# How To Use The Edge Index

Bend the pages of the book nearly double and hold them that way with your left hand.

Locate the letter you want in the Edge Index.

Match up the 1- or 2-line symbol next to the letter you have selected with the corresponding 1- or 2-line symbol on the page edge, and open there.

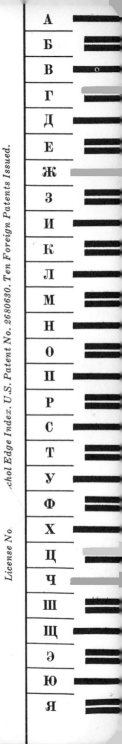

License No ................ .chol Edge Index. U.S. Patent No. 2680630. Ten Foreign Patents Issued.

# Russian-English Chemical and Polytechnical Dictionary

# Russian — English

## Chemical and Polytechnical

# DICTIONARY

LUDMILLA IGNATIEV CALLAHAM

SECOND EDITION PREPARED WITH THE ASSISTANCE OF E. B. UVAROV OF INTERLANGUAGE DICTIONARIES PUBLISHING CO.

JOHN WILEY & SONS, INC., NEW YORK AND LONDON

To my husband
John R. Callaham

# Preface

When I was compiling the first edition of this dictionary (then entitled *Russian-English Technical and Chemical Dictionary*), there was nothing I wanted so much as to emulate Patterson's *German-English Dictionary for Chemists*. Of all the foreign-English dictionaries I had used in my technical work, none could compare with his in organization, dependability, and consistency. I particularly liked his including a general vocabulary so that I could translate without the use of a second dictionary.

I, too, set my sights high—and spent seven solid years on that first edition alone. But the time never comes when a lexicographer can say, "This job is well done at last—I am really finished." He is never finished, never really satisfied. He just stops long enough to get one edition out, then starts work on the next. It becomes a way of life and I have become happily reconciled to a lifetime of endless word-hunting.

Since chemistry reaches out into so many fields and so many directions, I finally found myself with a dictionary that was as much polytechnical as it was chemical: Inorganic and organic chemistry; physical and nuclear chemistry; analytical chemistry; chemical engineering and broad chemical technology are naturally given the most complete and detailed coverage.

Then it became only logical—and therefore necessary—to develop comprehensive coverage of terms used in the major chemical process industries: resins and plastics; synthetic rubber; man-made fibers; ceramics; petroleum refining; pulp and paper; pharmaceuticals; food processing; fertilizers; insecticides and fungicides; paints and varnishes; light metals.

Emphasis on chemical process technology inevitably led to comprehensive coverage of related technical fields: mineralogy, metallurgy, mining and geology; general engineering, mechanical engineering, machinery, and metalworking; electrical engineering; automatic control systems; nucleonics; agriculture, pharmacy and botany ... and finally, in addition, the more frequently used terms in medicine; aeronautics; electronics; meteorology; physics, mathematics, and other pure sciences.

This work is intended chiefly for English-speaking scientists and engineers with a fair knowledge of Russian. It therefore includes a general vocabulary consisting of all types of words that might appear in the technical literature. Most of these non-technical terms acquire either special, or entirely different, meanings when used in a technical context. Then, of course, it is much handier to use one volume rather than two.

Judging from the letters I have received from users of my dictionary, I have succeeded in producing a reference that is regarded by many as "the technical man's general dictionary." Although such a dictionary must necessarily be superficial in many fields, it does serve as a starting point. It helps the user become oriented so he can decide what specialized dictionaries he needs to consult further.

As in the first edition, every effort was made to check each term in several reliable sources, both Soviet and American. A limited number of terms could be found in only one good source, but these were also included if they appeared particularly useful.

In the compilation of the first edition, I leaned heavily on my husband, John R. Callaham. With his many years of experience as an editor and a chemical engineer, he was able to help me check English equivalents, organize synonyms, and arrive at English equivalents for Russian definitions taken from Soviet sources. In working on this second edition, I received much valuable help from a number of sources. First, I had the conscientious collaboration of Mr. E. B. Uvarov, who devoted a full half year of his time to this second edition and then stood by, ready and willing to give advice and answer questions throughout the period of revision.

Mr. Uvarov and I each went through the entire first edition independently, deleting terms that seemed dispensable (to make room for more new entries), making changes that seemed desirable, and adding many new terms. Each of us went through a selected list of Soviet sources to collect new words, somewhat as I had done for the first edition. The large quantity of material now available made it impossible to go through each book as meticulously as I had done originally. Mr. Uvarov also made a special point of checking organic nomenclature and adding those pharmaceutical terms that he considered important. He also added terms received from: Dr. A. E. Stubbs, Dr. H. M. Leicester, Dr. Paul Sutton, Mr. Ben H. Ashe, Dr. L. Light, and Mr. C. N. Turton.

Then I had the help of a group of geologists who collaborated with one another and with me to make the new edition more useful in translating geological material. These are: Professor Earl Ingerson, University of Texas; Dr. Michael Fleischer and Dr. James Clarke, U.S. Geological Survey; Dorothy B. Vitaliano of Bloomington, Indiana; and others.

And, finally, I am deeply indebted to those users of my dictionary who, during the past fifteen years, have taken the time to send me so many new terms and excellent suggestions. There is no better source of words than the specialist who reads Russian as part of his job responsibilities. He is so intent on finding the precise meaning of a word that he does not stint on the time he spends going through various references. He values words in relation to their environment, not as unrelated bits of information. Nor is there any better guarantee of a word's accuracy than receiving it independently from three or more such authoritative sources.

I would especially like to acknowledge the contributions of some of these specialists: Professor H. L. Olin, who prodded my publisher and me until we started serious work on this revision; Kurt Gingold; Dr. Francis C. Frary; M. Zimmerman (U.S.S.R.); Dr. Herman Walde; and all the others who wrote letters to me and often included lists of ten to forty words for my dictionary. These words not only added to my dictionary, and/or verified various entries, but also showed me the type of words serious users want to find.

The Introduction on the following pages explains the organization of this book in greater detail and offers suggestions for translating words not included herein. I shall be grateful for any further suggestions regarding improvements, omissions, and errors.

L. I. C.

*Glen Ridge, New Jersey*
*August, 1962*

# Reference Works

*Орфографический словарь русского языка,* С. И. Ожегов и А. Б. Шапиро, Академия наук СССР, Москва 1958.

*Экспортно-импортный словарь,* Б. Т. Колпаков, Москва, 1952.

*Словарь иностранных слов,* И. В. Лехин и Ф. Н. Петров, Москва, 1955.

*Словарь местных географических терминов,* Э. и В. Мурзаевы, Москва, 1959.

*Краткий политехнический словарь,* Ю. А. Степанов, Москва, 1956.

*Органическая химия,* И. С. Иоффе, Ленинград, 1956.

*Общая и неорганическая химия,* Ю. В. Ходаков, Москва, 1959.

*Общая химическая технология,* С. И. Вольфкович, Москва-Ленинград, 1952.

*Краткий справочник химика,* В. И. Перельман, Москва, 1954.

*Машины и аппараты химических производств,* И. И. Чернобыльский, Москва, 1959.

*Краткий фотографический словарь,* А. А. Лапаури и В. И. Шеберстов, Москва, 1956.

*Англо-русский метеорологический словарь,* Л. И. Мамонтова и С. П. Хромов, Ленинград, 1959.

*Англо-русский электротехнический словарь,* Л. Б. Гейлер и Н. И. Дозоров, Москва, 1955.

*Англо-русский словарь по радиоэлектронике,* Москва, 1959.

*Англо-русский радиотехнический словарь,* Л. П. Герман-Прозорова и Н. И. Виноградова, Москва, 1957.

*Англо-русский словарь по автоматике и контрольно-измерительным приборам,* Л. К. Пташный, Москва, 1957.

*Технический словарь по топливу и маслам,* К. К. Папок и Н. А. Рагозин, Москва, 1955.

*Англо-русский горный словарь,* Л. И. Барон и Н. Н. Ершов, Москва, 1958.

*Англо-русский горнотехнический словарь,* Б. М. Косминский, С. Д. Матвеев и В. Д. Терпигорева, Москва, 1958.

*Русско-английский геологический словарь*, Т. А. Софиано, Москва, 1960.

*Англо-русский словарь по целлюлозно-бумажному производству*, А. Я. Элиашберг и др., Москва, 1958.

*Англо-русский словарь по каучуку и резине*, Ф. И. Яшунская, Москва, 1944.

*Краткая энциклопедия, Атомная энергия*, В. С. Емельянов, 1958.

*Краткий немецко-русский словарь по ядерной физике и ядерной технике*, Ю. М. Капланская и др., Москва, 1958.

*Русско-английский ядерный словарь*, Д. И. Воскобойник и М. Г. Циммерман, Москва, 1960.

*Англо-русский словарь по ракетной технике*, А. М. Мурашкевич, Москва, 1958.

*Энциклопедический сельскохозяйственный словарь-справочник*, Москва, 1959.

*Русско-английский сельскохозяйственный словарь*, Б. Н. Усовский и др., Москва, 1960.

*Определитель высших растений европейской части СССР*, С. С. Станков и В. И. Талиев, Москва, 1949.

*Ботанический словарь—Русско-английско-немецко-французско-латинский*, Н. Н. Давыдов, Москва, 1960.

*Латинско-русский словарь для ботаников*, Н. Н. Забинкова и М. Э. Кирпичников, Москва, 1957.

*Словарь-справочник фитопатолога*, П. Н. Головин, Москва, 1959.

*Практикум по общей биологии*, В. В. Маховко, Москва, 1960.

*Словарь-справочник энтомолога*, В. Н. Щеголев, Москва, 1958.

*Определитель насекомых*, Н. Н. Плавильщиков, Москва, 1950.

*Сельскохозяйственная энтомология*, В. Н. Щеголев, Москва, 1955.

*Краткий справочник по применению ядов для борьбы с вредителями и болезнями растений*, А. Л. Эфимов, Москва, 1958.

*Латино-русский медицинский словарь*, С. И. Вольфсон, Москва, 1957.

*Англо-русский медицинский словарь*, М. П. Мультановский и А. Я. Иванова, Москва, 1958.

*Лекарственные средства*, М. А. Машковский, Москва, 1957.

*Химия антибиотических веществ*, М. М. Шемякин и А. С. Хохлов, Москва-Ленинград, 1953.

*Учебник нормальной анатомии человека*. Н. К. Лысенков, В. И. Бушкович, и М. Г. Привес, Ленинград, 1958.

# Reference Works

*Encyclopedia of Science and Technology*, McGraw-Hill Book Co., New York, 1960.

*Webster's New International Dictionary of the English Language*, 2nd Edition, Unabridged, G. & C. Merriam Co., Springfield, Mass., 1960.

*The Merck Index of Chemicals and Drugs*, 7th Edition, Merck & Co., Inc., Rahway, N. J., 1960.

*The Condensed Chemical Dictionary*, 5th Edition, A. and E. Rose, Reinhold Publishing Corp., New York, 1956.

*Industrial Chemicals*, W. L. Faith, D. B. Keyes, and R. L. Clark, John Wiley & Sons, Inc., New York, 1950.

*Chemical Engineers' Handbook*, J. H. Perry, McGraw-Hill Book Co., Inc., New York, 1950.

*Selected Process Industries*, R. N. Shreve, McGraw-Hill Book Co., Inc., New York, 1950.

*Handbook of Chemistry and Physics*, 41st Edition, 1959–60.

*Chemical Abstracts*.

*Van Nostrand Chemist's Dictionary*, D. Van Nostrand Co., Inc., Princeton, N. J., 1953.

*A Dictionary of Named Effects and Laws in Chemistry, Physics and Mathematics*, D. W. G. Ballentyne and L. E. Q. Walker, Chapman and Hall, London, 1958.

*Organic Chemistry*, L. F. and M. Fieser, Reinhold Publishing Corp., New York, 1956.

*The Physical Chemistry of the Silicates*, W. Eitel, University of Chicago Press, 1954.

*Chemical Engineering*, J. M. Coulson and J. F. Richardson, Pergamon Press, London and New York, 1959.

*Chambers' Technical Dictionary*, C. F. Tweney and L. E. C. Hughes, The Macmillan Co., New York, 1959.

*Van Nostrand Scientific Encyclopedia*, 3rd Edition, D. Van Nostrand Co., Inc., Princeton, N. J., 1958.

*A Dictionary of Scientific Terms*, I. F. and W. D. Henderson (5th Edition by J. H. Kenneth), Oliver and Boyd, London, 1953.

*A Dictionary of Mechanical Engineering Terms*, 7th Edition, J. G. Horner and S. Abbey, Philosophical Library, Inc., New York, 1955.

*The Machinist Dictionary*, F. H. Colvin, Simmons-Boardman Publishing Corp., New York, 1956.

*Metals and Alloys Dictionary*, M. Merlub-Sobel, Chemical Publishing Co., Inc., Brooklyn, N. Y., 1944.

*Dictionary of Electrical Terms*, S. R. Roget, Pitman and Sons, Ltd., London, 1947.

*Electronics and Nucleonics Dictionary*, N. M. Cooke and J. Markus, McGraw-Hill Book Co., Inc., New York, 1960.

*A Glossary of Terms in Nuclear Science and Technology*, The American Society of Mechanical Engineers, New York, 1957.

*A Glossary of Terms Used in the Detergents Industry*, G. Carriere, Elsevier Publishing Co., New York, 1960.

*Mathematics Dictionary*, G. James and R. C. James, D. Van Nostrand Co., Inc., Princeton, N. J., 1959.

*American Pocket Medical Dictionary*, 19th Edition, W. B. Saunders Co., Philadelphia, Pa., 1953.

*Blakiston's New Gould Medical Dictionary*, McGraw-Hill Book Co., New York, 1956.

*A Dictionary of Geography*, W. G. Moore, Penguin Books Ltd., Harmondsworth, Middlesex, England, 1959.

*Russian-English Dictionary*, A. I. Smirnitsky, K. P. Schick, Brooklyn, N. Y.

*Russian for the Scientist*, J. and L. Turkevich, D. Van Nostrand Co., Inc., Princeton, N. J., 1959.

*Scientific Russian*, G. E. Condoyannis, John Wiley & Sons, Inc., New York, 1959.

*Official List of Abbreviations Used in the Referativnyi Zhurnal Khimiya, Their English Translation, and the Corresponding Abbreviations Used in Chemical Abstracts*, Edited by Joseph J. Gwirtsman.

Also:

*Five-Language Dictionary (Paints, Lacquers and Varnishes, Surface Treatment, Corrosion)*, R. Santholzer and J. Korinsky, Technical Literature Publishing House, Prague, 1956.

# Abbreviations

| | | | |
|---|---|---|---|
| *a.* | adjective | *instr.* | instrumental |
| *abbr.* | abbreviation | *m.* | masculine noun |
| *acc.* | accusative | mach. | machinery |
| *act.* | active | math. | mathematics |
| acous. | acoustics | mech. | mechanics |
| *adv.* | adverb | med. | medicine |
| aero. | aeronautics | met. | metallurgy, metals |
| agr. | agriculture | meteor. | meteorology |
| anat. | anatomy | micros. | microscopy |
| astron. | astronomy | mil. | military |
| bact. | bacteriology | min. | mineralogy, mining |
| biol. | biology | *n.* | neuter noun |
| bot. | botany | naut. | nautical |
| cer. | ceramics | obs. | obsolete |
| chem. | chemistry | pal. | paleontology |
| com. | commerce | *part.* | participle |
| *comp.* | comparative | *pass.* | passive |
| *conj.* | conjunction | petr. | petrology, petrography |
| cryst. | crystallography | pharm. | pharmacy, |
| *dat.* | dative | | pharmaceuticals |
| elec. | electricity, electrical | phot. | photography |
| | engineering | phys. | physics |
| elec. comm. | electrical communication | physiol. | physiology |
| esp. | especially | *pl.* | plural |
| expl. | explosives | *pr.* | present |
| *f.* | feminine noun | *prep.* | preposition |
| *fut.* | future | *prepos.* | prepositional |
| *gen.* | genitive | *pron.* | pronoun |
| geol. | geology | pyro. | pyrotechnics |
| geom. | geometry | rad. | radio |
| horol. | horology | *sing.* | singular |
| illum. | illumination | spec. | specifically |
| *imp.* | imperative | surv. | surveying |

| | | | |
|---|---|---|---|
| tech. | technical | *v.* | verb |
| tel. | telephone | vet. | veterinary |
| telev. | television | zool. | zoology, including |
| text. | textiles, textile industry | | entomology |
| typ. | typography | *3* | 3rd person |

# Russian Alphabet

| STANDARD | | ITALICS | NAME | TRANSLITERATION |
|---|---|---|---|---|
| А | а | *а* | ah | a |
| Б | б | *б* | beh | b |
| В | в | *в* | veh | v |
| Г | г | *г* | geh | g |
| Д | д | *д* | deh | d |
| Е | е | *е* | yeh | e |
| Ж | ж | *ж* | zheh | zh |
| З | з | *з* | zeh | z |
| И | и | *и* | ee | i |
| Й | й | *й* | ee kratkoye | ï |
| К | к | *к* | ka | k |
| Л | л | *л* | el | l |
| М | м | *м* | em | m |
| Н | н | *н* | en | n |
| О | о | *о* | aw | o |
| П | п | *п* | peh | p |
| Р | р | *р* | ehr | r |
| С | с | *с* | ess | s |
| Т | т | *т* | teh | t |
| У | у | *у* | oo | u |
| Ф | ф | *ф* | ef | f |
| Х | х | *х* | hha | kh |
| Ц | ц | *ц* | tseh | ts |
| Ч | ч | *ч* | tcheh | ch |
| Ш | ш | *ш* | sha | sh |
| Щ | щ | *щ* | shcha | shch |
| Ъ | ъ | *ъ* | mute hard sign | — |
| Ы | ы | *ы* | yeri | y |
| Ь | ь | *ь* | mute soft sign | — |
| Э | э | *э* | eh oborotnoye | e |
| Ю | ю | *ю* | yoo | yu |
| Я | я | *я* | ya | ya |

# Introduction

In the compilation of this dictionary, it was necessary to adhere to certain specific procedures for the sake of consistency. Regular users of the dictionary will find it convenient to familiarize themselves with these procedures, which are outlined below.

**Alphabetical Order.** All Russian terms are entered in strictly alphabetical order. Words derived from one root are listed in a single paragraph in order to save space by avoiding short lines. This system is also helpful in understanding the meaning of any specific word. Looking at the synonyms and equivalents given for a verb, for example, a translator can readily formulate the necessary noun endings. Hyphenated compound words are listed in the paragraph under the first word.

**Synonyms.** English equivalents are preferably of American usage and spelling, rather than British. Every attempt was made to avoid little-used or obsolete synonyms for English equivalents. Wherever possible, the meaning of English equivalents is made clear by means of suitable synonyms and parenthetical explanations. It would be simple and convenient if each Russian term had just so many cut-and-dried English equivalents. A lexicographer's job would then be a great deal easier. Unfortunately, there is almost no end to the possibilities, for writers use all sorts of terms quite loosely. I tried to track down as many meanings as I could, knowing that no one can get them all.

Many changes have taken place since my first edition was published in 1947. Numerous words have moved out of their original fields and assumed new and unexpected meanings. Ordinarily one would not expect a word like "napkin" to appear in a technical dictionary, but it also means filter pad. Although most terms have assumed more and more meanings, some have actually become narrower in their scope.

**Prefixes and Suffixes.** A very large number of prefixes is included, as well as the commoner suffixes, even more than in the first edition. This should be of great help in constructing words not included in the dictionary. I have also tried to give the English equivalents of prefixes of Latin or Greek origin. If other technically trained people are like me, they do not always remember the exact meaning of each prefix they meet. If I can save some of my users the trouble of referring to still another dictionary, then I feel that my time has been well spent.

**Abbreviations.** A wide range of abbreviations, including a fairly complete list of the units of measure, was found by combing the Soviet journals and encyclopedias. Such abbreviations are given in strictly alphabetical order in the text. If they consist of two or more parts, they are alphabetized as one word.

**Idioms.** If consisting of an adjective and a noun, idioms are usually listed under the modifying adjective unless the noun is much more distinctive. Other types of two- and three-word idioms are listed under what is considered to be the key word. Except in rare cases, each idiom appears only under one word. This avoids repetition and cross references which occupy space without serving any useful purpose. Certain idioms appear more than once because they are very typical and can serve as examples of how similar terms should be translated. Every effort was made to avoid including phrases of which the literal translation would also be idiomatic in English. However, some such idioms are given as examples or suggestions to the reader so that he can readily handle similar idioms. The volume of the dictionary could have easily been doubled by including many of the more obvious terms.

**Old and Modern Terms.** Obsolete and little-used Russian words are frequently included, since many old articles containing such words require translation. Emphasis is made, however, on Soviet terminology. The Russian words are spelled as they were found in Soviet periodicals, reference books, and dictionaries. Some of these may not always be in the approved form, but, since their purpose is to help in the translation of Soviet technical articles, it was considered desirable to give such words as they appeared in the literature. Камфара and камфора are good examples. The first is the approved form, as given in the *Soviet Orthographic Dictionary*, but the second is the one seen most frequently in chemistry textbooks. It is also well to remember that spellings have changed in the last fifteen years. If you cannot find a word spelled with a single consonant, look for it with a double consonant.

**Russianized Words.** When words are encountered which do not appear in this dictionary and the meaning of which is not readily determined, it is well to remember that Soviet writers frequently use foreign words written with Russian letters. For example, the German words *Träger*, *Abscheider*, and *Vorstoss* appear as **трегер, абшайдер,** and **воршТосс** in Russian and retain their original meanings. The French term *terre de Sienne* becomes **тердесьен,** and the English word *timer* is **таймер.** Another custom is to add verb, noun, and adjective endings to a man's name; for example, **шерардизовать,** to sherardize; **шерардизация,** sherardization; **томасовский** *a.*, Thomas. Wherever possible, names have been included in the dictionary, since Russian spelling usually makes them difficult to recognize. Walker, for example, is **Уокер** in Russian. Since many minerals are named after men, these also serve as an indication of the English spelling of such names.

**Chemical Compounds.** Since the number of chemical compounds is extremely large, only the most common and exemplary ones were chosen for each element. In general, those given should be sufficient to assist in the translation of almost any compound. With a few exceptions, Russian organic nomenclature is very similar to the English. The Russian alphabet, however, made it desirable to include a fairly wide range of organic compounds.

**Latin Equivalents.** Since plants usually have a large number of regional popular names, their Latin equivalents have been included to aid in their exact identification. Particular attention was paid to plants of special economic importance in the U.S.S.R. A popular plant name often refers to more than one variety, so it is not always possible to find all the proper Latin names. Latin equivalents have also been included in certain other instances (such as insect names) in the life sciences where confusion may result.

## GRAMMATICAL STRUCTURE

Technical Russian is not particularly difficult, since sentence structure is very similar to the English, but it is necessary to have at least an elementary knowledge of Russian grammar. Both nouns and adjectives are declined, and recognition of their endings, as well as those of conjugated verbs, is necessary to understand the meaning of a sentence. It is also convenient for looking up the particular word in the dictionary, since all nouns are indexed under the nominative case, all adjectives under the masculine singular form, and verbs under the infinitive. All idioms starting with a particular adjective are listed in a paragraph under the masculine form, even if the feminine form would appear elsewhere if considered alphabetically.

**Nouns.** Russian nouns have three genders, the recognition of which is important in the determination of modifying adjectives and clauses. The masculine nominative usually ends in a hard consonant, —ь or —й; the feminine in —а, —я, —ь; the neuter in —о, —е, —мя, —тя; the plural in —ы, —и, —а, —я, —ья.

**Adjectives.** All adjectives agree with the noun they modify in gender, number, and case. The masculine nominative singular endings are —ый, —ой, —ий; the feminine, —ая, —яя; the neuter, —ое, —ее; the plural, —ые, —ие. The comparative degree is usually formed by replacing —ый or —ой with —ее, —ей or —е; the superlative, by adding —ейший or —айший to the stem. Past and present participles have been considered as adjectives in this dictionary.

**Adverbs.** A large proportion of adverbs are formed by changing the adjective endings —ый and —ой to —о; —ский to —ски; and sometimes —ий to —е. The adverb form is also used to express the impersonal verb, as холодно, which is translated "it is cold."

**Verbs.** As is customary, verbs are indexed under the infinitive form, the ending of which is usually one of the following: —ть, —ать, —еть, —ить, —оть, —уть, —ыть, —ять, —йти, —зть, —зти, —сть, —сти, —чь. The reflexive form is often used to express the passive voice and is formed by adding —ся or —сь to the infinitive.

**Word Endings.** The table on the following pages is essentially the same as the one I worked out fifteen years ago for my first edition. It provides some of the frequently occurring technical Russian word endings, with their English equivalents and Russian and English examples. These suggested translations should not be regarded as the only possible ones. They are given merely to help in the translation of words not included in this book.

I have also prepared another table which should be helpful to students of Russian. It gives a brief résumé of typical noun and adjective declensions, as well as verb conjugations. I have included a fairly large number of irregular verb forms in the text, as suggested by one of my users.

# Common Russian Technical Word Endings

| RUSSIAN ENDINGS | ENGLISH EQUIVALENTS | RUSSIAN EXAMPLES | ENGLISH EQUIVALENTS |
|---|---|---|---|
| —аемость,<br>—имость,<br>—уемость,<br>—яемость *f.* | —ability,<br>—ibility,<br>—ubility | поглощаемость<br>смесимость<br>растворимость | absorbability<br>miscibility<br>solubility |
| —аемый,<br>—имый,<br>—уемый,<br>—яемый *a.* | —able, —ible,<br>—uble, —ed | поглощаемый<br>смесимый<br>растворимый<br>требуемый | absorbable<br>miscible<br>soluble<br>required |
| —аза *f.* | —ase | лактаза | lactase |
| —ал, —аль *m.* | —al | ацетал,<br>ацеталь | acetal |
| —алевый,<br>—аловый,<br>—альный *a.* | —al, —alic | ацеталевый<br>фталевый | acetal<br>phthalic |
| —альный,<br>—ильный,<br>—яльный *a.* | —ing | плавильный | smelting |
| —альня,<br>—ильня,<br>—ная, —ня<br>—яльня *f.* | —ery, —ry,<br>—ing mill,<br>—ing shop,<br>—ing works | плавильня<br><br>валяльня<br>литейная | smeltery,<br>smelting works,<br>foundry<br>fulling mill<br>casting shop |
| —ан *m.* | —an, —ane | меркаптан<br>бутан | mercaptan<br>butane |

| RUSSIAN ENDINGS | ENGLISH EQUIVALENTS | RUSSIAN EXAMPLES | ENGLISH EQUIVALENTS |
|---|---|---|---|
| —ание,<br>—ение *n.* | —ation, —ence,<br>—ing, —sion,<br>—tion | выпаривание<br>сцепление<br><br>поглощение | evaporation<br>coherence<br>cohesion<br>absorption |
| —ановый *a.* | —an, —ane,<br>—anic, —anoic | меркаптановый<br>бутановый<br><br>циановый | mercaptan<br>butane<br>butanoic<br>cyanic |
| —арность,<br>—ярность *f.* | —arity | молекулярность | molecularity |
| —арный,<br>—ярный *a.* | —ar, —arian,<br>—ary | молекулярный<br>утилитарный<br>санитарный | molecular<br>utilitarian<br>sanitary |
| —ат *m.*,<br>—атный *a.* | —ate | сульфат,<br>сульфатный | sulfate |
| —атель,<br>—итель *m.* | —ant, —ator,<br>—ent, —er,<br>—ing agent | ускоритель<br><br>поглотитель<br><br>окислитель | accelerant,<br>accelerator<br>absorbent,<br>absorber<br>oxidizer,<br>oxidizing agent |
| —ательный,<br>—ительный,<br>—очный *a.* | —ent, —ing,<br>—ive | поглотительный<br><br>сортировочный<br>уничтожительный | absorbent,<br>absorbing<br>sorting<br>destructive |
| —атор,<br>—ятор *m.*<br>—аторный,<br>—яторный *a.* | —ator, —er | генератор,<br>генераторный<br>трансформатор | generator<br><br>transformer |
| —вший,<br>—вшийся<br>(—авший, | —ed, —en,<br>—ened, —t | потонувший<br>сгустившийся | drowned, sunken<br>coagulated,<br>thickened |

| RUSSIAN ENDINGS | ENGLISH EQUIVALENTS | RUSSIAN EXAMPLES | ENGLISH EQUIVALENTS |
|---|---|---|---|
| —евший,<br>—ивший,<br>—увший),<br>—дший,<br>—лый,<br>—ший *a.* | | сгоревший | burnt |
| —еватый,<br>—оватый *a.* | —ish | красноватый | reddish |
| —евые,<br>—ные,<br>—овые *pl.* | —aceae, —ata,<br>—eae | гераниевые<br>целомные<br>сцитаминовые | Geraniaceae<br>Coelomata<br>Scitamineae |
| —ен *m.* | —en, —ene | глутен<br>бутен | gluten<br>butene |
| —еновый *a.* | —en, —ene,<br>—enic, —enoic | глутеновый<br>бутеновый<br>нафтеновый | gluten<br>butene, butenoic<br>naphthenic |
| —ентность,<br>—енциозность,<br>—енция *f.* | —ence, —ency | турбулентность<br>тенденциозность,<br>тенденция | turbulence<br>tendency |
| —ентный *a.* | —ent | турбулентный | turbulent |
| —ер *m.* | —er | дистиллер | distiller |
| —есть,<br>—ность,<br>—ость *f.* | —ism, —ity,<br>—ness | аморфность<br>твердость | amorphism<br>rigidity,<br>hardness |
| —з (—ез,<br>—из, —оз) *m.* | —sis | гидролиз<br>осмоз | hydrolysis<br>osmosis |
| —зионный,<br>—сионный *a.*<br>—зия,<br>—сия *f.* | —sion | телевизионный<br>телевизия | television |
| —ивность *f.* | —ivity | селективность | selectivity |

| RUSSIAN ENDINGS | ENGLISH EQUIVALENTS | RUSSIAN EXAMPLES | ENGLISH EQUIVALENTS |
|---|---|---|---|
| —ивный *a.* | —ive | селективный | selective |
| —ид *m.*, —идный *a.* | —ide | сульфид, сульфидный | sulfide |
| —иевый *a.* | —ic, —ium | таллиевый | thallic, thallium |
| —изация *f.*, —изирование, —изование *n.* | —ization, —izing, —yzing | гомогенизация анализирование | homogenization, homogenizing analyzing |
| —изированный, —изованный *a.* | —ized, —yzed | гомогенизованный анализированный | homogenized analyzed |
| —изировать, —изовать *v.* | —ize, —yze | гомогенизовать анализировать | homogenize analyze |
| —изм *m.* | —ism | аморфизм | amorphism |
| —изна, —ота *f.* | —ness | краснота | redness |
| —ий *m.* | —ium, —um | кальций алюминий | calcium aluminum |
| —ийский, —ский *a.* | —ian, —ic | пермский | Permian, Permic |
| —ик, —ист *m.* | —ant, —er, —ic, —ist, —yst | помощник аналист, аналитик механик химик | assistant, helper analyzer, analyst mechanic chemist |
| —ика *f.* | —ics | механика | mechanics |
| —ил *m.* | —il, —ile, —yl | бензил нитрил | benzil; benzyl nitrile |
| —иловый, —ильный *a.*, *see also under* —альный | —il, —ile, —ilic, —yl, —ylic | бензиловый нитриловый каприловый | benzil, benzilic; benzyl nitrile capryl, caprylic |

| RUSSIAN ENDINGS | ENGLISH EQUIVALENTS | RUSSIAN EXAMPLES | ENGLISH EQUIVALENTS |
|---|---|---|---|
| —ин *m.* | —in, —ine | глутин | glutin |
| | | анилин | aniline |
| —иновый *a.* | —in, —ine, —inic | глутиновый | glutin, glutinic |
| | | анилиновый | aniline |
| —ирование *n.* | —ating, —ation, —ing, —ion | метилирование | methylating, methylation |
| | | окклюдирование | occlusion |
| —ированный *a.* | —ated, —ed | метилированный | methylated |
| | | окклюдированный | occluded |
| —ировать *v.* | —ate, —e | метилировать | methylate |
| | | окклюдировать | occlude |
| —истый *a.* | —ous, —y | медистый | cuprous |
| | | тинистый | slimy |
| —ит *m.* | —ite, —itis, —yte | гранит | granite |
| | | неврит | neuritis |
| | | электролит | electrolyte |
| —итный, —итовый *a.* | —ite, —itic, —ytic | гранитный, гранитовый | granite, granitic |
| | | электролитный | electrolytic |
| —ификация *f.*, —ифицирование *n.* | —ification | ректификация | rectification |
| —ифицированный *a.* | —ified | ректифицированный | rectified |
| —ифицировать *v.* | —ify | ректифицировать | rectify |
| —ический, —ичный, —ный, —овый *a.* | —ic, —ical, —ous | медный | cupric |
| | | амфотерный | amphoteric |
| | | химический | chemical |
| | | аморфический, аморфный | amorphous |
| —ия *f.* | —ia, —ion, —ism, —ium, —y | анемия | anemia |
| | | флюксия | fluxion |
| | | рацемия | racemism |
| | | трапеция | trapezium |
| | | теория | theory |

| RUSSIAN ENDINGS | ENGLISH EQUIVALENTS | RUSSIAN EXAMPLES | ENGLISH EQUIVALENTS |
|---|---|---|---|
| —ник, —чик, —щик *m.* | —er, —or | сборщик<br>проводник | assembler<br>conductor |
| —нный (—анный, —енный, —янный) *a.* | —ed | поглощенный | absorbed |
| —оза *f.* | —ose | целлюлоза | cellulose |
| —озный *a.* | —ose, —ous | фистулозный | fistulose, fistulous |
| —оид *m.* | —oid | коллоид | colloid |
| —оидальный *a.* | —oid, —oidal | коллоидальный | colloid, colloidal |
| —ойский *a.* | —oic | мезозойский | Mesozoic |
| —ол, —оль *m.* | —ol, —ole | алкоголь<br>тиазол | alcohol<br>thiazole |
| —оловый, —ольный *a.* | —ol, —ole, —olic | алкогольный<br><br>тиазоловый | alcohol,<br>alcoholic<br>thiazole |
| —он *m.* | —on, —one | электрон<br>ксантон | electron<br>xanthone |
| —онный, —оновый *a.* | —on, —one, —onic | электронный<br><br>ксантоновый | electron,<br>electronic<br>xanthone,<br>xanthonic |
| —ор *m.* | —or | активатор | activator |
| —тический (—атический, —етический, —итический, —отический) *a.* | —tic | осмотический<br>гидролитический | osmotic<br>hydrolytic |
| —тый (—атый, —етый, —итый, —отый, —утый, —ытый, —ятый) *a.* | —ed, —en, —n | тянутый<br>битый | pulled, drawn<br>beaten |

| RUSSIAN ENDINGS | ENGLISH EQUIVALENTS | RUSSIAN EXAMPLES | ENGLISH EQUIVALENTS |
|---|---|---|---|
| —ционный (—ационный, —иционный, —яционный) *a.* | —ing, —tion, —tional | агитационный<br><br>фрикционный | agitating, agitation<br><br>friction, frictional |
| —ция (—ация, —иция, —яция) *f.* | —ing, —tion | агитация | agitating, agitation |
| —чатый, —щатый *a.* | —ar, —ated | трубчатый | tubular, tubulated |
| —щий (—ающий, —еющий, —ущий, —ующий, —ющий, —ящий, —яющий) *a.* | —ent, —ing, —ive | поглощающий<br><br><br>окисляющий | absorbent, absorbing, absorptive<br>oxidizing |
| —щийся (—ающийся, etc.) *a.* | —able, —ible, —ing, —ive | окисляющийся<br><br>сцепляющийся | oxidizable, oxidizing<br>cohesive |

а *abbr.* (ампер) ampere; (ар) are; а. *abbr.* (аршин) arshine.

а *conj.* but, and; а так как and since, now as; а то or else.

Å *abbr.* (ангстром) ångstrom.

ААИ *abbr.* (амплитудный анализатор импульсов) pulse height analyzer.

ааронова борода (bot.) arum.

АБ *abbr.* (препарат Боргарда) а copper sulfate-carbonate seed disinfectant.

абажур *m.* shade, screen.

абака *f.* abacus; abaca (Manila hemp).

абампер *m.* (elec.) abampere.

абасин *m.* Abasin, acetylcarbromal.

Аббе конденсатор (micros.) Abbe condenser.

аббревиа/тура, —ция *f.* abbreviation.

абграт/пресс *m.*, —штамп *m.* trimming press.

абдом/ен *m.* abdomen; —инальный *a.* abdominal.

абелит *m.* (expl.) abelite.

абельмош/а семена abelmosk, musk seed; —евое волокно abelmosk fiber.

Абел/я прибор Abel tester (for flash point); испытание по —ю Abel test.

аберрация *f.* aberration.

абзац *m.* paragraph, item.

абзетцер *m.* chain and bucket excavator.

абиет/ен *m.* abietene, diterebentyl; —ин *m.* abietin; —иновая кислота abietic acid, sylvic acid; —ит *m.* abietite (a sugar).

абиковиромицин *m.* abikoviromycin.

абисс/аль *f.* abyssal zone, abyssal fauna; —альный *a.* abyssal; —олит *m.* abyssolith.

абитуриент *m.* matriculant, college student.

абихит *m.* (min.) abichite, clinoclasite.

АБК *abbr.* (ацидофильная бульонная культура) acidophilus culture.

аблактиров/ание *n.* ablactation, wean-ing; —ка *f.* inarching (method of plant grafting).

абляция *f.* ablation.

абон/емент *m.* subscription; —ент *m.* subscriber; —ировать *v.* subscribe.

абориген *m.* aborigine, native.

аборт *m.* abortion; miscarriage; —ивный *a.* abortive.

абрадировать *v.* abrade, wear off.

абраз/ив *m.*, —ивный *a.*, —ивный материал, —ионный материал abrasive; —ионный *a.* abrasion, abrasive; —ит *m.* abrasite (an aluminum oxide abrasive); —ия *f.* abrasion, wearing away.

абрастол *m.* abrastol, calcium beta-naphtholsulfonate.

абраумзальц *m.* abraum salts (potash salts of Stassfurt).

абревиатура *see* аббревиатура.

абрико/с *m.*, —сный, —совый *a.* (bot.) apricot (*Prunus armeniaca*); —тин *m.* apricot liqueur.

абрин *m.* abrin, jequiritin; abrine, N-methyltryptophan.

абрис *m.* contour, outline, sketch.

абс. *abbr.* (абсолютный) absolute; абс. вл. *abbr.* (абсолютная влажность) absolute humidity; абс. выс. *abbr.* (абсолютная высота) absolute elevation; абс. ед. *abbr.* (абсолютная единица) absolute unit.

абсент, абсент *m.* absinth; —ат *m.* absinthate; —ин *m.* absinthin; —ово-кислый *a.* absinthic acid, absinthate (of); —овокислая соль absinthate; —овый *a.* absinthic; —овая кислота absinthic acid; соль —овой кислоты absinthate; —ол *m.* absinthol, thujol.

абсолютиров/ание *n.* dehydration (of alcohol); —ать *v.* dehydrate.

абсолютн/о *adv.* absolutely; ideal (black

body); —ый *a.* absolute; —ый нуль absolute zero.

**абсорб/ент** *m.* absorbent; —ер *m.* absorber; absorbent; —ированный *a.* absorbed; —ировать *v.* absorb; —ируемый *a.* absorbable; —ирующий *a.* absorbing, absorbent, absorptive; —ирующее средство absorbent; —циометр *m.* absorptiometer; —циометрический *a.* absorptiometric; —ционный *a.* absorption, absorptive; —ционная колонна absorption column; —ционная способность absorptive power, absorptivity; —ция *f.* absorption.

**абстатампер** *m.* (elec.) abstatampere.

**абстра/гировать** *v.* abstract; —ктный *a.* abstract; —кция *f.* abstraction.

**абсурд** *m.* absurdity; —ность *f.* absurdness; ineptness; —ный *a.* absurd, incongruous, foolish; inept.

**абсцесс** *m.* (med.) abscess.

**абсцисса** *f.* (math.) abscissa.

**абс. эл. ст. ед.** *abbr.* (абсолютная электростатическая единица) absolute electrostatic unit.

**абцуг,** —овый шлак *m.* dross, scum, spec. scum on molten lead, sharp slag.

**абшайдер** *m.* separator; refiner.

**абштрих** *m.* scum, dross, spec. scum of arsenates, etc., on molten lead.

**ав, а-в** *abbr.* (ампервиток) ampere-turn.

**ав—** *see also* **ау—**.

**аванкамера** *f.* antechamber, precombustion chamber.

**аванс** *m.* advance, down payment, deposit; —ировать *v.* advance.

**авантаж** *m.* advantage, profit; —ный *a.* advantageous, profitable.

**авантюрин** *m.* aventurine (a glass); (min.) aventurine; —ный, —овый *a.* aventurine, spangled.

**аванцистерна** *f.* preceding tank, preliminary tank; feed tank

**аварийно-защитный** *a.* emergency, safety.

**авар/ийный** *a.* accident, emergency; **а. рабочий** trouble shooter; **а. режим** emergency conditions; malfunction; **а. стержень** (nucl.) scram rod, emergency safety rod; **а. тормоз** emergency brake; —ийная установка emergency service; —ия *f.* accident,

breakdown, trouble; wreck; emergency; damage, injury.

**аваруит** *m.* (min.) awaruite (nickeliferous metallic iron).

**авгелит** *m.* (min.) augelite.

**авгит** *m.* (min.) augite (aluminous pyroxene); —ит *m.* (petr.) augitite; —овый *a.* augitic, augite; —овая масса (petr.) augite rock, pyroxenic mass.

**август** *m.* August.

**Августина процесс** Augustin process (for silver).

**авдио—** *see* **аудио—**.

**авезасит** *m.* (petr.) avezacite.

**авенацеин** *m.* avenacein (antibiotic).

**авенин** *m.* avenine (alkaloid); avenin, legumin.

**авентурин** *see* **авантюрин**.

**авиа—** *prefix* aviation, airplane, air, aerial; —база *f.* air base; —бензин *m.* aviation gasoline; —бомба *f.* aerial bomb; —горизонт *m.* gyrohorizon; —двигателестроение *n.* aircraft engine construction; —двигатель *m.* airplane motor, aircraft engine; —звено *n.* flight; —камера *f.* inner tube (of airplane tire); —крыло *n.* airplane wing; —линия *f.* airway; airline.

**авиалит** *m.* Avialite (copper-aluminum-iron alloy).

**авиа/магистраль** *f.* major airline; —масло *n.* aviation oil; —матка *f.*, —носец *m.* aircraft carrier; —маяк *m.* beacon; —мет *abbr.* (авиационная метеорологическая станция) aereometeorological station; —механик *m.* airplane mechanic; —мотор *m.* airplane motor; —обучение *n.* training in aviation, air training; —опрыскивание *n.* (agr.) aircraft spraying; —опрыскиватель *m.* sprayer plane; —опыливатель *m.* crop duster; —отряд *m.* flight; —подкормка *f.* (agr.) spreading fertilizer by plane; —покрышка *f.* airplane tire tread, tire; —прибор *m.* aircraft appliance factory; —прицел *m.* bomb sight; —разведка *f.* aerial reconnaissance; —тика *see* авиация; —тор *m.* aviator; —трасса *f.* air route; —хим *abbr.* (авиация и химия) aviation and chemistry.

### Feminine Plural Noun Endings        Neuter Plural Noun Endings

| | | | | | | | |
|---|---|---|---|---|---|---|---|
| Nom. | масс/ы | сол/и | реакц/ии | мил/и | тел/а | пол/я | знан/ия |
| Gen. | масс | —ей | —ий | —ь | тел | —ей | —ий |
| Dat. | —ам | —ям | —иям | —ям | —ам | —ям | —иям |
| Acc. | —ы | —и | —ии | —и | —а | —я | —ия |
| Instr. | —ами | —ями | —иями | —ями | —ами | —ями | —иями |
| Prepos. | о —ах | —ях | —иях | —ях | о —ах | —ях | —иях |

### Typical Regular Verb Endings—Present Tense

| читать | терять | греть | образовать |
|---|---|---|---|
| я чит/аю | я тер/яю | я гр/ею | я образ/ую |
| ты —аешь | ты —яешь | ты —еешь | ты —уешь |
| он, она | он, она, оно | он, она, оно | он, она, оно |
| —ает | —яет | —еет | —ует |
| мы —аем | мы —яем | мы —еем | мы —уем |
| вы —аете | вы —яете | вы —еете | вы —уете |
| они —ают | они —яют | они —еют | они —уют |

| малевать | говорить | учить |
|---|---|---|
| я мал/юю | я говор/ю | я уч/у |
| ты —юешь | ты —ишь | ты —ишь |
| он, она | он, она | он, она |
| —юет | —ит | —ит |
| мы —юем | мы —им | мы —им |
| вы —юете | вы —ите | вы —ите |
| они —ююют | они —ят | они —ат |

### Past Tense Endings

| | |
|---|---|
| *m.* | чита/л |
| *f.* | —ла |
| *n.* | —ло |
| *pl.* | —ли |

### Future Imperfective

Formed by future of **быть** followed
by the infinitive: **я буду читать**, etc.

# Declensions

### Masculine Singular Adjective Endings

| | | | | Typical Regular Masculine Singular Noun Endings | | | |
|---|---|---|---|---|---|---|---|
| | | | | Hard | Soft | Soft | Soft |
| Nom. | перв/ый | дорог/ой | син/ий | стол | словар/ь | случ/ай | критер/ий |
| Gen. | —ого | —ого | —его | —а | —я | —ая | —ия |
| Dat. | —ому | —ому | —ему | —у | —ю | —аю | —ию |
| Acc. | like nom. or gen. | | | стол | —ь | —ай | —ий |
| Instr. | —ым | —им | —им | —ом | —ем | —аем | —ием |
| Prepos. | о —ом | —ом | —ем | —е | —е | —ае | —ии |

### Feminine Singular Adjective Endings

| | | | | Typical Regular Feminine Singular Noun Endings | | | |
|---|---|---|---|---|---|---|---|
| | | | | Hard | Soft | Soft | Soft |
| Nom. | перв/ая | дорог/ая | син/яя | масс/а | сол/ь | реакц/ия | мил/я |
| Gen. | —ой | —ой | —ей | —ы | —и | —ии | —и |
| Dat. | —ой | —ой | —ей | —е | —и | —ии | —е |
| Acc. | —ую | —ую | —юю | —у | —ь | —ию | —ю |
| Instr. | —ой, | —ой, | —ей, | —ой, | —ью | —ией, | —ей, |
| | —ою | —ою | —ею | (—ою) | | (—иею) | (—ею) |
| Prepos. | о —ой | —ой | —ей | —е | —и | —ии | —е |

### Neuter Singular Adjective Endings

| | | | | Typical Regular Neuter Singular Noun Endings | | |
|---|---|---|---|---|---|---|
| | | | | Hard | Soft | Soft |
| Nom. | перв/ое | дорог/ое | син/ее | тел/о | пол/е | знан/ие |
| Gen. | —ого | —ого | —его | —а | —я | —ия |
| Dat. | —ому | —ому | —ему | —у | —ю | —ию |
| Acc. | —ое | —ое | —ее | —о | —е | —ие |
| Instr. | —ым | —им | —им | —ом | —ем | —ием |
| Prepos. | о —ом | —ом | —ем | —е | —е | —ии |

### Plural Adjective Endings— All Genders

| | | | | Masculine Plural Noun Endings | | | |
|---|---|---|---|---|---|---|---|
| Nom. | перв/ые | дорог/ие | син/ие | стол/ы | словар/и | случ/аи | критер/ии |
| Gen. | —ых | —их | —их | —ов | —ей | —аев | —иев |
| Dat. | —ым | —им | —им | —ам | —ям | —аям | —иям |
| Acc. | like nom. or gen. | | | —ы | —и | —аи | —ии |
| Instr. | —ыми | —ими | —ими | —ами | —ями | —аями | —иями |
| Prepos. | о —ых | —их | —их | —ах | —ях | —аях | —иях |

авиаци/онный *a.* aviation; aeronautical (meteorology); —я *f.* aviation.

авиетка *f.* small plane.

авизо *n.* aviso, letter of advice.

авиньон *m.* (text.) avignon; —ские красильные ягоды Avignon berries (dye).

авитаминоз *m.* avitaminosis, vitamin deficiency.

Авогадро число Avogadro number.

авокадо *n.* (bot.) avocado (*Persea Americana*).

авось *adv.* perhaps, maybe; на а. at random, haphazardly; пойти на а. *v.* venture at random.

авран *m.* (bot.) hedge hyssop (*Gratiola*).

аврикула *f.* (bot.) auricula.

аврипигмент *see* аурипигмент.

австр. *abbr.* (австрийский) Austrian.

австрал/ен *m.* australene, pinene; —ийский *a.* Australian; —ийский орех (bot.) Australian nut (*Macadamia ternifolia*); —ит *m.* (petr.) australite, obsidian pebbles.

австрийский *a.* Austrian.

авт. л. *abbr.* (авторский лист) author index.

авто— *prefix* auto—, automatic; automobile; car-borne (equipment); —база *f.* service station; garage; —бим *m.* a leather substitute; —блокировка *f.* automatic blocking; self-locking, self-catching; —броневик *m.* armored car; —бус *m.* bus; —вагон *see* автомотриса; —вентиль *m.* automobile tire valve; —воз *m.* carrier, truck; —гараж *m.* garage.

автогенный *a.* autogenous.

автогир *see* автожир.

автодин *m.* (pharm.) autodyne, phenoxyglycerin; (rad.) autodyne.

авто/дрезина *see* автомотриса; —жир *m.* gyroplane, autogyro; helicopter; —камера *f.* inner tube (of tire); —катализ *m.* autocatalysis; —кисление *n.* autooxidation; —клав *m.*, —клавировать *v.* autoclave; —клавированный *a.* autoclaved; —кластический *a.* (petr.) autoclastic; —коллимация *f.* (optics) autocollimation; —л *m.* a lubricating oil; —лаки *pl.* automobile lacquers; —лиз *m.* autol-

ysis; —лист *m.* sheet steel for automobiles; —лит *m.* (petr.) autolith.

автомат *m.* automaton, automat, robot; automatic machine; винторезный а. automatic screw threader; —изация, —ика *f.* automation; —изм *m.* automatism, automatic performance; —ический *a.* automatic, auto—, self-acting; automatically adjusting; power-driven, power-operated, power; —ическая подача automatic feed, power feed.

автомашина *f.* motor vehicle, car.

автомобиль *m.*, —ный *a.* automobile, car; а.-платформа *m.* flat truck; а.-цистерна *f.* tank truck; грузовой а. truck.

автомолит *m.* (min.) automolite, zinc spinel, zinc gahnite.

автоморф/изм *m.* automorphism; —ный *a.* automorphic (function); (petr.) automorphic, euhedral, idiomorphic; частично—ный hypidiomorphic, subhedral.

авто/мотриса *f.* railway motor car, rail car; —номный *a.* autonomous, independent, self-contained; —пилот *m.* mechanical pilot; autopilot, automatic pilot; —плуг *m.* mechanical plow; —податчик *m.* power feed; —покрышка *f.* automobile tire, tire tread; —проводимость *f.* (elec.) auto-conduction; —промышленность *f.* automobile industry; —псия *f.* (med.) autopsy.

автор *m.* author.

авторадио/граф, —снимок *m.* (tracer technology) autoradiograph, radio-autograph; —графия *f.* autoradiography; —метр *m.* car-borne radiometer.

авторегулировка *f.* automatic control (system).

авторемонтная мастерская auto repair shop, garage.

автореферат *m.* author's abstract.

авторизованный *a.* authorized.

авторитет *m.* authority, power; —ный *a.* authoritative.

авторс/кий *a.* author's; а. лист author index; —кое право copyright; —тво *n.* authorship.

авторучка *f.* fountain pen.

**авто/сани** *pl.* motor sleigh; —**син** *m.*, —**синный** *a.* (elec.) autosyn, selsyn, synchro; —**сома** *f.* (biol.) autosome; —**сомальный, —сомный** *a.* autosomal; —**сообщение** *n.* motor communication; —**стоп** *m.* automatic stop; —**страда** *f.* highway; —**строение** *n.* automobile construction; —**сцепка** *f.* automatic coupler; —**типия** *f.* (phot.) autotype; —**томия** *f.* (biol.) autotomy, self-division; —**тракторный** *a.* motor and tractor; automotive; —**транспорт** *m.* motor transport; —**трансформатор** *m.* (elec.) autotransformer, compensator; —**фазировка** *f.* phase stability (in accelerators); automatic phase stabilization; —**фретаж** *m.*, —**фретирование** *n.* self-loading; —**хром** *m.* (phot.) autochrome.

**автохтон** *m.* (geol.) autochthon; —**ный** *a.* autochthonous, indigenous.

**авто/цидные пояса** insecticide-impregnated strips (of burlap or paper); —**шина** *f.* automobile tire.

**А/Г** *abbr.* (отношение альбуминов к глобулинам) albumin-globulin ratio, A/G.

**агав/а** *f.* (bot.) agave; —**оза** *f.* agavose.

**агальматолит** *m.* (min.) agalmatolite; pagodite; pyrophyllite.

**агамный** *a.* (biol.) agamic, parthenogenetic; (bot.) agamous, cryptogamous.

**агар-агар** *m.* agar-agar.

**агарикус** *m.* agaric, white agaric.

**агаритрин** *m.* agarythrine.

**агарицин** *m.* agaricin; —**овая кислота** agaricic acid, agaric acid.

**агаро/вый** *a.* agar; —**ид** *m.* agaroid.

**агат** *m.* (min.) agate (a variegated chalcedony).

**агатин** *m.* agathin, cosmin.

**агатис** *m.* (bot.) agathis.

**агато/вый** *a.* agate; —**подобный** *a.* agate-like.

**агглом ер/ат** *m.* agglomerate, sinter, sinter cake; —**ационный** *a.* agglomeration; —**ационный обжиг** sinter roasting, sintering; —**ационная печь** sintering furnace; —**ация** *f.*, —**ирование** *n.* agglomeration, sintering; —**ирующее средство** agglomerant.

**агглютин/ация** *f.* agglutination; —**ин** *m.* agglutinin; —**ировать** *v.* agglutinate; —**ирующий** *a.* agglutinating.

**агградация** *f.* aggradation.

**аггрег/ат** *m.*, —**атный** *a.* aggregate; set, outfit, unit; assembly; plant, plant unit; apparatus; **топочный а.** furnace unit; —**атное состояние** state of aggregation; —**ация** *f.* aggregation.

**агент** *m.* agent, factor; —**ant, —ent; дезактивирующий а.** decontaminant; —**ский** *a.* agent, acting; —**ство** *n.*, —**ура** *f.* agency.

**агеострофический** *a.* (meteor.) ageostrophic.

**агиларит** *m.* (min.) aguilarite (silver selenide).

**агирный** *a.* (cryst.) triclinic.

**агит/атор** *m.* agitator, stirrer; —**ационнопенный процесс** (flotation) agitation-froth process; —**ационный** *a.* agitation; —**ация** *f.* agitation, stirring; —**ировать** *v.* agitate, stir.

**агликон** *m.* aglycone.

**агломерат** *see* **аггломерат.**

**аглу—** *see* **агглю—.**

**аглюкон** *m.* aglucone.

**агглютинировать** *see* **агглютинировать.**

**агматин** *m.* agmatine, aminobutyl guanidine.

**агнец** *m.* lamb; **непорочный а.** (bot.) Agnus castus (*Vitex agnus-castus*).

**агностерин** *m.* agnosterol.

**агометр** *m.* (elec.) agometer.

**агона, —льная кривая** *f.* agonic line.

**агониадин** *m.* agoniadin, plumierin.

**агоническая линия** agonic line.

**агония** *f.* agony.

**агпаитовый** *a.* (petr.) agpaitic.

**агранулоцитоз** *m.* (med.) agranulocytosis.

**аграрный** *a.* agrarian, agricultural.

**агрегат** *see* **аггрегат.**

**агресси/вный** *a.* aggressive; —**я** *f.* aggression.

**агриколит** *m.* (min.) agricolite (related to eulytite).

**агрикультур/а** *f.*, —**ный** *a.* agriculture.

**агрилит** *m.* (met.) Agrilite (copper-tin-lead, etc., alloy).

**агро—** *prefix* agro—, agricultural; —**база** *f.* agricultural base; —**биология** *f.* agrobiology, agricultural biology;

—**мелиорация** *f.* land improvement; —**метеорология** *f.* agricultural meteorology;—**метр** *m.* (geodesy) agrometer.

**агроном** *m.* agronomist, agriculturist; **а.-механизатор** *m.* agricultural engineer; —**ический** *a.* agronomic, agricultural; —**ия** *f.* agronomy, agriculture.

**агро/почвенный** *a.* agropedological; —**почвоведение** *n.* agropedology, agronomic soil science; —**пульверизатор** *m.* sprayer; —**пункт** *m.* agricultural experiment station; —**техника** *f.* agricultural technology; —**учеба** *f.* agricultural training.

**Агрофак** *abbr.* (**Агрономический факультет**) Faculty of Agronomy.

**агро/фон** *m.* soil preparation; soil fertility; —**химический** *a.* agrochemical; —**химия** *f.* agrochemistry, agricultural chemistry.

**агроцибин** *m.* agrocybin.

**агрумовые масла** citrus oils.

**А Г соль** *f.* nylon salt, hexamethylenediamine adipate.

**агума** *f.* soybean meal.

**агурин** *m.* Agurin, theobromine sodium acetate.

**агуттан** *m.* aguttan.

**адалин** *m.* Adalin, Uradal, carbromal.

**адамант** *m.* diamond; —**овый** *a.* adamantine; firm, steadfast.

**адамеллит** *m.* (petr.) adamellite (a diorite).

**адам/ин** *m.* (min.) adamite; —**ит** *m.* adamite (abrasive).

**адамово яблоко** (anat.) Adam's apple.

**адамон** *m.* adamon.

**адамсит** *m.* (min.) adamsite (a variety of mica); adamsite (poison gas).

**адансон/ин** *m.* adansonine; —**ия** *f.* (bot.) baobab (*Adansonia digitata*).

**адапт/ация** *f.* adaptation; —**ер** *m.* adapter; (rad.) pickup; —**ировать** *v.* adapt.

**адвек/тивный** *a.* (meteor.) advective, advection; —**ция** *f.* advection.

**адвокат** *m.* lawyer, attorney; advocate; —**ура** *f.* bar.

**адгези/онный** *a.*, —**я** *f.* adhesion.

**аддисонова болезнь** (med.) Addison's disease, bronzed skin.

**аддитивн/ость** *f.* additivity; —**ый** *a.* additive.

**аддукт** *m.* (chem.) adduct, inclusion complex.

**адекватн/о** *adv.* adequately, sufficiently; equally; —**ость** *f.* adequacy; —**ый** *a.* adequate, sufficient; equal (to).

**аделит** *m.* (min.) adelite.

**аден/аза** *f.* adenase, adenosine monophosphate; —**иловая кислота** adenylic acid; —**ин** *m.* adenine, 6-aminopurine; —**ит** *m.* adenitis, gland inflammation; —**озин** *m.* adenosine, adenine riboside.

**аденоид** *m.*, —**ный** *a.* (med.) adenoid.

**адергнейс** *m.* (petr.) banded gneiss.

**адермин** *m.* (obs.) adermin, vitamin $B_6$.

**адиабат/а** *f.* adiabatic curve; —**ический,** —**ичный,** —**ный** *a.* adiabatic.

**адиактинический** *a.* adiactinic.

**адиант,** —**ум** *m.* (bot.) maidenhair, Venus hair (*Adiantum capillus veneris*).

**адип/ил** *m.* adipyl; —**иновая кислота** adipic acid, hexanedioic acid; —**иновый альдегид** adipic dialdehyde, adipaldehyde; —**оин** *m.* adipoin, 2-hydroxycyclohexanone.

**администра/тивный** *a.* administrative; —**ция** *f.* administration.

**адмиралтейс/кий металл** admiralty metal; —**тво** *n.* shipyard, navy yard, dockyard.

**адмитанц** *m.* (elec.) admittance.

**адмонский двойной купорос** Salzburg vitriol (mixed cupric and ferrous sulfate).

**адник** *m.* (met.) Adnic (copper-nickel-tin alloy).

**адон/идин** *m.* adonidin; —**илен** *m.* adonilen; —**ин** *m.* adonin; —**ис** *m.* (bot.) adonis; —**ит** *m.* adonite, adonitol.

**адрагант** *m.*, —**гумми** tragacanth (gum).

**адренал/ин** *m.* adrenaline, epinephrine; —**он** *m.* adrenalone.

**адренохром** *m.* adrenochrome.

**адрес** *m.* address; **а.-календарь,** —**ная книга** directory; —**ант** *m.* addresser, sender; —**ат** *m.* addressee; —**овать** *v.* address, direct; refer.

**адрианопольский красный** Turkey red.

**адск/ий камень** lunar caustic, silver nitrate; **—ое масло** curcas oil; castor oil; very poor grade of olive oil.

**адсорб/ат** *m.* adsorbate; **—ент** *m.* adsorbent; **—ер** *m.* adsorber; adsorbent; **—ирование** *n.*, **—ционный** *a.*, **—ция** *f.* adsorption; **—ированный** *a.* adsorbed; **—ировать** *v.* adsorb; **—ционная способность** adsorptive capacity, adsorbability.

**АДУ** *abbr.* (**аппаратура дистанционного управления**) remote control equipment.

**адул/арий**, **—яр** *m.* (min.) adularia, adular (a form of orthoclase feldspar).

**адурол** *m.* (phot.) adurol.

**адус/ация**, **—сация** *f.* (met.) malleablizing.

**АДФ** *abbr.* (**аденозиндифосфорная кислота**) adenosine diphosphate, ADP.

**адхезия** *see* **адгезия**.

**адъективные красители** mordant dyes.

**адъюнкт** *m.* adjunct, assistant.

**адыры** *pl.* adyry (low foothills bordering the Ferghana depression).

**АЕ** *abbr.* (**антигенные единицы**) antigen units.

**АЕМ** *abbr.* (**атомная единица массы**) atomic mass unit, amu.

**ажгон** *m.* (bot.) an herb (*Trachyspermum copticum* or *T. ammi*); ajowan (fruit of *Carum copticum*).

**ажур/ый** *a.* openwork; skeleton; fret (saw); **—ая работа** openwork.

**азал/еин** *m.* azalein, fuchsin, aniline red; **—ея**, **—ия** *f.* (bot.) azalea.

**азар/ил** *m.*, **—иловый** *a.* asaryl; **—ин** *m.* azarin (dye); *see also* **азарон**; **—овое масло** asarum oil; **—он** *m.* asarone, asarin, asarum camphor; **—оновая кислота** asaronic acid, 2,4,5-trimethoxybenzoic acid.

**азафрин** *m.* azafrin.

**азбест** *see* **асбест**.

**азбол/ин** *m.* asbolin; **—ит** *m.* (min.) asbolite, earthy cobalt.

**азбука** *f.* alphabet.

**азеботин** *m.* asebotin.

**азелаин** *m.* azelain; **—овая кислота** azelaic acid, nonanedioic acid; **соль —овой кислоты** azelate; **—овокислый** *a.* azelaic acid; azelate (of); **—овокислая соль** azelate.

**азела/ол** *m.* azelaol, cycloöctanol; **—он** *m.* azelaone, cycloöctanone.

**азеотроп** *m.* azeotrope; **—ический**, **—ный** *a.* azeotropic.

**азерб.** *abbr.* (**азербайджанский**) Azerbaidzhan.

**ази—** *prefix* azi—.

**азиатикозид** *m.* asiaticoside.

**азиатский** *a.* Asiatic.

**азибензил** *m.* azibenzil.

**азид** *m.* azide; **а. натрия** (expl.) sodium azide.

**азид—**, **азидо—** *prefix* azid—, azido—, triazo—; **—ометан** *m.* azidomethane.

**азимина, трехдольная а.** *f.* (bot.) papaw (*Asimina triloba*).

**азимино—** *prefix* azimino—, azimido—; **—бензол** *m.* aziminobenzene, benzotriazole.

**азиминовое дерево** *see* **азимина**.

**азимут** *m.* azimuth; **—альный** *a.* azimuthal; **—альный круг** azimuth adjustment slide rule.

**азин** *m.*, **—овый** *a.* azine; **—окраски** *pl.* azino dyes.

**азиэтан** *m.* aziethane, diazoethane.

**Азия** Asia.

**Аз/нефть** *abbr.* (**Азербайджанское центральное нефтяное управление**) Board of Azerbaidzhan Oil Works, or Azneft; **—НИИЗ** *abbr.* (**Азербайджанский научно-исследовательский институт земледелия**) Azerbaidzhan Research Institute of Agriculture.

**азо—** *prefix* azo—; **—бензол** *m.* azobenzene; **—голубой** *m.* azo blue; **—ид** *see* **азид—**; **—имид** *m.* azoimide, hydrazoic acid.

**азойский** *a.* (geol.) azoic (without life).

**азо/кислотный** *a.* azo acid; **—краски**, **—красители** *pl.* azo dyes; **—кси** *prefix* azoxy-; **—ксибензол** *m.* azoxybenzene; **—ксисоединение** *n.* azoxy compound; **—л** *m.* azole; **—метин** *m.* azomethyne; **—нафталин** *m.* azonaphthalene.

**азосоединение** *n.* azo compound.

**азосочетание** *n.* nitrogen coupling.

**азот** *m.* nitrogen, N; **двуокись —a** nitrogen peroxide; **закись —a** nitrous oxide; **окись —a** nitric oxide; **—выделяющие бактерии** *see* **азотобактер**;

—**емия** *f.* (med.) azotemia, uremia; —**изация** *see* **азотирование.**
**азотин** *m.* (expl.) azotine.
**азотиров/ание** *n.* nitration; (met.) nitriding; —**анный** *a.* nitrated; nitrided; —**анная сталь** nitriding steel, nitralloy; —**ать** *v.* nitrate; nitride.
**азотисто/амиловый эфир** amyl nitrite; —**аммониевая соль** ammonium nitrite; —**водородная кислота** hydrazoic acid; **соль** —**водородной кислоты** hydrazoate; —**калиевая соль** potassium nitrite; —**кальциевая соль** calcium nitrite; —**кислый** *a.* nitrous acid; nitrite (of); —**кислый натрий** sodium nitrite; —**кислая соль** nitrite; —**медная соль** cupric nitrite; —**метиловый эфир** methyl nitrite; —**натриевая соль** sodium nitrite; —**этиловый эфир** ethyl nitrite.
**азотист/ый** *a.* nitrous, nitrogenous, nitride (of); **а. алюминий** aluminum nitride; **а. ангидрид** nitrous anhydride, nitrogen trioxide; **а. бор** boron nitride; **а. кальций** calcium nitride; —**ая известь** calcium cyanamide; —**ая кислота** nitrous acid; **соль** —**ой кислоты** nitrite.
**азотно/амиловый эфир** amyl nitrate; —**аммониевая соль** ammonium nitrate; —**бариевая соль** barium nitrate.
**азотноват/ая кислота** hyponitric acid (old name for nitrogen peroxide); —**истая кислота** hyponitrous acid; **соль** —**истой кислоты** hyponitrite; —**истоаммиачная соль** ammonium hyponitrite; —**истокислый** *a.* hyponitrous acid; hyponitrite (of); —**истокислая соль** hyponitrite; —**истосеребряная соль** silver hyponitrite; —**ый ангидрид** nitrogen peroxide.
**азотно/висмутовая соль** bismuth nitrate; **основная** —**висмутовая соль** bismuth subnitrate; —**глицериновый эфир** glycerol trinitrate, nitroglycerin; —**железистая соль** ferrous nitrate; —**железная соль** ferric nitrate; —**калиевая соль** potassium nitrate; —**кальциевая соль** calcium nitrate; —**кислотный** *a.* nitric acid; —**кислый** *a.* nitric acid; nitrate (of); —**кислый калий** potassium nitrate;

—**кислый сплав** niter cake; —**кислая соль** nitrate; —**медная соль** cupric nitrate; —**метиловый эфир** methyl nitrate; —**натриевая соль** sodium nitrate; —**ртутистая соль** mercurous nitrate; —**ртутная соль** mercuric nitrate; —**серебряная соль** silver nitrate; —**стибиловая соль** antimonyl nitrate; —**стронциевая соль** strontium nitrate; —**этиловый эфир** ethyl nitrate.
**азотн/ый** *a.* nitric, nitrogen, nitrogenous; **а. ангидрид** nitric anhydride, nitrogen pentoxide; —**ая кислота** nitric acid; **соль** —**ой кислоты** nitrate.
**азотобактер** *m.* Azotobacter, nitrogen-fixing bacteria; —**ин** *m.* bacterial fertilizer.
**азотолуол** *m.* azotoluene.
**азот/ометр** *m.* azotometer; —**углеродистый титан** titanium carbonitride; —**офиксация** *f.* nitrogen fixation; —**содержащий** *a.* nitrogen-containing.
**азо/фенол** *m.* azophenol; —**форовый** *a.* azophor; —**фоска** *f.* a nitrogen-phosphorus-potassium fertilizer.
**азул/ен** *m.* azulene; —**ин** *m.* azulin; —**миновая кислота** azulmic acid, azulmin.
**азур** *m.* (micros.) azure blue dye; —**ин** *m.* azurine; —**ит** *m.* (min.) azurite, chessylite, azure stone.
**АИЗ** *abbr.* (Ассоциация изобретателей) Association of Inventors.
**АИМ** *abbr.* (амплитудно-импульсная модуляция) pulse-amplitude modulation, PAM.
**аир** *m.* (bot.) sweet flag (*Acorus calamus*); —**ный** *a.* sweet flag, calamus; —**ное масло** calamus oil.
**аистник** *m.* (bot.) storksbill (*Erodium*).
**айв/а** *f.*, —**овый** *a.* (bot.) quince (*Cydonia*).
**айкинит** *m.* (min.) aikinite, needle ore.
**айлант** *m.* (bot.) ailanthus (*Ailanthus glandulosa*); —**овая кислота** ailanthic acid.
**аймафибрит** *see* **гемафибрит.**
**айован** *see* **ажгон.**
**Айри спиралы** (cryst.) Airy's spirals.
**айрол** *m.* Airol, bismuth oxyiodogallate.
**айсберг** *m.* iceberg.

**Айткена счетчик** Aitken (nuclei) counter.

**Айх металл, —а металл** Aich's metal (a type of gun metal).

**академ/ик** *m.* academician, member of the academy; **—ист** *m.* academist; **—ический** *a.* academic; **—ия** *f.* academy.

**акадиалит** *m.* (min.) acadialite (a variety of chabazite).

**акажу-дерево** *n.* mahogany (wood); **a.-камедь** acajou (gum).

**аказгин** *m.* akazgine.

**акакатехин** *m.* acacatechin.

**акалит** *see* **галалит.**

**акант** *m.* (bot.) bear's breech (*Acanthus*).

**акантит** *m.* (min.) acanthite (a silver sulfide).

**акантобделлы** *pl.* (zool.) Acanthob-dellida.

**акантов/ое масло** bear's breech oil; **—ые** *pl.* (bot.) Acanthaceae.

**аканф** *see* **акант.**

**акар/иазис** *m.* acariasis, mite infestation; **—ид** *m.* acarid, mite; **—ицид** *m.* acaricide (a mite killer); **—оид** *m.*, **—оидная смола** acaroid resin, yacca gum.

**акац/етин** *m.* acacetin; **—иевое масло** acacia oil; **—иин** *m.* acaciin.

**акация** *f.* (bot.) acacia; **белая a.** black locust (*Robinia pseudoacacia*); **желтая a.** Siberian acacia (*Caragana arborescens*).

**аква/вит** *m.* aqua vitae (brandy or whiskey); **—даг** *m.* Aquadag (a graphite lubricant); **—жел** *m.* aquagel (an alkali-treated bentonite clay).

**аквамарин** *m.*, **—ный, —овый** *a.* (min.) aquamarine (a variety of beryl).

**акварельные краскн** water colors.

**аквариум** *m.* aquarium.

**акведук, —т** *m.* aqueduct, conduit.

**аквизитор** *m.* buyer.

**аквилегия** *f.* (bot.) aquilegia.

**акво—** *prefix* aquo—.

**акер/ит** *m.* (petr.) akerite (a variety of syenite); **—манит** *m.* (min.) akermanite.

**акилей** *see* **аквилегия.**

**акклиматиз/ация** *f.*, **—ирование** *n.* acclimatization; **—ованный** *a.* acclimatized.

**аккомодация** *f.* accommodation, adaptation.

**аккомпанировать** *v.* accompany.

**аккордная работа** piece work.

**аккракопал** *m.* accra copal; **—овая кислота** accra-copalic acid; **—оловая кислота** accra-copalolic acid.

**аккредит/ив** *m.* letter of credit, bill of credit; **—ированный** *a.* accredited; **—ировать, —овать** *v.* accredit, give credit, open credit (with).

**аккреция** *f.* accretion.

**аккумулиров/ание** *n.* accumulation, storage; **—анный** *a.* accumulated, stored; accumulative; **—ать** *v.* accumulate, store, store up, collect; retain (heat).

**аккумулятор** *m.*, **—ный** *a.* (elec.) accumulator, storage cell, storage battery; reservoir; **—ная** *f.* battery room; **—ный сосуд** accumulator jar; **—ный элемент** battery cell, storage cell; **—ная батарея** storage battery; **—ная кислота** battery acid (a strength of sulfuric acid).

**аккумуляция** *see* **аккумулирование.**

**аккуратн/о** *adv.* accurately, exactly; neatly; **—ость** *f.* accuracy, exactness, precision; neatness; **—ый** *a.* accurate, exact, precise, punctual; neat.

**аклин/а, —аль** *f.*, **—ическая линия** aclinic line, magnetic equator; **—ический** *a.* aclinic.

**акмит** *m.* (min.) acmite (a pyroxene).

**акобальтозный** *a.* (vet.) cobalt-deficient.

**акоин** *m.* acoin, acoine, guanicaine.

**аколитин** *m.* acolytine.

**акон/еллин** *m.* aconelline; **—ин** *m.* aconine; **—ит** *m.* (bot.) aconite (*Aconitum*); **—итин** *m.* aconitine, acetylbenzoylaconine; **—итовая кислота** aconitic acid, 1,2,3-propene tricarboxylic acid; **соль —итовой кислоты, —итовокислая соль** aconitate; **—овая кислота** aconic acid.

**акр** *m.* acre.

**акрид/ан** *m.* acridan, 5,10-dihydroacridine; **—ил** *m.* acridyl; **—ин** *m.* acridine; **—иновый** *a.* acridine, acridinic; **—иновая кислота** acridic acid, acridinic acid; **—иновые краски** acridine dyes; **—ол** *m.* acridol; **—он** *m.* acridone, ketodihydroacridine.

**акрил** *m.* acryl; —**ил** *m.* acrylyl; —**овый** *a.* acryl, acrylic; —**овый альдегид** acrylaldehyde, acrolein, propenal; —**овая кислота** acrylic acid, propenoic acid; **соль** —**овой кислоты,** —**овокислая соль** acrylate; —**овая смола** acrylic resin; —**онитрил** *m.* acrylonitrile, propenenitrile; —**офенон** *m.* acrylophenone.

**акри/т** *m.* acritol; —**флавин** *m.* acriflavine; —**хин** *m.* acrichin (Soviet term for quinacrine hydrochloride).

**акроза** *f.* acrose.

**акроидес** *m.* acaroid resin, accroides gum.

**акрокамера** *f.* a type of combustion chamber.

**акрол/еин** *m.* acrolein, acrylaldehyde; —**ит** *m.* acrolite (synthetic resin).

**акромегалия** *f.* (med.) acromegaly.

**акрофлекс** *m.* Acroflex (rubber antioxidant).

**акрофут** *m.* acre-foot.

**акселер**— *see* **акцелер**—.

**аксессуары** *pl.* accessories.

**аксиальн/о-симметричный** *a.* axisymmetric; —**ый** *a.* axial; axial-flow (pump).

**аксин** *m.* axin; —**ит** *m.* (min.) axinite.

**аксиолит** *m.* (petr.) axiolite (a type of spherulitic aggregates).

**аксиома** *f.* axiom; principle.

**аксис** *m.* axis.

**аксонометрический** *a.* axonometric.

**акт** *m.* act, event; statement, report; document; (law) deed; **а. ионизации** ionizing event; **на а. деления** per fission.

**акт.** *abbr.* (**активный**) active; (**актуальный**) actual.

**АКТГ** *abbr.* (**адренокортикотропный гормон**)adrenocorticotropic hormone, ACTH.

**актив** *m.* assets; active members.

**актив/атор** *m.* activator, promoter; —**ационный** *a.,* —**ация** *f.,* —**ирование** *n.* activation; —**изировать,** —**ировать** *v.* activate, promote, accelerate; —**ин** *m.* (pharm.) Activin; —**ированный** *a.* activated; —**ирующее вещество** activating agent; —**нодействующий** *a.* active; —**ность** *f.* activity; radioactivity; —**ный** *a.*

active; industrious; operating; (nucl.) radioactive (sample), fissionable (material); —**ная зона** active section, core (of nuclear reactor); —**ная масса** filling paste, grid plug (of storage battery).

**актидион** *m.* actidione, cycloheximide.

**актин** *m.* actin; —**идиевые** *pl.* (bot.) Actinidiaceae; —**идия** *f.* (bot.) actinidia; —**иды** *pl.* actinides (elements); —**изм** *m.,* —**ичность** *f.* actinism; —**ий** *m.* actinium, Ac; **эманация** —**ия** actinon, An; —**ин** *m.* actinine; —**ический,** —**ичный** *a.* actinic.

**актино**— *prefix* actino— (rays, radiated structure); —**граф** *m.* actinograph; —**иды** *see* **актиниды;** —**лизин** *m.* actinolysin; —**лит** *m.* (min.) actinolite (a variety of amphibole); —**логия** *f.* actinology.

**актинометр** *m.* actinometer; —**ический** *a.* actinometric; —**ия** *f.* actinometry.

**актино/микоз** *m.* (vet.) actinomycosis; —**миксидии** *pl.* (zool.) Actinomyxidia; —**мицелин** *m.* actinomycelin; —**мицетин** *m.* actinomycetin; —**мицеты** *pl.* (bact.) Actinomycetes; —**мицин** *m.* actinomycin; —**н** *m.* actinon, An; —**родин** *m.* actinorhodine; —**рубин** *m.* actinorubin; —**скопия** *f.* actinoscopy; —**уран** *m.* actinouranium, AcU; —**фотометр** *m.* actinic photometer; —**химия** *f.* actinochemistry; —**электричество** *n.* actinoelectricity.

**актитиазовая кислота** actithiazic acid.

**актный** *a. of* **акт.**

**актовый зал** assembly hall.

**актол** *m.* Actol, silver lactate.

**актомиозин** *m.* actomyosin.

**актуальн/ость** *f.* actuality; —**ый** *a.* actual; present; urgent; timely.

**акула** *f.* (zool.) shark; **собачья а.** dog fish.

**акуметр** *m.* acoumeter.

**акундар/овая кислота** akundaric acid; —**ол** *m.* akundarol.

**акусти/ка** *f.* acoustics; —**ческий** *a.* acoustic.

**акушер** *m.* (med.) obstetrician; —**ский** *a.* obstetric; —**ство** *n.* obstetrics.

**акцелер/атор** *m.* accelerator; —**ация** *f.* acceleration; —**ен** *m.* accelerene, *p*-nitrosodimethylaniline; —**ограф** *m.* accelerograph; —**ометр** *m.* accelerometer.

**акцент** *m.* accent, accentuation; —**ировать**, —**овать** *v.* accent, accentuate.

**Акцентр** *abbr.* (Управление научных и научно-художественных учреждений академического центра) Board for Academic and Arts and Science Institutes of the Academic Center.

**акцепт** *m.* (com.) acceptance; —**ант** *m.* acceptor; —**ировать**, —**овать** *v.* accept; —**ование** *n.* acceptance; —**ор** *m.*, —**орный** *a.* (chem.) acceptor.

**акцессорный** *a.* accessory.

**акцидентный** *a.* accidental.

**акциз** *m.* (com.) excise; —**ная проба** test for asphalt-tar constituents in petroleum; —**ные** *pl.* the tars determined by this method.

**акци/онер** *m.* (com.) stockholder, shareholder; —**онерный** *a.* joint-stock; —**я** *f.* share, stock; **торговля** —**ями** jobbing.

**ал**— *see also* **аль**—.

**алабамий** *m.* alabamium, alabamine, Ab.

**алабанд/ин**, —**ит** *m.* (min.) alabandite, alabandine, manganblende.

**алабастриновый** *a.* alabastrine.

**алаит** *m.* (min.) alaite.

**алакреатин** *m.* alacreatine, guanidopropionic acid; —**ин** *m.* alacreatinine.

**алалит** *m.* (min.) alalite (a variety of diopside pyroxene).

**аламозит** *m.* (min.) alamosite.

**алан/ил** *m.* alanyl; —**ин** *m.* alanine, 2-aminopropanoic acid; —**иновый** *a.* alanine.

**алант/ин** *m.* alantin, inulin; —**овая кислота** alantic acid, inulic acid; —**овое масло** elecampane oil, inula oil; —**ол** *m.* alantol, pinguin; —**олактон** *m.* alantolactone, helenin.

**алануровая кислота** alanuric acid.

**алас** *m.* meadowland surrounding a lake.

**алая** *see under* **алый**.

**албана** *f.* albane.

**алболит** *see* **альболит**.

**алвеолярный** *see* **альвеолярный**.

**алгебра** *f.* algebra; —**ический** *a.* algebraic.

**алгидный** *a.* (med.) algid, cold.

**алгин** *m.*, —**овая кислота** algin, alginic acid.

**алгодонит** *m.* (min.) algodonite (native copper arsenide).

**алголовый краситель** algol dye.

**алгорифм** *m.* (math.) algorithm.

**алдегид** *see* **альдегид**.

**алдрин** *m.* aldrin (insecticide).

**алебастр** *m.* (min.) alabaster (a variety of gypsum); plaster of Paris; —**овый** *a.* alabaster, alabastrine.

**алевр/ит** *m.*, —**итовый** *a.* silt, aleurite; —**олит** *m.* siltstone, aleurolite.

**алейдрин** *m.* aleudrin, dichloroisopropyl carbamate.

**алейр/итиновая кислота** aleuritic acid; —**одиды** *pl.* white flies (Aleyrodidae); —**ометр** *m.* aleurometer (for testing flour); —**он** *m.* aleurone; —**онат** *m.* aleuronate; —**оновый** *a.* aleurone, aleuronic.

**александри/йский** *a.* Alexander; **а. лист** (pharm.) senna leaves; —**йская бумага** royal paper; —**т** *m.* (min.) alexandrite (a variety of chrysoberyl).

**алексин** *m.* (immunology) alexin, complement.

**алембик** *m.* alembic, retort, distilling vessel.

**алембротовая соль** alembroth (mercury ammonium chloride).

**аленка** *see* **оленка**.

**алепские чернильные орешки** Aleppo galls.

**алетр/ис** *m.* (bot.) Aletris; —**оид** *m.* aletroid, aletrin.

**алеть** *v.* redden, glow.

**алеуродиды** *see* **алейродиды**.

**алеутский** *a.* Aleutian.

**алжирский металл** Algerian metal (tin alloy).

**аливал** *m.* alival, iodopropyleneglycol.

**алидада** *f.* (surv.) alidade.

**ализарин** *m.* alizarin; —**овый** *a.* alizarin, alizaric; —**овая кислота** alizaric acid, phthalic acid; **соль** —**овой кислоты**, —**овокислая соль** alizarate; —**овое масло** alizarin oil, Turkey red oil; —**овые краски** alizarin dyes.

**аликантная сода** kelp (ashes).

**аликв/антный** *a.* (math.) aliquant; —**отный** *a.* aliquot.

**алипин** *m.* alypin.

**алит** *m.* (cement) alite.

**алитиров/ание** *n.* calorizing, coating with aluminum; —**ать** *v.* calorize, aluminize, alite.

**алифа** *see* **олифа.**

**али/фатический** *a.* aliphatic; —**циклический** *a.* alicyclic.

**алкадиен** *m.* alkadiene.

**алкали** *n.* alkali, *see also* **щелочь;** —**зация** *f.* alkalization; —**зировать** *v.* alkalize; —**метр** *m.* alkalimeter; —**метрический** *a.* alkalimetric; —**метрия** *f.* alkalimetry; —**ческий** *a.* alkaline.

**алкалоз** *m.* (med.) alkalosis.

**алкалоид** *m.,* —**ный** *a.* alkaloid.

**алк/амин** *m.* alkamine, amino alcohol; —**ан** *m.* alkane.

**алканн/а** *f.,* —**ый** *a.* (bot.) alkanna; —**ин** *m.* alkannin, anchusin; —**ая кислота** alkannic acid.

**алкар/ген** *m.* alkargen, cacodylic acid; —**зин** *m.* alkarsin, cacodyl oxide.

**алкен** *m.* alkene; —**ирование** *n.* alkenylation.

**алкермес** *m.* alkermes, kermes (dye).

**алкидн/ый** *a.* alkyd; —**ая смола** alkyd resin.

**алкил** *m.* alkyl; **сернистый а.** alkyl sulfide; —**амин** *m.* alkylamine; —**ен** *m.* alkylene; —**иден** *m.* alkylidene; —**ирование** *n.* alkylation; —**ированный** *a.* alkylated; —**ировать** *v.* alkylate, introduce alkyl (into); —**ирующее средство** alkylating agent; —**овый** *a.* alkyl.

**алкин** *m.* alkyne.

**алклэд** *see* **алькльэд.**

**алкогель** *m.* alcogel.

**алкогол/из** *m.* alcoholysis; —**изация** *f.* alcoholization; **иметр, —ометр** *m.* alcoholometer; —**иметрия, —ометрия** *f.* alcoholometry; —**ический** *a.* alcoholic; —**ь** *m.* alcohol; —**ьный** *a.* alcohol, alcoholic; —**ят** *m.* alcoholate.

**алкозоль** *m.* alcosol.

**алкокси—** *prefix* alkoxy—; —**алкилировать** *v.* convert into an alkoxy compound by alkylation; —**ариловать** *v.* convert into an alkoxy compound by arylation; —**лировать** *v.* alkoxylate.

**алкон** *m.* alkone.

**алкорноковая кора** alcornoco bark.

**алкумит** *m.* Alcumite (a copper-aluminum-iron-nickel alloy).

**алла/гит** *m.* (min.) allagite (an alteration product of rhodonite); —**ктит** *m.* (min.) allactite, allaktit; —**линит** *m.* (petr.) allalinite (an altered gabbro); —**нит** *m.* (min.) allanite, orthite.

**аллановая кислота** allanic acid.

**алланто/ин** *m.* allantoin, glyoxyl diureide; —**иновая кислота** allantoic acid, dicarbamidoacetic acid; **соль —иновой кислоты, —иновокислая соль** allantoate; —**ксаидин** *m.* allantoxaidine; —**ксановая кислота** allantoxanic acid.

**аллантуровая кислота** allanturic acid, glyoxalylurea.

**аллел/изм** *m.* (biol.) allelism; —**о-** *prefix* allelo— (reciprocally); —**отропический** *a.* allelotropic; —**отропия** *f.* allelotropism, equilibrium isomerism; —**ь** *m.* allele, allelomorph.

**аллемонтит** *m.* (min.) allemontite.

**аллен** *m.* allene, propadiene.

**аллерг/ен** *m.* (immunology) allergen; —**ия** *f.* allergy.

**аллея** *f.* alley, avenue.

**аллигатор** *m.,* —**ный** *a.* alligator.

**аллигация** *f.* alloy.

**аллил** *m.,* —**овый** *a.* allyl; —**ен** *m.* allylene, propyne; —**овый альдегид** allyl aldehyde, acrolein; —**овый спирт** allyl alcohol, 2-propen-1-ol.

**аллитуровая кислота** allituric acid.

**аллицин** *m.* allicin (antibacterial principle of garlic).

**аллобар** *m.* allobar (a form of element).

**аллоза** *f.* allose.

**алло/каин** *m.* allocain; —**клаз** *m.* (min.) alloclase, alloclasite (an impure glaucodot); —**коричная кислота** allocinnamic acid; —**ксазин** *m.* alloxazine.

**аллоксан** *m.* alloxan, mesoxalylurea; —**овая кислота** alloxanic acid; **соль —овой кислоты, —овокислая соль** alloxanate; —**тин** *m.* alloxantin.

**алло/мерия** *f.* (cryst.) allomerism; —**мерный** *a.* allomerous, allomeric; —**морфизм** *m.* (cryst.) allomorphism; —**морфный** *a.* allomorphic.

**аллонж** *m.* adapter; extractor (for zinc vapors); fly leaf.

**аллоновая кислота** allonic acid.

**аллопалладий** *m.* (min.) allopalladium.

**аллослизевая кислота** allomucic acid.

**алло/триоморфный** *a.* (cryst.) allotriomorphic, anhedral; **—тропизм** *m.*, **—тропия** *f.* allotropy, allotropism; **—тропический** *a.* allotropic.

**аллофан** *m.* (min.) allophane; **—овая кислота** allophanic acid, urea-carboxylic acid; **соль —овой кислоты, —овокислая соль** allophanate.

**аллохроит** *m.* (min.) allochroite (a variety of andradite garnet).

**аллохтон** *m.* (geol.) allochthon; **—ный** *a.* allochthonous (not formed in situ).

**аллувиальный** *see* **аллювиальный.**

**аллурановая кислота** alluranic acid.

**аллюв/иальный** *a.* (geol.) alluvial, superficial; **—иальное олово** (min.) alluvial tin, stream tin; **—ий** *m.* alluvium.

**алм—** *see* **альм—.**

**алмаз** *m.* diamond; **а. для резки стекла** diamond point.

**алмазилиум** *see* **альмасилиум.**

**алмаз/ный** *a.* diamond; **а. блеск** (min.) adamantine luster; **а. бур** diamond drill; **а. порошок** diamond dust; **а. шпат** (min.) adamantine spar, corundum; **—одержатель** *m.* diamond holder; **—оподобный** *a.* diamond-like, adamantine; **—содержащий** *a.* diamond-bearing; **—чик** *m.* diamond cutter.

**алмандин** *m.* (min.) almandine, almandite (a variety of garnet).

**ало** *adv.* reddishly; *n.* halo; **—ватый** *a.* reddish.

**аловольт** *m.* alowalt (abrasive).

**алодайн** *m.* Alodyne (coating on aluminum).

**алое** *see* **алоэ**; **—тин** *m.* aloetin (resin); **—тиновая кислота** aloetic acid, tetra-nitro-anthraquinone.

**алоин** *m.* aloin; **—оза** *f.* aloinose.

**алой** *see* **алоэ**; **—ный** *a.* aloe; aloe-fiber.

**алоксит** *m.* aloxite (fused alumina abrasive).

**алонж, —а** *see* **аллонж.**

**алоперин** *m.* aloperine (a Sophora alkaloid).

**алость** *f.* ruby color, ruby redness.

**алоэ** *n.* (bot.) aloe; **американское а.** agave; **смола а.** aloetin (resin).

**алперм** *m.* Alperm (aluminum-iron alloy).

**алпинин** *m.* alpinin.

**алстон/идин** *m.* alstonidine; **—ин** *m.* alstonine, chlorogenine; **—ит** *m.* (min.) alstonite, bromlite; **—ия** *f.* (bot.) alstonia.

**алтаит** *m.* (min.) altaite (lead telluride).

**алтеин** *m.* altheine.

**алтей** *m.*, **—ный** *a.* (bot.) Althaea.

**альтернант** *m.* (math.) alternant.

**алтро/за** *f.* altrose; **—новая кислота** altronic acid.

**алудель** *m.* aludel (condensing vessel).

**алудур** *m.* Aludur (aluminum-magnesium alloy).

**алумнол** *m.* Alumnol.

**алунд, —ум** *m.* alundum (abrasive).

**алун/ит** *m.* (min.) alunite, alumstone; **—итизированный** *a.* alunitized; **—оген** *m.* (min.) alunogen, feather alum.

**алфавит** *m.* alphabet; **—ный** *a.* alphabetic; **—ный указатель** index.

**алфальф/а** *f.* (bot.) alfalfa (*Medicago sativa*); **—он** *m.* alfalfone.

**алфенид** *see* **альфенид.**

**алфер** *m.* Alfer (iron-aluminum alloy).

**алфил** *m.* alphyl, alkyl-phenyl.

**алхим/ик** *m.* alchemist; **—ия** *f.* alchemy.

**ал/ый** *a.* reddish, blood red, ruby-colored; **—ая кислота** scarlet acid, phosgenated J acid.

**алыча** *f.* (bot.) cherry plum (*Prunus divaricata* or *P. cerasifera*).

**альбакор** *m.* (zool.) albacore.

**альбедо** *n.* albedo (reflection factor).

**альберт/ит** *m.* (min.) albertite (a variety of mineral asphalt); **—ол** *m.* albertol (a phenol-formaldehyde resin).

**альбидин** *m.* albidin.

**альбизия** *f.* (bot.) albizzia.

**альбин** *see* **апофиллит.**

**альбин/изм** *m.* (biol.) albinism; **—ос** *m.* albino.

**альбион-металл** *m.* Albion metal (a lead-tin laminate).

**альбит** *m.* (min.) albite (a plagioclase feldspar); **—изация** *f.* albitization; **—овый** *a.* albite.

**альбо—** *prefix* albo— (white, whitish); **—лен** *m.* albolene; **—лит** *m.* (cement) albolite, albolith.

**альбом** *m.* album.

**альбо/мицин** *m.* albomycin; —**феррин** *m.* alboferrin, iron phosphoalbuminate.

**альбумин** *m.* albumin; albumen; —**ат** *m.* albuminate; —**иметр** *m.* albuminometer; —**ин** *m.* albuminin; —**ный**, —**овый** *a.* albumin, albuminoid, albuminous; albumen; (phot.) albumin (paper); —**оза** *f.* albuminose; —**озный** *a.* albuminous; —**оид** *m.* albuminoid; —**урия** *f.* (med.) albuminuria.

**альбум/оза** *f.* albumose; —**оид** *m.* albumoid.

**альвеин** *m.* alvein.

**альвеолярный** *a.* alveolar.

**альга** *f.* (bot.) alga.

**альгаробилла** *f.* algarobilla, algaroba.

**альгаротов порошок** algaroth powder, antimony oxychloride.

**альгин** *see* **алгин.**

**альгология** *f.* algology, phycology.

**альдазин** *m.* aldazine.

**альдамин** *m.* Aldamin, aldol-α-naphthylamine.

**альдегид** *m.,* —**ный** *a.* aldehyde; **а. муравьиной кислоты** formaldehyde; **уксусный а.** acetaldehyde; —**аммиак** *m.* aldehyde ammonia; —**ин** *m.* aldehydine; —**ная смола** aldehyde resin; —**окислота** *f.* aldehyde acid, aldehydic acid.

**альд/им** *m.* aldime; —**ин** *m.* aldine.

**альдо/бионовая кислота** aldobionic acid; —**за** *f.* aldose; —**кетен** *m.* aldoketene; —**ксим** *m.* aldoxime; —**лаза** *f.* aldolase, zymohexase; —**ль** *m.,* —**льный** *a.* aldol, 3-hydroxybutanal; —**льная конденсация** aldol condensation; —**новая кислота** aldonic acid; —**пентоза** *f.* aldopentose.

**аль/дрей** *m.* Aldrey (aluminum-magnesium alloy); —**дюраль** *m.* Aldural (aluminum-coated Duralumin sheet); —**зен** *m.* Alzene (aluminum-zinc alloy).

**альзоль** *m.* alsol, aluminum acetotartrate.

**алькана** *see* **алканна.**

**аль/клад,** —**клед,** —**клэд** *m.* Alclad (aluminum-coated Duralumin); —**кусин** *m.* Alcusin (aluminum-copper-silicon casting alloy); —**маг** *m.* *abbr.* (**алюми-** ниево-магниевый сплав) aluminum-magnesium alloy.

**альманах** *m.* almanac, calendar.

**альмандин** *see* **алмандин.**

**альмасилиум** *m.* Almasilium (aluminum alloy).

**альмедина** *f.* almedine (a rubber-like material).

**альмелек** *m.* Almalec (aluminum alloy).

**Альмена-Ниландера проба** Almen-Nylander test (for sugar).

**аль/неон** *m.* Alneon (aluminum-zinc alloy); —**ни** *m.* Alni (aluminum-nickel-copper alloy); —**нико** *n.* Alnico (aluminum-nickel-cobalt alloy).

**альноит** *m.* (petr.) alnoite (melilite basalt).

**альпа/ка** *f.* alpaca (wool); (met.) *see* **аргентан;** —**кс** *m.* Alpax (aluminum-silicon alloy).

**альпийский** *a.* Alpine.

**альсифер** *m.* Alsifer (aluminum-silicon-iron alloy).

**альтакс** *m.* Altax (a dibenzothiazole disulfide rubber accelerator).

**альтернарин** *m.* alternarin.

**альтернатива** *f.* alternative, choice.

**альтернатор** *m.,* —**ный** *a.* (elec.) alternator.

**альтернирующий** *a.* alternating.

**альти/граф** *m.* recording altimeter; —**метр** *m.* altimeter, altitude finder; —**туда** *f.* altitude.

**альтма** *f.* Altma (aluminum alloy).

**альтроза** *see* **алтроза.**

**альфа** *f.* alpha (α); **а., а.-трава** *f.* (bot.) alfa, esparto grass (*Stipa tenacissima* or *Lygeum spartum*); **а.-излучатель** *m.* (nucl.) alpha emitter; **а.-излучение** *n.* alpha-particle emission, alpha radiation; **а.-лучи** *pl.* alpha rays; **а.-нафтол** *m.* α-naphthol; **а.-распад** *m.* alpha disintegration, alpha decay; —**льфа** *see* **алфалфа;** —**метр** *m.* conductivity-type gas analyzer.

**альфа-част/ица** *f.,* —**ичный** *a.* alpha-particle; **счетчик** —**иц** alpha counter.

**альфенид** *m.* Alfenid (nickel-plated silver alloy).

**альфовый** *a.* alfa, esparto.

**альфоль** *m.* Alfol (aluminum foil).

**алюм/ель** *m.* Alumel (nickel alloy);

—илит *m.* alumilite; —инат *m.* aluminate.

алюминиево/калиевая соль potassium aluminate; —калиевые квасцы potash alum; —кислый *a.* aluminic acid; aluminate (of); —кислый натрий, —натриевая соль sodium aluminate; —кислая соль aluminate; —кобальтовая соль cobalt aluminate.

алюминиев/ый *a.* aluminum, aluminiferous; —ая кислота aluminic acid; соль —ой кислоты aluminate; —ая крупка aluminum shot; —ые квасцы potash alum.

алюминие/натриевая соль sodium aluminate; —фтористый натрий sodium aluminum fluoride, cryolite.

алюмин/ий *m.* aluminum, Al; азотнокислый *a.* aluminum nitrate; гидрат окиси —ия aluminum hydroxide; окись —ия aluminum oxide, alumina; углеродистый *a.* aluminum carbide; фтористый *a.* aluminum fluoride; (min.) cryolite; хлорид —ия, хлористый *a.* aluminum chloride.

алюминит *m.* (min.) aluminite, websterite.

алюмино/силикат *m.* aluminosilicate; —термический *a.* aluminothermic; —термия *f.* aluminothermy.

алюмо— *prefix* alumo—, *see also* алюмино—; —железистый *a.* pedalferic (soil); —кальцит *m.* (min.) alumocalcite.

аляск/аит *m.* (min.) alaskaite (argentiferous galenobismutite); —ит *m.* alaskite (a rock of the granite clan).

АМ *abbr.* (аммиакат мочевины) urea ammonia liquor (fertilizer).

амазон/ит *m.*, —ский камень (min.) amazonite, amazonstone (a variety of microcline feldspar).

Амазонка the Amazon (river).

амалиновая кислота amalic acid, amalinic acid.

амальгам/а *f.* amalgam (an alloy of mercury); —атор *m.* amalgamator; —ационный *a.* amalgamation; —ационный стол amalgamating table, amalgamator; —ация *f.*, —ирование *n.* amalgamation; —ированный *a.* amal-

gamated; —ировать *v.* amalgamate; —ирующий *a.* amalgamating.

амандин *m.* amandin.

амарант *m.* (bot.) amaranth (*Amaranthus*).

амарантит *m.* (min.) amarantite.

амарантовые *pl.* (bot.) Amaranthaceae.

амарил, —лис *m.* (bot.) amaryllis; —лисовые *pl.* (bot.) Amaryllidaceae.

амар/ин *m.* amarin; —овая кислота amaric acid; —он *m.* amaron, tetraphenylpyrazine.

аматол *m.* (expl.) amatol.

амаузит *m.* (petr.) amausite, petrosilex.

АМБ *abbr.* (препарат автохтонной микрофлоры Б) autochthonous microflora B fertilizer.

амбар *m.*, —ный *a.* storehouse, granary.

амбатоаринит *m.* (min.) ambatoarinite.

амбер/ит *m.* (expl.) amberite; —лит *m.* Amberlite (ion-exchange resin); —оид *m.* amberoid, pressed amber.

амбиполярный *a.* ambipolar.

амбиция *f.* ambition.

амбли/гонит *m.* (min.) amblygonite, hebronite; —стегит *m.* (min.) amblystegite (a variety of hypersthene).

амбра *f.* amber, succinite (fossil resin); серая а. ambergris.

амбразура *f.* embrasure; port hole; breast (of blast furnace).

амбр/еин *m.* ambrein; —еиновая кислота ambreic acid; соль —еиновой кислоты, —еиновокислая соль ambreate; —ин *m.* ambrine; —ит *m.* ambrite (fossil resin).

амбро/вый *a.* amber; —зин *m.* (min.) ambrosine (resin); —зия *f.* (bot.) ragweed (*Ambrosia*); ambrosia (fungus); —ин *m.* (elec.) ambroin (insulating material).

амбулатория *f.* dispensary.

амбушюр *m.*, —a *f.* opening; mouthpiece (of telephone).

амеб/а *f.* (zool.) ameba; —иаз *m.* (med.) amebiasis; —ный *a.* amebic; —овидный *a.* amebiform, ameboid; —оцид *m.* amebicide.

амезит *m.* (min.) amesite.

амелиорация *f.* melioration, improvement.

амер. *abbr.* (американский) American.

американка *f.* American (woman); (min).

washer, washing device (for gold ores); (oil well drilling) sand pump.

**американск/ий** *a.* American; **—ие орехи** (bot.) Brazil nuts (*Bertholletia excelsa*).

**америций** *m.* americium, Am.

**аметист** *m.* (min.) amethyst (a crystalline form of quartz); **—овый** *a.* amethyst, amethystine.

**амиант** *m.*, **—овый** *a.* (min.) amianthus, asbestos; **—оид** *m.* amiantoid, byssolite (a form of asbestos).

**амигдал/ат** *m.* amygdalate; **—ин** *m.* amygdalin; **—иновая кислота** amygdalic acid, mandelic acid; **соль —иновой кислоты, —иновокислая соль** amygdalate; **—оза** *f.* amygdalose; **—оид** *m.* (petr.) amygdaloid (amygdaloidal basalt); **—оидный** *a.* amygdaloid, amygdaloidal, almond-like.

**амигдо—** *prefix* amygdo—.

**амид** *m.* amide; **—ин** *m.* amidine.

**амидиров/ание** *n.* amidation; **—ать** *v.* amidate, convert into an amide.

**амидо—** *prefix* amido—; amino—; **—ген** *m.* amidogen, amino group; **—группа** *f.* amido group (or radical); amino group; amides; **—л** *m.* amidol; **—пирин** *m.* amidopyrine; **—сульфоновая кислота** amidosulfonic acid, sulfaminic acid; **—толуол** *m.* aminotoluene, toluidine; **—янтарная кислота** amidosuccinic acid.

**амикрон** *m.* amicron (particle).

**амил** *m.* amyl, pentyl; **уксуснокислый а.** amyl acetate; **хлористый а.** amyl chloride; **—аза** *f.* amylase; **—амин** *m.* amylamine, pentylamine; **—ан** *m.* amylan (a gum); **—бензиловый эфир** amyl benzyl ether; **—ен** *m.* amylene, 1-pentene; **—о—** *prefix* amylo—.

**амиловый** *a.* amyl; **а. альдегид** amyl aldehyde, valeraldehyde, pentanal; **а. ацетат** amyl acetate; **а. спирт** amyl alcohol, pentanol; **а. эфир масляной кислоты** amyl butyrate; **а. эфир уксусной кислоты** amyl acetate.

**амило/ген** *m.* amylogen; **—декстрин** *m.* amylodextrin; **—за** *f.* amylose; **—ид** *m.*, **—идный** *a.* amyloid; **—ин** *m.* amyloin, maltodextrin; **—кластический** *a.* amyloclastic, amylolytic; **—лиз** *m.* amylolysis; **—метр** *m.* amylometer; **—пектин** *m.* amylopectin;

**—псин** *m.* amylopsin; **—форм** *m.* amyloform.

**амин** *m.* amine; **—азин** *m.* Aminazine, chlorpromazine; **—арсон** *m.* Aminarsone, Carbarsone; **—ирование** *n.* amination; **—ировать** *v.* aminate, convert into an amine; **—ная группа** *see* **аминогруппа.**

**амино—** *prefix* amino—; **—бензойная кислота** aminobenzoic acid; **—вый** *a.* amine; **—группа** *f.* amino group (or radical); amines; **—кислота** *f.* amino acid; **—кровин** *m.* a blood-protein hydrolyzate; **—пептидаза** *f.* aminopeptidase; **—соединение** *n.* amino compound, amine; **—спирт** *m.* amino alcohol; **—уксусная кислота** aminoacetic acid; **—фераза** *f.* aminopherase, transaminase; **—форм** *m.* aminoform, hexamethylenetetramine; **—этанол** *m.* aminoethanol, ethanolamine; **—янтарная кислота** aminosuccinic acid.

**амир/илен** *m.* amyrilene; **—ин** *m.* amyrin; **—ол** *m.* amyrol.

**амитал** *m.* Amytal, amobarbital.

**амицетин** *m.* amycetin.

**амм.** *abbr.* (аммиак) ammonia; (аммиачный) ammonium, ammoniacal.

**аммел/ид** *m.* ammelide, cyanuramide; **—ин** *m.* ammeline, cyanurodiamide.

**амметр** *see* **амперметр.**

**аммиа/к** *m.* ammonia, ammonia gas; **едкий а.** aqua ammonia, ammonium hydroxide; **сернокислый а.** ammonium sulfate; **спиртовой раствор —ка** spirits of ammonia; **—кат, —т** *m.* ammoniate, ammine; (fertilizers) ammoniate; ammonia liquor.

**аммиачн/ожелезные квасцы** ammonium iron alum; **—охромовые квасцы** ammonium chrome alum; **—ый** *a.* ammonium, ammonia, ammoniacal; **—ая вода** ammonia water, ammonia liquor, aqua ammonia; **—ая селитра** ammonium nitrate; **—ая смола** gum ammoniac; **—ая сода** ammonia soda, sodium carbonate; **—ая соль** ammonium salt; **—ые квасцы** ammonium alum.

**аммин** *m.* ammine.

**аммон/ал** *m.* (expl.) ammonal; **—иак** *m.*

**ammoniac plant** (*Dorema ammonia-cum*); **—иевый** *a.* ammonium, *see also* **аммиачный.**

**аммонизиров/ание** *n.* ammoniation; **—анный** *a.* ammoniated; **—ать** *v.* ammoniate.

**аммон/ий** *m.* ammonium; **азотнокислый а.** ammonium nitrate; **гидрат окиси —ия, гидроокись —ия** ammonium hydroxide; **сернистый а.** ammonium sulfide; **сернокислый а., сульфат —ия** ammonium sulfate; **хлористый а.** ammonium chloride; **—ийный** *a.* ammonium, *see also* **аммиачный.**

**аммо/нит** *m.* (expl., pal.) ammonite; **—нификация** *f.* ammonification; **—ноидеи** *pl.* (pal.) Ammonoidea; **—фос** *m.* ammophos (an ammonium phosphate fertilizer); **—фоска** *f.* ammophoska (a complete fertilizer).

**амнезия** *f.* (med.) amnesia.

**амо** *abbr.* (автомобильный завод) automobile factory.

**амортиз/атор** *m.* shock absorber, bumper; (elec.) damper; buffer; **—ацион-ный** *a.* shock-absorbing; amortization, sinking (fund); **—ационная пружина, —ирующее устройство** shock absorber; **—ация** *f.*, **—ирова-ние** *n.* amortization, depreciation; absorption (of shock), cushioning; (elec.) damping; buffer action; **—иро-ванный, —ованный** *a.* shockproof; damped; **—ировать** *v.* absorb (shock); damp.

**аморф/изм** *m.*, **—ность** *f.* amorphism; **—ический, —ный** *a.* amorphous, shapeless, formless.

**ампангабеит** *m.* (min.) ampangabéite.

**ам. пат.** *abbr.* (американский патент) United States patent.

**ампелит** *m.* (petr.) ampelite, cannel coal, carbonaceous schist.

**ампелопсин** *m.* ampelopsin.

**ампельный** *a.* (bot.) hanging, creeping.

**ампер** *m.*, **—ный** *a.* (elec.) ampere; **а.-секунда** ampere-second; **а.-час** ampere-hour; **—аж** *m.* amperage; **—весы** *pl.* ampere balance; **—виток** *m.* ampere-turn; **—метр** *m.* ampere meter, ammeter; **—ова дуга** ampere arc; **—ометрический** *a.* amperometric (titration).

**амплидин** *m.*, **—ный** *a.* (elec.) amplidyne.

**амплитуд/а** *f.* amplitude, range; crest, crest value; (pulse) height; (geol.) slip, shift, displacement (on fault), throw separation; **коэффициент —ы** (elec.) peak factor, crest factor; **—ный** *a.* amplitude; maximum, crest, peak (value); **—ный анализатор импуль-сов** pulse height analyzer; **—ный селектор** pulse height selector.

**амплифика/тор** *m.* amplifier; **—ция** *f.* amplification.

**ампул/а** *f.* ampoule, ampulla; **—ообоб-ный** *a.* (biol.) ampullaceous, flask-shaped.

**ампут/ация** *f.* amputation; **—ировать** *v.* amputate.

**амрад гумми** amrad gum.

**АМС** *abbr.* (агрометеорологическая станция) agrometeorological station.

**амуниция** *f.* (mil.) equipment; munitions.

**АМФ** *abbr.* (аденозинмонофосфат) adenosine monophosphate.

**амфибия** *f.* (zool.) amphibia, amphibian; (aero.) amphibian.

**амфибол** *m.* (min.) amphibole, hornblende; **зеленый а.** green amphibole, smaragdite; **—изация** *f.* (petr.) amphibolization; **—ит** *m.* amphibolite (a metamorphic rock); **—овый** *a.* amphibole, amphibolic; **—олит** *m.* amphibololite (igneous amphibolite).

**амфиген** *m.* (min.) amphigène, leucite; **—ит** *m.* amphigenite (amphigene-containing lava).

**амф/идная соль** amphoteric salt; **—ион** *m.* amphoteric ion.

**амфиподы** *pl.* (zool.) Amphipoda.

**амфитеатр** *m.* amphitheater; **горный а.** (geol.) cirque.

**амфи/хроический** *a.* amphichroic; **—хро-матический** *a.* amphichromatic.

**амфо/делит** *m.* (min.) amphodelite (an altered anorthite); **—лит** *m.* ampholyte, amphoteric electrolyte; **—тер-ность** *m.* amphoteric character; **—тер-ный** *a.* amphoteric; **—тропин** *m.* amphotropin, methenamine camphorate.

**АН** *abbr.* (Академия наук) Academy of Sciences.

**анабад/уст, —эст** *m.* anabadust (anabasine sulfate-lime insecticide).

**анабазин** *m.* anabasine, nicotimine.

**анабатический** *a.* (meteor.) anabatic.

**ана/биоз** *m.* (med.) anabiosis, resuscitation; **—болизм** *m.* (biol.) anabolism, constructive metabolism; **—гирин** *m.* anagyrine; **—дол** *m.* alphaprodine hydrochloride.

**анакард/иевые** *pl.* (bot.) Anacardiaceae; **—ия** *f.*, **—овое дерево** cashew (*Anacardium*); **—овый** *a.* cashew; anacardic; **—овая кислота** anacardic acid; **соль —овой кислоты, —овокислая соль** anacardate.

**анали/з** *m.* analysis; **не поддающийся —зу** unanalyzable; **—затор, —ст, —тик** *m.* analyst, analyzer; (met.) assayer; **—зирование** *n.* analyzation, analysis; **—зированный** *a.* analyzed; **—зировать** *v.* analyze; **—тика** *f.* analytics; **—тически** *adv.* analytically; **—тический** *a.* analytical.

**аналог** *m.* analog; (geol.) correlative; **—ический, —ичный** *a.* analogous, similar, corresponding; analog (computer); **—ия** *f.* analogy, resemblance, similarity; parity.

**анальг/езин** *m.* analgesine, antipyrine; **—ен** *m.* analgen; **—етик** *m.* analgesic; **—ин** *m.* Analgin, dipyrone.

**ана/льцим, —льцит** *m.* (min.) analcite, analcime; **—мезит** *m.* (petr.) anamesite (crystalline basalts).

**анамиртин** *m.* anamirtin.

**анамнез** *m.* (med.) anamnesis.

**анаморф/изм** *m.* anamorphism; **—ный** *a.* anamorphous, anamorphic; **—оз** *m.* anamorphosis.

**ананас** *m.* (bot.) pineapple (*Ananas sativus*); **—ный, —овый** *a.* pineapple; **—ная эссенция** pineapple extract; **—овые** *pl.* Bromeliaceae.

**анапаит** *m.* (min.) anapaite, tamanite.

**ана/плазмоз** *m.* (vet.) anaplasmosis (like Texas fever); **—стигматический** *a.* (optics) anastigmatic; **—стомоз** *m.* (med.) anastomosis.

**анатаз** *m.* (min.) anatase, octahedrite.

**анатексис** *m.* (geol.) anatexis, refusion.

**анатоксин** *m.* anatoxin.

**анатом, —ик** *m.* anatomist; **—ирование** *n.* dissection; **—ировать** *v.* dissect; anatomize; **—ический** *a.* anatomical; **—ия** *f.* anatomy; dissection.

**анауксит** *m.* (min.) anauxite.

**ана/фаза** *f.* (biol.) anaphase; **—филаксия** *f.* (med.) anaphylaxis; **—филактин** *m.* anaphylactin; **—форез** *m.* (chem., med.) anaphoresis.

**анаэроб, —ионт** *m.* (biol.) anaerobe; **—иоз** *m.* anacrobiosis; **—ный** *a.* anaerobic.

**ангал/амин** *m.* anhalamine; **—ин** *m.* anhaline; **—онидин** *m.* anhalonidine; **—онин** *m.* anhalonine.

**ангар** *m.* hangar, shed.

**ангармоничность** *f.* anharmonicity.

**ангелик/а** *f.* (bot.) angelica; **—овая кислота** angelic acid, *cis*-2-methyl-2-butenoic acid; **—овое масло** angelica oil, angelica root oil; **—овый альдегид** angelic aldehyde.

**ангелин** *m.* angelin, rhatanin.

**ангидремия** *f.* (med.) anhydremia.

**ангидр/ид** *m.* anhydride; **—изация** *f.* dehydration; **—ит** *m.* (min.) anhydrite.

**ангидро—** *prefix* anhydro—.

**ангина** *f.* (med.) angina; tonsillitis, quinsy.

**ангио—** *prefix* (bot., med.) angio— (vessel); **—логия** *f.* angiology.

**англ.** *abbr.* (английский) English; British (patent).

**англезит** *m.* (min.) anglesite.

**английск/ий** *a.* English; **а. красный** English red, colcothar; **а. порошок** algaroth, antimony oxychloride; **а. цемент** marble cement, Keene's cement; **—ая болезнь** (med.) rickets; **—ая булавка** safety pin; **—ая синь** English blue; **—ая соль** *see* горькая соль; **—ая цепь** short-link chain; **—ие белила** white lead.

**Англия** England.

**ангоб** *m.* (cer.) engobe.

**ангорская шерсть** Angora wool.

**ангостур/ин** *m.* angosturine; **—овая кора** (pharm.) angostura bark.

**ангстрем** *m.* (phys.) ångström (unit).

**анда-ассу** *n.* (bot.) anda-assu (*Joannesia princeps*).

**андалузит** *m.*, **—овый** *a.* (min.) andalusite.

**андез/ин** *m.* (min.) andesine (an intermediate plagioclase feldspar); **—ит** *m.* andesite (a porphyritic rock).

**андерсонит** *m.* (min.) andersonite.

**андирин** *m.* andirin.

**андовое масло** anda-assu oil, oil of anda (from *Joannesia princeps*).

**анд/орит** *m.* (min.) andorite (zinkenite group); **—радит** *m.* andradite, common calcium-iron garnet.

**андраза** *f.* andrase (enzyme).

**андро—** *prefix* andro—; **—генез** *m.* (biol.) androgenesis; **—зин** *m.* androsine; **—медотоксин** *m.* andromedotoxin; **—стан** *m.* androstane; **—стерон** *m.* androsterone.

**Анды** the Andes.

**ане/вризм** *m.* (med.) aneurism; **—врин, —йрин** *m.* aneurin, vitamin $B_1$.

**анем/ический, —ичный** *a.* anemic; **—ичность, —ия** *f.* anemia.

**анемо—** *prefix* anemo— (wind); **—граф** *m.* (meteor.) anemograph; **—логия** *f.* anemology; **—метр** *m.* anemometer, wind gage; **—метрический** *a.* anemometric, wind (measuring).

**анемон** *m.*, **—а** *f.* (bot.) anemone; **—ин** *m.*, **—овая камфара** anemonin, pulsatilla camphor; **—иновая кислота** anemoninic acid; **—овая кислота** anemonic acid.

**анемо/скоп** *m.* (meteor.) anemoscope; **—тахометр** *m.* air speed meter; **—фикация** *f.* utilization of wind power.

**анемузит** *m.* (min.) anemousite (a feldspar).

**анероид** *m.* (meteor.) aneroid, aneroid barometer; **—ный** *a.* aneroid; **—ограф** *m.* aneroidograph.

**анесте/зин** *m.* Anesthesin, benzocaine; **—зировать** *v.* anesthetize; **—зирующее средство, —тик** *m.*, **—тическое средство** anesthetic; **—зия** *f.* anesthesia.

**анетол** *m.* anethole, anise camphor.

**анзерин** *m.* anserine, N-methylcarnosine.

**аниз—** *see* **анизо—**; **анис—**.

**анизо—** *prefix* aniso— (unequal, dissimilar; not); (chem.) aniso—, anise; **—метрический** *a.* anisometric, not isometric; **—параклаз** *m.* (geol.)

strike fault, longitudinal fault; **—тропический, —тропный** *a.* anisotropic; **—тропия, —тропность** *f.* anisotropy; **—тропия, —тропное излучение** anisotropic emission.

**анил** *m.* anil, indigo (dyestuff); **—ид** *m.* anilide; **—ид уксусной кислоты** acetanilide; **—изм** *m.* (med.) anilism, aniline poisoning; **—ин** *m.* aniline, phenylamine; **азотнокислый —ин** aniline nitrate; **солянокислый —ин, хлористоводородный —ин** aniline hydrochloride.

**анилино—** *prefix* anilino—.

**анилин/овый** *a.* aniline; **а. бурый** aniline brown, triaminoazobenzene; **—овая краска** aniline dye; **—овая соль** aniline salt, aniline hydrochloride; **—овая точка** aniline point; **—овая черная** aniline black (an azine dye); **—сульфоновая кислота** anilinesulfonic acid.

**анимал/изация** *f.* animalization; **—ьный** *a.* (biol.) holozoic (nutrition).

**аниме, смола** anime (gum).

**анимик/ейская система** (geol.) Animikean series, Upper Huronian; **—ит** *m.* (min.) animikite (a mixture of silver, galena, and niccolite).

**анимин** *m.* animine.

**анион** *m.* anion; **—ит** *m.*, **—итный** *a.* anion exchanger, anion-exchange resin; **—ный** *a.* anion, anionic.

**анионообменн/ик** *m.* anion exchanger; **—ый** *a.* anion-exchange.

**анис** *m.* (bot.) anise (*Pimpinella anisum*); **—ал** *m.* anisal, anisylidene; **—ет** *m.*, **—овка** *f.* anisette, anise liqueur; **—идин** *m.* anisidine, methoxyaniline; **—идино—** *prefix* anisidino—; **—ил** *m.* anisyl; anisil; **—илиден** *m.* anisylidene; **—ный** *see* **анисовый**.

**анисово/кислый** *a.* anisic acid; anisate (of); **—кислая соль** anisate; **—этиловый эфир** ethyl anisate.

**анисов/ый** *a.* anise, anisic; **а. альдегид** anisaldehyde; **а. спирт** anisalcohol, anisyl alcohol; **—ая вода, а. ликер** anise liqueur, anisette; **—ая кислота** anisic acid, *p*-methoxybenzoic acid; **соль —ой кислоты** anisate; **—ое масло** anise oil; **—ое семя** aniseed.

**анисо/ил** *m.* anisoyl; **—ин** *m.* anisoin, dimethoxybenzoin; **—л** *m.* anisole, phenyl methyl ether; —лин *m.* anisolin; —ловый *a.* anisole.

**анисуровая кислота** anisuric acid.

**анит** *see* укроп; —ин *m.* anytin, anitin (a germicide).

**анкер** *m.* anchor; stay, tie rod; anker (measure).

**анкерит** *m.* (min.) ankerite.

**анкерн/ый** *a.* anchor; tension (chain); **а. зажим** (elec.) anchor ear; **а. спуск** anchor escapement; —**ая балка** tie beam; —**ая плита** anchor plate, tie plate.

**анкеровка** *f.* anchoring.

**анкета** *f.* questionnaire, form; inquiry.

**анкилоз** *m.* (med.) ankylosis.

**аннабергит** *m.* (min.) annabergite.

**анналин** *m.* annaline, calcium sulfate.

**анналы** *pl.* annals, records.

**аннато** *n.* annato (vegetable dyestuff).

**аннекс/ировать** *v.* annex; —ия *f.* annexation.

**аннелид** *m.* annelid, segmented worm.

**аннигиляц/ионный** *a.*, —ия *f.* annihilation, destruction, demolition; —**ионное излучение** (nucl.) annihilation radiation.

**аннидалин** *m.* annidalin, thymol iodide.

**аннит** *m.* (min.) annite (a variety of lepidomelane).

**аннот/ация** *f.* annotation; —**ировать** annotate.

**аннулиров/ание** *n.* annulment, cancelation, nullification; extinguishment; —**анный** *a.* annulled, canceled; —**ать** *v.* annul, cancel, nullify; abolish, destroy.

**анод** *m.* (elec.) anode; —**изация** *f.* (met.) anodic oxidation, anodizing.

**анодин** *m.* anodyne; —**ин** *m.* anodynin.

**анодирование** *see* анодизация.

**анодн/ый** *a.* anode, anodic; inverse (voltage of tube); **а. шлам** (met.) anode slime, anode mud; —**ая батарея** anode battery, plate battery; —**ое покрытие** (met.) anodizing, anodic oxidation; —**ое растворение** anodic dissolution; —**ые рейки** anode strips.

**аноксия** *f.* anoxia, oxygen deficiency.

**анол** *m.* anol, propenylphenol.

**анолит** *m.* anolyte.

**аномал/ия** *f.* anomaly, abnormality; —**ьный** *a.* anomalous, abnormal, unusual, irregular.

**аномит** *m.* (min.) anomite (a form of meroxene biotite).

**анона** *f.* (bot.) custard apple (*Anona*).

**анонимный** *a.* anonymous, unknown.

**аноновый** *a.* (bot.) custard apple.

**анормальный** *a.* abnormal, anomalous.

**анортит** *m.* (min.) anorthite, indianite; —**овый** *a.* anorthite.

**анорто/зит** *m.* (petr.) anorthosite (a granitoid labradorite); —**клаз** *m.* (min.) anorthoclase (a feldspar).

**АНП** *abbr.* (апатито-нефелиновая порода) apatite and nepheline rocks (for fertilizer).

**ансамбль** *m.* ensemble, aggregate; the whole.

**антабус** *m.* Antabuse, tetraethylthiuram disulfide.

**антагон/изм** *m.* antagonism; —**истический** *a.* antagonistic.

**антантрен** *m.* anthanthrene.

**Антаркти/да** *f.* Antarctica (the continent); —**ка** *f.* Antarctic (region).

**антарктический** *a.* Antarctic.

**антверпенская лазурь, а. синяя** Antwerp blue (an iron blue).

**антгельминтный** *a.* (med.) anthelmintic.

**антекл/аза** *f.* (geol.) anteclase; —**иза** *f.* anteclise (broad structural uplift).

**антелий** *m.* anthelion (kind of halo).

**антем/ен** *m.* anthemene, octadecylene; —**идин** *m.* anthemidine; —**ол** *m.* anthemol, camomile camphor.

**антенн/а** *f.*, —**ый** *a.* (rad.) antenna, aerial; (zool.) antenna.

**антестерин** *m.* anthesterol.

**антецедент** *m.* antecedent.

**анти—** *prefix* anti—; non—; —**альдоксим** *m.* antialdoxime.

**антиар/ин** *m.* antiarin; —**оза** *f.* antiarose; —**ол** *m.* antiarol; —**оновая кислота** antiaronic acid.

**анти/бактериальный** *a.* antibacterial; —**биотик** *m.*, —**биотический** *a.* antibiotic; —**вещество** *n.* antibody; —**вибратор** *m.* (mach.) shock absorber; —**вирус** *m.* (med.) antivirus; —**вирусный** *a.* antiviral; —**геморрагический** *a.* antihemorrhagic;—**ген**

*m.* (immunology) antigen; **—гигиеничный** *a.* unsanitary; **—гнилостное средство** preservative.

**антигорит** *m.* (min.) antigorite (a lamellar serpentine).

**антигризутное взрывчатое вещество** (min.) safety explosive.

**антидерапан** *m.* antiskid; guide path.

**антидетон/атор** *m.* antiknock, antiknock compound; **—ационный, —ирующий** *a.* antiknock; **показатель —ационных качеств** antiknock rating.

**анти/дот** *m.* antidote; **—затухание** *n.* antidamping; **—катализатор** *m.* anticatalyst, catalyst poison; **—катод** *m.* anticathode; **—каустик** *m.* anticaustic, antialkali.

**антиклин/аль** *m.* (geol.) anticline, anticlinal fold; **—альный** *a.* anticlinal; **—орий** *m.* anticlinorium.

**анти/коагулянт** *m.* anticoagulant; **—коллектор** *m.* (flotation) defrothing agent, depressant; **—коррозийный** *a.* anticorrosive, corrosion-resisting, antirust, rust preventive; **—ксерофтальмин** *m.* antixerophthalmic vitamin, vitamin A; **—логарифм** *m.* (math.) antilogarithm.

**антилопа** *f.* (zool.) antelope.

**антилуетин** *m.* antiluetin.

**антимицин** *m.* antimycin.

**антимон/ат** *m.* antimonate; **—ид** *m.* antimonide; **—ий** *m.* antimony, *see also* **сурьма**; **—ий крудум** (pharm.) antimonium crudum (antimony sulfide); **—ил** *m.* antimonyl; **—илкалий** *m.* tartar emetic; **—ин** *m.* antimonine, antimony lactate; **—ит** *m.* (min.) antimonite, stibnite, antimony glance.

**анти/накипин** *m.* antifouling compound, boiler compound; rust preventive; **—научный** *a.* unscientific; **—нейтрино** *n.* (nucl.) antineutrino; **—нейтрон** *m.* antineutron; **—нервин** *m.* antinervin; **—нозин** *m.* antinosin; **—ноннин** *m.* antinonnin; **—нуклон** *m.* antinucleon; **—обледенитель** *m.* (aero.) deicer; **—окислитель, —оксидант** *m.* antioxidant, age resistor; **—параллельный** *a.* antiparallel.

**антион** *m.* (phot.) Anthion, potassium persulfate.

**антипатия** *f.* antipathy, aversion.

**анти/пеллагрический витамин** antipellagra vitamin, nicotinic acid; **—пертит** *m.* antiperthite (an igneous rock).

**антипиретический** *a.* antipyretic.

**антипирин** *m.* antipyrine, Analgesine; **салициловокислый а.** antipyrine salicylate, Salipyrin.

**анти/под** *m.* (phys.) antipode; **—производная** *f.* (math.) antiderivative; **—протон** *m.* antiproton, negative proton; **—рахитический витамин** antirachitic vitamin, vitamin D; **—санитарный** *a.* unsanitary; **—сейсмический** *a.* earthquake-proof.

**антисеп/син** *m.* antisepsin, acetanilide bromide; **—тик** *m.* antiseptic; **—тика** *f.* antisepsis; **—тин** *m.* antiseptin; **—тический** *a.*, **—тическое средство** antiseptic; **—тол** *m.* antiseptol, cinchonine iodosulfate.

**анти/сиккатив** *m.* antisiccative, antidrier, humidifier; **—симметричный** *a.* antisymmetric; **—скорч** *m.* (rubber) antiscorch; **—скорчинг** *m.* antiscorching; **—совпадение** *n.* anticoincidence (in detectors).

**антиспазм/атический** *a.*, **—атическое средство** antispasmodic; **—ин** *m.* antispasmine, narceine sodium salicylate.

**анти/стерильный витамин** antisterility vitamin, vitamin E; **—теза** *f.* antithesis, contrast; **—тело** *n.* antibody; **—термин** *m.* antithermin; **—тиреойдный** *a.* antithyroid; **—токсин** *m.* antitoxin; **—токсический** *a.* antitoxic; **—тромбин** *m.* antithrombin; **—узел** *m.* (phys.) antinode; **—фебрин** *m.* antifebrin, acetanilide; **—фермент** *m.* antiferment; antienzyme; **—формин** *m.* Antiformin (alkaline sodium hypochlorite solution); **—фриз** *m.* antifreeze; **—фрикционный** *a.* antifriction; **—фунгин** *m.* Antifungin, magnesium borate; **—хлор** *m.* antichlor, spec. sodium thiosulfate.

**антициклон** *m.* (meteor.) anticyclone; **—ический** *a.* anticyclone, anticyclonic.

**анти/цинготный витамин** antiscorbutic

vitamin, vitamin C; —**частица** *f.* antiparticle.

**античный** *a.* antique.

**антодин** *m.* Antodyne, phenoxypropanediol.

**антозонит** *m.* (min.) antozonite (an odoriferous fluorite).

**антокориды** *pl.* (zool.) Anthocoridae.

**антокс** *m.* Antox (rubber antioxidant).

**антоксантин** *m.* anthoxanthin.

**антонов огонь** (med.) gangrene.

**Антонова правило** Antonoff's rule (for interfacial tension).

**антофиллит** *m.* (min.) anthophyllite (an amphibole).

**антоциан** *m.* anthocyan; —**идин** *m.* anthocyanidin.

**антр**— *prefix* anthr—.

**антра**— *prefix* anthra—; —**галлол** *m.* anthragallol, alizarin brown; —**зин** *m.* anthrazine, anthracene; —**кноз** *m.* anthracnose (plant disease).

**антрако/з,** —**зис** *m.* (med.) anthracosis, black-lung; —**лит,** —**нит** *m.* (min.) anthraconite, anthracolite (a bituminous marble); —**метр** *m.* anthracometer (for determining carbon dioxide).

**антракс** *m.* (med.) anthrax.

**антраксолит** *m.* (min.) anthraxolite.

**антр/амин** *m.* anthramine, aminoanthracene; —**анил** *m.* anthranyl; anthranil; —**анило**— *prefix* anthranilo—; —**аниловая кислота** anthranilic acid, *o*-aminobenzoic acid; —**анол** *m.* anthranol, 9-hydroxyanthracene; —**анон** *m.* anthranone, dihydroketoanthracene.

**антра/пиридин** *m.* anthrapyridine; —**флавин** *m.* anthraflavin; —**флавон** *m.* anthraflavone; —**хинолин** *m.* anthraquinoline, naphthoquinoline; —**хинон** *m.* anthraquinone; —**хиноновые краски** anthraquinone dyes; —**хиноносульфоновая кислота** anquinonesulfonic acid.

**антрацен** *m.,* —**овый** *a.* anthracene; —**овый синий** anthracene blue, alizarin blue; —**овое масло** anthracene oil.

**антрац/ил** *m.* anthracyl; —**ит** *m.* anthracite, hard coal; —**итовый** *a.* anthracite, anthraciferous.

**антреприза** *f.* enterprise.

**антресоль** *f.* entresol; mezzanine.

**антрил** *m.* anthryl.

**антро/иная кислота** anthroic acid, anthracenecarboxylic acid; —**ксан** *m.* anthroxan, anthranil; —**л** *m.* anthrol, hydroxyanthracene; —**н** *m.* anthrone, anthranone.

**антропо**— *prefix* anthropo— (man); —**ид** *m.* (zool.) anthropoid; —**логия** *f.* anthropology.

**анурия** *f.* (med.) anuria.

**анфельция** *f.* ahnfeltia (a seaweed).

**анфлераж** *m.* (perfumery) enfleurage.

**анхуз/ин** *m.* anchusin; —**овая кислота** anchusic acid; **соль —овой кислоты,** —**овокислая соль** anchusate.

**анциаевая кислота** anzic acid.

**анцилит** *m.* (min.) ancylite.

**анчар** *m.* (bot.) upas tree (*Antiaris toxicaria*).

**анчоус** *m.,* —**ный,** —**овый** *a.* anchovy.

**аншла/г** *m.* try square; set edge; —**жная полка** beam (of a square); —**жный угольник** back square; try square.

**аншлаш** *m.* stopping device.

**аншлиф** *m.* (micros.) polished section; (min., etc.) section, ground surface.

**аншпуг** *m.* crowbar.

**анэлектрический** *a.* anelectric.

**анэстезин** *see* **анестезин.**

**анютины глазки** (bot.) pansy, heart's ease (*Viola tricolor*).

**аорт/а** *f.* (anat.) aorta; **воспаление —ы,** —**ит** *m.* (med.) aortitis, inflammation of the aorta; —**ный,** —**овый** *a.* aortic.

**апарель** *m.* approach ramp.

**апат/елит** *m.* (min.) apatelite; —**ит** *m.* (min.) apatite, fluor-apatite.

**апат/ический,** —**ичный** *a.* apathetic, torpid, languid; —**ия** *f.* apathy.

**апекс** *m.* apex.

**апелл/ировать** *v.,* —**яция** *f.* (law) appeal.

**апельсин** *m.,* —**ный,** —**овый** *a.* (bot.) orange (*Citrus sinensis*); —**ные** *pl.* Aurantiaceae.

**апендицит** *see* **аппендицит.**

**апериодич/еский,** —**ный** *a.* aperiodic; —**ность** *f.* aperiodicity.

**аперт/ометр** *m.* (optics) apertometer; —**ура** *f.,* —**урный** *a.* aperture, orifice, opening.

**апжонит** *m.* (min.) apjohnite, manganese alum.

апи/генин *m.* apigenin, trihydroxy-flavone; —ин *m.* apiin; —кальный *a.* apical; —нол *m.* apinol, *l*-menthone; —оза *f.* apiose; —ол *m.* apiole, parsley camphor; —оловая кислота apiolic acid; —онин *m.* apyonin, auramin; —онол *m.* apionol, phentetrol.

апирон *m.* apyron, lithium acetylsalicylate.

аплазия *f.* (med.) aplasia.

апланат *m.* aplanat, aplanatic lens; —ический, —ичный *a.* aplanatic.

апплике *see* аpplике.

апл/ит *m.* (petr.) aplite, haplite (an igneous rock); —ом *m.* (min.) aplome, haplome (a variety of andradite garnet).

апо— *prefix* apo—; —атропин *m.* apo-atropine; —гамия *f.* (bot.) apogamy.

апогей *m.* culmination, peak; (astron.) apogee.

апо/камфорная кислота apocamphoric acid, campho acid; —кодеин *m.* apo-codeine; —конин *m.* a tar compound for road building; —кринный, —криновый *a.* apocrine (glands); —лизин *m.* apolysin; —морфин *m.* apomorphine; —нал *m.* aponal.

апоплек/сия *f.* (med.) apoplexy; —тик *m.*, —тический *a.* apoplectic.

апо/реин *m.* aporeine; —рфин *m.* apor-phine; —сафранин *m.* aposafranine, benzeneinduline; —стема *f.* (med.) apostem, abscess.

апостиль *m.* marginal note.

апо/стильб *m.* apostilb (unit of brightness); —строф *m.* apostrophe; —тезин *m.* Apothesine; —фема *f.* (math.) apothem; —фермент *m.* apoenzyme.

апофиза *f.* (geol., biol.) apophysis, off-shoot, tongue.

апофиллит *m.* (min.) apophyllite, fisheye.

апо/хинин *m.* apoquinine, homoquinine; —холевая кислота apocholic acid.

апохромат *m.*, —ическая линза apo-chromat, apochromatic lens; —ический *a.* apochromatic.

апоцианин *m.* apocyanine.

аппалачский *a.* Appalachian.

аппарат *m.*, —ный *a.* apparatus, instrument, device; (phot.) camera; —er, —or; а. для растворения dissolver;

выпарной а. evaporator; —ная *f.* instrument room, control room; —ный щит (automobile) dashboard; —ура *f.*, —урный *a.* apparatus, equipment, outfit; оснащение измерительной —урой instrumentation.

аппенди/кс *m.* appendix; —цит *m.* (med.) appendicitis.

аппетит *m.* appetite; —ный *a.* appetizing.

апплика/та *f.* (math.) *z*-coordinate; —тор *m.* applicator, applier; —ция *f.* application.

апплике *n.* silver plate, plated ware.

аппр— *see also* апр—.

аппрет *m.*, —ирование *n.* filling; sizing; (text.) dressing, finishing; —ированный *a.* finished; —ировать *v.* dress, finish; —ура *f.* filler, size; finish, dressing, finishing; —урный *a.* finishing; —урная масса size; —урщик *m.* finisher.

апрель *m.* April.

апрессин *m.* Apressin, hydralazine hydrochloride.

априорный *a.* prior, antecedent.

апроб/ация *f.* approbation; —ировать, —овать *v.* approbate, approve.

апроксим/ация *f.*, —ирование *n.* (math.) approximation; —ированный *a.* approximated, approximate.

апте/ка *f.* drug store, pharmacy; —карский, —чный *a.* pharmaceutical; —карь *m.* druggist, pharmacist; —чка *f.* medicine chest; —чное дело pharmacy, pharmaceutics; —чные товары drugs, pharmaceuticals.

ар *m.* are (100 sq. m.).

араб/ин *m.* arabin; —иновая кислота arabic acid, *d*-tetrahydroxyvaleric acid; —иноза *f.* arabinose, gum sugar; —ит, —итол *m.* arabitol; —онил *m.* arabonyl; —оновая кислота arabonic acid.

арабск/ий, аравийск/ий *a.* Arabian; —ая камедь gum arabic.

Аравия Arabia.

арагонит *m.* (min.) aragonite.

арак *m.* arrack (liquor from malted rice).

арал/игенин *m.* araligenin; —ин *m.* aralin.

аралкил *m.* aralkyl.

**аранжировать** *v.* arrange, set, put in order.

**арароб/а** *f.* araroba, goa powder; —**инол** *m.* ararobinol.

**арасан** *m.* mineral spring, thermal spring.

**арастра** *f.* (min.) drag-stone mill.

**араукария** *f.* (bot.) araucaria; **чилийская а.** monkey puzzle (*Araucaria imbricata*).

**арахид/ный** *a.* peanut; —**ное масло** peanut oil; —**оновая кислота** arachidonic acid; —**ы** *see* **арахис.**

**арахин** *m.* arachin; —**овая кислота** arachidic acid, arachic acid, eicosanoic acid; —**овый спирт** arachidic alcohol, eicosyl alcohol.

**арахис** *m.* (bot.) peanut (*Arachis hypogaea*).

**арбитр** *m.* arbitrator; —**аж** *m.* arbitration; —**ажный** *a.* arbitrary; —**ажный анализ** umpire analysis.

**арбуз** *m.*, —**ный** *a.* (bot.) watermelon (*Citrullus vulgaris*).

**арбу/стерин** *m.* arbusterol; —**тин** *m.* arbutin, arbutoside.

**аргал** *see* **аргол.**

**Аргана газовая горелка, аргандова горелка** Argand burner.

**аргелевые листья** (pharm.) argel leaves.

**аргемон/ин** *m.* argemonine; —**овое масло** argemone oil.

**аргент/амин** *m.* argentamine; —**ан** *m.* argentan, German silver, nickel silver; —**ин** *m.* (met.) argentine (a tin sponge); (min.) argentine (a lamellar variety of calcite).

**аргентинский** *a.* Argentine, Argentinian.

**аргентит** *m.* (min.) argentite, silver glance.

**аргенто/бисмутит** *m.* (min.) argentobismutite, matildite; —**метр** *m.* argentometer; —**пирит** *m.* (min.) argentopyrite (probably a variety of sternbergite).

**аргилл/изация** *f.* argillization; —**ит** *m.* argillite, pelite (an argillaceous sedimentary rock); —**итовый** *a.* argillitic, argillo—.

**аргин/аза** *f.* arginase (an enzyme); —**ин** *m.* arginine.

**аргиресцин** *m.* argyroescin.

**аргирит** *m.* (min.) argyrit, argentite.

**аргиро—** *prefix* argyro— (silver); —**дит**
*m.* argyrodite, silver sulfogermanate; —**ид,** —**фан** *m.* a silver-plated nickel silver; —**метрический** *a.* argyrometric; silver-weighing (balance); —**метрия** *f.* argyrometry; —**пирит** *m.* (min.) argyropyrite (probably a variety of sternbergite).

**арго/л** *m.* argol, crude tartar; —**н** *m.*, —**новый** *a.* argon, A; —**нин** *m.* argonin, silver caseinate; —**флавин** *m.* argoflavin; —**хром** *m.* argochrome.

**аргулан** *m.* argulan.

**аргумент** *m.* argument, reasoning; (math.) argument, amplitude; **а. функции** (math.) independent variable.

**арденнит** *m.* (min.) ardennite, dewalquite.

**ардометр** *m.* ardometer (optical pyrometer).

**area** *f.* area; —**л** *m.*, —**льный** *a.* areal.

**арек/а** *f.*, —**овая пальма** (bot.) areca palm, spec. betel palm (*Areca catechu*); —**аидин** *m.*, —**аидиновый** *a.* arecaidine; —**аин** *m.* arecaine, *n*-methylguvacine; —**овые орехи** betel nuts; —**олидин** *m.* arecolidine; —**олин** *m.* arecoline.

**арена** *f.* arena, field, area; list.

**аренд/а** *f.*, **сдавать в —у** *v.* rent, lease.

**арендалит** *m.* (min.) arendalite (a variety of epidote).

**аренд/атор** *m.* lessee, tenant; —**ная плата** rent; —**ный договор** lease; —**ование** *n.* renting, leasing; —**ованный** *a.* rented, leased; —**овать** *v.* rent, lease.

**аренит** *m.* arenite (fragmental, grained rock).

**Арентса сифон** Arents tap (for lead).

**арео/метр** *m.* areometer, hydrometer; **а. пикнометр,** —**пикнометр** *m.* areopycnometer; —**метрический** *a.* areometric; —**метрия** *f.* areometry, hydrometry.

**арест** *m.* arrest, seizure; —**ованный** *a.* arrested; —**овать** *v.* arrest, seize.

**арецин** *m.* arecin, areca red.

**аржанец** *m.* (bot.) timothy (*Phleum pratense*).

**арзено—** *see* **арсено—.**

**арибин** *m.* aribine, loturine.

**аридн/ость** *f.* aridity; —**ый** *a.* arid.

**аризонит** *m.* (min.) arizonite.

**арил** *m.* aryl; —**ирование** *n.* arylation; —**овать** *v.* arylate, introduce an aryl group.

**арист/ида** *f.* (bot.) aristida; —**ол** *m.* Aristol, thymol iodide; —**олохин** *m.* aristolochine; —**отипная бумага** (phot.) a silver chloride printing paper; —**охин,** —**охинин** *m.* aristochin, aristoquinine, diquinine carbonic ester.

**арит** *m.* (min.) arite (an intermediate of niccolite and breithauptite).

**аритм/ический,** —**ичный** *a.* arrhythmic, not rhythmic; —**ичность,** —**ия** *f.* (med.) arrhythmia.

**арифмет/ика** *f.* arithmetic; —**ический** *a.* arithmetical; —**ическая прогрессия,** —**ический ряд** arithmetical progression; **среднее** —**ическое** arithmetical mean.

**арифмометр** *m.* arithmometer, calculating machine, adding machine.

**арицин** *m.* aricine, quinovatine.

**арк**— *prefix* arc—; —**а** *f.* arc, arch.

**аркан** *m.* rope, lasso.

**арканз/асский камень** (petr.) Arkansas stone (a novaculite); —**ит** *m.* (min.) arkansite (a variety of brookite).

**арканит** *m.* (min.) arcanite (a potassium sulfate).

**аркатом** *m.* atomic-hydrogen arc welding.

**арккверит** *m.* (min.) arquerite (a variety of amalgam).

**арк/косинус** *m.* (math.) arc cosine, inverse cosine; —**овидный** *a.* arcuate; —**оген** *m.* (welding) arcogen.

**аркоз** *m.,* —**а** *f.* (petr.) arkose (a feldspar sandstone); —**овый** *a.* arkosic.

**арксинус** *m.* (math.) arc sine, inverse sine.

**Арктика** Arctic regions.

**арктический** *a.* arctic, northern.

**арктувин** *m.* arctuvine.

**арм.** *abbr.* (армянский) Armenian.

**арматур/а** *f.* fittings, fixtures, accessories, hardware; outfit, equipment; mounting; reinforcement; (elec.) armature; **а. котла** boiler fittings; —**ный** *a.* fitting, fixture; armature.

**арм/ейский** *a.* army; —**инженер** *m.* army engineer.

**армиров/ание** *n.* armoring, reinforcement; —**анный** *a.* armored, reinforced; —**анное стекло** wire glass; —**ать** *v.* armor, reinforce, sheathe, stiffen.

**армия** *f.* army.

**армко-железо** *n.* (met.) Armco iron.

**Арм ССР** *abbr.* (Армянская Советская Социалистическая Республика) Armenian Soviet Socialist Republic.

**Армстронга кислота** Armstrong acid.

**армуд** *see* айва.

**армянский** *a.* Armenian.

**арнаутка** *f.* (bot.) hard wheat (*Triticum durum*).

**арни/ка** *f.* (bot.) arnica (spec. *Arnica montana*); —**мит** *m.* arnimite (a basic copper sulfate); —**цин** *m.* arnicin.

**ароидные** *pl.* (bot.) Araceae.

**аромадендрал** *m.* aromadendral.

**аромат** *m.* aroma, scent, odor, perfume; —**изация** *f.* aromatization (production of aromatic compounds); —**ика** *f.,* —**ический,** —**ичный,** —**ный** *a.* aromatic; —**ический ряд** aromatic series; —**ическое вещество** aromatic principle; —**ическое соединение** aromatic compound; —**ические травы** aromatic herbs; —**ность** *f.* aroma.

**аронник** *see* арум; —**овые** *see* ароидные.

**арорут** *see* аррорут.

**арочный** *a.* arch, arched.

**арренал** *m.* arrhenal, sodium methyl arsenite.

**арретир** *m.,* —**ное устройство,** —**овка** *f.,* —**овочное приспособление** arrest, arrester, stop, stopping device, checking device, detent, detainer; locking device, holding device, catch; —**овать** *v.* arrest, stop, check; secure, lock; —**овочный** *a.* arresting, stopping, stop.

**арройо** *n.* arroyo.

**арро/рут,** —**урут** *m.* arrowroot (a starch); **вест-индский а.** (bot.) West Indian arrowroot (*Maranta arundinacea*).

**арс/аниловая кислота** arsanilic acid, *p*-aminophenylarsinic acid; —**ацетин** *m.* arsacetin, acetylatoxyl.

**арсенал** *m.* arsenal, armory; **морской а.** dockyard.

**арсен/ат** *m.* arsenate; —**диметил** *m.*

dimethylarsine; —диэтил *m.* diethyl-arsine; —ид *m.* arsenide; —ик *m.* arsenic, *see also* мышьяк; —иоплеит *m.* (min.) arseniopleite; —иосидерит *m.* (min.) arseniosiderite; —ит *m.* arsenite; (min.) *see* арсенолит.

арсено— *prefix* arseno—; —бензол *m.* arsenobenzene; —бисмит *m.* (min.) arsenobismite (hydrous bismuth arsenate); —зобензол *m.* arsenosobenzene, phenyl arsenoxide; —зосоединение *n.*, —ксид *m.* arsenoso compound, arsenoxide; —ламприт *m.* (min.) arsenolamprite (bismuth-containing arsenic); —лит *m.* (min.) arsenolite, white arsenic; —пирит *m.* (min.) arsenopyrite, mispickel; —соединение *n.* arseno compound.

арсен/сульфурит *m.* (min.) arsensulfurite (a variety of sulfur); —фенол *m.* arsenphenol.

арсепидин *m.* arsepidine, arsenidine.

арси/н *m.* arsine, arsenous hydride; —ндол *m.* arsindole; —но— *prefix* arsino—; —новая кислота arsinic acid; —триол *m.* arsitriol.

арсмаль *m.* a copper-arsenic insecticide.

арсон/иевые соединения arsonium compounds; —ий *m.* arsonium.

арсфенамин *m.* arsphenamine, Salvarsan.

арт. *abbr.* (артиллерийский).

артанитин *m.* arthanitin.

артарин *m.* artarine.

артезианский *a.* artesian (well).

артель *f.* artel, workmen's association, company; crew (of workers).

артемиз/ин *m.* artemisin, oxysantonin; —ия *f.* (bot.) artemisia.

артер/енол *m.* arterenol; —иальный *a.* arterial; —иит *m.* (med.) arteritis; —ин *m.* arterin; —иосклероз *m.* arteriosclerosis, hardening of the arteries; —ия *f.* artery.

артикул *m.* type, grade of merchandise.

артикуляция *f.* articulation.

артиллер/ийский *a.* artillery; —ист *m.* artillery-man; —ия *f.* artillery.

артист *m.* artist.

артишок *m.* (bot.) artichoke (*Cynara scolymus*).

Артмет *abbr.* (Трудовая артель об-

работки металлов) The Labor Association of Metal Workers.

артоза *f.* artose.

артрит *m.* (med.) arthritis, inflammation of the joints.

арум *m.* (bot.) arum.

арунд/инария *f.* (bot.) arundinaria; —о *n.* (bot.) reed (*Arundo donax*).

арфа *f.* harp; (agr.) seed-sorting screen; (aeolian) tones.

арфведсонит *m.* (min.) arfvedsonite (an amphibole).

арфонад *m.* arfonad (a sulfonium compound).

Архбюро *abbr.* (Архивное бюро) Bureau of Archives, Hall of Records.

арх/ей *m.* (geol.) Archean; —ейский *a.* Archean, ancient; —еозой *m.* Archeozoic; —еология *f.* archeology; —еоптерикс *m.* Archeopterix.

архив *m.* archives, records; Государственный а. Record Office.

Архимед Archimedes; закон —а, принцип —а Archimedes' principle.

архимедов винт Archimedean screw.

архимицеты *pl.* (bot.) Archimycetes.

архипелаг *m.* archipelago.

архитект/ор *m.* architect; —ура *f.* architecture; —урный *a.* architectural.

арцрунит *m.* (min.) arzrunite.

арча *f.* (bot.) juniper (*Juniperus*).

арчак *m.* saddle tree; (tech.) bow.

арч/евый, —овый *a.* (bot.) juniper.

аршин *m.*, —ный *a.* arshine (linear unit, 71.12 cm.).

арык *m.* impound, irrigation ditch.

а.с. *abbr.* (абсолютно сухой) absolutely dry; а-с *abbr.* (ампер-секунда) ampere-second.

аса, —н *see* асафетида.

асапрол *m.* asaprol, abrastol.

асафетида *f.* asafetida (a gum resin).

асб *abbr.* (апостильб) apostilb.

асбест *m.*, —овый *a.* (min.) asbestos (a variety of amphibole or chrysotile); а.-сырец *m.* crude asbestos; синий а. blue asbestos, crocidolite; —ин *m.* asbestine; —ит *m.* asbestos insulation; —овидный *a.* asbestiform, fibrous; —олин *m.* asbestolin (a paste for bearings).

асбо/картон *m.* asbestos board; —лан *m.* (min.) asbolan, asbolite (an earthy wad); —**пеколит** *m.* asbopekolite (an asbestos-pitch composition); —**фанера** *f.*, —**цементные материалы** asbestos-cement materials, asbestos-cement sheeting; —**шифер** *m.* artificial slate.

**асейсмический** *a.* (geol.) non-seismic.

**аселлин** *m.* asellin; —**овая кислота** asellic acid.

**асеп/сис** *m.*, —**тика** *f.* asepsis; —**тин** *m.* aseptin; —**тиновая кислота** aseptic acid; —**тический** *a.* aseptic; —**тол** *m.* aseptol, *o*-phenolsulfonic acid.

**АСИ** *abbr.* (**амплитудный селектор импульсов**) pulse height selector.

**асидерит** *m.* (min.) asiderite (an ironless stony meteorite).

**асидол** *m.* mixture of water-insoluble naphthenic acids.

**асимин/а,** —**овое дерево** *see* **азимина;** —**ин** *m.* asiminine.

**асимметр/ический,** —**ичный** *a.* asymmetric, asymmetrical, unsymmetrical; —**ия** *f.* asymmetry.

**асимптот/а** *f.* (geom.) asymptote; —**ический** *a.* asymptotic.

**асинергия** *f.* (med.) asynergy, faulty coordination.

**асинхрон/ичный,** —**ный** *a.* asynchronous, non-synchronous.

**асканит** *m.* askanite (an acid-activated clay).

**аскарид/а** *f.* ascarid (parasitic worm); —**иновая кислота** ascaridic acid, ascaridolic acid; —**овые** *pl.* (zool.) Ascaroidea; —**оз** *m.* (med.) ascariasis; —**ол** *m.* ascaridole.

**аскарит** *m.* ascarite (an asbestos material).

**асклеп/идин** *m.* asclepidin; —**ин** *m.* asclepin.

**асколи/зация** *f.* Ascoli test for anthrax in hides; —**ровать** *v.* test hides for anthrax.

**аско/лой** *m.* Ascoloy (aluminum alloy); —**мицеты** *pl.* (bot.) Ascomycetes; —**рбиновая кислота** ascorbic acid, vitamin C; —**хитоз** *m.* Ascochyta infection (of plants).

**асманит** *m.* (min.) asmanite (a form of meteoric silica).

**аспараг,** —**ус** *see* **спаржа;** —**ин** *m.* asparagine, α-aminosuccinamic acid;

—**иновая кислота** aspartic acid, aminosuccinic acid; **соль** —**иновой кислоты,** —**иновокислая соль** aspartate.

**аспарт/ил** *m.* aspartyl; —**овая кислота** *see* **аспарагиновая кислота.**

**аспект** *m.* aspect, appearance.

**аспергилл/ин** *m.* aspergillin; —**овая кислота** aspergillic acid.

**аспид** *m.* (petr.) slate; (zool.) asp; —**ин** *m.* aspidin; —**инол** *m.* aspidinol.

**аспидн/оголубой** *a.* slate blue; —**ый** *a.* slate, slaty; schistous; scaly, flaky, foliated; —**ый камень** slate (a metamorphic rock); —**ый сланец,** —**ая доска** slate; blackboard.

**аспидо/замин** *m.* aspidosamine; —**спермин** *m.* aspidospermine.

**аспирант** *m.* aspirant, fellow, alumnus.

**аспира/тор** *m.* aspirator, suction apparatus; —**ционный** *a.*, —**ция** *f.* aspiration, suction.

**аспирин** *m.* aspirin, acetylsalicylic acid.

**аспит** *m.* shield volcano.

**ассамар** *m.* assamar.

**ассениз/ационный** *a.* sanitary, sanitation; **а. насос** cesspool pump; —**ация** *f.* sanitation; —**ировать** *v.* make sanitary.

**ассигн/ация** *f.* assignation; bank note, note; —**ование** *n.* assigning, assignment; appropriation; allotment; —**овать** *v.* assign, appoint, grant, allot; appropriate; —**овка** *f.* assignment, grant.

**ассимил/ированный** *a.* assimilated; —**ировать** *v.* assimilate; —**ируемость** *f.* assimilability; —**ируемый** *a.* assimilable; —**ят,** —**ятор** *m.* assimilator; —**яторный** *a.* assimilatory; —**яция** *f.* assimilation.

**ассист/ент** *m.* assistant; —**ировать** *v.* assist, be an assistant.

**ассортимент** *m.* assortment, choice, selection; set, outfit.

**ассоци/ативный** *a.* associative; —**ация** *f.* association; combination; —**ированный** *a.* associated; —**ировать** *v.*, —**ироваться** *v.* associate, join, unite (with).

**астазиров/ание** *n.* (phys.) astatizing; —**ать** *v.* astatize, make astatic.

**астазия** *f.* (med.) astasia.

**астат/ий, —ин** *m.* astatine, At; **—ический** *a.* astatic, unstable; floating
(action); **—ичность** *f.* astaticism.

**астен/ия** *f.* (med.) asthenia; **—олит** *m.*
(geol.) asthenolith; **—осфера** *f.* (geol.)
asthenosphere.

**астер/изм** *m.* (cryst.) asterism; **—ин** *m.*
asterin; **—оид** *m.* (astron.) asteroid,
minor planet.

**астигматизм** *m.* (optics) astigmatism.

**астильба** *f.* (bot.) astilbe.

**астма** *f.* (med.) asthma; **—тик** *m.*, **—тический** *a.* asthmatic.

**Астона закон** Aston rule (of isotopes).

**астра** *f.* (bot.) aster.

**астрагал** *m.* (bot.) astragalus; (anat.)
astragalus, ankle bone.

**астраканит** *see* **астраханит.**

**астрал/ин** *m.* astral oil, kerosene; **—ит**
*m.* astralite (a glass); (expl.) astralite;
**—ьный** *a.* astral.

**астраханит** *m.* (min.) astrakanite (bloedite).

**астро/ида** *f.* (geom.) astroid; **—лин** *m.*
astrolin; **—лябический** *a.*, **—лябия**
*f.* (astron.) astrolabe (instrument);
**—навигация** *f.* astronavigation;
**—навтика** *f.* astronautics; **—ном** *m.*
astronomer; **—номический** *a.* astro-
nomical; **—номия** *f.* astronomy;
**—физика** *f.* astrophysics; **—филлит**
*m.* (min.) astrophyllite.

**асфальт** *m.* asphalt, mineral pitch; petroleum asphalt; **сибирский а.** (min.)
Siberian asphalt, dopplerite; **—ен** *m.*
asphaltene; **—ирование** *n.* asphalting, impregnation with asphalt; **—ированный** *a.* asphalted, impregnated
with asphalt; **—ировать** *v.* asphalt;
**—ит** *m.* (min.) asphaltite (a hydrocarbon complex).

**асфальто/бетон** *m.* asphalt concrete;
**—вый** *a.* asphalt, asphaltic, asphalt-
bearing; **—вый камень** asphalt stone
(a limestone impregnated with asphalt); **—вый толь** asphalt sheet,
asphalt roofing; **—вая замазка** asphalt cement; **—тип** *m.* (phot.)
asphaltotype.

**асфиксия** *f.* (med.) asphyxia.

**асфод/елина** *f.* (bot.) asphodeline; **—ель,
—иль** *f.* asphodel (*Asphodelus*).

**асхистовый** *a.* (petr.) aschistic, not
differentiated.

**АСХН** *abbr.* (Академия сельскохозяйственных наук) Academy of Agricultural Sciences.

**асцен/дент** *m.* (meteor.) ascendent;
**—зия** *f.* ascension.

**асцит** *m.* (med.) ascites.

**ат** *abbr.* (атмосфера техническая) technical atmosphere; atmosphere; **ат.**
*abbr.* (атомный) atomic; **ата** *abbr.*
(атмосфера абсолютная) absolute
atmosphere.

**атабрин** *m.* Atabrine; quinacrine.

**атак/а** *f.* attack; **угол —и** angle of incidence.

**атакамит** *m.* (min.) atacamite.

**атаковать** *v.* attack.

**атакси/ческий** *a.* ataxic; **—я** *f.* (med.)
ataxia.

**атамантин** *m.* athamantin.

**атбасарка** *f.* a locust (*Dociostaurus
kraussi*).

**ат. в.** *abbr.* (атомный вес) atomic weight.

**атебрин** *see* **атабрин.**

**ат. ед. массы** *abbr.* (атомная единица
массы) atomic mass unit, amu.

**ател/естит** *m.* (min.) atelestite (adamantine bismuth arsenate); **—ит** *m.* (min.)
atelite (a copper hydroxychloride).

**атеросклероз** *m.* (med.) atherosclerosis.

**атероспермин** *m.* atherospermine.

**ати** *abbr.* (атмосфера избыточная) gage
atmosphere.

**атизин** *m.* atisine.

**атиконовая кислота** aticonic acid.

**атипический** *a.* atypical, irregular.

**Аткинсона проба** Atkinson test.

**атлантический** *a.* Atlantic.

**атлас** *m.* (text.) satin; atlas (maps);
**—истый** *a.* satin, satiny; **—истый
шпат** (min.) satin spar (a variety of
aragonite or gypsum); **—ит** *m.* (min.)
atlasite (probably a mixture of atacamite and azurite); **—ить** *v.* make as
smooth as satin; **—ный** *a.* satin; **—ное
дерево** satinwood; **—овый голубой**
atlas blue.

**атлет** *m.* athlete; **—ика** *f.* athletics.

**атм.** *abbr.* (атмосфера) atmosphere;
(атмосфера барометрическая) barometric atmosphere; (атмосферный)
atmospheric.

**атмо/генный** *a.* (petr.) atmogenic; **—кластический** *a.* (petr.) atmoclastic; **—лиз** *m.* atmolysis; **—лит** *m.* (geol.) atmolith; **—метр** *m.* atmometer.

**атмостойкий** *a.* weatherproof.

**атмосфер/а** *f.* atmosphere; air; **техническая a.** technical atmosphere (735.5 mm. of mercury column); **—ический, —ный** *a.* atmospheric; air, vent (tube); **—ное давление** atmospheric pressure; **—ные осадки** atmospheric precipitation, atmospheric condensation.

**ат. н.** *abbr.* (атомный номер) atomic number.

**атоксил** *m.* atoxyl, sodium arsanilate; **—овая кислота** atoxylic acid, arsanilic acid.

**атолл** *m.* atoll (coral, circular island).

**атом** *m.* atom; **вес —а** atomic weight; **знак —а** atomic symbol; **однородные —ы** atoms of the same element; **разнородные —ы** atoms of different elements; **порядковое число —ов** atomic number; **—арный** *a.* atomic; nascent; **—изатор** *m.* atomizer; **—изм** *m.* atomism, atomic theory; **—истика** *f.* atomics; atomic theory; **—истический** *a.* atomistic; atomic; **—ический** *a.* atomic; **—ник** *m.* nuclear scientist; **—новодородный** *a.* atomic-hydrogen (welding); **—ность** *f.* atomicity, valence, valency; (alcohols) number of hydroxyl groups.

**атомн/ый** *a.* atomic; nuclear (physics); *suffix* **—hydric** (alcohol); **a. вес** atomic weight; **единица —ого веса** atomic weight unit, awu; **a. котел, a. реактор** nuclear reactor; **a. номер, —ое число, —ое порядковое число** atomic number; **a. объем** atomic volume; **—ая единица массы** atomic mass unit, amu; **—ая техника** nucleonics; **—ая энергия** atomic energy; nuclear power; **—ое обозначение** atomic symbol; **—ое учение** atomic theory.

**атомо—** *prefix* atomic; nuclear-powered; **—воз** *m.* nuclear-powered locomotive.

**атофан** *m.* Atophan, cinchophen.

**атра/ктилен** *m.* atractylene; **—ктилол** *m.* atractylol; **—норин** *m.* atranorin.

**атремон** *m.* atremone, chromone-2-carboxylic acid.

**атрепсия** *f.* athrepsia, marasmus.

**атрибут** *m.* attribute; **—ивный** *a.* attributive.

**атро—** *prefix* atro—; **—глицериновая кислота** atroglyceric acid, $\alpha$-phenylglyceric acid; **—лактиновая кислота** atrolactic acid, $\alpha$-phenyllactic acid; **—ментин** *m.* atromentin.

**атроп/амин** *m.* atropamine, apoatropine; **—изм** *m.* atropism, atropine poisoning; **—ил** *m.* atropyl; **—ин** *m.*, **—иновый** *a.* atropine, *dl*-hyoscyamine; **сернокислый —ин, сульфат —ина** atropine sulfate; **—овая кислота** atropic acid, $\alpha$-phenylacrylic acid.

**атро/пурол** *m.* atropurol; **—сцин** *m.* atroscine, *i*-scopolamine; **—фироваться** *v.*, **—фия** *f.* (med.) atrophy.

**АТС** *abbr.* (Автоматическая телефонная станция) Automatic Telephone Station.

**аттенюатор** *m.* (rad.) attenuator.

**аттест/ат** *m.* testimonial, certificate; **—ация** *f.* attestation, testimony; **—овать** *v.* testify, certify; recommend.

**АТФ** *abbr.* (аденозинтрифосфат) adenosine triphosphate, ATP.

**ауаровое масло** awara-kernel oil.

**аугментация** *f.* augmentation, increase.

**ауди/енция** *f.* audience; **—оллой** *m.* Audiolloy (nickel-iron alloy); **—ометр** *m.* audiometer; **—он** *m.* (elec.) audion, electric tube; **—тория** *f.* auditorium.

**ауерлит** *see* **ауэрлит.**

**АУК** *abbr.* (аминоуксусная кислота) aminoacetic acid.

**аукс/анометр** *m.* auxanometer (for measuring rate of plant growth); **—ин** *m.* auxin; **—ограф** *m.* auxograph; **—охром** *m.*, **—охромная группа** (chem.) auxochrome.

**аукубин** *m.* aucubin.

**аукцион** *m.* auction.

**аур/адин** *m.* auradin, neroli camphor; **—амин** *m.* auramine; **—аминовое основание** auramine base; **—антидин** *m.* aurantidin; **—антин** *m.* aurantine; **—антиоглиокладин** *m.* aurantioglioctadin; **—анция** *f.* aurantia (dye); **—ат** *m.* aurate; **—еолин** *m.*

aureolin, primulin; —еомицин *m.* aureomycin, chlortetracycline; —еотрицин *m.* aureothricin; —ин *m.* aurin, *p*-rosolic acid.

**аури/пигмент** *m.* (min.) orpiment, yellow arsenic; —хальцит *m.* aurichalcite.

**ауро/кол** *m.* aurocol; —тиол *m.* aurothiol.

**аускультировать** *v.* (med.) auscultate.

**аустенит** *m.* (met.) austenite; —ный, —овый *a.* austenite, austenitic.

**аутбридинг** *m.* (zool.) outbreeding.

**аутенит** *see* **аутунит.**

**аутигенный** *a.* (petr.) authigenic.

**ауто—** *prefix* auto—; automobile, *see also* авто—; —катализ *m.* autocatalysis.

**аутунит** *m.* (min.) autunite, lime uranite.

**ауэр/бахит** *m.* (min.) auerbachite; —лит *m.* (min.) auerlite (thorium silicophosphate); —металл *m.* Auer metal.

**афазия** *f.* (med.) aphasia.

**афаниновая кислота** aphanic acid.

**афанит** *m.* (petr.) aphanite, diabase; —овый *a.* aphanitic, diabasic.

**афвиллит** *m.* (min.) afwillite (a hydrous calcium silicate).

**афган/истанский, —ский** *a.* Afghanistan.

**афел/ий** *m.* (astron.) aphelion; —инус *m.* parasitic wasp (*Aphelinus mali*); —ины *pl.* Aphelinidae.

**афенил** *m.* afenil, calcium chloride urea.

**афидиус** *m.* a braconid wasp (*Aphidius granarius*).

**афин—** *see* **аффин—.**

**афин/ий** *m.* athenium, An; —янский *a.* Athenian.

**афиш/а** *f.* bill, poster, placard; —ировать *v.* make a display (of); —ная краска lithographic color.

**афридол** *m.* afridol, sodium hydroxymercuric toluate.

**африканск/ий** *a.* African; —ая пенька bowstring hemp.

**афро/дит** *m.* (min.) aphrodite; —метр *m.* (brewing) aphrometer; —сидерит *m.* (min.) aphrosiderite (a variety of chlorite).

**афтершок** *m.* (geol.) aftershock.

**афтиталит** *m.* (min.) aphthitalite, glaserite.

**аффект** *m.* affect; temporary insanity; —ированный *a.* affected.

**афферентный** *a.* afferent.

**аффин/аж** *m.*, —ирование *n.* (met.) refining; —ация *f.* (sugar) affination; —ировать *v.* refine; —ный *a.* affine, related, adjoining; (math.) affine (transformation); —ость *f.* affinity.

**ахи/бромин** *m.* achibromin; —леин, —ллеин *m.* achilleine, —лленовое масло achillea oil; —ллесово сухожилие, —ллово сухожилие (anat.) Achilles' tendon; —ллетин *m.* achilletin.

**АХЛ** *abbr.* (агрохимическая лаборатория) agrochemical laboratory.

**ахматит** *m.* (min.) achmatite (a variety of epidote).

**ахолия** *f.* (med.) acholia.

**ахондрит** *m.* (petr.) achondrite (a meteorite).

**ахро/ит** *m.* (min.) achroite (a variety of tourmaline); —мат *m.* achromatic lens; —матизм *m.* achromatism; —матический *a.* achromatic, colorless; —одекстрин *m.* achroödextrin.

**АХТТ** *abbr.* (Ассоциация химии твердого топлива) Solid Fuel Chemistry Association.

**аце—** *prefix* ace—; —диамин *m.* acediamine, ethenylamidine; —нафтен *m.* acenaphthene.

**ацеотропический** *see* **азеотропический.**

**ацет—** *prefix* acet—; —ал, —аль *m.*, —алевый *a.* acetal, 1,1-diethoxyethane; —альдазин *m.* acetaldazine; —альдегид *m.* acetaldehyde, ethanal; —альдегид-аммиак acetaldehyde ammonia; —альдоксим *m.* acetaldoxime, aldoxime;—альдол *m.*acetaldol, aldol.

**ацет/амид** *m.* acetamide, ethanamide; —амидин *m.* acetamidine, ethanamidine; —анилид *m.* acetanilide; —ат *m.* acetate; —атный шелк acetate silk (rayon); —енил *m.* acetenyl, ethynyl.

**ацетил** *m.* acetyl, ethanoyl; **перекись —а** acetyl peroxide; **хлористый а.** acetyl chloride; —ацетон *m.* acetylacetone.

**ацетилен** *m.*, —овый *a.* acetylene, ethyne; —истая медь cuprous acetylide;

—истое серебро silver acetylide; —овый генератор acetylene gas producer; —овая сажа acetylene black; —окислородная сварка oxyacetylene welding.

ацетил/ид *m.* acetylide;—иден *m.* acetylidene; —ирование *n.* acetylation, acetylization;—ированный *a.* acetylized; —ировать *v.* acetylate, acetylize; —ируемый *a.* acetylizable, capable of acetylation; —мочевина *f.* acetylurea;—овый, —ьный *a.* acetyl; —овый альдегид acetaldehyde; —салициловая кислота acetylsalicylic acid, aspirin; —серная кислота acetylsulfuric acid; —целлюлоза *f.* acetylcellulose, cellulose acetate; —целлюлозный *a.* cellulose acetate, acetate (silk).

ацет/иметр *m.* acetimeter (obs. for hydrometer); —иметрия *f.* acetimetry; —ин *m.*, —иновый *a.* acetin.

ацето— *prefix* aceto—; —ин *m.* acetoin, 3-hydroxy-2-butanone; —клетчатка *f.* cellulose acetate; —ксим *m.* acetoxime, 2-propanone oxime; —л *m.* acetol, 1-hydroxy-2-propanone; —метр *m.* acetometer; —н *m.* acetone, 2-propanone; —нил *m.* acetonyl; —нилацетон *m.* acetonylacetone; —нитрил *m.* acetonitrile, ethanenitrile.

ацетонов/окислый *a.* acetonic acid; acetonate (of); —окислая соль acetonate; —ый *a.* acetone; —ый спирт acetone alcohol, acetol; —ая кислота acetonic acid, α-hydroxyisobutyric acid; —ое масло acetone oil.

ацето/пирин *m.* acetopyrine; —уксусная кислота acetoacetic acid; —уксусный эфир acetoacetic ester, spec. ethyl acetoacetate; —фенетидин *m.* acetophenetidin, phenacetin; —фенон *m.* acetophenone, phenyl methyl ketone; —форм *m.* acetoform; —хлорин *m.* Soviet term for vinyl chloride -vinyl acetate copolymer fiber (Vinyon).

ацетуровая кислота aceturic acid, acetylglycine.

аци— *prefix* aci—.

ацид/иметр *m.* acidimeter (obs. for hydrometer); —иметрия *f.* acidi-

metry; —ит *m.* acid rock, acidic rock; —оз *m.* (med.) acidosis; —ол *m.* Acidol, betaine hydrochloride; —ометр *m.* acidometer; —офилин *m.* acidophilus milk; —офильный *a.* (biol.) acidophilic, acidophile; acidophilus (milk); —улин *m.* Acidulin, glutamic acid hydrochloride.

ациклический *a.* acyclic.

ацил *m.*, —ьный *a.* acyl; —ирование *n.* acylation; —ировать *v.* acylate.

ацитрин *m.* Acitrin, cinchophen ethyl ester.

АЦС *abbr.* (антиретикулярная цитотоксическая сыворотка) antireticular cytotoxic serum, ACS.

а-ч *abbr.* (ампер-час) ampere-hour.

Ачесона электропечь, Ачсона электропечь (elec.) Acheson furnace.

ашарит *m.* (min.) ascharite, szaibelyite.

Ашберри сплав Ashberry metal.

аширит *m.* (min.) dioptase.

аш-кислота *f.* H acid (dye intermediate).

аэр/атор *m.* aerator; —ация *f.*, —ирование *n.*, —ированность *f.* aeration; —ировать *v.* aerate.

аэро— *prefix* aero—, air; airborne; *see also* авиа—; —бный *a.* (biol.) aerobic; —бомба *f.* air bomb; —генный, —геновый *a.* aerogenic; eolian; —граф *m.* paint sprayer, air brush; aerograph; meteorograph; —двигатель *m.* airplane engine; —динамика *f.* aerodynamics; —динамический *a.* aerodynamic; —дром *m.* airdrome, airport, airfield; —золь *m.* aerosol; —изыскание *n.* aerial survey; —кулер *m.* air cooler; —лак *m.* (airplane) dope; —лит *m.* (geol.) aerolite, stony meteorite; —лифт *m.* air lift (pump); —логический *a.* (meteor.) aerological; —логия *f.* aerology; —лодка *f.* seaplane; —магнитный *a.* aeromagnetic; —магнитометр *m.* airborne magnetometer.

аэрометр *m.* aerometer; —ический *a.* aerometric; —ия *f.* aerometry.

аэромеханик *m.* aeromechanic, airplane mechanic; —a *f.* aeromechanics.

аэрон *m.* Aeron (an aluminum alloy); Aeron (an antiemetic).

аэронав/игатор *m.* air navigator; —игация *f.* aerial navigation; —т *m.*

aeronaut; —тика *f.* aeronautics; —тический *a.* aeronautical.

аэро/номический *a.* (meteor.) aeronomic; —опыливатель, —пыл.) —разбрасыватель *m.* crop duster; —план *m.* airplane; —порт *m.* airport; —почта *f.* air mail; —пыль, —смесь *f.* dust-laden air, dust cloud; —разведка *f.* airborne prospecting; —сев *m.* aerial sowing; —сил *m.* Aerosil (silica powder); —солоскоп *m.* aerosoloscope (counter for air particles); —спорин *m.* aerosporin, polymyxin A.

аэростат *m.* (aero.) aerostat, balloon, airship, dirigible; змейковый **a.** kite balloon; управляемый **a.** dirigible, airship; —ика *f.* aerostatics.

аэро/сфера *f.* aerosphere; —съемка *f.* aerial surveying, airborne surveying or mapping; —тэнк *m.* air tank (reservoir for purifying waste waters);

—упругость *f.* aeroelasticity; —фильный *a.* aerophilic, capable of absorbing air; —фильтр *m.* air filter; —фит *m.* (bot.) aerophyte, epiphyte, air plant; —флот *m.* (min.) aerofloat (flotation agent); —фобный *a.* aerophobic, incapable of absorbing air; —фон *m.* aerophone; —фор *m.* aerophore, breathing apparatus; —форм *m.* airoform, airol.

аэрофото/аппарат *m.* aerial camera; —графия *f.* aerial photography; —снимок *m.* aerial photograph; —съемка *f.* aerial photographic survey.

АЭС *abbr.* (атомная электростанция) nuclear power station.

аяконин *m.* ajaconine.

Аякс-Виатта печь (elec.) Ajax-Wyatt furnace.

аяцин *m.* ajacine.

# Б

б *see* бы; *abbr.* (бар) bar; (барн) barn; (бел) bel; б. *abbr.* (бывший) former.

Б *abbr.* (Бомэ) Baumé, Bé; code for niobium in steel mark.

баба *f.* ram, monkey, drop weight; (peasant) woman.

бабабуданит *m.* (min.) bababudanite.

бабануха *f.* leaf beetle (*Phaedon cochleariae*).

бабасу *n.* babassu (oil).

баббит *m.* babbitt (alloy for bearings).

бабелькварц *m.* (min.) babel quartz.

бабингтонит *m.* (min.) babingtonite.

Бабинэ принцип Babinet's principle.

бабка *f.* head, headstock (of lathe); chuck (of drilling machine); monkey, drop weight; задняя **б.** tailstock (of lathe); передняя **б.** headstock.

баблах *m.* bablah, Indian gallnuts (fruit of *Acacia bambolah* and *Acacia cinerea*).

Бабо закон (phys.) Babo's law.

бабоч/ка *f.* butterfly; —ки *pl.* Lepidoptera; клапан —кой (mach.) butterfly valve; —ницы *pl.* moth flies (*Psychodidae*).

бабуин *m.* (zool.) baboon.

бабушник *see* алоэ.

баб/ье лето Indian summer; —ья соль (bot.) samphire (*Crithmum maritimum*).

бавалит *m.* (min.) bavalite (near chamosite).

баварская голубая Bavarian blue.

Бавено закон, бавенский закон (cryst.) Baveno law (twinning).

багаж *m.*, —ный *a.* baggage, luggage, goods; —ник *m.* luggage carrier.

баган *m.* heap, pile; horizontal pile (in charcoal burning).

багас *m.* bagasse.

багер *m.* dredger, excavator.

багет *m.* baguet, molding.

баг/ийский *a.* Bahia; трава —ия Bahia grass (*Paspalum notatum*).

багор *m.* (boat) hook, gaff, harpoon.

багратионит *m.* (min.) bagrationite (a variety of allanite).

багрение *n.* spearing, harpooning (fish).

багрецовый *a.* purple.

багрить *v.* spear.

багр/оветь *v.* turn reddish purple; —овый, —янокрасный *a.* reddish purple; —яник *m.* (bot.) Judas tree (*Cercis*); —янки *pl.* red algae (*Florideae* or *Rhodophyceae*); —яный *a.* purple.

**багульник** *m.*, **болотный б.** (bot.) wild rosemary (*Ledum palustre*).

**бадан** *m.* (bot.) Bergenia.

**бадделеит** *m.* (min.) baddeleyite (zirconium dioxide).

**бад/ейка** *f.* tub, bucket; little bowl, little basin; **—ьевой** *a.* bucket; **—ьевой подъемник** bucket hoist, bucket; **—ья** *f.* bucket, tub, pail; kettle; trough.

**бадьян** *m.*, **б.-трава** *f.*, **—овый** *a.* (bot.) star anise (*Illicium anisatum*).

**бадяги** *pl.* (zool.) Spongillidae.

**бажра** *f.* a grass (*Pennisetum typhoideum*).

**баз** *m.* corral, pen, yard.

**база** *f.* base, basis, foundation, starting point; (surv.) datum line.

**базальный** *a.* basal.

**базальт** *m.* (petr.) basalt; **—ин** *m.* basaltine, augite; **—овый** *a.* basalt, basaltic; **—овая порода** basaltic rock; **—овое стекло** (petr.) basalt glass, tachylite, hyalomelane; **—ообразный** *a.* basaltiform, columnar.

**базанит** *m.* (min.) basanite, touchstone (a variety of jaspar).

**базар** *m.*, **—ный** *a.* market.

**Базедова болезнь** (med.) Basedow's disease, exophthalmic goiter.

**базельская зелень** Basel green, Paris green.

**базиди/альные грибы**, **—омицеты** *pl.* (bot.) Basidiomycetes; **—й** *m.* (bot.) basidium; (*pl.*) basidia; **—оспор** *m.* basidiospore, fruit-bearing basidia.

**базилик** *m.* (bot.) basil (*Ocimum basilicum*); **—овая мазь** (pharm.) basilicon ointment; **—овое масло** basil oil.

**баз/ировать**, **—ироваться** *v.* base (on); **—ис** *m.*, **—исный** *a.* basis, base, foundation; (cryst.) basal plane; level (of erosion); **—ит** *m.* basic rock; mafic rock; **—овый** *a.* basic.

**баилит** *see* **Бейли металл.**

**байбак** *m.* steppe marmot (rodent).

**байдар/а**, **—ка** *f.* canoe, dugout (boat).

**байевое масло** bay oil, myrcia oil.

**Байера способ** Bayer process (for aluminum oxide); **Б. теория напряжения** Baeyer tension (or strain) theory.

**байка** *f.* (text.) baize; frieze.

**байкал/еин** *m.* baicalein, 5,6,7-trihy-

droxyflavone; **—ин** *m.* baicalin; **—ит** *m.* (min.) baikalite (a variety of pyroxene).

**байкуру** *n.* baycuru root.

**байлеит** *see* **бейлиит.**

**байонетный** *a.* bayonet; **б. затвор** bayonet catch, bayonet joint; **б. цоколь** (elec.) bayonet cap (of lamp).

**байпас** *m.*, **—ный** *a.* by-pass.

**бак** *m.* tank, cistern, vat, tub, reservoir, container.

**бакале/йный** *a.*, **—я** *f.* grocery.

**бакан** *m.* beacon; buoy; lake (pigment).

**баканкозин** *m.* bakankosine.

**бакаут** *m.*, **—овое дерево** (bot.) lignum vitae, guaiac (*Guaiacum officinale*); **—овый** *a.* guaiac.

**бакел/изация** *f.* bakelization; **—ит** *m.*, **—итовый** *a.* bakelite (phenol-formaldehyde resin); **—итированный** *a.* treated with bakelite.

**бакен** *m.* beacon.

**бакерит** *m.* (min.) bakerite (hydrated calcium borosilicate).

**баккалавр** *m.* bachelor (holder of degree); **степень —а** bachelor degree; baccalaureate.

**баккатин** *m.* baccatine.

**бакла/га**, **—жка** *f.* flask, canteen.

**баклажан** *m.* (bot.) eggplant (*Solanum melongena*).

**бакланец** *m.* small rocky island, rock.

**баклуш/а** *f.* chip; block (of wood); cast iron wheel; **—ка** *f.* gate pin.

**баксин** *m.* orlean, annatto.

**бакстромит** *m.* (min.) bäckströmite, pseudo-pyrochroite.

**бактер/иальный**, **—ийный** *a.* bacterial; **—изовать** *v.* bacterize, subject to bacterial action; **—ии** *pl.* bacteria; **—иоз** *m.* bacteriosis, bacterial plant disease; **—иолиз** *m.* (med.) bacteriolysis; **—иолизин** *m.* bacteriolysin; **—иолог** *m.* bacteriologist; **—иологический** *a.* bacteriological; **—иология** *f.* bacteriology; **—иоподобный**, **—оидный** *a.* bacteroid; **—оскопический** *a.* bacterioscopic; **—оскопия** *f.* bacterioscopy; **—иоубивающий**, **—ицидный** *a.* bactericidal; **—иоубивающее средство**, **—ицид** *m.* bactericide; **—иофаг** *m.* bacteriophage; **—ия** *f.* bacterium.

**баку/ин** *m.* bakuin (lubricating oil from Baku petroleum); —**ол**, —**оль** *m.* bakuol.

**бак/ча**, —**ша** *see* **бахча.**

**бакштаг** *m.* backstay, guy, guy rope.

**балаган** *m.* booth, exhibit.

**баламутить** *v.* stir up, disturb, agitate, make muddy.

**баланс** *m.* balance, equilibrium, steadiness; **нейтронный б.** neutron economy; —**ер** *m.* (elec.) balancer.

**балансир** *m.*, —**ный** *a.* bob, bob weight, balance bob; beam, balance beam, equalizer, equalizing lever, reciprocating lever; rocking shaft; balance wheel; **б.**, —**овочное устройство** balancer; —**ный брус** balance bar.

**балансиров/ание** *n.* balancing; —**анный** *a.* balanced, in equilibrium; —**ать** *v.* balance, compensate.

**баланус** *m.* (zool.) barnacle.

**балас** *m.* (min.) balas (a variety of spinel).

**балат/а** *f.*, —**овый** *a.* balata (a latex).

**балахон** *m.* kind of loose overall, coverall.

**балда** *f.* knob; heavy hammer; bulldozer.

**балдахин** *m.* canopy.

**балд/риан**, —**ырьян** *see* **валериана.**

**балза** *f.* balsa wood.

**балинит** *m.* a wood-resin laminate.

**балка** *f.* beam, girder; ravine, gorge, gully; runway.

**балканский** *a.* Balkan.

**балкон** *m.* balcony.

**балл** *m.* mark; point, number (in a scale).

**баллас** *m.* ballas (variety of diamond).

**балласт** *m.* ballast, stabilizer; inert material; **б. газа** inert constituent (usually nitrogen and carbon dioxide); **грузить** —**ом** *v.* ballast; —**ирование** *n.*, —**ировка** *f.* ballasting; graveling (of roads); —**ированный** *a.* ballasted; —**ировать** *v.* ballast; —**ный** *a.* ballast; —**ное сопротивление** (elec.) ballast resistance (or resistor); —**овыгружатель** *m.* ballast unloader; gravel unloader; —**оочиститель** *m.* ballast cleaner.

**баллист/ика** *f.* ballistics; —**ит** *m.* (expl.) ballistite; —**ический** *a.* ballistic.

**баллон** *m.*, —**ный** *a.* balloon; (gas) cylinder, (acid) carboy, flask, bottle, vessel, container, tank; bulb (of thermometer); (med.) rubber bulb, syringe; —**ет** *m.* (aero.) ballonet.

**баллотиров/ание** *n.*, —**ка** *f.* ballot, poll, vote by ballot.

**балльн/ость** *f.* intensity (of an earthquake); —**ый** *a. of* **балл.**

**балоптикон** *m.* balopticon (a projector).

**балоч/ка** *f.* small beam; arm; —**ный** *a.* beam, girder; —**ная сталь** girder steel.

**балтийский** *a.* Baltic.

**балхашит** *m.* balkhashite (a bitumen).

**балык** *m.*, —**овина** *f.* cured fillet of sturgeon or other large fish.

**бальзам** *m.* balsam, balm; —**ин** *m.* (bot.) balsam (*Impatiens balsamina*); —**иновые** *pl.* (bot.) Balsaminaceae.

**бальзамиров/ание** *n.*, —**ка** *f.* embalming; —**анный** *a.* embalmed; —**ать** *v.* embalm; —**щик** *m.* embalmer.

**бальзам/ито** *n.* (pharm.) balsamito; —**ический,** —**ный** *a.* balsam, balsamic, balmy; —**ка** *f.*, —**ное яблоко** (bot.) balsam apple (*Momordica balsamina*); —**ная пихта** (bot.) balsam fir (*Abies balsamea*); —**ник** *m.*, —**ное дерево** balsam tree.

**бальма** *f.* overhang, rock shelter.

**Бальмера серия** Balmer series (of spectrum lines).

**бальмэна** *pl.* fluorescent colors.

**бальнео—** *prefix* balneo— (bath); —**грязевый** *a.* mud-bath.

**бальный** *a.* mark, point (value).

**бальтиморит** *m.* (min.) baltimorite (a picrolite serpentine).

**Бальца-Шимана реакция** Balz-Schiemann reaction (for fluorobenzenes).

**балюстрада** *f.* balustrade, guard rail.

**балясина** *f.* baluster; rung (of ladder).

**бамбук** *m.* (bot.) bamboo (*Bambusa*); **черный б.** black bamboo (*Phyllostachys nigra*); —**овые** *pl.* Bambuseae; —**овый** *a.* bamboo; (bot.) bambusaceous.

**бамия** *f.* (bot.) okra (*Hibiscus esculentus*).

**БАН** *abbr.* (**Белорусская Академия наук**) Belorussian Academy of Sciences; (**Библиотека Академии наук СССР**) Library of the Academy of Sciences, USSR.

**банальный** *a.* banal, commonplace, trite.

**банан** *m.* (bot.) banana (*Musa*); **райский б.** plantain (*M. paradisiaca*); **текстильный б.** Manila hemp (*M. textilus*); **фруктовый б.,** —**овое дерево** banana (*M. sapientum*); —**овые** *pl.* Musaceae; —**овый** *a.* banana; —**овый воск** pisang wax.

**бандаж** *m.* bandage; tire, band, banding; belt, belting; binding; (med.) truss.

**бандажно/гибочная машина** tire-bending machine; —**прокатный стан** tire-rolling mill, strip-rolling mill; —**токарный станок** tire lathe.

**бандажн/ый** *a.* bandage; tire, band; belt; **б. стан** tire mill, strip mill; —**ое железо** band iron, hoop iron.

**бандероль** *f.* wrapper; printed matter.

**бандолин** *m.* bandoline.

**Бандровского основание** Bandrowski's base.

**банистерин** *m.* banisterol.

**банк** *m.* bank.

**банк/а** *f.* jar; beaker; (med.) cup; bank, shoal; **ставить** —**и** *v.* (med.) cup.

**банкаброш** *m.* (text.) flyer, fly frame.

**банкет** *m.* (min.) banket (auriferous conglomerate); embankment.

**банк/ир** *m.* banker; —**овый** *a.* bank, banking.

**банкрот** *m.* bankrupt, insolvent; —**ство** *n.* bankruptcy, failure.

**банкуловое масло** bancoul nut oil.

**банник** *m.* (tube) brush, cleaner; reamer, scraper; (mil.) sponge, (gun) swab.

**баночный** *a.* jar, pot, glass.

**бант** *m.* knot, bow.

**баня** *f.* bath; bath house; **водяная б.** water bath, hot water bath; **паровая б.** steam bath; Turkish bath.

**баобаб** *m.* (bot.) baobab (*Adansonia digitata*); —**овая кора** adansonic bark; —**овое масло** baobab oil.

**бапти/зин** *m.* baptisin; —**зия** *f.* (bot.) baptisia; —**зоид** *m.* baptisoid; —**токсин** *m.* baptitoxine, cytisine.

**бар** *m.* bar (unit of pressure); bar, ledge.

**барабан** *m.* drum; roll, roller, cylinder; barrel; —**но-фрезерный станок** drum milling machine; —**но-шлифовальный станок** drum sander; —**ный** *a.* drum; —**ный грохот** rotating screen;

(min.) trommel; —**ный конвертер** (met.) barrel-type converter; —**ная мельница** (met.) rattler, tumbling barrel; —**ная перепонка** (anat.) tympanum; —**ная щелочь** commercial caustic soda.

**баран** *m.* sheep, ram; (mech.) battering ram; —**ец** *m.* (bot.) lamb succory (*Arnoseris*); *see also* **плаун**; —**ий** *a.* sheep; mutton; sheepskin; —**ий горох** (bot.) chickpea (*Cicer*, spec. *C. arietinum*); —**ий лоб** roche moutonnée (glacier-worn rock); —**ина** *f.* mutton; —**ка** *f.* ring-shaped roll, doughnut; (automobile) steering wheel; —**ка** *f.*, —**ник** *m.*, —**ья трава** (bot.) wolf's bane (*Arnica montana*); —**ок** *m.* (tech.) plane; —**чик** *m.* (text.) reel; (bot.) cowslip (*Primula officinalis*).

**барат** *m.* (viscose process) baratte, xanthation churn.

**бараш/ек** *m.* lamb; (mech.) wing nut; thumbscrew; —**ки** *pl.* fleece; froth, foam, breaking crests (of waves); (bot.) *see* **баранчик**; —**ковый** *a.* lambskin; wing (nut); thumb (screw).

**барба/лоин** *m.* barbaloin; —**мил** *m.* Barbamyl, amobarbital sodium.

**барбарис,** —**ник** *m.*, —**ный,** —**овый** *a.* (bot.) barberry (*Berberis*); —**овые** *pl.* Berberidaceae.

**барбатиновая кислота** barbatic acid.

**барбет** *m.* (mil.) barbette.

**барбиерит** *m.* (min.) barbierite.

**барбит/ал** *m.* barbital, diethylbarbituric acid; —**урат** *m.* barbiturate; —**уровая кислота** barbituric acid, malonylurea.

**барбот/аж** *m.* bubbling; —**ажный** *a.* bubbling, bubble; air-lift (system); —**ер** *m.* bubbler, diffuser; —**ировать** *v.* bubble, pass through a liquid.

**барботин** *m.* (cer.) barbotine.

**барбулька** *f.* (zool.) mullet.

**барвинок** *m.* (bot.) periwinkle (*Vinca*).

**бард/а** *f.*, —**енный,** —**яной** *a.* malt grains, distillery grains, residues; vinasse, slops, spent wash; (agr.) sterile soil; —**яной уголь** distillery grains ash (fertilizer).

**барел** *m.* barrel (unit of measure).

**барельеф** *m.*, —**ный** *a.* bas-relief.

**баретный напильник** barette file, cant file.

**бареттер** *m.* (rad.) barretter, ballast resistor.

**барех** *m.* kelp.

**баржа** *f.* barge.

**барид** *m.* snout beetle (*Baris*).

**бариев/ый** *a.* barium; **б. уранит** (min.) barium uranite, uranocircite.

**бар/ий** *m.* barium, Ba; **бромистый б.** barium bromide; **гидрат окиси —ия** barium hydroxide; **карбид —ия, углеродистый б.** barium carbide; **окись —ия** barium oxide, baryta; **перекись —ия** barium peroxide; **сернокислый б., сульфат —ия** barium sulfate; **хлористый б.** barium chloride.

**барил/ит** *m.* (min.) barylite; **—ла, —лья** *f.* barilla.

**бариль** *see* **баррель.**

**барильет** *m.* gas-collecting pipe.

**бар/ион** *m.* barion (particle with nuclear charge); **—ированный** *a.* barium-coated.

**бари/силит** *m.* (min.) barysilite; **—стронцианит** *m.* (min.) barystrontianite; **—стый** *see* **баритовый.**

**барит** *m.* baryta, barium oxide; (min.) barytes, barite, heavy spar; **едкий б.** barium hydroxide; **сернокислый б.** barium sulfate; **—о—** *prefix* baryto—.

**баритов/ый** *a.* barytic, baryta, baryto—; **б. желтый, б. крон** barium yellow, barium chromate; **б. шпат** *see* **барит; —ая вода** baryta water; **—ая селитра** barium nitrate; **—ая слюда** (min.) oellacherite (barium-containing muscovite); **—ые белила** baryta white, blanc fixe, permanent white (barium sulfate).

**барито/кальцит** *m.* (min.) barytocalcite; **—целестин** *m.* (min.) barytocelestite; **—цинковые белила** lithopone.

**барицентр** *m.* barycenter, center of gravity; **—ический** *a.* barycentric.

**бари/ческий** *a.* (meteor.) baric; barometric; **—я** *f.* barye (unit of pressure).

**барка** *f.* barge; (dye) vat; **—с** *m.* launch; longboat.

**баркевикит** *m.* (min.) barkevikite (an amphibole near arfvedsonite).

**баркометр** *m.* barkometer (hydrometer for tanning liquors).

**Барлоу колесо** (elec.) Barlow's wheel.

**барн** *m.* barn (unit of nuclear cross section).

**баро—** *prefix* baro— (weight, pressure); **—грамма** *f.* barogram; **—граф** *m.* barograph, recording barometer; **—камера** *f.* pressure chamber; **—клинный** *a.* baroclinic; **—метр** *m.* barometer; **—метрический** *a.* barometric; **—миль** *m.* baromil (barometer unit); **—реле** *n.* pressure relay, air relay; **—скоп** *m.* baroscope; **—стат** *m.* barostat; **—термограф** *m.* barothermograph; **—тропный** *a.* barotropic; **—циклономер** *m.* barocyclonometer.

**барочн/ик** *m.* bargeman, barge owner; **—ый** *a.* barge; **—ый груз** barge freight.

**баррандит** *m.* (min.) barrandite.

**барранкос** *m.* barranca (ravine or bank).

**баррель** *m.* barrel (unit of measure).

**барретер** *see* **бареттер.**

**баррикада** *f.* barricade.

**барс** *m.* (zool.) panther.

**барсу/к** *m.*, **—чий** *a.* (zool.) badger.

**Барта реакция** Bart reaction.

**барутин** *m.* barutin.

**бархан** *m* barchan, sand dune.

**бархат** *m.* (text.) velvet; **амурский б., —ное дерево** Amur cork (*Phellodendron amurense*); **бумажный б.** (text.) velveteen; **—ец** *m.*, **—ки, —цы** *pl.* (bot.) marigold (*Tagetes*); **—источерный** *a.* velvet black; **—истый** *a.* velvet, velvety; **—ный** *a.* velvet; barette (file).

**барыш** *m.* profit, gain; **—ничать** *v.* job; speculate.

**барьер** *m.*, **—ный** *a.* barrier, enclosure, rail, bar; **б. деления** fission barrier.

**бас** *m.* bass; **—истый** *a.* bass, deep.

**баскский** *a.* Basque.

**басма** *f.* a black dye.

**басон** *m.* galloon, braid, trimming.

**бассанит** *m.* (min.) bassanite.

**бассейн** *m.*, **—овый** *a.* tank, reservoir, basin; pond; pool; (coal) field; **б.-грязевик** sump, sump tank; **—овый реактор** (nucl.) pool-type reactor.

**бассетит** *m.* (min.) bassetite (similar to autunite).

**бассиев/о масло,** —**ое масло** bassia oil.

**бассистерин** *m.* bassisterol.

**бассор/ин** *m.* bassorin, tragacanthose; —**иновая кислота** bassoric acid; —**ская камедь** bassora gum.

**бастион** *m.* bastion, bulwark.

**баст/ит** *m.* (min.) bastite (eustatite altered to serpentine); —**незит** *m.* (min.) bastnäsite.

**бастовать** *v.* strike, go on strike.

**бастр** *m.* brown sugar, raw sugar.

**бастующий** *a.* striking, on strike.

**БАСХН** *abbr.* (Белорусская академия сельскохозяйственных наук) Belorussian Academy of Agricultural Sciences.

**Бата металл** Bath metal (brass alloy).

**батавские слезки** Prince Rupert's drops, glass tears.

**батальон** *m.* battalion.

**батан** *m.* batten (lumber); (text.) slay.

**батар/ейка** *f.* small battery; —**ейная** *f.* battery room; —**ейный** *a.* battery; —**ея** *f.* battery; set, bank, range; —**ея котлов** bank of boilers; —**ея накала** filament battery, "A" battery; —**ея сухих элементов** dry battery.

**батат** *m.* sweet potato (*Ipomoea batatas*).

**батер** *see* **белоголовец.**

**бати**— *prefix* bathy— (deep); —**альный** *a.* bathyal, deep-sea.

**батиковать** *v.* batik (paint on silk).

**батиловый спирт** batyl alcohol.

**батиметр** *m.* bathymeter; attenuation meter.

**батист** *m.* (text.) batiste, cambric, lawn.

**батисфера** *f.* bathysphere, diving sphere.

**баткак** *m.* batkak (black saline silt).

**бато**— *prefix* batho— (depth, height); *see also* **бати**—; —**лит** *m.* (petr.) batholite, batholith; —**литовый** *a.* batholitic; —**метр** *m.* bathometer (for measuring ocean depth); —**порт** *m.* caisson; —**хром** *m.* bathochrome.

**батрак** *m.* hired laborer, workman.

**батрахит** *m.* (min.) batrachite (a variety of monticellite).

**баттенсы** *pl.* battens (lumber).

**баттерфлей** *m.* (mech.) butterfly; **затвор б.** butterfly gate.

**батун** *m.* Welsh onion (*Allium fistulosum*).

**батчелорит** *m.* (min.) batchelorite.

**бауденовский** *a.* Bowden.

**Бауер-Барфа процесс** (met.) Bower-Barffing process.

**баул** *m.* trunk, grip, case.

**баулит** *m.* (petr.) baulite, krablite.

**баум/гауерит** *m.* (min.) baumhauerite; —**лерит** *m.* bäumlerite, baeumlerite.

**Бауш-Лом** (optics) Bausch and Lomb.

**баф/иин** *m.* baphiin; —**ия** *f.* (bot.) camwood, barwood (*Baphia nitida*).

**бахада** *f.* (geol.) bajada.

**бахром/а** *f.,* —**очный** *a.* fringe; outskirt; (anat.) fimbria; —**чатокрылые** *pl.* (zool.) thrips (*Thysanoptera*); —**чатый** *a.* fringed, fimbriate.

**бахтарма** *f.* flesh side of hide.

**бахч/а** *f.* field of melons, cucumbers, squash; —**евой** *a.* (bot.) cucurbitaceous; —**еводство** *n.* cultivation of melons, etc.

**баци/лизин** *m.* bacilysin; —**липин** *m.* bacilipin.

**бацилл/а** *f.* bacillus; **культура бацилл** bacilliculture; —**ин** *m.* bacillin; —**омицин** *m.* bacillomycin; —**оподобный** *a.* bacilliform, bacillar; —**оубивающее средство** bacillicide; —**ярный** *a.* bacillary.

**бацитрацин** *m.* bacitracin.

**баццит** *m.* (min.) bazzite.

**бачок** *m.* tank, small tank.

**башен/ка** *f.* turret, tower; —**ница** *f.* (bot.) tower cress (*Arabis turrita* or *Turris glabra*); —**ный** *a.* tower; —**ный процесс** tower process; Mills-Packard process (for sulfuric acid manufacture); —**ный холодильник** cooling tower.

**башм/ак** *m.* shoe; socket; chock; clip; —**ачник** *m.* shoemaker; —**ачный** *a.* shoe; —**ачная вакса** shoe polish; —**ачок** *m.* (bot.) lady's slipper (*Cypripedium*).

**башня** *f.* tower, turret.

**баштан** *see* **бахча.**

**баэль** *f.* (bot.) bel (*Aegle marmelos*).

**б.г.** *abbr.* (без года) year not given (in bibliography).

**БГУ** *abbr.* (Белорусский государственный университет) Belorussian State University).

**БГХ** *abbr.* (бензолгексахлорид) benzene hexachloride.

**бделий** *m.* bdellium (a gum resin).

**бдительн/ость** *f.* vigilance, watchfulness; **—ый** *a.* vigilant, watchful, alert.

**б.е.** *abbr.* (белковая единица) protein unit.

**Бе** *abbr.* (градусы Бомэ) degrees Baumé.

**беб/еерин, —ирин** *m.* bebeerine; **—еериновая кислота** bebeeric acid; **—ееру** *n.* bebeeru bark.

**беватрон** *m.* (nucl.) bevatron (synchrotron).

**бег** *m.* run, running, course; **—ание** *n.* running; wandering; **—ать** *v.* run, run about; **—ать от** *v.* avoid; **—ающий** *a.* running; (zool.) cursorial; *see also* **бегущий.**

**бегемот** *m.* (zool.) hippopotamus.

**беген/овая кислота** behenic acid, docosanoic acid; **—овое масло** behen oil, oil of ben; **—олевая кислота** behenolic acid, 13-docosynoic acid; **—олил** *m.* behenolyl; **—он** *m.* behenone.

**бегл/ец** *m.* fugitive; refugee; **—ость** *f.* fluency; **—ый** *a.* fluent, rapid; sketchy, superficial, brief; cursory (inspection); fugitive.

**бегов/ой** *a.* race; **—ая дорожка** (mach.) race.

**бегом** *m.* (elec.) begohm (unit of resistance).

**бегон/иевые** *pl.* (bot.) Begoniaceae; **—ия** *f.*, **—иевый** *a.* begonia.

**бегство** *n.* flight, escape, hasty retreat.

**бегун** *m.* runner; traveler; millstone; crusher roll (of mill); **—ковая мельница** crusher-roll mill; **—ковая тележка** trailer; **—ок** *m.* runner; traveler, traveling roller, roller; jockey pulley; race (for ball bearings); **—ы** *pl.* edge-runner mill.

**бег/ут** *pr. 3 pl. of* **бежать; —учий, —ущий** *a.* running; traveling (wave); scanning (beam); **—ущий слой** striation (in discharge tubes); **с —ущей волной** traveling-wave.

**бегхауз** *m.* bag house; filter plant.

**бед/а** *f.* misfortune, trouble, mishap, predicament; **как на —у** to make matters worse; **на —у** unfortunately.

**бедантит** *m.* (min.) beudantite.

**бедерный** *see* **бедренный.**

**бедн/еть** *v.* grow poor; **—ость** *f.* poverty, bareness, barrenness; **—ота** *f.* poverty, ore).

**бедрен/ец** *m.* (bot.) pimpinella; **б.-камнеломка** *f.*, **каменистый б.** burnet saxifrage (*P. saxifraga*); **эфирное масло —ца, —цовое масло** pimpernel oil.

**бедр/енный, —яный** *a.* hip; (anat.) femoral; **—енная кость** femur, thigh bone; **—о** *n.* femur, hip, thigh; ham, haunch.

**бедрок** *m.* (geol.) bedrock.

**бедств/енный** *a.* distress; disastrous; **—ие** *n.* calamity, disaster; emergency; distress; **сигнал —ия** distress signal, SOS; **—овать** *v.* be in distress; live in poverty.

**беербахит** *m.* (petr.) beerbachite (a type of dike).

**беж** *m.* beige; unbleached serge.

**беж/ать** *v.* run, course, flow; **—енец** *m.* refugee.

**без** *prep. gen.* without; minus, less, free (of); **б. четверти шесть** a quarter to six o'clock, five forty-five.

**без—** *prefix* in—, ir—, un—, —less, —free, de—, non—; *see also* **бес—; —аварийный** *a.* trouble-free, faultless; **—азотистый** *a.* nitrogen-free.

**безалаберн/ость** *f.* lack of order, inconsistency; **—ый** *a.* without system, inconsistent; negligent, careless.

**безалкалоидный** *a.* alkaloid-free.

**безапелляционный** *a.* peremptory.

**безбедн/ость** *f.* security; **—ый** *a.* competent; secure, comfortable, well-off.

**безболезненн/о** *adv.* painlessly, without pain; **—ость** *f.* painlessness; perfect health; **—ый** *a.* painless; healthy.

**безбоязненный** *a.* fearless, brave.

**безбрачный** *a.* celibate; (bot.) agamous.

**безбреж/ность** *f.*, **—ье** *n.* vast, infinite; **—ный** *a.* vast, boundless, unlimited.

**безбурный** *a.* stormless, calm.

**безвариантный** *a.* invariant.

**безваттный** *a.* (elec.) wattless, idle, reactive (component).

**безверье** *n.* disbelief.

**безвестн/ость** *f.* obscurity; —**ый** *a.* obscure, unknown.

**безветр/еный** *a.* windless, calm; —**ие** *n.* want of wind, calm.

**безвинный** *a.* innocent, guiltless.

**безвихрев/ой** *a.* vortex-free, eddy-free; irrotational; —**ое течение** irrotational flow.

**безвкус/ие** *n.*, —**ица** *f.*, —**ность** *f.* tastelessness, flatness, insipidity; —**ный** *a.* tasteless, flat, insipid.

**безвлажный** *a.* dry, arid.

**безвласти/ость** *f.* lack of authority; —**ый** *a.* powerless, helpless, impotent.

**безвласый** *a.* hairless.

**безвод/ность** *f.*, —**ье** *n.* anhydrous state; dryness, aridity; —**ный** *a.* anhydrous, free of water; dry, arid; —**ная соль** anhydrous salt; —**ородный** *a.* hydrogen-free.

**безвозвратн/о** *adv.* irrevocably; —**ый** *a.* irrevocable, irreversible.

**безвоздушн/ый** *a.* airless, deaerated, vacuum; —**ое пространство** vacuum.

**безвозмездн/о** *adv.* free, gratis; —**ый** *a.* free of charge, without cost.

**безволокнистый** *a.* fiber-free; snap (bean).

**безволос/ица** *f.* baldness; —**ый** *a.* bald, hairless; glabrous, smooth.

**безвредн/о** *adv.* harmlessly; —**ость** *f.* harmlessness; —**ый** *a.* harmless.

**безвременни/к** *m.*, —**ца** *f.* (bot.) meadow saffron (*Colchicum* spec. *C. autumnale*); **семена** —**ка** colchicum seed.

**безвремен/но** *adv.* not at the proper time, prematurely; —**ность** *f.* inopportuneness, untimeliness, prematureness; —**ный** *a.* inopportune, untimely, ill-timed, premature; —**ье** *n.* improper time; unseasonable weather.

**безвыгодн/ость** *f.* disadvantage; —**ый** *a.* disadvantageous.

**безвыездн/о** *adv.* without leaving; —**ый** *a.* never leaving; uninterrupted.

**безвыходн/ость** *f.* helplessness, hopelessness; —**ый** *a.* helpless, hopeless, desperate, having no way out.

**безвязкостный** *a.* non-viscous, inviscid.

**безглавый** *see* **безголовый.**

**безглазый** *a.* eyeless, without eyes; blind.

**безгласный** *a.* voiceless, mute.

**безголов/ые** *pl.* (zool.) Acephala; —**ый** *a.* headless, acephalous.

**безграмотн/ость** *f.* illiteracy; —**ый** *a.* illiterate, ignorant.

**безграничн/о** *adv.* infinitely, ad infinitum, without a limit; —**ость** *f.* infinity, limitlessness; —**ый** *a.* infinite, limitless; unbounded (function).

**безгранный** *a.* anhedral.

**безгрунтовая эмаль** one-coat enamel.

**бездарн/ость** *f.* want of talent; —**ый** *a.* untalented, ungifted, incapable.

**бездейств/енность** *f.* inactivity; ineffectiveness, inefficiency; —**енный, —ующий** *a.* inactive, inert, passive; idle, inoperative; —**ие** *n.* inaction, inertia, inertness; standstill, stop; **быть в** —**ии** *v.* (mach.) be out of service, be out of commission, not run; —**овать** *v.* remain inactive, slacken.

**бездел/ица** *f.* trifle; —**ка, —ушка** *f.* novelty, knick-knack; —**ье** *n.* idleness.

**безденежный** *a.* poor; free, gratuitous.

**без-дерево** *see* **бузина.**

**бездетный** *a.* childless.

**бездефицитный** *a.* self-supporting.

**бездеятельн/о** *adv.* passively; —**ость** *f.* inactivity, inertia; —**ый** *a.* passive, inactive, stagnant, inoperative.

**бездивергентный** *a.* non-divergent.

**бездна** *f.* chasm, gulf, deep, abyss; a great number (of), a great deal (of).

**бездождие** *n.* want of rain, drought.

**бездоказательный** *a.* unproved, unsubstantiated, not based on evidence.

**бездольный** *a.* (bot.) acotyledonous.

**бездомный** *a.* houseless, homeless.

**бездонный** *a.* bottomless, very deep.

**бездорож/ица** *f.*, —**ье** *n.* lack of roads, impassable roads; —**ный** *a.* pathless, impassable, roadless.

**бездоходн/о** *adv.* without profit, unprofitably; —**ость** *f.* barrenness, unproductiveness; —**ый** *a.* unprofitable.

**бездымный** *a.* smokeless; **б. порох** smokeless gunpowder.

**бездыханный** *a.* lifeless, inanimate.

**безжизненн/ость** *f.* lifelessness; —**ый** *a.* lifeless, inanimate, dull, dead.

**беззаботный** *a.* careless, unconcerned.

**беззаветный** *a.* supreme, unlimited, unrestrained; allowed.

**беззаконн/ик** *m.* transgressor, violator;

—ичать v. violate the law; —о adv. illegally; —ость f. illegality; —ый a. illegal.

беззамковые pl. (zool.) Inarticulata.

беззародышный a. (biol.) inembryonate.

беззарядный a. uncharged, neutral.

беззатей/ливый, —ный a. simple.

беззащитный a. defenseless, unprotected.

беззвездный a. starless.

беззвучный a. soundless, noiseless, silent.

беззольный a. ashless, ash-free.

беззубый a. toothless; (zool.) edentate, edentulous.

безиндукционный a. (elec.) non-inductive.

безискр/истый, —овой a. sparkless.

безконечный see бесконечный.

безкорыстный a. disinterested.

безлепестковый a. (bot.) apetalous.

безлес/ный a. woodless, treeless, bare; —ье n. lack of forests.

безликий a. faceless.

безлист/венный, —ный, —ый a. leafless.

безличный a. impersonal.

без/лодочный a. (glass drawing) without debiteuses; —лопастный a. bladeless.

безлюд/ный a. thinly populated, desolate, sparsely settled; —ство, —ье n. deficiency of population.

безмассовый a. massless.

безмен m. steelyard; spring balance.

безмерн/о adv. immeasurably; —ость f. immeasurableness, immensity, excess; —ый a. immeasurable, immense, excessive; boundless, infinite.

безместный a. having no place.

безмолв/ный a. silent, unspoken; implicit (promise); —ствовать v. be silent.

безмятежный a. imperturbable, placid, undisturbed, tranquil, quiet.

безнагрузочный a. idle, standby.

безнадежн/ость f. hopelessness; —ый a. hopeless, desperate.

безнадзорный a. unsupervised.

безналичный расчет payment by check.

безнамеренный a. unintentional.

безног/ие pl. (zool.) Apoda, —ий a. without feet; (zool.) apodal, apodous.

безо see без.

безоар m. —овый a. (vet.) bezoar;

—овая кислота bezoardic acid, ellagic acid.

безобидный a. inoffensive, harmless.

безобраз/ить v. mutilate, disfigure; —ность f. unseemliness; —ный a. unseemly, hideous; disfigured, deformed.

безоговорочный a. unconditional.

безоконный a. windowless (counter, etc.).

безопасливый a. incautious, rash.

безопасн/о adv. safely, without danger; it is safe; —ость f. safety, security; коэффициент —ости safety factor, margin of safety; мера —ости safeguard, safety measure; техника —ости accident prevention; —ый a. safe, secure; safety; permissible (load).

безоружный a. unarmed, defenseless.

безосновательн/о adv. groundlessly, without basis; —ый a. groundless, unfounded.

безостановочн/о adv. continuously, without stopping; —ость f. continuousness; —ый a. continuous, unceasing, ceaseless, uninterrupted; non-stop (flight).

безотбойный a. pressing, urgent.

безответственн/ость f. irresponsibility; —ый a. irresponsible, unaccountable.

безотговорочный a. without excuse.

безотказный a. dependable, reliable, trouble-free; infallible.

безотл/агательно adv. without delay, urgently, immediately; —агательность f. urgency; —агательный, —ожный a. urgent, pressing.

безотлучн/о adv. constantly, without leaving; —ость f. constant presence; —ый a. constantly present.

безотменный a. irrevocable.

безотносительн/о adv. without reference (to), irrespectively (of); —ость f. irrespectivity; —ый a. irrespective (of), irrelative; absolute.

безотчетный a. involuntary, instinctive, unconscious; unaccountable.

безошибочн/о adv. correctly, without error; —ость f. infallibility; —ый a. faultless, infallible, correct, unerring.

безплодный see бесплодный.

безработ/ица f. unemployment; период —ицы dead season; —ные pl. the unemployed; —ный *a.* unemployed.

**безрадиоактивный** *a.* non-radioactive, cold.

**безраздельный** *a.* inseparable.

**безразлич/ие** *n.* indifference, apathy; —но *adv.* irrespective, no matter which; it makes no difference; —ный *a.* indifferent, apathetic, insensible; neutral (point, zone).

**безразмерный** *a.* dimensionless.

**безрассудный** *a.* reckless, foolhardy, imprudent.

**безрезультатн/о** *adv.* without result, to no effect, in vain; —ость *f.* futility, inefficiency, ineffectiveness; —ый *a.* futile, without result, ineffective, inefficient; barren (well).

**безрельсовый** *a.* railless; б. транспорт highway transportation.

**безрессорный** *a.* without springs.

**безродный** *a.* without relatives.

**безропотный** *a.* resigned, submissive.

**безрукий** *a.* armless; clumsy, awkward.

**безваттный** *see* **безваттный.**

**безубыточн/о** *adv.,* —ый *a.* without loss.

**безугольный** *a.* having no angles; without coal; carbon-free.

**безударный** *a.* unstressed, unemphasized.

**безудержный** *a.* unchecked, unrestrained.

**безуклон/ный,** —чивый *a.* undeviating, straight.

**безукоризненный** *a.* irreproachable, faultless, blameless.

**безум/еть** *v.* go mad, become insane; —ец *m.* madman, lunatic; —ие *n.* insanity, dementia; —ный *a.* insane, mad.

**безупречный** *a.* faultless, irreproachable.

**безуронный** *a.* without loss or prejudice.

**безурядица** *f.* disorder, confusion.

**безусадочный** *a.* non-shrinking.

**безусловн/о** *adv.* absolutely, positively, unconditionally; —ость *f.* absoluteness, certainty; —ый *a.* absolute, positive, unconditional, categorical; irrespective; unconditioned (reflex).

**безуспешн/о** *adv.* unsuccessfully, without success; —ость *f.* lack of success, failure; —ый *a.* unsuccessful.

**безустанный** *a.* incessant, untiring.

**безусый** *a.* (zool.) without feelers.

**безуточный** *a.* (text.) weftless.

**безучаст/ие** *n.,* —ность *f.* indifference, apathy; —ный *a.* indifferent, apathetic.

**безцельный** *a.* useless, aimless.

**безшумный** *see* **бесшумный.**

**безъядерный** *a.* (biol.) anuclear.

**безызвести/ость** *f.* obscurity, uncertainty; —ый *a.* obscure, unknown.

**безым/енный,** —янный *a.* nameless, anonymous; б. палец fourth finger; —янная кость innominate bone, hip bone.

**безындукционный** *a.* non-inductive.

**безыскровый** *see* **безискровой.**

**безысходный** *a.* perpetual, continual.

**бейделлит** *m.* (min.) beidellite.

**бейлеит** *see* **бейлиит.**

**Бейли металл** Bailey metal.

**бейлиит** *m.* (min.) bayleyite (a magnesium-uranium carbonate).

**Бейльби слой** (met.) Beilby layer.

**Бейс-Балло закон** (meteor.) Buys Ballot's law.

**бейц/евание** *n.,* —овка *f.* staining (of woods); (met.) scouring, pickling.

**Бека лампа** Beck arc lamp.

**бекасики** *pl.* snipe flies (*Rhagionidae*).

**Бекке полоска** (optics) Becke line.

**беккелит** *m.* (min.) beckelite.

**беккерел/евы лучи** Becquerel rays; —ит *m.* becquerelite (uranium mineral).

**бекман/ия** *f.* slough grass (*Beckmannia*); —овский аппарат Beckmann apparatus (for determining molecular weight); —овское превращение Beckmann rearrangement.

**бекмес** *m.* concentrated fruit juice.

**бекон** *m.* bacon.

**бел** *m.* (elec. comm.) bel (unit).

**беладонна** *see* **белладонна.**

**белевой** *see* **бельевой.**

**белемнит** *m.* (geol.) belemnite (an extinct cephalopod).

**белена** *f.,* черная (bot.) henbane (*Hyoscyamus niger*).

**белен/ие,** —ье *n.* bleaching; blanching (of wax, metals); —ый *a.* bleached.

**белесоватый** *see* **беловатый.**

**бел/еть** *v.* grow white, whiten, bleach; —и *pl.* (med.) leucorrhea; —изна *f.* whiteness, white; —ики *pl.* beliki (For the Alapaevsk iron ore deposits the term means a mass of white clastic diluvial mesozoic rocks; for the Tukansk deposits, weathered and whitened clay schists; for the Berezovsk deposits, weathered beresites.)

**белила** *pl.* white mineral pigment, whiting; **свинцовые б.** white lead; **цинковые б.** zinc white, zinc oxide.

**белиль/ный** *a.* bleaching; **б. бак** bleacher, bleach tank; **б. порошок, —ная известь** bleaching powder, calcium hypochlorite; **б. раствор, —ная ванна** bleaching liquor, bleach; **—ная вода, —ная жидкость** Javel water, potassium hypochlorite; **—ная сода** bleaching soda (mixture of crystalline soda and sodium silicate); **—ная соль** bleaching salt; **—ное средство** bleaching agent, bleach, decolorant; **—ня** *f.* bleachery; **—щик** *m.* bleacher.

**белит** *m.* (cement) belite.

**белить** *v.* whiten, bleach; whitewash (building); blanch (metal, wax).

**бел/ичий** *a.* squirrel; **—ичье колесо** (mach.) squirrel cage; **—ка** *f.* squirrel; *gen. of* **белок; —ки** *pl. of* **белок;** *pl.* belki (in Siberia, the flattened mountain summits covered with snow).

**белков/ина** *f.,* **—ое вещество** albumin, protein; **—о-углеводный** *a.* protein-carbohydrate; **—ый** *a.* albumin, protein, albuminous.

**белладон/ин** *m.* belladonnine; **—на** *f.* (bot.) belladonna (*Atropa belladonna*); **—ное масло** belladonna oil.

**Белля способ** (met.) Bell's process (dephosphorizing); **Б. телефон** Bell telephone.

**бело—** *prefix* white.

**белов/атость** *f.* whitishness; **—атый** *a.* whitish; **—ой экземпляр** clean copy.

**белоглазка** *f.* loess with lime nodules.

**белоголов, —ец** *m.* (bot.) meadow sweet (*Spiraea ulmaria*); **—ица** *f.* cotton grass (*Eriophorum*); **—ка** *f.* a clover (*Trifolium montanum*); **—ник** *m.* yarrow (*Achillea nobilis*).

**бело/зерный** *a.* white-grained; **—зор** *m.* (bot.) parnassia; **—к** *m.* albumen (of egg); albumin, protein; white (of eye).

**белокалильн/ость** *f.,* **—ый жар** incandescence, white heat; **—ый** *a.* incandescent, white hot, glowing.

**бело/копытник** *m.* (bot.) coltsfoot (*Tussilago* or *petasites*); **—кровие** *n.* (med.) leukemia; **—крылка** *f.* whitefly, spec. greenhouse whitefly (*Trialeurodes vaporariorum*); **—крыльник** *m.* (bot.) water arum (*Calla palustris*); **—кудренник, вонючий** black horehound (*Ballota nigra*); **—курый** *a.* fair, blond; **—листник** *m.* (bot.) sweet sultan (*Centaurea moschata*); **—лицый** *a.* fair-skinned.

**белонит** *m.* (petr.) belonite.

**белорусс.** *abbr.* (**белорусский**) Belorussian.

**Белоруссия** Belorussia.

**бело/русский** *a.* Belorussian; **—снежный** *a.* snow-white; **—тал** *m.* (bot.) osier willow (*Salix amygdalina* or *S. viminalis*); **—телый** *a.* fair-skinned, white-skinned.

**бело/турка** *f.* (bot.) hard wheat (*Triticum durum*); **—ус** *m.,* **торчащий —ус** matgrass (*Nardus stricta*); **—цветник** *m.* snowflake (*Leucojum*).

**белочный** *see* **белковый.**

**белу/га** *f.* (zool.) beluga; **—жий клей** fish glue; **—ха** *f.* (zool.) white grampus.

**бел/ый** *a.* white; **б. камень** granulite, whitestone (metamorphic rock); **б. металл, б. сплав** white metal, antifriction metal; **—ое вещество** (anat.) white substance.

**бель** *f.* linen yarn; (calico) white reserve; white rust (plant disease).

**бельг.** *abbr.* (**бельгийский**) Belgian.

**бельгийская печь** Belgian furnace (for zinc).

**Бельгия** Belgium.

**белье** *n.* linen; (cer.) glazed and fired undecorated china; **нижнее б.** underwear; **—вой** *a.* linen.

**бельмо** *n.* (med.) cataract.

**бельтинг** *m.* belting.

**бельэтаж** *m.* first floor (above ground floor).

**беляк** *m.* (zool.) white hare; shoal (of fish); foam (of waves); beliak [(geol.) white kaolinic clay derived from feldspathic rocks; (pal.) mountain hare (*Lepus timidus*)].

**белянк/а** *f.* (bot.) white mushroom (*Lactarius*); spring snowflake (*Leucojum* *vernum*); **капустная б., репная б.** cabbage butterfly; —**и** *pl.* (zool.) Pieridae.

**бементит** *m.* (min.) bementite (a hydrous manganese silicate).

**бем/ерия** *f.* (bot.) ramie (*Boehmeria*); —**ит** *m.* (min.) boehmite (a hydrated alumina).

**бемское стекло** Bohemian glass (a sodium-potassium plate glass).

**Бенара ячейка** Benard cell, convection cell.

**бенбери** *n.* a rubber mixer.

**бенгальск/ий** *a.* Bengal; **б. огонь** Bengal light; —**ая зелень** Bengal green.

**бенедиктин** *m.* benedictine (a liqueur).

**бенз**— *prefix* benz—, benzo—; —**аконин** *m.* benzaconine, benzoylaconine; —**акридин** *m.* benzacridine, phenonaphthacridine.

**бензал, —ь** *m.* benzal, benzylidene; —**азин** *m.* benzalazine, benzaldehyde azine; —**ацетон** *m.* benzalacetone, cinnamyl methyl ketone; —**ацетофенон** *m.* benzalacetophenone, cinnamyl phenylketone.

**бенз/альдазин** *m.* benzaldazine; —**альдегид** *m.* benzaldehyde, benzenecarbonal; —**альдоксим** *m.* benzaldoxime; —**альхлорид** *m.* benzal chloride, benzylidene chloride; —**амид** *m.* benzamide, benzenecarbonamide; —**амидо**— *prefix* benzamido—; —**амин** *m.* benzamine; —**амон** *m.* Benzamon (a miotic); —**анилид** *m.* benzanilide, benzoylaniline; —**антрен** *m.* benzanthrene, naphthanthracene; —**антрон** *m.* benzanthrone; —**ацетин** *m.* benzacetin; —**гидроль** *m.* benzhydrol; —**едрин** *m.* Benzedrine, amphetamine.

**бензен** *see* **бензол**; —**ил** *m.* benzenyl; **хлористый —ил** benzenyl chloride.

**бензид** *m.* benzide, phenyl; —**ин** *m.*, —**иновый** *a.* benzidine; **хлористоводородный —ин** benzidine hydrochloride.

**бензил** *m.* benzyl; benzil, dibenzoyl; **хлористый б.** benzyl chloride; —**амин** *m.* benzylamine, phenylmethylamine; —**ацетат** *m.* benzyl acetate; —**бензоат** *m.* benzyl benzoate; —**диоксим** *m.* benzildioxime; —**ен** *m.* benzylene.

**бензилиден** *m.* benzylidene, benzal; **хлористый б.** benzylidene chloride, benzal chloride; —**ацетон** *m.* benzylidene acetone.

**бензилов/ый** *a.* benzyl; **б. спирт** benzyl alcohol, phenyl carbinol; **б. эфир** benzyl ether, benzyl oxide; **б. эфир уксусной кислоты** benzyl acetate; —**ая кислота** benzilic acid, diphenylglycolic acid; **соль —ой кислоты, —окислая соль** benzilate.

**бензил/пенициллин** *m.* benzylpenicillin; —**целлюлоза** *f.* benzylcellulose.

**бензимер** *see* **бензиномер**.

**бензимид**— *prefix* benzimid—; —**азол** *m.* benzimidazole.

**бензин** *m.*, —**овый** *a.* gasoline; benzine, ligroin, solvent naphtha; —**овый двигатель, —овый мотор, —омотор** *m.* gasoline engine or motor; —**овая колонка** gasoline pump; —**оизмеритель, —омер** *m.* gasoline gage; —**охранилище** *n.* gasoline tank.

**бензо**— *prefix* benzo—, benz—; gasoline; —**ат** *m.* benzoate; —**диазин** *m.* benzodiazine.

**бензое** *see* **бензойное дерево.**

**бензозол** *m.* benzosol, guaiacol benzoate.

**бензоил** *m.* benzoyl; **перекись —а** benzoyl peroxide; **хлорид —а, хлористый б.** benzoyl chloride; —**ацетон** *m.* benzoylacetone; —**бензойная кислота** benzoylbenzoic acid; —**гваякол** *m.* guaiacol benzoate; —**ен** *m.* benzoylene; —**ирование** *n.* benzoylation; —**ированный** *a.* benzoylated; —**ировать** *v.* benzoylate; —**овый** *a.* benzoyl.

**бенз/оин, —оий** *m.* benzoin, gum benzoin.

**бензойно/амиловый эфир** amyl benzoate; —**аммониевая соль** ammonium benzoate; —**бензиловый эфир** benzyl benzoate; —**кальциевая соль** calcium benzoate; —**кислый** *a.* benzoic acid; benzoate (of); —**кислый натрий** sodium benzoate; —**кислая соль** benzoate; —**ментиловый эфир** menthyl benzoate; —**метиловый эфир** methyl benzoate; —**натриевая соль** sodium benzoate; —**ртутная соль** mercuric benzoate; —**фениловый эфир** phenyl benzoate; —**этиловый эфир** ethyl benzoate.

**бензойн/ый** *a.* benzoin, benzoic; **б. альдегид** benzaldehyde; **б. ангидрид** benzoic anhydride; **б. эфир гваякола** guaiacol benzoate; **—ая кислота** benzoic acid, benzenecarboxylic acid; **соль —ой кислоты** benzoate; **эфир —ой кислоты** benzoic acid ester, benzoate; **—ая смола** *see* **бензой;** **—ое дерево** (bot.) benzoin tree (*Styrax benzoin*).

**бенз/окаин** *m.* benzocaine, ethyl *p*-aminobenzoate; **—околонка** *f.* gas (gasoline) pump; **—оксазин** *m.* benzoxazine; **—окси—** *prefix* benzoxy—.

**бензол** *m.*, **—овый** *a.* benzene, phene; **—еиновая кислота** benzoleic acid; **—ин** *m.* benzine; (pharm.) benzolin.

**бензолсульфо/кислота** *f.*, **—новая кислота** benzenesulfonic acid; **—намид** *m.* benzenesulfonamide; **—новоэтиловый эфир** ethyl benzenesulfonate; **—хлорид** *m.* benzenesulfonyl chloride.

**бензольн/ый** *a.* benzene; **—ое кольцо** benzene ring.

**бензо/нафтол** *m.* benzonaphthol, naphthol benzoate; **—нитрил** *m.* benzonitrile, benzenecarbonitrile; **—пиррол** *m.* benzopyrrole, indole; **—рез** *m.* oxygen-gasoline cutting torch; **—сульфоназол** *m.* benzosulfonazole; **—фенон** *m.* benzophenone, diphenyl ketone; **—хинолин** *m.* benzoquinoline, α-anthrapyridine; **—хинон** *m.* benzoquinone; **—хранилище** *n.* gas tank.

**бенз/пинакон** *m.* benzpinacone, benzopinacol; **—пирен** *m.* benzpyrene.

**бенинкопал** *m.* benin copal; **—иновая кислота** benincopalinic acid; **—овая кислота** benincopalic acid; **—оловая кислота** benincopalolic acid.

**бенит** *m.* barley sugar.

**бенитоит** *m.* (min.) benitoite.

**беннер** *m.*, **—овский станок** Banner (tire) machine.

**бентический** *see* **бентонический.**

**бентонит** *m.*, **—овая глина** (min.) bentonite (a volcanic, montmorillonite clay); **—овый** *a.* bentonite, bentonitic.

**бент/онический, —онный** *a.* (biol., geol.) benthonic, sea-bottom; **—ос**

*m.* benthos (sea-bottom flora and fauna).

**бенч** *m.* (geol.) bench.

**Бера закон** (optics) Beer's law.

**бераунит** *m.* (min.) beraunite (an iron phosphate).

**бербер/ин** *m.*, **—иновый** *a.* berberine; **—оновая кислота** berberonic acid, 2,4,5-pyridinetricarboxylic acid.

**берг/амотное масло, —амотовое масло** bergamot oil; **—аптен** *m.* bergaptene, bergamot camphor; **—аптеновая кислота** bergaptenic acid; **—аптол** *m.* bergaptol.

**берггрюн** *m.* (min.) mountain green, malachite.

**бергин/изация** *f.*, **—ирование** *n.*, **Бергиуса процесс** berginization, Bergius process (motor fuels from coal).

**бергманская трубка** Bergmann tubing.

**берг/шляг** *m.* sudden detachment of a piece of rock from the walls of a mine; **—шрунд** *m.* marginal crevasse.

**Бердана амальгаматор** (min.) Berdan pan.

**бердо** *n.* (text.) reed.

**берег** *m.* shore, coast, seashore, seacoast.

**берег** *past sing.*, **—ли** *past pl.* of **беречь.**

**берегов/ой** *a.* shore, coastal; **—ушка** *f.* brine fly (*Ephydra*); **—ушки** *pl.* ephydrid flies (*Ephydridae*).

**берегу/т** *pr. 3 pl.* of **беречь;** **—щий** *a.* keeping, preserving.

**бередить** *v.* irritate (a sore).

**береж/еный** *a.* kept, preserved; **—ет** *pr. 3 sing.* of **беречь;** **—ливость** *f.* economy, thrift; **—ливый** *a.* economical.

**бережн/ость** *f.* caution, prudence; **—ый** *a.* cautious, prudent, careful.

**береза** *f.* (bot.) birch (*Betula*).

**березит** *m.* (petr.) beresite, aplite (a muscovite granite).

**берез/ка** *f.* (bot.) small birch; European bindweed (*Convolvulus arvensis*); **—ник, —няк** *m.* birch grove; **—овик** *m.* birch mushroom (*Boletus scaber*).

**березовит** *m.* (min.) beresovite.

**березов/ица** *f.* birch sap, birch wine; **—ые** *pl.* (bot.) Betulaceae; **—ый** *a.* birch; **—ый деготь** birch tar oil; **—ая кора** birch bark.

**берека** *f.*, **лечебная б.** (bot.) wild service tree (*Sorbus torminalis*).

беремен/еть *v.* conceive; —ная *a.* pregnant; —ность *f.* pregnancy.

беренгелит *m.* berengelite (an asphaltlike mineral).

береск/ит, —лед, —лет *m.* (bot.) spindle tree (*Euonymus*).

берест *m.* (bot.) elm (*Ulmus*).

берест/а *f.*, —о *n.* birch bark; —овый, —яный *a.* birchbark; —овый деготь birch tar oil.

берет *pr. 3 sing. of* брать.

беречь *v.* take care (of), look (after); keep, preserve; spare; respect; —ся *v.* guard (against), beware (of).

Бержерона классификация Bergeron classification (of air masses).

бери-бери *f.* (med.) beriberi.

берил, —л *m.* (min.) beryl; благородный б. emerald (gem).

берилл/ат *m.* beryllate; —левый *a.* beryllium, *see also* берилловый; —левая соль beryllium salt; —ий *m.* beryllium, Be; гидрат окиси —ия beryllium hydroxide; окись —ия beryllium oxide, beryllia; сернокислый —ий beryllium sulfate.

бериллов/окалиевая соль potassium beryllate; —окислая соль beryllate; —ый *a.* beryllium; —ая земля beryllia, beryllium oxide; —ая кислота beryllic acid (beryllium hydroxide); соль —ой кислоты beryllate.

берилло/ид *m.* (cryst.) berylloid; —нит *m.* (min.) beryllonite.

берите *imp. of* брать.

беркелий *see* берклий.

Беркланд *see* Биркеланд.

берклий *m.* berkelium, Bk.

берковец *m. obs.* weight of 360 lb.

беркут *m.* (zool.) golden eagle.

берлин/ит *m.* (min.) berlinite (an aluminum phosphate); —ский *a.* Berlin; —ская зелень Prussian green; —ская лазурь Berlin blue, Prussian blue, ferric ferrocyanide.

берма *f.* berm, bench; shoulder (of road).

бермудская трава Bermuda grass.

Бернулли теорема Bernoulli's theorem.

беровский *a.* Baer (knoll).

беррит *m.* (elec.) berrite (insulator).

Бертело бомба Berthelot bomb, Berthelot's calorimeter.

бертелэйзен *m.* (metal work) hatchet stake.

бертиерит *m.* (min.) berthierite.

Берт/ло *see* Бертело; —оле Berthollet.

бертоллетов/а соль Berthollet's salt, potassium chlorate; —о серебро Berthollet's silver, fulminating silver.

бертрандит *m.* (min.) bertrandite.

бертьер/ин, —ит *m.* (min.) berthierite.

беру/т *pr. 3 pl. of* брать; —щий *a.* taking.

берце *n.* (anat.) tibia, shin bone.

берцел/ианит *m.* (min.) berzelianite; —иит, —ит *m.* berzelite.

Берцелиуса лампа Berzelius lamp.

берцов/ый *a.* crural, leg; (anat.) tibial; большая —ая кость tibia; больше-б. *a.* tibial; малая —ая кость fibula; мало-б. *a.* fibular.

бес— *see also* без—.

беседовать *v.* converse, talk.

бескарбонатный *a.* non-calcareous.

бескварцевый *a.* quartz-free.

бескильница *f.* alkali grass (*Puccinellia*).

бескислородный *a.* oxygen-free.

бесклассовый *a.* classless.

бесконечно *adv.* endlessly, infinitely, ad infinitum, forever; б. малый *a.* infinitesimal, infinitely small; б. малая величина (math.) infinitesimal value; —сть *f.* infinity, endlessness, perpetuity.

бесконечн/ый *a.* infinite, endless, everlasting, perpetual; б. винт perpetual screw, worm, screw conveyer; —ая величина (math.) infinite, infinite value; —ая цепь endless chain; —ое полотно conveyer belt.

бесконтрольн/о *adv.* without control; —ый *a.* uncontrolled.

бес/корковый *a.* crust-free; blended (cheese); —кормица *f.* lack of fodder; —корыстный *a.* disinterested; —костный *a.* boneless.

бескров/ие *n.*, —ность *f.* (med.) anemia; —ный *a.* anemic.

бескрылый *a.* wingless; (zool.) apterous.

беслерия *f.* (bot.) besleria.

беспамятн/ость *f.* forgetfulness; —ый *a.* forgetful, absentminded; в —ом состоянии unconscious.

**бесперебойн/ость** *f.* steadiness, continuity; **—ый** *a.* steady, uninterrupted, trouble-free, smooth, continuous.

**бесперево́дный** *a.* non-transferable.

**бесперемен/о** *adv.* without change; **—ый** *a.* changeless, unchangeable, invariable.

**беспересадочный** *a.* non-stop, through.

**бесперый** *a.* featherless; apodal (fish).

**беспечный** *a.* unconcerned, careless.

**беспилотный** *a.* (aero.) pilotless, robot.

**беспламенный** *a.* flameless.

**беспланов/ость** *f.* lack of planning; **—ый** *a.* haphazard, random.

**бесплатн/о** *adv.* free of charge, gratis; **—ый** *a.* free, free of charge.

**беспло́д/ие** *n.*, **—ность** *f.* sterility, infertility, barrenness; fruitlessness, futility; **—ный** *a.* sterile, barren; fruitless, futile; (bot.) acarpous; arid (land).

**бесплотный** *a.* immaterial.

**бесповоротн/ость** *f.* irreversibility, irrevocability; **—ый** *a.* irreversible, non-reversible, irrevocable.

**бесподобн/ость** *f.* incomparableness; **—ый** *a.* incomparable, unrivaled.

**беспозвоночный** *a.* invertebrate.

**беспокоить** *v.* disturb, bother, trouble, harass; **—ся** *v.* worry, be anxious (about); take care (of).

**беспокой/ный** *a.* restless, agitated, disturbed, turbulent; **—ство** *n.* unrest, agitation, disturbance; worry, trouble, turbulence.

**беспокровный** *a.* naked.

**беспо́лезн/о** *adv.* uselessly, in vain, of no use; **—ость** *f.* uselessness; inefficiency, ineffectiveness; **—ый** *a.* useless; inefficient, ineffective; dead.

**беспо́лый** *a.* sexless, neuter, asexual; (biol.) agamic, agamous.

**бесполюсный** *a.* poleless, without poles.

**беспомощ/ость** *f.* helplessness; **—ый** *a.* helpless.

**беспорист/ость** *f.* density; **—ый** *a.* non-porous, dense.

**беспорочный** *a.* faultless; spotless.

**беспоряд/ок** *m.* disorder, confusion; clutter; **—очно** *adv.* in disorder, confusedly; **—очность** *f.* disorderliness; **—очный** *a.* disorderly, confused, irregular, random (scattering), disordered (motion); (bot.) inordinate.

**беспосадочный** *a.* non-stop (flight).

**беспочвенн/о** *adv.* without basis, without foundation; **—ость** *f.* groundlessness; **—ый** *a.* groundless, unfounded, ill-founded, without sound basis.

**беспошлинн/о** *adv.*, **—ый** *a.* custom-free, duty-free; **—ая торговля** free trade.

**беспредельн/о** *adv.* infinitely, ad infinitum; **—ость** *f.* infinity, boundlessness; **—ый** *a.* infinite, boundless, limitless, unlimited, without end; unbounded (function).

**беспредметный** *a.* objectless, aimless.

**беспрекословный** *a.* indisputable; absolute, unquestioning.

**беспрепятственн/о** *adv.* free (to), at liberty, without hindrance; **—ый** *a.* unimpeded, unchecked, free.

**беспрерывн/о** *adv.* continuously, without interruption; **—ость** *f.* continuity, continuance, continuousness; **—ый** *a.* continuous, uninterrupted, perpetual, ceaseless, incessant, unremitting; **—ый процесс** continuous process.

**беспрестанный** *see* **беспрерывный**.

**беспрецедентный** *a.* unprecedented.

**беспри́быльн/о** *adv.* without profit, without advantage; **—ый** *a.* profitless, unprofitable; disadvantageous.

**беспримерн/о** *adv.* without example; **—ый** *a.* unmatched, unparalleled.

**беспримесный** *a.* pure, uncontaminated; (met.) unalloyed.

**беспристраст/ие** *n.*, **—ность** *f.* impartiality; **—но** *adv.* impartially, without bias, without prejudice; **—ный** *a.* impartial, unprejudiced, unbiased.

**бесприце́льный** *a.* aimless, random, haphazard.

**беспричинн/о** *adv.* without reason; **—ый** *a.* without reason or cause, unjust, causeless; gratuitous.

**бес/проволочный** *a.* wireless; **—проигрышный** *a.* safe, sure; **—просыпный** *a.* unbroken (sleep); **—процентный** *a.* without interest, bearing no interest; **—пыльный** *a.* dust-free.

**бессвязн/ость** *f.* inconsistency, incoherence; **—ый** *a.* inconsistent, incoherent, disconnected.

**бесселева функция** (math.) Bessel's function.

**бессемейный** *a.* unmarried, single.

**бессеменн/одольный** *a.* (bot.) acotyledonous; **—ый** *a.* seedless.

**Бессемера конвертер, бессемеров конвертер** (met.) Bessemer converter.

**бессемеров/ание** *n.* (met.) bessemerizing, Bessemer process; **—ать** *v.* bessemerize, convert cast iron into steel by Bessemer process; **—о железо, —ское железо** Bessemer iron; **—ский** *a.* Bessemer; **—ский конвертер, —ская реторта** Bessemer converter, Bessemer (for steel).

**бессемянный** *see* **бессеменный.**

**бессердечниковый** *a.* coreless.

**бессерный** *a.* sulfur-free.

**бессил/ие** *n.* impotence, feebleness; **—ьный** *a.* impotent, feeble.

**бессировать** *v.* lower.

**бессистемн/о** *adv.* without system, haphazardly, at random; **—ый** *a.* unsystematic, haphazard.

**бесследн/о** *adv.* without any trace, leaving no trace; **—ый** *a.* without trace, not to be traced, traceless.

**бесслов/есный, —ный** *a.* mute, dumb.

**бессменн/о** *adv.* without change; **—ость** *f.* changelessness, permanency; **—ый** *a.* changeless, permanent, fixed, set.

**бессмерт/ие** *n.*, **—ность** *f.* immortality; **—ить** *v.* immortalize; **—ник** *m.* (bot.) everlasting flowers (*Helichrysum arenarium*); **—ный** *a.* immortal, everlasting, eternal; **—ная трава** *see* **амброзия.**

**бессмысл/енность** *f.*, **—ица** *f.* nonsense, absurdity, senselessness; **—енный** *a.* senseless, absurd.

**бессовестный** *a.* dishonest, unscrupulous.

**бессодержательный** *a.* empty.

**бессознательн/о** *adv.* unconsciously, involuntarily; **—ость** *f.* unconsciousness; **—ый** *a.* unconscious, involuntary.

**бессолевой** *a.* salt-free.

**бессонн/ица** *f.* insomnia, sleeplessness; **—ый** *a.* sleepless.

**бесспорн/о** *adv.* indisputably, without contradiction; **—ость** *f.* indisputability, incontrovertibility; **—ый** *a.* indisputable.

**бессребреник** *m.* disinterested person.

**бессрочный** *a.* not limited to any definite time, indefinite; termless; permanent.

**бесстебельный** *a.* stemless; (bot.) acaulescent.

**бессточн/ый** *a.* without drainage; internal-drainage (basin); **—ая область** closed drainage.

**бесстрастный** *a.* indifferent, apathetic.

**бесструктурный** *a.* structureless, formless.

**бессуставчатый** *a.* (zool.) inarticulate.

**бессчетный** *a.* innumerable, countless.

**бессяжковые** *pl.* (zool.) Protura.

**бестактный** *a.* tactless, indelicate.

**бесталантный** *a.* untalented, incapable.

**бестарный** *a.* unpackaged, bulk, loose.

**бест-бар** *m.* (met.) best bar.

**бестелесный** *see* **бесплотный.**

**бестканевый** *a.* non-textile; without fabric; without tissue.

**бестоварье** *n.* shortage of goods.

**бестол/ковщина, —ковица, —очь** *f.* disorder, confusion, chaos; **—ковый** *a.* confused; unintelligible.

**бестужевские капли** Bestuscheff's tincture, ethereal tincture of iron chloride.

**бесфланцевый** *a.* flangeless, rimless; flush.

**бесформенн/о** *adv.* without form, without shape; **—ость** *f.* shapelessness, formlessness, amorphism; **—ый** *a.* shapeless, formless, amorphous.

**бесфосфорный** *a.* phosphorus-free; (met.) dephosphorized.

**бесхлеб/ица** *f.* famine, starvation; **—ный** *a.* without grain, barren.

**бесхлопотный** *a.* trouble-free.

**бесхозный** *a.* ownerless; no man's (land); (law) in abeyance.

**бесхозяйственный** *a.* thriftless.

**бесцветн/ость** *f.* colorlessness, achromatism; **—ый** *a.* colorless, achromatic; obscure (heat).

**бесцельн/о** *adv.* aimlessly, at random; **—ость** *f.* aimlessness; **—ый** *a.* aimless, purposeless, haphazard.

**бесценн/о** *adv.* beyond price; **—ость** *f.* inestimable value; **—ый** *a.* priceless, inestimable, invaluable.

**бесценок** *m.* an absurdly low price.

**бесцентровый** *a.* centerless.

**бесчест/ить** *v.*, —ье *n.* dishonor, discredit; —ный *a.* dishonest, dishonorable.

**бесчешуйный** *a.* scaleless, without scales.

**бесчисленн/ость** *f.* innumerable quantity; —ый *a.* innumerable, countless.

**бесчувств/енность** *f.*, —ие *n.* insensibility; —енный *a.* insensible, unfeeling, impassive, numb.

**бесшерст/ный,** —ый *a.* without wool; hairless.

**бесшовный** *a.* jointless, seamless (pipe).

**бесшумный** *a.* noiseless, silent.

**бета** *f.* beta ($\beta$); **б.-излучатель** *m.* (nucl.) beta-emitter (a radionuclide); **б.-латунь** *f.* beta-brass (copper-zinc alloy); **б.-луч** *m.*, **б.-лучевой** *a.* (nucl.) beta ray; **б.-нафтол** *m.* $\beta$-naphthol; **б.-распад** *m.* (nucl.) beta disintegration; beta decay; **б.-частица** *f.* beta particle; —ин *m.* betaine, trimethyl glycocoll; —радиоактивный *a.* beta-radioactive; —трон *m.* (nucl.) betatron, induction accelerator; —уранотил *m.* (min.) betauranotil; —фит *m.* betafite (an uranium mineral).

**бетел/евый орех** betel nut; —ь *m.* (bot.) betel palm (*Areca catechu*); **перечный** —ь betel pepper (*Piper betle*).

**бетол** *m.* betol, $\beta$-naphthyl salicylate.

**бетон** *m.* concrete.

**бетоника** *f.* (bot.) betony (*Betonica*).

**бетон/ирование** *n.* concreting, treating with concrete; —ированный *a.* concrete, treated with concrete; —ировать, —ить *v.* concrete, treat with concrete, lay concrete (on); —ит *m.*, —ный камень, —ный массив concrete (building) stone; —ный *a.* concrete; mortar (structure); —ное литье concrete grout; —олитная башня concrete pourer; —олом, —оразбиватель *m.* concrete breaker; —омешалка ,—ьерка *f.* concrete mixer; —осмешивающий *a.* concrete mixing; —щик *m.* concrete worker.

**бетруксиновая кислота** betruxinic acid.

**Бетт/ертона способ** Betterton process (for lead refining); —са способ Betts' process (for lead refining).

**бетул/аза** *f.* betulase; —ин *m.* betulin,
betula camphor, betulinol; —инамаровая кислота betulinamaric acid; —иновая кислота betulinic acid; —инол *m.* betulinol; —оретиновая кислота betuloretinic acid.

**беч** *m.* batch, charge.

**бечев/а** *see* бичева; —ка *f.* twine, binder twine, packthread.

**бешен/ство** *n.* madness; (med.) hydrophobia, rabies; —ый *a.* mad, furious, raging; turbulent; rabid; —ый огурец (bot.) squirting cucumber (*Ecballium elaterium*); —ая вишня, —ая ягода *see* белладонна.

**бзл.** *abbr.* (бензол) benzene (as solvent).

**бзн.** *abbr.* (бензин) benzine, ligroin (as solvent).

**би—** *prefix* bi—, di—.

**Биаля реакция** Bial's (pentose) test.

**би/антрил** *m.* bianthryl; —ацен *m.* biacene, biacenaphthylidene; —ацетил *m* biacetyl, 2,3-butanedione;—ацетилен *m.* biacetylene, butadiyne.

**биберит** *m.* (min.) bieberite (hydrous cobalt sulfate).

**библио/граф** *m.* bibliographer; —графический *a.* bibliographic; —графия *f.* bibliography; —лит *m.* bibliolite, bookstone (a laminated schistose rock); —тека *f.* library; —текарь *m.* librarian; —течный *a.* library.

**бибрихский шарлаховый** Biebrich red (dye), scarlet red.

**бивариантный** *a.* bivariant.

**бивень** *m.* incisor, tusk.

**биверит** *m.* (min.) beaverite (a basic hydrous sulfate).

**бивший** *past act. part. of* бить.

**бигаконитин** *m.* bikhaconitine.

**бигарадия** *see* апельсин, горький.

**бигидрат** *m.*, —ный *a.* dihydrate.

**бигнон/иевые** *pl.* (bot.) Bignoniaceae; —иевый *a.* bignonia; —ия *f.* trumpet creeper (*Bignonia*).

**бигумаль** *m.* bigumal (hydrochloride), chlorguanide hydrochloride (antimalarial).

**бидезил** *m.* bidesyl, dibenzoyldibenzyl.

**бидистиллат** *m.* doubly distilled water.

**бидон** *m.* can, container, vessel, carboy.

**биен/ие** *n.* beat, pulse, pulsation, palpitation; wobble, play (of wheel);

sagging, slack (of belt); **частота —ий** beat frequency.

**бизаболен** *see* **бисаболен.**

**бизон** *m.* (zool.) bison.

**бикарбонат** *m.* bicarbonate, spec. sodium bicarbonate.

**биквадрат** *m.* (math.) biquadrate, fourth power; **—ный** *a.* biquadratic; **—ное уравнение** (math.) biquadratic equation.

**бикрон** *m.* bicron (one billionth of a meter).

**бикс/биит** *m.* (min.) bixbyite (an iron manganese oxide); **—ин** *m.* bixin (coloring matter).

**Бикфорда шнур, бикфордов шнур** Bickford (safety) fuse.

**бил** *past 3 sing. of* **бить.**

**билатеральный** *a.* bilateral.

**билеин** *m.* bilein.

**билет** *m.* ticket, pass, permit; (bank) note.

**били/вердин** *m.* biliverdin; **—вердиновая кислота** biliverdic acid; **—ксантин** *m.* bilixanthin.

**б. или м.** *abbr.* **(более или менее)** more or less.

**били/н** *m.*, **—новый** *a.* bilin; **—нейрин** *m.* bilineurine; **—нигрин** *m.* bilinigrin; **—позол** *m.* biliposol; **—празин** *m.* biliprasin (pigment); **—рубин** *m.* bilirubin, hematoidin; **—рубиновая кислота** bilirubinic acid; **—соидановая кислота** bilisoidanic acid; **—траст** *m.* Bilitrast, iodoalphionic acid.

**биллет** *see* **билет.**

**биллион** *m.*, **—ный** *a.* billion; **—ная часть** one billionth.

**биллитонит** *m.* (petr.) billitonite.

**биллон** *m.* billon (a coinage alloy); **—овое серебро** billon silver.

**билль** *m.* bill.

**било** *n.* beater, dasher (in churn); (text.) scutch blade.

**билоидановая кислота** biloidanic acid, norsolanellic acid.

**бильгарциоз** *m.* (med.) bilharziasis, schistomiasis.

**бильд/аппарат** *m.* photograph transmitter, picture transmitter; **—передача** *f.* transmission of photographs; **—связь, —телеграфия** *f.* phototelegraphy.

**бильная мельница** hammer mill.

**биметалл** *m.* bimetal; **—изм** *m.* bimetallism; **—ический** *a.* bimetallic.

**бимолекулярный** *a.* bimolecular.

**бимс** *m.*, **—овый** *a.* beam; **—овое железо** bulb bar.

**бинарн/ый** *a.* binary; binomial (nomenclature); **б. пересчет** scale of two; **б. счетчик, —ая пересчетная схема** binary scaler, scale of two circuit.

**бинауральный** *a.* (acous.) binaural.

**бингамовская вязкость** Bingham viscosity.

**биндгеймит** *m.* (min.) bindheimite (a hydrous lead antimonate).

**бинд/енол** *m.* bindenol; **—он** *m.* bindone.

**биннит** *m.* (min.) binnite (a variety of tennantite).

**бинодаль** *f.* binodal (in phase diagram).

**бинок/ль** *m.* binoculars, binocular glasses; (field) glasses; **—улярный** *a.* binocular.

**бином** *m.* (math.) binomial; **коэффициенты —а** binomial coefficients; **—иальный, —инальный** *a.* binomial, binominal.

**бинормаль** *f.* (math.) binormal.

**бинт** *m.* bandage, ligature; **—овать** *v.* bandage, swathe.

**био—** *prefix* bio—; biological.

**биоген/езис** *m.* (biol.) biogenesis; **—етический** *a.* biogenetic; **—ный** *a.* (bot.) biogenous, parasitic.

**биогерм** *m.* (geol.) bioherm.

**биограф** *m.* biographer; **—ический** *a.* biographic; **—ия** *f.* biography.

**биодинам/ика** *f.* (biol.) biodynamics; **—ический** *a.* biodynamic.

**—биоз** *m. suffix* (biol.) **—biosis.**

**биоза** *f.* biose; disaccharide.

**биоклиматический** *a.* bioclimatic.

**биоксалат** *m.* bioxalate.

**биолит** *m.* (min.) biolith.

**биолог** *m.* biologist; **—ически** *adv.* biologically; **—ический** *a.* biological; **—ия** *f.* biology.

**био/м** *m.* (biol.) biome, formation; **—магнетизм** *m.* biomagnetism, animal magnetism; **—масса** *f.* biomass; **—метрия** *f.* biometry, statistical biology; **—мицин** *m.* Biomycin, Aureomycin, chlortetracycline; **—ника** *f.* bionics (mathematical biology); **—плазма** *f.* bioplasm, protoplasm;

—**препараты** *pl.* biologicals (immune serums, vaccines, etc.); —**псия** *f.* (med.) biopsy; —**с** *m.* bios (a yeast extract); —**синтез** *m.* biosynthesis; —**статика** *f.* biostatics; —**стерин** *m.* biosterin; biosterol; —**стерол** *m.* biosterol (obs. for vitamin A); —**сфера** *f.* biosphere; —**та** *f.* biota; —**тин** *m.* biotin, vitamin H; —**тит** *m.* (min.) biotite, magnesium-iron mica; —**тический** *a.* biotic, relating to life; biological.

**биотовский закон** (optics) Biot's law.

**био/топливо** *n.* biofuel, biological fuel; —**трон** *m.* (rad.) biotron; —**фабрика** *f.* biofactory, biologicals-manufacturing plant; —**физика** *f.* biophysics; —**фор** *m.* biophore.

**биохим/ик** *m.* biochemist; —**ический** *a.* biochemical; —**ия** *f.* biochemistry.

**био/хинол** *m.* bioquinol, quinine iodobismuthite; —**хора** *f.* (ecology) biochore; —**ценоз** *m.* (biol.) biocenosis; —**церин** *m.* biocerin.

**бипирамида** *f.* (cryst.) bipyramid, double-edged pyramid; —**льный** *a.* bipyramidal.

**биплан** *m.* (aero.) biplane.

**биполярн/ость** *f.* bipolarity; —**ый** *a.* bipolar.

**бипризма** *f.* (optics) biprism.

**бирж/а** *f.*, —**евой** *a.* (com.) exchange, stock exchange; —**евик** *m.*, —**евой маклер** stock broker.

**бирка** *f.* tally, score; tag, nameplate.

**Биркеланд-Эйде способ** Birkeland-Eyde process (for nitrogen fixation).

**биркование** *n.* branding; tagging, labeling.

**бирманский** *a.* Burmese, Burman.

**бирмингамский** *a.* Birmingham.

**бирюз/а** *f.*, —**овый** *a.* (min.) turquoise.

**бирючина** *f.* (bot.) privet (*Ligustrum*).

**бис**— *prefix* bis—; —**аболен** *m.* bisabolene; —**аболол** *m.* bisabolol.

**бисазо**— *prefix* bisazo—, tetrazo—.

**бисбееит** *m.* (min.) bisbeeite (a hydrous copper silicate).

**бисдиазо**— *prefix* bisdiazo—, tetrazo—.

**бисектриса** *see* **биссектриса.**

**бисер** *m.* beads; —**ный** *a.* bead, beaded; pearl (polymerization).

**бисиликат** *m.* disilicate.

**биск** *m.* (cer.) bisque.

**бискайский** *a.* Biscayan.

**Бискайский залив** Bay of Biscay.

**бисквит** *m.*, —**ный** *a.* biscuit; (cer.) biscuit, bisque; **обжигать** —**а, обжигать на б.** (cer.) give a biscuit firing; —**ный обжиг** biscuit firing.

**бископлаурин** *m.* biscoclaurine.

**бисмалит** *m.* (geol.) bysmalith.

**Бисмарка бурый, бисмаркбраун** *m.* Bismarck brown, triaminoazobenzene.

**бисмит** *m.* (min.) bismite.

**бисмут**— *see* **висмут**—; —**ин** *see* **висмутин**; —**ит** *m.* (min.) bismutite.

**бисмуто**—*prefix* bismutho—, bismuto—; —**за** *f.* bismutose, bismuth albuminate; —**сферит** *m.* (min.) bismutosphaerite.

**биссект/ор** *m.* (geom.) bisecting plane; —**риса** *f.* (geom.) bisector, bisecting line; (cryst.) bisectrix.

**биссолит** *m.* (min.) byssolite (a variety of asbestos).

**биссус** *m.* (zool.) byssus.

**бистер, бистр** *m.* bister (a pigment).

**бистунки** *pl.* beaded wires.

**бисульф/ат** *m.* bisulfate; **б. натрия** sodium bisulfate; —**ид** *m.* bisulfide; —**ит** *m.* bisulfite.

**бисфеноид** *m.* (cryst.) bisphenoid.

**бит** *m.* bit (unit of measure of information).

**битартрат** *m.* bitartrate.

**битва** *f.* battle, fight, combat, action.

**бительная машина** (text.) beetle.

**битенг** *m.* (aero.) bitt.

**битер** *m.* beater.

**битиит** *m.* (min.) bityite.

**битовнит** *see* **бытовнит.**

**бит/ок** *m.* beetle, maul, heavy wooden mallet; (beef) cutlet; —**ком набитый** packed, tight, crowded.

**биттит** *m.* (elec.) bittite.

**битулитный** *a.* bitulithic.

**битум** *m.* bitumen, asphalt; —**инизация** *f.* bituminization; —**инизировать** *v.* bituminize; —**инит** *m.* (min.) bituminite; —**инозность** *f.* bituminosity; impregnation (with bitumen); —**инозный, —ный** *a.* bituminous; asphalt, asphaltic; —**инол** *m.* bituminol, ammonium sulfobituminolate.

**бит/ый** *a.* beaten, cracked, broken; whipped; **—ь** *v.* beat, whip; hammer; break; gush, spurt (of stream); churn (butter); strike (the hour); (belt) flap, sag, whip; (wheel) wobble, play; *f.* foil, sheet; **—ь на** *v.* aim (at); **не —ь** *v.* (wheel) run true, be in alignment; **медная —ь** sheet copper, hammered copper; **—ье** *n.* beating; breaking; **—ься** *v.* beat, throb, pulsate; strive (for).

**битюминозный** *see* **битуминозный.**

**биурат** *m.* biurate.

**биурет** *m.* biuret, allophanamide.

**бифенил** *m.* biphenyl, phenylbenzene; **—ен** *m.* biphenylene.

**бифилярн/ый** *a.* bifilar, double-wound; **—ая обмотка** (elec.) bifilar winding.

**биформин** *m.* biformin; **—овая кислота** biforminic acid.

**бифуркация** *f.* bifurcation.

**бихлорид** *m.* bichloride.

**бихромат** *m.* bichromate.

**бицепс** *m.* (anat.) biceps.

**бицикл** *m.* bicycle.

**бициклический** *a.* bicyclic (compounds).

**бицикло—** *prefix* bicyclo—.

**бициллин** *m.* Bicillin, benzathine penicillin G.

**бич** *m.* whip; (biol.) flagellum; (mach.) beater; scourge, plague.

**бичев/а** *f.* towline, tow rope; **тянуть —у** *v.* tow; **—ание** *n.* towing; flagellation; **—ать** *v.* tow; flagellate, whip, lash; **—ка** *f.* twine, whipcord.

**бичевник** *m.* sloping beach.

**бишофит** *m.* (min.) bischofite.

**БКГ** *abbr.* (баллистокардиограмма) (med.) ballistocardiogram.

**благо** *n.* the good, welfare; **общее б.** common good, public welfare.

**благовидный** *a.* good-looking; plausible.

**благовол/ение** *n.* goodwill; favor, kindness; **—ить** *v.* favor, regard with goodwill; have the kindness (to).

**благовон/ие** *n.* aroma, fragrance; **—ный** *a.* aromatic, fragrant.

**благодар/ить** *v.* thank; **—ность** *f.* thanks, gratitude, appreciation; **в —ность** in acknowledgment; **—ный** *a.* grateful, appreciative; **—я** owing; thanks (to).

**благоденств/енный** *a.* prosperous, thriv-

ing; **—ие** *n.* prosperity; **—овать** *v.* prosper, thrive, flourish.

**благодетель** *m.* benefactor; **—ный** *a.* beneficial; **—ствовать** *v.* benefit.

**благо/деяние** *n.* benefit, boon; **—желательный** *a.* well-disposed (to), favorable; **—звучие** *n.* euphony, harmony; **—избранный** *a.* well-chosen; **—й** *a.* good, favorable.

**благонадежный** *a.* reliable, dependable.

**благонамерен/ие** *n.*, **—ность** *f.* good intention; **—ный** *a.* well-meant.

**благополуч/ие** *n.* welfare, well-being; **—но** *adv.* all right, safely; **—ный** *a.* safe; satisfactory.

**благоприят/но** *adv.* favorably; **—ность** *f.* favorableness; **—ный** *a.* favorable, opportune, propitious; contributory (factor); **—ный момент, —ный случай** opportunity; **—ное условие** facility; **наиболее —ный** optimum, optimal; **—ствовать** *v.* favor, foster, be conducive (to).

**благоразум/ие** *n.* common sense, reasonableness; **в пределах —ия** within reason; **—ный** *a.* reasonable, sensible, wise, cautious, prudent.

**благородный** *a.* noble; honorable; generous; precious (stone); **б. газ** inert gas; **б. металл** noble metal; precious metal.

**благосклонный** *a.* favorable, well-disposed.

**благо/состояние** *n.* welfare, prosperity, well-being; **—творить** *v.* do good, benefit; **—успешный** *a.* successful.

**благоустро/ение** *n.* good organization; **—енный** *a.* well-organized, well-arranged, well-managed; **—ивать, —ить** *v.* put in good order; **—йство** *n.* good order; public welfare.

**благоух/ание** *n.* fragrance, pleasant odor; **—анный, —ающий** *a.* fragrant, sweet-smelling; **—ать** *v.* give off fragrance.

**бладан** *m.* Bladan base (a tetraethyl pyrophosphate insecticide).

**бланк** *m.* form, blank, letterhead; **ставить б.** *v.* endorse; **—ирование** *n.*, **—ирующий** *a.* blanking.

**бланкит** *m.* sodium hydrosulfite.

**бланков/ый** *a.* blank, form; **—ая надпись** endorsement.

**бланконадписатель** *m.* endorser.

**бланфикс** *m.* blanc fixe, barium sulfate.

**бланфордит** *m.* (min.) blanfordite (a variety of pyroxene).

**бланwidров/ание** *n.* blanching, scalding; —**анный** *a.* blanched, scalded; —**ать** *v.* blanch, scald.

**бласт/ический** *a.* blastic (texture); —**омикоз** *m.* (med.) blastomycosis; —**омицеты** *pl.* (bot.) Blastomycetes; —**ула** *f.* (biol.) blastula.

**блау/газ** *m.* Blaugas (*not* blue gas); —**офен** *m.* (met.) flowing furnace (a type of reverberatory furnace).

**блев/ать,** —**нуть** *v.,* —**отина** *f.* vomit.

**бледит** *m.* (min.) bloedite, astrakanite.

**бледн/еть** *v.* grow pale, turn pale, lose color; —**ить** *v.* make pale; —**о** *adv.* pale; —**оватый** *a.* rather pale, palish; —**ожелтый** *a.* pale yellow; —**оокрашенный** *a.* pale-colored, dull; —**ость** *f.* paleness; —**ый** *a.* pale, light-colored; faint, weak (color).

**блей/вейс** *m.* white lead; —**штейн** *m.* (met.) lead matte.

**блек**— *see* **блэк**—.

**блек/локоричневый** *a.* dull brown, fallow dun; —**лость** *f.* fading; —**лый** *a.* faded, withered, colorless; pale (color); —**лая руда** (min.) fahlerz, tetrahedrite, gray copper ore; —**нуть** *v.* fade, wither.

**блекота** *see* **белена.**

**блекрот** *m.* black rot (plant disease).

**бленда** *f.* (min.) blende, spec. zinc blende, sphalerite; (optics) diaphragm; (phot.) lens hood; (min.) lantern.

**блес/к** *m.* luster, gloss, glitter, shine, glare, flash; brilliance, brightness, luminescence, luminosity; (min.) glance; (met.) fulguration, flash; **придавать б.** *v.* add luster, burnish; —**нуть** *v.* flash.

**блест/еть** *v.* shine, glitter, sparkle; —**ка** *f.* spangle, beadlet (ornament); —**кость** *f.* brilliancy; —**як,** —**ян** *m.* (min.) galena; (sometimes) mica; —**янки** *pl.* sap-feeding beetles (*Nitidulidae*); —**ящий** *a.* lustrous, brilliant, bright, shiny, sparkling, luminous.

**блеф** *m.* bluff.

**ближ/айший** *a.* near, next, proximate; —**е** *comp. of* **близкий, близко** nearer, closer; —**невосточный** *a.* Near Eastern; —**ний** *a.* near, next, neighboring; —**ний порядок** (cryst.) short-range order.

**близ** *prep. gen.* near, around, at hand, in the vicinity (of), close (to); —**иться** *v.* approach, draw near; —**кий** *a.* near, close, close by; —**ко** *adv.* near, at hand, near by, close, closely; —**кодействующий** *a.* short-range; —**лежащий** *a.* adjacent, contiguous (to), neighboring, near.

**близна** *f.* (text.) a flaw (in the web).

**близнец** *m.* twin.

**близорук/ий** *a.* near-sighted, myopic; —**ость** *f.* myopia.

**близост/ь** *f.* nearness, proximity, vicinity, neighborhood, closeness, imminence; **по** —**и** near at hand, within call.

**блик** *m.,* —**ование** *n.* flash; high-light, spot of light; (met.) fulguration, blick, flashing (as of molten silver); refining (of silver); —**ованный,** —**овый** *a.* refined; —**овать** *v.* flash, lighten; refine (silver); —**овое золото** refined gold still containing silver; —**овое серебро** silver containing 5–10% impurities.

**блин** *m.* pancake.

**блинд/аж** *m.* (mil.) blindage, sheeting; —**ированный** *a.* blinded, sheeted with iron, iron-clad, armored, armor-clad.

**блист/ание** *n.* shining, glittering; —**ательно** *adv.* brilliantly; —**ать** *see* **блестеть.**

**блистр** *m.* (met.) blister, blister copper.

**Бло драже** (pharm.) Blaud's pill.

**блок** *m.* block, pulley; unit, assembly, set; (uranium, fuel) lump, slug; (polymerization) bulk; **б.-диаграмма** block diagram; **б.-противовес** counterweight block; **б.-резина** cut sheet (of rubber); **в** —**ах** lump, lumped (uranium); **сложный б.** hoisting tackle, tackle; —**ада** *f.* blockade; —**гауз** *m.* blockhouse; —**инг-генератор** *m.* (electron.) blocking oscillator.

**блокир/ование** *n.,* —**овка** *f.* blocking, obstruction; locking, interlocking, interlocking gear; —**ованный** *a.*

blocked, obstructed; —**овать** *v.* block, obstruct; lock, interlock; —**овочный** *a.*, —**ующий** *a.* block, blocking, stop; locking, interlocking.

**блокнот** *m.* writing pad, tablet, notebook.

**блоковый** *a.* block, pulley.

**бломстранд/ин** *m.* (min.) blomstrandine; —**ит** *m.* blomstrandite.

**блох/а** *f.* (zool.) flea; —**и** *pl.* Aphaniptera; —**овник** *m.* (bot.) pennyroyal (*Mentha pulegium* or *Hedeoma pulegioides*).

**блоч/ный** *a. of* **блок**; block; lumped; **б. полимер** block polymer; —**ок** *m.* (uranium, fuel) slug, lump.

**блошин/ый** *a.* flea; —**ая мята** *see* **блоховник**; —**ая окраска** puce color; —**ого цвета** puce-colored.

**блош/истый**, —**ливый** *a.* full of fleas, flea-infested; —**ки** *pl.* fleas; —**ник** *m.* (bot.) fleabane (*Erigeron canadense*); —**ница** *f.* fleabane (*Pulicaria*); —**ный** *a.* flea; —**ное семя** psyllium seed.

**блужд/ание** *n.* wandering, straying; —**ать** *v.* wander, stray; —**ающий** *a.* wandering, stray, erratic; circulating; —**ающий нерв** (anat.) vagus.

**блуз/а** *f.* blouse, shirt; —**ник** *m.* laborer.

**блум** *see* **блюм**.

**блэк/бенд** *m.* (min.) blackband ore (a form of earthy siderite); —**варниш** *m.* black varnish (a cheap asphalt paint).

**блюдет** *pr. 3 sing. of* **блюсти**.

**блюд/ечко** *n.* saucer; —**о** *n.* dish, plate.

**блюду/т** *pr. 3 pl. of* **блюсти**; —**щий** *a.* keeping; observing.

**блюдце** *n.* saucer; (biol.) patella; scutellum; (geol.) small, usually shallow, depression; —**образный** *a.* saucer-shaped; (biol.) patelliform, patellate; scutellate.

**блюл** *past 3 sing. of* **блюсти**.

**блюм** *m.* (met.) bloom; —**инг** *m.* blooming, blooming mill, bloomery; —**сы** *pl.* blooms.

**блюсти** *v.* keep, guard, preserve, fulfil, observe; —**тельный** *a.* careful, watchful.

**бляха** *f.* metal plate.

**БМЭ** *abbr.* (Большая Медицинская Энциклопедия) Large Medical Encyclopedia.

**БО** *abbr.* (береговая оборона) coastal defence.

**боа** *m.* (zool.) boa.

**боб** *m.* (bot.) bean.

**бобер** *see* **бобр**.

**бобиерит** *m.* (min.) bobierrite (a magnesium phosphate).

**бобина** *f.* bobbin, spool, reel; ignition coil.

**боб/ковая руда**, —**овая (железная) руда** (min.) bean ore, pea ore, pisolitic ore; —**овидный**, —**ообразный** *a.* bean-like, bean-shaped, pisolitic; leguminous; —**овина** *f.* bean plant; —**овник** *m.* (bot.) dwarf almond (*Amygdalus nana*); *see also* **трифоль**; —**овые** *pl.*, —**овые растения** legumes, leguminous plants; —**овый** *a.* bean; leguminous; —**овая мука** bean meal; —**овое масло** bean oil, spec. soybean oil.

**бобр** *m.*, —**овый** *a.* (zool.) beaver; —**ик** *m.* (text.) castor, coarse woolen fabric; —**овик**, —**овник** *m.* (bot.) Spanish broom (*Spartium junceum*); *see also* **трифоль**; —**овица** *see* **клевер**; —**овая руда** *see* **бобовая руда**; —**овая струя** (pharm.) castor, castoreum.

**бобслей** *m.* bobsled.

**бобы** *pl.* beans; **б. какао** cocoa beans.

**бобыш/ек** *m.* cam; —**ка** *f.* boss, lug; nipple.

**бов/енит** *m.* (min.) bowenite (a variety of serpentine); —**лингиг** *m.* bowlingite (a variety of saponite); —**манит** *m.* bowmannite (identical with hamlinite).

**Бог** *m.* God; god.

**богар/а** *f.* boghara, unirrigated land; —**ный** *a.* dry (farming).

**богат/еть** *v.* get rich, grow rich, thrive, prosper; —**ство** *n.* riches, wealth, fortune; —**ства** *pl.* resources, mineral wealth; **естественные** —**ства** natural resources; —**ый** *a.* rich, wealthy; high-grade, high (in), rich (in); abundant, copious.

**богатырский** *a.* athletic, robust; giant.

**богемск/ий** *a.* Bohemian; —**ая земля** mineral green (copper carbonate).

**богомол** *m.* (zool.) praying mantis.

**богород/ичник** *m.* (bot.) bistort (*Polygonum bistorta*); —**ская трава** (bot.) wild thyme (*Thymus serpyllum*).

**богульник** *see* **багульник.**

**богхед** *m.*, **—ский уголь** boghead, boghead coal (a variety of cannel coal).

**бод** *m.* baud (telegraph unit of speed).

**боденбендерит** *m.* (min.) bodenbenderite.

**бодр/ить** *v.* brace, stimulate; **—иться** *v.* take courage; **—ость** *f.* courage, nerve; cheerfulness; **—ый** *a.* brisk; cheerful.

**бодрюш** *m.* goldbeater's (gastight) skin.

**Бодуина реакция** Baudouin test (for sesame oil).

**бодяк** *m.* (bot.) thistle (*Cirsium*).

**бое/вой** *a.* combat, fighting; war (gas); sledge (hammer); **—головка** *f.* (mil.) warhead; **—запас** *m.* ammunition.

**боек** *m.* block; head (of hammer); firing pin; striker, knife.

**боенск/ий** *a.* slaughter-house; **—ие отходы** slaughter-house waste; **—ое дело** slaughtering.

**бое/припасы** *pl.* ammunition; **—способность** *f.* fighting efficiency; **—ц** *m.* soldier, fighter.

**бож/ий** *a.* God's; **б. дар**, **—ья благодать**, **—ья милость** (bot.) hedge hyssop (*Gratiola officinalis*); **—ье дерево** (bot.) southernwood (*Artemisia abrotanum*); **—ья коровка** ladybird beetle.

**боз/е-частица** *f.*, **—он** *m.* (nucl.) boson (Bose particle); **безмассовый —он** classon; **Бозе-Эйнштейна статистика** Bose-Einstein statistics.

**бой** *m.* combat, battle, action; breakage, breaking; broken material, crushed material, rubble; cullet, broken glass; face (of hammer); (text.) picking.

**Бойда огнемет** Boyd flame thrower.

**бойк/ий** *a.* smart, brisk, alert; **—ость** *f.* briskness, alertness.

**бойкот** *m.*, **—ировать** *v.* boycott.

**бойлер** *m.* boiler.

**Бойля закон** (phys.) Boyle's law.

**бойница** *f.* porthole, vent.

**бойня** *f.* slaughter house, abattoir.

**бок** *m.* side, flank; wall; **б.-о-б.** side by side, alongside; **в б.** to the side, sideways; **к —у** to the side, laterally; **на б.** on the side, sideways; **по —ам** on each side; **по —у** set aside; **с —у** at the side (of), by the side (of), at hand; **с —у на б.** from side to side.

**бокал** *m.* beaker, glass.

**боккран** *m.* trestle crane.

**боковик** *m.* measuring jaw.

**боков/ой** *a.* side, lateral, by-; secondary, accessory, supplementary; sidelong, glancing (blow); marginal; wall (rock); **б. канал** by-pass; **б. разрез** lateral incision; **—ая грань**, **—ая поверхность** lateral face, flat side, facet; **—ая жидкость** (electrophoresis) auxiliary liquid; **—ая качка** rolling; **—ая реакция** side reaction; **—ая цепь** side chain; **—ое спускное течение** (distillation) side stream, slip stream.

**боковушка** *f.* margin, edge.

**боком** *adv.* sideways, sidewise, edgewise.

**бокс** *m.* box; boxing (sport); (leather) box calf; (hospital) isolation ward or room.

**боксит** *m.* (min.) bauxite (aluminum ore); **—овый** *a.* bauxite, bauxitic.

**боксование** *see* **буксование.**

**бол** *see* **болюс.**

**болван/ить** *v.* rough-hew, rough-cast; **—ка** *f.* (met.) block, pig, mold; ingot, bar, rod; dummy; **чугун в —ках** pig iron.

**болверк** *m.* bulwark.

**болг.** *abbr.* (**болгарский**).

**болгарский** *a.* Bulgarian.

**болдо** *see* **больдо.**

**боле**, **—е** *adv.* more; *see* **больше.**

**болезн/енность** *f.* sickliness; painfulness; **—енный** *a.* sickly; painful; **—етворный** *a.* pathogenic, disease-producing; **—етворный микроорганизм** pathogen; **—ь** *f.* disease; sickness, illness.

**болеит** *m.* (min.) boléite.

**боле/ть** *v.* be ill, suffer (from); pain, ache; **—утоляющий** *a.*, **—утоляющее средство** sedative, anodyne, analgesic.

**Боливия** Bolivia.

**болиголов** *m.* (bot.) poison hemlock (*Conium*, spec. *C. maculatum*).

**болид** *m.* (meteor.) bolide, fire-ball; meteor (usually explosive).

**болометр** *m.* bolometer (for measuring radiant heat); **—ический** *a.* bolometric.

**болона** *f.* excrescence, gall (on trees).

**болонский камень** (min.) Bologna stone (a variety of nodular barite).

**болот/ина** *f.* marshland, fen; bog, morass;

—**истый,** —**ный** *a.* bog, boggy, swampy, marshy; —**ник** *m.* a swamp plant; spec. waterstarwort (*Callitriche*); —**никовые** *pl.* (bot.) Callitrichaceae; Helobiae; —**никоцветные** *pl.* (bot.) Helobiae; —**ница** *f.* (bot.) spike rush (*Eleocharis*); —**ный газ** marsh gas, methane; —**ный торф** bog peat; —**ная вода** peat water; —**ная руда** bog iron ore, bog ore (an ore of iron or manganese); —**о** *n.* bog, swamp, marsh, morass.

**болт** *m.* bolt; pin; **б.-барашек** wing bolt; **скреплять** —**ами** *v.* bolt.

**болт/ание** *n.* shaking, stirring; —**анка** *f.* (aero.) bump; bumpiness; —**ать** *v.* shake, stir, mix; —**аться** *v.* dangle, swing; —**ающийся** *a.* dangling, swinging.

**болтов/ой** *a.* bolt; pin; **б. шарнир** pin hinge; —**ое крепление** bolting.

**болторезн/ый** *a.* bolt-threading, bolt-cutting ; **б. станок** bolt-cutting lathe, bolt-threading machine; —**ая головка** threading die.

**болтушка** *f.* mix, mash; batter; **б.-мешалка** *f.* (cement) mixer.

**болус** *see* **болюс.**

**боль** *f.* pain, ache; pang, stab; **причинять б.** *v.* pain, hurt.

**больд/ин** *m.* boldine; —**о листья** boldo leaves; —**оглюцин** *m.* boldoglucin.

**больни/ца** *f.,* —**чный** *a.* hospital, infirmary; —**чный служитель** orderly; —**чная палата** hospital ward.

**больн/о** *adv.* painfully; very, exceedingly; —**ой** *a.* sick, unwell, ill; sore; *m.* patient, sick person; —**ые** *pl.* the sick.

**Больцмана уравнение** (nucl.) Boltzmann equation.

**большак** *m.* highway; eldest son.

**больше** *comp. of* **большой, много** more, larger, bigger; **как можно б.** as much as possible; **много б.** much more; **тем б.** so much the more; **чем б., тем** the more . . . the; *prefix* macro—, large; —**берцовый** *a.* (anat.) tibial; —**берцовая кость** tibia; —**головки** *pl.* thick-headed flies (*Conopidae*); —**головый** *a.* macrocephalic.

**больш/ий** *a.* greater, larger, major; —**ей частью** for the greater part, for the most part; **самое** —**ее** at the most;

—**инство** *n.* majority, generality; —**ой** *a.* big, large, bulky, great, high; strong (current); coarse (grain); heavy (machine); **прицавать** —**ое значение** *v.* make much (of); —**ущий** *a.* enormous, uncommonly large, huge, colossal, mammoth.

**болюс** *m.* (min.) bole, bolus (a variety of halloysite clay); **белый б.** white bole, kaolin; **красный б.** red bolus.

**бол/ячка** *f.* sore, scab; boil; —**ящий** *see* **больной.**

**бомб/а** *f.* bomb; (gas) cylinder; (depth) charge; **сбрасывать** —**ы** *v.* bomb.

**бомбаж** *m.* bulging (of cans from food spoilage).

**бомбардир,** —**овщик** *m.* bomber; —**ование** *n.,* —**овка** *f.* bombardment, bombarding; impingement; bombing; **внесенный** —**овкой** bombardment-introduced (radioactivity); —**овать** *v.* bombard; bomb; —**уемый** *a.* bombarded, struck; —**уемый электронами** electron-bombarded; —**ующий** *a.* bombarding.

**Бомбей, бомбейский** *a.* Bombay.

**бомбиостерин** *m.* bombiosterol.

**бомбировка** *f.* camber.

**бомбить** *v.* bomb.

**бомбо/воз** *m.* bomber, bomber plane; —**держатель** *m.* bomb rack (of plane); —**мет** *m.* bomb-throwing device, bomber; —**метание** *n.* bomb dropping, bombing; —**сбрасыватель** *m.* bomb release, dropping gear; —**убежище** *n.* bomb shelter; —**упорный** *a.* bombproof.

**Боме** *see* **Бомэ.**

**бомонтит** *m.* (min.) beaumontite (a variety of heulandite).

**Бомэ** Baumé, Bé; **ареометр Б.** Baumé hydrometer; **градусов Б.** degrees Baumé.

**бон/а** *f.* check, order; paper money; —**ы** *pl.* bond.

**бонанца** *f.* bonanza (a body of rich ore).

**бонгкрековая кислота** bongkrek acid.

**бондар/ить** *v.* cooper; —**ный** *a.* cooper's; —**ное предприятие,** —**ня** *f.* cooperage, cooper's shop; —**ь** *m.* cooper, hooper.

**бондеризация** *f.* (met.) bonderizing.

бондрат *m.* a babbitt metal containing arsenic and cadmium.

бониновая кислота boninic acid.

бонит/ер, —ировщик *m.* classifier, grader; judge (of livestock); —ет *m.* (forestry) index of quality and yield; —ировать *v.* evaluate, appraise; judge; —ировка *f.* valuation, appraisement (of land); grading; judging; (biol.) bonitation; —ировочный *a.* evaluation (unit).

бонифик/атор *m.* ameliorant; —ация *f.* bonification, amelioration, improvement.

бонус *m.* bonus, premium.

боотит *m.* (min.) boothite.

бор *m.* boron, B; drill; pine forest; (bot.) millet grass (*Milium*); bristly fox-tail grass (*Setaria*); азотистый б. boron nitride; иодистый б. boron iodide.

бора *f.* bora, cold northerly wind.

Бора теория Bohr's theory.

бор/акс *m.* borax, sodium tetraborate; —аль *m.* boral, aluminum borotartrate; Boral ($B_{12}Al$, light material for neutronic shielding); —ан *m.* borane, boron hydride; —ат *m.* borate; —ацит *m.* (min.) boracite.

Боргарда препарат a basic copper sulfate-carbonate seed disinfectant.

бордо *n.* claret; claret color; —вый, —сский *a.* Bordeaux; —вый красный Bordeaux red, claret; —сская жидкость Bordeaux mixture (insecticide).

бордс/овый фут board foot (unit of measure); —ы *pl.* boards.

бордюр *m.*, —ный *a.* border, edging; curb, border stone; (geol.) limb; —ный камень curbstone.

боре/альный *a.* boreal (region); —й *m.* Boreas, north wind.

бор/ется *pr. 3 sing. of* бороться; —ец *m.* wrestler; (bot.) aconite (*Aconitum*).

боржом *m.* Borzhom mineral water.

борзый *a.* swift, fleet, quick.

бориккит *m.* (min.) borickite.

бор/ил *m.* boryl; —ин *m.* borine; —ирование *n.* borating; (met.) boronizing; —ировать *v.* borate; boronize.

борист/ый *a.* boron; boride (of); б. алюминий aluminum boride; —ая камера boron (ionization) chamber; —ая сталь boron steel.

боркальк *m.* a mixture of aluminum powder and lime used for reducing furnace slag; calcium borate.

бормагниевый *a.* boron-magnesium.

бормашина *f.* (dentist's) drill.

борметил *m.* bormethyl, trimethylborine.

Борна формула Born's equation.

борн/ейская камфора, —еол *m.* borneo-camphor, borneol; —ивал *m.* bornyval, bornyl isovalerate.

борнил *m.*, —овый *a.* bornyl; хлористый б. bornyl chloride; —амин *m.* bornylamine, 2-aminocamphane; —ацетат *m.* bornyl acetate; —ен *m.* bornylene; —овый спирт *see* борнеол; —оксалат *m.* bornyl oxalate.

борнит *m.* (min.) bornite, peacock ore, variegated copper ore.

борно— *prefix* boro—; —аммониевая соль ammonium borate; —вольфрамовая кислота borotungstic acid.

борновское приближение Born approximation.

борно/кальциевая соль calcium borate; —кислый *a.* boric acid; borate (of); —кислый натрий sodium borate; —кислая соль borate; —магниевая соль magnesium borate;—муравьиная кислота boroformic acid; —натриевая соль sodium borate; —натрокальцит *see* боронатрокальцит; —салициловая кислота borosalicylic acid; —свинцовистая соль lead borate.

борн/ый *a.* boric, boracic; б. ангидрид boric anhydride, boron oxide; б. глицерин boroglyceride, glyceryl borate; б. счетчик boron counter (tube); —ая кислота boric acid, boracic acid; соль —ой кислоты borate; —ая мазь boric acid ointment; —ое мыло borax soap.

боров *m.* horizontal flue; hog, pig.

боровертин *m.* borovertin.

боровик *m.* (bot.) mushroom (*Boletus edulis*); —а *see* брусника.

боровковый *a.* flue; б. порог baffle; breast wall.

бороводород *m.* boron hydride, borane.

боровок *m.* baffle, baffle plate, baffler; furnace bridge.

**боровольфрамовая кислота** borotungstic acid.

**боровский радиус** (nucl.) Bohr radius.

**боровый** *a. of* боров.

**борода** *f.* beard.

**бородав/ка** *f.* wart; **—ник** *m.* (bot.) nipplewort (*Lampsana communis*); **—ник, —очник** *m.* greater celandine (*Chelidonium majus*); **—чатость** *f.* warty condition; wart disease (of plants); **—чатый** *a.* warty.

**бород/атый** *a.* bearded; (bot.) barbate; **—ач** *m.* (bot.) beard grass (*Andropogon*); **—ка** *f.* beard, tuft; barb; (zool.) byssus; (mech.) bit; **—ок** *m.* punch, puncher; broach; knock-out rod; **—чатый** *a.* barbed; (bot.) barbate.

**борозд/а, —ка** *f.* furrow, ridge; trench; slot, groove, flute; trail; (anat.) sulcus, fissure; **—ильный** *a.* grooving, channeling (machine); **—ить** *v.* (agr.) furrow, plow; groove; **—ник** *m.* trenching plow; (agr.) marker; **—ной** *a.* furrow; groove; **—чатость** *f.* striation; **—чатый** *a.* grooved, channeled, fluted; striated.

**борол** *m.* borol (sodium potassium borosulfate).

**боролся** *past sing. of* бороться.

**борона** *f.* (agr.) harrow.

**боронатрокальцит** *m.* (min.) boronatrocalcite, ulexite.

**боронение** *see* боронование.

**боронец** *see* плаун.

**борон/ить, —овать** *v.* harrow; **—ование** *n.,* **—ьба** *f.* harrowing.

**бороскоп** *m.* boroscope (device for inspecting inside of tubes).

**бороться** *v.* fight, struggle, combat.

**борофтор/истоводородный, —оводородный** *a.* hydrofluoboric; **—истый водород, —оводородная кислота** hydrofluoboric acid, fluoboric acid; **соль —оводородной кислоты** fluoborate, fluoboride.

**боррелидин** *m.* borrelidin.

**борт** *m.* edge, rim, border, hem; flange, flanged edge, bead, crimp; bead (of tire); bort (an impure industrial diamond); side (of ship); curbstone; **загибать б.** *v.* bead; **за —ом** overboard; **—механик** *m.* ship engineer; air mechanic.

**бортнич/анье, —ество** *n.* apiculture; **—ать** *v.* keep bees.

**борт/овой** *a. of* борт; edge, border; flange; **б. камень** curbstone; **б. фрикцион** (mach.) steering clutch; **—овая качка** rolling (of ship); **—озагибочный пресс** flanger; **—техник** *m.* ship engineer; air mechanic.

**борштанга** *f.* boring bar.

**борщ** *m.* borsch (a type of soup); **—евик** *m.* (bot.) cow parsnip (*Heracleum*); **—евник** *see* аконит.

**борьба** *f.* struggle, fight, combat, combating; campaign, drive; (pest) control; (accident) prevention; (noise) abatement.

**борэт/ан** *m.* borethane; **—ил** *m.* borethyl.

**борю/тся** *pr. 3 pl. of* бороться; **—щийся** *a.* fighting, combating.

**бос/иком** *adv.,* **—ой** *a.* barefoot.

**босон** *see* бозон.

**босоногий** *see* босой.

**бот** *m.* boat, skiff; overshoe.

**ботани/зирка** *f.* (bot.) specimen box; **—зировать** *v.* botanize; **—к** *m.* botanist; **—ка** *f.* botany; **—ческий** *a.* botanical.

**ботв/а** *f.* tops of root-bearing plants; haulm, stem (of grass); **—орез** *m.,* **—отеребильный аппарат** (agr.) haulm remover.

**ботин/ок** *m.* boot, shoe; **—ки** *pl.* shoes.

**ботрио/ген** *m.* (min.) botryogen; **—микоз** *m.* (vet.) botryomycosis.

**ботулизм** *m.* botulism (food poisoning).

**Бофора шкала** (meteor.) Beaufort scale.

**боуэнит** *see* бовенит.

**боч.** *abbr.* (бочка) barrel.

**бочаг** *m.,* **—а** *f.* deep pool.

**бочар** *m.* cooper; **—ничать** *v.* cooper; **—ничество** *n.* cooperage, coopering; **—ный** *a.* cooper's; barrel; **—ня** *f.* cooperage, cooper's shop.

**боч/енок** *m.* small barrel, keg; **—ка** *f.* barrel, cask, keg; tub, vat; body (of shaft); (aero.) roll, snap roll.

**бочком** *see* боком.

**боч/кообразный** *a.* barrel-shaped, barrel; (biol.) dolioform; **—онок** *see* боченок.

**бояз/ливый** *a.* fearful, apprehensive; **—нь** *f.* fear, apprehension; (med.) phobia.

**боярышн/ик** *m.* (bot.) hawthorn (*Crataegus*); **—ица** *f.* (zool.) pierid butterfly (*Aporia crataegi*).

**боя/ться** *v.* fear, be afraid (of), dread; **—щийся** *a.* fearing.

**БПК** *abbr.* (биохимическое потребление кислорода) biochemical oxygen demand.

**бра** *n.* sconce, bracket, wall bracket.

**браваизит** *m.* (min.) bravaisite.

**бравший** *past act. part. of* **брать.**

**Бравэ решетка** (cryst.) Bravais lattice.

**брага** *f.* a homemade beer.

**браг/гит** *m.* (min.) braggite; **—ит** *m.* (min.) bragite, fergusonite.

**брадзот** *m.* (vet.) braxy.

**бради—** *prefix* brady— (slow); **—кардия** *f.* (med.) bradycardia; **—кинин** *m.* bradykinin.

**брадэна головка** (oil wells) bradenhead, stuffing-box casing-head.

**бражники** *pl.* hawk or sphinx moths (*Sphingidae*).

**браз.** *abbr.* (бразильский) Brazilian.

**бразил/еин** *m.* brazilein; **—ин** *m.* brazilin, brasilin; **—ит** *m.* brazilite (an oil-bearing rock); baddeleyite; **Бразилия** Brazil; **—копаловая кислота** brazilcopalic acid; **—овая кислота** brasilic acid; **—ьский** *a.* Brazil, Brazilian; **—ьское дерево** brazilwood.

**брайтова болезнь** (med.) Bright's disease, acute or chronic nephritis.

**брайтсток** *m.* bright stock (a high-quality oil).

**брак** *m.* union, marriage; (tech.) flaw; refuse, scrap; rejected material; (paper) broke.

**бракебушит** *m.* (min.) brackebuschite.

**бракер/аж** *m.* sorting, grading; **—овочная** *f.* grading room.

**бракет** *m.* bracket.

**брако/ванный** *a.* condemned, rejected, non-acceptable; defective, faulty; refuse, waste; **—вать** *v.* condemn, reject, refuse, discard, cast out; **—вка** *f.* condemning, rejection; sorting, grading; inspection; **—вщик** *m.* inspector, examiner; **—дел** *m.* bungler, bungling workman; **—молка** *f.* (paper) cone breaker, kneader.

**бракониды** *pl.* braconid wasps (*Braconidae*).

**брал** *past sing. of* **брать.**

**бранд/вахта** *f.* fire watch, guard ship; **—ер** *m.* fire boat, fire ship.

**брандизит** *m.* (min.) brandisite, disterrite (a variety of seybertite).

**бранд/мауер** *m.* fire wall, fireproof wall; **—мейстер** *m.* fire warden; **—спойт** *m.* fire engine, fire pump; (hose) nozzle.

**брандтит** *m.* (min.) brandtite.

**Бранли когерер** (rad.) Branley coherer.

**браннерит** *m.* (min.) brannerite (a uranium titanate).

**браслет** *m.* bracelet; (rubber) band.

**брассид/иновая кислота** brassidic acid, 12-docosenoic acid; **—он** *m.* brassidone.

**бросси/ловая кислота** brassylic acid; **—новая кислота** *see* **брассидиновая кислота.**

**брат** *m.* brother; earth pillar; **—ание** *n.* fraternization; **—аться** *v.* fraternize; **—ия** *f.* fraternity; brotherhood; *pl.* brothers.

**брать** *v.* take, obtain; withdraw, remove; turn (right' or left); follow (an example); **б. на себя** take upon oneself, assume; **не б.** fail; **—ся** *v.* undertake.

**браузе** *n.* sprinkler, spray.

**Брауна реактив** Braun's reagent; **Б. трубка** Braun tube, a potash bulb.

**браунинг** *m.* (mil.) Browning.

**браунит** *m.* (min.) braunite.

**брауиколь** *f.* (bot.) kale (*Brassica oleracea* var. *acephala*); winter cabbage (*B. crispa*).

**брауновский** *a.* Brownian (movement).

**браунивей/гская зелень, —н** *m.* Brunswick green, green copper carbonate.

**брахи—** *prefix* brachy— (short); **brachi—,** brachial; **—дома** *f.* brachydome; **—опода** *f.* (zool.) brachiopod; **—ось** (cryst.) brachyaxis; **—пирамида** *f.* brachypyramid; **—стохрона** *f.* (math.) brachistochrone; **—типный** *a.* brachy-type.

**брачный** *a.* (zool.) nuptial, breeding.

**брашпиль** *m.* windlass, capstan.

**бревенчатый** *a.* log, beam, timber.

**бревий** *m.* brevium, uranium X[2].

**бревно** *n.* log, beam; **—катка** *f.* log roller; **—таска** *f.* log hauler, log conveyer.

**брегерит** *m.* (min.) bröggerite (a variety of uraninite).

**бред** *m.* delirium; впасть в б. *v.* grow delirious.

**бредень** *m.* drag net.

**бредина** *f.* (bot.) goat willow (*Salix caprea*).

**бред/ить** *v.* be delirious; —овой *a.* delirious.

**бреет** *pr. 3 sing. of* **брить.**

**брезг/ать,** —овать *v.* have an aversion (to), disdain, be squeamish (about); —ливый *a.* squeamish, particular.

**брезент** *m.,* —овой *a.* tarpaulin, canvas; burlap; —овое пальто tarpaulin.

**брезилеин** *see* **бразилеин.**

**брейнерит** *m.* (min.) breunerite, brown spar (a variety of magnesite).

**брейслакит** *m.* (min.) breislakite (a variety of ilvaite).

**Брейта-Вигнера формула** (nucl.) Breit-Wigner formula.

**брейтгауптит** *m.* (min.) breithauptite, antimonial nickel.

**брекватер** *m.* breakwater, jetty.

**брекер** *m.* breaker.

**брекч/иа,** —ия *f.* breccia (a fragmental rock); —иевидный *a.* (petr.) brecciated; —ирование *n.* brecciation; —ированный *a.* brecciated.

**бременский зеленый** Bremen green, green copper carbonate; б. синий Bremen blue, blue copper carbonate.

**бремсберг** *m.* slope, gradient, incline.

**бремя** *n.* burden, load, weight.

**бренди** *m.* brandy.

**бренн/ость** *f.* perishability, instability, fragility; —ый *a.* perishable, fragile.

**бреславльская палочка** (bact.) *Salmonella breslau.*

**брести** *see* **бродить.**

**брест-колесо** *n.* breast wheel.

**бретелька** *f.* shoulder strap.

**бретонский** *a.* (geol.) Bretonian.

**брешь** *f.* breach, gap, break, notch, flaw.

**брею/т** *pr. 3 pl. of* **брить;** —щий *a.* shaving; (aero.) low-level.

**бриг** *m.* brig (a boat).

**бригад/а** *f.,* —ный *a.* brigade, squad, crew, team (of workers); —ир *m.* brigade foreman.

**бриггсовый логарифм** (math.) Briggs' logarithm, common logarithm.

**бридер** *m.* (nucl.) breeder.

**бриз** *m.* breeze.

**БРИЗ** *abbr.* (Бюро содействия рационализации и изобретательства) Office for the Promotion of Industrial Efficiency and Inventions.

**бризантн/ость** *f.,* —ое действие (expl.) brisance; —ый *a.* brisant, disruptive, shattering; —ые взрывчатые вещества high explosives, disruptives.

**брикет** *m.* briquet; brick fuel; (feed) pellet; —ирование *n.* briquetting; pelleting;—ированный *a.* briquetted; —ировать *v.* briquet; —ировочный, —ный *a.* briquetting, briquet.

**Брикнера цикл** (meteor.) Brückner cycle.

**брил** *past sing. of* **брить.**

**бриллиант** *m.* diamond; —индиго brilliant indigo; —овый *a.* diamond; brilliant; —овый желтый brilliant yellow; —овый черный, —овая чернь brilliant black; —овые лаки brilliant lacquers (alcohol-base lacquers).

**Бриллуэна функция** (phys.) Brillouin function.

**брильянт** *see* **бриллиант.**

**Брина метод** Brin process (for preparing oxygen).

**Бринел/я проба** (met.) Brinell test; твердость по —ю Brinell hardness.

**брио—** *prefix* bryo— (moss); —зои *pl.* (zool.) Bryozoa; —идин *m.* bryoidin; —логия *f.* bryology; —нан *m.* bryonane; —нидин *m.* bryonidin; —нин *m.* bryonin; —ния *f.* (bot.) bryony (*Bryonia*); —нол *m.* bryonol (a phytosterolin); —резин *m.* bryoresin.

**бристольск/ий** *a.* Bristol; б. картон, —ая бумага Bristol board.

**Бриталь-процесс** *m.* Brital process (of aluminum polishing).

**британ/ия** *f.,* —ский металл Britannia metal, Britannia (tin-antimony-copper alloy); —ский *a.* British; —ская тепловая единица British thermal unit (Btu).

**бритва** *f.* razor.

**британ-гум** *m.,* б.-гумми *n.* British gum, dextrin.

**бритолит** *m.* (min.) britholite.

**бриттолизация** *f.* brittolizing (of motor fuels).

**брить, —ся** *v.* shave; **—е** *n.* shave, shaving.

**бровалол** *m.* brovalol, bornyl bromovalerate.

**бров/ка** *f.* lip, brow (of hill, deposit); **—ь** *f.* eyebrow.

**брод** *m.* ford.

**бродил/о** *n.* leaven; **—ьность** *f.* fermentability; **—ьный** *a.* zymotic, fermentation, fermentative; **—ьный грибок** (bot.) yeast plant; **—ьный запал** ferment, leavening; **—ьный процесс** fermentation process, fermentation; **—ьня** *f.* fermentation room.

**брод/ить** *v.* ferment; wander, roam, stray; **—яжки** *pl.* young larvae; **—ячий** *a.* nomad, migratory; restless; erratic; **—ящий** *a.* zymotic, fermentation, fermenting; wandering, straying.

**брожен/ие** *n.* fermentation; **вызывать б.** *v.* ferment; **измеритель —ия** zymometer; **приходить в б.** *v.* ferment, start fermenting.

**брокантит** *see* брошантит.

**брокат** *m.* bronze powder; (text.) brocade.

**брокателло** *n.* broccatello (a variegated marble).

**брокатель** *f.* (text.) brocatel.

**брокенский призрак** Brocken bow (or specter), glory.

**брокер** *m.* (com.) broker; **—аж** *m.* brokerage.

**броккол/и, —ь** *f.* (bot.) broccoli (*Brassica oleracea botrytis* or *B. o.* var. *italica*).

**бром** *m.* bromine, Br; (pharm.) bromide; **гидрат —a** bromine hydrate; **хлористый б.** bromine chloride.

**бром— —** *prefix* brom—, bromo—; **—ал, —аль** *m.* bromal, 2,2,2-tribromoethanal; **гидрат —ала** bromal hydrate; **—алин** *m.* bromalin, bromethylformin; **—амид** *m.* bromamide, aniline tribromide.

**бромангидрид** *m.* acid bromide; **б. серной кислоты** sulfuryl bromide; **б. уксусной кислоты** acetyl bromide.

**броманилин** *m.* bromaniline.

**бромаргирит** *m.* (min.) bromargyrite (member of the cerargyrite group).

**бромат** *m.* bromate; **—ология** *f.* bromatology (science of foods and diet).

**бром/ацетон** *m.* bromacetone; **—бензол** *m.* bromobenzene; **—бутадиен** *m.* bromobutadiene; **—гидрат** *m.* bromine hydrate; hydrobromide; **—гидрин** *m.* bromhydrin; **—гидрирование** *n.* hydrobromination, addition of hydrogen bromide; **—елиевые** *pl.* (bot.) Bromeliaceae; **—етон** *m.* brometone; **—ид** *m.* bromide; **—ид натрия** sodium bromide; **—ипин** *m.* bromipin; **—ирит** *m.* (min.) bromyrite (a member of the cerargyrite group).

**бромиров/ание** *n.* bromination, treatment with bromine; **—анный** *a.* brominated; **—ать** *v.* brominate.

**бромистоводородн/ый** *a.* hydrobromic; hydrobromide (of); **б. хинин** quinine hydrobromide; **—ая кислота** hydrobromic acid, hydrogen bromide; **соль —ой кислоты** bromide.

**бромист/ый** *a.* bromine; (lower or —ous) bromide; **б. бензил** benzyl bromide; **б. водород** hydrogen bromide; **б. калий** potassium bromide; **б. натрий** sodium bromide; **б. этилен** ethylene bromide; **—ая медь** cuprous bromide; **—ое железо** ferrous bromide; **—ое серебро** silver bromide.

**бром/ит** *m.* bromite; **—лит** *m.* (min.) bromlite, alstonite; **—малеиновая кислота** bromomaleic acid; **—метил** *m.* methyl bromide.

**бромноват/ая кислота** bromic acid; **соль —ой кислоты** bromate; **—истая кислота** hypobromous acid; **соль —истой кислоты** hypobromite; **—истокальциевая соль** calcium hypobromite; **—истокислый** *a.* hypobromous acid; hypobromite (of); **—истокислая соль** hypobromite.

**бромновато/бензиловый эфир** benzyl bromate; **—калиевая соль** potassium bromate; **—кислый** *a.* bromic acid; bromate (of); **—кислый натрий** sodium bromate; **—кислая соль** bromate; **—натриевая соль** sodium bromate.

**бромн/ый** *a.* bromine; (higher or —ic) bromide; **—ая вода** bromine water; **—ая кислота** perbromic acid; **соль —ой кислоты** perbromate; **—ая медь**

cupric bromide; —ое железо ferric bromide.

**бромо—** *prefix* bromo—.

**бромоводород** *m.* hydrogen bromide; —ный *see* бромистоводородный.

**бромо/камфора** *f.* bromocamphor, monobromated camphor; —кись *f.* oxybromide; —колл *m.* bromocoll, brominated tannin gelatin; —л *m.* bromol, tribromophenol; —прен *m.* bromoprene, 2-bromobutadiene-1,4; —серебряный *a.* silver bromide (emulsion); —форм *m.* bromoform, tribromomethane.

**бром/стирол** *m.* bromostyrol, bromostyrene; —толуол *m.* bromotoluene; —уксусная кислота bromoacetic acid; соль —уксусной кислоты bromoacetate; —уксусноэтиловый эфир ethyl bromoacetate; —урал *m.* bromural; —циан *m.* cyanogen bromide; —юр *see* бромид.

**броне/автомашина** *f.*, —автомобиль *m.* armored car; —башня *f.* (aero.) turret; —бойный *a.* armor-piercing; —вик *m.* armored car; (zool.) armadillo.

**бронев/ой** *a.* armor, armoring, sheathing; б. лист, —ая плита armor plate; —ая обмотка (elec.) drum winding.

**броне/кабель** *m.* (elec.) armored cable; —машина *f.* armored car; —носец *see* броневик; —носный *a.* armor-clad, armored; iron-clad, steel-clad; —поезд *m.* armored train; —силы, —средства *pl.* armored forces; —ц *see* плаун.

**бронза** *f.* (met.) bronze.

**бронзиров/альный** *see* бронзовый; б. порошок bronzing powder; —ание *n.*, —ка *f.* bronzing; —анный *a.* bronzed; —ать *v.* bronze.

**бронзит** *m.* (min.) bronzite (a variety of enstatite); bronzite (alloy).

**бронзов/альный** *see* бронзовый, бронзировальный; —ание *see* бронзирование; —атоокрашенный *a.* bronze-colored; —ки *pl.* scarabaeid beetles (*Cetoniinae*); —ость *f.* bronzing (plant disease).

**бронзов/ый** *a.* bronze, bronzy; б. штейн concentration metal (from smelting of copper sulfide ores); —ая болезнь *see*

аддисонова болезнь; —ая зелень bronze green; —ые краски bronze colors, bronze powders.

**бронзо/литейный** завод bronze foundry; —подобный *a.* bronze-like, bronzy.

**бронпров/ание** *n.* armoring, armor-plating; —анный *a.* armored, armor-plated; armor-clad, metal-clad; steel-clad; jacketed; —анный латунью brass-armored; —ать *v.* armor, armor plate.

**бронтометр** *m.* (meteor.) brontometer.

**бронх** *m.* (anat.) bronchus; —и *pl.* bronchi; —иальный *a.* bronchial; —ит *m.* (med.) bronchitis.

**брон/я** *f.* armor, casing, jacket; guard plate (of blast furnace); обшивать —ею *v.* armor, armor-plate.

**брос/ание** *n.* throwing, casting, flinging; priming (in boilers); abandonment; projection; угол —ания angle of departure; —ать, —ить *v.* throw, cast; give up, quit, abandon, leave, drop; project; —аться, —иться *v.* throw oneself, plunge; —овый *a.* worthless, unproductive (land); —овый экспорт (com.) dumping; —ок *m.* hurl, throw; rush, surge; (mach.) kick; (aero.) bump.

**Броуна-Пирс опухоль** (med.) Brown-Pierce tumor.

**броунов/о движение,** —ское движение Brownian movement.

**брошантит** *m.* (min.) brochantite.

**брошенный** *a.* thrown; abandoned.

**броширов/ание** *n.*, —ка *f.* stitching (of books); —анный *a.* stitched; —ать *v.* stitch.

**брошь** *f.* (tech.) broach.

**брошюра** *f.* brochure, pamphlet, booklet.

**брудер** *m.* brooder (for poultry).

**брук/ит** *m.* (min.) brookite (a form of titanium dioxide); —хейвенский *a.* Brookhaven.

**брульон** *m.* draft, sketch, outline.

**брунирование** *see* брюнирование.

**брунцфигит** *m.* (min.) brunsvigite (a chlorite near metachlorite).

**бруньятеллит** *m.* (min.) brugnatellite.

**брус** *m.* beam, girder, joist, squared beam, tie beam; bar, block, brick, cake.

**брусит** *see* бруцит.

**брусков/ый** *a.* bar; hewn; brick-shaped; **—ая щетка** block brush; **—ое железо** bar iron.

**брусни/ка, —ца** *f.*, **—чный** *a.* (bot.) red bilberry, foxberry (*Vaccinium vitis idaea*); **—чник** *m.* red bilberry bush.

**брус/овка** *f.* file; **—овой** *a.* girder, joist, beam; **—ок** *m.* (met.) ingot, bar, pig; slug, block; brick; rail, rod.

**бруссонеция** *f.*, **бумажная б.** (bot.) paper mulberry (*Broussonetia papyrifera*).

**бруствер** *m.* breastwork, parapet, rampart.

**брус/чатка** *f.*, **—чатый** *a.* block, square beam; (geol.) mullion, rodding (structure); **—ья** *see* **брус**; cross bars; skids.

**брутто** *adv.*, **—вый** *a.* gross, gross weight; **б.-формула** empirical formula; **вес б.** gross weight.

**бруц/еллез** *m.* (med.) brucellosis; **—ин** *m.* brucine, dimethoxystrychnine; **—иновая кислота** brucinic acid; **—ит** *m.* (min.) brucite.

**брушбрекер** *m.* (agr.) brush breaker.

**брушит** *m.* (min.) brushite.

**БРФ** *abbr.* (**физический бериллиевый реактор**) physical beryllium reactor.

**брыжей/ка** *f.* (anat.) mesentery; **—ный** *a.* mesenteric.

**брыз/галка** *f.*, **—гало** *n.* sprinkler, sprayer; spraying rose, rose; **—гание, —ганье** *n.* sprinkling; splashing, spatter; jet, spurt; **—гать, —нуть** *v.* sprinkle; splash, spatter; jet, squirt; **—гаться** *v.* splash, spatter; **—ги** *pl.* spray, splash, spatter; **давать —ги** *v.* spurt; **—гозащищенный, —гонепроницаемый, —гостойкий** *a.* splashproof; **—гоуловитель** *m.* spray trap.

**брыкать, —ся** *v.* kick.

**брынза** *f.* a Caucasian cheese.

**брэгговское правило** (nucl.) Bragg's rule.

**брюкв/а** *f.*, **—енный** *a.* (bot.) turnip (*Brassica napus rapifera*).

**брюки** *pl.* trousers.

**брюнет** *m.*, **—ка** *f.* brunette.

**брюниров/ание** *n.* (met.) browning; bronzing; burnishing, polishing; **—анный** *a.* browned; burnished; **—ать** *v.* brown; burnish, polish.

**брюссельская капуста** (bot.) Brussels sprouts (*Brassica oleracea gemmifera*).

**Брюстера закон** (optics) Brewster's law.

**брюстерит** *m.* (min.) brewsterite (member of the heulandite group).

**брюхо** *n.* abdomen, stomach, belly; maw; **—ногие** *pl.* (zool.) Gastropoda; **—реснычные** *pl.* (zool.) Hypotricha.

**брюшин/а** *f.* (anat.) peritoneum; **воспаление —ы** (med.) peritonitis; **—ный** *a.* peritoneal.

**брюшко** *n.* (zool.) abdomen.

**брюшн/ой** *a.* abdominal, ventral, celiac; **б. тиф** (med.) typhoid fever; **—ая полость** abdominal cavity; **—отифозная палочка** (bact.) *Salmonella typhosa.*

**БССР** *abbr.* (**Белорусская Советская Социалистическая Республика**) Belorussian Soviet Socialist Republic.

**БСЭ** *abbr.* (**Большая Советская энциклопедия**) Large Soviet Encyclopedia.

**Б.Т.** *abbr.* (**Биржа труда**) Labor Exchange.

**бубон** *m.* (med.) bubo; **—ный** *a.* bubonic; **—ная чума** bubonic plague.

**Буво-Бланка реакция** Bouveault-Blanc reaction.

**бугай** *see* **бык.**

**Буге закон** (optics) Bouguer's law.

**бугель** *m.* bow, loop, stirrup, hoop; guard; (elec.) bow collector.

**Бугера** *see* **Буге.**

**бугор** *m.* heap, mound, hill, hillock; protuberance; nipple; **—ок** *m.* tubercle; **—чатка** *f.* (med.) tuberculosis; **—чатый** *a.* tubercular, tuberculosis; tubercle; nodular.

**бугристый** *a.* hummocky, hilly.

**будем** *fut. 1 pl. of* **быть.**

**будень** *m.* workday, weekday.

**будет** *fut. 3 sing. of* **быть.**

**будильник** *m.* alarm clock.

**будинаж** *m.* boudinage.

**будировать** *v.* oppose.

**будить** *v.* wake, rouse, call, raise.

**будка** *f.* booth, stall; cabin; (mil.) sentry box; (locomotive) cab.

**будничн/ость** *f.* triviality; **—ый** *a.* trivial, unimportant, petty; weekday; **—ый день** weekday, workday.

**будоражить** *v.* disturb, upset, alarm.

**будочка** *see* **будка.**

**будра** *f.*, **плющевидная б.** (bot.) ground ivy (*Glechoma hederacea*).

**будто,** —**бы** *conj.* as if, as though, that.

**буду** *fut. 1 sing.*; —**т** *fut. 3 pl.*; —**чи** *pr. act. gerund of* **быть.**

**будущ/ее** *n.* the future; —**ий** *a.* future, coming, next, ensuing; **в** —**ем году** next year; **на** —**ее время** for the future; —**ность** *f.* future, coming years; career.

**будь,** —**те** *imp. of* **быть; б. что будет** come what may; **не б. вас, он бы ушел** but for you, he would have gone.

**буек** *m.* buoy.

**буер** *m.* ice boat, ice breaker.

**буер/ак** *m.*, —**ачный** *a.* ravine, gorge, deep gully; —**ачистый** *a.* full of ravines.

**буж/дение,** —**ение** *n.* wakening, rousing.

**буженина** *f.* pork.

**буза** *f.* bouza (millet beverage); (min.) rock salt, halite.

**бузин/а** *f.*, —**ный,** —**овый** *a.* (bot.) elder (*Sambucus*).

**бузун** *see* **буза.**

**буй** *m.* buoy, float; beacon.

**буйвол** *m.*, —**овый** *a.* buffalo.

**буй/но** *adv.* violently; vigorously; —**ность** *f.*, —**ство** *n.* violence, turbulence; —**ный** *a.* violent, turbulent, ungovernable; vigorous; lush (growth); —**ствовать** *v.* storm, rage, behave violently.

**бук** *m.* (bot.) beech (*Fagus*).

**букарка** *f.* snout beetle (*Coenorrhinus pauxillus* or *Rhynchites p.*).

**букашка** *f.* small insect.

**букв/а** *f.* letter, character; **б. в** —**у** literatim; —**ально** *adv.* literally, word for word, verbatim; —**альность** *f.* literalness; —**альный** *a.* literal; verbal; —**арный** *a.* alphabetic; —**енный** *a.* letter, by letter; (min.) graphic.

**буквица** *f.*, **аптечная б.** (bot.) betony (*Betonica officinalis*); **белая б.** cowslip, primrose (*Primula*).

**буквопечатающий** *a.* printing.

**букет** *m.*, —**ный** *a.* bouquet, flavor; perfume, scent, aroma; bunch, clump (of plants); —**ировать** *v.* (agr.) block, bunch, thin.

**буккер** *m.* drill plow.

**букко** *n.* bucco (leaves), buchu.

**букландит** *m.* (min.) bucklandite (a variety of epidote or of allanite).

**буковица, лекарственная** *see* **буквица.**

**буков/ые** *pl.* (bot.) Fagaceae; —**ый** *a.* beech, beechen; beechwood; beechnut; —**ый жолудь** beechnut.

**букс** *m.* (bot.) box (*Buxus sempervirens*).

**букса** *f.* axle box; box; bushing.

**буксбаум** *see* **буксовое дерево.**

**буксин** *m.* buxine; buckskin.

**буксир** *m.* tow, towline; tug, tugboat; —**ный,** —**овочный** *a.* tow, tug; —**ный трос** towline; —**ование** *n.* towing, tugging; hauling, haul; —**овать** *v.* tow, tug, have in tow; haul.

**буксов/ание** *n.* slipping, skidding; —**ать** *v.* slip, skid, spin.

**букс/овое дерево** boxwood; —**ус** *m.* (bot.) box, boxwood (*Buxus*).

**букшпан** *see* **бакаут.**

**булава** *f.* mace, club.

**булавастик** *m.* (bot.) clavaria.

**булавка** *f.* pin.

**булавница** *see* **булавастик.**

**булаво**— *prefix* (biol.) clavi—, club; —**видный** *a.* club-shaped; (biol.) clavate; —**усые** *pl.* butterflies and skippers (*Rhopalocera*).

**булавочн/ый** *a.* pin; —**ая коррозия** pitting.

**буланжерит** *m.* (min.) boulangerite.

**буланый** *a.* dun, cream-colored.

**булань** *see* **булинь.**

**булат** *m.* damask steel, Damascus steel; **индийский б.** India steel, wootz.

**булгунняхи** *pl.* (geol.) hydrolaccoliths.

**булдырьян** *see* **валериана.**

**булев/а,** —**ский** *a.* (math.) Boolean.

**булинь** *m.* bowline.

**бул/ка,** —**очка** *f.* roll, bun; —**очная** *f.* bakery.

**булыжн/ик** *m.*, —**ый** *a.* cobblestone, pebble, rubble, shingle.

**бульб** *m.*, —**овый** *a.* bulb.

**буль-блок** *m.* (wire drawing) bull block.

**бульбокапнин** *m.* bulbocapnine.

**бульва** *f.* (bot.) Jerusalem artichoke (*Helianthus tuberosus*).

**бульвар** *m.*, —**ный** *a.* boulevard, avenue.

**бульверк** *m.* bulwark, rampart, fortification, defense.

**бульдозер** *m.* (mach.; met.) bulldozer.

**булька** *f.* boule (synthetic ruby); pellet.

булькать *v.* bubble, gurgle.
бульон *m.*, —ный *a.* broth.
Бульрича соль Bullrich's salt (sodium bicarbonate).
бумага *f.* paper; битая б. papier-maché.
бумаго/делательная машина paper-making machine; —массная пряжа paper yarn, paper twine; —прядильный *a.* textile, cotton-spinning; —прядильная фабрика, —прядильня *f.* cotton mill; —резательный *a.* paper-cutting.
бумаж/ка *f.* slip of paper; —ник *m.* wallet, billfold; —но— *prefix*, —ный *a.* paper; (text.) cotton; *see also* бумаго—; —ная масса, —ное тесто paper pulp; —ная нить, —ная пряжа cotton thread; —ная фабрика paper mill.
бумазея *f.* (text.) fustian.
бумеранг *m.* boomerang.
буна *f.* Buna (rubber); dike dam.
бундук *m.* (bot.) Kentucky coffee tree (*Gymnocladus canadensis*).
Бунзена горелка Bunsen burner.
бунзен/ин, —ит *m.* (min.) bunsenite (a nickel monoxide); —овская горелка *see* Бунзена горелка.
бункер *m.*, —ный *a.* bin, bunker, hopper; —ный затвор bin gate; —ный фидер hopper, feed bin; —ная вагонетка hopper car; —ная сеялка (agr.) seed drill; —ное топливо oil-distillation residues.
бунт *m.* revolt, mutiny; bale, pack; bunch, bundle; coil (of wire); —арский *a.* seditious;—арство *n.* sedition.
Бунте бюретка Bunte gas buret.
бунтовать *v.* revolt, rebel; raise, stir up; bale, packet, bundle; —ся *v.* revolt.
буплерол *m.* bupleurol.
бур *m.* auger, borer, drill, perforator; boring bit, bit; cutter.
бур/а *f.* borax, sodium tetraborate; сплавленный шарик —ы borax bead.
бурав *m.* auger, borer, drill, perforator; (med.) broach; —ец *m.* (zool.) borer; —ить *v.* bore, drill, perforate, pierce; —ление *n.* boring, drilling; —ница *f.* (zool.) miner; —чатый *a.* auger-shaped; —чик *m.* gimlet, borer.
бурак *m.* (bot.) beet (*Beta vulgaris*);

(pyrotechnics) rocket, marron; (text.) coiler; can.
буран *m.* snowstorm.
бурат *m.* (min.) trommel, washing drum; (flour) grading screen.
бурачная *f.* beetroot cellar.
бурачник *m.*, —овый *a.* (bot.) borage (*Borago officinalis*); —овые *pl.* Boraginaceae.
бурачок *m.* (bot.) alyssum.
бурбон *m.* (bot.) a cotton plant (*Gossypium purpurascens*); —ский чай (bot.) bourbon tea (*Angraecum fragans*).
бургундск/ий *a.* Burgundy; б. вар, —ая смола Burgundy pitch; —ая жидкость a copper sulfate-sodium carbonate fungicide.
бурда *f.* slops, waste water; (zool.) skin fold.
бур-де-суа (text.) spun silk.
бурдюк *m.* wineskin.
бурелом *m.* windbreak; wind-fallen wood.
бурение *n.* boring, drilling.
бурет *m.* (text.) bourette; silk noils.
буреть *v.* grow brown, turn brown.
буриль/ный *a.* boring; б. молоток (min.) hammer drill; —щик *m.* borer, driller.
бур/имость *f.* resistance to drilling (of rock); —ить *v.* bore, drill; —ка *f.* drill hole, blast hole.
буркеит *m.* (min.) burkeite.
буркун *m.* an alfalfa (*Medicago falcata*); б., желтый б., луговой б. yellow melilot (*Melilotus officinalis*); —чик *m.* an alfalfa (*Medicago lupulina*).
бурл/ение *n.* swirling, churning; —ивость *f.* tempestuousness, turbulence; —ивый *a.* tempestuous, turbulent; —ить *v.* bubble, boil, churn, swirl.
бурно *adv.* vigorously, violently.
бурнонит *m.* (min.) bournonite, wheel ore.
бурн/ость *f.* violence, storminess, intensity; —ый *a.* violent, vigorous, brisk, stormy, turbulent, tempestuous.
бурова́тый *a.* brownish.
буро/вая *f.* borehole; —взрывная работа blasthole drilling.
буровить *v.* bubble, ferment.
буров/ой *a.* drilling, boring; б. журнал drillhole log; б. резец, —ое долото

boring bit; **б. станок** drill; **—ая вышка** (oil) derrick; **—ая грязь, —ая муть,** drill mud, sludge; **—ая мука** bore meal, borings, drillings; **—ая скважина** bore; drill hole; (oil) well.

**буровый** *a.* borax, boracic.

**бурозем** *m.* brown soil.

**бурокислый** *see* **борнокислый.**

**буроугольный** *a.* lignite.

**бурс/а** *f.* (anat.) bursa, sac; **—ин** *m.* bursine, choline; **—иновая кислота** bursic acid; **—ит** *m.* (med.) bursitis.

**бурт, —ик** *m.*, **—овой** *a.* bead, crimp, rib, shoulder, collar, swelling; storage pile; **—оукладчик** *m.* piling machine.

**бурун** *m.* surf, breaker.

**бурунд/ук** *m.* (zool.) chipmunk; **—учная руда** (min.) banded ore.

**бур/ый** *a.* brown, fallow, chestnut; **б. уголь** (min.) brown coal, lignite; **—ая руда** (min.) vivianite; limonite; sphalerite.

**бурьян** *m.* (bot.) weeds.

**буря** *f.* storm, gale.

**бус** *m.* bead; (min.) smalls, slack, fines.

**бусин/а, —ка** *f.* bead.

**буссоль** *f.* compass, surveying compass; **б. наклонения** inclinometer; **б.-угломер** aiming circle.

**бустамит** *m.* (min.) bustamite (a form of rhodonite).

**бустер** *m.*, **—ный** *a.* booster.

**бусы** *pl.* beads.

**бут** *m.* quarrystone, rubble, rubblestone, débris; container.

**бута/диен** *m.* butadiene; **—диеновый каучук** butadiene rubber; **—дион** *m.* (pharm.) phenylbutazone; **—мид** *m.* tolbutamide, tolylsulfonylbutylurea.

**бутан** *m.* butane; **—дикислота, —диовая кислота** butanedioic acid, succinic acid; **—диол** *m.* butanediol, butylene glycol; **—дион** *m.* butanedione; **—овая кислота** butanoic acid; **—оил** *m.* butanoyl, butyryl; **—ол** *m.* butanol, butyl alcohol; **—олид** *m.* butanolide, butyrolactone; **—он** *m.* butanone, methylethyl ketone; **—оновая кислота** butanone acid, acetoacetic acid.

**бутара** *f.* (min.) trommel, sizing trommel, washing drum.

**бутезин** *m.* butesin, butyl-*p*-aminobenzoate.

**бутен** *m.* butene, butylene; dimethylene; **—ал** *m.* butenal, crotonaldehyde; **—ил** *m.* butenyl; **—овая кислота** butenic acid, butenoic acid; **—ол** *m.* butenol.

**бутень** *m.* (bot.) chervil (*Chaerophyllum*).

**бутерброд** *m.*, **—ный** *a.* sandwich.

**бутил** *m.* butyl; **хлористый б.** butyl chloride; **—альдегид** *see* **бутиральдегид;** **—амин** *m.* butylamine, aminobutane; **—ацетат** *m.* butyl acetate; **—ен** *m.* butylene, butene; **бромистый —ен** butylene bromide; **—иден** *m.* butylidene; **—каучук** *m.* butyl rubber.

**Бутилье** Boutillier.

**бутил/меркаптан** *m.* butyl mercaptan; **—метиловый эфир** butyl methyl ether.

**бутиловый** *a.* butyl; **б. альдегид** *see* **бутиральдегид; б. спирт** butyl alcohol, butanol; **б. эфир уксусной кислоты** butyl acetate.

**бутил/пропионат** *m.* butyl propionate; **—целлозольв** *m.* butyl Cellosolve (a solvent); **—ьный** *see* **бутиловый.**

**бутин** *m.* butine, butyne; butyn.

**бутир/альдегид** *m.* butyraldehyde, butanal; **—амид** *m.* butyramide, butanamide; **—ат** *m.* butyrate; **—ил** *m.* butyryl; **—ин** *m.* butyrin, triglycerol butyrate; **—иновая кислота** butyric acid, butanoic acid.

**бутиро—** *prefix* butyro—; **—ин** *m.* butyroin, 5-hydroxy-4-octanone; **—лактон** *m.* butyrolactone; **—метр** *m.* butyrometer; **—н** *m.* butyrone, 4-heptanone; **—нитрил** *m.* butyronitrile, butanenitrile.

**бутить** *v.* fill with rubble.

**бутов/очный, —ый** *a.* rubble; **б. материал** filling, filler; **б. камень** rubblestone, quarrystone.

**бутокси—** *prefix* butoxy—.

**бутон** *m.* bud; **—изация** *f.* budding.

**бутыл/ка** *f.* bottle; **разливать в —ки** *v.* bottle; **—кообразный** *a.* bottleshaped; **—ок** *m.* corkage; **—омоечный** *a.* bottle-washing.

**бутылочн/ый** *a.* bottle; **б. камень** (min.) bottlestone, moldavite (a kind of glass); **б. элемент** (elec.) bichromate cell; —**ого цвета** *a.* bottle-green.

**бутыль** *f.*, —**ный** *a.* large bottle, carboy, vessel; (gas) cylinder.

**буфа/гин** *m.* bufagin; —**нин** *m.* buphanine; —**нитин** *m.* buphanitine.

**буфер** *m.* buffer, bumper, shock absorber, cushion, cushioning; **б.-компенсатор** compensating buffer; **воздушный б., масляный б.** dashpot; **паровой б.** steam cushion; —**ность** *f.* buffering, buffer action; —**ный** *a.* buffer, floating; —**ный раствор** buffer solution; —**ная склянка** capacity vessel.

**буферовка** *f.* (met.) buffing, polishing.

**буфет** *m.* buffet, snack bar; cupboard; **б.-автомат** dumbwaiter; —**ная** *f.* pantry.

**буфо/нин** *m.* bufonin; —**талин** *m.* bufotalin; —**таловая кислота** bufotalic acid; —**танин** *m.* bufotanine; —**токсин** *m.* bufotoxin.

**Бухара** Bukhara.

**бухарник** *m.*, **шерстистый б.** (bot.) velvet grass (*Holcus lanatus*).

**бухгалтер** *m.* accountant, bookkeeper; —**ия** *f.* bookkeeping; —**ский** *a.* accountant, accounting.

**бухнуть** *v.* swell, dilate.

**бухта** *f.* bay, inlet; coil, bundle.

**бухтарма** *f.* flesh side of leather.

**бухточка** *f.* inlet, basin, cove.

**буча** *f.* row, disturbance.

**буч/ение** *n.* (text.) bucking, steeping (in lye), scouring; filling with rubble; —**енный** *a.* scoured, bucked; —**еный** *a.* filled with rubble; —**ильный** *a.* bucking, steeping; —**ильный сок** steeping liquor; —**ильня** *f.* bucking house; —**ить** *v.* buck, steep (in lye), scour.

**бушевать** *v.* storm, rage.

**бушель** *m.* bushel (measure).

**бушинг** *m.* bushing.

**БФЛ** *abbr.* (**биофизическая лаборатория**) biophysical laboratory.

**БЦЖ палочка** (bact.) BCG bacillus, bacillus Calmette-Guerin.

**б.ч.** *abbr.* (**большая часть**) a large part; (**большей частью**) for the most part.

**бы** *sign of conditional and subjunctive moods*: should, would; **где бы** wher-ever; **кто бы ни** whoever; **что бы ни** whatever.

**быв/ало** *past of* **бывать**: used to; **как ни в чем не б.** as if nothing were the matter; —**алость** *f.* experience; —**алый** *a.* experienced, skilled; past; —**ать** *v.* be, exist, occur; happen; be held, take place; visit, frequent; —**ший** *a.* former, late, ex—.

**бык** *m.* bull, ox; pier; buttress.

**был** *past sing. of* **быть**.

**былин/а**, —**ка** *f.* blade (of grass).

**был/о** *past of* **быть**; nearly, on the point of; —**ой** *a.* past, bygone.

**быль** *f.* fact, event, past occurrence.

**былье** *n.* herbs, plants, vegetables.

**быстрина** *f.* rapid, swift course, race.

**быстро** *adv.* quickly, rapidly, swiftly, with speed; readily; —**вязущий**, —**схатывающийся** *a.* quick-setting (cement); —**горящий** *a.* quick-burning; readily combustible; —**движущийся** *a.* high-speed, fast; —**действующий** *a.* quick-acting, rapid-action, high-speed, fast; —**летящий** *a.* fast-moving; —**размыкающий** *a.* quick-break; —**распадающийся** *a.* short-lived; —**режущий** *a.* fast-cutting, high-speed; —**режущая сталь** high-speed steel; —**сгорающий** *a.* free-burning; —**сканирующий** *a.* rapid-scanning, high-speed (spectrometer); —**сменный** *a.* quick-change; —**сохнущий** *a.* quick-drying.

**быстрота** *f.* speed, velocity, rapidity, quickness; rate; frequency.

**быстро/течный** *a.* transient; —**ток** *m.* chute; —**умный** *a.* quick-witted; —**устанавливающийся** *a.* quick-adjusting, readily adjustable; —**ходный** *a.* high-speed, fast, rapid; express (train).

**быстрый** *a.* quick, fast, rapid, prompt; **б. ход** high speed.

**быт** *m.* way of life, living conditions; —**ие** *n.* being, existence; —**ность** *f.* stay, sojourn, presence,

**бытовн/ит** *m.* (min.) bytownite (a plagioclase feldspar); —**ортит** *m.* bytownorthite (bytownite-anorthite).

**бытовой** *a.* actual, everyday; domestic; **б. газ** illuminating gas.

**быть** *v.* be, exist; —**е** *see* **бытие.**

**быч/ачий, —ий** *a.* bull's, bovine, ox, ox-like; beef; **—ье копытное масло, жир из —ьих копыт** neat's-foot oil; **—ья желчь** oxgall; **—ина** *f.* oxhide; **—ок** *m.* young bull; goby (fish).

**Бьеркнеса модель** Bjerknes (cyclone) model.

**бьет** *pr. 3 sing. of* **бить.**

**бьеф:** (hydraulics) **верхний б.** upper water; **нижний б.** under water.

**бью/т** *pr. 3 pl. of* **бить; —щий** *a.* beating; **—щийся** *a.* beating, pulsating.

**б.э.** *abbr.* (**белковый эквивалент**) protein equivalent.

**Бэв** *abbr.* (**биллион электрон-вольт**) billion electron volts, Bev; **б.э.в.** *abbr.* (**безазотистые экстрактивные вещества**) nitrogen-free extracts.

**бэйевое масло** *see* **байевое масло.**

**Бэйли печь** Baily furnace (electric-resistance type).

**Бэлля способ** *see* **Белля способ.**

**бэр** *abbr.* (**биологический эквивалент рентгена**) roentgen equivalent, man; rem.

**БЭТ** *abbr.* Brunauer, Emmett, and Teller, BET.

**бювар** *m.* blotting pad.

**бювет** *m.* pump room.

**бюджет** *m.*, **—ный** *a.* budget; **предусматривать в —е** *v.* budget (for), estimate.

**бюкс** *m.*, **—a** *f.* weighing bottle.

**бюллетень** *m.* bulletin; weather chart.

**бюретка** *f.* buret.

**бюро** *n.* bureau, office, department; desk.

**Бюхнера воронка** Büchner funnel.

**бязь** *f.* (text.) coarse calico; sheeting.

# В

**в** *prep. acc. to indicate direction; prepos. to indicate location;* in, into; on; at, per; *prefix* in, into; **в стакан** into the beaker; **в стакане** in the beaker; **в час** per hour, hourly.

**в.** *abbr.* (**век**) century; (**вольт**) volt; **В.** *abbr.* (**восток**) East; code for tungsten in steel mark.

**ва** *abbr.* (**вольтампер**) volt-ampere.

**вавеллит** *m.* (min.) wavellite.

**вага** *f.* crowbar, bar, lever; weighing machine; swingletree.

**вагильный** *a.* migratory, wandering, free-ranging.

**вагнер/ит** *m.* (min.) wagnerite; **—овский реактив** Wagner's reagent (for alkaloids).

**вагон** *m.* (railroad) car, coach; truck, wagon; **в.-весы** scale car; **в.-деррик** derrick car, wrecking car; **в.-кран** traveling crane; **в.-лаборатория** testing car; **в.-ледник, в.-холодильник** refrigerator car; **в.-мастерская** repair car; **в.-платформа** flatcar, gondola car; **в.-цистерна** tank car.

**вагонетка** *f.* trolley, truck, lorry, car, wagon; **в.-транспортер** transfer car.

**вагонн/ый** *a.* car; **в. зеленый, —ая зелень** a chrome green; **в. парк** rolling stock.

**вагоно/вожатый** *m.* motorman, engi-neer; **—опрокидыватель** *m.* car dumper; **—ремонтная мастерская** car repair shop; **—строение** *n.*, **—строительный** *a.* car building.

**вагран/ка** *f.*, **—очный** *a.* (met.) cupola, cupola furnace.

**ВАГТ** *abbr.* (**Всесоюзный аэрогеологический трест**) All-Union Aerogeological Trust.

**вад** *m.* (min.) wad, bog manganese.

**вади** *n.* wadi, dry wash, dry stream bed.

**вадоз/ная вода** vadose (mineral) water; **—овая зона** (geol.) vadose zone.

**важенка** *f.* female reindeer, doe.

**важн/ейший** *a.* major, paramount; **—о** *adv.* importantly, significantly; it is important; **—ость** *f.* importance, significance, concern; **функция —ости** (nucl.) importance function; **—ый** *a.* important, significant.

**ваза** *f.* vase, bowl.

**вазелин** *m.*, **—овый** *a.* Vaseline, petrolatum; **—овое масло** liquid petrolatum, mineral oil.

**вазицин** *m.* vasicine.

**вазо—** *prefix* vaso—; **—моторный** *a.* (anat.) vasomotor; **—прессин** *m.* vasopressin.

**ВАИ** *abbr.* (**Всесоюзная ассоциация инженеров**) All-Union Association of Engineers.

**вайд/а** *f.*, **красильная в.**, **—овый** *a.* (bot.) woad (*Isatis tinctoria*).

**вайербарс** wire bars.

**вайя** *f.* (bot.) frond.

**вакан/сия** *f.* vacancy, vacant site, empty place; **—тный** *a.* vacant, empty.

**вакка** *f.* (petr.) wacke (a residual deposit); **серая в.** graywacke (a variety of sandstone).

**Ваккенродера жидкость** Wackenroder solution (containing trithiodisulfonic acid).

**вакковый** *a.* (petr.) wacke.

**вакса** *f.* shoe polish, blacking.

**вакуметр** *see* **вакууммметр.**

**вакуоля** *f.* (biol.) vacuole.

**вакуум** *m.*, **—ный** *a.* vacuum; **испарение в —е** vacuum evaporation; **перегонка под —ом** vacuum distillation, reduced-pressure distillation; **в.-бак** *m.* vacuum tank; **в.-котел** vacuum pan; **в.-насос** vacuum pump; suction pump; **в.-сушило**, **в.-эксикатор** vacuum drier, vacuum desiccator; **в.-фильтр** vacuum filter, suction filter; **—ирование** *n.* evacuation; vacuum evaporation; **—ировать** *v.* evauacte; **—метр** *m.* vacuum gage, vacuometer; **—ноплотный, —плотный** *a.* vacuumtight, airtight.

**вакценовая кислота** vaccenic acid.

**вакцин/а** *f.* (med.) vaccine; **—ация** *f.*, **—ационный** *a.* vaccination; **—ейрин** *m.* vaccineurine; **—ировать** *v.* vaccinate.

**вал** *m.* roller, roll; shaft, axle; drum; bank, embankment; (geol.) swell, arch; bulwark; **мощность на —у** shaft horsepower; **окружать —ом** *v.* bank.

**валаит** *m.* (min.) valaite.

**валамин** *m.* valamin, amylene-hydrate isovalerate.

**валежн/ик** *m.*, **—ый** *a.* windfall, brushwood, deadwood.

**валек** *m.* battledore, beetle, paddle; curl; singletree; *see also* **валок.**

**валенный** *a.* thrown down; felled (trees).

**валент/ийский век** (geol.) Valentian stage; **—инит** *m.* (min.) valentinite.

**валентн/ость** *f.*, **—ый** *a.* valence.

**валенцианит** *m.* (min.) valencianite (a variety of andularia orthoclase).

**валеный** *see* **валяный.**

**валер/альдегид** *m.* valeraldehyde, pentanal; **—амид** *m.* valeramide, pentanamide; **—анилид** *m.* valeranilide; **—ен** *m.* valerene, amylene.

**валериан** *m.*, **—а** *f.* (bot.) valerian (*Valeriana officinalis*); **—ат** *m.* valerate, valerianate; **—ница** *f.* corn salad (*Valerianella*).

**валерианово/амиловый эфир** amyl valerate; **—висмутовая соль** bismuth valerate; **основная —висмутовая соль** bismuth subvalerate; **—железная соль** ferric valerate; **—калиевая соль, —кислый калий** potassium valerate; **—кислый** *a.* valeric acid; valerate (of); **—кислая соль** valerate; **—ментиловый эфир** menthyl valerate; **—этиловый эфир** ethyl valerate.

**валерианов/ые** *pl.* (bot.) Valerianaceae; **—ый** *a.* valerian, valeric; **—ый альдегид** *see* **валеральдегид; —ый ангидрид** valeric anhydride, pentanoic anhydride; **—ый корень** valerian root; **—ая кислота** valeric acid, valerianic acid, pentanoic acid; **соль —ой кислоты** valerate; **—ое масло** valerian oil.

**валер/ил** *m.* valeryl, pentanoyl; **хлористый в.** valeryl chloride; **—илен** *m.* valerylene, 2-pentyne; **—ин** *m.* valerin; **—ол** *m.* valerol; **—олактон** *m.* valerolactone; **—он** *m.* valerone, diisobutyl ketone; **—онитрил** *m.* valeronitrile, butyl cyanide.

**валерьян/а** *see* **валериана; —овый** *see* **валериановый.**

**валец** *m.* roller, cylinder.

**валивать** *see* **валить.**

**вали/дол** *m.* validol, menthol valerate; **—зан** *m.* valisan, bornyl bromovalerate.

**валик** *m.* roller, cylinder, drum; spindle, shaft; inker, inking roller; bead, molding; fillet, ridge.

**вал/ил** *m.* valyl, diethyl valeramide; **—илен** *m.* valylene; **—ин** *m.* valine; **—инол** *m.* valinol.

**валиснерия** *see* **валлиснерия.**

**валить** *v.* throw down, overturn, upset;

fell (trees); heap up; come in thick clouds (smoke); fall in great flakes (snow); **в. в кучу** heap, heap up; **—ся** *v.* fall, tumble down, collapse.

**величная кожа** roller leather.

**валка** *f.* felling, cutting down (of trees).

**валкий** *a.* shaky, unsteady, rickety.

**валковать** *v.* (agr.) windrow.

**валковый** *a.* roller.

**Валлаха перегруппировка** Wallach rearrangement.

**валлийский** *a.* Welsh; **Валлис** Wales.

**валлиснерия** *f.* tape grass (*Vallisneria*).

**Валлона процесс, валлонский процесс** (met.) Wallon process (for iron).

**валов/ой** *a.* gross, total; wholesale; empirical (formula); bulk (analysis, etc.); **в. выход** gross yield, gross returns; total yield, overall yield; **в. доход** gross returns, gross receipts.

**валок** *m.* roller, roll, cylinder; (agr.) swath, windrow.

**валонея** *f.* (tanning) valonia.

**валпургин** *see* **вальпургит.**

**валтерит** *m.* (min.) waltherite.

**валуевит** *m.* (min.) waluewite, valuevite.

**валу/ек, —й** *m.* (bot.) a mushroom (*Agaricus emeticus*).

**валун** *m.* boulder; rubble; **—ы** *pl.* (geol.) detritus, rock waste; float; **—ный** *a.* boulder; rubbly; **—ная глина** (geol.) boulder clay; glacier till; **—чатая руда** (min.) nodular ore.

**валховит** *m.* (min.) walchowite, retinite (a resinous hydrocarbon).

**вальволиновое масло** valvolin oil (a lubricant).

**вальденовское обращение** Walden inversion.

**вальдшнеп** *m.* (zool.) woodcock.

**вальм/а** *f.* (building) hip; **—овая крыша** hipped roof.

**вальпургит** *m.* walpurgite (uranium mineral).

**вальц** *m.* roll, roller; **—евание** *see* **вальцовка;** **—евать** *see* **вальцовать;** **—езагибочный станок** bending roller.

**вальцетокарн/ый станок** roll-turning lathe; **—я** *f.* roll shop.

**вальцов/анный** *a.* rolled, milled, pressed; **—ать** *v.* roll, mill; **—ка** *f.* rolling, milling; rotary process; **—щик** *m.*

rolling-press operator; **—ый** *a.* roller, rolling.

**вальцы** *pl. of* **вальц.**

**вальян** *m.* (text.) doffer.

**валют/а** *f.,* **—ный** *a.* currency; **—ный курс** rate of exchange; **—ное совещание** Foreign Currency Control Board.

**валюшка** *f.* (cer.) wad, clot, bat, mass.

**валяльн/ый** *a.* (text.) fulling, milling; **—ая глина,** **—ая глинка** fuller's earth (a type of clay); **—ая машина** fulling machine, milling machine; **—ая фабрика,** **—я** *f.* fulling mill; **—ое мыло** fuller's soap.

**вал/яльщик** *m.* fuller; **—яние** *n.* rolling; kneading; felting, matting; (text.) fulling, milling; **—яный** *a.* rolled; kneaded; fulled, milled; **—ять** *v.* roll; knead; full; felt (wool); **—яться** *v.* roll about, lie about.

**вам** *dat. of* **вы,** to you, for you; **—и** *instr.* by you, with you.

**ВАМИ** *abbr.* (Всесоюзный алюминиево-магниевый институт) All-Union Aluminum and Magnesium Institute.

**ВАН** *abbr.* (Вестник Академии Наук) Bulletin of the Academy of Sciences.

**ванад** *see* **ванадий; —ат** *m.* vanadate; **—атометрия** *f.* vanadatometry (quantitative analysis using a vanadium reagent).

**ванадиево/аммониевая соль** ammonium vanadate; **—кислый** *a.* vanadic acid; vanadate (of); **—кислый натрий,** **—натриевая соль** sodium vanadate; **—кислая соль** vanadate; **кислая —кислая соль** divanadate.

**ванадиев/ый** *a.* vanadium, vanadic; **в. ангидрид** vanadic anhydride, vanadium pentoxide; **—ая кислота** vanadic acid; **соль —ой кислоты** vanadate; **—ая соль** vanadic salt.

**ванад/ий** *m.* vanadium, V; **одноокись —ия** vanadium monoxide, vanadous oxide; **пятиокись —ия** vanadium pentoxide, vanadic anhydride; **трехокись —ия** vanadium trioxide, vanadic oxide; **хлористый в.** vanadous chloride, vanadium dichloride; **хлорный в.** vanadic chloride, vanadium trichloride.

**ванад/ил** *m.* vanadyl; **сернокислый в.**

**ванадил** vanadyl sulfate, vanadium sulfate; —**инит** m. (min.) vanadinite.

**ванадист/ый** a. vanadium, vanadous; —**ая кислота** vanadous acid; **соль** —**ой кислоты** vanadite; —**ая соль** vanadous salt; —**ая сталь** vanadium steel.

**ванадовый** see **ванадиевый.**

**вангресс** m. (met.) front hearth of shaft furnace.

**Ванда формула** Vand's equation (for viscosity of suspensions).

**Ван-де-Граафа генератор** Van de Graaf generator (electrostatic accelerator).

**Ван-Дейка коричневый** van Dyck brown (pigment).

**ванденбрандеит** m. (min.) vandenbrandeite, urano-lepidite.

**ван-дер-ваальсовские силы** van der Waals forces.

**вандрут** m. (min.) supporting beam.

**ванер** see **ваннер.**

**ванилин** m. vanillin; —**овый** a. vanillin, vanillic; —**овый спирт** vanillic alcohol; —**овая кислота** vanillic acid.

**ванил/лил** m. vanillyl; —**лин** see **ванилин;** —**лон** m. vanillone; —**ь** f. (bot.) vanilla (*Vanilla planifolia*); —**ьный** a. vanillic, vanilla.

**ванн/а** f. bath; (dyeing) dip, steep; tub, tank, vat; —**ая** f. bathroom.

**ваннер** m. (min.) vanner, slime washer, concentrator; —**ная отсадочная машина** vanning jig.

**Ваннера пирометр** Wanner's pyrometer.

**ванн/очка** f. little bath; (phot.) developing dish; —**ый** a. bath.

**ваноксит** m. (min.) vanoxite.

**Ван-Слайка метод** Van Slyke method (of protein hydrolysis).

**ванта** f. guy, guy rope; **накладывание вант** guying.

**Вант-Гоффа закон** van't Hoff's law.

**вантгоффит** m. (min.) vanthoffite.

**вантовый** a. guy, guying, guy rope.

**вантуз** m. air escape valve; air hole, vent.

**вапа** f. (text.) resist; (wall) paint.

**ваплерит** m. (min.) wapplerite (near pharmacolite).

**вапор** m. a lubricating oil for steam-engine cylinders; —**изация** f. vaporization; —**иметр** m. vaporimeter.

**вапплерит** see **ваплерит.**

**вар** m. pitch, pine tar; cobbler's wax; (elec.) var (volt-ampere-reactive); var (visual-aural range); **белый в., бургундский в.** Burgundy pitch.

**варан** m. monitor (a lizard).

**Варбурга закон** Warburg's law.

**варвикит** m. (min.) warwickite.

**варвицит** m. (min.) varvicite (manganese ore).

**варганить** v. bungle, botch, spoil, make a mess (of).

**вардит** m. (min.) wardite.

**вардовать** v. (met.) assay.

**варево** n. pottage, soup, concoction.

**варен/ие** see **варка;** —**ый** a. boiled, cooked, digested; scoured (silk); —**ье** n. jam, preserves.

**вариант** m. variant, variation, different reading, modification, alternative, alternate; —**ность** f. variance; —**ный** a. variant, varying, alternate, alternative.

**вари/ат** m. variate; —**атор** m. (elec.) variable-ratio transformer; (thermionics) buncher; —**ационный** a., —**ация** f., —**ирование** n. variation; —**ировать** see **варьировать.**

**варикозный** a. (med., bot.) varicose.

**вариокуплер** m. (rad.) variocoupler.

**вариол/ит** m. (petr.) variolite, pearl diabase (spherulitic basalt glass); —**итовый,** —**ический** a. variolitic; —**ы** pl. (petr.) varioles, spherulites, variolites.

**вариометр** m. (elec.) variometer; (aero.) vertical speed indicator, climb indicator.

**варистор** m. (elec.) varistor.

**варисцит** m. (min.) variscite.

**вар/ить** v. boil, cook, steam, digest; brew (beer); scour (silk); found (glass); —**иться** v. boil, digest, cook, be boiled; —**ка** f. boiling, cooking, digestion; brewing; scouring.

**Варнитсо** abbr. (**Всесоюзная ассоциация работников науки и техники для содействия социалистическому строительству СССР**) All-Union Association of Scientific and Technical Workers for active participation in Socialist Construction in the USSR.

**варн/ица,** —**я** f., —**ичный** a. boilery;

brewery; salt pan; —ый *see* варочный.

**варовик** *m.* hand leather.

**варовина** *f.* waxed thread.

**варочн/ый** *a.* boiling, cooking, digestion; в. котел digester; —ая камера, —ое отделение boiling room; brewing house, brew house.

**варрант** *m.,* —ный *a.* (com.) custom house license; dock warrant.

**вартит** *m.* (min.) warthite, bloedite.

**Варшава** Warsaw.

**варьиров/ание** *n.* variation; (thermionics) bunching; —ать *v.* vary, change, diversify, modify.

**варя** *see* варка.

**вас** *acc. of* вы, you; about you, for you.

**васил/ек** *m.* (bot.) cornflower (*Centaurea*); —исник *m.* meadow rue (*Thalictrum*); рогатые —ьки delphinium; —ьковый *a.* cornflower, cornflower blue.

**вассерглас** *m.* water glass, specif. sodium silicate solution; калиевый в. potassium silicate.

**васхегиит** *m.* (min.) vashegyite.

**ВАСХНИЛ** *abbr.* (Всесоюзная академия сельскохозяйственных наук имени В. И. Ленина) Lenin All-Union Academy of Agricultural Sciences.

**ват/а** *f.* cotton, cotton wool, wadding; (glass) wool; на —е wadded, padded.

**ватер** *m.* (text.) ringspinning frame.

**ватержакет** *m.,* —ный *a.* water jacket; —ная печь water-jacketed furnace; —ное охлаждение jacket cooling.

**ватериевое масло** Malabar tallow (from *Vateria indica*).

**ватерклозет** *m.,* —ный *a.* toilet.

**ватерлиния** *f.* water line, water mark.

**ватерпас** *m.* level (the instrument); —ный *a.* level, horizontal.

**ватерпруф** *m.* raincoat.

**ватман** *m.* high-quality drawing paper.

**ватный** *a.* cotton, wadded, quilted.

**ВАТО** *abbr.* (Всесоюзное автомобильно-тракторное объединение) All-Union Automobile and Tractor Association.

**ваточник** *m.* (bot.) milkweed (*Asclepias*).

**ватт** *m.,* —ный *a.* (elec.) watt; tidal marsh; число в. number of watts, wattage; в.-секунда watt-second; в.-час watt-hour; мощность в в.-часах,

отдача в в.-часах watt-hour efficiency; —метр *m.,* —метровый *a.* (elec.) wattmeter; —ность *f.* wattage.

**вау** *m.* (bot.) dyer's weed, weld (*Reseda luteola*); желтый в. luteolin (dye).

**вафля** *f.* waffle, wafer.

**вахня** *f.* (zool.) wachna cod.

**вахта** *f.* watch, duty; в., в.-трава (bot.) buckbean (*Menyanthes trifoliata*).

**вахтенный** *a.* lookout; в. журнал logbook.

**вахтер** *m.* watchman; janitor.

**ваш** *gen. of* вы, your.

**вашгерд** *m.* (min.) buddle, ore concentrator.

**вашеты** *pl.* (leather) split hides.

**Вашингтон** Washington.

**ваял/о** *n.* chisel, graver; —ьный *a.* chisel, sculpture;—ьная глина modeling clay.

**вая/ние** *n.,* —тельное искусство sculpture; —тель *m.* sculptor; —ть *v.* chisel, sculpture.

**вб** *abbr.* (вебер) weber.

**вбегать, вбежать** *v.* run in, run into, rush into; flow into.

**вбив/ание** *n.,* —ка *f.* driving in; packing in; —ать *v.* drive in, drive, hammer; wedge, pack in, ram.

**вбир/ание** *n.* absorption, soaking up; —ать *v.* absorb, soak up, take up, take in.

**вбит/ый** *a.* driven in; packed in; —ь *see* вбивать.

**ВБЛ** *abbr.* (ветеринарно-бактериологическая лаборатория) veterinary and bacteriological laboratory.

**вблизи** *adv.* near, nearby, in the neighborhood (of), in the vicinity, at hand.

**ВБО** *abbr.* (Всесоюзное ботаническое общество) All-Union Botanical Society.

**вбок** *adv.* to the side, laterally.

**вбр/асывать, —осить** *v.* throw in; —ошенный *a.* thrown in; included.

**вбрыз/гивание** *n.* injection; —гивать, —нуть *v.* inject; spray in; —нутый *a.* injected.

**вв** *abbr.* (взрывчатые вещества) explosives; **вв.** *abbr.* (века) ages.

**ввал/ивать, —ить** *v.* heap into; —иваться, —иться *v.* tumble in; fall in.

**ввальцовывать** *v.* roll in.

**введение** *n.* leading in; introduction; preface (of book).

**ввезти** *see* **ввозить.**

**вверг/ать, —нуть** *v.* plunge, throw in, precipitate; **—аться** *v.* fall into.

**ввер/енный** *a.* entrusted (to); **—ить** *see* **вверять.**

**ввер/нуть, —тывать** *v.* screw in, twist in, turn in; **—тка** *f.*, **—тывание** *n.* screwing in; **—тный** *a.* screw-in, screw; **—тная пробка, —тыш** *m.* screw stopper.

**вверх** *adv.* up, upward, upwards; **в. дном** upside down, bottomside up; **движение в., перемещение в., подъём в., ход в.** lifting movement, upward motion, ascent; upstroke (of piston); **тяга в.** upward pull, lift; updraft; **—у** *adv.* above, overhead, at the top (of).

**вверчивать** *see* **ввертывать.**

**вверять** *v.* entrust, trust; commit.

**ввести** *see* **вводить.**

**ввиду** *prep. gen.* in view of.

**ввин/тить, —чивать** *v.* screw in; **—ченный** *a.* screwed in; **—чивание** *n.* screwing in.

**в-во** *abbr.* (**вещество**) substance.

**ввод** *m.* leading in, induction, admission, introduction; inlet; (elec.) lead, lead-in; (computer) input; **—имый** *a.* input; introducible; **—ить** *v.* lead in, introduce, feed (into), inject; insert, drive in; (math.) interpolate.

**вводн/ый** *a.* introductory; incoming, inlet, leading in; (computer) input; parenthetical; quoted, cited; **в. изолятор** (elec.) inlet bell; **в. провод** lead-in, leading-in wire; **в. элемент** input component; **—ое отверстие** inlet; **—ое предложение** parenthesis; parenthetic clause.

**вводящ/ий** *a.* leading-in; **—ая труба** inlet pipe, feed line.

**ввоз** *m.*, **—ка** *f.* import, importation; carrying in; **—ить** *v.* import, bring in; **—ный** *a.* imported; import (duty); **—ные товары** imports, imported commodities.

**ввол/акивать, —очить** *v.* drag in.

**вволю** *adv.* as much as desired, in any amount, to any degree.

**ввосьмеро** *adv.* eight times; **в. больше** eight times as much; **в. меньше** one eighth; **—м** *adv.* eight (together).

**ВВР** *abbr.* (**водо-водяной реактор**) water-moderated water-cooled reactor.

**ВВС** *abbr.* (**Военно-воздушные силы**) Air Force.

**ввяз/анный** *a.* tied in, involved, implicated; **—ать, —ывать** *v.* tie in, involve, implicate; knit in; **—аться, —ываться** *v.* interfere, meddle; **—ывание** *n.* tying in, implication.

**ВГБО** *abbr.* (**Всесоюзное гидробиологическое общество**) All-Union Hydrobiological Society.

**вгиб** *m.* an inward bend; **—ание** *n.* bending inward; **—ать** *v.* bend in, curve inward.

**вгладь** *adv.* flush, even; **сварить в.** *v.* flush weld; **сварка в.** flush welding.

**вглубь** *adv.* in the depth (of), deep (into), deeply; **в. страны** inland.

**вгляд/еться, —ываться** *v.* observe closely, examine, peer (at).

**вгнездиться** *v.* take root in.

**вгон** *m.*, **—ка** *f.* driving in; **—ять** *v.* drive, drive in, force in.

**вгорячую** *adv.* hot; **ковать в.** *v.* (met.) forge hot; **тянутый в.** (met.) hot-drawn.

**вгребать, вгрести** *v.* rake in.

**вгружать, вгрузить** *v.* load, freight.

**вгрызаться** *v.* bite into, catch.

**ВГУ** *abbr.* (**Воронежский государственный университет**) Voronezh State University.

**вдаваться** *v.* devote oneself (to).

**вдавить** *see* **вдавливать.**

**вдавл/ение, —ивание** *n.* pressing in, caving in; impression, depression; **—енный** *a.* pressed in; depressed, sunken; **—ивать** *v.* press in, crush in, bend in; force, force in; imbed; impress, imprint.

**вдалбливать** *v.* knock in, work in.

**вдал/еке, —и** *adv.* in the distance, far off, far; **—ь** *adv.* into the distance.

**вдаться** *see* **вдаваться.**

**вдви/гание** *n.* moving in, pushing in; **—гать, —нуть** *v.* move in, push in, shift in, squeeze in; **—гаться, —нуться** *v.* move in, go in, enter; **—жной** *a.* movable, sliding; **—нутый** *a.* moved in, pushed in.

вдво/е *adv.* double, twice; di—; **в. больше** twice as much; **в. меньше** half, half as much, half as big; **складывать в.** fold in two, double; **—ем** *adv.* together, two (together); **—йне** *adv.* twice, twofold, doubly.

вдевать *v.* put in; thread (a needle).

вдевятеро *adv.* ninefold, nine times; **в. больше** nine times as much; **в. меньше** one ninth; **—м** *adv.* nine (together).

вдел/анный *a.* fitted in, set in, built-in, embedded; inlaid; **—ать, —ывать** *v.* fit in, set in, incase, embed; inlay (with); **—ка** *f.*, **—ывание** *n.* fitting in, setting in, incasing, embedding.

вдер/гать, **—гивать, —нуть** *v.* pull in, draw in, retract.

вдесятеро *adv.* ten times, tenfold; **в. больше** ten times as much; **в. меньше** one tenth; **—м** *adv.* ten (together).

вдет/ый *a.* put in, drawn in; **—ь** *see* вдевать.

вдобавок *adv.* besides, in addition.

вдов/а *f.* widow; **—ец** *m.* widower.

вдоволь *adv.* enough, plenty, sufficiently.

вдогонку *adv.* in pursuit (of).

вдоль *adv.* lengthwise, longitudinally; *prep. gen.* along, by; **в. по** along; разрезывание в. longitudinal cutting.

вдохнов/ение *n.* inspiration; **—енный** *a.* inspired; **—ить, —лять** *v.* inspire; **—ляться** *v.* take inspiration (from).

вдохнуть *see* вдыхать.

вдребезги *adv.* to pieces, to fragments.

вдруг *adv.* suddenly, all at once.

вдув/аемый *a.* blown in; **в. воздух** air blast; **—ание** *n.* injection, blast; **—атель** *m.* insufflator; blower; **—ать** *v.* blow in, inject, force in.

вдум/аться, **—ываться** *v.* consider carefully, go into the matter; действовать **—чиво** *v.* exercise judgment; **—чивый** *a.* thoughtful, considerate.

вдут/ый *a.* blown in, injected; **—ь** *see* вдувать.

вдых/ание *n.* inhalation; **—ательный** *a.* respiratory; **—ать** *v.* inhale.

вебер *m.* (elec.) weber (unit).

Вебера закон Weber's law.

вебнерит *m.* (min.) webnerite, andorite.

вебстерит *m.* (min.) websterite, aluminite.

вевелит *m.* (min.) whewellite (calcium oxalate).

вегазит *m.* (min.) vegasite.

вегет/арианец *m.*, **—арианский** *a.* vegetarian; **—ативный** *a.* vegetative; **—ационный** *a.* vegetation, vegetative; growing (season); greenhouse (culture); **—ация** *f.* vegetation.

**—вед** *m. suffix* scientist.

вед/ать *v.* know; manage, control, supervise; **—ение** *n.* knowledge; management, supervision; leading, guiding, conducting; working, practice; disposal; *suffix* science; **—ение дела** business transaction; **—ение счетов** bookkeeping; **—енный** *a.* led, conducted.

ведерный *a.* pail, bucket; vedro (unit of measure).

ведет *pr. 3 sing. of* вести.

Веджа печь Wedge furnace.

ведом/о: без его **—а** without his knowledge; **—ость** *f.* journal, report; register, list, record; payroll; **—ость расхода** charge sheet, expense sheet; **—ости** *pl.* newspapers.

ведомств/енный *a.* departmental; **—о** *n.* department, office, service.

ведомый *a.* known (to); dependent (on); guided, controlled; driven; **в. вал** driven shaft; **в. механизм** follower; **в. шкив** driven pulley, follower.

ведро *n.* pail, bucket; vedro (unit of measure, 12.299 liters).

ведут *pr. 3 pl. of* вести.

ведущ/ий *a.* leading, leader, guiding; driving; pilot, steering; master, control; advanced; **в. вал** drive shaft; **в. механизм** driving gear; **в. подшипник** guide bearing; **в. ролик, в. шкив** guide pulley, guide roller, guide; drive pulley, drive; **в. ток** *a.* (elec.) current-carrying, live; **—ое колесо** driving wheel, driver; guide pulley.

ведший *past act. part. of* вести.

ведь *conj.* well then, (well) but, why.

ведьма *f.* (geom.) witch.

ведя *pr. gerund of* вести.

веелерит *m.* wheelerite (a fossil resin).

веер *m.*, **—ный** *a.* fan; (mil.) sheaf; **—ная пальма, —ник** *m.* (bot.) fan palm (*Corypha*); **—о—** *prefix* fan, rhipido—; **—окрылые** *pl.* twisted-wing parasites

(*Strepsiptera*); —оносцы *pl.* wedge-shaped beetles (*Rhipiphoridae*); —о-образный *a.* fan-shaped, fan-type, radiating; (biol.) flabelliform, flabellate.

вежеталь *m.* toilet water.

вежливый *a.* courteous, polite.

вез *past sing. of* везти.

везде *adv.* everywhere; в., где угодно anywhere; —сущий, —сущный *a.* omnipresent, ubiquitous.

везен/ие *n.* transportation; —ный *a.* conveyed, carried, transported.

везерометр *m.* weatherometer (for testing coatings).

везикул/а *f.* vesicle; —ит *m.* (med.) vesiculitis; —ярный *a.* vesicular, vesicle.

везти *see* возить.

везувиан *m.* (min.) vesuvian, idocrase.

Везувий Mount Vesuvius.

везувин *m.*, —ный *a.* vesuvin, triamino-azobenzene.

везущий *a.* carrying, conveying; driving.

веибуллит *m.* (min.) weibullite.

вейгелия *f.* (bot.) weigela.

Вейля реакция Weyl's test (for creatinine in urine).

Веймара сплав Weimar alloy (copper-manganese-aluminum alloy).

вейник *m.* reed grass (*Calamagrostis*).

вейсит *m.* (min.) weissite.

век *m.* century; age; lifetime; (geol.) epoch, stage; средние —а the Middle Ages; освященный —ами time-honored, aged; отжить свой век to have outlived its usefulness, to be outmoded.

веко *n.* eyelid.

веков/ечный *a.* everlasting, eternal; —ой *a.* secular, ancient.

вексел/едатель *m.* (com.) drawer (of bill); —едержатель *m.* holder (of bill), payee; —енадписатель *m.* indorser; —ь *m.*, —ьный *a.* bill (of exchange), draft, promissory note; —ьный курс rate of exchange.

вектолит *m.* Vectolite (mixture of iron and cobalt oxides).

вектор *m.* (math.) vector; в.-потенциал (rad.) vector potential; —иальный, —ный *a.* vector, vectorial.

вел *past sing. of* вести.

велдона процесс *see* Вельдона способ.

велен/евый *a.* —ь *f.* vellum (paper).

веление *n.* order, command; instructions.

велер *m.* selector.

велерит *m.* (min.) wöhlerite.

велеть *v.* order, bid, tell, instruct.

вели *past pl. of* вести.

велик/ан *m.* giant; —ий *a.* great, big.

Великобритания Great Britain.

великовозрастный *a.* overgrown.

великодуш/ие *n.* generosity, magnanimity; —ный *a.* generous.

великолепный *a.* magnificent, splendid, superb, excellent.

велич/айший *a.* greatest, extreme; —ать *v.* glorify, extol, praise; —ество *n.* majesty; —ие *n.* grandeur, greatness.

величин/а *f.* size, dimension, measure; (math.) value, magnitude, quantity, amount; volume, bulk; degree, extent (of error), scope; intensity (of force, etc.); bigness, greatness; в натуральную —у full size; на значительную —у to a considerable extent; определять —у *v.* measure.

веллсит *m.* (min.) wellsite (a barium-bearing phillipsite).

вело/камера *f.* bicycle (inner) tube; —сипед *m.*, —сипедный *a.* bicycle; —сипедный кран walking crane.

велосит *m.* velosite (a lubricating oil).

велось *past sing. of* вестись.

велошина *f.* bicycle tire.

вельбот *m.* whaleboat.

вельвет *m.*, —ин *m.*, —овый *a.* velveteen.

вельвичия *f.* (bot.) welwitschia.

вельд *m.* (geol.) Wealden stage.

Вельдона способ Weldon process (in manufacturing chlorine).

вельзикол *see* хлордан.

вельц-печь *f.* rotary kiln.

Вельша способ (met.) Welsh process.

велюр *m.* (text.) velour; a suede leather.

Вена Vienna.

вена *f.* vein; воспаление вен (med.) phlebitis; расширение вен varicose veins.

венг. *abbr.* (венгерский) Hungarian.

венгерка *f.* a variety of plum.

венгерский *a.* Hungarian.

Венгрия Hungary.

венепункция *f.* (med.) venipuncture.

Венера *f.* (astron.) Venus.

венерин башмачок (bot.) lady's slipper

(*Cypripedium*); **в. волос, в. волосок** (bot.) maidenhair (*Adiantum capillus-veneris*); **—ы волосы** (min.) Venus hairstone, sagenitic quartz.

**венерический** *a.* (med.) venereal.

**венесекция** *f.* (med.) venesection.

**венец** *m.* crown, aureole, corona, rim; (anat.) radiation.

**венец/ейский, —ианский** *a.* Venetian; **в. красный** Venetian red, ferric oxide; **—ианская ярь** verdigris; **—ианские белила** Venetian white (white lead and barite).

**Венеция** Venice.

**Венецуэла** Venezuela.

**венечный** *a.* crown; (anat.) coronary; (bot.) coronate; **в. шов** (med.) coronal suture.

**вензель** *m.* monogram, initials.

**веник** *m.* broom, sweeper.

**венированный** *a.* veneer.

**венис/а** *f.*, **—овый** *a.* (min.) garnet; *see also* **гранат, гранатовый.**

**венит** *m.* (petr.) venite, veined gneiss.

**веницейский** *see* **венецейский.**

**венич/ек** *m.* whisk broom, brush; (bot.) panicle; **—ный** *a.* broom; (bot.) paniculate.

**венозный** *a.* venous, vein.

**венок** *m.* wreath, garland.

**венск/ий** *a.* Viennese, Vienna; **в. зеленый** Vienna green; **—ая едкая паста** Vienna paste, Vienna caustic (potassium hydroxide with lime); **—ая известь** French chalk; **—ое питье** (pharm.) senna tea.

**вентерь** *m.* fish trap.

**вентилир/ование** *see* **вентиляция; —о-ванный, —уемый** *a.* ventilated; **—о-вать** *v.* ventilate, air.

**вентиль** *m.*, **—ный** *a.* valve.

**вентиля/тор** *m.*, **—торный** *a.* ventilator, fan, blower; **вытяжной в.** aspirator, aspirating pump; exhaust fan; **—ци-онный** *a.* ventilation, ventilating; vent (hole); **—ция** *f.* ventilation, airing, aeration.

**вентральный** *a.* ventral, abdominal.

**Вентури трубка** Venturi tube.

**венч/ать** *v.* crown, top; marry; **—ающий** *a.* crowning; **—ающая часть** crown, top.

**венчик** *m.* rim; (bot.) corolla, crown.

**ВЕП** *abbr.* (высота единицы передачи) height of a transfer unit, H.T.U.

**вер/а** *f.* faith, belief, trust, credit; **при-нять на —у** *v.* take on trust.

**вератр/ат** *m.* veratrate; **—идин** *m.* verat-ridine; **—ил** *m.* veratryl; veratril; **хлористый —ил** veratryl chloride; **—иловый** *a.* veratryl.

**вератрин** *m.*, **—овый** *a.* veratrine; **—овая кислота, вератровая кислота** veratric acid, dimethoxybenzoic acid; **соль —овой кислоты** veratrate; **—овокислый** *a.* veratric acid; vera-trate (of); **—овокислая соль** vera-trate.

**вератро/идин** *m.* veratroidine; **—ил** *m.* veratroyl; **—л** *m.* veratrole, dimeth-oxybenzene; **—н** *m.* veratrone.

**верба** *f.* (bot.) willow (*Salix*).

**вербальный** *a.* verbal.

**вербан/ол** *m.* verbanol; **—он** *m.* verba-none.

**вербейник** *m.* (bot.) loosestrife (*Lysi-machia*).

**вербен/а** *f.*, **—овый** *a.* (bot.) verbena; **—алин, —алозид** *m.* verbenalin, ver-benaloside; **—ен** *m.* verbenene; **—овое масло** verbena oil; **ост-индское —овое масло** lemongrass oil; **—ол** *m.* verbenol; **—он** *m.* verbenone.

**верблю/д** *m.*, **—жий** *a.* camel; **одногор-бый в.** dromedary; **—дка** *f.* (bot.) a grass (*Corispermum*); **—дки** *pl.* (zool.) Rhaphidioptera; **—жья колючка** al-hagi (*Alhagi camelorum*).

**вербовать** *v.* recruit, enlist.

**верболоз** *m.* (bot.) bay willow (*Salix pentandra*).

**верва** *f.* cobbler's thread.

**вер-гинье** *n.* Guignet's green.

**вердикт** *m.* verdict.

**Вердэ постоянная** Verdet's constant.

**верев/ка** *f.*, **—очный** *a.* cord, rope, string; line, tackle; **—ки** *pl.* cordage.

**вереница** *f.* row, file, line; **в. импульсов** (phys.) pulse train.

**верес** *see* **можжевельник.**

**вереск** *m.*, **—овый** *a.* (bot.) heather (*Calluna* or *Erica*); **—овые** *pl.* Eri-caceae.

**веретеница** *f.* (zool.) slow worm.

**веретен/ный** *a.* spindle; **—о** *n.* spindle;

pivot, axle, arbor; broach; —ообразный *a.* spindle-shaped; (biol.) fusi-
form; taper, tapered.

**верея** *f.* gate post, door post, jamb.

**верж/е** *n.* laid paper; —ированный *a.*
laid.

**верит/ельные грамоты** credentials; —ь
*v.* believe, trust, have faith.

**верификация** *f.* verification.

**веркблей** *m.* (met.) crude lead, raw lead
(usually containing silver).

**верлит** *m.* (min.) wehrlite (a foliated bismuth telluride).

**вермель** *m.* vermeil, gilded silver;
gilding.

**вермикулит** *m.* vermiculite (a micaceous
mineral).

**вермилион** *m.* (min.) vermilion, cinnabar.

**вермишель** *f.*, —ный *a.* vermicelli.

**вермут** *m.*, —овый *a.* absinth (liqueur);
vermouth; (bot.) wormwood (*Artemisia absinthium*).

**вернее** *comp. of* верно, верный rather,
more accurately.

**Вернеля печь** Verneuil furnace.

**вернер/ит** *m.* (min.) wernerite, common
scapolite; —овская координацион-
ная теория Werner's coordination
theory.

**Вернета голубой** Vernet's blue.

**верниер** *see* верньер.

**вернин** *m.* vernine.

**верно** *adv.* correctly, accurately, right,
faithfully; it is correct.

**вернонин** *m.* vernonine.

**верность** *f.* correctness, accuracy, precision; (elec. comm.) fidelity; loyalty.

**вернуть** *v.* return, give back; get back,
regain, retrieve, recover; —ся *v.*
return, come back, get back.

**верн/ый** *a.* correct, accurate; reliable,
sure; significant (digit); faithful, loyal,
true.

**верньер** *m.*, —ный *a.*, —ная шкала
vernier.

**верование** *n.* belief, creed, faith.

**веродиген** *m.* verodigen.

**верон/ал** *m.* veronal, barbital; —ика *f.*
(bot.) veronica; —ская зелень,
—ская земля Verona green, Verona
earth.

**веростерин** *m.* verosterol.

**веротерпимый** *a.* tolerant.

**вероятие** *see* вероятность.

**вероятн/о** *adv.* probably; it is probable; —ость *f.* probability, likelihood,
expectancy; potential; по всей —ости
in all probability; коэффициент
—ости probability factor; теория
—ости law of probability; —ый *a.*
probable, likely.

**Версаль** Versailles.

**версен** *m.* Versene (chelating agent).

**версинус** *m.* (math.) versed sine.

**версия** *f.* version.

**верста** *f.* verst (unit of measure, 1.067
km.).

**верстак** *m.* bench, work bench.

**верст/ание** *n.* (typ.) making up (pages),
composing; —атка, —ать *f.* composing stick; —ать *v.* compose, make
up; impose; —аться *v.* compare oneself; come up to, attain.

**верстачный** *a.* bench, work bench.

**верстка** *f.* (printing) imposition; impression; form.

**верстовой** *a.* verst; в. столб mile post.

**вертеж** *m.* giddiness, vertigo.

**вертел** *m.* (anat.) trochanter.

**вертеп** *m.*, —ный *a.* cave, den, cavity,
recess; —истый *a.* cavernous.

**вертеть** *v.* turn, twirl, spin; (elec.) reverse; —ся *v.* turn around, whirl,
spin, revolve, rotate.

**вертикал** *m.* (astron.) vertical; vertical
flue; —ь *f.* vertical, vertical line;
—ьно *adv.* vertically; —ьнострогаль-
ный станок vertical planing machine;
—ьность *f.* verticality; —ьный *a.*
vertical, upright, erect; —ьный
разрез, —ьная наводка, —ьная проекция elevation, front view.

**вертиметр** *m.* vertimeter.

**вертициллезный** *a.* (bot.) verticilli-
aceous.

**вертлю/г** *m.*, —жный *a.* swivel, pivot,
axis; trochanter (of insect).

**вертлявый** *a.* restless, mobile.

**верт/олет** *m.* helicopter; —опрах *m.*
weather vane; —унья *f.* (zool.) bud
moth; —ушка *f.* rotator, rotor, impeller; vane; ventilator; revolving
stand; revolving door; turntable;
dial; current meter; —ячий *a.* whirling; rotatory; —ячка *f.* (vet.) avertin;

—ячки *pl.* whirligig beetles (*Gyrinidae*); —ящийся *a.* revolving, rotating; —ящийся крест turnstile.

верфь *f.* dockyard, shipyard, dock, wharf.

верх *m.* top, upper part, summit; hood (of car); брать в. *v.* get the upper hand (of), get the better (of), overcome.

верхне/бойное колесо overshot wheel; —бродильный *a.* top-fermented, top-fermenting, surface-fermentation; —камский *a.* upper Kama river; —меловой *a.* (geol.) upper Cretaceous; —челюстной *a.* (anat.) maxillary.

верхн/ий *a.* superior, upper, top, overhead; в. класс (concentration) oversize; в. привод overhead drive; в. провод overhead line; в. резервуар overhead tank; gravity tank; в. свет skylight; Верхнее озеро Lake Superior; —яя поверхность upper surface, top; —яя часть top.

верхов/енство *n.*, —ность *f.* supremacy, superiority; —ный *a.* supreme; —ой *a.* top, upper; upland, high; surface (fermentation); saddle (horse); *m.* rider; —одка *f.* (geol.) perched water table; —ый *a.* upper; upstream; —ье *n.* source, upper part (of river).

верхоглядничать *v.* be superficial.

верхом *adv.* astride, mounted; on horseback; heaped, to the top; upwards, above; сидеть в. на *v.* ride; ложка с в. heaping spoonful.

верхуш/ка *f.*, —ечный *a.* top, summit; (geom.) apex.

верчение *n.* rotating; boring.

верша *f.* creel, lobster pot.

верш/ать, —ить *v.* accomplish, execute, conclude; crown, top; —енный *a.* accomplished, concluded; crowned, topped; —ина *f.* top, summit, pinnacle, crown; (geom.) vertex, apex; point, cutting point (of tool); peak (of curve); crest (of hill); —инный *a.* apical; —ковый *a.*, —ок *m.* summit, top, peak; vershock (old unit of length, 4.445 cm.).

вес *m.* weight; importance, consequence; в. брутто gross weight; в. нетто net weight; излишек —а overweight; на

—у suspended, freely suspended; overhanging; собственный в. gravity; удельный в. specific gravity.

вес. *abbr.* (весовой) weight, by weight.

веселый *a.* cheerful, happy.

весельный *a.* oar, oar-like.

веселящий газ laughing gas (nitrous oxide).

весенний *a.* spring.

вес/ить *v.* weigh; —кость *f.* weight, weightiness, heaviness.

весло *n.* oar, paddle; —ногие *pl.* (zool.) Copepoda; —образный *a.* oar-like, oar-shaped.

весн/а *f.* spring; —ою *adv.* in the spring.

весну/шка *f.* freckle; —щатый *a.* freckled.

веснянк/а *f.* stone fly; (bot.) erophila; —и *pl.* stone flies (*Plecoptera*).

весов/ой *a.* weight, gravimetric; в. анализ gravimetric analysis; в. мерник, —ое устройство weighing device, weigher; в. номер weight ratio; —ая платформа platform scales, platform balance, counter scales; —ая скорость mass flow rate; —ая функция (nucl.) weighting function; —ая часть part by weight; —ая чашка balance pan; —щик *m.* weigher, weigh master.

весом/ер *see* весовой мерник; —ость *f.* ponderability; weightiness; weight; —ый *a.* ponderable, weighable.

ВЕСТ *abbr.* (ведомственный стандарт) departmental standard.

вести *v.* conduct, run, carry on, carry out; lead, drive; в. реакцию carry out a reaction; в. себя behave, conduct oneself; в. счета keep accounts.

вестиб/улярный *a.* vestibular; —юль *m.* vestibule, entrance, antechamber, anteroom.

Вестингауз Westinghouse.

Вест-Индия West Indies.

вестись *reflexive of* вести.

вестник *m.* messenger, herald; journal.

вестов/ой *a.* signal; orderly; в. колокол warning bell, alarm; —ая труба overflow pipe; —ое очко overflow.

Вестона элемент (elec.) Weston cell.

веструмит *m.* westrumite (an oil emulsion).

вестфальский уголь Westphalian coal

**Вестфаля весы** Westphal balance.

**весть** *f.* news, tidings, report; *v. see* **вести.**

**весцелиит** *m.* (min.) veszelyite.

**вес. ч.** *abbr.* (**весовая часть**) part by weight.

**весы** *pl.* scales, balance; **в.-дозатор** bagging scale; **точные в.** precision balance.

**весь** *a. and pron.* all, the whole, total, complete; **в. свет** the whole world; **всего** altogether, in all, all told, total; but, only; **во всю** fully; **при всем том** for all that.

**весьма** *adv.* extremely, very, much.

**вет—** *prefix and abbr.* veterinary; **—бак- лаборатория** *f.* veterinary bacteriological laboratory.

**ветв/истость** *f.* branchiness; **—истоусые** *pl.* (zool.) Cladocera; **—истый** *a.* branching; dendritic; (bot.) ramose; **—иться** *v.* branch, ramify; **—ление** *n.* branching, ramification.

**ветврач** *m.* veterinarian.

**ветв/ь** *f.* branch, arm; bough, twig; side; (railroad) siding; dendrite; **соотно- шение —ей** (nucl.) branching ratio; **—ящийся** *a.* branching, tree-like, dendritic; **—ящаяся структура** (min.) dendritic structure.

**ветер** *m.* wind.

**ветеринар** *m.,* **—ный** *a.* veterinary; **—ия** *f.* veterinary science.

**ветерок** *m.* breeze.

**ветивен** *m.* vetivene; **—овая кислота** vetivenic acid; **—ол** *m.* vetivenol.

**ветивер/ия** *f.,* **—овый** *a.* (bot.) vetiver (*Vetiveria zizanioides*); **—овое масло** vetiver oil.

**ветка** *see* **ветвь.**

**ветла** *f.* (bot.) white willow (*Salix alba*).

**ветлазарет** *m.* veterinary hospital.

**вето** *n.* veto.

**ветош/ка,** **—ь** *f.* rag; **—ник** *m.* ragman.

**ветпункт** *m.* veterinary hospital.

**ветреница** *f.* (bot.) wind flower (*Ane- mone*).

**ветрен/ник** *see* **ветрянка;** **—ый** *a.* windy.

**ветро/вал** *m.* windfall; **—вой** *see* **ветря- ной;** **—вое стекло** windshield; **—гон** *m.* weathercock; **—гонный** *a.* (pharm.) carminative; **—двигатель** *m.* wind-

mill; wind motor, wind-driven gener- ator; fan; **—задерживающие полосы** windbreaks; **—кальная сталь** air- hardened steel; **—лом** *m.* windbreak; **—мер** *m.* wind gage, anemometer; **—опыляемый** *a.* wind-pollinated, anemophilous; **—рез** *m.* wind cutter, chimney hood; **—указатель** *m.* (aero.) wind indicator; **—чет** *m.* (aero.) wind-speed indicator.

**ветря/к** *m.,* **—нка** *f.* air vane, vane; windmill; wind turbine.

**ветрян/ой** *a.* wind, *see also* **ветро—; в. двигатель,** **—ая мельница** windmill; **в. конус** (meteor.) wind sleeve, cone; **—ая печь** natural draft furnace.

**ветрян/ый** *a.;* **—ая оспа** (med.) chicken- pox.

**ветрячный** *a.* wind-driven, fan-driven.

**ветучасток** *m.* veterinary center.

**ветх/ий** *a.* old, dilapidated, decrepit; **—ость** *f.* oldness, decay, decrepit state.

**ветчина** *f.* ham.

**ветшать** *v.* get old, fall into decay, age.

**вех** *m.,* **ядовитый в.** (bot.) water hem- lock, cowbane (*Cicuta virosa*).

**веха** *f.* landmark, boundary mark; sur- veying rod, surveyor's stake; pole, peg, stake, staff, rod, beacon.

**вечер** *m.,* **—ний** *a.* evening; **—ом** in the evening, at nightfall; **под в.** toward evening, at dusk; **—еет** dusk is falling; **—ница** *f.* (zool.) bat; (bot.) hesperis.

**вечно** *adv.* perpetually, always; **—жив** *m.* (bot.) periwinkle, myrtle (*Vinca minor*); **—зеленый** *a.* evergreen; **—плавающий** *a.* (biol.) holoplankton- ic; **—плавающие тела** holoplankton, aquatic life; **—сть** *f.* perpetuity.

**вечн/ый** *a.* perpetual, endless, everlast- ing, eternal; **—ая мерзлота** perma- frost; **—ое движение** perpetual mo- tion.

**веш/алка** *f.* hanger, rack, stand, (hat) tree; peg; **сушка на —алках** rack curing; **—ать** *v.* hang, hang up, sus- pend; weigh.

**вешний** *a.* spring, vernal.

**вешняк** *m.* floodgate, sluice gate, sluice.

**вещ/ание** *n.* (rad.) broadcasting; **—ат- ельный** *a.* broadcast, broadcasting; **—ать** *v.* broadcast; prophesy.

**вещевой** *a.* pertaining to things, articles; ammunition; **в. мешок** knapsack, kit bag; **в. склад** warehouse.

**веществ/енность** *f.* substantiality; **—енный** *a.* substantial, material; real (number); (zool.) somatic; **—о** *n.* substance, material, matter, stuff; agent; composition; tissue; **простое —о** element.

**вещь** *f.* thing, object, article; piece of work.

**вея/лка, —льница** *f.* (agr.) winnowing machine; **—льный, —тельный** *a.* winnowing; **—льщик, —тель** *m.* winnower; **—ние** *n.* winnowing; blowing (of wind); (new) idea; **—ный** *a.* winnowed; **—ть** *v.* winnow, fan; blow gently.

**вжив** *adv.* alive, living.

**вжимать** *v.* squeeze in, force in, force.

**вз—** *see also* **вос—.**

**взад** *adv.* back, backwards; **в. и вперед** back and forth, to and fro, reciprocating; **—и** *adv.* behind, in the background.

**взаем** *see* **взаймы.**

**взаимно** *adv. and prefix* mutually, reciprocally; inter—, *see also* **взаимо—;** **в. заменимый, —обменный** *a.* interchangeable (part); **в. замкнутый** interlocked, intermeshed; **в. уничтожающийся** *a.* compensating (errors); **—проникающий** *a.* interpenetrating; **—связанный** *a.* linked, coupled; **—сть** *f.* reciprocity.

**взаимн/ый** *a.* mutual, reciprocal, inter—; *see also* **взаимо—;** **в. затвор, —ая сцепка** interlock; **—ая связь** linking, coupling; interrelation, interconnection; **—ое положение** relative position; **—ое проникновение** interpenetration.

**взаимо—** *prefix* inter—, *see also* **взаимно; —влияние** *n.* interference.

**взаимодейств/ие** *n.* interaction, reciprocal action, reciprocity; (chem.) reaction; cooperation; interference (of wells); **продукты —ия** reaction products; **—овать** *v.* interact; react; **—ующий** *a.* interacting; reacting; cooperative; **—ующая смесь** reaction mixture.

**взаимозаменяем/ость** *f.* interchangeability; **—ый** *a.* interchangeable, replaceable, duplicate; **—ая часть** counterpart, duplicate, spare part, standby part.

**взаимозамыкающий** *a.* interlocking.

**взаимоисключающ/ий** *a.* incompatible; **—ие минералы** mineral incompatibilities.

**взаимо/калибровка** *f.* intercalibration; **—обмен** *m.* interchange; **—обменный** *a.* interchangeable; **—отношение** *n.* relation, interrelation, correlation; **—положение** *n.* relative position; **—помощь** *f.* mutual assistance; **—проникающий** *a.* interpenetrating; **—растворение** *n.* mutual solution.

**взаимосвяз/анный** *a.* interrelated, interdependent; coupled (effect); **—ь** *f.* interrelationship, correlation, interdependence.

**взаймы** *adv.* as a loan, on credit; **брать в.** *v.* borrow; **дать в.** *v.* lend, advance.

**взакрой: забивка в.** clinch nailing; **сварка в.** split welding.

**взамен** *adv.* instead, in return, in exchange.

**взамок** *adv.* lock; **соединение в.** lock joint; **соединенный в.** lock-jointed, lock-seamed.

**взаперти** *adv.* under lock and key, locked.

**взаправду** *adv.* actually, in truth.

**взачет** *adv.* on account, in part payment.

**взбалам/утить, —учивать** *v.* stir, agitate; **—ученный** *a.* stirred, agitated.

**взбалтыв/ание** *n.* shaking, shaking up, agitation; **—ать** *v.* shake, shake up, agitate, shake thoroughly, churn.

**взбе/гание** *n.* running up; **—гать, —жать** *v.* run up.

**взбивать** *v.* beat up, whip; churn (butter).

**взбираться** *v.* get up, mount, ascend.

**взбит/ый** *a.* beaten up, whipped; churned (butter); **—ь** *see* **взбивать.**

**взболт/ать, —нуть** *see* **взбалтывать.**

**взборонить** *v.* (agr.) harrow.

**взбр/асывать, —осить** *v.* throw up, toss up; **—ос** *m.* ramp; uplift; (geol.) upthrust, upthrow; **—ошенный** *a.* thrown up, thrust up; upthrust.

**взбрыз/гивание** *n.* spraying, splashing up, spurting; —**гивать**, —**нуть** *v.* spray, splash up, spurt.

**взбудораж/ивать**, —**ить** *v.* disturb.

**взвал/ивать**, —**ить** *v.* load.

**взвар** *m.* decoction.

**взвед/ение** *n.* leading up (to); resetting; cocking (of gun); —**енный** *a.* led up (to); erected, raised; cocked.

**взвесить** *see* **взвешивать.**

**взвести** *see* **взводить.**

**взве/сь** *f.*, —**шенное вещество** suspension, suspended matter; —**шенность** *f.* suspension, suspended state; —**шенный** *a.* suspended, in suspension; weighed; weighted; fluidized (bed); —**шенное состояние** suspension; —**шенное среднее** weighted mean; —**шивание** *n.* suspension; weighing; —**шивать** *v.* suspend; weigh; consider; —**шивающий** *a.* suspending; weighing; weighting (factor).

**взвиваться** *v.* rise, fly up, be raised.

**взвин/тить**, —**чивать** *v.* wind up; excite; raise (prices).

**взвиться** *see* **взвиваться.**

**взвихривание** *see* **взметание.**

**взвод** *m.* leading up; cocking recess (of gun); notch; (mil.) platoon; —**ить** *v.* lead up; erect, raise.

**взволнов/ать**, —**ывать** *v.* disturb, agitate, stir; —**аться** *v.* be agitated.

**взвыть** *v.* howl, set up a howl.

**взгля/д** *m.* look, glance; view, opinion, outlook; aspect; **в. назад** retrospect; **на в.** in appearance; **при —де на** on looking at; **с первого —да** at first sight; —**дывать**, —**нуть** *v.* look at, glance.

**взгорье** *n.* hill.

**вздваивать** *v.* double up.

**вздор** *m.* nonsense; —**ность** *f.* absurdity; —**ный** *a.* absurd; quarrelsome.

**вздорожать** *v.* rise in price.

**вздохнуть** *see* **вздыхать.**

**вздрагивать** *v.* shudder, start, wince.

**вздремнуть** *v.* nap, doze.

**вздрогнуть** *see* **вздрагивать.**

**вздув/ание** *n.* swelling, bulging, inflation; (geol.) heave; —**ать** *v.* inflate; run up (prices); —**аться** *v.* swell, bulge, inflate, blow out.

**вздумать** *v.* take it into one's head, get the idea.

**вздут/ие** *n.*, —**ость** *f.* swelling, bulging, bulge, inflation; —**ый** *a.* swelled, inflated, blown up; —**ь** *see* **вздувать.**

**вздым/ание** *n.* rising; uplift (of mountains); —**аться** *v.* rise, swell, heave; —**ающийся** *a.* rising; upward.

**вздыхать** *v.* sigh, take a breath.

**взим/аемый** *a.* taxable; —**ание** *n.* levy, collection (of taxes); —**ать** *v.* levy, collect, raise.

**взир/ать** *v.* consider, look (at); **не —ая на** in spite of, notwithstanding.

**взламывать** *v.* break open, force open.

**взлет** *m.* upward flight, take-off (of plane); **коэффициент —а** lift coefficient; take-off factor; —**ать**, —**еть** *v.* fly up, take off; —**но-посадочная полоса** landing and take-off strip.

**взлом** *m.* breaking open, breaking in, break; —**анный**, —**ленный** *a.* broken; —**ать**, —**ить** *see* **взламывать.**

**взмах** *m.* stroke, sweep, sweeping motion, swing; —**ивать**, —**нуть** *v.* flap, wave, swing.

**взмет** *m.* breaking (of soil).

**взмет/ание** *n.* whirling, flying up, lifting up, rising (of dust, etc.); —**ать**, —**нуть**, —**ывать** *v.* throw up, fling up, raise.

**взморник** *m.* (bot.) wrack grass (*Zostera*).

**взморье** *n.* beach.

**взму/тить**, —**щать** *v.* muddy, make turbid; —**ченный** *a.* muddied, turbid; —**ченный асбест** asbestos slurry; **во —ченном состоянии** in suspension; turbid; —**чивать** *v.* suspend.

**взмыл/енный** *a.* foamy, frothy; —**иваться**, —**иться** *v.* foam, lather, froth.

**взнос** *m.* payment, fee, dues; instalment.

**взобраться** *see* **взбираться.**

**взогн/анный** *a.* sublimated; —**ать** *see* **возгонять.**

**взойти** *see* **восходить, всходить.**

**взор** *m.* look, glance, gaze.

**взорв/анный** *a.* exploded, blown up, blasted; —**ать** *see* **взрывать.**

**взраст/ать**, —**и** *v.* grow, grow up; increase.

**взрез** *m.*, —**ание** *n.*, —**ка** *f.*, —**ывание** *n.*

cutting open, dissecting; —ать, —ывать *v.* cut open, dissect.

**взросл/ость** *f.* maturity, adult stage; —ый *a.* adult, grown up, mature.

**взрыв** *m.* explosion, detonation, fulmination; blast; burst, bursting, rupture, blow up; outbreak, outburst; —аемость *f.* explosiveness; —ание *n.* explosion, bursting; blasting, demolishing, blowing up; —атель *m.* fuse, igniter; —ать *v.* explode, detonate, fulminate; blast, demolish, blow up, dynamite; dig up; —аться *v.* explode, burst, blow up, go off; —ающий *a.* exploding, explosive; —ающийся *a.* explosive; —ник *m.* (min.) blaster.

**взрывн/ой** *a.* explosive, *see also* взрывчатый; —ая горошина (pyrotechnics) torpedo; —ая граната high-explosive grenade; —ая работа blasting; demolishing; —ая сила explosive force; brisance; —ое действие explosive action.

**взрыво/безопасный, —упорный** *a.* explosionproof, safe; —опасность *f.* explosion hazard; —опасный *a.* dangerously explosive; —чный *see* взрывной.

**взрывчатость** *f.* explosiveness.

**взрывчат/ый** *a.* explosive; fulminating (silver); в. воздух firedamp (explosive mixture of methane and air); в. желатин blasting gelatin, nitrogelatin; в. состав, —ое вещество explosive; бризантное —ое вещество high explosive; detonating explosive; —ая сила explosive force.

**взрыт/ие** *n.* digging up; —ь *v.* dig up.

**взрых/ить, —ять** *v.* turn up, loosen (soil).

**взывать** *v.* appeal, invoke; call (for).

**взыск/ание, —ивание** *n.* penalty, fine; —ательный *a.* exacting, strict, severe; —ать, —ивать *v.* exact, claim; search.

**взя/вший** *a.* having taken; —тие *n.* taking; —тка *f.* bribe; —ток *m.* honey flow, nectar flow; —тый *a.* taken; given (value); in question; —ть *v.* take; —ться *v.* take hold (of); undertake.

**виадук** *m.* viaduct.

**ВИАМ** *abbr.* (Всесоюзный институт авиационных материалов) All-Union Institute of Aviation Materials.

**ВИАП** *abbr.* (Всесоюзный институт агропочвоведения) All-Union Institute of Agronomical Soil Science.

**вибратор** *m.*, —ный *a.* vibrator; (rad.) oscillator; (tel.) buzzer.

**вибрационн/ый** *a.* vibration, vibrating, shaking; в. грохот, —ое сито vibrating screen, vibration screen; в. компенсатор vibration absorber.

**вибрация** *see* вибрирование.

**вибрион** *m.* (bact.) vibrio.

**вибрир/ование** *n.* vibration, jarring, shaking; oscillation; —овать *v.* vibrate, jar, shake; oscillate; —ующий *a.* vibrating, vibratory, vibration.

**вибро/анализатор** *m.* vibration analyzer; —граф *m.* vibrograph; —датчик *m.* vibration pickup, vibration transducer; —мельница *f.*, —помол *m.* vibrational mill, vibratory mill; —метр *m.* vibrometer, vibration meter; —преобразователь *m.* vibrating rectifier; —стойкий *a.* vibration-proof, shock-proof; —стойкость *f.* resistance to vibration; —испытание на —стойкость vibration test.

**виварий** *m.* vivarium.

**виверра** *f.* (zool.) civet (cat).

**вивианит** *m.* (min.) vivianite.

**вивиант** *m.* Prussian blue, Berlin blue (a ferric ferrocyanide pigment).

**виви/пария** *f.* (biol.) viviparism, viviparous reproduction; —секция *f.* vivisection.

**вивший** *past act. part. of* вить.

**вигантол** *m.* vigantol (a derivative of ergosterol).

**Вигнера эффект** (nucl.) Wigner effect, discomposition effect.

**вигольд** *m.* wiegold (a copper-zinc-aluminum alloy).

**вигон/ь** *f.*, —евый *a.* (zool.) vicugna; vicugna wool.

**вигорит** *m.* (expl.) vigorite.

**вид** *m.* aspect, look, appearance, form, shape; view, prospect, outlook; type, kind, sort; (biol.) species; mode (of oscillations); condition, state; в. сбоку side view, profile; в. сзади back view, rear view; **в. спереди** front view; **в —ах** for the sake (of); **в —е in the form** (of); as, by way (of); **в любом —е** in any form, in any shape; **в —у** in view (of); as, whereas; **в —у того, что** in view of the fact that, considering that; **внешний в.** appearance; **делать в., показывать в.** *v.* pretend, feign; **для —у** for form's sake, as a matter of form; **иметь —ы** *v.* aim (at); **иметь в —у** *v.* have in mind, intend, contemplate; imply; **ни под каким —ом** by no means, under no consideration; **никаких —ов на** there is no prospect (of); **при —е** at the sight (of); **придавать в.** *v.* fashion, shape, mold; **с —у in** appearance; **упускать из —у** *v.* lose sight (of), overlook.

**Видаля проба** (med.) Widal test (for typhoid); **В. черный** Vidal black (a sulfide dyestuff).

**вид/анный** *a.* seen; **—ать** *v.* see often; **—ение** *n.* vision, sight.

**видео** *n.* video, television; **—усилитель** *m.* video amplifier; **—частота** *f.* video frequency, picture frequency.

**видер** *m.* (agr.) weeder, cultivator.

**видеть** *v.* see, view; **—ся** *v.* meet.

**видиа режущий металл, в.-сплав** (met.) widia (cemented tungsten carbide).

**видим/о** *adv.* evidently, visibly, obviously; **—ость** *f.* visibility, visual range; semblance, appearance; **зона —ости** field of vision; **слабая —ость** (aero.) poor visibility; **—ый** *a.* visible, observable, apparent; **—ый горизонт** skyline; **делать —ым** *v.* visualize.

**видм/анштеттова структура** (met.) Widmanstätten pattern; **—ерова колонка** (fractionation) Widmer column.

**видн/еться** *v.* be seen, show; **—о** *adv.* apparently, evidently; **—ость** *f.* visibility, noticeability; **—ый** *a.* visible, noticeable, conspicuous, prominent, observable; *suffix* like, resembling, **—shaped**.

**видов/ой** *a.* species; **—ое богатство, —ое обилие** range of species.

**видоизмен/ение** *n.* modification, version, variety; change, alteration, conversion, metamorphosis; **—енный** *a.* modified; **—яемый** *a.* modifiable,

changeable, mutable; **—ять** *v.* modify, change, alter.

**видоискатель** *m.* (phot.) viewfinder.

**ВИЗ** *see* **ВНИИЗ**.

**виза** *f.* visa, permit.

**визави** *adv.* opposite (each other).

**визг** *m.* squeal, scream, shriek.

**визерин** *m.* (min.) wiserine (a variety of octahedrite).

**визж/ание** *n.* squealing, squeak; spluttering (of arc); **—ать** *v.* squeal, squeak, shriek.

**визига** *f.* dried spinal cord of sturgeon.

**визио—** *see* **видео; —нер** *m.* visionary.

**визир** *m.* sight; (phot.) viewfinder; **—ка** *f.* (surv.) ranging rod; **—ный** *a.* sighting; **—ный крест** (surv.) reticule; **—ная линия** sighting line, guide line; **—ная трубка** telescopic sight, panoramic sight; **—ное отверстие** peep hole; **—ное приспособление** (optics) finder.

**визиров/ание** *n.* sighting, sight; **обратное в.** (surv.) backsight; **прямое в.** foresight; **—ать** *v.* sight; level.

**визит** *m.,* **—ный** *a.* visit, call; **—ация** *f.* visit; inspection; **—ер** *m.* visitor, caller.

**ВИЗР** *abbr.* (Всесоюзный институт защиты растений) All-Union Institute of Plant Protection.

**визуал/изация** *f.* visualization; **—ьный** *a.* visual; direct (reading).

**виикит** *m.* wiikite (uranium mineral).

**вика** *f.* (bot.) vetch (*Vicia*).

**Вика игла** (cement) Vicat needle.

**викаллой** *m.* Vicalloy (cobalt-vanadium alloy).

**викарирующий вид** representative species.

**викасол** *m.* vicasol.

**Викерс: твердость по —у** (met.) Vickers hardness.

**вико—** *prefix* (agr.) vetch.

**виксатин** *m.* oilcloth.

**виктория** *f.* Victoria; (bot.) victoria; **в. голубой** Victoria blue (a dye); **в. новый голубой** new Victoria blue; **в. зеленый, в. зелень** Victoria green, malachite green.

**викунья** *see* **вигонь**.

**вил** *past sing. of* **вить**.

**ВИЛАР** *abbr.* (Всесоюзный институт

лекарственных и ароматических растений) All-Union Institute of Medicinal and Aromatic Plants.

**вилк/а** *f.* fork, crotch, yoke; (mil.) bracket; (elec.) plug; (text.) flyer; **соединение —ой** forked connection, Y-connection.

**вилкеит** *m.* (min.) wilkeite (a variety of apatite).

**вилковый** *see* **вилочный; в. захват** fork catch.

**вилкообразн/ый** *a.* fork-shaped, forked, Y-shaped; **в. рычаг** yoke lever; **—ая трубка** Y-tube.

**виллемит** *m.* (min.) willemite (a zinc silicate).

**виллиам/ит** *m.* (min.) williamite, willyamite; **—сит** *m.* (min.) williamsite (a variety of serpentine); **—сонова синь** Williamson's blue, Prussian blue.

**виллиаумит** *m.* (min.) villiaumite.

**вилок** *m.* cabbage head.

**вило/образный** *a.* furcate, forked, bifurcate; **—чковая железа** (anat.) thymus gland; **—чный** *a.* fork; **—чный ключ** spanner, wrench; **—чный контакт** (elec.) plug, attachment.

**вилт** *see* **вильт.**

**вилуит** *m.* (min.) wiluite (a variety of vesuvianite).

**вилуйская вениса** (min.) grossular, grossularite (a variety of garnet).

**вилы** *pl.* (agr.) pitchfork; fork, crotch.

**Вильгеродта реакция** Willgerodt reaction (for amides).

**вильд** *see* **вельд.**

**Вильда защита** (meteor.) Wild fence.

**вильнуть** *see* **вилять.**

**Вильсона камера** (phys.) Wilson chamber, cloud chamber.

**вильт** *m.* wilt, wilt disease (of plants).

**Вильфлея обогатитель** (min.) Wilfley concentrator; **В. стол** Wilfley table.

**вильчат/ый** *a.* fork, forked, Y-shaped; **в. конец** forking; **в. рычаг** yoke lever; **с —ым захватом** fork (lift).

**вильямс—** *see* **виллиамс—.**

**вил/яние** *n.* wobble, wobbling (of wheel), shifting; **—ять** *v.* wobble, wriggle, shift.

**ВИМС** *abbr.* (Всесоюзный институт минерального сырья) All-Union Institute of Mineral Resources.

**вина** *f.* fault, guilt, blame; cause.

**Вина закон** (phys.) Wien's (displacement) law; **В. мостик** (elec.) Wien bridge.

**вина/ктин** *m.* vinactin; **—лин** *m.* vinaline.

**виндроуэр** *m.* (agr.) windrower.

**винегрет** *m.* mixed salad; mixture.

**винил** *m.* vinyl, ethenyl; **хлористый в.** vinyl chloride; **—ацетат** *m.* vinyl acetate; **—бензол** *m.* vinylbenzene, styrene; **—ен** *m.* vinylene; **хлористый —ен** vinylene chloride, ethylene dichloride; **—иден** *m.* vinylidene; **—ит** *m.* vinylite (a synthetic resin); **—овый, —ьный** *a.* vinyl; **—овый спирт** vinyl alcohol, ethenol; **—цианид** *m.* vinyl cyanide.

**винительный** *a.* (grammar) accusative.

**ВИНИТИ** *abbr.* (Всесоюзный институт научной и технической информации) All-Union Institute of Scientific and Technical Information).

**винить** *v.* accuse, blame.

**винкель** *m.* square, trysquare; (math.) vinculum.

**винно/аммониекалиевая соль** potassium ammonium tartrate; **—железистый** *a.* ferrotartaric; **—железистая соль** ferrous tartrate; **—железная соль** ferric tartrate; **—желтый** *a.* wine-yellow; **—калиевая соль** potassium tartrate; **кислая —калиевая соль** potassium bitartrate; **—калиевонатриевая соль, —калиенатриевая соль** sodium potassium tartrate; **—кальциевая соль** calcium tartrate.

**виннокаменн/окислый** *see* **виннокислый; —ый** *a.* tartaric, *see also* **винный; —ая кислота** tartaric acid, spec. *d-*tartaric acid; **соль —ой кислоты** tartrate.

**виннокисл/ый** *a.* tartaric acid; tartrate (of); **в. кали-натр, в. натрий-калий** sodium potassium tartrate; **в. хинин** quinine tartrate; **—ая соль** tartrate; **кислая —ая соль** bitartrate.

**винно/метиловый эфир** methyl tartrate; **—натриевая соль** sodium tartrate; **кислая —натриевая соль** sodium bitartrate; **—натриевокалиевая соль** sodium potassium tartrate; **—стибилокалиевая соль** potassium anti-

monyl tartrate, tartar emetic; —этиловый эфир ethyl tartrate.
винн/ый *a.* wine, vinous; tartaric; **в. камень** tartar (on teeth); cream of tartar, potassium bitartrate; **в. корень**
*see* **богородичник; в. спирт** ethyl
alcohol; **в. уксус** wine vinegar; —**ая
кислота** tartaric acid; **соль —ой кислоты** tartrate; **кислая соль —ой кислоты** bitartrate; —**ая ягода** (dried)
fig.
**вино** *n.* wine; **красное в.** claret.
винов/атый *a.* guilty, to blame; —**ник**
*m.* culprit, offender; —**ность** *f.* guilt,
blame; —**ный** *a.* guilty, at fault,
faulty.
**виногонный** *a.* distillatory, distilling.
**виноград** *m.* (bot.) grape, grapes (*Vitis*);
**в. изабелла, в. лабруска** fox grape
(*Vitis labrusca*); **культурный в.** wine
grape (*Vitis vinifera*); —**арство** *n.*
(agr.) viticulture; viniculture; —**ина**
*f.* grape; —**ник** *m.* vineyard.
**виноградно/аммониевая соль** ammonium racemate; —**кислый** *a.* racemic
acid; racemate (of); —**кислая соль**
racemate; —**этиловый эфир** ethyl
racemate.
виноградн/ые *pl.* (bot.) grape family
(*Vitaceae*); —**ый** *a.* grape; racemic;
—**ый сахар** grape sugar, glucose;
—**ая кислота** racemic acid, paratartaric acid; **соль —ой кислоты** racemate; —**ая чернь** vine black (a pigment); —**ое масло** grape seed oil.
вино/дел *m.* viniculturist; —**делие** *n.*
viniculture, wine making; —**курение**
*n.* distillation (of alcoholic beverages);
—**куренный завод** distillery.
**винт** *m.* screw; propeller, screw propeller; **в.-барашек, барашковый в.**
thumbscrew; **бесконечный в.** screw
conveyer.
**винтергреновое масло** wintergreen oil.
**винтерова кора** Winter's bark.
винт/ик *m.* little screw; —**ить** *v.*,
—**овальный** *a.* screw; —**овальная
доска, —овальня** *f.* screw plate, die
plate.
**винтовка** *f.* rifle; **в.-дальномер** rifle with
range finder, precision gun.
винтов/ой *a.* screw, spiral, helical; **в.
домкрат** screw jack, jack; **в. жом, в.**

пресс screw press, fly press; **в. ключ**
nut wrench; **в. конвейер, в. транспортер** screw conveyer, worm conveyer; **в. цоколь** (elec.) screw cap (of
bulb); —**ая гайка** screw nut, nut;
—**ая доска** *see* **винтовальная доска;**
—**ая зубчатая передача, —ая передача, —ое зацепление** helical gear;
worm gear; —**ая крышка** screw cap
(closure); —**ая линия** (math.) helical
line, helix; spiral; —**ая муфта** sleeve
nut; —**ая нарезка** thread (of screw);
—**ая пружина** helical spring; —**ое
колесо** helical wheel.
**винтовочный** *a.* rifle.
**винтом** *adv.* spirally.
винто/образный *a.* screw-shaped, spiral;
—**образная линия** helical line, helix;
—**рез** *m.* screw plate, die, tap.
винторезн/ый *a.* screw-cutting; **в. патрон, —ая головка** screw die, threading, die, die; **в. станок** screw-cutting
lathe, thread-milling machine, threader; —**ая гребенка, —ая плашка**
thread chaser, chaser; —**ая доска**
screw plate, die plate.
**виньетка** *f.* vignette.
**Виньолы рельс** Vignole's rail.
виола/ит *m.* (min.) violaite (a highly
pleochroic pyroxene); —**кверцитрин**
*m.* violaquercitrin, osyritrin; —**ксантин** *m.* violaxanthin; —**мин** *m.* viol-
amine; —**н** *m.* (min.) violan (a
diopside pyroxene); —**нин** *m.* viol-
anine; —**новая кислота** violanic
acid; —**нтрол** *m.* violanthrole; —**цеин**
*m.* violacein.
**виолевый** *a.* violet.
**Виолля эталон** Violle's standard, Violle's
platinum unit.
вио/луровая кислота violuric acid;
—**мицин** *m.* viomycin; —**стерол** *m.*
viosterol (vitamin D); —**форм** *m.*
vioform, iodochlorohydroxyquino-
line.
**виппер** *m.* (min.) whipper, dumper.
**ВИР** *see* **ВНИИР.**
вираж *m.* (aero.) veering, banking, turning; (phot.) toner;; —**ировать** *v.* veer,
turn.
вираг/ионный *a.* virgate, rod-like;
—**ия** *f.* (geol.) virgation.
**виргинский** *a.* Virginian.

**вириал** *m.*, **—ьный** *a.* (math.) virial.

**вирид/ин** *m.* viridine; (min.) viridine (a variety of andalusite); **—ит** *m.* (min.) viridite.

**вирировать** *v.* (phot.) tone, shade.

**вирту/альный** *a.* virtual; **—оз** *m.* virtuoso.

**виру/лентность** *v.* (med.) virulence; **—лентный** *a.* virulent; **—с** *m.*, **—сный** *a.* virus; **—сология** *f.* virology.

**висеть** *v.* hang, be suspended.

**вискаутчин** *m.* viscaoutchin.

**виски** *f.* whiskey; *pl. of* **висок.**

**вискоз/а** *f.*, **—ный** *a.* viscose (cellulose xanthate solution);**—иметр** *m.* viscosimeter (for measuring viscosity); **—ин** *m.* (chem.) viscosin; viscosine (light lubricating oil); **—ный шелк** viscose rayon; **—ное волокно** viscose fiber (regenerated cellulose).

**висло/крылка** *f.* sialid (fly); **—крылые** *pl.* Megaloptera; **—плодник** *m.* (bot.) cremocarp; **—ухий** *a.* flap-eared, lop-eared.

**висмут** *m.* bismuth, Bi; **азотнокислый в.** bismuth nitrate; **основной азотнокис-лый в.** bismuth subnitrate; **карбонат —а, углекислый в.** bismuth carbonate; **основной углекислый в.** bismuth subcarbonate; **окись —а** bismuth oxide, specif. bismuth trioxide; **пятиокись —а** bismuth pentoxide; **хлористый в.** bismuth chloride, bismuth trichloride.

**висмут/ат** *m.* bismuthate; **—ил** *m.* bismuthyl; **хлористый —ил** bismuthyl chloride; **—ин** *m.* (chem.) bismuthine; (min.) bismuthinite, bismuth glance; **—истый** *a.* bismuth, bismuthous; **—истая соль** bismuthous salt; **—ит** *m.* (min.) bismutite; **—оводород** *m.* bismuth hydride.

**висмутовокисл/ый** *a.* bismuthic acid; bismuthate (of); **—ая соль** bismuthate.

**висмутов/ый** *a.* bismuth, bismuthic; **в. ангидрид** bismuthic anhydride, bismuth pentoxide; **в. блеск** (min.) bismuth glance, bismuthinite; **в. глет** bismuth litharge, bismuth oxide; **в. шпат** (min.) bismuth spar, bismutite; **—ая белая, —ые белила** bismuth white; **—ая кислота** bismuthic acid; **соль —ой кислоты** bismuthate; **—ая обманка** (min.) bismuth blende, eulytite; **—ая охра** (min.) bismuth ocher, bismite; **—ая синь** bismuth blue; **—ая соль** bismuthic salt; **—ое золото** (min.) bismuth gold, maldonite; **—ое серебро** (min.) bismuth silver, chilenite; schapbachite.

**виснуть** *v.* hang, droop.

**висок** *m.* (anat.) temple.

**високос** *m.*, **—ный год** leap year.

**височн/ый** *a.* (anat.) temple, temporal; **—ая кость** temporal bone.

**вистра** *f.* (text.) a viscose wool.

**ВИСХМ** *abbr.* (Всесоюзный институт сельскохозяйственной микробиологии) All-Union Institute of Agricultural Microbiology.

**висцеральный** *a.* (anat.) visceral.

**висцин** *m.* viscin.

**висюлька** *f.* pendant; icicle.

**вися/чий, —щий** *a.* hanging, suspended; pendulous, pendant; aerial; (bot.) cernuous; **в. замок** padlock; **в. клапан** drop valve; **в. мост** suspension bridge.

**вита/-гляс** *m.* Vita glass (permeable to ultraviolet ray); **—ллий** *m.* Vitallium (cobalt-chromium-molybdenum alloy).

**витальный** *a.* (biol.) vital.

**витамин** *m.*, **—ный** *a.* vitamin; **—озность** *f.* vitamin content, vitamin potency.

**витать** *v.* be absent-minded.

**Витворта резьба** (British standard) Whitworth thread.

**витгамит** *m.* (min.) withamite (a variety of epidote).

**витексин** *m.* vitexine.

**вителин** *m.* vitellin.

**витерит** *m.* (min.) witherite (a native barium carbonate).

**витиатин** *m.* vitiatine.

**витие** *see* **витье.**

**витиеватый** *a.* ornate, flowery.

**витковый** *a. of* **виток;** turn; loop.

**витнеит** *m.* (min.) whitneyite (a copper arsenide).

**витова пляска** *see* **виттова пляска.**

**вит/ой** *a.* twisted, spiral; **—ок** *m.* coil; loop; whorl, convolution; (elec.) turn.

**ВИТР** *abbr.* (Всесоюзный научно-исследовательский институт методики и техники разведки) All-Union Scientific Research Institute of Methods and Techniques of Prospecting.

**витраж** *m.* stained glass (panel); stained glass work.

**витрен** *m.* vitrain (a variety of bituminous coal); —изированный *a.* vitrainized.

**витрина** *f.* showcase, store window.

**витриолизация** *f.* vitriolization, conversion into sulfuric acid or sulfate.

**витрит** *m.* vitrite (vitrifiable material).

**витрификация** *f.* vitrification.

**витрофир** *m.* (petr.) vitrophyre (a type of porphyry); —овый *a.* vitrophyric.

**Витстона мостик** (elec.) Wheatstone bridge.

**Витта теория цветности** Witt color theory.

**виттихенит** *m.* (min.) wittichenite.

**виттова пляска** (med.) St. Vitus' dance.

**вит/ый** *a.* twisted, spun; —ь *v.* twist, spin, wind, twine; —ье *n.* twisting, twining, torsion; —ься *v.* twist, spin.

**ВИУА** *abbr.* (Всесоюзный институт удобрений и агропочвоведения) All-Union Research Institute of Fertilizers and Agronomical Soil Science; **ВИУАА** *abbr.* (Всесоюзный институт удобрений, агротехники и агропочвоведения) All-Union Research Institute of Fertilizers, Agricultural Technology and Agronomical Soil Science.

**вихляться** *v.* dangle.

**вихор** *m.* tuft.

**вихрев/ой** *a.* vortical, vortex; whirling, turbulent, eddy; **в. ветер** whirlwind; —ая нить vortex; —ое движение eddy, whirl; —ое кольцо vortex ring; —ые токи (elec.) eddy currents.

**вихр/евость** *f.*, —ь скорости vorticity; —еобразование *n.* formation of a vortex; —ь *m.* vortex; whirl, whirlwind, whirlpool, eddy, eddying.

**Вица протрава** a chromium acetonitrate solution.

**вици/анин** *m.* vicianin; —аноза *f.* vicainose; —лин *m.* vicilin.

**вициналь** *f.* vicinal form; —ный *a.* vicinal.

**вишенный** *see* вишневый.

**виши** *f.* Vichy (water).

**вишнево/калильный жар** (met.) cherry-red heat; —красный *a.* cherry-red.

**вишне/вый** *a.* cherry; cerise (color); **в. клей** cherry gum; —вая кора cherry tree bark; —слива *see* алыча.

**вишня** *f.* (bot.) cherry (*Prunus cerasus*).

**ВИЭВ** *abbr.* (Всесоюзный научно-исследовательский институт экспериментальной ветеринарии) All-Union Research Institute of Experimental Veterinary Science.

**вкапыв/ание** *n.* digging in; —ать *v.* dig in, drive in.

**вкат/ить, —ывать** *v.* roll in, wheel in; —иться, —ываться *v.* roll in.

**ВКГ** *abbr.* (векторкардиограмма) (med.) vectorcardiogram.

**вкл.** *abbr.* (включительно) inclusively.

**вклад** *m.* deposit, investment; endowment, contribution; —ка *f.* laying in, putting in; insertion, insert; —чик *m.* investor, depositor; —ывание *n.* laying in, putting in, insertion, enclosing; —ывать *v.* put in, enclose; invest; embed; sheathe, put up; line; contribute.

**вкладыш** *m.* (axle) bearing, bushing, lining, brass; insert, insertion piece; **в. подпятника** thrust bearing; **кольцевой в. подпятника** collar step; **в. подшипника** bearing bush, bushing.

**вклеивать, вклеить** *v.* glue in, cement in.

**вклейка** *f.* gluing in, cementing in; inset, glued-in piece.

**вклепанный** *a.* riveted.

**вклин/ение, —ивание** *n.* wedging in; —ивать, —ить *v.* wedge in.

**включ/атель** *m.* (elec.) switch; —ать *v.* include, enclose, insert; put (into service); occlude (gas); (elec.) switch on, turn on, plug in, make contact, connect, cut in, close (switch); put in gear, engage, throw in (clutch); —ать скорость put in gear; —аться *v.* engage, interlock; —ающий *a.* enclosing; including; engaging; actuating; cut-in; —ающий механизм engaging gear; —ая including, inclusive, comprising.

включен/ие n. inclusion, enclosure, insertion; occlusion (of gas); incorporation; (elec.) switching on, connection; (petr.) xenolith; —ия pl. impurities; газовые —ия occluded gas, entrapped gas; клеточное в. (biol.) inclusion body; коробка —ия (elec.) junction box; положение —ия (elec.) on position; схема —ия (elec.) wiring diagram, wiring scheme.

включ/енный a. included, enclosed; occluded (gas), entrapped; incorporated; embedded; (elec.) switched on, on, connected; in gear, engaged; —ительно adv. inclusively; —ить see включать.

вкол/ачивать, —отить v. drive in, knock in, ram, pack in.

вконец adv. entirely, totally, wholly.

вкоп/анный a. dug in; embedded, buried; —ать v. dig in; bury; —ка f. digging in; burying.

вкорен/ение n. inculcation, rooting in; —ить, —ять v. inculcate, enroot; —иться, —яться v. take root.

вкоротке adv. soon, before long.

вкось adv. on a slant, slanting, on a bias, obliquely, awry, crookedly.

вкрадываться v. creep in, slip in.

вкрапл/ение n., —енность f. dissemination, impregnation; —енник m. (petr.) phenocryst, inset, impregnation; —енный a. disseminated, impregnated, ingrained; —ивать, —ять v. disseminate, impregnate (ore).

вкрасться see вкрадываться.

вкратце adv. briefly, in short.

вкрест adv. transversely, transverse (to).

вкривь see вкось.

вкруг see вокруг.

вкрутить v. screw in, twist in.

вкрутую adv. hard-boiled (egg).

вкручивать see вкрутить.

вку/с m. taste, flavor; appetite, liking; придавать в. v. flavor; пробовать на в. v. taste; —сить, —шать v. taste, partake (of); —сный a. tasty, delicious; —совой a. taste; —совые качества, —совые свойства palatability.

вл. abbr. (влажность) humidity.

влаг/а f. moisture, humidity, dampness; (med.) humor; количество —и moisture content, humidity.

влагалищ/е n. sheath, case; (anat., bot.) vagina; (bot.) ocrea; —ный a. vaginal.

влагать see вкладывать.

влаго— prefix moisture, hygro—; water; —емкость f. water capacity, moisture capacity; specific retention (of moisture by soil); —задержание n. moisture retention; —зарядка f., —зарядковый a. water supply;—изоляция f. waterproofing; —мер m. moisture meter; —непроницаемый, —упорный a. moistureproof, moisture-resistant, dampproof; —содержание n. moisture content; —стойкость f. moisture resistance.

влад/елец, —етель m. owner, possessor, proprietor; —ение n. possession, ownership; property; domain, territory; —еть v. possess, own, have; manage, handle (tool).

влажн/о adv. damply, moistly, wet; —оадиабатический a. (meteor.) moist-adiabatic, saturated-adiabatic; —ость f. moisture, humidity, damp, dampness, wet, wetness; moisture content; содержание —ости moisture content, humidity; —ый a. moist, damp, humid, wet.

вламываться v. break into.

влапу: соединение в. lap joint.

власку: соединение в. scarf joint.

власоглавы pl. (zool.) Trichiuroidea.

власт/вовать v. dominate, rule, reign; —ный a. commanding, authoritative; having the authority (to); —ь f. power, authority, rule.

влачить v. drag.

влево adv. to the left, counterclockwise; взять в. v. turn to the left; вращающийся в. (optics) levorotatory.

влез/ание n. getting in; intrusion; —ать, —ть v. climb in, get in; intrude.

влек past sing.; —ут fut. 3 pl.; —ущий pres. act. part. of влечь.

влет/ать, —еть v. fly in, fly into; —ающий a. incoming, entering; oncoming (neutron, etc.).

влеч/ение n. inclination, bent, tendency; —енный a. drawn, attracted; —ь v.

attract, draw; —ь за собой involve, entail.

вли/вание n. pouring in, infusion, injection; —вать, —ть v. pour (in), run in, infuse, inject; merge, blend; —ваться v. be poured in, pour in, flow in; —тый a. poured in.

влия/ние n. influence, action, effect; agency; control; оказать в., —ть v. influence, affect, act, work (on); функция —ния nucleus, kernel (of integral equation); weighting function; —тельный a. influential.

влож/ение n. putting in, enclosure; —ить see вкладывать.

вломиться see вламываться.

вм. abbr. (вместе) together; (вместо) instead; В/М abbr. (вода-масло) water-in-oil (emulsion), W/O.

вмаз/ать, —ывать v. cement in, putty in, paste in, plaster in, embed; —ка f., —ывание n. cementing in, pasting in; —чик m. paster.

вмен/ение n. imputation, imposition; —ить, —ять v. impute, impose (upon), lay to the charge (of); —ить себе consider; —яемый a. imputable; responsible, of sound mind.

вмерзать v. freeze in.

вместе adv. together, collectedly, jointly; в. с тем in addition to that, also, moreover; and at the same time.

вмести/лище n. receptacle, container, vessel; tank, storage tank; —мость, —тельность f. capacity, holding capacity, storage capacity; roominess, room, spaciousness; space, volume; contents; scope; —тельный a. roomy, spacious, large; —ть see вмещать; —ться v. fit in.

вместо prep. gen. instead (of), for, in place (of), in lieu (of); в. того, чтобы instead of.

вмеш/ательство n. interference, intervention; —ать, —ивать v. mix in, add; —аться, —иваться v. interfere, intervene, interpose.

вмещ/ать v. hold, contain, enclose, accommodate; put in, insert; —аться v. go in, fit in; —ающий a. holding, containing, enclosing; —ающая порода country rock, surrounding rock; —ение n. putting in, insertion;

housing; —енный a. put in, inserted; held, contained, housed.

вмиг adv. in a flash, suddenly.

ВМО abbr. (Всесоюзное микробиологическое общество) All-Union Microbiological Society.

вмокрую adv. wet.

вмонтиров/анный a. built in, fixed, stationary, immovable; —ать v. build in, fix.

ВМТ abbr. (верхняя мертвая точка) upper dead center.

вмуров/анный a. embedded; immured; —ать v. embed; immure.

вмятина f. hollow, dent.

ВН abbr. (вакуум-насос) vacuum pump.

внавалку see внасыпную.

внаем, внаймы adv. to let, to rent.

внакладку see внахлестку.

внаклон adv. on a slant, slant-wise, at an angle.

внакрой, внапуск see внахлестку.

внасыпную adv. bulk; груз в. bulk load, bulk freight.

внахлестку adv. lap, lapped, overlap; сваривание в., сварка в. lap welding; scarf welding; соединение в., шов в. lap joint, overlapping joint.

вначале adv. at the beginning, at first.

внашивать see вносить.

ВНД abbr. (высшая нервная деятельность) (physiol.) higher nervous activity.

вне prep. gen. out of, outside (of), beyond, without; regardless of, without regard (for); prefix extra—, ex—; —аэродромный a. cross-country (flight); —атмосферный a. (astron.) extra-atmospheric, extraterrestrial; —галактический a. (astron.) extra-galactic; —городской a. out-of-town.

внедр/ение n. inculcation, implantation, instillation; introduction, injection; adoption (of system); (geol.) intrusion; фаза —ения interstitial phase; —енный a. implanted, instilled; embedded; intruded; interstitial (atom); —ить, —ять v. inculcate, implant, instil; introduce, inject; rub in; embed; intrude, thrust; —иться, —яться v. take root.

внезапн/о adv. suddenly, unexpectedly;

—ость *f.* suddenness, surprise; —ый *a.* sudden, unexpected, abrupt.

вне/земной *a.* (astron.) extraterrestrial; —кишечный *a.* (med.) abenteric; (med., anat.) parenteral; —корневое удобрение leaf-feeding spray; —маточный *a.* (anat.) extrauterine; —осевой *a.* extra-axial, side (blow); —очередной *a.* extra, special; top-priority; —очередность *f.* top priority.

внес/ение *n.* introduction, bringing in, insertion, entering, entry; payment, deposit (of money); placement, application (of fertilizer); машина для —ения feeder, injector; —ти *see* вносить.

внетропический *a.* extratropical.

внешкольный *a.* extracurricular.

внешнеобразованный *a.* externally generated.

внешний *a.* outer, exterior, external, outside, outward; extraneous; surface, superficial; formal; foreign (trade); male (screw thread); в. диаметр outside diameter; в. размер overall dimension, overall size; в. электрон outer electron, orbital electron; —ие члены (math.) extremes; —ость *f.* exterior, outside, outward form, form, appearance; external parts; superficiality.

внештатный *a.* not on the staff, outside.

Внешторг *abbr.* (Министерство внешней торговли) Ministry of Foreign Trade.

внеяд/ерный, —ренный *a.* extranuclear; (chem.) exocyclic.

ВНИВИ *abbr.* (Всесоюзный научно-исследовательский витаминный институт) All-Union Scientific Research Institute of Vitamins.

ВНИГНИ *abbr.* (Всесоюзный научно-исследовательский геологоразведочный нефтяной институт) All-Union Scientific Research Geological Prospecting Petroleum Institute; ВНИГРИ *abbr.* (Всесоюзный нефтяной научно-исследовательский геолого-разведочный институт) All-Union Petroleum Scientific Research Geologic Prospecting Institute.

вниз *adv.* down, downwards, under-neath; в. по падению down; в. по склону, в. под гору downhill; направленный в. downcast, downward; сверху в. downward; ход в. descent, down stroke (of piston).

внизу *adv.* beneath, below, under, underneath, at the foot (of); downstairs.

ВНИИА *abbr.* (Всесоюзный научно-исследовательский институт антибиотиков) All-Union Scientific Research Institute of Antibiotics; ВНИИВСЭ *abbr.* (Всесоюзный научно-исследовательский институт ветеринарной санитарии и эктопаразитологии) All-Union Scientific Research Institute of Veterinary Sanitation and Ectoparasitology; ВНИИГ *abbr.* (Всесоюзный научно-исследовательский институт галургии) All-Union Scientific Research Institute of Halurgy; ВНИИГАЗ *abbr.* (Всесоюзный научно-исследовательский институт природных газов) All-Union Scientific Research Institute of Natural Gas; ВНИИГеофизика *abbr.* (Всесоюзный научно-исследовательский институт геофизических методов разведки) All-Union Scientific-Research Institute of Geophysical Methods of Prospecting; ВНИИЗ *abbr.* (Всесоюзный научно-исследовательский институт зерна и продуктов его переработки) All-Union Scientific Research Institute of Grain and its By-Products; ВНИИК *abbr.* (Всесоюзный научно-исследовательский институт керамики) All-Union Scientific Research Institute of Ceramics; (Всесоюзный научно-исследовательскйи институт искусственной кожи) All-Union Scientific Research Institute of Artificial Leather; ВНИИР *abbr.* (Всесоюзный научно-исследовательский институт растениеводства) All-Union Scientific Research Institute of Plant Growing; ВНИИС *abbr.* (Всесоюзный научно-исследовательский институт стекла) All-Union Scientific Research Institute of Glass; ВНИИСВ *abbr.* (Всесоюзный научно-исследовательский институт стеклянного волокна) All-Union Scientific

Research Institute of Glass Fiber; **ВНИИТБ** *abbr.* (**Всесоюзный научно-исследовательский институт по технической безопасности**) All-Union Scientific Research Institute of Industrial Safety.

**вник/ать,** —**нуть** *v.* investigate, see into.

**вниман/ие** *n.* attention, care, heed, note, notice, regard; **обращать в.** *v.* pay attention, notice; **обращать в. на себя** *v.* attract attention; **оставить без** —**ия** *v.* ignore; **предлагать** —**ию** *v.* call attention (to), propose; **принимая во в.** in view (of), in consideration (of); **не принимая во в.** disregarding; **достойный** —**ия** noteworthy; noticeable.

**внимательн/о** *adv.* attentively; —**ость** *f.* attentiveness; —**ый** *a.* attentive.

**внимать** *v.* listen, hear; grant.

**ВНИМП** *abbr.* (**Всесоюзный научно-исследовательский институт молочной промышленности**) All-Union Scientific Research Institute of the Dairy Industry; **ВНИМЭМК** *abbr.* (**Всесоюзный научно-исследовательский институт масличных и эфиромасличных культур**) All-Union Scientific Research Institute of Oil and Essential-Oil Crops; **ВНИТО** *abbr.* (**Всесоюзное научное инженерно-техническое общество**) All-Union Scientific Engineering and Technical Society; **ВНИХФИ** *abbr.* (**Всесоюзный научно-исследовательский химико-фармацевтический институт**) All-Union Scientific Research Institute of Pharmaceutical Chemistry.

**внов/е** *adv.* newly, recently, lately; —**ь** *adv.* again, afresh, freshly, anew, new, over again, once more; re—.

**внос** *see* **внесение;** —**имый** *a.* introduced; insertion; —**ить** *v.* bring in, carry, get in; introduce, run in, add; insert, enter, list, book; pay in; place, apply (fertilizer); —**ка** *see* **внесение.**

**внук** *m.* grandson.

**внуран** *see* **меркаптофос.**

**внутр.** *abbr.* (**внутренний**) internal.

**внутренне—** *prefix* inside, internal; —**шлифовальный станок** internal grinder.

**внутренн/ий** *a.* inner, inside, interior, internal, endo—; inward; inherent, intrinsic, self—; residual (stress); indoor; inland (water); epeiric (sea); female (screw thread); domestic, home (trade); (anat.) intestinal; **в. диаметр** inside diameter; —**ее горение** internal combustion; —**ее сопротивление** internal resistance; —**ей секреции** endocrine (gland); —**о** *adv.* inside, internally, inwardly; —**ость** *f.* interior, inside; —**ости** *pl.* (anat.) viscera, intestines, bowels.

**внутреродность** *f.* (math.) endomorphism.

**внутри** *prep. gen.* in, within, inside; *prefix* intra—, endo—; —**атомный** *a.* intra-atomic; atomic, nuclear (energy, power); —**брюшинный** *a.* (anat.) intraperitoneal; —**брюшной** *a.* intra-abdominal; —**венный** *a.* intravenous; —**венозный** *a.* intravenous; —**горный** *a.* intermontane; —**грудной** *a.* intrathoracic; —**заводский** *a.* intrafactory; —**зеренный** *a.* intragranular; —**клеточный** *a.* intracellular, endocellular; endo—(enzyme); —**комплексный** *a.* chelate (compound, etc.); —**кристаллический** *a.* intracrystalline; —**массовый** *a.* (meteor.) air-mass (shower); —**молекулярный** *a.* intramolecular; —**мышечный** *a.* intramuscular; —**охлажденный** *a.* internally cooled; —**пазовый** *a.* inner; —**растительный** *a.* systemic (insecticide); —**секреторный** *a.* (physiol.) endocrine; —**сердечный** *a.* (anat.) endocardial; —**сортовой** *a.* intravarietal; —**союзный** *a.* domestic (in USSR); —**тропический** *a.* intertropical; —**формационный** *a.* intraformational; —**черепной** *a.* (anat.) intracranial; —**шлифовальный станок** internal grinder; —**ядерный** *a.* intranuclear.

**внутрь** *adv. and prep. gen.* in, inside, inwards, inward, into; **в. страны** inland.

**внуш/аемость** *f.* suggestibility; —**ать,** —**ить** *v.* suggest, prompt, inspire, impress; —**ение** *n.* suggestion; **поддающийся** —**ению** open to suggestion; —**енный** *a.* suggested; —**ительный** *a.* imposing, impressive.

внят/но *adv.* audibly; —ность *f.* audibility, distinctness, intelligibility; —ный *a.* audible, distinct; —ь *see* внимать.

во *see* в.

вобрать *see* вбирать.

вовек *adv.* eternally, everlastingly.

вовле/кать, —чь *v.* draw in, implicate, involve; —каться *v.* be taken up; —чение *n.* implication; —ченный *a.* drawn in, involved.

во-время *adv.* in time, on time.

вовсе *adv.* at all; в. нет not at all.

во-вторых *adv.* secondly, in the second place.

вовчинец *see* волчьи ягоды.

воган *m.* a vitamin A concentrate.

вогезит *m.* (petr.) vogesite (a syenite porphyry).

Вогезы the Vosges (mountains).

вогнать *see* вгонять.

вогнут/о— *prefix* concavo—; —овыпуклый *a.* concavo-convex; —ость *f.*, —ая поверхность concavity; —ый *a.* concave, bent in; —ое место dent; —ь *see* вгибать.

вод. *abbr.* (водяной) water, aqueous.

—вод *suffix* guide; conductor.

вод/а *f.* water; движущая в., рабочая в. power water; желтая в. (med.) glaucoma; не пропускающий —ы water-proof, watertight; охлаждение —ой water cooling; присоединение —ы hydration; с выделением —ы, с отдачею —ы with loss of water, accompanied by dehydration; сила —ы water power; содержащий —у containing water, hydrated; удалять —у *v.* dehydrate.

водвор/ение *n.* installation; settlement; establishment; —ить, —ять *v.* install; settle; —иться, —яться *v.* settle.

ВОДГЕО *abbr.* (Всесоюзный научно-исследовательский институт водоснабжения, канализации, гидротехнических сооружений и инженерной гидрогеологии) All-Union Scientific Research Institute of Water Supply, Canalization, Hydrotechnical Construction and Engineering Hydrogeology.

водило *n.* pole.

вод/итель *m.* driver, leader; —ить *see* вести; —ить компанию *v.* associate; —иться *v.* live, inhabit, breed.

водка *f.* vodka; крепкая в. aqua fortis, nitric acid; царская в. aqua regia, nitrohydrochloric acid.

водн. *abbr.* (водный) water, aqueous.

водник *m.* water-transport worker; water reservoir.

водно— *prefix* water, aqueous, *see also* водо—; —растворимый *a.* water-soluble; —сосудистый *a.* water-vascular; —спиртовый *a.* water-alcohol; —сть *f.* water content; —суспензионный *a.* water-suspension.

водн/ый *a.* water, aqueous, hydrous; *see also* водяной; *suffix* —hydrate; в. остаток water residue, hydroxyl; в. раствор aqueous solution; —ая культура hydroponics; —ая окись hydroxide;—ая соль hydrated salt;—ая энергия water power.

водо— *prefix* water, hydraulic, aqua—; —бой *m.*, —бойный *a.* fountain, jet; —бойная стенка (hydraulics) apron; —боязнь *f.* (med.) hydrophobia, rabies; —вместилище *n.* reservoir; —вод *m.* water line, water pipe; water conduit, canal; —водяной *a.* water-moderated water-cooled (nuclear reactor); water-to-water (heat exchanger); —воз *m.* water carrier; —возная бочка water cask.

водоворот *m.*, —ный *a.* whirlpool, whirl, swirl, eddy, vortex.

водовыпускн/ой *a.* water-discharge; в. кран water cock, water faucet; —ая труба water discharge pipe, drain.

вододействующий *a.* hydraulic; water (wheel).

водоем *m.* reservoir, cistern, tank, water tank, basin, well; pond, impound; (bot.) pennywort (*Hydrocotyle*); —истый, —кий *a.* containing or absorbing a great deal of water; watery; —кость *f.* water-retaining capacity; reservoir capacity; —ный *a.* reservoir, tank.

водо/жил *m.* (bot.) yellow root (*Hydrastis canadensis*); —защищенный *a.* watertight; (elec.) hose-proof; —зор *m.* hydroscope; —измещение *n.* displacement, tonnage; —качальный *a.*

water-pumping; —качка *f.* water tower; water supply station, pumping station.

водокрас *m.* (bot.) frogbit (*Hydrocharis morsus ranae*); —овые *pl.* (bot.) Hydrocharitaceae.

водолаз *m.* diver; —а *f.*, —ный шлем diving helmet; —ничать *v.* be a diver; —ный *a.* diving, diver's.

водо/лечебный *a.* (med.) hydropathic; —лечение *n.* hydropathy, water cure; —люб *m.* water scavenger beetle (*Hydrophilus*); (bot.) pennywort (*Hydrocotyle*).

водомер *m.*, —ный *a.* water meter, water gage; —ный кран try cock, gage cock; —ная рейка depth gage; —ное стекло water gage, gage glass.

водо/мет *m.*, —метный *a.* jet, fountain; —моина, —мойня *f.* gully, ravine; —нагреватель *m.* water heater; —наливной *a.* water-filling.

водонапорн/ый *a.* water-pressure; в. бак elevated tank; в. насос hydraulic pump; —ая башня water tower.

водонепро/мокаемость, —ницаемость *f.* waterproofness; —никаемый, —ницаемый *a.* waterproof, impervious (to water), water-tight.

водоносн/ый *a.* water-supplying, water-bearing, aquiferous; в. грунт, —ая порода water-bearing soil.

водо/обильный *a.* watered; —описание *n.* hydrography.

водоотвод *m.* drain, drainage, draining; —ная труба drain, drain pipe, waste pipe; —ное отверстие discharge outlet, drain outlet.

водо/отдача *f.* yield of water; water loss; —отделитель *m.* water separator, water trap; —отливный *a.* water-emptying, drain; —отливный эжектор, —отливная помпа bilge pump; —отнимающий *a.* dehydrating; —отнимающее средство dehydrating agent, dehydrant; —охладительный *a.* water-cooling; —охлаждаемый *a.* water-cooled.

водоочиститель *m.* water purifier, water clarifier; —ный *a.* water-purifying; —ный бассейн purifying tank.

водо/очищение *n.* water purification, water treatment; —пад *m.*, —пад-

ный *a.* waterfall, cascade, cataract; —падь *f.* decrease of water; —плавающий *a.* (biol.) planktonic; —плавающие тела plankton; —пленочный насос rotary jet pump; —поглощающий *a.* water-absorbing, hygroscopic; —подготовка *f.* water treatment; —подогреватель *m.* water heater.

водоподъемн/ый *a.* water-lifting; в. таран hydraulic ram; —ая труба water-raising pipe, ascending pipe.

водо/пой *m.* water trough, watering place (for stock); —приводный канал race-way; —приемник *m.* water intake; —приемный *a.* water-receiving; —приемный колодец drain, sump; —пробный кран gage cock (of boiler).

водопровод *m.* water pipe, water supply line, water conduit, aqueduct; water supply; —ец *m.* hydraulic engineer; —ный *a.* water-conducting; tap (water); —ный кран water faucet; —ная задвижка sluice gate; —ная магистраль water main; —ная раковина sink, basin; —ная система water supply system, water distributing system; —ная станция, —ные сооружения water works, water supply station; —ная труба water pipe, water supply line; —чик *m.* plumber.

водопроницаем/ость *f.* water permeability; —ый *a.* permeable (to water).

водо/разборный кран hydrant; —раздел *m.* watershed, water divide; interfluve, interfluve area; —раздельный хребет divide; —распыление *n.* water spraying; —распылительный *a.* water-spray; —распылительное сопло spray nozzle; —растворимый *a.* water-soluble.

водород *m.* hydrogen, H; перекись —а hydrogen peroxide; сернистый в. hydrogen sulfide; хлористый в. hydrogen chloride.

водород/истый *a.* hydrogen; hydride (of); в. натрий sodium hydride; —но- *prefix* hydrogen; —но-ионный показатель, —ный показатель pH value; —ный *a.* hydrogen, hydrogenous; —ный газ hydrogen gas.

**водородо/воздушная смесь** hydrogen-air mixture; —**кислородный** *a.* oxyhydrogen; —**подобный** *a.* hydrogen-like.

**водородосернисто/кислый** *a.* hydrosulfurous acid; hydrosulfite (of); в. **натрий, —натриевая соль** sodium hydrosulfite; —**кислая соль** hydrosulfite.

**водородосернист/ый** *a.* hydrosulfurous; hydrosulfide (of); в. **натрий** sodium hydrosulfide; —**ая кислота** hydrosulfurous acid, hyposulfurous acid; **соль —ой кислоты** hydrosulfite.

**водоросл/ь** *f.* (bot.) alga, seaweed; **багряные —и, красные —и** red algae (*Rhodophyceae*); **бурые —и** brown algae (*Phaeophyceae*); **зеленые нитчатые —и** green algae (*Ulothricales*); **кремневые—и** diatoms (*Bacillarieae*); **сине-зеленые —и** blue-green algae (*Cyanophyceae*).

**водосбор** *m.* water basin; drainage collecting system; (bot.) columbine (*Aquilegia*); —**ник** *m.* (water-collecting) header; —**ный** *a.* water-collecting; catch (basin); —**ное кольцо** (min.) water ring.

**водослив** *m.*, —**ный** *a.* overflow, runoff, spillway, weir; —**ный штрек** water level, drift at water level; —**ная плотина** spillway dam.

**водо/снабжение** *n.* water supply, water works, water service; —**содержащий** *a.* water-containing, hydrated; —**спуск** *m.*, —**спускной** *a.* floodgate; drain.

**водостойк/ий** *a.* water-resistant; —**ость** *f.* water resistance, stability in water, water-resisting property.

**водосто/к** *m.*, —**чный** *a.* drain, sump, runoff, outlet; gully; seepage; —**чный жолоб** gutter; —**чный колодец** catch pit; —**чная канава** gully, wash; —**чная труба** drain pipe, discharge pipe, sewer pipe.

**водо/струйный** *a.* water-jet; —**струйный насос** water-jet pump; aspirator; —**ток** *m.*, —**течь** *f.* current of water; leak; —**терапия** *f.* water cure; —**ток** *m.* current of water; —**точный** *a.* giving water; flowing, running; —**трубный котел** water-tube boiler;

—**тяга** *f.* drain pipe;—**удерживатель-ный** *a.* water-retaining.

**водоуказатель** *m.*, —**ный прибор**, —**ное стекло** water gage.

**водоумягчитель** *m.* demineralizer, water softener.

**водоупорн/ость** *f.* water resistance; —**ый, водоустойчивый** *a.* water-resistant, waterproof, watertight, impervious (to water).

**водо/хозяйство** *n.* aquiculture; —**храни-лище** *n.* reservoir, cistern, tank, water supply tank; —**черпалка** *f.* water engine; pump; —**черпание** *n.* drawing of water; —**чистилище** *n.* filtering basin, filtering tank.

**водочный** *a.* vodka; в. **завод** distillery; в. **огарок** niter cake (a crude sodium acid sulfate).

**водру/жать, —зить** *v.* erect, set up.

**ВОДСАНТЕХ** *abbr.* (Институт водоснабжения и сантехники) Institute of Water Supply and Sanitary Technology.

**вод. ст.** *abbr.* (водяной столб) water gage.

—**вод/ство** *suffix* breeding, raising; growing, culture; cultivating, farming; —**ческий** *a.* breeding, raising.

**водяника** *f.* (bot.) crowberry (*Empetrum nigrum*).

**водянист/ость** *f.* wateriness; (med.) serosity; —**ый** *a.* watery, aqueous, hydrous; (med.) serous; —**ый голубой** sea blue.

**водяница** *see* **водяника.**

**водянка** *f.* (med.) dropsy; в. **яичка** (med.) hydrocele.

**водян/ой** *a.* water, aqueous; aquatic; hydraulic; *see also* **водный, водо**—; в. **газ** water gas; в. **затвор** water seal, hydraulic seal; в. **пар** steam, water vapor; **перегонка с —ым паром** steam distillation; в. **столб** water column; water gage; —**ая баня** water bath, hot-water bath; —**ая сила** water power; —**ое число** water equivalent, thermal capacity; —**ые часы** hydroscope.

**водящ/ий** *a.* leading, guiding; —**ее приспособление** guide, carrier.

**воевать** *v.* make war (upon), fight.

**воедино** *adv.* together, jointly.

**воен/изация** *f.* militarization; **—инженер** *m.* military engineer; **—мор** *m.* sailor, navy man; **воен.-мор.** *abbr.* (военноморской); **—номорской** *a.* naval; **—нообязанный** *a.* subject to military service; **—нохимический** *a.* chemical warfare; **—ный** *a.* military; **—ные запасы** munitions; **—порт** *m.* military harbor; **—техник** *m.* military technician.

**воет** *pr. 3 sing. of* выть.

**вожа/к** *m.*, **—тый** *a.* leader; driver.

**вожд/ение** *n.* leading, driving; **—ь** *m.* leader, chief.

**вожжа** *f.*, **—ть** *v.* rein.

**воз—** *see also* вос—.

**воз** *m.* wagon, cart, van; cartload.

**возблагодарить** *v.* thank.

**возбран/ить**, **—ять** *v.* prohibit, forbid.

**возбуд/имость** *f.* excitability; **—итель** *m.* stimulant, incentive, inducer, provoker; activator; energizer; (elec.) exciter, driver; **—ительный** *a.* stimulating, exciting; exciter; **—ительный контур** (elec.) exciting circuit; **—ить** *see* возбуждать.

**возбужд/аемый** *a.* excitable; **—аемая энергия** energy input; **—ать** *v.* excite, stimulate, stir, arouse, provoke, call forth, induce; create, give rise (to); (elec.) excite, energize, drive; actuate, establish (magnetic field); **—аться** *v.* get excited; run up, build itself up; **—ающий** *a.* exciting, stimulating; **—ающее средство** stimulant, excitant.

**возбужден/ие** *n.* excitement, stimulation, agitation; activation; (elec.) excitation, exciting; **в. компаунд, смешанное в.** (elec.) compound excitation; **обмотка —ия** exciting winding; **потеря —ия** excitation loss; **реостат —ия** (elec.) field rheostat; **функция —ия** (nucl.) excitation function; **цепь —ия** exciting circuit; **—ный** *a.* excited, stimulated.

**возведение** *n.* raising, erection; **в. в степень** (math.) involution.

**возвести** *see* возводить.

**возве/стительный** *a.* giving notice; **—стить**, **—щать** *v.* announce, give notice, notify, advertise; **—щение** *n.* announcement, notice.

**возводить** *v.* raise; fabricate, construct; **—ся** *v.* be raised, be elevated.

**возврат** *m.* return, returning, recovery; regression; reset; **—имый** *a.* revertible; retrievable, salvageable, recoverable; **—ить** *see* возвращать.

**возвратно-поступательн/о** *adv.* back and forth, to and fro; **двигаться в.** *v.* reciprocate; **—ый** *a.* reciprocating; **—ое движение** reciprocation, reciprocal motion, alternate motion; see-saw motion, rocking motion.

**возвратный** *a.* returning, return, recurring, retrogressive; (med.) relapsing; reflexive (verb).

**возвращ/ать** *v.* return; recall; recover; **—аться** *v.* return, come back, recur, revert; **—аться назад** *v.* regress; **—ающий** *a.* returning; recovering; **—ающийся** *a.* returning; resurgent; **—ение** *n.* return, returning; recovery; restoring, restitution, restoration; reversion, recurrence; regression; back stroke (of piston); **—енный** *a.* returned; recovered; restored.

**возвыш/ать, возвысить** *v.* raise, lift up, elevate, exalt; **—аться** *v.* be raised; rise, rise above; **—ение** *n.* raising, elevation; rise, increase; **—енность** *f.* height, elevation, eminence; protuberance; hill, mountain; (geom.) altitude; **—енный** *a.* elevated, lofty; raised, increased.

**возглавлять** *v.* head.

**возгла/сить, —шать** *v.* proclaim, publish.

**возгон** *m.* sublimate; (min.) encrustation; **—ка** *f.* sublimation; volatilization; **—очный** *a.* sublimation; **—очная печь** subliming furnace; **—щик** *m.* (met.) volatilizer; **—яемость** *f.* sublimability; **—яемый, —яющийся** *a.* sublimable; volatilizable; **—ять, —яться** *v.* sublimate, sublime.

**возгор/аемость** *see* воспламеняемость; **—ание** *n.* inflammation, ignition; **точка —ания** flash point; **—аться, —еться** *v.* get inflamed, catch fire; **—ающийся** *a.* inflammable, ignitable, combustible.

**возда/вать, —ть** *v.* render; reward.

**воздвиг/ание** n. erection, raising; **—ать, —нуть** v. erect, raise, set up.

**воздейств/ие** n. influence, action, effect, reaction; **—овать** v. influence, act, affect, react, attack; **—ующее устройство** actuator.

**воздел/анный** a. cultivated; **—ать, —ывать** v. cultivate, till, farm; **—ывание** n. cultivation.

**воздерж/ание** n., **—анность** f., **—ность** f. abstinence; **—анный** a. abstinent, temperate; restrained; **—ать, —ивать** v. restrain, repress; **—аться, —иваться** v. abstain, refrain (from).

**воздух** m. air; **кислород —а** atmospheric oxygen; **удаление —а** deaeration.

**воздухо—** prefix air; **—воз** m. (min.) pneumatic engine, locomotive; **—выпускной кран** air cock, escape valve.

**воздуходувка** f. blower, blowing machine, blast engine; bellows; ventilating fan, ventilator; air compressor, pneumatic pump; **паровая в.** steam blower; **поршневая в.** air pump.

**воздуходувн/ый** a. air-blowing, blast; **в. мех** bellows; **в. прибор** blast apparatus; **в. счетчик** bellows meter; **—ая коробка** blast box; **—ая машина** blower, blowing machine, pressure blower; **—ая труба** (met.) blast pipe, tuyere pipe; **—ая установка** blower plant; blast apparatus.

**воздухо/летательные аппараты** aircraft; **—мер** m. aerometer; **—мерия** f. aerometry; **—нагреватель** m. (met.) hot-blast stove, blast heater; **—непроницаемый** a. airproof, airtight, impermeable to air; **—отвод** m. offtake, drawoff; **—отводная труба** drawoff, drawoff pipe; **—отсасывающий** a. air-ejector, exhaust; **—отсасывающий насос** air ejector, exhaust pump; **—охладительный** a. air-cooling; **—охладительная установка** air-cooling apparatus; **—охлаждаемый** a. air-cooled; **—очиститель** m. air purifier, air cleaner.

**воздухоплав/ание** n. aeronautics, aerial navigation; aerostatics; aerostation; **—атель** m. aeronaut; **—ательный** a. aeronautical; aerostatic; **—ательные аппараты** aircraft.

**воздухо/подводящий** a. air-supply, air-feed; **—подобный** a. air-like, airy; **—подогреватель** m. air preheater; **—приводная труба** (met.) blast pipe, tuyere pipe; **—провод** m. air line, air duct, air conduit; flue; (met.) blast pipe, blast main; **—проводящий** a. air-conducting; **—разделительный аппарат** air-fractionating apparatus; **—сборник** m. air collector; **—эквивалентный** a. air-equivalent.

**воздушно—** prefix air, see also **воздухо—**; **в.-водяной** a. air-to-water (heat exchanger); **—гашеный** a. air-slaked (lime); **—охлаждаемый** a. air-cooled; **в.-реактивный** a. air-breathing jet (engine); **—сть** f. airiness; **—сухой** a. air-dried, air-dry, wind-dried; **—эквивалентный** a. air-equivalent.

**воздушн/ый** a. air; pneumatic; aerial, overhead; elevated (train); open-air (ionization chamber); see also **воздухо—**; **в. винт** (aero.) airscrew, propeller; **в. зазор** air gap, section gap; **в. змей** kite; (pyrotechnics) serpent; **в. канал** air duct, air passage, flue; **в. клапан, в. шибер** air valve; **в. манометр** blast indicator; **в. насос** air pump, pneumatic pump; air compressor; **в. провод** aerial, antenna; aerial line; **в. резервуар, —ая камера, —ая коробка** air chamber, air box; (met.) blast box, tuyere box; **в. сифон** air lift, monte-jus; **в. флот, —ые силы** (mil.) air force; **в. шар** balloon; **—ая баня** air bath; **—ая канатная дорога** cableway; **—ая линия, —ая проводка** overhead line; **—ая машина** pneumatic engine; **—ая прослойка** air seal; **—ая сеть** aerial; **—ая яма** air pocket; **—ое сообщение** air route; **—ое сопло** air-blast nozzle; **—ое успокоение** air cushioning; **—ые души** humidifiers.

**воздымать** v. rise.

**возжа** see **вожжа**.

**возж/ение, —игание** n. lighting, kindling; **—ечь, —игать** v. light, kindle.

**воззв/ание** n. proclamation, appeal; **—ать** see **взывать**.

**воззр/ение** n. view, opinion, outlook; **—иться** v. stare (at).

**возить** v. convey, transport, carry, cart,

drive; —ся *v.* fuss (over), take much trouble (over).

возлагать *v.* place, lay, rest (on); confer, bestow; charge, entrust (with); —ся *v.* rest (on).

возле *prep. gen.* beside, by, near.

возле/жать, —чь *v.* recline.

возлож/ение *n.* laying (upon); —ить *see* возлагать.

возме/стить, —щать *v.* compensate, repay, make good, make up, supply; substitute, replace; —щение *n.* compensation, reparation; replacement.

возможн/о *adv.* possibly; it is possible; в. скорее as soon as possible; насколько в., сколько в. as much as possible, as far as possible; —ость *f.* possibility, feasibility, opportunity, chance; —ости *pl.* resources, potentialities, opportunities; давать —ость *v.* enable; по —ости as far as possible; if possible; —ый *a.* possible, feasible, practicable, potential; probable.

возмужал/ость *f.* manhood, puberty; —ый *a.* mature, adult, in one's prime.

возмутительный *a.* shocking, disgraceful.

возму/тить, —щать *v.* disturb, agitate, stir up, rouse; make indignant, exasperate; —щаться *v.* resent; —щающий *a.* disturbing; —щающий эффект, —щение *n.* disturbing effect; —щающая сила disturbing force; —щение *n.* disturbance; trouble, derangement, disorder; indignation; (astron.) perturbation; теория —щения (nucl.) perturbation theory; —щенный *a.* disturbed; perturbed; indignant.

вознагра/дить, —ждать *v.* reward, recompense, remunerate, compensate; —ение *n.* reward, compensation; fee, pay; —жденный *a.* rewarded, compensated (for).

вознести *see* возносить.

возник/ание, —новение *n.* rising up, rise, emergence, origination, genesis, formation; onset; —ать, —нуть *v.* arise, rise (from), come up, spring up, crop up, emerge, develop, originate; —ающий *a.* originating, rising (from); nascent.

возносить *v.* raise, raise up.

возня *f.* trouble, fuss, care.

возобнов/ить, —лять *v.* renew, restore; resume, recommence; —ление *n.* renewal, restoration; resumption; re—; —ление леса reforestation; —ленный *a.* renewed, restored; —ляемый *a.* renewable; —ляющийся *a.* regenerative.

возогнанный *a.* sublimed.

возонавиватель *m.* (hay) loader.

возраж/ать *v.* object, take exception (to), disapprove, retort; —ающий *a.* objecting; *m.* objector.

возраждать *see* возрождать.

возражение *n.* objection, retort, rejoinder.

возразить *see* возражать.

возраст *m.* age; в. по гелию helium age; —ание *n.* growth, increase, rise; —ать, —и *v.* grow, increase, rise, accelerate; —ающий *a.* increasing, rising, ascending; progressive.

возрожд/ать, возродить *v.* regenerate, renew; reactivate; —аться *v.* regenerate, revive; —ающий *a.* regenerative; —ение *n.* regeneration; reactivation; —енный *a.* rejuvenated, regenerated, reactivate; reactivated.

возчик *m.* driver, carter, carrier.

возыметь *v.* conceive, form; have (effect).

возьм/ет *fut. 3 sing.*; —ите *imp.* of взять.

воин *m.* soldier, warrior, army man; —ский *a.* military, army.

вой *m.* howl, howling, whine.

войло/к *m.* felt, felting; (biol.) tomentum; сбивать в. *v.* felt; —кообразный *a.* felt-like, matted; —чник *m.* felt maker; —чноопушенный *a.* tomentose; —чный *a.* felt, felted; tomentose; —чная болезнь *see* ризоктониоз; —чная трава *see* повилика.

вой/на *f.* war, warfare; —ско *n.* army; —ска *pl.* troops, forces.

войти *see* входить.

вокальный *a.* vocal.

вокеленит *m.* (min.) vauquelenite.

вокзал *m.* (railroad) station, terminal.

вокруг *adv. and prep. gen.* round, around.

вол *m.* bullock, ox.

волвянка *see* волнуха.

**волдыр/еватый** *a.* covered with blisters; pimply; **—ь** *m.*, **—ный** *a.* blister, lump, swelling.

**волевой** *a.* volitional; resolute, determined.

**волемит,** **—ол** *m.* volemite, volemitol, heptaheptanol.

**волк** *m.* (zool.) wolf; **пчелиный в.** *see* **филант;** **в.-машина** (text.) disintegrator; (paper) thrasher, thresher.

**волконожье** *see* **плаун.**

**волконскоит** *m.* (min.) volchonskoite.

**волластон/ит** *m.* (min.) wollastonite, tabular spar; **—овский** *a.* Wollaston (wire).

**волн/а** *f.* wave, surge, billow, breaker; **длина** **—ы** wavelength; **серия волн, цуг волн** wave train.

**волнение** *n.* agitation, commotion, disturbance; churning; heaving, swell (of sea).

**волнист/ость** *f.* waviness, undulation, ripple; **—ый** *a.* wavy, undulating, undulatory, rolling, ripply; curving, sinuous; corrugated (iron); crimped (wire); buckled, warped; **—ая текстура** (geol.) ropy texture (of lava).

**волно—** *prefix* wave, ondo—.

**волновать** *v.* agitate, disturb, stir up; **—ся** *v.* be agitated; be upset, worry; wave, billow, surge.

**волно/видный** *see* **волнообразный;** **—вод** *m.*, **—водный** *a.* (rad.) wave guide; **—вой** *a.* wave; **—вой коэффициент,** **—овая постоянная** wavelength constant; **—вая функция** (quantum mechanics) wave function; **—вомеханический** *a.* wave-mechanics, wave-mechanical; **—искатель** *m.* (rad.) wave detector; **—лом** *m.* breakwater, groyne, jetty; **—мер** *m.* (elec.) wavemeter, ondometer; frequency meter.

**волнообраз/ный** *a.* wave-like, wavy, undulating, undulatory, ripple; pulsating (current); **—ная обмотка** (elec.) wave winding; **—ное движение** undulation; **—ователь** *m.* (rad.) oscillator.

**волно/отвод,** **—рез** *see* **волнолом;** **—повышающий** *a.* (rad.) booster; **—прибойный** *a.* wave-cut; **—прибойные знаки** ripple marks; **—стойкий** *a.*

surgeproof; **—указатель,** **—уловитель** *m.* (rad.) wave detector.

**волну/ха,** **—шка** *f.* (bot.) a mushroom (*Lactarius torminosus*).

**волнянки** *pl.* tussock moths (*Orgyidae, Lymantriidae*).

**воло/вий** *a.* ox, oxen; **в. язык, аптечный** **—вик,** **—глодка** *f.* (bot.) oxtongue (*Anchusa officinalis*); **—вик** *m.* bugloss (*Anchusa*).

**вологодская сажа** an ivory black.

**володушка** *f.*, **круглолистная в.** (bot.) hare's ear (*Bupleurum rotundifolium*).

**волок** *m.* portage; (tech.) draw plate; *past sing. of* **волочь.**

**волокнина** *f.* fibrin.

**волокнисто—** *prefix* fibro—, fibrous, fiber; **—образный** *a.* fibroid; **—пористый** *a.* fibroporous; **—сть** *f.* fibrousness, fibrous structure; **—эластичный** *a.* fibro-elastic.

**волокнист/ый** *a.* fibrous, stringy, filamentous; **в. шлак** slag; volcanic scoria; **—ая структура** columnar structure; fibrous structure; **—ые агрегаты** (geol.) columnar aggregates.

**волокно** *n.* fiber, filament, thread; grain (of wood); **—дерка** *f.* (text.) disintegrator; **—отделитель** *m.*, **—отделительная машина** fiber-extracting machine; (cotton) gin; **—отделительный** *a.* fiber-separating, fiber-extracting.

**волоком** *adv.* by traction.

**волокон/це** *n.* fibril; **—чатый** *a.* filamentary.

**волокут** *pr.* 3 *pl. of* **волочь.**

**волокуша** *f.* scraper; rake.

**воломит** *m.* wolomite (a tungsten alloy).

**волонтер** *m.* volunteer.

**волос** *m.*, **—ы** *pl.* hair.

**волосатик** *m.* a hair; (zool.) hair worm; (bot.) maidenhair (*Adiantum*); **—овые** *pl.* (zool.) Nematomorpha.

**волос/атость** *f.* hairiness; **—атый** *a.* hairy, shaggy; (bot.) pilose; **—ина** *f.* hairline, hairline crack; **—исто—** *prefix* hairy; (biol.) trich—, tricho—; **—истокрылые** *pl.* caddice flies and worms (*Trichoptera*); **—истый** *a.* capillary, *see also* **волосатый;** **—ки** *pl.* (cross) hairs.

**волоснец** *m.* (bot.) wild rye (*Elymus*).

**волосн/ой** *a.* hair; capillary; hairline (crack); fret (saw); **в. сосуд** capillary (blood vessel); **—ая соль** *see* **волосяная соль; —ая трубка** capillary tube; **—ость** *f.* capillarity, capillary attraction; **действие —ости** capillary action.

**волосо/видный** *a.* hair-like; capillary; fibrolitic; **—вина** *f.* fine crack, seam; **—к** *m.* a hair; filament, fiber; hair spring.

**волосян/ой** *a.* hair; capillary; **в. гигрометр** (meteor.) hair hygrometer; **в. канал** capillary duct; **—ая соль** hair salt, silky epsomite (a fibrous form of alunogen).

**волоч/ающийся** *a.* dragging, trailing; **—ение** *n.* dragging, drag; traction; drawing (of wire); **ось —ения** drag axis; **—енный** *a.* dragged; drawn.

**волочильн/ый** *a.* drawing; **в. глазок, —ое очко** hole of draw plate, draw hole; **в. завод** drawing mill; **в. станок** draw bench, wire-drawing machine; **—ая доска, —я** *f.* draw plate; **—ая матрица** drawing die.

**волоч/ильщик** *m.* wire drawer; **—ить, —ь** *v.* drag, trail; pull, draw (wire), draw out; prolong; **—иться** *v.* drag.

**волошский орех** (bot.) walnut (*Juglans regia*).

**волунтал** *m.* voluntal, trichloroethylurethan.

**Волфа процесс** *see* **Вольфа процесс.**

**волхонскоит** *m.* (min.) wolchonskoite.

**волчан** *see* **волчий боб.**

**волчанка** *f.* (med.) lupus vulgaris.

**волч/ец** *m.* (bot.) thistle; (met.) tungsten; **благословенный в., кудрявый в.** blessed thistle (*Cnicus benedictus*); **железистый в., железный в.** (min.) wolframite; **—еягодник** *m.* (bot.) daphne, spec. mezereon (*Daphne mezereum*); **—ий** *a.* wolf, lupine; **—ий боб** (bot.) lupine (*Lupinus*); **—ий корень** *see* **аконит; —ий перец, —ье лыко, —ьи ягоды, —ник** *m.* mezereon (*Daphne mezereum*); **—ье молоко** spurge (*Euphorbia*); **—ье сито** carline thistle (*Carlina vulgaris*); **—ья печь** (met.) blast furnace; **—ок** *m.* gyroscope, gyrostat; hydrometer; (bot.) sucker; (bot.) anoplanthus or

orobanche; (text.) porcupine cylinder; **—онок** *m.* wolf cub.

**волшебный** *a.* magic; **в. орех** (bot.) witch hazel (*Hamamelis*); **в. фонарь** projector.

**волынка** *f.* (music) bagpipes; dawdling.

**Вольвилля способ** Wohlwill process (gold refining).

**вольвическая лава** an acidproof lava used in making chemical apparatus.

**вольготный** *a.* free.

**вольер** *m.* open-air cage; poultry yard.

**вольн/ичать** *v.* take liberties; **—о** *adv.* freely, voluntarily; **—одумец** *m.* free thinker, liberal; **—омыслие** *n.* free thinking; **—онаемный** *a.* civilian; **—оопределяющийся** *a.* (mil.) volunteer; **—опрактикующий** *a.* privately practicing; *m.* private practitioner; **—ослушатель** *m.* outsider (student); **—ость** *f.* freedom, liberty; **—ый** *a.* free.

**вольский** *a.* Volsk.

**вольт** *m.* (elec.) volt; **в.-ампер** volt-ampere; **число в.** voltage.

**вольта** a machine oil; a light cotton fabric.

**Вольта явление** Volta effect.

**вольта/ж** *m.* (elec.) voltage; **—ит** *m.* (min.) voltaite; **—ический** *a.* (elec.) voltaic; **—метр** *m.* voltameter; **—метрический** *a.* voltametric; **—мпер** *m.* volt-ampere; **—мперметр** *m.* volt-amperemeter, voltammeter; **—скоп** *m.* voltascope (current detector); **—стат** *m.* voltastat (voltage control).

**Вольтекса способ** Voltex (welding) process.

**вольтижировать** *v.* vault.

**вольтметр** *m.*, **—овый** *a.* (elec.) voltmeter.

**вольтов столб** voltaic pile; **—а дуга** voltaic arc, electric arc.

**вольтодобавочная машина** (elec.) booster.

**вольтол/евые масла, —ы** voltols, voltolized oils; **—изация** *f.* voltolization (process for production of lubricating oils); **—изованный** *a.* voltolized.

**вольтоскоп** *m.* spark plug tester.

**вольтотрансформатор** *m.* (elec.) voltage transformer, transformer.

**вольтцин** *m.* (min.) voltzine, voltzite.

**Вольты** элемент voltaic cell.

**Вольфа процесс** (flotation) Wolf process.

**вольфартова муха** a fly (*Wohlfartia magnifica*).

**вольфахит** *m.* (min.) wolfachite (near corynite).

**вольфрам** *m.* tungsten, W; **азотистый в.** tungsten nitride; **трехокись** —a tungsten trioxide, tungstic anhydride; **трехсернистый в.** tungsten trisulfide.

**вольфрам/ат** *m.* tungstate; **в. натрия** sodium tungstate; —**истый** *a.* tungsten; —**ит** *m.* (min.) wolframite.

**вольфрамо**— *prefix* tungsten.

**вольфрамово/кальциевая соль** calcium tungstate; —**кислый** *a.* tungstic acid; tungstate (of); —**кислый натрий, —натриевая соль** sodium tungstate; —**кислая соль** tungstate; —**свинцовистая соль** lead tungstate.

**вольфрамов/ый** *a.* tungsten, tungstic; **в. ангидрид** tungstic anhydride, tungsten trioxide; **в. голубой** wolfram blue, mineral blue (a tungsten oxide); **в. камень** (min.) scheelite; —**ая желтая** tungsten yellow (a variety of tungsten bronze); —**ая кислота** tungstic acid; **соль** —**ой кислоты** tungstate;—**ая лампа** tungsten lamp; —**ая охра** (min.) tungstic ocher, tungstite; —**ая соль** tungsten salt.

**вольфрамо/натриевая соль** *see* **вольфрамовонатриевая соль;** —**сернистый** *a.* sulfotungstate (of).

**вольфсбергит** *m.* (min.) wolfsbergite, chalcostibite.

**вольцин** *see* **вольтцин.**

**волюм/енометр** *m.* volumenometer; —**етр, —инометр, —метр, —ометр** *m.* volumeter; —**етрический** *a.* volumetric; —**инозный** *a.* voluminous.

**волюта** *f.* volute.

**вол/я** *f.* will; freedom, liberty; —**ей-неволей** *adv.* willing or not, one way or another; **по доброй** —**е** willingly, of one's own accord; **сила** —**и** will power; **пускать на** —**ю** *v.* set free, liberate.

**Вомедак** *abbr.* (**Военно-медицинская академия**) Military Medical Academy.

**вон** *adv.* out, away; over there.

**вонз/ать, —ить** *v.* thrust, prod.

**вонь** *f.* stench, stink, bad odor.

**вонюч/ий** *a.* malodorous, putrid, stinking; (min.) fetid; **в. камень** (min.) stinkstone (any fetid stone, spec. anthraconite); —**ая смола** asafetida (gum); —**ка** *f.* (zool.) skunk; (bot.) asafetida (*Ferula asafetida*); peppergrass (*Lepidium*); bean trefoil (*Anagyris foetida*).

**вонять** *v.* have a bad smell.

**вообра/жаемый** *a.* imaginary, unreal, fictitious, non-existent, hypothetical; virtual; —**жать, —зить** *v.* imagine, fancy, conceive, figure; —**жение** *n.* imagination, idea; —**женный** *a.* imagined, assumed; —**зимый** *a.* imaginable.

**вообще** *adv.* generally, in general.

**воодушев/ить, —лять** *v.* inspire, fill with enthusiasm; —**ление** *n.* enthusiasm.

**вооруж/ать, —ить** *v.* arm, outfit; **в. против** instigate against; —**аться, —иться** *v.* take up arms; —**ение** *n.* armament, arming, arms, armature; fitting out, rigging; —**енный** *a.* armed; fitted out.

**вооч/ию, —ью** *adv.* with one's own eyes, for oneself.

**ВОП** *abbr.* (**Всесоюзное общество почвоведов**) All-Union Society of Soil Scientists.

**во-первых** *adv.* firstly, in the first place.

**вопить** *v.* cry out, howl.

**вопло/тить, —щать** *v.* embody, personify.

**вопреки** *prep. dat.* in spite (of), notwithstanding, despite, regardless (of), contrary.

**вопро/с** *m.* question, query, interrogation; problem, point; **под** —**сом** open to question; —**сительный** *a.* interrogative; interrogatory; question (mark); —**сить, —шать** *v.* question; —**сник** *m.* questionnaire; —**шающий** *a.* interrogative.

**ворван/ь** *f.*, —**ный** *a.* train oil, fish oil, blubber; **в. тюленья** seal oil.

**ворваться** *see* **врываться.**

**воробей** *m.* sparrow; —**ник** *m.* (bot.) gromwell (*Lithospermum officinale*).

**воробьевит** *m.* (min.) worobieffeite, vorobyevite (a variety of beryl).

**воробьиный** *a.* sparrow.

**воров/ать** *v.* steal, thieve, pilfer; tap (electricity, etc.); —**ство** *n.* stealing; tapping; tampering (with power, etc.).

**ворон** *m.* raven; —**а** *f.* crow.

**воронен/ие** *n.* (met.) burnishing, polishing; browning; bronzing; bluing, tinting (by oxidation); —**ый** *a.* burnished, polished; browned; blued; —**ая сталь** blue steel.

**воронец** *m.* (bot.) cohosh (*Actaea*).

**вороний** *a.* crow, crow's; **в. глаз** (bot.) paris.

**ворон/ило** *n.* burnisher, polisher; —**ить** *v.* (met.) burnish, polish; brown; bronze; blue, tint (by oxidation).

**воронк/а** *f.* funnel; hopper; crater; eddy; sinkhole, sink; cone (of depression); *see also under* **форда в.; капельная в.** drop funnel, dropping funnel; —**о-образный** *a.* funnel-shaped, funneled; hopper-shaped; cone-shaped.

**ворон/ой** *a.* black; —**ье** *n.* crows and ravens.

**ворот** *m.* windlass, winch, capstan, reel; drum, shaft; hoist, hauler, pull; collar.

**ворота** *pl.* gate, gateway.

**воротило** *n.* mill handle.

**воротить** *v.* recall; —**ся** *v.* come back, return.

**воротн/ик** *m.* collar, flange, lip; —**ичок** *m.* little collar.

**воротн/ый** *a.* gate, portal; windlass, winch; —**ая вена** (anat.) portal vein.

**вороток** *m.* tap wrench.

**ворох** *m.* heap, pile; —**нуть** *see* **ворошить.**

**ворочать** *v.* turn, roll; (elec.) reverse; —**ся** *v.* turn, rotate.

**ворош/илка** *f.* agitator; (agr.) tedder; —**ить** *v.* stir, disturb; turn (hay).

**ворс** *m.*, —**а** *f.* pile, nap, fleece.

**Ворса элемент** Vorce cell (for chlorine).

**ворс/ильный,** —**овальный** *a.*, —**ование** *n.* (text.) teasing; —**ильщик** *m.* teaseler; —**инка** *f.* hair, fiber; (biol.) villus; —**инчатый** *a.* wooly, fluffy, tomentose; —**истый** *a.* nappy, fluffy, fleecy, friezed; —**ить,** —**овать** *v.* tease, raise the nap; —**овальная машина** napping frame; —**овальная шишка** (text.) teasel; —**овальная**

**шишка,** —**янка** *f.* (bot.) teasel (*Dipsacus*), spec. fuller's teasel (*D. fullonum*); —**янковые** *pl.* Dipsaca-ceae.

**вортекс** *m.* vortex.

**Вортингтона насос** Worthington pump.

**ворчать** *v.* grumble, complain; growl.

**вос—** *prefix* up, off, away; re—, again.

**восемнадцат/ый** *a.* eighteenth; —**ь** eighteen.

**восемь** eight; —**десят** eighty; —**сот** eight hundred; —**ю восемь** eight times eight.

**воск** *m.* wax.

**воскли/кнуть,** —**цать** *v.* exclaim, ejaculate; —**цательный** *a.* exclamation (mark); —**цательная совка** a cutworm (*Agrotis exclamationis*).

**воско—** *prefix* wax, cer—; —**беление** *n.* wax bleaching; —**белильный завод,** —**белильня** *f.*, —**бойная** *f.*, —**бойный завод** wax refinery; —**битие** *n.* wax refining; —**боина** *f.*, —**бой** *m.* beeswax (residual); —**видный** *a.* waxy, ceraceous.

**восков/ина** *f.* (zool.) cere; —**ка** *f.* tracing paper; wax paper; —**ник** *m.* (bot.) wax myrtle, bayberry (*Myrica cerifera*); —**никовые** *pl.* (bot.) Myricaceae.

**восков/ой** *a.* wax, waxy, waxen; **в. пластырь** (pharm.) cerate; **в. плющ** (bot.) waxflower (*Hoya carnosa*); **в. спирт** ceric alcohol; —**ая бумага** tracing paper; wax paper; —**ая кислота** ceric acid, cerotic acid, heptacosanoic acid; **соль** —**ой кислоты** cerotate; —**ая моль** bee moth; —**ая пальма** (bot.) wax palm (*Ceroxylon*); —**ая трава** (bot.) honeywort (*Cerinthe*); —**ое дерево** *see* **восковник;** —**ые краски** oil paints containing wax.

**воско/носный** *a.* ceriferous, wax-producing; —**образный,** —**подобный** *a.* wax-like, waxy, ceraceous; —**топка** *f.* wax refinery; —**цветник** *m.* (bot.) honeywort (*Cerinthe*).

**воскрес/ать,** —**нуть** *v.* rise again; revive; —**енье** *n.*, —**ный** *a.* Sunday; —**ить,** **воскрешать** *v.* resuscitate, revive.

**воспал/ение** *n.* (med.) inflammation; **в.**

легких pneumonia; —енный *a.* inflamed, sore; —ительный *a.* inflammatory; —ить, —ять *v.* inflame; —иться *v.* get inflamed; blaze.

воспар/ить, —ять *v.* soar, fly up.

воспит/ание *n.* education, upbringing, training; —анник *m.*, —анница *f.* pupil; —анный *a.* well-bred; brought up, trained; —атель *m.* tutor, trainer; educator; —ательный *a.* educational; —ать, —ывать *v.* bring up, raise, rear; train, educate.

воспламенен/ие *n.* ignition, inflammation, combustion; kindling, setting fire (to); камера —ия combustion chamber; проба на в. flash test; температура —ия, точка —ия flash point (of oils); ignition point, kindling point.

воспламен/итель *m.* igniter, ignition device, lighting device; ignition charge; —ить, —ять *v.* inflame, ignite, kindle; —иться, —яться *v.* ignite, catch fire; —яемость *f.* combustibility, inflammability, ignitability; —яемый, —яющийся *a.* combustible, inflammable, ignitable; —яющаяся смесь ignition mixture.

восполн/ить, —ять *v.* fill in, make up, complete; fulfill.

воспользоваться *v.* profit (by), take advantage (of), use, employ.

воспомин/ание *n.* remembrance, recollection; —ать *v.* remember, recollect.

воспрепятствовать *v.* hinder, prevent.

воспре/тительный *a.* prohibitive; —тить, —щать *v.* prohibit, forbid; —щение *n.* prohibition.

восприимчив/ость *f.* suspectibility, receptivity; магнитная в. susceptibility; —ый *a.* susceptible, receptive, sensitive.

восприн/имаемость *f.* perceptibility; —имаемый *a.* perceptible, discernible; —имание, —ятие *n.* taking, receiving, acceptance; —имать, —ять *v.* take, receive; take up, imbibe, absorb; perceive; —имающий *a.* receiving; sensing; —имающий элемент sensitive element, sensing unit.

восприят/ие *n.* perception, sensing;

объект —ия, результат —ия percept.

воспроизв/едение, —одство *n.* reproduction, breeding, regeneration; зона —одства (nucl.) blanket; коэффициент —одства conversion ratio; прирост —одства (nucl.) breeding gain; цикл —одства breeding cycle; —ести, —одить *v.* reproduce; produce; —одимый *a.* reproducible; —одительный *a.* reproductive; —одящий *a.* reproducing, breeding, fertile (medium).

воспротив/иться, —ляться *v.* oppose, resist; —ление *n.* resistance.

воспылать *v.* flame out, flare.

воссиять *v.* begin to shine.

воссоедин/ение *n.* reunion; recombination (of ions); —ять *v.* reunite; —яться *v.* rejoin; recombine.

воссозда/вать *v.* reconstruct; —ние *n.* reconstruction.

восставать *v.* revolt, rebel, rise.

восстанавлив/аемость *see* восстановляемость; —аемый *a.* reducible; —ать *v.* reduce, deoxidize; reinstate, reestablish, restore, recondition; regenerate, reclaim, recover; recuperate, revive, revivify; erect (a perpendicular); vindicate; —ающий *a.* reducing; —ающая способность reducing power; recovery characteristics (of counter); —ающийся *a.* reducible.

восстание *n.* rise; uprising, rebellion.

восстанов/имый *see* восстановляемый; —итель *m.* reducer, reducing agent; regenerator, restorer, renovator.

восстановительн/ый *a.* reducing, reduction; regenerating, restoration; в. цех (met.) reduction works; —ая печь reduction furnace; —ая способность reducing power; —ое пламя reducing flame; —ое средство reducing agent; —ые работы recovery.

восстановить *see* восстанавливать.

восстановл/ение *n.* reduction, deoxidation; reestablishment, resumption, renewal, restoration, reconditioning; regeneration, recovery; (instrumentation) recovery time; revivification; re—; в. цикла recycling; —енный *a.* reduced; restored; recovered; —яемость *f.* reducibility; —яемый, —яющийся *a.* reducible; —ять *see*

**восстанавливать; —ющий** *a.* reducing.

**восстать** *see* **восставать.**

**вост.** *abbr.* (**восточный**) east, eastern.

**восток** *m.* east, orient.

**востор/г** *m.* delight, enthusiasm, zeal; **—женный** *a.* enthusiastic, zealous.

**восточный** *a.* eastern, oriental.

**востребование** *n.* demand.

**восхвал/ение** *n.* eulogy, praises; **—ять** *v.* laud, praise, extol.

**восхи/тительный** *a.* delightful; **—тить, —щать** *v.* delight; **—щаться** *v.* admire.

**восхо/д** *m.* rise, rising, ascent; **—дить** *v.* rise, ascend; **—дящий** *a.* rising, ascending, anabatic; upward; uptake (flue); **—дящий боровок** uptake, upcast; **—дящая труба** riser; **отливать —дящей струей** *v.* cast from bottom; **—ждение** *n.* ascent, ascension, climbing.

**восьмер/ичный** *a.* octuple; **—ка, —о** eight; (aero.) figure eight; **—ник** (cryst.) eight-fold twin.

**восьми—** *prefix* oct—, octa—, octo—, eight; **—валентный** *a.* octavalent; **—гранник** *m.* octahedron; **—гранный** *a.* octahedral; **—десятилетний** *a.* octogenarian; **—десятый** *a.* eightieth; **—кратный** *a.* octuple; **—летний** *a.* octennial; **—лучевые** *pl.* (zool.) Octocorallia;—**ног** *m.* (zool.) octopus; **—ногие** *pl.* Octopoda; **—сложный** *a.* octosyllabic; **—угольник** *m.* octagon; **—угольный** *a.* octagonal.

**восьмой** *a.* eighth.

**вот** *adv.* here; **в. и все** that is all.

**вотировать** *v.* vote.

**воткать** *v.* interweave, weave in.

**воткнуть** *see* **втыкать.**

**вотум** *m.* vote.

**вофатокс** *see* **метафос.**

**вошли** *past pl. of* **войти.**

**вошь** *f.* louse; **травяная в.** aphid.

**вощ/анка** *f.* wax paper; oil cloth; (bot.) *see* **восковая трава; —аной, —аный** *a.* wax, waxen, waxed; **—ение** *n.* waxing; **—еный** *a.* waxed; **—еная бумага** wax paper; **—ина** *f.* unrefined beeswax; **—ить** *v.* wax.

**вою/т** *pr. 3 pl.*; **—щий** *pres. act. part. of* **выть.**

**вояж** *m.* travel; trip; **—ер** *m.* traveling salesman; **—ировать** *v.* travel.

**впад/ать** *v.* fall in; flow, discharge; **—ающий** *a.* falling into; flowing into, inflowing; **—ение** *n.* inflow; mouth, issue (of river); **—ина** *f.* hollow, cavity, depression, concavity, dent, indentation; recess, notch, gap, space; sag; trough (of wave); valley (of curve); (geol.) basin, trough, depression; orbit, socket (of eye); **—истый** *a.* full of cavities.

**впа/ивание** *n.,* **—йка** *f.* soldering in, sealing in; **—ивать** *v.* solder in, seal in; **—й** *m.* sealing in, seal-in, seal.

**впал/ость** *f.* hollowness, concavity; **—ый** *a.* hollow, concave, sunken.

**впараллель** *adv.* in parallel.

**впасть** *see* **впадать.**

**впаять** *see* **впаивать.**

**впервые** *adv.* first, for the first time.

**вперевязку: стык в.** broken joint.

**вперед** *adv.* on, forward, ahead, forth, onward; first; fast (of clock); **взад и в.** back and forth, to and fro; **движение в.** onward motion, advance, progress; **забегать в.** *v.* forestall; **идущий в.** advancing, progressive; **подвигаться в.** *v.* advance, progress; **ход в.** forward running; forward, stroke; **—и** *adv.* in front, before, ahead (of); in future.

**впере/крой, —крышку, —крышу** *see* **внахлестку; —межку** *see* **попеременно; —мешку** *adv.* pell-mell; in disorder.

**впечатл/евать, —еть** *v.* impress, imprint; engrave; **—ение** *n.* impression, sensation; **—ительность** *f.* impressibility; susceptibility; **—ительный** *a.* impressionable, susceptible, sensitive.

**впивать** *v.* drink in, absorb, suck in; **—ся** *v.* dig in, hold on.

**впис/анный** *a.* written in, entered, inscribed; **в. угол** inscribed angle; **—ать, —ывать** *v.* enter, inscribe, write in; (geom.) inscribe.

**впит/анный** *a.* absorbed; **—ать, —ывать** *v.* absorb, soak up, take up; **—аться** *v.* be absorbed, soak in; **—ывание** *n.* absorption, soaking in; **—ывающий** *a.* absorbent, absorbing;

—ывающий в себя absorptive; saturant, saturable; —ь *see* впивать.
впих/ать, —ивать, —нуть *v.* push in, squeeze in.
вплавь *adv.* swimming, by swimming.
впластов/анный *a.* embedded; interbedded, interstratified; —ываться *v.* be embedded; interbed, interstratify.
вплес/кивать, —нуть *v.* splash in, pour carelessly, dump in.
вплет/ание, —ение *n.* interweaving, intertwining; implication; —ать, вплести *v.* interweave, intertwine, interlace; plait in, splice in; implicate, involve; —енный *a.* interwoven, interlaced; implicated, involved.
вплотную *adv.* close, close by, closely, up to, against; в. к up against, close to.
вплоть *adv.* up to, till; close; в. до down to.
вплы/вать, —ть *v.* swim in, float in.
вполдерева: соединение в. halving.
вполз/ать, —ти *v.* crawl in, creep in, worm through.
вполне *adv.* fully, entirely, wholly, totally, completely, thoroughly, quite, perfectly; не в. incompletely, under, sub—.
вполовину *adv.* half.
вполу/накрой, —нахлест, —нахлестку *adv.* half-lap; соединение в. half-lap joint; scarf joint, scarf.
впопад *adv.* timely, to the point.
впопыхах *adv.* hurriedly, hastily.
впору *adv.*: быть в. *v.* fit; be fit (for).
впослед/ние *adv.* for the last time; —ствии *adv.* afterwards, later on, subsequently.
впотай *adv.* flush, even; головка в. countersunk head; клепка в. flush riveting; углубление в. countersinking.
впотьмах *adv.* in the dark.
вправду *adv.* really, seriously.
вправе, быть *v.* have a right (to).
вправ/ить, —ливать, —лять *v.* set, set to rights; в. вывих set a bone (joint); —ка *f.* setting, resetting.
вправо *adv.* to the right, clockwise (rotation); взять в. *v.* turn to the right; вращающийся в. dextrorotatory.

впредь *adv.* henceforth, in the future; в. до pending, until.
впрессованный *a.* pressed in, embedded, built in, set in; press-fitted.
впритык *adv.* butt, butt-joint; flush, against, end to end; накладка в., располагать в. *v.* butt; сваривать в. *v.* butt-weld; соединение в., сращивание в. butt joint, abutting joint.
впроголодь *adv.* half starving.
впрок *adv.* for the future, for keeping, for preservation; заготовлять в. *v.* preserve, cure, lay in, store; идти в. *v.* be of use, be of profit.
впрочем *adv.* however, though; not that; nevertheless; on the other hand.
впрыг/ивать, —нуть *v.* jump in, leap in.
впрыскив/ание *n.* injection, injecting, spraying in; —ательный *a.* injection; —ать, впрыскать *v.* inject, squirt in, spray in; —ающий *a.* injecting, spray; —ающий холодильник jet condenser; —ающее сопло spray nozzle.
впрыснут/ый *a.* injected; —ь *see* впрыскивать.
впрягать *v.* harness.
впуск *m.* letting in, admission, introduction, ingress, intake, inlet; в. воздуха air intake; опережение —а, предварение —а admission lead; ход —а admission stroke, instroke; —ать *v.* let in, introduce, admit, inject, run in.
впускн/ой *a.* admission, admitting, intake, inlet; в. клапан inlet valve, intake valve; —ая труба feed pipe, supply pipe; inlet pipe, intake pipe; —ое отверстие inlet, intake; —ое устройство injector.
впустить *see* впускать.
впустую *adv.* in vain, to no purpose.
впут/анный *a.* implicated, involved; —ать, —ывать *v.* implicate, involve; —аться, —ываться *v.* be mixed up (with), be enmeshed; interfere.
впущенный *a.* admitted, let in, injected.
впятеро *adv.* five times, fivefold; в. больше five times as much; в. меньше one fifth; —м *adv.* five (together).
враб/атываться, —отаться *v.* work in, run in.
вра/г *m.* enemy, foe; —жда *f.* enmity; —ждебный *a.* hostile, antagonistic.
вразбежку *adv.* alternate, alternately;

размещение в. staggering; расположенный в. staggered, alternated; стыки в. alternate joints.

вразбро/д *adv.* separately, without order; —с *adv.* scattered, haphazard.

вразвилку *adv.* forked, pronged; ось в. forked axle.

вразрез *adv.* contrary; (elec.) in series; идти в. *v.* oppose.

вразум/ительный *a.* perspicuous, comprehensible, intelligible; persuasive; —ить, —лять *v.* explain, teach, make one comprehend; —иться *v.* understand, comprehend; —ление *n.* teaching, explaining, making one comprehend.

врасплох *adv.* by surprise, unawares.

врассечку *adv.* (elec.) in series.

врассыпную *adv.* in all directions.

враст/ание *n.* growing in, ingrowing; intergrowth, interlocking; —ать, —и *v.* grow in; intergrow, interlock; —ающий *a.* ingrowing; interlocking.

врастяжку *adv.* at full length, flat, prone.

врасщеп *adv.* split, forked; сварка в. split welding, fork welding, V-welding; соединение в. split joint.

врать *v.* lie, tell a lie.

врач *m.* doctor, surgeon, physician; —ебный *a.* medical; —евание *n.* doctoring, treating; —евать *v.* doctor, treat, cure.

враща/емый *a.* rotatable; —тель *m.* rotator.

вращательн/о-качающийся стол (ore concentration) rotary shaking table; —ый *a.* rotary, rotatory, rotatable; rotation, rotational; —ое движение rotary motion, rotation.

вращать *v.* revolve, rotate, turn; circulate (a liquid); circle; wind; drive; —ся *v.* revolve, rotate, turn, gyrate, circle; (mach.) run; —ся вокруг revolve (around), circle.

вращающ/ий *a.* rotating; в. момент torque; —ийся *a.*, вращаясь rotary, rotatory, rotating, revolving, revolvable; turning, gyrating, slewing; swivel; pivoted; (mach.) running; live (center); spinning (nucleus); —ийся влево (optics) levorotatory; —ийся вправо dextrorotatory; —ийся круг rotating disk, armature;

—ийся поперечник jib, boom; —ийся поршень impeller (of pump); —ийся стол turntable, revolving platform; —аяся печь revolving furnace, rotary furnace, rotating furnace; —аяся сила rotatory power, specific rotation; —аяся сушильная печь rotary dryer.

вращен/ие *n.* rotation, rotary motion, revolution, revolving, turning, gyration, slewing; pivoting; (mach.) running; circulation (of liquid); круговое в. revolution; левое в. (optics) levorotation; counterclockwise rotation; момент —ия moment of rotation; torque; ось —ия pivot, pivot axis; правое в. (optics) dextrorotation; clockwise rotation; точка —ия pivot, fulcrum.

вращполе *n.* rotating field.

ВРД *abbr.* (воздушно-реактивный двигатель) air-breathing jet engine.

вред *m.* harm, damage, injury, hurt; причинять в. *see* вредить.

вредител/ь *m.* (agr.) pest; blight; wrecker, saboteur; —и *pl.* vermin, pests; —ьский *a.* harmful; —ьство *n.* sabotage.

вредить *v.* harm, damage, injure, hurt, impair.

вредн/о *adv.* harmfully; it is harmful; —ость *f.* harm, damage, injury; harmfulness; —ый *a.* harmful, injurious, deleterious, detrimental, destructive; noxious (gas); over-(dose); —ое пространство idle space, dead space; clearance (in cylinder); obnoxious volume.

вредоносн/ый *see* вредный; —ые испарения noxious vapors.

врез/ание *n.* incision, gash, notch, bite; —анный *a.* incised, notched; serrated, saw-toothed; —ать, —ывать *v.* cut in, cut, engrave; fit in; embed; incise, entrench (meanders in a river); —аться, —ываться *v.* cut one's way in, bite into, run into; —ка *f.* cutting in, engraving; fitting in, setting in; inset map; —ной *a.* cut in; fit in, set in; —ной замок deadlock.

времена *pl.* of время.

временн/ик *m.* annals; —о *adv.* temporarily; —о назначенный *m.* acting officer, presiding officer; —о помогающее средство (pharm.) palliative; —ой *a.* time; —ость *f.* temporariness, provisionality; —ый *a.* temporary, provisional, tentative; intermittent; auxiliary; —ый контакт intermittent contact; —ая мера, —ое приспособление makeshift, expedient; —ое сопротивление temporary resistance, breaking-down point, breaking point, critical point.

**врем/я** *n.* time; (grammar) tense; —ена *pl.* times, the times; —енами, по —енам at times, sometimes, every now and then, intermittently; в. года season; в. от —ени from time to time, every now and then; в свое в. in due time, in due course; во-в. in time, at the right time, in season; к тому —ени by that time, by then; на некоторое в. for some time, for a while; постоянная —ени time constant; регулируемый по —ени timed; со —енем in time; тем —енем in the meantime, meanwhile; —яисчисление *n.* chronology.

**вровень** *adv.* level, flush (with).

**вроде** *prep. gen.* like, such as; нечто в. a kind of.

**врожденн/ость** *f.* innateness, inherency; —ый *a.* innate, inherent, inborn, native, natural, original; congenital (disease).

**врозницу** *adv.* retail, at retail.

**врозь** *adv.* apart, asunder, separately.

**вросший** *a.* intergrown.

**врс.** *abbr.* (верста) verst.

**вруб** *m.* cut, notch, channel; (min.) crosscutting; —ать, —ить *v.* chop in, cut in; groove, notch; (elec.) switch on, throw in (switch); —ка *f.* cut, notch; notching, grooving; соединять —кой *v.* mortise; —ленный *a.* cut in, notched, grooved; switched on.

**врубов/ой** *a.* chopping, cutting; в. молот pickax, pick; —ая машина (min.) cutting machine, cutter.

**вру/н** *m.*, —нья *f.* liar; —т *pr. 3 pl. of* врать.

**вруч/ать, —ить** *v.* hand, give, deliver, entrust; —ение *n.* handing, committing, entrusting; delivery; presentation.

**вручную** *adv.* hand, by hand, manual, manually; откованный в. hand-forged; отсортированный в. hand-picked; подача в. hand feed, manual feed; приводимый в. hand-operated, manual; сделанный в. handmade, manual.

**врш.** *abbr.* (вершок) vershock.

**вры/вать, —ть** *v.* dig in; —ваться *v.* burst in.

**вряд, в. ли** *adv.* scarcely, hardly; в. ли it is doubtful (whether), it is not likely.

**в.с.** *abbr.* (водяной столб) water column; (воздушносухой) air-dry; вс— *see also* вос—.

**вса/дить, —живать** *v.* set in, embed; thrust, plunge, drive in; plant; —дник *m.* rider; —женный *a.* set in, embedded; planted.

**всаливание** *n.* salting in.

**всасыв/аемость** *f.* absorbability; —аемый *a.* absorbable; suction; —аемый воздух suction air; —ание *n.* suction, sucking, drawing in; absorption; intake, induction; indraft; —ать *v.* suck, suck in, draw, draw in; absorb.

**всасывающ/ий** *a.* sucking, suction, pull; absorbing, absorptive; intake; в. вентилятор suction fan, exhaust fan; в. клапан suction valve, inlet valve; в. насос suction pump; в. ход admission stroke; —ая система exhaust system; —ая склянка suction bottle; —ая способность absorbing capacity; —ая труба suction pipe, intake; —ее действие sucking action, suction, pull; —ее окно, —ее устройство intake.

**всачиваться** *v.* seep in, be absorbed.

**все** *n. of* весь; *pl.* all, everybody, everyone; *adv.* always, all the time; still; only, all; в. еще still; в. же nevertheless; во —м in all respects.

**все—** *prefix* omni—, pan—, all; —возможный *a.* every kind of, all kinds of, various; —волновый *a.* all-wave; long (counter).

**всегда** *adv.* always, at all times, constantly, ever; —жив *see* барвинок; —шний *a.* usual, habitual, customary, normal.

ВСЕГЕИ *abbr.* (Всесоюзный научно-исследовательский геологический институт) All-Union Scientific Research Geological Institute; ВСЕГИНГЕО *abbr.* (Всесоюзный научно-исследовательский институт гидрологии и инженерной геологии) All-Union Scientific Research Institute of Hydrology and Engineering Geology.

всего *see* весь; в.-навсего in all; but.

всед/енный, —невный *a.* daily, everyday.

всек *abbr.* (вольтсекунда) volt second.

всел/ение *n.* settling, quartering; establishment, installation; —енная *f.* universe; —енский *a.* universal; —ить, —ять *v.* settle; suggest; instil; —иться, —яться *v.* settle, move in.

всемерн/о *adv.* in every possible way; —ый *a.* of every kind, all possible.

всемеро *adv.* seven times; sevenfold; в. больше seven times as much; в. меньше one seventh; —м *adv.* seven (together).

все/мирный *a.* universal; world, worldwide; —направленный *a.* omnidirectional; —народный *a.* public, of all the people; —общий *a.* common, general, universal; —объемлющий *a.* universal; —охватывающий *a.* all-embracing, comprehensive; —поглощающий *a.* omnivorous; —пожирающий *a.* all-devouring; —постигающий *a.* omnipercipient.

всероссийский *a.* All-Russian.

всерьез *adv.* in earnest, seriously.

всес. *abbr.* (всесоюзный) All-Union.

все/светный *a.* universal, common; —сословный *a.* of all classes; —союзный *a.* Union, All-Union.

всесторонн/е *adv.* closely; thoroughly; comprehensively, in detail; —ий *a.* close; thorough, comprehensive, detailed.

все-таки *adv.* however, though, all the same, for all that, still.

всеуслышание: во в. publicly, openly.

всецел/о *adv.* wholly, completely, entirely, altogether; —ый *a.* whole, complete, entire, full.

всечасн/о *adv.*, —ый *a.* hourly.

всеядн/ый *a.* omnivorous; —ые животные (zool.) Omnivora.

вскакив/ание *n.* jumping up; —ать *v.* jump up, spring up, bounce up.

вскальзыв/ание *n.* slipping in; —ать *v.* slip in, slide in.

вскапыв/ание *n.* digging up; excavating; —ать *v.* dig up, trench; excavate.

вскармливать *v.* bring up, rear.

вски/дать, —дывать, —нуть *v.* toss up, throw up, lift up.

вскип/ание *n.* boiling up; effervescing, effervescence; blistering, seeds (in glaze); —ать, —еть *v.* boil, boil up, boil over; effervesce; bubble up, froth, foam; ferment; —ающий *a.* boiling up, boiling over; effervescing; —ятить *v.* boil, bring to a boil; scour; —ятиться *v.* boil, come to a boil.

вскло/коченный, —ченный *a.* matted, felted, entangled.

всколых/ать, —нуть, всколебать *v.* stir up.

вскольз/нуть *see* вскальзывать; —ь *adv.* slightly, superficially, casually.

вскоп/анный *a.* dug up, furrowed; —ать *see* вскапывать.

вскоре *adv.* soon, shortly after.

вскормить *see* вскармливать.

вскочить *see* вскакивать.

вскры/вать, —ть *v.* open; find out, reveal; dissect; lance (an abscess); —тие *n.* opening; discovery; dissection, autopsy; —тый *a.* opened; revealed, discovered; dissected; —ша *f.* (min.) removal, stripping; strip pit; debris; capping, overburden.

вслед *adv. and prep. dat.* after, following; в. за behind; послать в. *v.* forward; —ствие *prep. gen.* in consequence of, owing to, on account of.

вслу/х *adv.* aloud; —шаться, —шиваться *v.* listen.

всматриваться, всмотреться *v.* look into, examine, scrutinize, observe.

всов/ать, —ывать *v.* slip in, slide in, thrust in, insert.

всос/анный *a.* sucked in, pulled in, drawn in; suction; absorbed; —ать *see* всасывать.

вспадать *v.* occur; в. на ум occur (to one).

вспаивать *v.* nurse with milk.
вспархивать *v.* fly up.
вспарывать *v.* rip open.
вспасть *see* вспадать.
вспа/ханный *a.* plowed, tilled; —хать, —хивать *v.* plow, till, cultivate; —хивание *n.*, —шка *f.* plowing, tilling.
вспенив/ание *n.* foaming, frothing; —атель *m.* (min.) frothing agent; —ать, вспенить *v.* froth, foam, lather; —аться *v.* froth; —ающий *a.* frothing; —ающий реактив, —ающее средство frothing agent.
всплес/к *m.* splash, splashing; surge; —кивание *n.* splashing; stirring; (met.) rabbling; —кивать, —нуть *v.* splash; stir; rabble.
всплош/ную, —ь *adv.* without interruption, continuously; in succession.
всплы/вание, —тие *n.* floating, floating up, emersion; —вать, —ть *v.* float, float up, come to the surface, rise to the surface, emerge; —вающий *a.* supernatant; —вной *a.* floating; flotation (process); —тый *a.* floated.
вспоить *see* вспаивать.
всполаскивать *see* всполоскать.
всполашивать *see* всполошить.
всполз/ание *n.* creeping; —ать *v.* creep.
всполос/кать, —нуть *v.* rinse.
всполошить *v.* raise an alarm; rouse, startle; —ся *v.* take alarm.
вспом/инать, —нить *v.* recollect, recall, remember, think (of); —инаться *v.* come back to one's mind.
вспомогательн/ый *a.* auxiliary, accessory, subsidiary; relief, emergency, spare; booster; в. агрегат, —ое устройство booster; в. двигатель servomotor, auxiliary motor; —ая установка branch establishment; subsidiary plant; —ая часть accessory; —ое средство means.
вспороть *see* вспарывать.
вспорхнуть *see* вспархивать.
вспот/елый *a.* perspiring, perspired; —еть *v.* perspire, become perspired, sweat.
вспрыг/ивать, —нуть *v.* jump up.
вспрыс/кивание *n.* sprinkling, spraying, injection; —кивать, —нуть *v.* sprinkle, spray, inject.

вспух/ать, —нуть *v.* swell; —лый *a.* swollen.
вспуч/енный *a.* swollen, distended, inflated; raised; —ивание *n.* swelling, swelling up, expanding, inflation, blowing up; buckling, bulging; (cer.) bloating; effervescing; (geol.) heave, heaving; —ивать, —ить *v.* swell, swell up, puff up, blow up, distend; raise; —иваться *v.* swell up, bulge, blow out; effervesce, ferment; (met.) blister; —ивающийся *a.* swelling; heaving; —ина *f.* swelling; blister.
вспыл/ить *v.* fire up, get angry; —ьчивый *a.* hot-tempered, hasty, irritable.
вспых/ивание *see* вспышка; —ивать, —нуть *v.* flash, flare up, burst into flames, deflagrate; scintillate; —ивающий *a.* flashing, flaring; deflagrating.
вспышк/а *f.* flash, flare, blaze; ignition, spark; scintillation; outburst, outbreak, explosion, detonation, fulmination; deflagration; (astrophysics) burst; давать —у *v.* fulminate; flare, flash; момент —и ignition point; проба на —у flash test; сгорание со —ою deflagration; температура —и, точка —и flash point.
вспять *adv.* backwards, back.
встав/ание *n.* rising, getting up; —ать *v.* get up, stand up, rise.
встав/ить, —лять *v.* put in, insert, intercalate, set (in), fit (in), embed, incase, secure, fix in; introduce; —ка *f.* insert, insertion piece, inset; insertion, setting in; interpolation; —кодержатель *m.* (elec.) fuse holder; —ление *n.* insertion, introduction, installation; —ленный *a.* inserted, set in; installed, mounted; nested; inlaid; —ной *a.* inserted, insertion; plug-in; detachable; —ной зуб false tooth; (mech.) bit; —ной-вытяжной *a.* push-pull; —очный *a.* insertion (piece); intercalary (growth).
встар/ину, —ь *adv.* in olden times.
встать *see* вставать.
встревож/енный *a.* anxious, worried, agitated, upset; —енье *n.* alarm; —ить *v.* alarm, give the alarm.

встреп/ать *v.* ruffle, shake up; —ка *f.* shaking, thrashing.

встре/тить, —чать *v.* meet, encounter, find; —чаться *v.* meet, come across; be found, occur (of natural resources); —ча *f.* meeting, encounter; линия —чи line of impact; угол —чи angle of incidence; —чно-параллельный *a.* antiparallel; —чный *a.* counter (flow, plan, etc.); back; contrary, opposite; head (wind).

встроенный *a.* built in, fixed.

встря/ска *f.*, —хивание *n.* shaking, shaking up, jarring; jar; stirring up; —хиватель *m.* shaker; (rad.) scrambler; —хивать, —хнуть *v.* shake, agitate; —хивающий *a.* shaking; —хивающий стол jarring table, vibrating table, vibrator; —хивающий транспортер jigging conveyer; —хивающая решетка vibrating screen, shaking screen; —хивающая формовочная машина (molding) joltramming machine.

вступ/ать, —ить *v.* enter, step in; —аться, —иться *v.* intercede (for); —ающий *a.* entering, incoming; —ительный *a.* introductory, admission, ingoing, incoming; entrance (examination); —ление *n.* entry, entrance; introduction; opening, inlet; prelude, preface.

встык *adv.* butt; приделанный в. butted; сваривать в. *v.* butt-weld; сварка в. butt welding; соединение в. butt joint (of pipe), abutting joint.

ВСУ *abbr.* (Военно-санитарное управление) Medical department; (ветросиловая установка) wind power plant.

всунут/ый *a.* put in, inserted; —ь *see* всовывать.

всухую *adv.* dry; шлифованный в. dry ground; шлифовать в. *v.* dry grind.

всх. *abbr.* (всходы) seedlings; (всхожесть) germinating capacity.

ВСХВ *abbr.* (Всесоюзная сельскохозяйственная выставка) All-Union Agricultural Fair; ВСХО *abbr.* (Всесоюзное сельскохозяйственное общество) All-Union Agricultural Society.

всхо/д *m.* ascent, rise; —ды *pl.* young growth, sprouts, shoots; seedlings; —дить *v.* mount, ascend; (bot.)

sprout, germinate; —дозащитный *a.* protective-mulch; —жесть *f.* germinating capacity, germination; —жий *a.* germinating.

всып/ание *n.*, —ка *f.* filling, pouring in (dry material); —анный *a.* poured in; —ать *v.* fill (with), pour in; —ной *a.* pouring; random, haphazard.

всырую *adv.* wet, damp; формовка в. (met.) green sand molding.

ВСЭ *abbr.* (ветеринарносанитарная экспертиза) veterinary and sanitary inspection.

всюду *adv.* everywhere, anywhere.

вся *f. of* весь; —кий *a. and pron.* any, every; anyone, anybody, everyone, everybody; —чески *adv.* in every way; —ческий *a.* of every kind, every type.

вт *abbr.* (ватт) watt.

втайне *adv.* secretly, confidentially.

вталкив/ание *n.* forcing in, pressing in; —ать *v.* push in, force in, thrust in; —аться *v.* run into, collide (with).

втаптыв/ание *n.* treading down; —ать *v.* tread down, trample on.

втаскив/ание *n.* dragging in; —ать *v.* drag in, pull in, haul in.

втач/ать, —ивать *v.* stitch in.

втащить *see* втаскивать.

втек/ание *n.* inflowing, inflow, influx; —ать *v.* flow in, run in; давать —ать run in; —ающий *a.* inflowing; influent (stream); —ающая жидкость inflow.

втереть *see* втирать.

втеч/ение *see* втекание; —ь *see* втекать.

втирать *v.* rub in, smear in.

втис/кать, —кивать, —нуть *v.* press in, thrust in, force in; —киваться *v.* squeeze oneself into.

втолкнуть *see* вталкивать.

втоптать *see* втаптывать.

втор— *abbr.* (вторичный) secondary; *sec-* (compounds).

вторг/аться, —нуться *v.* trespass, encroach (upon), break in, intrude; raid, invade; intervene; —ающийся *a.* (geol.) intrusive, irruptive.

вторец: обтачивать в. *v.* face.

вторжение *n.* intrusion, inroad; invasion; outbreak; (geol.) irruption.

вторичн/о *adv.* a second time, again;

re—; secondarily; **в. нагревать** *v.* reheat; —**оротые** *pl.* (zool.) Deuterostoma; **в. -эмиттирующий** *a.* secondary-emission; —**ый** *a.* secondary; re—; reiterative; product (nucleus); —**ая реакция** secondary reaction; —**ое замерзание** refreezing, regelation.

**вторник** Tuesday.

**втор/ой** *a.* second;—**ого порядка** secondary; **во** —**ых** in the second place, secondly; —**оклассный** *a.* second-class, secondary; —**окурсник** *m.* sophomore.

**второпях** *adv.* hastily, hurriedly.

**второ/разрядный, —сортный** *a.* second-rate, inferior; —**сортная руда** (min.) seconds; —**степенный** *a.* secondary, less important, minor, accessory.

**втридорога** *adv.* exorbitant.

**втро/е** *adv.* three times, threefold; (fold) in three; **в. больше** three times as much; **в. меньше** one third; —**ем** *adv.* three (together); —**йне** *adv.* threefold.

**вт-с, втсек** *abbr.* (ватт-секунда) watt-second.

**втуз** *m.,* —**овский** *a. abbr.* (высшее техническое учебное заведение) higher technical school.

**втул/ка** *f.,* —**очный** *a.* bush, bushing, sleeve, sleeve pipe, socket, collar, boss; spigot, faucet; stopper, plug, bung, insert; hub (of wheel); pad; **в. стакана** (mach.) bush, bushing; —**очный ключ** socket wrench; —**очный подшипник** bush bearing; —**очная муфта** sleeve coupling.

**втупик** *adv.* dead end; **ставить в.** *v.* perplex, baffle, puzzle.

**втч, вт-ч** *abbr.* (ватт-час) watt-hour; **в т.ч.** *abbr.* (в том числе) among them.

**вты/кать** *v.* thrust into, drive into, stick into, plug in; —**чной** *a.* plug-in.

**втя/гивание** *n.* drawing in, pulling in, sucking, suction; —**гивать, —нуть** *v.* draw in, draw, pull in, pull, haul in; retract; suck in, absorb; implicate, involve; —**гиваться, —нуться** *v.* be drawn in; get used (to), get accustomed (to); —**жной** *a.* suction; plunger; —**нутый** *a.* drawn in, pulled in, sucked in.

**вуал/ирование** *n.* blooming, hazing (of coatings); —**ирующий** *a.* masking; —**ь** *f.* film, veil; (phot.) fog.

**ВУАН** *abbr.* (Всеукраинская академия наук) The Ukrainian Academy of Science; **ВУГИ** *abbr.* (Всесоюзный научно-исследовательский угольный институт) All-Union Scientific Research Coal Institute.

**Вуда металл, В. сплав** Wood's alloy (bismuth-lead-tin-cadmium alloy).

**вудвардит** *m.* (min.) woodwardite (a copper aluminum sulfate).

**Вудр/еффа шпонка, —уфа шпонка, —уффа шпонка** Woodruff key.

**вуз** *m.,* —**овский** *a. abbr.* (высшее учебное заведение) higher institute of learning; university, college.

**вулк/абестон** *m.* Vulcabeston (insulator); —**алоза** *f.* Vulcalose (insulator); —**алок процесс** Vulcalock process (lining metal surface with rubber).

**вулкан** *m.* volcano; **действующий в., огнедышащий в.** active volcano.

**вулканиз/ат** *m.* vulcanized rubber; —**атор** *m.* vulcanizer; —**ационный** *a.,* —**ация** *f.* vulcanization, cure; **ускоритель** —**ации** rubber accelerator; —**ированный, —ованный** *a.* vulcanized; —**ировать, —овать** *v.* vulcanize; —**м** *m.* (geol.) volcanism; —**ование** *n.* vulcanization.

**вулканит** *m.* vulcanite (a hard rubber).

**вулканическ/ий** *a.* volcanic; **в. пепел** volcanic ash, volcanic tuff, tuff; —**ая порода** volcanic rock; —**ого происхождения** of volcanic origin, volcanic; igneous; plutonic; —**ое стекло** (petr.) volcanic glass, obsidian.

**вулканоид** *m.* mud volcano.

**вулканолог/ический** *a.* volcanological; —**ия** *f.* volcanology.

**вулка/нский** *a.* (geol.) vulcanian (eruption); —**нфибра** *f.* vulcanized fiber (leather substitute); —**фор** *m.* Vulcafor (an English rubber accelerator); —**цит** *m.* Vulcacite (a German rubber accelerator).

**вулпиновая кислота** vulpinic acid, vulpic acid.

**вульгарный** *a.* (biol.) common.

**вультекс** *m.* vultex (vulcanized rubber latex).

**Вульфа склянка** Woulfe bottle.

**вульфенит** *m.* (min.) wulfenite (a lead molybdate).

**вульфова склянка** *see* **Вульфа склянка.**

**Вурстера красный** Wurster's red.

**вурц/илит** *m.* wurtzilite (an asphaltic mineral); **—ит** *m.* wurtzite (a zinc sulfide).

**вута** *f.* bracket (in reinforced concrete construction).

**Вут/за сталь, —ца сталь, вутц** *m.*, **вуц** *m.* wootz, wootz steel, Indian steel.

**вуцин** *m.* vuzine, isooctylhydrocupreine.

**вход** *m.* entry, entrance, entering, admission, access; intake, inlet, mouth; (computer) input; **на —е** inlet (temperature, etc.); input (velocity, etc.); **—ить** *v.* enter, come in, get in, walk in; penetrate; become (a habit); be taken (into consideration); **—ной** *a.* entrance, entering, entry, inlet; input; re-entrant (angle); **—ное отверстие** inlet, intake; **—ящий** *a.* incoming, entering, entrance, ingoing; male (screw thread); **—ящий журнал** book of entries.

**вхождение** *n.* entering, entry, walking in.

**вхолодную** *adv.* cold; **ковать в.** *v.* forge cold; hammer-harden; **окраска в.** cold dyeing.

**вхолостую** *adv.* idle, empty, no-load; **идя в., работа в., работающий в.** (mach.) idling, running idle, running without a load; **работать в.** *v.* idle, run idle.

**ВХТУ** *abbr.* (**Высшее химико-технологическое училище**) Higher School of Chemical Engineering.

**вце/дить, —цеживать** *v.* filter in; pour in; transfuse; **—женный** *a.* filtered in.

**вцеп/иться, —ляться** *v.* catch hold (of), hold fast, cling.

**ВЦСПС** *abbr.* (**Всесоюзный центральный совет профессиональных союзов**) The All-Union Central Council of Trade Unions.

**ВЧ** *abbr.* (**высокочастотный**) high-frequency.

**вчера** *adv.* yesterday; **в. вечером** last night; **—шний** *a.* yesterday's.

**вчерне** *adv.* in the rough, unfinished.

**вчетверо** *adv.* four times; (fold) in four; **в. больше** four times as much; **в. меньше** one fourth; **—м** *adv.* four (together).

**вчинать** *v.* begin, take the initiative.

**вчистую** *adv.* clean, final, in final form; **обрабатывать в.** *v.* finish, dress.

**вчит/аться, —ываться** *v.* read attentively, become absorbed.

**вшестеро** *adv.* six times; **в. больше** six times as much; **в. меньше** one sixth; **—м** *adv.* six (together).

**вши** *pl. of* **вошь**; true lice (*Anoplura*).

**вшивать** *v.* sew in, stitch in.

**вшив/еть** *v.* become louse-infested; **—ица** *f.* (bot.) lousewort (*Pedicularis*).

**вшив/ка** *f.* sewing in; **—ной** *a.* sewn in.

**вшив/ость** *f.* (med.) pediculosis; **—ый** *a.* louse-infested; louse; **—ая трава** (bot.) stavesacre (*Delphinium staphysagria*).

**вширь** *adv.* broadwise.

**вшит/ый** *a.* sewn in; **—ь** *see* **вшивать.**

**вшпунт** *adv.* groove; **обшивка в.** grooved-tongued boarding; **соединение в., сплачивание в.** groove and tongue joint; cleat.

**въед/аться** *v.* corrode, eat into; **—чивость** *f.* corrosiveness; **—чивый** *a.* corrosive.

**въезд** *m.*, **—ной** *a.* drive, approach, avenue.

**въезжать** *v.* enter, drive in, move into.

**въесться** *see* **въедаться.**

**въехать** *see* **въезжать.**

**вы** *pron. pl.* you.

**вы—** *prefix* ex—, out of.

**выбалансировать** *v.* balance.

**выбег** *m.* running out, coasting; (mach.) running down; overshoot, overswing (of pointer); **—гать, —жать** *v.* run out.

**выбел/ивание, —ка** *see* **беление; —ить** *see* **белить.**

**выбив/ание** *n.*, **—ка** *f.* beating out, hammering out, knocking out, dislodging; stamping, chasing, embossing; **—ать** *v.* beat out, hammer out, knock out, drive out, dislodge; force open; stamp, punch (trade-mark, etc.); chase, emboss, coin; **—аться из сил** *v.* do one's utmost, be exhausted; **—ной** *a.* knock-out; stamping, punching; chasing, embossing; bursting (charge of shrapnel).

**выбир/атель** *m.* selector; (elec.) selector switch; **—ать** *v.* choose, select, single out; pick, pick out, cull; (min.) dig up, take up; recover; —**аться** *v.* be chosen; get out, move.

**выбит/ый** *a.* knocked out; stamped, punched; knocked-on (atom; electron); overgrazed (pasture); —**ь** *see* **выбивать.**

**выбо/ина** *f.*, —**й** *m.* hollow, dent, indentation, spot; rut.

**выбой/ка** *f.*, —**чатый** *a.* siftings, fines; (text.) printed linen.

**выбор** *m.* choice, selection, choosing; sample; option; election; **без** —**а** at random; **возможность** —**а** option; **остановить свой в.** *v.* fix on, decide on; —**ы** *pl.* election; —**ка** *f.* selection, excerpt; sample; recovery; —**ный** *a.* chosen; elective, elected, electoral; —**очный** *a.* selective; sample, sampling; random, spot (check); in patches; —**щик** *m.* voter.

**выбраживать** *see* **выбродить.**

**выбраковывать** *v.* cull, discard.

**выбранный** *a.* chosen, selected.

**выбрасыв/ание** *n.* throwing out, discarding; projection (of rays); discomposition, knocking out (of atom); —**атель** *m.* ejector, extractor, knockout, knock-out rod, shedder, lift-out attachment, lifting-out device; —**ать** *v.* throw out, discard, reject; eject; knock out; shed; project (rays); —**аться** *v.* be thrown away, be discarded; jump out.

**выбрать** *see* **выбирать.**

**выбри/вать,** —**ть** *v.* shave thoroughly.

**выбродить** *v.* ferment, work.

**выбро/с** *m.* ejection; overshooting; **в. пламени** backfire; —**ски,** —**сы** *pl.* ejections, discharge; refuse, rubbish; —**сать,** —**сить** *see* **выбрасывать;** —**шенный** *a.* thrown out, ejected, rejected.

**выбур/авливать,** —**ивать** *v.* drill out.

**выбы/вать,** —**ть** *v.* leave, quit.

**вывал/ивать,** —**ить** *v.* tumble out, throw out, dump, dump out, tip over; —**иваться** *v.* fall out.

**вывар/енный** *a.* boiled, extracted; degummed (silk), scoured; —**ивание** *n.* boiling, boiling out, extraction, decocting; (text.) scouring; —**ивать,** —**ить** *v.* boil, boil out, extract; boil

down, boil off; digest; —**ивать клей** (text.) degum; —**ка** *f.* boiling; extraction, residue; (pharm.) decoction; brewing, brew; refining; (dyeing) mordant; —**очный** *a.* boiling, extraction; —**очная соль** sodium chloride, common salt.

**вывед/ать,** —**ывать** *v.* investigate, find out; —**ение** *n.* drawing out; removal; —**еный** *a.* brought out, revealed, exposed, uncovered.

**вывезти** *see* **вывозить.**

**вывер/енный** *a.* adjusted, aligned; calibrated; —**ить** *see* **выверять;** —**ка** *f.* adjustment, alignment, centering, lining up; gaging; control.

**вывернуть** *see* **вывертывать, выворачивать.**

**выверочн/ый** *a.* straightening, aligning, adjustment; **в. винт** adjusting screw; fine adjustment; —**ая доска** straightedge.

**вывертывать** *v.* unscrew, twist out, *see also* **выворачивать;** —**ся** *v.* get out.

**вывер/щик** *m.* adjuster; —**ять** *v.* adjust, align, line up, straighten; verify, test, check; gage, calibrate; set (a watch); —**яющийся** *a.* adjustable.

**вывес/ить** *see* **вывешивать;** —**ка** *f.* sign, signboard.

**вывести** *see* **выводить.**

**выветр/елый** *a.* weathered, abraded, wind-worn, wind-sculptured; —**енный** *a.* aired; weathered, eroded, abraded; —**ивание** *n.* airing, ventilation; weathering, disintegration, erosion, eolation; seasoning; efflorescence (of salts); **кора** —**ивания** mantle (weathering crust); —**ивать,** —**ить** *v.* air, ventilate; season; —**иваться,** —**иться** *v.* be aired; weather, disintegrate, erode; effloresce; —**ивающийся** *a.* efflorescent; —**ившийся** *a.* weathered, wind-blown.

**вывешивать** *v.* hang out; *see also* **взвешивать.**

**вывин/тить,** —**чивать** *v.* unscrew, screw out; —**ченный** *a.* unscrewed, screwed out, loosened.

**вывих** *m.* dislocation, sprain; (med.) luxation; —**ивать,** —**нуть** *v.* dislocate, sprain; —**нутый** *a.* dislocated, out of joint, sprained.

**вывод** *m.* conclusion, deduction, inference, corollary; result, consequence, development; (math.) derivation; (elec.) tapping; outlet, escape; leading out; **отсюда в., что** the result is that; in conclusion; **сделать —ы** *v.* draw conclusions, conclude; **—ить** *v.* lead out, take out, bring out, help out (of); conclude, deduct, infer; develop, evolve; (math.) derive; breed, hatch (chickens); exterminate, eradicate; take out (stain); erect (building); **—ить его из себя** try his patience; **—ка** *f.* starting up (of plant); heating-up campaign (of glass furnace); **—ковый** *a. of* **выводок;** (biol.) proliferous; **—ковая камера** (pal.) brood pouch.

**выводн/ой** *a.* leading out; (physiol.) excretory; reserve (field); **—ая труба** outlet pipe; delivery pipe.

**выводок** *m.* hatch, brood (of birds).

**выводящий** *a.* outgoing, exit; (physiol.) excretory.

**вывоз** *m.* export, exportation; **—ить** *v.* export; remove, take out, wheel out; **—ной** *a.* export.

**вывор/ачивание** *n.* turning inside out, reversing; **—ачивать, —отить** *v.* turn inside out, reverse; sprain (joint); **—от** *m.* reverse, under side; **—отный, —оченный** *a.* inverted, reversed.

**вывяливать** *v.* dry or cure in open air.

**выгад/ать, —ывать** *v.* economize, save, spare; gain (time); **—ка** *f.*, **—ывание** *n.* economy, saving; gain.

**выгар** *m.*, **—ки** *pl.* slag, dross, cinder, scoria; volcanic scoria.

**выгиб** *m.* bend, outward curve, flexure, warping; **—ание** *n.* curving out, arching; **—атель** *m.* adjuster; **—ать** *v.* curve, bend, camber, buckle, bend out; **—аться** *v.* arch, bulge.

**выгла/дить, —живать** *v.* smooth down, smooth, plane; iron, press (clothes).

**выглублять** *v.* raise out of the ground.

**выгля/деть, —дывать, —нуть** *v.* look, appear, seem; look out, glance out.

**выгнать** *see* **выгонять.**

**выгнут/ость** *f.* convexity, bulging; **—ый** *a.* convex, cambered; **—ое бревно** camber beam; **—ь** *see* **выгибать.**

**выгов/аривать, —орить** *v.* pronounce, utter; stipulate, specify; lecture, reprimand; **в. себе** reserve for oneself; **—ор** *m.* pronunciation, accent; lecture, reprimand, reproof, rebuke, admonition.

**выгод/а** *f.* profit, advantage, benefit, gain, interest; **—но** *adv.* profitably; it is profitable, it is economical; **—ность** *f.* economy, advantageousness; utility, efficiency; **—ный** *a.* profitable, advantageous, beneficial, gainful, remunerative, favorable; efficient.

**выгон** *m.* distillation; pasture, pasturage; **—ка** *f.* distillation; forcing (of plants); **—очный** *a.* distillation; forcing, forced (plant); **—ять** *v.* drive out, expel, force out; chase away; distil; force.

**выгораживать** *v.* fence out, exclude; screen, shield, defend.

**выгор/ание** *n.* burning out, dying out; thorough combustion; burn-out, pitting; (nucl.) burn-up; **—ать, —еть** *v.* burn out, burn down, die out; fade (of color); **—елый** *a.* burned out; faded.

**выгородить** *see* **выгораживать.**

**выгравир/ованный** *a.* carved out; sunken; **—овать** *v.* carve out.

**выгреб** *m.* raking out; cesspool; **—ать, выгрести** *v.* rake out, scrape out, draw out; **—ки** *pl.* rakings, scrapings; **—ной** *a.* raking; **—ная яма** cesspool.

**выгруз/ить, выгружать** *v.* unload, dump, drop, discharge; **—ка** *f.* unloading, discharging, discharge; freight handling; **—очный** *a.* unloading, discharge, discharging; **—очный ящик** discharge box, discharge hopper.

**выгул** *m.*, **—ьный** *a.* range, pasture.

**выдавать** *v.* distribute, give out, issue, give away, deliver; pay out (rope); draw (a bill on); **в. себя** pass for, pretend to be; **—ся** *v.* protrude, project, jut, overhang; swell out; be embossed.

**выдав/ить, —ливать** *v.* press out, press, squeeze out, squeeze, force out, extrude; spin (on lathe); **—ка** *f.*, **—ливание** *n.* squeezing out, extrusion; stamping, pressing; spinning (on lathe); —**ленный** *a.* squeezed out, extruded; stamped, pressed out; sunken.

**выдаивать** *v.* milk dry, strip (a cow).

**выдалблив/ание** *n.* excavation; slotting; —**ать** *v.* excavate, hollow out, dig out.

**выдать** *see* **выдавать.**

**выдача** *f.* distribution, delivery, delivering; ration; conveying; output (of mine); drawing (of coal).

**выдающийся** *a.* prominent, outstanding, distinguished; protruding, projecting.

**выдви/гать** *v.* put forward, introduce, promote; **в. вперед** push forward, promote, advertise; —**гаться** *v.* move out; become successful; —**гающийся** *a.* prominent, outstanding; —**жение** *n.* promotion, advance, advancement.

**выдвижн/ой** *a.* extensible, extension-type, pull-out, draw-out, telescopic; sliding (door, window); **в. калибр** slide gage; **в. ящик** drawer.

**выдвинуть** *see* **выдвигать.**

**выдел/анный** *a.* produced, manufactured; (leather) tanned, dressed; —**ать** *see* **выделывать.**

**выделен/ие** *n.* isolation, separation, separating out; formation; settling, precipitating, precipitation, deposit; evolution, generation, liberation (of heat, gas, etc.); emanation, exhalation, emission; escape, loss; (physiol.) secretion, excretion, discharge; (met.) segregation; elimination, extraction; recovery; discrimination; **в. осадка** precipitation; **в. фосфора** dephosphorization; **момент —ия, состояние —ия** nascent state; **водород в момент —ия** nascent hydrogen; **способствующий —ию** secretory.

**выдел/енный** *a.* isolated, separated, separated out; formed; precipitated, settled out; evolved, liberated, given off, yielded; secreted; preferred (axis); parting (silver); **в. счетчиком** counterdefined; —**ившийся** *a.* separated; precipitated; evolved (gas); —**итель** *m.* separator, discriminator (math.) eliminant; —**ительный** *a.* (physiol.) secretory (gland); excretory (system); —**ить** *see* **выделять.**

**выдел/ка** *f.*, —**ывание** *n.* manufacture,

production; (leather) tanning, dressing; —**ывать** *v.* make, manufacture, produce, prepare; tan, dress.

**выдел/яемость** *f.* separability; precipitability; —**яемый** *a.* separable; precipitable; —**ять** *v.* isolate, separate, separate out; settle out, precipitate, deposit; evolve, liberate, give off (gas, heat, etc.); set free, yield, exhale; drive out, drive off, eliminate; lose; (physiol.) secrete, discharge, excrete, exude; withdraw, take away, extract; segregate; distinguish, discriminate; —**яться** *v.* separate out; precipitate out; be given off, liberated; escape, emanate (from); segregate; stand out; receive one's share; —**яющий** *a.* giving off, yielding; secretory; —**яющийся** *a.* separating out; precipitating; escaping (gas); prominent, outstanding, selective.

**выдергивать** *v.* jerk, pull, draw (out).

**выдерж/анный** *a.* seasoned; exposed, set out, put out; sustained, kept, maintained; self-restrained; postponed; —**ать, —ивать** *v.* age, season (lumber); stand, bear, endure, withstand, hold out; pass (a test); hold, sustain, keep, maintain; (met.) soak; run (an edition); **не —ивать** fail; —**ивание** *n.* seasoning; enduring, withstanding; holding, keeping.

**выдержк/а** *f.* extract, passage; firmness, endurance, stamina; aging; (phot.) exposure; (met.) soaking; **в. времени** delay, time lag; **с —ой времени** delayed-action, time-lag; timed; **резервуар —и** (nucl.) decay tank.

**выдернуть** *see* **выдергивать.**

**выдирать** *v.* rip up, rip out, tear out.

**выдолб/ить** *see* **выдалбливать;** —**ленный** *a.* hollowed out; slotted.

**выдох** *m.* expiration; —**лый, —шийся** *a.* evaporated, flat; —**нуться** *see* **выдыхаться.**

**выдра** *f.* (zool.) otter; (broaching and punching) metal scrap.

**выдразнивание** *n.* teasing, poling; **окончательное в.** (met.) toughening by poling.

**выдрать** *see* **выдирать.**

**выдув/альщик** *m.* (glass) blower; —**ание** *n.*, —**ка** *f.* blowing out, blow-off, expulsion, discharge; deflation; eolation, wind erosion; —ать *v.* blow, blow out, blow off; deflate; —ной *a.* blow, blow-out; —ной клапан blow valve.

**выдум/ать, —ывать** *v.* invent, devise, contrive, think out, imagine; —ка *f.* invention, fiction, fabrication; —щик *m.* inventor.

**выдуть** *see* **выдувать.**

**выдых/ание** *n.* expiration; evaporation, exhalation; —ать *v.* expire, exhale, breathe out; —аться *v.* expire; evaporate, volatilize; fade (of odor).

**выед/ание** *n.* corrosion; —ать *v.* eat out, corrode, pit.

**выез/д** *m.* departure, excursion; —дка *f.* breaking in, training; —жать *v.* leave, depart; —жать на exploit.

**выем/ка** *f.*, —очный *a.* hollow, recess, depression, dent, indentation; notch, notching, gap; groove, furrow, channel, channeling, flute, chamfer; (min.) cutting, excavation, digging; drawing, removal, extraction (of ore); dugout, ditch, gutter; housing; sample; угол —ки (surv.) angle of elevation; —чатокрылые моли gelechiid moths (*Gelechiidae*); —чатый *a.* notched, emarginate, sinuate.

**выесть** *see* **выедать.**

**выехать** *see* **выезжать.**

**выжать** *see* **выжимать, выжинать.**

**выждать** *see* **выжидать.**

**выжечь** *see* **выжигать.**

**выжив/аемость** *f.* survival; survival rate; —ание *n.* survival; driving out; —ать *v.* survive, outlive; drive out.

**выжиг/ание** *n.* burning out; roasting; cauterizing; —ать *v.* burn, burn out, burn up; roast, remove by roasting, calcine; sear, cauterize; brand; (welding) penetrate.

**выжид/ание** *n.* waiting; —ательный *a.* expectant; —ать *v.* wait for an opportunity, take one's time.

**выжим/ание** *n.* squeezing, squeezing out, pressing; centrifuging; stripping; —ать *v.* squeeze, squeeze out, press, press out, force out; centrifuge; wring, wring out; extract; —ки *pl.* husks, residue, refuse.

**выжинать** *v.* (agr.) reap clean.

**выжить** *see* **выживать.**

**вызв/анный** *a.* produced, caused (by); induced; (tel.) called; в. облучением radiation-induced; —ать *see* **вызывать.**

**вызвол/ить, —ять** *v.* help, rescue.

**выздор/авливание, —овление** *n.* recovery, convalescence; —авливать, —оветь *v.* recover, improve, get well, convalesce; —авливающий *a.* convalescent; —овевший *a.* recovered.

**вызов** *m.* summons; (tel.) call; provocation, challenge.

**вызолотить** *v.* gild.

**вызрев/ать** *v.* ripen, grow ripe; —ший *a.* ripened; hardwood (cutting).

**вызыв/аемый** *a.* call, called; producible; effected, caused; —ать *v.* provoke, stir, arouse; give rise (to), bring about, cause, effect; elicit, call forth, evoke, induce, produce; draw, draw out; excite, generate (current); exert (pressure); (tel.) call, call up; send for, summon; —аться *v.* volunteer, offer; —ающий *a.* provocative; causing, bringing about; —ной *a.* (tel.) call, calling.

**выигр/ать, —ывать** *v.* win, gain, profit; —ыш *m.* gain, profit; коэффициент —ыша gain factor; —ышный *a.* winning; advantageous, effective.

**выиск/ть.**, —ивание *n.* search; —ать, —ивать *v.* hunt (for); find out, discover.

**выйный** *a.* (anat.) nuchal.

**выйти** *see* **выходить.**

**выка** *see* **вика.**

**выказ/ать, —ывать** *v.* show, display, manifest; —ной *a.* exhibited.

**выкалывать** *v.* prick out.

**выкапыв/ание** *n.* excavation; —ать *v.* dig up, dig out, excavate, unearth.

**выкармливать** *v.* fatten; bring up, rear.

**выкат** *m.*, —ывание *n.* rolling out; —ать, —ывать *v.* roll out, wheel out.

**выкач/анный** *a.* pumped out; —ать, —ивать *v.* pump, pump out, empty, evacuate, exhaust, deflate; —ивание *n.*, —ка *f.* pumping, pumping out, evacuation, exhaustion, deflation.

**выки/дать, —дывать, —нуть** *v.* throw out, reject; (med.) miscarry, abort; —дыш *m.* miscarriage, abortion.

**выкип/ать,** —еть *v.* boil away, evaporate by boiling; **пределы** —ания boiling range; **—елый** *a.* boiled away; **—ятить, —ячивать** *v.* boil out, boil; scald.

**выклад/ка** *f.,* **—ывание** *n.* laying out, unpacking; calculation, computation; lining, facing; (met.) fettling; **делать —ки** *v.* compute; **—ывать** *v.* lay out, take out, unpack; line, face; **—ывать кирпичом** *v.* brick.

**выклев/ать, —ывать** *v.* peck out.

**выклинив/ание** *n.* thinning, thinning out, wedging out, cropping out, pinching, tapering (of vein); **—аться** *v.* thin out, wedge out, crop out, pinch out, taper, die out, play out.

**выключ/аемый** *a.* capable of being switched off; **в. элемент** spare cell; **—атель** *m.* (elec.) switch, disconnecting switch, (contact) breaker, cut-out; releasing device, release; **—ать, —ить** *v.* disconnect, disengage, uncouple, release; turn off (current, gas), cut off, cut out, shut off; (elec.) switch off, break (contact); shut down, put out of service; throw out (of gear); **—ающий** *a.* disconnecting, disengaging, releasing; cut-off.

**выключен/ие** *n.* disconnecting, disengaging, release; cutting out; turning off (of current, gas), shutting off; (elec.) switching off, breaking (contact); shutting, shutdown, shutting down; **муфта —ия** release clutch; **положение —ия** off position; **—ный** *a.* disconnected; turned off, cut off, off; (elec.) switched off, dead; out of gear.

**выков/ать, —ывать** *v.* (met.) forge, hammer, hammer out, draw out.

**выковыр/ивать, —ять** *v.* pick out.

**выколачивать** *v.* knock out, beat out.

**выколка** *f.* pricking out, cutting out.

**выколот/ить** *see* **выколачивать; —ка** *f.* knock out, knock-out rod; drift.

**выколоть** *see* **выкалывать.**

**выкопать** *see* **выкапывать.**

**выкормить** *see* **выкармливать.**

**выкорчев/ать, —ывать** *v.* grub up, uproot; **—ывание** *n.* grubbing.

**выкрадывать** *v.* steal; tap (current, etc.).

**выкраивать** *v.* cut, cut out (by pattern).

**выкрасить** *v.* paint.

**выкрасть** *see* **выкрадывать.**

**выкраш/енный** *a.* painted; **—ивать** *see* **выкрасить.**

**выкрашиваться** *v.* break off, chip.

**выкристаллизов/ание** *n.* crystallization, crystallizing out; efflorescence; **—анный** *a.* crystallized out; **—ать, —ываться, —ываться** *v.* crystallize out, crystallize; effloresce.

**выкроить** *see* **выкраивать.**

**выкройк/а** *f.* pattern; **снять —у** *v.* cut out a pattern.

**выкру/гливать, —глить** *v.* round off; **—жать, —живать, —жить** *v.* round, scoop, chamfer; **—жка** *f.* rounding off; fillet, recess, chamfer.

**выкру/тить, —чивать** *v.* twist out, unscrew; wring out; centrifuge; **—титься, —чиваться** *v.* extricate oneself (from a difficulty); **—чивание** *n.* twisting out, unscrewing; wringing out; centrifuging; decomposition of aluminate in Bayer process.

**выкуп** *m.* repurchase.

**выкупать, —ся** *v.* bathe.

**выкуп/ать, —ить** *v.* redeem, buy back; buy out; **—ной** *a.* redeemable; **—ное право** right of repurchase.

**выкур/ивать, —ить** *v.* smoke, smoke out, fumigate; distil.

**выл** *past sing. of* **выть.**

**вылавливать** *v.* catch, get out; trap; recover.

**выламывать** *v.* break open; break off; **—ся** *v.* break out; chip.

**вылеж/ать, —ивать** *v.* lie out; **—аться, —иваться** *v.* age.

**вылез/ать, —ть** *v.* climb out, get out; fall out, come out.

**вылеп/ить, —лять** *see* **лепить.**

**вылет** *m.* flying out, departure, escape (of neutrons, etc.); overhang, overhang beam, overhanging length (of beam); boom (of crane); sweep (of lathe); gap; **длина —a** range (as of a water jet); **линия —a** line of departure; **—ать, —еть** *v.* fly out, escape; **—ающий** *a.* escaping, out-going, emitted.

**вылеч/ивание** *n.* curing, healing; **—ивать, —ить** *v.* cure, heal; **—иваться,**

—**иться** v. be cured, recover, get well.

**вылив/ание** n. pouring out, pouring off, decantation; —**ать** v. pour, pour out, pour off, decant; discharge; cast; —**аться** v. pour out, run out, flow out, be discharged.

**вылин/явший** a. faded, washed out; —**ять** v. fade out, lose color.

**вылит/ый** a. poured out, decanted; cast; —**ь** see **выливать**.

**выловить** see **вылавливать**.

**вылож/енный** a. laid out; lined; в. свинцом lead-lined; —**ить** see **выкладывать**.

**вылом** m., —**ка** f. breaking out; quarry; —**ать**, —**ить** see **выламывать**; —**ки** pl. (met.) scum, cobbings, dross.

**вылу/дить**, – **живать** v. tin, tinplate, coat with tin; —**женный** a. tinned.

**вылуп/иться**, —**ляться** v. hatch.

**вылущ/ение** n. (med.) enucleation; —**ить** see **лущить**.

**вымаз/ать**, —**ывать** v. soil, smear, daub; —**аться**, —**ываться** v. get dirty.

**выман/ивать**, —**ить** v. coax, entice; swindle.

**вымарать** see **вымарывать**.

**вымаривать** v. starve out, destroy.

**вымарыв/ание** n. expurgation; —**ать** v. soil, smear, dirty; expurgate, strike out, delete.

**вымасл/ивать**, —**ить** v. oil, grease.

**выматывать** v. wind up, wind out; deplete, drain, exhaust.

**вымачив/ание** n. steeping, soaking, maceration, wetting; —**ать** v. steep, soak, macerate, wet.

**вымащивать** v. pave.

**вымен** m., —**ивать**, —**ять** v. exchange, barter; —**енный** a. exchanged; —**ивание** n. exchanging, bartering.

**вымеобразный** a. mammatus (cloud).

**вымереть** see **вымирать**.

**вымерз/ание** n. winterkilling; —**ать**, —**нуть** v. freeze, freeze out, be destroyed by frost; —**лый** a. frozen, frost-bitten, destroyed by frost.

**вымер/ивание** n. measuring; —**ивать**, —**ить**, —**ять** v. measure, gage.

**вымерший** a. extinct.

**выме/сти**, —**тать** v. sweep out.

**выметывание** n. (bot.) tasseling, heading.

**вымешивать** v. stir, mix well; knead.

**вымир/ание** n. dying off, extinction; —**ать** v. die out, become extinct.

**вымогать** v. extort, wring out (a promise).

**вымоина** f. gully, washout, gulch, ravine.

**вымок/ать**, —**нуть** v. get wet, be drenched; soak, be steeped; (flax) be retted.

**вымол/ачивать**, —**отить** v. thrash out, beat out (grain); —**отка** f. thrashing.

**выморажив/ание** n. freezing out, destruction by frost; —**ать** v. freeze, freeze out, kill by frost.

**выморить** see **вымаривать**.

**вымор/оженный** a. frozen, frost-bitten, killed by frost; —**озить** see **вымораживать**; —**озок** m. frost-bitten plant.

**вымостить** see **вымащивать**.

**вымот/анный** a. depleted; —**ать** see **выматывать**.

**вымоч/енный** a. wetted, steeped, soaked; —**ить** see **вымачивать**; —**ка** f. wetting, soaking; wet rot (of seeds).

**вымощенный** a. paved.

**вымпел** m. pennant, streamer; (aero.) dropped message bag.

**вымыв/ание** n. washing, washing out; —**ать** v. wash, wash out.

**вымыл/ивать**, —**ить** v. soap.

**вымыс/ел** m. invention, fiction; —**лить** v. invent, contrive, devise.

**вымыт/ый** a. washed, washed out; —**ь** see **вымывать**.

**вымышлять** see **вымыслить**.

**вымя** n. udder (of cow).

**вынашивать** v., —**ся** see **выносить**; wear out (clothes, etc.).

**вынес/енный** a. taken out; remote, outlying; extension; external (instrument); sustained, tolerated; —**ти** see **выносить**.

**выним/ание** n. taking out, removal, withdrawal; —**ать** v. take out, remove, withdraw, draw out, extract.

**вынос** m. carrying out, bearing out; loss (on erosion); debris cone; outlying point; branch office; —**ить** v. take out, carry out; sustain, endure, undergo, tolerate, hold out, stand; pass (a resolution); —**ка** f. marginal note, footnote.

**выносли́в/ость** *f.* endurance, hardiness, resistance, strength; (radiation) tolerance; **преде́л —ости** (met.) endurance limit, fatigue limit; **—ый** *a.* enduring, hardy, sturdy, rugged.

**вынужд/а́ть, вы́нудить** *v.* force, compel, oblige; **—енный** *a.* forced, constrained; **быть —енным** *v.* have to, be obliged to.

**вы́нут/ый** *a.* removed, withdrawn, taken out; **—ь** *see* **вынима́ть.**

**выны́р/ивать, —нуть** *v.* come to the surface, emerge.

**выня́ньчить** *v.* nurse, tend.

**вып.** *abbr.* (вы́пуск) issue.

**вы́пад** *m.*, **—ка** *f.* falling out, precipitation; **—ать** *v.* fall out, fall, drop out, come out, separate out, precipitate; **—а́ющий** *a.* falling out, precipitating; (radiation) fallout; **—ение** *n.* falling out, falling, fall, precipitation, precipitate, deposit; (med.) prolapse; (radiation) fallout.

**вы́пал** *m.* discharge; **в. шпура** blast; **—ивать, —ить** *v.* fire, discharge; singe, scorch.

**выпалыв/а́ние** *n.* weeding; **—ать** *v.* weed.

**выпар/енный** *a.* evaporated, concentrated; **—ивание** *n.* evaporation, concentration; steaming; **я́ма для —ивания соли** salt pan; **—иватель, —итель** *m.* evaporator, concentrator; vaporizer; carburetor; **—ивать, —ить** *v.* evaporate, concentrate; steam; **—иваться** *v.* evaporate, vaporize; **—ительный** *a.* evaporating; **—ительная ча́шка** evaporating dish; **—ка** *f.* evaporated residue, concentrate; evaporator; **—ной, —ный** *a.* evaporating; **—ной аппара́т** evaporator; **—ная се́кция** stripping section, stripper (of fractionating column).

**вы́пасть** *see* **выпада́ть.**

**выпах/анный** *a.* plowed up; depleted (soil); **—ать, —ивать** *v.* plow, plow up.

**выпа́чкать** *v.* soil, dirty.

**выпека́ть** *v.* bake, bake thoroughly.

**выпен/ивать, —ить** *v.* clear from froth, clear from scum; **—иваться, —иться** *v.* froth out, froth over.

**вы́пер/еть** *see* **выпира́ть; —тый** *a.* pushed out, bulging.

**вы́печь** *see* **выпека́ть.**

**выпив/а́ть** *v.* drink, drink up; **—ший** *a.* drunk; having drunk.

**выпил/ивание** *n.* sawing, sawing out; **—ивать, —ить** *v.* saw, saw out; file out.

**выпир/а́ние** *n.* heaving (of plants); **—а́ть** *v.* protrude, bulge out.

**выпис/ать, —ывать** *v.* write (for), order (by mail); write out, copy, extract; **—ываться** *v.* be ordered; **—ка, —ь** *f.* extract, copy, copied passage; **—ной** *a.* mail order.

**вы́пить** *see* **выпива́ть.**

**выпих/ивать, —нуть** *v.* push out.

**выплав/ить, —лять** *v.* melt, melt out, extract (by melting); (met.) smelt, smelt down; **—ка** *f.*, **—ление** *n.* melting, extraction; (met.) smelting, founding; **—ленный, —ной** *a.* melted out, extracted; smelted; **—ок** *m.* piece of smelted ore.

**выпла́/та** *f.* paying, paying off; **—тить, —чивать** *v.* pay, pay off.

**выплев/а́ть, —ывать** *v.* spit out.

**выплес/ка́ть, —кивать, —нуть** *v.* splash out, spatter, spill; **—ки** *pl.* splashes, spattering, spillage.

**выпле/сти, —та́ть** *v.* plait, braid.

**вы́плод** *m.* breeding (of insects).

**выплы/ва́ть, —ть** *v.* swim out, emerge, float up.

**вы́плюнуть** *see* **выплёвывать.**

**выпола́живать** *v.* smooth, flatten (out).

**выпола́скивать** *v.* rinse out, flush.

**выполз/а́ть, —ти** *v.* creep out, get out.

**выполн/е́ние** *n.* execution, fulfillment, realization, accomplishment, achievement, completion, performance; filling (of cavity); **—имость** *f.* executability; feasibility, practicability; **—имый** *a.* executable, workable; feasible, practicable; **—ить, —ять** *v.* carry out, execute, accomplish, achieve, fulfill, perform, make, carry on; fill (an order); discharge (duties); **—я́ться** *v.* be satisfied (of equation).

**вы́полоскать** *see* **выпола́скивать.**

**вы́полоть** *see* **выпа́лывать.**

**вы́пор** *m.* air gate, air hole; overflow

gate, overflow lip, overflow; —**ажни-**
**вать, —ожнить** *v.* empty, drain.
**выпот** *m.* sweating; leaking (of boiler);
(volcano) fumarolic sublimate; (med.)
exudate; —**евание** *n.* sweating, exudation; bleeding (of plasticizer); —**еть**
*v.* sweat out; exude, ooze.
**выправ/ить, —лять** *v.* correct, set right,
straighten, smooth, flatten; planish;
dress; direct; —**ка** *f.* correction,
straightening, smoothing; posture,
bearing; —**ление** *n.* correcting,
straightening.
**выпрастывать** *v.* empty; work free (of),
get out; —**ся** *v.* work free (of).
**выпрашивать** *v.* solicit, get (by asking).
**выпр/евать, —еть** *v.* sweat out; perish
(of plants under snow); boil away;
boil enough; —**елый** *a.* evaporated.
**выпрессовывать** *v.* press out, squeeze
out.
**выпров/аживать, —одить** *v.* see off the
premises, accompany, escort.
**выпросить** *see* **выпрашивать.**
**выпростать** *see* **выпрастывать.**
**выпряд/ать, —ывать** *v.* spin, spin out.
**выпрям/итель** *m.* (elec.) rectifier; —**и-**
**тельный** *a.* rectifier, rectifying; —**ить,**
—**лять** *v.* straighten, unbend, erect;
(elec.) rectify; right (an airplane);
-**ление** *n.* straightening, rectification; —**ленный** *a.* straightened; rectified; —**ляющий** *a.* straightening;
rectifying.
**выпрясть** *see* **выпрядать.**
**выпукл/о** *adv.* convexly; —**овогнутый**
*a.* convexo-concave; —**ость** *f.* convexity, curvature, camber; promi-
nence, bulge, bulging, protuberance;
embossing; —**ый** *a.* convex, arched,
arching; buckled, bulging; protuber-
ant, prominent; raised, embossed;
—**ая работа** embossing.
**выпуск** *m.* outlet, escape, exhaust;
release; discharging, discharge, tapping, tap, flushing, emptying, draining, withdrawal; deflation; expulsion;
output, productive capacity, delivery;
issue, number (of journal); vintage;
—**ание** *n.* letting out, discharging,
discharge, drawing off; emission;
deflation; —**ать** *v.* let out, empty,
discharge, drain, run off, run out,

flush, draw off, tap; eject, release,
set free; issue, publish; omit, leave
out; manufacture, put out, deliver.
**выпускн/ой** *a.* exhaust, outlet, discharge;
exit; **в. валик, в. ролик** drawing-off
roller; **в. клапан** escape valve, release
valve, safety valve; **в. штуцер** exhaust (of motor); —**ая труба** outlet,
outlet pipe, exhaust pipe, waste pipe;
—**ое отверстие** outlet, discharge hole,
vent; tap, tap hole.
**выпустить** *see* **выпускать.**
**выпут/ать, —ывать** *v.* disentangle,
extricate, disengage.
**выпуч/енный** *a.* bulging, protruding;
—**енное место, —ивание** *n.,* —**ина** *f.*
bulging, bulge, swelling; buckling;
—**ивать, —ить** *v.* bulge, swell,
protrude.
**выпущен/ие** *see* **выпускание;** —**ный** *a.*
let out, discharged, etc., *see* **выпуск-**
**ать.**
**выпыт/ать, —ывать** *v.* question, elicit.
**выпя/тить, —чивать** *v.* protrude, stick
out; —**чиваться** *v.* project, overhang.
**выраб/атывать, —отать** *v.* manufacture, produce; improve, perfect, develop (a method); generate; work,
mine; work out, exhaust, deplete;
—**атываться, —отаться** *v.* be worked
out, be finished; develop; wear;
—**отанный** *a.* manufactured, produced; improved, developed; generated; worked; worked out, exhausted,
spent (solution); —**отка** *f.* manufacture, manufacturing, production; development; generation; working, mining; produce, yield, output, productive capacity; delivery; wear; exhaustion, depletion.
**выравн/енность** *f.* uniformity; —**ивание**
*n.* leveling, lining up, alignment;
trimming; equalization, compensation; —**иватель** *m.* equalizer, compensator; flattener; (agr.) leveler;
—**ивать, —ить, —ять** *v.* level, level
off, align, line up, straighten, smooth,
smooth out, plane; adjust, equalize,
balance; —**ивающий** *a.* leveling,
straightening; equalizing, compensating.
**выраж/ать** *v.* express, convey, utter;

—аясь in terms of; expressing oneself; —ение *n.* expression, phrase, term; в денежном —ении in terms of money; —енный *a.* expressed; —енный в, —енный через expressed in, in terms of.

выраз/ительный *a.* expressive, significant, indicative; —ить *see* выражать.

вырас/ание *n.* growing; germination; —ать, —и *v.* grow, grow up; —ить, выращивать *v.* grow, raise, cultivate; bring up, rear, nurture; incubate (microorganisms).

вырвать *v.* vomit; tear out, force out.

вырез *m.* cut, opening, notch, groove, rabbet, indentation; —ание *n.* cutting, cutting out, grooving, engraving; —анный *a.* cut out, engraved; —ать, —ывать *v.* cut, cut out; carve, engrave; eliminate, extirpate; —ка *f.* cut, cut-out; clipping; pattern; indentation; tenderloin (of beef).

вырисов/ать, —ывать *v.* draw carefully; —аться, —ываться *v.* appear, be visible in outline.

выровн/енный *a.* straightened, leveled; trimmed; —ять *see* выравнивать.

выро/дившийся, —жденный *a.* degenerated; confluent (function); —диться, —ждаться *v.* degenerate; —док *m.*, —дочный *a.* degenerate; —ждение *n.* degeneration.

вырон/ить, —ять *v.* let fall, drop, lose.

вырост *m.* protuberance, excrescence; —ать, —и *see* вырастать; —ной *a.* breeding, nursery (pond).

выруб *m.* cut, notch; —ать, —ить *v.* chop out; cut off, cut out; cut down, fell (trees); —ка *f.* cutting out; felling; notching, notch, indentation; punching; (metal) blank; —ленный *a.* cut out, cut off; cut down, felled; punched.

вырубной *a.* cutting, chopping; в. пресс, в. штамп, в. штемпель cutting machine, cutting punch, stamping machine, punching die, blanking punch.

выругать *v.* scold, reprimand.

выруч/ать, —ить *v.* rescue, help, relieve, release; gain, profit; recover (expenses); —ка *f.* rescue, assistance, support; gain, profit, proceeds, receipts.

выры/вание *n.* digging, digging out; drawing, extraction; реакция —вания (nucl.) pickup (reaction); —вать, —ть *v.* dig, dig out, unearth, excavate, uncover; pull out, tear; draw, extract; —ваться *v.* break loose, escape, get free; —тый *a.* dug out, excavated, uncovered.

выс. *abbr.* (высота) height, altitude.

высад/ить *see* высаживать; —ка *f.* landing, debarkation, getting off; (agr.) transplantation; —ной, —очный *a.* landing; transplanted; —ная головка snap head (of rivet); —ок *m.* transplanted plant; —очный пресс, —очная машина (forging) upsetter.

высаж/енный *a.* landed, put out; transplanted, set out; —ивать *v.* put out; put off; set down, land; (agr.) transplant, set out; (forging) upset, jump up; precipitate; —иваться *v.* land, alight, get down, descend; settle out, precipitate; —ивающийся *a.* settling out, precipitating.

высалив/ание *n.*, —ающий *a.* salting out; —атель *m.* salting out agent; —ать *v.* salt out.

высасыв/ание *n.* sucking out, drawing out, exhaustion; —ать *v.* suck out, draw out, draw off (air), exhaust, evacuate.

высачив/ание *n.* oozing, leaking, exudation; —аться *v.* ooze out, leak, trickle.

высверл/енный *a.* drilled, bored; bore (hole); —ивание *n.* drilling, boring; —ивать, —ить *v.* drill (out), bore (out).

высвечивание *n.* scintillation; de-excitation.

высвобо/дить, —ждать *v.* set free; disengage; —жденный *a.* set free, released.

высев *m.*, —ной *a.* seeding; —ать *v.* sow, seed; —ающий *a.* sowing, seeding.

высе/вки *pl.* siftings, screenings, fines; spec. bran; —ивание *n.* sifting out, screening; —ивать *v.* sift out, screen; sow (a field).

высекать *v.* hew, cut, cut out, carve, sculpture; stamp, punch; strike (a fire).

**высел/ить, —ять** *v.* eject, evict; **—иться, —яться** *v.* move.

**высеребрить** *v.* silver-plate.

**высеч/ка** *f.* hewing, cutting, cutting out, cut; (min.) slice, trench; **—ь** *see* **высекать.**

**высеять** *see* **высеивать.**

**выси/деть, —живать** *v.* wait; hatch (eggs).

**выситься** *v.* tower, rise.

**выскаблив/ание** *n.* scraping out; (med.) abrasion (of the uterus); **—ать** *v.* scrape out, scrape off; erase.

**высказ/анный** *a.* expressed, explicit; **—ать, —ывать** *v.* express, say; **—аться, —ываться** *v.* speak out, speak one's mind.

**выскакив/ание** *n.* springing out, slipping out; **—ать** *v.* spring out, slip out, jump out, work out, emerge.

**выскальзыв/ание** *n.* slip, slipping out; **—ать** *v.* slip, slip out.

**выскобл/енный** *a.* scraped out; **—ить** *see* **выскабливать.**

**выскользнуть** *see* **выскальзывать.**

**выскочить** *see* **выскакивать.**

**выскре/бать, —бывать, —сти** *v.* scrape out, scratch out; **—бывание** *n.* scraping out, scraping off.

**выслать** *see* **высылать.**

**высле/дить, —живать** *v.* trace, track down, search out.

**выслу/га** *f.* service; **—живать, —жить** *v.* deserve, merit; qualify (for); **—живаться** *v.* be promoted, advance.

**выслуш/ать, —ивать** *v.* listen, hear; (med.) examine, auscultate; **—ивание** *n.* listening, hearing; examination.

**высмаливать** *v.* tar, pitch.

**высматривать** *v.* look out (for), be on the alert (for).

**высмеивать** *v.* ridicule, scoff (at).

**высмолить** *see* **высмаливать.**

**высмотреть** *see* **высматривать.**

**высовывать** *v.* thrust out, put out, protrude; **—ся** *v.* protrude, project.

**высок/ий** *a.* high, tall, towering; eminent; **котел —ого давления** high-pressure boiler; **—о** *adv.* high, highly.

**высоко—** *prefix* high, highly; **—активный** *a.* highly active; highly radioactive, high-activity, hot; **—вакуумный** *a.* high-vacuum; **—вольтный** *a.* high-

voltage; **—вязкий** *a.* high-viscosity; **—горный** *a.* high-mountain, high-altitude; **—градусный** *a.* of a high degree; high-grade; highly concentrated; **—дисперсный** *a.* highly dispersed; **—интенсивный** *a.* high (flux); **—ионизированный** *a.* highly ionized; **—качественный** *a.* high-quality, high-grade, fine; high-strength; high-test (gasoline); rich (ore); high-fidelity; high-definition; **—кипящий** *a.* high-boiling, having a high boiling point; **—концентрированный** *a.* highly concentrated; **—кормный** *a.* (biol.) eutrophic; **—кремнистый** *a.* high-silicon; **—кучевые облака** (meteor.) altocumulus.

**высоко/легированный** *a.* high (alloy); **—марганцовистый** *a.* high-manganese; **—молекулярный** *a.* high-molecular, of high molecular weight; **—мощный** *a.* high-power, high-capacity; (mach.) heavy duty; **—огнеупорный** *a.* highly refractory; **—омный** *a.* (elec.) high-resistance; **—плавкий** *a.* high-melting; **—пробный** *a.* high-test (gasoline); high-grade; fine; sterling (silver); **—продуктивный, —производительный** *a.* very productive, highly efficient; high-duty; **—проходный фильтр** (elec.) high-pass filter; **—процентный** *a.* high-percentage, high-grade, rich (ore); **—радиоактивный** *a.* highly radioactive, hot; **—развитый** *a.* highly developed.

**высоко/сводчатый** *a.* high-domed; **—скоростной** *a.* high-speed; **—слоистое облако** (meteor.) altostratus; **—сортный** *see* **высококачественный; —ствольный** *a.* high, full-grown (tree); **—температурный** *a.* high-temperature; **—точный** *a.* high-precision, precision; **—углеродистый** *a.* high-carbon; **—удойная** *a.* highly productive (cow); **—урожайный** *a.* heavy-producing; **—фосфористый** *a.* high-phosphorus; **—хромистый** *a.* high-chromium; **—частотный** *a.* high-frequency; **—чувствительный** *a.* highly sensitive, extremely sensitive; **—эластичность** *f.* rubber-like elasticity, Mackian elasticity.

**высортиров/ать** *v.* sort, sort out, cull; —ка *f.* sorting, culling.

**высосать** *see* **высасывать.**

**высот/а** *f.* height, altitude, elevation; depth; pitch (of tone); (geol.) throw (of fault); degree (of temperature); reading (of barometer); (floor) line; на —ах high-level; набирать —у *v.* (aero.) climb; —ность *f.* height, altitude; —ный *a.* altitude; high-altitude, high-level; tall; high-flying; upper-air; upper-level; —ный репер (surv.) bench mark; —омер *m.* altimeter, altitude gage, height finder.

**высох/нуть** *see* **высыхать**; —ший *a.* dry, shriveled.

**высочка** *f.* (met.) liquation, segregation.

**выспаться** *v.* have enough sleep.

**выспрашивать, выспросить** *v.* question, enquire.

**выстав/ить, —лять** *v.* put out, set out, expose; display, exhibit; —ка *f.* exhibition, display, show; (agr.) fair; —ление *n.* putting out, setting out, exposure; —ленный *a.* put out, set out, exposed; —очный *a.* exhibitory, exhibition, display; —очный зал exhibit room, exposition room, show room.

**выстаивать** *v.* stand (a given time); withstand; lose strength, color, or flavor; —ся *v.* mature.

**выстил/ать** *v.* pave, floor, cover, lay; line; —ка *f.* flooring; pavement; lining.

**выстир/ать, —ывать** *v.* wash, wash out, launder.

**выстлать** *see* **выстилать.**

**выстоять** *see* **выстаивать.**

**выстрагивать** *v.* plane.

**выстраивать** *v.* build, erect, set up; align, line up.

**выстрел** *m.* shot, discharge, report, detonation; —ить *v.* shoot, fire, go off.

**выстри/гать, —чь** *v.* clip, shear.

**выстрогать** *see* **выстрагивать.**

**выстро/ить** *see* **выстраивать**; —йка *f.* building, construction.

**высту/дить, —жать, —живать** *v.* cool.

**выстукив/ание** *n.* percussion; (med.) tapping; —ать *v.* subject to percussion; tap.

**выступ** *m.* projection, protuberance, pro-trusion, jut, overhang, overhanging; (biol.) process; (geol.) ledge, shelf, bench, ridge; extension; lug, cog, cam, boss, catch, horn; cusp, point (of crystal); baffle; clutch; flange, shoulder, rib; embossing; jetty; сварка —ами projection welding.

**выступ/ать, —ить** *v.* come forward, step forward; project, protrude, jut, jut out; (geol.) crop out, emerge; be embossed; —ающий *a.* projecting, outstanding; —ающая часть appendage; protuberance; —ающийся *a.* projecting, jutting, overhanging; —ление *n.* appearance.

**выстывать** *v.* cool, become cool.

**высунут/ый** *a.* thrust out, protruding; —ь *see* **высовывать.**

**высуш/енный** *a.* dried, desiccated; seasoned (lumber); вес —енного материала dry weight; —ивание *n.* drying, desiccation; —ивать, —ить *v.* dry, desiccate; drain (land); —ивающий *a.* drying, desiccating, siccative; —ивающее вещество drying agent, desiccant.

**высчитывать** *v.* reckon, compute, calculate.

**высш/ий** *a.* higher, superior, highest, supreme; в. спирт higher alcohol; —ая степень maximum; —ая точка climax, acme, peak (of curve); top, summit (of mountain); —ие учебные заведения universities.

**высыл/ать** *v.* send out, ship; exile, deport; —ка *f.* shipping; deportation.

**высып/анный** *a.* poured out; —ать *v.* pour out, empty; —аться *v.* be poured out, run out, spill, shed; sleep enough; —ка *f.* pouring out, emptying; vysypka (rock fragments scattered around showing the presence of bedrock).

**высых/ание** *n.* drying, desiccation; —ать *v.* dry, dry up; run dry (of stream); fade, wither; —ающий *a.* drying; —ающее масло siccative oil, drier.

**высь** *f.* height; top, summit, crest.

**выталкив/ание** *n.* pushing out, ejection, expulsion, extrusion; —атель *m.* pusher, push rod, ejector, knock-out; lift-out attachment, lifting-out device, withdrawing device; extruder; —**ать** *v.* push out, force out, eject, expel, extrude; knock out.

**выта́плив/ание** *n.* melting down; (met.) smelting out; —**ать** *see* **вы́топить.**

**выта́скив/ание** *n.* pulling out, extraction, drawing out, withdrawal; —**ать** *v.* pull out, extract, draw, draw out, haul out.

**выта́чивать** *v.* turn (on lathe); sharpen; bore out, cut (grooves).

**вы́тащить** *see* **выта́скивать.**

**вы́тек/ание** *n.* flowing out, running out, effluence, efflux; outlet, discharge; **ско́рость** —**ания** rate of discharge; **температу́ра** —**ания** outlet temperature, exit temperature; —**ать** *v.* flow out, run out, stream, issue, discharge, be discharged, escape; result, follow, ensue; —**ающий** *a.* flowing out, running out, discharging, draining; resultant; effluent (stream); —**ающий пото́к,** —**ающая жи́дкость** effluent.

**вы́тереть** *see* **вытира́ть.**

**вы́терпеть** *v.* endure, bear, stand.

**вы́тесать** *see* **вытёсывать.**

**вытесн/е́ние** *n.* displacement, dislodgment, substitution; —**енный** *a.* displaced, dislodged, supplanted; expelled; —**и́тель** *m.* displacer; —**и́ть,** —**у́ть,** —**я́ть** *v.* displace, dislodge, supplant, supersede; replace; liberate; force out, drive out, expel; exclude, crowd out, extrude.

**вытёсывать** *v.* hew into shape.

**вы́течь** *see* **вытека́ть.**

**вытира́ть** *v.* wipe, dry.

**вы́тисн/ить,** —**уть,** —**ять** *v.* impress, imprint, stamp.

**вы́толк/ать,** —**нуть** *see* **выта́лкивать.**

**вы́топ/ить** *v.* heat; melt out; clarify (fat); —**иться** *v.* be heated; melt out; —**ка** *f.* melting out; (met.) liquation, segregation; —**ки** *pl.* residue of melted fat; (met.) scum, slag, dross.

**вы́торгов/ать,** —**ывать** *v.* bargain (for), gain by trade.

**вы́точ/енный** *a.* cut, bored out; sharpened; **в. жёлобок** recess, groove; —**ить** *see* **выта́чивать;** —**ка** *f.* turning (on lathe); recess, groove, hollow chamfer; spot.

**вы́трав/ить,** —**ливать,** —**лять** *v.* cor-

rode, eat away, erode, etch; —**ка** *f.*, —**ле́ние** *n.*, —**ливание** *n.* corrosion, pitting, etching, erosion; (dyeing) discharge; **си́ла** —**ле́ния** causticity, corrosiveness; **ситцепеча́тание** —**кой** (dyeing) discharge printing; **фигу́ра** —**ле́ния** etched figure; —**ленный** *a.* corroded, etched, eroded; —**ляющий** *a.* corroding, corrosive; —**ляющее сре́дство** caustic, corrosive; mordant.

**вы́требовать** *v.* send for, order, demand.

**вытря́с/ать,** —**ти** *v.* shake out.

**вытря́х/ать,** —**ивать,** —**нуть** *v.* shake out, let fall, jolt out, dump out.

**выть** *v.* howl.

**вытя́гив/ание** *n.* extraction, drawing out; drawing off, exhaustion (of air); extension, extending, pulling out, elongation, drawing, stretching, spread; —**ать** *v.* extract, remove, draw out; draw off, exhaust (air); extend, pull out, elongate, lengthen, prolong; draw, stretch, stretch out, spread; —**аться** *v.* be extracted; stretch, draw out, extend; expand.

**вытя́жка** *f.* extract; (pharm.) tincture, infusion; drawn shell, shell; flue; (text.) draft; stretch of staple; *see also* **вытя́гивание.**

**вытяжн/о́й** *a.* drawing; exhaust; blistering (plaster); **в. ва́лик** drawing roller; **в. вентиля́тор** aspirator, exhaust fan; **в. колпа́к, в. шкаф** exhaust hood, fume hood, hood; **в. насо́с** vacuum pump; **в. пресс** drawing press; **в. трос** (parachute) rip cord, release cord; **в. штамп** drawing die; —**ая возду́шная труба́** air suction pipe, exhaust pipe; —**ая систе́ма** exhaust system; —**ая труба́** exhaust pipe; chimney, flue, draft flue; ventilating pipe; —**ая тя́га** suction draft, induced draft; —**ая ша́хта** air hole, air vent.

**вытя́нут/ый** *a.* extracted, drawn out; stretched out, elongated, prolonged; prolate (nucleus); exhausted (air); —**ь** *see* **вытя́гивать.**

**выу́ч/ивать,** —**ить** *v.* teach; learn; —**иться** *v.* learn; —**ка** *f.* teaching, training.

**выха́живать** *v.* raise, rear (stock); tend, care for (convalescent); ferment (beer).

**вы́хват/ить,** —**ывать** *v.* snatch out,

snatch away; —ывание n. snatching.

выхлоп m. exhaust, discharge, expulsion; в. пара steam exhaust, steam escape.

выхлопатывать see выхлопотать.

выхлопн/ой a. exhaust, escape, waste; в. газ exhaust gas, waste gas; —ые газы exhaust; в. горшок muffler; в. пар exhaust steam; в. патрубок, —ая труба exhaust pipe, escape pipe; в. штуцер exhaust (of motor); —ое отверстие exhaust, outlet, exit.

выхлопотать v. obtain, procure, get (by suing).

выход m. yield (of product), output; outlet, exit, vent, egress, outflow, escape, discharge, discharging; emergence; seepage (of oil); issue (of journal); publication (of book); (geol.) outcrop, emersion; в. 90% теории the yield is 90% of the theoretical; в. на альдегид yield of aldehyde; в. пара steam escape; в. по yield of; yield on the basis of; в. по току (electrochem.) current efficiency; в. смешения mixing efficiency; большой в. high yield; на —е outlet (temperature, etc.); output (velocity); доза на —е (radiation) exit dose; работа —а work function (of electrons); с 90% —ом по теории with a yield of 90% of the theoretical; угол —а angle of emergence.

выходец m. emigrant; он в. he comes (from).

выходить v. go out, come out, come forth, get out, emerge, issue; yield; escape; appear, be published, be issued; front, face, open on (of building); see also выхаживать.

выходн/ой a. outgoing, discharge; output; exit; в. день day off; в. слой (geol.) outcrop; —ая кривая (chromatography) elution curve; —ая скорость rate of discharge; delivery speed; —ое отверстие outlet, vent.

выхо/дящий a. coming out, outgoing; (geol.) outcropping; —ждение n. coming out, going out.

выхол/аживание n. cooling; —аживать, —одить v. cool thoroughly, chill.

выхол/ащивать, —остить v. geld, castrate.

выхухоль f. (zool.) muskrat.

выцвест/и, —ь see выцветать.

выцвет/ание n. fading, bleaching, discoloration; efflorescence (of salt); в. серы (rubber) blooming; —ать v. fade, bleach, lose color; effloresce; (bot.) finish blooming; —ший a. faded, discolored; —ы pl. efflorescence.

выце/дить, —живать v. filter; decant, pour off; —женный a. filtered; decanted.

вычекан/енный a. coined, chased; —ивать, —ить v. coin, chase, emboss.

вычерк/ивание n. crossing out, deleting; obliteration; cancellation; —ивать, —нуть v. cross out, delete, strike out, strike off, obliterate, efface, rule out, erase; cancel, cancel out; —нутый a. crossed out, deleted; canceled.

вычерн/ивать, —ить v. blacken, black out, paint black.

вычерп/ать, —нуть, —ывать v. bail out, dip out, dredge, scoop; —ка f. (paper) test sheet; —нутый, —анный a. bailed out, dredged, scooped; —ывание n. bailing out.

вычер/тить v. trace, pencil, map out, lay out; —чивание n. tracing, mapping, laying out, layout.

вычес/ать v. comb, comb out; —ки pl. refuse, combings.

вычесть v. deduct, subtract.

вычесывать see вычесать.

вычет m. deduction; теория —ов residue theory.

вычисл/ение n. calculation, computation, figuring, reckoning, estimate, rating; —енный a. calculated, computed, estimated; —енная стоимость estimate; —итель m., —ительная машина computer, computing machine; calculator, calculating machine; —ить, —ять v. compute, calculate, figure out, estimate; cipher; numerate; —яемый a. (math.) enumerable, denumerable, countable.

вычистить see вычищать.

вычит/аемое n. (math.) subtrahend; —аемый a. deductible; —ание n. deduction; (math.) subtraction; —ать v. deduct; subtract.

вычит/ать, —ывать v. read thoroughly, read through; find (in a book).

**вычищать** v. clean, clean out, cleanse, scrape out.

**вышвыр/ивать,** —**нуть,** —**ять** v. throw out, spatter.

**выше** comp. of **высокий, высоко,** higher, taller, above; —**исчисленный** a. above-numbered, above-calculated; —**кипящий** a. higher-boiling; —**лежащий** a. superincumbent; —**лежащий пласт** (geol.) superstratum, overlying stratum; —**объявленный,** —**означенный,** —**реченный,** —**сказанный,** —**указанный,** —**упомянутый** a. above, foregoing, aforesaid, previously mentioned, above-mentioned; —**приведенный** a. shown above, given above.

**вышиб** m., —**ание** n., —**ка** f. knocking out, breaking out; —**ать,** —**ить** v. knock out, break out, drive out.

**вышив/альный** a. embroidery; —**ать** v. embroider; —**ка** f. embroidery.

**вышин/а** f. height; —**ой в** in height.

**вышка** f. tower, watch tower; (oil well) derrick; (mech.) pulpit; garret.

**выштампов/анный** a. stamped out; —**ать** v. stamp out, punch; eliminate, eradicate.

**выштукатурить** see **штукатурить.**

**выщел/ачивание** n. lixiviation, leaching, leaching out; —**ачивать,** —**очить** v. lixiviate, leach, leach out, extract, dissolve out; (text.) steep; —**оченный** a. lixiviated, leached out; buck (ashes).

**выщуп/ать,** —**ывать** v. feel, search by touch, probe; —**ывание** n. feeling, probing.

**выяв/ить,** —**лять** v. show, make apparent, expose; develop; —**ление** n. exposure; development, appearance; —**ление качества** behavior.

**выясн/ение** n. clarification, explanation; —**енный** a. cleared up, explained; —**ить,** —**ять** v. clear up, make clear, clear, explain; look (into), inquire, examine, investigate; find out, ascertain, prove; develop.

**вьет** pr. 3 sing. of **вить.**

**вью/га** f., —**жный** a. snowstorm.

**вьюк** m. pack, load, burden.

**вьюн** m. (zool.) groundling (fish).

**вьюн/ковые** pl. (bot.) Convolvulaceae; —**ок** m. bindweed (Convolvulus).

**вьюрок** m. reel.

**вьют** pr. 3 pl. of **вить.**

**вьюч/ить** v. load, pack; —**ный** a. pack; —**ный обоз** pack train; —**ная лошадь** pack horse.

**вьюшка** f. damper; reel.

**вьющ/ий** pr. act. part. of **вить;** —**ийся** a. (bot.) climbing, creeping, trailing; —**ееся растение** vine.

**ВЭИ** abbr. (Всесоюзный электротехнический институт) All-Union Electrical Engineering Institute.

**ВЭТТ** abbr. (высота эквивалентной теоретической тарелки) height equivalent of a theoretical plate, H.E.T.P.

**вюрм** m. (geol.) Würm.

**Вюрца колба** Würtz flask.

**вюстит** m. (min.) wüstite.

**вяжет** pr. 3 sing. of **вязать.**

**вяжущ/ий** a. binding, cementing; astringent, stringent; **в. материал,** —**ее вещество,** —**ее средство** binder, binding material, cement; astringent; matrix.

**вяз** m. (bot.) elm (Ulmus).

**вяз/альный** a. binding; (text.) knitting; —**альщик** m. binder; knitter; —**ание** n. binding, tying; knitting; —**анка** f. bundle, bunch, sheaf; —**анный** a. knitted; bound; —**ательный** a. binding; —**ать** v. bind, tie; knit; be astringent; —**аться** v. be compatible (with), be consistent (with).

**вязига** f. dried spinal cord of sturgeon.

**вязка** f. binding, tying; bundle; binder twine; clamp.

**вязк/ий** a. viscous (liquid); sticky, pasty, stringy; tough, tenacious, tensile, ductile, malleable; —**ость** f. viscosity; body (of oil); stickiness, adhesiveness; strength, toughness, tenacity, ductility.

**вязнуть** v. stick, sink (in).

**вязов/ые** pl. (bot.) Ulmaceae; —**ый** a. elm.

**вязочный** a. binding, tying.

**вял/ение** n. sun-curing; jerking (of meat); —**еный** a. dried, cured; jerked; —**ить** v. sun-cure, dry-cure; jerk.

**вял/ость** f. flabbiness; —**ый** a. flabby, flaccid, limp, inert, sluggish, dull.

**вянуть** v. wither, wilt, droop.

# Г

**г** *abbr.* (грамм) gram; (гекто—) hecto—; **г.** *abbr.* (год) year; (гора) mountain; (город) city; **Г** *abbr.* [грамм (сила)] gram (force); (гига—) giga—; code for manganese in steel mark.

**га** *abbr.* (гектар) hectare.

**гаагский** *a.* Hague.

**габардин** *m.* (text.) gabardine.

**габарит** *m.*, —**ный** *a.* clearance, overall size; clearance diagram; dimension, size, profile, bulk (of machine); —**ный контур** outline; —**ный чертеж** outline drawing; —**ная высота** clearance height.

**габбро** *n.* gabbro (an igneous rock); —**видный,** —**подобный** *a.* gabbroid; —**вый** *a.* gabbro, gabbroic; —**норит** *m.* gabbronorite.

**Габера процесс** Haber process (for nitrogen fixation).

**габион** *m.*, —**ный** *a.* gabion.

**габит/ет** *m.* (biol.) habitat; —**ус** *m.* habitus, habit, appearance.

**габронематоз** *m.* (vet.) habronemiasis.

**гавайский** *a.* Hawaiian.

**гаванна** *f.* Havana (cigar).

**гаван/ь** *f.*, —**ный** *a.* port, harbor.

**гаверсинус** *m.* (math.) haversine, half of versed sine.

**Гавр** Le Havre.

**гага** *f.* (zool.) eider.

**гагат** *m.*, —**овый** *a.* (min.) jet; —**оподобный** *a.* jet-like.

**гагачий пух** eiderdown.

**гад** *m.* (zool.) reptile.

**гад/ание** *n.* guessing, guesswork; —**ательно** *adv.* hypothetically, by conjecture, by guesswork; —**ательный** *a.* hypothetical, conjectural; —**ать** *v.* guess, conjecture, surmise.

**гадина** *f.* (zool.) reptile; vermin.

**гад/ить** *v.* soil; spoil, damage; —**кий** *a.* dirty, foul; disgusting, bad; —**кость** *f.* dirty stuff; odiousness.

**Гадлея принцип** (meteor.) Hadley's principle.

**гадолин/ий** *m.*, —**овый** *a.* gadolinium, Gd; **окись** —**ия** gadolinium oxide; —**ит** *m.* (min.) gadolinite; —**овая земля** gadolinia, gadolinium oxide.

**гадость** *see* **гадкость.**

**Гадфильда процесс** (met.) Hadfield process.

**гадю/ка** *f.*, —**чий** *a.* (zool.) adder, viper; —**чий лук** (bot.) grape hyacinth (*Muscari*).

**гаечн/ый** *a.* nut; female, inside (thread); **г. барашек** wing nut; **г. замок** lock nut; **г. ключ** wrench, monkey wrench; **г. пресс** nut-making machine.

**гажение** *n.* outgassing, gas removal.

**газ** *m.* gas; gauze (material); **сбавить г.** *v.* (mach.) throttle down; —**ация** *f.* fumigation; —**гольдер** *m.* gas holder, gasometer, gas container, gas tank; —**ер** *see* **газовик.**

**газет/а** *f.*, —**ный** *a.* newspaper, journal.

**газиатор** *m.* gas heater, gas stove.

**газиров/ание** *n.* gassing, aeration; gas recovery; —**анный** *a.* gassed, aerated; —**ать** *v.* gas, aerate, aerify, bubble up.

**газифи/катор** *m.* gasifier; —**кация** *f.* gasification, production of gas; carburetion; —**цировать** *v.* gasify.

**газлифт** *m.* gas lift, air lift.

**газо—** *prefix* gas; —**анализатор** *m.* gas analyzer; —**баллон** *m.* gas cylinder; —**бетон** *m.*, —**бетонный** *a.* porous concrete; —**видный** *a.* gaseous, gasiform; —**вать** *v.* gas; —**вик** *m.* gas generator, gas producer; —**воз** *m.* gas-driven locomotive; —**воздуходувная машина** gas-driven blower; —**воспламенитель** *m.* gas lighter; —**всасыватель** *m.* gas exhauster; —**вщик** *m.* gas fitter; —**выделение** *n.* evolution of gas, generation of gas; degassing; **мощность —выделения** emanating power.

**газов/ый** *a.* gas, gaseous, *see also* **газо—**; gauze; **г. завод** gas works, gas plant; **г. канал** flue; **г. рожок** gas jet; **г. счетчик** gas meter; —**ые часы** gas meter; —**ая вода** gas liquor, coal gas liquor; —**ая колонка** (geol.) geyser; —**ая магистраль** gas main, gas pipeline, gas line; —**ая постоянная** gas constant; —**ая сажа** gas black, carbon black; —**ая съемка** oil prospecting (by gas analysis); —**ая ткань** wire gauze; —**ая топка** gas heat; —**ое масло** gas oil;

diesel oil; —ое усиление (instrumentation) gas amplification; —ые сети gas-piping system, gas-distributing system.

**газоген** *m.* gasogen.

**газогенератор** *m.* gas generator, gas producer, producer; —ный *a.* gas-producing; —ная установка gas works, gas plant.

**газо/динамо** *n.* gas-driven dynamo; —диффузионный *a.* gas-diffusion, gaseous-diffusion; —добывание *n.* production of gas, gasification; —дувка *f.* gas blast; gas blower; —ем *m.* gas holder, gasometer; —испытатель *m.* gas tester; eudiometer; —йль *m.* gas oil.

**газокалильн/ый** *a.* incandescent; г. колпачок, —ая сетка incandescent mantle; г. свет incandescent gas light.

**газокамера** *f.* (vet.) gas-treatment building.

**газолин** *m.*, —овый *a.* gasoline, gas.

**газомер** *m.*, —итель *m.* gas meter; gasometer, gas holder, gas tank.

**газомет** *m.* gas ejector.

**газометр** *see* газомер; —ический *a.* gasometric; —ия *f.* gasometry.

**газомото/воз** *m.* gas-driven locomotive; —р *m.* gas engine, gas motor, internal-combustion engine.

**газон** *m.* lawn, grass.

**газо/наполненный** *a.* gas-filled; —нанолнительная станция (gasoline) filling station; —непроницаемый *a.* gas-tight, gasproof, impermeable to gas.

**газонокосилка** *f.* lawn mower.

**газоносн/ость** *f.* gas-bearing capacity; —ый *a.* gas-bearing, gas, gaseous.

**газообразн/ость** *f.* gaseousness; —ый *a.* gaseous, gasiform; —ое тело gas; —ое топливо gaseous fuel; fuel gas.

**газообраз/ование** *n.* gasification, gas formation, evolution of gas; volatilization, vaporization; —ователь *m.*, —ующий аппарат gas producer, gas generator, gasifier; —ующий *a.* gas-forming.

**газоотвод** *m.* gas bleeder, offtake, gas uptake (of blast furnace); gas vent, gas conduit; —ный *a.* bleeding, offtake, vent; —ный канал gas flue;

—ная труба, —ящая труба gas outlet; exhaust pipe.

**газо/отделитель** *m.* gas separator, gas trap; —отравленный *a.* gassed, poisoned by gas; —отсасывающий *a.* gas-suction, exhaust; —охладитель *m.* gas condenser.

**газоочист/итель** *m.* gas purifier, scrubber; —ительный, —ный *a.* gas-purifying; —ка *f.* gas purification, scrubbing.

**газо/плотный** *a.* gas-tight, gasproof; —поглотитель *m.* gas absorber, getter; —подводящий *a.* gas-intake, gas-feed; —полный *a.* gas-filled; —привод *m.* gas inlet, gas feed; —приемник *m.* gas collector; —приемный *a.* gas-collecting, gas-receiving; —провод *m.* gas pipe, gas pipeline, gas main, gas conduit, flue, gas supply; —проводчик *m.* gas fitter; —производитель *m.* gas producer, gas generator; —промыватель *m.* gas purifier, scrubber; —промывная башня gas scrub tower, scrubber; —проницаемость *f.* gas permeability, permeability to gas; —проницаемый *a.* gas-permeable, permeable to gas; —разрядный *a.* gas-discharge.

**газораспределитель** *m.* gas distributer, gas header; —ный *a.* gas-distributing.

**газо/сборник** *m.* gas collector; —сварка *f.* gas welding; —светный *a.* gas-discharge; fluorescent (lamp); —свещение *n.* gas illumination; —сос *m.* exhauster; —сжигательный *a.* gas-burning; —сушитель *m.* gas drier; —техника *f.*, —технический *a.* gas engineering; —трон *m.* (electron.) discharge-tube rectifier, gas-filled tube rectifier; —турбина *f.* gas turbine, gas-driven turbine; —убежище *n.* (mil.) gasproof shelter; —удерживающий *a.* gas-retaining; —уловитель *m.* gas trap, gas catcher, gas separator, gas take, gas collector; —упорный *a.* gasproof; —фикация *see* газификация; —ход *m.* gas conduit; —хранилище *n.* gas holder, gas storage tank; —хромирование *n.* diffusion chromizing; —чиститель gas purifier, scrubber.

**газящий** *a.* gassing.

**Гаити** Haiti.

**Гайда процесс** (min.) Hyde (flotation) process.

**Гайдена способ** Hayden process (for refining copper).

**гайденит** *m.* (min.) haydenite (a variety of chabazite).

**гайдингерит** *m.* (min.) haidingerite.

**гайдроп** *m.* guide rope.

**гайерит** *see* **гауерит.**

**гайк/а** *f.* nut, female screw; **г.-барашек, барашковая г.** wing nut, butterfly nut; **—онарезной станок, —орезный станок** nut-cutting machine.

**гайлюссит** *see* **гейлюссит.**

**гайморит** *m.* (med.) highmoritis.

**гайнальдия** *f.* (bot.) haynaldia.

**гайот** *m.* guyot.

**гайпер/ник** *m.* Hypernic (an iron-nickel alloy); **—сил** *m.* Hipersil (silicon-iron alloy), *see also* **гиперсил.**

**гак** *m.* hook.

**гакманит** *m.* (min.) hackmanite (a variety of sodalite).

**галаадский бальзам** balm of Gilead.

**галагепто/за** *f.* galaheptose; **—новая кислота** galaheptonic acid.

**галазон** *m.* halazone.

**галакт/аза** *f.* galactase; **—ан** *m.* galactan, gelose; **—ика** *f.* (astron.) Galaxy; **—ин** *m.* galactin; **—ит** *m.* (min.) galactite (a variety of natrolite); **—ический** *a.* (astron.) galactic.

**галакто—** *prefix* galacto— (milk; galactose); **—з** *m.* galactosis, milk formation; **—за** *f.* galactose, pentahydroxyhexanol; **—замин** *m.* galactosamine; **—зид** *m.* galactoside, cerebroside; **—метр** *m.* galactometer; **—новая кислота** galactonic acid, pentahydroxyhexoic acid.

**галактуроновая кислота** galacturonic acid.

**галалит** *m.* galalith (casein plastic).

**гал/ама камедь** Galam gum; **—ангин** *m.* galangin (a resin); **—ангол** *m.* galangol; **—антамин** *m.* galanthamine; **—бан** *m.* galbanum (gum resin from *Ferula*); **—ган** *m.* galanga (root of *Alpinia officinarum*).

**галегин** *m.* galegine, isopentenyl guanidine.

**гален** *m.*, **—ит** *m.* (min.) galena, galenite,

lead glance; **—обисмутит** *m.* (min.) galenobismutite; **—овы препараты** (pharm.) galenicals; **—овый** *a.* (min.) galena; **—оид** *m.* galenoid.

**галепо—** *prefix* halepo—.

**галерея** *f.* gallery; tunnel.

**галета** *f.* ship biscuit; press cake; disc coil.

**галечн/ик** *m.*, **—иковый** *a.* gravel, pebble; (geol.) conglomerate; **—иковая руда** (min.) nodular ore; **—ый** *a.* pebble, shingle; **—ая мельница** pebble mill.

**галил** *m.* galyl.

**галип/ен** *m.* galipene; **—идин** *m.* galipidine; **—ин** *m.* galipine; **—оидин** *m.* galipoidine; **—ол** *m.* galipol; **—от** *m.* galipot (oleoresin from *Pinus pinaster*).

**галит** *m.* (min.) halite, rock salt, natural sodium chloride.

**галл** *m.* gall.

**галл/ал** *m.* gallal, aluminum gallate; **—аминовая кислота** gallamic acid; **—анилид** *m.*, **—анол** *m.* gallanilide, gallinol, gallanol; **—ат** *m.* gallate; **—ацетофенон** *m.* gallacetophenone; **—еин** *m.* gallein, pyrogallolphthalein.

**галлерея** *see* **галерея.**

**галлерит** *m.* (min.) hallerite (a lithium-bearing paragonite mica).

**галлефлинта** *see* **геллефлинта.**

**галли—** *prefix* galli-, gallic.

**галлиевая соль** gallium salt, gallic salt.

**галлизин** *m.* gallisin.

**галлизировать** *v.* (wine) gallize.

**галл/ий** *m.* gallium, Ga; **закись —ия** gallous oxide, gallium monoxide; **окись —ия** gallic oxide, gallium trioxide; **хлористый г.** gallous chloride, gallium dichloride; **хлорный г.** gallium chloride, spec. gallic chloride.

**галлипот** gallipot (a jar); *see also* **галипот.**

**галлит** *m.* (min.) hallite (a variety of mica).

**галли/фаровая кислота** gallipharic acid; **—цин** *m.* gallicin, methyl gallate.

**галлицы** *pl.* gall gnats (*Cecidomyiidae*).

**галло—** *prefix* gallo—, gallous; **—бромол** *m.* gallobromol, dibromogallic acid.

**галловеевский котел** Galloway boiler.

**галлово/железная соль** ferric gallate;

—кальциевая соль calcium gallate;
—кислый *a*. gallic acid; gallate (of);
—кислая соль gallate; —кислое
железо iron gallate; —метиловый
эфир methyl gallate; —свинцовая
соль lead gallate.

галлов/ый *a*. gallic; —ая кислота gallic
acid, 3,4,5-trihydroxybenzoic acid;
соль —ой кислоты gallate.

галло/ген *m*. gallogen, ellagic acid; —дубильная кислота gallotannic acid.

галлоизит *m*. halloysite (a clay mineral).

галло/ил *m*. galloyl; —ксантин *m*.
galloxanthin; —л *m*. gallol.

галлон *m*., —ный *a*. gallon (measure).

галлообразование *n*. (bot.) gall formation.

галлоцианин *m*. gallocyanin.

галлуазит *see* галлоизит.

галлюцинация *f*. hallucination.

Галля цепь Gall's chain, sprocket chain;
Г. явление *see* Холля явление.

галм/ееподобный *a*. (min.) calamine-
like; —ей *m*. calamine, hemimorphite;
—ейный камень calamine stone,
smithsonite.

гало *n*. (meteor.) halo; *prefix* halo—
(salt).

галоген *m*. halogen; —алкил *m*. alkyl
halide; —ангидрид *see* галогеноангидрид;—арил *m*. aryl halide; —ация
*f*., —ирование *n*. halogenation; —ид
*m*. halide; halogen; —ированный *a*.
halogenated; —ировать *v*. halo-
genate, halogenize.

галогенн/ый *a*. halogen, halogenous, halide; г. водород hydrogen halide; —ая
кислота halogen acid.

галогеноангидрид *m*. acid halide; a non-
metal halide (such as phosphorus halide); г. серной кислоты sulfuryl
halide.

галогеноводород *m*. hydrogen halide,
haloid acid; —ная кислота halogen
hydracid, hydrohalic acid; соль —ной
кислоты halide.

галогенопроизводные *pl*. halogen derivatives.

галогидрин *m*. halohydrin.

галоид *m*., —ный *a*. halogen; halide;
—алкил *see* галогеналкил; —гидрин
*see* галогидрин; —ирование *see* гало-
генация; —ированный *see* галогени-

рованный; —ный алкил alkyl halide;
—ный винил vinyl halide; —ный
металл metal halide; —ная соль
halide, haloid; —ные производные
*see* галоидопроизводные.

галоидо— *prefix* halogeno—; —ангидрид *see* галогеноангидрид; —водород
*see* галогеноводород; —производные
*pl*. halogen derivatives.

галометр *m*. halometer (for salt determination); —ический *a*. halometric;
—ия *f*. halometry.

галопиров/ание *n*. galloping, galloping
motion; —ать *v*. gallop.

гало/трихит *m*. (min.) halotrichite, iron
alum; —фит *m*. (bot.) halophyte;
—фитовый *a*. halophytic; —фобное
растение (bot.) halophobe; —химический *a*. halochemical; —химия *f*.
halochemistry; —хромия *f*. halo-
chromism.

галош/а *f*., —ный *a*. overshoe, rubber.

галс *m*. tack.

галсту/к *m*., —чный *a*. necktie.

галтель *m*., —ный *a*. hollow chamfer,
fillet; —ный резец recessing tool.

галтов/ание *n*., —ка *f*. tumbling; —атв
*v*. tumble.

галтоза *f*. galtose.

галун *m*., —ный *a*. galloon, lace.

галургия *f*. halurgy (science of salt).

галь *f*. (text.) heald.

гальбан *m*. galbanum (gum resin);
—овое масло galbanum oil.

гальваниз/атор *m*. galvanizer; —ация
*f*., —ирование *n*. galvanization, electroplating; —ированный *a*. galvanized, plated; —ировать *v*. galvanize,
electroplate, plate; —м *m*. galvanism.

гальваническ/и *adv*. by galvanization; г.
оцинковывать *v*. galvanize; г. плаки-
ровать, г. покрывать *v*. galvanize,
electroplate; —ий *a*. galvanic, voltaic;
electro—; —ий покров electro-
deposit; —ий цех galvanizing shop,
electroplating shop; —ий элемент
galvanic cell, galvanic battery (obs.);
—ое золочение electrogilding.

гальвано *n*., изготовлять г. *v*. electrotype.

гальванограф *m*. (elec.) galvanograph;
—ия *f*. galvanography.

**гальвано/каустика** *f.* (med.) galvano-cautery, electrocautery; —**магнитизм** *m.* galvanomagnetism; —**магнитный** *a.* galvanomagnetic.

**гальванометр** *m.* (elec.) galvanometer; **постоянная** —а galvanometer constant; —**ический** *a.* galvanometric; —**ия** *f.* galvanometry.

**гальванопласт** *m.* galvanizer; —**ика** *f.* galvanoplastics, electroforming; —**ический, —ичный** *a.* galvanoplastic, electroforming; electrometallurgic; —**ическое заведение** galvanizing plant, electroplating plant.

**гальванопокрытие** *n.* electrodeposition, plating.

**гальваноскоп** *m.* (elec.) galvanoscope, current detector, quadrant electrometer; —**ический** *a.* galvanoscopic.

**гальваностег/ировать** *v.* electroplate; —**ически отложенный** electrodeposited; —**ический** *a.* electrolytic (plating), electroplating; —**ическое покрытие** electroplating, electrodeposition; —**ия** *f.* galvanostegy; electroplating, electrodeposition.

**гальвано/техника** *f.* electrolytic metallurgy; —**типия** *f.* electrotype; —**тропизм** *m.* (biol.) galvanotropism; —**хромия** *f.* (met.) galvanic coloring.

**галька** *f.* pebble, shingle, rubble; nodule; pebbles (fuel).

**гальмей** *see* **галмей.**

**Гальтона кривая** (math.) Galtonian curve.

**гамак** *m.* hammock.

**гамамел/идин** *m.* hamamelidin; —**ин** *m.* hamamelin; —**иса кора** hamamelis bark, witch hazel bark.

**гамартит** *m.* (min.) hamartite, bastnäsite.

**гаматионовая кислота** hamathionic acid, euxanthic acid.

**гамаша** *f.* gaiter, legging.

**гамбергит** *m.* (min.) hambergite.

**гамбин** *m.* gambin (a nitroso dye).

**гамбир** *m.* gambier, pale catechu; —**ная камедь** gambier gum.

**гамбузия** *f.* gambusia (fish).

**Гамбург, гамбургский** *a.* Hamburg.

**гамет/а** *f.* (biol.) gamete; —**о**— *prefix* gameto—, gamete.

**гамильтониан** *m.* (math.) Hamiltonian, Hamiltonian operator.

**гамит** *m.* hamite (shell).

—**гамия** *f.* *suffix* (biol.) —gamy (union for reproduction).

**гамлинит** *m.* (min.) hamlinite, goyazite.

**гамма** *f.* gamma ($\gamma$); gamut, range; **г.-аппарат** *m.* gamma (therapy) unit; **г.-железо** *n.* gamma iron; **г.-излучатель** *m.* gamma emitter; **г.-излучение** *n.* gamma radiation; **г.-лучи** *pl.* gamma rays; **г.-радиометр** *m.* gamma-ray counter; **г.-уран** *m.* gamma uranium; **г.-установка** *f.* gamma unit, gamma-ray source; —**граф** *m.* (nucl.) gammagraph.

**Гаммета уравнение** Hammett equation (for reaction rates).

—**гамный** *a.* *suffix* (biol.) —gamous (uniting for reproduction).

**гамовский** *a.* Gamow.

**гангл/ий** *m.* (anat.) ganglion, nerve center; —**иозный** *a.* ganglionic; gangliar, ganglioid.

**гангрен/а** *f.* (med.) gangrene; —**озный** *a.* gangrenous.

**гандшпуг** *see* **ганшпуг.**

**ганзенская желтая** Hansa yellow.

**ганистер** *m.* (petr.) ganister (a refractory quartzitic sandstone).

**ганит** *m.* (min.) gahnite, zinc spinel.

**Ганкока отсадочная машина** (min.) Hancock jig.

**ганкокит** *m.* (min.) hancockite (an epidote).

**ганксит** *m.* (min.) hanksite.

**ганнайит** *m.* (min.) hannayite.

**гано/идный** *a.* (zool.) ganoid; —**ин** *m.* ganoin; —**малит** *m.* (min.) ganomalite; —**филлит** *m.* (min.) ganophyllite.

**гантел/еобразный** *a.* dumbbell-like; —**и** *pl.* dumbbell.

**Гануса метод** Hanus (iodine number) method.

**ганшпуг** *m.* hand spike, lever.

**гаолян** *m.* (bot.) sorghum, spec. kaoliang (*Sorghum vulgare*).

**гап** *m.* gap, gap block.

**гапло**— *prefix* haplo— (single, simple); —**ид** *m.* (biol.) haploid, haploid cell; —**споридии** *pl.* (zool.) Haplosporidia.

гапто— *prefix* hapto— (contact, combination); —тропия *f.* (bot.) haptotropism; —форная группа haptophore.

гараж *m.* garage.

гарансин *m.* garancin (dye).

гарант *m.* guarantor; —ийный *a.* guarantee; —ирование *n.* guaranteeing; —ированный *a.* guaranteed, assured; —ировать *v.* guarantee; —ия *f.* guarantee, security, assurance.

гарве/изация *f.*, —ирование *n.* (met.) harveyizing (cementation process); —изированный *a.* harveyized; —изированная сталь Harvey steel; —изировать *v.* harveyize.

Гарвея процесс (met.) Harvey process.

гаргойль *m.* Gargoyle (lubricating oil).

гаргревский *a.* Hargreaves.

Гаргривс-Берда элемент Hargreaves-Bird (electrolytic) cell.

гардемарин *m.* midshipman.

гарденин *m.* gardenin.

гарденит *m.* (met.) hardenite (obs.), martensite.

гардения *f.* (bot.) gardenia.

гардина *f.* curtain.

гардинол *m.* gardinol (a detergent).

гардистонит *m.* (min.) hardystonite (member of melilite group).

Гаркинза теория Harkins theory.

гаркрец *m.* (met.) refinery slag.

гарлемск/ий бальзам, —ое масло Haarlem oil (sulfurated linseed oil).

гарлицин *m.* garlicine.

гармал/а *f.* (bot.) harmel, wild rue (*Peganum harmala*); —ин *m.* harmaline.

гарман *m.* harman, aribine.

гармахерский горн copper furnace, (copper) refining hearth; г. сок refinery slag.

Гарме способ (met.) Harmet's process.

гарм/ин *m.* harmine; —иновая кислота harminic acid; —ол *m.* harmol; —оловая кислота harmolic acid.

гармон/ика *f.* harmonic; harmonic curve; (music) accordion; в виде —ики bellow type; —иковая мембрана bellows; —ическая *f.* (phys.) harmonic; —ический *a.* harmonic, harmonious, rhythmic; —ический ряд (math.) harmonic progression; —ическая

кривая harmonic curve; —ичность *f.* harmonicity; —ия *f.* harmony, concord.

гармотом *m.*, баритовый г. (min.) harmotome.

гармошка *f.* bellows.

гарнец *m.* peck (measure).

гарниерит *m.* (min.) garnierite, noumeite.

гарнизон *m.* garrison, post.

гарнир *m.*, —овать *v.* garnish, trim.

гарниссаж *m.* (met.) lining, slag hardened on walls of blast furnace.

гарнитура *f.* fittings, mountings, trimmings; set, outfit; (text.) card clothing.

гарновка *see* арнаутка.

гарное масло fuel oil.

гарнцовый *a.* peck (measure).

гарньерит *see* гарниерит.

гарп/иус *m.*, —иусный *a.* rosin, colophony; —иусное масло rosin oil; —олин *m.* harpolin (a rosin-formaldehyde resin).

гарпун *m.*, —ный *a.* harpoon.

Гарриса способ Harris process (for lead refining).

гарт *m.* type metal (a lead-antimony alloy), —блей *m.* hard lead, antimonial lead.

гартит *see* гарденит.

гартовый *a.* type-metal.

гарус *m.*, —ный *a.* (text.) worsted yarn; —ина *f.* worsted thread.

Гарфильда валки (met.) Garfield rolls.

Гарца отсадочная машина (min.) Harz jig, plain eccentric jig.

гарц/бургит *m.* (petr.) harzburgite (a variety of peridotite); —евское решето *see* Гарца отсадочная машина.

гарь *f.* burning; fumes; cinder, ashes, dross; slash fire.

гас/ило *n.*, —ильщик *m.*, —итель *m.* extinguisher, quencher; damper; —ильный, —ительный *a.* extinguishing, damping, quenching; —итель *m.* damper; —ить *v.* extinguish, quench; damp; slake (lime); darken, put out (light); —нуть *v.* be extinguished; go out, die out; be slaked.

гасталдит *m.* (min.) gastaldite (a variety of glaucophane).

гастер— *see* гастр—.

**гастеромицеты** *pl.* (bot.) Gasteromycetes.

**гастингсит** *m.* (min.) hastingsite (a type of amphibole).

**гастр**—, **—о**— *prefix* gastr—, gastro— (stomach); **—ин** *m.* gastrin; **—ит** *m.* (med.) gastritis; **—ический** *a.* gastric; **—оподы** *pl.* (zool.) Gastropoda; **—отрихи** *pl.* (zool.) Gastrotricha; **—оэнтерит** *m.* (med.) gastroenteritis; **—ула** *f.* (biol.) gastrula.

**гасящ/ий, —ийся** *see* **гасительный; —ая схема** quenching circuit.

**г-ат** *see* **г-атом.**

**гатер** *m.* horizontal frame saw.

**гатить** *v.* dam up; build a road (on swampy ground).

**г-атом** *abbr.* (грамм-атом) gram-atom.

**гатура** *f.* (map drawing) hachure.

**гатчет/ин, —тин** *m.* (min.) hatchettine, hatchettite, mountain tallow.

**Гатчетта бурый** Hatchett's brown (copper ferrocyanide).

**гатчеттолит** *m.* (min.) hatchettolite (a tantalo-niobate of uranium).

**Гатше/ра краска, —та коричневая** *see* **Гатчетта бурый.**

**гатшетин** *see* **гатчетин.**

**гать** *f.* dam, dike, embankment, causeway.

**Гау ферма** Howe girder.

**гауби/ца** *f.*, **—чный** *a.* (mil.) howitzer.

**гауерит** *m.* (min.) hauerite (a natural manganese disulfide).

**—гауз** *suffix* house.

**Гаукинса элемент** Hawkins cell.

**гаультер/иевое масло, —овое масло** gaultheria oil, wintergreen oil; **—ин** *m.* gaultherin, monotropitoside; **—о-лин** *m.* gaultherolin, methyl salicylate.

**гаус** *see* **гаусс.**

**гаусман/ит, —нит** *m.* (min.) hausmannite.

**гаусс** *m.* gauss (unit of magnetic induction); **—ова, —овый** *a.* Gauss, Gaussian.

**гауч-пресс** *m.* (paper) couch; gage press.

**гафний** *m.* hafnium, Hf.

**гафтонит** *m.* (min.) haughtonite (a variety of biotite mica).

**гач** *m.* crude, fairly oil-free paraffin.

**гашен/ие** *n.* extinguishing, putting out, quenching; extinction, dying out;

slaking (lime); **—ка** *f.* slaked lime; **—ый** *a.* extinguished, quenched; slaked.

**гашетка** *f.* (guided missiles) firing button.

**гаширование** *n.* warping.

**гашиш** *m.* hashish.

**гашпиль** *m.* (leather) paddle wheel tank.

**гаюин, —ит** *m.* (min.) haüynite, haüyne; **—овый порфир** haüynitic porphyry.

**гб** *abbr.* (гильберт) gilbert.

**гвадальказарит** *m.* (min.) guadalcazarite.

**Гваделупа** Guadaloupe.

**гвай/кан** *see* **гваяковое дерево; —ол** *m.* guaiol, tiglic aldehyde; **—эн** *m.* guaiene; **—юла** *see* **гваюла.**

**Гватемала** Guatemala.

**гваэтол** *m.* guaethol, thanatol.

**гваюл/а** *f.* (bot.) guayule (*Parthenium*); **—овый каучук** guayule rubber.

**гвая/дол** *m.* guaiadol; **—к** *m.* guaiacum, guaiac gum; (bot.) *see* **гваяковое дерево;** *prefix* guaiac—; **—камфол** *m.* guaiacol camphorate; **—квин** *m.* guaiaquin.

**гваяков/ый** *a.* guaiac; **г. желтый** guaiacum yellow; **—ая кислота** guaiacic acid; **—ая смола** guaiacum, guaiac gum; **—ое дерево** (bot.) guaiacum, lignum vitae (*Guaiacum officinale*).

**гваяк/ол** *m.*, **—оловый** *a.* guaiacol, o-methoxyphenol; **бензойнокислый г., бензоат —ола** guaiacol benzoate; **—оловый эфир угольной кислоты** guaiacol carbonate; **—оновая кислота** guaiaconic acid.

**гваяц/ен** *m.* guaiacene, tiglic aldehyde; **—етин** *m.* guaiacetin, sodium pyrocatechin; **—ин** *m.* guaiacin.

**гветол** *m.* guethol.

**Гвиана, гвианский** *a.* Guiana.

**гвинейск/ий** *a.* Guinea; **г. перец** red pepper, paprika; **—ая зелень** Guinea green.

**гвозд/арь** *see* **гвоздочник; —евой** *a.* nail; **—едер** *m.* nail extractor; **—ик** *m.* tack.

**гвоздика** *f.* clove; (bot.) pinks (*Dianthus*).

**гвоздильн/ый** *a.* nail, nail-making; **г. молоток** spike driver; **—я** *f.* nail header, heading tool, riveting stock; nail mold.

**гвоздить** *v.* nail, drive a nail.

гвоздичн/ик *m.* (bot.) statice; avens (*Geum*); —ые *pl.* Caryophyllaceae; —ый *a.* clove; —ый перец (bot.) allspice (*Pimenta officinalis*); —ое дерево clove tree (*Eugenia aromatica* or *E. caryophyllata*); —ое масло oil of cloves; —ые головки cloves (spice).

гвоздо/образный *a.* nail-shaped; —чник *m.* nail maker, nail manufacturer; nailer; —чный *see* гвоздильный.

гвозд/ь *m.* nail; peg, spike; pin; большой г. spike; деревянный г. peg, dowel; шляпка —я nail head; —яник *m.* nail box; —яной *a.* nail.

гвт *abbr.* (гектоватт) hectowatt; гвт-ч *abbr.* (гектоватт-час) hectowatt-hour.

гг. *abbr.* (годы) years; (города) cities.

ГГУ *abbr.* (Горьковский государственный университет) Gorki State University.

где *adv.* where, wherever, wherein; г.-либо, г.-нибудь, г.-то somewhere, anywhere; г. бы, г. бы ни wherever.

геантиклиналь *m.* (geol.) geanticline.

геарксутит *see* гирксутит.

Геберлейна агломерационный процесс (met.) Heberlein (sintering) process.

гебронит *m.* (min.) hebronite, amblygonite.

геве/а *see* хевея; —ен *m.* heveen.

геветтит *m.* (min.) hewettite.

гевея *see* хевея.

геданит *m.* (min.) gedanite (a fossil resin related to amber).

геддановая кислота gheddic acid.

геденбергит *m.* (min.) hedenbergite (a calcium-iron pyroxene).

гедеом/овое масло hedeoma oil, American pennyroyal oil; —ол *m.* hedeomol.

гедер/агенин *m.* hederagenin; —агениновая кислота hederageninic acid; —ин *m.* hederine; —иновая кислота hederic acid; —оза *f.* hederose.

гедифан *m.* (min.) hedyphane (a calcium variety of mimetite).

гедихиумовое масло hedychium oil.

гедонал *m.* hedonal, methylpropylcarbinol urethan.

гедрит *m.* (min.) gedrite (a variety of anthophyllite).

гедроин *m.* hedroin.

геевое масло ghee (a semifluid butter).

гезароль *m.* Gesarol, DDT.

гезенк *m.* (min.) blind pit, blind shaft, staple, winze.

гейбахит *m.* (min.) heubachite.

Гейгера счетчик Geiger counter; Г.-Неттола закон Geiger-Nuttall relation.

гейгеровская область Geiger region.

гейзенберговский принцип Heisenberg principle.

гейзер *m.* (geol.) geyser; —ит *m.* (min.) geyserite (a variety of opal).

Гейзинга лак Heising varnish.

гейкиелит *m.* (min.) geikielite (a natural magnesium iron titanate).

Гейланда диаграмма (elec.) Heyland diagram.

гейландит *m.* (min.) heulandite (a zeolite).

Гейли метод (met.) Gayley process.

гейлюс/ит, —сит *m.* (min.) gaylussite.

Гей-люссака башня Gay-Lussac tower (for sulfuric acid manufacture).

гейммит *m.* heumite (a dike rock).

гейнтцит *m.* (min.) heintzite, kaliborite.

Гейслера сплавы Heusler alloys (manganese-copper-aluminum ferromagnetic alloy); Г. трубка Geissler tube.

Гейтлера-Лондона теория Heitler-London (covalence) theory.

гекбомит *m.* (min.) högbomite, hoegbomite.

гекельный станок (text.) hackling machine, hackling bench.

гекза— *see* гекса—.

гекли *n.* (text.) hackle.

гекса— *prefix* hexa— (six); *see also* шести—.

гексабром— *prefix* hexabrom—, hexabromo—; —ное число hexabromide number.

гексагидрит *m.* (min.) hexahydrite.

гексагидро— *prefix* hexahydro—; —азепин *m.* hexahydroazepine, hexamethyleneimine; —бензойная кислота hexahydrobenzoic acid.

гексагидрокси— *prefix* hexahydroxy—.

гексагидро/салициловая кислота hexahydrosalicylic acid; —толуол *m.* hexahydrotoluene.

гексагира *f.* (cryst.) sixfold axis of symmetry.

**гексагональн/о—** *prefix* hexagonal; **—ый** *a.* hexagonal, six-sided.

**гекса/декан** *m.* hexadecane, dioctyl; **—децен** *m.* hexadecene, cetene; **—децил** *m.* hexadecyl; **—децилен** *m.* hexadecylene, cetene; **—диен** *m.* hexadiene; **—диин** *m.* hexadiine, bipropargyl.

**гекса/кисоктаэдр** *m.* (cryst.) hexakisoctahedron, hexoctahedron; **—козан** *m.* hexacosane; **—козановая кислота** hexacosanic acid; **—контан** *m.* hexacontane.

**гексал** *m.* hexal; **—ин** *m.* hexalin, cyclohexanol.

**гексаметил** *m.*, **—овый** *a.* hexamethyl; **—ен** *m.* hexamethylene, cyclohexane; **—ентетрамин** *m.* hexamethylenetetramine.

**гекса/мидин** *m.* hexamidine, Mysoline; **—н** *m.* hexane, caproyl hydride; **—нал** *m.* hexanal, caproaldehyde; **—нафтен** *m.* hexanaphthene, cyclohexene; **—нитро—** *prefix* hexanitro—.

**гексан/овый** *a.* hexane; **—овая кислота** hexanoic acid, caproic acid; **—ол** *m.* hexanol, hexyl alcohol; **—он** *m.* hexanone, ethylpropyl ketone.

**гекса/симметричная поверхность** (cryst.) hexasymmetrical plane; **—тен** *m.* a hexachlorocyclohexane insecticide; **—триен** *m.* hexatriene; **—фенил** *m.* hexaphenyl.

**гексахлор—** *prefix* hexachlor—, hexachloro—; **—ан** *m.* hexachloran, hexachlorocyclohexane (same as Lindane); **—этан** *m.* hexachloroethane, carbon trichloride.

**гекса/циклический** *a.* hexacyclic; **—эдр** *m.* (cryst.) hexahedron, cube; **—эдрический** *a.* hexahedral, cubic.

**гексен** *m.* hexene, tetrahydrobenzene; **—ал** *m.* hexenal, sodium barbiturate; Hexenal, hexobarbital; **—ил** *m.* hexenyl; **—овая кислота** hexenoic acid, propylacrylic acid.

**гексетон** *m.* hexetone.

**гексил** *m.*, **—овый** *a.* hexyl, enanthyl; **хлористый г.** hexyl chloride; **—ен** *m.* hexylene, hexene; **—ил** *m.* hexylyl; **—овый спирт** *see* гексанол; **—овая кислота** hexylic acid, caproic acid.

**рекс/ин** *m.* hexine, hexyne; **—ит** *m.* hexitol, a hexahydric alcohol.

**гексо—** *prefix* hexo—; **—биоза** *f.* hexobiose; **—д** *m.* hexode, six-electrode tube.

**гексоз—** *prefix* hexose—; **—а** *f.* hexose.

**гексо/н** *m.* hexone, methylisobutyl ketone; **—ний** *m.* hexonium, hexamethonium; **—новая кислота** hexonic acid; **—триоза** *f.* hexotriose.

**гексуроновая кислота** hexuronic acid.

**гектар** *m.* hectare (2.471 acres).

**гектический** *a.* hectic.

**гекто—** *prefix* hecto— (hundred); **—ватт** *m.* (elec.) hectowatt; **—ватт-час** *m.* hectowatt-hour; **—грамм** *m.* hectogram; **—граф** *m.* hectograph; **—графический** *a.* hectographic; **—литр** *m.* hectoliter; **—метр** *m.* hectometer; **—пьеза** *f.* (elec.) hectopiezoelectric unit.

**гелвин** *m.* (min.) helvite, helvine.

**гелволевая кислота** helvolic acid.

**гелебор** *see* геллебор.

**гелен/ин** *m.* helenin, inula camphor; **—ит** *m.* (min.) helenite (an ozoceritelike wax); gehlenite (a calcium aluminum silicate).

**гелеобраз/ный** *a.* gel-like, gelatinous, jelly-like, gelatinoid; **—ование** *n.* gelatination, gelatinization, jellification.

**гелепин/иновая кислота** helepininic acid; **—оловая кислота** helepinolic acid.

**гели** *pl.* of **гель.**

**гелиант/ин** *m.* helianthin; **—овая кислота** helianthic acid; **—рон** *m.* helianthrone, benzodianthrone.

**гелигнит** *m.* gelignite (a gelatin dynamite).

**гел/иевый** *a.*, **—ий** *m.* helium, He.

**геликоид** *m.* helicoid; **—альный** *a.* helicoid, helical, spiral, coiled; **—ин** *m.* helicoidin.

**геликоптер** *m.* (aero.) helicopter.

**геликсин** *m.* helixin (an antibiotic).

**гелио—** *prefix* helio— (sun); **—гравюра** *f.* (typ.) heliogravure, photoengraving; **—граф** *m.* (surv.) heliograph; **—графия** *f.* heliography; **—дор** *m.* (min.) heliodor (a gem variety of beryl); **—лампа** *f.* heliolamp; **—метр**

*m.* (astron.) heliometer; —и *m.* helion, alpha-particle; —скоп *m.* helioscope; —стат *m.* heliostat; —сушка *f.* sun drying; —сфера *f.* heliosphere; —техника *f.* solar energy technology.
гелиотроп *m.* (bot.) heliotrope (*Heliotropium*); (min.) heliotrope (a subspecies of quartz); (surv.) heliotrope, heliograph; —изм *m.* (bot.) heliotropism; —ин *m.* heliotropin; heliotropine (the alkaloid); —ический *a.* heliotropic; —овый *a.* heliotrope, heliotropic; —овая кислота heliotropic acid, piperonylic acid.
гелио/физика *f.* heliophysics; —филлит *m.* (min.) heliophyllite, ecdemite; —фильный *a.* heliophilous, sunloving; —фит *m.* (bot.) heliophyte; —центрический *a.* (astron.) heliocentric.
гели/хризумовое масло helichrysum oil; —цидин *m.* helicidin; —цин *m.* helicin, salicylaldehyde glucoside.
гелландит *m.* (min.) hellandite.
геллебор *m.* (bot.) hellebore (*Helleborus*); —еин *m.* helleborein; —етин *m.* helleboretin; —ин *m.* helleborin.
Геллезена элемент (elec.) Hellesen cell.
Геллера процесс Heller process (of gasification).
геллефлинта *f.* (petr.) hälleflinta.
гелминт *see* гельминт.
гелмитол *m.* Helmitol, Citramin.
гелоз/а *f.* gelose; —ин *m.* gelosine.
гель *m.* gel, jelly.
гельбин *m.* barium yellow, barium chromate.
гельветский ярус (geol.) Helvetian stage.
гельвин *see* гелвин.
гельдерберг/иан *m.*, —ская формация (geol.) Helderbergian formation.
гельзем/ий корень gelsemium root; —ин *m.* gelsemine; —инин *m.* gelseminine; —ининовая кислота gelsemininic acid, gelsemic acid; —иновый *a.* gelsemine, gelseminic; —иновая кислота gelseminic acid, scopoletin; —ицин *m.* gelsemicine.
гелькозол *m.* helcosol, bismuth pyrogallate.
гельмгольцевый *a.* Helmholtz, Helmholtzian.

гельминт *m.* (zool.) helminth, an intestinal parasitic worm; —оз *m.* (med.) helminthiasis; —ологический *a.* helminthologic; —ология *f.* helminthology.
гем *m.* heme (of hemoglobin).
гема— *prefix* hema—.
гемамель-таннин *m.* hamamelitannin.
гемантин *m.* hemanthine.
гемат/еин *m.* hematein; —иметр *m.* hematimeter.
гематин *m.* hematin; —овый *a.* hematinic; —овая кислота hematinic acid; —ометр *m.* hematinometer.
гематит *m.* (min.) hematite, red iron ore; (met.) a high-quality foundry iron; почковидный г. kidney ore (a reniform variety of hematite); —овый *a.* hematite, hematitic; —овая руда hematite; —оподобный *a.* hematitic.
гемато— *prefix* hemato—, blood; —ген *m.* hematogen; —глобулин *m.* hematoglobulin, oxyhemoglobin; —зис *m.* (med.) hematosis; —идин *m.* hematoidin, bilirubin; —ксилин *m.* hematoxylin; —лиз *m.* hematolysis; —лит *m.* (min.) hematolite; —литический *a.* hematolytic; (min.) hematolitic; —логия *f.* hematology; —порфирин *m.* hematoporphyrin, porporino; —стибиит *m.* (min.) hematostibiite (probably same as manganostibiite).
гематур/иновая кислота hematurinic acid; —ия *f.* hematuria.
гемафибрит *m.* (min.) hemafibrite.
гемеллит/ен, —ол *m.* hemellitol, hemimellitene; —овая кислота hemellitic acid, 2,3-xylic acid.
гемера *f.* (geol., pal.) hemera.
гемерокалис *m.* (bot.) day lily (*Hemerocallis*).
геми— *prefix* hemi—, semi—; —альбумоза *f.* hemialbumose, propeptone.
гемимеллит/ен *m.* hemimellitene, 1,2,3-trimethylbenzene; —овая кислота hemimellitic acid, 1,2,3-benzenetricarboxylic acid; —ол *m.* hemimellitol.
гемиморф/изм *m.* (cryst.) hemimorphism; —ит *m.* (min.) hemimorphite, calamine; —ный *a.* (cryst.) hemimorphic.
гемин *m.* hemin, hematin chloride.
геми/пиновая кислота hemipinic acid,

hemipic acid, 3,4-dimethoxyphthalic acid; —пиоцианин *m.* hemipyocyanine; —пирамида *f.* (cryst.) hemipyramid; —сфера *f.* hemisphere; —сферический *a.* hemispheric, hemispherical.

гемит *m.* (elec.) Hemit (insulating material).

гемитроп/ический, —ный *a.* (cryst.) hemitropic, hemitrope, twinned.

гемицеллюлоза *f.* hemicellulose.

гемиэдр *m.* (cryst.) hemihedron; —ический *a.* hemihedral; —ия *f.* hemihedrism.

гемлок *m.* (bot.) hemlock (*Tsuga*).

гемма *f.* gem, jewel; (biol.) gemma.

гемо— *prefix* hemo— (blood); —глобин *m.* hemoglobin; —л *m.* hemol; —лиз *m.* hemolysis; —лизин *m.* hemolysin; —литический *a.* hemolytic; —пиррол *m.* hemopyrrole.

геморр/агический *a.* (med.) hemorrhagic; —агия *f.* hemorrhage; —оидальный, —ойный *a.* hemorrhoid, hemorrhoidal; —ой *m.* hemorrhoid.

гемо/споридии *pl.* (zool.) Hemosporidia; —статический *a.* (med.) hemostatic; —статическое средство hemostatic, styptic; —терапия *f.* (med.) hemotherapy; —торакс *m.* hemothorax; —цианин *m.* hemocyanin; —эритрин *m.* hemoerythrin.

Гемпеля бюретка Hempel gas buret; Г. дефлегматор Hempel's distilling tube.

Гемфри насос Humphrey (gas) pump.

ген *m.* (biol.) gene; *suffix* —gen, —gene.

ген. *abbr.* (генеральный) general; (генетика) genetics; (генетический) genetic.

генвудит *m.* (min.) henwoodite (a hydrated phosphate of aluminum and copper).

Гендерсона процесс (met.) Henderson process.

генеалог/ический *a.* genealogical; —ия *f.* genealogy.

генезер/етол *m.* geneserethol; —ин *m.* geneserine.

генезис *m.* genesis, origin, source; *suffix* —genesis, —geny.

генейкозан *m.* heneicosane; —овая кислота heneicosanic acid.

генекен *m.* (bot.) henequen, Yucatan sisal (*Agave fourcroydes*).

генерал/изация *f.* generalization; —ьный *a.* general.

генератор *m.* generator, dynamo; oscillator; (gas) producer; —ный *a.* generator, generating; —ный агрегат (elec.) generator, generating unit; —ный газ generator gas, producer gas; —ная станция (elec.) power station, powerhouse.

генер/атриса *f.* (geom.) generatrix; —ация *f.*, —ирование *n.* generation; oscillation; —ированный *a.* generated; —ировать *v.* generate, produce; —ирующий *a.* generating; oscillating.

генет/ика *f.* (biol.) genetics; —ический *a.* genetic.

гени/альный *a.* great, brilliant; —й *m.* genius.

генистеин *m.* genistein, 4′,5,7-trihydroxyisoflavone.

генитальный *a.* genital, sexual.

генна *f.* henna (dye).

ген/ный *a.* (biol.) gene; *suffix* —genic, —genous; -inducing, -causing, -producing; produced by, arising in; —о prefix geno— (race, kind; sex); —овариация *f.* genovariation; —отип *m.* genotype; —отипный *a.* genotypic.

генплан *m.* State economic production plan.

генри *n.* (elec.) henry (unit of induction); закон Г. Henry's law; —метр *m.* henrymeter, inductance meter.

Гентеле зелень Gentele's green, copper stannate.

гентиа/марин *m.* gentiamarin; —нин *m.* gentianin; —нит *m.* gentianite; —ноза *f.* gentianose.

генти/енин *m.* gentienin; —зин *m.* gentisin, gentianin; —зиновая кислота gentisic acid, 2,5-dihydroxybenzoic acid; —ин *m.* gentiin.

гентио/биоза *f.* gentiobiose; —генин *m.* gentiogenin; —пикрин *m.* gentiopicrin.

гентит *m.* (min.) genthite, nickel gymnite (probably a variety of garnierite).

гентриаконтан *m.* hentriacontane.

генуинный *a.* genuine, real; natural; congenital (disease or deformity).

Генуя, генуэзский *a.* Genoa.

генциан/а *f.* (bot.) gentian (*Gentiana*); —оза *see* гентианоза.

гео— *prefix* geo— (earth, land); —биотический *a.* (biol.) geobiotic; —ботанический *a.* geobotanical; —генезис *m.* geogeny (rare); —гнозия *f.* geognosy, structural geology.

географ *m.* geographer; —ический *a.* geographic; —ия *f.* geography.

геодез/ист *m.* geodesist; —ический *a.* geodetic; (math.) geodesic; —ия *f.* geodesy, large-scale surveying.

геодин *m.* geodin.

геозот *m.* geosote, guaiacol valerate.

геоид *m.* geoidal surface, geoid.

геокронит *m.* (min.) geocronite.

геолог *m.* geologist; —ический *a.* geological; —ическое летосчисление geochronology; —ия *f.* geology.

геомагнитный *a.* geomagnetic.

геометр *m.* geometrician; —альный, —ический *a.* geometric; —ический ряд geometric progression; —ическое место (math.) locus; —ически *adv.* geometrically; —ия *f.* geometry; configuration.

гео/морфный *a.* geomorphic; —морфология *f.* geomorphology; —номия *f.* geonomy; —потенциал *m.* geopotential.

георгийский *a.* (geol.) Georgian.

георгина *f.* (bot.) dahlia.

гео/синклиналь *f.* (geol.) geosyncline; —строфический *a.* (meteor.) geostrophic; gradient (wind); —тектоника geotectonics, tectonic geology; —тектонический *a.* geotectonic, structural.

геотерм/ика, —ия *f.* (geol.) geothermy; —ический *a.* geothermal; —ическая ступень geothermal step; —ометр *m.* geothermometer.

геотропизм *m.* (bot.) geotropism.

геофиз/ик *m.* geophysicist; —ика *f.* geophysics; промысловая —ика geophysical well logging; —ический *a.* geophysical.

геофон *m.* geophone.

геоффраин *m.* geoffrayin, rhatanin.

геохим/ический *a.* geochemical; —ия *f.* geochemistry.

геохронолог/ический *a.* geochronolog-ical; —ия *f.* geochronology, geologic time.

геоцентрический *a.* (astron.) geocentric.

геоцерин/овая кислота geocerinic acid; —он *m.* geocerinone.

гепарин *m.* heparin.

гепатит *m.* (min.) hepatite (fetid barite); (med.) hepatitis.

гепта— *prefix* hepta— (seven); *see also* семи—; —гональный *a.* heptagonal.

гептадекан *m.* heptadecane; —овая кислота heptadecanoic acid, margaric acid; —он *m.* heptadecanone, pelargone.

гепта/диен *m.* heptadiene; —козан *m.* heptacosane.

гептальдегид *m.* heptaldehyde, heptanal.

гептаметилен *m.* heptamethylene, suberane.

гептан *m.* heptane; —ал *m.* heptanal; —овая кислота heptanoic acid, enanthic acid; —ол *m.* heptanol, heptyl alcohol; —он *m.* heptanone.

гептахлор *m.* heptachlor (insecticide).

гептаэдр *m.* heptahedron; —ический *a.* heptahedral.

гептен *m.* heptene, pentylethylene; —ил *m.* heptenyl; —илен *m.* heptenylene, heptine.

гептил *m.*, —овый *a.* heptyl; —ацетат *m.* heptyl acetate; —ен *m.* heptylene, heptene; —овый спирт *see* гептанол.

гепт/ин *m.* heptine, heptyne, pentylacetylene; —ит *m.* heptitol, a heptahydric alcohol; —од *m.* (thermionics) heptode, pentagrid; —оза *f.* heptose; —уроновая кислота hepturonic acid.

Гепфнера процесс Höpfner process (for copper).

геран/евые, —иевые *pl.* (bot.) Geraniaceae; —иал *m.* geranial, citral; —иевый *a.* geranium, geranic; —иевая кислота geranic acid, 3,7-dimethyl-2,6-octadienoic acid; —иевое масло geranium oil; турецкое —иевое масло palmarosa oil; —иецветные, —еобразные *pl.* (bot.) Geraniales; —ий *see* герань.

геранил *m.*, —овый *a.* geranyl; муравьинокислый г., формиат —а geranyl formate; —ацетат *m.* geranyl acetate.

геран/иол *m.* geraniol; —иум *m.*, —ь *f.* (bot.) geranium; pelargonium.

**герапатит** *m.* herapathite, quinine sulfate periodide.

**гератоль** *m.* geratol (for purification of acetylene).

**гербарий** *m.* (bot.) herbarium.

**Герберта метод** (met.) Herbert (hardening) process.

**гербицид** *m.* herbicide, weed killer.

**гербов/ый** *a.* stamped; **г. сбор** stamp duty; **—ая марка** stamp.

**герд** *m.* (min.) buddle.

**гердерит** *m.* (min.) herderite (a fluophosphate of beryllium and calcium).

**геренгрундит** *m.* (min.) herrengrundite.

**Гересгофа печь** Herreshoff furnace.

**геркулой** *m.* Herculoy (a copper alloy).

**герман/ат** *m.* germanate; **—иеводород** *m.* germanium hydride, germane; **—иевокислый** *a.* germanic acid; germanate (of); **—иевокислая соль** germanate; **—иевый** *a.* germanium, germanic; **—иевая кислота** germanic acid (germanic hydroxide); **соль —иевой кислоты** germanate; **—иевая соль** germanic salt, germanium salt.

**германиефтороводородн/ая кислота** fluogermanic acid, hydrofluogermanic acid; **соль —ой кислоты** fluogermanate.

**герман/ий** *m.* germanium, Ge; **двуокись —ия, окись —ия** germanium dioxide, germanic oxide; **закись —ия** germanous oxide, germanium monoxide; **хлористый г.** germanous chloride, germanium dichloride; **хлорный г.** germanic chloride, germanium tetrachloride; **—ит** *m.* (min.) germanite.

**Германия** Germany.

**германский** *a.* German.

**гермафродит** *m.* (biol.) hermaphrodite.

**гермет/изация** *f.* hermetic sealing, sealing, making airtight; **—изированный, —изованный** *a.* hermetically sealed; **—ически** *adv.* hermetically; **—ический** *a.* hermetic, tight, airtight; pneumatic (sprayer); **—ичность** *f.* hermetic state, hermetic nature, tightness.

**герми/нативный** *a.* germinative; **—натор** *m.* germinator; **—цид** *m.* germicide.

**германофенил** *m.* hermophenyl.

**герм. пат.** *abbr.* (германский патент) German patent.

**гербиарин** *m.* herniarin, 7-methoxycoumarin.

**героин** *m.* heroin, diacetylmorphine.

**геро/ический, —йский** *a.* heroic; **—й** *m.* hero.

**герониевая кислота** geronic acid, 2-dimethyl-6-ketoheptoic acid.

**герпетология** *f.* (zool.) herpetology.

**гередорфит** *m.* (min.) gersdorffite.

**Герти генератор** Heurty generator.

**гертц** *see* **герц.**

**Геру дуговая печь** (met.) Heroult furnace; **Г. процесс** Heroult process (for aluminum manufacture).

**герхардтит** *m.* (min.) gerhardtite.

**герц** *m.* (elec. comm.) hertz, cycle per second.

**герцин/ит** *m.* (min.) hercynite, iron spinel; **—ский** *a.* (geol.) Hercynian.

**герцовый** *a.* Hertz, Hertzian.

**гершелит** *m.* (min.) herschelite, seebachite (a variety of chabazite).

**Гершеля явление** (phot.) Herschel effect.

**геспер/етин** *m.* hesperetin; **—етиновая кислота** hesperetic acid; **—етол** *m.* hesperetol, 5-vinyl guaiacol; **—иден** *m.* hesperidene, *d*-limonene; **—идин** *m.* hesperidine (alkaloid); hesperidin (glucoside).

**Гесса закон** Hess' law (of constant heat summation).

**гессен/ка** *f.*, **—ская муха** Hessian fly; **—ский пурпур** Hessian purple (dye).

**гессит** *m.* (min.) hessite (silver telluride).

**Гесслера сплав** *see* **Гейслера сплавы.**

**гессонит** *m.* (min.) hessonite, cinnamon stone (a variety of grossularite garnet).

**гетеро—** *prefix* hetero— (different); *see also* **разно—; —атом** *m.* heteroatom, a heterocyclic atom; **—ауксин** *m.* heteroauxin, 3-indolylacetic acid (root stimulant).

**гетероген/изация** *f.* heterogenization; **—ит** *m.* (min.) heterogenite (probably an alteration product of smaltite); **—ность** *f.* heterogeneity; **—ный** *a.* heterogeneous.

**гетеродин** *m.*, **—ный** *a.* (rad.) heterodyne.

гетерозигот/а *f.* (biol.) heterozygote;
—ность *f.* heterozygosity; —ный *a.*
heterozygous.
гетеро/зис *m.* (biol.) heterosis, hybrid
vigor; —лиз *m.* heterolysis; —лит *m.*
(min.) hetaerolite, zinc-hausmannite.
гетероморф/изм *m.* heteromorphism;
—ит *m.* (min.) heteromorphite; —ный
*a.* heteromorphous, heteromorphic.
гетеро/пический *a.* (geol.) heteropic;
—поликислота *f.* heteropoly acid;
—полярный *a.* heteropolar; —статический способ (elec.) heterostatic
method (for using quadrant electrometer); —томный *a.* (min.) hetero-
tomous; —трофный *a.* (physiol.)
heterotrophic; —хлоридиновые *pl.*
(zool.) Heterochloridina; —циклический *a.* heterocyclic.
гетит *m.* (min.) goethite.
гето/крезол *m.* hetocresol, cresol meta-
cinnamate; —л *m.* hetol, sodium
cinnamate.
геттангский ярус (geol.) Hettangian
stage.
Гефнера свеча Hefner unit, Hefner
candle (0.9 candlepower).
ги *see* геевое масло.
гиал/иновый *a.* glassy; (biol.) hyaline,
clear, transparent; —ит *m.* (min.)
hyalite (a variety of opal); —итовое
стекло hyalithe (a glass).
гиало— *prefix* hyalo—, hyal— (clear,
glass).
гиалограф/ический *a.* (phot.) hyalo-
graphic; —ия *f.* hyalography.
гиалоидный *see* гиалиновый.
гиало/кристаллический *a.* hyalocrystal-
line; —мелан *m.* (petr.) hyalomelane
(a basalt-obsidian); —пилитовая
структура (geol.) hyalopilitic texture;
—плазма *f.* (biol.) hyaloplasm; —сидерит *m.* (min.) hyalosiderite (a
variety of chrysolite); —текит *m.*
(min.) hyalotekite; —техника *f.* glass
manufacture; —фан *m.* (min.) hyalo-
phane (a barium-bearing adularia
orthoclase).
гиалургия *f.* hyalurgy, glass manufacture.
гиалуроновая кислота hyaluronic acid.
гиананхин *m.* hyananchin.
ГИАП *abbr.* (Государственный инсти-

тут азотной промышленности) State
Institute of the Nitrogen Industry.
гиацинт *m.*, —овый *a.* (bot.) hyacinth
(*Hyacinthus*); (min.) hyacinth, zircon;
восточный г. (bot.) hyacinth (*Hyacinthus orientalis*); (min.) oriental
hyacinth, corundum; цейлонский г.
(min.) Ceylon hyacinth; jargon; —ин
*m.* hyacinthin, phenylacetic aldehyde.
гиб *m.* bend, bending; г. с перегибом
backward and forward bending (test).
гиббенит *m.* (min.) hibbenite (a variety
of hopeite).
гибберелл/а *f.* gibberella (a fungus);
—ин *m.* gibberellin; —овая кислота
gibberellic acid, gibberellin X.
Гиббса правило фаз Gibbs' phase rule.
гиббсит *m.* (min.) gibbsite, hydrargillite.
гибель *f.* ruin, destruction, catastrophe,
wreck, loss; —ный *a.* destructive,
disastrous, catastrophic.
гибискус *m.* (bot.) hibiscus.
гибк/а *f.* bending; —ий *a.* flexible, supple, pliable, pliant, bendable, ductile;
springy, elastic; —ость *f.* flexibility,
pliability, ductility; elasticity; plasticity.
гибнерит *see* гюбнерит.
гибнуть *v.* perish; disappear.
гибочный *a.* bending.
гибрид *m.* (biol.) hybrid; (petr.) hybrid
rock, contaminated rock; —изация *f.*
hybridization; —ный *a.* hybrid.
гибсит *see* гиббсит.
гибшит *m.* (min.) hibschite.
ГИВ *abbr.* (Государственная инспекция
по ветеринарии) State Veterinary
Inspection; ГИВД *abbr.* (Государственный институт высоких давлений)
State Institute of High Pressures.
гига— *prefix* giga— (denoting a magnitude of $10^9$).
гигант *m.* giant; —ин *m.* gigantin;
—олит *m.* (min.) gigantolite (a variety
of pinite); —ский *a.* gigantic, huge,
mammoth.
гигиен/а *f.* hygiene, hygienics, sanitation; —ист *m.* hygienist; —ический,
—ичный *a.* hygienic, sanitary.
гигрин *m.* hygrine; —овая кислота
hygric acid.
гигро— *prefix* hygro— (wet, moist);
—граф *m.* hygrograph.

**гигрол** *m.* hygrol, colloidal mercury.

**гигрометр** *m.* (meteor.) hygrometer; **—ический** *a.* hygrometric; **—ия** *f.* hygrometry, determination of humidity.

**гигроскоп** *m.* hygroscope; **—ический,** **—ичный** *a.* hygroscopic, moisture-absorbing; absorbent (cotton); **—ичность** *f.* hygroscopicity, hygroscopic nature.

**гигро/филит** *m.* (min.) hygrophilite, chlorocalcite; **—фильный** *a.* (biol.) hygrophilous; **—фит** *m.* (bot.) hygrophyte; **—электрометр** *m.* hygroelectrometer.

**гид** *m.* guide.

**Гида процесс** *see* **Гайда процесс.**

**гидантоин** *m.* hydantoin, glycolylurea; **—овая кислота** hydantoic acid, glycoluric acid.

**гидато/генезис** *m.* (geol.) hydatogenesis; **—генный** *a.* hydatogenous, hydatogenic; **—пневматолитический** *a.* (geol.) hydatopneumatolytic.

**гидденит** *m.* (min.) hiddenite (a variety of spodumene).

**гиднокарпов/ая кислота** hydnocarpic acid; **—ое масло** hydnocarpus oil.

**гидр.** *abbr.* (гидролитический) hydrolytic.

**гидр—** *prefix* hydr—; **—а** *f.* (zool.) hydra (polyp); **—ы** *pl.* Hydrida.

**гидравлика** *f.* hydraulics, hydromechanics.

**гидравлическ/ий** *a.* hydraulic; **г. затвор** hydraulic seal, water seal; **г. подъемник** hydraulic lift, jigger; **г. раствор** hydraulic mortar; **г. таран, г. поршень** hydraulic ram; **г. удар** water hammer; **—ая разработка** hydraulic mining, hydraulicking; **—ая сила** water power.

**гидравличность** *f.* hydraulicity.

**гидрази—** *prefix* hydrazi—; **—д** *m.* hydrazide; **—дин** *m.* hydrazidine; **—л** *m.* hydrazyl; **—метилен** *m.* hydrazimethylene.

**гидразин** *m.,* **—иевый, —овый** *a.* hydrazine, diamine; **гидрат —а** hydrazine hydrate; **сернокислый г., сульфат —а** hydrazine sulfate.

**гидрази/но—** *prefix* hydrazino—; **—но-кислота** *f.* hydrazino acid;—**уксусная**

кислота hydraziacetic acid.

**гидразо—** *prefix* hydrazo—; **—бензол** *m.* hydrazobenzene, 1,1-diphenylhydrazine; **—кислота** *f.* hydrazo acid; **—н** *m.* hydrazone; **—соединение** *n.* hydrazo compound; **—толуол** *m.* hydrazotoluene.

**гидр/амин** *m.* hydramine; **—ангин** *m.* hydrangin.

**гидрант** *m.* (fire) hydrant; (zool.) hydranth.

**гидр/аргиллит** *m.* (min.) hydrargillite, gibbsite; **—аргирол** *m.* hydrargyrol, mercuric phenylthionate.

**гидрастин** *m.* hydrastine (alkaloid); hydrastin; **сернокислый г., сульфат —а** hydrastine sulfate; **—ин** *m.* hydrastinine.

**гидраст/ис** *m.,* **канадский г.** (bot.) golden-seal (*Hydrastis canadensis*); **—овая кислота** hydrastic acid.

**гидрат** *m.* hydrate; **г. закиси** hydroxide (lower or **—ous** hydroxide); **г. закиси железа** ferrous hydroxide; **г. закиси меди** cuprous hydroxide; **г. окиси** hydroxide (higher or **—ic** hydroxide); **г. окиси аммония** ammonium hydroxide; **г. окиси железа** ferric hydroxide; **г. окиси меди** cupric hydroxide.

**гидрат/ация, —изация** *f.* hydration; **—изированный, —ированный** *a.* hydrated; **—изировать** *v.* hydrate; **—ный** *a.* hydrate, hydrated; **—ная вода** water of hydration; **—огенный** *a.* aqueous, water.

**гидратропов/ый альдегид** hydratropaldehyde; **г. спирт** hydratropic alcohol;—**ая кислота** hydratropic acid, alpha-phenylpropionic acid.

**гидр/ацетин** *m.* Hydracetin, acetylphenylhydrazine; **—ид** *m.* hydride; **—ин** *m.* hydrin.

**гидринд/ен** *m.* hydrindene, indan; **—ил** *m.* hydrindyl; **—иновая кислота** hydrindic acid, *o*-aminomandelic acid; **—он** *m.* hydrindone, indone.

**гидриров/ание** *n.* hydrogenation; **—анный** *a.* hydrogenated; **—ать** *v.* hydrogenate, hydrogenize.

**гидро—** *prefix* hydro—, hydr—, water, hydraulic; **—аккумулирование** *n.* water storage; **—ароматический** *a.* hydroaromatic; **—биология** *f.* hydro-

biology; —борацит *m.* (min.) hydro-
boracite; —бромид *m.* hydrobromide;
—гель *m.* hydrogel; —гематит *m.*
(min.) hydrohematite, turgite; —ген
*see* водород; —генератор *m.* (elec.)
hydraulic generator.
гидроген/изат *m.* hydrogenation product; —изация *f.* hydrogenation;
—изованный *a.* hydrogenated;
—изовать *v.* hydrogenate; —ный
*a.* hydrogen, hydrogenous.
гидро/геология *f.* hydrogeology; —граф
*m.* hydrograph; hydrographer; —графический *a.* hydrographic; —графия
*f.* (navigation) hydrography.
гидродинам/ика *f.* hydrodynamics; —и-
ческий *a.* hydrodynamic; —ометр *m.*
hydrodynamometer.
гидро/добыча *f.* hydraulic mining; —доломит *m.* (min.) hydrodolomite;
—затвор *m.* hydro seal, water seal;
—золь *m.* hydrosol; —идные *pl.*
(zool.) Hydrozoa; —иды *pl.* Hy-
droida; —изогипса *f.* contour of
water table; —изоляция *f.* waterproofing (of basements, etc.); —иодид
*m.* hydroiodide; —какодил *m.* cacodyl
hydride; —карбонат *m.* hydrocarbo-
nate; —карбюр *m.* a light oil; —каучук *m.* hydrorubber; —клапан *m.*
pressure-operated valve; —кластический *a.* (geol.) hydroclastic; —ко-
раллы *pl.* (zool.) Hydrocorallinae;
—коричная кислота hydrocinnamic
acid; —котарнин *m.* hydrocotarnine;
—коффеиновая кислота hydro-
caffeic acid.
гидроксамовая кислота hydroxamic
acid.
гидроксантан *m.* xanthane hydride.
гидрокси— *prefix* hydroxy—; —бензол
*m.* hydroxybenzene; —кислота *f.* hydroxy acid; —л *m.*, —льный *a.*
hydroxyl; —ламин *m.* hydroxylamine; —лирование *n.* hydroxylation;
—лировать *v.* hydroxylate.
гидроксимовая кислота hydroximic
acid.
гидроксисоединение *n.* hydroxy compound.
гидроксоновая кислота hydroxonic acid.
гидрокумарон *m.* hydrocoumarone.
гидрол *m.* hydrol, water molecule.

гидролиз *m.* hydrolysis; —ат *m.* hydrolyzate; —ация *f.* hydrolyzing, hydrolysis; —ировать, —овать *v.* hydrolyze; —ный *a.* hydrolytic; —ующий
*a.* hydrolyzing.
гидролит *m.* hydrolyte; —ический *a.*
hydrolytic; —ическое расщепление
hydrolytic dissociation, hydrolysis.
гидролог *m.* (geol.) hydrologist; —ический *a.* hydrologic; —ия *f.* hydrology.
гидро/магнезит *m.* (min.) hydromagnesite; —медузы *pl.* (zool.) Hydro-
medusae; —металлургия *f.* hydro-
metallurgy; —метаморфизм *m.* (geol.)
hydrometamorphism; —метеорология *f.* hydrometeorology.
гидрометр *m.* hydrometer; —ический *a.*
hydrometric; —ическая вертушка
current meter (for streams); —ия *f.*
hydrometry; —ограф *m.* hydrometro-
graph.
гидро/механика *f.* hydromechanics, fluid
mechanics; —модуль *m.* (agr.) water
consumption per unit of time and
area; —монитор *m.* (min.) monitor;
hydraulic excavator; —мотор *m.*
hydraulic motor.
гидрон *m.*, —овый *a.* hydrone; —ал *m.*
hydronal, polychloral; —алиум *m.*
Hydronalium (an aluminum alloy);
—астуран *m.* (min.) hydro-uraninite.
гидро/окись *f.* hydroxide; г. алюминия
aluminum hydroxide; —передача *f.*
hydraulic transmission; —перекись *f.*
hydroperoxide; —план, —самолет *m.*
hydroplane, seaplane; —пневмати-
ческий *a.* hydropneumatic; контейнер —почты (nucl.) hydraulic rabbit;
—привод *m.* hydraulic drive or servo;
—пульт *m.* hydropult, hand sprayer;
(min.) hydraulic hose; —разработка
*f.* hydraulic mining; —сепаратор *m.*
(min.) hydroclassifier.
гидросернист/ый *a.* hydrosulfurous, hydrosulfite (of); г. натрий, —онатриевая соль sodium hydrosulfite;
sodium hyposulfite; —ая кислота
hydrosulfurous acid, hyposulfurous
acid; соль —ой кислоты hydrosulfite.
гидро/сеть *f.* drainage system; —силикат *m.* hydrosilicate; —силовая
установка (elec.) water power station,
hydroelectric power station; —скоп

*m.* hydroscope (moisture detector); —смесь *f.* hydraulic fluid (spec. alcohol-glycerin mix); —стабилизация *f.* stabilization of liquid fuel by hydrogenation; —станция *f.* hydrostation.

гидростат/ика *f.* hydrostatics; —ический *a.* hydrostatic; —ическое давление hydrostatic pressure, liquid (at rest) pressure.

гидросульф/ат *m.* hydrosulfate; —ид *m.* hydrosulfide; —ит *m.* hydrosulfite.

гидро/сфера *f.* (geol.) hydrosphere, earth's surface water; —талькит *m.* (min.) hydrotalcite; —терма *f.* thermal spring; —термальный, —термический *a.* hydrothermal.

гидротехн/ик *m.* hydraulic engineer; —ика *f.*, —ический *a.* hydraulic engineering; —ическое сооружение hydraulic structure, hydraulic work.

гидро/тионовая кислота hydrosulfuric acid, hydrogen sulfide; —торит *m.* (min.) hydrothorite; —трансформатор *m.* torque converter; —троилит *m.* (min.) hydrotroilite; —турбина *f.* hydraulic turbine; —турбогенератор *m.* (elec.) hydroelectric generator; —усилитель *m.* (aero.) booster; —установка *f.* hydroelectric plant; —фан *m.* (min.) hydrophane (a variety of common opal).

гидрофильн/ость *f.* hydrophily, hydrophilic nature; —ый *a.* hydrophilic.

гидрофит *m.* (bot.) hydrophyte.

гидрофоб/изация *f.* waterproofing, water-repellency treatment; —ия *f.* (med.) hydrophobia; —ность *f.* hydrophoby, hydrophobic nature; —ный *a.* hydrophobic.

гидро/фон *m.* hydrophone, submarine detector; —фор *m.* hydrophore; —фталевая кислота hydrophthalic acid; —халцедон *m.* (min.) hydrochalcedony, enhydrite; —химия *f.* chemical hydrology; —хинон *m.* hydroquinone, *p*-dioxybenzene.

гидро/целлюлоза *f.* hydrocellulose; —централь *m.* central hydroelectric power station; —церит *m.* (min.) hydrocerite (probably same as cerite); —церуссит *m.* (min.) hydrocerussite; —цинкит *m.* (min.) hydrozincite;

—штурмовик *m.* (aero.) naval fighter; —экстрактор *m.* hydroextractor, whizzer (centrifuge); —элеватор *m.* hydraulic elevator; a jet pump; —электрический *a.* hydroelectric; —электрическая станция, —электростанция *f.* hydroelectric power station; —энергетика *f.*, —энергетический *a.*, —энергия *f.* water power.

гидрюр *m.* hydrogenation product; perhydro compound.

гидуриловая кислота hydurilic acid.

гиельмит *m.* (min.) hjelmite, hielmite.

гиен/а *f.* (zool.) hyena; —анхин *m.* hyenanchin; —овая кислота hyenic acid, tricosylacetic acid.

гиератит *m.* (min.) hieratite.

гиетный *a.* hyetal, rain.

ГИЗ *abbr.* (Государственное книгоиздательство) The State Publishing House.

гизекит *m.* (min.) gieseckite (a variety of pinite).

гизингерит *m.* (min.) hisingerite.

Гизлегпром *abbr.* (Государственное издательство легкой промышленности) State Light Industry Publishing House.

гийот *m.* guyot.

гик *m.* pitch and tar, residue of coal tar.

ГИКИ *abbr.* (Государственный исследовательский керамический институт) State Ceramics Research Institute.

гикомакс *m.* Hycomax (iron-cobalt-nickel-aluminum-copper alloy).

гикори *n.* hickory (wood).

гилея *f.* tropical forest.

Гиллебранда анализ (min.) Hillebrand analysis.

Гиллери линейка (met.) Guillery ruler (for hardness test).

Гилля способ (met.) Gill's method.

гилпинит *see* гильпинит.

Гильбера правила (meteor.) Guilbert's rules.

гильберт *m.* (elec.) gilbert (unit of magnetomotive force); —ит *m.* (min.) gilbertite (a variety of hydromuscovite).

Гильберта преобразование (math.) Hilbert transform.

гильз/а *f.*, —овый *a.* case, hull, husk;

(mil.) cartridge case, shell case; sleeve, sleeve pipe, socket, bush, bushing; (text.) tube.

**Гильо способ** Guillot method.

**гильотин/а** *f.*, **—ировать**, **—ный** *a.*, **—ные ножницы** guillotine.

**гильош** *m.*, **—ировать** *v.* guilloche (a pattern).

**гиль/пинит** *m.* (min.) gilpinite; **—сонит** *m.* gilsonite (a variety of native asphalt).

**гиляби** *pl.* (petr.) bentonite.

**Гималаи** the Himalaya.

**гиматомелановая кислота** hymatomelanic acid.

**гименомицеты** *pl.* (bot.) Hymenomycetes.

**гиминовая кислота** hyminic acid.

**гимназ/ист** *m.* student; **—ия** *f.* gymnasium, a preparatory school.

**гимнаст** *m.* athlete; **—ика** *f.* gymnastics.

**гимнемовая кислота** gymnemic acid.

**гимнит** *m.* (min.) gymnite, deweylite.

**гимно—** *prefix* gymno— (bare, uncovered).

**гимнот** *m.* (zool.) surinam eel.

**гимолальные соли** hymolal salts (detergent).

**гиму** *n.* Hymu (molybdenum-nickel-iron alloy).

**гиназа** *f.* gynase.

**гингерол** *m.* gingerol.

**гингивит** *m.* (med.) gingivitis.

**гиндрицин** *m.* gindricine.

**гинезин** *m.* gynesine, trigonelline.

**гинеколог** *m.* (med.) gynecologist; **—ический** *a.* gynecological; **—ия** *f.* gynecology.

**гинецей** *m.* (bot.) gynecium.

**гинея** *f.* guinea (money).

**ГИНЗ** *abbr.* (Государственный институт здравхранения) The State Health Institute.

**ГИНИ** *abbr.* (Государственный научно-исследовательский нефтяной институт) State Petroleum Research Institute.

**гини** *pl. of* **гинь**.

**гинкго** *n.*, **—вое дерево** (bot.) ginkgo tree (*Ginkgo biloba*); **—вая кислота** ginkgoic acid.

**гино/вал** *m.* gynoval, isobornyl isovalerate; **—кардин** *m.* gynocardine;

**—кардовая кислота** gynocardic acid.

**гинокитол** *m.* hinokitol.

**гинсдалит** *m.* (min.) hinsdalite (related to the hamlinite group).

**гинтцеит** *m.* (min.) hintzeite, kaliborite.

**гинь** *f.* winding tackle, purchase tackle.

**Гинье зелень, гиньетова зелень** Guignet's green (chrome pigment).

**гио—** *prefix* (anat.) hyo—; **—идный** *a.* hyoid.

**гиобертит** *see* **джиобертит**.

**г-ион** *abbr.* (грамм-ион) gram-ion.

**гиоргиозит** *m.* (min.) giorgiosite (probably a variety of hydromagnesite).

**гиортдалит** *m.* (min.) hiortdahlite, guarinite.

**гиосци/амин** *m.* hyoscyamine, daturine; **сернокислый г., сульфат —амина** hyoscyamine sulfate; **—н** *m.* hyoscine, scopolamine; **бромистоводородный —н, бромгидрат —на** hyoscine hydrobromide.

**гиохоловая кислота** hyocholic acid.

**гипа/биссальный** *a.* hypabyssal (igneous rock); **—конитин** *m.* hypaconitine.

**гипаутоморфный** *a.* (petr.) hypautomorphic, hypidiomorphic, subhedral.

**гипафорин** *m.* hypaphorine, trimethyltryptophan.

**гипер—** *prefix* hyper—, super—, over.

**гипербол/а** *f.* (geom.) hyperbola; **—ический** *a.* hyperbolic; **—оид** *m.* hyperboloid.

**гипер/борейский** *a.* hyperborean, northern; **—генный** *a.* (geol.) supergene; **—емия** *f.* (med.) hyperemia; **—из** *m.* cumene hydroperoxide; **—ицин** *m.*, **—ициновый** *a.* hypericin.

**гиперко** *n.* Hiperco (iron-chromium-cobalt alloy).

**гиперком/мутация** *f.* (elec.) overcommutation; **—паунд** *m.* (elec.) overpounded generator; **—паундирование** *n.* overcompounding; **—паундированный** *a.* overcompounded.

**гипер/ник** *m.* Hipernik, Hypernik (iron-nickel alloy); **—ол** *m.* hyperol, ortizon; **—он** *m.* (nucl.) hyperon; **—осколок** *m.*, **—ядро** *n.* hyperfragment; **—сил** *m.* Hipersil, Hypersil (iron-silicon alloy); **—синхронный** *a.* hypersynchronous; **—стен** *m.* (min.) hypersthene (a pyroxene); **—стеновый** *a.*

hypersthene, hypersthenic; —тонический *a.* hypertonic; —трофия *f.*
(med.) hypertrophy; —эвтектоидный
*a.* (met.) hypereutectoid.
гипидиоморфный *a.* (petr.) hypidiomorphic, subhedral.
гипна/л *m.* hypnal, antipyrine chloralhy-
drate; —цетин *m.* hypnacetine.
гипновый *a.* (bot.) hypnum.
гипноз *m.* (med.) hypnosis.
гипнон *m.* hypnone, acetophenone.
гипнот/изер *m.* hypnotist, hypnotizer;
—изировать *v.* hypnotize; —изм *m.*
hypnotism; —ический *a.* hypnotic.
гипо— *prefix* hypo—, sub—, under;
—борат *m.* hypoborate; —бромит
*m.* hypobromite; —витаминоза *f.*
(med.) hypovitaminosis; —галоген-
ный *a.* hypohalogenous; —геевая
кислота hypogeic acid, 7-hexade-
cenoic acid; —генный *a.* (geol.) hypo-
gene; (bot.) hypogenous; —дерма *f.*
(zool.) hypodermis; —иодит *m.* hypoiodite; —кристаллический *a.* hypo-
crystalline, partly crystalline; —ксантин *m.* hypoxanthine, 6-oxypurine;
—ксия *f.* (med.) hypoxia, oxygen
deficiency; —нитрит *m.* hyponitrite;
—пус *m.* (zool.) hypopus; —синхронный *a.* (elec.) hyposynchronous;
—склерит *m.* (min.) hyposclerite (a
variety of albite feldspar).
гипосульф/ат *m.* hyposulfate; —ит *m.*
hyposulfite; thiosulfate.
гипо/теза *f.* hypothesis; —тенуза *f.*
(geom.) hypotenuse; —термальный
*a.* hypothermal; —тетический *a.*
hypothetical; —тонический *a.* hypo-
tonic; —трохоида *f.* (geom.) hypo-
trochoid; —физ *m.* (anat.) hypophysis, pituitary body; —фосфат *m.*
hypophosphate; —фосфит *m.* hypophosphite; —хлорит *m.* hypochlorite.
гипохондр/ик *m.*, —ический *a.* hypochondriac; —ия *f.* hypochondria.
гипо/центр *m.* (geol.) hypocenter, seismic center; (zool.) hypocentrum;
—циклоида *f.* (geom.) hypocycloid.
гиппоманин *m.* hippomanin.
гиппопотам *m.* (zool.) hippopotamus.
гиппур/ан *m.* hippuran, sodium iodo-
hippurate; —ат *m.* hippurate; —ил

*m.* hippuryl; —ит *m.* (geol.) hippur-
ite; —итовый *a.* hippuritic.
гиппуров/ая кислота hippuric acid,
benzaminoacetic acid; соль —ой
кислоты, —окислая соль hippurate;
—окислый *a.* hippuric acid; hippurate (of); —окислый аммоний ammonium hippurate.
гипс *m.* (min.) gypsum; plaster of Paris;
землистый г. (min.) earthy gypsum;
сырой г. gypsum, plaster stone;
—обетон *m.* plaster with filler;
—овать *v.* treat with gypsum; plaster; —овидный *a.* gypseous.
гипсов/ый *a.* gypsum, gypseous; plaster;
г. камень gypseous stone, plaster
stone; hard deposit of calcium sulfate;
г. слепок, —ая отливка plaster cast;
—ая земля, —ая мука (min.) earthy
gypsum; —ая форма plaster mold.
гипсодонт *m.* (zool.) hypsodont.
гипсолит *m.* (building) plaster; gypsum;
—овая плита plasterboard, sheet-
rock.
гипсометр *m.* hypsometer (for determining altitude); —ический *a.* hyp-
sometric; —ия *f.* hypsometry.
гипсо/носный, —содержащий *a.* gyp-
siferous, gypseous; —подобный *a.*
gypseous; —термометр *see* гипсометр.
гипсохром *m.* hypsochrome; —овый *a.*
hypsochromic.
гипт/агин *m.* hiptagin; —олид *m.*
hyptolide.
ГИПХ *abbr.* (Государственный институт прикладной химии) State Institute of Applied Chemistry.
гира *f.* (cryst.) axis of symmetry.
Гира печь Geer oven.
гиральдит *m.* hyraldite (bleaching preparation).
гирботол *m.* girbotol (for gas purification).
гиргол *m.* hyrgol (colloidal solution of
mercury).
гирка *f.* (bot.) a variety of wheat.
гирксутит *m.* (min.) gearksutite.
гирло *n.* branch (of river); narrow strait.
гирлянд/а *f.*, —ный *a.* garland, wreath,
chain.
гирный *a.* weight (of balance).
гиро— *prefix* gyro— (ring; gyral;

spiral); —ида *f.* (cryst.) rotation-inversion axis; —идальный, —эдрический *a.* (cryst.) gyroidal, plagihedral; (optics) rotatory; —компас *m.* gyrocompass, directional gyro; —лит *m.* (min.) gyrolite (a zeolite); —магнитный *a.* gyromagnetic; —скоп *m.* gyroscope; —стат *m.* gyrostat; —трон *m.* gyrotron; —форин *m.* gyrophorin; —форовая кислота gyrophoric acid; —частота *f.* gyrofrequency.

гирс/иновая кислота *see* гирциновая кислота; —утовая кислота hirsutic acid.

гирудин *m.* hirudin.

гирцин *m.* hircine; —овая кислота hircinic acid; соль —овой кислоты, —овокислая соль hircinate.

гиря *f.* weight (of balance).

гисмондин *m.* gismondite (an alteration mineral of plagioclase feldspar).

гиссопин *m.* hyssopine.

гист/азарин *m.* hystazarin, 2,3-dihydroxyanthraquinone; —амин *m.*, —аминовый *a.* histamine, 4-imidazolylethylamine.

гистерез/иметр, —ометр *m.* hysteresis meter; —ис *m.* (phys.) hysteresis, lagging; —ис вращения rotating hysteresis; вязкий —ис, ползучий —ис hysteresis lag, magnetic creeping; петля —иса hysteresis loop; —ный *a.* hysteresis, hysteretic, lag.

гистерогенный *a.* (min.) hysterogenetic.

гисти/дин *m.* histidine; —о— *see* гисто—; —оцит *m.* (biol.) histiocyte.

гисто— *prefix* (biol.) histo—, tissue.

гистограмма *f.* (statistics) histogram; (petr.) differential granulometric composition diagram.

гистолиз *m.* (biol.) histolysis, breaking down of tissues.

гистолог *m.* histologist; —ический *a.* histological; —ия *f.* histology.

гистон *m.* histon.

гитагенин *m.* githagenin.

гиталин *m.* gitalin.

гитар/а *f.*, —ный *a.* guitar; (mech.) swinging arm, bracket, swing frame gear, quadrant, adjustment plate.

гито/генин *m.* gitogenin; —гениновая

кислота gitogenic acid; —ксигенин *m.* gitoxigenin; —ксин *m.* gitoxin.

гиттия *f.* (geol.) gyttja (a sapropelic black mud).

Гитторфа трубка Hittorf's tube.

гифа *f.* (bot.) hypha; filament.

ГК *abbr.* (гибберелловая кислота) gibberellic acid.

гл *abbr.* (гектолитр) hectoliter; гл. *abbr.* (глава) chapter; head, chief.

глав. *abbr.*, глав— *prefix* (главный) main, chief, principal.

глав/а *f.* chapter (of book); head, chief, foreman; —арь *m.* leader, chief; —бух *m.* chief accountant; —енство *n.* supremacy, priority; —енствовать *v.* take the lead, be at the head; have priority.

Главземхоз *abbr.* (Главное управление земельным хозяйством) The Main Department of Agriculture.

главк *m.* main administrative board.

главко— *prefix* glauco—; —дот *m.* (min.) glaucodot (a cobalt iron sulfarsenide); —нит *m.*, —нитовый песок (min.) glauconite, green sand; —нитовый *a.* glauconitic; —пикрин *m.* glaucopicrine; —фан *m.* (min.) glaucophane (member of amphibole series); —хроит *m.* (min.) glaucochroite (member of chrysolite group).

Глав/мервес *abbr.* (Главная палата мер и весов) The Bureau of Weights and Measures; —наука *abbr.* (Главное управление научными учреждениями) The Central Scientific Board.

главнейший *a.* chief, predominant.

главн/ый *a.* chief, principal, main, predominant, leading, primary; major (axis); (mech.) master; —ым образом chiefly, mainly, principally, for the most part.

Главпрофобр *abbr.* (Главное управление по профессиональному образованию) The Board of Professional Training.

главрач *m.* chief surgeon.

Главсельхоз *abbr.* (Главное управление сельскохозяйственной промышленности) The Board of Agricultural Industry.

глагол *m.* verb.

глаголь *m.* (min.) prop, strut, pillar.

**гладил/ка** *f.* polisher, burnisher, burnishing stick; (foundry) sleeker; smoother, flatter; plane; trowel; stamp, die; **—о** *n.* polisher, burnisher.

**гладиль/ный** *a.* polishing; smoothing, ironing; **—ная доска** ironing board; **—ная машина** ironing machine, ironer; **—щик** *m.* polisher, smoother, ironer.

**гладиоловая кислота** gladiolic acid.

**гладиолус** *m.* (bot.) gladiolus.

**глад/ить** *v.* polish, smooth, planish, plane, level; iron (cloth); **—кий** *a.* smooth, polished, even, flat, plane; (text.) unfigured; fluent; **—ко** *adv.* smoothly; **—коствольный** *a.* smoothbore (gun); **—кость** *f.* smoothness, evenness; **—ыш** *m.* (bot.) laserwort (*Laserpitium*); mushroom (*Lactarius volemus*); **—ыши** *pl.* (zool.) backswimmers (*Notonectidae*); **—ь** *f.* smooth surface, even surface.

**глаже** *comp. of* **гладкий, гладко,** smoother; **—ние, —нье** *n.* smoothing, polishing; ironing (cloth); (text.) satining; **—нный** *a.* smoothed, polished; ironed.

**глаз** *m.* eye; **бросающийся в —а** conspicuous, outstanding; **воспаление г.** (med.) ophthalmia; **на г.** approximately, by rule of thumb; **—астый** *a.* large eyed; quick-sighted.

**Глазго** Glasgow.

**глазерит** *m.* (min.) glaserite, aphthitalite.

**глазет** *m.,* **—овый** *a.* (text.) silk brocade.

**глазеть** *v.* gaze, stare (at).

**глазиров/ание** *n.,* **—ка** *f.* glaze, glazing; varnish; frosting; **—анный** *a.* glazed; varnished; frosted, iced, candied; **—ать** *v.* glaze; varnish; frost, ice.

**глазковатый** *a.* (zool., petr.) ocellar; birdseye (fracture).

**глазн/ица** *f.,* **—ая впадина** eye socket, orbit; **—ой** *a.* eye, ocular, optic; ophthalmic; **—ой нерв** optic nerve; **—ая линза** (optics) eyepiece; **—ая трава** (bot.) eyebright (*Euphrasia*); **—ое яблоко** (anat.) eyeball.

**глазо/видный** *a.* (zool.) ocellate; (zool., petr.) ocellar; **—двигательный** *a.* (anat.) oculomotor; **—едка** *f.* sulfur dioxide.

**глазок** *m.* eye, eyelet; (zool.) ocellus; eyepiece; inspection hole, peephole, sight; glory hole (of furnace); slot, aperture, hole (of die); mesh (of screen); lug, ear; **на г.** *see under* **глаз.**

**глазо/мер** *m.* visual estimation; **—мерный** *a.* by eye, by sight, approximate; **—образный** *a.* eye-shaped, oculiform.

**глазур/енный, —ованный** *a.* glazed; enameled, lacquered; **—ить, —овать** *v.* glaze; enamel, lacquer; **—ование** *n.,* **—овка** *f.* glaze, glazing; enamel, enameling; **—ообжигательная печь** (cer.) glaze kiln; **—ь** *f.* glaze, varnish; enamel, lacquer; gloss; frosting, icing; **нанести —ь** *v.* glaze; **порок —и** glaze wave; **свинцовая —ь** (cer.) lead glaze, lead glazing.

**гланда** *f.* gland, specif. tonsil.

**глас** *m.* voice; **—ить** *v.* say, run, go; **—ность** *f.* publicity, public knowledge, notoriety; **—ный** *a.* public, open, notorious; vowel (letter).

**глаубер/ит** *m.* (min.) glauberite (a calcium sodium sulfate); **—ова соль** Glauber's salt, sodium sulfate decahydrate.

**глауко—** *see* **главко—; —ма** *f.* (med.) glaucoma; **—нит** *see* **главконит.**

**глауцин** *m.* glaucine; **—овая кислота** glaucinic acid.

**гляциальный** *a.* glacial.

**гледичия** *f.* (bot.) honey locust (*Gleditschia triacanthos*).

**глее/ватый** *a.* gleyey; **—вый горизонт** gley; **—вая почва** gley soil; **—образование** *n.* gley formation process.

**глезер** *m.* (paper) glazer; **—ование** *n.* glazing.

**глей** *m.* gley.

**глейкометр** *m.* (brewing) gleucometer (a hydrometer).

**глет** *m.,* **—овый** *a.* litharge, lead monoxide.

**глетчер** *m.* (geol.) glacier.

**глеукометр** *see* **глейкометр.**

**глиадин** *m.* gliadin, vegetable protein.

**глик—** *prefix* glyc—; gluc— (when referring to glucose or its derivatives).

**глико—** *prefix* glyco—; gluco—; **—бром** *m.* glycobrom; **—ген** *m.* glycogen, glucogen, animal starch.

**гликоз/ал** *m.* glycosal, glycerol salicylate; **—амин** *m.* glycosamine; **—ид** *m.* glycoside; **—урия** *f.* (med.) glycosuria.

**гликокол,** **—л,** **—ь** *m.* glycocoll, glycine.

**гликол** *m.* glycol, 1,2-ethanediol; **хлоргидрин** **—а** glycol chlorohydrin; **—диацетат** glycol diacetate.

**гликолево/кислый** *a.* glycolic acid; glycolate (of); **—кислая соль** glycolate; **—этиловый эфир** ethyl glycolate.

**гликолев/ый** *a.* glycol; **г. альдегид** glycolaldehyde, hydroxyethanal; **г. эфир янтарной кислоты** glycol succinate; **—ые эфиры** glycol ethers; **—ая кислота** glycolic acid, hydroxyethanoic acid; **соль —ой кислоты** glycolate.

**гликол/ид** *m.* glycolide, 2,5-*p*-dioxanedione; **—из** *m.* glycolysis; **—ил** *m.* glycolyl; **—итический** *a.* glycolytic, glycoclastic; **—урил** *m.* glycoluril, acetylenediureine; **—уровая кислота** glycoluric acid, hydantoic acid; **—ь** *see* гликол.

**глико/стерин** *m.* glycosterin, diethylene glycol distearate; **—фосфолипин** *m.* glycophospholipin; **—холевая кислота** glycocholic acid; **—холевокислый** *a.* glycocholic acid; glycocholate (of); **—холевокислая соль** glycocholate; **—циамин** *m.* glycocyamine, guanidoacetic acid.

**глина** *f.* clay; (met.) loam; **белая г., фарфоровая г.** kaolin, China clay; **жирная г.** loam; bituminous clay; **пластическая г.** potter's clay, plastic clay; **формовая г.** putty; **г.-наполнитель** filler clay.

**глин/ец** *m.* clay sand; **квасцовый г.** alum shale; **—изация** *f.* argillization; **—ий** *see* глинозем.

**глинисто—** *prefix* argillo—; **—сть** *f.* clayiness; (geol.) shaliness.

**глинистый** *a.* clay, clayey, argillaceous; **г. железняк** (min.) clay ironstone; **г. известняк** argillaceous limestone, argillocalcite; **г. песчаник** argillaceous sandstone; **г. раствор** clay mortar; drilling mud; **г. сланец** (clay) slate, argillite.

**глини/ца** *f.*, **—ще** *n.* clay pit; loam pit.

**глинка** *f.* clay.

**глино—** *prefix* clay; **—бетон** *m.* a sand-gravel-clay building mixture; **—битный** *a.* clay, adobe; pisé (building); **—вал** *m.* clay kneader; **—железистый** *a.* argilloferruginous.

**глинозем** *m.* alumina, aluminum oxide; **белый г.** kaolin, China clay; **водный г., гидрат —а** aluminum hydroxide; **сернокислый г., сульфат —а** aluminum sulfate; **уксуснокислый г.** aluminum acetate; **—истый, —ный** *a.* alumina, aluminous; **—ный силикат** aluminum silicate; **—ная соль** aluminum salt.

**глино/копня, —копия** *see* глиница; **—мешалка** *f.* clay mixer; **—мялка** *f.* pug mill, clay mill; **—носный** *a.* clayey, argillaceous; **—резка, —резная машина** *f.* clay cutter, clay-cutting machine.

**глинтвейн** *m.* mulled wine.

**глинян/ый** *a.* clay, clayey, argillaceous; (met.) loam; **г. раствор** clay mortar; drilling mud; **—ая масса** (cer.) body, clay slip; **—ая отливка** loam casting; **—ая посуда** earthenware, pottery; **—ая форма** loam mold; **—ое мыло** aluminous soap.

**глиоксал, —ь** *m.* glyoxal, ethanedial; **—аза** *f.* glyoxalase; **—евая кислота, —овая кислота** glyoxalic acid, glyoxylic acid, oxoethanoic acid; **—идин** *m.* glyoxalidine; **—ин** *m.* glyoxaline.

**глиокс/ил** *m.* glyoxyl; **—илевая кислота, —иловая кислота** *see* глиоксалевая кислота; **—им** *m.* glyoxime.

**глио/розеин** *m.* gliorosein; **—токсин** *m.* gliotoxin.

**глиптал/евые смолы** glyptal resins, alkyd resins; **—и** *pl.* glyptals, alkyds.

**глипти/ка** *f.*, **—ческий** *a.* glyptic, engraving.

**глипто/генезис** *m.* (geol.) earth sculpture; **—графия** *f.* glyptography.

**глисс/ада** *f.*, **—адный** *a.* (aero.) landing beam; glide path, glide slope; **—ер** *see* гидроплан; **—ировать** *v.* glide, skim (over water).

**глист** *m.*, **—а** *f.* helminth, intestinal worm; **ленточный г.** tapeworm; **—ник** *m.*, **—ница** *f.* (bot.) wormwood (*Artemisia absinthium*); **—огонный** *a.*, **—огонное средство** vermifuge, anthelmintic.

**глифограф/ический** *a.* glyphographic; —**ия** *f.* glyphography.

**глифтали** *see* **глиптали.**

**глицер/ат** *m.* glycerate; —**ид** *m.* glyceride; —**ил** *m.* glyceryl, propenyl.

**глицерин** *m.* glycerin, glycerol; *prefix* glycero—; **азотнокислый г., нитрат** —**а** nitroglycerin; **триацетат** —**а** triacetin; **щелочный г., г. из подмыльных щелоков** soap lye glycerin.

**глицерино**— *prefix* glycero—.

**глицеринов/ый** *a.* glycerin; **г. альдегид** glyceraldehyde; —**ая кислота** glyceric acid, 2,3-dihydroxypropanoic acid.

**глицерино/серная кислота** glycerosulfuric acid; **соль** —**серной кислоты,** —**сернокислая соль** glycerosulfate; —**фосфорная кислота** glycerophosphoric acid; **соль** —**фосфорной кислоты,** —**фосфорнокислая соль** glycerophosphate; —**фосфорнокислый аммоний** ammonium glycerophosphate; —**фосфорнокислый калий** potassium glycerophosphate.

**глицеро**— *prefix* glycero—; —**за** *f.* glycerose; —**фосфат** *m.* glycerophosphate.

**глицид** *m.* glycide, glycidol, 2,3-epoxy-1-propanol; —**ная кислота** glycidic acid, epoxypropionic acid.

**глиций** *see* **глуциний.**

**глицил** *m.* glycyl; —**глицин** *m.* glycylglycine.

**глицин** *m.,* —**овый** *a.* glycine, glycocoll, aminoethanoic acid; glycin; —**альдегид** *m.* glycinaldehyde; —**ангидрид** *m.* glycine anhydride, 2,5-piperazinedione; —**ин** *m.* glycinin; —**ия** *f.* (bot.) wisteria.

**глицирр/етин** *m.* glycyrrhetin; —**изин** *m.* glycyrrhizin; —**изиновая кислота** glycyrrhizic acid.

**гл. о.** *see* **гл. обр.**

**глобальный** *a.* global; total, entire.

**глоби/гериновая грязь** (geol.) globigerina ooze; —**н** *m.* globin.

**глобоид** *m.* (bot.) globoid; —**альный** *a.* globoid, globate, globular.

**гл. обр.** *abbr.* (**главным образом**) chiefly, principally.

**глобул/а** *f.* globule; —**арин** *m.* globularin; —**ин** *m.* globulin; —**ит** *m.* (geol.) globulite, crystallites; —**ол** *m.* globulol; —**ярный** *a.* globular.

**глобус** *m.,* —**ный** *a.* globe, sphere.

**Гловера башня** Glover tower; **гловерная кислота, гловерова кислота** Glover acid (sulfuric acid).

**глокерит** *m.* (min.) glockerite.

**глоксиния** *f.* (bot.) gloxinia.

**гломеропорфировый** *a.* (petr.) glomeroporphyric.

**глория** *f.* (meteor.) glory.

**глосса** *f.* gloss; a kind of flounder.

**глоссарий** *m.* glossary.

**глоссит** *m.* (med.) glossitis.

**Глостер** Gloucester.

**глот/ание** *n.* swallowing, gulping, deglutition; —**ательный** *a.* deglutitory; —**ать,** —**нуть** *v.* swallow, gulp; —**ка** *f.* throat, gullet; (anat.) pharynx; —**ок** *m.* swallow, mouthful, gulp; —**очный** *a.* throat; pharyngeal.

**глохнуть** *v.* grow deaf; (bot.) dry, wither.

**глуб/же** *compr.* *of* **глубокий, глубоко,** deeper; —**ина** *f.* depth, profoundness; degree (of conversion); **большие** —**ины** deep sea; **на** —**ине** deepseated, deep.

**глубинн/ый** *a.* depth; deep-seated; subsurface, buried; (geol.) plutonic; (bot.) hypogeal; **г. калибр** depth gage; **г. разрыв** depth charge; —**ая бомба** depth bomb; —**ая горная порода** (geol.) intrusive rock, intrusion; —**ая доза** (radiobiology) depth dose; —**ое внедрение** (geol.) plutonic intrusion.

**глубино/измерительный прибор,** —**мер** *see* **глубомер.**

**глубок/ий** *a.* deep, deep-seated, penetrating, thoroughgoing, profound; depth; —**о** *adv.* deep, deeply; —**о находящийся** deep-seated.

**глубоко**— *prefix* deep; low, intense (cooling, etc.); —**водный** *a.* deep-sea; —**мысленный** *a.* profound, serious; —**отпущенный** *a.* (met.) deep-drawn, cold-work drawn; —**полимеризованный** *a.* highly polymerized; —**столбчатый** *a.* deep-columnar; —**сть** *f.* depth, profundity; —**фокусный** *a.* deep-focus (earthquake).

**глуб/омер** *m.* depth gage, depthometer; —**ь** *see* **глубина, вглубь.**

**глуп/еть** *v.* grow stupid; —**ить** *v.* do

something foolish; —**ость** *f.* foolishness, folly; stupidity; —**ый** *a.* foolish, stupid; —**ыш** *m.* (zool.) fulmar.

**глута/зин** *m.* glutazine, beta-imidoglutarimide; —**коновая кислота** glutaconic acid, pentenedioic acid; —**мин** *m.* glutamine; —**миновая кислота**, —**новая кислота** glutamic acid, alpha-aminoglutaric acid.

**глутаро/вый ангидрид** glutaric anhydride; —**вая кислота** glutaric acid, pentanedioic acid; —**нитрил** *m.* glutaronitrile, pentanedinitrile.

**глут/атион** *m.* glutathione; —**ен** *m.*, —**е-новый** *a.* gluten; —**енин** *m.* glutenin; —**еновая мука** gluten meal, gluten flour; —**ин** *m.* glutin; —**иновая кислота** glutinic acid, pentinedioic acid.

**глуто/за** *f.* glutose; —**л**, —**ль** *m.* glutol; —**лин** *m.* glutolin, formalin gelatin.

**глухарь** *m.* (zool.) wood grouse, wood cock.

**глухо** *adv.* dully.

**глуховецкий** *a.* Glukhov.

**глух/ой** *a.* deaf; dull (sound); dead-end, blind (passage); blank; thick (forest); opal, opaque (glass); —**г. конец** dead end; **г. переулок** cul-de-sac; **г. фланец** blank flange, blind flange; —**ая муфта** end sleeve; —**ое соединение** closed coupling; —**онемой** *a.* deaf-mute; —**ота** *f.* deafness.

**глуц**— *see* **глюк**—; —**ид** *m.* glucide; —**ин** *m.* glucin, sodium aminotriazinesulfonate.

**глуцин/ий** *m.*, —**овый** *a.* glucinum, Gl (obs.), beryllium; —**овая земля** glucina, beryllia, beryllium oxide; —**овая кислота** glucinic acid.

**глуш/ение** *n.* extinguishing, damping down, banking (of fire); choking; (elec.) damping; opacification (of glass, etc.); —**илка** *f.* blank plug; —**итель** *m.* damper, damping device; silencer, muffler, exhaust muffler; baffle, baffler, buffer, attenuator; opacifier; —**ить** *v.* damp down, bank (fire); deafen; deaden (sound); quench, slake; suppress; plug (pipe); choke (plants); —**ь** *f.* thicket.

**глыб/а** *f.*, —**ка** *f.* lump, clod, chunk, clump, block, block mass; heap; (met.) bloom, stamp; —**истый**, —**о-** **ватый** *a.* lumpy; —**овая гора** (geol.) block mountain, fault-block mountain; —**овая лава** block lava; —**овое строение** (geol.) block faulting; —**од-роб**, —**одробитель** *m.* clod breaker.

**глюк**— *prefix* gluc—; —**ал** *m.* glucal.

**глюко**— *prefix* gluco—, *see also* **глико**—; —**ванилин** *m.* glucovanillin; —**ванилиновая кислота** glucovanillic acid; —**галловая кислота** glucogallic acid; —**ген** *see* **гликоген**; —**гидразон** *m.* glucohydrazone.

**глюкоз/а** *f.* glucose, grape sugar, dextrose; glucose г. dextroglucose; —**азон** *m.* glucosazone; —**амин** *m.* glucosamine; —**ан** *m.* glucosan (a polysaccharide); —**ен** *m.* glucosene; —**ид** *m.* glucoside; —**имин** *m.* glucosimine (obs. term for amino sugar); —**ин** *m.* glucosin; —**он** *m.* glucosone; —**офосфорная кислота** glucosophosphoric acid.

**глюко/новая кислота** gluconic acid, pentahydroxyhexoic acid; **соль** —**новой кислоты** gluconate; —**протеин** *m.* glucoprotein; —**фор** *m.* glucophore; —**холевая кислота** glucocholic acid.

**глюкуронов/ая кислота** glucuronic acid, glycuronic acid; **соль** —**ой кислоты**, —**окислая соль** glycuronate.

**глют**— *see* **глут**—.

**глюциний** *see* **глуциний**.

**гляд/елка** *f.* inspection hole, peephole, sight; —**ение** *n.* looking; —**еть** *v.* look, look at, look after; watch; see.

**глянец** *m.* polish, luster, gloss, glaze, brightness; **наводить г.** *v.* polish, gloss, glaze.

**глянуть** *see* **глядеть**.

**глянц/вейс** *m.* brilliant white (gypsum-aluminum hydroxide mixture); —**гольд** *m.* (cer.) brilliant gold; —**евание** *n.* polishing, glossing, glazing; —**еватый** *a.* shiny; —**евать**, —**овать** *v.* polish, gloss; —**евитый** *a.* glossy, lustrous, shiny; —**евый**, —**овый** *a.* glossy, lacquered; —**зильбер** *m.* (cer.) silver colored paint; —**крахмал** *m.* gloss starch; —**ованный** *a.* polished, glossed.

**гляци/ация** *f.* (geol.) glaciation; —**о**— *prefix* glacio—, glacier.

**Гмелина соль** Gmelin's salt, potassium ferricyanide.

**гмелин/ит** *m.* (min.) gmelinite (a zeolite); **—овая синь** ultramarine.

**ГМК** *abbr.* (гидразид малеиновой кислоты) maleic hydrazide.

**г-моль** *abbr.* (грамм-моль) mole, gram molecule.

**ГМТ** *abbr.* (гексаметилентетрамин) hexamethylenetetramine.

**гн** *abbr.* (генри) henry.

**гнаивать** *see* **гноить.**

**гнать** *v.* drive, chase; distil; race (engine).

**гнедой** *a.* bay (colored).

**гнезд/о** *n.,* **—ный, —овой** *a.* nest, cradle; pit, depression, hollow; socket, couple; seat (of valve); housing (of machine); mesh (of screen); rabbet, groove, mortise; (bot.) nidus; pocket (of ore); (min.) druse; paragraph (of dictionary); (elec.) receptacle, plug-in socket; bunch, cluster; hill (of corn, etc.); seed bed; (tel.) jack; **г. и шип** mortise and tenon; **осадок —ами** (geol.) nodular deposit; **—овой посев** planting in hills; **—овая печь** pit furnace; **—овье** *n.* breeding site.

**гнейс** *m.* (petr.) gneiss; **—овый** *a.* gneissic, gneissoid, gneiss; **—оподобный** *a.* gneiss-like, gneissoid.

**гне/сти** *v.* press, squeeze; **—т** *m.* press, pressure, weight; oppression.

**гнетовые** *pl.* (bot.) Gnetaceae.

**гнивший** *past act. part. of* **гнить.**

**гнид/а** *f.,* **—ный** *a.* (zool.) nit; **—ник** *m.* (bot.) stavesacre (*Delphinium staphysagria*).

**гни/ение** *n.* decay, decomposition, putrefaction, rot; **сухое г.** dry rot; **—ет** *pr. 3 sing. of* **гнить; —лец** *m.* foul brood (disease of bees); **—лой** *a.* decayed, rotten, putrid, putrescent; **—локровие** *n.* (med.) septicemia, blood poisoning.

**гнилост/ность, —ь** *f.* decay, putrefaction, rottenness, putrescence; **—ный** *a.* putrid, putrescent; septic.

**гнил/ушка** *f.* piece of rotten wood, punk; **—ь** *f.* rottenness, putrefaction; rot, mold (plant disease); **мокрая —ь** damp rot; **серая —ь** gray mold, botrytis rot.

**гни/ть** *v.* rot, decay, decompose, putrefy; **—ючесть** *f.* putridness; **—ючий** *a.*

liable to decay, putrescible; **—ющий** *a.* putrescent, rotting.

**гное/видный** *a.* (med.) puriform; **—ние,** **—течение** *n.* suppuration; **—родный** *a.* pyogenic; **—точивый** *a.* suppurative.

**—гнозия** *f. suffix* —gnosy (branch of knowledge).

**гно/истый, —йливый, —йный** *a.* suppurative, purulent; **—ить** *v.* rot, putrefy; suppurate, fester; manure (soil); **—иться** *v.* suppurate, fester, discharge matter; **—й** *m.* pus, matter; **—йник** *m.* abscess; **—йничковый** *a.* pustulous; **—йничок** *m.* pustule; **—йное выделение** pus.

**гномон** *m.* (geom., etc.) gnomon; **—ический** *a.* gnomonic.

**гноскопин** *m.* gnoscopine, *dl*-narcotine.

**гно/ючий, —ящийся** *a.* purulent, festering.

**гнус** *m.* blood-sucking flies.

**ГНТК** *abbr.* (Государственный научно-технический комитет) State Scientific and Technical Committee (in the Council of Ministers, USSR).

**гну/тый** *a.* bent, curved; **—ть** *v.* bend, curve, flex, buckle; deflect; **—щийся** *a.* flexible, elastic.

**гнюс** *m.* (zool.) electric ray.

**гоанг-нан** *m.* hoangnan (bark).

**Гоби** Gobi desert.

**гован** *m.* gowan (decomposed granite).

**Говарда мешалка** Howard mixer.

**говлит** *m.* (min.) howlite.

**говор** *m.* talk, rumor; speech, speaking; **—итель** *see* **громкоговоритель; —ить** *v.* talk, say, speak, tell; **—ить о** indicate; **не —я** to say nothing (of); **—ят** it is said, it is claimed; **—ной раструб** **—ная воронка** (tel.) mouthpiece.

**говя/дина** *f.,* **—жий** *a.* beef.

**гогманит** *m.* (min.) hohmannite (a ferric silicate similar to amarantite).

**год** *m.* year, annum.

**годен** *see* **годный.**

**годжкинсонит** *m.* (min.) hodgkinsonite.

**година** *f.* time, year.

**годить** *see* **погодить, ждать; —ся** *v.* suit, fit, apply, do, be useful.

**годичн/ость** *f.* a year's time; **—ый** *a.* yearly, annual; lasting a year.

**годн/ость** *f.* suitability, fitness, availability, serviceability; **—ый** *a.* suitable, suited, fit, proper; available; serviceable; effective; applicable, adaptable.

**годов/алый** *a.* one-year-old, yearling; **—ик** *m.* yearling; **—ой** *a.* annual, yearly; **—щина** *f.* anniversary.

**годо/граф** *m.* (math.) hodograph; (seismology) hodograph, travel time curve; locus, trajectory; **—скоп** *m.* hodoscope (for tracing path of charged particles).

**ГОИ** *abbr.* (Государственный океанографический институт) State Institute of Oceanography; (Государственный оптический институт) State Optical Institute.

**годы** *pl.* of **год**; years, age.

**гойяцит** *m.* (min.) goyazite, hamlinite.

**гокутолит** *m.* (min.) hokutolite (a lead-bearing variety of barite).

**гол.** *abbr.* (голова, голов) head.

**голадин** *m.* holadin.

**голарренин** *m.* holarrhenine.

**голдфильдит** *m.* (min.) goldfieldite.

**голен/астый** *a.* long-legged; **—ище** *n.* boot top; **—ь** *f.* shin, shank; tarsus (of bird).

**голец** *m.* loach (fish); char (fish); (geol.) bald peak, bald mountain.

**голик** *m.* besom, broom; beacon.

**голл.** *abbr.* (голландский) Dutch.

**голландер** *m.* (paper) hollander, beating machine; (agr.) huller.

**Голландия** Holland, the Netherlands.

**голландск/ий** *a.* Dutch; **г. металл** Dutch metal (a copper-zinc alloy); **—ая сажа** an ivory black; **—ие белила** Dutch white (white lead pigment).

**голлендер** *see* **голландер.**

**голм/ий** *see* **гольмий; —квистит** *m.* (min.) holmquistite (a lithium-bearing variety of anthophyllite).

**голо** *adv.* nakedly, barely; poorly.

**голо—** *prefix* (biol.) gymno— (naked, bare); holo— (complete, whole, entire).

**голов/а** *f.* head; loaf (of sugar); **приходить в —у** *v.* occur; **—астик** *m.* (zool.) tadpole; **—астый** *a.* large-headed; **—ач** *m.* mudfish; humpback whale; beetle (*Lethrus*).

**головешка** *see* **головня.**

**головизна** *f.* jowl.

**головка** *f.* small head; cap, capping; knob; attachment, end, tip; block; (drill) bit; (chisel) point; (garlic) clove; **г. дестиллата** (petroleum) head, light distillate; **поворотная г.** swivel head.

**головневые** *pl.* (bot.) Ustilagineae.

**головн/ой** *a.* head, cephalic; leading; **—ая боль** headache; **—ая насадка** cap; **—ая установка** pilot plant; **—ое сооружение** (hydraulics) headwork.

**головня** *f.* charred log, firebrand; blight, smut; **пыльная г.** smut (*Ustilago*); **твердая г.** kernel smut.

**голово—** *prefix* head, cephalo—; **—грудь** *f.* (zool.) cephalothorax; **—кружение** *n.* vertigo, giddiness, dizziness; **—ломка** *f.* puzzle, problem; **—ногие** *pl.* (zool.) Cephalopoda; **—образный** *a.* head-shaped, cephaliform.

**головчат/ый** *a.* bulbous; (bot.) capitate; **—ое железо** bulb iron.

**—головые** *pl. suffix* **—cephala.**

**гологиалиновый** *a.* holohyaline, completely glassy.

**голод** *m.* hunger, famine; **морить —ом, томить —ом** *v.* starve; **—ание** *n.,* **—овка** *f.* starvation; malnutrition; deficiency; **—ать** *v.* starve; **—ающий** *a.* starving; **—ный** *a.* hungry.

**голозерный** *a.* (bot.) naked.

**голокаин** *m.* holocaine, phenacaine.

**гололед** *m.,* **—ица** *f.* glaze, glazed frost; **—ица** *f.* ice-covered ground.

**голо/морфный** *a.* (math.) holomorphic; **—планктонный** *a.* (biol.) holoplanktonic.

**голоплодный** *a.* (bot.) gymnocarpous.

**голос** *m.* voice; vote, ballot.

**голосем/енной, —янный** *a.* (bot.) gymnospermous; **—янные** *pl.* Gymnospermae.

**голословн/о** *adv.* without proof, without foundation; **—ость** *f.* lack of proof, unsubstantiated nature; **—ый** *a.* proofless, unsubstantiated by proof, unfounded, assumed.

**голосов/ание** *n.* vote, voting, ballot, poll; **—ать** *v.* vote, cast a ballot; **—ой** *a.* vocal, voice; **—ая щель**

(anat.) glottis; —ые связки vocal chords.

голо/тип *m*. (zool.) holotype; —турия *f*. (zool.) holothurian, sea cucumber; —турии *pl*. Holothurioidea.

голоцен *m*. (geol.) Holocene (epoch).

голоэдр *m*. (cryst.) holohedron; —ический *a*. holohedral.

голтель *m*. molding plane, cornice plane.

голуб/ель, —ика *f*. (bot.) blueberry (*Vaccinium*); spec. bog bilberry (*V. uliginosum*); —еть *v*. become azure, become blue; —ец *m*. mountain blue, azurite; —изна *f*. blue, azure.

голубиный *a*. pigeon.

голуби/ца, —чник *see* голубика.

голубки *pl*. (bot.) columbine (*Aquilegia*).

голуб/оватый *a*. bluish; —ой *a*. blue, sky-blue, azure; —осерый *a*. blue-gray.

голубушка *f*. (bot.) oxytropis.

голубь *m*. pigeon, dove.

голубянки *pl*. (zool.) hair-streaks, gossamer wings (*Lycaenidae*).

голубят/ина *f*. squab, pigeon meat; —ничать *v*. raise pigeons; —ня *f*. dovecote, pigeon coop.

голый *a*. bare, naked, nude, uncovered.

голыш *m*. pebble, shingle, flint, flint stone, cobblestone; —евый *a*. pebbly.

голь *f*. bareness, nakedness; poverty.

гольд/глет *m*. a kind of litharge; —фильдит *m*. (min.) goldfieldite; —шмидтит *m*. (min.) goldschmidtite (a gold-silver telluride).

голье *n*., —вой *a*. (leather) clean raw hide.

гольм/иевый *a*. holmium, holmic; —ий *m*. holmium, Ho; окись —ия holmium oxide; хлорный —ий holmic chloride.

гольтский ярус (geol.) Gault stage.

Гольтца машина (elec.) Holtz machine.

гольф *m*. golf.

гольф/стрем, —штрем *m*. gulf stream.

гольян *m*. (zool.) minnow.

голяк *m*. hide of premature lamb.

гомак *m*. gohmak (a substitute for ebonite).

гоманнит *m*. (min.) hohmannite (a variety of amarantite).

гоматропин *m*. homatropine.

гомбо *see* бамия.

гоменол *m*. an essential oil from *Melaleuca viridiflora*.

гомео— *prefix* homeo—, homo—.

гомеоморф/изм *m*., —ия *f*. homeomorphism; —ный *a*. homeomorphous.

гомеопат *m*. (med.) homeopathist; —ия *f*. homeopathy.

гомеополярн/ый *a*. homeopolar, homopolar; —ая связь homopolar bond; covalent bond.

гоми *n*. (bot.) foxtail millet (*Setaria italica*).

гомилит *m*. (min.) homilite.

гоммелин *m*. gommeline, dextrin.

гоммоз *see* гуммоз.

гомо— *prefix* homo— (same, like).

гомоген/изатор *m*. homogenizer; —изация *f*. homogenizing, homogenization; (met.) diffusion annealing; —изировать, —изовать *v*. homogenize; —изованный *a*. homogenized; —ность *f*. homogeneity, homogeneousness; —ный *a*. homogeneous.

гомо/динамичный *a*. homodynamic; —динный *a*. (rad.) homodyne.

гомозигот/а *f*. (biol.) homozygote; —ность *f*. homozygosity; —ный *a*. homozygous.

гомо/камфора *f*. homocamphor; —клиналь *m*. (geol.) homocline.

гомолог *m*. homolog; —ический *a*. homologous; —ический ряд homologous series; —ия *f*. homology.

гомоморф/изм *m*. (biol.) homomorphism; —ный *a*. homomorphous, homomorphic.

гомо/полярный *a*. homopolar; *see also* гомеополярный; —таксиальный *a*. (geol.) homotaxial; —тетичный *a*. (math.) homothetic; —тетия *f*. homothety, like placement; —типный *a*. (zool.) homotypic, normal; —тропин *see* гоматропин; —фталевая кислота homophthalic acid; —циклический *a*. homocyclic; —цистеин *m*. homocysteine.

гомути *n*. gomuti (fiber).

гомфокарпин *m*. gomphocarpine.

гон *m*. bout, run, pass.

гонада *f*. gonad, sexual gland.

гонг *m*. gong.

гонданг *m*. gondang (wax).

Гондвана *f*. Gondwana Land.

гондол/а *f.*, —ьный *a.* gondola (freight car or river boat); balloon car; г.-вагон (railroad) gondola.

Гондурас Honduras.

гондурол *m.* hondurol.

гонец *m.* express messenger.

гонидий *m.* (bot.) gonidium.

гониевый *a.* (anat.) gonial.

гониометр *m.* goniometer; прикладной г. protractor; —ический *a.* goniometric; —ия *f.* goniometry, direction finding.

—гония *f.* *suffix* —gony (generation, reproduction).

гон/ка *f.* driving, chase; distillation; raft, float (of wood); г., —ная машина *suffix* separator, extractor, centrifuge; —ный *a.* *suffix* —iferous, producing, inducing; extracting.

гонобобель *see* голубика.

гонококк *m.* (med.) gonococcus.

гонорар, —ий *m.* fee, compensation; royalty.

гонорея *f.* (med.) gonorrhea.

гоночный *a.* driving; distillation; race, racing; г. автомобиль racer.

гонт *m.* shingle; gravel.

ГОНТИ *abbr.* (Государственное объединенное научнотехническое издательство) State United Technical Publishing House.

гонт/ина *f.*, —овой, —овый *a.* shingle; —овщик *m.* shingle manufacturer.

гончар *m.* (cer.) potter; —ничать *v.* be a potter.

гончарн/ый *a.* potter's; ceramic, earthenware; clay, argillaceous; г. круг potter's wheel; г. станок potter's lathe; г. сурик minium, red lead; —ая глина potter's clay, ball clay; —ая масса, —ое тесто (cer.) paste, body; —ая печь kiln; —ая труба earthenware pipe; —ое искусство ceramics; —ые изделия pottery, earthenware; —я *f.* pottery.

гончарство *n.* potter's trade; ceramics.

гонщик *m.* racer.

гонять *v.* drive, chase; distil; race (a motor); —ся *v.* pursue.

гопеит *m.* (min.) hopeite.

гопкалит *m.* hopcalite (gas mask filter).

Гопкинсона испытание (elec.) Hopkinson test.

гоппер-фидер *m.* feed hopper.

гор. *abbr.* (городской) municipal, urban, city.

гор/а *f.* mountain, hill; г.-останец residual mountain; в —у uphill; стоять —ой за *v.* back to the limit.

горазд *a.* clever, quick, good (at); —о *adv.* much, far, by far.

горб *m.* hump, hunch, protuberance, bulge, camber; —атить *v.* hump; —атки *pl.* humpbacked flies (*Phoridae*); tumbling flower beetles (*Mordellidae*); —атый *a.* humpbacked, hunchback.

горбахит *m.* (min.) horbachite.

горбач *m.* compass plane.

горб/ина *f.* hump, small hump, bump; —истый *a.* knotty (wood); —ить *v.* bend, crook; —уша *f.* (agr.) sickle; —ыль *m.* slab.

Горвуда процесс (min.) Horwood (flotation) process.

горд *see* гордовина.

горд/еин *m.* hordein; —енин *m.* hordenine.

гордиев узел Gordian knot, very involved problem.

гордиться *v.* be proud (of), take pride (in).

гордов/ина *f.*, —ый *a.* (bot.) viburnum.

горд/ость *f.* pride; —ый *a.* proud.

горе *n.* grief, misfortune; —вать *v.* grieve.

горел/ка *f.* burner, (gas) jet; (welding) torch; —ый *a.* burnt, scorched, smoked.

горельеф *m.* high relief.

гор/ение *n.* combustion, burning, blazing; теплота —ения heat of combustion; —еть *v.* burn; shine, blaze.

горец *see* горлец.

горечавк/а *f.* (bot.) gentian (*Gentiana*); —овые *pl.* Gentianaceae.

горечь *f.* bitterness, bitter taste; bitter principle.

горжа *f.* gorge, ravine.

горизонт *m.* horizon, prospect, skyline; level, level line, floor; layer, bed; (water) table; вне —а out of sight; —аль *f.* horizontal, level; contour line; установка по —али horizontal adjustment.

горизонтальн/о *adv.* horizontally, on a

level; —**осверлильный станок** boring lathe; —**ость** *f.* horizontal position; —**ый** *a.* horizontal, level, flat; —**ая линия, —ая плоскость** level; —**ая съемка** leveling.

**горилла** *f.* (zool.) gorilla.

**горист/ость** *f.* mountainousness, mountainous state; —**ый** *a.* mountainous.

**горицвет** *m.*, **весенний г.** (bot.) adonis (*Adonis vernalis*).

**горичник** *m.*, **аптечный г.** (bot.) brimstone-wort (*Peucedanum officinale*).

**горка** *f.* hill, knoll, ridge; (aero.) vertical climb; cabinet; gravity (seed) cleaner; (mech.) backfall of roll.

**горлец** *m.*, **змеиный г.** (bot.) bistort, snakeweed (*Polygonum bistorta*).

**горло** *n.* throat; neck (of vessel); vent (of volcano); **с длинным —м** long-necked; —**вина** *f.* manhole; crater, orifice, mouth, vent; throat; neck (of vessel); top (of furnace); —**вой** *a.* throat; —**вая трубка** throttle pipe; —**вая чахотка** (med.) laryngeal phthisis; —**перый** *a.* jugular.

**горл/ышко** *n.* neck, mouth, spout; throat, gullet; —**янка** *f.* (bot.) bottle gourd (*Lagenaria vulgaris*); crookneck (*Cucurbita pepo condensa*).

**гормон** *m.*, —**альный, —ный** *a.* hormone; —**отерапия** *f.* hormone therapy.

**горн** *m.* (met.) hearth, forge, furnace; (cer.) kiln.

**горнблендит** *m.* hornblendite (an igneous rock).

**горнил/о** *see* **горн; —ьный** *see* **горновый.**

**горнито** *n.* (geol.) hornito.

**горнов/ой, —ый** *a.* hearth, forge, furnace; —**ой** *m.* furnace attendant; —**ая сварка** forge welding.

**горнозавод/ский** *a.* metallurgical; —**чик** *m.* foundry owner.

**горнокаменн/ый** *a.*, —**ая порода** rock.

**горно/промышленность** *f.* mining industry; —**рабочий, —служащий** *m.* miner; —**рудный** *a.* mining; —**спасательный** *a.* (mine) rescue.

**горност/ай** *m.*, —**аевый, —айвый, —аячий** *a.* (zool.) ermine; —**аевые моли** ermine moths (*Yponomeutidae*).

**горн/ый** *a.* mountain, mountainous; mining; surveying (compass); air

(sickness); **г. воск** (min.) mineral wax, ozocerite; **г. инженер** mining engineer; **г. кряж** ridge, range (of mountains); **г. лен** (min.) mountain flax, amianthus (a form of asbestos); **г. песок** pit sand; **г. проход** mountain pass; **г. трут, —ая губка, —ое молоко** (min.) mountain milk (a form of spongy calcite); **г. хрусталь** (min.) rock crystal (a form of colorless quartz); —**ая бумага** (min.) mountain paper, mountain cork (a form of asbestos); **открытая —ая выработка** open pit mining, open cut mining; —**ая голубая, —ая синь** mineral blue, blue verditer (basic copper carbonate); —**ая зелень** mountain green, malachite; —**ая кожа** (min.) mountain leather (a form of asbestos); —**ая мука** mountain meal, kieselguhr; —**ая порода** rock; —**ая пробка** mountain cork (a form of asbestos); —**ая система** range (of mountains); —**ая смола** mineral tar, mineral pitch, bitumen; —**ая техника** mining engineering; —**ое дело** mining, mining industry; —**ое дерево** mountain wood, ligneous asbestos; —**ое искусство** mining; —**ое масло** petroleum, naphtha; mineral oil; —**ое мыло** mountain soap (a kind of clay); —**ое сало** mineral tallow, hatchetite; —**ые квасцы** rock alum, alunite, alumstone.

**горн/як** *m.*, —**яцкий** *a.* miner; mining engineer or student.

**город** *m.* town, city; **главный г.** capital.

**городить** *v.* hedge, fence, enclose.

**город/ишко** *n.* small town, village; —**овой** *see* **городской.**

**город/ок** *m.* small town; lumber yard; —**сад** *m.* garden city; —**ской** *a.* city, municipal, civil.

**городчатый** *a.* crenulate.

**горо/дьба** *f.* enclosure, fence; —**жение** *n.* enclosing, fencing.

**горообраз/ование** *n.* (geol.) orogeny; orogenesis; —**ующий** *a.* orogenic.

**горох** *m.* (bot.) pea (*Pisum*); —**овидный** *a.* pea-shaped, pisiform; pisolitic.

**гороховник** *m.* (bot.) dyer's broom (*Genista tinctoria*); locust tree (*Robinia*).

горохов/ый *a.* pea; pea-green; **г. камень** (min.) pea stone, pisolite; **—ая руда** pea ore (a form of iron ore); **—ое дерево** (bot.) acacia.
горош/ек *m.* little pea; pea coal; **душистый г.** (bot.) sweet pea (*Lathyrus odoratus*); **кормовой г.** (bot.) vetch (*Vicia sativa*); **сушенный г.** dried peas; **гравий —ком** pea gravel; **—ина, —инка** *f.* a pea; **—ковый** *a.* pea; **—чатый** *see* **гороховидный.**
горсейксит *m.* (min.) gorceixite (hamlinite group).
горский *a.* mountain.
горст *m.* (geol.) horst, upthrust, uplift.
горсть *f.* handful.
горсфордит *m.* (min.) horsfordite.
гортан/ный *a.* (anat.) laryngeal; **—ь** *f.* larynx, throat.
гортензия *f.* (bot.) hydrangea.
гортикультура *f.* horticulture.
гортон/олит *m.* (min.) hortonolite; **—сфера** *f.* Hortonsphere (a gas holder).
горч/авка, **—анка** *see* **горечавка; —айший** *a.* most bitter; worst; **—ак** *m.* (bot.) smartweed (*Polygonum hydropiper*); persicaria (*Polygonum persicaria*); gentian (*Gentiana*); acroptilon; **—ать** *see* **горькнуть; —е** *comp. of* **горький,** more bitter; **—ить** *v.* make bitter; have a bitter taste.
горчи/ца *f.,* **—чный** *a.* (bot.) mustard (*Sinapis*); **—чник** *m.* mustard plaster; **—чный газ** mustard gas, dichlorodiethyl sulfide.
горшечник *m.* potter; **круг —a, станок —a** potter's wheel.
горш/ечный, **—ковый** *a.* pot, potter's; **г. камень** (min.) potstone, soapstone; **г. товар** pottery, earthenware; **г. шлак** (met.) first-run slag; **—ая глина** potter's clay, ball clay; **—ая мельница** barrel mill; **—ая руда** (min.) galena; **—ая печь** potter's kiln; **—ое дерево** (bot.) lecythis; **—кообразный** *a.* pot-shaped; **—кообразный круг** pot (grinding) wheel; **—ок** *m.* pot, vessel.
горьк/ий *a.* bitter; **г. шпат** *see* **шпат; —ая вода** bitter water (containing Epsom salts); (pharm.) bitter-almond water; **—ая кора** bitter bark, spec.

amargoso; **—ая настойка, —ие капли** bitters; **—ая соль** Epsom salts, magnesium sulfate heptahydrate; **—ое вещество** bitter principle; **—ое дерево** (bot.) quassia; **—лый** *a.* rancid, rank; grown bitter; **—нуть** *v.* become bitter; grow rancid, rank; **—о** *adv.* bitterly; **—оватый** *a.* somewhat bitter, bitterish.
горьковский *a.* Gorki.
горькозем *m.,* **—истый** *a.* magnesia; **—истая слюда** (min.) magnesium mica.
горько/миндальный *a.* bitter-almond; **—сладкий** *a.* bitter-sweet; **—соленый** *a.* acrid; **—сть** *f.* bitterness.
горюч/ее *n.* fuel; **газовое г.** gaseous fuel; fuel gas; **жидкое г.** liquid fuel; fuel oil; **твердое г.** solid fuel, natural fuel; **—есть** *f.* combustibility, inflammability.
горюч/ий *a.* combustible, inflammable, ignitable; **г. газ** fuel gas; gas of combustion, flue gas; **г. материал** fuel, combustible material; **—ее масло** fuel oil.
горяче/катаный *a.* hot-rolled; **—ломкий** *a.* (met.) hot-short; **—ломкость** *f.* hot-shortness, hot-short state; **—спелый** *a.* (met.) too hot; (of iron) kishy; **—тянутый** *a.* (met.) hot-drawn; **—чный** *a.* burning, feverish; **—чный бред** (med.) delirium.
горяч/ий *a.* hot; (nucl.) hot, highly radioactive; **г. сросток** soldered joint; **—ая камера** (nucl.) hot cell, hot cave (of hot laboratory); **—ить** *v.* warm, heat; **—иться** *v.* get warm; **—ка** *f.* (med.) fever; **белая —ка** delirium tremens; **гнилая —ка** typhus; **—ность** *f.* warmth, heat; zeal, enthusiasm; **—о** *adv.* warmly, hotly; eagerly.
горящий *a.* burning.
гос— *abbr.* (**государственный**) state.
Гос/издат *abbr.* (**Государственное книгоиздательство**) State Publishing House, State Publishers; **—книга** *abbr.* (**Государственное книгоиздательство и книготорговля**) The State Press and Book-trading House.
госларит *m.* (min.) goslarite (a zinc sulfate).
госналог *m.* state tax.

**госпиталь** *m.*, **—ный** *a.* (military) hospital; **походный г.** ambulance.

**Госплан** *abbr.* (**Государственная плановая комиссия**) State Planning Commission.

**господств/о** *n.*, **—ование** *n.* domination, supremacy, prevalence; **—овать** *v.* dominate, predominate, prevail; govern; **—ующий** *a.* dominant, predominant, prevailing, prevalent.

**госпредприятие** *n.* state enterprise.

**госраспределение** *n.* state distribution.

**Госсельсклад** *abbr.* (**Государственный сельскохозяйственный склад**) State Warehouse for Agricultural Produce.

**госсип/етин** *m.* gossypetin; **—ин** *m.* gossypin (cotton cellulose); **—овая кислота** gossypic acid; **—оза** *f.* gossypose, raffinose; **—оид** *m.* gossypoid; **—ол** *m.* gossypol.

**госслужащий** *m.* government employee.

**госснабжение** *n.* state supply.

**Гос/союз** *abbr.* (**Государственный союз трудовых и производственных артелей**) State Union of Labor and Industrial Associations; **—строй** *abbr.* (**Всероссийская государственная строительная контора**) The Office of State Construction.

**ГОСТ** *abbr.* (**Государственный общесоюзный стандарт**) All-Union State Standard.

**гост/еприимный** *a.* hospitable; **—иница** *f.* hotel; **—иный** *a.* visitor's, guest; **—ить** *v.* be on a visit (to), stay (with).

**Госторг** *abbr.* (**Государственная экспортная-импортная контора**) State Export and Import Company.

**госторговля** *f.* state trade.

**гость** *m.* guest, visitor; (min.) metasome.

**государств/енный** *a.* state; government, public; national; federal; **—о** *n.* state; government.

**госучреждение** *n.* state institution.

**госфонд** *m.* state fund.

**Госхимтехиздат** *abbr.* (**Государственное химико-техническое издательство**) State Chemical-Technical Publishers.

**гот/ический** *a.* Gothic; **—ландский** *a.* (geol.) Gothlandian, Silurian.

**готов** *see* **готовый.**

**готовальн/ик** *m.*, **—я** *f.* set or case of drawing instruments.

**готов/ить** *v.* prepare, make ready; **—ность** *f.* preparedness, readiness, disposition; **—ый** *a.* ready, prepared, fabricated, ready-made, finished, final; disposed, willing.

**готская жельть** a chrome yellow; **г. зелень** a chrome green.

**гофельгумми** *n.* gofel gum.

**Гофмана реакция** Hofmann's reaction.

**гофманские капли** Hoffmann drops (a mixture of alcohol and ether).

**Гофмейстера ряд** Hofmeister series, lyotropic series.

**гофр** *m.* corrugation, crimp; corrugated metal sheet.

**гофриров/ально-закаточный станок** crimping, beading, and flanging machine; **—альный** *a.* crimping; **—ание** *n.*, **—ка** *f.* crimping, corrugation; **—анный** *a.* corrugated (iron); crimped (wire, cloth, etc.); embossed (fabric); **—анная мембрана, —анная трубка** bellows; **—ать** *v.* corrugate, crimp.

**гофрузид** *m.* gofruside.

**Гофти** *abbr.* (**Государственный физико-технический институт**) State Physical-Technical Institute.

**гошкорнит** *m.* (min.) hauchecornite.

**Гоэлро** *abbr.* (**Государственная комиссия по электрофикации России**) State Commission on the Electrification of Russia.

**гиз** *abbr.* (**гектопьеза**) hectopiezo-electric unit.

**г-р** *abbr.* (**грамм-рентген**) gram-roentgen; **гр.** *abbr.* (**группа**) group; radical.

**граб** *m.* (bot.) hornbeam (*Carpinus*); spec. white beech (*C. betulus*).

**грабар** *m.* excavator, excavating machine.

**грабеж** *m.* robbery, plunder.

**грабельный** *a.* rake, rabble.

**грабен** *m.* (geol.) graben.

**грабин/а**, **—ник** *see* **граб**; **—ный** *a.* hornbeam.

**грабит/ельский** *a.* predatory; exorbitant; **—ь** *v.* rob.

**грабли** *pl.* rake, rabble; ladder (of concentration classifier).

**грабшти/к, —х, —хель** *m.* burin, graver, engraving tool.

**гравелит** *m.* gritstone.

**гравер** *m.* engraver; a bark beetle.

**гравие/мойка** *f.* gravel washer; **—сортировка** *f.* gravel sorter, gravel classifier; gravel sorting.

**гравий** *m.,* **—ный** *a.* gravel, grit; **горный г., карьерный г.** pit gravel.

**гравилат** *m.,* **—ный** *a.* (bot.) avens (*Geum*).

**гравиметр** *m.* gravimeter, gravity meter; hydrometer; **—ический** *a.* gravimetric; **—ия** *f.* gravimetry.

**гравировальн/ый** *a.* engraving, carving; **г. станок** engraving machine, engraver; **—ая доска** copper or steel plate, engraver's cut; **—ая игла** etching needle, style.

**гравиров/альщик** *see* **гравер; —ание** *n.,* **—ка** *f.* engraving, etching; scratch; **—анный** *a.* engraved, etched; (min.) glyptic; **—ать** *v.* engrave, etch, carve.

**гравистый** *a.* gravelly.

**гравитац/ионный** *a.* gravitation, gravitational, gravity; **—ионная сортировка** (min.) gravity concentration; **—ия** *f.* gravitation; gravity concentration.

**гравитон** *m.* graviton, gravitation quantum.

**гравюра** *f.* engraving, print, cut.

**Грагама закон** *see* **Греэма закон.**

**град** *m.* hail; shower, volley.

**град.** *abbr.* (**градус**) degree.

**град/ация** *f.* gradation, grading, scale; shading; **—иент** *m.* gradient, grade, slope; (meteor.) lapse rate.

**градина** *f.* hailstone, hail.

**градир/ный** *a.,* **—ование** *n.,* **—овка** *f.* graduation, evaporation; **г. аппарат** graduator; **г. камень** a cake of calcium, magnesium, and other carbonates formed during salt manufacture; **—ня** *f.* graduating tower, (salt) graduation house; cooling tower, cooler, water-cooling system; **—овать** *v.* graduate, evaporate.

**градо/битие** *n.* damage done by hail; **—вой** *a.* hail.

**грдуатор** *m.* graduator; (elec.) induction coil.

**градуиров/ание** *n.,* **—ка** *f.* graduation, calibration, division; rating (of light bulbs); **—анный** *a.* graduated, calibrated, divided; **—анный диск** dial, face; **—ать** *v.* graduate, calibrate, divide; standardize, gage.

**градус** *m.,* **—ный** *a.* degree; **—ник** *m.* thermometer; **—о-день** *m.* (meteor.) degree day.

**граждан/ин** *m.* citizen; **—ский** *a.* civil, civic, social; **—ский инженер** civil engineer; **—ское строительство** civil engineering; **—ство** *n.* citizenship.

**гралекс** *m.* a leather substitute.

**грам/ин** *m.* gramine; **—иновая кислота** graminic acid, tyrocidine hydrochloride; **—ицидин** *m.* gramicidin.

**грамм** *m.* gram; **г., —а** *f. suffix* **—gram;** diffraction pattern; **г.-атом** gram atom; **г.-ион** gram ion; **г.-калория** gram calorie, small calorie; **г.-молекула, г.-частица** gram molecule, mole; **г.-рентген** (radiobiology) gram-roentgen; **г.-эквивалент** gram equivalent.

**Грамма кольцевой якорь** (elec.) Gramme ring armature.

**граммат/ика** *f.* grammar; **—ит** *m.* (min.) grammatite, tremolite (a variety of amphibole); **—ический** *a.* grammatical.

**граммовый** *a.* gram; **г. эквивалент** *see* **грамм-эквивалент.**

**граммолекул/а** *see* **грамм-молекула; —ярный** *a.* gram-molecular, molar.

**граммофон** *m.,* **—ный** *a.* phonograph.

**грамот/а** *f.* reading and writing; charter, record; deed; certificate; **—ность** *f.* literacy; **—ный** *a.* literate.

**грамотрицательный** *a.* (bact.) Gram-negative.

**грампластинка** *f.* phonograph record.

**грамположительный** *a.* (bact.) Gram-positive.

**гран** *m.* grain (weight); tiny quantity.

**гранат** *m.* (min.) garnet; (bot.) pomegranate (*Punica granatum*); **благородный г., красный г.** (min.) carbuncle, red gem garnet or ruby; **богемский г.** *see* **пироп; железистый г.** iron garnet (a variety of andradite garnet); **черный г.** black garnet, melanite.

**граната** *f.* grenade, shell.

**гранатанин** *m.* granatanine, 1,5-imino-cyclooctane.

**гранатизированный** *a.* (min.) garnet-ized, garnetiferous.

**гранатин** *m.* granatine.

**гранат/ка** *f.* pomegranate (fruit); a superior grade of sodium chloride crystals; **—ник, —овое дерево** *see* **гранат; —ный, —овый** *a.* (min.) garnet; (bot.) pomegranate; **—овая порода** garnet rock; **—овые** *pl.* (bot.) Punicaceae.

**гранатодубильная кислота** granato-tannic acid.

**гранатомет** *m.* rifle-grenade thrower.

**гранатонин** *m.* granatonine, pseudopel-letierine.

**гранатоподобный** *a.* (min.) garnet-like.

**грандидиерит** *m.* (min.) grandidierite.

**грандиозн/ость** *f.* grandeur, magnificence; **—ый** *a.* grand, magnificent.

**гране/ние** *n.* cutting (of gems); **—ный** *a.* cut, ground, faceted; fluted, canted; diamond-cut (glass); **—центрированный** *a.* (cryst.) face-centered.

**гранилит** *m.* (petr.) granilite (a granite).

**гранил/о** *n.* cutter; **—ьный** *a.* cutting; **—ьная мастерская, —ьня** *f.* diamond-cutting shop; **—ьщик** *m.* diamond cutter, gem cutter.

**гранистый** *a.* faceted.

**гранит** *m.* (petr.) granite; **буквенный г., письменный г.** graphic granite; **—изация** *f.* granitization; **—ит** *m.* (petr.) granitite (a biotite granite); **—ный, —овый** *a.* granite, granitic.

**гранито/видный, —подобный** *a.* (petr.) granitoid, granite-like; **—гнейс** *m.* gneissoid granite, gneissic granite; **—ид** *m.* granitoid rock; **—идный** *a.* granitoid; **—идная структура** granitoid texture; **—оль** *m.* a leather substitute.

**гранить** *v.* cut, grind, facet, cut into facets.

**границ/а** *f.* boundary, boundary line, border; line, limit, limitation, end, cut-off; (Compton) edge; landmark; frontier; confines; **в —ах** within, in the range (of); **за —ей** abroad; **имеющий общую —у** coterminous (with).

**гранич/ащий** *a.* adjacent, adjoining; **—ение** *n.* demarcation; **—ить** *v.*

border (on), be contiguous (to), abut; **—ный** *a.* border, boundary, limiting; cut-off; grenz (X-rays); **—ный слой** boundary layer, interface; **—ная скорость** boundary velocity; cut-off velocity; **—ная точка** end point; threshold; **—ные условия** (math.) boundary conditions.

**гранка** *f.* (typ.) galley proof, slip.

**—гранн/ик** *m.* *suffix* **—**hedron; **—ый** *a.* *suffix* **—**hedral.

**гранобластический** *a.* (petr.) grano-blastic.

**грановитый** *a.* faceted.

**грано/диорит** *m.* (petr.) granodiorite; **—зан** *m.* an ethylmercuric chloride seed fungicide equivalent to Ceresan; **—лит** *m.* (cement) granolith; **—фир** *m.* granophyre.

**Гранта топливо** Grant's fuel.

**гранул/а** *f.*, **—ь** *m.*, **—я** *f.* granule, small grain, shot; **—еза, —оза** *f.* granulose; **—езный** *a.* granulose, granulous; **—ема** *f.* (med.) granuloma; **—ирование** *n.*, **—яция** *f.*, **—яционный** *a.* granulation, granulating; **—ированный** *a.* granulated, granular; **—ировать** *v.* granulate; **—ит** *m.* (petr.) granulite; **—итовый** *a.* granulitic; **—ометрический** *a.* granulometric, grain-size, particle-size; fineness (ratio); **—оцит** *m.* (anat.) granulo-cyte; **—оцитопения** *f.* (med.) granulocytopenia; **—ярный** *a.* granular; **—ятор** *m.*, **—яционная машина** granulator, granulating machine.

**гран/ь** *f.* facet, face (of crystal), side, plane; edge (of tool); margin; (math.) bound; **—ью, —ями** facet-ways.

**ГРАО** *abbr.* (Главная российская астрономическая обсерватория) Main Russian Observatory.

**граптолит** *m.* (geol.) graptolite (fossil).

**Грасгофа критерий** Grashof number.

**грат** *m.* bur, fin, edge, ridge.

**гратио/золетин** *m.* gratiosoletin; **—золин** *m.* gratiosolin; **—лин** *m.* gratiolin; **—ловая кислота** gratioloic acid.

**граувакк/а** *f.*, **—овый** *a.* (petr.) gray-wacke.

**—граф** *m.* *suffix* **—**graph; **—grapher.

**графа** *f.* column (of a table); range; straight line.

**график** *m.* graph, plot, curve; diagram; chart, table; schedule; **составление —a** scheduling; **—a** *f.* graphing, plotting.

**график/ка** *f.* marking tool, marking awl, mark scraper, scratch awl; **—ьный** *a.* marking, ruling.

**графин** *m.* decanter, bottle.

**графит** *m.* graphite, black lead, plumbago; **—изация** *f.*, **—ирование** *n.*, **—ование** *n.* graphitization; coating with graphite; **—ированный** *a.* graphitized; **—ировать** *v.* graphitize; **—истый** *a.* graphitic; **—ит** *m.* (min.) graphitite (same as graphite); **—ный**, **—овый** *a.* graphite, graphitic; lead (pencil); **—ный уголь** graphitic carbon; **—ная спель** (met.) kish, graphite segregations; **—овая кислота** graphitic acid; **—овая смазка** graphite lubricant, graphite lubrication.

**графито/ид** *m.* graphitoid (a type of anthracite coal); **—образный** *a.* graphitic.

**граф/ить** *v.* rule, draw lines; (math.) graph; **—ически** *adv.* graphically; **—ический** *a.* graphic, diagrammatic, schematic; eutectic (texture); *suffix* —graphic; diffraction; **—ическая характеристика** curve; **—ическое изображение** graphic representation, diagram; **—ия** *f. suffix* —graphy; diffraction; **—леный** *a.* ruled; divided into columns.

**графо/логия** *f.* graphology; **—метр** *m.* (surv.) graphometer; **—статика** *f.* graphostatics.

**графтонит** *m.* (min.) graftonite.

**грахамит** *see* **греэмит.**

**грацилярии** *pl.* (zool.) gracilariids (*Gracilariidae*).

**гребенка** *f.* comb; chaser, chasing tool; manifold; (text.) hackle; (tel.) distributing block.

**гребенник** *see* **гравилат.**

**гребен/ный** *a.* combed; **—ные очески** combings; **—очный** *a.* comb.

**гребенчат/ый** *a.* comb, comb-shaped, comb-like; (biol.) pectinate, pectinal; cristate; **г. подшипник** collar thrust bearing; **г. шип**, **—ая пята**, **—ая цапфа**, **—ая шейка** collar journal,

thrust journal, cam journal; **—ая структура** comb structure (of ores).

**гребень** *m.* comb; summit, peak, crown, ridge (of hill); crest (of wave); (anat.) crista, crest, ridge; collar, flange (of wheel); ledge; hackle (for flax); (weaving) lease reed; (meteor.) wedge.

**гребешок** *m.* comb; crest.

**греб/ковый** *a.* rake, rabble; hoe-type; **—ло** *n.* strickle; paddle, oar; **—ля** *f.* raking; pull.

**гребне/вание** *n.* ridging; **—видный** *see* **гребенчатый; —вик** *m.* (bot.) dog's-tail grass (*Cynosurus*); **—вики** *pl.* (zool.) Ctenophora; **—вой** *a.* of гребень, comb; ridge; **—держатель** *m.* comb holder; **—чесальная машина** hackling machine, comber; **—чесание** *n.* (text.) combing.

**гребник** *see* **гравилат.**

**гребн/ой** *a.* paddle; **г. вал** propeller shaft; **г. винт** screw propeller, propeller; **—ое колесо** paddle wheel.

**гребок** *m.* raker, rabble, hoe; strickle.

**грегамит** *see* **греэмит.**

**грегарин/ы** *pl.* (zool.) Gregarina (parasites); **—овидный** *a.* gregariniform.

**Грегема закон** *see* **Греэма закон.**

**греенокит** *see* **гринокит.**

**греж** *m.*, **—a** *f.* raw silk, greige, reeled silk.

**грейдер** *m.* grader.

**грейзен** *m.* (petr.) greisen (a pneumatolytic derivative of granite); **—изация** *f.* greisenization.

**грейнахеровский** *a.* Greinacher.

**грейпфрут** *m.* (bot.) grapefruit (*Citrus paradisa*).

**Грейт-Фолса конвертер** Great Falls converter.

**грейфер** *m.*, **—ный** *a.* gripper, claw; grab, grab bucket; **—ный кран** grab crane, bucket crane; **—ный экскаватор** clamshell excavator.

**грелка** *f.* heater, warming pan; hot water bottle.

**греметь** *v.* fulminate, detonate; rattle, rumble.

**гремуче/кислый** *a.* fulminic acid; fulminate (of); **—кислая ртуть** mercury fulminate; **—кислая соль** fulminate; **—медная кислота** cuprofulminic acid; **соль —медной кислоты, —меднокислая соль** cuprofulminate; —**медная соль** cupric fulminate;—**ртутная соль** mercury fulminate; —**серебряная соль** silver fulminate, fulminating silver; —**цинковая соль** zinc fulminate.

**гремуч/ий** *a.* fulminating, detonating; rattling; **г. воздух** (mining) firedamp; detonating gas; **г. газ** detonating gas, specif. oxyhydrogen gas; **г. камень** (min.) eaglestone (nodular clay ironstone); **г. порох, г. порошок, —ая смесь** fulminating powder, detonating powder, percussion powder; **г. сахар** (expl.) nitrosaccharose; **г. студень** nitrogelatin, blasting gelatin, gelatin dynamite; —**ая змея, —ник** *m.* rattlesnake; —**ая кислота** fulminic acid; **соль —ой кислоты** fulminate; —**ая ртуть** fulminating mercury, mercury fulminate; —**ая хлопчатая бумага** pyroxylin; —**ее золото** fulminating gold, aurodiamine; —**ее серебро** fulminating silver.

**грена** *f.* silkworm eggs.

**гренадилл** *m.* granadilla (fruit of passiflora).

**гренадин** *m.* grenadine, pomegranate syrup.

**гренаж** *m.* silkworm breeding.

**гренай** *m.* (met.) buckshot cinder.

**гренарня** *f.* silkworm breeding room.

**гренвильская свита** (geol.) Grenville series.

**Гренландия** Greenland.

**гренок** *m.* rusk, toast (bread).

**грест/и, —ь** *v.* rake; row, paddle, pull.

**греть** *v.* heat, warm.

**Греффе метод** (math.) Graeffe's method.

**грех** *m.* sin, fault.

**Греца критерий** Graetz number.

**Греция** Greece.

**грецкий орех** (bot.) walnut (*Juglans regia*).

**греч.** *abbr.* (**греческий**) Greek.

**греча** *see* **гречиха.**

**греческий** *a.* Greek.

**греч/иха** *f.*, —**невый** *a.* (bot.) buckwheat (*Fagopyrum esculentum*); **красильная г.,красильная —ка** polygony (*Polygonum tinctorium*); —**ишные** *pl.* Polygonaceae; —**невая крупа** buckwheat (the grain).

**грешить** *v.* err, make a mistake, do wrong.

**Греэма закон** Graham law.

**греэмит** *m.* (min.) grahamite (a native asphalt-like material).

**ГРИ** *abbr.* (**Государственный радиевый институт**) State Radium Institute.

**гриб** *m.* mushroom; fungus; —**ы** *pl.* mushrooms; fungi; —**ы-водоросли** Phycomycetes; **сумчатые —ы** Ascomycetes; **учение о —ах** mycology.

**грибков/ый** *a.* fungous, mushroom, mushroom-like, fungoid; —**ая кислота** fungic acid; **соль —ой кислоты, —окислая соль** fungate; —**ое вещество, —ая клетчатка, —ое начало** fungin.

**гриб/ница** *f.* mushroom spawn; mycelium; —**ной** *see* **грибковый;** —**ной сахар** mycose, trehalose; —**овидный, —ообразный** *a.* mushroom, mushroom-shaped, fungiform, fungoid; —**ожил** *m.* mushroom beetle (*Fungiculus*); —**ок** *m.* little mushroom; fungus; —**ки** *pl.* fungi; **образование —ков** fungoid growth; —**окорень** *m.* (bot.) mycorhiza.

**грива** *f.* mane, crest.

**гривенник** *m.* silver coin worth 10 kopecks.

**Гривс-Этчеля печь** Greaves-Etchell furnace (for steel).

**григорианский** *a.* Gregorian (calendar).

**гридик** *m.* (rad.) grid leak.

**гризе/ин** *m.* grisein; —**олютеин** *m.* griseolutein; —**офульвин** *m.* griseofulvin.

**гризли** *n.* (mining) grizzly; grizzly bear.

**гризутин** *m.* (expl.) grisoutine.

**грильяж** *m.* roasting.

**грим** *m.* rouge, make-up.

**Грина печь** Green (electric arc) furnace.

**гриналит** *m.*, —**овый** *a.* greenalite (a non-potash mineral resembling glauconite).

**гринда** *f.* (zool.) pilot whale.

**гриндел/ин** *m.* grindeline; —**ия** *f.*, —**ия трава** (bot.) gum plant, tar weed (*Grindelia*); —**оид** *m.* grindeloid.

**гринель** *f.* broom straw.

**грино/вит** *m.* (min.) greenovite (a manganesian variety of titanite); **—кит** *m.* greenockite (a cadmium sulfate).

**гринсбон** *m.* (text.) gingham.

**гриньяровская реакция** Grignard reaction.

**грипп** *m.*, **—озный** *a.* (med.) grippe, influenza.

**Грисгейма красный** Griesheim red.

**грит** *m.* grit.

**гриф** *m.* stamp, stamped signature; touch, feel, handle; (music) fingerboard, neck; (zool.) vulture.

**грифа** *f.* grifa, lithium acetyl salicylate.

**грифель** *m.* slate; slate pencil; **—ная доска** slate; **—ный сланец** (geol.) grapholite, writing slate.

**грифит** *m.* (min.) griphite.

**грифолин** *m.* grifolin.

**Гриффита белила** Griffith white, lithopone.

**гриффитит** *m.* (min.) griffithite.

**гроб** *m.* coffin.

**Грове элемент** (elec.) Grove cell.

**гроза** *f.* storm, thunderstorm.

**грозд/евидный, —еобразный** *a.* botryoidal; grape-like, in grape-like clusters; (zool.) racemose; **—евидная структура** (min.) botryoidal structure; **—ь** *m.*, **—ный, —овый** *a.* cluster, bunch (of grapes); (bot.) raceme.

**грозить** *v.* threaten, menace.

**грозненский** *a.* Grozny.

**грозный** *a.* threatening, menacing; stern.

**грозов/ой** *a.* storm, thunderstorm; **г. разрядник** lightning arrester, lightning protector; **г. шквал** thundersquall; **—ое облако** thundercloud, cumulo-nimbus.

**грозо/защита** *f.* lightning protection; **—отметчик** *m.* storm indicator; **—писец** *m.* (meteor.) brontograph; **—стойкий, —упорный** *a.* lightning-proof.

**грозящий** *a.* threatening, imminent.

**гром** *m.* thunder.

**громад/а** *f.* mass, bulk; heap, pile; huge building; **—ина** *f.* huge thing; **—ность** *f.* hugeness, vastness, enormity; **—ный** *a.* huge, vast, enormous, mammoth.

**громдола** *see* **валериана.**

**громить** *v.* destroy, ruin.

**громк/ий** *a.* loud, noisy; **—о** *adv.* loudly; **—оговоритель** *m.* (rad.) loudspeaker; **—оговорящий** *a.* loud-speaking; loudspeaker; **—ость** *f.* loudness, volume; **регулятор —ости** volume control.

**громо/вой** *a.* thunder, thunderous; **—вая стрела** thunderbolt; fulgurite, lightning tube; **—гласный** *a.* loud.

**громозд/ить** *v.* heap up, stack, pile up; **—иться** *v.* tower; **—кий** *a.* cumbrous, cumbersome, unwieldy, awkward, bulky, massive; **—кость** *f.* awkwardness; bulk.

**громоотвод** *m.*, **—ный** *a.* lightning rod, lightning conductor.

**громче** *comp. of* **громкий, громко** louder.

**громыхать** *v.* rumble, rattle.

**гророилит** *m.* (min.) groroilite (a variety of earthy manganese or wad).

**гросс** *m.* gross (twelve dozen).

**гроссбух** *m.* (com.) ledger.

**гроссул/ар, —яр** *m.* (min.) grossularite.

**грот** *m.* grotto, cavern.

**гротескный** *a.* grotesque.

**гротит** *m.* (min.) grothite (a variety of yttrium-containing titanite).

**гротовый** *a.* grotto, cavern.

**грох/нуть** *v.* drop with a crash; **—нуться** *v.* crash, rattle down; **—от** *m.* crash, rattle, roar; screen, sifter, sieve, riddle, grizzly; **—отать** *v.* rattle, roar; **—отить** *v.* screen, riddle, sieve, sift, bolt; **—очение** *n.* screening, sifting; **—оченый** *a.* screened, sifted.

**грош/евый, —овый** *a.* very cheap.

**груббер** *m.* (agr.) grubber, cultivator; **г.-борона** cultivator harrow.

**груб/еть** *v.* harden, roughen, coarsen; **—о** *adv.* roughly, coarsely; **—оватый** *a.* rather coarse; **—оволокнистый** *a.* coarse-fibered, coarse-grained; **—озернистый** *a.* coarse-grained, coarse; **—омозаичный** *a.* (building) cyclopean; **—ообломочный** *a.* coarsely fragmental; **—ость** *f.* roughness, coarseness; clumsiness, crudeness; **—ый** *a.* rough, coarse; crude, raw; gross; clumsy; hard (usage).

**груда** *f.* heap, pile, mass, congestion, cluster.

**груд/ина** *f.* (anat.) sternum; **—ника** *f.* (bot.) abutilon; **—ница** *f.* (med.)

mastitis; (tech.) breast beam; (bot.) linosyris.

**грудн/ой** *a.* breast, chest, thoracic; pectoral; **г. порошок** (pharm.) pectoral powder, specif. compound licorice powder; **г. проток** (anat.) thoracic duct; **—ая доска** (paper) apron board; **—ая жаба** (med.) angina pectoris; **—ая железа** (anat.) mammary gland; **—ая клетка, —ая полость** (anat.) chest, thorax; **—ая кость** (anat.) breastbone, sternum; **—ая плева** (anat.) pleura; **—ая упорка** breast plate.

**груд/обрюшная преграда** (anat.) diaphragm; **—ь** *f.* breast, chest; (zool.) thorax; front (of blast furnace).

**груз** *m.* load, burden, weight; charge; goods, consignment, cargo, freight, shipment, lading; (pendulum) bob; **общий г.** gross weight; **транспортировка —ов** shipping, freight traffic, freight handling; **тяжелый г.** dead weight; heavy load.

**груз.** *abbr.* (**грузинский**) Georgian.

**груздь** *m.* (bot.) pepper mushroom (*Agaricus* or *Lactarius piperatus*).

**грузило** *n.* plumb, plumb bob, plumb line, sounding lead.

**грузинский** *a.* Georgian (USSR).

**грузить** *v.* load; freight, ship; handle.

**Грузия** Georgia (USSR).

**груз/кий** *a.* heavy, weighty; **—но** *adv.* heavily laden; **—нуть** *v.* sink; **—ный** *a.* heavy, massive; loaded.

**грузо/вик** *m.* motor truck, truck, lorry; van, wagon; freight car; **г.-цистерна** tank truck; **—вместимость** *f.* load-carrying capacity, carrying capacity; **—вое** *n.* tonnage, tonnage dues.

**грузов/ой** *a.* load, loading; freight; **г. автомобиль** truck; **г. пароход, —ое судно** freighter, cargo ship; **г. подъемник** freight elevator; **г. транспорт, —ые перевозки** freight traffic.

**грузо/захватное приспособление** load-lifting mechanism, hoisting device; **—напряженность** *f.* density of freight traffic; **—оборот** *m.* freight turnover; **—отправитель** *m.* consigner.

**грузоподъемн/ик** *m.* freight elevator; **—ость** *f.*, **—ая способность** lifting capacity, lifting power, lifting force

(of magnet); load-lifting capacity, load capacity, carrying capacity; **—ый** *a.* load-lifting, hoisting; **—ый кран** crane, derrick; **—ый механизм** hoisting device, elevating mechanism; **—ая машина** elevating machine, elevator; **—ая петля** sling; **—ая тележка** jack; **—ая цепь** chain sling; **—ое приспособление** lifting tackle.

**груз/ополучатель** *m.* consignee; **—оспособность** *f.* capacity; **—ошина** *f.* truck tire; **—чик** *m.* loader; stevedore, longshoreman.

**грундбукса** *f.* (mach.) bottom box, bottom.

**грунерит** *m.* (min.) grunerite (a variety of amphibole)

**грунт** *m.* ground, bottom; soil, earth, land; priming (color), ground coat, first coat (of paint); **—ование** *n.* grounding; undercoat, priming; **—овать** *v.* ground, prime, coat, give the first coat; size; (dyeing) bottom; (calico printing) prepare; **—оведение** *n.* soil science; **—овка** *f.* ground coat, priming, prime coat, first coat (of paint).

**грунтов/ой, —очный** *a.* ground, soil; dirt (road); prime; **г. лак** filler; knotting varnish; jobbing varnish; **г. слой** prime coat, first coat; **—ая вода** ground water, subsurface water; **—ая труба** ground pipe.

**грунтомер** *m.* soil density meter.

**грунтонос** *m.*, **—ка** *f.* (min.) core lifter.

**группа** *f.* group, bunch, cluster, batch; set, series, assembly; bank (of machines); block (of words); (chem.) radical; **г. ионов** ion cluster.

**группиров/ание** *n.*, **—ка** *f.* grouping, classification; tabulation; batching, bunching, concentration; **—анный** *a.* grouped, classified; tabulated; **—атель** *m.* (thermionics) buncher; **—ать** *v.* group, classify; tabulate; bank; **—аться** *v.* group, gather.

**группов/ой** *a.* group, gang; **г. выключатель** (elec.) group switch; branch switch; **—ое включение** series connection, series parallel connection.

**групповыбиратель** *m.* (elec. comm.) selector.

грустный *a.* melancholy, sad; lamentable.

груша *f.* (bot.) pear (*Pyrus communis*); (elec.) bulb; (met.) converter, pear (of converter); земляная г. (bot.) Jerusalem artichoke (*Helianthus tuberosus*).

грушанк/а *f.* (bot.) pyrola; —овые *pl.* Pyrolaceae.

груше/видный, —образный *a.* pear-shaped, pyriform; —вый *a.* pear; —вое масло pear oil, amyl acetate.

грушовка *f.* pear wine; (bot.) pyrola.

грыж/а *f.*, —евой, —ный *a.* (med.) hernia, rupture; операция —и herniotomy; —ная трава, —ник *m.*, —овник *m.* (bot.) rupture wort (*Herniaria glabra*).

грыз/ение *n.* gnawing; —ть *v.* gnaw, nibble, bite; —ун *m.* rodent; wood beetle.

Грэм, Грэхем *see* Греэма закон.

грюн/ерит *m.* (min.) grünerite (a variety of amphibole); —коль *f.* green cabbage; —лингит *m.* (min.) grünlingite; —штейн *m.* (petr.) greenstone.

гряд/а *f.* layer, stratum, bed; ridge; (mountain) chain; bank (of clouds, etc.); —иль *f.* (plow) beam; —ка *f.* (garden) bed; —оделатель *m.* (agr.) ridger.

грязевик *m.* mud drum, mud box, mud collector, mud trap; sludge pan, sump, bottom outlet; sediment tank.

грязевой *a.* mud, sludge; г. гейзер (geol.) mud pot; г. насос sludge pump.

грязе/отстойник *m.* mud sump, sump; sediment tank; —приемный барабан mud drum —уловитель *m.* mud trap, catch basin; —черпалка *f.* mud dredger.

грязн/ить *v.* soil, dirty; pollute, contaminate; —иться *v.* get dirty; get contaminated; —оватый *a.* rather dirty, dingy (color); —ота *f.* dirtiness; —ый *a.* dirty, muddy, soiled; sludgy, slimy, oozy; contaminated, impure.

грязь *f.* dirt, mud, soil; slime, sludge, ooze, slurry; silt, sediment; (cer.) slip; scum, scoria; contamination, impurity.

гс. *abbr.* (гаусс) gauss.

ГСИ *abbr.* (Государственная санитарная инспекция) State Sanitary Inspection.

ГСМ *abbr.* (горюче-смазочные материалы) fuels and lubricants.

ГСХОС *abbr.* (Государственная сельскохозяйственная опытная станция) State Agricultural Experiment Station.

ГТД *abbr.* (газотурбинный двигатель) gas turbine engine.

ГУ *abbr.* (государственное учреждение) state institution, state office.

гуа— *see under* гва—; —ва *f.* (bot.) guava (*Psidium guajava*).

гуако *n.* (pharm.) guaco.

гуаназ/а *f.* guanase; —ил *m.* guanazyl; —ол *m.* guanazole.

гуанидин *m.* guanidine, aminomethanamidine; углекислый г., карбонат —a guanidine carbonate; —о— *prefix* guanidino—; —офосфорная кислота guanidinophosphoric acid, phosphagen.

гуанидо— *prefix* guanido—; —уксусная кислота guanidoacetic acid.

гуанил *m.*, —овый *a.* guanyl; —овая кислота guanylic acid.

гуан/ин *m.* guanine, imidoxanthine; —о *n.* guano, bird manure; —овулит *m.* (min.) guanovulite.

гуаран/а *f.* guarana (paste from seeds of *Paullinia cupana*); —ин *m.* guaranine, caffeine.

гуаринит *m.* (min.) guarinite, hiortdahlite.

гуацин *m.* guacin.

гуаяк, —овое дерево *see* гваяковое дерево.

губ - *abbr.* (губернский) district.

губа *f.* lip; bay, gulf; jaw (of vise, etc.); —стый *a.* thick-lipped.

губель *m.* fillister, rabbeting plane.

губерн/атор *m.* governor; —ия *f.* district, province; —ский *a.* district, regional.

Губерта тормоз Hubert's brake.

губит/ельный *a.* destructive, injurious, fatal; —ь *v.* destroy, ruin.

губк/а *f.* sponge; jaw (of vise); (mech.) bit; древесная г. (bot.) tree fungus (*Polyporus fomentarius*); —и *pl.* (zool.) sponges (*Porifera*); —оватый *see* губчатый.

**губ/ной** *a.* lip, labial; **—овидный** *a.* lip-like, lip-shaped; **—оногие** *pl.* (zool.) Chilopoda; **—оцветные** *pl.* (bot.) Labiatae; **—оцветный** *a.* labiate.

**губчат/ость** *f.* sponginess; **—ый** *a.* spongy, sponge; fungous; blown, porous; **—ое железо** (met.) sponge iron, porous iron.

**гувацин** *m.* guvacine.

**Гудвина газовая сажа** Goodwin's gas black.

**гудение** *n.* hum, humming, buzzing.

**гудерманиан** *m.* (math.) Gudermannian.

**гудеть** *v.* hum, drone, buzz.

**гуджир** *m.* gudzhir (efflorescence of mirabilite, soda, etc., on the ice surface of salt lakes).

**Гудзонов залив** Hudson Bay.

**Гудир** Goodyear (brand).

**гудок** *m.* horn, siren, whistle, blast.

**гудрон** *m.* asphalt, tar; spec. a crude residue from petroleum refining; **—атор** *m.* asphalt spreader; **—ирование** *n.* asphalting, tarring (of road); **поверхностное —ирование** asphalt surfacing; **—ированный** *a.* tarred (road); **—ировать** *v.* asphalt, tar.

**гуж** *m.* tug; **—евой** *a.* land (transport); **—ом** *adv.* by vehicle, by land.

**гуза** *f.* (bot.) Asiatic cotton (*Gossypium hirsutum*); **г.-пая** *f.* guza-paya (cotton stems and bolls).

**гузнек** *m.* gooseneck.

**гузо/ломка** *f.* (cotton) boll breaker; **—уборочная машина** cotton-stem picker.

**гуитерманит** *m.* (min.) guitermanite.

**Гука закон** Hooke's law; **Г. шарнир** Hooke's joint, universal joint.

**Гукера элемент** Hooker (chlorine) cell.

**гул** *m.* boom, rumble, din; buzz, humming (of wires).

**гулкий** *a.* hollow (sound).

**гуло/гептоза** *f.* guloheptose; **—гептоновая кислота** guloheptonic acid; **—за** *f.* gulose; **—новая кислота** gulonic acid.

**Гульдберга и Вааге закон** Guldberg and Waage law, law of mass action.

**гульсит** *m.* (min.) hulsite.

**гулявник** *m.* (bot.) hedge mustard (*Sisymbrium*).

**Гуляра раствор, гулярдова вода** Gou-

lard's extract (solution of basic lead acetate).

**гумай** *m.* (bot.) Johnson grass, Guinea grass (*Sorghum halepense*).

**гумат** *m.* humate.

**гумбо** *n.* gumbo (clay).

**гумбольдт/илит** *m.* (min.) humboldtilite (a variety of melilite); **—ин** *m.* humboldtine; **—ит** *m.* humboldtite, datolite.

**гумбрин** *m.* gumbrin (a bleaching clay).

**гуменный** *a.* threshing floor, barn.

**гумиластик** *see* **гуммиластик.**

**гумин** *m.* humin.

**гуминов/окислый** *a.* humic acid; humate (of); **—окислая соль, соль —ой кислоты** humate; **—ый** *a.* humus, humic, mold; **—ая кислота** humic acid.

**гумит** *m.* (min.) humite (a basic magnesium fluosilicate).

**гумификация** *f.* humification.

**гумма** *f.* (med.) gumma (a tumor).

**гумми** *n.* gum; **—аммиак, —аммониак** *m.* gum ammoniac, ammoniacum; **—арабик** *m.* gum arabic; **—балата** *f.* balata; **—гут** *m.* gamboge; **—гутовые** *pl.* (bot.) Guttiferae; **—даммар** *m.* dammar; **—копал** *m.* copal; **—лак** *m.* gum lac; shellac; **—лаковая кислота** laccaic acid; **—ластик** *m.* (India) rubber; **—рование** *n.* lining with rubber, rubberizing.

**гуммит** *m.* (min.) gummite (an alteration product of uraninite).

**гуммитрагант** *m.* tragacanth (gum).

**гуммоз** *m.* gummosis (plant disease); **—ный** *a.* gummous, gumlike, gummy.

**гуммон** *m.* gummon (insulating material).

**гумно** *n.* threshing floor, barn floor.

**гумо/аммофос, —фос** *m.* humoammophos (fertilizer); **—аммофоска** *f.* humoammophoska (complete organomineral fertilizer); **—ген** *m.* humogen (fertilizer); **—ральный** *a.* (biol.) humoral.

**гумоцериновая кислота** humoceric acid.

**гумул/ен** *m.* humulene; **—ин** *m.* humulin, lupuline; **—иновая кислота** humulinic acid; **—инон** *m.* humulinone; **—одубильная кислота** humulotannic acid; **—он** *m.* humulone.

**гумус** *m.* humus, mold; **—ность** *f.*

humus content; —ный, —овый *a.* humus, mold, humic; —ообразование *n.* humus formation.

**гунит** *m.* gunite (sand-cement mixture).

**ГУП** *abbr.* (гамма-установка, промышленная) industrial gamma-unit.

**Гупера состав** Hooper (insulating) material.

**гупи** *n.* guppy (fish).

**Гупса процесс** Hoopes process (for aluminum refining).

**гур** *m.* (min.) guhr, kieselguhr.

**гура** *f.* (bot.) sand-box tree (*Hura crepitans*); (geol.) butte.

**гургофит** *m.* (min.) gurhofite (a variety of calcareous dolomite).

**гуреаулит** *m.* (min.) hureaulite.

**Гурон** Lake Huron.

**гуронский** *a.* (geol.) Huronian.

**гурт** *m.* drove, herd, flock (of cattle).

**гурт/ик** *m.* the milling (of a coin); —ить *v.* mill.

**гурт/овой** *a.* herd; wholesale; —овщик *m.* herdsman; wholesale merchant; —ом *adv.* all together, collectively.

**гурьб/а** *f.* crowd; —ой *adv.* in a crowd.

**гурьюн/-бальзам**, —овый бальзам gurjun balsam; —овая кислота gurjunic acid; —овое масло gurjun oil.

**ГУС** *abbr.* (Государственный ученый совет) The State Scientific Council.

**гусак** *m.* gander.

**гусар** *m.* hussar; rider (on a balance).

**Гусевский завод** the Gus Works (Ukraine).

**гусек** *m.* gosling; ogee, flute; bucket (of dam).

**гусени/ца** *f.*, —чный *a.* (zool.) caterpillar; (mach.) caterpillar track, track; —чный палец track pin; —чный трактор caterpillar (tractor), crawler; —чный ход caterpillar tread.

**гус/енок** *m.* gosling; —иный *a.* goose; —иный лук (bot.) gagea; —иная лапка (bot.) goosefoot (*Chenopodium glaucum*); —иная трава silver weed (*Potentilla anserina*); goose grass (*Galium aparine*).

**гусматик** *m.* a safety tire; patching paste.

**гуссакит** *m.* (min.) hussakite (a variety of xenotime).

**густ/еть**, —иться *v.* thicken, become thick, condense, solidify; —ить *v.* thicken, condense, concentrate.

**густо** *adv.* thickly, densely; —ватый *a.* rather thick, viscous; —ветвистый *a.* thick-branched.

**густой** *a.* thick, dense, viscous; heavy (oil); intimate (mixture); deep, rich (color); bushy (growth); fine (screen); soupy (fog).

**густо/лиственный** *a.* bushy, bushy-leaved; —насаженный *a.* thickset, close; —опушенный *a.* (bot.) hoary, canescent; —растущий *a.* bushy, dense, thick-growing; —та *f.* thickness, density, viscosity; consistency, body (of oil); depth, richness (of color); spacing, population (of plants); степень —ты consistency; density; —тертая краска pigment paste.

**гус/ыня** *f.* goose (female); —ь *m.* goose, gander; —ьком *adv.* single file; tandem; —ятина *f.* goose meat.

**ГУТ** *abbr.* (гамма-установка, терапевтическая) therapeutic gamma-unit.

**гутта** *f.*, —перча *f.*, —перчевый *a.* gutta-percha; —перчевое дерево (bot.) gutta-percha tree (*Isonandra gutta* or *Eucommia ulmoides*); —перченос *m.* gutta-percha-yielding plant.

**гутчинсонит** *m.* (min.) hutchinsonite.

**Гуча тигель** Gooch crucible, Gooch filter.

**гущ/а** *f.* dregs, grounds, sediment; mash; —е *comp. of* густой, thicker; делать —е *v.* thicken, condense; deepen (color).

**гуява** *see* гуава.

**ГФК** *abbr.* (глицерофосфорная кислота) glycerophosphoric acid.

**ГФО** *abbr.* (Главная физическая обсерватория) The Main Physical Observatory.

**ГХА** *abbr.* (гексахлорацетон) hexachloroacetone; **ГХБ** *abbr.* (гексахлорбензол) hexachlorobenzene; **ГХЦГ** *abbr.* (гексахлороциклогексан) hexachlorocyclohexane.

**гц** *abbr.* (герц) hertz, cycles per second.

**гьельмит** *m.* (min.) hielmite, hjelmite.

**Гэв** *abbr.* (гигаэлектрон-вольт) gigaelectron-volt (billion electron-volt).

**гэз** *m.* gaize (an argillaceous sandstone).

**г-экв** *abbr.* (грамм-эквивалент) gram-equivalent.

**гэлюссит** *see* **гейлюссит.**

**ГЭС** *abbr.* (гидроэлектростанция) hydroelectric power plant; (государственная электрическая станция) State power plant.

**ГЭТК** *abbr.* (гексаэтилтетрафосфат) hexaethyl tetraphosphate.

**ГЭЦ** *abbr.* (гидроэлектроцентраль) central hydroelectric power plant.

**Гюбля раствор** Hübl solution.

**гюбнерит** *m.* (min.) hübnerite, huebnerite (a manganese tungstate).

**гюгелит** *m.* (min.) hügelite.

**Гюйгенса принцип** (phys.) Huygens principle.

**Гюльднера генератор** Güldner producer.

**гюнцский век** (geol.) Gunzian stage.

# Д

**д** *abbr.* (деци—) deci—; Д code for copper in steel mark; Д. *abbr.* (доктор) Doctor.

**да** *adv.* yes; *conj.* but, and.

**дав/ание** *n.* giving, donation; —ать *v.* give, donate; afford, provide; yield, produce; let, allow; легко —аться *v.* come easily.

**давешний** *a.* recent.

**давидит** *m.* (min.) davidite (near ilmenite).

**давило** *n.* weight, press.

**давильн/ый** *a.* press, pressing; д. пресс stamp, stamping machine; winepress; —я *f.* winepress, press.

**давильщик** *m.* presser.

**давин** *m.* (min.) davyne (near microsommite).

**давить** *v.* press, squeeze; —ся *v.* choke.

**давка** *f.* press, crowd, crush, throng.

**давлен/ие** *n.* pressure; compression; stress; д. воздуха atmospheric pressure; air pressure; д. на поверхность surface pressure; котел высокого —ия high-pressure boiler; коэффициент —ия pressure ratio; линия —ия line of pressure; line of action (in gears); пар низкого —ия low-pressure steam; под —ием pressurized; смазка под —ием pressure lubrication; указатель —ия pressure gage; испарение под уменьшенным —ием reduced-pressure evaporation, vacuum evaporation.

**давн/ий, —ишний** *a.* ancient, old, long-established, of long standing; с —их пор for a long time.

**давно** *adv.* long ago, long before; д. тому назад long ago; —сть *f.* remoteness, oldness, antiquity; (law) prescription.

**давнуть** *see* **давить.**

**давший** *past act. part. of* **давать.**

**даг.** *abbr.* (дагестанский) Dagestan.

**дагенан** *m.* Dagenan, sulfapyridine.

**дагерротип** *m.*, —ный *a.* (phot.) daguerreotype; —ия *f.* daguerreotypy.

**дагинголовая кислота** dagingolic acid.

**дагусса** *f.* yard grass (*Eleusine indica*).

**дадил, —ь** *m.* dadyl (a component of turpentine).

**да/дут** *fut. 3 pl.*; —ет *pr. 3 sing. of* **давать.**

**даже** *adv.* even.

**дазиметр** *m.* dasymeter; —ический *a.* dasymetric, density-measuring.

**даивать** *see* **доить.**

**дайка** *f.* (geol.) dike.

**Дайнса анемограф** Dines anemograph.

**дайте** *imp. of* **давать.**

**дакеит** *m.* (min.) dakeite, schroekingerite.

**дакр/ен** *m.* dacrene; —иолин *m.* dacryolin.

**дактил/ический, —овый** *a.* dactylic; —ограмма *f.* dactylogram, fingerprint.

**дал** *past sing. of* **давать.**

**Даламбера принцип** (mech.) D'Alembert principle.

**далее** *comp. of* **далеко,** farther; и так д. et cetera, and so forth.

**далек/ий** *a.* distant, far, remote; д. от цели wide of the mark; —о *adv.* far, far off; by far, much.

**дали** *past pl. of* **давать.**

**далин** *m.* dahlin (dye); inulin, alant starch.

**далина** *see* **даль.**

**далит** *m.* (min.) dahllite (a variety of staffelite).

**далия** *f.* (bot.) dahlia.

**даль** *f.* distance, remoteness; **—невидение** *n.* television; **—нейший** *a.* further, ulterior; furthest, furthermost; **в —нейшем** in the future, later on, subsequently; below; **—непривозный** *a.* imported; **—ний** *a.* distant, far off, remote, long; (tel.) long-distance; cross-country (flying); **—ний порядок** (cryst.) long-range order; **—него действия** long-range.

**Дальний** *a.* Dalny, Dairen.

**дально—** *prefix* distance, tele—.

**дальнобойн/ость** *f.*, **—ый** *a.* long range; **—ое орудие** long-range gun.

**дальновид/ение** *n.*, **—ность** *f.* foresight, clear-sightedness; **—ный** *a.* far-sighted.

**дальнодейств/ие** *n.* remote control; **—ующий** *a.* remote-control; long-range.

**дальнозорк/ий** *a.* far-sighted, presby-opic; **—ость** *f.* far-sightedness; **старческая —ость** (med.) presbyopia.

**дально/измерение** *n.* telemetry, tele-metering; **—мер** *m.* telemeter; range finder; **—стный** *a.* distance, range.

**дальност/ь** *f.* distance, farness, remoteness; mileage; range, compass, radius; **д. действия, д. передачи, д. полета** range; **определение —и** (radar) ranging; **отклонение по —и** longitudinal deviation; **предельная д.** critical range, range limit.

**дальноуправляемый** *a.* remote-controlled.

**Дальтона закон** Dalton's law.

**дальтонизм** *m.* (med.) daltonism, color blindness.

**дальше** *сотр.* of **далеко, далекий,** further, farther; forward, onward, right on; beyond; **проходить д.** *v.* proceed, move on.

**даманн-асфальт** a mixture of sand, gravel, or slag with bitumen or tar.

**дамас/к** *m.*, **—кированная сталь, —ская сталь** damask steel, Damascus steel; **—кирование** *n.*, **—кировка** *f.* dam-asking; **—кированный** *a.* damasked; **—кировать** *v.* damask, damascene.

**дамасценин** *m.* damascenine; **—овая кислота** damasceninic acid.

**дамба** *f.* dam, dike, levee, jetty.

**дамбоза** *f.* dambose, *i*-inositol.

**даменит** *m.* (expl.) dahmenite.

**дамиана** *f.* damiana (leaves).

**даммар** *m.*, **—овая смола, —ская смола** dammar gum; **—иловая кислота** dammarylic acid; **—овый** *a.* dammar.

**дамурит** *m.* (min.) damourite (a hydrous form of muscovite); **—изация** *f.* damouritization.

**ДАН** *abbr.* (**Доклады Академии Наук**) Proceedings of the Academy of Science.

**данаин** *m.* danain.

**дана/ит** *m.* (min.) danaite (a variety of arsenopyrite); **—лит** *m.* danalite.

**данбурит** *m.* (min.) danburite.

**Даниеля элемент** (elec.) Daniell cell.

**Дания** Denmark.

**даннеморит** *m.* (min.) dannemorite.

**данник** *m.* tributary.

**данн/ое** *n.* datum, given or known quantity; ground, basis; **—ые** *pl.* data, facts; findings; **—ый** *a.* given, present, under consideration, in question.

**дантикул** *m.* dentil, indentation, notch.

**дантист** *m.* dentist.

**дань** *f.* tribute, contribution, tax; **обложить —ю** *v.* tax, impose a tax.

**ДАОС** *abbr.* (**Долгопрудная агрохимическая опытная станция имени Д. Н. Прянишникова**) Pryanishnikov Dolgoprudnaya Agrochemical Experiment Station.

**дар** *m.* gift, donation, grant.

**дарапскит** *m.* (min.) darapskite (a native sodium nitrate and sulfate).

**Дарвина теория** Darwin's theory.

**дарвин/изм** *m.* darwinism; **—истический, —овский** *a.* Darwinian.

**дар/ение** *n.* donation, presentation; **—еный** *a.* donated, presented; **—итель** *m.* donor, grantor; **—ить** *v.* donate, grant, give, present.

**дармин** *m.* darmin; **—ное масло** worm-seed oil.

**дармо/вой** *see* **даровой;** **—ед** *m.* parasite; **—едничать** *v.* be parasitic.

**даров/ание** *n.* donation, granting, conferring, gift, endowment; talent; —**анный** *a.* donated, granted, conferred; —**ать** *v.* donate, grant, give, confer.

**даровитый** *a.* gifted, clever, talented.

**даров/ой** *a.* free, gratuitous; —**щина,** —**щинка** *f.* present, gift, donation.

**даром** *adv.* free of charge, gratis; in vain, to no purpose; **д. что** although, though; **не д.** with reason; no wonder.

**Дарсе металл** D'Arcet metal (a bismuth-lead-tin alloy).

**дарси** *m.* darcy (unit of permeability).

**дарсонвализация** *f.* (med.) d'Arsonvalism, high-frequency electrical treatment; **д'Арсонваля ток** d'Arsonval current.

**дарственн/ый** *a.* donation; **д. акт** grant; —**ая запись** deed, settlement.

**даст** *fut. 3 sing. of* **давать.**

**дат.** *abbr.* (**датский**) Danish.

**дата** *f.* date.

**датель** *m.* giver, donator, donor.

**датиров/ание** *n.* dating, age determination; —**анный** *a.* dated; nominal (pressure); —**ать** *v.* date; —**очный** *a.* date, dating.

**датисц/етин** *m.* datiscetin; —**ин** *m.* datiscin.

**датолит** *m.* (min.) datolite.

**датск/ий** *a.* Danish; —**ие белила** Danish white (a finely ground chalk).

**датурин** *m.* daturine, hyoscyamine; —**овая кислота** daturic acid, margaric acid.

**датчик** *m.* pickup, pickup unit; (elec.) transducer; monitor, controller; sender, transmitter; generator; sensitive element; data unit; **д. вибраций** vibration pickup; **д. времени** timer; **д. температуры** temperature gage; **д.-измеритель** sensory element, pickup.

**дать** *see* **давать.**

**Дау элемент** Dow (electrolytic) cell.

**даукостерин** *m.* daucosterol.

**дау-металл** *m.* Dowmetal (a magnesium alloy).

**Даунса метод** Downs (electrolytic) process.

**даунтонский век** (geol.) Downtonian stage.

**даурицин** *m.* dauricine.

**Даусона газ** Dawson (producer) gas.

**даусонит** *m.* (min.) dawsonite (a basic carbonate of aluminum and sodium).

**дауцин** *m.* daucine.

**дауэкс** *m.* Dowex (ion-exchange resins).

**ДАФ** *abbr.* (**диаммонийфосфат**) diammonium phosphate.

**дафн/андрин** *m.* daphnandrine; —**етин** *m.* daphnetin, 7,8-dihydroxycoumarin; —**ин** *m.* daphnin; —**ит** *m.* (min.) daphnite (a variety of chlorite).

**дацит** *m.* dacite (an igneous rock); —**овый** *a.* dacitic.

**дач/а** *f.* giving, paying; (agr.) rate; plot, lot; summer house, resort; —**ный** *a.* resort.

**даю/т** *pr. 3 pl. of* **давать;** —**щий** *a.* giving; data.

**дб** *abbr.* (**децибел**) decibel.

**д.б.** *abbr.* (**должно быть**) probably.

**ДВ** *abbr.* (**длинные волны**) long waves; **Д.В.** *abbr.* (**Дальний Восток**) the Far East.

**два** two.

**двадцати/гранник** *m.* (cryst.) icosahedron; —**гранный** *a.* icosahedral; —**летие** *n.* twenty-year period; —**летний** *a.* twenty-year; —**четырехгранник** *m.* (cryst.) icositetrahedron.

**двадцат/ый** *a.* twentieth; —**ь** twenty.

**дважды** *adv.* twice, twofold.

**Двайт-Лойд** *see* **Дуайт.**

**двенадцати/гранник** *m.* (cryst.) dodecahedron; —**гранный** *a.* dodecahedral; —**перстная кишка** (anat.) duodenum; —**ричный** *a.* duodecimal; —**угольник** *m.* (geom.) dodecagon.

**двенадцат/ый** *a.* twelfth; —**ь** twelve.

**двер/ной** *a.* door, gate; **д. проем** doorway; —**ная створка** valve; —**ца** *f.* door, gate; —**цесниматель** *m.* door extractor (of coke oven); —**ь** *f.* door.

**двести** two hundred.

**двигание** *n.* moving, removing, stirring.

**двигатель** *m.* engine, motor; propeller, driver; impellent, motive power; —**ный** *a.* engine, motor; propellent, impellent, motive; —**ная сила** motive power, moving force, impetus, impulse; **источник** —**ной силы** prime mover.

**двиг/ать** *v.* move, set in motion, stir, slide, drive; —**аться** *v.* move, travel;

(mach.) run, work, operate; —**ающий**
*see* **движущий.**

**движен/ие** *n.* motion, movement, stir;
travel; traffic; **затор в** —**ии** traffic
congestion, traffic jam; **количество**
—**ия** momentum; **момент количества**
—**ия** angular momentum; **начало**
—**ия** start; **приводить в д.** start, set
in motion; **сила** —**ия** *see* **двигатель-
ная сила; скорость** —**ия** traveling
speed; **энергия** —**ия** kinetic energy.

**движет** *pr. 3 sing. of* **двигать.**

**движим/ость** *f.* mobility; movables, personal property; —**ый** *a.* movable,
mobile; moved, propelled, actuated.

**движитель** *see* **двигатель.**

**движок** *m.* slide, runner; arm (of
apparatus).

**движущ/ий** *a.* moving, motive, impellent, driving, propelling; operating
(mechanism); —**ая сила** driving
force, motive power, motive force;
momentum, impetus, impulse; —**ее
колесо** driving wheel; —**ийся** *a.*
moving, running, working, operating.

**двинут/ый** *a.* moved, set in motion; —**ь**
*see* **двигать.**

**двое** two; —**брачный** *a.* bigamous;
—**кратный** *a.* twofold, reiterated;
—**мыслие** *n.* ambiguity, indecision;
—**ние** *n.* dividing; rectification, distillation; second plowing; —**связ-
ность** *f.* double bond; —**тес** *m.*,
—**тесный гвоздь** two-inch nail, plank
nail; —**точие** *n.* colon.

**двоильн/ый** *a.* dividing; rectifying; —**ая
машина** (leather) splitting machine.

**дво/ить** *v.* double; divide in two; (chem.)
rectify, distil; (agr.) plow a second
time; —**ичный** *a.* binary; —**ичное
число** binary digit, bit; —**йка** *f.* pair,
two; second plowing.

**двойник** *m.* double, twin, counterpart,
duplicate; —**ование** *n.*, —**овое срастание** (cryst.) twinning; —**овый** *a.*
twin, duplicate, twinned; —**овый
кристалл** twin crystal, twin; —**овая
ось** twinning axis; —**овая плоскость**
twinning plane.

**двойничн/ик** *m.*, —**ый** *a.* twin.

**двойн/ой** *a.* double, twofold, duplex,
dual, binary; two-ply; di—, twin;
(bot.) geminate; —**ого действия**

double-acting; —**ое лучепреломление**
birefringence, double refraction; —**ое
соединение** binary compound; —**ое
управление** dual control; —**я** *f.* twins;
double, duplicate.

**двойственн/ость** *f.* duality, duplicity;
ambiguity; —**ый** *a.* dual, double;
ambiguous, non-committal.

**двойчат/ка** *f.* double kernel; —**ый** *a.*
double; (bot.) geminate.

**двор** *m.*, —**ной** *a.* yard, court; —**ник** *m.*
yard man.

**двояк/ий** *a.* double, twofold, duplex;
ambiguous; —**о** *adv.* doubly, in two
ways.

**двояко/вогнутый** *a.* concavo-concave,
biconcave, double concave; —**выпуклый** *a.* convexo-convex, biconvex,
double convex, lenticular; —**выпук-
лое стекло** lens; —**дышащие** *pl.*
(zool.) Dipnoi; —**преломляющий** *a.*
birefringent, double-refracting; —**сть**
*f.* doubleness, duplicity; ambiguous-
ness, ambiguity.

**ДВС** *abbr.* (**двигатель внутреннего сгорания**) internal combustion engine.

**дву**— *prefix* di—, bi—, two, double, *see
also* **двух**—; —**аммониевый** *a.* diammonium; —**атомный** *see* **двухатом-
ный;** —**борнокислая соль** diborate;
—**брюшная мышца** (anat.) digastric
muscle; —**валентность** *f.* bivalence;
—**валентный** *a.* bivalent; —**вариантный** *a.* bivariant; —**видный** *a.* dimorphous.

**двувинно/каменнокислая соль,** —**кислая соль** bitartrate; —**кислый калий**
potassium bitartrate.

**дву/водный гидрат** dihydrate; —**воль-
фрамовокислая соль** ditungstate;
—**главый** *a.* two-headed, double-
headed; —**гнездный** *a.* (bot.) bilocu-
lar; —**годовалый, годовой** *a.* two-
year, biennial; —**горбый** *a.* two-
humped; double-peaked (curve);
—**горлый** *a.* two-necked (bottle);
—**губый** *a.* (bot.) bilabiate; —**доль-
ные** *pl.* (bot.) dicotyledons; —**дольный** *a.* dicotyledonous; —**домный** *a.*
(bot.) diclinous; —**дужный** *a.* (zool.)
diapsid; —**жаберные** *pl.* (zool.) Di-
branchia, —**жаберный** *a.* dibranchi-
ate; —**женный** *a.* (bot.) digynous;

—жильный *a.* twin, twin-core (cable); —зернянка *see* эммер.

двузначн/ость *f.* ambiguity; —ый *a.* ambiguous; two-digit (number).

дву/зуб *m.*, —зубка *f.* diodont (fish); —карбоксильный, —карбоновый *a.* dicarboxylic; —кислотный *a.* diacid; —колка *f.* two-wheeled cart; —кольчатый *see* двухкольчатый; —копытный *a.* cloven-footed; —коробчатый *a.* (bot.) bicapsular; —красочный *a.* dichromatic; —кратный *a.* twofold, double, reiterated, two-stage; —кремнекислая соль disilicate.

двукрыл/ые *pl.* (zool.) Diptera; —ый *a.* dipterous, two-winged.

дву/летний *a.* (bot.) biennial; —линейный *a.* bilinear; —личный *a.* double-faced, hypocritical; —мерный *a.* two-dimensional; —мерная поверхность (cryst.) dimetric surface, tetragonal surface; —молекулярный *a.* bimolecular; —молочная кислота dilactic acid; —мужий *see* двутычинковый; —мускульный *a.* (zool.) dimyarian; —направленный *a.* bidirectional; —натриевый *a.* disodium; —нитный *a.* bifilar.

двуног/а *f.* bipod; —ий *a.* two-legged; —ое животное (zool.) biped.

двуокись *f.* dioxide; д. серы sulfur dioxide; д. углерода carbon dioxide.

дву/основный *a.* dibasic; diatomic, dihydric; —осность *f.* biaxiality; —осный *a.* biaxial; —палый *a.* (zool.) didactylous.

двупарно/ногие *pl.* (zool.) Diplopoda, Chilognatha; —усые *pl.* Teleiocereta.

дву/пламенный *a.* double-flame; —плечий *a.* double-arm (lever); —полый *a.* bisexual; —полье *n.* two-field rotation of crops; —полюсный *see* двухполюсный.

двупреломл/ение *n.* (cryst.) birefringence, double refraction; —яющий *a.* double-refracting.

двурезцов/ые *pl.* (zool.) Diprotodontia; —ый *a.* diprotodont.

дву/рядный *see* двухрядный; —салициловая кислота disalicylic acid.

двусерн/ая кислота disulfuric acid, pyrosulfuric acid; —истокислая соль bisulfite; —истокислый натрий, —и-стонатриевая соль sodium bisulfite; —истый *a.* disulfide (of); —окислая соль bisulfate; —окислый натрий, —онатриевая соль sodium bisulfate.

дву/сеточный *a.* double-grid; —скатный *a.* with two sloping surfaces; gable (roof); —слойные *pl.* (zool.) Diploblastica; —слойный *a.* diploblastic; two-ply, two-layer.

двусмысленн/ость *f.* ambiguity; —ый *a.* ambiguous, equivocal, doubtful, obscure.

двуствол/ка *f.*, —ьное ружье double-barreled gun.

двустворчат/ые *pl.* (zool.) Bivalvia; —ый *a.* bivalve, bivalvular; double-wing; —ый клапан wing valve.

двустенный *see* двухстенный.

двусторонн/ий *a.* bilateral, double-sided, reversible, two-way; duplex; double-pointed, double-ended; dual (control); amphoteric (oxide); —ее весло paddle.

дву/ступенчатый *a.* double-stage, two-stage, two-step; —тавровая балка I-beam, H-beam; —тычинковый, —тычиночный *a.* (bot.) diandrous.

двуугле/калиевая соль potassium bicarbonate; —кислый *a.* bicarbonate (of); —кислый натр, —кислая сода, —натриевая соль sodium bicarbonate; —кислая соль bicarbonate.

дву/уксуснокислая соль diacetate; —урановокислая соль diuranate; —урановокислый натрий, —урановонатриевая соль sodium diuranate; —устка *f.* fluke (parasitic worm); —утробка *f.* (zool.) marsupial; —ухий *a.* double-ear (phone).

двух— prefix bi—, di—, two, double; *see also* дву—; —атомный *a.* diatomic, bivalent; dihydric (alcohol); —боевой *a.* duplex, double-faced (hammer); —бороздчатый *a.* double-groove, double-furrow.

двухвалковый *a.* two-roll, two-high (rolling mill); д. прокатный стан, д. стан two-high rolling mill, duo mill.

двух/вариантный *a.* bivariant; —видовый *a.* two-mode; —витковый *a* double-coil, double-turn; two-loop.

двухвостки *pl.* (zool.) Diplura.

двух/годичный *a.* two-year, biennial; —гранный *a.* (geom.) dihedral; two-surfaced, bounded by two surfaces; —групповой *a.* two-group; —диапазонный *a.* dual-range; —дневный *a.* two-day; —желобчатый *a.* double-groove, double-grooved; —жидкостный *a.* double-fluid; double-solvent (extraction); —жильный *see* двужильный;—замещенные *pl.* disubstitution products, di-derivatives; —замещенный фосфат кальция dicalcium phosphate; —заходная резьба double (screw) thread; —зональный *a.* two-region.

двух/камерная печь double-chamber furnace; —колейный *a.* double-track; —коленчатый *a.* double-knee, double-throw; —кольчатый *a.* dicyclic; binuclear; —конечный *a.* double-end, double-pointed; —контактный *a.* double-contact; double-prong (plug); —контурный *a.* two-circuit;—копытный *see* двукопытный; —кулачковый *a.* (mech.) double-jawed.

двух/лемешный *a.* double-furrow (plow); —ленточный *a.* double-strand, two-strand; —летний *a.* two-year; (bot.) biennial; —лобный *see* двухбоевой.

двухлористый *a.* dichloride (of).

двух/лучевой *a.* two-beam, double-beam; —мерный *a.* two-dimensional; —местный *a.* two-seater (plane, automobile); —месячный *a.* two-month, bimonthly; —минеральная порода binary rock; —ниточная резьба, —оборотная резьба double (screw) thread; —одовой *see* двухходовой.

двух/опорный *a.* double-seat, double-beat (valve); —основный *a.* dibasic; —палубный *a.* double-deck; —позиционный, —положенный *a.* two-position; —полосный *a.* double-band; —полупериодный *a.* full-wave (rectifier); —полюсный *a.* (elec.) bipolar, double-pole, two-pole; —поставный *a.* double-blade (saw frame); —поточный *a.* double-flow; —проводный *a.* double (line), double-wire, two-wire; —проходной *a.* two-way.

двух/путевой, —путный *a.* double-track; two-way; —раздельный *a.* two-part; —резцовый *a.* duplex

(lathe); —рельсовый *a.* double-track; double-rail.

двухромово/калиевая соль, —кислый калий potassium bichromate; —кислая соль bichromate; —кислый натрий, —натриевая соль sodium bichromate.

двух/рядный *a.* double, double-row, two-series; —сотый *a.* two-hundredth; —срезный *a.* double-shear; —станинный *a.* double-sided, double-standard; —створчатый *see* двустворчатый; —стенный *a.* double-walled; —стоечный *see* двухстанинный; —сторонний *a.* two-way; —стрендовая веревка double-strand rope; —ступенчатый *see* двуступенчатый; —тактный *a.* two-stroke, two-cycle (engine); push-pull; —тарифный метр (elec.) double-rate meter, two-rate meter; —томный *a.* two-volume (book); —ударный *a.* (radiobiology) double-hit; —фазный *a.* two-phase, diphase; —фокусный *a.* bifocal; —хлористый *see* двухлористый; —ходовой *a.* two-way; two-pass (furnace); double-thread (screw).

двухцветни/ость *f.* dichroism, dichromatism; —ый *a.* dichroic, dichromatic.

двух/целевой *a.* dual-purpose; —цепной *a.* double-chain, twin-chain; (elec.) double-circuit; —цилиндровый *a.* two-cylinder; double-barreled; —частичный *a.* two-body (force); —шарнирный *a.* double-hinged, double-jointed; —шкальный *a.* two-scale; double-dial; —шпиндельный *a.* duplex; —ъядерный *a.* binuclear; —ъярусный, —этажный *a.* two-story, double-deck, double-level; —электродный *a.* two-electrode (tube).

двуцветный *see* двухцветный.

двучлен *m.*, —ный *a.* (math.) binomial.

дг *abbr.* (дециграмм) decigram.

ДД *abbr.* (дихлорпропандихлорпропилен) dichloropropane-dichloropropylene mixture; ДДД *abbr.* (дефицит давления диффузии) diffusion pressure deficit; ДДТ *abbr.* (дихлордифенилтрихлорэтан) dichlorodiphenyltrichloroethane, DDT.

де— *prefix* de—, des—, *see also* дез—.

деазот/изация *f.*, —ирование *n.* denitration, denitriding; —ированный *a.* denitrated; —ировать *v.* denitrate, denitride.

дейсер *m.* (aero.) deicer.

деактивация *see* дезактивирование.

деаэр/атор *m.* deaerator; —ация *f.* deaeration; —изационный *a.* deaeration, deaerating; —ированный *a.* deaerated; —ировать *v.* deaerate.

дебае/вский *a.*, Дебай Debye; —грамма *f.* Debye powder pattern, X-ray powder diagram.

дебаркадер *m.* platform, landing.

дебат/ировать *v.* debate, discuss, argue; —ы *pl.* debate, dispute, argument.

Дебая-Гюккеля уравнение Debye and Hückel equation; Д.-Шеррера метод (cryst.) Debye and Scherrer method.

дебелый *a.* fleshy, corpulent.

дебензине *n.* a debenzened oil.

Деберейнера триады Döbereiner's rule of triads.

дебет *m.* (com.) debit.

дебильность *f.* moderate congenital retardation.

дебит *m.* yield, output; discharge, flow (of a river).

дебитор *m.* debtor.

деблокир/ование *n.*, —овка *f.* clearing, releasing; —ованный *a.* cleared, released, relieved; —овать *v.* clear, release, relieve; —ующий *a.* releasing.

дебнеровский фиолетовый Döbner's violet.

дебри *n.* jungle, thicket; maze; —стый *a.* full of thick forests.

де-Бройля соотношение (phys.) de Broglie relation.

девальвация *f.* devaluation, depreciation.

Деваля испытание Deval (attrition) test.

Деварда сплав Devarda's alloy (a copper-aluminum-zinc alloy).

девастация *f.* extermination of sources of infection.

девать *v.* put, dispose (of).

девейлит *m.* (min.) deweylite (near serpentine).

Деви лампа (min.) Davy lamp, davy.

девиация *f.* deviation.

девиз *m.*, —ный *a.* motto, device, emblem.

девиндтит *m.* dewindtite (a uranium mineral).

девиометр *m.* deviometer.

Девиса печь (met.) Davis furnace.

девитри/т *m.* devitrite (a sodium calcium silicate); —фикация *f.* devitrification.

девич/ий *a.* virgin, maiden; —ья кожа (pharm.) althea paste; белая —ья кожа gum paste; коричневая —ья кожа licorice root paste.

девон *m.*, —ский период (geol.) Devonian period.

девственн/ый *a.* virgin, maiden; primeval; parthen—, partheno—; —ое размножение (biol.) parthenogenesis.

девулканизация *f.* devulcanization.

девяност/о ninety; —ый *a.* ninetieth.

девясил *m.* (bot.) elecampane (*Inula*).

девятер/ичный *a.* nonary; —ной *a.* ninefold.

девяти/десятый *a.* ninetieth; —кратный *a.* ninefold; —сотый *a.* nine-hundredth; —угольник *m.* (geom.) nonagon.

девят/ка nine; —надцатый *a.* nineteenth; —надцать nineteen; —ый *a.* ninth; —ь nine; —ьсот nine hundred.

дегаз/ационный *a.*, —ация *f.* degasification, degassing; decontaminating; (vacuum system) outgassing; —ер, —ификатор *m.* degasifier, degasser; —ированный *a.* degasified, degassed; —ировать *v.* degasify.

дегатировать *see* декатировать.

дегельминтизация *f.* (vet.) worming.

дегенер/ат *m.* degenerate; —ативность *f.* degeneracy; —ативный *a.* degenerate; —ация *f.* degeneration; —ированный *a.* degenerated, degenerate, vestigial; —ировать *v.* degenerate.

дегерминатор *m.* (agr.) degerminator.

дегидраза *f.* dehydrase, dehydrogenase.

дегидрат/ация *f.*, —ационный *a.* dehydration; —ировать *v.* dehydrate; —ирующее вещество dehydrating agent, dehydrator, dehydrant; —ор *m.* dehydrator.

дегидрацетовая кислота dehydracetic acid, methyl acetopyronone.

дегидрация *see* дегидратация.

**дегидрир/ование** *n.* dehydrogenation; **—ованный** *a.* dehydrogenated; **—о-вать** *v.* dehydrogenate, dehydrogenize; **—ующий** *a.* dehydrogenating.

**дегидро—** *prefix* dehydro—.

**дегидрогениз/ация** *f.*, **—ационный** *a.* dehydrogenation; **—овать** *v.* dehydrogenate.

**дегидрокси—** *prefix* dehydroxy—.

**дегидро/слизевая кислота** dehydromucic acid, 2,5-furandicarboxylic acid; **—тиотолуидин** *m.* dehydrothiotoluidine; **—холевая кислота** dehydrocholic acid; **—циклизация** *f.* dehydrocyclization.

**дегоржировать** *v.* disgorge.

**деготь** *m.* tar, pitch; **каменноугольный д.**, **коксовый д.** coal tar.

**дегра** *f.* (leather) degras, wool fat.

**деград/ация** *f.* degradation, deterioration; **—ировать** *v.* deteriorate, degenerate.

**дегте/картон** *m.* tar paper; **—образный** *a.* tarry, tar-like; **—отделитель** *m.* tar separator.

**дегтярн/ый** *a.* tar, tarry; **—ая вода** (pharm.) tar water; tar water, specif. (gas) ammoniacal liquor; **—ое масло** tar oil; carbonization tar oil, esp. from lignite; **—я** *f.* tar works.

**дегуммировать** *v.* degum.

**дегустатор** *m.* taster.

**дедвейт** *m.* dead weight, dead load.

**дедекиндово сечение** (math.) Dedekind cut.

**деду/ктивный** *a.* deductive; **—кция** *f.* deduction; **—цировать** *v.* deduce.

**дееспособн/ость** *f.* competence; **—ый** *a.* competent.

**дежа** *f.* pan trough.

**дежекци/я** *f.*, **—онный** *a.* dejection.

**дежур/ить** *v.* be on duty; **—ный** *a.* on duty; *m.* attendant; **—ный журнал** log; **—ный машинист** shift engineer; **—ство** *n.* being on duty, attendance; **с —ством on** duty.

**дез—** *prefix* des—, de—; dis—; **—авуировать** *v.* repudiate, disavow; **—агрегация** *f.* disaggregation, disintegration.

**дезактив/ационный** *a.*, **—ация** *f.*, **—ирование** *n.* deactivation; (nucl.) decontamination; **—ированный** *a.* deactivated; decontaminated; **—ировать**

*v.* deactivate; decontaminate; **—ирующий агент** decontaminating agent, decontaminant.

**дезами/дизация** *f.* deamidization; **—нирование** *n.* deamination.

**дезил** *m.* desyl.

**дезинсек/тор** *m.* insect-exterminating unit; **—ционный** *a.*, **—ция** *f.* disinfestation, extermination of insects.

**дезинтегр/атор** *m.* disintegrator, pulverizer; dust extractor (for gases); **—ация** *f.* disintegration; **—ированный** *a.* disintegrated; **—ировать** *v.* disintegrate.

**дезинфек/тант** *m.*, **—ционное средство** disinfectant; **—тор** *m.* disinfector; **—ционный** *a.* disinfection, disinfecting, disinfectant; **—ция** *f.* disinfection.

**дезинфицир/овать** *v.* disinfect; **—ующий** *a.* disinfecting, disinfectant; **—ующее вещество**, **—ующее средство** disinfectant.

**дезодор/атор** *m.* deodorizer, deodorant; **—ация** *f.*, **—изация** *f.*, **—ирование** *n.* deodorization; **—ированный** *a.* deodorized; **—ировать** *v.* deodorize.

**дезоксалевая кислота** desoxalic acid.

**дезокси—** *prefix* desoxy—; **—бензоин** *m.* desoxybenzoin, phenylbenzyl ketone; **—дация** *f.* deoxidation, reduction; **—соединение** *n.* desoxy compound; **—холевая кислота** desoxycholic acid.

**дезорбция** *see* десорбция.

**дезорганиз/ация** *f.* disorganization, confusion, disorder, chaos; **—ованный** *a.* disorganized, confused, chaotic; **—овать**, **—овывать** *v.* disorganize.

**дезориентация** *f.* disorientation.

**деионизация** *f.* deionization.

**дейка** *see* дайка.

**действенн/ость** *f.* efficiency, effectiveness; **—ый** *a.* efficient, effective, operative.

**действ/ие** *n.* action, work, working, operation, performance, functioning, running (of machine), service; agency, effect, influence, efficacy; treatment, reaction; **—ием** by the action (of), by means (of); **интенсивность —ия, сила —ия** effective force, working power, efficiency; **коэффициент полезного —ия** efficiency; **оказывать д.** *v.* work, operate, take effect; **поле —ия** domain, field of action; **приведенный в д.** started, actuated; **приводить в д.** *v.* start, work, operate, actuate; **прямого —ия** direct-action; **способ —ия** mode of operation; kind of action; **химическое д.** chemical reaction.

**действительн/о** *adv.* actually, in fact, indeed, in reality; **—ость** *f.* reality, actuality, fact; efficiency, effectiveness, practicality; validity; operation; **в —ости** in reality, in fact; **—ый** *a.* real, true, actual, virtual; effective, efficient; valid; net (price); **—ая отдача** practical efficiency; **—ая производительность** effective capacity; **делать —ым** *v.* validate.

**действ/овать** *v.* act, operate, work, run, function, proceed; attack, react, treat; affect; **начать д.** take effect, start; **не д.** fail, be out of order; **—ующий** *a.* active, acting, actuating, working, at work; efficient, effective; virtual; in gear; *m.* operator; **—ующая сила** effective force, working power, efficiency; **—ующая среда** agent; **—ующее значение** virtual value; **—ующее начало** active principle; **—ующее поле** field of action; **закон —ующих масс** law of mass action, mass law, law of chemical kinetics.

**Дейстера стол** (min.) Deister (concentration) table.

**дейтер/ид** *m.* deuteride; **—иевый** *a.*, **—ий** *m.* deuterium, D (heavy hydrogen); **—изованный** *a.* deuterium; deuterated; **—изовать, —ировать** *v.* deuterate; **—о—** *prefix* deutero— (second, secondary; deuterium); **—генный** *a.* (geol.) deuterogenic; **—н** *see* **дейтрон**; **—оокись** *f.* deuterium oxide, heavy water; **—плазма** *f.* (biol.) deuteroplasm.

**дейт/он, —рон** *m.*, **—ронный** *a.* deuteron (deuterium nucleus).

**дейция** *f.* (bot.) deutzia.

**дек** *m.*, **—а** *f.* deck; **—а** *f.* sound board, sounding board (of musical instrument).

**дека—** *prefix* deca—, ten.

**декабрь** *m.* December.

**дека/гидронафталин** *m.* decahydronaphthalene, decalin; **—гон** *m.* (geom.) decagon; **—грамм** *m.* decagram; **—да** *f.* decade.

**декаден/т** *m.*, **—ский, —тский** *a.* decadent; **—ство, —тство** *n.* decadence.

**декадный** *a.* decade; decimal.

**декалесценция** *f.* (met.) decalescence.

**декалин** *m.* decalin.

**декалитр** *m.* decaliter (10 liters).

**декалькомания** *f.* (printing) decalcomania.

**декальцифи/кация** *f.* decalcification; **—ровать** *v.* decalcify.

**декаметр** *m.* decameter (10 meters).

**декан** *m.* dean; (chem.) decane; **—ал** *m.* decanal, decyl aldehyde; **—ол** *m.* decanol, decyl alcohol; **—он** *m.* decanone.

**декант/атор** *m.* settling basin; **—ация** *f.*, **—ирование** *n.* decantation; **—ированный** *a.* decanted, poured off; **—ировать** *v.* decant, pour off.

**декапиров/ание** *n.*, **—ка** *f.* (met.) dip, pickle, pickling, scouring; passivation; **—ать** *v.* dip, pickle, scour, clean.

**декаподная среда** *m.* decapod.

**декарбоксилиров/ание** *n.* decarboxylizing; **—ать** *v.* decarboxylize.

**декарбонизация** *f.* decarbonization.

**декартовый** *a.* (math.) Cartesian (Descartes).

**декатил** *m.* decatyl, decyl.

**декатиров/ание** *n.*, **—ка** *f.* (text.) decatizing, steaming; **—ать** *v.* decatize.

**декатонна** *f.* ten tons.

**декаэдр** *m.* (cryst.) decahedron; **—ический** *a.* decahedral.

**декларация** *f.* declaration.

**деклин/атор, —ометр** *m.* (phys.) declination compass; declinometer; **—ация** *f.* declination; magnetic declination.

**деклуазит** *m.* (min.) descloizite.

**дековый** *a.* deck.

**декогер/ер** *m.* (rad.) decoherer; **—ировать** *v.* decohere.

**декодировать** *v.* decode.

**декокт** *m.* decoction.

**деколориметр** *m.* (sugar) decolorimeter.

**декомпресс/ия** *f.* decompression; **—ор** *m.* decompressor.

**декор/ативный, —ационный** *a.* decorative, ornamental; **—ация** *f.,* **—ирование** *n.* decoration; **—ировать** *v.* decorate.

**декортик/атор** *m.,* **—ационная машина** decorticator, stripping machine; **—ация** *f.* decortication, stripping.

**декохерер** *see* **декогерер.**

**декре/мент** *m.* decrement, decrease; **—метр** *m.* decremeter.

**декрет** *m.* decree, statute.

**дексель** *m.* adz.

**декстр/ан** *m.* dextran; **—ин** *m.,* **—иновый** *a.* dextrin, starch gum.

**декстро—** *prefix* dextro— (to the right, clockwise); **—за** *f.* dextrose, $d$-glucose; **—соединение** *n.* dextro compound, dextrorotatory compound.

**дел** *past sing. of* **девать, делать.**

**дел.** *abbr.* (**деление**) division, fission.

**делан/ие** *n.* making, doing; **—ный** *a.* made, done; studied, affected, simulated.

**делатинит** *m.* (min.) delatynite (a fossil resin).

**делать** *v.* make, do, produce; render, cause; **—ся** *v.* be made, be done; become, get, grow, turn; happen.

**делафоссит** *m.* (min.) delafossite.

**делациллин** *m.* Delacillin, penicillin sodium.

**делег/ат** *m.* delegate; **—ация** *f.,* **—ирование** *n.* delegation; **—ировать** *v.* delegate, authorize.

**дележ** *m.,* **—ка** *f.,* **—ный** *a.* share, sharing.

**делен/ие** *n.* division, partition, graduation; dividing, splitting, sharing; indexing; dial; unit, interval; (biol., nucl.) fission; **наносить —ия** *v.* divide, subdivide, graduate; index; **осколки —ия** fission fragments; **продукт —ия** fission product; **размножение —ием** (biol.) fission; **—ный** *a.* divided, split; indexed.

**делессит** *m.* (min.) delessite (a variety of chlorite).

**делеция** *f.* deletion.

**—делие** *n. suffix* industry; manufacture, making.

**деликатн/о** *adv.* delicately, cautiously, carefully, precisely; **—ость** *f.* delicacy, carefulness, precision; **—ый** *a.*

delicate, considerate; cautious, careful, precise.

**делим/ое** *n.* (math.) dividend; **—ость** *f.* divisibility; (cryst.) cleavability, cleavage; (nucl.) fissionability; (petr.) fissility; **—ый** *a.* divisible; cleavable; fissionable.

**делинт/ер** *m.* delinter, lint extractor; **—еровка** *f.,* **—еровочный** *a.* delinting; defibrating; **—ировать** *v.* delint.

**делирий** *m.* (med.) delirium.

**делитель** *m.* (math.) divisor, denominator; divider, separator; **д. на 16** scale of sixteen; **общий наибольший д.** greatest common divisor; **—ность** *f.* divisibility.

**делительн/ый** *a.* dividing, separating; index, indexing; (nucl.) fission; **д. диск, д. круг** index dial; **д. инструмент, —ая головка, —ое приспособление** indexing head, spacing attachment; graduator; **д. кран** separatory stopcock; **—ая воронка** separatory funnel; **—ая машина** graduating machine.

**делить** *v.* divide, share, apportion, part; cleave, split; **—ся** *v.* be divided; cleave, split; share.

**дел/о** *n.* business, transaction, deal, concern, matter, thing, point; enterprise; occupation; work, act, deed; (law) case; (mil.) engagement; **—а** *pl.* business, things, affairs, doings, occasions, proceedings; **д. в том, что** the fact is, the point is; **в самом —е** really, in truth, actually; **вести д.** *v.* supervise, manage; **иметь д.** *v.* deal (with); **к —у** to the point, directly; **между —ом** in one's spare time, at odd moments; **на самом —е** as a matter of fact, actually; **первым —ом** first of all; **по —у** on business.

**делов/итость** *f.* business ability; **—итый** *a.* business-like; **—ой** *a.* business, business-like, skilled.

**делокановая кислота** delocanic acid.

**делопроизвод/итель** *m.* secretary, clerk; **—ство** *n.* business correspondence.

**делоренцит** *m.* (min.) delorenzite.

**дельвоксит** *m.* (min.) delvauxite (possibly a hydrated dufrenite).

**дельн/о** *adv.* capably, sensibly; **—ость** *f.* capability, sense, cleverness; **—ый**

*a.* capable, sensible, clever; (met.) raw.

**дельсемин** *m.* delsemine.

**дельт/а** *f.* delta (Δ, δ); delta (of river); **д.-железо** delta iron; **д.-излучение** *n.* delta radiation; **д.-лучи** *pl.* delta rays; **д.-металл, —оин** *m.* delta metal; **—овидный, —овый** *a.* deltoid; **—оиддодекаэдр, —оэдр** *m.* (cryst.) deltoid dodecahedron, deltohedron.

**дельтруксиновая кислота** deltruxinic acid.

**дельфизин** *m.* delphisine.

**дельфин** *m.* (zool.) dolphin.

**дельфин/ат** *m.* delphinate; **—идин** *m.* delphinidin; **—ин** *m.* delphinin (glucoside); delphinine (alkaloid); **—ит** *m.* (min.)delphinite (a variety of epidote); **—иум** *m.* (bot.) delphinium; **—овая кислота** delphinic acid; **соль —овой кислоты, —овокислая соль** delphinate; **—оидин** *m.* delphinoidine.

**дельфокурарин** *m.* delphocurarine.

**дельфтский фаянс** (cer.) delft.

**делюв/иальные отложения, —ий** *m.* talus, rock slide.

**делянка** *f.* allotment, plot (of land).

**делячество** *n.* utilitarian attitude.

**делящийся** *pres. act. part. of* делиться; fissionable.

**демагнетизатор** *m.* demagnetizer.

**демантоид** *m.* (min.) demantoid (a variety of andradite garnet).

**демаркац/ия** *f.*, **—ионный** *a.* demarcation; **—ионная линия** line of demarcation, dividing line.

**деменция** *f.* (med.) dementia.

**демерейдж** *see* демураж.

**демерол** *m.* demerol, meperidine.

**деметилирование** *n.* demethylation.

**деметон** *see* меркаптофос.

**демидовит** *m.* (min.) demidovite (a variety of chrysocolla).

**деминерализовать** *v.* demineralize.

**демиссин** *m.* demissine.

**демобилиз/ация** *f.* demobilization; fixation (of nutrients, etc.); **—ировать** *v.* demobilize.

**демодул/ировать** *v.* (rad.) demodulate; **—яция** *f.* demodulation.

**демонстр/ант** *m.* demonstrator; **—ативно** *adv.* demonstratively, with demonstration; **—ативный** *a.* demonstra-tive; **—атор** *m.* demonstrator, exponent; **—ационный** *a.* demonstration, demonstrating; **—ационный склад** showroom, exhibit; **—ация** *f.*, **—ирование** *n.* demonstration; **—ированный** *a.* demonstrated; **—ировать** *v.* demonstrate.

**демонт/аж** *m.*, **—ирование** *n.* dismounting, dismantling, stripping; **—ировать** *v.* dismount, dismantle, take to pieces, take apart, take down, strip.

**демпинг** *m.* (com.) dumping.

**демпфер** *m.* damper, shock absorber, buffer; (elec.) damper, damper winding; **—ная цепь** (elec.) damping circuit.

**демпфиров/ание** *n.* damping, shock absorption, buffer action; **—анный** *a.* damped; **—ать** *v.* damp.

**демпфирующий** *a.* damping.

**демультипликатор** *m.* (mach.) a supplementary gear box; reducing gear.

**демураж** *m.* demurrage (of ship).

**денатур/ализация** *f.* denaturalization; **—ализировать** *v.* denaturalize; **—ант, —атор** *m.*, **—ирующее средство** denaturant, denaturing agent; **—ат** *m.* denatured alcohol; **—ация** *f.*, **—ирование** *n.* denaturing; **—ированный** *a.* denatured; **—ировать** *v.* denature.

**дендироль** *m.* (paper) dandy roll.

**дендрит** *m.* (cryst.) dendrite; **—ный, —овый** *a.* dendritic, tree-like, arborescent; **—ное строение** dendritic structure.

**дендро/идный** *a.* dendroid, dendritic; **—лит** *m.* dendrolite (fossil plant); **—метр** *m.* dendrometer (for measuring trees).

**денежн/ик** *m.* (bot.) pennycress (*Thlaspi arvense*); **—ый** *a.* monetary; money (order); **—ый знак** paper money, paper bill; **—ая повинность** tax, duty.

**денет** *fut. 3 sing. of* девать.

**дензиметр** *see* денсиметр.

**дензнак** *see* денежный знак.

**денитр/ация** *f.*, **—ирование** *n.*, **—ование** *n.* denitration; **—ировать, —овать** *v.* denitrate; **—ификация** *f.* denitrification; **—ифицирующий** *a.* denitrifying; **—ующий** *a.* denitrating.

Деннштедта печь Dennstedt furnace (for analysis).

денси/метр *m.* densimeter, hydrometer; —тометр *m.* (phot.) densitometer.

дент/алий, —альный *a.* dental; —ин *m.* dentine (of teeth).

денудация *f.* (geol.) denudation, erosion.

денут *fut. 3 pl. of* девать.

Деннштедта печь *see* Деннштедта печь.

день *m.* day.

деньги *pl.* money, currency; dues; бумажные д. bank notes, bills, paper money; наличные д. cash.

денье *n.*, д.-титр (text.) denier.

депарафинизация *f.* deparaffination.

департамент *m.* department, division; —ский *a.* departmental.

депеграмма *f.* (meteor.) depegram.

депеша *f.* dispatch, message, telegram.

депиля/торий *m.* depilatory; —ция *f.* depilation.

депланировать *v.* smooth, make even.

депо *n.* depot, station; warehouse.

депозит *m.* deposit.

деполимериз/ация *f.* depolymerization; —овать *v.* depolymerize.

деполяриз/атор *m.* depolarizer; —ация *f.* depolarization; —овать *v.* depolarize.

депонировать *v.* deposit.

депортация *f.* deportation.

депресс/ант, —ор *m.* (min.) depressor, depressing agent; (oils) pour-point depressant; —иометр *m.* depression meter; —ионный *a.* depression, depressor; —ия *f.* depression, lowering.

депс/анон *m.* depsanone, 1,2-dihydrodepsenone; —енон *m.* depsenone, 4-benzoylbenzofuran; —ид *m.* depside.

депутат *m.* representative, delegate.

дерапаж *m.* skidding, slipping.

дератизация *f.* rat (and mouse) extermination.

дербенник *m.* (bot.) loosestrife (*Lythrum*); —овые *pl.* Lythraceae.

дербилит *m.* (min.) derbylite (an antimotitanate of iron).

дерг/ание, —анье *n.* twitching, pulling; —анный *a.* twitched, jerked, pulled; —ать *v.* twitch, jerk, pull, tug.

деревей *m.* (bot.) yarrow, milfoil (*Achillea millifolium*).

деревен/ение *n.* lignification; —еть *v.* lignify, become wood.

дерев/енский *a.* rural, country; —ня *f.* village; country.

дерево *n.* tree; wood; д.-камень petrified wood; —обделочная *f.* wood-working shop; —обделочный, —обрабатывающий *a.* wood-working.

деревцо *n.* sapling, small tree.

деревяжка *see* деревяшка.

деревян/еть *v.* lignify, become wood; —истый *a.* ligneous, woody; —истый опал (min.) wood opal, opalized wood; —ка *f.* (bot.) tormentilla; —ность *f.* woodiness; —ный *a.* wooden, wood; woody, ligneous; *see also* древесный; —ое масло low-grade olive oil.

деревяшка *f.* stump, piece of wood.

дер/еза *f.* (bot.) lyceum; —ен *m.* dogwood (*Cornus*); —енные *pl.* Cornaceae.

дерет *pr. 3 sing. of* драть.

держава *f.* state, empire, dominion, power; orb, globe, mound.

державка *f.* holder, hold, stand, support, carrier, bracket.

держав/ный *a.* potent, powerful, reigning; —ствовать *v.* reign, rule.

держан/ие *n.* keeping, maintaining, holding, preserving; —ный *a.* kept, maintained, held; —ый *a.* secondhand, used.

держ/атель *m.* holder, adapter, chuck; *see also* державка; —ать *v.* keep, hold, retain; take (examination); —аться *v.* keep to, hold (on), cling, adhere; hold out, hold up, bear up; behave; —ащий *a.* holding; —и-дерево *n.* (bot.) Christ's thorn (*Paliurus*).

дерз/ать, —нуть *v.* dare, presume; risk, hazard; —кий *a.* daring, audacious.

дерив/ат *m.* derivative; —ация *f.* derivation, origin, source; drawing off (from main stream); (ballistics) lateral deviation, drift.

дерик *see* деррик.

дерм/а *f.* (anat.) derma, dermis; *suffix* —derm, —dermis; —альный, —ический *a.* dermal, dermic, cutaneous; —атин *m.* a leatherette; —атит *m.* (med.) dermatitis; —ато— *prefix* dermato— (skin, hide); —атол *m.* dermatol, bismuth subgallate;

—атолог *m.* dermatologist; —атология *f.* dermatology; —атомикоз *m.* (med.) dermatomycosis.

дермол *m.* dermol, bismuth chrysophanate.

дерн *m.* turf, sod, peat; —ина *f.* sod; individual plant in turf; —истость *f.* turfiness; —истый *a.* turfy, soddy.

дернить *v.* depilate.

дерно/во— *prefix,* —вый *a.* turf, sod; soddy (soil); —вый торф peat sod; —вая руда (min.) meadow ore, bog iron ore; —рез *m.* sod-breaking plow; —резка *f.* turf cutter, grass cutter; —сним *m.* (agr.) skim coulter.

дернут/ый *see* дерганный; —ь *see* дергать.

деррид *m.* derrid (a resin).

деррик *m.* derrick; д.-вышка derrick (for drilling); д.-кран derrick crane, derrick; вагон-д. derrick car.

деррис *m.* derris (insecticide).

Дерсита сплав *see* Дарсе металл.

деру/т *pr. 3 pl.;* —щий *pr. act. part. of* драть.

дерю/га *f.,* —жина *f.,* —жный *a.* sacking, sack cloth.

дес. *abbr.* (десятина) a unit of area.

десант *m.,* —ный *a.* descent, landing.

десерт *m.,* —ный *a.* dessert.

десили/кация *f.* desiliconization; —цировать *v.* desiliconize.

десквамация *f.* desquamation, scaling, peeling, exfoliation.

десмидиевые *pl.* Desmidiaceae (algae).

десмин *m.* (min.) desmine, stilbite.

десмо— *prefix* desmo— (bond, ligament).

десмотроп *m.* desmotrope; —ия *f.* desmotropism, dynamic isomerism; —ный *a.* desmotropic.

десна *f.* (anat.) gum.

десорбция *f.* desorption.

дестабилизирующий *a.* disturbing.

дестевой *a.* quire.

дестиллировать *see* дистиллировать.

дестрибютор *m.* distributor.

дестрикт/иновая кислота destrictinic acid; —овая кислота destrictic acid.

деструин *m.* destruin.

деструк/тивный *a.* destructive; —ция *f.* destruction, breakdown; degradation (of polymers, etc.).

десть *f.* quire (of paper).

десульф/ация *f.,* —ирование *n.,* —урация *f.* desulfuration, desulfurization; —ировать *v.* desulfurize; (petroleum) sweeten; —итация *f.* elimination of sulfurous acid; —уризатор *m.* desulfurizer.

десятер/ичный, —ной *a.* tenfold; —о ten.

десяти— *prefix* deca—, ten; —водный *a.* decahydrate; —гранник *m.* (cryst.) decahedron; —гранный *a.* decahedral; —дневка *f.* ten-day period; —кратный *a.* tenfold; —летие *n.* decade, tenth anniversary; —летний *a.* ten-year, decennial; —на *f.,* —ный *a.* tenth part; unit of land measure (2.70 acres); —ногие *pl.* (zool.) Decapoda; —сильник *m.* (bot.) tansy (*Tanacetum vulgare*); —угольник *m.* (geom.) decagon; —угольный *a.* decagonal.

десятичн/ый *a.,* —ая дробь decimal; д. знак decimal point.

десятник *m.* foreman.

десят/ок *m.,* —ый *a.* tenth; —ь ten.

детал/изация *f.,* —ировка *f.* detail, detail of design; —изировать *v.* detail; —ь *f.* detail, piece, part, component, member, feature; —ьно *adv.* in detail; —ьный *a.* detailed, detail, minute.

детандер *m.* reduction valve; (refrigeration) compressed-gas motor.

деташер *m.* detacher.

детва *f.* larva (of bees).

детдом *m.* children's home.

детект/ирование *n.* detection; (rad.) rectification; —ировать *v.* detect, find, catch; rectify; —ор *m.,* —орный *a.* detector; pickup; rectifier.

детерминант *m.* determinant.

дети *pl.* children.

детойль *m.* a DDT insecticide.

детон/атор *m.* (expl.) detonator, detonator cap, primer, percussion cap; —ация *f.,* —ационный *a.* detonation, explosion; knock (of motor); ингибитор —ации antiknock; величина —ации, степень —ации, —ационная стойкость knock rating (of fuel), octane number; —ировать *v.* detonate, explode; knock: —ирующий *a.*

detonating; knocking; high (explosives); —**ометр** *m.* (aero.) engine knock indicator.

**дето/родный** *a.* genital; —**рождение** *n.* child bearing, procreation.

**детрит** *m.*, —**овый** *a.* (geol.) detrital; —**ус** *m.* detritus, rock waste.

**детс/кий** *a.* child's, juvenile; **д. сад** nursery; —**кое место** (anat.) placenta; —**тво** *n.* childhood, infancy.

**дет/ый** *a.* put; —**ь** *see* **девать.**

**дефазированный** *a.* out of phase.

**дефека/т** *m.* defecate, defecation mud; —**тор** *m.* (sugar) defecator, clarifier; —**ционный** *a.* defecation, clarifying; —**ционный котел** defecating pan, clarifier; —**ционная грязь** defecation slime; —**ция** *f.* defecation, clarification; excrement, discharge.

**дефект** *m.* defect, shortcoming, damage, flaw, blemish; **д. массы** (nucl.) mass defect; —**ивный** *a.* defective, faulty; —**ный** *a.* imperfect; —**овочный** *a.* defective; defective-part (list); —**оскоп** *m.* defectoscope; —**оскопия** *f.* defectoscopy, flaw detection.

**деферризация** *f.* deferrization, iron removal.

**дефибр/ер** *m.* fiber separator; (paper) pulp grinder; —**ерные камни** pulping rolls; —**инирование** *n.* defibrination, fibrin removal; —**ировать** *v.* defiber; grind (wood for pulp).

**дефил/е** *n.* (mil.) defile; ravine, gorge; —**ировать** *v.* defile, file.

**дефис** *m.* (typ.) hyphen.

**дефицит** *m.* deficit; —**ность** *f.* deficiency, shortage, unavailability; —**ный** *a.* deficit, deficient, difficultly available.

**дефлагра/тор** *m.* deflagrator; —**ция** *f.* deflagration, burning up.

**дефлегм/атор** *m.* dephlegmator, fractionating column; still head; reflux condenser; —**ация** *f.* dephlegmation, fractionation; **коэффициент —ации** reflux ratio; —**ировать** *v.* dephlegmate, fractionate, reflux.

**дефлект/ометр** *m.* deflectometer; —**ор** *m.* deflector.

**дефлок/кулирование, —улирование** *n.*, —**уляция** *f.* deflocculation; —**улиро-ванный** *a.* deflocculated; —**улировать** *v.* deflocculate; —**улирующий реагент** deflocculating agent, deflocculant.

**дефляция** *f.* deflation; (geol.) deflation, wind erosion.

**деформ/ационный** *a.*, —**ация** *f.*, —**ирование** *n.* deformation, distortion, warping; strain; —**ированный** *a.* deformed, distorted; —**ировать** *v.* deform, distort; strain; —**ироваться** *v.* be distorted, warp, buckle; —**ирующий** *a.* deforming; straining.

**дефолиа/нт** *m.* defoliant; —**ция** *f.* defoliation.

**дефосфориз/ация** *f.* dephosphorization; —**ировать** *v.* dephosphorize; —**ован-ный** *a.* dephosphorized.

**дефрост/ация** *f.* defrosting, thawing; —**ер** *m.* defroster.

**дехлор/ация** *f.*, —**ирование** *n.* dechlorination; —**ированный** *a.* dechlorinated; —**ировать** *v.* dechlorinate.

**дехолин** *m.* Decholin, dehydrocholic acid.

**децелер/ация** *f.* deceleration; —**ометр** *m.* decelerometer.

**децентрализ/ация** *f.* decentralization, scattering; —**овать** *v.* decentralize, scatter.

**деци—** *prefix* deci— (one tenth); —**бел** *m.* (sound) decibel; —**грамм** *m.* decigram.

**децил** *m.* decyl, decatyl; —**ен** *m.* decylene, decene; —**еновая кислота** decylenic acid.

**децилитр** *m.* deciliter (0.1 liter).

**децилов/ый** *a.* decyl; **д. альдегид** decyl aldehyde, decanal; **д. спирт** decyl alcohol, 1-decanol; —**ая кислота** decylic acid, capric acid.

**деци/льон** *m.* decillion; —**мальный** *a.* decimal; —**метр** *m.* decimeter (0.1 meter); —**метровый** *a.* decimetric, micro- (waves); —**молярный** *a.* decimolar.

**децин** *m.* decine, decyne.

**деци/непер** *m.* (elec.) decineper; —**нор-мальный** *a.* decinormal.

**дешев/еть** *v.* fall in price, cost less; —**изна** *f.* cheapness, low price, good bargain; —**ить** *v.* cheapen, undercharge; —**ле** *comp. of* **дешево,** cheaper; —**о** *adv.* cheaply, inexpensively, at a low price; —**ый** *a.* cheap, inexpensive.

дешенит *m.* (min.) dechenite.

дешифр/атор *m.* decoder; —ирование, —ование *n.* decoding, deciphering; —ировать *v.* decode, decipher.

деэмуль/гатор *m.* demulsifier; —сация *f.* demulsification.

деэтилирование *n.* deëthylation.

деятель *m.* worker, man; д. науки scientific man; —но *adv.* actively; —ность *f.* activity, work; profession, occupation; —ный *a.* active, busy, energetic; practical.

дж *abbr.* (джоуль) joule.

Джаксона *see* Джексона.

джамбоэ *n.* djamboe, guava leaves.

джар *m.* (elec.) jar (unit of capacitance).

джасп/еризация *f.* (min.) jasperization; —ероидный *a.* jasperoid; —илит *m.* jaspilite (a form of jasper).

джатекс *m.* jatex (a rubber latex).

джек *m.* jack; (min.) jackhammer.

Джекоби сплав Jacoby metal (a lead-antimony-tin alloy).

джекорин *see* иекорин.

Джексона подающий транспортер (agr.) Jackson feeder.

джем *m.* jam.

джемпер *m.* jumper.

джемсонит *m.* (min.) jamesonite.

дженкинзит *m.* (min.) jenkinsite.

дженколовая кислота jenkolic acid, djenkolic acid.

дженни *n.* (text.) jenny.

джень-шень *see* джин-шень.

джервин *see* иервин.

Джерса нагревательный колодец (met.) Gjer's soaking pit.

джерси *n.* (text.) jersey.

джеспилит *see* джаспилит.

джеффер/изит *m.* (min.) jefferisite (a vermiculite); —сонит *m.* jeffersonite (a manganese-zinc pyroxene).

джиг *m.*, —гер *m.* jig, jigger.

джизлан *m.* cotton-boll cicada.

джилпинит *m.* (min.) gilpinite, johannite.

джин *m.* (text.) gin; gin (liquor); —ирование *n.* ginning; —ированный *a.* ginned; —ировать *v.* gin.

джин-шень *m.* (bot.) ginseng (*Panax ginseng*).

джиобертит *m.* (min.) giobertite (a variety of magnesite).

джойнтер *m.* (building) jointer.

Джонваля турбина Jonval turbine.

джонка *f.* junk (boat).

Джонса реактив (met.) Jones' reagent.

джон/сонова трава (bot.) Johnson grass (*Sorghum halepense*); —стонит *m.* (min.) johnstonite, vanadinite; —струпит *m.* (min.) johnstrupite.

джордан *m.* (paper) Jordan, conical refiner.

джорджианский *see* георгийский.

джоул/ево тепло Joule effect, heat effect; —ометр *m.* joule meter; —ь *m.* joule (unit of work); Джоуля закон Joule's law.

Джоши эффект (elec.) Joshi effect.

джузгун *m.* (bot.) calligonum.

джунгли *pl.* jungle.

джут *m.*, —овый *a.* (bot.) jute (*Corchorus*).

джэк *see* джек.

дзельква *f.* (bot.) zelkova.

дзета *f.* zeta (Z, ζ).

ди— *prefix* di—, bi—.

диабаз *m.* diabase (a basic igneous rock); —овый *a.* diabase, diabasic; —овый миндальный камень (petr.) amygdaloidal greenstone.

диабантит *m.* (min.) diabantite (a variety of chlorite).

диабет *m.* (med.) diabetes; —ик *m.* diabetic; —ин *m.* diabetin, fructose; —ический *a.* diabetic.

диаген/ез *m.* diagenesis, recombination, rearrangement; —етический *a.* diagenetic.

диагно/з *m.* (med.) diagnosis; ставить д. *v.* diagnose; —ст *m.* diagnostician; —стика *f.* diagnostics; —стический *a.* diagnostic.

диагометр *m.* diagometer (an electroscope).

диагональ *f.* diagonal, diagonal line; —ный *a.* diagonal, oblique.

диаграмм/а *f.* diagram, drawing, plan, figure; pattern; chart, record sheet; graph; —ный *a.* diagrammatic.

диаграф *m.* diagraph (drawing instrument).

диада *f.* dyad.

диадохит *m.* (min.) diadochite (a variety of destinezite).

диаз/ен *m.* diazene, diazete; —ин *m.*, —иновый *a.* diazine.

диазо— *prefix* diazo—; —амино— *prefix* diazoamino—, azimino—; —амино-бензол *m.* diazoaminobenzene, 1,3-diphenyltriazene; —бензол *m.* diazobenzene; —гидрат *m.* diazohydrate; —кси— *prefix* diazoxy—; —л *m.* diazole; —лин *m.* diazoline; —метан *m.* diazomethane, azimethane; —ниевое соединение diazonium compound; —реакция *f.* diazo test (for urine); —соединение, —тело *n.* diazo compound; —соль *f.* diazo salt.

диазот/ат *m.* diazotate; —ация *f.*, —ирование *n.* diazotization, diazotizing; одностоуонее —ирование monodiazotization;—ировать *v.* diazotize; —ирующий *a.* diazotizing; —ирующийся *a.* diazotizable.

диазоуксусн/ая кислота diazoacetic acid; соль —ой кислоты, —окислая соль diazoacetate; —ый эфир, —оэтиловый эфир ethyl diazoacetate.

диазо/фенол *m.* diazophenol; —черный пигмент diazo black; —этан *m.* diazoethane, aziethane.

диазтин *m.* diazthine, thiodiazine.

диакарб *m.* Diacarb, acetazolamide.

диакисдодекаэдр *m.* (cryst.) dyakisdodecahedron, diploid.

диа/клаза *f.* (geol.) diaclase; —клинальный *a.* diaclinal; —критический *a.* (elec.) diacritical.

диактинический *a.* (phot.) diactinic.

диакусти/ка *f.* diacoustics; —ческий *a.* diacoustic.

диализ *m.* dialysis, ultrafiltration; —ат *m.* dialyzate; —атор *m.* dialyzer; dialyzator;—ированный, —ованный *a.* dialyzed; —ировать, —овать *v.* dialyze; —ирующий *a.* dialyzing.

диалин *m.* dialin, dihydronaphthalene.

диалит *m.* (elec.) dialite (insulator).

диалитический *a.* dialytic.

диалкил *m.*, —овый *a.* dialkyl; —ен *m.* dialkylene.

диаллаг *m.*, —он *m.* (min.) diallage (a variety of pyroxene).

диаллил *m.*, —овый *a.* diallyl; —амин *m.* diallylamine, di-2-propenylamine.

диалогит *m.* (min.) dialogite, rhodochrosite.

диалуров/ая кислота dialuric acid, 5-hydroxybarbituric acid; соль —ой кислоты, —окислая соль dialurate.

диаль *m.* Dial, 5,5-diallylbarbituric acid; —дегид *m.* dialdehyde.

диам. *abbr.* (диаметр) diameter.

диамагн/етизм, —итизм *m.*, —итность *f.* diamagnetism; —итный *a.* diamagnetic.

диамантовый желтый diamond yellow; д. черный diamond black (an azo dye).

диаметр *m.* diameter; bore, caliber; —ально *adv.* diametrically, in diameter; —альный *a.* diameter, diametric.

диам/ид *m.* diamide; —идо— *prefix* diamido—; —ил *m.*, —иловый *a.* diamyl; —ин *m.* diamine.

диамино— *prefix* diamino—; —бензол *m.* diaminobenzene; —вый *a.* diamine; —дифенил *m.* diaminodiphenyl, benzidine; —фенол *m.* diaminophenol.

диаммофос *m.* diammonium hydrogen phosphate (fertilizer).

дианизидин *m.* dianisidine, dimethoxybenzidine.

дианил/ин *m.* dianiline; —овый желтый dianil yellow.

дианино дерево *see* Дианы дерево.

диантр/ахинон *m.* dianthraquinone; —ацил *m.* dianthracyl; —ил *m.* dianthryl, bianthryl.

Дианы дерево arbor Dianae (silver tree).

диапазон *m.*, —ный *a.* range, compass, scope; diapason (rad.) band; д. мощности power range.

диапировый *a.* diapiric.

диапозитив *m.* (phot.) diapositive, positive slide.

диарея *f.* (med.) diarrhea.

диарил *m.*, —ьный *a.* diaryl.

диарсин *m.* diarsine, biarsine.

диас *m.* (geol.) Dyas (obs. for Permian system).

диаспирин *m.* diaspirin, succinylsalicylic acid.

диаспор *m.* (min.) diaspore (a hydrous aluminum oxide); —а *f.* (bot.) diaspore.

диаста/з *m.* (med.) diastasis; д., —за *f.*, —тический фермент diastase, amylase; —зиметрия *f.* diastasimetry;

—зический *a.* diastasic, diastatic;
—тический *a.* diastatic.
диастереоизомер *m.* diastereoisomer, diastereomer.
диастол/а *f.* (biol.) diastole; —ический *a.* diastolic.
диастрофизм *m.* (geol.) diastrophism.
диатез *m.* (med.) diathesis.
диатерм/ический, —ичный *a.* diathermic, diathermal; —ичность *f.* diathermy, diathermance; —ия *f.* diathermy; —ометр *m.* diathermometer.
диатол *m.* diatol, diethyl carbonate.
диатом/а *f.* (bot.) diatom (a member of the *Bacillariophyta*); —ин, —ит *m.*, —овая земля diatomite, diatomaceous earth; —ный, —овый *a.* diatomic; —овые водоросли diatoms.
диатрема *f.* (geol.) diatreme, volcanic vent.
диафан *m.* unglazed porcelain; —ометр *m.* diaphanometer (for measuring transparency); —оскоп *m.* diaphanoscope.
диафиз *m.* (anat.) diaphysis.
диафорит *m.* (min.) diaphorite.
диафрагм/а *f.*, —овый *a.* diaphragm, membrane; (phot.) stop; —ировать *v.* (optics) stop down, diaphragm.
диахилон *m.* diachylon (ointment).
диацет/амид *m.* diacetamide, diacetylamine; —ат *m.* diacetate; —ил *m.* diacetyl, biacetyl; —илен *m.* diacetylene, butadiine; —илморфин *m.* diacetyl morphine, heroine; —илтаннин *m.* diacetyl tannin, tannigen; —ин *m.* diacetin, glyceryl diacetate; —он *m.*, —оновый *a.* diacetone, acetylacetone; —оновый спирт diacetone alcohol.
диаципиперазин *m.* diacipiperazine.
диашистовый *a.* (geol.) diachistic.
дибенз— *prefix* dibenz—, dibenzo—; —амид *m.* dibenzamide, benzoyl benzamide; —енил *m.* dibenzenyl; —ил *m.*, —иловый *a.* dibenzyl; —илиден *m.* dibenzylidene; —оил *m.* dibenzoyl; —ойная кислота dibenzoic acid.
диборнил *m.* dibornyl.
дибром— *prefix* dibrom—, dibromo—; —бензол *m.* dibromobenzene.
дибути/л *m.*, —ловый *a.* dibutyl; —рин *m.* dibutyrin, glyceryl dibutyrate.

дивало *n.* (bot.) scleranthus.
дивалолактон *m.* divalolactone; —овая кислота divalolactonic acid.
диванадил *m.* divanadyl.
дивариантный *a.* bivariant.
дивар/инол *m.* divarinol, propylresorcinol; —овая кислота divaric acid.
диверг/ентный, —ирующий *a.* divergent; —енция *f.* divergence; —ировать *v.* diverge.
диверсин *m.* diversine.
дивертер *m.* (elec.) diverter.
дивиденд *m.* (com.) dividend.
диви-диви *n.* divi-divi (pods of *Caesalpinia coriaria*).
дивиз/ия *f.* division; —ор *m.* divisor.
дивий мед, д. хлеб (bot.) carob (*Ceratonia siliqua*).
дивина *f.* (bot.) mullein (*Verbascum*).
дивинил *m.* divinyl; bivinyl, 1,3-butadiene; —овый *a.* divinyl; —овый каучук butadiene rubber.
дивинная кислота ditartaric acid.
див/ить *v.* astonish, surprise; —иться *v.* wonder, be surprised (at); —ный *a.* wonderful, marvelous; —о *n.* wonder, marvel; —оваться *v.* wonder, marvel (at).
дивольфрамовая кислота ditungstic acid.
дигален *m.* Digalen (digitalis preparation).
дигалловая кислота digallic acid, tannic acid.
дигедральный *a.* dihedral.
дигексагональный *a.* (cryst.) dihexagonal.
дигексил *m.* dihexyl; dodecane.
дигентизиновая кислота digentisic acid.
дигериров/ание *n.* digestion; —анный *a.* digested; —ать *v.* digest.
дигестор *m.* digester.
дигидр—, —о— *prefix* dihydr—, dihydro—; —ит *m.* (min.) dihydrite (copper phosphate); —обензол *m.* dihydrobenzene; —окси— *prefix* dihydroxy—; —ол *m.* dihydrol.
дигитал/евая кислота digitalic acid; —еин digitalein; —игенин *m.* digitaligenin; —ин *m.* digitalin; —ис *m.* (pharm.) digitàlis; —оза *f.* digitalose.
дигито/вая кислота digitic acid; —генин *m.* digitogenin; —геновая кислота

digitogenic acid; —ксигенин *m*. digitoxigenin; —ксин *m*. digitoxin; —ксоза *f*. digitoxose, 3,4,5-trihydroxyhexanal; —нин *m*. digitonin.

дигликол *m*. diglycol; —евая кислота diglycolic acid, oxydiethanoic acid.

ди/глицерин *m*. diglycerin; —глицил *m*. diglycyl; —гоксин *m*. digoxin; —гуанил *m*. diguanyl; —дезил *m*. didesyl.

дидим, —ий *m*. didymium (mixture of neodymium and praseodymium).

дидодекаэдр *m*. (cryst.) didodecahedron, diploid; —ический *a*. didodecahedral.

диен *m*. diene; —овый ряд diene series, diolefines.

диет/а *f*. diet; —етика *f*. dietetics; —етический, —ический *a*. dietetic, dietary; —отерапия *f*. diet therapy.

дижерминатор *m*. degerminator, germ separator.

диз— *see also under* дис—.

дизел/ь, —ьмотор *m*., двигатель —я, —ьный *a*. diesel (engine); —ьное топливо diesel fuel, diesel oil.

дизентер/ийный *a*. (med.) dysenteric; —ия *f*. dysentery.

дизодиль *m*. (min.) dysodile (a native hydrocarbon).

дизъюнктивный *a*. disjunctive.

диизат/иновая кислота diisatinic acid; —оген *m*. diisatogen.

диизо— *prefix* diiso—; —бутил *m*., —бутиловый *a*. diisobutyl.

ди/имид *m*. diimide; —имин *m*. diimine; —имино— *prefix* diimino—.

диинд/ил *m*. diindyl, dindyl; —оген *m*. diindogen, indigotin.

дииод— *prefix* diiod—, diiodo—; —ид *m*. diiodide.

дииодо— *prefix* diiodo—; —бензол *m*. diiodobenzene; —уксусная кислота diiodoacetic acid, diiodacetic acid.

Дика проба (med.) Dick test (for scarlet fever).

дикаин *m*. tetracaine, amethocaine.

дикакодил *m*. dicacodyl.

дикальцийфосфат *m*. dicalcium phosphate.

дикамфо— *prefix* dicampho—.

дикарбо/ксильная кислота, —новая кислота dicarboxylic acid.

дикарвакрол *m*. dicarvacrol.

дикарь *m*. savage.

дикето— *prefix* diketo—; —н *m*. diketone.

дик/ий *a*. wild, savage; odd, extravagant, absurd; —ое мясо (med.) proud flesh.

дикинсонит *m*. (min.) dickinsonite.

диклин/изм *m*. (bot.) diclinism, dicliny; —ический, —овый *a*. diclinous; (cryst.) diclinic.

Дикмана реакция Dieckmann reaction (for cyclic ketones).

дико *adv*. wildly, recklessly, irresponsibly.

дикобраз *m*. (zool.) porcupine.

диковин/а, —ка *f*. wonder, rarity; —ный *a*. odd, rare, unusual.

дикод/еин *m*. dicodeine; —ид *m*. dicodid, dihydrocodeinone.

Дикона способ Deacon process (for chlorine).

дикон/овая кислота diconic acid; —хинин *m*. diconchinine, diquinidine.

дико/растущий *a*. (bot.) wild; —сть *f*. wildness; wild state; absurdity.

дикрезил *m*. dicresyl.

диксантил *m*. dixanthyl.

диксгениновая кислота dixgeninic acid.

диксилил *m*. dixylyl.

диктамнин *m*. dictamnin.

диктио— *prefix* dictyo— (net); —каулез *m*. (vet.) dictyocaulosis.

диктов/ание *n*., —ка *f*. dictation; —анный *a*. dictated; —ать *v*. dictate.

дикто/граф *m*. dictograph; —р *m*. (rad.) announcer; speaker; —фон *m*. dictaphone.

дикумарон *m*. dicoumarone.

дикумил *m*. dicumyl, dicumenyl.

Дила процесс (met.) Diehl (cyanide) process.

дилакт/аминовая кислота dilactamic acid; —ил *m*. dilactyl.

дилакцерил *m*. dilacceryl.

дилат/ация *f*. dilation, expansion; —ометр *m*. dilatometer; —ометрия *f*. dilatometry.

дилаудид *m*. dilaudid, dihydromorphinone hydrochloride.

дилейцил *m*. dileucyl.

дилемма *f*. dilemma, fix, perplexity.

дилемовое масло dilem oil, Java oil.

дилетант *m*. amateur.

дилизин *m*. dilysine.

**дили/монен** *m.* dilimonene; **—туровая кислота** dilituric acid, 5-nitrobarbituric acid; **—хестериновая кислота** dilichesteric acid.

**диллениевые** *pl.* (bot.) Dilleniaceae.

**дилувиальный** *see* **дилювиальный.**

**Дильса-Альдера реакция** Diels-Alder reaction.

**дильсы** *pl.* deal (lumber).

**дилюв/иальный** *a.* (geol.) diluvial; **—ий** *m.*, **д. нанос** diluvium.

**дим/азон** *m.* dimazon, diacetylaminoazotoluene; **—едон** *m.* dimedon, dimethyl cyclohexanedione; **—едрол** *m.* Dimedrol, diphenylhydramine.

**димезитил** *m.*, **—овый** *a.* dimesityl.

**диментил** *m.*, **—овый** *a.* dimenthyl.

**димер** *m.* dimer; **—изация** *f.* dimerization (a polymerization); **—ный** *a.* dimeric.

**димет/акриловая кислота** dimethacrylic acid; **—ано—** *prefix* dimethano—.

**диметил** *m.*, **—овый** *a.* dimethyl; **—амин** *m.* dimethylamine; **—аминофенол** *m.* dimethylaminophenol; **—анилин** *m.* dimethyl aniline; **—ен** *m.* dimethylene; **—кетон** *m.* dimethyl ketone, acetone; **—овый эфир** dimethyl ether, methyl ether; **—овый эфир серной кислоты, —сульфат** methyl sulfate; **—цинк** *m.* zinc dimethyl.

**диметокси—** *prefix* dimethoxy—.

**димир/истин** *m.* dimyristin; **—цен** *m.* dimyrcene.

**диморф/изм** *m.* dimorphism; **—ный** *a.* dimorphous, dimorphic.

**димочевина** *f.* diurea.

**дина** *f.* dyne (unit of force).

**динам/а** *f.* dyname (one thousand kilogram-meters); **—бин** *m.* dynambin; **—етр** *m.* dynameter; **—изм** *m.* dynamism; **—ик** *m.* (rad.) dynamic speaker; **—ика** *f.* dynamics; **—ит** *m.*, **—итный** *a.* dynamite; **—ический** *a.* dynamic; **—ный** *a.* dynamo.

**динамо** *n.*, **—машина** *f.* (elec.) dynamo, (dynamoelectric) generator; **—граф** *m.* dynamograph, recording dynamometer; **—двигатель** *see* **динамотор.**

**динамометр** *m.* dynamometer; **—ический** *a.* dynamometric.

**динамон** *m.* (expl.) dynammon.

**динамотор** *m.* (elec.) dynamotor, rotary transformer.

**динамоэлектрический** *a.* dynamoelectric.

**динантский ярус** (geol.) Dinantian series, Avonian series.

**динас** *m.*, **—овый кирпич** Dinas brick (a type of silica refractory brick).

**динатрон** *m.* (thermionics) dynatron.

**динафт—**, **—о—** *prefix* dinaphth—, dinaphtho—; **—азин** *m.* dinaphthazine, dibenzophenazine; **—акридин** *m.* dinaphthacridine; **—антрацен** *m.* dinaphthanthracene, dibenzanthracene; **—ил** *m.*, **—иловый** *a.* dinaphthyl; **—илен** *m.* dinaphthylene; **—оксантен** *m.* dinaphthoxanthene; **—ол** *m.* dinaphthol.

**динглерова зелень** Dingler green (a pigment of calcium and chromium phosphates).

**диндил** *m.* dindyl, diindyl.

**динезин** *m.* Dinesine, diethazine.

**диникотиновая кислота** dinicotinic acid, 3,5-pyrinedicarboxylic acid.

**динит** *m.* (min.) dinite.

**динитро—** *prefix* dinitro—; **—бензол** *m.* dinitrobenzene; **—глицерин** *m.* dinitroglycerin; **—толуол** *m.* dinitrotoluene; **—фенол** *m.* dinitrophenol.

**динод** *m.* (electron.) dynode.

**динозавр** *m.* (pal.) dinosaur.

**диогенал** *m.* diogenal.

**диод** *m.* (thermionics) diode, diode tube.

**диоза** *f.* diose.

**диокс/азин** *m.* dioxazine; **—азол** *m.* dioxazole; **—ан** *m.* dioxane, diethylene dioxide; **—андион** *m.* dioxanedione; **—диазин** *m.* dioxdiazine.

**диокси—** *prefix* dioxy— (frequently used for dihydroxy—); **—альдегид** *m.* dihydroxyaldehyde; **—антрахинон** *m.* dihydroxyanthraquinone; **—ацетон** *m.* dihydroxyacetone; **—бензол** *m.* dihydroxybenzene.

**диокс/ид** *m.* dioxide; **—икетон** *m.* dihydroxyketone; **—им** *m.* dioxime; **—ин** *m.* dioxine, β-oxynaphthoquinoxime; dioxin; **—инафталин** *m.* dihydroxynaphthalene; **—индол** *m.* dioxindole; **—ихинон** *m.* dihydroxyquinone; **—ол** *m.* dioxole; **—олан** *m.* dioxolan.

**ди/октаэдр** *m.* (cryst.) dioctahedron,

ditetragonal pyramid; —октил *m.* dioctyl; —ол *m.* diol, glycol; —олеин *m.* diolein, glycerol dioleate; —олео— *prefix* dioleo—; —олефин *m.* diolefin; —онин *m.* dionine, ethylmorphine hydrochloride.

**диопси/д,** —т *m.* (min.) diopside, alalite (a variety of pyroxene).

**диоптаз** *m.* (min.) dioptase.

**диоптр** *m.* (optics) diopter (instrument); —ика *f.* dioptrics; —ический *a.* dioptric; —ия *f.* diopter (unit of power of lens).

**диорама** *f.* diorama.

**диорит** *m.* diorite (a granitoid rock); —овый *a.* diorite, dioritic.

**диорселиновая кислота** diorsellinic acid, lecanoric acid.

**диорто—** *prefix* diortho—.

**диоскор/еин** *m.* dioscorein; —ейные *pl.* (bot.) Dioscoreaceae; —ея *f.* (bot.) Chinese yam (*Dioscorea*); —ин *m.* dioscorine.

**диос/мелеоптен** *m.* diosmeleoptene; —пирос *m.* (bot.) date plum, persimmon (*Diospyros*); —фенол *m.* diosphenol, buchu camphor; —цин *m.* dioscin.

**диотан** *m.* diothane.

**дипальмитин** *m.* dipalmitine, glycerol dipalmitate.

**дипентен** *m.* dipentene, terpene.

**дипик/олиновая кислота** dipicolinic acid, pyridinedicarboxylic acid; —рил *m.* dipicryl.

**дипир** *m.* (min.) dipyre (a variety of scapolite).

**дипирамида** *f.* bipyramid.

**дипирид/ил** *m.* dipyridyl; —ин *m.* dipyridine, nicotyrine.

**диплацин** *m.* (pharm.) Diplacin.

**диплекс** *m.* (telegraphy) diplex.

**дипло—** *prefix* diplo— (double); —зал *m.* Diplosal, salicylosalicylic acid; —ид *m.*, —идный *a.* (biol.; cryst.) diploid; —кокк *m.* (bact.) diplococcus; —коккин *m.* diplococcin.

**диплом** *m.* diploma; **университетский д.** degree, university degree; —ированный *a.* graduated, graduate; licensed (engineer); registered (nurse).

**дипломицин** *m.* diplomycin.

**дипломн/ый** *a.* diploma; —ая работа thesis.

**диплоэдр** *m.* (cryst.) diploid, dyakisdodecahedron.

**дипно—** *prefix* dypno—; —н *m.* dypnone.

**диполь** *m.* dipole; (electric) doublet; (rad.) dipole antenna; —ьный *a.* dipole, dipolar.

**Диппеля масло** Dippel's oil, bone oil.

**дипрен** *m.* diprene.

**дипроп/аргил** *m.* dipropargyl, bipropargyl; —ил *m.*, —иловый *a.* dipropyl; —илкетон *m.* dipropylketone, butyrone.

**дипсевдо—** *prefix* dipseudo—.

**диптеро—** *prefix* diptero— (two-winged); —карповые *pl.* (bot.) Dipterocarpaceae.

**Дирака уравнение** (quantum mechanics) Dirac equation; **дираковская частица** Dirac particle, fermion.

**дирезорци/ловая кислота** diresorcylic acid; —нол *m.* diresorcinol.

**директ/ива** *f.* instructions, letter of instructions, directions; —ивный *a.* instruction, directional; —ор *m.* director, manager, head; sender; —орраспорядитель managing director; —риса *f.* (geom.) directrix.

**дирекц/ионный** *a.* directions, directional; —ия *f.* direction, management, board (of directors).

**дирижабль** *m.* dirigible, airship.

**дирижер** *m.* regulator.

**Дирихле признак сходимости** (math.) Dirichlet's test for convergence.

**дирицинолеин** *m.* diricinolein.

**диродан** *m.* dithiocyanogen.

**дис—** *prefix* dis—; *see also under* диз—.

**дисазо/бензол** *m.* disazobenzene; —соединение *n.* disazo compound.

**дисалицил/ид** *m.* disalicylide, salosalicylide; —овая кислота disalicylic acid, salicylic anhydride.

**дисаналит** *m.* (min.) dysanalyte.

**дисахарид** *m.* disaccharide.

**дисгармон/ировать** *v.* be out of keeping, clash, conflict (with); —ирующий *a.* conflicting, incongruous (with); —ия *f.* disharmony, conflict.

**дисгрегация** *f.* disgregation, disintegration.

**диселенид** *m.* diselenide.

диселено— *prefix* diseleno—.

дисил/ан *m.* disilane, silicoethane; —икат *m.* disilicate.

дисириновая кислота disyringic acid.

диск *m.* disk, disc, plate; slice.

дискант *m.*, —овый *a.* (acous.) treble.

дискатол *m.* discatol.

дисквалифицировать *v.* disqualify.

дисков/ание *n.* (tel.) dialing; (agr.) disking; —ый *a.* disk, disc, plate; —ый фрезер cutting disk.

диско/идальный *see* дискообразный; —лит *m.* (geol.) discolith, discoidal coccolith; —мицеты *pl.* (bot.) Discomycetes.

дисконт *m.* (com.) discount; —ировать *v.* discount.

дискообразный *a.* disk-like, disk-shaped, discoid, discoidal.

дискразит *m.* (min.) dyscrasite, antimonsilver.

дискредит/ация *f.* —ирование *n.* discrediting; —ировать *v.* discredit.

дискрет/а *f.* (statistics) sample; —ный *a.* discrete, distinct; —ное представление (cybernetics) sampling analysis.

дискримин/ант *m.* (math.) discriminant; —атор *m.* discriminator.

диску/ссионный *a.* controversial; —ссия *f.* discussion, controversy; —тировать *v.* discuss.

дислизин *m.* dyslysin.

дисло/кация *f.* dislocation, disturbance; —цированный *a.* dislocated; —цировать *v.* dislocate, disturb.

дислуит *m.* (min.) dysluite (a zinc- manganese-iron gahnite).

дисмембратор *m.* crusher.

дисмутация *f.* dismutation, disproportionation.

дисодил *see* дизодиль.

диспансер *m.* (med.) dispensary; clinic; —изация *f.* dispensary system.

диспепс/ический *a.* (med.) dyspeptic; —ия *f.* dyspepsia.

дисперг/атор *m.* disperser; dispergator, a peptizing agent; —ирование *see* дисперсия; —ированный *a.* dispersed; —ированная медь (met.) copper rain; —ировать *v.* disperse, scatter, diffuse; —ирующий *a.* dispersing, dispersive; —ирующий реагент (flotation) dispersion reagent.

дисперс/ионный *a.* dispersion, dispersing; —ионная среда dispersion medium; —ионное средство dispersion agent; —ионное твердение (met.) precipitation hardening, age hardening; —ия *f.* dispersion, scattering; (statistics) standard deviation; —ность *f.* degree of dispersion; particle size; —ный *a.* dispersed; —ное вещество dispersed material, dispersed phase; —оид *m.* dispersoid.

диспетчер *m.* dispatcher; —изация *f.* dispatching; traffic control; —ская *f.* control room; (aero.) control tower; —ский *a.* dispatcher, dispatching.

диспрозий *m.* dysprosium, Dy.

диспропорц/ионирование *n.* (chem.) disproportionation; —ия *f.* disproportion.

диспут *m.* dispute, discussion, argument; —ировать *v.* discuss, argue.

диссектор *m.* dissector.

диссертация *f.* dissertation, thesis.

диссидент *m.* dissenter, nonconformist.

диссиметричный *a.* asymmetric, unsymmetrical.

диссимиляция *f.* dissimilation.

диссипа/тивный *a.* dissipative; —ция *f.* dissipation, diffusion, dispersion.

диссол/ьвер *m.* dissolving tank; —юция *f.* dissolution; dissolving.

диссонанс *m.* dissonance, discord.

диссоци/ация *f.* dissociation; —ировать *v.* dissociate, break up, break down, split up; —ирующийся *a.* dissociable.

диссугаз *m.* acetylene (dissolved in acetone).

дистанц/иометрирование *n.* ranging; —ионирующий *a.* spacer (plate, etc.); —ионноуправляемый *a.* remote-controlled; —ионный *a.* distant, remote, tele—; distance; range; remote-control; space, spacer (plate, rib, etc.); time (fuse); —ионный термометр telethermometer; —ионная деталь spacer; —ионная трубка fuse; —ионное управление remote control; —ия *f.* distance, range; interval.

дистеарин *m.* distearin.

дистектический *a.* dystectic.

дистен *m.* (min.) disthene, kyanite.

дистилл/ат, —ят *m.* distillate; —ер,

—**ятор** *m.* distiller, still, spec. strong ammonia liquor still (in Solvay process); condenser; —**ерная жидкость** (Solvay) still waste; —**ирование** *n.*, —**яционный** *a.*, —**яция** *f.* distillation, distilling; —**ированный** *a.* distilled; —**ировать** *v.* distill.

**дистильбен** *m.* distilbene.

**дистирол** *m.* distyrene.

**дистрибутивный** *a.* distributive.

**дистрофия** *f.* (med.) dystrophy.

**дисульф/ат** *m.* disulfate, pyrosulfate; bisulfate; —**ид** *m.* disulfide.

**дисульфо**— *prefix* disulfo—; —**нат** *m.*, **соль** —**новой кислоты** disulfonate; —**новая кислота** disulfonic acid.

**дисциплин/а**, —**ированность** *f.* discipline; —**арный** *a.* disciplinary; —**ированный** *a.* disciplined, trained; —**ировать** *v.* discipline, train.

**дита** *f.* dita bark, alstonia; —**ин** *m.* ditaine, echitamine; —**мин** *m.* ditamine.

**Дитеричи уравнение** Dieterici equation.

**дитерпен** *m.* diterpene.

**дитетра/гональный** *a.* ditetragonal;—**эдр** *m.* (cryst.) ditetrahedron; —**эдрический** *a.* ditetrahedral.

**дити/азин** *m.* dithiazine; —**азол** *m.* dithiazol; —**ан** *m.* dithiane, diethylene disulfide; —**ен** *m.* dithiene; —**енил** *m.* dithienyl.

**дитимол** *m.* dithymol.

**дитио**— *prefix* dithio—; —**анилин** *m.* dithioaniline; —**кислота**, —**новая кислота** dithionic acid; —**л** *m.* dithiole, disulfole; —**н** *m.* dithion (sodium dithiosalicylate mixture); —**нат** *m.*, **соль** —**новой кислоты** dithionate; —**салициловая кислота** dithiosalicylic acid; **соль** —**салициловой кислоты** dithiosalicylate; —**угольная кислота** dithiocarbonic acid; —**фос** *m.* a tetraethyl dithiopyrophosphate insecticide.

**дитолил** *m.* ditolyl, dimethyldiphenyl; —**амин** *m.* ditolylamine.

**дитразин** *m.* ditrazine, diethylcarbamazine citrate.

**дитригон** *m.* (cryst.) ditrigon, symmetrical octahedron; —**альный** *a.* ditrigonal.

**дитрихит** *m.* (min.) dietrichite.

**дитроит** *m.* (petr.) ditroite.

**дитчер** *m.* ditcher, ditching machine.

**дитя** *n.* child, infant.

**диур/анат** *m.* diuranate; —**ез** *m.* (med.) diuresis; —**еид** diureide; —**етин** *m.* diuretin, theobromine sodium salicylate; —**етический** *a.*, —**етическое средство** (pharm.) diuretic.

**диф**— *prefix* differential.

**дифацил** *m.* diphacyl, adiphenine.

**дифен**— *prefix* diphen—, dipheno—; —**ат** *m.* diphenate; —**ид** *m.* diphenide.

**дифенил** *m.*, —**овый** *a.* diphenyl; biphenyl; —**амин** *m.* diphenylamine, phenyl aniline; —**ен** *m.* diphenylene; **окись** —**ена** diphenylene oxide; **сернистый** —**ен** diphenylene sulfide;—**ил** *m.* diphenylyl; —**ин** *m.* diphenyline; —**кетон** *m.* diphenyl ketone, benzophenone; —**метан** *m.* diphenyl methane, benzylbenzene.

**дифенимид** *m.* diphenimide.

**дифено**— *prefix* dipheno—; —**вая кислота** diphenic acid, bibenzoic acid; **соль** —**вой кислоты** diphenate; —**л** *m.* diphenol; —**хинон** *m.* diphenoquinone.

**диференциал** *see* **дифференциал.**

**диферуловая кислота** diferulic acid.

**дифлуан** *m.* difluan.

**дифлуор**— *prefix* difluor—, difluoro—; —**ен** *m.* difluorene, didiphenyleneethylene; —**енилен** *m.* difluorenylene.

**дифманометр** *m.* differential manometer.

**диформ/амид** *m.* diformamide; —**ил** *m.* diformyl, glyoxal.

**дифосген** *m.* diphosgene, trichloromethyl chloroformate.

**дифосф/ат** *m.*, **соль** —**орной кислоты** diphosphate; —**орная кислота** diphosphoric acid, pyrophosphoric acid.

**дифракция** *see* **диффракция.**

**дифталил** *m.* diphthalyl.

**дифтер/ит** *m.*, —**ия** *f.* (med.) diptheria; —**итный** *a.* diptheritic.

**дифференц/иал** *m.* (math.) differential; differential gear; **вал** —**иала** differential shaft; —**иальный** *a.* differential; —**иальное исчисление** (math.) differential calculus; —**иатор** *m.*, —**ирующая схема** (elec.) differentiator, differentiating circuit; —**иация** *f.*,

**—ирование** n. differentiation; **—ированный** a. differentiated; **—ировать** v. differentiate; distinguish.

**диффлюэнция** f. ice blow.

**диффра/гированный** a. diffracted; **—гировать** v. diffract; **—ктаевая кислота** diffractic acid; **—кция** f., **—кционный** a. diffraction; **—кционная решетка** diffraction grating.

**диффу/зат** m. diffusate; **—зионный** a., **—зия** f. diffusion; **—зионный сок** (sugar) raw juice; **—зионный ток** diffusion current; **—зионная способность** diffusibiltiy; **коэффициент —зии** diffusion coefficient, diffusivity; **—зно—** prefix diffusely, diffuse; **—зный** a. diffuse, scattered; **—зометр** m. diffusometer; **—зор** m. diffuser; **—зорное кольцо** diffusion ring; **—ндировать** v. diffuse, spread, scatter; pass through a membrane; **—ндируемый** a. diffusible.

**дихан** m. Dichan, dicyclohexylammonium nitrite.

**дихин/идин** m. diquinidine; **—ицин** m. diquinicine; **—о—** prefix diquino—; **—оил**, **—олил** m. diquinoyl, diquinolyl; **—олин** m. diquinoline; **—олопиридин** m. diquinolopyridine.

**дихлор—**, **—о—** prefix dichlor—, dichloro—; **—амин** m. dichloramine; **—ацетон** m. dichloroacetone; **—бензол** m. dichlorobenzene; **—гидрин** m. dichlorohydrin; **—ид** m. dichloride; **—ицид** m. dichloricide, p-dichlorobenzene; **—уксусная кислота** dichloroacetic acid; **—этан** m. dichloroethane; **—этилен** m. dichloroethylene.

**дихотом/ический** a. (bot.) dichotomous; **—ия** f. (biol.) dichotomy, bifurcation.

**дихро/изм** m., **—ичность** f. (cryst.) dichroism; **—ит** m. (min.) dichroite, cordierite, iolite; **—ичный** a. dichroic.

**дихром/ат** m., **соль —овой кислоты** dichromate, bichromate; **—атизм** m. dichromatism; **—атический** a. dichromatic; **—овая кислота** dichromic acid.

**дихро/скоп** m. (cryst.) dichroscope; **—соль** f. dichroic salt.

**дицентрин** m. dicentrine.

**дицетил** m. dicetyl, dotriacontane.

**дициан** m. dicyanogen, cyanogen gas;

dicyan; **—диамид** m. dicyandiamide, cyanguanidine; **—ид** m. dicyanide; **—ин** m. dicyanine.

**дициклическ/ий** a. dicyclic; **—ое соединение** dicyclic compound.

**дицикло—** prefix dicyclo—, bicyclo—; **—гептан** m. bicycloheptane; **—пентил** m. dicyclopentyl.

**дицим/ил** m. dicymyl; **—ол** m. dicymene.

**дицинаммил** m. dicinnamyl.

**дич/ать** v. become wild, grow wild; **—ок** m. seedling; wilding; **—ь** f. game, wild life; thicket; nonsense, absurdity.

**диэлаидо—** prefix dielaido—.

**диэлдрин** m. an insecticide similar to aldrin.

**диэлектр/ик** m. (elec.) dielectric, nonconductor; insulator; **—ит** m. dielectrite (insulator); **—ический** a. dielectric, non-conducting; **—ическая постоянная**, **—ическая проницаемость** dielectric constant, permittivity.

**диэнантил** m. dienanthyl.

**диэозин** m. dieosine.

**диэрез** m. rupture, separation.

**диэта** see **диета**.

**диэтил** m. diethyl; **—анилин** m. diethyl aniline; **—барбитуровая кислота** diethylbarbituric acid, veronal.

**диэтилен** m., **—овый** a. diethylene; **двуокись —а** diethylene dioxide, dioxane; **—диамин** m. diethylenediamine, piperazine.

**диэтил/карбонат** m. diethyl carbonate; **—овый** a. diethyl; **—овый эфир** diethyl ether, ordinary ether; **—овый эфир винной кислоты** diethyl tartrate; **—овый эфир фталевой кислоты** diethyl phthalate; **—сульфат** m. diethyl sulfate; **—цинк** m. zinc diethyl.

**дк** abbr. (дека—) deca—; **дкг** abbr. (декаграмм) decagram; **дкл** abbr. (декалитр) decaliter; **дкм** abbr. (декаметр) decameter.

**ДКФ** abbr. (дикальцийфосфат) dicalcium phosphate.

**дл** abbr. (децилитр) deciliter; **дл.** abbr. (длина) length; (доля) a unit of weight.

**дланевидный** a. palmate.

**длин/а** f. length, stretch, run (of wire); height (of catalyst bed); **в—у, по—е**

longitudinally, lengthwise; endwise; **во всю —у** full length; **на единицу —ы** linear.

**длинно** *adv.* long, lengthily; **—ватый** *a.* somewhat long; **—волновой** *a.* longwave; **—волокнистый** *a.* long-fibered, long-staple; **—звеньевая цепь** longlink chain; **—пламенный** *a.* longflame (coal); **—плечий** *a.* long-armed; **—пробежный** *a.* long-range; **—сеточная машина** (paper) Fourdrinier machine; **—столбчатый** *a.* longcolumnar; **—усые** pl. (zool.) Nematocera; **—фокусный** *a.* long-focus.

**длинный** *a.* long, lengthy.

**длительн/о** *adv.* long, a long time; **—ость** *f.* length, duration, continuance; period, time; (pulse) width; **—ый** *a.* long, lasting, prolonged, protracted; continuous (operation); longterm (experiment).

**длить** *v.* protract, prolong, draw out, delay; **—ся** *v.* last, continue.

**для** *prep. gen.* for, to; **д. того, чтобы** in order that, so that, so as to; **д. чего** why?

**длящийся** *a.* lasting, permanent.

**дм** *abbr.* (дециметр) decimeter; **дм² ** *abbr.* (квадратный дециметр) square decimeter; **дм³** *abbr.* (кубический дециметр) cubic decimeter; **дм.** *abbr.* (дюйм) inch.

**ДММ** *abbr.* (диметилмочевина) dimethylurea; (молотковая дробилка) hammer mill.

**дн** *abbr.* (дина) dyne; **дн.** *abbr.* (дней) days; **д.н.** *abbr.* (действующее начало) primary nutrient.

**ДНВФ** *abbr.* (динитроортовторфенол) dinitro-*o*-sec-phenol.

**дне** *prepos. of* **день** and **дно.**

**днев/ка** *f.* day's rest, rest, stop; **—ник** *m.* diary, journal, record; **—ной** *a.* day, daytime, diurnal; **—ной свет** daylight; **коэффициент —ного освещения** daylight factor.

**днем** *adv.* in the daytime, during the day, by day; **д. и ночью** day and night, twenty-four hours a day, continuously.

**Днепр** the Dnieper (river); **—острой** Dnieprostroy.

**днище** *n.* bottom; bilge.

**ДНК** *abbr.* (дезоксирибонуклеиновая кислота) desoxyribonucleic acid, DNA.

**дно** *n.* bottom; ground; head (of drum); (welding) root; face (of cathode-ray tube); **вверх —м** upside down.

**ДНОК** *abbr.* (динитроортокрезол) dinitro-*o*-cresol.

**дноуглубитель** *m.* dredge.

**ДНРБ** *abbr.* (динитророданбензол) dinitrothiocyanobenzene; **ДНФ** *abbr.* (динитрофенол) dinitrophenol.

**до** *prep. gen.* before, prior; until, pending, till; to, up to, as far as; about, approximately; with; **до сих пор** up to now; **дело до него** business with him; **ему не до этого** he has no time for that.

**до—** *prefix with verbs* ad—, up to; to the end, completely, until ready; to finish; till, as far as, up to, far enough, sufficiently; *with adj.* hypo—, sub—.

**добав/ить, —лять** *v.* add, append, annex; admix, make up, fill up; boost (voltage); **—ка** *f.,* **—ок** *m.* addition, introduction; admixture, impurity; addition agent; accessory; **—ление** *n.* addition, adding, supplement, appendix; **—ленный** *a.* added, mixed (with); **—ляемое** *n.,* **—ляющийся** *a.* (math.) addend.

**добавочн/ый** *a.* additional, supplementary, accessory, auxiliary, extra; filler; admixed; (elec.) booster, boosting; after (effect, etc.); extension (pipe, rod); surplus (value); **д. агент** addition agent; **д. налог** surtax; **д. усилитель** booster; **—ая плата** bonus.

**добе/гать, —жать** *v.* run up to, reach.

**добела** *adv.* to white heat, white hot; **раскаленный д.** white hot, incandescent.

**добивать** *v.* finish off, dispatch; **—ся** *v.* aim (for), try to get, strive (for).

**добирать** *v.* finish gathering; **—ся** *v.* attain, reach, come, get (to).

**добить** *see* **добивать; —ся** *v.* obtain, get, attain, gain, secure, succeed; **—ся своего** have one's way, succeed.

**дображив/ание** *n.* after-fermentation, secondary fermentation; **—ать** *v.* finish fermenting.

**добрать** *see* **добирать.**

**добре/елит** *m.* (min.) daubréelite; **—ит** *m.* daubreite.

**добро** *n.* good; property, goods, chattels.

**добровол/ец** *m.* volunteer; **—ьно** *adv.* voluntarily; **—ьность** *f.* voluntariness; **—ьный** *a.* voluntary, free, willing, spontaneous; cooperative; **—ьческий** *a.* voluntary.

**доброкачественн/ость** *f.* good quality, soundness; factor of merit; **—ый** *a.* good-quality, sound; (med.) benign.

**добро/нравный** *a.* well-behaved, orderly; **—совестность** *f.* conscientiousness; **—совестный** *a.* conscientious, scrupulous; **—та** *f.* kindness, goodness; quality; **—тность** *f.* quality; quality factor, *Q*-factor; коэффициент **—тности** factor of merit; **—тный** *a.* good-quality, good; *suffix* **—**quality.

**добр/ый** *a.* good, kind; **—ое имя** reputation.

**добы/вание** *n.* extraction, mining, recovery; **—вать, —ть** *v.* extract, mine, recover, quarry; obtain, derive, acquire, procure, gain; **—ваться** *v.* be mined, come (from); **—вающая промышленность** extractive industry (mining, agriculture, etc.); **—тый** *a.* derived; **—ча** *f.* extraction, mining, recovery, crop (of ore); output (of mine), yield; production, generation; gain, profit.

**довар/енный** *a.* boiled enough; **—ивание** *n.* final boiling; **—ивать, —ить** *v.* finish boiling, boil sufficiently; digest.

**доведен/ие** *n.* bringing (to); finishing up; **—ный** *a.* brought, led (to); finished, finished up.

**довер/енность** *f.* trust, confidence; warrant, power of attorney; **—енный** *a.* trusted; *m.* proxy, agent; **—ие** *n.* trust, confidence; reliability; **—итель** *m.* constituent, principal; **—ительный** *a.* confidential; **—ить** *see* **доверять.**

**доверов порошок** (pharm.) Dover's powder.

**доверху** *adv.* up to the top, full.

**доверчив/ость** *f.* confidence, trust; **—ый** *a.* confiding, trusting.

**доверш/ать, —ить** *v.* consummate, finish, complete; **—ение** *n.* consummation, completion, accomplishment;

**—енный** *a.* consummated, completed, accomplished.

**доверять** *v.* trust, believe, credit.

**довес/ить** *see* **довешивать; —ок** *m.* make-weight.

**довести** *see* **доводить.**

**довешивать** *v.* make up the weight; finish weighing.

**довод** *m.* reason, argument.

**довод/ить** *v.* lead, bring (to), reduce; attain, reach; finish, finish up; refine; grind, polish, lap; **—иться** *v.* happen; **—ка** *f.*, **—очный** *a.* finish, finishing; grinding, lapping.

**довоенный** *a.* prewar.

**довольн/о** *adv.* enough, sufficiently; rather, fairly; **—ый** *a.* content, satisfied (with).

**довольств/ие** *n.* ration, allowance, allotment, portion, supply; вещевое д. personal equipment; **—о** *n.* ease, prosperity, content; **—овать** *v.* satisfy, provide; **—оваться** *v.* be satisfied (with).

**довсоновский газ** *see* **Доусона газ.**

**догад/аться, —ываться** *v.* guess, suspect, think (of); **—ка** *f.* surmise, guess; **—ливость** *f.* ingenuity; **—ливый** *a.* ingenious, shrewd.

**доггер** *m.* (geol.) dogger.

**догиалиновый** *a.* dohyaline.

**доглинг** *m.* bottle-nose (a whale).

**догляд/еть, —ывать** *v.* observe, notice; see to the end.

**догма** *f.*, **—т** *m.* dogma, theory, doctrine, maxim; **—тический, —тичный** *a.* dogmatic, positive, authoritative.

**догнать** *see* **догонять.**

**догов/ариваться, —ориться** *v.* negotiate, treat, arrange, make terms, come to an understanding; **—ор** *m.* agreement, contract, treaty, pact; **—орный** *a.* contract, stipulated, agreed.

**догон** *m.*, **—ка** *f.* overtaking; **—ять** *v.* overtake, catch up, reach.

**догор/ать, —еть** *v.* burn low, burn out, finish burning.

**догру/жать, —живать, —зить** *v.* finish loading, add; recharge, replenish; **—зка** *f.* additional charge.

**додавать** *v.* make up, pay up, add.

**додаивать** *v.* strip (a cow).

**дода/нный** *a.* made up, added; paid up; —**ть** *see* **додавать;** —**ча** *f.* making up, addition.

**додекагон** *m.* (geom.) dodecagon.

**додекан** *m.* dodecane; —**ал** *m.* dodecanal, lauraldehyde;—**овая кислота** dodecanoic acid, lauric acid; —**ол** *m.* dodecanol, dodecyl alcohol.

**додекаэдр** *m.* (cryst.) dodecahedron; —**ический** *a.* dodecahedral.

**додел/анный** *a.* finished off, completed; —**ать,** —**ывать** *v.* finish off, complete; touch up; —**ывание** *n.* completion.

**додеценал** *m.* dodecenal.

**додецил** *m.,* —**овый** *a.* dodecyl; —**амин** *m.* dodecylamine, aminododecane; —**ен** *m.* dodecylene, decylethylene; —**овый спирт** dodecyl alcohol, 1-dodecanol; —**овая кислота** dodecylic acid.

**додум/аться,** —**ываться** *v.* conclude, come to a conclusion; think up, hit on (idea).

**доезжать** *v.* arrive, reach, attain.

**доение** *n.* milking.

**доехать** *see* **доезжать.**

**дожар/ивать,** —**ить** *v.* finish roasting.

**дождаться** *v.* wait (for), expect.

**дождев/альный** *a.,* —**ание** *n.* sprinkling, overhead irrigation; —**атель** *m.* sprinkler; —**ик** *m.* raincoat; (bot.) puffball (*Lycoperdon*); —**ой** *a.* rain, rainy, pluvial, hyetal; spray (nozzle); —**ой червь** earthworm; —**ое облако** rain cloud, nimbus;. —**ые осадки** rainfall, precipitation.

**дожде/мер** *m.* rain gage; —**мерное ведро** rain-gage receiver; —**носный** *a.* rainy, pluvial; —**писец** *m.* pluviograph; —**приемник** *m.* rain gully, gully.

**дожд/ить** *v.* rain; —**ливый** *a.* rainy; —**ливый период** rain spell; rainy season; —**ь** *m.* rain; cascade, shower.

**дожечь** *see* **дожигать.**

**дожив/ание** *n.* living (to a given time); **кривая** —**ания** (biol.) survival curve; —**ать** *v.* live (until); stay (the rest of).

**дожигать** *v.* burn up, finish burning; burn sufficiently; —**ся** *v.* burn out, finish burning, smolder.

**дожидать,** —**ся** *see* **дождаться.**

**дожить** *see* **доживать.**

**доз/а** *f.* dose, portion; (radiobiology) dose, dosage; **д. половинной выживаемости** median lethal dose, MLD; **мощность** —**ы** dose rate, dosage rate; **полной** —**ой** full-scale (irradiation).

**дозаривание** *n.* after-ripening; artificial ripening.

**дозаря/д** *m.,* —**жающий** *a.* (elec.) milking.

**дозатор** *m.* dosing apparatus, measuring device; batcher, batchmeter; proportioning hopper, hopper dispenser; **д. времени** timing unit.

**дозвол/ение** *n.* permission; —**енный** *a.* permitted, authorized; legal; —**ительный** *a.* permissible; —**ить,** —**ять** *v.* permit, allow, authorize, grant.

**дозвуковой** *a.* (acous.) subsonic.

**дозиметр** *m.* dosimeter, dose meter (for measuring radiation); **д. местности** area monitor; —**ист** *m.* health physicist, radiation supervisor; —**ический** *a.* dosimetric; health-monitoring; —**ическая служба** radiation monitoring service; —**ическая физика** health physics; —**ия** *f.* dosimetry, (radiation) monitoring, radiation control.

**дозиров/ание** *n.,* —**ка** *f.* dosing, dosage; measuring out, dispensing, proportioning; (chem.) batching; monitoring; determination; —**анный** *a.* measured out, proportioned; —**ать** *v.* dose; measure out, proportion; **весовая** —**ка** proportioner, proportioning feeder; —**очный** *a.* dosing, dosage; proportioning, metering.

**дозирующий прибор** *see* **дозатор, дозиметр.**

**дозна/вание** *n.* inquiring, finding out; —**ваться,** —**ться** *v.* inquire (about), find out, ascertain, question; —**ние** *n.* inquiry, search, investigation.

**дозор** *m.,* —**ный** *a.* patrol; (night) watch; **ходить** —**ом** *v.* patrol.

**дозре/вание** *n.* ripening; —**вать,** —**ть** *v.* ripen, finish ripening; —**лый** *a.* completely ripe.

**доильн/ик** *m.* milk pail; —**ый** *a.* milking; —**я** *f.* dairy.

**доиск/аться** *v.* find out, ascertain, determine, establish; —**ивание** *n.* finding out, seeking out; —**иваться** *v.* search, try to find out, inquire.

**доисторический** *a.* prehistoric.

до/ить *v.* milk; —йка *f.* milking; —йная *a.* milch (cow); —йник *m.* milk pail.

дойти *see* доходить.

док *m.*, ставить в д. *v.* dock.

ДОК *abbr.* (дезоксикортикостерон) desoxycorticosterone.

докадмиевый *a.* sub-cadmium.

доказ/ательный *a.* demonstrative, convincing, conclusive; —ательство *n.* demonstration, argument, proof, evidence; —ать, —ывать *v.* demonstrate, argue, prove, show, substantiate; —уемый *a.* demonstrable.

доканчив/ание *n.* finishing, completing; —ать *v.* finish, complete, end up.

докапывать *v.* finish digging; —ся *v.* find out, uncover, reveal.

докембрий *m.*, —ский *a.* (geol.) Precambrian.

докер *m.* docker.

доклад *m.* report, paper, talk, lecture; —ная записка memorandum, report; —чик *m.* reporter; speaker, lecturer; —ывать *v.* report, present (a paper); announce; add.

докозан *m.* docosane; —овая кислота docosanoic acid, behenic acid; —ол *m.* docosanol.

доконать *v.* finish, break, destroy.

доконч/енный *a.* finished, ended, completed; —ить *see* доканчивать.

докопать *see* докапывать.

докрасна *adv.* to red heat, to redness; раскаленный д. red hot.

докритический *a.* subcritical.

доктор *m.* doctor, physician; степень —а, —ская степень doctorate, doctor's degree (Ph.D.); —ант *m.* student preparing for doctor's degree; —ская проба doctor test (for sulfur in gasoline).

доктрина *f.* doctrine, teaching, tenet.

докуда *adv.* how far? until when?

докука *f.* annoyance, worry.

документ *m.* document, deed, instrument; —альный *a.* documentary.

докуп/ать, —ить *v.* buy in addition, buy more; —ка *f.* additional purchase.

докучать *v.* annoy, trouble, worry.

долац *m.* dolina, sink hole.

долбеж *m.*, —ка *f.* mortise; —ный *a.* grooving, slotting; —ная головка slotting attachment.

долб/ить, —нуть *v.* chisel, hollow, chip, cut, pick; (mil.) batter; —ление *n.* chiseling, hollowing, slotting, mortising; —ня *f.* beater, beetle, ram, rammer; —як *m.* cog-wheel cutter, gear-wheel cutter.

долг. *abbr.* (долгота) longitude.

долг *m.* debt, obligation, duty; loan; —и *pl.* debts, liabilities, arrears; в д. on credit, on trust.

долгий *a.* long, protracted, prolonged.

долго *adv.* long, a long time; —вато *adv.*, —ватый *a.* rather long; —вечность *f.* longevity, lasting quality, durability; life (of machine); —вечный *a.* long-lived, long-lasting, durable, permanent.

долговой *a.* debt.

долго/временный *a.* durable, lasting, permanent; of long duration; —денствие, —летие *n.* longevity, long life; —живущий *a.* long-lived; —летний *a.* long, long-established, of many years' standing; —ножки *pl.* crane flies (*Tipulidae*); —носики *pl.* weevils (*Curculionidae*); —прочность *f.* durability; —срочный *a.* long-term, long, lasting, long-range, of long duration; —та *f.* length; (geog.) longitude.

долевой *a.* per unit; (anat.) lobar.

долее *comp. of* долго, longer.

долерит *m.* (petr.) dolerite (a basalt); —овый *a.* doleritic.

долерофанит *m.* (min.) dolerophanite (a copper sulfate).

долж/енствовать *v.* be obliged, be forced (to); owe; он —ен he must, he has to; —но one must; —но быть probably; это —но быть it must be; this is probably; —ник *m.* debtor; —ное *n.* due; воздавать —ное *v.* do justice (to).

должност/ной *a.* official, functional; —ное лицо official, functionary; —ь *f.* office, function, post, position; исполняющий —ь acting, acting for.

должн/ый *a.* due, proper, right, owing; быть —ым *v.* owe.

долив/ать *v.* add (by pouring), fill up, pour full; —ка *f.* addition.

долин/а *f.*, —ный *a.* valley, trough; length; д. волны wavelength.

долит/ый *a.* added, poured full; —ь *see* доливать.

**долихо—** *prefix* dolicho— (long, narrow).

**доллар** *m.* dollar.

**доложить** *see* докладывать.

**долой** *interjection* away, off, down.

**доломит** *m.* (min.) dolomite, pearl spar; **—изация** *f.* dolomitization; **—изированный** *a.* dolomitized; **—изировать, —изовать** *v.* dolomitize; **—ный, —овый** *a.* dolomite, dolomitic.

**доломол** *m.* dolomol (magnesium stearate).

**долот/ной, —чатый** *a.* chisel; **—ная сталь** drilling steel; **—о** *n.* chisel, gouge; (drill) bit; **—ообразный** *a.* chisel-shaped; **—чатая головка** chisel point.

**доль/ка** *f.* lobule, small lobe; **—ный** *a.* lobate, lobe-like; **—чатый** *a.* lobed.

**дольше** *see* долее.

**дол/я** *f.* share, portion; allotment, quota; part, segment; fraction, particle; fate, lot; (bot., anat.) lobe; unit of weight **—44.435 mg.; миллионные —и** parts per million; **вносить —ю** *v.* subscribe, contribute a share; **входить в —ю с** *v.* become partners with; **выпадать на —ю** *v.* fall to the lot (of); **книга в четвертую —ю листа** quarto.

**дом** *m.* house, home; **—а** at home; **вне —а** outdoors, outside, in the open; abroad.

**дом.** *abbr.* (домашний) domestic.

**домат/ический, —овый** *a.* (cryst.) domatic.

**домашн/ий** *a.* domestic, home, home-made, household; **—ее хозяйство** domestic economy; household; **—яя птица** poultry; **—яя хозяйка** housewife.

**домейкит** *m.* (min.) domeykite (a copper arsenide).

**домен** *m.* domain.

**домен/ный** *a.,* **—ная печь** (met.) blast furnace; **д.** metallurgical (coke); **д. свинец** pig lead; **д. цех** blast-furnace plant; **д. шлак** blast-furnace slag; **—щик** *m.* blast-furnace operator.

**доместикация** *f.* domestication.

**доместицин** *m.* domesticine.

**домик** *m.* little house, booth.

**доминант/а** *f.,* **—ный** *a.* (biol.) dominant.

**доминион** *m.* dominion.

**доминир/овать** *v.* dominate, predominate; **—ующий** *a.* dominating, predominant.

**домит** *m.* domite (a trachyte rock).

**домкрат** *m.,* **—ный** *a.* jack, screw jack, lifting jack.

**домн/а** *f.* (met.) blast furnace; **—ица** *f.* bloomery (furnace).

**домовитый** *a.* economical, thrifty.

**домовладелец** *m.* house owner, landlord.

**домовый** *a.* house; **д. гриб** (bot.) a timber-destroying fungus (*Merulius lacrimans*).

**домогаться** *v.* solicit, sue, seek.

**домой** *adv.* home, homeward.

**домо/рощенный** *a.* home-grown, home-produced; **—строение** *n.* house building.

**домы/вать, —ть** *v.* finish washing.

**донаксин** *m.* donaxine, gramine.

**донарит** *m.* (expl.) donarite.

**донатор** *m.,* **—ный** *a.* donor.

**донашивать** *v.* wear out, finish wearing.

**Донбасс** *abbr.* (Донецкий угольный бассейн) Donets Coal Basin, Donbas.

**донга** *f.* donga, dry wash.

**донес/ение** *n.* report, dispatch, account, message; **—ти** *see* доносить.

**Донецкий бассейн** *see* Донбасс.

**донизу** *adv.* to the bottom.

**донимать** *v.* worry, exasperate.

**донка** *f.* donkey pump.

**донкихотский** *a.* quixotic, foolish.

**Доннана равновесие** Donnan equilibrium.

**донник** *m.* (bot.) sweet clover (*Melilotus*); heading (for barrels).

**донн/ый** *a.* ground, bottom; (biol.) benthonic; **д. лед** ground ice; **д. осадок** bottoms, residue, sludge; **—ая фаза** (salt system) solid phase.

**доноокругловочный станок** head-rounding machine (for barrels, drums).

**донор** *m.* (phys.) donor; blood donor.

**донос/ить** *v.* carry up to; report, denounce; wear out (clothes); **—чик** *m.* informer.

**донышко** *n.* bottom; header (of tube).

**донять** *see* донимать.

**доотказа** *adv.* all the way in, as far as possible, tight, home (of fitted part).

**доохла/дитель** *m.* after-cooler, recooler, secondary cooler; **—ждать** *v.* cool again, recool; —ждение *n.* after-cooling.

доп. *abbr.* (дополнение) supplement.

допа *f.* dopa, 3,4-dihydroxyphenylalanine.

допан *m.* (pharm.) Dopane.

допе/кать, —чь *v.* finish baking.

допла/та *f.,* —чивание *n.* additional payment, remaining payment; —тить, —чивать *v.* pay in addition, pay up; —ченный *a.* paid up.

доплерит *see* допплерит.

доплы/вать, —ть *v.* swim up to, float up to, reach.

доподлинн/о *adv.* to a certainty, for certain; —ый *a.* certain, authentic, genuine.

дополаскивать *v.* finish rinsing.

дополн/ение *n.* supplement, complement, addition; —енный *a.* supplemented, added, made up, completed; —ительный *a.* supplementary, additional, subsidiary, extra, spare, accessory, auxiliary; admixed; complementary (angle; color); side (reaction); —ительная величина (math.) complement; —ительная функция (math.) cofunction; —ить, —ять *v.* supplement, complete, add, complement, make up, fill up.

дополучить *v.* receive in addition.

допотопный *a.* antiquated, antediluvian.

допплер/ит *m.* (min.) dopplerite (a natural oxygenated hydrocarbon); —овское смещение Doppler shift, Doppler frequency.

допр/ашивать, —осить *v.* examine, question; —оситься *v.* get by asking; —ос *m.* examination, questioning, interrogation.

допуск *m.* allowance; admission, admittance; tolerance, permissible variation, clearance limit; д. на allowance for; единица —а tolerance unit; —аемость *f.* admissibility; —аемый *a.* admissible, safe, permissible, *see also* допустимый; —ать *v.* admit, receive; permit, allow, tolerate; grant, assume, consider probable; accept; take for granted; —ающий *a.* permitting; accessible.

допустим/ый *a.* admissible, permissible, allowable, acceptable, safe; —ая доза tolerance dose; —ая концентрация maximum permissible concentration (of dust, gas, etc.); —ая нагрузка permissible load, safe load; carrying capacity; —ая нагрузка током current-carrying capacity; —ая точность (measurement) tolerance; —ое отклонение permissible variation; tolerance.

допустить *see* допускать.

допущен/ие *n.* admission; permission, allowance, tolerance; assumption; —ный *a.* admitted; permitted, allowed, tolerated; authorized.

допыт/аться *v.* find out, discover, disclose; —ываться *v.* question, investigate.

дораб/атывать, —отать *v.* finish working.

дора/стать, —сти *v.* grow up to, reach; —щивание *n.* growing up to; maturing (of vegetables in cold frames).

дореволюционный *a.* prerevolutionary.

доремол *m.* doremol.

дормиол *m.* dormiol, amylene chloral.

дорн *m.* mandrel, spindle, shaft (for piecing together rubber articles).

Дорна эффект Dorn effect.

дорновой *a. of* дорн.

дорный *a.* split, fissured, cracked.

дорог/а *f.* road, way, passage, path; —ой in passing, on the way; в —е en route, on the way; давать —у *v.* make way (for), give way (to); уступать —у *v.* let pass.

дорого *adv.* dear, expensive, high; —визна *f.* expensiveness; —й *a.* dear, expensive, costly, high-priced.

дородный *a.* corpulent, obese, fat.

дорож/ать *v.* rise in price; —е *comp. of* дорого, дорогой, more expensive; —ить *v.* value, prize; —иться *v.* overcharge, ask too much (for).

дорож/ка *f.* path, track, trail, walk; —ник *m.* grooving plane; —ный *a.* road, highway; —ный отдел highway department; —ный струг grader.

Дорра агитатор Dorr agitator.

дорсальный *a.* dorsal.

дортмундский чан Dortmund tank (for sewage).

дортуар *m.* dormitory.

досад/а *f.* vexation, disappointment;

—ить *see* досаждать, досаживать;
—но *adv.* it is a pity, it is too bad;
—ный *a.* vexing, disappointing, unfortunate; —овать *v.* be displeased (with).

досаждать *v.* annoy, irritate.
досаживать *v.* finish planting, add.
досинхронный *a.* hyposynchronous.
доск/а *f.*, —овый *a.* board, plank; (instrument) panel; slab, plate (for engraving); классная д. blackboard; обшивать —ами *v.* plank, board up; —овый фут board foot (unit of measurement).

доскональный *a.* precise, detailed.
досл/анный *a.* sent up, sent on; —ать *see* досылать.
дословн/о *adv.* word for word, literally, verbatim; —ый *a.* literal, verbatim.
дослуж/ивать, —ить *v.* serve until, serve out, serve one's time.
дослуш/ать, —ивать *v.* hear out, hear to the end.
досм/атривать, —отреть *v.* see to the end; inspect, examine.
досолить *v.* add more salt.
досохнуть *see* досыхать.
доспе/вание *n.* ripening, maturing; —вать, —ть *v.* ripen, finish ripening; —лый *a.* ripe, mature.
доспехи *pl.* armor.
досрочн/о *adv.* ahead of schedule; —ый *a.* premature, early.
доставать *v.* get, obtain, procure; reach; bring; suffice; —ся *v.* fall to one's lot.
достав/ить, —лять *v.* deliver, convey, transmit; furnish, supply, give, yield, bring, afford; —ка *f.*, —ление *n.* delivery; transportation; furnishing, supply, procuring; yield, recovery; —ленный *a.* delivered, conveyed, furnished, supplied, yielded; —очный *a.* delivery; —щик *m.* supplier.
достаивать *v.* stand to the end.
достаток *m.* prosperity; income.
достаточн/о *adv.* sufficiently, adequately, satisfactorily; it is sufficient; —ость *f.* sufficiency, adequacy; competence; —ый *a.* sufficient, adequate, ample, satisfactory; competent.
достать *see* доставать.
дости/гаемость, —жимость *f.* attainability, accessibility, practicability;

—гаемый, —жимый *a.* attainable, accessible, approachable, practicable; —гать, —гнуть, —чь *v.* reach, attain, get, obtain, achieve, gain; come (up to), arrive; amount, run (to); не —гать *v.* fail; —гнутый *a.* attained, reached; —жение *n.* attainment, achievement, improvement, progress.

достоверн/ость *f.* authenticity, truth; confidence; граница —ости confidence limit; показатель—ости различия (math.) statistically reliable difference; —ый *a.* authentic, reliable, proved, certain, trustworthy; significant; —ая руда proved ore, positive ore; —ые запасы (min.) proved resources.

достодолжный *a.* due, proper, just.
достоинство *n.* quality, merit, virtue.
достойный *a.* worth, worthy, deserving.
достопримечательн/ость *f.* curiosity, rarity; —ый *a.* notable, remarkable.
достояние *n.* property; contribution.
достоять *see* достаивать.
достраив/ание *n.* finishing construction; —ать *v.* finish building, add on (building).
дострел *m.* shooting, perforation.
достро/ить *see* достраивать; —йка *see* достраивание.
доступ *m.* access, approach, entrance, admission, inlet, passage; закрыть д. *v.* make inaccessible; —но *adv.* easily, simply, accessibly; —ность *f.* accessibility, access, availability; —ный *a.* accessible, within reach, available, approachable, practicable; легко —ный easily available, within easy reach.
досуг *m.* leisure, spare time.
досу/ха *adv.* to dryness, until dry, dry; —шивать, —шить *v.* finish drying.
досчатый *see* дощатый.
досылать *v.* send on, send the remainder.
досып/анный *a.* filled up, added; —ать *v.* fill up, add; sleep enough, finish sleeping; —ка *f.* filling up, addition.
досыта *adv.* to satiety, sufficiently.
досыхать *v.* get dry, become dry.
досье *n.* file, papers.
досюда *adv.* this far, up to here.
досяг/ать, —нуть *v.* attain, reach,

accomplish; —**аемость** *f.* reach, range, attainability, extent; —**аемый** *a.* within reach, attainable, approachable.

**дотация** *f.* subsidy, grant.

**доте/кать,** —**чь** *v.* flow up to.

**дотла** *adv.* utterly, completely.

**дотоле** *adv.* hitherto.

**дотрагиваться** *v.* touch.

**дотриаконтан** *m.* dotriacontane.

**дотронуться** *see* **дотрагиваться.**

**дотуда** *adv.* up to there, to that place.

**дотя/гивать,** —**нуть** *v.* drag up to, draw up to; last out; —**гиваться,** —**нуться** *v.* reach (with difficulty), hold out, last.

**Доусона газ** Dowson (producer) gas.

**ДОФА** *abbr.* (**диоксифенилаланин**) dihydroxyphenylalanine.

**дофиновый голубой** Dauphin blue.

**дох/лый** *a.* dead (animal); —**лятина** *f.* carrion; —**нуть** *v.* die.

**дохнуть** *see* **дышать.**

**доход** *m.* income, returns, revenue, profit, gain; —**ить** *v.* come (to), go (to), reach, attain; extend (to), go as far (as); amount, run (to), total; ripen, develop; —**ность** *f.* profitableness, earning capacity; income; —**ный** *a.* profitable, paying; —**ные статьи** revenues.

**доцент** *m.* lecturer, reader; associate professor.

**дочерн/ий** *a.* daughter, filial, subsidiary, secondary; (nucl.) daughter, decay-product; —**ее вещество** daughter, decay product.

**дочиста** *adv.* completely.

**дочит/ать,** —**ывать** *v.* finish reading.

**дочь** *f.* daughter.

**дошкольный** *a.* preschool.

**дошлый** *a.* experienced, skilful.

**дошник** *m.* tank, vat.

**дощ/атый** *a.* board, plank; tabular; **д. настил, д. ход** boardwalk; —**ечка** *f.* small plank; tablet, slab, plate; —**ник** *m.* tan vat.

**доэвтектоидный** *a.* (met.) hypoeutectoid.

**дояр** *m.,* —**ка** *f.* (agr.) milker.

**ДПН** *abbr.* (**дифосфопиридиннуклеотид**) diphosphopyridine nucleotide, DPN, coenzyme I.

**др.** *abbr.* (**другое**) the other, the rest; (**другие**) others; **д-р** *abbr.* (**доктор**) doctor.

**дравит** *m.* (min.) dravite (a variety of tourmaline).

**драга** *f.* drag, dredge, dredger.

**драгант** *m.* tragacanth (gum).

**драг/ер** *m.* dredger; —**ирование** *n.* dredging; —**ировать** *v.* dredge, drag, scoop or drag out; —**лайн** *see* **дреглайн.**

**драгоценн/ость** *f.* jewel, gem, precious stone; valuable; —**ый** *a.* precious, valuable; —**ый камень** precious stone, gem.

**драгун трава** (bot.) tarragon (*Artemisia dracunculus*).

**драек** *m.* dowel.

**драже** *n.* sugar plum; (pharm.) lozenge.

**дражиров/ание** *n.,* —**очный** *a.* coating, pelleting (of seeds); —**анный** *a.* coated, pelleted.

**дражное дело** *see* **драгирование.**

**дразн/ение** *n.* teasing, exciting; (met.) poling; —**илка** *f.* pole, stirrer; —**ить** *v.* tease, excite; pole, stir.

**драйер** *m.* dryer, drying machine.

**драка** *f.* fight.

**дракон** *m.* dragon (lizard); —**ил** *m.* draconyl; —**иловая кислота** draconylic acid; —**ический** *a.* (astron.) draconic; —**ова кровь** dragon's blood (resin); —**овая кислота** draconic acid, anisic acid; —**овое дерево** (bot.) dragon tree (*Dracaena draco*).

**дран/ица** *f.,* —**ка** *f.,* —**ь** *f.,* —**ичный** *a.* lath, lathing, batten, shingle; shaving, chip, boring, turning; —**ый** *a.* torn, tattered.

**драп** *m.* thick cloth; —**ировать** *v.* drape; —**ировка** *f.,* —**ри** *n.* drapery.

**дратва** *f.* wax-end; lacing (of belt); (pitched) thread.

**драть** *v.* tear, pull, strip off; —**ся** *v.* fight.

**драфт** *m.* glass rod.

**драхма** *f.* dram (old unit of weight).

**драцена** *f.* (bot.) dracaena (*Cordyline* or *Dracaena draco*).

**драциловая кислота** dracylic acid.

**драчев/ый напильник** bastard file; —**ая насечка** bastard cut.

**ДРБ** *abbr.* (**динитророданбензол**) dinitrothiocyanobenzene.

дребедень *f.* rubbish, trash; loose texture.

дребезги *see* вдребезги.

дребезж/ание *n.* jar, jarring, rattling; —ать *v.* jar, rattle.

древес/ина *f.* wood; lignin; wood pulp, wood cellulose; —ница, въедливая leopard moth (*Zeuzera pyrina*); —нокислый *see* древесноуксуснокислый; —нослоистый *a.* laminated wood; —ность *f.* woodiness.

древесноугольный *a.* charcoal, wood charcoal; д. чугун charcoal iron.

древесноуксусн/ая кислота pyroligneous acid (an impure acetic acid); соль —ой кислоты, —окислая соль pyrolignite; —окислый *a.* pyroligneous acid; pyrolignite (of); —окислое железо iron pyrolignite, iron liquor.

древесн/ый *a.* wood, woody, ligneous; fibrous; arboreal; wood-pulp (paper); д. воск (agr.) grafting wax; д. картон fiber-board; д. настой *see* древесноуксуснокислое железо; д. порошок, —ая мука wood meal, sawdust; д. сахар wood sugar, xylose; д. спирт wood alcohol, methyl alcohol; д. уголь charcoal; д. уксус wood vinegar, pyroligneous acid (an impure acetic acid); —ая замазка wood cement, joiner's putty; (agr.) grafting clay; —ая камедь wood gum, xylan; —ая масса wood pulp; —ая слабительная губка (pharm.) agaric; —ая стружка wood shavings, excelsior; —ая шерсть, —ое мочало wood fiber, excelsior; —ое масло wood oil; specif. tung oil; —ое топливо fire wood; —ые опилки sawdust.

древко *n.* shaft, pikestaff.

древн/е— *prefix* paleo—, ancient; —екрылые насекомые (zool.) Paleoptera; —ий *a.* ancient, old; early; —ость *f.* antiquity, ancient times.

древо/вал *m.* feller, felling machine; tree uprooter; —видность *f.* woodiness; —видный, —подобный *a.* woody, ligneous, xyloid; arborescent, dendritic, tree-like; —дел *m.* woodworker, cabinetmaker; —еды *pl.* (zool.) Xylophaga; —измерение *n.* dendrometry; —насаждение *n.* plantation of trees;

—терка *f.* (paper) pulp grinder; —точец *m.* (zool.) borer; —точцы *pl.* carpenter moths (*Cossidæ*).

древпластики *pl.* wood plastics.

дреглайн *m.* drag line, drag-line excavator.

дредноут *m.* (mil.) dreadnought.

дрезина *f.* trolley, hand car.

дрейкантер *m.* (geol.) dreikanter; (cryst.) trihedron.

дрейф *m.*, —овый, —ующий *a.* drift, drifting; угол —а drift angle; —овать *v.* drift, drive.

дрек *m.* grapnel.

дрель *f.* drill.

дрема *f.* (bot.) melandrium; silene; lychnis.

дрем/ать *v.* doze, slumber; —ливый *a.* somnolent, sleepy.

дремлик *m.* (bot.) orchid (*Orchis moria*); болотный д. orchid (*Epipactis palustris*).

дрем/лющий *a.* dozing; —ота *f.* drowsiness; —отный *a.* drowsy, somnolent.

дремучий *a.* dense, thick (forest).

дрен *m.*, —а *f.* drain; —аж *m.*, —ажный *a.* drainage, drain; —ажировать, —ировать *v.* drain, draw off; —ажный канал drain, gutter; —ирование *n.* draining, drainage; —ированный *a.* drained.

дренчер *m.*, —ное оборудование drencher.

дресва *f.* gravel.

дрессер *m.* dresser.

дрессиров/ать *v.* train; —ка *f.*, —очный *a.* training; (met.) dressing off, trimming, leveling.

дрешер *m.* (paper) thresher, thrasher.

дриадовые *pl.* (bot.) Dryadaceae.

дриттельзильбер *m.* tiers-argent (a silver-aluminum alloy).

дрифтер *m.* (min.) drifter (a rock drill).

дробеструйная очистка (foundry) cleaning with a blast of metal shot.

дробилка *f.* crusher, breaker; (hammer) mill; д.-мешалка disintegrator.

дробильн/ый *a.* crushing; д. прибор, —ая машина crusher; —ые вальцы crusher rolls, crushing rolls.

дроб/ина *f.*, —инка *f.* small shot, pellet; (brewery) residues, dregs, spent grains, mash; —ить *v.* crush, stamp, pulverize, grind, granulate; divide, split up, break down; **—ление** *n.* crushing, grinding, granulation, breaking, breaking down; **—леный** *a.* crushed, ground, granulated.

**дроб/ность** *f.* divisibility; **—ный** *a.* fractional; divided, broken; split (application); **—ная перегонка** fractional distillation; **—овидный** *a.* buckshot; **—овой** *a.* shot; **—овой эффект** (thermionics) shot effect, shot noise; **—овая коронка** (min.) core bit; **—ь** *f.* (math.) fraction; (met.) shot; **периодическая—ь** repeating decimal.

**дробянка** *f.* (bot.) schizophyte.

**дробящий** *a.* crushing; disruptive.

**дров/а** *pl.*, **—яной** *a.* wood, firewood; **—окол** *m.*, **—околка** *f.*, **—окольный станок** cleaver, wood-splitter; **—осек** *m.* woodsman, lumberjack, tree feller; **—осеки** *pl.* long-horned beetles (*Cerambycidae*).

**дроги** *pl.* dray cart.

**дрогист** *m.* druggist.

**дрогнуть** *v.* shake; move, jerk; waver, falter.

**дрож/ание** *n.* vibration, shaking, shivering, tremor; flickering; jarring; **—ать** *v.* vibrate, shake, shiver; flicker; jar; jerk; **—ащий** *a.* vibrating, shivering.

**дрожд/и** *see* **дрожжи**; **—яной** *a.* yeasty, yeast-like; dreggy.

**дрожжевание** *n.* fermentation.

**дрожжев/ой** *a.* yeast; **д. грибок** yeast fungus, yeast plant; **—ая кислота** nucleic acid; **—ая клетка** yeast cell; **—ые грибы** (bot.) Saccharomyces, yeast fungi.

**дрожж/еподобный** *a.* yeast-like, yeasty; **—и** *pl.* yeast, leaven; **задавать —и** *v.* (brewing) add yeast to the wort; pitch; **прессованные —и** yeast cake; **ставить на —ах** *v.* leaven; **хлеб на —ах** yeast bread.

**дрожки** *pl.* droshky.

**дрожь** *f.* shiver, chill, tremor.

**дрозд** *m.* (zool.) thrush.

**дрозометр** *m.* (meteor.) drosometer.

**дрозофила** *f.* fruit fly (*Drosophila*).

**дрок** *m.* (bot.) furze (*Ulex*); broom (*Genista*); **красильный д.** dyer's broom (*G. tinctoria*).

**дромадер** *m.* (zool.) dromedary.

**дронт** *m.* (zool.) dodo.

**дросс** *m.* (met.) dross, slag.

**дроссел/евать,** **—ировать** *v.* throttle, choke; baffle; **—ирование** *n.* throttling, choking; **—ирующий** *a.* throttling.

**дроссель** *m.*, **—ный** *a.* throttle, choke; (elec.) choke coil; **д.-клапан,** **—ный клапан** throttle, throttle valve; butterfly valve; **—ный эффект** (heat) Joule-Thomson effect; **—ная заслонка** baffle plate; **—ная катушка** (elec.) choke coil, inductor.

**дроссовый** *a.* (met.) dross.

**дротик** *m.* dart; spear.

**дроты** *pl.* glass tubes, glass tubing.

**дрочник** *see* **дрок, красильный.**

**друг** *m.* friend; **д. —а** each other, one another; **д. за —ом** one after another, in succession; **—ие** *pl.* others, the rest.

**другой** *a.* other, another, different; **кто-то д.** someone else; **тот и д.** both; **ни тот ни д.** neither.

**Друде уравнение** (light dispersion) Drude equation.

**друж/ба** *f.* friendship; **—елюбный,** **—еский,** **—ественный** *a.* friendly.

**дружина** *f.* brigade.

**дружить** *v.* be friends (with).

**дружковский** *a.* Druzhkovka.

**дружн/о** *adv.* amicably; unanimously, in unison, together; **—ый** *a.* friendly, harmonious, unanimous; (math.) amicable (numbers); **—ая весна** spring with rapid and continuous thawing of snow.

**друз/а** *f.* (min.) druse; node, nodule; **—овидный,** **—овый,** **—ообразный** *a.* drusy.

**друмлин** *m.* (geol.) drumlin.

**друммондов свет** Drummond limelight.

**друшла/г,** **—к** *see* **дуршлаг.**

**дрыг/ание** *n.* jerking, twitching; **—ать,** **—нуть** *v.* jerk, twitch.

**дрюит** *m.* drewite (a calcium carbonate deposit).

**дряб/лость** *f.* flabbiness; **—лый** *a.* flabby, flaccid, limp; **—нуть** *v.* become flabby, wither.

**дрягиль** *m.* carrier, porter.

**дряква** *f.* (bot.) cyclamen.

**дрян/ной** *a.* worthless; **—ь** *f.* trash.

дрях/ление *n.* aging; —леть, —нуть *v.* age, grow decrepit; —лость *f.* senility; decrepit state; —лый *a.* senile, infirm; decrepit.

ДСП *abbr.* (древеснослоистый пластик) wood-resin laminate.

ДТ *abbr.* (дизельный трактор) diesel tractor.

Дуайт-Ллойда машина Dwight-Lloyd (sintering) machine.

дуалин *m.*, —овый *a.* (expl.) dualin.

дуал/истический *a.* dualistic; —ьность *f.* duality.

дуант *m.*, —ный *a.* (nucl.) duant, dee, D-electrode (of cyclotron).

дуб *m.* (bot.) oak (*Quercus*).

дуб/ас, —ень *m.* tanbark (from oak).

дубильно/алюминиевая соль aluminum tannate; —железистая соль ferrous tannate; —кислый *a.* tannic acid; tannate (of); —кислый висмут bismuth tannate; —кислая соль tannate; —кислое железо iron tannate.

дубильн/ый *a.* tanning, tannic; д. куб tan vat, tan pit; д. материал tanning agent; д. раствор tannin solution; д. сок tan liquor; —ая кислота tannic acid, digallic acid; —ой кислоты tannate; —ая кора tanbark; —ое вещество tannin, tannic acid; —я *f.* tannery, tanyard.

дубильщик *m.* tanner.

дубина *f.* club, cudgel.

дубинидин *m.* dubinidine.

дуб/итель *m.* tanning material, tanning agent; —ить *v.* tan; —ление *n.* tanning; —леный *a.* tanned; —леный жирами oil-tanned, chamois.

дубл/ер *m.* doubler; —ет *m.* doublet, dipole; duplicate; —етов метод (mass spectrometry) doublet method; —икат *m.* duplicate, replica, counterpart.

дублиров/ание *n.* doubling, duplication; —анный *a.* doubled; —ать *v.* double, duplicate; fold; —очный *a.* doubling, double; duplicating.

дуб/ло *n.*, —овина *f.*, —овая кора tanbark (from oak); кукурузный —ляк a beetle (*Pentodon idiota*); —няк *m.* oak grove, oak wood; —оватый *a.* coarse; —овик *m.* a variety of mushroom; —овый *a.* oak, oaken; —овые ягодки *see* дубянка.

дубоизин *see* дубуазин.

дубрава *f.* oak woods.

дубров/ка *f.* (bot.) ajuga; д., —ник *m.* germander (*Teucrium*).

дубуазин *m.* duboisine, *l*-hyoscyamine.

дубянка *f.* (bot.) mistletoe (*Viscum album*).

дувший *past act. part. of* дуть.

дуг/а *f.* arch, arc, bow, curve; rib; сводить —ой *v.* arch, curve.

дуглас/ит *m.* (min.) douglasite (a potassium-iron chloride); —ова пихта Douglas fir, Oregon pine.

дуго/вой *a.* arch, arc, arched, curve, curved; д. переброс arcing over; д. фонарь arc lamp; —вая печь (elec.) arc furnace; —гаситель *m.* arc arrester; (magnetic) blowout; —образно *adv.* in an arch; (bent) double; —образный *a.* arched, curved, bow-shaped; —стойкий *a.* arc-resistant, non-arcing; —стойкость *f.* arc resistance.

дуд/арь *m.* mine worker; —ка *f.* a shallow open mine, open pit; bell pit.

дудник *m.* (bot.) angelica.

дует *pr. 3 sing. of* дуть.

дужка *f.* little bow, bow, ear; profile (of airplane wing).

ДУК *abbr.* (автодезоустановка) (vet.) portable disinfecting unit.

дукер *see* дюкер.

дуктил/иметр, —ометр *m.* ductilimeter; —ометрия *f.* ductilimetry; —ьность *f.* ductility; —ьный *a.* ductile.

дул *past sing. of* дуть.

дулевский *a.* Dulevo.

дуло *n.* bore, muzzle, mouth (of cannon).

дулькамар/ин *m.* dulcamarin; —ретин *m.* dulcamarrhetin.

дульн/ый *a.* bore, muzzle, mouth; —ая пробка tampion.

дульц/ин *m.* dulcin; dulcine, dulcitol; —ит *m.*, —итол *m.* dulcite, dulcitol; —ификация *f.* dulcification, sweetening.

дуля *f.* (bot.) a variety of pear.

дума *f.* thought; council, assembly; —ть *v.* think; believe, suppose, imagine; intend, mean.

думдум *m.* dumdum (bullet).

думкар *m.* dump car, dumping wagon.

думмис *m.* dummy piston.

думпкар *see* думкар.

Дунай the Danube (river).

дунда/зит *m.* (min.) dundasite; —кин *m.* dundakine; —товая кислота dundathic acid.

дунит *m.* dunite (a peridotite rock).

дуновение *n.* whiff, breath, puff, blowing.

дунст *m.* fine shot; coarse meal.

дунуть *v.* blow, puff.

дуо duo, two-high (rolling mill); д.-стан, стан д. duo mill, two-high rolling mill, twin rolling mill.

дуоденальный *a.* (anat.) duodenal.

дуодецимальный *a.* duodecimal.

дуотал *m.* duotal, guaiacol carbonate.

дуп *m.* (text.) doup.

дуплекс *m.* duplex, twin; д.-процесс (met.) duplex process; —ный *a.* duplex, double, twofold.

дуплет *see* дублет.

дупл/истый *a.* hollow, empty; —о *n.* hollow, cavity, void.

дурайрон *m.* Duriron (an acid resisting alloy).

дурак *m.* fool.

дурал/ий *m.* Duralium (an aluminum-base alloy); —ой *m.* Duraloy (a ferrous alloy); —юмин, —юминий *m.* Duralumin (an aluminum-base alloy).

дурана металл, дуран-металл Durana metal (a copper-zinc base alloy).

дурангит *m.* (min.) durangite.

дуранда *f.* oil cake.

дурацкий *a.* stupid, foolish.

дурденит *m.* (min.) durdenite.

дурен *m.* durene, durol; —ол *m.* durenol.

дуреть *v.* become stupid.

дуриан *see* дурио.

дуридин *m.* duridine, aminodurine.

дурил *m.* duryl; —ен *m.* durylene; —овая кислота durylic acid, 2,4,5-trimethylbenzoic acid.

дуримет *m.* Durimet (a ferrous alloy).

дурио *n.* (bot.) durian (*Durio zibethinus*).

дурман *m.* (bot.) thorn apple (*Datura stramonium*); narcotic, intoxicant; dizziness; экстракт —а (pharm.) stramonium extract; —ить *v.* intoxicate, stupefy; —овая кислота daturic acid.

дурнеть *v.* grow ugly.

дурница *f.* (bot.) bog bilberry, whortleberry (*Vaccinium uliginosum*).

дурнишник *m.* (bot.) cocklebur (*Xanthium*).

дурн/ой *a.* bad, wrong, poor; unfavorable, tough; (med.) venereal (disease); —ая земля badland; —ое питание malnutrition; —опьян *see* дурман; —ота *f.* giddiness, vertigo.

дуро/л *see* дурен; —метр *see* дюрометр; —хингидрон *m.* duroquinhydrone, tetramethylquinhydrone; —хинон *m.* duroquinone.

дурр/а *f.*, —о *n.* durra (a grain sorghum).

дуршлаг *m.* colander, strainer.

дурь *f.* foolishness.

дуст *m.* (agr.) dust.

дут/ый *a.* blown (up), inflated, extended; pneumatic (tire); —ь *v.* blow, inflate; blast.

дуть/е *n.* blowing, blast, blasting, draft; горячее д. hot air blast, hot blast; на полном д. full blast (furnace); под —ем in blast; подавать д., стоять на д. *v.* blow, blast; проба через д. bubble test; blow test; сушка —я blast drying, forced-draft drying.

дуфренит *see* дюфренит.

дух *m.* odor, scent; breath; spirit, morale; (spectrography) satellite line; в этом —е in this way, in this manner; одним —ом immediately, in a second; присутствие —а presence of mind.

духа *f.* (met.) air hole (of casting mold).

духи *pl.* perfume, scent, essence.

духовка *f.* oven, kiln.

духовн/ая *f.* will; —ый *a.* spiritual.

духо/вой *a.* wind, air; hot-air (heat); д. канал (anat.) windpipe; —вая печь *see* духовка; —мер *m.* wind gage; blast meter; —та *f.* close air, stuffiness.

дучка *f.* (min.) ramp, slope, incline.

душ *m.* shower, shower bath.

душ/а *f.* soul, mind, spirit; —евный *a.* sincere, cordial; emotional; mental (illness); —еполезный *a.* edifying; —еприказчик *m.* (law) executor.

душист/ый *a.* fragrant, sweet-smelling, scented, odorous, perfumed; —ое вещество perfume, aromatic principle.

душить *v.* stifle, choke, throttle, smother; scent, perfume.

**душица** *f.* (bot.) wild marjoram (*Origanum vulgare*).

**душн/ик** *m.* vent, air vent, air hole, ventilator, aspirator; —**ый** *a.* close, hot, stifling, suffocating, oppressive, sultry.

**дую/т** *pr. 3 pl. of* **дуть**; —**щий** *a.* blowing; —**щийся** *a.* (geol.) heaving.

**ДФН** *see* **ДПН.**

**ДХЭ** *abbr.* (дихлорэтан) dichloroethane.

**дыба** *f.* rack, beam, post.

**дым** *m.*, —**ить**, —**иться** *v.* smoke, fume; —**ка** *f.* haze, mist, fog; —**комер** *m.* haze meter; —**ление** *n.* (agr.) smudging; —**ный** *a.* smoky, fuming.

**дымов/ой** *a.* smoke; **д. газ** flue gas, stack gas; **д. канал** flue, chimney flue; —**ая завеса** smoke screen; —**ая заслонка** damper; —**ая труба** chimney, smokestack, stack, flue.

**дымогарн/ый** *a.* smoke-consuming; **д. котел** fire-tube boiler; —**ая коробка** firebox; —**ая трубка** fire tube.

**дымо/непроницаемый** *a.* smoketight, smokeproof; —**образование** *n.* formation of smoke; —**отводная труба** chimney; —**отводный колпак,** —**отводчик** smoke deflector, chimney hood; —**поглощающий** *a.* smoke-consuming; —**сжигание** *n.*, —**сожигание** *n.*, smoke combustion; smoke abatement; —**сжигающий** *a.* smoke-consuming, smoke-burning; —**сос** *m.* exhaust fan; flue gas pump; —**стойкий,** —**упорный** *a.* fume-resistant; —**ход** *m.* flue, chimney; —**ходы** *pl.* flue system.

**дымчат/о-серый** *a.* smoky gray; —**ый** *a.* smoky, smoke-colored; smoked (glass).

**дымянк/а** *f.* (bot.) fumitory (*Fumaria*); —**овые** *pl.* Fumariaceae.

**дымящий** *a.* smoking; fuming (sulfuric acid, etc.); smoldering (embers); —**ся** *a.* smoky.

**дын/ник** *m.* (agr.) melon bed; —**ный** *a.* melon; —**ная груша** a tropical fruit (*Solanum muricatum* var. *teleutogenum*); —**ное дерево** papaya (*Carica papaya*); —**я** *f.* melon, muskmelon (*Cucumis melo*).

**дыр/а,** —**ка** *f.* hole, tear, gap, perforation, aperture; (electron) vacancy; —**ко-промежуточный** *a.* vacancy-interstitial; —**окол,** —**опробиватель** *m.* puncher, punch, perforator; —**омер** *m.* hole gage.

**дыропробивн/ой** *a.* punching, piercing, perforating; **д. пресс, д. станок, д. штамп,** —**ая машина** punch, puncher, punching machine, punch press; perforator.

**дыр/опроводный шлямбур** drift, punch; —**очка** *f.* little hole, small aperture; —**очный** *a.* hole; —**чатый,** —**явый** *a.* full of holes, perforated; —**явить** *v.* make a hole, pierce, perforate.

**дых/ало** *n.* windpipe; blow hole; —**альце** *n.* (zool.) spiracle, breathing orifice; —**ание** *n.* breathing, respiration.

**дыхательн/ый** *a.* respiratory; **д. аппарат** respirator; **д. клапан** breather valve; —**ая система** (zool.) respiratory system; —**ое горло** (anat.) windpipe.

**дышать** *v.* breathe, respire.

**дышло** *n.*, —**вой,** —**вый** *a.* shaft, pole, beam; connecting rod.

**Дьюара сосуд** Dewar flask.

**Дэви лампа** *see* **Деви лампа.**

**дэннаж** *m.* (nautical) dunnage.

**ДЭС** *abbr.* (дуговая электросварка) electric arc welding.

**дээрация** *see* **деаэрация.**

**дюбель** *m.*, —**ный** *a.* dowel, pin, key.

**дюбуазин** *see* **дубуазин.**

**дю-Виньо синтез** du Vigneaud synthesis (of biotin).

**Дюгема-Маргулеса уравнение** Duhem-Margulus equation.

**дюгонговый жир** dugong oil (substitute for cod-liver oil).

**дюжий** *a.* sturdy, strong, robust.

**дюжина** *f.* dozen, twelve.

**дюжинный** *a.* common, ordinary.

**дюз** *m.*, —**a** *f.* nozzle; small aperture.

**дюйм** *m.* inch (2.54 cm.); —**овка** *f.* inch plank; —**овый** *a.* inch, one-inch.

**дюкер** *m.* inverted siphon, sag pipe.

**Дюлонга-Пти закон** Dulong and Petit law.

**Дюма способ** Dumas method.

**дюм/азин** *m.* dumasin; —**озовое масло** dumosa oil; —**онтит** *m.* dumontite (a uranium mineral); —**ортьерит** *m.* (min.) dumortierite.

**дюн/а** *f.*, —**ный** *a.* dune, sand dune.

**дюнштейн** *m.* (met.) thin matte.

**Дюпон** du Pont (U.S. chemical firm).

**дюпрен** *m.* Duprene (synthetic chloroprene rubber).

**дюр—** *see also* **дур—**; **—ен** *m.*, **—еновый** *a.*, **—эн** *m.* (min.) durain; **—ометр** *m.* (met.) durometer, hardness tester; **—утоль** *m.* solid coconut oil.

**дюфрен/ит** *m.* (min.) dufrenite, kraurite; **—уазит** *m.* (min.) dufrenoysite.

**дюшесс** *m.* (bot.) a variety of pear.

**дягиль**, **—ник** *m.* (bot.) angelica.

**дятел** *m.* (zool.) woodpecker.

**дятл/ина**, **—овина** *f.* (bot.) red clover, trifolium (*Trifolium pratense*).

# Е

**ев—** *see also under* **эв—**, **эй—**.

**евген/ика** *f.* eugenics; **—ический** *a.* eugenic.

**евгенов/ый блеск** (min.) polybasite; **—ая кислота** *see* **эйгеновая кислота.**

**евкалипт** *m.* (bot.) eucalyptus.

**евклидово пространство** (geom.) Euclidean space.

**Евр/азия** Eurasia; **—атом** *abbr.* (Европейское сообщение по атомной энергии) European Atomic Energy Alliance, Euratom.

**еврей** *m.* Jew; **—ский** *a.* Jewish, Hebrew; **—ский камень** (min.) Jewstone, marcasite; (petr.) Jewstone.

**Европа** Europe.

**европ/еец** *m.*, **—ейский** *a.* European; **—ий** *m.* europium, Eu.

**евстахиева труба** (anat.) Eustachian tube.

**евфорбий** *see* **эвфорбий.**

**евший** *past act. part. of* **есть.**

**егей** *m.* (bot.) carex.

**Егера решетка** Jäger screen.

**Египет** Egypt.

**египетск/ий** *a.* Egyptian; **—ая синь** Egyptian blue (a copper pigment); **—ая яшма** (min.) Egyptian jasper.

**его** *gen. of* **он, оно,** his, its; *acc.* him, it.

**ед** *abbr.* (единица допуска) tolerance unit; **ед.** *abbr.* (единица) unit; **ЕД** *abbr.* (единица действия) (biol.) active unit.

**—ед** *m. suffix* **—phage, eater.**

**еда** *f.* meal, food.

**едва** *adv.* barely, hardly scarcely; **е. . . . как** no sooner . . . than; **е. ли** hardly, scarcely, not likely, it is doubtful; **е. не** nearly.

**еденный** *a.* eaten.

**едет** *pr. 3 sing. of* **ехать.**

**ед. изм.** *abbr.* (единица измерения) unit of measurement.

**един/ение** *n.* unity, accord; union; **—ить** *v.* unite.

**единиц/а** *f.* unit; unity, one; **—ах, в —ах** in units (of), in terms (of); **весовой —ы** per unit weight; **за —у, на —у** per unit, each.

**единичн/ость** *f.* singleness; **—ый** *a.* single, unit, unitary, one, only.

**едино—** *prefix* uni—, mono—; **—брачный** *a.* (zool.) monogynous; (bot.) monoecious; **—временно** *adv.* once only; **—временный** *a.* once, one-time; isochronous; **—главый** *a.* singleheaded, one-headed; **—гласие**, **—душие** *n.* unanimity, accord, unison; **—гласный**, **—душный** *a.* unanimous.

**единокров/ие** *n.*, **—ность** *f.* consanguinity, affinity; blood relationship; **—ный** *a.* consanguineous.

**единоличный** *a.* personal, individual.

**единомысл/енный** *a.* unanimous, agreeing; **—ие** *n.* agreement of opinion.

**единомышленн/ик** *m.* adherent, upholder; **—ый** *a.* unanimous, of the same opinion.

**единоначалие** *n.* one-man management.

**единообраз/ие** *n.* uniformity, sameness; **—ный** *a.* uniform, same.

**едино/племенный** *a.* of the same race; **—рог** *m.* unicorn; narwhal (whale); **—родный** *a.* unigenital, only begotten; **—утробный** *a.* (anat.) uterine.

**единственн/о** *adv.* only, solely; **—ость** *f.* oneness, soleness, singleness; **—ый** *a.* only, sole, unique, single.

**един/ство** *n.* unity, harmony; **—ый** *a.* single, only, sole; united, common.

**едк/ий** *a.* caustic, corrosive; burning, stinging, acrid, sharp, pungent (taste); **е. газ** corrosive gas; **—ое вещество,** **—ое средство** caustic, corrosive; **—ие щелочи** caustic alkalis, alkali hydroxides.

**едкость** *f.* causticity, corrosiveness; acridness, pungency; **е. протравы** causticity.

**едо/к** *m.* eater, consumer; **—мый** *a.* edible.

**едут** *pr. 3 pl. of* **ехать**.

**едя/т** *pr. 3 pl. of* **есть**; **—щий** *a.* eating.

**ее** *gen. and acc. of* **она**, her.

**еж** *m.* (zool.) hedgehog; **е.-трансформатор** (rad.) hedgehog transformer; **морской е.** (zool.) sea urchin.

**ежа** *f.* (bot.) orchard grass (*Dactylis*).

**ежевика** *f.* (bot.) blackberry (*Rubus*); bramble; **сизая е.** dewberry (*R. caesius*).

**ежевка** *f.* (bot.) a variety of wheat (*Triticum compactum*).

**ежегодн/ик** *m.* yearbook, annual, annual publication; **—о** *adv.* yearly, every year, annually, per annum; **—ый** *a.* yearly, annual, anniversary.

**ежеголов/ка** *f.*, **—ник** *m.* (bot.) bur reed (*Sparganium*); **—никовые** *pl.* Sparganiaceae.

**ежедекадно** *adv.* every ten days.

**ежедневн/о** *adv.* daily, per diem; **—ый** *a.* daily, every day, diurnal.

**ежели** *conj.* if, in case.

**еже/месячник** *m.* monthly (publication); **—месячно** *adv.*, **—месячный** *a.* every month, monthly; **—минутно** *adv.* every minute; continually; **—минутный** *a.* occurring every minute; continual, incessant; **—мухи** *see* **тахины**; **—недельник** *m.* weekly (publication); **—недельно** *adv.*, **—недельный** *a.* every week, weekly; **—суточно** *adv.*, **—суточный** *a.* every day; **—часно** *adv.*, **—часный** *a.* every hour, hourly.

**ежиться** *v.* shrink, shrivel.

**ежов/ник** *m.* (bot.) echinochloa; **—ый** *a.* hedgehog, sea urchin, echinal.

**езд/а** *f.* drive, riding; **—ить** *v.* drive, ride, go, journey; **—ок** *m.* rider.

**ей** *dat. of* **она**, her, to her.

**ек—** *see under* **эк—**.

**ел** *past sing. of* **есть**.

**елань** *f.* glade.

**еле** *adv.* hardly, scarcely, narrowly.

**елевый** *a.* spruce, fir.

**елей** *m.*, **—ный** *a.* olive oil; anointing, unguent; **—ность** *f.* oiliness.

**еленец** *m.* horn beetle.

**елец** *m.* dace (fish).

**ели** *past pl. of* **есть**.

**ел/ка** *f.*, **—ь** *f.* spruce (*Picea*); **кладка в —ку** herringbone brickwork; **—овый** *see* **елевый**; **—очный** *a.* Christmas tree, spruce, fir; (cryst.) arborescent, tree-like; herringbone (design); **—очный дефлегматор** rod-and-disk type fractionating column.

**емк.** *abbr.* (**емкость**) capacity.

**емк/ий** *a.* large-capacity; capacious, roomy; *suffix* consuming; **—остно-резистивный** *a.* (elec.) capacitance-resistance.

**емкост/ный** *a.* capacity; capacitive; **—ная нагрузка** (elec.) capacitive load, leading load; **—ное сопротивление** (elec.) capacitive reactance; **—ь** *f.* capacity, cubic content; (elec.) capacitance; vessel.

**ему** *dat. of* **он**, **оно**, him, to him, it, to it.

**ендова** *f.* a pouring vessel with a spout.

**енол** *m.*, **—ьный** *a.* (tautomerism) enol; **—изация** *f.* enolization.

**енот** *m.*, **—овый** *a.* (zool.) raccoon.

**епанча** *f.* mantle, cloak.

**ералаш** *m.* disorder, jumble; absurdity.

**еремеевит** *m.* (min.) jeremejevite, eremeyevite; eichwaldite.

**ере/сь** *f.* heresy; **—тик** *m.* heretic; **—тический** *a.* heretical, dissenting.

**ерик** *m.* erik (shallow channel in the Volga delta).

**еритрин** *see* **эритрин**.

**ерошить** *v.* ruffle, dishevel; **—ся** *v.* bristle.

**ерунда** *f.* nonsense, absurdity.

**ерунок** *m.* bevel, bevel square.

**ерш** *m.* jag, ragbolt; broach; jagged rod; brush, wire brush; ruff (fish).

**ершиться** *v.* be obstinate, resist.

**если** *conj.* if, in case, as long as; **е. бы** if; **е. бы не** but for, if not for; **е. не** if not, but for, unless; **е. . . . то** if . . . then; **е. только** if only, providing; **е. только вообще** if at all; **е. только не** unless; **е. уже** if anything.

**ест** *pr. 3 sing. of* **есть**.

**естественн/ик** *m.* naturalist; **—о** *adv.* naturally, of course; it is natural; **—онаучный** *a.* natural-science; **—ость** *f.* naturalness; **—ый** *a.* natural, native, inherent, inborn, innate; —ый газ natural gas; —ые богатства natural resources; дело —ое it is a matter of course; с —ым охлаждением self-cooled.

**естество** n. nature, substance; —ведение, —знание n. natural science; —испытание n. natural history; —испытатель m. naturalist.

**есть** v. eat; *present of* **быть**, is, there is.

**ефес** m. hilt, handle.

**ехать** v. drive, ride, go.

**ехидн/а** f. (zool.) echidna (*Tachyglossus*); —ый a. spiteful, malicious.

**ешьте** *imp. of* **есть**.

**еще** adv. still, yet, as yet, more, any more, again, else, but; е. в even in.

**ею** *instr. of* **она**, by her, with her.

# Ж

**ж** *see* **же**.

**ж., Ж** abbr. (журнал) journal.

**жаба** f. (zool.) toad; (med.) quinsy, tonsilitis; грудная ж. (med.) angina pectoris.

**жаберн/одышащие** pl. (zool.) Branchiata; —ый a. gill, gill-like, branchial.

**жабий** a. toad; ж. глаз (min.) toad's eye tin (a cassiterite).

**жабник** m. (bot.) cudweed (*Filago*, *Antennaria*, etc.).

**жабр/ей**, —ий m. (bot.) hemp nettle (*Galeopsis* spec. *G. tetrahit*).

**жабро**— *prefix* (zool.) branchi—, branchio—; —видный a. branchiate, branchiform; —ногие pl. branchiopods.

**жабры** pl. (zool.) gills, branchia.

**жавелев/а вода**, —ая вода Javel water (a bleaching agent).

**жаворонок** m. (zool.) lark.

**жад** m. (min.) jade; —еит m. jadeite.

**жадн/ичать** v. be greedy; —о adv. greedily, avidly, eagerly; —ость f. greed, greediness, avidity, avarice; —ый a. greedy, avaricious.

**жажд/а** f. thirst, craving, appetite; —ать v. be thirsty (for), hunger; —ущий a. thirsty, hungry.

**жакет** m. jacket.

**жаккардова машина** (text.) jacquard.

**жал** *past sing. of* **жать**.

**жалейка** *see* **жилейка**.

**жаление** n. regretting.

**жаленье** n. stinging, sting.

**жалеть** v. regret, be sorry (for), sympathize; spare.

**жалить** v. sting, prick, bite.

**жалк/ий** a. sorry, pitiful, shabby, miserable; —о *see* **жаль**.

**жало** n. sting, stinger; dart.

**жалоб/а** f. complaint, grievance, claim; заявить —у v. make a complaint; —ный a. sad, grievous; —щик m. plaintiff.

**жалован/ие** n. grant, donation, granting, conferring; —ный a. granted, presented, gratuitous; —ье n. salary, wages, pay; на —ии salaried.

**жаловать** v. give, grant, bestow; favor, like; —ся v. complain, deplore.

**жалон** m. (surv.) stake, pole; —ировать v. stake out, mark out.

**жалост/ный** a. regretful, sad, deplorable; —ь f. pity, compassion, mercy.

**жаль** v. *impersonal* it is a pity; ему ж. he is sorry, he regrets.

**жальный** a. sting, stinging.

**жалюзи** pl. jalousie, louver; grating.

**жаменовская свеча** Jamin candle.

**Жамэна эффект** (phys.) Jamin effect.

**жар** m. heat, glow; (med.) fever, temperature; —а f. heat, hot weather.

**жаргон** m. jargon; (min.) jargon (a Ceylon zircon or inferior diamond).

**жар/ение** n., —ильный a. frying; roasting; —еный a. fried; roasted; —ить v. fry; roast.

**жарк/ий** a. hot, sultry (weather); ж. пояс torrid zone; —о adv. hot; it is hot.

**жаров/ня** f. roaster; brazier; chafing dish; —ой a. heat, fire; —ая труба fire tube, flue, furnace flue; —ая туша hearth.

**жаропонижающ/ий** a. (med.) febrifugal, antipyretic; —ее средство febrifuge, antipyretic.

**жаро/производительная способность** heating effect, heating power, pyrometric effect; —прочность f. resistance to heat, high-temperature strength; —прочный *a.* high-temperature, heat-resisting (retaining mechanical properties at high temperatures); —стойкий *a.* high-temperature, heat-resisting (not deteriorating at high temperatures); —стойкость *f.* thermal stability; —трубный *a.* fire-tube, flue (boiler, etc.).

жароупорн/ость *f.* resistance to heat; —ый *a.* heat-resisting, heatproof, fire-resistant; —ый элемент heat resistor.

жасмин *m.*, —ный *a.* (bot.) jasmine (*Jasminum*); —ник *m.* woodruff (*Asperula odorata*); —ное масло jasmine oil.

жасмон *m.* jasmone.

жат/ва *f.* harvest, crop, produce, reaping; —венный *a.* harvesting, reaping; —венная машина, —ка *f.* reaper, reaping machine, harvesting machine; —ый *a.* reaped, harvested; squeezed, pressed; —ь *v.* reap, harvest, mow, gather in; squeeze, press, pinch, strain.

ЖАХ *abbr.* (Журнал аналитической химии) Journal of Analytical Chemistry.

жбан *m.* can, kind of jug, tub.

жва/ка, —чка *f.* cud, chew; chewing gum; —ло *n.* mandible (of insect); —чные *pl.* (zool.) Ruminantia; —чный *a.* chewing, ruminant.

жгли *past pl. of* жечь.

жгут *m.* braid, plait, band; gasket, packing material (for stuffing boxes); *pr. 3 pl. of* жечь.

жгут/иковые, —оносцы *pl.* (zool.) flagellates (*Flagellatae* or *Mastigophora*).

жгуч/есть *f.* causticity, corrosiveness; —ий *a.* caustic, corrosive, burning, stinging.

жгущий *pres. act. part. of* жечь.

ж.д. *abbr.* (железная дорога) railroad; ж-д *abbr.* (железнодорожный) railroad.

жд/анный *a.* awaited, expected; —ать *v.* wait, expect; —ет *pr. 3 sing.*; —ут *pr. 3 pl. of* ждать.

же *conj.* but, and; as to, now, then; even.

жевание *n.* mastication, chewing.

жевательн/ый *a.* masticatory, chewing; —ая резина chewing gum.

жевать *v.* masticate, chew.

жег *past sing. of* жечь.

жединский век (geol.) Gedinnian stage.

жезл *m.* rod, staff.

желан/ие *n.* wish, desire; по —ию as desired, if desired, at will; —ный *a.* desired, wished (for), welcome.

желательн/о *v.* it is desirable; если ж. if desired; —ость *f.* desirability; —ый *a.* desirable, desired.

желатин *m.* gelatin; —ация *f.*, —ирование *n.* gelatinization, gelation; (rubber) agglomeration; —ированный *a.* gelatinized, gelated; —ировать *v.* gelatinize, gelate, gel.

желатин/ный, —овый *a.* gelatin, gelatinous; ж. лист sheet gelatin.

желатино/зный *a.* gelatinous, jelly-like; —образный, —подобный *a.* gelatinous, gelatinoid, gelatiniform.

жел/ать *v.* wish, want, desire; be willing; —ающий *a.* wishing, wanting, desiring.

желва/к *m.* concretion, nodule; (med.) tumor, scirrhus; —чный *a.* nodular, knotty, lumpy.

желе *n.* jelly, gel.

желез/а, —ка *f.* (anat.) gland; ж. внутренней секреции endocrine gland.

железисто— *prefix* iron, ferro—, ferrous; —железистая соль ferrous ferrite; —железно— *prefix* ferrosoferric; —кремнистый сланец (petr.) ferruginous chert; —натриевая соль sodium ferrite; —серый *a.* iron gray.

железистосинерод/истоводородная кислота, —оводородная кислота ferrocyanic acid; соль —истоводородной кислоты ferrocyanide; —истый *a.* ferrocyanide (of); —истый калий potassium ferrocyanide; —истое железо ferrous ferrocyanide; —ное железо ferric ferrocyanide.

железисто/сть *f.* ferruginosity, ferruginous nature; —цианистый *see* железистосинеродистый.

железист/ый *a.* iron, ferrous, ferruginous, ferriferous, chalybeate; (anat.) glandular; ж. голыш (petr.) sinopite, sinople; ж. источник chalybeate spring; ж. препарат (pharm.) iron tonic, iron preparation; ж. цинковый шпат (min.) ferruginous calamine;

—ая вениса (min.) iron garnet (andradite); —ая вода ferruginous water, chalybeate water; —ая глина iron clay; —ая грязь ferruginous mud; —ая кислота ferrous acid; соль —ой кислоты ferrite; —ая слюда (min.) micaceous iron ore (a form of hematite); —ая соль ferrous salt;—ое вино (pharm.) iron wine.

**железка** *f.* (anat.) glandule.

**железнение** *n.* (electrolytic) iron plating.

**железница** *f.* (bot.) ironwort (*Sideritis*); (vet.) demodecosis, Demodex infestation.

**железно—** *prefix* iron, ferri—, ferric; —аммиачные квасцы, —аммониевые квасцы ammonium ferric alum.

**железнодорожн/ик** *m.* railroad man; —ый *a.* railroad, railway; —ая сеть railroad system.

**железно/калиевая соль** potassium ferrate; —кислый *a.* ferric acid; ferrate (of); —кислая соль ferrate; —литиевая слюда (min.) iron-lithia mica, zinnwaldite; —синерод— *see* железосинерод—.

**железн/ый** *a.* iron, ferric; **ж. блеск** (min.) iron glance, specular iron (a form of hematite); **ж. каменный мозг** (min.) lithomarge containing iron; **ж. колчедан** (min.) iron pyrites, pyrites, pyrite; **ж. купорос** iron vitriol, copperas, melanterite (hydrous ferrous sulfate); **ж. лак** iron varnish; **ж. лист** iron plate, sheet iron; **ж. лом** scrap iron; **ж. мордан** iron mordant, iron liquor; **ж. сплав** (met.) iron alloy, ferroalloy; **ж. сурик** iron minium, red ocher; **ж. шпат** (min.) spathic iron, siderite; **ж. элемент** (elec.) iron cell; —ая дорога railroad, railway; —ая жесть (met.) sheet iron; —ая замазка iron cement; —ая кислота ferric acid; соль —ой кислоты ferrate; —ая лазурь (min.) blue iron-earth, vivianite; —ая охра iron ocher, colored oxides of iron; —ая почка (petr.) eaglestone (ironstone concretion); —ая протрава *see* железный мордан; —ая свинка, —ая чушка iron pig; —ая слюда (min.) micaceous hematite; —ая сметана (min.) specularite; micaceous hematite; —ая соль ferric

salt; —ая трава (bot.) vervain (*Verbena*); ironweed (*Vernonia*); —ая фиолетовая colcothar, Prussian red, rouge; —ая шляпа (petr.) iron hat, gossan; —ое дерево (bot.) lignum vitae (*Guaiacum officinale*); hackberry, nettletree (*Celtis*); argan tree (*Argania sideroxylon*); —ые капли (pharm.) tincture of iron; —ые квасцы iron alum, ferric alum (ferric potassium sulfate); —ые товары hardware; —ые цветы iron flowers (ferric chloride).

**железняк** *m.* (min.) iron ore, ironstone; (bot.) vervain (*Verbena*); Jerusalem sage (*Phlomis*); **бурый ж.** (min.) limonite, brown hematite, brown iron ore; **землистый бурый ж.** yellow ocher (a form of limonite); **луговой бурый ж.** bog iron ore, lake iron ore; **красный ж.** hematite; **землистый красный ж.** red iron ocher.

**желез/о** *n.* iron, Fe; **ж. в болванках** (met.) pig iron, pig, crude cast iron; **азотнокислая закись** —а ferrous nitrate; **азотнокислая окись** —а ferric nitrate; **азотнокислое железо** iron nitrate; **бористое ж., борное ж.** ferroboron, iron boride; **бромистое ж.** ferrous bromide; **бромное ж.** ferric bromide; **ванадиевое ж.** (met.) ferrovanadium; **вольфрамистое ж.** (met.) ferrotungsten; **гидрат закиси** —а ferrous hydroxide; **гидрат окиси** —а ferric hydroxide; **двувалентное ж., закисное ж.** ferrous iron; **двусернистое ж.** ferric sulfide; **закисная соль** —а, **соль закиси** —а ferrous salt; **закись** —а ferrous oxide; **соединение закиси** —а ferrous compound; **закись-окись** —а ferrosoferric oxide, magnetic iron oxide; **ковкое ж., сварочное ж., тягучее ж.** wrought iron, malleable iron; **окисная соль** —а, **соль окиси** —а ferric salt; **окисное ж., трехвалентное ж.** ferric iron; **окись** —а ferric oxide; **соединение окиси** —а ferric compound; **сернистое ж.** ferrous sulfide; **сернокислая закись** —а ferrous sulfate; **сернокислая окись** —а ferric sulfate; **сернокислое ж.** iron sulfate; **углеродистое ж.** iron carbide; **уксуснокислая закись** —а ferrous acetate; **хлористое ж.** ferrous chloride; **хлорное ж.** ferric chloride.

**железо—** *prefix* iron, ferro—; ferri—, ferric; *see also* **железно—**; **—аллофан** *m.* (min.) ferriallophane; **—аммиачные квасцы, —аммониевые квасцы** ferric ammonium alum; **—бетон** *m.*, **—бетонный** *a.* ferroconcrete, reinforced concrete; **—делательный завод** (met.) iron works, iron mill; **—любивый** *a.* (biol.) siderophilic; **—магнитный** *a.* ferromagnetic; **—никелевый колчедан** (min.) pentlandite; **—обрабатывающая промышленность** iron-working industry, ferrous industry, iron industry; **—плавильный завод** iron foundry; **—подобный** *a.* iron-like, ferruginous; **—прокатный стан** iron rolling mill; **—родановая кислота** ferrithiocyanic acid.

**железосинерод/истоводородная кислота, —оводородная кислота** ferricyanic acid; **соль —истоводородной кислоты** ferricyanide; **—истый калий** potassium ferricyanide; **—истый натрий** sodium ferricyanide; **—истое железо** ferrous ferricyanide; **—ное железо** ferric ferricyanide.

**железо/скобяные изделия** hardware; **—содержащий** *a.* iron-containing, ferruginous, ferriferous, chalybeate; **—цианистый** *see* **железосинеродистый.**

**железы** *gen. and pl. of* **железа.**

**железообразный** *a.* jelly-like, gelatinous.

**желоб** *m.* groove, gutter, trough, channel, trench, furrow, canal, conduit, chute, spout; **наклонный ж., спускной ж.** chute; **—истый, —коватый** *a.* grooved, channeled; (bot.) canaliculate; (zool.) canalicular; **—ить** *v.* groove, channel, flute, chamfer; **—ление** *n.* grooving, channeling, fluting; **—оватый, —ообразный** *a.* U-shaped, trough-shaped; **—ок** *m.* groove, flute, slot.

**желобчат/ый** *a.* grooved, fluted, channeled; corrugated, ribbed; **ж. транспортер** trough conveyer; **—ое железо** U-iron; corrugated iron; **—ое колесо** sheave, grooved pulley wheel.

**желонка** *f.* (min.) sludge pump, sand pump.

**желт/еть** *v.* yellow, turn yellow; **—изна, —ина** *f.* yellowness, yellowishness; **—инник, —ник** *m.* (bot.) sumac (*Rhus,* spec. *R. cotinus*); **—ить** *v.* color yellow, paint yellow.

**желто—** *prefix* yellow.

**желтоват/о—** *prefix* yellowish; **—ый** *a.* yellowish; **—ость** *f.* yellowishness, yellowness.

**желто/гузка** *f.* a tussock moth (*Euproctis similis*); **—зеленый** *a.* yellowish green; **—зем** *m.* zheltozem, yellow soil; (min.) yellow ocher (a variety of limonite); **—к** *m.* yolk (of an egg); **—калильный жар** yellow heat; **—корень** *m.* (bot.) yellowroot (*Xanthorrhiza*); turmeric (*Curcuma*); goldenseal (*Hydrastis*); **—коричневый** *a.* yellowish brown, fawn colored; **—лен** *m.* (bot.) brimstonewort (*Peucedanum officinale*); **—подзолистый** *a.* yellow-podzolic soil; **—фиоль** *f.* (bot.) wallflower (*Cheiranthus*); **—цвет** *m.* (bot.) golden rod (*Solidago*); *see also* **желтуха;** dyer's broom; weld; **—чник** *m.* yolk gland; **—чный** *a.* yolk, vitelline.

**желту/ха** *f.* (med.) yellow jaundice; yellows (plant disease); (bot.) ragwort (*Senecio jacoboea*); dyer's broom (*Genista tinctoria*); weld, dyer's weed (*Reseda luteola*); **—шник** *m.* (bot.) erysimum; swallowwort, celandine (*Chelidonium majus*); **—шный** *a.* (med.) icteric.

**желт/ый** *a.* yellow; **ж. корень, —як** *m.* (bot.) turmeric (*Curcuma*); **ж. пигмент** carotin; **—ая вода** (med.) glaucoma; **—ое дерево** fustic, yellowwood (dye); (bot.) sumac (*Rhus cotinus*); **—ое тело** (anat.) corpus luteum; **—ь** *f.* yellow (pigment); **баритовая —ь** barium yellow (barium chromate); **—яница** *f.*, **—яница трава** (bot.) safflower (*Carthamus*); **—янка** *f.* (bot.) weld, dyer's weed (*Reseda luteola*).

**желудевый** *m.* acorn.

**желуд/ок** *m.* stomach; **катарр—ка** (med.) gastritis; **—очек** *m.* (zool.) ventricle, chamber, cavity; **—очно—** *prefix* gastro—; **—очно-кишечный** *a.* gastroenteritic; **—очный** *a.* stomachic, gastric; **—очный сок** gastric juice.

**жёлудь** *m.* acorn.

желч/е—, —но— *prefix* chole—, cholo— (bile, gall);—ение *n.* yellow fermentation (of tobacco); —ность *f.* (med.) jaundice; —ный *a.* bilious, bile; choleric (person); gall (bladder; stones); —ь *f.* gall, bile; вещество —и bilin; разлитие —и (med.) jaundice; bilious attack.

жемчу/г *m.*, —жина *f.* pearl; (met.) bead; —жница *f.* pearl shell; (zool.) pearl oyster; (vet.) pearl disease; —жночистый *a.* as bright as a pearl.

жемчужн/ый *a.* pearl, pearly, pearl-colored; ж. блеск (min.) pearl glance; —ая накипь (min.) pearl sinter (a variety of opal); —ое зерно pearl; —ые белила (cosmetics) pearl powder.

жен— *prefix see* женский.

жена *f.* wife; —тый *a.* married.

женевский *a.* Geneva, Genevan.

женить *v.* marry.

женомуж/ие *n.* (bot.) gynandria, gynandry; —ий *a.* gynandrous.

женский *a.* female, feminine, woman's; ж. волос (bot.) maidenhair (*Adiantum*).

Жентеле зелень *see* Гентеле зелень.

женщина *f.* woman.

жень-шень *m.* (bot.) ginseng (*Panax*).

жеод *m.*, —а *f.* (geol.) geode; nodule.

Жерара правило Gerhardt law.

жердняк *m.* forest planting.

жердь *f.* pole, rod.

жеребейка *f.* (foundry) gagger, chaplet block.

жереб/енок *m.* foal, colt; —ец *m.* stallion; —иться *v.* foal.

жеребок *see* жеребейка.

жеребьевка *f.* sorting, allotment.

жерех *m.* (zool.) a carp-like fish.

жерло *n.* mouth, orifice, crater, vent.

жернов *m.*, —ой камень, —ой *a.* millstone, burrstone; верхний ж. runner.

жертв/а *f.* sacrifice, victim; —ователь *m.* donor; —овать *v.* sacrifice, give.

жерух *m.* (bot.) cress, peppergrass (*Lepidium*); —ха *f.*, —шник *m.* watercress (*Nasturtium* or *Roripa*).

жест *m.* gesture, motion, action.

жестер *see* жостер.

жестк/ий *a.* stiff, rigid, inflexible, tough, sturdy, stable; hard (water, etc.); drastic (conditions); —о *adv.* stiffly,

rigidly; roughly; —оватый *a.* stiff, somewhat hard;—окрылые *pl.* beetles and weevils (*Coleoptera*); —окрылый *a.* coleopterous; —оопушенный *a.* (bot.) hispid; —ость *f.* stiffness, rigidity, inflexibility; hardness (of water); коэффициент —ости (mech.) rigidity; фактор —ости (radiation) hardness factor; электрическая —ость (elec. comm.) elastance;—офокусирующий *a.* strong-focusing.

жестокий *a.* cruel, hard, severe.

жестче *compr. of* жесткий, жестко; —ние *n.* stiffening, hardening; aging.

жесть *f.* tin, tin plate, sheet iron; алюминиевая ж. sheet aluminum; белая ж. tin plate; черная ж. black plate, sheet iron (untinned iron plate).

жестян/ик, —ник, —щик *m.* tinsmith, tinner; —ицкая *f.* tinning shop, plating shop; —ка *f.* tin, tin box, tin can, can; —ой *a.* tin.

жете *n.* jetel fiber.

жетон *m.* medal; counter.

жечь *v.* burn, roast; corrode.

жжен/ие *n.* burning, roasting, firing, calcining; —ка *f.* roasted, ground clay; —ый *a.* burned, roasted, fired, calcined, charred; burnt (umber; alum).

жив *see* живой.

жив-во *abbr.* (животноводство) livestock raising.

живет *pr. 3 sing. of* жить.

живетский век (geol.) Givetian stage.

живит/ельный *a.* restorative, vivifying, regenerative; —ь *v.* restore, vivify, regenerate, animate, revive.

живица *f.* soft resin, oleoresin, galipot.

живность *f.* poultry, fowl.

живо *adv.* promptly, quickly.

живодерня *f.* slaughterhouse.

живодрев *see* жизненное дерево.

жив/ое *n.* the quick, the living flesh; —ой *a.* alive, living, animate, lively, active, brisk; bright, rich, vivid (color); (spring) water; —ая сила kinetic energy; manpower; —окость *f.* delphinium; —оловка *f.* animal trap.

живопись *f.* painting, pictorial art.

живоро/дный, —дящий *a.* (zool.) viviparous; —ждение *n.* viviparity.

**живо/росль** *f.* (zool.) zoophyte; **—сече-ние** *n.* vivisection; **—сть** *f.* animation, liveliness, briskness.

**живот** *m.* stomach, abdomen.

**животвор/ить** *v.* vivify, reanimate, revive; **—ный, —ящий** *a.* vivifying, life-giving, resuscitating.

**животновод** *m.* stock breeder; **—ство** *n.* livestock breeding, animal husbandry; **—ческий** *a.* stock (farm).

**животное** *n.* animal; animal life, fauna.

**животнорастение** *n.* (zool.) zoophyte.

**животн/ый** *a.* animal; **ж. крахмал** animal starch, glycogen; **ж. уголь** animal charcoal, bone black; **—ая кислота** zoönic (acetic) acid; **соль —ой кислоты, —окислая соль** zoönate; **—ое масло** animal oil, specif. bone oil.

**животрепещущий** *a.* of vital importance; actual.

**живу/т** *pr. 3 pl. of* **жить; —честь** *f.* viability, tenacity; **—чий** *a.* of great vitality, tenacious of life, long-lived, hardy; **—чая трава, —чка** *f.* (bot.) bugle (*Ajuga reptans*); houseleek (*Sempervivum*).

**жив/ущий** *a.* living; **—чик** *m.* (zool.) spermatozoon; **—ший** *past act. part. of* **жить; —ьем** *adv.* alive; **—я** *adv.* living.

**жигалка** *f.* stable fly (*Stomoxys calcitrans*).

**Жигмонди фильтр** Zsigmondy filter.

**жигун, —ец** *m.* (bot.) pellitory of Spain (*Anacyclus pyrethrum*).

**жиденький** *a.* liquid, watery.

**жидк/ий** *a.* liquid, fluid, watery, thin; light (oil); **ж. воздух** liquefied air, liquid air; **ж. прут** flexible rod; **—ая садка** (met.) molten charge; **—ое состояние** liquid state, liquidity, fluidity; **—ое тело** liquid, fluid; **мера —их тел** liquid measure, fluid measure; **—ое топливо** liquid fuel; fuel oil.

**жидко** *adv.* in liquid form; *prefix* liquid; **—металлический** *a.* liquid-metal; **—плавкий** *a.* liquid, fluid; **—плавкость** *f.* fluidity; **—стность** *f.* liquidity, fluidity; **—стный** *a.* liquid, fluid; fluid-flow (pump); hydraulic (brake); **—стный затвор, —стное уплотнение**

liquid seal; **—сть** *f.* liquid, fluid, liquor; liquidity, fluidity; **—теку-честь** *f.* fluidity; fluid flow; flowability (of molten metal); **—текущий** *a.* fluid, non-viscous; fluid-flow; **—фаз-ный** *a.* liquid-phase.

**жидовская вишня** (bot.) alkekengi berries, winter cherry (*Physalis alkekengi*); **ж. смола** (min.) Jew's pitch (a bitumen).

**жиж/а, —ица** *f.* liquid, liquor, juice; **—енный** *a. suffix* liquid, liquefied; **—ка** *f.* pyroligneous distillate.

**жизнедеятельн/ость** *f.* activity, active life; **—ый** *a.* active, vital.

**жизненн/ость** *f.* vitality, life; **—ый** *a.* vital, life's; viable; **—ое дерево** (bot.) arbor vitae (*Thuja occidentalis*).

**жизнеописание** *n.* biography, life.

**жизнеспособн/ость** *f.* viability, vitality; germinating power (of seed); **—ый** *a.* viable, capable of living, live (seeds).

**жизнь** *f.* life, existence, living; **претвор-ить в ж.** *v.* put into practice, realize.

**жиклер** *m.* jet, jet discharge, jet nozzle, jet tube (of carburetor).

**жил** *past sing. of* **жить.**

**жил— *prefix, see* **жилищный.**

**жила** *f.* vein; (geol.) vein, lode, seam; (med.) catgut; (bot., zool.) nerve; filament, strand, core (of cable); **ж.-проводник** (geol.) lead vein, leader; **расширение —ы** (med.) aneurysm; **сложная ж.** (min.) lode, vein; **сухая ж.** (anat.) tendon, sinew.

**жилейка** *f.* pipes.

**жилец** *m.* dweller, tenant.

**жилистый** *a.* fibrous, stringy, sinewy, veiny.

**жилиться** *v.* strain oneself, strive (for).

**жилищ/е** *n.,* **—ный** *a.* residence, habitation, abode, dwelling, house; **—ное строительство** housing.

**жилк/а** *f.* fiber, nerve, rib, vein; **—ова-ние** *n.* veining, venation; **—оватый** *a.* fibrous, stringy; veined.

**жиловатый** *see* **жилистый.**

**жилой** *a.* inhabited, habitable, residential; **ж. дом** dwelling, residence.

**жилоч/ка** *f.* small vein, fibril; **—ный** *see* **жильный.**

**жил/строительство** *n.* house building, housing; **—ье** *see* **жилище.**

**жильн/ый** *a.* vein, veiny; **ж. материал,** **—ая порода** (min.) veinstone, gangue, matrix; **ж. минерал** vein mineral, gangue mineral, gangue; **ж. пояс,** **—ая полоса, —ая толща, —ое месторождение** (min.) vein, lode, seam.

**жимолост/ные** *pl.* (bot.) Caprifoliaceae; **—ь** *f.* honeysuckle (*Lonicera*).

**жинзенг** *see* **джин-шень.**

**жир** *m.* fat, tallow; oil; suint, yolk (of wool); **дубленый —ами** oil-tanned.

**жиразолевый опал** (min.) girasol, opal.

**жирант** *m.* (com.) indorser.

**жирасоль** *see* **жиразолевый опал.**

**жират** *m.* indorsee.

**жираторн/ый** *a.* gyratory, gyrating; **—ая дробилка** gyratory (rock breaker).

**жираф** *m.* (zool.; min.) giraffe.

**жирационный** *a.* gyration, gyratory, gyrating.

**жиреть** *v.* fatten, get fat.

**жирно—** *prefix* fat, fatty, aliphatic; rich (in); **—ароматический** *a.* aliphatic-aromatic; **—известковый** *a.* fat-lime; rich in lime; **—кислый** *a.* fatty acid; **—молочность** *f.* butter-fat yielding capacity (of cow); **—размолотый** *a.* (paper) wet-beaten; **—сть** *f.* fatness, greasiness, oiliness; richness, fertility (of soil); wetness (of paper pulp).

**жирн/ый** *a.* fat, greasy, oily; fatty, aliphatic; rich, fertile; (typ.) heavy, bold; lardaceous (fracture); bituminous (peat); **ж. карандаш** China pencil, glass-marking pencil; **ж. корень** (pharm.) symphytum root; **ж. ряд** aliphatic series, fatty series; **—ая глина, —ая земля** (foundry) loam; **—ая кислота** aliphatic acid, fatty acid; **—ая мазь** pomade; **—ое масло** fatty oil, tallow oil; **—ое пятно** grease spot, grease stain; **—ое соединение,** **—ое тело** aliphatic compound.

**жиро** *n.* (com.) indorsement.

**Жиро печь** (elec.) Girot furnace.

**жиро—** *prefix* fat, fatty, aliphatic, lipo—; adipo—; (mech.) gyro—, *see also* **гиро—.**

**жиров/ание** *n.* lubrication, oiling, greasing; (bot.) vigorous growth; **—ать** *v.* lubricate, oil, grease.

**жировик** *m.* (med.) tumor; (min.) steatite, soapstone (a massive variety of talc); **китайский ж.** (min.) agalmatolite, pagodite.

**жиров/ой** *a.* fatty, aliphatic; tallowy, sebaceous; (anat.) adipose; **ж. обмен** lipometabolism; **—ая кислота** *see* **жирная кислота; —ая ткань** (anat.) adipose tissue; **—ое вещество** fat, fatty matter; **—ое дерево** (bot.) tallow tree (*Sapium sebiferum*); **—ое седение** fat bloom (on chocolate); **—ые отбросы** refuse fat, scrap fat.

**жировоск** *m.* adipocere; corpse fat.

**жироклинометр** *m.* gyrolevel.

**жиромер** *m.* butyrometer.

**жирометр** *m.* gyrometer.

**жиро/непроницаемый** *a.* greaseproof; **—обменный** *a.* lipometabolic; **—отложение** *n.* adipopexis, fat storage; **—подобный** *a.* fatty, oily, tallowy, sebaceous; **—пот** *m.* suint, yolk (of wool).

**жирораствор/имый** *a.* fat-soluble, liposoluble; **—яющий** *a.* fat-dissolving; **—яющий реактив** fat solvent.

**жирорасщепл/ение** *n.* cleavage of fat, lipolysis; **—яющий** *a.* fat-splitting, fat-cleaving, lipolytic.

**жироректор** *m.* (aero.) gyrorector.

**жироскоп** *m.* gyroscope, gyrostat, gyro; **—ический** *a.* gyroscopic, gyro—.

**жиросодержащий** *a.* fat-containing, fatty.

**жиростат/ика** *f.* gyrostatics; **—ический** *a.* gyrostatic.

**жиро/удаляющий реагент** fat extractant; **—уловитель** *m.* grease trap.

**жирянка** *f.* (bot.) butterwort (*Pinguicula*).

**жисмондит** *m.* (min.) gismondite.

**жите/йский** *a.* worldly; everyday; **—ль** *m.* inhabitant, resident, dweller; **—льство** *n.* abode, dwelling; **—льствовать** *v.* reside, live, inhabit.

**жит/ец** *m.* a brome grass (*Bromus secalinus*); **—ник** *m.* field mouse; **—ница** *f.* granary, corn crib, barn; **—ный** *a.,* **—о** *n.* corn, barley, wheat, grain; **—няк** *m.* wheat grass (*Agropyron*).

**жить** *v.* live, be alive, exist, subsist; **—е** *n.* life, being, existence.

**жмаки** *see* **жмыхи.**

**ЖМГ** *abbr.* (жидкометаллическое горючее) liquid-metal fuel.

**жмет** *pr. 3 sing. of* **жать,** press.

**жмурить** *v.* squint, close (the eyes).

**жму/т** *pr. 3 pl.;* —**щий** *pr. act. part. of* **жать,** press.

**жмых** *m.,* —**и** *pl.* oil cake, mill cake; —**одробилка** *f.* oil-cake grinder.

**жне/емолотилка** *f.* (agr.) combine; —**йка** *f.* harvester, reaper, reaping machine; —**т** *pr. 3 sing. of* **жать;** —**ц** *m.* reaper.

**жн/ива** *f.,* —**итво** *n.* reaping, crop, harvest; —**иво,** —**ивье** *n.* stubble, stubble field; —**ут** *pr. 3 pl.;* —**ущий** *pr. act. part. of* **жать,** reap.

**ЖНХ** *abbr.* (Журнал неорганической химии) Journal of Inorganic Chemistry.

**жолоб** *see* **желоб.**

**жолудь** *see* **желудь.**

**жом** *m.,* —**овый** *a.* press; (puddling) squeezer; (med.) tourniquet; bagasse, beet pulp.

**жонкил/евый** *a.,* —**ь** *m.,* —**я** *f.* (bot.) jonquil (*Narcissus jonquilla*).

**жордан** *see* **джордан.**

**жорнов** *see* **жернов.**

**жосефинит** *m.* (min.) josephinite (a native iron-nickel alloy).

**жостер** *m.* dried buckthorn berries (of *Rhamnus cathartica*).

**ЖОХ** *abbr.* (Журнал общей химии) Journal of General Chemistry.

**ж. прикл.-хим., ЖПХ** *abbr.* (Журнал прикладной химии) Journal of Applied Chemistry.

**жрать** *v.* devour, guzzle.

**жребий** *m.* allotment, lot, fate, destiny.

**ж. резин. пром., ЖРП** *abbr.* (Журнал резиновой промышленности) Journal of the Rubber Industry.

**ЖРФХО** *abbr.* (Журнал русского физико-химического общества) Journal

of the Russian Physical and Chemical Society.

**ж. тех. физ., ЖТФ** *abbr.* (Журнал технической физики) Journal of Technical Physics.

**жужелиц/а** *f.* (met.) slag, dross, scoria; —**евые,** —**ы** *pl.* ground beetles (*Carabidae*).

**жужж/ание** *n.* humming, buzzing; —**ать** *v.* hum, buzz, drone.

**жук** *m.* beetle, bug, weevil; (met.) sow (a furnace accretion); —**и** *pl.* (zool.) Coleoptera; kinks (in wire).

**Жульена металл** (met.) hard lead.

**журав/ель,** —**ль** *m.* (mach.) sweep, lever arm; —**ельник** *see* **герань;** —**ец** *m.,* —**линый** *a.,* —**ль** *m.* (zool.) crane; —**чик** *m.* lime nodule.

**журить** *v.* reprove, rebuke, censure.

**журнал** *m.,* —**ьный** *a.* journal; log; **периодический ж.** periodical, review.

**журчалк/а** *f.* bulb fly (*Eumerus*); —**и** *pl.* flower flies, hover flies (*Syrphidae*).

**журчать** *v.* ripple, purl, gurgle.

**жут/кий** *a.* horrible; —**ь** *f.* fright, terror.

**жучина** *f.* wound, tapping (of trees).

**жучок** *m.* beetle, bug.

**ж. физ. хим., ЖФХ** *abbr.* (Журнал физической химии) Journal of Physical Chemistry.

**ЖФХО** *abbr.* (Журнал физико-химического общества) Journal of the Physical and Chemical Society.

**ж. хим. пром., ЖХП** *abbr.* (Журнал химической промышленности) Journal of Chemical Industry.

**ЖХО** *abbr.* (Журнал химического общества) Journal of the Chemical Society.

**ЖЭТФ** *abbr.* (Журнал экспериментальной и теоретической физики) Journal of Experimental and Theoretical Physics.

**Жюрена закон** (phys.) Jurin's law.

**жюри** *m.* jury.

# З

**з.** *abbr.* (западный) western; (золотник) unit of weight; **З.** *abbr.* (запад) west.

**за** *prep. acc. to indicate motion; instr. to indicate location;* after, behind, beyond, out of; for, as; per; during; **за**

**единицу** per unit; **за и против** pro and con; **за исключением** with the exception (of), except; **итти за** *v.* follow, go after; **ни за что** on no account, by no means; **приняться за** *v.* set to.

**ЗА** *abbr.* (**зенитная артиллерия**) anti-aircraft artillery.

**за—** *prefix* beyond, trans—; behind; ad—; *with verbs to indicate the beginning of action;* —**алеть** *v.* redden; —**атлантический** *a.* transatlantic.

**забав/а** *f.* amusement; —**лять** *v.* entertain, amuse; —**ный** *a.* entertaining.

**Забайкаль/е,** —**ская область** Transbaikal region.

**забаллотиров/ать,** —**ывать** *v.* vote against, blackball.

**забастов/ать** *v.,* —**ка** *f.* (labor) strike.

**забвение** *n.* oblivion.

**забе/г** *m.* overshooting, overswinging (of needle); —**гать,** —**жать** *v.* run in, drop in; stray; outrun; —**гающий** *a.* leading.

**забел/ивать,** —**ить** *v.* whiten.

**забеременеть** *v.* become pregnant.

**забив/ание** *n.,* —**ка** *f.* driving (in); stopping up, clogging; (rad.) jamming; —**ать** *v.* drive (in), hammer in, ram, force in; stop up, clog, block up, fill in; begin to beat; slaughter (cattle); flood, glut (the market); —**аться** *v.* clog up, get clogged up.

**забир/аемый** *a.* input; —**ать** *v.* take (away); —**аться** *v.* get in, steal in.

**забирка** *f.* (min.) prop wall.

**забирное отверстие** intake.

**забит/ый** *a.* driven in; stopped up, clogged, plugged up; (blasting) stemmed; —**ь** *see* **забивать.**

**заблаговременн/о** *adv.* in advance, early; —**ый** *a.* done in time, early.

**заблагорассудить** *v.* think fit.

**заблестеть** *v.* begin to shine.

**заблу/диться,** —**ждаться** *v.* lose one's way, get lost, go astray, stray; be mistaken, err; —**ждение** *n.* fallacy, error, mistake, delusion.

**забоина** *f.* nick, dent.

**забой** *m.* driving in; (min.) face; slaughter (of cattle); —**ка** *f.* (blasting) stemming; —**ник** *m.* beetle, rammer, tamper; —**щик** *m.* miner, cutter; slaughterer.

**заболачивать** *v.* swamp.

**заболев/аемость** *f.* morbidity; sick rate; —**ание** *n.* illness, sickness; falling ill; —**ать, заболеть** *v.* fall ill, get sick.

**заболон/ники** *pl.* bark beetles (*Scoly-*

*tidae*); —**ь** *f.* (bot.) alburnum, sapwood.

**заболоченный** *a.* swamped; stagnant.

**заболтать** *see* **болтать.**

**забор** *m.* fence, enclosure, partition, hedge; goods taken on credit; advance payment; **з. воздуха** air intake; **обнести** —**ом** *v.* fence in; —**ник** *m.* sampler; —**ный** *a.* fence, partition; intake; ration (book); —**ное отверстие** intake.

**забортовка** *f.* beading.

**забот/а** *f.* care, anxiety, trouble, responsibility; —**иться** *v.* take care (of), look after, be responsible (for); —**ливость** *f.* carefulness, anxiousness; —**ливый** *a.* careful, thoughtful, solicitous.

**забраков/ание** *n.,* —**ка** *f.* rejection, refusal; —**анный** *a.* rejected, refused, condemned; —**ать,** —**ывать** *v.* reject, refuse, condemn.

**забрало** *n.* visor.

**забранный** *a.* taken, taken away.

**забрасыв/ание** *n.* throwing, spattering; abandonment; stoking, firing (furnace); —**ать** *v.* throw, spatter; abandon, neglect; stoke, fire.

**забрать** *see* **забирать.**

**забредить** *v.* become delirious.

**забрести** *v.* go astray, stray.

**забронировать** *v.* reserve, assign.

**забро/с** *see* **забрасывание;** —**санный,** —**шенный** *a.* thrown, spattered; abandoned, neglected; —**сать,** —**сить** *see* **забрасывать.**

**забрыз/ганный** *a.* splashed, spattered; —**гать,** —**гивать,** —**нуть** *v.* splash, spatter; —**гивание** *n.* splashing, spattering.

**забурник** *m.* drill, borer, bore.

**забут** *m.* packing; —**ить** *v.* fill in, pack; bank up; —**ка,** —**овка** *f.* filling-in work, packing material, rubblework, rubble masonry.

**забы/вать,** —**ть** *v.* forget, leave out, omit; —**вчивость** *f.* forgetfulness, absentmindedness; —**вчивый** *a.* forgetful, absentminded, careless.

**зав—** *abbr.* (**заведующий**) manager, director, chief.

**завал** *m.* fall, avalanche; (med.) obstruction, constipation; —**енный** *a.* heaped up, loaded, filled, clogged up;

—**ивание** *n.* heaping up, filling up, clogging up; —**ивать,** —**ить** *v.* heap up, load, fill, cover up, encumber, clog, choke; —**иваться** *v.* be covered up, be mislaid, be misplaced; —**ка** *f.* priming, charging, filling; (furnace) charge; —**очная машина** charging machine, charger.

**завальцовывать** *v.* roll in.

**завар/енный** *a.* welded, sealed; scalded, scoured; —**иванье** *n.,* —**ка** *f.* welding up; infusing, brewing; —**ивать,** —**ить** *v.* weld, seal; infuse, brew; scald, treat with hot water; scour; —**ной** *a.* boiled; —**ное тесто** dough made with hot water or milk.

**завастривать** *see* **заострять.**

**заведение** *n.* establishment, institution; custom, habit, usage.

**заведомо** *adv.* with knowledge (of), known to be; **з. зная** knowing beforehand, having previous knowledge.

**завед/ующий,** —**ывающий** *m.* manager, director, chief, head, superintendent; *a.* managing, directing; —**ывание** *n.* management, superintendence; —**ывать** *v.* manage, superintend, direct.

**завезти** *see* **завозить.**

**завербовать** *v.* recruit.

**завер/ение** *n.* assurance; assertion; —**ить** *v.* assure; witness, certify.

**завернуть** *see* **завертывать.**

**заверт/ка** *f.* screw driver; wrapping up; knob, catch, latch; —**ывание** *n.* wrapping up; involution; screwing up; —**ывать** *v.* wrap, wrap up, envelop, muffle up, cover; screw up; turn off (faucet).

**заверш/ать,** —**ить** *v.* complete, consummate, crown, top off; —**ающий** *a.* concluding, closing, final; —**ение** *n.* completion, accomplishment; —**енный** *a.* completed, accomplished, final.

**заверять** *see* **заверить.**

**завес/а** *f.,* —**очный** *a.* curtain, screen; mist; —**ить** *see* **завешивать;** —**ка** *f.* rack.

**завести** *see* **заводить.**

**завет** *m.* testament, will.

**завешив/ание** *n.* curtaining, screening; —**ать** *v.* curtain, screen, veil.

**завещ/ание** *n.* will, testament; —**атель** *m.* testator; —**ать** *v.* will, leave, bequeath.

**завзятый** *a.* inveterate; confirmed.

**завив/ание** *n.,* —**ка** *f.* twisting, curling, winding, coiling action, convolution, folding; —**ать** *v.* twist, curl, crimp; —**ающийся** *a.* twisting, curling.

**завидный** *a.* enviable.

**завин/тить,** —**чивать** *v.* screw up.

**зависание** *n.* sticking, hanging (of furnace charge).

**зависеть** *v.* depend (on), turn (on).

**зависимост/ь** *f.* dependence, relation; characteristic; (math.) function; **з. от энергии** energy dependence; **в** —**и от** depending on, in relation to; **быть в** —**и от** *v.* depend on; **изменение в** —**и от** variation with; **взаимная з.** interdependency; **изображать з. от, откладывать в** —**и от, наносить в** —**и от** *v.* plot against (in graph); **кривая** —**и давления от температуры** temperature-pressure curve.

**зависим/ый** *a.* dependent, subordinate; —**ое переменное** (math.) dependent variable.

**зависть** *f.* envy.

**зависящ/ий** *a.* depending; **з. от энергии** energy-dependent; **все** —**ие меры** all possible precautions.

**завит/ой,** —**ый** *a.* twisted, curled; —**ок** *m.* curl, spiral, scroll; coil; knot (in wood); (anat.) helix (of ear); —**ь** *see* **завивать.**

**завихрен/ие** *n.* swirling, whirl, whirlpool, eddy, eddying, vortex; (aero.) whirlwind, backwash; —**ность** *f.* (phys.) vorticity.

**зав/канц** *abbr.* (**заведующий канцелярией**), —**конт** *abbr.* (**заведующий конторой**) office manager; —**ком** *abbr.* (**заводский комитет**) factory committee.

**завлад/евать,** —**еть** *v.* take possession (of), occupy, seize, encroach.

**завод** *m.* works, plant, factory, mill, shop; custom; (mech.) starter; **автоматический з.** self-starter; **своего** —**а** domestic.

**завод/ить** *v.* wind, wind up, crank, start (motor); acquire; found, set up, establish; bring, take, lead in; —**ка** *f.*

winding up, starting; graining, seeding (of crystals); **автоматическая —ка** self-starter; **—ной** *a.* winding, cranking, starting; **—ная рукоятка, —ная ручка** starting crank, crank.

**заводнять** *v.* flood.

**заводоуправление** *n.* works management, plant management.

**заводск/ий** *a.* works, plant, mill, factory; **з. паспорт, —ая марка, —ая табличка** trademark, nameplate.

**заводчик** *m.* manufacturer, factory owner.

**заводь** *f.* backwater, pool; settling basin.

**завоев/ать, —ывать** *v.* conquer.

**завозить** *v.* bring in, deliver en route.

**завол/акивать** *v.* cloud up; (med.) heal up, close; **—ока** *f.* (med.) seton.

**завор/ачивать, —отить** *v.* turn up, *see also* **завёртывать; —от** *m.* turn, turning; **—от кишок** (med.) volvulus; **—оченный** *a.* turned up, cocked.

**завсегдашний** *a.* usual, customary.

**завтра** *adv.* tomorrow.

**завтрак** *m.* lunch, breakfast; **—ать** *v.* lunch, have lunch, eat breakfast.

**завтрашний** *a.* tomorrow's.

**Завхоз** *abbr.* (Заведующий хозяйственной частью) Head of the Economic Division.

**завыв/ание** *n.*, **—ать** *v.* howl.

**завысить** *see* **завышать.**

**завыть** *see* **завывать.**

**завыш/ать** *v.* overstate; overestimate; **—енный** *a.* overstated; too high (result, value); oversized.

**завяд/ание** *n.* wilting; **—ать** *v.* wilt, wither, fade.

**завяз/анный** *a.* tied, bound; **з. корень, —ник** *m.*, **—ный корень** (bot.) tormentilla; **—ать** *see* **завязнуть, завязывать; —ка** *f.* tie, string, band, bond; **—ной** *a.* tying; **—нуть** *v.* stick (in mud); sink, enter (of splinter).

**завязыв/ание** *n.* tying, binding; **—ать** *v.* tie, bind, knot; **—ать отношения** enter into relations (with).

**завязь** *f.* (bot.) ovary, germ.

**завя/лый** *a.* faded, withered, wilted; **—нуть** *v.* fade, wither, wilt.

**загадать** *see* **загадывать.**

**загадить** *see* **загаживать.**

**загад/ка** *f.* riddle, enigma, puzzle; **—оч-**

**ный** *a.* enigmatic, puzzling; **—ывать, —ывать вперед** *v.* conjecture.

**загаживать** *v.* pollute, soil, dirty, contaminate.

**загар** *m.* sunburn, tan; tarnish; (desert) varnish.

**загас/ать, —нуть** *v.* go out, die out; **—ить** *v.* extinguish; switch off.

**загвоздка** *f.* difficulty.

**загиб** *m.* bend, fold, crease, bead, flange, edge (of rim); **—ание** *n.* bending, folding, creasing; recurvature; **—ание кромок** beading; **—ать** *v.* bend, fold, crease, turn in, turn back, turn down; **—аться** *v.* bend, fold, curl; **—ной** *a.* folding, folded; **—очный** *a.* bending, creasing; **—очный станок, —очная машина** creasing machine; flanging machine.

**загибщик** *m.* deviator.

**загипсов/ание** *n.* cementing, plastering; **—ать** *v.* cement, plaster.

**заглав/ие** *n.* title, designation; **—ный** *a.* title (page); capital (letters).

**загла/дить, —живать** *v.* smooth, even, level; **з. вину** make up (for).

**заглаз/а** *adv.* behind one's back; amply, more than enough; **—но** *adv.* without seeing, without having seen.

**заглинизирование** *n.* silting, accumulation of mud.

**заглох/лый** *a.* choked up, smothered; **—нуть** *v.* choke up, be choked, smother; (agr.) overgrow (with).

**заглублять** *v.* lower; work deeper (into).

**заглуш/ать, —ить** *v.* drown, smother, stifle, choke; suppress; damp, bank (fire); soothe, alleviate (pain); deaden (sound); opacify (glass, etc.); **—ающий** *a.* smothering, choking; damping; **—ение** *n.* smothering, choking, suffocating; suppression; damping; banking; **—енный** *a.* choked, suppressed; damped, banked; opacified; **—ка** *f.* choke, plug, stopper, end cap; dead end; blank flange, blind flange; silencing device, silencer.

**загля/дывать, —нуть** *v.* look in, peek.

**загнать** *see* **загонять.**

**загнив/аемость** *f.* putrescibility; **—ание** *n.* rotting, decay; stagnation; (med.) suppuration, festering; **—атель** *m.* septic tank; **—ать** *v.* rot, decay fester; —ший *a.* rotted; stagnant; festered.

**загнут/ый** *a.* bent, folded; recurved; —ь *see* загибать.

**загов/аривать,** —орить *v.* begin to speak; address; —ор *m.* plot, conspiracy.

**заголовок** *m.* title, heading, headline.

**загон** *m.,* —ка *f.* enclosure, pen, corral (for cattle); strip (of plowed land); —щик *m.* drover, herdsman; —ять *v.* drive, drive in, corral, stable.

**загоражив/ание** *n.* enclosure; enclosing, fencing; —ать *v.* enclose, fence; obstruct, block, block up; close, stop, shut off, cut off.

**загор/ание** *n.* ignition, firing; sunburn; —ать, —еть *v.* become tanned, get sunburnt, tan; —аться, —еться *v.* ignite, catch fire; —ающийся *a.* igniting, inflammable; ignition (mixture); —елый *a.* tan, sunburnt.

**загорный** *a.* ultramontane, tramontane.

**загород/ить** *see* загораживать; —ка *f.* partition, fence.

**загородный** *a.* suburban; rural.

**загорожени/ый** *a.* enclosed, fenced; —ое место enclosure.

**загорт/ать** *v.* cover; —ач *m.* covering device.

**загот/авливать,** —овить, —овлять *v.* store, stock up; prepare, provide; put up, preserve (food); —овитель *m.* purchasing agent; —овительный, —овочный *a.* storage, storing; preparing; —овительный стан (met.) billet mill; —овка *f.* store, stock; procurement; preparation, provision; (state) purchase; intermediate product, half-finished material; (met.) blank, billet, bar; плоская —овка (met.) ingot slab; полая —овка, пустотелая —овка hollow billet, hollow ingot (for pipe manufacture); —овление *n.* preparing, storing, stocking; —овленный *a.* prepared, ready; stored; fabricated (parts); —пункт *m.* storage place, warehouse; —щик *m.* storer, provider; maker, preparer.

**загра/дитель** *m.* stopper, barrier, rejector; (elec. comm.) trap; —дительный, —ждающий *a.* obstructing,

barrier; boundary; —дить, —ждать *v.* obstruct; dam, shut in; —ждение *n.* obstructing, stopping; barrier, obstacle; —жденный *a.* obstructed, blocked.

**загран/ицей** *adv.* abroad, in foreign countries; —ичный *a.* foreign, foreign-made.

**загре/бать,** —сти *v.* rake, rake together; з. жар bank the fire.

**загривок** *m.* nape (of neck); withers (of horse).

**загромо/ждать,** —здить *v.* encumber, block up, barricade, clog; —ждение *n.* blocking up, clogging.

**загруб/ение** *n.* hardening, roughening; (med.) callosity; —еть *v.* become hardened, get rough, become calloused.

**загру/жать,** —зить *v.* charge, load, fill; з. топку, з. топливо stoke, fire; —женный *a.* charged, loaded, filled, fed; —зка *f.* charge, contents; charging, loading, filling, priming; stoking, firing.

**загрузочн/ый** *a.* charging, loading, feeding; з. горшок, з. ковш, з. ящик, —ая воронка hopper, feed hopper, feed box, bin; з. желоб, з. лоток, з. рукав feed chute, loading chute, charge chute; з. механизм, —ое приспособление charging device, charger; —ая машина charging machine, charger; fueling machine.

**загрузчик** *m.* charger; stoker.

**загрунтов/анный** *a.* sized, primed; —ать, —ывать *v.* size, prime, apply a ground coat; —ка *f.* sizing, priming, ground color, first coat (of paint).

**загрязн/ение** *n.* impurity, contaminant; contamination, pollution, soiling; clouding; accumulation of mud; clogging; химическое з. chemical impurity; —енный *a.* impure, contaminated, polluted; clogged up; —ить —ять *v.* render impure, contaminate, pollute; clog up, choke; —иться, —яться *v.* get contaminated, pick up dirt; clog up; —яющий *a.* contaminating; —яющее вещество contaminant.

**загубить** *v.* ruin.

**загу/стевание** *n.,* —стка *f.* thickening,

solidification, concentration; —**сте-вать,** —**стеть** *v.* thicken, solidify, condense; —**ститель** *m.*thickening agent; —**щенный** *a.* thickened; close, thickset.

**зад** *m.* back, rear, tail.

**задавать** *v.* set, assign, give; put, ask (a question); —**ся** *v.* set oneself (a goal).

**задав/ить,** —**ливать** *v.* crush; —**ленный** *a.* crushed.

**задалживание** *n.* downtime.

**задан/ие** *n.* task, assignment, mission; —**ный** *a.* assigned, given, fixed, set, preset; prescribed.

**задатки** *pl.* disposition, instincts, inclination.

**задаток** *m.* deposit, down payment.

**задатчик** *m.* controller, control-point adjustment, setter; **з. мощности** power controller.

**зад/ать** *see* **задавать;** —**ача** *f.* problem; task, undertaking; crux, point, question; —**ающий** *a.* giving, assigning; master.

**задви/гать,** —**нуть** *v.* begin to move; bolt, bar, push-in; shut; —**гаться** *v.* start moving, stir; —**жка** *f.* bolt, bar, catch, fastener, fastening; gate, slide gate, slide plate; gate valve, slide valve; —**жной** *a.* sliding, drawable; —**нутый** *a.* bolted, barred, pushed in; shut.

**задворки** *pl.* backyard.

**задев/ание** *n.* catching, grazing, interference; —**ать** *v.* catch, graze, brush against, interfere; provoke, irritate; **не** —**ать** *v.* clear.

**задел/анный** *a.* stopped up, sealed, closed; fixed, embedded; built-in; —**ать,** —**ывать** *v.* stop up, seal, close, fasten; terminate; fix, embed, cement; cover (seeds); —**ка** *f.,* —**ывание** *n.* stopping up, sealing, closing; seal; building in; covering, embedding (of seeds); placement, application (of fertilizer).

**задергивать** *v.* draw, pull in.

**задерж/ание,** —**ивание** *n.* delay, detention, arrest; inhibition, retardation, retention, holding back; —**анный** *a.* delayed, inhibited, retarded, stopped; retained; —**анное совпадение**delayed coincidence; —**ать,** —**ивать** *v.* delay,

inhibit, retard, hold back, detain, impede, moderate; intercept; stop, check, arrest, block, suppress; keep, retain, hold over, entrap; —**аться,** —**иваться** *v.* lag; remain, be retained.

**задерживающ/ий** *a.* retarding, inhibiting, restraining; intercepting; stop; retentive, retaining; holding back; check (valve); lock (mechanism); —**ая сила** coercive force; —**ая способность** retentivity, retentiveness; —**ее действие** inhibitory action.

**задержка** *f.* delay, lag, setback; check, stop, catch; impediment; entrapment.

**задерн/елый** *a.* planted with grass; —**ение** *n.* ground cover.

**задернуть** *see* **задергивать.**

**задет/ый** *a.* caught; —**ь** *see* **задевать.**

**задир** *m.* fin, rib; —**ание** *n.* scratching, scoring; seizing (of bearings); —**ать** *v.* begin to tear, scratch, score; —**аться** *v.* begin to tear; seize.

**заднежаберные** *pl.* (zool.) Opisthobranchia.

**задненавесной** *a.* rear-mounted.

**задн/ий** *a.* back, rear, end, tail, posterior; **з. конец,** —**яя часть** tail, tail end, back; **з. план** background; **з. проход** (anat.) anus; **з. свет** tail light; **з. ход** backing, backing up, reverse running; return movement, return stroke (of piston); —**его хода** *a.* backing, backward; **дать з. ход** *v.* back, reverse; —**яя стойка** back rest; —**яя сторона** reverse, wrong side.

**задник** *m.* heelpiece (of relay); counter (of shoe).

**задолго** *adv.* long in advance.

**задолж/алый** *a.* indebted, in debt; —**ать** *v.* be in debt, incur debts; —**енность** *f.* indebtedness, debt, liabilities.

**задом** *adv.* backwards; **з. наперед** back to front.

**задорина** *f.* splinter.

**задохнуться** *see* **задыхаться.**

**задрайка** *f.* knob, catch, bolt bar.

**задр/анный** *a.* torn, scuffed; scratched, scored; —**ать** *see* **задирать.**

**задув/ание** *n.,* —**ка** *f.* blowing out, extinguishing; blowing in, starting up (blast furnace); beginning to blow; —**ать** *v.* blow out, extinguish, put out; blow in, start up; begin to blow;

—очный *a.* blowing; blow-in; —очный кокс bed charge; —очная колоша (met.) blow-in burden, starting-up charge.

задум/анный *a.* planned; —ать, —ывать *v.* plan, conceive, intend; —аться, —ываться *v.* be thoughtful, ponder.

задут/ый *a.* blown out, extinguished; blown in (furnace); —ь *see* задувать.

задуш/ать, —ить *v.* suffocate, choke, throttle, stifle; —ение *n.* suffocating, suffocation, choking, throttling, stifling; —енный *a.* suffocated, choked.

задхлый *a.* musty, musty-smelling.

зады *pl.* the past; повторять з. *v.* repeat.

задыхаться *v.* suffocate; be out of breath.

задышать *v.* begin to breathe.

заед/ание *n.* gripping, catching, sticking, jamming, seizing (of bearings), jam; —ать *v.* grip, catch, stick, jam, seize, hook, hook in, hook into, bind in, dig in.

заез/д *m.* event; dropping in; —жать *v.* drop in.

заем *m.* loan; делать з. *v.* raise a loan; —ный *a.* loan; borrowed; —ное письмо acknowledgment of debt, I.O.U.

заершенный *a.* jagged, ragged, notched, irregular; з. болт ragbolt.

заехать *see* заезжать.

зажат/ие *n.* pressing, squeezing; bite; —ый *a.* pressed, squeezed, held, fastened, fixed; —ь *see* зажимать.

заж/ечь *see* зажигать; —женный *a.* ignited, lit.

зажив/ание, —ление *n.* healing; —ать *v.* close, heal; —ить, —лять *v.* heal.

заживо *adv.* alive; during one's life.

зажиг/алка *f.* lighter; —ание *n.* ignition, lighting, firing, kindling, setting fire (to); искра —ания ignition spark; —атель *m.* lighter, lighting device, igniter, firing device.

зажигательн/ый *a.* ignition, igniting, incendiary; з. прибор ignition device, firing device; з. шнур, —ая трубка fuse; —ая бомба incendiary bomb; —ая искра ignition spark; —ое стекло burning lens.

зажигать *v.* ignite, light, set fire (to);

—ся *v.* ignite, catch fire, begin burning.

зажим *m.* clamp, clip, fastener, grip, gripping device, clutch, chuck, lock; cleat; (elec.) terminal, binding post; pinchcock (for rubber tubing); з.-капельник dropping cock, drip cock; пружинный з. clip; —ание *n.* clamping, gripping, pressing; (med.) strangulation, constriction; —ать *v.* clamp, grip, grasp, fasten, fasten down, fix, clip, catch, cramp, press, pinch, clutch; —ающий *a.* clamping, gripping; —ающий конус gripping jaw.

зажимн/ой, —ый *a.* clamping, gripping, grip, binding; з. винт set screw, adjusting screw; (elec.) clamp screw, terminal screw; з. конденсатор compression condenser; з. конец (elec.) terminal; з. кулачок, —ая губа, —ая колодка, —ая щека chuck jaw, gripping jaw, jaw; з. патрон vise; chuck; —ая гайка lock nut, grip nut; —ая доска (elec.) terminal board; —ая скоба clip, clasp; —ое кольцо grip ring, clamping ring, locking ring; —ое приспособление, —ое устройство gripping device, clamping device, jaw, clutch, chuck; —ые клещи clamp, clamp tongs.

зажинать *v.* begin to reap.

зажит/ок *m.* earnings; —очный *a.* wealthy, well-off; —ь *see* заживать.

зажор *m.*, —а *f.* accumulation of water under snow; ice jam.

зазеленеть *v.* turn green.

заземлен/ие *n.* (elec.) grounding, ground, ground system, ground connection; провод —ия, —ный кабель ground wire; —ный *a.* grounded, ground.

заземл/итель *m.* grounding electrode; —ительный, —яющий *a.* (elec.) grounding, ground; —ительный провод ground wire; —ить, —ять *v.* ground.

зазор *m.* clearance, space, gap, margin; slit, slot; give, slack, free play, backlash; tolerance; shame, dishonor; —ный *a.* shameful, dishonorable.

зазубр/енность *f.* crenation, crenulation; —енный *a.* notched, jagged, toothed, indented, cogged, serrated, hackly (fracture); pointed; —ивать, —ить *v.* notch, jag, indent, dent, score, serrate; **—ина** *f.* notch, jag, indentation, indent, dent, barb, feather.

**заикаться** *v.* stammer, stutter.

**заил/ение, —ивание** *n.* filling in (of canals, etc.), silting, accumulation of mud; (min.) extinguishing fires with mud; **—енный** *a.* silt-covered, filled with mud; **—ивать** *v.* silt up, fill with mud.

**заимо/давец, —датель** *m.* creditor; **—дательство** *n.* lending; **—образно** *adv.*, **—образный** *a.* on credit, as a loan.

**заимствов/ание** *n.* borrowing; derivation; (elec.) consumption; **—анный** *a.* borrowed; **—ать** *v.* borrow, copy; derive.

**заиндев/елый** *a.* covered with hoar frost, hoar; **—ение** *n.* formation of hoar frost; **—еть** *v.* be covered with hoar frost.

**заинтересов/ать, —ывать** *v.* interest, attract attention.

**зайгерование** *see* **зейгерование.**

**займище** *n.* floodplain.

**займы** *pl.* loans, borrowing.

**зайти** *see* **захаживать.**

**зайчик** *m.* light spot; *see also* **заяц.**

**Закавказье** Transcaucasia.

**закадмиевый** *a.* epicadmium.

**заказ** *m.* order, command; **на з.** to order; **—ать, —ывать** *v.* order, have made; **—ной** *a.* ordered; registered (letter); **—чик** *m.* client, customer.

**закал** *see* **закалка; —енный** *a.* hardened, hard, tempered, chilled, quenched; seasoned, hardy (person); **—енная сталь** chilled steel, tempered steel; **—енное стекло** toughened glass.

**закалив/аемость** *f.* hardenability; **— ание** *see* **закалка; —ать, закалить** *v.* harden, temper, chill, quench; **—ать по поверхности** (met.) caseharden; **—ающий** *a.* hardening, tempering.

**закалка** *f.* hardening, tempering, temper, quenching, chilling; **з. в масле** oil hardening; **з. поверхности, поверхностная з.** (met.) casehardening.

**закалочн/ая** *f.* hardening shop, tempering shop; **—ый** *a.* hardening, tempering; **—ая ванна** quenching bath; **—ая жидкость** quenching liquid,

hardening liquid; **—ая печь** hardening furnace, tempering furnace; **—ая среда, —ое средство** hardening agent, tempering agent.

**закалывать** *v.* stab, slaughter, butcher.

**закалять** *see* **закаливать.**

**закаменеть** *see* **каменеть.**

**закамуфлировать** *v.* camouflage.

**заканчивать** *v.* finish, end, complete, conclude, accomplish.

**закапать** *v.* spot, stain; begin dripping.

**закапчив/ание** *n.* blackening with smoke; **—ать** *v.* blacken with smoke, soot.

**закапывать** *v.* dig in, inter, embed; fill up.

**закармлив/ание** *n.* fattening, feeding up; **—ать** *v.* fatten, feed up, overfeed.

**закат** *m.* setting, decline; (rolling) lap; **з. солнца** sunset.

**закат/ать, —ить, —ывать** *v.* roll, roll up.

**закач/ать, —ивать** *v.* start rocking; pump (in); **—ка** *f.* injection.

**заква/сить, —шивать** *v.* leaven, raise; **—ска** *f.* leaven, ferment; yeast.

**закид/ать, —ывать** *v.* cast beyond; abandon, neglect; fill up (ditch).

**закип/ать, —еть** *v.* start boiling, simmer.

**закированн/ый песок, —ая почва** (geol.) brea; mineral tar.

**закис/ать, —нуть** *v.* sour, get sour; **—лый, —ший** *a.* sour, soured.

**закисн/ый** *a.* (lower or **—**ous) oxide; **—ая соль** (lower or **—**ous) salt; **—ая соль железа** ferrous salt; **—ое железо** ferrous iron.

**закис/ь** *f.* (lower or **—**ous) oxide (formerly protoxide); **з. железа** ferrous oxide; **азотнокислая з. железа** ferrous nitrate; **з. меди** cuprous oxide; **сернокислая з. меди** cuprous sulfate; **з.-окись** mixed oxide; **гидрат —и** (lower or **—**ous) hydroxide; **гидрат —и железа** ferrous hydroxide.

**заклад** *m.* mortgage, pledge; **—ка** *f.* laying (of foundation); marking out; establishment, planting (of orchard); backing, packing; (min.) rubbish; **пустая —ка** rubbish; **—ной** *a.* mortgage; laying, insertion; **—чик** *m.* mortgagor; rivet setter; **—ывать** *v.* mortgage, pawn; lay (foundation), establish; block up, wall up, embed; harness (horses).

**закле/ивать, —ить** v. glue up, paste up, stop up; **—йка** f. gluing up, stopping up.

**заклейм/енный** a. stamped, marked; **—ить** v. stamp, mark, brand.

**заклеп/анный** a. riveted; **—ать, —ывать** v. rivet; clinch; **—ка** f. rivet, clinch, clincher, iron pin, cramp; **—ковидная сварка** rivet weld; **—ник** m. riveting hammer; **—ный, —очный** a. rivet, riveting; clinch; **—очный шов** rivet joint; **—очное отверстие** rivet hole; **—очнообкатная машина** rivet spinner; **—ывание** n. riveting.

**заклепыв/ание** n. riveting; **—ать** v. rivet, clinch.

**заклин/ение, —ивание** n., **—ка** f. wedging, blocking; arching; sticking, jamming, catching; **—енный** a. wedged, fixed, fastened, jammed; **—ивать, —ить** v. wedge, wedge up, fasten with a wedge, block, block up; **—ивать на** fasten to; **—иваться** v. wedge, jam.

**заключать** v. include, enclose, contain; confine, shut in; conclude, come to the conclusion, deduce, infer; **з. в себе** include, comprise, comprehend, embody, embrace; house, hold; **—ся** v. consist (of); end, finish, result (in).

**заключен/ие** n. inclusion; enclosure; custody, imprisonment; occlusion; conclusion, deduction, inference; corollary; closing, finishing up; **—ный** a. enclosed, included, occluded; embedded; concluded.

**заключ/ительный** a. final, closing, conclusive; terminal; **—ить** see **заключать.**

**заковыка** f. impediment, hitch.

**закожный** a. subcutaneous.

**закоксоваться** v. get clogged with coke.

**закол/ачивать, —отить** v. nail up, nail the lid on, board up.

**заколоть** see **закалывать.**

**закон** m. law, rule, principle; expression, relationship; **—ность** f. legitimacy, legality, validity; **—ный** a. legal, valid, legitimate, rightful; **—овед, —оведец** m. lawyer; **—оведение** n. law, jurisprudence.

**законодатель** m. legislator; **—ный** a. legislative; **—ство** n. legislation.

**закономерн/ость** f. regularity; mechanism; rule; principles, conformity to principle; **—ый** a. regular; conforming to an established rule.

**законопа/тить, —чивать** v. calk up, pack, plug; **—ченный** a. calked, packed.

**законо/преступление** n. infringement of the law, transgression; **—проект** m. bill.

**законтрактов/анный** a. contracted; **—ать, —ывать** v. make a contract, enter into contract, bind by contract.

**законуривание** n. (min.) making the first cut.

**законч/енность** f. completeness; finish; **—енный** a. completed, complete, finished, final; **—ить** see **заканчивать.**

**закопать** see **закапывать.**

**закоп/телость, —ченность** f. smokiness, sootiness; **—телый, —тельный** a. smoky, smoke-stained, blackened by smoke, sooty; **—тить** see **закапчивать; —ченный** a. smoky, sooty; smoked (glass).

**закорачив/ание** n., **—ающий** a. (elec.) shorting, short-circuiting; **—атель** m. short-circuiter; **—ать** v. short-circuit, short out.

**закорен/елый** a. deep-rooted, inveterate, ingrained; **—еть** v. take root.

**закоротить** see **закорачивать.**

**закорюка** see **заковыка.**

**закоулок** m. secluded spot; back street.

**закоченеть** see **окоченеть.**

**закрадываться** v. steal in, creep in.

**закраина** f. edge, rim, border, flange, flanged edge; tip; shelf.

**закрасить** v. paint, cover with paint.

**закрасться** see **закрадываться.**

**закрашивать** see **закрасить.**

**закреп** m., **—а, —ка** f. catch, clip, tack, fastening; dowel, joint pin; **—итель** m. fixer, fixing agent, fixative; (insecticides) sticker; **—ить** see **закреплять.**

**закрепл/ение** n. securing, fixing, fixing in, fastening; gripping, holding, attaching, strengthening, tightening (of screw); attachment, securing device, anchor; safety device; (phot.) fixing;

fixation (of dye); —**енный** *a.* secured, fixed, fastened, attached, mounted; fast, tight; —**ять** *v.* secure, fix, fasten, attach, mount, clamp, tighten; —**ять на** fasten to.

**закрепляющ/ий** *a.* fixing, fastening, clamping; з. **состав,** —**ее средство** fixing agent, fixative; —**ая ванна** (phot.) fixing bath; —**ая среда** mounting medium; —**ее приспособление** fastener, clamp, holding device.

**закрепная гайка** lock nut.

**закритический** *a.* (nucl.) supercritical.

**закрой** *m.* cut; —**ка** *f.* cutting out; —**ник** *m.* molding plane; —**щик** *m.* cutter.

**закром** *m.* bin, corn crib, granary.

**закругл/ение** *n.* rounding, rounding off, chamfering; curvature, curve; —**енный** *a.* rounded, rounded off, truncated (cone, etc.); —**ить,** —**ять** *v.* round, round off, make round, chamfer.

**закружить** *v.* make dizzy; —**ся** *v.* get dizzy.

**закру/тень** *m.,* —**тка** *f.* tommy bar; —**тить,** —**чивать** *v.* twist, curl, crimp; —**чиваться** *v.* twist, kink; —**тка** *f.* torsion; (med.) tourniquet; artery clamp; —**ченный** *a.* twisted, curled; —**ченное место** kink; —**чивание** *n.* twisting, curling, involution; coiling action; torsion; **угол** —**чивания** angle of twist; —**чивающийся** *a.* twisting, curling.

**закрывать** *see* **закрыть.**

**закрылок** *m.* (aero.) flap.

**закрыт/ие** *n.* closing, shutting, enclosure; —**оплодные** *pl.* (bot.) Pyrenomycetes; —**ый** *a.* closed, shut, locked, stopped up, sealed; enclosed, housed, sheltered, shielded; crossed (belt); box (groove); —**ого типа** enclosed (machine); —**ь** *v.* close, shut, shut down, shut off, stop, cut off, turn off (faucet); cover, shelter, house, enclose.

**закукливаться** *v.* (zool.) pupate.

**закулистый** *a.* secret, hidden, concealed; behind the scenes.

**закуп** *m.,* —**ка** *f.* purchase; —**ать,** —**ить** *v.* buy in, purchase; —**ной** *a.* purchased.

**закупор/енный** *a.* corked, stopped up, sealed, plugged; —**ивание** *n.,* —**ка** *f.* corking, stopping up, sealing; choking, clogging, obstruction (in pipes); (med.) embolism; —**ивать,** —**ить** *v.* cork, stop up, seal, bung, cap; clog, plug, plug up, choke, obstruct; pack, make tight; —**иваться,** —**иться** *v.* get clogged up, block up; —**ившийся** *a.* clogged up, blocked, plugged.

**закуп/очный** *a.* purchase; —**щик** *m.* buyer, purchaser.

**закуска** *f.* snack, hors d'oeuvre.

**закут/ать,** —**ывать** *v.* wrap up, muffle.

**закхеево масло** *see* **захеево масло.**

**зал** *m.,* —**а** *f.* hall, room.

**заламывать** *v.* begin to break.

**залатать** *v.* patch, mend.

**залег/ание** *n.* lying down; (geol.) occurrence, stratification, bed; —**ать** *v.* lie down; (geol.) occur, be deposited; —**ать на** overlie; —**ать под,** —**ать ниже** underlie; —**ающий** *a.* lying; occurring, deposited, buried, embedded.

**залеж/авшийся,** —**алый** *a.* long-lain (goods); —**аться,** —**иваться** *v.* lie a long time, age with lying; —**ный** *a.* long-fallow, unused, idle (land); —**ь** *f.* long-lain goods; (geol.) deposit, bed, stratum, layer; waste land.

**залеп/ить,** —**лять** *v.* paste up, seal.

**залесен/ие** *n.* reforestation; —**ность** *f.* extent of forests.

**залет/ать,** —**еть** *v.* fly in; start flying; fly off, fly away, fly beyond.

**залеч/ивать,** —**ить** *v.* cure, heal; —**иваться,** —**иться** *v.* heal up, close up.

**залечь** *see* **залегать.**

**залив** *m.* gulf, bay, cove, inlet; molded edge (of cast); —**ание** *n.,* —**ка** *f.* pouring over, flooding, drenching; filling up, priming (engine); lining (of bearing); —**ать** *v.* pour over, flood, drench, wet, drown, flush; fill up, prime; fill in, line; seal (with); —**ающий** *a.* flooding, filling, lining; —**ающий свет** floodlight; —**ное** *n.* jelly.

**заливн/ой** *a.* flooded; *see also* **заливочный;** з. **кран** priming cup (of tractor); з. **лед** bay ice; —**ая пробка** priming plug (of pump).

**заливочн/ый** *a.* pouring, flooding; з. **желоб** pouring spout; з. **кран** (foundry) casting crane; —**ая масса** sealing compound; casting resin; —**ая чаша** pouring basin.

**заливчик** *see* **залив.**

**ализ** *m.* (aero.) fairing.

**залипание** *n.* sealing.

**залит/ый** *a.* poured over, flooded; filled; lined (bearing); з. **маслом** oil-immersed; —**ь** *see* **заливать.**

**залог** *m.* deposit, pledge, guarantee, security; mortgage; (grammar) voice.

**залож/ение** *n.* laying (of foundation); —**енный** *a.* laid; mortgaged; —**ить** *see* **закладывать.**

**залом/ать,** —**ить** *see* **заламывать.**

**залп** *m.*, —**овый** *a.* volley, discharge.

**залужение** *n.* sowing (field) to grass.

**зальбанд** *m.* (min.) casing, selvage.

**зальмрот** *m.* salmon red (dye).

**зальцбургский купорос** eagle vitriol (a mixture of ferrous and cupric sulfates).

**зам.** *abbr.*, **зам**— *prefix* (**заместитель**) substitute; (**заместительный**) substitute, acting.

**замаз/ать,** —**ывать** *v.* cement, putty, plaster, plaster up, daub, fill up, stop (a hole); —**ка** *f.* cement, putty, plaster, lute, paste; —**ывание** *n.* cementing, puttying, plastering.

**заманчив/ость** *f.* temptation; —**ый** *a.* tempting, alluring, enticing.

**замарать** *v.* soil, dirty, smear; blot out, efface.

**замаривать** *see* **заморить.**

**замарывать** *see* **замарать.**

**замаскиров/ать,** —**ывать** *v.* disguise, screen, camouflage, mask.

**замасл/ивать,** —**ить** *v.* oil, grease, lubricate.

**заматывать** *v.* wind, twist, entwine.

**замачив/ание** *n.* wetting, moistening; —**ать** *v.* wet, damp, moisten, humidify, soften, dip, soak, steep; ret (fiber).

**замащивать** *v.* pave.

**замбониев столб** Zamboni's dry cell.

**замедлен/ие** *n.* slowing down, retardation, lag, deceleration, delay, delayed action; **без** —**ия** readily; **длина** —**ия** (nucl.) slowing-down length; —**ный** *a.* slowed down, retarded, delayed, deferred-action; —**ного действия** delayed-action.

**замедл/ивать,** —**ить,** —**ять** *v.* slow down, retard, delay, defer, prolong, detain; ease, ease up, moderate; suppress, inhibit; —**иваться,** —**иться,** —**яться** *v.* slow down, decelerate, slacken; —**итель** *m.* retarder, inhibitor; (speed) reducer; (nucl.) moderator; —**яющий** *a.* retarding, inhibiting; timing (relay); —**яющая способность** (nucl.) slowing-down power, moderating power.

**замен/а** *f.* substitution, replacing, replacement; substitute, equivalent; change, changing, interchanging, renewing; з. **каучука** rubber substitute; —**енный** *a.* substituted; —**имость,** —**яемость** *f.* interchangeability, exchangeability; —**имый,** —**яемый** *a.* interchangeable, exchangeable, renewable, replaceable, detachable; —**итель** *m.* substitute; eliminator; —**ить,** —**ять** *v.* substitute, replace, renew; exchange, interchange, supersede; —**яющий** *a.* substituting, substitution, replacing, interchanging; (med.) prosthetic.

**замер** *m.* measuring; survey; test, probe.

**замереть** *see* **замирать.**

**замерз/ание** *n.* freezing, congealing, solidification, chilling; **температура** —**ания, точка** —**ания** freezing point; pour point (of oil); —**ать,** —**нуть** *v.* freeze, congeal, solidify; —**ающий** *a.* freezing; —**лый,** —**ший** *a.* frozen.

**замерная лента** measuring tape.

**замертв/елый** *a.* benumbed, numb; —**о** *adv.* in a dead faint.

**замерять** *v.* gage, measure.

**замес** *m.* batch, mix; —**ить** *see* **замешать.**

**замести** *see* **заметать.**

**заместитель** *m.* substitute; assistant; —**ный** *a.* substitute, substituting; —**ство** *n.* substitution; **по** —**ству** by proxy.

**заместить** *see* **замещать.**

**заметать** *v.* sweep; cover up; sew up.

**заме/тить,** —**чать** *v.* notice, take notice, observe, remark; mark, note; —**тка** *f.* notice, note, memorandum; —**тки**

*pl.* notes; **—тный** *a.* noticeable, discernible; marked, appreciable; outstanding; **—чание** *n.* noticing; remark, observation, comment, note; **—чательный** *a.* remarkable, striking, unusual, uncommon, singular.

**замеш/анный** *a.* mixed, mixed in, kneaded; connected (with), involved (in); **—ательство** *n.* confusion, disorder; embarrassment; **—ать, —ивать** *v.* mix, mix in, knead; involve, entangle, implicate.

**замещ.** *abbr.* (**замещенный**) substituted.

**замещ/аемый** *a.* replaceable, displaceable; **—ать** *v.* substitute, replace, displace, supersede; change, convert; **—ающий** *a.* substituting, replacing; **—ение** *n.* substitution, replacement, displacement; change, conversion; **двойное —ение, обменное —ение** (chem.) double decomposition; **—енный** *a.* substituted, replaced, displaced.

**замзав** *abbr.* (**заместитель заведующего**) acting manager.

**заминать** *v.* tread on, press down, stamp on; suppress, put a stop (to).

**заминка** *f.* hesitation, confusion, delay.

**замир/ание** *n.* dying away; (rad.) fading; **—ать** *v.* (sound) die, die away, fade; sink, stop beating (of heart).

**замкнут/ость** *f.* reticence; (elec.) closed state (of circuit); **—ый** *a.* closed, locked; box (groove); inland (sea); **—ый накоротко** (elec.) short-circuited; **—ый цикл** closed cycle: **—ая цепь** closed circuit, loop; **—ь** *see* **замыкать.**

**замковые** *pl.* (zool.) Articulata.

**замок** *m.* lock; catch; scarf, scarf joint; hinge; castle; **в з.** scarfwise; **висячий з.** padlock; **французский з.** stock lock.

**замок/ать, —нуть** *v.* get wet.

**замонтировать** *v.* build in.

**заморажив/ание** *n.* freezing, congealing, refrigerating; **—атель** *m.* freezer; refrigerant; **—ать** *v.* freeze, congeal, refrigerate, chill; **—ающий** *a.* freezing; **—ающее средство** refrigerant.

**заморить** *v.* starve, underfeed.

**заморо/женный** *a.* frozen, congealed; iced; **—зить** *see* **замораживать;**

**—зки** *pl.* first autumn or late spring frosts.

**заморский** *a.* overseas, foreign.

**заморыш** *m.* starveling, starver.

**замостить** *see* **замащивать.**

**замотать** *see* **заматывать.**

**замочить** *see* **замачивать.**

**замочн/ый** *a.* lock; з. **наличник** plate (of lock); **—ая скважина** keyhole.

**замощенный** *a.* paved.

**замужество** *n.* marriage.

**замуров/анный** *a.* immured, walled in; built-in; embedded; **—ать, —ывать** *v.* immure, wall in; build in, embed; bank up; **—ка** *f.* immurement.

**замутить** *v.* make muddy, make turbid, disturb; **—ся** *v.* become turbid.

**замуч/енный** *a.* worn out, exhausted; **—ивать, —ить** *v.* tire out, exhaust.

**замш/а** *f.*, **—евый** *a.* chamois, suede; **—евание** *n.* chamoising; **—евать** *v.* chamois, oil-tan; **—иться** *v.* become cottony, lose its nap.

**замывать** *v.* wash off, wash away.

**замык/ание** *n.* locking, fastening, closing, completion; з. **накоротко, короткое з.** (elec.) short-circuiting; **—атель** *m.* (elec.) switch; contactor; locking mechanism; **—ать** *v.* lock, close, close up; **—ать цепь** (elec.) close a circuit, make contact; **—аться** *v.* close up, join; form (a circle); **—ающая** *f.* closing line; **—ающий** *a.* locking, closing.

**замыс/ел, —л** *m.* project, scheme, plan; **—лить** *v.* plan, intend; **—ловатость** *f.* intricacy; **—ловатый** *a.* intricate, complicated, complex, involved.

**замыть** *see* **замывать.**

**замычка** *f.* bolt, catch, lock.

**замышлять** *see* **замыслить.**

**замять** *see* **заминать;** **—ся** *v.* become confused, falter, stop short.

**занаве/с** *m.*, **—ска** *f.*, **—сь** *f.* curtain; screen; **—сить, —шивать** *v.* curtain, screen, cover; **—шенный** *a.* curtained, screened, covered.

**занашивать** *v.* wear out.

**Зандмейера реакция** Sandmeyer's reaction.

**зандр** *m.* outwash plain, driftless area.

**зандцемент** *m.* sand cement.

**занемо/гать, —чь** *v.* fall ill.

**занести** *see* **заносить.**

**зани/жать, —зить** *v.* understate; underestimate, put too low; **—женный** *a.* understated; too low (result, value); undersized.

**занимаемость** *f.* occupancy.

**занимательн/ость** *f.* interest; **—ый** *a.* interesting, entertaining.

**занимать** *v.* borrow; occupy, take possession (of); engage, hold, tie up; **—ся** *v.* study, work (at), be occupied (with), deal (with).

**заново** *adv.* anew, re—.

**заноз/а** *f.* splinter; **—истый** *a.* splintery, hackly, jagged; **—ить** *v.* get a splinter in.

**занорыш** *m.* cavity.

**занос** *m.* accumulation, drift; skidding (of automobile, etc.); (aero.) side slip; (med.) mole; **—ить** *v.* put down, register, enter; carry away; carry, bring in (a disease); wear out; choke up (with), block up (with); skid (of automobiles); **—ный** *a.* brought in, imported (disease); drift; skidding.

**заносчивый** *a.* arrogant, overbearing.

**занят/ие** *n.* occupation, employment, business, pursuit; seizure; **часы —ия** business hours; **—ой** *a.* busy; **—ый** *a.* occupied, busy; **—ь** *see* **занимать.**

**заоблачный** *a.* beyond the clouds.

**заодно** *adv.* at the same time, together.

**заокеанский** *a.* transoceanic.

**заостр/ение, —ивание** *n.* sharpening, pointing; point, tip; **—енность** *f.* keenness, taper; **—енный** *a.* pointed, sharp, tapered, acute, acicular; **—ить, —ять** *v.* sharpen, point, grind down, taper down; **—яющийся** *a.* tapering.

**заочн/о** *adv.* without seeing; **—ый** *a.* out of sight; by default; correspondence (course).

**зап.** *abbr.* (**западный**) west, western.

**запад** *m.* west, occident.

**запад/ать** *v.* fall in; **—ина** *f.* sink, sinkhole; (pal.) patella.

**западный** *a.* western, west.

**западня** *f.* trap, snare, mesh.

**запаечный** *a.* sealing.

**запаздыв/ание** *n.* retardation; hysteresis, lag, lagging, delay; time lag (of magnetization, etc.); tardiness, lateness; **угол —ания** (elec.) angle of lag;

**—ать** *v.* be late; delay, lag, creep, retard; **—ающе-критический** *a.* (nucl.) delayed-critical (reactor); **—ающий** *a.* lagging; delayed (neutron, etc.).

**запа/ивать** *v.* solder, seal up; **—йка** *f.* soldering, sealing, seal.

**запаков/ать, —ывать** *v.* pack, wrap up.

**запал** *m.* fuse, lighter, primer, cap, blasting charge; vent, touch hole; ignition, firing; premature drying (of seeds); (vet.) pulmonary emphysema; **автоматический з.** ignition device, igniter; **неисправный з., неправильный з.** misfire.

**запалзывать** *v.* creep in, crawl in.

**запал/ивать, —ить** *v.* ignite, kindle, light, fire; **—ьник** *m.* ignition device, igniter, blasting fuse; ignition chamber.

**запальн/ый** *a.* ignition, igniting, firing; (nucl.) seed; **з. прибор** ignition device, igniter; **з. шар** ignition chamber; **—ая свеча** spark plug; **—ая ячейка** (nucl.) seed unit.

**запальщик** *m.* blaster.

**запараллелить** *v.* connect in parallel.

**запар/ивание** *n.,* **—ка** *f.* steaming, spec. high-pressure steaming; soaking, steeping; (agr.) scalding (of straw, etc.); **—ивать** *v.* steam; **—ник** *m.* scalding unit.

**запарн/ый** *a.* steaming; **з. аппарат** steam chamber, steam chest; **—ые краски** (dyeing) steam colors; **печатание —ыми красками** steam printing.

**запас** *m.* store, stock, supply, reserve, reserve stock, storage; provision, allowance, margin; **—ы** *pl.* reserves; resources; **з. прочности, коэффициент —а** coefficient of safety, safety factor; **з. товаров** stock in trade; **в з., про з.** in stock, in store; **проверять з.** *v.* take stock, take inventory; **—ание** *n.* storage, accumulation; **—ать, —ти** *v.* stock, store, accumulate, reserve; **—ливый** *a.* thrifty, provident; **—ная** *f.* storeroom, stockroom; **—ной, —ный** *a.* reserve, auxiliary, spare, duplicate, standby (equipment); emergency (exit); **—ной путь** siding; **—ная часть** spare part, spare.

**запасть** *see* **западать.**

запасы *pl. of* запас; reserves.

запатентованный *a.* patented.

запах *m.* odor, smell, scent, perfume, aroma; без —а odorless; издавать з. *see* запахнуть; лишение —а, удаление —а deodorization.

запах/ать, —ивать *v.* plow in.

запахнуть *v.* smell, give off odor, exhale.

запачкать *v.* soil, dirty.

запаш/ка *f.* land for plowing; tillage; plowing under (or in); —ник *m.* share; shallow plow.

запа/янный *a.* soldered; closed, sealed (tube, ampoule); —ять *see* запаивать.

зап.-герм. пат. *abbr.* (патент Западной зоны Германии) German Western Zone patent.

запека *f.* zapeka (brown iron cement in auriferous sands).

запек/ать *v.* bake well, bake brown; —аться *v.* clot, congeal, coagulate (of blood); cake, sinter; —шийся *a.* clotted, coagulated; caked, sintered.

запер/еть *see* запирать; —тый *a.* closed, locked; blocked, barred.

запечат/анный *a.* sealed; —ать *see* запечатывать.

запечатле/вать, —ть *v.* impress, imprint.

запечатыв/ание *n.* sealing; —ать *v.* seal, seal up.

запеч/енный *a.* baked well; —ь *see* запекать.

запил *m.* notch, gash; —енный *a.* notched; —ивать, —ить *v.* mark with a saw or file, notch; begin to saw or file.

запинаться *v.* hesitate, falter.

запир/ание *n.* closing, shutting, locking, fastening; occlusion; —ательный *a.* locking, lock; (anat.) obturator; —ательная мышца (anat.) constrictor; —ательство *n.* denial, disavowal; —ать *v.* close, close up, shut, shut off, seal, lock, lock in, fasten, bolt; deny; —ающий *a.* locking; cut-off (voltage).

запис/анный *a.* recorded, on record, record; —ать *see* записывать; —ка *f.* note, memorandum, report; —ки *pl.* notes, records, journal, memoirs; proceedings; —ной *a.* writing; note (book); first-rate, regular.

записыв/ание *n.* taking notes, putting down, recording, transcribing; —ать *v.* make a note (of), put down, write down, mark down, record, register; —аться *v.* enter, join, become a member (of); —ающий *a.* recording.

запись *f.* entry, record, recording, transcription; registration; writing; note; symbol; з. на ленте, з. на пленке tape recording.

запих/ать, —ивать, —нуть *v.* push in.

заплавлять *v.* close by melting, seal.

запла/та *f.* patch, piece; wage, salary, pay; —тать *v.* patch, mend; —тить *v.* pay; —ченный *a.* paid.

заплесн/евелый, —евший *a.* mildewed, moldy; —еветь *v.* mildew, grow moldy; —ение *n.* mildewing, growing moldy.

запле/сти, —тать *v.* braid, plait.

заплечик *m.* shoulder, collar, bead; (met.) bosh (of a shaft furnace); кожух —а bosh jacket; —и *pl.* bosh.

заплечье *n.* shoulder blade.

запломбиров/анный *a.* filled (tooth); sealed; —ать *v.* fill; seal.

заплы/вать, —ть *v.* swim in, float in; come in; be filled (with mud, etc.); з. жиром grow over with fat, get very fat.

заповедать *see* заповедовать.

заповедн/ик *m.* national forest, game reservation; —ый *a.* forbidden, prohibited, interdicted.

заповед/овать, —ывать *v.* command, order.

заподлицо *adv.* flush (with).

запозд/авший, —алый *a.* late, retarded, overdue; —алость *f.* lateness, backwardness; —ание *see* запаздывание; —ать *see* запаздывать.

заполн/ение *n.* filling, filling in, filling up, charging, priming; (adsorption) surface coverage; коэффициент —ения (elec.) space factor; —енный *a.* filled, charged; —итель *m.* filler; aggregate (in concrete); —ить, —ять *v.* fill, fill in, fill up, charge; stop (a hole); —иться, —яться *v.* fill up; —яющий *a.* filling; —яющий материал filler, filling.

запом/инание *n.* memorizing; remembering; storage (of data); —инать, —нить *v.* memorize, remember, keep in mind; store; —**инающий** *a.* memory; —**инающее устройство** (data) storage.

**запонка** *f.* stud.

**запор** *m.* bolt, bar, lock, latch, hasp, fastener, catch, stop, shut-off device; locking, fastening; (med.) constipation; —**но-выпускной** *a.* shut-off (valve).

**запорн/ый** *a.* locking, closing, shut-off, shutting-off; з. **клапан** shut-off valve, stop valve; з. **кран** stopcock; —**ая жидкость** sealing fluid, seal; —**ое приспособление** closing device, plug.

**запот/евание** *n.* perspiring, sweating; moisture condensate; —**елый** *a.* perspired, sweated, covered with moisture, dim (glass); —**еть** *v.* perspire, sweat, become covered with moisture.

**заправила** *f.* rule; *m.* boss, chief.

**заправ/ить,** —**лять** *v.* service, repair, set right; fill up, fuel, charge, prime (engine); dress, grind, sharpen (instrument); set, prepare; season (food); trim (lampwick); —**ка** *f.,* —**очный** *a.* servicing, repairing; filling, fueling, charging, priming; dressing, grinding, sharpening; setting, preparing; seasoning; dressing, fertilization (of soil); —**ленный под** fritted hearth bottom.

**заправочн/ый** *see* **заправка;** з. **валик** (paper) pinch roll; з. **пункт** (gasoline) filling station; з. **чан** (tanning) dressing vat; —**ая колонка** (filling station) pump.

**заправский** *a.* true, real, regular.

**заправщик** *m.* fuel tank.

**запрашивать** *v.* inquire, send an inquiry, write for information.

**запрессов/анный** *a.* pressed, press-fitted; —**ка** *f.* pressing.

**запрет** *see* **запрещение;** —**ительный** *a.* prohibitive, prohibitory; —**ить** *see* **запрещать;** —**ный** *a.* prohibited, forbidden.

**запречь** *see* **запрягать.**

**запрещ/ать** *v.* prohibit, forbid; —**ение** *n.* prohibition; embargo; ban; **первого** —**ения** (nucl.) first-forbidden; —**енный** *a.* prohibited, forbidden; —**енный переход** (quantum mechanics) forbidden transition.

**заприходовать** *v.* debit.

**запрод/ажа** *f.* sale, conclusion of a sale; advance contract; —**ать** *v.* agree to sell, sell on partial payment.

**запрос** *m.* inquiry, interrogation; need, requirement; overcharging; **цена без** —**а** fixed price; —**ить** *see* **запрашивать;** —**ный** *a.* request (form).

**запру/да** *f.* dam, dike, embankment, bar; mill pond, puddle; —**дить,** —**живать** *v.* dam, dam up; —**жение** *n.* damming, diking; backing up; —**женный** *a.* dammed, impounded, retained; —**женная вода** backwater.

**запря/гать,** —**чь** *v.* harness, put (to); —**жка** *f.* harnessing; team (of horses).

**запуск** *m.* (mach.) start-up; **процесс** —**а** start-up procedure; —**ать** *v.* start; neglect.

**запуст/елый** *a.* neglected, desolate, waste, barren, desert; —**ение** *n.* neglect, desolate state, barrenness; —**еть** *v.* go to waste, grow desolate; —**ить** *see* **запускать.**

**запут/авшийся** *a.* caught, entrapped, entangled; —**анность** *f.* complicatedness, complication; —**анный** *a.* complicated, involved, intricate; tangled, tortuous, knotted, knotty; confused; —**ать,** —**ывать** *v.* complicate; involve, implicate; tangle; —**аться,** —**ываться** *v.* become involved, get entangled, be caught; —**ывание** *n.* complication; entanglement.

**запущенн/ость** *f.* neglect; —**ый** *a.* neglected, run-down.

**запылать** *v.* flame up.

**запыл/ивать,** —**ить** *v.* dust, cover with dust; —**иваться,** —**иться** *v.* become dusty, get covered with dust.

**запяст/ный** *a.* (anat.) carpal; —**ье** *n.* wrist, carpus; bracelet.

**запятая** *f.* comma.

**запятн/анный** *a.* spotted, stained; —**ать** *v.* spot, stain; dishonor.

**запятовидный** *a.* comma, comma-shaped.

**зараб/атывание** *n.* earning; —**атывать,** —**отать** *v.* earn, merit, deserve; —**отная плата** salary, wages; —**оток** *m.* earnings.

**заравнивать** *v.* level, even up, flatten.

**зараж/ать** *v.* infect, contaminate; inoculate; —**ение** *n.* infection, contagion;

blood poisoning, septicemia; inoculation, seeding (of crystal); (parasitic) infestation; (nucl.) contamination; —**енный** *a.* infected, contaminated; inoculated.

**зараз** *adv.* at one sitting (or stroke).

**зараз/а** *f.* infection, contamination, contagion; —**ительность** *f.* infectiousness; —**ительный** *a.* infectious, contagious, catching; (nucl.) contaminating; —**ить** *see* **заражать.**

**заразих/а** *f.* (bot.) broom rape (*Orobanche*); —**овые** *pl.* Orobanchaceae.

**заразн/ый** *see* **заразительный;** —**ое начало** (med.) virus.

**заранее** *adv.* beforehand, previously, early; **з. предвиденный** foregone (conclusion); **оплаченный з.** prepaid.

**зараст/ать,** —**и** *v.* grow over, be overgrown (with).

**заратит** *m.* (min.) zaratite, emerald nickel.

**зарево** *n.* glow, redness.

**зарегистриров/ание** *n.* registration; —**анный** *a.* registered, recorded, on record; —**анная заявка** patent claim; —**ать** *v.* register, record.

**зарез/ать,** —**ывать** *v.* butcher, slaughter.

**заржав/евший,** —**елый,** —**ленный** *a.* rusted, rusty, corroded; —**еть** *v.* rust.

**зарница** *f.* summer lightning.

**заровнять** *see* **заравнивать.**

**зародить** *see* **зарождать.**

**зародыш** *m.* (anat.) fetus, embryo; (biol.) germ; (bot.) seed, bud; nucleus, seed (of crystal); **з. стебля** (bot.) plumule; **образование**—**ей,** —**евание** *n.* nucleation; —**евый** *a.* embryonic; —**евая клетка** germ cell; —**евое действие** germination; —**еубивающее вещество** germicide.

**зарожд/ать** *v.* bear, produce, generate, conceive; —**аться** *v.* be born; engender; —**ающийся** *a.* incipient, nascent; —**ение** *n.* conception, origin; onset; formation, generation; —**енный** *a.* conceived, produced.

**зарос/ль** *f.* weeds, overgrowth, thicket, brushwood; —**тать,** —**ти** *see* **зарастать;** —**ток** *m.* (bot.) prothallus, prothallium; —**ший** *a.* overgrown (with).

**зарплата** *f.* wages, salary.

**заруб** *see* **зарубина;** —**ать** *see* **зарубить.**

**зарубежн/ый** *a.* foreign, beyond the border; —**ая печать** foreign press.

**заруб/ина,** —**ка** *f.* mark, incision, notch, dent, indentation, nick, cut; —**ить** *v.* mark, notch, cut.

**зарубц/еваться,** —**евываться,** —**овываться** *v.* (med.) cicatrize, heal with a scar.

**зарухание** *n.* devitrification.

**заруч/ать,** —**ить** *v.* sign; —**аться,** —**иться** *v.* secure, make sure (of); —**ный** *a.* signed.

**зарыблен/ие** *n.* stocking with fish; —**ный** *a.* stocked.

**зары/вать,** —**ть** *v.* bury, inter, dig, dig in; —**ваться,** —**ться** *v.* bury oneself, dig in; risk, go to extremes; —**тие** *n.* burying, digging in; —**тый** *a.* buried.

**заря** *f.* glow, redness; dawn, daybreak; evening glow, sunset; outset, start.

**зарябить** *v.* ripple, ruffle.

**заряд** *m.* charge, loading; blasting charge (of explosive); cartridge; (elec.) charge, charging; **напряжение** —**а** (elec.) charging voltage; —**ить** *see* **заряжать;** —**ка** *see* **заряжение;** —**ник** *m.,* —**ный агрегат,** —**ная установка** battery charger; —**ный,** —**овый** *a.* charge, charging; loading; —**ный ящик** (mil.) caisson; —**овая независимость** (nucl.) charge independence; —**но-отсчетное устройство,** —**носчитывающее устройство** charger-reader; —**ово-инвариантный,** —**овонезависимый** *a.* charge-independent.

**заряж/аемый** *a.* chargeable, charged; —**ать** *v.* charge, load; (elec.) charge; —**ающий** *a.* charging; —**ающая машина** charging machine, charger; —**ение** *n.* charging, charge, loading; —**енный** *a.* charged, loaded, fed; (elec.) live, charged.

**заса/дить,** —**живать** *v.* plant, set; drive (spike, etc.); imprison, shut in, put in; —**дка** *f.* planting; driving, driving in.

**засаливать** *v.* salt, pickle, corn.

**засал/ивать,** —**ить** *v.* soil, grease; —**иваться,** —**иться** *v.* get greasy, glaze; clog up; —**ившийся** *a.* glazed (polishing wheel).

**засаривать** *see* **засорить.**

**засасыв/ание** *n.*, **—ающий** *a.* sucking in, suction; **—ать** *v.* suck in, draw in; **—ающий насос** suction pump; **—ающая банка** suction flask.

**засахар/енный** *a.* candied; **—ивание** *n.* sugaring, candying; saccharification; **—ивать** *v.* sugar, preserve in sugar, candy; **—иваться** *v.* saccharify.

**засветка** *f.* illumination; irradiation, exposure.

**засвидетельствов/ание** *n.* witnessing, testifying; authentication, certification; **—ать** *v.* witness, testify, attest, certify.

**засев** *m.*, **—ание** *n.*, **—ка** *f.* sowing, planting; seeding; sown area; **з. облаков** cloud seeding; **—ать** *v.* sow, plant; seed; inoculate; **—ать под** sow to.

**засевший** *a.* stuck, caught, plugged.

**засед/ание** *n.* conference, meeting, session; **журнал —аний** minute book; **—атель** *m.* assessor; **присяжный —атель** juror, juryman; **—ать** *v.* sit in, take part in a conference or meeting, hold meetings; stick, stick fast.

**засека** *f.* abatis.

**засекать** *v.* make a cut; intersect.

**засекре/тить**, **—чивать** *v.* make secret; restrict, classify (information); **—ченный** *a.* secret, confidential; security-restricted.

**засел/ение** *n.* population, colonization; **—енный** *a.* populated; **—ить, —ять** *v.* populate, people, colonize.

**засесть** *see* **заседать.**

**засеч/ка** *f.* cut, canker; indentation, notch; (surv.) intersection; **обратная з.** (surv.) resection; **—ь** *see* **засекать.**

**засе/янный** *a.* sown, planted; **—ять** *see* **засевать.**

**засилье** *n.* predominance.

**заск/акивание** *n.* engagement; **—акивать** *v.* catch, engage, snap (into), get into place; **—ок** *m.* engagement; catch.

**заскорузлый** *a.* hardened, calloused.

**заскочить** *see* **заскакивать.**

**заслон** *m.* screen; lock, barrier; shelter belt; **—ение** *n.* shielding, screening; **угол —ения** (illumination) angle of cut-off; **—ить, —ять** *v.* shield, screen,

shade; **—ка** *f.*, **—очный** *a.* door, gate, slide, flap, baffle; damper, choke; fire screen; (anat.) valve (of heart); **—очная теория** (meteor.) barrier theory.

**заслуг/а** *f.* merit, desert; **—и** *pl.* services.

**заслуж/енный** *a.* deserved, merited; estimable, honored; **—ивать, —ить** *v.* deserve, merit, earn; **—ивающий** *a.* deserving, worthy (of).

**засмол/ение** *n.* pitching, tarring; resinification; **—ить, засмаливать** *v.* pitch, tar; resinify.

**заснеженный** *a.* snow encrusted.

**заснят/ый** *a.* photographed; **—ь** *v.* photograph.

**засов** *m.* bolt, bar, hasp, catch; **—ать, —ывать** *v.* push, thrust, shove, poke (in).

**засол** *m.*, **—ка** *f.* salting, pickling; **—ение** *n.* salinization (of soil); **—енность** *f.* salinity; **—енный** *a.* saline; salt (marsh); **—ить** *v.* salt, pickle.

**засор/ение** *n.* stoppage, obstruction, choking up, choking, plugging; soiling, dirtiness, contamination, impurity; (med.) constipation; **—енность** *f.* contaminated state; weediness; **—енный** *a.* stopped, stopped up, choked, clogged up, plugged up; soiled, contaminated; constipated; weedy (garden); **—ить , —ять** *v.* stop up, obstruct, choke, choke up, clog, plug up, block; soil; litter; **—иться, —яться** *v.* clog up, block up, get plugged up.

**засос** *m.* inflow; **—анный** *a.* sucked in, drawn in, suction; **сухо —анный** dry-suction.

**засох/нуть** *see* **засыхать; —ший** *a.* dried, withered.

**заспиртовывать** *v.* alcoholize.

**засрочный** *a.* beyond the term, overdue.

**заст.** *abbr.* (застывание) solidification.

**застава** *f.* gate, gateway, gates, toll gate, barrier; (mil.) outpost.

**заставить** *v.* compel, force, oblige, make, cause, impel; block, bar.

**заставка** *f.* (typ.) space; fuse.

**заставл/енный** *a.* compelled, forced; blocked, barred; **—ять** *see* **заставить.**

**заставные буквы** (typ.) title types.

**застаив/ание** *n.* stagnation; hanging,

sticking (of furnace charge); —аться *v.* stagnate, stand too long.

засте/гивать, —гнуть *v.* fasten, hook, hook up, clasp, button; —жка *f.* fastener, fastening, clasp, hasp, hook; механическая —жка zipper.

застекл/енный *a.* glazed, vitrified; glassed-in, glass-covered; —ить, —овать *v.* glaze, vitrify; glass in.

застиг/ать, —нуть *v.* catch unawares.

заст/илать, —лать *v.* cover, sheathe, lay; cloud, overcast; —илка *f.* covering.

заст/ой *m.* stagnation, dead season, standstill; deadlock, crisis; (med.) congestion, obstruction, stasis; время —оя dull season; —ойный *a.* stagnant (water); dead, dull; congested.

застолбить *v.* (min.) peg, mark out (a claim).

застопор/ивание *n.* stopping, clogging, choking; —ившийся *a.* clogged, choked, plugged; —ивать, —ить *v.* stop, clog, plug; cut off (steam).

застоявшийся *a.* stale, stagnant.

застрахов/анный *a.* insured; —ать, —ывать *v.* insure.

застр/евание *n.* sticking, jamming; —евать, —януть, —ять *v.* stick, get stuck, jam; —явший *a.* stuck, clogged.

застудить *v.* chill; —ся be chilled; catch cold.

застудневание *n.* coagulation, gelation.

застуж/ать, —ивать *see* застудить; —енный *a.* chilled.

заступ *m.* pick, pickax; spade.

заступ/ать, —ить *see* заменять; —аться, —иться *v.* intercede, plead (for); —ление *n.*, —ничество *n.* intercession; —ник *m.* defender; patron.

засты/вание *n.* congealing, solidification, freezing; проба —вания (oils) pour test; температура —вания, точка —вания solidification point, pour point; —вать, —нуть, —ть *v.* congeal, solidify, freeze, harden, gel, set; get cold, get chilled; —вающий *a.* congealing; —вший *a.* congealed, solidified, hardened.

засты/нуть, —ть *see* застывать.

засунуть *see* засовывать.

засух/а *f.* drought, dryness, dry period; zasukha (dry lake in the steppes); —оустойчивый *a.* drought-resistant.

засуш/енный *a.* dried, shriveled; —ивать, —ить *v.* dry, dry up; —ка *f.* drying; —ливость *f.* aridity; —ливый *a.* drying; arid.

засчит/ать, —ывать *v.* take into consideration, take into account, include.

засып/ать *v.* cover, fill, fill in, fill up, charge; —ка, —ь *f.* covering, filling (in), charging, stoking; (met.) charge, burden; —ной *a.* charging; —ной ковш, —ная воронка charging hopper, feed hopper; —ная яма hopper, bin; —ное отверстие charging hole.

засыхать *v.* dry, shrivel, shrink, wither.

затапливать *v.* fire, fire up, light a fire, make a fire, kindle; heat; flood, deluge, submerge, drown.

затачивать *see* заточить.

затвердев/ание *n.* hardening, solidification, congealing; setting (of cement); степень —ания consistency; температура —ания, точка —ания solidification point; freezing point; coagulation point; —ать *v.* harden, solidify, set, congeal, bind, grow hard, grow firm; —ший *a.* hardened, solidified, congealed.

затверд/елость *f.* hardness; —елый *a.* hardened, firm, set, indurate, caked; —ение *see* затвердевание; —еть *see* затвердевать; —итель *m.* hardener.

затвор *m.*, —ный *a.* bolt, bar, lock, fastening; closing device, shut-off, trap, stopper; gate, valve; (liquid) seal; (phot.) shutter; (rifle) lock; з. у шлюза floodgate, water gate; герметический з. hermetic seal; —енный *a.* shut, closed; slaked (lime); —ить, —ять *v.* shut, close, shut off; slake (lime), mix (cement).

затевать *v.* undertake, begin, venture.

затекать *v.* flow in, fill.

затем *adv. and conj.* after this, after that, then, further, next; thereupon, whereupon, subsequently; as, inasmuch as; seeing that; з. что *conj.* because, since; as, inasmuch as, seeing that; з. чтобы in order that; а з. and then, and later.

затемн/ение *n.* darkening, blackout,

eclipse; dim-out; —енный *a.* darkened, subdued, blacked out; —итель *m.* dimmer; —ить, —ять *v.* darken, obscure, black out; shade.

затен/ивать, —ить, —ять *v.* shade, darken; —итель *m.* shade.

затереть *see* затирать.

затечь *see* затекать.

затея *f.* undertaking, enterprise; —ть *see* затевать.

затир/ание *n.*, —ка *f.* rubbing over, smoothing out; (pigments) grinding; (brewing) mashing; —ать *v.* rub over, smooth out; (brewing) mash; not work smoothly.

затих/ать, —нуть *v.* abate, quiet down.

затишье *n.* calm, calmness, stillness; временное з. lull, interval of calm.

заткнут/ый *a.* plugged, stopped up; —ь *see* затыкать.

затм/евать, —ить *v.* eclipse, obscure, darken; —ение *n.* eclipse; полное —ение total eclipse.

зато *conj.* in return; but then, whereas.

затоваривание *n.* overproduction, surplus, excess of supply, glut (on the market).

затон *m.* cove, backwater; (hydraulics) crawl; —уть *v.* sink, submerge, be submerged.

затопить *see* затапливать.

затопл/ение *n.* inundation, flooding; —енный *a.* flooded, drowned, submerged; —ять *v.* inundate, flood, drown, submerge, immerse, deluge.

затор *m.* blocking, stoppage, obstruction, trouble; (brewing) mash.

затормо/женный *a.* braked; retarded, restrained; deferred, delayed (reaction); —зить *v.* brake, apply the brakes.

заторный *a.* (brewing) mash.

заточ/ать, —ить *v.* confine, imprison.

заточ/ить *v.* sharpen, point, grind; —ка *f.*, —ный *a.* sharpening, pointing, grinding, dressing, rounding off; —ный станок sharpener, grinder.

затрав/ка *f.*, —ник *m.* fuse; primer, priming, priming device; з. (cryst.) inoculation, seeding; seed; внесение —ки seeding; —ленный *a.* primed, filled; —лять *v.* prime; inoculate, seed; —очный *a.* inoculating,

seeding; —очный кристалл seed.

затрагивать *v.* touch upon, affect.

затра/та *f.* expense, expenditure, outlay; consumption; input (of work); —ченный *a.* expended; consumed; —чивать *v.* spend; consume, use.

затронуть *see* затрагивать.

затропический *a.* extratropical.

затрудн/ение *n.* difficulty, inconvenience, trouble; crux (of the matter); без —ения readily; —енное дыхание labored breathing; —ительность *f.* difficulty; —ительный *a.* difficult, inconvenient; intricate, puzzling; —ить, —ять *v.* trouble, cause trouble, encumber, hamper.

затуман/ивать, —ить *v.* cloud, obscure (by fog); —иваться, —иться *v.* cloud up, grow cloudy, get foggy, get dim.

затуп/ившийся, —ленный *a.* dulled, blunt; —ить, —лять *v.* dull, blunt; —иться, —ляться *v.* get dulled, become blunt.

затух/ание *n.* extinguishment, dying out, damping; (elec. comm.) attenuation; (radioactive) decay; магазин —ания attenuator; постоянная —ания attenuation constant; —ать, —нуть *v.* go out slowly, be extinguished, die out, taper out; damp, attenuate; (rad.) die, die away, fade; —ающий *a.* dying; transient (term).

затушев/ать, —ывать *v.* shade, tint.

затуш/енный *a.* extinguished, out; —ить *v.* extinguish, put out.

затхл/ость *f.* stuffiness, staleness; —ый *a.* stuffy, stale, close, musty, moldy; —ая вода stagnant water, bilge water.

затыкать *v.* stop, stop up, plug, cork, bung; pack; choke up, obstruct.

затыловочный токарный станок relieing lathe, gear-milling lathe.

затыл/ок *m.* back of the head; (anat.) occiput; —очный *a.* occipital, cervical.

затычка *f.* plug, bung, stopper; spiggot.

затягив/ание *n.* tightening; (rad.) coupling-hysteresis effect; —ать *v.* tighten, draw close, fasten down, screw up; draw out, protract, delay; heal (wound); draw in, involve, implicate.

затяжка *f.* tightening; tie, tie-beam,

bridging; delay, prolongation (of time).

**затяжной** *a.* tightening; lingering (illness); **з. болт** draw bolt; **з. трос** stay wire.

**затянут/ый** *a.* tightened; delayed, prolonged; **—ь** *see* **затягивать.**

**заурановый** *a.* transuranium.

**заурядный** *a.* ordinary, commonplace.

**заусен/ец** *m.*, **—ица** *f.*, **—ок** *m.* projecting edge, barb, burr, fin, rib, seam.

**заушн/ица** *f.* (med.) mumps, parotitis; **—ый** *a.* (anat.) parotid.

**зафиксированный** *a.* fixed.

**заформовать** *v.* mold, shape.

**зафрахтов/ание** *n.* chartering; **—анный** *a.* chartered; **—ать** *v.* charter, freight.

**захаживать** *v.* go in, drop in, come in, enter.

**захват** *m.* clamp, hold, holding device, grapple, grip, catch, clutch; grab, grab bucket; gripping, engagement, fastening; capture, entrapment; encroachment, inroad; taking up, seizure; recharge (of well); premature drying (of grain); **з. электронов** electron capture; **сечение —а, —ное сечение** capture cross section; **угол —а** angle of nip (between rolls); **ширина —а** working width; **—ить** *see* **захватывать;** **—ка** *f.* detent, detainer, catch, checking device; **—ный** *see* **захватывающий; —чик** *m.* (chem.) acceptor; (soil) invader; (geol.) pirate stream.

**захватыв/ание** *n.* gripping, catching, seizing; taking; capture, trapping, entrapment; **—атель** *m.* grip, clamp, fastener; **—ать** *v.* grip, catch, grasp, engage, bite; seize, take, take hold (of), trap; capture (particles, electrons); include, cover, deal (with); enclose; encroach, occupy, take possession (of), take over; make an inroad upon.

**захватывающ/ий** *a.* gripping, catching; **з. замок** catch lock; **з. ковш** grab bucket, grab; **—ая способность** hold; **—ее приспособление, —ее устройство** gripping device, clamp, jaw, catch.

**захваченный** *a.* gripped; captured, entrained, entrapped.

**захворать** *v.* fall ill.

**захеево масло** bito oil, zachun oil.

**захлеб/нуться, —ываться** *v.* choke; (distillation) flood; **—ывание** *n.* flooding (of column); **точка —ывания** flooding point.

**захлестыв/ание** *n.* whipping, lashing; sagging (of belt); entanglement (of wires); **—ать** *v.* whip, lash; sag; entangle; sprinkle, wet.

**захлоп/ать** *v.* begin to clap or flap; **—ка** *f.* flap; **—нуть** *v.* slam shut.

**заход** *m.* setting; (sun) set; (aero.) turn; **—ить** *see* **захаживать;** set (of sun).

**захождение** *n.* (biol.) transgression.

**захолодить** *v.* freeze, chill.

**захолустный** *a.* provincial, isolated.

**захоронение** *n.* burial (of radioactive waste).

**зацементировать** *v.* cement in.

**зацентровка** *f.* centering, alignment.

**зацеп/а, —ка** *f.* catch, detent, detainer, checking device, stop; hook, latch; cam, cog; **—ить** *see* **зацеплять.**

**зацеплен/ие** *n.* catching, hooking, gearing, meshing, engagement, contact; **в —ии** in gear, geared, engaged; **вводить в з.** throw in gear, put in gear; **входить в з.** gear, mesh, engage; **линия —ия** line of contact; line of action; **—ный** *a.* caught, hooked, geared, engaged.

**зацепл/ять** *v.* catch, hook, gear, mesh, engage, bite, lock; **—яющий** *a.* hooking, engaging.

**зачастую** *adv.* often, frequently.

**зачат/ие, —ье** *n.* conception, beginning; **—ок** *m.* embryo, rudiment; **—очный** *a.* incipient, embryonic; rudimentary; **—очный член** rudiment, vestige; **в —очном состоянии** in embryo; **—ь** *v.* conceive, become pregnant; begin, commence.

**зачекан/енный** *a.* calked; **—ивать** *v.* calk in, *see also* **чеканить; —ка** *f.* calking.

**зачем** *adv.* why, what for, wherefore.

**зачерк/ивание** *n.* crossing out, striking out, deletion; **—ивать, —нуть** *v.* cross out, strike out, delete.

**зачерп/нуть, —ывать** *v.* scoop, ladle; **—ывание** *n.* scooping, ladling; **проба —ыванием** ladle sampling.

**зачер/тить, —чивать** v. draft, draw, sketch, trace, cover with lines; **—чен-ный** a. drafted, sketched, traced.

**зачесть** see **зачитывать.**

**зачет** m. test, examination; compensation; instalment, part payment; **в з.** in payment (of); **это не в з.** it does not count; **—ный** a. instalment, on account.

**зачинать** see **зачать.**

**зачинить** v. mend, fix.

**зачисл/ить, —ять** v. include, enter; enlist, enroll; take on (staff).

**зачистка** f. (met.) dressing, trimming.

**зачитывать** v. take into consideration; take in payment (of).

**зачищ/ать** v. clean, strip, trim (off); **—енный** a. cleaned, trimmed, bare (wire).

**зашеек** m. (anat.) nape of neck.

**зашершаветь** v. become rough.

**зашифровывать** v. code, cipher.

**зашкаливание** n. off-scale reading.

**зашлаковывание** n. slagging.

**зашнуров/ать, —ывать** v. lace.

**заштрихов/анный** a. crosshatched; **—ывать** v. crosshatch.

**зашунтиров/анный** a. shunted, switched; **—ать** v. shunt, switch.

**защебен/ивать, —ить** v. fill up with rubble.

**защелк/а** f. catch, latch, trigger, pawl, click, detent, detainer, stop, trip, checking device, arresting device; **—ивать, —нуть** v. fasten; latch, snap; **—ивающий механизм** lock mechanism.

**защем/ить, —лять** v. pinch, bite, fasten; choke, jam; **—иться, —ляться** v. get pinched, hook, hook in, dig in, bite; **—ление** n. pinching; choking; **—ленный** a. pinched, fastened; choked; entrapped.

**защит/а** f. defense, protection, safeguard, guard; precaution; shelter, cover; shield, shielding (against radiation); (soil) conservation; **з. от нейтронов** (nucl.) neutron shield; **—ить** see **защищать; —ник** m. defender, protector, defense counsel.

**защитн/ый** a. protecting, protective, guard; (nucl.) shield, shielding; khaki (color); seal (coat of paint); (micros.)

cover (glass); **з. газ** gas envelope; **з. кожух, —ая коробка** (nucl.) jacket, can; **з. слой** protective layer, protective film; **з. угол** (illum.) angle of cut-off; **з. щит** face shield; **з. экран** (nucl.) shield; **—ая доска, —ая плита** baffle plate, baffle; **—ое действие** screening effect; **—ое средство** preservative; preventive; prophylactic; **—ое устройство** protective device, safety device.

**защищ/аемый, —енный** a. defended, protected, guarded, screened, shielded, sheltered, enclosed; suffix —proof; **— ать** v. defend, protect, guard, screen, shield, shelter, cover; advocate.

**заэвтект/ический** a. (met.) hypereutectic; **—оидный** a. hypereutectoid.

**заяв/итель** m. applicant; **—ить, —лять** v. declare, announce; state, claim; **—ка** f. declaration, statement; claim, mining claim, location; **—ление** n. declaration, statement; application.

**заядлый** a. inveterate, confirmed.

**заяц** m. (zool.) hare.

**заяч/ий** a. hare; **з. корень** (bot.) wild ginger (Asarum); **—ье ушко** hare's ear (Bupleurum rotundifolium); **—ья капуста** stonecrop (Sedum purpureum); orpine (Sedum telephium); **—ьи ножки** club moss (Lycopodium clavatum).

**зва/ние** n. calling; status, rank, title; **—ный** a. called, invited; **—ть** v. call, invite, bid, summon; name.

**звезд/а** f. star; (mach.) spider; **морские —ы** (zool.) starfish (Asteroidea); **соединение —ой** (elec.) star connection; **—ный** a. star, stellar, stellate; sidereal (time); **—ная карта** star chart, celestial map.

**звездо/видный, —образный** a. star-shaped, star-like, stellate, asteroid; **—образная опора** (mach.) spider; **—чка** f. little star, star; asterisk; star wheel, sprocket; turnstile; spider; (met.) pick; (bot.) see **звездчатка.**

**звездчат/ка** f. (horol.) star wheel; (bot.) starwort (Stellaria); **—ость** f. (min.) asterism; **—ый** a. star-shaped, stellate, star, asteriated; **—ый остов** (mach.) spider.

**звенеть** v. ring, jingle, tinkle, clank.

**звен/о** *n.*, **—ьевой** *a.* link (of chain), ring, section, member, unit, component; team, group; monomer unit, mer in polymer chain; (geol.) member (of formation), bed; **—ьевой** *m.* team leader.

**звенящий** *a.* ringing, jingling; **з. камень** *see* **звонкий камень.**

**зверин/ец** *m.* menagerie, zoological park; **—ый** *a.* animal.

**зверобой, —ник, дырявый з.** *m.* (bot.) St. John's wort (*Hypericum perforatum*); **—ные** *pl.* Hypericaceae.

**звер/оводство** *n.*, **—оводческий** *a.* animal breeding, fur farming; **—осовхоз** *m.* state fur farm; **—ь** *m.* wild animal, wild beast.

**звон** *m.* ring; **—ец** *m.* (bot.) yellow rattle (*Rhinanthus crista galli*); (zool.) midge (*Chironomus*); **—ить** *v.* ring.

**звонк/ий** *a.* sonorous, resounding, clear; **з. камень** (petr.) clinkstone (obs.), phonolite; **—овый** *a.* bell; **—ость** *f.* sonorousness, clearness.

**звонок** *m.* bell.

**звук** *m.* sound, tone.

**звуко—** *prefix* phono—, phon—, sound.

**звуков/ой** *a.* sound, acoustic; sonic, soundwave; audible; with sound effects; audio (frequency); **—ая волна** sound wave; **—ая дорожка** sound track.

**звуко/генератор** *m.* audio-frequency oscillator; **—глушитель** *m.* silencer, muffler.

**звукозапис/ыватель** *m.*, **—ывающий аппарат** sound recorder, transcriber; **—ывающий** *a.*, **—ь** *f.* sound recording.

**звуко/изоляционный, —непроницаемый** *a.* soundproof; **—изоляция** *f.* soundproofing, sound insulation; **—локация** *f.* sound fixing and ranging; Sonar; **—мер** *m.* phonometer; **—метрия** *f.* (mil.) sound ranging; **—оператор** *m.* soundman, recordist; **—отражение** *n.* sound reflection; **—писец** *m.* sound recorder.

**звукопогло/титель** *m.* silencer, sound absorber; **—щательный, —щающий** *a.* sound-absorbing, soundproof; **—щение** *n.* sound absorption.

**звуко/приемный** *a.*, **—приставка** *f.*,

**—сниматель, —съемник** *m.* sound pickup; **—проводность** *f.* sound conductivity; **—проводный, —проводящий** *a.* sound-conducting; **—проекция** *f.* sound projection; **—проницаемость** *f.* sound transmission; **—стирающий** *a.* erasing; **—съемочный аппарат** sound (movie) camera; **—улавливание** *n.* sound ranging; **—уловитель** *m.* sound ranger, sound locator, sound detector; **—усилитель** *m.* sound amplifier; **—фикация** *f.* public address system.

**звуч/ание** *n.* sounding, sonorousness, vibration; **—ать** *v.* sound, resound; **—ащий** *a.* sounding; **—ность** *f.* sonorousness; **—ный** *a.* sonorous, resonant, sonant, loud.

**звякать** *v.* tinkle, jingle.

**з-д** *abbr.* (завод) plant, works; **з.д.** *abbr.* (западная долгота) western longitude.

**здание** *n.* building, edifice, structure.

**здесь** *adv.* here.

**здешний** *a.* local, of this place.

**ЗДМ** *abbr.* (закон действующих масс) law of mass action.

**здороваться** *v.* greet.

**здоров/енный** *a.* robust, hearty, strong; **—еть** *v.* become strong, get healthy; **—ый** *a.* healthy, sane, strong, robust, sound; **—ая структура** (met.) sound structure, soundness; **—ая трава** *see* **зверобой; —ье** *n.* health.

**здрав/ница** *f.* sanatorium, nursing home; health resort; **—о** *adv.* soundly, sanely.

**здравомысл/ие** *n.* common sense; **—ящий** *a.* sensible, sane, sober.

**здрав/оохранение** *n.* public health; **—отдел** *m.* health department; **—ствовать** *v.* be in good health, be well, thrive; **—ый** *a.* sound, sane; common (sense).

**зебра** *f.* (zool.) zebra.

**зебромал** *m.* zebromal, ethyl dibromcinnamate.

**зев** *m.* mouth, pharynx, throat, jaw, jaw opening, gap, opening, span (of wrench); (text.) shed; **воспаление —а, катар —а** (med.) pharyngitis; **—ать, —нуть** *v.* yawn, gape; miss (an opportunity); —**ный** *a.* (anat.) pharyngeal.

**Зегера конус** Seger cone, fusible cone.

**зедлицкая соль** *see* **зейдлицкая соль.**

**Зеебека эффект** (elec.) Seebeck effect.

**Зеемана эффект** (phys.) Zeeman effect.

**зеин** *m.* zein.

**зейбахит** *m.* (min.) seebachite, herschelite (a form of chabazite).

**зейбертит** *m.* (min.) seybertite, clintonite.

**зейгерн/ый** *a.* (met.) liquation; **з. горн, з. шесток** liquation hearth; **з. шлак** liquation slag; —**ая печь** liquation furnace; —**ая работа** liquation process, liquation; —**ые крецы** liquation dross.

**зейгеров/ание** *n.* (met.) liquation, liquation process; segregation; —**анный** *a.* liquated; —**ать** *v.* liquate; segregate.

**Зейдлица порошок, зейдлицкий порошок** Seidlitz powder; **зейдлицкая соль** Epsom salt, magnesium sulfate heptahydrate.

**зеймер** *m.* edger, trimmer.

**зелен/еть** *v.* turn green; —**ика, —ица** *f.* spores of club moss; —**ка** *f.* (bot.) club moss (*Lycopodium clavatum*); blakstonia.

**зелено—** *prefix* green, greenish; —**вато—** *prefix* greenish; —**ватый** *a.* greenish, olive; —**глазка** *f.* a fly (*Chlorops pumilionis*); —**желтый** *a.* greenish yellow; —**каменный** *a.*, —**каменная порода** (petr.) greenstone.

**зелен/чак** *m.* (min.) jade; —**щик** *m.* green grocer, vegetable grocer; —**ый** *a.* green; —**ый песок** (min.) green sand, glauconite; —**ый пигмент** chlorophyll; —**ь** *f.* greens, vegetables; green (pigment).

**зелье** *n.* herb; potion.

**зельтерская вода** Seltzer water.

**зем.** *abbr.* (**земельный**) soil.

**земек** *m.* Zamak (a zinc-base die-casting alloy).

**земельный** *a.* land, agrarian, soil, agricultural; earth (metals).

**земл.** *abbr.* (**земледелие**) agriculture; (**земледельческий**) agricultural.

**земле—** *prefix* earth, land; —**битная стена** rammed earth wall, pisé de

terre wall; —**вание** *n.* hauling in soil; —**ведение** *n.* geography.

**землевлад/елец** *m.* landlord, landowner, landholder; —**ение** *n.* land ownership.

**земледел/ец** *m.* farmer, cultivator, tiller, agriculturist; —**ие** *n.* farming, cultivation, agriculture; —**ка** *f.* (foundry) sand-conditioning plant, department for preparation and treatment of loam, sand, etc.; —**ьческий** *a.* agricultural.

**землекоп** *m.*, —**ный** *a.* excavator, digger.

**землемер** *m.* land surveyor, geodesist; —**ный** *a.* surveying, geodetic; —**ный циркуль** surveyor's compass.

**земле/пользование** *n.* land utilization; —**ройка** *f.* (zool.) shrew; —**сос** *m.*, —**сосная драга** hydraulic dredge, suction dredge; —**трясение** *n.* earthquake; —**уплотнитель** *m.* (steam) roller; —**устройство** *n.* land management.

**землечерп/алка** *f.* dredge, dredger, dredging shovel, scoop shovel, steam shovel; —**ание** *n.* excavation, dredging; —**ательный** *a.* dredging; —**ательная машина** dredge, dredger; —**ательные работы** dredging, excavation work.

**землистый** *a.* earthen, earthy, ocherous.

**земл/я** *f.* earth, ground, soil; land, country; **английская з.** (min.) tripoli, tripolite; **белая з.** terra alba, pipe clay; **голубая з.** (min.) blue earth, blue ground, kimberlite; **желтая з.** (min.) yellow ocher (a form of limonite); **редкие —и** rare earths; **щелочные —и** alkaline earths; **японская —я** catechu.

**земляк** *m.* fellow countryman, compatriot.

**землян/ика** *f.*, —**ичный** *a.* (bot.) strawberry (*Fragaria*).

**землянка** *f.* mud hut, dugout.

**землян/ой** *a.* earth, earthen, earthy; (elec.) ground; **з. воск** ozocerite, mineral wax, native paraffin; **з. орех** (bot.) peanut (*Arachis hypogaea*); **з. червяк** (zool.) earthworm; —**ая груша** (bot.) Jerusalem artichoke (*Helianthus tuberosus*); —**ая смола** (geol.) blackstone, ampelite, carbonaceous shale; —**ое масло** petroleum; —**ые краски** mineral pigments; —**ые**

монахи, —ые братья (geol.) earth pillars, earth columns; —ые работы excavation work.

земник *m.* ground coal.

земноводный *a.* amphibian, amphibious; terraqueous.

земн/ой *a.* terrestrial, earthly, earthy, telluric; з. зажим (elec.) ground terminal; з. шар the earth; globe; —ая ось earth's axis; —ое излучение terrestrial radiation.

Земотдел *abbr.* (Отдел землеустройства и земледелия) the Department of Agriculture.

зензубель *m.* molding plane.

зенит *m.* zenith; —ный *a.* zenith; anti-aircraft; —чик *m.* anti-aircraft gunner.

зенкель, зенкер *see* зенковка.

зенков/ание *n.*, —очный *a.* countersinking, counterboring; —ать *v.* countersink, counterbore; —ка *f.* countersink, countersink reamer, reamer, counterbore.

зеркало *n.* mirror; speculum (for optical instruments); surface (of liquid); (water) table; полировка под з. mirror finish.

зеркальнополированный *a.* mirror-finished, smooth, highly polished.

зеркальн/ый *a.* mirror; mirror-like, specular; highly polished, reflecting, shining; image (frequency, etc.); plate (glass); optical (isomerism); з. изомер enantiomer; з. металл speculum metal (a copper-tin alloy); з. чугун specular cast iron; —ая кора oak bark from trees under 20 years old; —ое изображение, —ое отражение mirror image, reflected image, specular reflection; —ые ядра mirror nuclei.

зерлик *m.* (bot.) hart's tongue (*Scolopendrium vulgare*); —а корневище polypody root (*Polypodium vulgare*).

зерн/ение *n.* granulation, granulating; —еный *a.* granulated; —истосланцеватый *a.* granular-cleavable; —истость *f.* granularity, grain; grain size, mesh; graininess, seediness, bittiness (of coatings); —источерепитчатый *a.* granular-interlocking; —истый *a.* granular, granulated,

grainy; clotted (oil); spheroidized (pearlite, etc.); —ить *v.* granulate, crush; knurl; mill; —о *n.* grain, granule, kernel, nodule, pellet; seed, corn, cereals; —а *pl.* grains; nibs, bits (in lacquer); номер —а grain size, mesh, fineness; —овик *m.* (bot.) seed vessel, pericarp.

зерновк/а *f.* (zool.) weevil; (bot.) caryopsis; —и *pl.* pea and bean weevils (*Bruchidae* or *Mylabridae*).

зернов/ой *a.* grain, granular; seed, corn, cereal; з. спирт grain alcohol; з. хлеб grain; —ые злаки cereals; —ые культуры grain crops.

зерно/дробилка *f.* grain mill; —очиститель *m.* grain cleaner; (corn) sheller; —очистка *f.* grain cleaning; cleaning shoe (of combine); —пульт, —пульт-погрузчик *m.* grain blower, grain loader; —склад *m.* grain storage; granary; —совхоз state grain farm; —сушилка *f.* grain dryer, seed dryer; —транспортер *m.* grain conveyer; —хранилище *n.* barn, granary; —ядный *a.* granivorous.

зернышко *n.* small grain, granule.

зеро *see* нуль.

зета *f.* zeta (Z, ζ).

зет-металл *see* зетовое железо.

зетов/ый *a.* Z, zee-, Z-shaped; —ая балка zee-beam; —ое железо Z-iron.

зефир *m.* zephyr (yarn, cloth).

зибелин *m.* zibeline, sable fur.

зига *f.* ridge (of corrugated metal).

зиг/бургит *m.* (min.) siegburgite (a fossil resin); —енит *m.* siegenite (a variety of linnaeite).

зигзаг *m.* zigzag; —ообразный *a.* zigzag, crisscross, staggered; serrated, notched, saw-like, toothed.

зигмашина *f.* creasing machine.

зигнемовые *pl.* (bot.) Zygnemaceae.

зиго— *prefix* (biol.) zygo— (yoke, pair; zygosis); —мицеты *pl.* (bot.) Zygomycetes; —спора *f.* zygospore; —та *f.* (biol.) zygote.

зизания *f.* (bot.) zizania.

зик-машина *see* зигмашина.

зильберглет *m.* litharge, lead monoxide.

зима *f.* winter.

зимаза *f.* zymase (yeast enzyme).

зим/ний *a.* winter, hibernal; —о— *prefix*

winter; zymo— (ferment, fermentation); —**ование** *n.*, —**овка** *f.* hibernation; —**овать** *v.* hibernate, winter, pass the winter; —**овник** *m.* winter abode; winter hive; (bot.) hellebore (*Helleborus*); colchicum; —**овниковые** *pl.* Melanthaceae.

**зимо/гексаза** *f.* zymohexase, aldolase; —**ген** *m.* zymogen.

**зимозеленка** *see* **зимолюбка**.

**зимозин** *see* **зимаза**.

**зимой** *adv.* in winter.

**зимол/из** *m.* zymolysis, zymohydrolysis; —**огия** *f.* zymology.

**зимолюбка** *f.* (bot.) wintergreen (*Pyrola* or *Chimaphila*).

**зимо/плазма** *f.* zymoplasm, thrombase; —**стерин** *m.* zymosterol.

**зимо/стойкий** *a.* winter-hardy, hardy (plant); —**стойкость** *f.* hardiness; —**ю** *adv.* in winter.

**зингибер/ен** *m.* zingiberene, methyl-4-propenylcyclohexane; —**ол** *m.* zingiberol.

**зинзив/ей**, —**ерь** *m.* (bot.) mallow (*Malva*).

**зинзубель** *see* **зензубель**.

**зинковка** *see* **зенковка**.

**зирки, червонные** *see* **вербена**.

**зия/ние** *n.* yawning, gaping; hiatus, chasm, gap; —**ть** *v.* yawn, gape, open; —**ющий** *a.* yawning, gaping.

**ЗЛ** *abbr.* (Заводская Лаборатория) Industrial Laboratory (journal).

**злак** *m.* grass; —**и** *pl.* cereals, grain; —**и, овые** *pl.* (bot.) Gramineae; —**овый** *a.* grassy, gramineous, herbaceous; —**овые мухи** chloropid flies (*Chloropidae*).

**златки** *pl.* metallic wood borers, flat-headed borers (*Buprestidae*).

**злато/глазки** *pl.* aphid lions (*Chrysopidae*); —**гузка** *f.* brown-tail moth (*Nygmia phaeorrhoea* or *Euproctis chrysorrhoea*); —**искр** *m.* (min.) aventurine; —**к** *m.* (bot.) asphodel (*Asphodelus*); —**тканый** *a.* (text.) gold-worked; —**цвет** *m.* (bot.) chrysanthemum (*Pyrethrum aureum*); —**цветный** *a.* gold-colored.

**зло** *n.* evil, wrong, harm; malice, anger; *adv.* maliciously; **употреблять во з.**

*v.* abuse, misuse; —**воние** *n.* bad odor, stink, stench; —**вонный** *a.* malodorous, bad-smelling, stinking, fetid; —**й** *a.* spiteful, malicious.

**злокачественн/ый** *a.* malignant; —**ая опухоль** (med.) malignant tumor; —**ое малокровие** pernicious anemia.

**зло/ключение** *n.* mishap; —**намеренный**, —**умышленный** *a.* ill-intentioned.

**злоупотребл/ение** *n.* misuse, maltreatment; —**ять** *v.* abuse, misuse, maltreat.

**змеевидный** *a.* serpent-like, serpentine, sinuous, zigzag; coil, spiral.

**змеевик** *m.* coil, coil pipe, spiral tube; worm; spiral drill; (bot.) bistort, snake weed (*Polygonum bistorta*); (min.) serpentine, serpentine rock, ophiolite; **з.-холодильник** condenser coil, cooling coil; **благородный з.** (min.) bowenite (a variety of massive serpentine); —**овый** *a.* coil, spiral, worm; (bot.) bistort; (min.) serpentine, ophiolitic.

**змее/головник** *m.* (bot.) dragon's head (*Dracocephalum*); —**хвостки** *pl.* (zool.) Ophiuroidea.

**зме/иный** *a.* snake; serpentine (curve); **з. камень** (min.), —**иная трава** (bot.) *see* **змеевик**; **з. корень**, —**йка** *f.* (bot.) snakeroot; —**иная кровь** dragon's blood (resin); —**иться** *v.* serpentinize; —**й** *m.* serpent; **бумажный** —**й, воздушный** —**й** kite; —**йка** *f.* spiral separator, seed sorter; —**йковый** *a.* kite; —**йковый аэростат** kite, kite balloon; —**я** *f.* snake, serpent.

**зморник** *m.* (bot.) zostera; —**овые** *pl.* Zosteraceae.

**знак** *m.* sign, symbol, mark, indication, token, omen, badge; **з. атома, химический** **з.** atomic symbol, chemical symbol; **з. иона** charge; **з. минерала** optic sign; —**овый** *a.* sign, symbol.

**знаком/ить** *v.* acquaint, introduce; inform; familiarize; —**иться** *v.* get acquainted, meet; study, investigate; —**ство** *n.* acquaintance (with), knowledge (of); —**ый** *a.* acquainted (with), familiar, known.

**знакопеременный** *a.* sign-changing, alternating.

**знаменатель** *m.* (math.) denominator;

common ratio (in geometrical progression); —ный *a.* denominative; significant, noteworthy, important.

**знамение** *n.* sign, phenomenon, token.

**знаменит/ость** *f.* celebrity, fame, eminence; —ый *a.* celebrated, famous, eminent.

**знаменовать** *v.* prove, show, indicate.

**знамя** *n.* banner.

**знание** *n.* knowledge, learning; science, skill.

**знати/ость** *f.* notability, eminence; —ый *a.* notable, eminent, distinguished.

**знаток** *m.* connoisseur, judge, expert.

**знать** *v.* know, have knowledge (of), be informed (of), be aware (of), be acquainted (with); be skilled (in); **дать з.** inform; **дать себя з.** reveal oneself, identify oneself.

**значащий** *a.* meaning; significant (figure, etc.).

**значек** *see* значок.

**значение** *n.* meaning, sense; importance, significance, consequence, import; value; **иметь з.** *v.* be important, matter; **конечное з.** final value.

**значимость** *f.* significance.

**значительн/о** *adv.* considerably, much, significantly; —ость *f.* significance, magnitude; —ый *a.* significant, important, considerable, notable, marked.

**значить** *v.* mean, signify; —ся в списке be mentioned.

**значность** *f.* valency, atomicity.

**значный** *a.* marking.

**значок** *m.* sign, emblem, badge.

**знающ/ий** *a.* knowing; expert, skilled; —ее лицо expert.

**знобить** *v.* chill, freeze; shiver.

**зноиха** *f.* (bot.) fool's parsley (*Aethusa cynapium*).

**зной** *m.* heat, sultriness; —ный *a.* hot, sultry, burning, torrid.

**зоб** *m.*, —ный *a.* crop, craw (of bird); (med.) goiter; —астый *a.* with a large crop; —ный корень (bot.) polypody root (*Polypodium*); —ная железа (anat.) thymus; —оватость *f.* (root) knot, cancer.

**зов** *m.* call, summons, invitation; —ет *pr. 3 sing. of* звать; —ущий *a.* calling; naming.

**зодиак** *m.* (astron.) zodiac; —альный *a.* zodiacal.

**зодчество** *n.* architecture.

**зол/а** *f.* ashes, cinders; **содержание —ы** ash content.

**золенгофенский камень** Solenhofen stone (a limestone).

**зол/ение** *n.*, —ка *f.* (tanning) liming; —истый *a.* ash, ashen; —ить *v.* lime.

**золоедины** *pl.* (met.) blowholes, air holes.

**золот/арник,** —ень *m.* (bot.) golden rod (*Solidago*); —ильный *a.* gilding.

**золотисто—** *prefix* gold, auro—, aurous; —желтый *a.* golden yellow; —золотой *a.* auroauric; —родановодородная кислота aurothiocyanic acid; —синеродоводородная кислота aurocyanic acid; —хлороводородная кислота chloroaurous acid.

**золот/истый** *a.* golden, gold-colored; gold, aurous; —ить *v.* gild.

**золотник** *m.*, —овый *a.* slide valve, gate valve; unit of weight (4.266 g.); —о-вый шток, —овая скалка slide rod, slide valve stem; —овое зеркало slide valve face.

**золот/о** *n.* gold, Au; **гидрат закиси —а** aurous hydroxide; **гидрат окиси —а** auric hydroxide, gold hydroxide, auric acid; **закись —а** aurous oxide; **соль закиси —а** aurous salt; **листовое з.** gold leaf, gold foil; **новое з.** Mannheim gold (a brass alloy); **окись —а** auric oxide, gold trioxide; **соль окиси —а** auric salt; **промывное з., шлихо-вое з.** (min.) placer gold, gold dust; **сернокислая закись —а, сернокислая соль закиси —а** aurous sulfate; **сернокислая окись —а, сернокислая соль окиси —а** auric sulfate; **синеро-дистое з.** aurous cyanide, gold monocyanide; **синеродное з.** auric cyanide, gold tricyanide; **хлористое з.** aurous chloride, gold monochloride; **хлорное з.** auric chloride, gold trichloride.

**золото—** *prefix* gold, auri—, auric; —бит, —боец *m.* (met.) gold beater; —бородник *m.* (bot.) chrysopogon; —глазки *see* златоглазки; —иска-тель *m.* gold prospector, gold miner.

**золот/ой** *a.* gold, golden, auric; **з. песок** gold dust; **з. прииск, —ая россыпь**

(min.) placer, placer deposit; —ая кислота auric acid, auric hydroxide; соль —ой кислоты aurate; —ая печать (bot.) golden-seal (*Hydrastis canadensis*); —ое число gold number.

золотокисл/ый *a.* auric acid; aurate (of); з. натрий sodium aurate; —ая соль aurate.

золото/носный *a.* gold-bearing, auriferous; —подобный *a.* gold-like, golden; —промывочное устройство (min.) gold washer; —промышленник *m.* gold miner; —промышленность *f.* gold mining; —родановодородная кислота thiocyanatoauric acid.

золотосинерод/истый *a.* cyanoaurate (of); з. калий potassium cyanoaurate; —оводородная кислота cyanoauric acid.

золото/содержащий *see* золотоносный; —тысячник *m.* (bot.) centaury (*Erythraea centaurium*).

золотохлор/истый *a.* chloroaurate (of); з. натрий sodium chloroaurate; —о-водородная кислота chloroauric acid.

золоточерпательная машина (min.) gold dredger, gold dredge.

золоту/ха *f.* (med.) scrofula; —шник *see* золотарник; —шный *a.* scrofulous.

золоудал/ение *n.* ash removal; —итель *m.* ash remover.

золочен/ие *n.* gilding, gold-plating; —ый *a.* gilded, gilt, gold-plated.

золь *m.* sol.

зольн/ик *m.* ash pit, ash dump, ash bin; cinder pit, cinder box; (tanning) lime pit; (bot.) cineraria; saltwort (*Salsola*); —ость *f.* ash content, percentage of ash; определение —ости ash determination; —ый *a.* ash, cinder; —ая вода lime water; —ая трава (bot.) kidney vetch (*Anthyllis vulneraria*).

зона *f.* zone, area, region, section; belt, band, range; —льность *f.* zonality, zonation, zoning; —льный *a.* zonal, regional.

зонгорин *m.* songorine.

зонд *m.* sound, probe; borer, drill; (meteor.) sounding balloon; —аж *m.*, —ирование *n.*, —ировочный *a.* sounding, probing; —ировать *v.* sound, probe; search, explore; bore;

—ировочный бур sounding borer, probe.

зон/ированный *a.* zoned; —овый *a.* zone.

зонт, —ик *m.* umbrella; canopy; cover; cupola, hood (of furnace); (bot.) umbel; —ичнокистевой *a.* (bot.) corymbose, corymbiform; —ичные *pl.* Umbelliferae; —ичный, —ообразный *a.* umbrella-shaped, umbellate.

зоо— *prefix* zoo— (animal); —ген *m.* zoogene; —генный *a.* zoogenic; —география *f.* zoogeography, faunal geography;—глеи,—глены *pl.* (bact.) zoogloea; —лит *m.* zoolith, zoolite, fossil animal; —литовый *a.* zoolithic.

зоолог *m.* zoologist; —ический *a.* zoological; —ия *f.* zoology.

зоо/мариновая кислота zoomaric acid, hexadecenoic acid; —ноз *m.* zoonotic disease; —парк *m.* zoological garden, zoo; —стерин *m.* zoosterol.

зоотехн/ик *m.* zootechnician, livestock expert; animal breeder; —ика, —ия *f.* zootechny, animal breeding; —ический *a.* zootechnic.

зоо/токсин *m.* zootoxin (such as snake venom); —ферма *f.* fur farm; —фит *m.* zoophyte; —химический *a.* zoochemical; —химия *f.* zoochemistry; —цид *m.* rodent poison.

зопник *m.* (bot.) phlomis.

зорк/ий *a.* sharp-sighted, far-sighted; —ость *f.* keen vision.

зор/я *f.* (bot.) lovage (*Levisticum officinale*); —ьное масло lovage oil.

ЗОС *abbr.* (зональная опытная станция) Zonal Experiment Station.

зрачок *m.* pupil (of eye).

зрел/ость *f.* ripeness, maturity; finished state; (med.) puberty, virility; —ый *a.* ripe, mature; —ьня *f.* apparatus for oxidizing mordants and aging dyes.

зрен/ие *n.* eyesight, vision; обман —ия optical illusion; поле —ия visual field; точка —ия point of view, viewpoint; угол —ия point of view; viewing angle, visual angle.

зреть *v.* ripen, mature, age.

зримый *a.* visible.

зритель *m.* spectator, observer; viewer.

зрительн/ый *a.* visual, optic, optical; specular; signal (communication);

**—ая трубка** telescope, spyglass, field glasses; **—ое стекло** (micros.) eyepiece.

**зря** *adv.* in vain, to no purpose, for nothing, uselessly; without thinking; **—шный** *a.* purposeless, for no purpose.

**ЗС** *abbr.* (замедляющая способность) moderating power.

**зуб** *m.* tooth; tuckstone; *see also* зубец; **в з.** end on; **режущий з.** blade.

**зубарь** *m.* toothed plane.

**зубец** *m.* tooth, cog, lug, catch, cam, projection, spur, barb; indent, dent, notch; dog (of clutch); merlon (of wall); prong, tine (of fork); pinnacle; (drill) bit.

**зубил/о** *n.*, **—ьный** *a.* chisel, point tool, calking iron, bit, punch; **вырубать —ом** *v.* gouge, chisel out; **обрубать —ом** *v.* trim, chisel off; **рубить —ом** *v.* chisel; **—ьная сталь** chisel steel.

**зубнина** *f.* (bot.) leadwort (*Plumbago*).

**зубн/ой** *a.* tooth, dental; **з. винный камень** tartar; **з. врач** dentist; **з. протез** artificial tooth, denture; **—ое вещество** (anat.) dentine; **—ое дерево** (bot.) prickly ash (*Xanthoxylum*); **—ое средство** dentifrice.

**зубовидный** *a.* tooth-like, odontoid; dent type (maize).

**зубоврач** *m.* dentist; **—ебный** *a.* dentist's, dental; **—евание** *n.* dentistry.

**зубо/закругляющий станок** gear-chamfering machine; **—к** *m.* little tooth; bit; rice coal; **—мер** *m.* tooth gage, gear gage; **—резный станок, —фрезерный станок** gear cutter, gear-milling machine; **—строгальный станок** gear planer, gear shaper; **—шлифовальный станок** gear-grinding machine.

**зубр** *m.* (zool.) bison.

**зубрить** *v.* indent, dent; learn by rote.

**зубровка** *f.* (bot.) sweet grass (*Hierochloe*).

**зубчат/ка** *f.* gear, gear wheel; rack and pinion; (bot.) eyebright (*Euphrasia*

*officinalis*); odontites; **—ость** *f.* serration.

**зубчат/ый** *a.* toothed, gear, geared, cogged, serrated, serrate, indented, dented, notched, jagged, scalloped; hackly (fracture); **з. блок** sprocket, sprocket wheel; **з. перебор, —ое зацепление** gear, gearing, transmission gear; **з. привод, —ая передача** gear drive, gear; **з. рельс, —ая полоса, —ая рейка** gear rack, rack; **—ое колесо** gear wheel, gear, cog wheel, pinion; **—ое кольцо** ring gear.

**зуб/чик** *see* зубец; **—чики** *pl.* (wave) ripple; **—ья** *pl.* teeth.

**зуд** *m.* itching, scabies; **—ень** *m.* (zool.) mite.

**зумм/ер** *m.* (elec. comm.) buzzer, hummer, vibrator; **—ерный** *a.* buzzer; humming; **—ирование** *n.* buzzing, humming.

**зумф, зумпф** *m.*, **—овый** *a.* sump, pit, draining pit in mine; **—овый шлих** (met.) ore slime, slimes; **—офен** *m.* (met.) pit furnace, soaking pit; **—штрек** *m.* (min.) sump, sump drift.

**зунд** *m.* sound, strait.

**зыб/кий** *a.* vacillating, unsteady, unstable; quaking; **—кость** *f.*, **—ление** *n.* vacillation, fluctuation; **—ун** *m.*, **—учий песок** quicksand; **—ун** *m.* floating mass of vegetation; **—учий** *a.* shifting, unsteady; **—ь** *f.* spongy ground; surge, swell (of sea).

**зычн/ость** *f.* loudness; **—ый** *a.* loud, sonorous.

**зэта** *see* зета.

**зюзник** *m.* (bot.) fetid horehound (*Ballota*); bugleweed (*Lycopus*).

**зюид** *m.* (nautical) south; **—овый** *a.* southern, south.

**зяб/кий** *a.* chilly, sensitive to cold; **—кость** *f.* chilliness; **—левый** *a.* autumn (plowing); **—лина** *f.* (geol.) frost cleft; **—нуть** *v.* feel chilly.

**зябра** *f.* (bot.) hemp nettle (*Galeopsis speciosa*).

**зябь** *f.* fall plowing; fall-plowed field.

# И

**и** *conj.* and, also, too; but, although; both; even, as well as; **и тот и другой** both.

**ИАН** *abbr.* (Известия Академии Наук) Bulletin of the Academy of Sciences.

**иатр**— *see* **ятр**—.

**ИБВ** *abbr.* (Институт биологии водохранилищ) Institute of Biology of Water Reservoirs.

**ибер/ийский** *a.* Iberian; **—ит** *m.* (min.) iberite (alteration product of cordierite).

**ибо** *conj.* because, for, as.

**ИБФ** *abbr.* (Институт биологической физики Академии Наук СССР) Institute of Biological Physics of the USSR Academy of Sciences; **ИБХ** *abbr.* (Институт биологической химии имени А. Н. Баха Академии Наук СССР) Bakh Institute of Biological Chemistry of the USSR Academy of Sciences.

**ИВ** *abbr.* (индекс вязкости) viscosity index.

**ива** *f.* (bot.) willow (*Salix*).

**иван-да-марья** *f.* (bot.) cow wheat (*Melampyrum nemorosum*).

**иванов хлеб** (bot.) carob tree (*Ceratonia siliqua*); **и. червяк** (zool.) firefly.

**иван-чай** *m.* (bot.) willow herb (*Chamaenerion* (or *Epilobium*) *angustifolium*).

**ивняк** *m.* osier bed, willow grove.

**ивов/ые** *pl.* (bot.) Salicaceae; **—ый** *a.* willow.

**иволга** *f.* (zool.) oriole.

**ИВП** *abbr.* (измеритель влажности почвы) soil moisture meter.

**ига/зурин**, **—сурин** *m.* igasurine; **—суровая кислота** igasuric acid.

**игелстромит** *m.* (min.) igelströmite (a variety of pyroaurite).

**ИГен** *abbr.* (Институт генетики Академии Наук СССР) Institute of Genetics of the USSR Academy of Sciences.

**игепон** *m.* Igepon (detergent).

**игл/а** *f.* needle, stylus; (zool.) spine; (bot.) thorn; spicule; pivot; (text.) card wire; (volcano) lava plug; (Pele's) tear; **—истый** *a.* needle-

shaped, acicular; **—ица** *f.* (bot.) butcher's broom (*Ruscus*).

**игло/ватый** *a.* prickly, spiny, thorny; **—видный**, **—образный** *a.* needle-shaped, needle, acicular; **—кожие** *pl.* (zool.) echinoderms.

**Игнатия**, **боб св.** (bot.) St. Ignatius' bean, ignatia bean (*Strychnos ignatia*).

**игнимбрит** *m.* (petr.) ignimbrite, welded tuff.

**игнитрон** *m.*, **—ный** *a.* (elec.) ignitron.

**игнорировать** *v.* ignore, disregard.

**иго** *n.* yoke.

**иголка** *see* **игла.**

**игольн/ик** *m.* needle case; **—ый** *a.* needle.

**игольчат/ый** *a.* needle, needle-shaped, acicular, spiny, spicular; **и. клапан** needle valve; **и. контакт** (elec.) point contact; **—ая лента** (text.) card clothing; **—ая маслянка** needle lubricator; **—ая руда** (min.) needle ore (aikinite in acicular crystals).

**игра** *f.* play, free play, freedom, slack, give, looseness, backlash; clearance; game, sport; freak (of nature); **и. валков** backlash; **продольная и.** axial clearance; **—ть** *v.* play.

**игрек** *m.* (math.) *y* (value); **и. сплав Y** alloy.

**игристый** *a.* sparkling, frothy, foaming.

**игрушка** *f.* toy, plaything.

**игуана** *f.* (zool.) iguana.

**иддингсит** *m.* (min.) iddingsite.

**идеал** *m.* ideal; **—ьность** *f.* the ideal; **—ьный** *a.* ideal, optimum; theoretical.

**идейный** *a.* idea, notion, conception; true to the idea (of).

**иденти/фикационный** *a.*, **—фикация** *f.* identification; **—фицировать** *v.* identify, determine; **—фицируемый** *a.* identifiable, identified; **—чность** *f.* identity; **—чный** *a.* identical.

**идет** *pr. 3 sing. of* **идти; дождь и.** it is raining.

**идея** *f.* idea, notion, conception.

**идио**— *prefix* idio— (separate, distinct; self-produced); **—бласт** *m.* (biol.)

idioblast, biophore; (geol.) idioblast (crystal).

идиоген/иты *pl.* (geol.) idiogenites; —ный *a.* idiogenous.

идиома *f.* idiom; —тический *a.* idiomatic.

идио/морфный *a.* (min.) idiomorphic, euhedral, automorphic; —синкразия *f.* idiosyncrasy, peculiarity; —статический *a.* (elec.) idiostatic.

идиот *m.* idiot, imbecile; —изм *m.*, —ия *f.* idiocy; —ический *a.* idiotic, imbecile.

идио/фанизм *m.* (cryst.) idiophanism; —фанный *a.* idiophanous; —хроматический *a.* (min.) idiochromatic; —электрический *a.* idioelectric, idioelectrical.

идит *m.* iditol (a hexahydric alcohol).

идите *imp. of* идти.

идитол *m.* a phenol-formaldehyde resin.

идоза *f.* idose, pentahydroxyhexanal.

идокраз *m.* (min.) idocrase, vesuvianite.

идоновая кислота idonic acid.

идосахарная кислота idosaccharic acid.

и др. *abbr.* (и другое) et cetera; (и другие) and others, et al.

идр/иален *m.* (min.) idrialene (a hydrocarbon from asphalt); —иалит *m.* idrialite (a natural oxygenated hydrocarbon); —ил *m.* idryl, fluoranthene.

ид/ти *v.* go; operate, run, work; progress, proceed; и. за follow; —ущий *a.*, —я going, running, operating; reaching; —ущий вверх rising; —ущий вниз descending, falling.

иезаконитин *m.* jesaconitine.

иезуитск/ий *a.* Jesuit; и. порошок Jesuit's powder (old name for quinine powder); и. чай Jesuit's tea, wormseed (fruit of *Chenopodium ambrosiodes*); —ая кора Jesuit's bark, cinchona bark.

иеко/леин *m.* jecolein; —леиновая кислота jecoleic acid; —рин *m.* jecorin (a protein); —риновая кислота jecoric acid.

иена *f.* yen (a Japanese coin).

иенит *m.* (min.) yenite, ilvaite, lievrite.

иенское стекло Jena glass.

иервин *m.* jervine.

иероглиф *m.* hieroglyph.

иетолин *m.* jetolin (aniline black).

иецекит *m.* (min.) ježekite.

иждивение *n.* expense, cost.

из *prep. gen.* out of, of, from, with; *prefix* ex—; *with verbs to mean* use up (by); *see also* ис—.

изадрин *m.* isopropylarterenol, Aludrine.

иза/зол *m.* isazol; —конитовая кислота isaconitic acid, isoaconitic acid; —коновая кислота isaconic acid, itaconic acid.

изалло/бара *f.* (meteor.) isallobar; —барический *a.* isallobaric; —терма *f.* isallotherm.

изамин *m.*, —овый *a.* isamine.

изамовая кислота isamic acid.

изановая кислота isanic acid.

изаномаль *m.* (meteor.) isanomal, isanomalous line; isabnormal line.

изарол *m.* Isarol, ichthammole.

изат/ан *m.* isatan, hydroxybioxindol; —ид *m.* isatide, dihydroxybioxindol; —ин *m.*, —иновый *a.* isatin, 2,3-indolinedione; —иновая кислота isatinic acid, isatic acid.

изато/вая кислота isatoic acid, N-carboxyanthranilic acid; —геновая кислота isatogenic acid; —ксим *m.* isatoxime, nitrosoindoxyl; —фан *m.* isatophan.

изатроп/ил *m.* isatropyl; —овая кислота isatropic acid.

изафеновая кислота isaphenic acid.

изба *f.* hut, cottage.

избав/ить, —лять *v.* release, rid (of), free (of); —иться, —ляться *v.* get rid (of); —ление *n.* release; —ленный *a.* released, rid, freed.

избе/гать, —гнуть, —жать *v.* avoid, escape, evade, dodge, avert; —жание *n.* avoiding, avoidance, escape, averting; во —жание in order to avoid.

избирател/ь *m.* elector, voter; selector; —и *pl.* electorate, body of electors.

избирательн/ость *f.* selectivity; —ый *a.* selective; electoral; —ый растворитель selective solvent; —ая способность selectivity.

избирать *v.* choose, select; elect.

избоина *f.* cake, oil cake.

избор/азживать, —оздить *v.* furrow, ridge; —ожденный, —оженный *a.* furrowed, ridged, striated.

**избр/ание** *n.* selection; election; **—анный** *a.* selected, chosen; **—ать** *see* **изби-рать.**

**избыт/ок** *m.* surplus, superfluity, excess; abundance, profusion, plenty; **и. нейтронов** (nucl.) neutron excess, difference number; **сумма —ков** (meteor.) accumulated excess; **—оч-ный** *a.* surplus, excess, excessive, in excess, superfluous, overflow; over— (pressure); gage (atmosphere); **—оч-ный размер** oversize.

**изв.** *abbr.* (известия) bulletin, journal.

**изваяние** *n.* sculpture.

**извед/ать, —ывать** *v.* learn, find out; investigate, try.

**изверг/ать, —нуть** *v.* erupt, throw out, eject, expel, emit, exclude; excrete; vomit; **—нутый** *see* **изверженный.**

**извержен/ие** *n.* eruption, ejection, emission, effusion, discharge, outbreak; excretion; **—ный** *a.* ejected, emitted; (geol.) igneous, eruptive, volcanic.

**известе—** *see* **известково—; —разбрасы-ватель** *m.* (agr.) lime spreader.

**извести** *see* **изводить.**

**извест/ие** *n.*, **—ия** *pl.* information, news, report; bulletin, journal; **—и-тель** *m.* indicator; signaling device; **—ительный** *a.* indicating; **—ить** *see* **извещать.**

**известк/а** *see* **известь; —ование** *n.* liming; **—овистый** *a.* calcareous, lime-like, lime-containing.

**известково—** *prefix* lime; **—желез-ная руда** calcareous iron ore; **—обжи-гательная печь** lime kiln; **—сть** *f.* calcareousness; **—хромистый гранат** (min.) calcium-chromium garnet, uva-rovite.

**известков/ый** *a.* lime, calcareous, calcif-erous, calcium; **и. азот** calcium cyanamide; **и. бак** (sugar) lime vat; **и. зольник** (tanning) lime pit; **и. камень** (petr.) limestone; **и. мергель** lime marl, calcareous marl; **и. поле-вой шпат** lime feldspar, anorthite; **и. раствор** lime mortar; whitewash; **и. туф** (min.) tufa, travertine; **и. шпат** (min.) calc spar, calcareous spar, calcite; **бурый и. шпат** dolo-mite, pearl spar; **и. щелок** lime lye (calcium hydroxide); **—ая вода** lime-water, calcium hydroxide suspension; **—ая зола** lime ash (chiefly calcium carbonate); **—ая кашица, —ое тесто** lime paste, lime cream; **—ая накипь** (min.) calcareous sinter, travertine; **—ая селитра** calcium nitrate; **—ая серная печень** lime hepar, sulfurated lime; **—ая синь** blue verditer; **—ая соль** calcium salt; **—ое молоко** milk of lime.

**известн/о** it is known; **ему и.** he knows; **—ость** *f.* reputation, repute, fame, publicity; **поставить в —ость, ставить в —ость** *v.* inform, let it be known; **пользующийся —остью, —ый** *a.* famous, well-known, cele-brated; certain.

**известняк** *m.* (petr.) limestone; **волнис-тый и., пенистый и.** (min.) aragonite; **волокнистый и., жилковатый и.** satin spar (a fibrous variety of calcite); **комовой и.** (min.) ballstone; **—овый** *a.* limestone, calcareous, calciferous.

**извест/ь** *f.* lime; **и.-пушонка, выветрив-шаяся и.** air-slaked lime; **и.-тесто** lime paste; **азотистая и.** calcium cyanamide; **белильная и., хлорная и.** bleaching powder, calcium hypo-chlorite; **венская и.** Vienna paste, Vienna lime (lime and potash); **гашеная и.** slaked lime, calcium hydroxide; **едкая и., жженая и., негашеная и.** quicklime, unslaked lime, calcium oxide; **карбонат —и, углекислая и.** calcium carbonate; **натечная и.** (min.) calcareous sinter, travertine; **раствор —и** mortar, grout; whitewash; **селитряная и.** calcium nitrate; **сернокислая и., сульфат —и** calcium sulfate; **содержащий и.** calciferous, calcium-containing, cal-careous; **фосфорнокислая и.** calcium phosphate.

**извещ/ать** *v.* inform, notify, let know; indicate; advertise; **—ение** *n.* infor-mation, notification, notice, advice.

**извив** *m.* winding, coil, fold; **—ание** *n.* winding, coiling; **—аться** *v.* wind, coil, twist, meander.

**извил/ина** *f.* bend, crook, curve, con-volution, tortuosity, meander; de-tour; **мозговые —ины** (anat.) con-volutions of the brain; **—истый** *a.*

winding, tortuous, sinuous, meandering.

**извин/ение** *n.* apology, excuse; **—итель-ный** *a.* excusable; **—ить, —ять** *v.* excuse, forgive, pardon.

**извит/ость** *f.* winding, twisting; **—ься** *see* **извиваться.**

**извлек/ание** *see* **извлечение; —ать** *v.* extract, derive, draw, draw out, withdraw, draw off, extricate, recover; derive profit; **—ающий** *a.* extracting, digesting, digestive; **—а-ющий раствор** extractant.

**извлеч/ение** *n.* extraction, recovery; abstract, résumé, compendium, summary; (math.) taking (the root of); **коэффициент —ения** extraction coefficient; **секция —ения** (isotopes separation) stripper; **—енный** *a.* extracted, drawn off; derived; **—ь** *see* **извлекать.**

**извне** *adv.* from without.

**изводить** *v.* exhaust, overwork; spend, use, consume; **—ся** *v.* overwork.

**извозчик** *m.* cab driver, driver.

**извор/ачиваться** *v.* avoid, dodge, elude; **—отливый** *a.* resourceful, clever.

**извра/тить, —щать** *v.* distort, misinterpret; corrupt, pervert; **—щение** *n.* distortion; perversion; inversion; **—щенный** *a.* distorted, perverted.

**изгар/ь, —ина** *f.* scale, forge scale, scoria.

**изгиб** *m.* bend, bending, deflection, inflection, curve, curvature, arc, flexure, kink; winding; (geol.) fold; elbow (of pipe); offset; **испытание на и.** bending test, flexing test; **линия —а** curvature; **момент —а, —аю-щий момент** bending moment, moment of flexure; **продольный и.** buckling; **—аемость** *f.* deflectivity; **—ание** *n.* bending, deflection, curving, buckling; **—ать** *v.* bend, deflect, curve; **—аться** *v.* buckle, sag; **—ающая сила** deflecting force.

**изгла/дить, —живать** *v.* efface, erase, wipe out, obliterate.

**изг/нание** *n.* expulsion; **—нать, —онять** *v.* expel, drive out.

**изгородь** *f.* hedge, enclosure, fence.

**изгот/авливать, —овить, —овлять** *v.* prepare, make, make up, produce, manufacture; make ready; carry out, execute; **—овитель** *m.* producer,

manufacturer; **—овление** *n.* preparation, production, manufacture; carrying out, execution (of an order); **—овленный** *a.* prepared, produced, manufactured.

**изд.** *abbr.* (**издание**) edition, publication; (**издательство**) press, publishing house.

**издав/ание** *n.* emission; **—ать** *v.* emit, give off, evolve, exhale; publish, issue.

**издавна** *adv.* long since, long ago.

**издал/ека, —и** *adv.* from afar, from a distance.

**издан/ие** *n.* edition, publication, issue; **—ия** *pl.* transactions (of a scientific organization); **—ный** *a.* published, issued.

**издатель** *m.* publisher; **—ство** *n.* publisher, publishing house, publishing firm.

**изд/ать** *see* **издавать; —ающий** *a.* emitting, exhaling, giving off; issuing.

**изд-во** *abbr.* (**издательство**) publishing house.

**издев/ательство** *n.,* **—ка** *f.* ridicule, mockery; **—аться** *v.* ridicule, deride.

**издел/ие** *n.* article, object, manufactured object, product, piece of work; **—ия** *pl.* ware; **промышленные —ия** goods of commerce, industrial goods.

**издерж/ать, —ивать** *v.* use, consume; spend (money), disburse; **—ка** *f.* expense, cost, expenditure, outlay, charge.

**издирать** *see* **изодрать.**

**изентроп/а** *f.* isentrope, adiabatic curve; **—ный** *a.* isentropic.

**изерин** *m.* (min.) iserine (a variety of ferriferous rutile).

**изжи/вать, —ть** *v.* exterminate, get rid (of), overcome; live, spend one's life.

**изжога** *f.* heartburn.

**из-за** *prep. gen.* because of, on account of, through; from; from behind.

**ИЗИФ** *abbr.* (**Институт прикладной зоологии и фитопатологии**) Institute of Applied Zoology and Phytopathology.

**излавливать** *v.* catch, seize, trap.

**излагат/ельный** *a.* explanatory; **—ь** *v.* state, give an account (of); expose; set forth, write up, report.

**изламывать** *v.* break, fracture.

**излеч/ение** *n.* recovery, cure, healing; **—ивать, —ить** *v.* cure, heal; **—имость** *f.* curability; **—имый** *a.* curable.

**изли/вать, —ть** *v.* pour, pour out, discharge; **—ваться, —ться** *v.* issue (from), flow out, well out, gush, effuse; **—вшийся** *a.* issuing, effusive; (geol.) effusive, extrusive.

**излиш/ек** *m.* surplus, excess; **—ество** *n.* excess; **—ества** *pl.* luxuries; **—ествовать** *v.* overindulge; **—не** *adv.* in excess, superfluously; it is not necessary; **—ний** *a.* excessive, superfluous, unnecessary.

**излия/ние** *n.* outpouring, outflow, discharge, effusion, eruption; **—ть** *see* **изливать.**

**изловить** *see* **излавливать.**

**изловчиться** *v.* manage, contrive.

**излож/ение** *n.* account, statement, exposition; presentation; **—енный** *a.* stated, written, exposed; **—ить** *see* **излагать.**

**изложница** *f.* (met.) mold, casting mold, chill, pan.

**излом** *m.* fracture, break, fissure, breaking, breaking off; breakdown; cross-sectional view; **нагрузка для —а** crippling load; **плоскость —а** cleavage plane; **—анный, —ленный** *a.* fractured, broken; **—ать, —ить** *see* **изламывать.**

**излуч/аемость** *f.,* **—ательная способность** emissivity, radiating power; **—аемый** *a.* emitted, radiated; **—атель** *m.* emitter, radiator; **—ательный** *a.* emitting, emissive; radiating; **—ать, —ить** *v.* emit, radiate, eradiate; **—аться, —иться** *v.* radiate, emanate (from); **—ающий** *a.* emitting, radiating, radiant; **—ение** *n.* emission, radiation, emanation; evolution (of light), photogenesis; projection (of sound); **биологическое действие —ения** biologic effectiveness of radiation, RBE; **—енный** *a.* emitted, radiated.

**излуч/ина** *f.* curve, bend, winding, meander; detour; **—истый** *a.* bent, winding, meandering, tortuous.

**измалывать** *v.* grind, crush, break up.

**изматывать** *v.* deplete, exhaust.

**измельч/ание, —ение** *n.* grinding, crushing, pulverization, breaking up; growing small, dwarfing; **—ать, —ить** *v.* grind, crush, pulverize, pound, stamp (ore); reduce to fragments, cut into small pieces; **—ающий** *a.* grinding, crushing; **—енный** *a.* ground, granulated, crushed, pulverized; **—итель** *m.* crusher, pulverizer.

**измена** *f.* treachery, treason.

**изменен/ие** *n.* change, alteration, variation, modification, conversion, transformation; fluctuation, deviation; correction; **—ный** *a.* changed, converted.

**измен/имый** *see* **изменяемый; —итель** *m.* changer, converter; **—ить** *see* **изменять.**

**изменчив/ость** *f.* variability; (biol.) mutability, mutation; **—ый** *a.* variable, changeable, inconstant, irregular, unsettled, floating; (geol.) metamorphic.

**измен/яемость** *f.* variability, changeability, alterability; **—яемый** *a.* variable, changeable, convertible; **—ять** *v.* change, alter, modify, vary, alternate; betray; **—яться** *v.* change, be changed; fluctuate; **—яющийся** *a.* variable.

**измер/ение** *n.* measuring, measurement, gaging; survey; dimension, size; determination; *suffix* **—metry; в трех —ениях, с тремя —ениями** three-dimensional; **—енный** *a.* measured, gaged; **—имость** *f.* measurability; **—имый** *a.* measurable, mensurable; **—итель** *m.* measurer, gage, meter; assayer.

**измерительн/ый** *a.* measuring, gaging; **и. прибор** measuring instrument, gage; meter; **и. сосуд** measure, measuring vessel, graduate; **и. цилиндр** graduated cylinder, graduate; **—ая лента, —ая рулетка** tape measure, tape; **—ая машина** gaging machine; **—ая труба** measuring tube, measuring pipet; buret.

**измер/ить, —ять** *v.* measure, gage, size; survey; determine; **—яемый** *a.* measurable.

**измод** *m.* (bot.) milkwort (*Polygala*).

**изможденный** *a.* exhausted, emaciated.

**измол/ачивать, —отить** v. (agr.) thresh; **—отый** a. ground; **—оть** see **измалывать.**

**измор/озь** f. hoarfrost, rime, (white) frost; **—ось** f. drizzle; sleet.

**измочал/ивать, —ить** v. shred, separate into shreds, separate into filaments.

**измыслить** see **выдумать.**

**изнанка** f. wrong side, reverse, inside.

**изначальный** a. primordial.

**изнашив/аемость** f. wearability, wearing property; **—ание** n. wear, wear and tear, wearing out; deterioration, depreciation; **—ать** v. wear out, wear away, fray; erode; **—аться** v. wear, wear out, wear away, fray; erode; deteriorate; **медленно —аться** wear well.

**изнеможение** n. exhaustion.

**износ** m. wear, wear and tear, wearing away, abrasion; deterioration; depletion, impoverishment (of mine); consumption (of electrode); **—ить** see **изнашивать.**

**износо/стойкий, —упорный** a. resistant to wear, long-lasting, durable; **—стойкость, —упорность** f. resistance to wear, wearing qualities, durability.

**изношенный** a. worn out, worn, outworn; eroded; used up, exhausted.

**изнур/ить, —ять** v. exhaust, wear out.

**изнутри** adv. from within, inside.

**изо—** prefix iso—; abbr. (**изоляционный**) insulating; see also **ис—; —азол** m. isoazole, isopyrrol.

**изоамил** m., **—овый** a. isoamyl; **—ацетат** m., **—овый эфир уксусной кислоты** isoamyl acetate; **—ен** m. isoamylene; **—овый спирт** isoamyl alcohol.

**изобар/а** f. isobar, constant-pressure line; isobar (a nuclide); **—ический, —ный** a. isobaric; **—ический потенциал, —но-изотермический потенциал** (thermodynamics) Gibbs free energy; **—ометрический** a. isobarometric.

**изобат/а** f. isobath, depth contour; **—итерма** f. isobathytherm.

**изобенз—** prefix isobenz—, isobenzo—.

**изобил/ие** n. abundance, plenty, profusion, fertility; **—овать** v. abound (in), be rich (in); **—ующий** a. abundant, rich (in); **—ьный** a. abundant,

plentiful, copious, fertile, heavy, full.

**изоблич/ать, —ить** v. detect, expose.

**изображ/аемый** a. imaginary; **—ать** v. represent, depict, describe, render, characterize; design; **—ение** n. picture, image, image formation; representation, description; **искажение —ения** (optics) aberration; **—енный** a. represented, described.

**изобразит/ельный** a. descriptive, imitative; graphic; **—ь** see **изображать.**

**изобрест/и, —ь** see **изобретать.**

**изобретатель** m. inventor, deviser; **—ность** f. inventiveness, resourcefulness, ingenuity; **—ный** a. inventive, resourceful, ingenious; **—ство** n. invention, development of inventions.

**изобрет/ать** v. invent, devise, contrive, develop; **—ение** n. invention, device; **—енный** a. invented, devised, developed.

**изобут/ан** m. isobutane; **—енил** m. 2-methylallyl (Russian nomenclature); **—ил** m., **—иловый** a. isobutyl; **—илацетат** m., **—иловый эфир уксусной кислоты** isobutyl acetate; **—илбензоат** m. isobutyl benzoate; **—илен** m. isobutylene; **—иловый спирт** isobutyl alcohol; **—ирил** m. isobutyryl.

**изовалерианов/ая кислота** isovaleric acid; **—оэтиловый эфир** ethyl isovalerate.

**изовела** f. isovel, equal-speed line.

**изоверин** m. (pharm.) N-isoamylcadaverine hydrochloride.

**изогалина** f. isohaline, equal-salinity line.

**изогамма** f. isogam.

**изогексан** m. isohexane.

**изогелия** f. (meteor.) isohel, isohelic line.

**изогенный** a. isogenetic, isogenous.

**изогеотерм/а** f. (geol.) isogeotherm, isogeothermal line; **—ический** a. isogeothermal.

**изогептан** m. isoheptane.

**изогидр/ический, —ичный** a. isohydric; **—ичность, —ия** f. isohydry.

**изогиет/а** f., **—ная линия** (meteor.) isohyet, isohyetal line.

**изогипса** f. isohypse, structure contour.

**изогира** f. (optics) isogyre.

**изогист** see **изогиета.**

**изогнут/ость** *f.* curvature, flexion, camber; **—ый** *a.* curved, bent, cranked; folded; camber (beam); **—ь** *see* **изгибать.**

**изогон/а** *f.*, **—аль** *m.* (magnetism) isogonic, isogonic line; **—альный** *a.* isogonal, equiangular; **—ический** *a.* isogonic.

**изоград/иент** *m.* isogradient; **—ный** *a.* isograde.

**Изода копер** (met.) Izod impact machine.

**изодиафера** *f.* isodiaphere (a nuclide).

**изодинам/а** *f.* (magnetism) isodynamic line; **—ический** *a.* isodynamic.

**изодоза** *f.* (radiobiology) isodose.

**изодрать** *v.* tear, rend, lacerate.

**изодрин** *m.* isodrin (insecticide).

**изозомы** *see* **толстоножки.**

**изоклазит** *m.* (min.) isoclasite.

**изоклиматический** *a.* isoclimatic.

**изоклин/а** *f.*, **—аль** *m.* isoclinal, isoclinal line; (geol.) isocline; **—альный, —ический** *a.* isoclinal, isoclinic; **—альная складка** isocline, overturn.

**изокоричная кислота** isocinnamic acid.

**изолейцин** *m.* isoleucine.

**изолента** *f.* insulating tape, friction tape.

**изолиния** *f.* (meteor.) isoline.

**изолир/ование** *n.*, **—овка** *f.* insulation; **—ованный** *a.* insulated, sealed; isolated; single; **—овать** *v.* insulate, seal; isolate, segregate; quarantine; **герметически —овать** seal off; **—овочный, —ующий** *a.* insulation, insulating; **—овочное вещество, —ующее средство** insulating material, insulator; **—ующее свойство** insulating power; **– уемый** *a.* insulated.

**изолог** *m.* isolog; **—ичный** *a.* isologous.

**изолятор** *m.*, **—ный** *a.* insulator; isolator; (hospital) isolation ward or room.

**изоляц/ионный** *a.* insulation, insulating; **и. материал** insulating material, insulator; **—ионная лента** (elec.) insulation tape, friction tape; **—ия** *f.* insulation, insulating, sealing; isolation, segregation; quarantine; **полная —ия** positive confinement (of radioactive waste); **с бумажной —ией** paper-insulated.

**изомасляная кислота** isobutyric acid.

**изоменаль** *m.* isomenal.

**изомер** *m.*, **—ное тело** isomer; **зеркальный и., несовместимый и.** enantiomer; **—а** *f.* isomer, equal-proportion line; **—изация** *f.*, **—ное превращение** isomerization; **—изм** *m.*, **—ия** *f.*, **—ное состояние** isomerism; **—ия боковой цепи** side-chain isomerism; **—ия положения** place isomerism; **—изованный** *a.* isomerized; **—изовать** *v.* isomerize; **—ный** *a.* isomeric; **—ный переход** (nucl.) isomeric transition.

**изометамерный** *a.* isometameric.

**изометрический** *a.* isometric, isometrical.

**изоморф/изм** *m.*, **—ность** *f.* isomorphism; **—ный** *a.* isomorphous, isomorphic.

**изомочевина** *f.* isourea, pseudourea.

**изонефа** *f.* isoneph, equal-cloudiness line.

**изонитр/ил** *m.* isonitrile, isocyanide; **—осоединение** *n.* isonitro compound.

**изономаль** *m.*, **—ная линия** (meteor.) isonomal.

**изооктан** *m.* isoöctane.

**изоосмотический** *see* **изосмотический.**

**изопага** *f.* (meteor.) isopag, equiglacial line.

**изопахита** *f.* (maps) isopach.

**изопентан** *m.* isopentane.

**изо/пикна** *f.* isopycn, equal-density line; **—пикнический** *a.* isopycnic; **—пический** *a.* (geol.) isopic, isopical; **—плера** *f.* isopleric line, constant-volume line; **—плета** *f.* isopleth.

**изопол** *m.* ysopol.

**изо/поликислота** *f.* isopolyacid; **—прал** *m.* isopral, trichloro-*i*-propanol; **—прен** *m.* isoprene, 2-methyl-1,3-butadiene; **—преновый каучук** isoprene rubber.

**изопропил** *m.*, **—овый** *a.* isopropyl; **—ацетат** *m.*, **—овый эфир уксусной кислоты** isopropyl acetate; **—овый спирт** isopropyl alcohol.

**изопьест/а** *f.*, **—ическая линия** (geol.) isopiestic, isopiestic line; isobaric line; **—ический** *a.* isopiestic.

**изорв/анный** *a.* torn, tattered, ragged; **—ать** *v.* tear, rend.

**изорефракт** *m.* isorefract, line of equal refractive indices.

**изороданов/ая кислота** isothiocyanic acid; **соль —ой кислоты, —окислая соль** isothiocyanate.

**изосафрол** *m.* isosafrole.

**изосейс/ма, —та** *f.* (geol.) isoseismal line, isoseism; **—мический** *a.* isoseismic, isoseismal.

**изосмотический** *a.* isosmotic, isotonic.

**изостазия** *f.* (geol.) isostasy.

**изостат/а** *f.* isostatic, isostatic curve, equal-pressure curve; **—ический** *a.* isostatic, in hydrostatic equilibrium.

**изостер/а** *f.* (chem.; meteor.) isostere; **—ический** *a.* isosteric; **—ия** *f.* isosterism.

**изотак/а** *f.* (meteor.) isotac; **—тический** *a.* (polymerization) isotactic; **—тичность** *f.* isotacticity.

**изотаха** *f.* isotach, equal-velocity line.

**изотера** *f.* (meteor.) isothere, isotheral line.

**изотерм/а** *f.* isotherm, isothermal curve, equal-temperature curve; **—ический** *a.* isothermic, isothermal; **—ическая закалка** isothermal hardening, austempering.

**изотима** *f.* isothyme, isoatmic line, equal-evaporation line.

**изотон** *m.* (nucl.) isotone (a nuclide); **—ический, —ный** *a.* isotonic, isosmotic; **—ия** *f.* isotonicity.

**изотоп** *m.* (phys.) isotope; **разделение —ов** (nucl.) isotope separation; **—ический, —ный** *a.* isotope, isotopic; **—ный индикатор** isotopic tracer; **—ный обмен** isotopic exchange; **—ное изобилие** isotopic abundance; **—ное смещение** isotope shift; **—ное число** isotopic number, neutron excess; **метод —ного разбавления** isotope dilution analysis.

**изотрон** *m.*, **—ный разделитель** isotron (isotope separator).

**изотроп/ический, —ный** *a.* isotropic; **—ия, —ность** *f.* isotropy, isotropism.

**изофациальный** *a.* isofacial.

**изофена** *f.* (meteor.) isophene.

**изоформ** *m.* isoform, *p*-iodoanisol.

**изофота** *f.* (phys.) isophot.

**изофталевая кислота** isophthalic acid.

**изохимена** *f.* (meteor.) isocheim.

**изохинолин** *m.* isoquinoline.

**изохиона** *f.* isochion, equal-snow line.

**изохор/а** *f.* isochore, isochore curve; **—ный** *a.* isochoric; **—ный потенциал, —но-изотермический потенциал** (thermodynamics) Helmholtz free energy, work function.

**изохром/атический, —атичный, —ный** *a.* isochromatic, orthochromatic.

**изохрон/изм** *m.*, **—ность** *f.* isochronism; **—ический, —ный** *a.* isochronous.

**изоциануровая кислота** isocyanuric acid.

**изоциклическ/ий** *a.* isocyclic; **—ое соединение** isocyclic compound.

**изощр/ение** *n.* exercise; inventiveness; **—ять** *v.* cultivate (the mind); **—яться** *v.* excel.

**изоэдрический** *a.* isohedral.

**изоэйгенол** *m.* isoeugenol.

**изоэнергета** *f.* isenergic, constant-energy line.

**изоэнтроп/а** *f.* isoentropic curve; **—ийный, —ический** *a.* isoentropic.

**из-под** *prep. gen.* from under.

**израз/ец** *m.*, **—цовый** *a.* tile.

**израсход/ованный** *a.* spent, used; **—овать, —ывать** *v.* spend, use, lay out; **—оваться** *v.* spend too much.

**изредка** *adv.* rarely, seldom; from time to time, now and then, now and again.

**израз/анный** *a.* cut, dissected; broken (country); **—ать, —ывать** *v.* cut (to pieces), dissect.

**изрешетить** *v.* riddle (with bullets), pierce in many places.

**изруб/ать, —ить** *v.* cut, chop, mince; **—ленный** *a.* cut, chopped, hashed.

**изры/вать, —ть** *v.* dig up; **—тый** *a.* dug up; pitted.

**изрядн/о** *adv.* rather, fairly well, tolerably; **—ый** *a.* tolerable, passable, fair.

**изуверство** *n.* fanaticism.

**изувеч/ивать, —ить** *v.* maim, mutilate.

**изум/ительный** *a.* amazing, astounding; **—лять** *v.* surprise, amaze.

**изумруд** *m.* (min.) emerald (a gem variety of beryl); **восточный и.** oriental emerald (a green variety of corundum); **—ный** *a.* emerald; bright green.

**изуродов/ание** *n.* mutilation; **—анный** *a.* mutilated; **—ать** *v.* mutilate, maim.

**изуч/ать, —ивать, —ить** v. study, investigate, learn; **—ение** n. study, investigation; **—енный** a. studied, investigated, learned.

**изъед/ать, изъесть** v. eat away, corrode; **—енный** a. corroded, pitted.

**изъяв/ить, —лять** v. express, testify; **—ление** n. testimony.

**изъязвлен/ие** n. pitting; (med.) ulceration; **—ный** a. pitted; ulcerous, ulcered.

**изъян** m. defect, flaw, fault; damage, loss.

**изъясн/ить, —ять** see **объяснять.**

**изъят/ие** n. removal, elimination, withdrawal; (legal) immunity; **—ь** v. remove, withdraw, eliminate; confiscate.

**изыск/ание** n. investigation, search, research; exploration, prospecting, survey; делать и., производить и. v. survey; (min.) prospect; **—ать, —ивать** v. investigate, search (for), try to find.

**изэнтроп/а** f. (thermodynamics) isentrope, isentropic line; **—ический** a. isentropic.

**изэтионовая кислота** isethionic acid, 2-hydroxyethanesulfonic acid.

**изюм** m. raisin.

**изящный** a. fine, exquisite.

**ийолит** m. (petr.) ijolite.

**ИК** abbr. (инфракрасный) infrared.

**икать,** v. hiccup.

**И-кислота** f. J acid.

**икнуть** see **икать.**

**иконоскоп** m. (telev.) iconoscope; **—ия** f. iconoscopy.

**икорный** a. roe, spawn; (anat.) calf.

**икосаэдр** m. (cryst.) icosahedron; **—ический** a. icosahedral.

**икоситетраэдр** m. icositetrahedron.

**икот/а** f., **—ный** a. hiccup, hiccuping; **—ник** m. (bot.) berteroa.

**икр/а** f. roe, spawn; caviar; calf (of leg); **—инка** f. fish egg; **—ометание** n. spawning; **—оножный** a. (anat.) sural, calf; gastrocnemius (muscle); **—яной** a. roe; (anat.) sural, calf; **—яной камень** (min.) roe stone, oölite.

**икс** m. (math.) x; **—лучи** pl. X-rays; **—образный** a. X-shaped.

**иксолит** m. (min.) ixolyte.

**иксообразный** see **иксобразный.**

**ил** m. silt, slime, mud, sludge, ooze, sediment, (flotation) slurry; (cer.) slip.

**ИЛ** abbr. (Издательство иностранной литературы) Foreign Literature Publishing House.

**ИЛАН** abbr. (Институт леса Академии Наук СССР) Institute of Forestry of the USSR Academy of Sciences.

**иланг/-иланг** m., **—иланговый** a. (bot.) ylang-ylang (Cananga odorata); **—ол** m. ylangol.

**илваит** see **ильваит.**

**илексантин** m. ilexanthin.

**илексит** see **улексит.**

**илем** see **ильм.**

**или** conj. or, either.

**илим** see **ильм.**

**илипе** see **иллипе.**

**илис/иловый спирт** see **илициловый спирт; —овый спирт** ilicic alcohol, amyrin.

**илист/ость** f. muddiness; **—ый** a. muddy, slimy, oozy, sludgy.

**илиц/иловый спирт** ilicyl alcohol; **—ин** m. ilicin.

**илл.** abbr. (иллюстрации) illustrations.

**иллиний** m. illinium (obs. for promethium).

**иллинум** m. Illinum (acid-resistant alloy).

**иллип/е** n. illipe, bassia fat; **—ен** m. illipene; **—овое дерево** (bot.) illipi butter tree (Bassia latifolia).

**иллит** m. (min.) illite.

**иллиум** m. Illium (a nickel-base alloy).

**иллудин** m. illudin.

**иллюв/иальный** a. (geol.) illuvial; **—ий** m. illuvial deposits.

**иллюз/ия** f. illusion, delusion; **—орный** a. illusory, illusive, deceptive.

**иллюмин/атор** m. illuminator; **—ация** f. illumination; **—ация, —овка** f. coloring map contours; **—ент** m. illuminant; **—ированный** a. illuminated, lit; **—ировать, —овать** v. illuminate, light; **—ометр** m. illuminometer, photometer.

**иллюстр/ация** f. illustration; **—ированный** a. illustrated; **—ировать** v. illustrate.

**илов/атый** *a.* muddy, slimy, oozy; —**атая глина,** —**ка** *f.* (geol.) loam; siltstone; —**ый процесс** (min.) a process for extraction of gold from mud by cyanidation.

**илоочиститель** *m.* desilter.

**иль** *see* **или.**

**ильваит** *m.* (min.) ilvaite, lievrite.

**Ильгнера система** (elec.) Ilgner system (for motor speed control).

**ильземаннит** *m.* (min.) ilsemannite (an oxidation product of molybdenite).

**ильм** *m.* (bot.) elm (*Ulmus*).

**ильмени** *pl.* ilmeni (lakes in the Volga delta).

**ильмен/ий** *m.* ilmenium (a mixture of niobium and tantalum); —**ит** *m.*, —**итовый** *a.* (min.) ilmenite, titanic iron ore; —**орутил** *m.* ilmenorutile (a variety of ferriferous rutile).

**ильм/няк,** —**овое дерево** *see* **ильм;** —**овые** *pl.* (bot.) Ulmaceae; —**овый** *a.* elm.

**ильный** *a.* mud, slime, ooze.

**им** *instr. of* **он, оно,** by him, with it; *dat. of* **они,** to them, them.

**им.** *abbr.* (**имени**) named after.

**ИМ-68** a coal flotation agent (mixture of aliphatic alcohols).

**имаг/инальная стадия,** —**о** *n.* (zool.) imago.

**имазатин** *m.* imasatin; —**овая кислота** imasatic acid, isamic acid.

**имазин** *m.* imazine.

**имбецильность** *f.* (med.) imbecility.

**имбибиция** *f.* imbibition, saturation.

**имбир/ь** *m.*, —**ный** *a.* (bot.) ginger (*Zingiber officinale*).

**Имгофа шлам** Imhoff sludge.

**имеется** *see under* **иметь.**

**имезатин** *m.* imesatin, 3-iminoöxindole.

**имени** *see under* **имя.**

**имение** *n.* property, possession, estate.

**именительный** *a.* (grammar) nominative.

**именно** *adv.* namely, to wit, precisely expressly, just; —**й** *a.* nominal, name.

**именов/ание** *n.* naming, name, denomination; —**анный** *a.* named, called; —**анное число** (math.) concrete number; —**ать** *v.* name, call, address; designate.

**имеринит** *m.* (min.) imerinite (a variety of soda-amphibole).

**иметь** *v.* have, possess; —**ся** *v.* be, have; **здесь имеется** here there is, here is; **у него имеется** he has.

**имеющий** *a.* having; —**ся** *a.* available.

**ими** *instr. of* **они,** by them.

**имид** *m.*, —**ный** *a.* imide; —**азол** *m.* imidazole, glyoxaline; —**азолил** *m.* imidazolyl; —**азолон** *m.* imidazolone, iminazolone.

**имидо**— *prefix* imido—; —**ген** *m.* imidogen, imido group; —**мочевина** *f.* imidourea, imidocarbamide, guanidine; —**тиоэфир** *m.* imidothio ester; —**угольная кислота** imidocarbonic acid.

**иминазол** *m.* iminazole.

**имино**— *prefix* imino—; —**группа** *f.* imino group; —**уксусная кислота** iminoacetic acid; —**этанол** *m.* iminoethanol.

**имит/атор** *m.* simulator; —**ационный** *a.*, —**ация** *f.* imitation; —**ировать** *v.* imitate, copy; —**ирующий** *a.* imitative, simulative.

**ИМК** *abbr.* (**индолилмасляная кислота**) indolylbutyric acid.

**имм.** *abbr.* (**иммунный**) immune.

**имманентн/ость** *f.* immanence; —**ый** *a.* immanent, inherent.

**иммельман** *m.* (aero.) Immelman turn.

**иммерс/ия** *f.*, —**ионный** *a.* immersion; **и. в масле** oil immersion.

**иммобилизация** *f.* immobilization; fixation; reversion, retrogradation.

**иммортель** *m.* (bot.) everlasting.

**иммун/изация** *f.*, —**изирование** *n.* immunization; —**изировать** *v.* immunize; —**итет** *m.* immunity; —**ненный, —ный** *a.* immune; —**ная сыворотка,** —**сыворотка** immune serum, antiserum; —**обиологический** *a.* immunobiological; —**ология** *f.* immunology.

**имп.** *abbr.* (**импульсы**) impulses, pulses.

**импедан/с,** —**ц** *m.*, —**сный** *a.* (elec.) impedance, apparent resistance.

**импеллер** *m.* impeller, blade.

**император** *m.*, —**ный** *a.* imperative.

**императорин** *m.* imperatorin, peucedanin.

**импер/иал** *m.* imperial (coin); deck, top

(of bus); —ия *f.* empire; —ский *a.* imperial, royal.

**имплантация** *f.* implantation.

**импликац/ионный** *a.* implicational, implicative; —ионная структура (geol.) graphic texture; —ия *f.* implication.

**имплоз/ивный** *a.* implosive; —ия *f.* implosion, bursting inwards.

**имп/мин** *abbr.* (импульсов в минуту) pulses per minute; counts per minute.

**импозантный** *a.* impressive, imposing.

**импонировать** *v.* impress, impose (upon).

**импорт** *m.* import, importation; —ер *m.* importer; —ировать *v.* import; —ный *a.* imported, import.

**импотен/тность** *f.*, —ция *f.* impotence; —тный *a.* impotent.

**импре/гнация** *f.*, —гнирование *n.* impregnation; —гнированный *a.* impregnated; —гнировать, —ньировать *v.* impregnate.

**имп/сек** *abbr.* (импульсов в секунду) pulses per second; counts per second.

**импсонит** *m.* (min.) impsonite (a variety of albertite).

**импульс** *m.* impulse, impetus, impact; momentum; (elec.) pulse; **и. напряжения** voltage pulse; **и. тока** current pulse; **амплитуда —а, высота —а** pulse height; **генератор —ов, —ный генератор** impulse generator; **датчик —ов** impulse transmitter; surge generator; **пространство —ов** momentum space; **усилитель —ов, —ный усилитель** pulse amplifier; —ер *m.* impulse starter; —ивный *a.* impulsive; —номодулированный *a.* pulse-modulated, pulsed; —но-приложенный *a.* step-function (voltage); —ный *a.* impulse, momentum; pulse, pulsed, impulsive; sampled (data); flash (bulb); —ная ионизационная камера pulse ionization chamber; **в —ном режиме** pulsed; —овидный *a.* pulse-like; —остойкий *a.* surgeproof.

**импфирование** *n.* water softening by means of hydrochloric or sulfuric acid.

**имуществ/енный** *a.* property; —о *n.* property, estate; stock, goods; assets; **опись —а** inventory.

**имущий** *a.* wealthy.

**им/я** *n.* name; —ени named for; **институт —ени Ленина** Lenin Institute; **от —ени** on behalf (of).

**ин.** *abbr.* (интенсивный) strong.

**инактив/ация** *f.* inactivation; —ировать *v.* inactivate.

**иначе** *adv.* otherwise, differently; or else.

**инбирь** *see* имбирь.

**инбридинг** *m.* (biol.) inbreeding.

**инваз/ионный** *a.*, —ия *f.* (parasitic) invasion, infestation.

**инвалид** *m.*, —ный *a.* invalid; —ность *f.* invalidism.

**инвар** *m.* Invar (an iron-nickel alloy).

**инвариант** *m.*, —ный *a.* (math.) invariant; —ность *f.* invariance.

**инвентар/изировать, вписать в —ь, составлять —ную опись** *v.* take inventory, take stock; —ная опись inventory; —ь *m.* inventory, stock, stock in trade; implements; **живой —ь** livestock.

**инверс/ионный** *a.* inversion; —ия *see* инвертирование; —ор *m.* (chem., geom.) inversor.

**инверт/аза** *f.*, —ин *m.* invertase, invertin, saccharase, sucrase; —ер *m.* (elec.) inverter, inverted rectifier.

**инвертиров/ание** *n.* inversion, inverting, reversal; **температура —ания** inversion point; —анный *a.* inverted; —анный сахар invert sugar (mixture of *d*-fructose and *d*-glucose); —ать *v.* invert, reverse.

**инверт/ный** *a.* invert; —ор *see* инвертер.

**инволютный** *a.* involute, coiled; —ция *f.* involution; (biol.) degeneration.

**ингаля/тор** *m.* inhaler; —ция *f.* inhalation.

**ингибин** *m.* inhibin.

**ингибитор** *m.*, —ный *a.* inhibitor, arrester.

**ингот** *m.* (met.) ingot; —изм *m.* ingot structure.

**ингредиент** *m.* ingredient, component.

**ингресс/ивный** *a.* ingressive, entering; —ия *f.* ingression, entrance.

**инд.** *abbr.* (индийский) Indian.

**инд/азин** *m.* indazine; —азол *m.* indazole, benzopyrazole; —азолон *m.* indazolone; —аллой *m.* Indalloy; —амин *m.*, —аминовый *a.* indamine, phenylene blue; —ан *m.* indan, hydrindene; —анил *m.* indanyl; —анон *m.* indanone, indone.

**индантрен** *m.,* —**овый** *a.* indanthrene (an anthraquinone vat dyestuff); —**овые красители** indanthrene dyes.

**индейка** *f.* turkey (hen).

**индейский** *a.* (American) Indian.

**индекс** *m.* index.

**инден** *m.* indene; —ил *m.* indenyl; —он *m.* indenone, indone.

**индепендент** *m.* independent.

**индианит** *m.* (min.) indianite, anorthite.

**индивид,** —**уум** *m.* individual; —**уалистический** *a.* individualistic; —**уальный** *a.* individual; independent, separate, self-contained, single; unit (drive).

**индиго** *n.* indigo (a blue vat dye); **белое и.** indigo white, leuco indigo, soluble indigo; **голубое и.** indigo blue; **красное и.** indigo red, indirubin.

**индигов/ый** *a.* indigo; **и. куб** indigo vat; —**ая кислота** indigotic acid; **соль** —**ой кислоты** indigotate; —**ая соль** indigo salt, *o*-nitrobenzaldehyde; —**ые краски** indigo dyes.

**индиго/ид** *m.,* —**идный** *a.* indigoid; —**кармин** *m.* indigocarmine, sodium indigotinsulfonate; —**лит** *m.* (min.) indigolite, indicolite (a variety of tourmaline); —**метр** *m.* indigometer; —**метрия** *f.* indigometry; —**носка** *f.* (bot.) indigo plant (*Indigofera tinctoria*); —**серная кислота** indigosulfuric acid, sulfindigotic acid; —**сульфоновая кислота** indigosulfonic acid; —**тат** *m.* indigotate; —**тин** *m.* indigotin, indigo blue, indigo.

**индиевая соль** indium salt.

**инд/ий** *m.* indium, In; **закись** —**ия** indium monoxide; **односернистый и.** indium monosulfide; **окись** —**ия** indium oxide; **сернистый и.** indium (sesqui-)sulfide; **хлористый и.** indium dichloride; **хлорный и.** indium trichloride.

**индийск/ий** *a.* Indian, India; **и. бальзам** balsam of Peru; **и. желтый,** —**ая желтая** Indian yellow; **и. куб** (dyeing) potash vat.

**индикан** *m.* indican.

**индикатор** *m.* indicator; marker; (radioactive) tracer; *suffix* —**scope**; **метод изотопных** —**ов,** —**ный метод** tracer technique; —**ный** *a.* indicator, indicating; indicated; —**ный механизм** indicating instrument, indicator; —**ная бумага** indicator paper, test paper; —**ная мощность,** —**ная сила** indicated horsepower; —**ные часы** dial indicator, dial gage; —**оподобный** *a.* indicator.

**индикатрис/а,** —**са** *f.* (math.) indicatrix.

**индикация** *f.* indication; presentation, display; tracing.

**индиколит** *see* индиголит.

**инд/ил** *m.* indyl; —**илиден** *m.* indylidene; —**ин** *m.* indin; —**ирубин** *m.* indirubin, indigo red.

**индифферентный** *a.* indifferent, inert.

**индицирование** *n.* indicating, indication; indexing.

**Индия** India.

**индо—** *prefix* indo—; —**анилин** *m.* indoaniline; —**ген** *m.* indogen.

**Индо-Китай** Indo-China.

**индокс/азеин** *m.* indoxazeine, benzisoxazole; —**ил** *m.,* —**иловый** *a.* indoxyl; —**иловая кислота** indoxylic acid; —**илсерная кислота** indoxyl-sulfuric acid.

**индо/л** *m.* indole, 1-benzazole; —**ленин** *m.,* —**лениновый** *a.* indolenine, iso-1-benzazole; —**лил** *m.* indolyl; —**лин** *m.* indoline, 2,3-dihydroindole; —**линон** *m.* indolinone; —**лол** *m.* indolol, indoxyl; —**лон** *m.* indolone; —**н** *m.* indone, hydrindone; —**нил** *m.* indonyl.

**индосс/амент** *m.,* —**о** *n.* (com.) indorsement; —**ант** *m.* indorser; —**ат** *m.* indorsee; —**ирование** *n.* indorsing, indorsement; —**ировать** *v.* indorse.

**Индостан** Hindustan.

**индо/фенин** *m.* indophenine; —**фенол** *m.* indophenol; —**форм** *m.* indoform.

**индукт/анц** *m.,* —**ивность** *f.* (elec.) inductance, inductivity; —**ивный** *a.* inductive.

**индуктир/ование** *see* индукция; —**ованный** *a.* induced; —**овать** *v.* induce; —**ующий** *a.* inducing, inductive.

**индукто—** *prefix* (elec.) inducto—, induction; —**метр** *m.* induction meter;

—р, —рий *m.*, —рный *a.* inductor, induction coil; (tel.) magneto.

индукци/онный *a.* induction, inductive; и. ролик, —онная катушка (elec.) induction coil; и. ускоритель (nucl.) induction accelerator; —я *f.* induction; (magnetic) density; вызванный —ей, обусловленный —ей induced; емкость —и inductive capacity, dielectric constant; коэффициент —и (elec.) inductance.

индулин *m.*, —овый *a.* induline.

индусский *a.* Hindu.

индустри/ализация *f.* industrialization; —альный *a.* industrial; —я *f.* industry.

индуцировать *see* индуктировать.

индю/к *m.* turkey (cock); —шачий *a.* turkey; —шка *f.* turkey (hen); —шонок *m.* turkey poult.

инеевидный *a.* frosted (finish).

инезит *m.* (min.) inesite.

иней *m.* hoarfrost, frost, rime.

инер/тность *f.* inertness; lag, sluggishness; —тный *a.* inert, inactive, passive; sluggish; —ционность *f.* (visual) persistence; —ционный *a.* inertia; sluggish; —ция *f.* inertia, inertness, reluctance, lag; момент —ции moment of inertia; радиус —ции radius of gyration; сила —ции inertia.

инж. *abbr.* (инженерный) engineering.

инжек/тированный *a.* injected; —тировать *v.* inject; —тор *m.* injector; accelerator; —торный *a.* injector, injection; —торного типа spray-type (equipment); —ция *f.* injection.

инженер *m.* engineer; и.-аквизитор, и.-вояжер sales engineer; и.-геолог geological engineer; и.-гидравлик hydraulics engineer; и.-испытатель, и.-экспериментатор testing engineer; и.-конструктор, и.-строитель construction engineer, design engineer; civil engineer; и.-консультант consulting engineer, advisory engineer; и.-металлург metallurgical engineer; и.-механик, и.-механизатор mechanical engineer; и.-производственник production engineer, works engineer; и.-химик chemical engineer; и.-электрик electrical engineer.

инженерн/ый *a.*, —ое дело engineering.

инжир *m.* (bot.) fig (*Ficus carica*).

Инжу *abbr.* (Инженерное училище) the School of Engineering.

инистый *a.* frosted, rimy.

инициал *m.* initial (letter).

инициатив/а *f.*, —ный *a.* initiative.

иници/атор *m.* initiator, starter; pioneer, organizer; —ировать *v.* initiate, start, trigger; —ирующий заряд, —ирующее вещество initiator, priming explosive.

инкапсуляция *f.* incapsulation, enclosure in a capsule.

инкарнатиловый спирт incarnatyl alcohol.

инкассировать *v.* collect.

инклин/атор, —ометр *m.* dipping compass, dip needle, inclinometer.

инклю/дированная целлюлоза "inclusion" cellulose, rendered water-free by a solvent-displacement method; —зия *f.* inclusion; (petr.) xenolith.

инконгруентный *a.* incongruent.

инконель *m.* Inconel (nickel-chromium alloy).

инкорпор/ация *f.* incorporation; —ировать *v.* incorporate, include.

инкремент *m.* increment, growth.

инкре/т *m.* (biol.) internal secretion, hormone; —ция *f.* incretion, internal secretion.

инкруст/ация *f.*, —ирование *n.* incrustation, scale formation, scale, crust; inlay, lining; —ированный *a.* incrusted; inlaid, lined; —ировать *v.* incrust, cover with a crust; inlay, line.

инкуб/атор *m.*, —аторный *a.* incubator; —аторий *m.* incubator house, hatchery; —аторная станция hatchery; —аторно-птицеводческая станция hatchery and poultry-breeding center; —ационный *a.* incubation, incubative; —ация *f.*, —ационный период incubation, period of incubation; —ировать *v.* incubate.

иннерв/ация *f.* (biol.) innervation, distribution of nerves; —ировать *v.* innervate.

иновидный *a.* different, different-looking.

иногда *adv.* sometimes, occasionally, in some cases, now and then.

**иноза** *see* **инозит.**

**инозем/ец** *m.* foreigner, stranger, alien; —**ный** *a.* foreign, outlandish, alien.

**иноз/ин** *m.* inosin; —**иновая кислота** inosinic acid, inosinphosphoric acid; —**ит** *m.* inositol, hexahydroxycyclohexane; —**итофосфат** *m.* inositol phosphate.

**иной** *a.* some, other.

**инокул/ирование** *n.*, —**яция** *f.* inoculation; —**ировать** *v.* inoculate.

**иноломин** *m.* inolomin.

**инообразный** *see* **иновидный.**

**иноплеменн/ик** *m.* foreigner, stranger, outsider; —**ый** *a.* foreign, strange.

**инородный** *a.* foreign, extraneous.

**иностран/ец** *m.* foreigner; —**ный** *a.* foreign.

**инсеквентный** *a.* (geol.) insequent.

**инсект/арий** *m.* insectarium; —**ицид** *m.* insecticide; —**окуция** *f.* insectocution (insect electrocution); —**офунгицид** *m.* combination insecticide-fungicide.

**инсипин** *m.* insipin, quinine diglycolsulfate.

**инсоляция** *f.* insolation, exposure to sun's rays; (meteor.) sun's radiation; (med.) sunstroke.

**инспек/тирование** *n.*, —**ция** *f.* inspection, examination; —**тировать** *v.* inspect, examine; —**тор** *m.* inspector; —**торат** *m.*, —**тура** *f.* inspector's job; —**торский** *a.* inspectorial, inspection.

**инспир/атор** *m.* inspirator; respirator; —**ация** *f.* inspiration, inhalation; —**ированный** *a.* inspired; —**ировать** *v.* inspire.

**инсталляция** *f.* installation.

**инстилляция** *f.* instillation.

**инстинкт** *m.* instinct; —**ивно** *adv.* instinctively; —**ивный** *a.* instinctive.

**институт** *m.* institute, institution.

**инструк/таж** *m.* instructions, directions; —**тировать** *v.* instruct, advise, direct; —**тор** *m.* instructor, adviser; —**ционный** *a.* instruction; —**ция** *f.* instruction, order; specification; instruction book, handbook, manual.

**инструмент** *m.* instrument, tool, implement; (collective) tools, spec. machine tools; **и.-эталон** master tool; **комплект** —**ов, набор** —**ов,** —**арий**

*m.* tool kit, set of tools; —**альная** *f.* toolroom, tool shed, tool shop —**альный** *a.* instrumental, instrument, tool; —**альная сталь** tool steel; —**альщик** *m.* tool maker; —**одержатель** *m.* tool holder.

**инсул/ин** *m.* insulin (a hormone); —**ит** *m.* insulite (insulating construction board).

**инсульт** *m.* (radiation; vet.) insult; (med.) stroke, attack.

**ин-т** *abbr.* (**институт**) institute.

**интактный** *a.* intact.

**интарвин** *m.* intarvin, glycerol trimargarate.

**интегр/ал** *m.* (math.) integral; —**альный** *a.* integral, whole; —**альное исчисление** integral calculus; —**атор** *m.* integrator, integrating instrument; —**атор импульсов,** —**ирующая схема** (elec.) integrating circuit; —**аф** *m.* integraph; —**ация** *f.*, —**ирование** *n.* integration; —**ированный** *a.* integrated; —**ировать** *v.* integrate; —**ируемый** *a.* integrated; integrable; —**ируемая функция,** —**ирующийся** *a.* integrand; —**ирующий** *a.* integrating, integrant; —**ирующий дозиметр** integrating dose meter.

**интеллигентн/ость** *f.* intelligence; —**ый** *a.* intelligent, educated, cultured.

**интендант** *m.* commissary; —**ский** *a.*, —**ство** *n.* commissariat.

**интенсивн/ость** *f.* intensity; rate; density (of smoke); (spectrum line) strength; magnitude (of earthquake); **и. потока** (radiation) flux; **и. частоты** frequency rate; —**ый** *a.* intensive, intense, high; heavy (traffic).

**интенси/метр** *m.* (nucl.) counting-rate meter, ratemeter; —**фикатор** *m.* intensifier; —**фикация** *f.* intensification; —**фицировать** *v.* intensify; increase the capacity; —**фицирующий** *a.* intensifying.

**интервал** *m.* interval, gap, space, spacing, interspace, intermediate space, pause, interruption; distance, range; **в** —**е температур** in the temperature range; —**ометр** *m.* timer.

**интервенция** *f.* intervention.

**интервью** *n.* interview; —**ировать** *v.* interview, question.

интергранулярный *a.* intergranular.
интеренин *m.* Interrenin (a hormone preparation).
интерес *m.* interest, profit; —но *adv.* interestingly; it is interesting; —ный *a.* interesting, attractive; —ованный *a.* interested; —овать *v.* interest, attract; —оваться *v.* become interested (in), take interest.
интер/костельный *a.* intercostal; —кристаллический *a.* intercrystalline; —медин *m.* intermedin (a hormone); —миттирующий *a.* intermittent; —национальный *a.* international.
интерпол/ирование *n.*, —яционный *a.*, —яция *f.* interpolation; —ировать *v.* interpolate.
интерпрет/ация *f.* interpretation; —ировать *v.* interpret, explain.
интер/сектинг *m.* intersecting; —септор, —цептор *m.* interceptor; (elec.) chopper; —сертальный *a.* (geol.) intersertal; —стициальный *a.* interstitial.
интерфер/енциальный, —енционный *a.*, —енция *f.* interference; —ировать *v.* interfere; —ометр *m.* (light) interferometer.
интерьер *m.* interior.
интимн/ость *f.* intimacy, closeness; —ый *a.* intimate, close.
интоксикация *f.* intoxication, toxin poisoning; (agr.) absorption of insecticide by plant.
интрамин *m.* intramine, contramine.
интрамолекулярный *a.* intramolecular.
интродукция *f.* introduction.
интру/дировать *v.* intrude; —зив *m.*, —зивная горная порода (geol.) intrusion, intrusive rock; —зивный *a.* intrusive; —зия *f.* intrusion.
интубация *f.* (med.) intubation.
интуиция *f.* intuition, instinct.
инул/аза *f.* inulase (an enzyme); —ин *m.* inulin, alantin, alant starch.
инфантильн/ость *f.* infancy; (med.) infantilism; —ый *a.* infantile.
инфаркт *m.* (med.) infarct.
инфекци/онный *a.* infectious, contagious, catching; —я *f.* infection, contagion.
инфильтр/ат *m.*, —ировать *v.* infiltrate; —ация *f.* infiltration, seepage.
инфлектор *m.* inflector, deflector.

инфл/уэнца, —уэнца *f.* (med.) influenza.
инфлюентная линия influence line.
инфляция *f.* inflation.
информ/ация *f.* information; —ировать *v.* inform; —отдел *m.* bureau of information.
инфра— *prefix* infra— (below); —звуковой *a.* subsonic, subaudio; —красный *a.* infrared (rays).
инфузия *f.* infusion.
инфузор/ии *pl.* (zool.) Infusoria; ресничные и. Ciliata; сосущие и. Suctoria; —ная земля (geol.) infusorial earth, kieselguhr, diatomaceous earth.
инфундировать *v.* infuse.
инцидент *m.* incident, occurrence, case.
инцизия *f.* incision, cut.
инцистиров/ание *n.* (biol.) encystment, cyst formation; —аться *v.* encyst.
инцухт *m.* (biol.) inbreeding.
инч *m.* inch.
инъек/тировать, инъицировать *see* инжектировать; —ция *see* инжекция.
иобирин *m.* yobirine.
иоганнит *m.* (min.) johannite (gilpinite).
иогимб/ин *m.* yohimbine; —овая кислота yohimbic acid; —овая кора yohimbe (bark of *Corynanthe yohimbe*).
иогурт *m.* yoghurt (cheese-like food).
иод *m.* iodine, I; азид —а, —азид iodine azide; бромистый и. iodine bromide; хлористый и. iodine chloride; насыщать —ом *v.* iodize.
иод— *prefix* iod—, iodo—; —алкил *m.* alkyl iodide; —ангидрид *m.* acid iodide; —анилин *m.* iodoaniline; —ат *m.* iodate; —ацетон *m.* iodoacetone; —бензол *m.* iodobenzene; —гидрин *m.* iodohydrin; —ид *m.* iodide.
иод/изм *m.* iodism, iodine poisoning; —ипин *m.* Iodipin; —ирит *m.* (min.) iodyrite, iodargyrite (native silver iodide).
иодиров/ание *n.* iodination, iodizing; —анный *a.* iodinated, iodized; —ать *v.* iodinate, iodize, iodate.
иодистоводородн/ый *a.* hydriodide (of); и. морфин morphine hydriodide; —ая кислота hydriodic acid; соль —ой кислоты iodide.
иодисто/калийный *a.* potassium iodide;

—**кислый** *a.* iodous acid; iodite (of); —**кислая соль** iodite.

**иодист/ый** *a.* iodine; (lower or —ous) iodide (of); **и. азот** nitrogen iodide; **и. бензил** benzyl iodide; **и. водород** hydrogen iodide; **и. калий** potassium iodide; **и. метил** methyl iodide; —**ая кислота** iodous acid; **соль —ой кислоты** iodite;—**ая медь** cuprous iodide; —**ая ртуть** mercurous iodide; —**ое железо** ferrous iodide.

**иодит** *m.* iodite; (min.) *see* **иодирит.**

**иод/магнийметил** *m.* methylmagnesium iodide; —**магнийэтил** *m.* ethylmagnesium iodide; —**метилат** *m.* methiodide.

**иодноватист/ая кислота** hypoiodous acid; **соль —ой кислоты** hypoiodite.

**иодновато/бариевая соль** barium iodate; —**железная соль** ferric iodate; —**кислый** *a.* iodic acid; iodate (of); —**кислый натрий**, —**натриевая соль** sodium iodate; —**кислая соль** iodate.

**иодноват/ый** *a.* iodic; **и. ангидрид** iodic anhydride, iodine pentoxide; —**ая кислота** iodic acid; **соль —ой кислоты** iodate.

**иоднокисл/ый** *a.* periodic acid; periodate (of); —**ая соль** periodate.

**иодн/ый** *a.* iodine; (higher or —ic) iodide (of); —**ая зелень** iodine green (a phenolphthalein dye); —**ая кислота** periodic acid; **соль —ой кислоты** periodate; —**ая медь** cupric iodide; —**ая настойка,** —**ая тинктура** tincture of iodine; —**ая ртуть** mercuric iodide; —**ое число** iodine number, Wijs number.

**иодо**— *prefix* iodo—; iodoxy—; —**бензол** *m.* iodoxybenzene; —**бромит** *m.* (min.) iodobromite; —**водород** *m.* hydrogen iodide, hydriodic acid gas; —**водородный** *see* **иодистоводородный**; —**зо**— *prefix* iodoso—; —**зобензол** *m.* iodosobenzene; —**зол** *m.* iodosol, thymol iodide; —**какодил** *m.* cacodyl iodide; —**кись** *f.* oxyiodide; —**крахмал** *m.,* —**крахмальный** *a.* starch iodide, iodized starch; —**крезол** *m.* iodocresol, iodocresine, traumatol.

**иодокси**— *prefix* iodoxy—.

**иодол** *m.* Iodol, tetraiodopyrrole.

**иодометан** *m.* iodomethane, methyl iodide.

**иодометр/ический** *a.* iodometric; —**ия** *f.* iodometry.

**иодон/ий** *m.,* —**иевый** *a.* iodonium (trivalent iodine).

**иодо/пропионовая кислота** iodopropionic acid; —**соединение** *n.* iodo compound, iodine compound; —**стерин** *m.* iodosterol; —**тирин** *m.* thyroiodine; —**фен** *m.* Iodophene, iodophthalein; —**форм** *m.,* —**формный** *a.* iodoform, triiodomethane; —**формин** *m.* iodoformin; —**этан** *m.* iodoethane, ethyl iodide; —**этилен** *m.* iodoethylene, vinyl iodide; —**эфир** *m.* iodo ether.

**иод/толуол** *m.* iodotoluene; —**циан** *m.* cyanogen iodide; —**эозин** *m.* iodeosin, erythrosin; —**юр** *m.* iodide.

**иолит** *m.* (min.) iolite, cordierite, dichroite.

**ион** *m.* ion; **выход пар —ов** ion-pair yield; **передвижение —ов, перенос —ов** ionic migration; **промежуточный и., средний и.** hybrid ion, amphoteric ion, zwitterion; **расщепление —ов** ionic cleavage, ionization.

**ион/ен** *m.* ionene; —**идин** *m.* ionidine.

**иониз/атор** *m.,* —**ирующее устройство** ionizer; —**ационный** *a.,* —**ация** *f.* ionization, electrolytic dissociation; —**ационный манометр** ionization gage, ion gage; —**ационная камера** ionization chamber; **постоянная —а-ции** ionization constant; **теплота —ации** heat of ionization; —**ированный** *a.* ionized; —**ировать,** —**ироваться,** —**овать** *v.* ionize; —**ируемый** *a.* ionizable; —**ирующий** *a.* ionizing; —**ирующий акт,** —**ирующее событие** ionizing event.

**ионий** *m.* ionium, Io.

**ионит** *m.* ion exchanger, ion-exchange resin; —**овый** *a.* ion-exchanger, ion-exchange.

**ионн/ый** *a.* ionic, ion; **и. обмен** ion exchange; —**ая сила** ionic strength; —**ая траектория** ionization path, ionization track.

**иоио/ген** *m.* ionogen; —**генный** *a.* ionogenic; —**избирательный** *a.* ion-selective; —**излучающий** *a.* ion-emitting;—**колориметр** *m.* ionocolorimeter (for *p*H determination); —**мер** *m. p*H meter; —**метр** *m.* ionometer; —**н** *m.* ionone; —**обмен** *m.* ion exchange; —**обменитель, —обменник** *m.* ion exchanger; —**обменный** *a.* ion-exchange (resin, etc.); —**образование** *n.* ion formation; —**сфера** *f.* ionosphere; —**сферный** *a.* ionospheric.

**ион/отерапия** *f.* (med.) ionotherapy, iontophoresis; —**офорез, —тофорез** *m.* iontophoresis.

**ИОНХ** *abbr.* (Институт общей и неорганической химии имени Н.С. Курнакова) the N.S. Kurnakov Institute of General and Inorganic Chemistry.

**иорд/ан** *see* **джордан;** —**анит** *m.* (min.) jordanite; —**исит** *m.* (min.) jordisite (a molybdenum sulfide).

**Иорк** York; —**шир** Yorkshire.

**иосейт** *m.* (min.) josëite.

**иосол** *m.* iosol, thymol iodide.

**иот/а** *f.* iota; **ни на** —**у** not at all.

**иотион** *m.* iothion, diiodopropyl alcohol.

**ИОХ(АН)** *abbr.* (Институт органической химии Академии Наук) Institute of Organic Chemistry of the Academy of Sciences.

**иохимбин** *see* **иогимбин.**

**Ипатиева реакция** Ipatiev reaction (for preparation of alcohols).

**ипекакуан/а** *f.* (bot.) ipecac (*Psychotria ipecacuanha*); —**ин** *m.* ipecacuanhin; —**овая кислота** ipecacuanhic acid.

**ипекамин** *m.* ipecamine.

**иперит** *see* **иприт.**

**ипом/еин** *m.* ipomoein; —**ея** *f.* (bot.) morning glory (*Ipomoea*); —**овая кислота** ipomic acid, sebacic acid.

**ипоте/ка** *f.* mortgage; —**чный** *a.* mortgage, hypothecary.

**ипохондр/ик** *m.*, —**ический** *a.* (med.) hypochondriac; —**ия** *f.* hypochondria.

**и пр.** *abbr.* (и прочее) and so forth.

**ипрал** *m.* Ipral, probarbital.

**иприт** *m.* (mil.) yperite, mustard gas.

**ИПС** *abbr.* (инкубаторно-птицеводческая станция) hatchery and poultry-breeding center.

**ипуанин** *m.* ipuanine, artificial emetine.

**ипуранол** *m.* ipuranol.

**ИПФК** *abbr.* (изопропилфенилкарбамат) isopropyl phenyl carbamate.

**Ирак** Iraq.

**ирбитский** *a.* Irbit.

**ирга** *f.* (bot.) June berry (*Amelanchier*).

**ИРЕА** *abbr.* (Институт химических реактивов) Institute of Chemical Reagents.

**ирен** *m.* irene.

**иретол** *m.* iretol, 5-methoxypyrogallol.

**иригизация** *f.* ihrigizing (addition of silicon to iron and steel).

**иридесценция** *f.* iridescence.

**иридиев/ый** *a.* iridium, iridic; —**ая чернь** iridium black, iridium trioxide.

**иридизация** *f.* iridescence.

**ирид/ий** *m.* iridium, Ir; **закись** —**ия** iridooxide, iridium monoxide; **соль закиси** —**ия** salt of bivalent iridium; **окись** —**ия** iridic oxide, iridium dioxide; **хлористый и.** iridochloride, iridium dichloride; **хлорный и.** iridic chloride, iridium tetrachloride.

**иридин** *m.* iridin.

**иридирующий** *a.* iridescent.

**ирид/истый** *a.* iridium, iridous; **и. осмий,** —**осмин** *m.* (min.) iridosmine, osmiridium (native osmium-iridium alloy); —**истая платина** platinum-iridium alloy; —**омирмецин** *m.* iridomyrmecin; —**официн** *m.* iridophycin (a phycocolloid).

**иризация** *f.* iridescence; irisation (of clouds).

**иризин** *m.* irisin.

**иризирующий** *a.* iridescent.

**ирис** *m.* (bot.) iris; iris (of eye); —**овая диафрагма** (phot.) iris diaphragm; —**овое масло** iris oil, orris oil.

**ирифан** *m.* iriphan.

**Ирландия** Ireland.

**ирландский** *a.* Irish; **и. мох** (bot.) Irish moss, carragheen (*Chondrus crispus*).

**ирный** *a.* calamus.

**ирон** *m.* irone.

**ирради/ация** *f.* irradiation; —**ировать** *v.* irradiate.

**иррациональн/ый** *a.* irrational; —**ая**

**величина, —ое число** (math.) irrational number, non-rational number.

**иррегулярный** *a.* irregular, uneven.

**ирриг/атор** *m.* irrigator; **—ация** *f.*, **—ационный** *a.* irrigation; **—ированный** *a.* irrigated; **—ировать** *v.* irrigate.

**ирруптивный** *a.* (geol.) irruptive.

**ис—** *prefix* ex—, away from, out of.

**иск** *m.* suit, action, claim; **предъявить и.** *v.* sue, prosecute, institute proceedings (against).

**иска/жать, —зить** *v.* alter, distort, deform, mutilate; misrepresent; **—жение** *n.*, **—женность** *f.* distortion, deformation; misrepresentation; **—женный** *a.* distorted, mutilated, abnormal.

**искан/ие** *n.* hunting, seeking; selection; dialing; **—ный** *a.* sought, looked for.

**искапывать** *see* **ископать.**

**искатель** *m.* seeker; selector, finder, locator; (scintillation) scanner; (phot.) view finder; **—ный** *a.* searching, seeking; **—ная трубка** (optics) object finder; **—ство** *n.* suit.

**искать** *v.* look (for), search, seek, hunt.

**исключ/ать** *v.* exclude, except, deduct; expel, turn out, release, discharge, eject, discard; (math.) eliminate; **—ающий** *a.* excluding; **взаимно —ающий** conflicting; **—ая** except, with the exception (of), barring, excluding.

**исключен/ие** *n.* exclusion, exception; expulsion, ejection, elimination; **в виде —ия** with this exception, as an exception; **за —ием** with the exception (of), except (for); **—ный** *a.* excluded, excepted; expelled, ejected, eliminated.

**исключительн/о** *adv.* exceptionally; exclusively, solely; **—ый** *a.* exceptional, unusual, exclusive; **—ое право** monopoly; patent right.

**исключить** *see* **исключать.**

**исковерк/ать, —ивать** *v.* distort, mutilate, spoil.

**исков/ой** *a.* claim; **—ое прошение** statement of claim.

**искомкать** *v.* crumple, crush, wrinkle up.

**иском/ый** *a.* sought (for), desired; **—ое число** unknown quantity.

**ископаем/ое** *n.*, **—ый** *a.* mineral, fossil; **полезное и.** mineral, mineral product; **полезные —ые** mineral wealth, mineral resources; **—ый уголь** coal.

**ископать** *v.* dig up, dig all over.

**искорен/ение** *n.* uprooting, extermination, eradication; **—ить, —ять** uproot, exterminate, eradicate, extirpate.

**искорка** *f.* little spark; scintillation.

**искоса** *adv.* askew, askance.

**искр/а** *f.* spark, flash; **выбрасывание искр** emission of sparks, sparking; scintillation; **зажигание —ой** spark ignition; **мечущий —ы** emitting sparks, sparking; scintillating, sparkling; **счетчик искр** scintillation counter; **—ение** *n.* (elec.) sparking, flashing; effervescing, sparkling.

**искренн/ость** *f.* sincerity, candor; **—ый** *a.* sincere, frank, honest, true, genuine.

**искрив/ившийся, —ленный** *a.* bent, curved; twisted, warped, distorted; **—ить, —лять** *v.* bend, curve; twist, distort; **—ляться** *v.* twist, warp, curl; **—ление** *n.* bend, curve; flexure, bending; twist, warp; twisting, warping, distortion.

**искрист/ость** *f.* effervescence, foaminess, frothiness; **—ый** *a.* effervescent, sparkling; scintillating, flashing.

**искрить** *v.* spark, flash; **—ся** *v.* (elec.) spark; sparkle, flash, scintillate; effervesce, fizz.

**искровой** *a.* spark, spark-like; **и. зажигатель** spark fuse, high-tension fuse; spark plug; **и. промежуток** spark gap; **и. разряд** spark discharge; **и. счетчик** scintillation counter.

**искрогаситель** *m.*, **—ное устройство** spark arrester, spark extinguisher, spark quencher; **—ный** *a.* spark-extinguishing, blow-out; **—ная катушка** (elec.) blow-out coil.

**искро/гашение, —тушение** *n.* arc suppression; spark quenching, spark extinguishing; **—ловитель, —уловитель** *m.*, **—уловительная камера** spark catcher, spark arrester; **—мер**

_m._ scintillometer; —**метность** _f._ triboluminescence; —**образование** _n._ spark formation, sparking; —**стойкий** _a._ non-arcing, non-sparking; —**стойкость** _f._ arc resistance; —**тушитель** _see_ **искрогаситель**; —**удержатель** _m._ spark arrester; —**указатель** _m._ spark indicator, spark detector.

**искрошить ,—ся** _v._ crumble.

**искряк** _m._ (min.) aventurine.

**искрящий** _a._ sparking; —**ся** _a._ sparkling, scintillating; effervescent.

**искусный** _a._ expert, skilful, clever.

**искусственн/о** _adv._ artificially; synthetically; —**ость** _f._ artificiality; —**ый** _a._ artificial, false; synthetic; man-made; —**ый каучук** synthetic rubber.

**искусство** _n._ art, craft; skill, proficiency, knack, cleverness, workmanship; practice.

**исландский** _a._ Iceland; **и. мох** (bot.) Iceland moss (_Cetraria islandica_); **и. шпат** (min.) Iceland spar, doubly refracting spar (a variety of calcite).

**ИСО** _abbr._ (**известково-серный отвар**) lime-sulfur spray.

**исп.** _abbr._ (**испанский**) Spanish.

**Испания** Spain.

**испанск/ий** _a._ Spanish; **и. перец** (bot.) red pepper, Cayenne pepper (_Capsicum_); —**ая мушка** Spanish fly; **белая —ая** Spanish white (bismuth subnitrate).

**испарен/ие** _n._ evaporation, evaporating, vaporization, exhalation; vapor, fume; **вредное и.** miasma, polluting exhalations; **жидкость —ия** condensate; **ядовитое и.** mephitis, deadly gas; —**ный** _a._ evaporated, vaporized, volatilized.

**испарина** _f._ perspiration, sweat; condensate.

**испаритель** _m._ evaporator, vaporizer; condenser, cooler; carburetor; evaporimeter, atmometer; —**ный** _a._ evaporative; —**ная секция** stripping section, stripper (of fractionating column); —**ная способность** evaporative capacity, volatility.

**испар/ить, —ять** _v._ evaporate, vaporize, volatilize, exhale; steam; —**иться, —яться** _v._ evaporate; fume; —**яе-**

**мость** _f._ evaporability, vaporizability, volatility; —**яемый** _a._ volatile; —**яющий** _a._ evaporating, vaporizing.

**испахать** _v._ plow up.

**испепел/ение** _n._ incineration, calcination; —**ить, —ять** _v._ incinerate, calcine, reduce to ashes.

**испещр/енный** _a._ speckled, spotted, mottled, variegated, streaked, striated; —**ять** _v._ speckle, mottle, streak.

**исподволь** _adv._ without hurry; gradually, by degrees, little by little.

**исподн/ий** _a._ under, bottom, from below; —**ик** _m._ bottom, bottom part, bottom die, bottom tool.

**исполиновый котел** (geol.) pot hole, kettle hole, wash hole.

**исполинск/ий** _a._ giant, gigantic, huge; —**ие щитни** (zool.) Gigantostraca.

**исполком** _m._ executive committee.

**исполн/ение** _n._ accomplishment, fulfillment, execution, observation, observance, completion; **приводить в и.** _v._ carry out, accomplish; —**енный** _a._ accomplished, fulfilled, complete; —**имость** _f._ feasibility, practicability; —**имый** _a._ feasible, practicable.

**исполнитель** _m._ executor, performer; executive; —**ный** _a._ executive; punctual, careful, attentive; —**ный двигатель** slave motor; —**ный механизм** actuating mechanism, actuator; slave (of a manipulator).

**исполн/ить, —ять** _v._ execute, fulfill, carry out, perform, consummate; —**яющий** _a._ fulfilling, carrying out; acting (for).

**использов/ание** _n._ utilization, use, employment; exploitation, development; consumption; recovery, salvaging (of waste); **процент —ания** recovery; efficiency; —**анный** _a._ used, used up, utilized, consumed, spent, stripped (gas); —**ать** _v._ use, make use (of), utilize, employ, consume; profit (by), take advantage (of).

**испольщик** _m._ sharecropper.

**испорошковывать** _v._ pulverize.

**испор/тить** _v._ spoil, injure, damage; —**ченность** _f._ bad condition, faultiness; putrescence; —**ченный** _a._

spoiled, rotten, decomposed, putrefied; injured, damaged, faulty; corrupt.

**исправ/ительный** *a.* corrective; **—ить, —лять** *v.* correct, adjust, readjust, rectify, remedy, fix, repair; amend, revise; discharge (duties); reclaim; **—иться, —ляться** *v.* improve; **—ление** *n.* correction, adjustment, readjustment, rectification, fixing, reparation; revision; reclamation; improvement; **—ленный** *a.* corrected, adjusted, fixed, repaired; revised; improved.

**исправн/о** *adv.* duly; **—ость** *f.* punctuality, exactness; good condition, working order; **в полной —ости** in good working order; **—ый** *a.* punctual, exact, accurate, precise; efficient, fit, serviceable, in good working order, sound; **—ое состояние** working order.

**испражн/ение** *n.* defecation, evacuation, bowel movement; **—ения** *pl.* feces, excrement; **—яться** *v.* defecate, evacuate, move the bowels.

**испробовать** *v.* try, test.

**испрям/ить, —лять** *v.* straighten.

**испуг** *m.* fright, fear, shock; **—ать** *v.* frighten, startle.

**испу/скаемый** *a.* emitted, given off; **—скание** *n.* emission, emanation; emergence; **—скатель** *m.* emitter; **—скательный, —скающий** *a.* emitting, emissive; **—скательная способность** emissive power, emissivity, radiating capacity; **—скать** *v.* emit, give off, exhale; eject; give, utter; expire; **—скаться** *v.* emerge; emanate; **—щенный** *a.* emitted.

**испыл/енность** *f.* pulverulence; **—енный** *a.* pulverized, pulverulent; **—ять** *v.* pulverize.

**испытание** *n.* test, testing, experiment, trial; assay, analysis, checking, examination; research, investigation; **и. в работе, и. в эксплуатации** field test, plant test; **и. на test for; и. на сжатие** compression test; **и. трением** friction test; **и.-экспресс** quick test.

**испыт/анный** *a.* tested, tried, examined, inspected, approved; **и. временем** time-tested; **—атель** *m.* tester, testing

apparatus; investigator, research man; analyst.

**испытательный** *a.* test, testing, experimental; **и. кран** try cock, gage cock; **и. полигон** proving ground; **и. прибор** tester, testing apparatus; **и. стол** laboratory bench; (tel.) test board.

**испыт/ать** *see* **испытывать; —уемый, —ующий** *see* **испытательный.**

**испытыв/аемый** *a.* test, tested, under consideration, in question; experienced; **—ать** *v.* test, put to test, try; investigate, examine, check; assay, analyze; undergo, sustain, experience; **—ать на** test for.

**иссе/кать, —чь** *v.* cut, slash; carve, chisel; **—чение** *n.* cut; carving.

**исследов/ание** *n.* investigation, research, study, survey; exploration; examination, analysis; **—ания** *pl.* investigations, research; **производить и.** *v.* investigate; survey; **—анный** *a.* investigated, studied, examined, tested; **—атель** *m.* investigator, researcher, (literature) searcher; explorer; **—ательский** *a.* research; exploratory; **—ать** *v.* investigate, do research (on), study, examine, inquire (into); search, explore; try, test; analyze; (met.) assay.

**иссоп** *m.* (bot.) hyssop (*Hyssopus officinalis*); **—ное масло** oil of hyssop.

**исс/охнуть, —ыхать** *v.* dry up, wither, shrivel; **—ушать, —ушить** *v.* dry, desiccate; shrink, shrivel; scorch; **—ушение** *n.* desiccation.

**иссяк/ать, —нуть** *v.* dry up, run dry; run low, run short; exhaust.

**истекать** *v.* elapse, expire; emanate (from), escape, flow out, run out; bleed.

**истереть** *see* **истирать.**

**истери/ка** *f.* hysteria, hysterics; **—ческий** *a.* hysterical.

**истерт/ость** *f.* worn condition; attrition, wearing down; **—ый** *a.* worn, abraded.

**истец** *m.* plaintiff; petitioner.

**истеч/ение** *n.* outflow, flow, discharge, efflux; emanation, emission, escape (of gas); expiration, lapse (of time); bleeding; (med.) flux; **диаграмма —ения** effluogram; **—ь** *see* **истекать.**

**истизин** *m.* Istizin, 1,8-dihydroxyan-thraquinone.

**истин/а** *f.* truth, fact, verity; **—ный** *a.* true, actual, real, virtual, veritable; intrinsic (luminosity); **—ное среднее** true mean.

**истир/аемость** *f.* wearability, wearing properties, wear; **—ание** *n.* grinding, crushing, pulverizing; wear, wearing away, attrition, abrasion, deterioration; (geol.) erosion; (met.) galling; **—атель** *m.* grinder, pulverizer, pulverizing machine; abrasive; **—ать** *v.* grind, crush, pulverize; wear down, abrade; erode; **—аться** *v.* wear, wear down, wear away; **—ающий** *a.*, **—ающее вещество** abrasive.

**истле/вать, —ть** *v.* rot, decay, decompose; **—вший** *a.* decomposed; **—ние** *n.* decomposition.

**Истмэна желтый** Eastman's yellow; **И. фильма** Eastman (photographic) film.

**истод** *m.* (bot.) milkwort (*Polygala*); **—овые** *pl.* Polygalaceae.

**исток** *m.* outflow, issue, discharge, discharging, outlet, flowing, effluxion, source.

**истолков/ание** *n.* interpretation, explanation, commentary; **—атель** *m.* interpreter, commentator; **—ательный** *a.* explanatory; **—ать, —ывать** *v.* interpret, explain, expound, comment.

**истол/очь** *v.* pound, crush, grind, stamp, break up; **—ченный** *a.* pounded, crushed, ground, broken up.

**истом/а** *f.* fatigue, weariness, lassitude, faintness; **—ить, —лять** *v.* weary, exhaust, tire; **—ление** *n.* exhaustion; **—ленный** *a.* exhausted.

**Истона циклы** (meteor.) Easton cycles.

**истоп/ить** *v.* melt down, melt, smelt; heat (stove); **—ник** *m.* stoker, fireman.

**истор/ик** *m.* historian; **—ический** *a.* historic, historical; **—ия** *f.* history.

**источ/ать, —ить** *v.* shed, spill, spout; bore (of worm).

**источник** *m.* source, origin; spring, fountain, well; supply, resource; **и. нейтронов** neutron source; **служить —ом** *v.* be a source (of), give rise (to), cause.

**истощать** *v.* exhaust, deplete, drain,

work out, spend, wear out, reduce in strength, impoverish; **—ся** *v.* be exhausted, be worn out; be worked out, become poor; run low, dwindle, die off.

**истощен/ие** *n.* exhaustion, depletion, draining, impoverishment; emaciation; (mil.) attrition; **—ный** *a.* exhausted, depleted, drained, worn out; spent (solution); emaciated.

**истощившийся** *a.* exhausted; extinct (volcano).

**истребитель** *m.* destroyer; fighter, fighter plane, pursuit plane; **—ный** *a.* destructive, destroying, exterminating.

**истреб/ить, —лять** *v.* destroy, exterminate, annihilate, obliterate; **—ление** *n.* destruction, extermination, annihilation.

**истрепанный** *a.* ragged, frayed.

**истый** *a.* true, real, thorough.

**ИСФХА АН СССР** *abbr.* (Известия сектора физико-химического анализа Академии Наук СССР) Bulletin of the Sector of Physicochemical Analysis, Academy of Sciences, USSR.

**ИСХ** *abbr.* (Институт сельского хозяйства) Institute of Agriculture.

**исход** *m.* issue, outlet, outcome, result; way out; **в —е** by the end of (a given time); **—ить** *v.* issue, originate, proceed (from), emanate, radiate, emerge.

**исходн/ый** *a.* original, initial, first; reference, base; parent; stock (plant); **и. материал, —ое сырье** starting material, raw material; feed; **и. пункт, —ая точка** initial point, starting point, point of departure, origin, base, basis; reference point; **и. район** zone of departure; **—ая пульпа** (concentration) feed pulp; **—ое вещество** initial product, raw material, parent substance; **—ое положение** initial position, starting point, first step.

**исходящий** *a.* issuing, emanating, coming (from); outgoing (calls, etc.).

**исхуд/авший, —алый, —елый** *a.* emaciated, thin, wasted; **—ать, —еть** *v.* become emaciated, waste away.

**исцарапанный** *a.* scratched; striated, grooved.

**исцел/ение** n. healing, recovery; —**имый** a. curable; —**ить,** —**ять** v. heal, cure.

**исчез/ание,** —**новение** n. disappearance, loss; —**ать,** —**нуть** v. disappear, vanish, dissipate, taper out, fade away; merge (into); die out, become extinct; —**ающий** a. disappearing, vanishing, dying out; elastic (deformation).

**исчерпыв/ать** v. scoop, empty, drain; exhaust, work out, deplete (ore); —**ающий** a. draining; exhaustive (study); —**ающая часть** (fractionation) stripping section.

**исчер/тить,** —**чивать** v. streak, stripe, line, cover with lines, striate; —**ченный** a. streaked, striated.

**исчисл/ение** n. calculation, computation; numeration; enumeration; calculus; **дифференциальное и.** (math.) differential calculus; —**енный** a. calculated; enumerated; —**ить,** —**ять** v. calculate, compute, estimate; numerate; enumerate.

**исштрихованный** a. streaked, striated.

**исщепать** v. split, splinter, chip.

**итабирит** m. (min.) itabirite, specular schist (a variety of hematite).

**итак** conj. thus, so; now, now then.

**итако/лумит** m. (min.) itacolumite, flexible sandstone; —**новая кислота** itaconic acid, methylenebutanedioic acid.

**итал.** abbr. (**итальянский**) Italian.

**Италия** Italy; **итальянский** a. Italian.

**итамаловая кислота** itamalic acid.

**и т. д.** abbr. (**и так далее**) etc.

**итер/ативный** a. (math.) iterative; —**ация** f. iteration; —**ированный** a. iterated, repeated.

**итог** m. sum, total, total amount, result; —**и** pl. results, returns; —**о** adv. altogether, in all; **в** —**е** on the whole, to sum up; **в конечном** —**е** in the end, in the long run; **подводить и.** v. sum up.

**и т. п.** abbr. (**и тому подобное**) and so on, and so forth, and the like.

**итрол** m. itrol, silver citrate.

**ИТС** abbr. (**Инженерно-техническая секция**) Engineering-Technical Section.

**иттерб/ий** m. ytterbium, Yb; **окись** —**ия** ytterbium oxide; **хлористый и.** ytterbium chloride; —**ит** m. (min.) ytterbite, gadolinite; —**овый** a. ytterbium; —**овая земля** ytterbia, ytterbium oxide.

**итти** see **идти.**

**иттр/иалит** m. (min.) yttrialite; —**иевый,** —**овый** a. yttrium, yttriferous, yttric; —**иевый шпат** (min.) xenotime (an yttrium phosphate); —**иевая земля** yttria, yttrium oxide; —**ий** m. yttrium, Y or Yt; **окись** —**ия** yttrium oxide; **сернокислый** —**ий,** **сульфат** —**ия** yttrium sulfate.

**иттро/гуммит** m. (min.) yttrogummite; —**колумбит,** —**танталит** m. yttrocolumbite, yttrotantalite; —**кразит** m. yttrocrasite; —**сфен** m. yttrosphene; —**титанит** m. yttrotitanite; —**флуорит** m. yttrofluorite; —**церит** m. yttrocerite (a variety of fluorite); —**эрзит** m. yttroersite.

**итурин** m. iturin.

**иудейск/ий** a. Jewish; —**ая смола** (min.) Jew's pitch (a bitumen).

**иудино дерево** (bot.) Judas tree (*Cercis siliquastrum*).

**ИУК** abbr. (**индолилуксусная кислота**) indolylacetic acid.

**ИФ** abbr. (**инозитофосфат**) inositol phosphate.

**ИФЗ** abbr. (**Институт физики земли им. О. Ю. Шмидта**) O. Yu. Schmidt Institute of Physics of the Earth.

**ИФК** abbr. (**изопропилфенилкарбамат**) isopropylphenyl carbamate; (**инозитофосфорная кислота**) inositolphosphoric acid.

**ИФХА** abbr. (**Институт физико-химического анализа**) Institute of Physicochemical Analysis.

**их** gen. and acc. of **они,** their, them.

**ихневмон** m. ichneumon (mammal); ichneumon fly; —**иды** see **наездники.**

**ихнология** f. (geol.) ichnology.

**ихор** m. (med.) ichor (discharge); (geol.) ichor (granitic liquid); —**озный** a. (med.) ichorous.

**ихт/альбин** m. ichthalbin, ichthyol albuminate; —**арган** m. Ichthargan, silver sulfoichthyolate; —**инат** see **ихтиол.**

**ихтио—** prefix ichthyo—, ichthy— (fish); —**дин** m. ichthyodin; —**з** m. (med.) ichthyosis, xerodermia; —**завр**

*m.* (pal.) ichthyosaur; —**кол,** —**коль**
*m.* ichthyocolla, fish glue, isinglass;
—**л***m.*,—**ловый** *a.* Ichthyol, ichthammol; —**лат** *m.* ichthyolate; —**лит** *m.*
ichthyolite, fossil fish; —**логия** *f.*
ichthyology; —**тический** *a.* (med.)
ichthyotic; —**фтальм,** —**фтальмит**
*m.* (min.) ichthyophthalmite (old
name for apophyllite).
**ихтулин** *m.* ichthulin.
**ИХФК** *abbr.* (**изопропил-N-3-хлорфен-
илкарбамат**) isopropyl N-(3-chloro-
phenyl) carbamate.
**ицерия** *f.* (zool.) cottony cushion scale
(*Icerya purchasi*).

**ишемия** *f.* (med.) ischemia.
**ишиас** *m.* (med.) sciatica.
**ишикаваит** *m.* ishikawaite (uranium
mineral).
**ищ/ет** *pr. 3 sing. of* **искать;** —**ущий** *a.*
seeking.
**июддит** *m.* (min.) juddite (a manganiferous amphibole).
**июдино дерево** *see* **иудино дерево.**
**ию/ль** *m.* July; —**нь** *m.* June.
**иятрен** *see* **ятрен.**
**йо**— *see under* **ио**—; —**тнийский** *a.*
(geol.) Jotnian.

# К

**к** *abbr.* (**кулон**) coulomb; **к.** *abbr.* (**копейка**) kopeck.
**к** *prep. dat.* to; toward; by; for; against;
**к тому же** besides, moreover; **к чему?**
what for? why?
**К** *abbr.* (**Каучук**) Caoutchouc (a journal);
code for cobalt in steel mark; **К.** *abbr.*
(**кандидат**) candidate.
**ка** *abbr.* (**килоампер**) kiloampere.
**кабаит** *m.* (min.) kabaite (a hydrocarbon).
**кабан** *m.*, —**ный** *a.* (zool.) boar; horizontal pile (in charcoal burning);
(aero.) cabane; —**ок** *m.* block of ice;
—**чик** *m.* pylon (of airplane).
**кабар/га** *f.* musk deer; —**говая струя,**
—**динский мускус** Carbardine musk.
**кабачок** *m.* (bot.) summer squash, pumpkin (*Cucurbita pepo*).
**кабеле/к** *m.* (elec.) pigtail; —**провод** *m.*
conduit; —**укладка** *f.* cable laying.
**кабель** *m.*, —**ный** *a.* cable; —**тов** *m.*
cable length; hawser (of ship); —**щик**
*m.* cable man.
**кабестан** *m.* capstan, winch.
**кабин/а,** —**ка** *f.* cabin, cab, cage, car;
**к. пилота** (aero.) cockpit; —**ет** *m.*
cabinet, closet; study; (reception)
room.
**кабл/ирование** *n.* cabling; —**ировать**
*v.* cable; —**ограмма** *f.* cablegram,
cable.
**каблу/к** *m.*, —**чный** *a.* heel.
**каботаж** *m.*, —**ный** *a.* coast, coasting.
**кабошон** *m.* cabochon, convex-cut gem.

**кабрерит** *m.* (min.) cabrerite (a magnesian variety of annabergite).
**кабрирование** *n.* (aero.) pitching.
**кав/а** *f.*, **к.-к., корень** —**ы** kava, kava-
kava (root of *Piper methysticum*).
**кавалер/ник** *m.*, —**ская звезда** (bot.) passion flower (*Passiflora*).
**кавальер** *m.* bank (of earth); dump pit.
**каверн/а** *f.* cavern; vesicle, pocket; flaw,
cavity; (anat.) sinus; —**овая вода**
(geol.) interstitial water; —**озный** *a.*
cavernous, honeycombed, porous,
vesicular.
**кавитац/ионный** *a.*, —**ия** *f.* cavitation;
cavity.
**Кавказ** Caucasus.
**кавказ/ит** *m.* kavkazite (sanidine granite from the Caucasus); —**ский** *a.*
Caucasian.
**кавычки** *pl.* quotation marks.
**кагат** *m.* (root crop storage) clamp, pit.
**кадаверин** *m.* cadaverine, 1,5-pentane-
diamine; —**ы** *pl.* cadaverines, pto-
maines.
**кадален** *m.* cadalene.
**кадастр** *m.* (land evaluation) cadaster.
**кад/ехол** *m.* cadechol, camphor-choleic
acid; —**инен** *m.* cadinene.
**кадка** *f.* tub, vat.
**кадмиев/ый** *a.* cadmium; **к. желтый,**
—**ая желть** cadmium yellow, cadmium sulfide; —**ая обманка** (min.)
greenockite.
**кадмиесодержащий** *a.* cadmium-con-
taining, cadmiferous.

**кадм/ий** *m.* cadmium, Cd; **азотнокислый к.**, **нитрат** —ия cadmium nitrate; **ацетат** —ия, **уксуснокислый к.** cadmium acetate; **бромид** —ия, **бромистый к.** cadmium bromide; **гидрат окиси** —ия cadmium hydroxide; **закись** —ия cadmous oxide; **окись** —ия cadmium oxide; **сернистый к.** cadmium sulfide.

**кадмиров/ание** *n.* cadmium plating; —**анный** *a.* cadmium-plated; —**ать** *v.* plate with cadmium.

**кадмия** *f.* cadmia (old name for zinc or zinc carbonate); **печная к.** (met.) tutty (an impure zinc oxide sublimate).

**кадмопон** *m.* cadmopone, cadmium lithopone.

**кадр** *m.*, —**овый** *a.* skeleton, frame, framework; outline; skeleton staff; (phot.) frame, exposure; —**ы** *pl.* personnel; **подготовка** —**ов** training of specialists.

**кадушка** *see* **кадка.**

**кады/к** *m.*, —**чный** *a.* (anat.) Adam's apple.

**кадь** *see* **кадка.**

**Кадэ жидкость** Cadet's liquid.

**каем/ка** *see* **кайма;** —**чатый** *a.* bordered.

**каепут** *see* **каяпутовое дерево.**

**кажд/огодно** *adv.* annually, every year; —**одневно** *adv.*, —**одневный** *a.* daily, every day; —**ый** *a.* each, every; *pron.* everyone, everybody, each one.

**кажется** *see* **казаться.**

**кажущийся** *a.* apparent, seeming.

**казак** *m.* Cossack.

**казалось** *see* **казаться.**

**казан** *m.*, —**ный** *a.* kettle, boiler.

**казарка** *f.* snout beetle (*Rhynchites bacchus*); barnacle.

**казарм/а** *f.* barracks; —**енный** *a.* barrack, barrack-like.

**казатель** *m.* indicator, guide, pointer.

**казаться** *v.* seem, appear; **кажется** it seems, it appears; **казалось** it seemed.

**казах** *m.*, —**ский** *a.* Kazakh.

**каза/цкий**, —**чий** *a.* Cossack.

**казеа/за** *f.* casease; —**новая кислота** caseanic acid.

**казеин** *m.*, —**овый** *a.* casein (milk protein); **растительный к.** vegetable casein; —**аза** *f.* caseinase, rennase; —**ат** *m.*, —**овокислая соль** caseinate, caseate; —**ат натрия**, —**овонатриевая соль** sodium caseinate; —**овая кислота** caseinic acid; **соль** —**овой кислоты** caseinate; —**овые краски** casein paints.

**каземат** *m.*, —**ный** *a.* casemate.

**казенник** *m.* breech (of firearms).

**казенный** *a.* government, state, public; fiscal; **на к. счет** at public expense.

**казимир/ин** *m.* casimirin; —**оедин** *m.* casimiroedine; —**оза** *f.* casimirose; —**оин** *m.* casimiroine.

**казна** *f.* treasury; —**чей** *m.* treasurer, paymaster, cashier; —**чейство** *n.* treasury, exchequer.

**казнить** *v.* execute, put to death.

**казнохранилище** *n.* treasury.

**казнь** *f.* execution, capital punishment.

**казолит** *m.* kasolite (uranium mineral).

**КазССР** *abbr.* (**Казахская Советская Социалистическая Республика**) Kazakh Soviet Socialist Republic.

**казуарин/а** *f.* (bot.) beefwood (*Casuarina*); —**овые** *pl.* Casuarinaceae.

**казус** *m.* (law) special case; —**ный** *a.* involved.

**каинит** *m.* (min.) kainite.

**каинк/а** *f.*, —**овый корень** cainca, cahinca (root of *Chiococca racemosa*); —**овая кислота** caincic acid, cahincic acid.

**каинозит** *m.* (min.) kainosite, cenosite.

**каинц/етин** *m.* caincetin; —**ин** *m.* caincin, cahincic acid.

**Каир** Cairo.

**каир/ин** *see* **кайрин;** —**нгорм** *m.* (min.) cairngorm, cairngorm stone (a smoky quartz); —**олин** *see* **кайролин.**

**кайапонин** *m.* cayaponine.

**кайенский перец** Cayenne pepper (dried fruit of *Capsicum*).

**кайепутен** *see* **каяпутен.**

**Кайетэ-матиаса закон** (phys.) Cailletet and Mathias law.

**кайл/а** *f.*, —**о** *n.*, —**овый** *a.* pick, hack; wedge.

**кайм/а** *f.* border, edging, edge, hem, fringe, rim, flange; —**ить** *v.* border, edge.

**кайноз/ит** *see* **каинозит;** —**ой** *m.* (geol.) Cenozoic era; —**ойский** *a.* Cenozoic.

**кайр/ин** *m.* kairine, methyl oxytetrahydroquinoline; **—олин** *m.* kairoline, methyl tetrahydroquinoline.

**кайса** *f.* dried apricots.

**как** *adv.* how, as, like; **к. будто** as if, as though; it looks, it appears; **к. бы** as if, as though; **к. бы не** lest; **к. бы ни** however, howsoever; **к. быть?** what is to be done? **к. вдруг** when suddenly; **к. если бы** as if; **к. есть** quite, absolutely, utterly; **к. же** without doubt, certainly, of course; **к.-либо** somehow; **к. например** as, for instance; **к. не** but; **к. ни** however; **к. ни в чем не бывало** as if nothing were the matter; **к.-нибудь** somehow, anyhow; **к.-раз** exactly, just, right, precisely; **к. . . . , так и** both . . . and; **к. таковой** as such; **к.-то** somehow; lately; **к. только** as soon as, when.

**какао** *n.*, **—вый** *a.* cacao, cocoa; **к. боб, боб к.**, **—вый боб** cocoa bean; **—вла** *f.* cacao husk; **—вое дерево, к.-шоколадное дерево** (bot.) cacao (*Theobroma cacao*); **—вое масло, к.-масло** cacao butter, theobroma oil; **—рин** *m.* cacaorin.

**каков** *pron. and a.* what kind of? how? what?

**какодил** *m.*, **—овый** *a.* cacodyl; **окись —а** cacodyl oxide, alkarsine; **хлористый к.** cacodyl chloride; **—ат** *m.*, **—овокислая соль, соль —овой кислоты** cacodylate; **—овая кислота** cacodylic acid, dimethylarsinic acid; **—овокислый** *a.* cacodylic acid; cacodylate (of).

**какой** *a.* what? which? **к.-либо, к.-нибудь** some, any; **к.-то** some.

**какоксен** *m.* (min.) cacoxene, cacoxenite.

**какотелин** *m.* cacotheline.

**кактус** *m.*, **—овый** *a.* (bot.) cactus; **—овые** *pl.* Cactaceae.

**кал** *m.* excrement, feces, dung.

**кал** *abbr.* (калория малая) small calorie.

**калабар/ин** *m.* calabarine; **—ские бобы** calabar bean (*Physostigma venenosum*).

**кала/верит** *m.* (min.) calaverite (a gold-silver telluride); **—ит** *m.* (min.) calaite, turquoise; **—мен** *m.* calamene; **—мин** *m.* (min.) calamine,

hemimorphite; **—минтон** *m.* calaminthone; **—мит** *m.* (min.) calamite (a variety of tremolite); **—мянка** *f.* (text.) calamanco.

**каландр** *m.*, **—овый** *a.* (text., paper) calender, calender roll; **—ирование, —ование** *n.* calendering, calender run, glazing; **—ированный, —ованный** *a.* calendered; **—ировать, —овать** *v.* calender, glaze.

**каланча** *f.* watch tower, fire tower, lookout.

**калач** *m.* calatch (sort of white bread).

**калган** *m.* (bot.) tormentil (*Potentilla tormentilla*); **к., —ный корень** galanga (root of *Alpinia officinarum*).

**калгон** *m.* Calgon, sodium hexametaphosphate.

**Кале** Calais.

**калев/ать** *v.* channel; **—ка** *f.*, **—очный** *a.* channel, channel molding; molding plane, fillister; **—очный паз** channel.

**каледон/ит** *m.* (min.) caledonite; **—ский** *a.* (geol.) Caledonian.

**калейдоскоп** *m.* kaleidoscope; **—ический** *a.* kaleidoscopic.

**калека** *m.* cripple.

**календар/ь** *m.*, **—ный** *a.* calendar; **—ное планирование** scheduling.

**календулин** *m.* calendulin.

**кален/ие** *n.* incandescence, making red hot, heating to redness; **белое к.** white heat, incandescence; **красное к.** red heat; **—ица** *f.* (glass) cooling arch; **—ый** *a.* red hot, heated to redness.

**калесценция** *f.* calescence.

**калечить** *v.* cripple, lame, mutilate, disable.

**кали** *n.* potash, potassium oxide; **к.-аппарат** potash bulb (for carbon dioxide absorption); **едкое к.** caustic potash, potassium hydroxide; **сернокислое к.** potassium sulfate; **углекислое к.** potassium carbonate.

**калиатур** *m.* (dye) caliatour wood.

**калибер** *see* **калибр**; **—ный** *a.* caliber, gage, standard; **—ная доска, —ная плитка** wire gage, wire gage plate; **—ная скоба** caliper gage.

**калиборит** *m.* (min.) kaliborite (a potash borite).

**калибр** *m.* caliber, gage, size, bore, bore

diameter; gage (of wire); groove (of roller); **к.-кольцо** ring gage; **к.-нутромер, к.-пробка** internal gage, plug gage, hole gage; **к.-скоба** caliper gage; **выдвижной к., раздвижной к.** sliding calipers, slide gage, vernier calipers.

**калибр/атор, —овщик** *m.* calibrator; **—ирование** *n.*, **—ование** *n.*, **—овка** *f.* calibration, standardization; grooving, groove designing (of roller); **—ованный** *a.* calibrated, gaged, graduated, standardized; **—ировать, —овать** *v.* calibrate, gage, graduate, standardize, adjust, test; groove (roller); **—ирующий** *a.* calibrating; **—овочный** *a.* caliber, calibration; **—овочная машина** gaging machine; **—омер, —ометр** *m.* gage.

**калиевохромовые квасцы** potash chrome alum.

**калиев/ый** *a.* potassium, potash, potassic; **к. полевой шпат, к. шпат** (min.) potash feldspar, orthoclase; **к. щелок** caustic potash (solution), potash lye; **—ая селитра** potassium nitrate; **—ая слюда** (min.) potash mica, muscovite, common mica; **—ая соль** potassium salt, potash salt; **—ое мыло** potash soap, soft soap; **—ое растворимое стекло** potash water glass, potassium silicate; **—ое стекло** potash glass; **—ые квасцы** potash alum; (min.) kalinite.

**кал/ий** *m.* potassium, K; **азотнокислый к., нитрат —ия** potassium nitrate; **ацетат —ия, уксуснокислый к.** potassium acetate; **бромид —ия, бромистый к.** potassium bromide; **гидрат окиси —ия** potassium hydroxide; **едкий к.** *see* **кали, едкое;** **иодистый к.** potassium iodide; **марганцевокислый к., перманганат —ия** potassium permanganate; **марганцовистокислый к.** potassium manganate; **окись —ия** potassium oxide; **синеродистый к., цианистый к.** potassium cyanide; **хлористый к.** potassium chloride; **хлорнокислый к.** potassium perchlorate.

**калийн/ый** *see* **калиевый; —ая соль** potassium salt; spec. a fertilizer or slug spray of ground sylvinite and potassium chloride.

**каликант** *m.* (bot.) calycanthus; **—ин** *m.* calycanthine.

**каликс** *m.* calyx, cup.

**калильн/ый** *a.* incandescent, glowing; **к. горн** (met., cer.) annealing hearth; **к. жар** red heat, glowing heat; **к. колпачок, к. чулок, —ая сетка** incandescent mantle; **к. свет** (elec.) incandescent light; **к. ящик** (met., cer.) annealing box; **—ая головка** ignition chamber; **—ая лампа** (elec.) incandescent lamp; **—ая печь** (met.) annealing furnace, glowing furnace; (cer.) hardening-on kiln; **—ая трубка** ignition tube.

**калильщик** *m.* annealer (operator).

**калимаг** *m.*, **—незия** *f.* a potassium-magnesium sulfate fertilizer.

**калина** *f.* (bot.) viburnum, spec. cranberry tree (*Viburnum opulus*); **к. кора** cramp bark.

**калинит** *m.* (min.) kalinite, potash alum.

**калитка** *f.* gate, wicket gate.

**калить** *v.* make red hot, incandesce.

**калифорн/ий** *m.* californium, Cf; **—ийский, —ский** *a.* California; **—ийская жидкость** *see* **ИСО; —ит** *m.* (min.) californite (a variety of vesuvianite).

**калицин** *m.* calycin.

**кали/че, —ше** *n.* (min.) caliche (usually impure Chile saltpeter).

**калка** *f.* (leather) stuffing.

**каллаит** *m.* (min.) kallait, turquoise.

**каллатур** *see* **калиатур.**

**каллиандр/а кора** calliandra bark; **—еин** *m.* calliandrein.

**каллиротрон** *m.* (rad.) kallirotron.

**каллитрол** *m.* callitrol; **—овая кислота** callitrolic acid.

**каллифоры** *pl.* blowflies, bluebottle flies (*Calliphoridae*).

**Калло элемент** (elec.) Callaud cell (a form of Daniell cell).

**каллус** *m.* (bot., med.) callus.

**Калье коэффициент** (phot.) Callier's Q factor.

**каллюс** *see* **каллус.**

**калм/егиновая кислота** calmeghinic acid; **—аллой** *m.* Calmalloy (nickel-copper-iron alloy); **—онал** *m.* calmonal, urethan calcium bromide.

**каломел/ол** *m.* calomelol, colloidal calomel; **—ь** *m.*, **—ьный** *a.* calomel, mercurous chloride; **растительный —ь** podophyllin (a resin).

**калоресценция** *f.* (phys.) calorescence.

**калори—** *prefix* calori—, heat; **—затор** *m.* calorizator; (mach.) hot bulb, ignition chamber; **—зация** *f.*, **—зирование** *n.* calorizing, coating with aluminum; **—зировать** *v.* calorize.

**калорийность** *f.* calorific value, heat value; fuel value, calorie value (of food).

**калориметр** *m.* calorimeter; **—ирование** *n.* calorimetric measurement; **—ический** *a.* calorimetric, calorific; **—ия** *f.* calorimetry, calorimetric measurement.

**калорифер** *m.* heater, heating element; radiator; (met.) hotblast stove.

**калорическ/ий** *a.* caloric, calorific, thermic, thermal; **к. двигатель, —ая машина** hot-air engine; **—ое значение** calorific value.

**калория** *f.* calorie; **большая к., техническая к.** large calorie, kilogram-calorie; **британская к.** British thermal unit, BTU; **малая к.** small calorie, gram-calorie.

**калотип** *m.* (phot.) calotype.

**калотта** *f.* (building) calotte.

**калоша** *f.* overshoe, rubber.

**калужница** *f.* (bot.) buttercup (*Caltha*).

**калумба** *see* **коломбо.**

**калусцит** *m.* (min.) kaluszite, syngenite.

**калуфер** *m.*, **—ный** *a.* (bot.) tansy (*Tanacetum*); costmary (*Chrysanthemum balsamita*).

**Кальбаум** Kahlbaum (German reagent firm).

**кальгумит** *m.* calhumite (mixture of lime and humic acids).

**кальдера** *f.* (geol.) caldera, crater.

**калька** *f.* tracing cloth, tracing paper; **бумажная к.** tracing paper.

**калька/ммон** *m.* calcammonia (mixture of lime and ammonium chloride); **—ренит** *m.* (petr.) calcarenite; **—рона** *f.* calcarone (a sulfur furnace used in Sicily); **—ронный способ** calcarone method; **—фанит** *m.* (min.) calcaphanite (a variety of diabase).

**калькгур** *m.* agaric mineral (a calcium carbonate).

**калькиров/ание** *n.* tracing; calking;

**—анный** *a.* traced; calked; **—ать** *v.* trace; calk.

**калько—** *see* **халько—.**

**калькул/ировать** *v.* calculate, estimate, figure out, work out; **—ятор** *m.* calculator, estimator; calculating machine; **—яционный** *a.* calculation, calculating; **—яция** *f.* calculation, estimate.

**кальмар** *m.* (zool.) squid.

**кальцеолярия** *f.* (bot.) calceolaria.

**кальци—** *prefix* calci—; **—евый** *a.* calcium; **—евая селитра** calcium nitrate; **—евая серная печень** *see* **известковая серная печень**; **—евая соль** calcium salt.

**кальц/ий** *m.* calcium, Ca; **к.-цианамид, цианамид —ия** calcium cyanamide; **гидрат окиси —ия** calcium hydroxide; **окись —ия** calcium oxide; **сернокислый к., сульфат —ия** calcium sulfate; **углекислый к.** calcium carbonate; **углеродистый к.** calcium carbide; **фосфат —ия, фосфорнокислый к.** calcium phosphate; **хлористый к.** calcium chloride; **хлорноватистокислый к.** calcium hypochlorite; **—иметр** *m.* calcimeter (for carbon dioxide determination).

**кальцин** *m.* calcine, calcined phosphate; **—а** *f.* (cer.) tin-lead ash.

**кальцин/ация** *f.*, **—ирование** *n.* calcination, roasting; **—ированный** *a.* calcined, roasted; **—ировать** *v.* calcine, roast.

**кальци/остронцианит** *m.* (min.) calciostrontianite; **—оторит** *m.* (min.) calciothorite; **—т** *m.* (min.) calcite, calc spar, calcareous spar; **—ферол** *m.* calciferol, vitamin $D_2$; **—фикация** *f.* (geol.) calcification.

**калютрон** *m.* calutron (isotope separator).

**кам** *m.* (geol.) kame (ridge of stratified drift).

**кам.** *abbr.* (**каменный**) stone.

**кама/ла** *f.* kamala (powder from *Mallotus philippinensis*); **—резит** *m.* (min.) kamarezite; **—цит** *m.* (min.) kamacite (a variety of nickeliferous meteoric iron).

**камбал** *m.* (dye) camwood.

**камбала** *f.* plaice, flatfish, flounder.

**камбий** *m.* (bot.) cambium.

**камбоджа** *f.* gamboge (gum resin).

**камбопиновая кислота** cambopinic acid.

**камвольный** *a.* (text.) worsted.

**камед/еобразный** *a.* gum-like, gummy; **—етечение** *n.* gummosis, resinous exudation (of trees); **—истый** *a.* gum, gummy, resinous; **—истая смола** gum resin; **—ный** *a.* gum; **—ный сахар** gum sugar, arabinose; **—ная загустка** gum water; **—ное дерево** (bot.) gum tree, sweet gum (*Liquidambar styraciflua*).

**камед/ь** *f.* gum, resin; **аравийская к.** gum arabic; **лишать —и** *v.* degum.

**камелек** *m.* hearth, fireplace.

**камелин/а** *f.* (bot.) dodder seed (*Camelina sativa*); **—овое масло** cameline oil.

**камелия** *f.* (bot.) camellia.

**камель** *m.* camel (a type of caisson).

**камен/еть** *v.* (geol.) petrify, fossilize, harden, become stone; **—истость** *f.* stoniness; **—истый** *a.* stony, stone-like, petrous, rocky; covered with stones.

**каменноугольн/ый** *a.* coal, carboniferous; coal-tar, *see also* **угольный**; **к. газ** coal gas; **к. деготь, —ая смола** coal tar; **—ое масло** coal-tar oil; **—ые красители** coal-tar dyes.

**каменн/ый** *a.* stone, stony, lithoidal; jewel (bearing); **к. век** stone age; **к. метеорит** (petr.) stony meteorite; achondrite; **к. мозг** (min.) lithomarge (a compact variety of kaolin); **к. уголь** coal, *see also* **уголь**; **—ая болезнь** (med.) lithiasis; **—ая кладка** stonework, masonry; **—ая посуда** stoneware; **—ая соль** (min.) rock salt, halite, sodium chloride; **—ое масло** petroleum.

**камено— ** *see* **камне—**; **—лом** *m.* quarrier, quarryman; **—ломка** *see* **камнеломка**; **—ломня** *f.* quarry, stone quarry, stone pit; **—сек, —тес** *m.* stone cutter; mason; **—сечный, —тесный** *a.* stone cutter's, stone cutting; **—тесное долото** stone chisel.

**камен/щик** *m.* mason, stone mason, brick layer; **—ь** *m.* stone, rock; cliff; (med.) calculus, stone; **—ь-плитняк** flagstone.

**камера** *f.* chamber, cell, compartment; room, office; (phot.) camera; inner tube (of tire); chest, bin, case; barrel (of pump); **к.-обскура** camera obscura.

**камеральный** *a.* office (work).

**камерн/ый** *a.* chamber, chambered, compartment; box (filter press); **к. способ** chamber process (for sulfuric acid manufacture); **—ая кислота** chamber acid (sulfuric acid); **—ая печь** compartment kiln; **—ые кристаллы** chamber crystals (nitrosyl sulfate).

**камерон** *m.* Cameron pump; **—щик** *m.* (min.) pump operator and mechanic.

**камертон** *m.*, **—ный** *a.* tuning fork; **—ный вибратор** (rad.) tuning fork oscillator.

**камея** *f.* cameo.

**камин** *m.*, **—ный** *a.* fireplace; chimney, smokestack.

**камлот** *m.* (text.) camelot.

**камне/бурильный станок** rock drilling machine, rock drill; **—видность** *f.* stoniness, stony appearance; **—видный** *a.* stony, stone-like, lithoidal; **—дробилка** *f.* stone crusher, rock crusher, ore crusher; **—ед** *see* **камнеточец**; **—лом** *see* **каменолом**.

**камнеломк/а** *f.* (bot.) saxifrage (*Saxifraga*); **—овые** *pl.* Saxifragaceae.

**камне/облицовка** *f.* stone surfacing, stone lining; **—образный** *see* **камневидный**; **—образующий** *a.* stone-forming, lapidific; **—печатание** *n.* lithography; **—печатный** *a.* lithographed, lithographic; **—растение** *n.* (bot.) lithophyte; **—резная пила** stone saw; **—сверлильный станок** rock drill; **—сечение** *n.* (med.) lithotomy; **—точец** *m.* (zool.) stone borer (*Pholas dactylus*).

**камомиллол** *m.* camomillol.

**камор/а** *f.* chamber; lock (of sluice); **—ка** *f.* closet, small room.

**кампания** *f.* campaign, drive; season; time; operating period, run (of furnace).

**кампанский век** (geol.) Campanian stage.

**кампеш** *m.*, **—евое дерево, —евый**, **—ный** *a.* (bot.) logwood (*Haematoxylon campechianum*).

**кампилит** *m.* (min.) kampylite (a variety of mimetite).

**камполон** *m.* campolon (liver extract).

**кампометр** *m.* kampometer (for measuring heat radiation).

**камптонит** *m.* camptonite (a dike rock).

**кам.-уг.** *abbr.* (каменноугольный) coal.

**камуфлет** *m.* (mil.) underground explosion.

**камуфляж** *m.* camouflage.

**камушек** *m.* small stone, pebble.

**камфан** *m.* camphane; —ил *m.*, —иловый *a.* camphanyl; —овая кислота camphanic acid; —ол *m.* camphanol; —он *m.* camphanone.

**камфара** *see* камфора.

**камфен** *m.* camphene; —гликол *m.* campheneglycol, 2,3-dihydroxycamphane.

**камфенил** *m.*, —овый *a.* camphenyl; —ан *m.* camphenilane, 2,2-dimethylnorcamphane; —ен *m.* camphenilene; —иден *m.* camphenilidene; —овая кислота camphenylic acid; —он *m.* camphenilone, 3-ketocamphanilane.

**камфен/овая кислота** camphenic acid; —ол *m.* camphenol; —оловая кислота camphenolic acid; —он *m.* camphenone, 1-methylcamphenilone.

**камферол** *m.* campherol.

**камфидин** *m.* camphidine.

**камфил** *m.*, —овый *a.* camphyl; —овая кислота camphylic acid; —овый спирт camphyl alcohol, borneol.

**камфо—** *prefix* campho—; —ген *m.* camphogen, cymene; —карбоксильная кислота, —карбоновая кислота camphocarboxylic acid, 2-keto-3-carboxycamphane; —кислота *f.* campho acid, carboxyl-apocamphoric acid.

**камфол** *m.* camphol, borneol; —актон *m.* campholactone; —ен *m.* campholene; —еновая кислота campholenic acid; —ид *m.* campholide; —овая кислота campholic acid.

**камфон** *m.* camphone; —ановая кислота camphonanic acid; —ен *m.* camphonene; —еновая кислота camphonenic acid; —овая кислота camphonic acid; —оловая кислота camphonolic acid.

**камфор/а** *f.* camphor, 2-ketocamphane;

однобромистая **к.** monobromated camphor; —ановая кислота camphoranic acid; —ен *m.* camphorene; —ил *m.*, —иловый *a.* camphoryl.

**камфорно/аммониевая соль,** —кислый аммоний ammonium camphorate; —кислый *a.* camphoric acid; camphorate (of); —кислая соль camphorate.

**камфорн/ый** *a.* camphor, camphoric; **к.** спирт spirit of camphor; —ая кислота camphoric acid; соль —ой кислоты camphorate; —ое дерево (bot.) camphor (*Camphora officinalis* or *Cinnamomum camphora*); —ое масло camphor oil; (pharm.) camphorated oil.

**камфо/роил** *m.* camphoroyl; —роксим *m.* camphoroxime; —роновая кислота camphoronic acid; —рфорон *m.* camphorphorone; —рхинон *m.* camphorquinone, 2,3-di-ketocamphane; —цееновая кислота camphoceenic acid.

**камфреновая кислота** camphrenic acid.

**камчат/ка** *f.*, —ный *a.* (text.) damask.

**камшафт** *m.* camshaft.

**камы** *pl. of* кам.

**камыш** *m.*, —евый *a.* cane, reed; (bot.) reed (*Phragmites communis*); rush (*Scirpus*); —евый мат rush matting.

**камышек** *see* камушек.

**камыш/ит** *m.* (construction) pressboard made of reeds; —овый *a.* rattan, rush.

**канав/а** *f.* gutter, channel, ditch, canal, trench; groove; raceway; опробование —ами trench sampling (in ore concentration); —ка *f.* groove, slot; incision, cut; с одной —кой single-groove; —окапатель *m.*, —окопательная машина trench digger, trenching plow, ditch digger.

**канад/ин** *m.* canadine, tetrahydroberberine; —иновая кислота canadinic acid; —иноловая кислота canadinolic acid; —ол *m.* canadol; —оловая кислота canadolic acid.

**канадский** *a.* Canada, Canadian; **к.** бальзам Canada balsam.

**канал** *m.* channel, canal, conduit, passage; (anat.) duct; bore (of gun);

channel (of nuclear reactor); **боковой к., побочный к.** side drain.

**канализационн/ый** *a.* sewage, waste; canalization; **к. насос** sewage pump, drain pump; **—ая вода** sewage, waste water; **—ая сеть** sewer system; **—ая труба** sewage pipe, sewer; water pipe, gas pipe or electric conduit; **—ые газы** sewer gases.

**канализ/ация** *f.* canalization; channeling; sewer system, sewerage, drainage, drain system; **—ировать** *v.* canalize; provide with a sewer system.

**канал/овый, —ьный** *a.* channel, canal; **к. эффект** (nucl.) channeling effect; **—ьная сажа** channel black; **—овые лучи** canal rays, positive rays; **—ьчатый** *a.* channeled, grooved; tubular.

**кананговое масло** cananga oil.

**канап** *see* **кенаф.**

**канар** *m.* bale of wool; harvesting sack.

**канар/еечник** *m.,* **—еечная трава** canary grass (*Phalaris*); **—еечниковые** *pl.* Phalarideae; **—еечный** *a.* canary, canary-colored; **—ейка** *f.* (zool.) canary.

**канат** *m.* cable, rope; **—ик** *m.* (anat.) funiculus, cord.

**канатник** *m.* (bot.) Chinese bell flower (*Abutilon avicennae*).

**канатно—** *see* **канато—; —башенный, —скребковый** *a.* drag-line (excavator).

**канатн/ый** *a.* cable, rope; funicular (railway, etc.); **к. привод, —ая передача** rope drive; **—ая дорога** cableway; **—ые изделия** cordage.

**канато/крутильная машина** rope-twisting machine; **—нажиматель** *m.* rope tightener; **—натягивающий** *a.* rope-tightening; **—скребковый** drag-line (excavator); **—тростильная дорожка** ropewalk.

**канатчик** *m.* ropemaker.

**канаус** *m.* (text.) taffeta.

**канва** *f.* canvas; outline, groundwork.

**канга** *f.* (petr.) canga (an iron breccia).

**кандалы** *pl.* shackles, fetters, handcuffs.

**канделил/ьский воск, воск —а** candelilla wax, gama wax.

**канделябр** *m.* candelabrum; chandelier, branched fixture.

**кандидат** *m.,* **—ский** *a.* candidate, applicant; Master (actually closer to a Doctor's degree).

**кандидулин** *m.* candidulin.

**кандык** *m.* (bot.) dog's tooth violet (*Erythronium dens-canis*).

**канегра** *f.* (bot.) tanner's dock (*Rumex hymenosepalus*).

**каникулы** *pl.* vacation, holidays.

**каниловый спирт** kanyl alcohol.

**канирин** *m.* kanirin, trimethylamine oxide.

**канистра** *f.* (oil) tank.

**канитель** *f.* gold thread, bullion, bullion fringe; long-drawn-out proceedings.

**канифас** *m.* (text.) dimity.

**канифоль** *f.,* **—ный** *a.* colophony, rosin.

**Каниццаро** *see* **Канниццаро.**

**канкринит** *m.* (min.) cancrinite.

**канкроид** *m.* (med.) cancroid.

**канна** *f.* (bot.) canna; **съедобная к.** Queensland arrowroot (*Canna edulis*).

**каннаб/ин** *m.* cannabine (alkaloid); cannabin (glucoside or resin); **—инол** *m.* cannabinol; **—оид** *m.* cannaboid.

**каннелюра** *f.* (architecture) flute.

**каннибальство** *n.* cannibalism.

**Канниццаро реакция** Cannizzaro reaction.

**каннов/ые** *pl.* (bot.) Cannaceae; **—ый** *a.* canna, cannaceous.

**канон/ерка** *f.* gunboat; **—ир** *m.* cannoneer, gunner; **—ит** *m.* (expl.) cannonite.

**канонический** *a.* (math.) canonical, standard.

**кант** *m.* edge, edging, border.

**канталупа** *f.* cantaloup, muskmelon.

**канталь** *m.* an iron-chromium-base heat-resistant alloy.

**кантар/ен** *m.* cantharene, dihydro-*o*-xylene; **—ид** *m.* Spanish fly (*Cantharis vesicatoria*); **—идин** *m.* cantharidin, lactone of cantharidic acid; **—идиновая кислота** cantharidic acid; **соль —идиновой кислоты, —идиновокислая соль** cantharidate; **—овая кислота** cantharic acid.

**кантарь** *see* **контарь.**

**кантовальн/ый** *a.* cant, canting, tilting; **к. аппарат, —ое устройство** tilter, turn-over device; **—ая пила** bevel saw.

**кантов/ание** *n.,* **—ка** *f.* canting, tilting;

beveling; (rolling) turning, manipulation; —атель *m.* tilter; manipulator; —ать *v.* cant, tilt; bevel, edge; —очный *a.* canting, tilting; beveling, edging; —очное приспособление beveling tool.

кантонит *m.* (min.) cantonite (a variety of covellite).

кануть *v.* disappear, drop.

канфильдит *m.* (min.) canfieldite (a silver and tin sulfide).

канфорка *f.* chafing dish.

канцеляр/ист *m.* clerk; —ия *f.* office; —ский *a.* office, clerical; —ские принадлежности stationery; —щина *f.* red tape, bureaucracy.

канцер *m.* (med.) cancer; —огенный *a.* carcinogenic, cancer-producing.

канцлер *m.*, —ский *a.* chancellor.

каныга *f.* (zool.) stomach contents.

каньон *m.* canyon.

канюля *f.* (med.) cannula.

каолин *m.*, —овый *a.* (min.) kaolin, China clay, porcelain clay; —изация *f.* kaolinization; —изированный *a.* kaolinized; —изировать, —изовать *v.* kaolinize; —ит *m.* kaolinite, kaolin.

кап *m.* knot in lumber; burl.

капа *f.* sealed end.

кап/ание *n.* dropping, dripping, trickle; —ать *v.* drop, drip, trickle, trickle off in drops; —ающий *a.* dripping; —еж *m.* drip.

капелина *f.* (med.) cupel.

капел/ирование *n.*, —яция *f.* cupellation (for silver and gold recovery); —ированный *a.* cupeled; —ировать *v.* cupel; —яционный *a.* cupellation, cupel; —яционный костяной порошок cupel dust, bone ash; —яционная печь cupel furnace, cupeling furnace, cupel.

капель *f.* dripping, trickling; (met.) cupel; —ка *f.* droplet; —ник *m.*, —ница *f.* (eye) dropper, dropping glass, dropping tube, dropping bottle; pipet; dripcock; (geol.) dropstone, stalactite; —но-жидкий *a.* sufficiently liquid to form drops.

капель/ный, —чатый *a.* drop, dropping, trickling; liquid-drop (model of nucleus); к. кран dripcock; к. электрод drop electrode; —ная воронка dropping funnel; —ная проба, —ное испытание drop test, spot test; —ная смазка drip lubrication.

капеля *f.* (met.) cupel.

капер/атовая кислота caperatic acid; —идин *m.* caperidin; —сник *m.*, —совый кустарник (bot.) caper (*Capparis spinosa*); —сы, —цы *pl.* capers.

капилляр *m.* capillary; —ность *f.* capillarity, capillary attraction; —ный *a.* capillary; —ный подъем capillary rise; —ная трубка capillary tube, capillary; —ное притяжение capillary attraction; —ное расслаивание pore filling.

капитал *m.* capital, stock, fund; основной к. stock capital, stock; —ист *m.* capitalist; —овложение *n.* investment.

капитальн/ый *a.* capital; chief, principal; thorough, fundamental, substantial; к. ремонт overhauling; —ое вложение, —ые затраты investment, outlay.

капитан *m.* captain.

капитель *f.* capital, head (of column).

капитулировать *v.* capitulate, give up.

капишон *see* капюшон.

капкан *m.* trap.

капле/защищенный, —стойкий, —упорный *a.* drip-proof; —образный *a.* drip-shaped, drop, dropwise; точка —падения drop point; —собиратель *m.* drip pan, drip cup, gutter; —указатель *m.* sight glass.

каплун *m.* capon; —ировать *v.* capon, castrate.

капля *f.* drop; —ми, по —м drop by drop.

капно/метрия *f.* capnometry; —скоп *m.* capnoscope, smoke gage.

капнуть *see* капать.

капок *m.*, —овый *a.* kapok (fibers).

капорцы *see* каперсы.

капот *m.* hood (of automobile); housing; cupola; —ировать *v.* nose over.

Каппа линии (elec.) Kapp lines.

капра/ровая кислота capraric acid; —т *m.* caprate.

капремонт *m.* overhauling.

**капризный** *a.* capricious, freakish.

**каприл** *m.*, —**овый** *a.* capryl, hexyl; —**ат** *m.*, —**овокислая соль** caprylate; —**ен** *m.* caprylene, octene; —**иден** *m.* caprylidene, 1-octyne; —**ин** *m.* caprylin; —**овая кислота** caprylic acid, octanoic acid; **соль** —**овой кислоты** caprylate; —**овый альдегид** caprylic aldehyde, octanal; —**овый спирт** capryl alcohol, hexyl alcohol.

**каприн** *m.* caprin; caprine, norleucine; —**овая кислота** capric acid, *n*-decanoic acid; **соль** —**овой кислоты**, —**овокислая соль** caprate; —**овоизоамиловый эфир** isoamyl caprate; —**овокислый** *a.* capric acid; caprate (of); —**овый альдегид** capric aldehyde, capraldehyde, decanal.

**капририл** *m.* capryryl, octanoyl.

**капро/ат** *m.* caproate; —**ил** *m.* caproyl; —**иловый спирт** caproyl alcohol, octyl alcohol; —**ин** *m.* caproin.

**капрок** *m.* (geol.) cap rock.

**капрон** *m.*, —**овый** *a.* caprone, 6-hendecanone; capron (Soviet name for polycaprolactam resin and fiber); —**ил** *m.*, —**иловый** *a.* capronyl; **хлористый** —**ил** capronyl chloride; —**овая кислота** caproic acid, hexanoic acid; **соль** —**овой кислоты**, —**овокислая соль** caproate; —**овое волокно** (polycaprolactam fiber); —**овокислый** *a.* caproic acid; caproate (of); —**овооктиловый эфир** octyl caproate; —**овый альдегид** caproic aldehyde, caproaldehyde, hexanal.

**капс/аицин** *m.* capsaicin; —**антин** *m.* capsanthin; —**антол** *m.* capsanthol.

**капсель** *m.* (cer.) sagger.

**капсельный двигатель** enclosed motor, shield-type motor; **к. насос** rotary pump.

**капси/кол** *m.* capsicol; —**кутин** *m.* capsicutin; —**цин** *m.* capsicine (alkaloid); capsicin (oleoresin).

**капсул/а** *f.* capsule; **заключение в** —**ю** encapsulation.

**капсул/арин** *m.* capsularin; —**есциновая кислота** capsulaescinic acid.

**капсульный** *a. of* капсула.

**капсюл/ь** *m.* percussion cap, priming cap, cap, cartridge primer; —**ьный** *a.*

**capsule**; percussion cap, cap; enclosed (motor); —**я** *see* капсула.

**каптаж** *m.* capture; piping (of water supply); harnessing (of river); capping (of well).

**каптакс** *m.* Captax (a mercaptobenzothiazole rubber accelerator).

**каптировать** *v.* capture, catch, collect; pipe (water or oil).

**каптол** *m.* captol, chloral tannin.

**капуст/а** *f.*, —**ный** *a.* (bot.) cabbage (*Brassica oleracea*); **квашенная к.**, **кислая к.** sauerkraut; **кочанная к.** (head) cabbage (*Brassica oleracea capitata*); **красная к.** red cabbage (*B. o. rubra*); **кудрявая к.** savoy (*B. o. bullata*); **лиственная к.** kale (*Brassica acephala*); **морская к.**, **черная к.** *see* катран; **цветная к.** cauliflower (*B. o. botrytis*); —**ница** *f.*, —**ная белянка** cabbage butterfly.

**капут-мортум** *m.* caput mortuum, colcothar.

**Капштадт** Cape Town.

**капюшон** *m.* hood, cowl; —**ообразный** *a.* hooded, cowled.

**карабин** *m.*, —**ный** *a.* carbine, rifle; snap hook; —**ный крючок** swivel.

**каравай** *m.* loaf; (rubber) cake.

**караван** *m.*, —**ный** *a.* caravan.

**карагач** *m.* (bot.) elm (*Ulmus*).

**карадокский ярус** (geol.) Caradocian stage.

**карадрина** *f.* (zool.) cutworm moth (*Laphygma exigua*).

**Караибское море** Carribean Sea.

**каракатица** *f.* (zool.) cuttlefish.

**караковый** *a.* dark bay, brown.

**каракуль** *m.* astrakhan (fur); karakul (sheep); —**ча** *f.* Persian lamb.

**карамелан** *m.* caramelan.

**карамелиз/ирование**, —**ование** *n.* caramelization, burning, charring (of sugar); —**ированный**, —**ованный** *a.* caramelized, burned, charred; —**ировать**, —**овать** *v.* caramelize, burn, char.

**карамель** *f.* caramel, burnt sugar.

**каран** *m.* carane.

**карандаш** *m.*, —**ный** *a.* pencil, crayon; —**еобразный** *a.* pencil-shaped.

**каранеол** *m.* caraneol, carol.

**каранская камедь** carana, gum carana.

карантин *m.*, —ный *a.* quarantine; —ное свидетельство bill of health.

караповое масло karapa oil.

карапузики *pl.* black beetles (*Histeridae*).

карасик *m.* cross file; (foundry) sleeker, smoother.

карат *m.*, —ный *a.* carat (unit of weight).

каратуз *m.* karatuz (common salt from the bottom of salt lakes).

карать *v.* punish, penalize.

караул *m.* watch, guard.

карб— *prefix* carb—, carbo—.

карбаз/ид *m.* carbazide; —ил *m.* carbazyl; —иловая кислота carbazylic acid; —иновая кислота carbazic acid; —ол *m.*, —оловый *a.* carbazole, diphenylenimide; —он *m.* carbazone.

карбам/ат *m.*, —инат *m.* carbamate, carbaminate; —ид *m.*, —идный *a.* carbamide (urea); —ил *m.*, —иловый *a.* carbamyl; —иловый эфир carbamilic ether, phenylurethan.

карбамино/вая кислота carbamic acid, aminoformic acid; соль —вой кислоты, —вокислая соль carbamate; —воаммониевая соль, —вокислый аммоний ammonium carbamate; —вокислый *a.* carbamic acid; carbamate (of); —воэтиловый эфир, —этиловый эфир ethyl carbamate, urethan.

карбамит *m.* carbamite (a rocket-fuel stabilizer).

карбанил *m.* carbanil, phenyl cyanate; —ид *m.* carbanilide, diphenylurea; —о— *prefix* carbanilo—; —овая кислота carbanilic acid, phenylcarbamic acid.

карбид *m.*, —ный, —овый *a.* carbide; к. кальция calcium carbide; —ка *f.* (min.) acetylene lamp; —ная печь carbide furnace; —ный генератор carbide generator (for acetylene); —ообразующий *a.* carbide-forming.

карб/иламин *m.* carbylamine, isocyanide; —иловая кислота carbylic acid; —инол *m.* carbinol, primary alcohol; methanol; —итол *m.* Carbitol, diethyleneglycol ethyl ether.

карбо— *prefix* carbo—; —бензоил *m.* carbobenzoyl; —вальт, —вольт *m.*

Carbowalt (abrasive); —ген *m.* (med.) oxygen with admixture of carbon dioxide; —ид *m.* carboid (a graphite mixture).

карбокси— *prefix* carboxy—, carboxyl; —л *m.*, —льная группа carboxyl; —лаза *f.* carboxylase, (an enzyme); —льный *a.* carboxyl, carboxylic; —льная кислота carboxylic acid.

карбол/инеум *m.* Carbolineum (a wood preservative); —ит *m.* carbolite (a carbide abrasive); carbolite (resin); —ка *f.*, —овая кислота carbolic acid, phenol; —овый *a.* carbolic, phenolic, phenic; —овая вода carbolic acid water, phenolated water; —овое масло carbolic oil; —ой *m.* (met.) Carboloy (cemented tungsten carbide); —он *m.* Carbolon (silicon carbide abrasive).

карбометокси— *prefix* carbomethoxy—.

карбо/метр *m.* carbometer (for carbon dioxide determination) —мицин *m.* carbomycin; —н *m.* carbon; (geol.) Carboniferous (period); —надо *n.* carbonado, black diamond.

карбонат *m.* carbonate; к. аммония ammonium carbonate; —ит *m.* (petr.) carbonatite; —ный, —овый *a.* carbonate; carbonaceous; calcareous (soil).

карбониз/атор *m.* carbonizer; —ация *f.*, —ационный *a.*, —ирование, —ование *n.* carbonization, carbonation; (met.) carburization; —ированный, —ованный *a.* carbonized; carburized; —ировать, —овать *v.* carbonize; carburize.

карбонил *m.*, —ьный *a.* carbonyl; сернистый к. carbonyl sulfide, carbon oxysulfide; хлористый к. carbonyl chloride, phosgene.

карбонит *m.* (expl.) carbonite.

карбонов/ый *a.* (geol.) carbonaceous, carbon-containing; carboniferous; —ая кислота, —окислый *a.* carboxylic acid.

карбоно/лит *m.* carbonolite, carbonaceous rocks; —мерт *m.* carbonometer.

карборунд, —ум *m.*, —овый *a.* carborundum, silicon carbide.

карбо/фос *m.* a Malathion insecticide;

—холин *m.* carbocholine, carbamyl-choline chloride; —цериновая кислота carboceric acid; —цианин *m.* (phot.) carbocyanine; —циклический *a.* carbocyclic (compound).

карбункул *m.* (min., med.) carbuncle.

карбур— *see* карбюр—; —ан *m.* (min.) carburan (near thucholite).

карбэтокси— *prefix* carbethoxy—.

карбюр/атор *m.*, —аторный *a.* carburetor; —ация *f.*, —изация *f.*, —ирование *n.* carburation, carburetion; (met.) carburization, carburizing; —изатор *m.* carbonizer; carburizing agent; —ированный *a.* carbureted; carburized; —ировать *v.* carburet; carburize.

карв/акрил *m.* carvacryl; —акрол *m.* carvacrol, 2-hydroxy-*p*-cymene; —ен *m.* carvene, *d*-limonene; —енон *m.* carvenone; —еол *m.* carveol, 2-hydroxylimonene; —естрен *m.* carvestrene, 1-*m*-terpene; —естрол *m.* carvestrol, 1-*m*-menthenol; —ил *m.* carvyl; —оксим *m.* carvoxime; —ол, —он *m.* carvol, carvone; —оментил *m.* carvomenthyl; —оментол *m.* carvomenthol, 2-*p*-menthanol.

карда *f.* (text.) card, card clothing.

кардамон *m.*, —ный, —овый *a.* (bot.) cardamom (*Ellettaria cardamomum*); гвинейский к. Guinea grains.

кардан *m.*, шарнир Кардана, —ный шарнир, —ная подвеска Cardan joint, universal joint; —ный вал, —ная передача Cardan shaft, propeller shaft.

кардиазол *m.* Cardiazol, pentamethylenetetrazol.

кардинальный *a.* cardinal, chief, principal.

кардио— *prefix* cardio— (heart); —грамма *f.* (med.) cardiogram; —граф *m.* cardiograph; —ида *f.* (math.) cardioid; —идный *a.* cardioid, heart-shaped; —идный кулак (horol.) heart cam, heart piece; —логия *f.* cardiology.

кардит *m.* (med.) carditis.

кард/машина, —ная машина *see* кардомашина; —ный *a.* (text.) card; —ный очес card waste; —ный холст, —ная лента card clothing.

кардобенедикт *m.* (bot.) blessed thistle (*Cnicus benedictus*).

кардов/ание *n.* (text.) carding; —ать *v.* card.

кардол, —ь *m.* cardol.

кардо/лента *f.* (text.) card clothing; —машина *f.*, —чесальная машина carding machine, carder; —наборная машина card-setting machine; —питатель *m.* card filler; —чесание *n.* carding; —чесанный *a.* carded.

Кардью вольтметр Cardew voltmeter.

карен *m.* carene.

карет/а *f.*, —ный *a.* carriage, coach; —ка *f.* carrier, carriage (of machine); (drilling) rig.

кариатур *see* калиатур.

кариес *see* кариоз.

кариин *m.* caryin.

кариинит *m.* (min.) caryinite.

карий *a.* hazel, brown.

карикатура *f.* caricature.

карил *m.* caryl.

карио— *prefix* (biol.) karyo—, caryo— (nucleus of cell).

кариоз *m.* (med.) caries; —ный *a.* carious.

кариокинез *m.* (biol.) karyokinesis, mitosis.

кариофилл/ен *m.* caryophyllene, light clove oil; —ин *m.* caryophyllin; —иновая кислота caryophyllinic acid.

кариоцит *m.* (physiol.) karyocyte, normoblast.

Кариуса метод Carius' (analysis) method.

карицин *m.* caricin.

кария *f.* (bot.) hickory (*Carya*).

каркамель *see* куркума.

каркас *m.* skeleton, frame, framework, chassis; body, form, shell, hull, housing, casing; carcass (of tire); (bot.) hackberry (*Celtis*).

каркать *v.* croak, caw.

карлик *m.* dwarf, pygmy; —овость *f.* dwarf state, stunted condition; —овый *a.* dwarf, dwarfish, stunted, diminutive.

карлсбадская соль Carlsbad salt.

кармазин *m.*, —ный, —овый *a.* crimson, scarlet; —овая краска crimson dye;

—овокрасный *a.* crimson, crimson red.

карма/н *m.*, —нный *a.* pocket; housing, container; —нный фонарь flashlight; —нная камера pocket (ionization) chamber; —шек *m.* (bot.) pocket; —шки сливы plum pockets (fungus disease).

кармелитов/ая вода, —ый спирт carmelite (toilet) water.

кармин *m.* carmine, coccinellin; —ный, —овый *a.* carmine, crimson; —овая кислота carminic acid, cochinilin; соль —овой кислоты, —овокислая соль carminate; —овокрасный *a.* carmine red; —овый шпат (min.) carmine spar, carminite; —охинон *m.* carminoquinone.

кармоизин *m.* carmoisin (food dye).

карналлит *m.* (min.) carnallite.

карнатур *see* калиатур.

карнауб/а *f.* (bot.) Brazilian wax palm (*Copernicia cerifera*); —иловый спирт carnaubyl alcohol; —овая кислота, —ская кислота carnaubic acid; —ский воск carnauba wax, Brazil wax.

карне/гиит *m.* (min.) carnegieite; —ол *see* сердолик; —олютесцин *m.* carneolutescin.

карниз *m.* cornice; (geol.) bench.

карнийский век (geol.) Carnian stage.

карнин *m.* carnine.

карнитин *m.* carnitine, novain.

Карно функция Carnot's function; К. цикл, К. круговой процесс Carnot's cycle.

карно/зин *m.* carnosine, alanylhistidine; —мускарин *m.* carnomuscarine; —тин, —тит *m.* (min.) carnotite.

кароб/ин *m.* carobine; —овая кислота carobic acid.

каровое озеро tarn, bog, fen.

Карозерс Carothers (name).

карол *m.* carol, 5-hydroxycarane; —иновая кислота carolinic acid; —овая кислота carolic acid.

карон *m.* carone, 5-ketocarane; —овая кислота caronic acid.

каротаж *m.*, —ный *a.* (mineral exploration) well logging, logging, coring; log.

каротин *m.*, —овый *a.* carotene, pri-

mary vitamin A; —оид *m.* carotinoid, polyene.

каротировать *v.* (mineral exploration) log.

кароттаж *see* каротаж.

карп *m.* carp (fish).

карп/аин *m.* carpaine; —амовая кислота carpamic acid.

карпо— *prefix* (biol.) carpo— (fruit); (anat.) carpo— (carpus, carpal).

карповый *a.* carp (fish).

карр *m.* sink hole.

Карра долото Carr bit.

карраген *see* ирландский мох.

каррарский мрамор Carrara marble.

карри *n.* karri (timber).

карролит *m.* (min.) carrollite (a variety of linnaeite).

карсель *m.* carcel unit (9.6 candles); —ская лампа Carcel lamp.

карст *m.* (geol.) karst.

карстенит *m.* (min.) karstenite, anhydrite.

карстовая воронка sink hole; к. пустота cavern.

карт/а *f.* card; map, chart; ставить на —у *v.* hazard, stake; чертить —у *v.* map, plot, chart.

картам/еин *m.* carthamein; —ин *m.*, —овая кислота carthamin, carthamic acid; —ова трава (bot.) safflower (*Carthamus tinctorius*).

картезианск/ий *a.* Cartesian; к. водолаз (phys.) Cartesian devil; к. порошок (min.) Carthusian powder, kermes mineral; —ие координаты (math.) Cartesian coordinates.

картель *f.* cartel; syndicate, trust.

картер *m.* crankcase, gear case; housing.

картеч/ь *f.*, —ный *a.* case shot, buckshot.

картин/а *f.* picture; figure; image; (diffraction, etc.) pattern; —ка *f.* picture, illustration; —ный *a.* picture, pictorial, picturesque.

картиров/ание *n.* mapping, mapping out; —ать *v.* map out.

картограф/ический *a.* cartographic; —ия *f.* cartography, mapping.

картон *m.*, —ный *a.* cardboard, carton, pasteboard, millboard, board; прессовый к. pressboard; —аж *m.* cardboard, cardboard boxes; —ажная

**фабрика** carton factory; **—ка** *f.* cardboard box, (paper) carton; piece of cardboard or composition board.

**картотека** *f.* card index, card catalog.

**картофеле/водство** *n.* potato growing; **—копалка** *f.*, **—копатель** *m.* potato digger; **—сажалка** *f.* potato planter; **—хранилище** *n.* potato cellar.

**картофель** *m.*, **—ный** *a.* (bot.) potato (*Solanum tuberosum*); **—ный жук** Colorado potato beetle; **—ное пюре** mashed potatoes.

**карточ/ка** *f.*, **—ный** *a.* card, index card.

**картошка** *see* **картофель.**

**картуз** *m.*, **—ный** *a.* (paper) bag, sack; cap, cartridge; pocket, pouch; **—ная бумага** wrapping paper.

**карус** *m.* (bot.) carex.

**карусельн/о-токарный станок, —ый станок** vertical boring and turning machine, boring and turning lathe; **—ый** *a.* rotary, revolving; turret-type; rotary-drum (dryer); rotary-hearth (furnace).

**Карфаген** Carthage.

**карфо/лит** *m.* (min.) carpholite; **—сидерит** *m.* carphosiderite.

**карциноген** *m.*, **—ное вещество** (med.) carcinogen; **—ез** *m.* carcinogenesis; **—ный** *a.* carcinogenic, cancer-producing.

**карцинома** *f.* carcinoma (a form of cancer).

**карьер** *m.*, **—ный** *a.* (min.) pit, open pit, open-cut mine, quarry; career; **во весь к.** at full speed; **разработка —ами** open-cut mining; **—а** *f.* career.

**касан/ие** *n.* (math.) contact, tangency; **линия —ия** line of contact, tangent; **поверхность —ия** contact surface; **точка —ия** point of contact.

**касательн/ая** *f.*, **—ая линия** (geom.) tangent; **по —ой** tangentially; **—о** *prep. gen.* about, touching (upon), concerning, relative (to); **—ость** *f.* relation, connection; **—ый** *a.* concerning, touching; tangent, tangential.

**касатик** *m.* (bot.) iris; **—овые** *pl.* Iridaceae.

**кас/аться** *v.* concern, touch (upon), deal (with), relate (to), regard, have respect (to), affect; touch, be in contact (with); **что —ается** as concerns, as regards, regarding, as to, as for; **—ающийся** *a.* concerning, touching (upon); tangent.

**каска** *f.* helmet.

**каскад** *m.* cascade; step, stage; **—но** *adv.* (elec.) in cascade; **—ный ливень, —ная лавина** cascade shower (of cosmic rays); **—ное соединение** cascade connection.

**каскар/а** *f.* cascara (bark of *Picramnia antidesma*); **к. амарга** cascara amarga; **к. саграда** cascara sagrada (bark of *Rhamnus purshiana*); **—илла** *f.*, **кора —иллы** cascarilla (bark of *Croton eluteria*); **—иллин** *m.* cascarilline; **—илловая кислота** cascarillic acid; **—ин** *m.* cascarin.

**Каспийское море** Caspian Sea.

**касса** *f.* cash, cash box, money drawer, cash register; (typ.) case; (savings) bank.

**кассава** *f.* cassava, manioca starch; **горькая к.** (bot.) bitter cassava (*Manihot utilissima*); **сладкая к.** sweet cassava (*Manihot aipi*).

**кассевая кислота** cassic acid, rhein.

**кассельская бурая краска** Cassel brown (pigment); **к. желтая** Cassel yellow (a form of lead oxychloride); **к. печь** (cer.) potter's kiln, pottery kiln.

**кассет/а** *f.* adapter; (phot.) film holder, cartridge, cassette; cell (of bomb); **—ка** *f.* box.

**кассиев пурпур** Cassius' purple, gold-tin purple; **—ый** *a.* Cassia; **—ое масло** Cassia oil, cinnamon oil.

**кассиопий** *m.* cassiopeium (lutecium).

**кассир** *m.* cashier; **—овать** *v.* annul, reverse, void; collect (coins).

**касситерит** *m.* (min.) cassiterite, tin oxide.

**кассия** *f.* (bot.) cassia; **стручковая к.** purging cassia (*Cassia fistula*).

**кассов/ый** *a.* cash; account (book); **—ая наличность** cash (money).

**кастанит** *m.* (min.) castanite.

**кастел/агенин** *m.* castelagenin; **—амарин** *m.* castelamarin; **—ин** *m.* castelin.

**каст/ин** *m.* castine; **—онин** *m.* castonin.

**кастор** *m.* (min.) castor, castorite (a crystalline variety of petalite); castor (woolen cloth); —**еум** *m.* (pharm.) castoreum, castor; —**ин** *m.* castorin; —**ка** *f.*, —**овое масло** castor oil, ricinus oil; —**овый** *a.* castor, castoric; —**овая кислота** castoric acid; **соль** —**овой кислоты,** —**овокислая соль** castorate.

**кастр/ация** *f.* castration; —**ировать** *v.* castrate, geld.

**кастрюля** *f.* pot, kettle, pan.

**ката** *f.* (bot.) khat (*Catha edulis*).

**ката**— *prefix* cata—; —**батический** *a.* (meteor.) catabatic; —**биотическая сила** (biol.) catabiotic force; —**болизм** *m.* catabolism, destructive metabolism.

**катавотр** *m.* (geol.) swallow hole, sink, sink hole.

**ката/генез** *m.* (zool.) catagenesis, retrogressive evolution; —**кластический** *a.* (geol.) cataclastic.

**катакомбы** *pl.* catacombs.

**катала́з/а** *f.* catalase (oxidizing enzyme); —**ометр** *m.* catalasometer.

**каталанский** *see* **каталонский.**

**катале́п/сия** *f.* (med.) catalepsy; —**тический** *a.* cataleptic.

**катализ** *m.* catalysis; —**ат** *m.* catalyzate, product of catalysis; —**атор** *m.* catalyzer, catalyst, catalytic agent; —**овать** *v.* catalyze.

**каталитическ/и** *adv.* catalytically, by catalysis; —**ий** *a.* catalytic; —**ий способ** catalytic process, contact process.

**каталич.** *abbr.* (**каталитический**).

**катало/г** *m.*, —**жный** *a.* catalog, booklet; —**гизировать** *v.* catalog, classify.

**каталонск/ий горн, к. сыродутный горн,** —**ая кузница** (met.) Catalan forge, bloomery (for iron ores); **к. сыродутный процесс** Catalan forge process.

**катальщик** *m.* roller; (clothes) mangler; fuller.

**катаморф/изм** *m.* (geol.) katamorphism; —**ный** *a.* katamorphic.

**катан/ие,** —**ье** *n.* rolling; (text.) mangling; wheeling; driving, riding; —**ка** *f.* wire rod, rolled wire; —**ый** *a.* rolled.

**катаплазма** *f.* (med.) cataplasm, poultice.

**катапульта** *f.* catapult.

**катар** *m.* (med.) catarrh; **к. желудка** gastritis.

**катаракт** *m.*, —**ный** *a.* cataract, waterfall; cataract (hydraulic brake); damper, shock absorber, dashpot; —**а** *f.* (med.) cataract.

**катар/альный** *a.* (med.) catarrhal; —**р** *see* **катар.**

**катарт/ин** *m.* cathartin; —**иновая кислота** cathartic acid; —**ический** *a.*, —**ическое средство** cathartic.

**катастроф/а** *f.* catastrophe, disaster; —**ический** *a.* catastrophic, disastrous.

**кататермометр** *m.* catathermometer.

**катать** *v.* roll; (text.) mangle; wheel, convey, drive.

**катафорез** *m.* (elec.) cataphoresis.

**катгин** *m.* cathine.

**категор/ический** *a.* categorical; —**ия** *f.* category, class.

**катен/арный** *a.* (math.) catenary; —**оид** *m.* catenoid.

**катер** *m.* launch, cutter.

**катет** *m.* (geom.) leg (of right triangle).

**катетер** *m.* (med.) catheter.

**катетометр** *m.* (phys.) cathetometer.

**катех/ин** *m.*, —**иновая кислота** catechin, catechuic acid; —**ол** *m.* catechol, catechin; pyrocatechol; —**у** *n.* catechu, black catechu; —**у-пальма** *f.* catechu palm (*Areca catechu*); **желтое** —**у, кубическое** —**у** gambier.

**катин** *m.* catine.

**катион** *m.* cation, positively charged ion; —**ит** *m.* cation exchanger, cation-exchange resin; —**ный** *a.* cation, cationic; —**ообменник** *m.* cation exchanger; —**ообменный** *a.* cation-exchange.

**катить** *v.* roll, wheel.

**катоген/ический,** —**ный** *a.* (geol.) katogene.

**катод** *m.* cathode, negative electrode; —**нолучевой** *a.* cathode-ray; —**нолучевая трубка** cathode-ray tube, CRT; —**ный** *a.* cathode, cathodic; —**ное восстановление** cathodic reduction; —**ное покрытие** cathodic deposition, cathodic coating; —**ные лучи** cathode rays.

**каток** *m.* roller, roll.

**католит** *m.* (electrolysis) catholyte.

**катон** *m.* kathon (herbicide).

**катоптри/ка** *f.* (optics) catoptrics; **—т** *m.* (min.) catoptrite; **—ческий** *a.* catoptric.

**катофорит** *m.* (min.) katophorite.

**каточек** *m.* block.

**катран** *m.* (bot.) sea kale (*Crambe*, spec. *C. maritima*).

**катун** *m.* (bot.) saltwort (*Salsola collina*).

**катучий** *a.* rolling; **к. кран** traveling crane.

**катуш/ка** *f.*, **—ечный** *a.* spool, bobbin, reel, roll; (elec.) coil; (zool.) planorbis; **—кодержатель** *m.* coil holder.

**катыш/ек**, **—ок** *m.* pellet.

**катюша** *f.* (mil.) katusha (a rocket gun similar to the American bazooka).

**катэху** *see* **катеху.**

**катящийся** *a.* rolling; roller (contact).

**каудальный** *a.* caudal, tail.

**каузальный** *a.* causal.

**кауло/сапонин** *m.* caulosaponin, leontin; **—филлин** *m.* caulophyllin; caulophylline (alkaloid from *Caulophyllum thalictroides*); **—филлоид** *m.* caulophylloid.

**Каул/са печь**, **—ься печь** (elec.) Cowles furnace (for aluminum).

**каупер** *m.*, **Каупера нагреватель** (met.) Cowper stove, hot-blast stove.

**каупрен** *m.* cauprene.

**каур/и** *n.* kauri, kauri gum, kauri resin; **—иновая кислота** kaurinic acid; **—оловая кислота** kaurolic acid.

**каурый** *a.* light chestnut (color).

**каусти/зация**, **—фикация** *f.*, **—цирование** *n.* causticization, causticizing; **—к** *m.* caustic; **—ка** *f.* (optics) caustic; *suffix* (med.) —cautery; **—цировать** *v.* causticize.

**каустич/еский** *a.* caustic; **к. поташ** caustic potash, potassium hydroxide; **—еская сода** caustic soda, sodium hydroxide; **—ность** *f.* causticity.

**каустобиолит** *m.* caustobiolith (organic accumulation such as oil shale, coal, petroleum).

**каутер** *m.* (med.) cautery (instrument).

**каучин** *m.* caoutchene (dipentene).

**каучук** *m.* caoutchouc, rubber, spec. raw rubber; **искусственный к.** synthetic rubber.

**каучуков/ый** *a.* rubber; **к. сок**, **—ое молоко** rubber latex; **—ая замазка** rubber cement; **—ая лента** rubber band; **—ая трубка** rubber tubing, rubber hose; **—ое дерево** (bot.) rubber tree.

**каучуконос** *m.* (bot.) rubber plant, rubber-yielding plant; **—ный** *a.* rubber-bearing; **—ное дерево** rubber tree.

**каучуко/образный**, **—подобный** *a.* rubbery, gum-like, gummy.

**кафедра** *f.* desk; (professorship) chair; university department.

**каф/ель**, **—ля** *f.*, **—ельный** *a.* (Dutch) tile.

**кафирин** *m.* kafirin (a protein).

**кафф/аловая кислота** caffalic acid; **—еин** *see* **кофеин.**

**кахексия** *f.* (med.) cachexia.

**кахель** *see* **кафель.**

**кахолонг** *see* **кашолонг.**

**кач/алка** *f.* rocking device, rocker; **—ание** *n.* rocking, swinging, swaying, shaking, oscillation, vibration; fluctuation; pumping; **—ание насосом** pumping; **плоскость —ания** plane of vibration; **—ательно-сочлененный** *a.* hinged; **—ательный** *see* **качающийся**; **—ать** *v.* rock, swing, sway, shake, oscillate, vibrate; pump; **—аться** *v.* rock, swing, oscillate, fluctuate; shake, wobble.

**качающ/ийся** *a.* rocking, swinging, pendulum, oscillating, oscillatory; vibrating, vibratory; jigging, shaking; tipping, tilting; fluctuating; **к. вентилятор** pivoting fan, oscillating fan; **к. грохот** vibrating screen; **—аяся опора** pivot journal; **—аяся печь** tilting furnace; **—аяся рамка** rocker.

**каче/ли** *pl.*, **—ль** *f.* swing; **—ние** *see* **качка.**

**качественный** *a.* qualitative, high-grade, fine; observational (measurement); **к. анализ** qualitative analysis.

**качеств/о** *n.* quality, grade; character, property, nature; **в —е** as, in the capacity of; **повышение —а, улучшение —а** refinement, improvement.

**качивать** *see* **качать.**

**качим** *m.* (bot.) gypsophila.

**кач/ка** *f.* rolling, tossing; looseness, free play, freedom; **—нуть** *see* **качать.**

**качурит** *m.* a construction board.

**каша** *f.* cereal, gruel; paste, pulp.

**кашалот** *m.* (zool.) sperm whale; **—овая ворвань** spermaceti oil.

**кашель** *m.* cough.

**кашемир** *m.* (text.) cashmere.

**кашеобразный** *a.* pasty, viscous.

**кашица** *f.* gruel; paste, viscous mass, slurry; (paper) pulp; (pharm.) electuary, confection; **пищевая к.** (physiol.) chyme.

**кашля/ние** *n.* coughing, cough; **—нуть, —ть** *v.* cough.

**кашмирет** *m.* (text.) cashmere twill.

**кашолонг** *m.*, **—овый** *a.* (min.) cacholong (a variety of opal).

**каштан** *m.* (bot.) chestnut (*Castanea*); **конский к.** horse chestnut (*Aesculus hippocastanum*); **—овобурый** *a.* chestnut brown, chestnut; **—овый** *a.* chestnut; chestnut brown, nut brown.

**кашу** *see* **катеху; —дубильная кислота** catechutannic acid.

**каюта** *f.* cabin, stateroom.

**каяпут/ен** *m.* cajeputene, terpene; **—ное масло, —овое масло** cajeput oil; **—овое дерево** (bot.) cajuput tree (*Melaleuca leucadendron*).

**кв** *abbr.* (**киловольт**) kilovolt; **кв.** (**квадратный**) square; **КВ** *abbr.* (**коротковолновый**) short-wave; (**короткие волны**) short waves; (**коэффициент воспроизводства**) reproduction factor, conversion ratio; **ква** *abbr.* (**киловольт-ампер**) kilovolt-ampere.

**квадр** *m.* cut stone.

**квадрант** *m.*, **—ный** *a.* quadrant.

**квадрат** *m.* square; **возводить в к., возвышать в к.** *v.* (math.) square; **метр в —е** square meter; **обработка на к.** squaring; **—ический, —ичный** *a.* quadratic; **—но-гнездовой** *a.* square-cluster (planting); **—ность** *f.* squareness.

**квадратн/ый** *a.* square; quadratic; (cryst.) tetragonal; **к. корень** (math.) square root; **к. метр** square meter; **к. режим** turbulent flow; **—ое содержание** square area, area; **—ое среднее** root mean square; **—ое уравнение** (math.) quadratic equation; **—ое число** square, square number.

**квадрат/рикса** *f.* (math.) quadratrix;

**—ура** *f.*, **—урный** *a.* quadrature, squaring; square area, area; **—урный прилив** neap tide.

**квадрильон** *m.* quadrillion.

**квадрифидин** *m.* quadrifidin.

**квадруплекс** quadruplex.

**квадруполь** *m.*, **—ный** *a.* quadrupole.

**квази—** *prefix* quasi—; **—линейный** *a.* quasilinear; **—периодический** *a.* (math.) quasiperiodic; **—связанный** *a.* quasibound; **—стационарный** *a.* quasistationary, quasistable; **—упругий** *a.* quasi-elastic.

**квакер** *m.* Quaker.

**квалифи/кация** *f.* qualification; **—цированный** *a.* qualified, regular; skilled, trained; **—цированный труд** skilled labor; **—цировать** *v.* qualify; **—цирующий** *a.* qualifying.

**квант** *m.*, **—овый** *a.* (phys.) quantum (unit of energy); bit (of information); **к. действия** Planck's constant; **к. света** photon; **теория —ов** quantum theory; **—ика** *f.* (math.) quantic; **—ование** *n.* quantization; **—ованный** *a.* quantized; quantum; **—ованная орбита** quantum orbit; **—овать** *v.* quantize; **—овомеханический** *a.* quantum-mechanical; **—овохимический** *a.* quantum-chemical; **—овый выход** quantum yield.

**кварта** *f.* quart (unit of measure).

**квартал** *m.* quarter (of year); (city) block; section; **—ьный** *a.* quarterly; block.

**квартир/а** *f.*, **—ный** *a.* apartment, lodging, tenement, residence; **—ант** *m.* tenant, lodger; **—ный вопрос** housing problem; **—овать** *v.* reside, lodge, live; **—охозяин** *m.* landlord.

**кварто** *n.* quarto; **стан к.** four-high rolling mill.

**квартов/ание** *n.* quartation (assay of gold or silver ore); quartering (of bulk materials); **—ать** *v.* quarter.

**кварц** *m.* (min.) quartz; **натечный к.** siliceous sinter, fiorite (a variety of chalcedony and opal).

**кварцев/ый** *a.* quartz, quartzitic; **к. песок** quartz sand, silica sand; **к. сланец** (geol.) quartzose schist; **—ая жильная толща** (min.) quartz reef, quartz lode or vein; **—ая лампа**

quartz lamp, quartz mercury vapor lamp.

**кварц/еносный** *a.* (min.) quartziferous, quartzose; **—еподобный** *a.* quartz-like, quartzitic, quartz; **—ин** *m.* (min.) quartzine (a form of fibrous chalcedony); **—ит** *m.* quartzite, quartz rock, granular quartz; **—итовый** *a.* quarzitic, quartziferous, quartzose; **—итовый песчаник** quartz sandstone.

**квас** *m.*, **—ной** *a.* kvass (a fermented drink); **—ы** *pl.* tanner's ooze; **—ильный** *a.* fermentation; **—ить** *v.* make sour; leaven (dough); **—иться, —нуть** *v.* turn sour, ferment.

**квасс/иевая кислота** quassic acid; **—ин** *m.* quassin; **—ия** *f.* quassia, bitterwood.

**квасце/вание** *n.* aluming; tawing, tanning with alum; **—вар** *m.* alum boiler, alum maker; **—варня** *f.* alum works; **—вать** *see* квасцовать; **—носный** *a.* aluminous, aluminiferous; **—подобный** *a.* alum-like, aluminoform, aluminous.

**квасцов/анный** *a.* alumed, treated with alum; tanned with alum; **—ать** *v.* alum, treat with alum; tan with alum; **—ик** *m.* (min.) aluminite, websterite.

**квасцов/ый** *a.* alum, aluminous, aluminiferous; **к. завод** alum works; **к. камень, —ая руда** (min.) alumstone, alunite; **к. сланец, —ая глина** (geol.) alum shale; **—ая земля** alumina, aluminum oxide; **—ая мука** alum powder; alum, aluminum potassium sulfate.

**квасцы** *pl.* alum; **жженые к.** burnt alum, calcined aluminum potassium sulfate; **калиевые к., нейтральные к., обыкновенные к.** potash alum; **каменные к.** *see* **квасцовый камень; натриевые к.** soda alum; **перистые к.** (min.) feather alum, alunogen; **римские к.** Roman alum (aluminum iron sulfate).

**кватернион** *m.* (math.) quaternion.

**квач** *m.* swab.

**кваш/а** *f.* leaven, leavened dough; **—ение** *n.* fermentation; **—енный** *a.* leavened; sour, acid; **—ня** *f.* kneading trough.

**кв. дм** *abbr.* (квадратный дециметр) square decimeter; **кв. дм.** *abbr.* (квадратный дюйм) square inch.

**Квебек** Quebec.

**квебрах/амин** *m.* quebrachamine; **—ин** *m.* quebrachine; **—ит** *m.* quebrachite, quebrachitol, methoxypinite; **—о** *n.*, **—овый** *a.* (bot.) quebracho (*Aspidosperma*).

**квенстедтит** *m.* (min.) quenstedtite (probably a variety of copiapite).

**кверху** *adv.* up, upwards.

**кверцет/агетин** *m.* quercetagetin; **—ин** *m.*, **—иновая кислота** quercetin, quercetinic acid, flavin.

**кверци/метин, —трин** *m.*, **—триновая кислота** quercimetin, quercitrin, quercitrinic acid; **—н** *m.* quercin; **—т** *m.* quercitol, cyclohexanpentol; **—тин** *m.* quercitin.

**кверцитрон** *m.*, **к. кора** quercitron (bark); **—овый дуб** (bot.) quercitron, dyer's oak (*Quercus tinctoria*).

**квершлаг** *m.* (min.) crosscut.

**квеста** *f.* cuesta (sloping plain or ridge).

**кветенит** *m.* (min.) quetenite (probably a variety of botryogen).

**квил/аивая кислота, —иевая кислота, —лаивая кислота** quillaic acid; **—лая** *f.* quillaia, soap bark.

**квинкви—** *prefix* quinqui—, quinque—; **—льон** *m.* quinquillion.

**квинстоунит** *m.* (min.) queenstownite, Darwin glass.

**квинтал** *m.* quintal (unit of 100 kg.).

**квинтильон** *m.* quintillion.

**квинтуплекс** *m.* quintuplex; (oil-well drilling) quintuplex measuring and control instrument.

**квинтэссенция** *f.* quintessence.

**квисквеит** *m.* (min.) quisqueite.

**квит** *m.* (bot.) quince (*Cydonia*).

**квитанция** *f.* receipt, acknowledgment.

**квитовое дерево** *see* квит.

**кв. км** *abbr.* (квадратный километр) square kilometer; **кв. м** *abbr.* (квадратный метр) square meter; **кв. мм** *abbr.* (квадратный миллиметр) square millimeter.

**к-во** *abbr.* (количество) quantity.

**кворум** *m.* quorum.

**квота** *f.* (com.) quota.

**кв. см** *abbr.* (квадратный сантиметр) square centimeter.

**квт** *abbr.* (киловатт) kilowatt; **квт-ч** *abbr.* (киловатт-час) kilowatt-hour.

**кв. фт.** *abbr.* (квадратный фут) square foot.

**кг** *abbr.* (килограмм) kilogram; **кг-моль** *abbr.* (килограмм-молекула) kilogram-molecule; **кг/см²** *abbr.* (кг на квадратный сантиметр) kilograms per square centimeter; **кГ** *abbr.* (килограмм-сила) kilogram (force); **кГм** *abbr.* (килограмм-метр) kilogrammeter; **кГм/сек** *abbr.* (кГм в секунду) kilogrammeters per second.

**КГУ** *abbr.* (Казанский государственный университет) Kazan State University; (Киевский государственный университет имени Шевченко) T. G. Shevchenko Kiev State University.

**кгц** *abbr.* (килогерц) kilohertz, kilocycles per second.

**кдж** *abbr.* (килоджоуль) kilojoule.

**к.е.** *abbr.* (кормовая единица) feed unit; (крахмальная единица) starch unit.

**кевеенавит** *m.* (min.) keweenawite.

**кевовое дерево** (bot.) a gum-yielding tree (*Pistacia mutica*).

**кег/ельный** *a.* skittle; pin; —**леобразный** *a.* top-shaped, turbinate.

**кегль** *m.* (typ.) point.

**кегля** *f.* skittle, pin.

**к.ед.** *see* **к.е.**; **КЕД** *abbr.* (крысиная единица действия) (physiol.) rat unit.

**кедр** *m.*, —**овый** *a.* (bot.) cedar (*Cedrus*); —**овое масло** cedar oil; cedarwood oil; —**овые орехи** pine kernels.

**кейльгауит** *m.* (min.) keilhauite, yttrotitanite.

**кейпер** *m.* (geol.) Keuper series.

**кеке масло** cay-cay butter.

**кекс** *m.* cake.

**кекур** *m.* kekur (bank of gravel pushed ashore by river ice; in Siberia, conical rocks on a sea coast).

**Келвина шкала** Kelvin (temperature) scale.

**келейный** *a.* cell.

**келифит** *m.* (min.) kelyphite (a garnet decomposition rim); —**овый** *a.* kelyphitic.

**Келлера раствор** Keller solution.

**келлин** *m.* khellin, kellin.

**келловейский ярус** (geol.) Callovian stage.

**келоид** *m.* (med.) keloid.

**келп** *m.* (bot.) kelp.

**Кельвина** *see* **Кельвина**.

**кельма** *f.* trowel.

**кельнск/ий** *a.*, **Кельн** Cologne; —**ая вода** eau de Cologne; —**ая земля**, —**ая умбра** Cologne brown, van Dyke brown.

**кельня** *f.* trowel.

**кельн** *see* **келп**.

**кельтий** *m.* obs. celtium (hafnium, Hf).

**келья** *f.* cell.

**кем** *instr. of* **кто**, by whom.

**Кембридж** Cambridge.

**кембрий** *m.*, —**ский период** (geol.) Cambrian period.

**кембрик** *m.*, —**овый** *a.* (text.) cambric.

**кемигам** *m.* Chemigum (a synthetic rubber).

**кеммерерит** *m.* (min.) kämmererite (a variety of penninite).

**Кемпбелля формула** (elec.) Campbell's formula.

**кемпфер/ид** *m.* kaempferide; —**ол** *m.* kaempferol.

**кенаф** *m.* (bot.) ambary (*Hibiscus cannabinus*).

**кенгуру** *f.* (zool.) kangaroo.

**кенд/озид** *m.* kendoside (*Apocynum* extract); —**ырь** *m.* (bot.) Indian hemp (*Apocynum*).

**Кенли тигельная печь** Canley furnace.

**кеннел/евый**, —**ьский** *a.* cannel (coal).

**кенотрон** *m.* (thermionics) kenotron.

**Кента мельница** Kent roller mill.

**кентролит** *m.* (min.) kentrolite (a rare lead silicate).

**кентук/ийский** *a.* Kentucky; —**ийское кофейное дерево** (bot.) Kentucky coffee tree (*Gymnocladus canadensis*); —**илиновая кислота** kentuckylinic acid.

**к.е.о.** *abbr.* (коэффициент естественной освещенности) daylight factor.

**Кеплера закон** (astron.) Kepler's law.

**кеплеровский** *a.* Keplerian.

**керазин** *m.* cerasin (gum resin); kerasin (a cerebroside); (min.) phosgenite, horn lead; —**оза** *f.* cerasinose.

**керам/ет** *see* **кермет;** —**зит** *m.* a porous clay filler (for cement); —**ика** *f.* ceramics; earthenware; —**иковый** *a.* ceramic, earthenware; clay, argillaceous; —**иковые изделия** pottery, earthenware; —**ический** *a.* ceramic; —**огалит** *m.* (min.) ceramohalite, hairsalt (a form of alunogen).

**кераргирит** *m.* (min.) cerargyrite, horn silver.

**кератин** *m.* (zool.) keratin; —**изация** *f.* keratinization, horn-formation; —**овая ткань** horny tissue, keratin.

**кepaт/ит** *m.* (med.) keratitis; —**оз** *m.* (med.) keratosis; —**офир** *m.* (petr.) keratophyre.

**кервель** *m.,* —**ный** *a.* (bot.) chervil (*Anthriscus*).

**керезин** *see* **церезин.**

**керит** *m.* (elec.) kerite (insulator).

**кермезит** *m.* kermesite, kermes mineral.

**кермек** *m.* (bot.) statice.

**кермес** *m.* kermes (dye); kermes insect (*Coccus ilicis*); (bot.) kermes berries; kermes mineral, kermesite.

**кермет** *m.* cermet, ceramet, metal-ceramic.

**кери** *m.* center, core, core sample; punch hole; base (of tube); **отливать с** —**ом** *v.* (foundry) hollow cast; —**ер** *m.* punch, prick punch.

**кернит** *m.* (min.) kernite, rasorite (a sodium borate).

**керно** *n.* prick punch; indentation, mark, prick; —**вать** *v.* punch, prick.

**керновый** *a.* core.

**кероген** *m.* (geol.) kerogen (bituminous material).

**керонафт** *m.* solution of naphthalene in kerosene.

**керосин** *m.,* —**овый** *a.* kerosene; —**ка** *f.* kerosene stove, oil burner; —**овый завод** oil refinery, petroleum refinery; —**орез** *m.* torch using liquid fuel.

**Керра эффект** (elec.) Kerr effect.

**керромаг** *m.* (met.) Cerromag.

**Кертиса диск** Curtis disk.

**керченит** *m.* (min.) kertschenite (a hydrated ferric phosphate).

**кесар/ево сечение,** —**ское сечение** (med.) Caesarean operation.

**кессон** *m.,* —**ный** *a.* caisson; —**ная болезнь** caisson disease, the bends.

**кета** *f.* (zool.) Siberian salmon.

**кет/азин** *m.* ketazin; ketazine, bisazimethylene; —**аль** *m.* ketal.

**кетгут** *m.* catgut.

**кет/ен** *m.* ketene; —**имид** *m.* ketimide; —**имин** *m.* ketimine; —**ин** *m.* ketine, 2,5-dimethylpyrazine; —**ипиновая кислота** ketipic acid, oxalodiacetic acid.

**кето**— *prefix* keto—, охо—; —**амин** *m.* ketoamine; —**гексоза** *f.* ketohexose; **к.-енольный** *a.* keto-enol (tautomerism); —**за** *f.* ketose; —**кислота,** —**нокислота** *f.* keto acid, ketonic acid; —**ксим** *m.* ketoxime; acetoxime; —**л,** —**носпирт,** —**спирт** *m.* ketol, ketone alcohol; —**л** *m.* ketole, indole.

**кетон** *m.* ketone; **диэтиловый к.** diethyl ketone; —**ный,** —**овый** *a.* ketone, ketonic; —**окислота** *see* **кетокислота;** —**оспирт** *see* **кетол;** —**сахар** *m.* ketonic sugar; —**соединение** *n.* keto compound, ketonic compound; —**форма** *f.* ketone form, ketonic ester type.

**кефаелин** *m.* cephaëline.

**кефал/антин** *m.* cephalanthin; —**етин** *m.* cephaletin; —**ин** *m.* cephalin, brain lipoid; —**оидин** *m.* kephaloidin.

**кефаль** *m.* (zool.) grey mullet.

**кефир** *m.,* —**ный** *a.* kefir (fermented liquor made from goat's milk with *Bacillus caucasicus*); —**ные грибки,** —**ные зерна** kefir yeast, kefir grains, kefir powder.

**кеффек/елит,** —**илит** *see* **кил.**

**КЗМ** *abbr.* (концентрированная эмульсия зеленого масла) concentrated emulsion of 61–63% green (petroleum) oil (insecticide); **КЗМВ** concentrated emulsion of 80% green (petroleum) oil.

**кзыл-кендырь** *see* **кендырь.**

**киан/етин** *m.* kyanethine, cyanethine; —**идин** *m.* kyanidine, 1,3,5-triazine.

**кианиз/ация** *f.* (wood preservation) kyanization, kyanizing; —**ированный,** —**ованный** *a.* kyanized; —**ировать,** —**овать** *v.* kyanize; —**ующий** *a,* kyanizing.

**кианит** *m.* (min.) kyanite, cyanite, disthene.

**кианол** *m.* kyanol (aniline).

**киафенин** *m.* kyaphenine, cyaphenine.

**кибделофан** *m.* (min.) kibdelophane, ilmenite.

**кибернетика** *f.* cybernetics.

**кив/атин** *m.* (geol.) Keewatin (epoch or group); —**инон** *m.* Keweenawan series; —**инонский** *a.* Keweenawan.

**кивсяк** *m.* (zool.) millipede.

**кигиляхи** *pl.* kigilyakhi (pillared rocks of irregular shape on a mountain slope).

**кид/ание** *n.* throwing; abandoning; —**анный** *a.* thrown; abandoned; —**ать** *v.* throw, fling, cast; abandon, leave, drop, quit; —**ка** *f.* (text.) picking.

**Киев** Kiev.

**КИЗ** *abbr.* (Казахский научно-исследовательский институт земледелия) Kazakh Research Institute of Agriculture.

**кизельгур** *m.* (geol.) kieselguhr, diatomaceous earth, infusorial earth.

**кизерит** *m.* (min.) kieserite.

**кизил** *m.*, —**овое дерево** (bot.) dogwood (*Cornus mas*); —**овые** *pl.* Cornaceae.

**кизиль** *see* **жидовская вишня**; —**ник** *m.* (bot.) cotoneaster.

**кий** *m.* cue.

**кил** *m.* kill (fuller's earth).

**кила** *f.* (med.) hernia, rupture; clubroot (plant disease).

**килев/ание** *n.* careening (of boat); —**ать** *v.* careen; —**идный** *a.* (bot.) carinate; —**ой** *a.* keel, bottom; —**ая качка** heaving (of ship).

**килл/арнейская складчатость** (geol.) Killarney folds; —**инит** *m.* (min.) killinite (a variety of pinite).

**кило**— *prefix* kilo— (denoting a magnitude of $10^3$); —**вар** *m.* (elec.) kilovar; —**ватт** *m.* kilowatt; —**ватт-час** kilowatt-hour.

**киловой** *a.* hernia, rupture.

**кило/вольт** *m.* (elec.) kilovolt; **к.-ампер** kilovolt-ampere; —**герц** *m.* kilohertz, kilocycles per second.

**килограмм** *m.* kilogram; **к.-калория** kilogram calorie, large calorie; **к.-**

**метр,** —**етр,** —**ометр** *m.* kilogrammeter; —**олекула** *f.* kilogram molecule.

**кило/дина** *f.* kilodyne; —**джоуль** *m.* kilojoule, large joule; —**калория** *f.* kilocalorie, large calorie; —**кюри** *n.* kilocurie; —**линия** *f.* kiloline (unit of magnetic flux); —**литр** *m.* kiloliter, stere; —**люмен** kilolumen; —**метр** *m.* kilometer; —**метраж** *m.* number of kilometers; mileage; —**моль** *m.* kilogram molecule; —**ом** *m.* (elec.) kilohm; —**тонна** *f.* kiloton (unit of explosive force); —**уатт** *see* **киловатт**; —**цикл** *m.* kilocycle; —**электронвольт** *m.* kiloelectron-volt, kev.

**килуран** *m.* kilurane (unit of radioactivity).

**киль** *m.* keel; (aero.) tail fin, fin surface.

**кильватер** *m.* ship's wake, dead water.

**килька** *f.* (zool.) sprat.

**кильная трава** *see* **грыжник**.

**киматолит** *m.* (min.) cymatolite (an alteration product of spodumene).

**ким/берлейский метод** (min.) Kimberly method; —**берлит** *m.* (petr.) kimberlite, blue earth; —**еридж** *m.*, —**е-риджский ярус** (geol.) Kimeridgian stage.

**кимограф** *m.* (med.) kymograph.

**кимолийская глина** (min.) cimolite.

**кимон** *m.* (bot.) cumin (*Cumenum cyminum*).

**кимофан** *m.* (min.) cymophane, chrysoberyl.

**Кина испытатель** (met.) Keen tester; **К. цемент** Keene's cement.

**киназа** *f.* kinase (enzyme activator).

**кингстон** *m.* Kingston (flooding) valve.

**киндерхук** *m.* (geol.) Kinderhook beds.

**кинемати/ка** *f.* (phys.) kinematics, science of motion; —**ческий** *a.* kinematic.

**кинематограф** *m.* cinematograph, motion picture, moving picture; —**иче-ский** *a.* cinematographic, moving picture.

**кинескоп** *m.* (telev.) kinescope, picture tube.

**кинестезия** *f.* (med.) kinesthesia.

**кинет/ика** *f.* (phys.) kinetics; —**ический** *a.* kinetic; —**ическая энергия** kinetic energy; —**огенезис** *m.* (zool.) kineto-genesis; —**оскоп** *m.* kinetoscope; —**офон** *m.* kinetophone.

**кинеч.** *abbr.* (**кинетический**).

**кинжал** *m.* dagger.

**кин/за** *see* **кориандр;** —**кан** *see* **кумкват.**

**Кинмайера амальгама** Kienmaier's amalgam, zinc-tin amalgam.

**кино** *n.* kino (gum); motion picture, movie.

**киноа** *f.* (bot.) quinoa (*Chenopodium quinoa*).

**киноварь** *f.* (min.) cinnabar; vermilion (pigment); **зеленая к.** cinnabar green; **красная к.** vermilion.

**киноин** *m.* kinoin (resin).

**кино/картина** *f.* motion picture, movie; —**лента** *f.* film; —**механик** *m.* movie technician; —**проектор** *m.*, —**установка** *f.* movie projector; —**промышленность** *f.* moving picture industry; —**съемка** *f.* motion-picture filming; —**фотопулемет** *m.* camera gun; —**хроника** *f.* newsreel.

**кинур/енин** *m.* kynurenine; —**еновая кислота** kynurenic acid, 4-hydroxy-quinaldic acid; —**ин** *m.* kynurin, 4-quinolinol; —**овая кислота** kynuric acid, carbostyrilic acid.

**кинут/ый** *a.* thrown; abandoned; —**ь** *see* **кидать.**

**киньон-насос** *m.* a compressed-air pump for conveying dust.

**киоск** *m.* booth.

**кип** *m.* kip (unit of force, 1000 lb); notch.

**кип.** *abbr.* (**кипение**) boiling.

**КИП** *abbr.* (**контрольно-измерительные приборы**) control and measuring instruments.

**кипа** *f.* bale, stack, pack.

**кипарис** *m.*, —**овый** *a.* (bot.) cypress (*Cupressus sempervirens*); —**овик** *m.* chamaecyparis; —**овые** *pl.* Cupressaceae.

**кипел/ка** *f.* quicklime, unslaked lime, calcium oxide; —**ый** *a.* boiled.

**кипен/ие** *n.* boiling, ebullition; bubbling, effervescence; **температура** —**ия, точка** —**ия** boiling point.

**кипер** *m.*, —**ная ткань** (text.) twill; —**ная лента** surgical tape.

**кипеть** *v.* boil; bubble.

**киповая планка** (min.) chock, timber.

**кипоразбиватель** *m.* bale breaker.

**Киппа аппарат** Kipp generator.

**кипрегель** *m.* (surv.) telescopic alidade.

**кипрей** *m.* (bot.) willow herb (*Epilobium*).

**кип/ун** *m.* bubbling or boiling spring; —**учий,** —**ящий** *a.* boiling; bubbling, effervescent; boiling-water (nuclear reactor); —**учий слой** fluidized bed; —**ятильник** *m.* boiler, hot-water heater; —**ятильный** *a.* boiling; —**ятильный куб** beaker; —**ятить** *v.* boil, bring to a boil; —**яток** *m.* boiling water; —**ячение** *n.* boiling; —**яченый** *a.* boiled.

**кир** *m.* (geol.) kir (solidified petroleum).

**КиР** *abbr.* (**Каучук и резина**) Caoutchouc and Rubber (a journal).

**киргиз** *m.*, —**ский** *a.* Kirgiz.

**кирза** *f.* (text.) kersey; subterranean frozen layer; **к. СК** a leather substitute.

**кирка** *f.* pick, pickax; scraper, scraping tool, hoe.

**кирказон** *m.* (bot.) birthwort (*Aristolochia*); —**овые** *pl.* Aristolochiaceae.

**кирков/ка** *f.* scarifying; —**щик** *m.* scarifier.

**кирочный** *a.* pick, pickax; scraper, hoe.

**кирпич** *m.* brick; **пережженный к.** clinker; —**еделательный** *a.* brick-molding (machine); —**собжигательная печь** brick kiln; —**ник** *m.* brickmaker; —**но-красный** *a.* brick-red.

**кирпичн/ый** *a.* brick; **к. завод** brickyard; —**ая кладка** brick laying; —**ая решетка** checkerwork (of bricks).

**Кирхгофа закон** Kirchhoff's law.

**кисе/евидный** *a.* muslin-like; —**йный** *a.* muslin.

**киселевание** *n.* (tanning) drenching.

**кисель** *m.* fruit jelly; (tanning) bark liquor, ooze; **к. из отрубей** (tanning) bran drench, bran steep; **морской к.** (zool.) jellyfish, medusa.

**кисея** *f.* (text.) muslin, gauze.

**кисл/еть** *see* **киснуть;** —**ица** *f.* (bot.) oxalis; crab (*Pyrus malus*); —**ичная соль** potassium bioxalate; —**ичные** *pl.* (bot.) Oxalidaceae.

**кисло** *adv.* sourly, acidly, acid; —**ватость** *f.* sourness; acidulousness, (slight) acidity, subacidity; —**ватый** *a.* sourish; acidulous, subacid; —**вка** *f.* (bleaching) souring machine.

**кислород** *m.* oxygen, O; **к. воздуха** atmospheric oxygen; —**но**— *see* **кислородо**—; —**ный** *a.* oxygen, oxygenous; —**ная бомба** oxygen cylinder; —**ная кислота** oxy acid, oxygen acid; —**ная соль** oxy salt.

**кислородо/ацетиленовая горелка** oxyacetylene torch; **к. сварка** oxyacetylene welding; —**водородный** *a.* oxyhydrogen (welding); —**отщепляющий** *a.* oxygen-removing, deoxidizing; —**содержащий** *a.* oxygen-containing, oxy—.

**кислосладкий** *a.* sourish sweet.

**кислот/а** *f.* acid; **ангидрид** —**ы**, **безводная к.** acid anhydride.

**кислотн/ость** *f.* acidity; **показатель степени** —**ости**, —**ое число** acid number; —**ый** *a.* acid; sour; —**ый окисел** acidic oxide; —**ая ванна** acid bath; —**ые красители** acid dyes; —**ые пары** acid fumes.

**кислото/измерение** *n.* acidimetry; —**мер** *m.* acidimeter; —**обработанный** *a.* acid-treated; —**образование** *n.* acid formation, acidification; —**образователь** *m.* acid former, acidifier; —**поглощающий** *a.* acid-absorbing; —**подобный** *a.* acid-like, of acid nature; —**стойкий**, —**упорный**, —**устойчивый** *a.* acidproof, acid-resisting; —**упорность** *f.* acid resistance, resistance to acid.

**кисл/ый** *a.* acid; sour; bi— (when used before a salt); **к. характер** acid nature; acid condition, acidity; —**ая соль** acid salt, bi-salt; —**ая сернистокислая соль** bisulfite; —**ая сернокислая соль** bisulfate; —**ая углекалиевая соль** potassium bicarbonate; —**ая углекислая соль** bicarbonate; —**ое свойство** acidity.

**кисля/нка** *f.* (bot.) barberry (*Berberis vulgaris*); —**тина** *f.* sour fruit or drink.

**киснуть** *v.* sour, turn sour, become acid.

**киста** *f.* (med.) cyst.

**кисте/вание** *n.* brushing; —**вик**, **зеленый** (bot.) blue mold, common mold (*Penicillium glaucum*); —**вой** *a.*

brush; bunch, cluster; (anat.) wrist, carpal; —**вой разряд** (elec.) brush discharge; —**носный** *a.* (bot.) racemose; —**образный** *a.* brush-shaped; (bot.) penicillate, penicilliform; —**рые** *pl.* Crossopterygii (fish); —**хвост** *m.* tussock moth (*Orgyia antiqua*).

**кистовидный** *a.* cystoid, cystiform.

**кист/очка** *f.* brush, small brush; —**очный** *see* **кистевой**; —**ь** *f.* brush; bunch, cluster; (bot.) raceme; (anat.) wrist.

**кит** *m.* (zool.) whale.

**кит.** *abbr.* (**китайский**).

**Китай** China.

**китайск/ий** *a.* Chinese; **к. воск** insect wax; **к. лен**, —**ая крапива**, —**ая трава** China grass, ramie fiber; **к. орех** *see* **арахис**; —**ая синь** Chinese blue, Prussian blue (pigment); —**ое масло** China wood oil, tung oil; —**ое серебро** packfong, German silver (copper-zinc-nickel alloy).

**кити**, —**ны** *pl.* (bot.) runners.

**кито/бойное судно** whaleboat; —**видный**, —**образный** *a.* cetacean, cetaceous; —**вый** *a.* whale, cetaceous; —**вый жир** whale oil; blubber; —**вый ус** whalebone; —**ловство** *n.* whaling.

**киур** *m.* mason's hammer.

**кифоз** *m.* (med.) kyphosis.

**кишеть** *v.* swarm.

**кишечн/ик** *m.* bowels, intestines; —**ополостные** *pl.* (zool.) Coelenterata; —**ый** *a.* intestinal, enteric, gut; —**ая палочка** (bact.) *Escherichia coli*; —**ая струна** catgut.

**киш/ка** *f.* (anat.) intestine, gut; (rubber) hose; **воспаление** —**ок** (med.) enteritis; **двенадцатиперстная к.** (anat.) duodenum; **прямая к.** rectum; **слепая к.** caecum; **толстая к.** colon.

**кишмиш** *m.* currant; seedless grapes.

**кишнец** *m.*, —**овый** *a.* (bot.) coriander (*Coriandrum sativum*).

**к121/тин** *see* **киватин**.

**кияк** *m.* giant rye grass (*Elymus giganteus*).

**киянка** *f.* wooden hammer, mallet.

**Кк** *abbr.* (**калийная соль**) potassium salt.

**ккал** *abbr.* (**килокалория**) large calorie.

**ккюри** *abbr.* (**килокюри**) kilocurie.

кл *abbr.* (**килолитр**) kiloliter; кл. *abbr.* (**класс**) class; (**клин**) plot, field; к.-л. *abbr.* (**какой-либо**) some, any.

**клавариевые** *pl.* (bot.) Clavariaceae.

**клавиатура** *f.* keyboard.

**клавицепсин** *m.* clavicepsin.

**клавиш/а** *f.*, —**ный** *a.* key.

**клавшиный** *a.* oscillating (mechanism).

**клад** *m.* treasure.

**кладбище** *n.* cemetery.

**кладенный** *past pass. part. of* **класть.**

**кладень** *m.* beam, sleeper, ground timber.

**кладестиновая кислота** cladestic acid.

**кладет** *pr. 3 sing. of* **класть.**

**кладка** *f.* laying; stack (of lumber); clutch (of eggs); egg mass (of fish).

**кладо—** *prefix* clado— (sprout).

**кладов/ая** *f.* storeroom, pantry; warehouse; —**щик** *m.* warehouse man.

**кладо/ния** *f.* cladonia (genus of lichens); —**новая кислота** cladonic acid; —**спориоз** *m.* scab caused by Cladosporium.

**клад/ут** *pr. 3 pl. of* **класть;** —**ущий** *a.* laying; —**чик** *m.* layer, setter; —**ь** *f.* load, cargo, freight; bridging plank.

**клажа** *f.* laying, setting, piling; load, cargo.

**Клайдена явление** (phot.) Clayden effect.

**Клайзена реакция** Claisen reaction.

**клал** *past sing. of* **класть.**

**клам/ера** *f.*, —**мер** *m.* cramp iron, clamp.

**клан** *m.* clan.

**клапан** *m.*, —**ный** *a.* valve, vent; к.-**бабочка** butterfly valve; **болезнь сердечных** —**ов** (med.) valvular disease of the heart; —**ная камера,** —**ная коробка** valve box.

**Клапейрона уравнение** Clapeyron equation.

**клапротит** *m.* (min.) klaprothite.

**кларен** *m.* clarain (constituent of coal).

**кларет** *m.* claret (wine).

**кларит** *m.* (min.) clarite (a variety of enargite).

**Кларка элемент** Clark cell.

**кларкеит** *m.* (min.) clarkeite.

**класс** *m.* class, sort, grade; category; (pal.) genus.

**классифи/катор** *m.* classifier; —**кация** *f.* classification, sorting, grading, sizing; separation; tabulation, grouping; —**цированный** *a.* classified, sorted, graded; —**цировать** *v.* classify, class, sort, grade, size, assort; tabulate.

**классический** *a.* classic, classical.

**классный** *a.* class.

**кластическ/ий** *a.* (geol.) clastic, fragmental; —**ие породы** clastic rocks.

**класто—** *prefix* clasto—.

**класть** *v.* lay, deposit, put, place, set.

**клаудетит** *m.* (min.) claudetite (an arsenic trioxide).

**Клаузиус-Клапейрона уравнение** Clausius-Clapeyron equation.

**клаузоне** *n.* (cer.) cloisonné.

**клаусталит** *m.* (min.) clausthalite.

**клебемасса** *f.* bituminous cement.

**клев/ание** *n.* pecking; (aero.) pitching; —**ать** *v.* peck, nibble, bite.

**Клеве кислота** Cleve's acid (dye intermediate).

**клевеит** *m.* (min.) cleveite (a variety of uraninite).

**клевеландит** *m.* (min.) cleavelandite (a variety of albite feldspar).

**клевер** *m.*, —**ный** *a.* (bot.) clover (*Trifolium*).

**клеветать** *v.* slander, cast aspersions (on).

**клев/ец** *m.* (mech.) tooth; —**ок** *m.* notcher; bite, biting.

**клеевар** *m.* glue boiler, gluemaker; —**ка** *f.* glue boiler, gluepot; —**ный завод** glue factory; —**очный** *a.* glue-boiling.

**клее/вой** *a.* glue, adhesive; к. **сахар** gelatin sugar; —**вое вещество** sizing material; gluten; adhesive; —**мешалка** *f.* glue mixer, glue churn; —**ние** *n.* gluing, pasting, cementing.

**клеен/ка** *f.*, —**очный** *a.* oilcloth, oilskin; linoleum; к.-**лощенка** buckram canvas.

**клееный** *a.* glued, pasted, cemented; к. **холст** buckram canvas.

**кле/ильный** *a.* gluing, pasting; —**ить** *v.* glue, gum, paste, cement; —**й** *m.* glue, gum, paste, cement; size, sizing, filling; **жидкий** —**й** size; **извлекать** —**й, лишать** —**я** *v.* degum.

**клейк/ий** *a.* gluey, sticky, gummy, viscous, adhesive; glue, adhesive; к. **пластырь** adhesive plaster; —**ое вещество** adhesive; sizing.

**клейковин/а** *f.*, —**ный** *a.* gluten.

клейкост/ь *f.* adhesiveness, stickiness, gumminess, viscosity; tack; повыситель —и tackifier.

клейм/ение *n.*, —овка *f.* branding, stamping, marking; —еный *a.* branded, stamped, marked; —ить *v.* brand, stamp, mark, impress, seal; —о *n.* brand, stamp, mark, seal; branding iron, marking iron; —овщик *m.* brander, marker.

клейн/ит *m.* (min.) kleinite, mercurammonite; -нишиновская формула (nucl.) Klein-Nishina formula.

клейстер *m.* paste, filling, sizing.

клейсто— *prefix* cleisto— (closed); —гамия *f.* (bot.) cleistogamy.

Клейтона-Эгнеля закон (meteor.) Clayton-Egnell law.

клементит *m.* (min.) klementite (an uncertain variety of chlorite).

клемм/а *f.* clamp, clip; (elec.) terminal; —ник *m.* terminal block.

клемшел *m.* clamshell (excavator).

клен *m.*, —овый *a.* (bot.) maple (*Acer*); —овая кислота aceric acid (supposed to be identical with malic acid); —овые *pl.* Aceraceae.

клепало *see* клепальный молот.

клепальн/ый *a.* riveting; к. молот, к. молоток riveting hammer, riveter; к. пресс, к. станок, —ая машина riveting machine, riveter.

клеп/альщик *m.* riveter; —анный *a.* riveted; —ать *v.* rivet; —ка *f.* riveting; stave, clapboard (of barrel).

клептомания *f.* (med.) kleptomania.

клерк *m.* clerk.

клер/ование *n.*, —овка *f.* clarification (of sugar); —овать *v.* clarify, clear, decolorize; —с *m.* (sugar) clear liquor.

клетевой *see* клеточный.

клетк/а *f.* cage; crate, box, casing, crib; (elevator) car; (biol.) cell; square; cubicle; mesh (of screen); —ообразная обмотка *see* клеточная обмотка.

клеточк/а *f.* little cage; (biol.) cell; —ообразный *a.* cellular.

клеточн/ый *a.* cage, crate; squirrel-cage (motor, etc.); cellular; к. сок (biol.) cell fluid; —ая обмотка (elec.) cage winding; —ое ядро (biol.) cell nucleus.

клетчатк/а *f.* cellulose; (biol.) cellular tissue; ксантогеновый эфир —и cellulose xanthate.

клетчатый *a.* square, squared, checkered; graph (paper); meshed; cellulose; (biol.) cellular.

клеть *f.* storeroom; cage, housing; bucket; stand (of rolling mill).

клешн/евидный *a.* claw-shaped; chelate (compound); —я *f.* claw, nipper.

клещ *m.* (zool.) tick, mite.

клещевин/а *f.*, —ный *a.* (bot.) castor plant (*Ricinus communis*); —ное масло castor oil.

клещ/евой *a.*, —и *pl.* tongs, forceps, nippers, pincers; vise; (zool.) mites and ticks (*Acarina*); к. тормоз clip brake; волосатые —и (zool.) Glycyphagidae; мучные —и Tyroglyphidae; хищные —и Cheyletidae; —ик *m.* mite.

клея/нка *see* клееварка; —щий *a.* adhesive.

кливаж *m.* cleavage; —ное расслоение foliation cleavage.

клиент *m.* client, customer; —ура *f.* clients, clientele.

клизма *f.* (med.) enema, syringe.

клик/ать, —нуть *v.* call.

кликушество *n.* hysterics, hysteria; epilepsy.

климаграмма *f.* (meteor.) climagram.

климат *m.* climate; —ический *a.* climatic; —ическая станция health resort; —олог *m.* climatologist; —ологический *a.* climatological; —ология *f.* climatology.

климениевые слои (geol.) Clymenia beds.

климогра/мма *f.*, —ф *m.* (meteor.) climograph.

клин *m.* wedge, key, cotter; cleat; chock; (agr.) field, plot; вбивать к. *v.* wedge (in); натяжной к., поперечный к. cotter, key; сходить на к. *v.* taper.

клингер *m.* water gage (in boiler).

клингерит *m.* an asbestos-rubber cement.

клини/ка *f.* clinic; —цист *m.* clinic physician; —ческий *a.* clinic, clinical.

клинкер *m.*, —ный *a.* clinker, brick.

клино— *prefix* wedge—, spheno—; clino— (incline); —видный *see* клинообразный; —вой *a.* wedge, key, cotter; wedge-shaped, V-shaped, V-(belt); —вая шпонка (taper) key.

**клиногумит** *m.* (min.) clinohumite.

**клинок** *m.* blade.

**клиноклаз,** —**ит** *m.* (min.) clinoclase, clinoclasite, aphanèse.

**клинолистовые** *pl.* (bot.) Sphenophylliae.

**клинометр** *m.* clinometer, incline level.

**клинообразный** *a.* wedge-shaped, wedge, cuneiform, sphenic, sphenoid, tapered, V-shaped; **к. интрузив** (geol.) sphenolith.

**клино/ось** *f.* (cryst.) clino-axis; —**пирамида** *f.* clinopyramid; —**ромбический** *a.* clinorhombic, monoclinic; —**ромбоэдрический** *a.* clinorhomboidal, triclinic; —**хлор** *m.* (min.) clinochlore, ripidolite (in part); —**цоизит** *m.* (min.) clinozoisite (considered an iron-free epidote); —**эдрит** *m.* (min.) clinohedrite; —**энстатит** *m.* (min.) clinoenstatite (a variety of pyroxene).

**клинтонит** *m.* (min.) clintonite (a variety of seybertite).

**клинчатый** *a.* wedge-shaped, tapered.

**клинчер** *m.* clincher, clencher; —**ная шина** beaded-edge tire.

**клиппер** *m.* clipper (boat).

**клипсы** *pl.* clips.

**клир/енс** *m.* clearance; —**инг** *m.* clearing.

**клир(р)фактор** *m.* (elec. comm.) klirr-factor, non-linear distortion factor.

**клистир** *m.* (med.) enema, syringe; stomach pump.

**клистрон** *m.,* —**ный** *a.* klystron (an electron tube).

**клит** *m.* a long-horned beetle.

**клитоцибин** *m.* clitocybine.

**клифстон** *m.* chalk.

**клиф/тонит** *m.* (min.) cliftonite (a variety of meteoric carbon); —**ф** *m.* cliff.

**клица** *f.* cleat, insulating clamp.

**клише** *n.* (typ.) cliché, stereotype block, engraving plate, cut.

**клм** *abbr.* (килолюмен) kilolumen; **клм-ч** *abbr.* (килолюмен-час) kilolumen-hour.

**клоака** *f.* cloaca, cesspool, sink.

**кловен** *m.* clovene.

**Клода способ** Claude's method (for liquefying air).

**клодетит** *m.* (min.) claudetite (an arsenic trioxide).

**клозет** *m.* toilet, lavatory.

**клок** *m.* flock, tuft; —**астый** *a.* flocky, tufty, tufted.

**клокотать** *v.* bubble, bubble up.

**клон** *m.* (biol.) clone.

**клонить** *v.* lean, incline.

**клоп** *m.,* —**овый** *a.* bug; —**ы** *pl.* true bugs (*Hemiptera*); spec. bedbugs (*Cimicidae*); —**овая ромашка** (bot.) bugbane (*Cimicifuga*); —**овник** *m.* a peppergrass (*Lepidium ruderale*); —**огонник** *m.* European bugbane (*Cimicifuga foetida*).

**клопфер** *m.* (telegraphy) sounder.

**клочень** *m.* bee moth (*Galleria mellonella*).

**клоч/кование** *n.* flocculation; —**коватый** *a.* flocculent, flocky; tufty; —**ок** *m.* flake, flock; shred, scrap; —**ья** *pl.* flakes; shreds, pieces, fragments.

**клуб** *m.* club; puff of smoke.

**клубен/ек** *m.* tubercle, nodule; —**ь** *m.,* —**ьковый** *a.* (bot.) tuber; nodule; —**ьковая бактерия** (bact.) rhizobium.

**клубиться** *v.* curl, wreath (of smoke).

**клубне/видный** *a.* tuber-like, tuberoid; —**вый** *a.* tuber, tuberous; —**луковица** *f.* corm, bulb; —**носный** *a.* tuberiferous; bulbiferous; —**образование** *n.* tuberization; —**плод** *m.* root, root crop.

**клубни/ка** *f.,* —**чный** *a.* (bot.) garden strawberry (*Fragaria elatior*).

**клубный** *a.* club.

**клуб/оватый** *a.* ball-like, globular; —**ок** *m.* ball (of thread), knot, tangle; puff (of smoke); —**очек** *m.* ball; —**очная машина** ball winder, balling frame.

**Клузиуса колонна** (isotopes separation) Clusius column.

**клуити/анол** *m.* cluytianol; —**ловый спирт** cluytyl alcohol; —**новая кислота** cluytic acid.

**клумба** *f.* flower bed.

**клуп/анодиевая кислота** clupanodic acid; —**анодоновая кислота** clupanodonic acid; —**еин** *m.* clupein.

**клуп/ик** *m.,* —**ка** *f.,* —**п** *m.* diestock, screwstock; hand tap.

**клык** *m.,* —**овый** *a.* tusk (of elephant); tooth, fang; detent, checking device; —**астый** *a.* having long tusks.

**клэрен** *m.* (coal) clarain.

**клюв** *m.* beak, bill; (zool.) rostrum;

—овидный, —ообразный *a.* beak-shaped, rostral, rostrate; (anat.) coracoid; —оголовые *pl.* (zool.) Rhynchocephalia.

клюза *f.* defile.

клюка *f.* rabble, poker; crutch.

клюкв/а *f.,* —енный *a.* (bot.) cranberry (*Oxycoccus palustris*).

клюнийский ярус (geol.) Clunian stage.

клюнуть *see* клевать.

клюфт *m.* (min.) cleft, fissure.

ключ *m.,* —евой *a.* key; wrench; monkey wrench; spring, fountain; (elec.) switch; английский к., французский к. monkey wrench; бить—ом *v.* spout, jet, well up, bubble up; кипеть—ом *v.* boil over; —евая вода spring water; —евая схема gating circuit, gate.

ключи/ца *f.* (anat.) clavicle, collarbone; —чный *a.* clavicular.

ключки *pl.* germinated seeds.

клюшка *see* клюка.

кляйзеновский *a.* Claisen (condensation).

клямера *f.* clinch rivet.

клястероспориоз *m.* Clasterosporium infection of fruit.

клятва *f.* oath, vow.

Кляузинга коэффициент (phys.) Clausing's factor.

клячка *f.* chewing gum.

км *abbr.* (километр) kilometer; км² *abbr.* (квадратный километр) square kilometer; км³ *abbr.* (кубический километр) cubic kilometer.

КМА *abbr.* (Курская магнитная аномалия) Kursk Magnetic Anomaly.

км/сек *abbr.* (километров в секунду) kilometers per second; км/ч, км/час *abbr.* (километров в час) kilometers per hour.

к.-н. *abbr.* (какой-нибудь) some, any.

кнебелит *m.* (min.) knebelite.

Кневенагеля реакция Knoevenagel reaction.

кнехт *m.* cleat.

книг/а *f.* book, volume; —оиздательство *n.* publishing house, publisher; —опечатание *n.* printing, press; —охранилище *n.* library.

книдиевая кислота cnidic acid.

книдоспоридии *pl.* (zool.) Cnidosporidia.

книж/ечка *f.* booklet, notebook; к., —ка

*f.* (zool.) psalterium, third stomach (of ruminants); —ка *f.,* —ный *a.* book.

книзу *adv.* down, downwards; тяга к. downward pull; downdraft.

кница *f.* gusset, bracket; (naut.) knee.

кницин *m.* cnicin.

кнопер *m.* oak gall.

кнопит *m.* (min.) knopite (calcium titanate).

кноп/ка *f.,* —очный, —чатый *a.* button, push button, knob; tack; snap fastener; —очный выключатель (elec.) press button switch, button switch; —очное управление press button control.

кнопперсы *pl.* gall nuts, galls.

КНР *abbr.* (Китайская Народная Республика) People's Republic of China.

кнудсеновский поток (phys.) Knudsen flow.

кнур *m.* (zool.) boar.

кнут *m.* whip.

княж/еника *f.* (bot.) raspberry (*Rubus arcticus*); —ик *m.* (bot.) clematis.

ко *see* к.

Ко *abbr.* (компания) Company.

КоА *abbr.* (кофермент А) coenzyme A.

коагель *m.* coagel.

коагулир/ование *n.* coagulation; —ованный *a.* coagulated; —овать *v.* coagulate; —уемость *f.* coagulability; —уемый *a.* coagulable; —ующий *a.* coagulating; —ующий реагент coagulant, coagulating agent.

коагул/юм, —ят *m.* coagulum, clot; coagulate; —янт *m.* coagulant, coagulating agent; —ятор *m.* coagulator; coagulant, coagulating agent; —яция *f.,* —яционный *a.* coagulation, coagulating.

коаксиальный *a.* coaxial.

коалесценция *f.* coalescence.

коалит *m.* coalite, semicoke.

коалиция *f.* coalition.

коаптация *f.* coaptation.

коацерв/ат *m.* coacervate (phase in colloidal solution); —ация *f.* coacervation.

кобальт *m.* cobalt, Co; азотнокислый к., нитрат —a cobalt nitrate; азотнокислая закись —a cobaltous nitrate;

**закись** —a cobaltous oxide; **соединение закиси** —a cobaltous compound; **соль закиси** —a cobaltous salt; **закись-окись** —a cobalto-cobaltic oxide; **землистый к., роговой к.** (min.) earthy cobalt, asbolite; **окись** —a cobaltic oxide; **соединение окиси** —a cobaltic compound; **соль окиси** —a cobaltic salt; **сернокислый к., сульфат** —a cobalt sulfate; **сернокислая окись** —a cobaltic sulfate; **синий к.** cobalt blue; **хлористый к.** cobaltous chloride; **хлорный к.** cobaltic chloride; **шпейсовый к.** (min.) cobalt speiss.

**кобальт/амин, —иак, —иамин** *m.* cobaltammine, cobaltiac; **—ин** *m.* (min.) cobaltite, cobalt glance. cobaltite, cobalt glance.

**кобальтиров/ание** *n.* cobalting, cobalt plating; **—анный** *a.* cobalt-plated; **—ать** *v.* cobalt, plate with cobalt.

**кобальтисто—** *prefix* cobalto—, cobaltous; **—синеродистый калий** potassium cobaltocyanide; **—синеродо-водородная кислота** cobaltocyanic acid.

**кобальт/истый** *a.* cobaltous, cobalto—, cobalt; **—ит** *see* **кобальтин.**

**кобальто—** *prefix* cobalti—, cobaltic; cobalto—; **—азотистоводородная кислота** cobaltinitrous acid; **—азотистокалиевая соль** potassium cobaltinitrite.

**кобальтов/ый** *a.* cobaltic, cobalti—, cobalt, cobaltiferous; **к. блеск** (min.) cobalt glance, cobaltite; **к. зеленый** cobalt green, cobalt zincate, Rinmann's green; **к. колчедан** (min.) cobaltpyrite, linnaeite; **к. купорос** cobalt vitriol, cobaltous sulfate; **к. обмет, —ые цветы** (min.) cobalt bloom, erythrite; **к. шпат** (min.) spherocobaltite, cobalt protocarbonate; **—ая синь** cobalt blue; **—ое синее стекло** cobalt glass.

**кобальто/кальцит** *m.* (min.) cobaltocalcite (a variety of calcite); **—марганцовая руда** (min.) cobaltiferous wad, asbolan, asbolite; **—менит** *m.* (min.) cobaltomenite (a cobalt selenite); **—никелевый колчедан** *m.* cobaltpyrite.

**кобальтосинеродист/ая кислота, —оводородная кислота** cobalticyanic acid; **—ый калий** potassium cobalticyanide.

**кобеллит** *m.* (min.) kobellite.

**кобка** *f.* bucket.

**кобловый** *a.* pollard, pollarded (tree).

**кобра** *f.* (zool.) cobra.

**кобура** *f.* leather case, holster.

**кобыл/а** *f.* mare; **—ий** *a.* mare's; **—ица** *f.* filly; **—ка** *f.* filly; bridge (of string instrument); locust, grasshopper; field cricket.

**ковалентн/ость** *f.* covalence; **—ый** *a.* covalent.

**ков/ало** *n.* forge hammer; **—альня** *f.* forge, smithy; **—ание** *see* **ковка; —аный** *a.* forged, beaten, hammered; wrought (iron); shod (horse).

**ковар** *m.* Kovar (a low-expansion alloy).

**ковари/антный** *a.* (math.) covariant; **—ационный** *a.*, **—ация** *f.* covariance.

**ковать** *v.* forge, beat, hammer; work; shoe (a horse); **к. вхолодную** hammer harden.

**ковелл/ин, —ит** *m.* (min.) covellite.

**ковер** *m.* carpet, rug.

**коверк/ание** *n.* distortion; **—ать** *v.* distort, mangle, twist, contort.

**коверсинус** *m.* (math.) coversed sine.

**ковк/а** *f.* forging, forge work, hammering; shoeing (of horse); **сварка —ой** hammer welding; **—ий** *a.* ductile, malleable, forgeable, flexible, supple; **—ий чугун** wrought iron; **—ость** *f.* ductility, malleability, forgeability, flexibility.

**ковочный** *a.* forging; forged.

**коврига** *f.* cake, round loaf.

**коврижки** *pl.* kovrizhki (hydrolaccoliths or other permafrost hummocks).

**ковро/вый** *a.* carpet; braided (cable); **—вая материя** carpeting; **—вые растения** ground cover; **—ткачество** *n.* carpet weaving.

**ковш** *m.*, **—евой, —овый** *a.* dipper, ladle, scoop, shovel; (feed) hopper; bucket; port, harbor; **—евой конвейер, —евой транспортер** bucket conveyer; **—евой экскаватор** bucket excavator; **—евая проба** panning (of gold); **—евая тележка** (foundry) ladle car; **—ово-ленточный** *a.* bucket and belt.

**ковыль** *m.*, **—ный** *a.* feather grass (*Stipa*).

**ковыр/нуть**, **—ять** *v.* pick (at).

**когазин** *m.* kogazin.

**когда** *adv.* when; **к. бы ни** whenever; **к.-либо, к.-нибудь** sometime, some day, any time; ever; **к.-так** if so, in that case; **к.-то** formerly, once, sometime.

**когезия** *f.* cohesion.

**когенит** *m.* (min.) cohenite (a meteoritic iron carbide).

**когер/ент** *m.* coherent; **—ентность** *f.*, **—ирование** *n.* coherence; **—ентный** *a.* coherent; **—ентное рассеяние** (phys.) Bragg scattering; **—ер** *m.* (rad.) coherer; **—ировать** *v.* cohere.

**кого** *acc. and gen. of* кто, whom.

**ког/отный** *a.* unguiculate, claw; **—оть** *m.* claw, nail, talon; catch; knuckle (of hinge); **—ти** *pl.* claws; grapplers (for climbing posts); **—теобразный** *a.* claw-shaped, claw-like, hooked, unguiform.

**код** *m.* code, key, cipher, signal book.

**кодак** *m.* (phot.) Kodak; **—ром** *m.* Kodachrome (color film).

**кодамин** *m.* codamine.

**кодеин** *m.* codeine, methylmorphine; **фосфат —а, фосфорнокислый к.** codeine phosphate; **—овая кислота** codeic acid; **—он** *m.* codeinone.

**кодекс** *m.* code.

**кодеонал** *m.* codeonal.

**код/ер**, **—ировщик** *m.*, **—ирующее устройство** coder, encoder; **—ирование** *n.*, **—ирующий** *a.* coding, encoding; **—ированный** *a.* coded, in code; **—ировать** *v.* code, encode; **—ифицировать** *f.* codify, systematize; **—овый** *a.* code.

**кое** *pron. n.* which, that; **к.-где** *adv.* somewhere; **к.-как** *adv.* anyhow, carelessly; with difficulty, somehow; **к.-какой** *a.* some, any; **к.-кто** *pron.* somebody, someone, some; **к.-куда** *adv.* somewhere; **к.-что** *pron.* something, a little.

**кожа** *f.* skin; (anat.) cutis; hide, leather; peel, paring (of fruit); **—н** *m.* leather coat; **—ный** *a.* leather, leathery.

**кож/евенный** *a.* tanning; leather; **к. завод** tannery; **—евенное дерево** (bot.) sumac (*Rhus*); **—евник** *m.* tanner, currier, leather-dresser; (bot.) sumac; **—евнический, —евничий** *a.* tanner's; **—евня** *f.* tannery; **—ееды** *pl.* skin beetles (*Dermestidae*); **—заменитель** *m.* leather substitute, artificial leather; **—имит** *m.* artificial sole leather; **—истокрылые** *pl.* earwigs (*Dermaptera*); **—ица** *f.* film, pellicle, thin skin; peel, husk; **—ный** *a.* skin, cutaneous; **—сырье** *n.* hides, raw hide.

**кожура** *f.* rind, skin, peel, pod.

**кожух** *m.* case, casing, housing, cover, covering, sheath, sheathing; mantle, hood, cowl, jacket; shell (of boiler); leather coat; **—отрубный, —отрубчатый** *a.* shell-and-tube (heat exchanger).

**коза** *f.* goat (female); crate; (brick) hod.

**козалит** *m.* (min.) cosalite.

**козачка** *f.* plow handle.

**коз/ел** *m.* goat (male); (met.) sow, salamander, bear (furnace scale); **—елец** *m.* (bot.) viper's grass (*Scorzonera*); *see also* козлобородник; **—елок** *m.* (aero.) chock; morocco leather; **винтовой —елок** jack, screw jack; **—ерог** *m.* (astron.) Capricorn; **—ий** *a.* goat, caprine; **—ья ива** goat willow (*Salix caprea*); **—ья трава** *see* козлятник.

**козимаза** *f.* cozymase, coenzyme I.

**козленок** *m.* kid; kid leather.

**Козлета способ** *see* кослеттизация.

**козл/ец** *see* змеевик; **—ина** *f.* goatskin; **—иный** *a.* goat; **—иться** *v.* kid, yean; **—обородник** *m.* (bot.) goat's beard, vegetable oyster (*Tragopogon*).

**козлов/ой** *a.* goat; trestle, gantry; **к. кран** gantry crane; **—ая кожа** goatskin.

**козлы** *pl.* trestle, horse, saw horse, bench; carriage (of crane).

**коз/лятник** *m.* (bot.) goat's rue (*Galega officinalis*); **—оводство** *n.*, **—оводческий** *a.* goat breeding.

**козыль, —ник** *m.* (bot.) ambrosia.

**козырек** *m.* visor; deflector, baffle plate; lip (of excavator scoop).

**козья** *see* козий.

**козявка** *f.* small beetle; **мавританская к.** cadelle (*Tenebroides mauritanicus*).

**коикс** *m.* (bot.) Job's tears (*Coix*).

**кой** *pron. m.* who, which, that; *see also* **кое.**

**койева кислота** kojic acid.

**койка** *f.* cot, hammock, berth.

**койлер** *m.* (text.) coiler.

**койот** *m.* (zool.) coyote.

**кок** *m.* (aero.) nacelle; cockpit.

**кока** *f.*, **—иновый куст** (bot.) coca (*Erythroxylon coca*); **—евая кислота** cocaic acid; **—ин** *m.*, **—иновый** *a.* cocaine, erythroxyline.

**кокард/а** *f.* cockade, badge; **—овая руда** (min.) cockade ore, cockscomb pyrite (a form of marcasite).

**кокил/ь** *m.*, **—ьный** *a.* (foundry) chill mold, chill; ingot mold; **отливать в —ях** *v.* cast cold; **отливка в —ях, —ьная отливка, —ьное литье** chill casting; **—ьноотлитый** *a.* chill-cast.

**кокимбит** *m.* (min.) coquimbite.

**кокк** *m.* coccus (a spherical bacterium).

**кокк/алиновая кислота** coccalinic acid, menispermic acid; **—огнин** *m.* coccognin; **—олит** *m.* (min.) coccolite (a variety of pyroxene); (zool.) coccolith; **—улин** *m.* cocculin.

**коклюш** *m.* (med.) whooping cough.

**коклюшка** *f.* bobbin, spindle.

**кокон** *m.*, **—овый** *a.* cocoon, follicle; **—овая нить** silk fiber; **—опряды** *pl.* tent caterpillars (*Lasiocampidae*).

**кокорыш** *m.* (bot.) small-leaved hemlock, fool's parsley (*Aethusa cynapium*).

**кокос** *m.*, **—овый** *a.*, **—овый орех** coconut; **—овая пальма** (bot.) coconut palm (*Cocos nucifera*); **—овое масло** coconut oil.

**Кокрофта-Уолтона ускоритель** (nucl.) Cockroft-Walton accelerator.

**кокс** *m.* coke.

**кок-сагыз** *m.* (bot.) kok-saghyz (*Taraxacum kok-saghyz*) (source of rubber).

**коксик** *m.* small coke, coke dust, coke fines, coke breeze.

**коксобензольный завод** benzol plant, benzene plant; coal-tar chemical plant.

**коксов/альный** *a.* coke, coking; **—альная печь, —альное стойло** coke oven; **—альщик** *m.* coke oven operator; **—ание** *n.* coking; **—ание в кучах** batch coking; **—ать** *v.* coke, convert into coke.

**коксов/ый** *a.* coke; **к. газ, газ —ых печей** coke oven gas; **к. мусор** *see* **коксик; к. пирог** coke mass; **—ая мука** powdered coke; **—ая печь** coke oven; **—ая смола** coke oven tar, coal tar.

**коксо/выталкиватель** *m.* coke pusher; **—обжигательная печь** coke oven; **—подобный** *a.* coke-like; **—химическое производство** by-product coke industry; coal-tar chemical industry.

**коксу/емость** *f.* coking capacity; **—ющий, —ющийся** *a.* coking.

**кокуида** *f.* (zool.) armored scale (*Coccodea*).

**кокумовое масло** cocum fat.

**кокцер/ил** *m.*, **—иловый** *a.* cocceryl; **—иловый спирт** cocceryl alcohol; **—иловая кислота, —иновая кислота** coccerylic acid, cocceric acid; **—ин** *m.* coccerin.

**кокцид/ии** *pl.* (zool.) Coccidia; **—иоз** *m.* (med.) coccidiosis.

**кокцин** *m.* coccin; **новый к.** (phot.) new coccin; **—елиды** *pl.* lady beetles (*Coccinelidae*); **—еллин** *m.* coccinellin, carmin; **—овый** *a.* coccin; coccineous, bright red; **—овая кислота** coccinic acid, hydroxymethylphthalic acid.

**кокшаровит** *m.* (min.) koksharovite (a variety of edenite amphibole).

**кол** *m.* stake, picket, pole; **посадка под к.** dibble planting.

**Кола способ** Cole's method.

**кола** *f.* (bot.) cola; **к. орехи** cola nuts; **—мин** *m.* colamine, 2-aminoethanol; **—теин** *m.* colatein; **—тин** *m.* colatin, colatannin.

**колба** *f.* flask; retort; shell, envelope; (elec.) bulb.

**колбаса** *f.* sausage, bologna; bustle pipe (of blast furnace).

**колбочка** *f.* small flask; (elec.) bulb.

**кол-во** *abbr.* (**количество**) quantity.

**колд-крем** *m.* cold cream.

**колдобина** *f.* small pit, hole.

**колдунник** *see* **колтунник.**

**колебан/ие** *n.* oscillation, fluctuation, variation, vacillation, range; vibration, swinging, rocking; flickering (of flame); **вид** —ия (rad.) mode; **гене-ратор** —ий (rad.) oscillator.

**колебательн/ый** *a.* oscillatory, oscillating, fluctuating; vibrating, vibration, vibrational; **к. контактор** vibrating contactor, chopper; **к. контур** (rad.) oscillatory circuit; **волна** —ого **движения** vibrational wave.

**колеб/ать** *v.* shake, agitate, vibrate; swing; —**аться** *v.* oscillate, fluctuate, vary, range; vibrate; falter, hesitate, waver; flicker; wobble, sway; —**аться в пределах** fluctuate, vary, range; —**лющийся** *a.* oscillating, oscillatory, fluctuating, variable; vibrating, vibratory; unsteady, wavering; flickering (flame).

**колеманит** *m.* (min.) colemanite.

**коленкор** *m.* (text.) calico.

**коленно-рычажн/ый механизм** toggle; —**ое соединение** toggle joint.

**колен/о** *n.*, —**ный** *a.* knee; elbow, bend; offset; tribe, race, line, generation; (bot.) joint, node; (geol.) limb, slope (of fold); curvature; —**ная чашка** (anat.) knee cap, patella.

**коленчат/ый** *a.* knee-like, geniculate; elbow, elbowed, angular, bent, crank, cranked; angle (thermometer, etc.); jointed, articulate; **к. вал,** —**ая ось** crankshaft; **к. рычаг** crank; —**ая труба** elbow, elbow pipe; —**ое соединение** elbow joint.

**колер** *m.* color, tint; (vet.) staggers.

**колерябия** *see* **кольраби.**

**колесико** *n.* small wheel, caster, caster wheel, ball caster, roller.

**колесн/ик** *m.* wheelwright; —**о-токарный станок** wheel lathe; —**ый** *a.* wheel, wheeled; paddle-wheel (steamer); axle (grease).

**колес/о** *n.* wheel; **к.-топчак** treadmill; **центр** —**а** spider; —**овидный** *a.* wheel-shaped, rotiform, rotate, trochoid.

**колет** *m.* collar; *pr. 3 sing. of* **колоть.**

**колеч/ко** *n.* small ring, annulet, link; —**ный** *a.* ring.

**колея** *f.* rut, track; (railroad) line, (rail) gage; **узкая к.** narrow gage.

**коли** *adv.* when; *conj.* if, since, as.

**коли/ка** *f.*, —**ки** *pl.* (med.) colic; —**статин** *m.* colistatin; —**стин** *m.*

colistin; —**т** *m.* (med.) colitis; —**цин** *m.* colicin.

**количественн/ый** *a.* quantitative; **к. анализ** quantitative analysis; —**ое числительное** cardinal number.

**количество** *n.* quantity, amount, number; **превосходить** —**м** *v.* exceed (in number).

**колк/а** *f.* splitting, cleaving, cleavage, fission; —**ий** *a.* split, fissured, cracked; cleavable, fissile.

**колкотар** *m.* colcothar, Prussian red, rouge.

**колл.** *abbr.* (**коллоидный**) colloidal.

**коллаген** *m.* collagen.

**колларгол** *m.* collargol.

**колле/га** *m.* colleague, associate; —**гия** *f.* staff, board, college; —**дж** *m.* college.

**коллектив** *m.* association, organized body; —**ный** *a.* collective; —**ное хозяйство** collective farm, cooperative farm.

**коллектор** *m.* collector, accumulator, receiver, receptacle, sampler; manifold, header; (elec.) commutator; (met.) collector, collecting agent, flotation promoter; —**ный** *a.* collecting, collector; commutator; —**ный двигатель** (elec.) commutator motor; —**ное масло** flotation oil, collecting oil.

**коллекци/онировать** *v.* collect; —**я** *f.* collection, set, complex.

**колленхима** *f.* (bot.) collenchyma.

**Колл. ж.** *abbr.* (**Коллоидный журнал**) Colloid Journal.

**коллигативный** *a.* colligative.

**коллидин** *m.* collidine.

**коллизия** *f.* collision.

**коллим/атор** *m.* (optics) collimator; —**ационный** *a.*, —**ация** *f.* collimation; —**ированный** *a.* collimated; —**ировать** *v.* collimate, render parallel.

**коллине/арность** *f.* collinearity; —**арный** *a.* colinear; —**ация** *f.* collineation.

**коллирит** *m.* (min.) collyrite.

**коллод/иальный, —ийный, —ионный** *a.* collodion; —**иальная вата, —ийная вата** collodion cotton, soluble guncotton, pyroxylin; —**ий, —иум** *m.* collodion.

**коллоид** *m.* colloid; —**альный, —ный** *a.*

colloid, colloidal; —альное движение colloidal movement, Brownian movement; —ная растворимость solubilization; —ное вещество colloid.

**коллоксилин** *m.* colloxylin, pyroxylin.

**коллотипия** *f.* (phot.) collotype.

**коллофан** *m.* (min.) collophanite.

**коллюв/ий** *m.*, —иальное отложение (geol.) colluvial deposit, colluvial soil.

**колоб** *m.* oil cake, cake.

**коловорот** *m.* brace (and bit).

**коловрат/ки** *pl.* (zool.) Rotifera, wheel animalcules; —ность *f.* vicissitude, mutability, inconstancy.

**коловратн/ый** *a.* circular, rotary, rotatory, revolving, gyrating; к. насос rotary pump; —ое движение gyration.

**коловращение** *n.* circular motion, rotation, revolution.

**коловый** *a.* stake, picket; pole (bean).

**кологарифм** *m.* (math.) cologarithm.

**колода** *f.* block, log, chunk; trough.

**колод/езник** *m.* well borer; —езный *a.*, —езь, —ец *m.* well, pit, shaft, sump; manhole; —езная печь (met.) soaking pit; отстойный —ец drain, sink, sewer.

**колод/ка** *f.*, —очный *a.* (mech.) shoe, block, check; last (for shoes); к.-гайка link block; тормозная к. brake shoe; —очный тормоз block brake, shoe brake.

**колодцекопатель** *m.* well driller.

**колок** *m.* peg, pin; grove (of trees).

**колок/винта, —винтида, —инт, —итина** see **колоцинт**.

**колокол** *m.* bell; bell jar; hopper; (aero.) whipstall; —ообразный, —оподобный *a.* bell-shaped, funnel-shaped, funneled; —ьный *a.* bell; —ьный металл, —ьная бронза bell metal (a copper-tin alloy).

**колокольчик** *m.* small bell; (bot.) campanula; —овые *pl.* Campanulaceae.

**колокотина** see **колоцинт**.

**коломазь** *f.* grease, axle grease.

**коломб/ин** *m.* columbin, calumbin; —иновая кислота colombic acid, calumbic acid; —о *n.* columba, calumba (dried root of *Jateorrhiza palmata*).

**коломбье** *n.* (paper) colombier.

**коломенка** *f.* kind of barge.

**колон/иальный** *a.* colonial, colony; —иальные товары groceries; —изировать *v.* colonize, settle; —ия *f.* colony.

**колон/ка** *f.*, —ковый *a.* column; core, core sample; band (of drops); —ковый бур (min.) core drill; —ковый ловитель core lifter; —кообразный, —нообразный *a.* columnar; —на *f.* column, pillar; tower; (elec.) pile; (cryst.) prism; ионизация —нами columnar ionization; на —не pillar type; —нада *f.* colonnade; —ный *a.* column, columnar; see also **колотый**; —ного типа column (dissolver, etc.).

**колорад/оит** *m.* (min.) coloradoite (a mercury telluride); —ские слои (geol.) Coloradian beds; —ский жук Colorado potato beetle.

**колор/изация** *f.* coloration, coloring; —иметр *m.* colorimeter; —иметрический *a.* colorimetric; —иметрия *f.* colorimetry, colorimetric analysis; —индекс *m.* color index; —ит *m.* coloring.

**колос** *m.* ear, spike (of wheat, corn, etc.); вторичный к. spikelet.

**колосеница** *f.* psyllium seed, fleaseed.

**колоси/стый** *a.* full of ears, heavy-eared (corn, etc.); —ться *v.* ear, form ears.

**колосник** *m.*, —овый *a.* fire grate bar, grate; —и *pl.* grate, grating; —овая решетка grate, fire grate, grating.

**колосняк** *m.* (bot.) wild rye (*Elymus*).

**колосо/вая трава** see **грыжник**; —видный, —образный *a.* spike-shaped, spicate; herringbone (design); —к *m.* spikelet; душистый —к sweet-scented vernal grass (*Anthoxanthum odoratum*); —подъемник *m.* (agr.) grain guard, lifter; —приемник *m.* feeder house (of combine); —уборник *m.* stripper.

**колоссальный** *a.* colossal, huge.

**колосяной** *a.* ear, spike.

**колот/ило** *n.*, —ушка *f.* mallet, beater, rammer; bumper, buffer; —ить *v.* beat, knock, thrash, pound; mill, thresh.

**колот/ый** *a.* split, cleaved; —ь *v.* split, cleave; pierce, prick, stab, thrust; —е *n.* cleaving; (med.) colic.

**колоф/ен** *m.* colophene; **—оловая кислота, —оновая кислота** colopholic acid, colophonic acid; **—оний** *m.* colophony, rosin; **—онит** *m.* (min.) colophonite (a variety of andradite garnet); **—онон** *m.* colophonone.

**колоцинт, колоцветник** *m.* (bot.) colocynth (*Citrullus colocynthis*); **—еин** *m.* colocynthein; **—ин** *m.* colocynthin.

**колоша** *f.* charge; **рудная к.** charge of ore.

**колошение** *n.* (bot.) heading, ear formation.

**колошник** *m.* mouth, charge hole (of furnace).

**колошников/ый** *a.* (met.) charge; blast furnace; **к. газ** blast furnace gas, waste gas; **—ая площадка** charging platform; **—ая пыль** blast furnace dust, flue dust; **—ые весы** charging scales.

**колпа/к** *m.*, **—чковый, —чный** *a.* cap, cover, cowl, hood, bell, helmet; cupola, dome (of furnace) (foundry) cope; (agr.) hotcap; **колесный к.** hub cap; **паровой к.** steam collector; **стеклянный к.** bell jar; **—чковая гайка** screw cap; **—чковая колонна** bubble tower, bubble-plate column; **—чковая тарелка** bubble plate, bubble-cap plate; **—чок** *m.* cap; bubble cap.

**кол/сек** *abbr.* (колебания в секунду) oscillations per second.

**колтун** *m.* (med.) plica polonica.

**колтунник** *m.* (bot.) club moss (*Lycopodium clavatum*).

**колумб/ат** *see* **ниобат**; **—иевый** *a.* Columbia; *see also* **ниобиевый**; **—ий** *m.* columbium, *obs. name for* niobium, *see* **ниобий**; **—ин** *see* **коломбин**; **—ит** *m.* (min.) columbite, niobite.

**Колумбия** Colombia; Columbia.

**колумелла** *f.* (biol.) columella.

**колун** *m.* ax, chopper.

**колх/амеин** *m.* colchameine; **—амин** *m.* colchamine; **—инин** *m.* colchinine; **—ицеин** *m.* colchiceine; **—ицин** *m.* colchicine; **—ициновая кислота** colchicinic acid.

**колхоз** *m.* kolkhoz, collective farm.

**колчедан** *m.* (min.) pyrite, pyrites; **волосистый к.** millerite (nickel sulfide); **гребенчатый к.** cockscomb pyrite (a variety of marcasite); **железный к., серный к.** iron pyrites, pyrite, fool's gold; **копьевидный к.** spear pyrite (a variety of marcasite); **лучистый к.** marcasite; **—ный, —овый** *a.* pyrite, pyritic; **—ные огарки** (met.) pyrite cinders; roasted pyrites; **—осодержащий** *a.* pyritiferous.

**колых/ание** *n.* rocking, swaying; fluctuation; **—ать, —нуть** *v.* rock, sway, shake, swing; **—аться, —нуться** *v.* rock, sway, swing; fluctuate; waver.

**колышек** *m.* peg, picket, prop.

**колышка** *f.* (text.) heald.

**коль** *conj.* if, when, though; *adv.* how much, how many.

**Кольбе реакция** Kolbe reaction.

**Кольби печь** Colby furnace.

**кольд-крем** *m.* cold cream.

**кользовое масло** colza oil, rape oil.

**колькотар** *see* **колкотар.**

**кольм** *m.* kolm (Swedish coal).

**кольмат/аж** *m.*, **—ация** *f.* improving land by silt deposition.

**кольнуть** *see* **колоть.**

**коль/раби, —ряби** *f.* (bot.) kohlrabi (*Brassica oleracea caulorapa*).

**Кольрауша закон** Kohlrausch's law.

**коль-скоро** *conj.* as soon as, as.

**кольца масло** *see* **кользовое масло.**

**кольцев/ание** *n.* cyclization; (elec.) completion of circuit; **—ать** *v.* girdle (trees); band (poultry); **—идный** *see* **кольцеобразный.**

**кольцев/ой** *a.* ring, ring-shaped, annular, circular, circumferential; cyclic; **к. ватер** (text.) ring-spinning machine; **к. грохот** (min.) ring grizzly; **к. зазор** (mach.) radial clearance; **к. подпятник** collar bearing, collar-step bearing; **к. счетчик** (nucl.) ring counter; **—ая обмотка** (elec.) ring winding, Gramme winding; **—ая печь** (cer.) annular kiln, Hofmann kiln; **—ая трубка** (nucl.) donut; **—ая цепь** link chain; **—ое соединение** ring compound, cyclic compound.

**кольцеобразный** *a.* ring-shaped, annular, circular, collar-shaped; cyclic.

**кольц/о** *n.* ring, collar; coil; link (of chain); washer; girdle, band; race, raceway (for ball bearings); (elec.) circuit; **замыкание** —a ring formation, cyclization; **разрыв** —a, **расщепление** —a ring cleavage, cyclic cleavage.

**кольч/атка** *f.* ring worm; —**атый** *a.* ring, ring-shaped, annular, annulate, annulated; cyclic; —**атый червь,** —**ец** *m.* segmented worm, annelid; —**атое соединение** ring compound, cyclic compound.

**кольчугалюминий** *m.* a Duralumin-type alloy.

**колюки** *see* **коровки.**

**колют** *pr. 3 pl. of* **колоть.**

**колюч/еголовые** *pl.* (zool.) Acanthocephala; —**есть** *f.* prickliness; —**ий** *a.* prickly, spiny, thorny; barbed (wire); —**ка** *f.* prickle, spine, thorn, burr, barb; **бесстебельная** —**ка,** —**ник** *m.* (bot.) carline thistle (*Carlina vulgaris*).

**колюшка** *f.* (zool.) stickleback.

**колющий** *a.* cleaving; piercing, stabbing, shooting (pain).

**ком** *m.* clot, lump, chunk, ball, clod; *prepos. of* **кто.**

**ком** *abbr.* (**килоом**) kilohm; **ком**— *abbr.* (**комитет**) committee; (**комиссия**) commission; (**комиссар**) commissar.

**кома** *f.* (med.) coma.

**комагматический** *a.* (geol.) comagmatic.

**команд/а** *f.* command; squad, detail, party, crew; —**ир** *m.,* —**ирский** *a.* commander; —**ировать** *v.* send on a mission; —**ировка** *f.* mission, business trip; —**ный** *a.* master; —**овать** *v.* command, give orders.

**комановая кислота** comanic acid, pyrone-alpha-carboxylic acid.

**команчи** *n.* (geol.) Comanchean series.

**комар** *m.,* —**иный** *a.* (zool.) mosquito; hollow punch, punch press; (met.) nibbling machine, blank-cutting machine; —**ы** *pl.* (zool.) Culicidae; —**ик** *m.* midge, gnat; —**ник** *m.* (bot.) fleabane, fleawort (*Inula squarrosa*).

**комбайн** *m.* (agr.) combine, combine harvester; —**ер** *m.* combiner; —**ировать** *v.* combine, harvest by combine.

**комбатант** *m.* combatant.

**комби**— *prefix* combined, combination;

—**корм** *m.,* —**кормовой** *a.* mixed feed, concentrate; combined fodder.

**комбин/ат** *m.* combine, concern; —**атор** *m.,* —**аторный** *a.* combiner; —**аторика** *f.* (math.) study of combinations; —**ация** *f.,* —**ирование** *n.,* —**ационный** *a.* combination; —**ационное рассеяние** (light) Raman effect; —**езон** *m.* overalls, coveralls; —**ированный** *a.* combined, combination; composite; multiple-unit; —**ировать** *v.* combine, arrange.

**Ком/внуторг** *abbr.* (**Комиссия по внутренней торговле**) Commission for Home Trade; —**госоор** *abbr.* (**Комитет государственных сооружений**) Committee for State Construction.

**комель** *m.* butt, butt end, thick end.

**комен/амид** *m.* comenamide; —**аминовая кислота** comenamic acid; —**дит** *m.* (min.) comendite (a variety of rhyolite); —**овая кислота** comenic acid.

**комета** *f.* comet.

**коминге** *m.* coaming, combing, curb.

**комисс/ар** *m.* commissar, commissioner; —**ариат** *m.* commissariat; —**ионер** *m.* commissioner, agent, middleman, broker, jobber; —**ионерство** *n.* brokerage, jobbing; —**ионный** *a.,* —**ия** *f.* commission, committee, board.

**комитет** *m.* committee, bureau.

**комический** *a.* comical, ridiculous.

**комками** *see* **комок.**

**комкать** *v.* crumple.

**комков/ание** *n.* (met.) nodulizing; —**атый** *a.* clotted, lumped, lumpy, cloddy.

**комма-бацилла** *f.* (biol.) comma bacillus, cholera bacillus.

**коммелин/а** *f.* (bot.) day flower (*Commelina*); —**овые** *pl.* Commelinaceae.

**коммеморативный** *a.* commemorative.

**коммент/арий** *m.* comment, remarks; —**ировать** *v.* comment, remark, observe.

**коммер/сант** *m.* merchant, dealer; —**ция** *f.* commerce, trade; —**ческий** *a.* commercial, mercantile; business (man); **ставить на** —**ческую ногу** *v.* commercialize, put on a commercial basis.

**коммивояжер** *m.* traveling salesman.

**коммун/а** f. commune; —**альный** a. communal, public, municipal; —**альная техника** municipal engineering; civil engineering; —**альные предприятия** public utilities; —**изм** m. communism.

**коммуника/тор** m. communicator; —**ционный** a., —**ция** f. communication; **лабораторные** —**ции** laboratory services, utilities.

**коммунист** m. communist; —**ический** a. communistic.

**коммут/ативный** a. (math.) commutative; —**атор** m., —**аторный** a. (elec.) commutator; (tel.) switchboard; —**ационный** a., —**ация** f., —**ирование** n. commutation; switching; —**ационный аппарат**, —**ационный механизм**, —**ационный прибор** switch; —**ационный щит**, —**ационная доска** switchboard; —**ационное устройство** switchgear; —**ированный** a. commutated; switched; —**ировать** v. commutate, commute, change over, reverse, switch; —**ирующий** a. commutating.

**комнат/а** f. room, apartment; —**ный** a. room, indoor.

**комовой** a. ball, lump, clot.

**комод** m. chest of drawers.

**ком/ок** m. lump, clump, clot, chunk; —**ками, в** —**ках** in lumps, lumpy, clotted; **осадок** —**ками** nodular deposit.

**комол** m. Comol (Remalloy—iron-molybdenum-cobalt alloy).

**комол/ость** f. (zool.) absence of horns; —**ый** a. hornless.

**комоч/ек** m. small clump, aggregate; **образовать** —**ки** v. clot.

**компактн/ость** f. compactness, density; —**ый** a. compact, dense, tight; concise; rugged; massive.

**компандор** m. (tel.) compandor.

**компан/ия** f. company, partnership; party, crew; —**ьон** m. partner, companion.

**компаратор** m. comparator; colorimeter.

**компартия** f. Communist party.

**компас** m., —**ный** a. compass.

**компатриот** m. compatriot.

**компаунд** m. compound, filler; (elec.) insulation compound; compound engine; **к.-динамомашина** (elec.) compound dynamo; **к.-машина, двигатель к.** compound engine; **к.-обмотка** compound winding; **турбина-к.** compound turbine.

**компаунд/ирование** n. compounding; —**ированный** a. compounded, compound, compound-wound; —**ировать** v. compound; —**ирующий** a. compounding; —**ный** a. compound, compound-wound.

**компенди/й**, —**ум** m. compendium, digest.

**компенс/атор** m. compensator, balancer, equalizer; expansion piece; expansion tank; —**ационный** a. compensation, compensating; expansion (piece); —**ация** f., —**ирование** n., —**ирующий** a. compensation, balancing, equalizing; —**ированный** a. compensated; —**ировать** v. compensate, make up (for).

**компетен/тность**, —**ция** f. competence, ability; —**тный** a. competent, able.

**компил/ировать** v. compile, collect; —**яция** f. compilation, collection.

**комплекс** m. complex; group (of atoms); (pal.) assemblage; —**ность** f. complexity; (soil) heterogeneity; —**ный** a. a. complex; multiple (investigation, approach); —**ный процесс** process with rational utilization of all important components; —**ометрический** a. complexometric (titration); —**ообразование** n., —**ообразующий** a. (chem.) complexing.

**комплект** m. set, kit, unit, outfit, assembly, series; —**ный** a. complete; —**ование** n. making up a set; manning, replacement in personnel; —**овать** v. complete (a set), supply, staff.

**комплекция** f. constitution, build.

**комплемент** m. (immunology) complement.

**компликация** f. complication.

**компо/зитный** a. composite; —**зиция** f. composition; —**нент** m. component, constituent; —**нировать**, —**новать** v. compose, group, arrange; combine; —**новка** f. composition, grouping.

**компост** m. compost.

**компостер** m. punch.

**компостиров/ание** n. (agr.) composting;

**—анный** *a.* composted; **—ать** *v.* compost, enrich with compost; punch.

**компот** *m.* stewed fruit.

**компр/есс** *m.* (med.) compress; **—есси-метр, —ессометр** *m.* compression gage; **—ессионный** *a.*, **—ессия** *f.*, **—имирование** *n.* compression; **—ессор** *m.*, **—ессорный** *a.* compressor; **—ессорная** *f.* compressor house; **—ессорная установка** compressor plant; **—имированный** *a.* compressed; **—имировать** *v.* compress.

**компром/етировать, приходить к —иссу** *v.*, **—исс** *m.* compromise; **не идущий на —исс** uncompromising.

**комптометр** *m.* comptometer.

**комптон/ит** *m.* (min.) comptonite (a variety of thomsonite); **—овское смещение** (radiation) Compton shift; **—овское явление, -эффект** Compton effect; **граница —овского поглощения** Compton edge.

**комсомол** *m.*, **—ьский** *a.* Komsomol, Young Communist League.

**кому** *dat. of* кто, to whom.

**комфорт** *m.*, **—ный** *a.* comfort; **—абельный** *a.* comfortable.

**комья** *pl. of* ком.

**конвалла/марин** *m.* convallamarin; **—ретин** *m.* convallaretin; **—рин** *m.* convallarin.

**конвейер** *m.* conveyer, elevator; **—ный** *a.* conveyer, conveying, traveling; **—ная работа** assembly line work; **—ная система** conveyer system.

**конвек/тивный, —ционный** *a.* convective, convection, convectional; **—ция** *f.* convection.

**конвенц/иональный** *a.* conventional; **—ия** *f.* convention; agreement.

**конверг/ентный** *a.* convergent; **—енция** *f.* convergence; **—ировать** *v.* converge.

**конверс/ия** *f.*, **—ионный** *a.* conversion.

**конверт** *m.* envelope, cover.

**конверт/ер, —ор** *m.*, **—ерный** *a.* (met., nucl.) converter; **—ирование** *n.* conversion; **—ированный** *a.* converted; **—ировать** *v.* convert.

**конвицин** *m.* convicin.

**конво/ировать** *v.*, **—й** *m.*, **—йный** *a.* convoy, escort.

**конволвулин** *m.* convolvulin, rhodeorhetin; **—овая кислота, —оловая кислота** convolvulic acid, convolvulinolic acid.

**конвульс/ивный** *a.* convulsive; whooping (cough); **—ия** *f.* convulsion.

**конгениальный** *a.* congenial.

**конгидрин** *m.* conhydrine, hydroxyconiine.

**конгломер/ат** *m.* conglomerate; **—ация** *f.* conglomeration.

**конго** *n.* Congo (dye); **к.-бумага, —вая бумага** Congo (filter) paper; **к.-голубой** Congo blue, trypan blue; **к.-каучук** Congo rubber; **к.-красный, —рот** *m.* Congo red (indicator); **—вая кислота** congoic acid.

**конгрегация** *f.* congregation.

**конгруэн/тность, —ция** *f.* congruence; **—тный** *a.* congruent, corresponding.

**конгсбергит** *m.* (min.) kongsbergite (a variety of native amalgam).

**кондельфин** *m.* condelphine.

**конденсат** *m.*, **—ный** *a.* condensate; water of condensation; **—ор** *m.*, **—орный** *a.* condenser; (elec.) capacitor; **—орный горшок** moisture trap.

**конденсационн/ый** *a.* condensation, condensing; **к. аппарат** condenser; **к. горшок** moisture trap, steam trap; condensing pot; **к. змеевик** spiral condenser, condenser coil; **—ая вода** water of condensation, condensed water; **—ая камера** condensing chamber.

**конденс/ация** *f.*, **—ирование** *n.* condensation; **температура —ации** dew point; **—ер, —ор** *m.*, **—орный** *a.* condenser, condensing lens; **—ированный** *a.* condensed; **—ировать** *v.* condense; **—ирующий** *a.* condensing.

**кондилома** *f.* (med.) condyloma.

**кондитер** *m.* confectioner; **—ские изделия** confectionery, candy; pastry.

**кондиционер** *m.* conditioner.

**кондици/онирование, —рование** *n.* conditioning, humidity control; **к. воздуха** air conditioning; **—онированный** *a.* conditioned; artificial; **—онировать** *v.* condition; **—онный** *a.* conditional; conditioned; quality standardized, certified (seed); **—я** *f.* condition, clause.

**кондовый** *a.* tall, high, full-grown (forest).

**кондуит** *m.* conduit.

**кондуктивн/ость** *f.* conductivity; **—ый** *a.* conductive.

**кондуктометрический** *a.* conductometric (titration).

**кондуктор** *m.*, **—ный** *a.* conductor; (mech.) jig; **—ная втулка** jig bushing; **—ная плита** plate jig; **—но-сверлильный станок** jig borer.

**кондукци/онный** *a.* conduction, conductive; **—я** *f.* conduction.

**кондуран/гин** *m.* condurangin; **—го** *n.* (bot.) condurango (*Gonolobus condurango*); **—стерин** *m.* conduransterin.

**коневодство** *n.* horse breeding.

**конек** *m.* ridge, gable (of roof).

**конель** *m.* Konel (nickel-base ferrous alloy).

**конесси, кора** conessi bark; **—н** *m.* conessine, wrightine.

**кон/ец** *m.* end, termination, close, consummation; extremity, tip; terminal; purpose, aim; distance, journey; length (of rope); outflow, issue, discharge; (elec.) lead; **—цом** end on; **острым —цом** edgewise; **—цы** *pl.* ends, butts, waste, scrap; **—цами** at the ends; **в один к.** one-way (trip); **в оба —ца** round trip; **в —це —цов** finally, eventually; **вид с —ца** end view; **на худой к.** at the worst; **под к.** toward the end, finally; **положить к.** *v.* make an end (of), put a stop (to); **сводить —цы с —цами** *v.* make both ends meet; **толстый к.** butt; **тонкий к.** tip.

**конечно** *adv.* of course, certainly, naturally, surely, no doubt; **—разностный** *a.* finite-difference.

**конечность** *f.* finiteness; limb, extremity.

**конечн/ый** *a.* final, ultimate, terminal, end; finite; **к. момент, —ая точка** end point (in titration, etc.); **к. продукт** end product, final product; **к. ряд** finite series; **—ая скорость** outlet velocity; **—ая температура** end temperature; outlet temperature; **—ая функция** finite function; **в —ом итоге** ultimately; **в —ом счете** all things considered.

**кониакский подъярус** (geol.) Coniacian substage.

**кони/ин, —лен** *m.* coniine, 2-propyl-piperidine; **—иновая кислота** coniic acid, conicic acid.

**кони/метр** *m.* (min.) konimeter (for measuring dust); **—н** *see* **кониин**.

**конина** *f.* horseflesh, horse meat.

**кони/нкит** *m.* (min.) koninckite; **—рин** *see* **кониин**; **—т** *m.* (min.) konite (a variety of dolomite).

**конифер/ил** *m.*, **—иловый** *a.* coniferyl; **—иловый спирт, —ол** *m.* coniferyl alcohol, coniferol; **—ин** *m.* coniferin.

**конихальцит** *m.* (min.) conichalcite.

**кониц/еин** *m.* coniceine; **—ин** *m.*, **—иновый** *a.* conicine.

**конич еск/ий** *a.* conic, conical, cone; bevel, beveled; tapered, tapering; **к. клапан** cone valve; **к. классификатор** (met.) cone classifier; **к. подпятник** cone bearing; **—ая шестерня, —ое** gear; **зубчатое колесо, —ое колесо** bevel gear; **—ое сечение** (geom.) conic section.

**коничность** *f.* conicity, angle of taper; conic shape.

**конкрет/изировать** *v.* define concretely, specify; **—ность** *f.* concreteness; **—ный** *a.* concrete.

**конкреци/онный** *a.* concretionary, nodular; **—я** *f.* concretion, nodule.

**конкур/ент** *m.* rival, competitor; **—ентный** *a.* concurrent; **—енция** *f.* competition; **вне —енции** unrivaled; **—ировать** *v.* compete; **—ирующий** *a.* competing, competitive, rival; **—с** *m.* competition; **—сный** *a.* competitive.

**коннарит** *m.* (min.) connarite.

**коннектор** *m.* connector.

**коннеллит** *m.* (min.) connellite, footeite.

**конн/о-моторный** *a.* horse-drawn and motor-driven (sprayer); **—ый** *a.* horse; horse-drawn.

**Коновалова закон** Konowaloff rule (of vapor pressures).

**коногон** *m.* (min.) drawer.

**конод** *m.* conode, tie line (in phase diagram).

**коноид** *m.*, **—альный** *a.* (geom.) conoid.

**конометр** *see* **кониметр**.

**коноп/атить** *v.* calk; **—атка** *f.* calking;

calking iron; —атный *a.* calking; —ать *f.* oakum; —ачение *n.* calking.

конопиды *pl.* thick-headed flies (*Conopidae*).

конопл/еводство *n.* hemp raising; —евые *pl.* (bot.) Cannabinaceae; —я *f.* hemp (*Cannabis sativa*); —яник *m.* hemp field; —яный *a.* hemp, hempen; —яная кислота linoleic acid; —яное масло hempseed oil.

коносамент *m.* (com.) bill of lading.

конперник *m.* Conpernik (iron-nickel alloy).

консеквентный *a.* consecutive, successive.

консерв/ативный *a.* conservative; —атор *m.* conserver; expansion tank, header tank; —ация *f.* conservation.

консервир/ование *n.*, —овка *f.* preserving, preservation, canning (of food); conservation; —ованный *a.* preserved, canned, tinned; conserved; —овать *v.* preserve, can, tin; conserve; —ующий *a.* preserving; conserving.

консерв/ный *a.* preserving, canning; к. завод cannery; —ы *pl.* preserves, canned food; мясные —ы canned meat; фруктовые —ы canned fruit.

консертальный *a.* (cryst.) consertal.

консилиум *m.* consultation, council.

консист/ентный *a.* consistent; —ентная смазка (lubricating) grease; —енция *f.* consistence, density; consistency, body; —ометр *m.* consistometer.

конский *a.* horse, equine; к. боб (bot.) broad bean, Windsor bean (*Vicia faba*); specif. horse bean (*Vicia faba equina*); к. ладан *see* копытень.

консоли *pl.* (com.) consolidated annuities; —дация *f.* consolidation; —дированный *a.* consolidated; —дировать *v.* consolidate.

консоль *f.*, —ный *a.* cantilever, angle bearer, bracket, arm; console; —ный кран cantilever crane, bracket crane; —ный подшипник bracket bearing; —ная балка, —ная ферма cantilever.

конспект *m.*, —ивный *a.* abstract, synopsis, summary, compendium; —ировать *v.* abstract, summarize.

консталин *m.* konstalin (a solid lubricant).

константа *f.* constant.

константан *m.* constantan (a nickel-copper alloy).

Константиновский завод the Konstantinovka (glass) works.

констатировать *v.* state, establish, ascertain.

константный *a.* constant.

констелляция *f.* (astron.) constellation.

конститу/тивный *a.* constitutive; —циональный *a.* constitutional; —ционный *a.*, —ция *f.* constitution; —ционная вода water of constitution, chemically combined water; —ционная формула constitutional formula.

конструиров/ание *n.* construction, designing, development; —ать *v.* construct, design, develop, engineer.

конструк/таль *m.* an aluminum alloy; —тивный *a.* constructive, constructional; —тор *m.* constructor, designer; —торский *a.* constructor; structural; —ционный *a.* construction, constructional, structural; —ционная сталь structural steel; —ция *f.* construction, structure, formation; design, make, build; последней —ции of recent design.

консул *m.*, —ьский *a.* consul.

консульт/ант *m.* consultant; —ативный *a.* consultative, consulting, advisory; —ация *f.* consultation, arbitration; —ировать *v.* consult, ask advice (of).

контаг/ий *m.* (med.) contagion; —иозный *a.* contagious.

контакт *m.* contact, connection, terminal; catalyst; к. (Петрова) spec. a detergent mixture of sulfonaphthenic acids (Russian equivalent of Twitchell reagent); граница —а interface; подвижный к. (elec.) slide contact, slider; —но-разрывный механизм (elec.) make-and-break mechanism.

контакт/ный, —овый *a.* contact; contacting (section of column); к. винт (elec.) contact screw, terminal; к. рельс contact rail, conductor rail; к. ролик contact roller; trolley wheel; к. способ contact process (for sulfuric acid manufacture); —ная кнопка (elec.) press button, switch button; —ная поверхность contact surface; interface; —ное вещество, —ное

**средство** contact agent, catalyst; —**op** *m.* (elec.) contactor, switch.

**контаминация** *f.* contamination.

**контарь** *m.* steelyard (a weighing device); quintal (100 kg.).

**контейнер** *m.* container, box; tank; (nucl.) rabbit, can.

**контекст** *m.* context.

**контингент** *m.* contingent, quota, share.

**континент** *m.* continent; —**альный** *a.* continental.

**континуум** *m.* (math.) continuum; **состояние** —a continuous state.

**контокоррент** *m.* (com.) account current.

**контор/а** *f.* office, bureau, board; —**ка** *f.* writing desk, desk; —**ская книга** account book, ledger; —**щик** *m.* clerk.

**контр**— *prefix* counter—.

**контравалентность** *f.* contravalence.

**контраг/ент** *m.* contractor; —**ированный** *a.* contracted (dimensionally).

**контрадик/торный** *a.* contradictory; —**ция** *f.* contradiction.

**контражур** *m.* (phot.) back-lit exposure.

**контракт** *m.* contract, agreement, terms; —**ант** *m.* contractor; —**ация** *f.* contracting; —**ировать, —овать** *v.* contract.

**контрак/тура** *f.* (med.) contracture; —**ция** *f.* contraction; compression.

**контрапрош** *m.* counterapproach.

**контраст** *m.* contrast; —**ировать** *v.* contrast, compare; —**ность** *f.*, —**ный** *a.* contrast; —**ность изображения** contrast range.

**контрафакция** *f.* infringement.

**контрацид** *m.* (met.) a nickel alloy.

**контргайка** *f.* lock nut.

**контргруз** *m.* counterweight, balance weight, counterbalance, counterpoise.

**контр-давление** *n.* back pressure.

**контрибуция** *f.* contribution; indemnity.

**контр/калибр** *m.* countergage, standard gage, control gage, master gage; —**клин** *m.* counterwedge; tightening key; —**миноносец** *m.* torpedo boat destroyer, destroyer.

**контролер** *m.* controller, inspector, supervisor, checker; monitor; (elec.) controller; **к. мер и весов** inspector of weights and measures; **главный к.** (elec.) master switch; —**ный** *a.* (elec.) controller.

**контролир/ование** *n.*, —**овка** *f.* control, controlling, supervision; —**ованный** *a.* controlled, control; —**овать** *v.* control, superintend, monitor, inspect, check; —**ующий агент** control agent, modifying agent.

**контроллер** *see* **контролер**.

**контроль** *m.* control, checking, inspection, supervision, monitoring; blank test, standard; —**ная** *f.* control room; —**но-измерительный** *a.* control and measurement; **производственная** —**но-измерительная аппаратура** process instrumentation; —**но-семенной** *a.* seed-testing.

**контрольн/ый** *a.* control, check, test, pilot, regulating; supervisory; monitoring; master; reference (point); **к. анализ** check analysis; **к. блок** monitor unit; **к. калибр** check gage, master gage, standard; **к. кран** gage tap; **к. щиток,** —**ая доска** dashboard, instrument board (or panel); —**ая книга** log; —**ая колба** control flask; —**ая линия** guide line; —**ое определение** control determination; —**ое устройство** monitor; —**ые инструменты** control instruments; inspection tools.

**контрпар** *m.* countersteam, counterpressure steam, back steam; —**ить** *v.* countersteam, give back steam.

**контрпоршень** *m.* counterpiston.

**контрпретензия** *f.* counterclaim.

**контрпривод** *m.*, —**ный вал** countershaft.

**контр/приказ** *m.* countermand; —**проверка** *f.* check determination; —**разведка** *f.* counterreconnaissance, counterespionage; —**рельс** *m.* guard rail, guide rail; —**ток** *m.* countercurrent, counterflow; —**фланец** *m.* counterflange; —**форс** *m.* counterfort, buttress, abutment.

**конту/женный** *a.* contused, bruised; —**зить** *v.* contuse, bruise; —**зия** *f.* contusion, shell shock.

**контур** *m.* contour, outline, form; loop, circuit; circumference, periphery; relief; boundary; **линия** —a contour line, contour; **набрасывать к.** *v.* outline; **—ный** *a.* contour, outline, in outline.

**конус** *m.* (geom.) cone; (gripping) jaw; bell (of blast furnace); **к. выноса** (geol.) alluvial fan; **угол —а** angle of taper; **усеченный к.** frustrum.

**конусн/ость** *f.* conicity, angle of taper; **—ый** *a.* cone, conic, conical; bevel; taper.

**конусо/видность, —образность** *f.* cone shape, conicity, taper; **—видный, —образный** *a.* cone-shaped, coniform, conoid, conical; taper, tapered.

**конфекц/ион** *m.*, **—ия** *f.* confection; **—ионный** *a.* confection; made, ready-made (clothes); **—ия** *f.* making, piecing (together), assembly.

**конференция** *f.* conference.

**конфет/а** *f.*, **—ный** *a.* candy; **—ы** *pl.*, confectionery.

**конфигурац/ионный** *a.*, **—ия** *f.* configuration, profile, contour; layout.

**конфиденциальный** *a.* confidential, private.

**конфиск/ация** *f.* confiscation; **—овать** *v.* confiscate.

**конфликт** *m.* conflict; **—ный** *a.* conflicting.

**конфлюэн/тный** *a.* confluent; **—ция** *f.* confluence.

**конфокальный** *a.* (math.) confocal.

**конформный** *a.* (math.) conformal.

**конх** *m.* conch, shell.

**конхи/нин** *m.* conquinine, quinidine; **—олин** *m.* conchiolin; **—т** *m.* (min.) conchite (a porous variety of aragonite).

**конхоида** *f.* (geom.) conchoid; **—льный** *a.* conchoidal, shell-like.

**конц.** *abbr.* (**концентрированный**) concentrated.

**конца** *see* **конец.**

**концев/ой** *a.* end, terminal, *see also* **конечный; к. зажим** (elec.) terminal, terminal clamp; **—ая шарошка** end mill, milling cutter.

**концентр/ат** *m.* concentrate; **—атор** *m.*, **—ационный аппарат** concentrator; **—ационный** *a.*, **—ация** *f.*, **—ирование** *n.* concentration, concentrating; **—ационный элемент** (elec.) concentration cell; **—ирован-**

**—ный** *a.* concentrated, strong; **—ировать** *v.* concentrate; **—ирующий** *a.* concentrating; **—ометр** *m.* device for continuous measurement of concentration (of sulfur in petroleum products).

**концентр/ический, —ичный** *a.* concentric; **—ичность** *f.* concentricity; **—ы** *pl.* (geom.) concentric circles.

**концепция** *f.* conception, concept, idea.

**конце/равнитель** *m.* trimming saw, crosscut saw; **—резка** *f.*, **—резная пила** cut-off saw.

**концерн** *m.* (com.) concern.

**концессия** *f.* concession, grant.

**кон-ция** *abbr.* (**концентрация**) concentration.

**концкорм** *m.* (agr.) concentrated feed, concentrate.

**конц/овка** *f.* (printing) tailpiece; runout (of film); **—ы** *pl. of* **конец.**

**конч/ать, —ить** *v.* finish, end, complete, conclude, terminate; **—аться** *v.* come to an end, expire, lapse; result, end (in); **—енный** *a.* finished, completed, done.

**кончик** *m.* tip, point, end.

**конъюг/ат** *m.* (biol.) conjugate; **—ация** *f.*, **—ирование** *n.* conjugation; **—ированный** *a.* conjugated, conjugate, paired, coupled; **—ированные двойные связи** conjugate double bonds.

**конъюнкт/ива** *f.* (anat.) conjunctiva; **—ивит** *m.* (med.) conjunctivitis; **—ивный** *a.* conjunctive; **—ура** *f.* conjuncture, juncture; (business) conditions.

**конь** *m.* horse, stallion.

**коньковый** *a.* ridge, gable.

**конья/к** *m.* cognac, brandy; **—чное масло** cognac oil; ethyl oenanthate (flavoring).

**конюшня** *f.* stable.

**конятник** *m.* China root (rhizome of *Smilax China*).

**коопер/атив** *m.* cooperative, cooperative store; **—ативный** *a.* cooperative; **—атор** *m.* cooperator; **—ация** *f.*, **—ирование** *n.* cooperation; **—ированный** *a.* affiliated; **—ировать** *v.* cooperate.

**Коопзем** *abbr.* (**Кооператив работников учреждений накромзема**) The

Employees' Cooperative Store at the Commissariat for Agriculture.

**кооптировать** v. coopt.

**коорди́н/ата** f. (math.) coordinate; **—атный** a. coordinate, coordinated; **—атор** m. coordinator; **—ационный** a., **—ация** f. coordination; **—ационная связь** coordination linkage; coordinate bond; **—ированный** a. coordinated, coordinate; **—ировать** v. coordinate.

**коп.** abbr. (копейка) kopeck.

**копа** f. pile, heap; 60 sheaves (of corn).

**копа/еноска** f., **—йский** a., **—йское дерево** (bot.) copaiba (*Copaifera officinalis*); **—ин** m. copahin; **—йва** f., **—йский бальзам** copaiba, balsam copaiba; **—йская кислота** copaivic acid.

**копал** m., **—овый, —ьный** a. copal (resin); **к. каури** kauri gum, kauri resin; copal; **—ин** m. (min.) copaline, copalite; copalin (resin from *Liquidambar styraciflua*); **—иновая кислота** copalinic acid; **—овый желтник, —овый кожевник** (bot.) sumac (*Rhus copallina*); **—овый лак** copal varnish; **—овая кислота** copalic acid; **—овая смола** copal, copal resin.

**коп/анец, —ань** m. pond, pool; **—ание, —анье** n. digging, excavation; **—атель** m. digger, excavator; **—ательный** a. digging; (zool.) fossorial; **—ать** v. dig, excavate; **—ач** m. (root crop) digger, plow.

**копе/ечник** m. (bot.) hedysarum; **—ечный** a., **—йка** f. kopeck (1/100 of a ruble); **—ечная руда** a form of bog iron ore.

**копеллидин** m. copellidine, 2-ethyl-6-methyl-piperidine.

**копеподы** pl. (zool.) Copepoda.

**копер** m. pile driver, ram impact machine, drop hammer; impact tester; (bot.) see **укроп.**

**коперниковая пальма** see **карнауба.**

**копи** pl. of **копь.**

**копиапит** m. (min.) copiapite, janosite, yellow copperas.

**копил/ка** f. receptacle; (coin) box; **—ьник** m. (met.) forehearth, receiver, settling reservoir.

**копир** m. copy, master form; (mach.) feeler mechanism.

**копирин** m. copyrine, 2, 7-benzodiazine.

**копир/ка** f. carbon paper; **—ный** a. copy.

**копирова́льно/-фрезерный станок** duplicate-milling machine, profiling machine; die-sinking machine; **—шлифовальный станок** profile grinding machine.

**копировальн/ый** a. copying, duplicating; **к. аппарат, —ое приспособление** duplicator; mimeographing machine; (phot.) printer; **к. станок** copying machine; **к. фрезерный станок** see **копировально-фрезерный станок; —ая бумага** carbon paper; tracing paper; **—ая краска** transfer color.

**копир/ование** n. copying, duplication; (phot.) printing; **—овать** v. copy, duplicate, imitate; trace; **—овщик** m. tracer; **—ующий** a. copying, duplicating; master-slave (manipulator); **—ующее сочленение** slave joint (of manipulator).

**копит/ель** m. storer, accumulator; **—ь** v. store, accumulate, save up, put by.

**коп/ия** f. copy, transcript, duplicate, counterpart; **снимать —ию** v. copy, make a copy, duplicate.

**копн/а** f. rick (of hay), shock (of wheat); **—ение** n. stacking, piling up; **—итель** m. stacker, shocker; **—ить** v. stack, pile up, shock.

**копнуть** see **копать.**

**кополимер** see **сополимер.**

**копотливый** a. sluggish; tedious.

**копот/ный** a. sooty, smoky, smoking; **—ь** f. soot, lampblack; smoke, fume, vapor.

**Коппа закон** Kopp's law.

**коппит** m. (min.) koppite.

**копра** f. copra (dried kernels of coconut); **—ол** m. copraol.

**копровый** a. pile-driver.

**копро/лит** m. (geol.) coprolite, fossil excrement; **—порфирин** m. coproporphyrin; **—станол, —стерин** m. coprostanol, coprosterol, dihydrocholesterol.

**копт/еть** v. smoke; **—ильня** f., **—ильная камера** smokehouse; **—ить** v. smoke, cure; **—ящий** a. smoking.

**копулиров/ание** *n.*, —**ка** *f.* (agr.) whipgrafting; —**ать** *v.* whipgraft.

**копуляция** *f.* copulation.

**копунктальный** *a.* (math.) copunctal, concurrent.

**копчен/ие** *n.* smoking, curing; fumigation; —**ый** *a.* smoked, cured.

**копчик** *m.* (anat.) coccyx; —**овый** *a.* coccygeal.

**копыт/ень,** —**ник** *m.* (bot.) asarum.

**копытн/оступающие** *pl.* (zool.) unguligrades; —**ый** *a.* hoof; hoofed, ungulate; —**ая мазь,** —**ое масло** (pharm.) neat's-foot oil, hoof ointment; —**ая мука** hoof-meal; —**ое животное** (zool.) ungulate.

**копыт/о** *n.* hoof; —**чатый** *a.* hoofshaped, ungulate.

**копь** *f.* mine, pit.

**копье** *n.* spear, lance; —**видный** *a.* spear-shaped, spicular, lanceolate.

**кор.** *abbr.* (корейский) Korean.

**кора** *f.* bark, rind, cortex; crust; (casting) skin; **земная к.** (geol.) crust.

**кораб/ельный** *a.* ship, marine; shipborne; **к. клей** marine glue; —**лестроение** *n.* shipbuilding;—**ль** *m.* ship, vessel.

**кора/зол** *m.* Corazol, pentylenetetrazol; —**лин** *m.* coralin.

**коралл** *m.* coral; —**ин** *m.* corallin, aurin, *p*-rosolic acid; —**ит** *m.* corallite.

**коралло/видный,** —**образный** *a.* corallike, coralloidal; —**вый** *a.* coral, coralline; —**вые полипы** (zool.) Anthozoa.

**корамин** *m.* Coramine, nikethamide.

**корацит** *m.* (min.) coracite (an alteration product of uraninite).

**корги** *pl.* korgi (small river bars; shoals in the Arctic Ocean).

**корд** *m.*, —**а** *f.* cord.

**кордиамин** *m.* Cordiamin, nikethamide.

**кордиерит** *m.* (min.) cordierite, iolite.

**кордил** *m.* cordyl, acetyl-cordol; —**ит** *m.* (min.) cordylite (a variety of parisite).

**кордильера** *f.* cordillera, mountain range.

**кордит** *m.* (expl.) cordite.

**кордицепин** *m.* cordycepin.

**кордная нить** (rubber) cord; **к. ткань** cord fabric; **к. шина** cord tire.

**Кордо резьба** Cordeaux (screw) thread.

**кордовая шина** *see* **кордная шина.**

**кордовская кожа** *see* **кордуан.**

**кордол** *m.* cordol, tribromsalol.

**кордон** *m.* cordon.

**кордриль** *m.* (min.) core drill.

**кордуан** *m.*, —**ский сафьян** cordovan, cordovan leather.

**корегонин** *m.* coregonin.

**кореит** *m.* (min.) agalmatolite.

**корейский** *a.* Korean.

**корекс** *m.* Corex (abrasive).

**корен/астый** *a.* thickset, stumpy, stocky; —**иться** *v.* root (in); be founded (on).

**коренн/ой** *a.* root; radical, fundamental, original, trunk, main; native, indigenous; thorough; **к. вал** crankshaft; **к. зуб** (anat.) molar; **к. подшипник** crank bearing; **к. рассол** spring brine, deep-well brine; —**ая порода** bedrock; —**ая свая** foundation pile.

**кор/ень** *m.* root; radix; (math.) radical; **вырывать с** —**нем** *v.* uproot, eradicate; **знак** —**ня** (math.) radical sign; **квадратный к.** (math.) square root; **кубический к.** cube root; **на** —**ню** standing (crop); **пускать** —**ни** *v.* take root.

**коретра** *f.* larva of Chaoborinae.

**корешок** *m.* little root, rootlet, radicle; stub (of receipt); butt, butt end.

**корж** *m.* (cer.) filter cake, cast; rock jutting from roof of mine.

**корз** *m.* coarse (low-grade rubber).

**корзин/а** *f.* basket, crate, crib; bucket; —**ка** *f.* basket; (bot.) calathide; —**коцветные** *pl.* (bot.) Aggregatae; —**чатый** *a.* basket, basket-like.

**корзит** *m.* (petr.) corsite, napoleonite (a variety of orbicular diorite).

**кориамиртин** *m.* coriamyrtin.

**кориандр** *m.*, —**овый** *a.* (bot.) coriander (*Coriandrum sativum*); —**ол** *m.* coriandrol, linalool.

**кори/арин** *m.* coriarine; —**бульбин** *m.* corybulbine; —**далин** *m.* corydaline; —**дин** *m.* corydine (alkaloid from *Corydalis cava*); coridine (aniline derivative).

**коридор** *m.*, —**ный** *a.* corridor, passage, passageway; **в** —**ном порядке** unstaggered.

**кори/кавамин** *m.* corycavamine; —**кавидин** *m.* corycavidine; —**кавин** *m.*

corycavine; —лин *m.* corylin; —ло-
филин *m.* corylophiline; —нин *m.*
corynin (a hydroxy acid); corynine,
yohimbine; —нит *m.* (min.) corynite
(antimony-containing gersdorffite).
**коринка** *f.* currants, currant.
**кориокавин** *m.* coryocavine.
**Кориолиса сила** (phys.) Coriolis force.
**кори/пальмин** *m.* corypalmine; —тубе-
**рин** *m.* corytuberine.
**кориц/а** *f.* cinnamon; **белая к.** canella,
canella bark; **китайская к.** Chinese
cinnamon, cassia bark; **цветы** —ы
cinnamon flowers, cassia buds.
**коричне/ватый** *a.* brownish; —вый *a.*
brown; —вая земля, —зем *m.* korich-
nezem, cinnamonic soil.
**коричник** *m.* (bot.) cinnamon (*Cinnamomum*); **настоящий к., цейлонский к.**
cinnamon (*Cinnamomum zeylanicum*).
**корично/амиловый эфир** amyl cinnamate; —бензиловый эфир benzyl
cinnamate; —бутиловый эфир butyl
cinnamate; —висмутовая соль bismuth cinnamate; —карбоновая кислота carboxycinnamic acid; —кислый *a.* cinnamic acid; cinnamate (of);
—кислый натрий, —натриевая соль
sodium cinnamate; —кислая соль
cinnamate; —этиловый эфир ethyl
cinnamate.
**коричн/ый** *a.* cinnamon; cinnamic; **к.
альдегид** cinnamic aldehyde, cinnamaldehyde, 3-phenylpropenal; **к. камень** (min.) cinnamon-stone, essonite
(a variety of grossularite garnet); **к.
лавр, —ое дерево** *see* **коричник; к.
спирт** cinnamic alcohol; **к. цвет**
cinnamon flowers, cassia buds; —ая
кислота cinnamic acid; **соль** —ой
кислоты cinnamate; —ое масло
cinnamon oil; **китайское** —ое масло
cassia oil.
**корка** *f.* crust, incrustation, scale, scab;
bark; peel, rind; (met.) scum; (casting)
skin.
**коркит** *m.* (min.) corkite (a beudantite).
**корков/атый** *a.* suberous; —о-столб-
**чатый** *a.* crust-columnar; —ый *a.*
(anat.) cortical; *see also* **пробковый;**
—ый асбест *see* **горная пробка;** —ая
пробка cork, stopper, plug.
**Корлиса клапан** Corliss valve.

**корм** *m.* feed, forage, fodder.
**корма** *f.* stern (of ship).
**корм/еж** *m.*, —ежка *f.* feed, feeding;
—ить *v.* feed, nourish; —ление *n.*
feeding; —ленный *a.* fed, nourished.
**кормо**— *prefix* feed, fodder; —вой *a.*
food, feed, feeding; nutrient (yeast);
(naut.) stern; —вой эквивалент
fodder equivalent; —вая единица
feed unit (equal to nutritional value
of 1 kg. of oats); —вая патока (sugar)
final molasses; —вая смесь (agr.)
feed, mash; —вая трава fodder grass,
forage grass; —дробилка *f.* feed
grinder; —кухня *f.* feed (preparing)
plant.
**кормофит** *m.* (bot.) cormophyte.
**кормоцех** *see* **кормокухня.**
**кормушка** *f.* feed box, feeder, trough,
rack.
**корналин** *m.* (min.) carnelian (a form of
chalcedony).
**корнать** *v.* cut short, crop.
**корнваллийский** *a.* Cornish.
**Корнваллис** Cornwall.
**корнваллит** *m.* (min.) cornwallite.
**корне**— *prefix* root, rhizo—; —вище *n.*
(bot.) rhizome, rootstock; —вой *a.*
root, radical, *see also* **коренной;** —вая
соль deep-well salt; —головые *pl.*
(zool.) Rhizocephala; —ед *m.* root
rot; (zool.) root borer; —еды *pl.*
(zool.) Hepialidae; —жил *m.* a bark
beetle (*Hylastes*); —ножки *pl.* (zool.)
Rhizopoda; —обитаемый *a.* root-
inhabited, root (zone); —отпрыско-
вый *a.* offset, shoot; —плод *m.* root
crop; —резка *f.* root cutter.
**корнерупин** *m.* (min.) kornerupine.
**корни** *pl. of* **корень.**
**корнин** *m.* cornin, cornic acid; cornine
(alkaloid).
**Корнинга стекло** Corning glass.
**корнишон** *m.* gherkin, small cucumber.
**корнубианит** *m.* (petr.) cornubianite (a
tourmaline hornfels).
**корну/оид** *m.* cornuoid; —тин *m.* cornu-
tine (ergot alkaloid); —тол *m.*
cornutol.
**корнуэльский** *see* **корнваллийский.**
**корнцанги** *pl.* (met.) assayer's tongs.
**корнюры** *pl.* gas conduits (for coke
ovens).

**короб** *m.* box, flat; basket; duct.
**коробить** *v.* warp, distort, deform, bend;
—**ся** *v.* warp, buckle, shrink.
**коробка** *f.* box, case, chest; housing,
compartment; hopper; can; tank;
body.
**коробление** *n.* warping, buckling, distortion, deformation, shrinkage.
**коробоч/ка** *f.* little box; (bot.) boll, pod;
—**ный** *a.* box, case; boll.
**коробчат/ый** *a.* box, box-type, box-like;
**к. замок** case lock; —**ая отливка**
(foundry) box casting; —**ое железо**
U-iron, channel iron.
**корова** *f.* cow.
**коровальт** *m.* Corowalt (abrasive).
**коров/ий** *a.* cow, bovine; —**ье масло**
butter; —**ки** *pl.* lady beetles (*Cocci-
nellidae*); —**ник** *m.* cow barn; (bot.)
angelica.
**коровой** *a.* crusted.
**коровяк** *m.* liquid cow manure; (bot.)
mullein (*Verbascum*).
**короед** *m.* bark beetle; —**ы** *pl.* engraver
or bark beetles (*Ipidae, Scolytidae*);
**к.-гравер** *m.* Pityogenes; **к.-крошка**
*f.* Crypturgus.
**корол/евский** *a.* king's, royal; **к. голубой**
king's blue, royal blue; —**евская
желть** king's yellow, orpiment; —**ек**
*m.* (met.) metallic regulus or button,
assay button, bead; —**ь** *m.* king;
—**ьковый** *a.* (met.) reguline, regulus;
button, assay (balance).
**коромысло** *n.* yoke, beam, balance beam,
(balance) arm; rocking shaft; bascule.
**корон/а** *f.* crown, corona; —**адит** *m.*
(min.) coronadite; —**ен** *m.* coronene;
—**ий** *m.* coronium, protofluorine;
—**иллин** *m.* coronillin.
**корон/ирование** *n.*, —**ирующий разряд**,
—**ный разряд** (dielectrics) corona,
corona discharge; —**ировать** *v.* display corona; —**ка** *f.* crown; (boring)
bit; —**ник** *m.* winter cutworm (*Agrotis segetum*); —**ный** *a.* crown, corona;
—**ный бур** crown drill; —**ная
шестерня** crown wheel; —**овать** *v.*
crown.
**короноповая кислота** coronopic acid.
**корончатый** *see* **коронный**.
**коро/обдирка** *f.*, —**обдирочник** *m.*,
—**очистный нож** barker, spudder;

—**обдирный**, —**обдирочный** *a.* barking, bark-stripping.
**коросил** *m.* Koroseal (plasticized polyvinyl chloride).
**короста** *f.* scab, mange.
**коротк/ий** *a.* short, brief; —**о** *adv.*
shortly, briefly; —**о говоря** in short,
in brief, in a few words.
**коротко**— *prefix* short; —**волновый** *a.*
short-wave; —**волокнистый** *a.* short-
staple, short-fibered; short-grained;
—**выдержанный** *a.* briefly exposed;
seasoned for a short time; (nucl.)
short-decayed; —**действующий** *a.*
short-range; —**живущий** *a.* short-
lived; —**замкнутый** *a.* (elec.) short-
circuited, short-circuit, shorted;
—**замыкатель** *m.* short-circuiting device; —**замыкающий** *a.* short-circuiting; —**звеньевая цепь** short-link
chain; —**крылые** *pl.* rove beetles
(*Staphylinidae*); —**крылый** *a.* short-
winged, brachypterous; —**надкрылые
жуки** short-winged beetles (*Brache-
lytra, Staphylinidae*); —**пламенный** *a.*
short-flame; —**плечий** *a.* short-arm
(balance); —**пробежный** *a.* short-
range; —**ствольный** *a.*short-barreled;
—**столбчатый** *a.* (min.) short-colum-
nar; —**сть** *f.* shortness, brevity;
—**усые** *pl.* short-horned flies (*Brachy-
cera*); —**фокусный** *a.* short-focus.
**коротоксигенин** *m.* corotoxigenin.
**короче** *comp. of.* **короткий, коротко,**
shorter.
**корочка** *diminutive of* **корка.**
**корпия** *f.* lint.
**корпора/тивный** *a.* corporate; —**ция** *f.*
corporation, body.
**корпорин** *m.* corporin, progesterone.
**корпулентный** *a.* corpulent, fat.
**корпус** *m.* body, carcass, frame, framework, chassis, hull; housing, case,
casing; (reactor) vessel; (evaporator)
effect; base (of plow); shell (of bomb);
(mil.) corps.
**корпускул/а** *f.* corpuscle; —**ярный** *a.*
corpuscular.
**корпусный** *a. of* **корпус.**
**корразия** *f.* (geol.) corrasion.
**коррегир/ование** *see* **коррекция**;—**овать**
*see* **корригировать**; —**ующий** *see*
**корректирующий.**

**коррект/ив** *m.* corrective; correction, amendment; —**ировать** *v.* correct, adjust; —**ировочный,** —**ирующий** *a.* correcting, adjusting; —**ность** *f.* correctness; —**ный** *a.* correct, proper; —**ор** *m.* corrector; proofreader; —**ура** *f.* correction; proof, proof page; proofreading; **править** —**уру** *v.* proofread; —**урный лист** proof page.

**коррекци/онный** *a.,* —**я** *f.* correction; к. **множитель** correction factor; —**онная величина** extent of correction.

**коррел/ировать** *v.,* —**ят** *m.* correlate; —**ятивный** *a.* correlative; —**яция** *f.* correlation.

**корреспонден/т** *m.* correspondent, reporter; —**ция** *f.* correspondence.

**корригировать** *v.* correct, adjust, fix.

**корродир/ованный** *a.* corroded; —**овать** *v.* corrode; —**ующий** *a.* corroding, corrosive; —**ующее средство** corrosive.

**коррозие/стойкий,** —**устойчивый** *a.* corrosion-resisting, non-corroding, rustproof; stainless (steel); —**устойчивость** *f.* resistance to corrosion.

**корроз/ийный,** —**ионный** *a.* corrosion; corrosive; —**ионная устойчивость** corrosion resistance; —**ионное растрескивание** corrosion cracking, stress corrosion; —**ионно—** *see* **коррозие—;** —**ия** *f.* corrosion; **локальная** —**ия, местная** —**ия** pitting.

**корсиканский глистогонный мох** Corsican moss (*Gracilaria helminthochorton*).

**корти/зон** *m.* cortisone; —**костерон** *m.* corticosterone; —**н** *m.* cortin (adrenal cortex extract); —**цин** *m.* corticin; —**циновая кислота** corticinic acid.

**корубин** *m.* Corubin (abrasive).

**корунд** *m.* (min.) corundum; **синий к.** sapphire; —**еллит** *m.* corundellite (margarite-coated corundum crystals); —**офилит** *m.* corundophilite (probably same as prochlorite).

**корча** *f.* spasm, cramp; stump with root.

**корчага** *f.* large pot, earthenware pot.

**корчев/альный** *a.,* —**ание** *n.,* —**ка** *f.* uprooting, grubbing; —**ать** *v.* uproot, grub.

**корч/ение** *n.* contraction (of nerves); —**ить** *v.* contort, convulse, contract.

**коршун** *m.* (zool.) kite, hawk.

**корыт/ный,** —**ообразный** *a.* trough, trough-shaped; —**ное железо** U-iron, channel iron; —**о** *n.* trough, pan, vat; hod; —**це** *n.* race (for ball bearings); saddle.

**корь** *f.* (med.) measles.

**корье** *n.* (tan) bark.

**корэльен** *m.* (geol.) Corallian.

**корюшка** *f.* (zool.) smelt.

**корявый** *a.* uneven, rough.

**коряга** *f.* stump with root.

**КОС** *abbr.* (колхозная опытная станция) Collective Farm Experiment Station.

**коса** *f.* scythe; braid, plait; sand bar.

**косарь** *m.* mower; chopper.

**косвенн/о** *adv.* indirectly, obliquely; —**одействующий** *a.* indirect; —**ый** *a.* indirect; oblique, cross; circumstantial (evidence).

**косейсмический** *a.* (geol.) coseismal.

**косеканс** *m.,* —**ный** *a.* (math.) cosecant.

**косил/ка** *f.* mower, mowing machine; —**очный** *a.* mowing.

**косина** *f.* obliquity, sloping, slope.

**косинус** *m.* (math.) cosine; —**оида** *f.,* —**оидальная кривая** cosine curve.

**косить** *v.* mow, cut; slant; —**ся** *v.* slope, slant.

**косица** *f.* braid, rope.

**кослеттизация** *f.* (met.) coslettizing (phosphoric acid treatment).

**косматый** *a.* shaggy, hairy.

**космети/ка** *f.* cosmetic, cosmetics; —**ческий** *a.* cosmetic; —**ческие изделия,** —**ческие средства** cosmetics.

**космический** *a.* cosmic.

**космогония** *f.* (astron.) cosmogony.

**космолин** *m.* cosmoline, petroleum jelly.

**космо/логия** *f.* cosmology; —**навтика** *f.* astronautics, interplanetary navigation; —**с** *m.* cosmos, outer space; —**трон** *m.* (nucl.) cosmotron (a proton accelerator).

**косналог** *m.* indirect tax, hidden tax.

**косн/еть** *v.* stagnate; stiffen; —**ость** *f.* inertness, sluggishness.

**коснуться** *see* **касаться.**

**косный** *a.* inert, stagnant, stale, sluggish.

**косо** *adv.* obliquely, slantwise, slanting, on a bias, sideways, askance, askew; —**вато** *adv.* somewhat obliquely; —**ватый** *a.* somewhat oblique.

**косовица** *f.* haying season; harvesting.
**косо/вичник** *m.* (min.) crosscut; —**глазие** *n.* squint; (med.) strabismus; —**гон** *m.* (mach.) pitman, connecting rod; —**гор** *m.* slant, incline, declivity, slope (of a hill); —**зубчатое колесо** spiral gear.
**косой** *a.* slanting, sloping; diagonal, transverse; sidelong, skew; oblique (angle).
**косо/нарезанный** *a.* (text.) bias-cut; —**прицельный** *a.* oblique; —**симметричный** *a.* skew-symmetric; —**слоистый** *a.* (geol.) obliquely laminated; —**слой** *m.* cross grain, curly grain; (geol.) oblique bed; —**слойность** *f.* twisted growth (of tree); —**сть** *f.* obliquity, bias; —**угольный** *a.* oblique-angled; canted, bevel, beveled; —**ур** *m.* bridgeboard, notch board (for stairs).
**коссаит** *m.* (min.) cossaite (a compact variety of paragonite).
**коссирит** *m.* (min.) cossyrite, aenigmatite.
**косте—** *prefix* osteo—, osseo—, bone; —**дробилка** *f.* bone grinder; —**неть** *v.* ossify; grow numb, get stiff; —**ный слой** (geol.) bone bed.
**костер** *m.* campfire, bonfire, wood fire; mound, heap, pile (in charcoal burning); (min.) chock; **к.**, —**я** *f.* (bot.) brome grass (*Bromus*); **кровельный к.** (bot.) military grass (*B. tectorum*); **ржаной к.** cheat, chess (*B. secalinus*).
**костил** *m.* costyl.
**кост/истый** *a.* bony, osseous; —**лявый** *a.* bony, gaunt; —**ный** *a.* bone, osseous; —**ная ткань** bony tissue.
**костовая кислота** costic acid, costusic acid.
**костоеда** *f.* (med.) caries.
**костол** *m.* costol.
**костоправ** *m.* osteopath, bone setter.
**косточк/а** *f.* small bone; stone, pit, seed, kernel (of fruit); (elec.) bushing; —**овыбиватель** *m.* seeder, pit remover; —**овые** *pl.* (bot.) Amygdalaceae.
**костр/а**, —**ика** *f.* chaff, scutch, tow, refuse from dressed flax.
**костров/ый** *a.* pile; **к. уголь** charcoal; —**ая крепь** (min.) chock; —**ое**

**углежжение** pile charring, heap charring.
**костыл/едер** *m.* spike puller; —**ек** *m.* crooked nail, cup-hook nail; —**ь** *m.*, —**ьный** *a.* crutch; spike, cramp, cotter, pin; dog nail, cup-hook nail; —**ьковый гвоздь** clasp nail; —**ьный гвоздь** spike nail; —**ьный** diamond-headed nail.
**кость** *f.* bone; **жженая к.** *see* **костяной уголь.**
**костюм** *m.* costume, suit.
**костяк** *m.* skeleton, framework.
**костян/ика** *f.* (bot.) stone bramble (*Rubus saxatilis*); —**ка** *f.* (bot.) drupe.
**костян/ой** *a.* bone; **к. уголь**, —**ая чернь** bone black, bone charcoal; —**ая зола** bone ash (tricalcium phosphate from bones); —**ая мука** bone meal; —**ое масло** bone oil, Dippel's oil; —**ое стекло** alabaster glass; **черная** —**ая** ivory black.
**косуля** *f.* (zool.) roe, roe deer; plow.
**косынка** *f.* connection plate, corner plate, gusset plate.
**косьба** *f.* mowing.
**косяк** *m.* jamb (of door); stand, pillar; herd (of horses); shoal (of fish).
**кот** *m.* tom cat, cat.
**котангенс** *m.* (math.) cotangent.
**котарн/ин** *m.* cotarnine; —**овая кислота** cotarnic acid.
**котеин** *m.* cotein, cotoin.
**котектический** *a.* cotectic.
**котел** *m.* boiler, kettle, cauldron; (nucl.) reactor; (geol.) pot hole, kettle hole; **к.-карлик** small boiler; **к.-утилизатор** *m.* waste-heat boiler; **паровой к.** boiler, steam boiler; —**ок** *m.* small kettle, pot; —**ьная** *f.* boiler room, boiler house.
**котельн/ый** *a.* boiler; (nucl.) reactor; **к. газ** boiler flue gas; **к. завод, к. цех** boiler works, boiler shop; **к. камень**, —**ая накипь** boiler scale; **к. мастер** boiler maker; —**ое железо** boiler plate; —**ое отделение** boiler room.
**котельщик** *m.* boiler maker.
**Котиаса способ** (met.) Cothias method (for casting).
**котик** *m.* little cat; seal; sealskin.
**котип** *m.* (biol.) cotype.
**котиров/ать** *v.* quote; —**ка** *f.* quotation.

**котлета** *f.* cutlet, chop.

**котло/ван** *m.* trench, ditch, foundation pit; **—вина** *f.* (geol.) hollow, basin, crater, trough, syncline; **—надзор** *m.* boiler inspection; **—образный провал** (geol.) cauldron, giant's cauldron, pot hole.

**кото** *see* **кото-кора.**

**котовик** *m.* (bot.) catnip (*Nepeta cataria*).

**кото/ин** *m.* cotoin; **-кора** *f.* coto bark; **—нетин** *m.* cotonetin.

**котон/изатор** *m.* (text.) cottonizer; **—изация** *f.* cottonizing; **—ин** *m.* cottonized fiber.

**который** *a. and pron.* which? what? which, that, who; **к.-нибудь** some, any.

**котрель** *m.* Cottrell precipitator; **Котреля процесс** Cottrell precipitation.

**коттигит** *m.* (min.) köttigite.

**Коттона-Мутона эффект** (phys.) Cotton-Mouton effect.

**коттонизация** *see* **котонизация.**

**коттонпикер** *m.* (agr.) cotton picker.

**Коттрелля аппарат** *see* **котрель.**

**котуннит** *m.* (min.) cotunnite.

**котятник** *m.* (bot.) ground ivy (*Glechoma hederacea*).

**коуз** *m.* pit, cistern.

**коупер** *see* **каупер.**

**коуш** *m.* eye, eye ring, dead eye.

**кофе** *m.* coffee; **аравийский к.** (bot.) coffee (*Coffea arabica*); **—дубильная кислота** caffetannic acid, chlorogenic acid.

**кофеин** *m.* caffeine, 1,3,7-trimethylxanthine; **лимоннокислый к.** caffeine citrate; **—изм** *m.* caffeinism, caffeine poisoning; **—ка** *f.* coffee bean.

**кофейник** *m.* coffee pot.

**кофейнокисл/ый** *a.* caffeic acid; caffeate (of); **—ая соль** caffeate.

**кофейн/ый** *a.* coffee; **к. боб** coffee bean; **—ая кислота** caffeic acid, 3,4-dihydroxycinnamic acid; **соль —ой кислоты** caffeate; **— ое дерево** (bot.) coffee tree (*Coffea*).

**кофеподобный** *a.* coffee-like.

**кофердам** *see* **коффердам.**

**кофермент** *m.* coenzyme; coferment.

**кофункция** *f.* (math.) cofunction.

**кофф/еин** *see* **кофеин;** **—ердам** *m.* coffer-

dam; **—инит** *m.* coffinite (uranium mineral).

**Коха колба** Koch flask.

**кохерер** *see* **когерер.**

**кохия** *f.* (bot.) kochia.

**Кохо** Cohoe (name).

**кохова палочка** Koch's bacillus.

**кохун** *m.* cohune (nut).

**коцин/ин** *m.* cocinin; **—овая кислота** cocinic acid; **—он** *m.* cocinone.

**кочан** *m.*, **—ный** *a.* head (of cabbage).

**кочевой** *a.* nomad, nomadic; migratory.

**кочегар** *m.* stoker, fireman; **—ка, —ня** *f.* stokehole, stokehold, boiler room; **—ный** *a.* firing, stoking; **—ная площадка** stoking platform; **—ное отделение** boiler room.

**коченеть** *v.* grow numb, get rigid.

**кочерга** *f.* poker, fire iron, (furnace) rake, rabble.

**кочет** *m.* cock.

**кочк/а** *f.* hillock; **—оватый** *a.* full of hillocks, hilly; **—оватое болото** everglade.

**кочубеит** *m.* (min.) kotschubeite (a variety of clinochlore).

**кош** *m.* corncrib.

**кошара** *f.* sheep pen.

**кошач/ий** *a.* cat; **к. глаз** (min.) cat's eye (a gem variety of Ceylon chrysoberyl or opalescent quartz); **к. дубровник, к. майоран** (bot.) cat thyme (*Teucrium marum*); **—ье золото** (min.) cat gold, yellow mica; **—ье серебро** cat silver, silvery mica; **—ья лапка** (bot.) cat's-foot (*Antennaria*); **—ья мята** *see* **котовик.**

**кошелек** *m.* purse, wallet.

**кошелка** *f.* kind of bag or basket.

**кошение** *n.* mowing.

**кошенил/евый** *a.*, **—ь** *f.* cochineal; **к. краситель** cochineal dye; **—евая кислота** cochenillic acid; **—ин** *m.* cochinilin, carminic acid; **дубовая —ь** kermes (insect); **—ьно-красный цвет** cochineal red.

**кошиновое масло** cochin (grass) oil.

**Коши-Римана уравнения** (math.) Cauchy-Riemann equations.

**кошк/а** *f.* (female) cat; drag; grapnel, grab; grapple fork; car, trolley, carriage (of crane); (geol.) spit, bar; **—и** *pl.* (climbing) grapplers.

**кошма** *f.* felting.

**кошмар** *m.* nightmare; **—ный** *a.* nightmarish.

**кошмить** *v.* felt.

**коэненит** *m.* (min.) koenenite.

**коэнзим** *m.* coenzyme.

**коэрци/метр** *m.* (elec.) coercive force meter; **—тивность** *f.*, **—тивная сила** coercivity, coercive force; **—тивный** *a.* coercive.

**коэф.** *abbr.* (**коэффициент**) coefficient.

**коэффициент** *m.* coefficient, factor; ratio; **к. полезного действия** efficiency, output; *look up idioms under more descriptive words, e.g.,* **расширения, коэффициент.**

**коэхлинит** *m.* (min.) koechlinite.

**кп** *abbr.* (**кислородный потенциал**) oxygen potential.

**кпд** *abbr.* (**коэффициент полезного действия**) efficiency.

**КПО** *abbr.* (**Кооперативно-промышленное общество**) The Industrial Co-operative Society.

**КПСС** *abbr.* (**Коммунистическая партия Советского Союза**) Communist Party of the Soviet Union, C.P.S.U.

**кр.** *abbr.* (**критический**) critical.

**краб** *m.* (zool.) crab.

**краблит** *m.* (geol.) krablite, baulite (a rhyolite tuff).

**кравчик** *m.* a beetle (*Lethrus*).

**краги** *pl.* leggings, leather gaiters.

**краденный** *past pass. part. of* **красть.**

**крае/ведение** *n.* study of a region, regional study; **—вой** *a.* region, district; rim, edge, marginal, fringe; end (effect); contact (angle); outer (layer, zone); corner (stone); **—вой поток** (elec.) fringing.

**кража** *f.* theft; larceny; tampering (with power).

**кра/й** *m.* edge, rim, border, margin, periphery; fringe, side, verge, extremity; tip, end; land, country, region; chuck (beef); **выливаться через к.** *v.* overflow; **на —ях, с —ю** at the edge, in the margin, marginal.

**крайне** *adv.* extremely, very, highly.

**крайн/ий** *a.* extreme, utmost, urgent; last, end, on the end, terminal; outer, outside; **к. член** (math.) extreme;

**—ее значение** extreme; limiting value; **—яя необходимость** emergency; **в —ем случае** as a last resort, in an emergency, failing this; **по —ей мере** at least.

**крайност/ь** *f.* extreme, extremity, need, exigence, emergency; excess; **впадать в —и** *v.* run to extremes; **до —и** in the extreme, to excess.

**кракен** *m.* crackene; **—хинон** *m.* crackene-quinone.

**крамер/иодубильная кислота** krameriotannic acid, ratanhia-tannic acid; **—ия** *f.* rhatany root (of *Krameria triandra* or *K. argentia*); **—овая кислота** krameric acid, rhatanic acid.

**крамповать** *see* **кардовать.**

**кран** *m.* cock, stopcock, tap, faucet, spigot; crane; **к.-брызгалка** spray cock; **к.-двунога** sheer legs, sheers; **к.-тренога** three-leg crane; **водомерный к.** gage cock; **пловучий к.** derrick boat; **поворотный к.** jib crane; **подвижный к.** traveling crane; **подъемный к.** crane.

**крандаллит** *m.* (min.) crandallite.

**крани/альный** *a.* (anat.) cranial; **—ология** *f.* craniology.

**кранный** *a.* cock, stopcock, faucet.

**кранов/щик** *m.* crane operator; **—ый** *a.* crane; **—ый вагон** crane truck; **—ая балка** jib, boom; **—ая тележка** crane trolley.

**кранцит** *m.* (min.) krantzite (a fossil resin).

**крап** *m.* specks, speckles; (bot.) madder (*Rubia tinctorum*).

**крапать** *v.* spot, speckle; trickle, drop.

**крапив/а** *f.* (bot.) nettle (*Urtica*); **глухая к.** dead nettle (*Lamium album*); **жгучая к.** stinging nettle (*Urtica urens*); **индийская к., китайская к.** *see* **рами; разноцветная к.** hemp nettle (*Galeopsis*); **—ник** *m.* (zool.) wren; **—ница** *f.* nettle rash; nettle butterfly (*Vanessa urticae*); **—ные** *pl.* (bot.) Urticaceae; **—ный** *a.* nettle, urticaceous; **—ная лихорадка** nettle rash.

**крапин/а, —ка** *f.* speck, speckle, spot; tracer, identification thread.

**крап/лак** *m.*, **—овый лак** madder lake.

**крап/овый, —повый** *a.* madder; **к. желтый** madder yellow, xanthin; **к. красный** madder red, alizarin; **—овое вещество** alizarin; **—п** *see* **крап.**

**крапчат/ость** *f.* mottling; **—ый** *a.* spotted, speckled, mottled, marbled.

**краруп/изация** *f.* (elec.) Krarup loading, continuous loading; **—изированный** *a.* continuously loaded; **—изировать** *v.* load continuously; **—овский кабель** Krarup cable.

**красав/ица, —ка** *f.* (bot.) belladonna (*Atropa belladonna*).

**красивый** *a.* beautiful, fine.

**красильн/ый** *a.* dye, tinctorial; **к. бак, к. чан** dye vat; **к. завод** dye works; **к. камень** (min.) dyestone, Clinton ore (an iron ore); **к. корень** (bot.) *see* **крап; к. лак** color lake, lake; **к. мох** orchilla weed (*Rocella tinctoria*); **к. отвар** dye liquor; **—ая барка** dye bath, dye vat; **—ая трава** (bot.) dyer's weed (*Reseda luteola*); **—ое вещество** dyestuff, dye; **—ое дерево** dyewood; **—ое растение** dye plant; **—ые материалы** dyestuffs.

**красиль/ня** *f.* dye works; **—щик** *m.* dyer.

**красит/ель** *m.* dye, dyestuff; coloring material, pigment; **—ь** *v.* dye, color, stain, paint.

**краск/а** *f.* paint, dye, color, pigment; dyeing, painting; **к. смешанного цвета** secondary color; **масляные —и** oil paints; **сухая к.** pastel color; **—оварка** *f.* (text.) color room; **—одувка** *f.*, **—ораспылитель** *m.* paint sprayer; **—отер** *m.*, **—отерка** *f.* color mill, color grinder; paint grinder; **—устранитель** *m.* paint remover.

**краснеть** *v.* redden, become red.

**красно/армеец** *m.* Red Army soldier (USSR); **—бурый** *a.* reddish brown, russet; **—ватый** *a.* reddish; **—деревец** *m.* cabinetmaker; **—дубленый** *a.* tanned (to a russet color); **—зем** terra rossa, a fossil red earth; krasnozem, red soil; **—калильный** *a.* red-hot, red-heat; red (heat); **—лесье** *n.* pine forest.

**красноломк/ий, —остный** *a.* (met.) red-short, hot-short, hot-brittle; **—ость** *f.* red-shortness, hot-brittleness.

**красно/пятнистый** *a.* red-spotted, stained red, with red stains; **—стойкость** *f.* (met.) red hardness; **—та** *f.* (med.) erythema; **—тал** *m.* willow (*Salix acutifolia*); **—флотец** *m.* sailor of USSR navy; **—хвост** *m.* (zool.) Dasychira.

**краснуха** *f.* red rot (of tree); (med.) erysipelas.

**красн/ый** *a.* red; cartilaginous (fish); **—ое дерево** mahogany.

**красота** *f.* beauty, fineness.

**красотел** *m.* European ground beetle.

**красочный** *a.* color; rich in color, brilliant; *see also* **красильный.**

**крассик** *m.* (geol.) krassyk (decomposed ferruginous schist).

**красть** *v.* steal; (elec.) tap (a wire).

**красящ/ий** *a.* dyeing, coloring; **к. валик** inking roll; **—ая сила, —ая способность** dyeing power, tinting power; **—ее вещество** dyestuff, dye, coloring matter, pigment, stain.

**кратер** *m.* crater; **—ная чаша** (geol.) crater basin.

**краткий** *a.* short, brief, concise.

**кратко/временный** *a.* short, of short duration, short-lived, short-term; temporary, transient, transitory, momentary; **—дневный** *a.* short, brief, of short duration; **—срочный** *a.* short, short-term, short-range; **—сть** *f.* shortness, brevity.

**кратн/ое** *n.*, **—ое число** (math.) multiple; **общее к.** common multiple; **общее наименьшее к.** least common multiple; **—ость** *f.* multiplicity factor; **—ый** *a.* multiple; **закон —ых отношений** law of multiple proportions.

**кратон** *m.* craton, shield.

**краурит** *m.* (min.) kraurite, dufrenite.

**крафт/-бумага** *f.*, **к.-пепер** *m.* kraft paper; **к.-целлюлоза** *f.* kraft pulp.

**крахмал** *m.* starch; **—ение** *n.* starching; **—истый, —оподобный** *a.* starchy, amyloid, amylaceous; **—ить** *v.* starch; **—о—** *prefix* starch, amylo—; **—ометр** *m.* amylometer.

**крахмаль/ный** *a.* starch; **к. сахар** starch sugar, (dextro)glucose; **—ная патока** starch syrup, glucose; **—щик** *m.* starch manufacturer.

**крац/бюрст** *m.*, **—овка** *f.*, **—овочная**

щетка scratching brush, stiff brush; —евание *n.* scratching, scratch finish; —овальный станок scratching machine; —эйзен *m.* scraper.

крашен/ие, —ье *n.* dyeing, coloring, painting; —ный *a.* dyed, colored, stained, painted.

краю *see under* край.

креат/ин *m.* creatine, guanidine methylglycine; —инин *m.* creatinine, methyl glycocyamidine; —отоксин *m.* creatotoxin, meat poison or ptomaine.

кребы *pl.* crab apples.

креветка *f.* (zool.) shrimp, prawn.

крегинг *see* крекинг.

кредит *m.* credit; —ив *m.* letter of credit; —ивная грамота credentials; —ный билет bank note; —овать *v.* credit (with); —ор *m.* creditor; —оспособный *a.* solvent.

креднерит *m.* (min.) crednerite.

крез/алол *m.* cresalol; —атин *m.* cresatin, *m*-cresyl acetate; —идин *m.* cresidine, aminocresol.

крезил *m.*, —овый *a.* cresyl; —ат *m.* cresylate; —ен *m.* cresylene, tolylene; —ит *m.* (expl.) cresylite; —овая кислота, —овый спирт *see* крезол.

крезокси— *prefix* cresoxy—, toloxy—.

крезол *m.*, —овый, —ьный *a.* cresol, cresylic acid, methylphenol; —овая смола cresol resin; —овый красный cresol red, cresol sulfonphthalein; —сульфоновая кислота cresolsulfonic acid.

крезорц/ил *m.* cresorcyl; —ин *m.* cresorcin, dimethylfluorescein; —инол *m.* cresorcinol, 2,4-dihydroxytoluene.

крезотиновая кислота cresotic acid, cresotinic acid, hydroxytoluic acid.

Крейза испытание Kreis test.

крейс/ер *m.* (naut.) cruiser; к.-разведчик scout; —ерская скорость cruising speed; —ирование *n.* cruising.

крейттонит *m.* (min.) kreittonite (a zinc-iron gahnite).

крейцкопф *m.*, —ный *a.* (mach.) crosshead.

крейцмейсель *m.* groove chisel, gouge.

крекер *m.* cracker; к.-вальцы cracker mill.

крек/инг *m.*, —ирование *n.* cracking (of petroleum); к.-бензин gasoline produced by cracking; к.-процесс cracking, cracking process; —ированный *a.* cracked; —ировать *v.* crack.

крем *m.* cream.

кремальер/а *f.* rack, rack and pinion; —ное начертание indented line.

крема/торий *m.* crematory, incinerator; —ция *f.*, —ционный *a.* cremation; —ционная печь incinerator.

кремень *m.* (min.) flint, pebble, flint nodule; silica, silex; chalcedony; египетский к. Egyptian jasper.

Кремера проба Cramer's (sucrose) test.

кремерзит *m.* (min.) kremersite.

Кремль Kremlin.

кремне— *prefix* silico—; —алюминиевая соль aluminum silicate; —борокальцит *m.* (min.) silicoborocalcite; —вка *f.* kremnyovka (kaolinic refractory clay).

кремнево— *prefix* silico—.

кремне/водород *m.* silicon hydride, hydrogen silicide; silicohydride, silane; —вокарбидный кирпич silicon carbide brick; —вольфрамовая кислота silicotungstic acid; соль —вольфрамовой кислоты silicotungstate; —вомолибденовая кислота silicomolybdic acid; —вомолибденовокислая соль silicomolybdate.

кремнев/ый *a.* silicon, silicic, siliceous, flinty, *see also* кремнистый; к. ангидрид, ангидрид —ой кислоты silicic anhydride, silica, silicon dioxide; —ая галька flint, flint pebble; —ая кислота silicic acid; гель —ой кислоты, студенистая —ая кислота silica gel, gelatinous silicic acid, colloidal silica; соль —ой кислоты silicate; —ое ружье flintlock, firelock.

кремнегел/ит, —ь *m.* silica gel.

кремнезем *m.* silica, silicon dioxide; водный к., гидрат —а hydrated silica; silicic acid; гель —а silica gel, colloidal silica; —истый, —ный *a.* siliceous, silicic, siliciferous.

кремне/калиевая соль potassium silicate; —кальциевая соль calcium silicate; —кислота *f.* silicic acid, silicon dioxide, silica; —кислый *a.* silicic acid; silicate (of); —кислый алюминий aluminum silicate; —кислая соль silicate; —магниевая соль magnesium silicate; —марганцовая соль manganese silicate; —медная соль cupric silicate; —молибденовая синь silicomolybdenum blue; —натриевая соль sodium silicate; —органический *a.* organosilicon; —содержащий *a.* silicon-containing, siliceous, siliciferous; —фосфат *m.* silicophosphate.

кремнефтор/истоводородная кислота, —оводородная кислота fluosilicic acid; соль —истоводородной кислоты fluosilicate, silicofluoride; —истый *a.* fluosilicate (of); —истый барий barium fluosilicate; —истый калий potassium fluosilicate.

кремн/ехлороформ *m.* silicochloroform; —ецинковая соль zinc silicate; —иевый *see* кремневый.

кремн/ий *m.* silicon, Si; водородистый к. silicon hydride, hydrogen silicide; двуокись —ия silicon dioxide, silica; карбид —ия, углеродистый к. silicon carbide, carborundum; хлористый к. silicon (tetra)chloride.

кремнисто— *prefix* silico—; —зеркальный чугун (met.) silicon spiegel, ferrosilicomanganese.

кремнист/ый *a.* siliceous, flinty, gravelly; silicide (of); flint (corn); к. водород hydrogen silicide, silicon hydride; к. малахит (min.) chrysocolla; к. марганец manganese silicide; (min.) manganese spar, rhodonite; к. металл metallic silicide; к. сланец (petr.) chert; к. туф, —ая накипь (min.) siliceous sinter; geyserite, fiorite, pearl sinter; —ая медь copper silicide; (met.) cuprosilicon; (min.) chrysocolla; —ая сталь silicon steel; —ое железо iron silicide; (met.) ferrosilicon.

кремницкие белила Kremnitz white, Crems white (white lead pigment).

кремовый *a.* cream, cream-colored.

кремортартар *m.* cream of tartar, potassium bitartrate.

кремские белила *see* кремницкие белила.

крен *m.* (naut.) heeling; (aero.) heel, bank; продольный к. pitch.

кренат *m.* crenate.

кренговать *v.* (naut.) careen.

крендель *m.* pretzel, cracknel.

кренить, —ся *v.* (naut.) heel; (aero.) bank.

кренкит *m.* (min.) kröhnkite.

кренерит *m.* (min.) krennerite (a gold-silver telluride).

кренов/ая кислота crenic acid; соль —ой кислоты, —окислая соль crenate.

крено/мер *m.* inclinometer; —метр *m.* (aero.) bank indicator.

креозол *m.* creosol, methoxycresol.

креозот *m.*, —овый *a.* creosote; углекислый к., —ал *m.* creosote carbonate, creosotal; —ное масло, —овое масло creosote oil.

креолин *m.* Creolin (disinfectant, insecticide).

креп *m.* (text.) crepe; —дешин *m.* crepe de Chine.

крепеж *m.* bracing, fastening; brackets; —ный *a.* fastening, holding, mounting; reinforcing; —ный лес (min.) supports, props.

крепит/ель *m.* binder, bond, brace; —ельный *a.* strengthening, reinforcing, fortifying, invigorating; confirming, corroboratory; —ь *v.* strengthen, fortify, brace, make fast.

креп/кий *a.* strong, solid, firm, sturdy, tough, hard; concentrated (solution); —ко *adv.* firmly, tightly, tight; —ление *n.* strengthening, bracing, fixing; stapling (to); attachment, linkage; fortification (of wine); прочность —ления holding power; с кольцевым —лением ring-mounted; —леный *a.* strengthened, braced; fortified; —нуть *v.* get stronger; harden, stiffen.

креповый *a.* crepy; (text.) crepe.

крепость *f.* strength, toughness, tenacity, stability; fortress; к. на разрыв breaking strength, tensile strength.

креп/чать *v.* grow stronger; —ь *f.* (min.) supports, props; lining of shaft; —ящий *a.* strengthening, bracing, supporting; holding, fastening.

кресло *n.* chair, armchair.

кресс *m.* (bot.) cress, peppergrass (*Lepidium*); водяной к. water cress (*Nasturtium officinale*); огородный к., садовый к., к.-салат garden peppergrass (*Lepidium sativum*).

**крест** *m.* cross, four-way piece; **к. на к.** crosswise; **—ец** *m.* (anat.) sacrum.

**крестовидн/ый** *a.* cross-shaped, cruciform, cruciate; **—ая муфта** four-way connection, crossing box.

**крестов/ик** *m.,* **—ый камень** (min.) staurolite; **—ина,** **—инка** *f.* cross, cross piece, cross connection, crossing, cross pipe, crosshead, cross beam; spider, center-piece, four-way piece; turnstile; (railroad) frog; **связывающая —ина** *f.,* **—ая связь** cross bond, cross brace; **—ичка** *f.* (zool.) Dociostaurus or Notostaurus; **—ник** *m.* (bot.) groundsel, ragweed (*Senecio*); **—ый** *a.* cross.

**кресто/образный** *see* **крестовидный**; **—цветные** *pl.* (bot.) Cruciferae.

**крестцов/ый** *a.* (anat.) sacral; **—ая кость** sacrum.

**крестьян/ин** *m.,* **—ский** *a.* peasant, country man, farmer.

**кретин** *m.* (med.) cretin; **—изм** *m.* cretinism.

**кретон** *m.* (text.) cretonne.

**крец** *m.,* **—а** *f.* waste metal (dross, cuttings, sweepings, etc.).

**крешер** *m.* crusher; crusher gage.

**крив/ая** *f.* (math.) curve, line; **к. давления** pressure curve; **кривизна —ой, наклон —ой, характер —ой, ход —ой** degree of curvature, slope of curve; **рабочая к.** characteristic curve; **температурная к. давления** temperature-pressure curve.

**крив/изна** *f.* curvature, curve, flexure, camber; crookedness, warping; bend, bending, slope; **—ить** *v.* curve, flex, bend; distort; **—иться** *v.* curve, bend; cant, tilt; **—о** *adv.* crookedly; on a slope; **—обокий** *a.* lopsided, one-sided; **—ой** *a.* crooked, curved, curve, bent; **—ая линия** curve; **—олинейный** *a.* curvilinear, curvilineal, curved.

**кривоцвет** *m.* (bot.) lycopsis.

**кривошип** *m.,* **—ный** *a.* crank, crankhandle, crankshaft; **ось —а, —ный вал** crankshaft; **плечо —a** crank arm; **—ная камера** crankcase; **—ная передача,** **—ношатунный механизм** crankgear; **—ношатунный привод,** **привод —ного механизма** crank drive.

**криз, —ис** *m.* crisis.

**кризо—** *see* **хризо—**.

**крик** *m.* cry, shout, scream.

**криминология** *f.* criminology.

**криноид** *m.* (zool.) crinoid; **—ный** *a.* crinoid, crinoidal.

**кринолин** *m.* crinoline.

**крио—** *prefix* cryo— (cold, freezing); **—ген** *m.* cryogen, freezing mixture; **—геника** *f.* cryogenics; **—генин** *m.* Cryogenine, 1-phenylsemicarbazide; **—генный** *a.* cryogenic.

**криогидрат** *m.* cryohydrate, cryosel; **—ная точка** cryohydric point.

**криолит** *m.* (min.) cryolite, Greenland spar; **—ионит** *m.* cryolithionite; **—овый** *a.* cryolite, cryolitic.

**криометр** *m.* cryometer, low temperature thermometer.

**криоскоп** *m.* cryoscope (for determination of freezing point); **—ический** *a.* cryoscopic; **—ия** *f.* cryoscopy.

**криофиллит** *m.* (min.) cryophyllite (a variety of lithium mica).

**крип** *m.* (met.) creep.

**крипт/ал** *m.* cryptal, 4-isopropylcyclohexene aldehyde; **—идин** *m.* cryptidine.

**крипто—** *prefix* crypto— (hidden, covered); krypto—; **—валентность** *f.* cryptovalence, abnormal valence; **—карин** *m.* cryptocarine; **—кластический** *a.* cryptoclastic, compact; **—кристаллический** *a.* cryptocrystalline, microcrystalline; **—ксантин** *m.* cryptoxanthin, caricaxanthin.

**криптол** *m.* Kryptol (resistance material for electric furnaces).

**крипто/лит** *m.* (min.) cryptolite (probably a variety of monazite); **—метр** *m.* cryptometer (for determining hiding power of paint); **—монады** *pl.* (zool.) Cryptomonadina; **—морфит** *m.* (min.) cryptomorphite.

**криптон** *m.* krypton, Kr.

**крипто/пертит** *m.* (min.) cryptoperthite (a variety of perthite); **—пин** *m.* cryptopine; **—пиррол** *m.* cryptopyrrole; **—скоп** *m.* cryptoscope, fluoroscope; **—тил** *m.* (min.) kryptotile (an alteration product of prismatine);

—фановая кислота cryptophanic acid; —фит *m.* (bot.) cryptophyte; —цианин *m.* cryptocyanine.

**кристадин** *m.* (rad.) oscillating crystal receiver.

**кристалл** *m.* crystal; к.-двойник twin crystal; плоскость —a crystal face.

**кристаллиз/атор** *m.* crystallizer, crystallizing basin, crystal pan; —ация *f.*, —ационный *a.* crystallization, crystallizing; —ационная вода water of crystallization; —ированный, —ованный *a.* crystallized; —ировать, —овать, —ироваться *v.* crystallize; —уемость *f.* crystallizability; —ующийся *a.* crystallizing, crystallizable.

**кристалл/ик** *m.* small crystal, crystal particle, crystalline particle; —ин *m.* crystallin; —ит *m.* (geol.) crystallite, crystalline grain.

**кристаллич/еский** *a.* crystalline, crystal, crystallized; granulated (sugar); —еская решетка crystal lattice; неясно к., скрытно к. cryptocrystalline; —ность *f.* crystallinity.

**кристалло/бластический** *a.* (geol.) crystalloblastic; —генезис *m.*, —гения *f.* crystallogeny; —генический *a.* crystallogenic; —гидрат *m.* crystal hydrate; —грамма *f.* crystallogram.

**кристаллограф** *m.* crystallographer; —ический *a.* crystallographic; —ия *f.* crystallography.

**кристалло/за** *f.* crystallose; —ид *m.*, —идальный *a.* crystalloid; —й *m.* Crystalloy (iron-silicon alloy); —логия *f.* crystallology.

**кристаллометр/ический** *a.* crystallometric; —ия *f.* crystallometry.

**кристалло/н** *m.* crystallon, seed crystal; —номия *f.* crystallonomy; —носный, —содержащий *a.* containing crystals, crystalliferous; —образный, —подобный *a.* crystal-like, crystalloid, crystalline; —химия *f.* crystal chemistry.

**кристальн/о** *adv.*, —ый *a.* crystal, crystalline; к. чистый crystal clear.

**крист/ианит** *m.* (min.) christianite, anorthite; —обалит *m.* cristobalite (a variety of silica).

**кристолон** *m.* Crystolon (a silicon carbide abrasive).

**кристофит** *m.* (min.) christophite (a ferriferous variety of sphalerite).

**крит** *m.* (nucl.) crit (critical mass); crith (unit of density).

**крит.** *abbr.* (критический) critical.

**критер/иальный** *a.* criterional; —ий *m.* criterion; (dimensional analysis) number, group.

**критик** *m.* critic, reviewer; —a *f.* criticism, censure; review (of book); —овать *v.* criticize; review.

**критическ/и** *adv.* critically; —ий *a.* critical, crucial; —ий предел critical limit, breaking-down point; —ая точка critical point; константа —ой точки critical constant; —ое обстоятельство emergency; —ое состояние criticality.

**крит/ичность** *f.* criticality; —масса *f.* (nucl.) critical mass.

**критмен** *m.* crithmene.

**критрадиус** *m.* critical radius.

**крица** *f.* (met.) bloom, ball, pig, bar.

**кричать** *v.* shout, yell, call out.

**кричн/ый** *a.* (met.) refinery; bloomery, bloom; к. горн refinery hearth; bloomery; к. мастер refiner; к. сок slag; к. чугун, —ое железо bloomery iron; —ое производство refinery process; blooming; —ые шлаки refinery slag cinders.

**кричтонит** *m.* (min.) crichtonite (a variety of ilmenite).

**кров** *m.* shelter, roof; home.

**кровав/ик, —ник** *m.* (min.) bloodstone (a variety of chalcedony or jasper); hematite, red iron ore; (bot.) bloodroot, tormentil (*Potentilla tormentilla*); —окрасный *a.* blood-red.

**кровав/ый** *a.* bloody, blood-stained; к. железняк (min.) hematite, red iron ore; —ая моча (med.) hematuria.

**кровать** *f.* bed.

**крове—** *see* крово—.

**кровелька** *f.* (bot.) aril.

**кровельн/ый** *a.* roof, roofing; к. желоб gutter; к. картон tar paper, roofing paper; к. материал roofing, roofing material; —ое железо roofing tin.

**кровельщик** *m.* roofer.

**кровеносн/ый сосуд** (anat.) blood vessel; —ое давление blood pressure.

кров/етворный *see* кровотворный; —е-щелочная соль *see under* кровяная соль; —инка *f.* blood particle.

кровля *f.* roof, roofing.

кровн/ость *f.* (zool.) thorough-bred state; —ый *a.* blood; thorough-bred.

крово— *prefix* blood, hemo—; —извлечение *n.* blood discharge; —излияние *n.* (med.) hemorrhage; —обращение *n.* (physiol.) circulation; —останавливающий *a.*, —останавливающее средство styptic; —переливание *n.* blood transfusion; —пийца *f.* leech; —подтек *m.* bruise, ecchymosis; —пролитие *n.* bloodshed; —пускание *n.* blood-letting, bleeding; —соски *pl.* tick and louse flies (*Hippoboscidae*); —сосущий *a.* blood-sucking; —творение *n.* blood formation, hemogenesis, hemopoiesis; —творный *a.* hemogenic, blood-producing; —течение *n.* bleeding, hemorrhage.

кровоточ/ивость *f.* (med.) hemophilia; —ивый *a.* bleeding; —ить *v.* bleed.

крово/харканье *n.* (med.) hemoptysis; —хлебка *f.* (bot.) burnet (*Poterium sanguisorba*); —хлебковые *pl.* Poteriaceae; —цветник *m.* bloodflower (*Haemanthus*).

кров/ь *f.* blood; истекать —ью *v.* bleed; сушеная к. blood meal.

кровян/ой *a.* blood, bloody; к. сгусток blood clot; к. уголь blood charcoal; —ая пластинка blood platelet; —ое тельцо blood corpuscle; подсчет —ых телец blood count; желтая —ая соль potassium ferrocyanide; красная —ая соль potassium ferricyanide; —окрасный *a.* blood-red.

кроет *pr. 3 sing. of* крыть.

кро/ить *v.* cut out, cut (by pattern); —йка *f.* cutting out.

кройте *imp. of* крыть.

кроки *n.* sketch, rough sketch.

крокидолит *see* кросидолит.

крокировка *f.* sketching, outlining.

крокодил *m.*, —овый *a.* (zool.) crocodile.

кроко/за *f.* crocose; —изит, —ит *m.* (min.) crocoisite, crocoite; —новая кислота croconic acid, crocic acid.

крокус *m.* (bot.) crocus; (min.) crocus, rouge (iron oxide).

крол/ик *m.*, —ичий *a.* rabbit; —ьчатник *m.* rabbit hutch.

кроме *prep. gen.* except, save, apart from; besides, in addition; к. того besides that, moreover, furthermore.

кромерские слои (geol.) Cromerian strata.

кром/ка *f.*, —очный *a.* edge, border, hem; rim, brim; bead, shoulder; (text.) list, selvage; —козагибочная машина, —козагибочный станок flanger, crimper; hemming machine; —кообрубочный станок trimmer.

кромсать *v.* shred, cut to pieces.

крон *m.* crown (glass); chrome pigment; желтый к. chrome yellow, Paris yellow (a lead chromate); красный к. chrome red (basic lead chromate); —а *f.* corona; corolla; crown (coin); crest, top (of tree); —блок *m.* crown block; —глас *m.* crown glass.

кронит *m.* (expl.) cronite.

кронциркуль *m.* outside calipers.

кронштейн *m.* cantilever, bracket, corbel, arm, gibbet; stand, support.

кропать *v.* botch, bungle; scribble.

кроп/ить *v.* sprinkle, spray; —ление *n.* sprinkling, spraying; batching (of jute).

кропотливый *a.* tedious, painstaking, minute, detailed, meticulous.

кросидолит *m.* (min.) crocidolite, blue asbestos.

кросс/бридинг *m.* (agr.) crossbreeding; —инг *m.* (min.) crossing; —ит *m.* (min.) crossite (a variety of amphibole).

Кросслея генератор Crossley generator.

кроссовер *m.* (biophysics) crossing over.

крот *m.* (zool.) mole.

крот/аконовая кислота crotaconic acid; —алин *m.* crotaline; —алотоксин *m.* crotalotoxin; —алярия *f.* (bot.) crotalaria; —ил *m.* crotyl.

кроткий *a.* mild, gentle, meek.

кротов/атель *m.* (agr.) mole plow; —ина *f.* molehill; —ый *a.* (zool.) mole; —ый дренаж (agr.) mole drainage; —ый камень (geol.) toadstone (a trap rock).

кротон *m.* (bot.) croton; —аллин *m.* crotonallin; —ат *m.* crotonate; —ил *m.*, —иловый *a.* crotonyl; —илен *m.*

crotonylene, 2-butyne; —иловый спирт crotonyl alcohol.

кротонов/ый *a.* croton, crotonic; к. альдегид crotonaldehyde, 2-butenal; —ая кислота crotonic acid, 2-butenoic acid; соль —ой кислоты, —окислая соль crotonate; —ое масло croton oil.

кротон/оид *m.* crotonoid; —ол *m.*, —оловая кислота crotonol, crotonolic acid.

крох/а *f.* crumb, grain; —и *pl.* remains, scrap; —кий *a.* friable, crumbly.

кроц/еин *m.* crocein (dye); —еиновая кислота croceic acid, 2-naphthol-8-sulfonic acid; —еиновый шарлаховый crocein scarlet; —етин *m.* crocetin; —ин *m.* crocin.

крош/ащийся *a.* crumbling, crumbly, friable; —енный *a.* crumbled; chopped up, minced; —ечка *f.* crumb, grain, very small particle; —ечный *a.* very small, minute; —ить *v.* crumble; chop up, mince; —иться *v.* crumble, be friable; —ка *f.* crumb; (zool.) Atomaria; *suffix* meal, dust; —коватость *f.* friability.

кроют *pr. 3 pl. of* крыть.

кроющ/ий *a.* covering, coating; к. материал covering material, coating; —ая способность covering power, hiding power, body (of paint).

КРС *abbr.* (комбинационное рассеяние света) Raman effect.

круг *m.* circle, ring, disk, wheel, orbit, circumference; range, scope, compass; period, cycle; на к. on the average; описывать к. *v.* (aero.) circle; поворотный к. turntable.

кругит *m.* (min.) krugite.

кругл/еть *v.* become round; —ить *v.* make round, round off.

кругло *adv.* round, roundly; —ватый *a.* roundish; —годичный *a.* year-round; —губцы *pl.* roundnose pliers; —донный *a.* round-bottomed (flask); —лобый молоток rounding hammer; —палочный станок rounding machine; —ресничные *pl.* (zool.) Peritricha; —ротые *pl.* (zool.) Cyclostomata; —суточно *adv.* round-the-clock; —суточный *a.* twenty four-hour, continuous; —та *f.* roundness,

round shape; —шлифовальный станок cylinder-and-cone grinding machine; —шовные *pl.*, —шовные мухи circular-seamed flies (*Cyclorrhapha*).

кругл/ый *a.* round, circular, annular, globular, spherical; к. год the year round; —ыш, —як *m.* rounded stone, roundstone; round timber, round beam.

кругов/ой *a.* circular, round, ring, circling; cyclic; endless (conveyer); continuous (drive); mutual (guarantee); circumferential (weld seam); к. нониус dial; к. полет (aero.) circuit; к. процесс cycle; —ая диаграмма (math.) complex plane locus; —ая система rotary system; circulating system; —ое движение circular motion, rotary motion, rotation, circling, circle; circulation; давать —ое движение, иметь —ое движение *v.* rotate; circulate; —ое обращение circulation; circuit.

круго/ворот *m.* rotation, circular motion; circulation; cycle; к. азота nitrogen cycle (in nature); —вращательный *a.* rotary, gyrating, circular, circulatory; —вращение *n.* rotation, circular motion; circulation; —зор *m.* scope, horizon, views, mental outlook; range, range of vision; —м *adv.* round, around, about; in a ring, in a circle; —оборот *m.* circuit; circulation; —оборот примесей circulating load of impurities; —образность *f.* roundness, round shape, circularity; —образный *a.* round, circular; —обращение *n.* rotation, circular motion; circulation.

кружал/о *n.*, —ьный *a.* center (for arch while building), curve piece, camber slip; rotating screen; —ьное ребро curve piece.

кружев/ницы *pl.* lace bugs (*Tingitidae*); —о *n.* lace; —овидный *a.* lace-like, lacy.

круж/ение *n.* turning, spinning, vertigo, dizziness; —ить *v.* turn, spin around, rotate; —иться *v.* turn, spin, gyrate, rotate; у него —ится голова he is dizzy.

кружка *f.* mug, jug, jar; (med.) irrigator.

**круж/ный** *a.* circuitous, roundabout; **—ок** *m.* small circle; disk, tablet, cake; association, society.

**крукезит** *m.* (min.) crookesite.

**Крукса трубка** Crookes (X-ray) tube; **круксовое темное пространство** Crookes dark space.

**крунода** *f.* (geom.) crunode.

**круп** *m.* (med.; zool.) croup.

**круп/а** *f.* groats, pearl barley; soft hail, graupel; **—инка** *f.* grain, granule; **—итчатый** *a.* grainy, granular; wheaten; **—ица** *f.* grain, crumb; **—ка** *f.* grit, grit sandstone; (sugar) coarse bone black; (bot.) whitlow grass (*Draba*).

**крупнеть** *v.* grow larger, grow heavier.

**крупно** *adv. and prefix* coarsely, in large particles; on a large scale; macro—; **—волокнистый** *a.* coarse-fiber; **—заводская промышленность** large-scale industry, manufacture on a large scale; **—зем** *m.* coarse earth; **—зернистый** *a.* coarse-grained, coarse-fibered, coarse; **—клетчатый** *a.* wide-mesh, wide-meshed; **—комковатый** *a.* buckshot; **—кристаллический** *a.* coarsely crystalline, macrocrystalline, phanerocrystalline; **—кусковой** *a.* lumpy, large-sized, in large pieces; **—масштабный** *a.* broad-scale; large-scale; **—молотый** *a.* coarsely ground.

**крупно/ноздреватый** *a.* coarsely porous; **—пильчатый** *a.* (bot.) runcinate; **—плодный** *a.* large-fruited; **—пунктирная линия** heavy dotted line; **—порфировый** *a.* (geol.) coarsely porphyritic, magnophyric; **—сланцеватая структура** (geol.) platy structure; **—сортный** *a.* heavy, large, large-size.

**крупн/ость** *f.* size, coarseness, thickness; **—ый** *a.* big, coarse; large-scale; heavy-duty (machine); standing (timber); lump (coal).

**круподер/ка, —ная машина** *see* **крупорушка.**

**крупонировать** *v.* butt, crop, round (hides).

**крупорушка** *f.* sheller, hulling mill.

**Крупп болезнь** (met.) Krupp's disease.

**крупп/ировать** *v.* (met.) kruppize, apply Krupp process; **—овский процесс** Krupp (cementation) process.

**круп/чатка** *f.* grainy wheaten flour; wheat-grinding mill; **—чатый** *a.* grainy, large-grained, coarse; **—яной** *a.* groats.

**крустифи/кация** *f.* (geol.) crustification; **—цированный** *a.* crustified.

**крутец** *m.* twisted flax tow.

**крутизна** *f.* steepness, sharpness; (elec. comm.) transconductance.

**крутик** *m.* (bot.) dyer's wood (*Isatis tinctoria*); indigo bush (*Amorpha fruticosa*).

**крут/ило** *n.* twisting pliers; **—ильный** *a.* torsion, torsional, twisting; **—ильный ватер** (text.) doubler; **—ильный динамометр** torsion dynamometer, torsion meter; **—ильные весы** torsion balance; **—ильщик** *m.* twister; **—ить** *v.* twist, ring, turn, whirl; (elec.) reverse; **—иться** *v.* turn, revolve, spin around, eddy, swirl; **—ка** *f.* twist; **—комер** *m.* twist counter.

**крут/о** *adv.* steeply, abruptly, sharply, severely; tightly; **—ой** *a.* steep, precipitous, abrupt, sharp, sudden; severe, tough; hard-boiled (egg).

**круток** *m.* coarse linen.

**круто/падающий** *a.* steeply dipping, steep; **—сть** *f.* steepness, abruptness, sharpness; pitch (of roof).

**крутящ/ий** *a.* twisting, torsion, torsional; **к. момент** torque; **—ее усилие** torsional force.

**круч/а** *f.* steep slope, steepness; **—е** *comp. of* **круто, крутой,** steeper, more abrupt.

**кручен/ие** *n.* twisting, torsion; distortion, buckling; **момент —ия** torque; **подвержение —ию** torsion, torsional stress; **—ый** *a.* twisted, spun; thrown (silk).

**крушение** *n.* wreck, ruin; accident; breakdown, collapse.

**крушиа** *f.* Crucia (spring steel).

**крушилка** *f.* disintegrator, disintegrating mill; crusher.

**крушин/а** *f.*, **—ный** *a.* (bot.) buckthorn (*Rhamnus*); **американская к.** cascara sagrada (*R. purshiana*); **игольная к., колючая к., слабительная к.** buckthorn (*R. cathartica*); **каменная к., красильная к.** dyer's buckthorn (*R. infectoria* or *R. tinctoria*); **эфирное**

масло —ы buckthorn oil; —ные, —овые *pl.* Rhamnaceae.

крушить *v.* shatter, destroy, wreck.

крыжовник *m.* (bot.) gooseberry (*Ribes grossularia*).

к-рый *abbr.* (который) who, which.

крыл *past sing. of* крыть.

крылат/ка *f.* wing nut; vane; winged seed; —ые *pl.* (zool.) Pterygogenea; —ый *a.* winged, alate; —ые насекомые Pterygota.

крыло *n.* wing; blade, vane, impeller; fender (of automobile); (geol.) limb (of fold); —видный, —образный *a.* wing-shaped, alar; (zool.) pterygoid; —ногие *pl.* (zool.) Pteropoda; —ухие *pl.* (zool.) Pterygota.

—крылые *pl. suffix* (biol.) —ptera.

крылышко *n.* small wing; vane.

крыльце *n.* (anat.) shoulder blade.

крыльцо *n.* porch, flight of steps, perron.

крыльчатка *see* крыльчатое колесо.

крыльчат/ый *a.* wing, vane; к. вентилятор fan, fan ventilator; к. насос vane pump; —ая гайка wing nut; —ое колесо vane wheel, blade wheel, impeller.

Крым Crimea.

крымза *f.* zinc sulfate.

крым/-сагыз *m.* (bot.) krym-saghyz (*Taraxacum megalorrhizon, T. gymnanthum* or *T. hybernum*); —ский *a.* Crimean.

крынка *f.* milk pot, jug.

крыс/а *f.*, —ий, —иный *a.* rat; —ид *m.* rat poison (α-naphthylthiourea); —оловка *f.* rat trap.

крыт/ый *a.* covered, capped; roofed; —ь *v.* cover, cap; roof; —ься *v.* be covered, be concealed.

крыца *see* крица.

крыш/а *f.*, настилать —у *v.* roof; —ка *f.*, —ечный *a.* cover, lid, hood, cap.

крэбы *pl.* crab apples.

крэк/инг, —ирование *see* крекинг.

крэшер *see* крешер.

Крюгера элемент Krüger cell.

крюк *m.* hook, crook; grapple, cramp iron; staple; pickax, pick; detour.

крючить *v.* bend (into a hook).

крюч/коватый *a.* hooked, jagged, hackly (fracture); к. ключ spanner, wrench; —кообразный *a.* hook-like, hooked,

crooked; —ник *m.* carrier, stevedore; —ок *m.* hook, catch, claw; lifting handle; rake.

кряду *adv.* together, running.

кряж *m.* block, log; ridge, crest; (bot.) local strain.

КСА прибор *abbr.* (прибор Климова-Синицина-Алеевой) Klimov-Sinitsyn-Aleeva apparatus (for testing stability of greases).

ксант/алин *m.* xanthaline; —ан *m.* xanthane; —ат *m.* xanthate; —атбарабан *see* барат; —атин *m.* xanthathin; —гидрол *m.* xanthydrol, 9-hydroxyxanthene; —еин *m.* xanthein; —еллин *m.* xanthellin; —ематин *m.* xanthematin.

ксантен *m.*, —овый *a.* xanthene, diphenylmethane oxide; —ол *m.* xanthenol, xanthydrol; —он *m.* xanthenone, xanthone.

ксантил *m.*, —овый *a.* xanthyl; —овая кислота xanthylic acid.

ксантин *m.*, —овый *a.* xanthine, 2,6-purinedione; —ин *m.* xanthinine; —овые основания xanthine bases, purines.

ксантит *m.* (min.) xanthite (a variety of vesuvianite).

ксанто— *prefix* xantho— (yellow); —арсенит *m.* (min.) xantharsenite (a variety of sarkinite).

ксантоген *m.* xanthogen; —амид *m.* xanthogenamide, thiourethan; —ат *m.* xanthate; —ил *m.* xanthogenyl; —илцеллюлоза *f.* cellulose xanthate; —ирование *n.* xanthation.

ксантогеново/кислый *a.* xanthic acid; xanthate (of); к. калий, —калиевая соль potassium xanthate; —кислая соль xanthate; —натриевая соль sodium xanthate; —этиловый эфир ethyl xanthate.

ксантоген/ый *a.* xanthogen, xanthogenic; к. эфир ethyl xanthate; —ая кислота xanthic acid, ethyloxydithiocarbonic acid; соль —ой кислоты xanthate.

ксанто/глобулин *m.* xanthoglobulin, hypoxanthine; —зин *m.* xanthosin, xanthinriboside; —кон *m.* (min.) xanthoconite; —креатинин *m.* xanthocreatinine; —ксилен, —ксилин *m.* xanthoxylene, xanthoxylin; —**ксилон** *m.* xanthoxylone; —**ксол** *m.* xanthoxol; —**лин** *m.* xantholine, santonica; —**мицин** *m.* xanthomycin.

**ксантон** *m.* xanthone, 9-xanthenone; —**овый** *a.* xanthone, xanthonic; —**овая кислота** xanthonic acid; —**овые краски** xanthone dyes.

**ксантопикр/ин** *m.* xanthopicrin; —**ит** *m.* xanthopicrite (resin).

**ксантопротеин** *m.* xanthoprotein; —**овая кислота** xanthoproteic acid; —**овая реакция** xanthoprotein reaction.

**ксанто/птерин** *m.* xanthopterin; —**пукцин** *m.* xanthopuccine; —**пурпурин** *m.* xanthopurpurin, purpuroxanthene; —**рамнин** *m.* xanthorhamnin.

**ксантор/идза** *f.* xanthorrhiza, yellow root; —**рея** *f.* xanthorrhoea (resin), accroides resin; —**тит** *m.* (min.) xanthorthite (an altered variety of allanite).

**ксанто/сидерит** *m.* (min.) xanthosiderite (probably a variety of limonite); —**струмарин** *m.* xanthostrumarin; —**токсин** *m.* xanthotoxin; —**тоновая кислота** xanthotonic acid; —**филл** *m.* xanthophyll; —**филлит** *m.* (min.) xanthophyllite; —**хелидоновая кислота** xanthochelidonic acid, acetonedioxalic acid.

**кселен** *see* **ксилен.**

**ксен/ен** *m.* xenene, biphenyl; —**ил** *m.* xenyl; —**иламин** *m.* xenylamine, *p*-biphenylamine.

**ксено/генит** *m.* (geol.) xenogenite; —**кристалл** *m.* (geol.) xenocryst; —**лит** *m.* (min.) xenolite (probably a variety of sillimanite); (geol.) xenolith, inclusion; —**морфный** *a.* (min.) xenomorphic.

**ксенон** *m.* xenon, Xe.

**ксенотим** *m.* (min.) xenotime (an yttrium phosphate).

**ксеро—** *prefix* xero— (dry); —**гель** *m.* xerogel; —**графия** *f.* xerography; —**новая кислота** xeronic acid; —**термический** *a.* xerothermic; —**фит** *m.* xerophyte, drought-resisting plant; —**форм** *m.* xeroform, bismuth tribromophenate.

**ксил/ан** *m.* xylan; —**ема** *f.* (bot.) xylem;

—**ен** *m.* xylain (constituent of coal); —**ендиол** *m.* xylenediol, benzenedicarbinol; —**енол** *m.* xylenol; —**идин** *m.*, —**идиновый** *a.* xylidine, dimethylaniline; —**идиновая кислота** xylidic acid, 4-methylisophthalic acid.

**ксилил** *m.*, —**овый** *a.* xylyl; **бромистый к.** xylyl bromide; —**ен** *m.* xylylene; —**енимин** *m.* xylylenimine, dihydroisoindole; —**овая кислота** xylic acid (xylylic acid), dimethylbenzoic acid; —**овый спирт** xylyl alcohol; —**ол** *m.* xylylol, xylenediol.

**ксили/н** *m.* xylin; —**т** *m.* xylite, xylitol.

**ксило—** *prefix* xylo— (wood); —**бетонный камень** a type of cement block; —**граф** *m.* xylographer; —**графия** *f.* xylography, wood engraving; —**за** *f.* xylose, wood sugar; —**зиевая кислота** xylosic acid; —**идин** *m.* xyloidine; —**ил** *m.* xyloyl; —**кетоза** *f.* xyloketose.

**ксилол** *m.* xylene, dimethylbenzene; —**ин** *m.* xyloline (yarn); —**ит** *m.* xylolith, wood-stone.

**ксилометр** *m.* xylometer.

**ксилон** *m.* xylon, wood cellulose; —**ит** *m.* xylonite, celluloid; —**овый** *a.* xylon, xylonic; —**овая кислота** xylonic acid.

**ксило/пал** *m.* xylopal, wood opal; —**рсин**, —**рцин** *m.* xylorcinol, dimethylresorcinol; —**томия** *f.* xylotomy; —**хинон** *m.* xyloquinone, dimethylquinone; —**хлорал** *m.* xylochloral.

**Кск** *abbr.* (**сернокислый калий**) potassium sulfate.

**ксонотлит** *m.* (min.) xonotlite (a zeolite).

**кстати** *adv.* to the point, to the purpose, opportunely; by the way.

**КСУ** *abbr.* (**Комиссия содействия ученым**) Assistance Committee for Scientists.

**КСХОС** *abbr.* (**комплексная сельскохозяйственная опытная станция**) Complex Agricultural Experiment Station.

**к-т** *abbr.* (**комбинат**) combine.

**к-та** *abbr.* (**кислота**) acid.

**ктипеит** *m.* (min.) ktypeite (probably a porous form of aragonite).

**кто** *pron.* who, who? **к. бы ни** whoever;

**к.-либо, к.-нибудь** somebody, someone, anybody; **к.-то** somebody.

**к.т.п.** *abbr.* (коэффициент теплопередачи) coefficient of heat transfer.

**ктыри** *pl.* robber flies (*Asilidae*).

**к-ть** *abbr.* (кислотность) acidity.

**куб** *m.* (math.) cube; vat; still; **в —е** cubed; **возводить в к.** *v.* cube, raise to the third power; **перегонный к.** still.

**куб.** *abbr.* (кубический) cubic.

**куба** *f.* Cuba wood, fustic wood.

**Куба** Cuba.

**кубанит** *m.* (min.) cubanite, chalmersite.

**кубанка** *f.* (bot.) a hard wheat (*Triticum durum*).

**кубарка** *f.* rake (used with tractor).

**кубарь** *m.* humming top, spinning top.

**кубатура** *f.* cubic content, cubage, volume; cubature, determination of volume.

**куб. дм** *abbr.* (кубический дециметр) cubic decimeter; **куб. дм.** *abbr.* (кубический дюйм) cubic inch.

**кубеб/а** *f.*, **—овый** *a.* cubeb (dried, unripened fruit of *Piper cubeba*); **—ен** *m.* cubebene; **—ин** *m.* cubebin, 3,4-dimethyleneoxy-*p*-oxystyrone; **—о-вая кислота** cubebic acid; **—овое масло** cubeb oil.

**кубель** *m.* box.

**кубик** *m.* small cube, cube-shaped block.

**кубицит** *m.* (min.) cubicite, cubic zeolite.

**кубическ/ий, кубичный** *a.* cubic, cubical; **к. корень** (math.) cube root; **к. шпат** (min.) cube spar, anhydrite; **—ая селитра** cubic saltpeter, sodium nitrate; **—ое уравнение** (math.) cubic equation; **—ие квасцы** cubic alum, potash alum.

**куб. км** *abbr.* (кубический километр) cubic kilometer; **куб. м** *abbr.* (кубический метр) cubic meter; **куб. мм** *abbr.* (кубический миллиметр) cubic millimeter.

**кубовидный** *a.* cubical, cuboid, cube-shaped.

**кубов/ый** *a.* cube; vat; still; **к. краситель, —ая краска** vat dye; **к. остаток** still residues, bottoms; **к. процесс, —ая окраска, —ое крашение** vat dyeing; **—ая руда** (min.) cube ore,

pharmacosiderite; **—ое железо** boiler plate.

**кубоит** *see* **кубицит.**

**кубок** *m.* beaker, bowl.

**кубо/метр** *m.* cubic meter; **—образный** *see* **кубовидный; —силицит** *m.* (min.) cubosilicite (a form of silica).

**кубрик** *m.* cockpit.

**куб. см** *abbr.* (кубический сантиметр) cubic centimeter.

**кубышка** *f.* jug; coin box; egg sac, clump of locust eggs; (bot.) yellow water lily (*Nuphar*).

**кувалда** *f.* hammer, sledge hammer.

**кувез** *m.* incubator (for premature babies).

**кувел/яж, —яция** *see* **кювеляж.**

**кувшин** *m.* pitcher, jug, jar; **—ка** *f.* (bot.) water lily (*Nymphaea*); **—ковые** *pl.* Nymphaeaceae.

**куда** *adv.* where? in what direction? **к. бы ни** wherever; **к. как** how very; **к. либо, к.-нибудь** somewhere, anywhere; **к. то** somewhere.

**куд/бер, —бир** *m.* cudbear, persio, orchil (food color).

**кудель** *f.* flax or hemp tow.

**кудрявый** *a.* curly, frizzly, crimped.

**Кузбас** *abbr.* **Кузнецкий бассейн.**

**кузка** *see* **кузька.**

**кузнец** *m.* blacksmith, smithy; **к.-инструментальщик** toolsmith.

**Кузнецк/ий бассейн** Kusnetsk coal fields (Siberia); **—строй** Kusnetskstroy.

**кузнечик** *m.* grasshopper; **—и, —овые** *pl.* Tettigoniidae or Locustidae.

**кузн/ечно-прессовый** *a.* forging and pressing; **—ечный** *a.* forging, forge; smith's, blacksmith's; wrought (iron); sledge (hammer); **—ечный цех, —ечная мастерская, —ица** *f.* smithy, blacksmith shop; forge, forge shop; **—ечный шлак** (met.) hearth cinder, forge cinder.

**кузов** *m.* basket; body (of vehicle); hood (of car); **к.-пикап** pickup body; **—остроение** *n.* bodywork.

**кузька** *f.* grain beetle (*Anisoplia austriaca*).

**кузьмичева трава** (bot.) ephedra.

**Кука пролив** Cook Strait.

**кукеит** *m.* (min.) cookeite.

**кукельван** see **кукольван.**

**кукерсит** m. kukersit (a bituminous shale).

**кукла** f. doll.

**куклородные** pl. (zool.) Pupipara.

**кукол/еотборник** m. cockle cylinder, cockle separator; —**ица** see **кукольван.**

**куколк/а** f. (zool.) chrysalis, pupa, cocoon; —**ообразный** a. pupiform.

**куколь** m., —**ный** a. (bot.) cockle, corncockle (*Agrostemma githago*); —**ван** m. fish berries (*Cocculus indicus* or *Anamirta cocculus*); —**вановые** pl. Menispermaceae.

**кукурбит/ин** m. cucurbitine; —**ол** m. cucurbitol.

**кукуруз/а** f., —**ный** a. (bot.) corn, maize (*Zea mays*); зубовидная к. dent corn (*Z. m. indentata*); кремнистая к. flint corn (*Z. m. indurata*); лопающаяся к. popcorn (*Z. m. everta*); пленчатая к., чешуйчатая к. pod corn (*Z. m. tunicata*); сахарная к. sweet corn (*Z. m. saccharata*).

**кукурузо/сажалка** f. corn planter; —**уборочная машина** corn picker; —**хранилище** n. corn crib.

**кукушк/а** f. cuckoo; switcher; (min.) dinky (small locomotive); —**ины слезки** (bot.) orchis (*Orchis maculata*).

**кулаж** m. loss, waste.

**кулак** m. fist; (tech.) see **кулачок**; hammer (of crusher).

**кулачков/ый** a. of **кулачок**; к. вал camshaft; к. механизм, —**ое распределение** cam gear; к. привод cam drive; —**ая дробилка** hammer mill.

**кулачкообразный** a. cam-shaped, jaw-shaped.

**кулачник** m. round coal.

**кулачн/ый** a. fist; (tech.) see also **кулачковый**; к. патрон jaw chuck; —**ая муфта** jaw clutch.

**кулач/ок** m., —**ковый** a. cam, cog, lug, tooth, pin, finger, projection; jaw (of chuck); pawl, catch, detent, detainer, checking device; tappet; приводной к., рабочий к. actuating cam; сгибающий к. bending block.

**кулевой** a. sack, sold by sacks.

**кулер, сахарный** caramel.

**кулеш** m. thin gruel, paste.

**Кулиджа трубка** Coolidge (X-ray) tube.

**кулинарный** a. culinary.

**кулис/а** f., —**ный** a. crank; link, connecting link; rocker; slot, slot hole, slideway; windbreak strip, strip (of land); —**ный камень** slide block, link block; guide shoe; rocker die (of steam engine); —**ный механизм**, —**ный привод** link gear; (elec.) rocker gear; —**ообразное строение** echelon structure.

**кулич** m. cake, sweet loaf.

**кулон** m. (elec.) coulomb (unit of quantity); закон **Кулона** Coulomb's law; —**метр**, —**ометр** m. coulometer; —**овский** a. Coulomb.

**култук** m. kultuk (deeply indented shallow bay).

**кулуар** m. chute, conduit.

**куль** m. bag, sack; pocket, pouch.

**кульверт** m. culvert.

**кульгардит** m. (min.) coolgardite.

**кульм** m. culm, anthracite coal.

**Кульмана зелень, кульмановская зелень** Kuhlmann's green, cuprous oxychloride.

**кульмин/ационный** a., —**ация** f. culmination, culminating; к. пункт climax; —**ировать** v. culminate, end, terminate.

**культив/атор** m. (agr.) cultivator; к.-**груббер**, к.-**скарификатор**, к.-**экстирпатор** grubber; —**ация** f., —**ирование** n. cultivation; —**ированный** a. cultivated; —**ировать** v. cultivate.

**культур/а** f. culture, cultivation; crop; полевые —**ы** crops; —**ный** a. cultured, cultural, cultivated; —**техник** m. (agr.) ameliorator; —**техника** f. amelioration, soil improvement.

**куляж** see **кулаж.**

**кум** m. coomb (old measure of 4 bushels).

**кумазоновая кислота** coumazonic acid.

**кумал** m. cumal, cumylene.

**кумалин** m. coumalin, 1,2-pyrone; —**овая кислота** coumalic acid.

**куманика** f. (bot.) bramble (*Rubus*).

**куманилид** m. cumanilide, cumophenamide.

**куманичный** a. blackberry, bramble.

**кумар/ан** m. coumaran, dihydrocoumarone; —**анон** m. coumaranone, 2(1)-benzofuranone; —**ил** m. coumaryl;

—иловая кислота coumarilic acid, 1-benzofurancarboxylic acid; —ин *m.* coumarin, 1,2-benzopyrone; —инкарбоновая кислота carboxycoumaric acid; —иновая кислота coumarinic acid, coumaric acid; —кетон *m.* coumarketone; —овый *a.* coumaric; —овый альдегид coumaraldehyde, *o*-hydroxycinnamaldehyde; —он *m.* coumarone, benzofuran; —оновая смола coumarone resin; —ун *m.* coumarouna bean, tonka bean.

кумач *m.* red calico.

кумб *see* кум.

куменгеит *m.* (min.) cumengeite.

кумен/ил *m.* cumenyl, cumyl; —ол *see* куминол; —уровая кислота *see* кумину́ровая кислота.

куметр *m.* (elec. comm.) *Q*-meter.

кумжа *f.* (zool.) salmon trout.

кумидин *m.* cumidine, cumenylamine; —овая кислота cumidic acid, dimethylphthalic acid.

кумил *m.*, —овый *a.* cumyl, cumenyl; —ен *m.* cumylene, cumal; —овая кислота cumylic acid, durylic acid.

кумин/ал *m.* cuminal, cumal; cumic aldehyde; —амид *m.* cuminamide, cumic amide; —амовая кислота cuminamic acid.

кумингтонит *m.* (min.) cummingtonite (a variety of amphibole).

куминил *m.* cuminyl; cuminil, dicuminoketone; хлористый к. cuminyl chloride.

куминов/ый *a.* cumin, cuminic, cumic; к. альдегид cumic aldehyde, cumaldehyde; к. спирт *see* куминол; —ая кислота cuminic acid, cumic acid, *p*-isopropylbenzoic acid; —ое масло cumin oil.

кумин/оин *m.* cuminoin, diisopropyl benzoin; —ол *m.* cuminol, cumic alcohol, *i*-propylbenzyl alcohol; —уровая кислота cuminuric acid.

кумкват *m.* (bot.) kumquat (*Fortunella*).

кумо/бензиловый спирт cumobenzyl alcohol; —л *m.* cumene, *i*-propylbenzene; —нитрил *m.* cumonitrile, cumenyl cyanide; —тиазон *m.* coumothiazone; —фенамид *m.* cumophen-

amide, cumanilide; —хинол *m.* cumoquinol; —хинон *m.* cumoquinone.

кумул/ированный *a.* cumulated; —иты *pl.* (petr.) cumulites (spherulitic aggregates of globules); —офировая текстура (geol.) cumulophyric texture; —ятивный *a.* cumulative; —ятивные отложения (geol.) cumulose deposits; —яция *f.* cumulation, accumulation.

кумы *pl.* kumy (quicksands in Central Asia).

кумыс *m.* koumiss (a drink made from mare's milk); kumyss, lac fermentatum.

Кундта закон Kundt's rule.

кунжут *m.*, —ный *a.* (bot.) sesame (*Sesamum indicum*); —ное масло sesame oil; —ные *pl.* (bot.) Pedaliaceae.

куни/аль *m.* a copper-base alloy; —ко *n.* Cunico (cobalt-nickel-copper alloy); —фе *n.* Cunife (copper-nickel-iron alloy).

кунцит *m.* (min.) kunzite (a spodumene).

куорин *m.* cuorin.

купа *f.* group, cluster.

купавка *f.* (bot.) camomile (*Anthemis*).

купаж *m.*, —ирование *n.* mixing (of liquids); mixture, blend, blending (of wines, etc.); dilution.

купальни/к *m.* (bot.) arnica; —ца *f.* globe flower (*Trollius europaeus*).

куп/альный *a.* bathing, bath; —альня *f.* bath (house); —ание, —анье, *n.* bathing, swimming; —ать, —аться *v.* bathe.

купе *n.* coupe; (railroad) compartment.

купелировать *see* капелировать.

купель *f.* (typ.) font.

купеляция *see* капелирование.

купена *f.* (bot.) Solomon's seal, sealwort (*Polygonatum*).

**Купер-Юитта лампа** Cooper-Hewitt lamp.

куп/ец *m.* merchant, tradesman; —ечеcкий *a.* mercantile.

купировать *v.* mix, blend; dilute, cut.

куп/ить *v.* buy, purchase; —ля *f.* buying, purchasing; purchase.

купол *m.*, —ьный *a.* cupola, dome, bowl, bell, crown (of furnace); canopy (of parachute); (min.) pot; (geol.) boss;

—**овидный,** —**ообразный** *a.* dome-shaped, arched; (geol.) quaquaversal, domal (structure); —**ообразование** *n.* dome-formation, doming; —**ьный свод** arched dome.

**купон** *m.* coupon.

**купорос** *m.* vitriol; **белый к., цинковый к.** white vitriol, zinc sulfate; **двойной к.** eagle vitriol (mixture of ferrous and cupric sulfates); **железный к., зеленый к.** green vitriol, copperas, ferrous sulfate heptahydrate; **медный к., синий к.** blue vitriol, copper sulfate; **свинцовый к.** lead vitriol, lead sulfate; **черный к.** an iron copperas; —**ить** *v.* vitriolate.

**купоросн/ый** *a.* vitriol, vitriolic; **к. завод** vitriol works, sulfuric acid plant; **к. куб** copperas vat; —**ое масло** oil of vitriol, commercial sulfuric acid (93%).

**купр/аза** *f.* cuprase; —**аммониевый** *a.* cuprammonium.

**купре/ан** *m.* cupreane, desoxycupreine; —**идан** *m.* cupreidane, desoxycupreidine; —**идин** *m.* cupreidine; —**ин** *m.* cupreine (alkaloid from cuprea bark); (min.) copper glance, chalcocite; —**ол** *m.* cupreol; —**ссин** *m.* cupressin.

**куприн** *m.* cuprine.

**куприт** *m.* (min.) cuprite, red copper ore.

**купро**— *prefix* cupro—; —**адамит** *m.* (min.) cuproadamite (a variety of adamite); —**бисмутит** *m.* cuprobismuthite (probably identical with emplectite); —**гемол** *m.* cuprohemol; —**деклоизит,** —**деклуазит** *m.* (min.) cuprodescloizite.

**купрокс** *m.,* —**ный** *a.* (rad.) copper oxide rectifier; cuprous oxide; —**ный выпрямитель** copper oxide rectifier.

**купро/магнезит** *m.* (min.) cupromagnesite; —**марганец** *m.* (met.) cupromanganese; —**н** *m.* cupron, α-benzoinoxime; (elec.) cupron cell; —**н-элемент** *m.,* —**новый аккумулятор** cupron cell, copper oxide cell; —**никель** *m.* (met.) cupronickel (copper-nickel alloy); —**нин** *m.* cupronine; —**отунит** *m.* (min.) cuproautunite; —**пирит** *m.* (min.) copper pyrites, chalcopyrite, yellow copper ore; —**пломбит,** —**плумбит** *m.* (min.)

cuproplumbite; —**склодовскит** *m.* (min.) cuprosklodowskite; —**тунгстит** *m.* cuprotungstite; —**уранит** *m.* (min.) cuprouranite; —**хлорид** *m.* cuprous chloride; —**шеелит** *m.* (min.) cuproscheelite.

**купфер/меритоль** *m.* a copper-calcium arsenate insecticide and fungicide; —**никель** *m.* (min.) copper nickel, niccolite, arsenical nickel; —**рон** *m.* Cupferron; —**штейн** *m.* (met.) copper matte.

**купчая** *f.* title, deed.

**купырь** *m.* (bot.) chervil (*Anthriscus*).

**купюра** *f.* cut; abridgment; (com.) note, bond.

**курага** *f.* dried apricots.

**курай** *m.* (bot.) saltwort (*Salsola kali* or *S. ruthenica*).

**курант** *m.* grinder (for paints).

**курар/е** *n.* curare (extract of *Strychnos toxifera*); —**ин** *m.* curarine.

**курба** *f.* (vet. *obs.*) inflammation of the hock.

**курбель** *m.* knob.

**курвиметр** *m.* curvometer.

**курган** *m.* (geol.) hill, tumulus (of lava).

**кургузить** *v.* curtail, cut back.

**курдю/к** *m.* fat tail (of sheep); —**чное сало** Kurduyk fat.

**курение** *n.* smoking, fuming; fumigation.

**курин** *m.* curine.

**курин/ый** *a.* chicken, hen's; —**ая слепота** (med.) night blindness, nyctalopia; (bot.) greater celandine (*Chelidonium*).

**курит/ельный** *a.* fumigating; —**ельное вещество** fumigant, fumigating agent; —**ь** *v.* smoke, cure; fumigate; distil; smoke (tobacco).

**курица** *f.* hen, chicken.

**куркасовое масло** curcas oil.

**курковый** *a.* (gun) cock.

**куркум/а** *f.* (bot.) turmeric (*Curcuma longa*); —**ен** *m.* curcumene; —**ин** *m.,* —**овый желтый** curcumin, turmeric yellow; —**овый** *a.* turmeric, curcuma; —**овый корень** turmeric root, hydratis; —**овая кислота** curcumic acid.

**курмак** *m.* coarse-grain millet (*Echinochloa macrocarpa*).

**курный** *a.* smoky; **к. каменный уголь** incompletely carbonized charcoal.

**куроводство** *n.* poultry breeding.

**курок** *m.* cock, hammer (of gun).

**куронгит** *m.* (min.) coorongite (a variety of elaterite).

**куропатка** *f.* (zool.) partridge.

**курорт** *m.*, **—ный** *a.* health resort; **—ология** *f.* treatment at health resorts.

**курослеп** *see* **калужница.**

**курри порошок** curry powder.

**Курроля соль** Kurrol salt, potassium polyphosphate.

**курс** *m.* course; track, path; (com.) rate of exchange; **держать к. на** *v.* head for, hold a course.

**курсив** *m.* (typ.) italics; **выделять —ом, набирать —ом** *v.* italicize; **—ный** *a.* italic, italicized.

**курсо/вой** *a.* course; **—граф** *m.* (aero.) avigraph, course recorder; **—указатель** *m.* course indicator.

**куртаж** *m.*, **—ный** *a.* (com.) brokerage, broker's business.

**курт/ка, —очка** *f.* jacket.

**курум** *m.* stone stream, rock stream, rock-train.

**курцин** *m.* curcin.

**Курциуса реакция** Curtius reaction.

**курчав/еть** *v.* curl; **—ка** *f.* (bot.) atraphaxis; **—ость** *f.* curliness; (leaf) curl; crimp (of wool); **—ый** *a.* curly.

**куры** *pl. of* **курица.**

**курьез** *m.* curiosity, curious phenomenon, oddity, strange thing, **—но** *adv.* curiously, in a strange way; **—ный** *a.* curious, strange, odd.

**курьер** *m.* messenger; **—ский** *a.* express.

**курья** *f.* kurya (long narrow oxbow, detached from river at upper end only).

**курят/ина** *f.* chicken (meat); **—ник** *m.* chicken coop.

**курящий** *a.* smoking, fuming.

**кусать** *v.* bite, sting.

**кусачки** *pl.* cutting pliers, nippers, wire cutter; **к.-плоскогубцы** flatnose (cutting) pliers.

**кусилол** *m.* cusylol (cupric citrate).

**кускам/идин** *m.* cuscamidine; **—ин** *m.* cuscamine.

**куски** *pl. of* **кусок.**

**куско, кора** cusco bark (a variety of cinchona bark).

**кусков/ой, —атый** *a.* lump.

**куско/гигрин** *m.* cuscohygrine; **—нидин** *m.* cusconidine; **—нин** *m.* cusconine.

**кускута** *f.* seed sorter; (bot.) dodder (*Cuscuta*).

**кус/ок** *m.* piece, lump, block, chunk, bar, slice, fragment; length; **—ками, в —ках** in pieces, lumpy, clotted; **из одного —ка** one-piece; **одним —ком** in block, whole; **по —кам** piece by piece, piecemeal; **разбить на —ки** *v.* break to pieces, shatter; **—очек** *m.* little piece, fragment.

**куспар/идин** *m.* cusparidine; **—ин** *m.* cusparine; **кора —ия** cusparia bark, angostura bark.

**куспидин** *m.* cuspidine.

**кусс/еин** *m.* koussein; **—ин** *m.* koussin, kossin; **—о** *n.*, **цветы —о** kousso (dried flower of *Hagenia abyssinica*).

**куст** *m.* bush, shrub; bunch; (min.) pocket; section, group; cluster (of points).

**кустарник** *m.* brushwood, scrub, undergrowth; **—овый плуг** ripper.

**кустар/ный** *a.* homemade; domestic (industry); **—щина** *f.* haphazard work, unsystematic method of working; **—ь** *m.* handicraftsman.

**кустерит** *m.* (min.) custerite.

**кустистый** *a.* bushy.

**кустован/ие** *n.* interconnecting; **—ный** *a.* interconnected; (tel.) bank.

**кусто/ватый** *a.* shrubby, bushy; **—рез** *m.* brush cutter.

**кусцы** *see* **кусачки.**

**кут/ание, —анье** *n.* wrapping, muffling; **—ать** *v.* wrap, wrap up, muffle up.

**кутикула** *f.* (biol.) cuticle, skin.

**кутин** *m.* cutin; **—овая кислота** cutic acid.

**кутоза** *f.* cutose.

**кутр/а** *f.*, **—овый** *a.* (bot.) Indian hemp (*Apocynum*); **—овые** *pl.* Apocynaceae.

**куфта** *f.* (text.) cut; reel; knot of yarn.

**кух/арка** *f.* cook; **—ня** *f.* kitchen; **—онный** *a.* kitchen, cooking.

**куч/а** *f.* pile, heap, mass, cluster, congestion, congregation; **в —е** in a pile, collectively, as a group; **обжиг в —ах**

heap roasting; **—евое облако** cumulus; **—еводождевое облако** cumulonimbus; **—еобразный** *a.* cumuliform (cloud).

**кучерявчик** *m.* (geol.) underclay.

**кучина** *f.* (bot.) mahaleb (*Prunus mahaleb*).

**кучинский** *a.* Kuchino.

**кучичингская группа** (geol.) Coutchiching group.

**куч/ка** *f.* small heap; **—ной** *a.* heap, mound; **—ность** *f.* cluster; close grouping, close planting.

**кушак** *m.* belt, girdle, sash.

**куш/анье** *n.* food, dish; **—ать** *v.* eat.

**кушетка** *f.* couch.

**кущение** *n.* (bot.) tillering.

**куэста** *see* **куеста.**

**кх** an obs. unit of crystal structure measurement equal to 1/1.00202 Å; **Кх** *abbr.* (**хлористый калий**) potassium chloride.

**КШ** *abbr.* (**кольцо и шар**) ring and ball (method for determination of softening points).

**кыштымит** *m.* (petr.) kyschtymite.

**Кьел/даля колба** Kjeldahl flask; **К. способ** Kjeldahl method (for nitrogen determination); **—лина печь** (met.) Kjellin (electric) furnace.

**к.э.** *abbr.* (**крахмальный эквивалент**) starch equivalent.

**КЭАМ** *abbr.* (**концентрированная эмульсия антраценого масла**) Carbolineum, concentrated emulsion of anthracene oil.

**Кэв** *abbr.* (**килоэлектрон-вольт**) kiloelectron volt.

**Кэвендиша опыт** (phys.) Cavendish experiment.

**КЭД** *abbr.* (**кожная эритемная доза**) erythema-producing dose (of radiation).

**кэк** *m.*, **—и** *pl.* cake, sinter cake.

**к. экв.** *see* **к.э.**

**кэпрок** *m.* (min.) cap rock.

**кыспак** *m.* kyspak (isolated table mountain underlain by sandstone).

**кювел/яж** *m.*, **—яция** *f.* (eng., min.) tubbing, lining.

**кювет** *m.* ditch, drain ditch; **—а, —ка** *f.* cell, container, vessel, tank; bulb; (phot.) tray; (glass) cuvette.

**кюльшиф** *m.* (brewing) cooling back, cooler.

**кюммель** *m.* kümmel (liqueur).

**Кюммеля болезнь** (med.) Kümmell's disease.

**кюмпель-пресс** *m.* circular flanging press.

**кюрасао** *n.* curacao; **к.-корка** curacao (orange) peel.

**кюри** *n.* curie, Curie unit (of radioactivity); **К. температура, К. точка** Curie point; **—грамма** *f.* curiegram; **—граф** *m.* curiegraph; **—й** *m.* curium, Cm; **—т** *m.* (min.) curite; **—терапия** *f.* Curie therapy, radium therapy.

**кяриз** *m.* kahriz (near horizontal underground water-collecting gallery, Near East).

# Л

**л** *abbr.* (**литр**) liter; **л.** *abbr.* (**левый**) left; counterclockwise; **Л** *abbr.* (**Ленинград**) Leningrad.

**лаб.** *abbr.* (**лаборатория, лабораторный**) laboratory.

**лабаз** *m.* granary; meal store; fodder shed; **—ник** *m.* corn dealer, flour merchant; (bot.) filipendula, spec. dropwort (*Filipendula hexapetala*).

**лабардан** *m.* salt cod.

**лабарраков раствор** Labarraque solution (sodium hypochlorite).

**лабиальный** *a.* (anat.) labial.

**лабильн/ость** *f.*, **—ое состояние** lability, labile state; **—ый** *a.* labile, unstable.

**лабиринт** *m.*, **—ный** *a.*, **—овый** *a.* labyrinth, maze.

**лабора/нт** *m.* laboratory worker; research man; **—тория** *f.*, **—торный** *a.* laboratory.

**лабрадор, —ит** *m.* (min.) labradorite, Labrador feldspar-stone (a plagioclase feldspar); **—овый** *a.* Labrador.

**лабурнин** *m.* laburnine.

**лав/а** *f.* (geol.) lava, clinker, volcanic magma; (min.) longwall, long working face; **волнистая л.** ropy lava, pahoehoe; **выемка —ами** longwall system; **поток** —ы lava flow, lava stream; **стекловидная л.** volcanic glass, obsidian; **шлаковая л.** scorified lava, scoria.

**Лаваля сопло** Laval's nozzle.

**лаванд/а** *f.* (bot.) lavender (*Lavandula officinalis*); —**ное масло, —овое масло, —уловое масло** lavender oil.

**лавдан** *see* **ладан.**

**лавендулин** *m.* lavendulin.

**лавенит** *m.* (min.) làvenite.

**лавзония** *f.* (bot.) henna plant (*Lawsonia alba* or *L. inermis*).

**лавин/а** *f.,* —**ный** *a.* avalanche, snow slide; avalanche, Townsend ionization; —**ообразный** *a.* avalanche-like.

**лавис** *m.* (engraving) wash; wash design.

**лавка** *f.* store, shop; bench.

**лавливать** *see* **ловить.**

**лаво—** *prefix,* —**вый** *a.* (geol.) lava, lavic, lavatic; —**пад** *m.* lava cascade; —**подобный** *a.* lava-like, lavic, lavatic.

**лавоч/ка** *f.* little store, shop; bench; —**ник** *m.* storekeeper, shopkeeper, retailer, retail merchant; —**ный** *a.* store.

**лавр** *m.* (bot.) laurel (*Laurus*); **благородный л.** laurel, sweet bay (*L. nobilis*); *prefix, see also* **лаур—.**

**лаврентьевский** *a.* (geol.) Laurentian.

**лавровиш/енник** *m.,* —**невое дерево,** —**ня** *f.* (bot.) cherry laurel (*Prunus laurocerasus*).

**лавровые** *pl.* (bot.) Lauraceae.

**лавров/ый** *a.* laurel; lauric; **л. альдегид** *see* **лауриновый альдегид; л. боб** *see* **пихурим;** —**ая камфора** laurel camphor; —**ая кислота** *see* **лауриновая кислота;** —**ое дерево** *see* **лавр;** —**ое масло** laurel berries oil; laurel oil; —**ое жирное масло** laurel oil; —**ое эфирное масло** laurel leaves oil.

**Лавуазье** Lavoisier (French chemist).

**лаг** *m.* (naut.) log; broadside.

**лага** *f.* sleeper; bolster.

**лагер/ь** *m.,* —**ный** *a.* camp.

**лагохилин** *m.* lagochilin.

**Лагранжа уравнение** (phys.) Lagrangian equation.

**лагуна** *f.* lagoon, pool.

**лагфаза** *f.* (bact.) lag phase.

**лад** *m.* harmony, concord; **дело идет на л.** things are progressing smoothly; **быть не в** —**ах с** *v.* be on bad terms with.

**ладан** *m.,* —**ный** *a.* ladanum; frankincense, olibanum, gum thus; —**ник** *m.* (bot.) rock rose (*Cistus tauricus* or *C. ladaniferus*); —**никовые,** —**ные** *pl.* Cistaceae; —**ное масло** ladanum oil; olibanum oil.

**ладинский век** (geol.) Ladinian stage.

**лад/ить** *v.* agree, be on good terms (with); fit, adapt, adjust; —**иться** *v.* go well, succeed; —**но** *adv.* well, in concord; all right, very well!; —**ный** *a.* harmonious, in accord, on good terms.

**ладожские свиты** (geol.) Ladogian series.

**ладон** *see* **ладан.**

**ладон/чатый** *a.* (biol.) palmate; —**ь** *f.* palm (of hand).

**ладье/видный,** —**образный** *a.* keel-shaped, carinate; boat-shaped, scaphoid; —**видная кость** (anat.) navicular; —**образная складка** (geol.) carinate fold, isoclinal fold.

**лаз** *m.* manhole.

**лазарево дерево** *see* **кампеш.**

**лазарет** *m.,* —**ный** *a.* infirmary; field ambulance; **плавучий л.** hospital ship.

**лаз/ейка,** —**ея** *f.* loophole, gap, opening; manhole; —**ить** *v.* climb, clamber.

**лаз/оревый** *see* **лазуревый; л. шпат,** —**улит** *m.* (min.) lazulite, azure spar; —**улитовый** *a.* lazulitic.

**лазур/евый,** —**ный** *a.,* —**ь** *f.* azure, sky blue; **л. камень,** —**ик** *m.* (min.) azure stone, lapis lazuli (a mixture of lazurite, haüynite, etc.); —**ит** *m.* lazurite; **берлинская** —**ь** Prussian blue (also called Jet-Red iron blue).

**лазящий** *a.* climbing, scansorial.

**лай** *m.* bark, barking.

**лайда** *f.* laida (treeless part of a forest and tundra landscape; low seacoast plain dissected by tortuous rills).

**лайк/а** *f.,* —**овый** *a.* kid (leather); —**овая кожа** kid, kidskin.

**лайм** *m.* (bot.) lime (*Citrus aurantifolia*).

**лайма** *f.* Lima bean (*Phaseolus limensis* or *P. lunatus*).

**Лаймана серия** (phys.) Lyman series.

**лайнер** *m.* liner; (mil.) inner tube.

**лак** *m.* lac; lake; varnish; lacquer; **л.-дей** lac dye; **китайский л., масляный л.** lac varnish, lacquer.

**лакиров/ание** *n.*, **—ка** *f.* lacquering; varnishing; **—анный** *a.* lacquered; varnished; patent (leather); **—ать** *v.* lacquer; varnish.

**лакка** *f.* lacca, lacca gum, lac; **—за** *f.* laccase; **—иновая кислота** laccainic acid, laccaic acid.

**лакколит** *m.* (geol.) laccolith, laccolite.

**лак-лак** *m.* lac lake.

**лакмус** *m.* litmus; **красильный л.** (bot.) dyer's croton (*Croton tinctorium*).

**лакмусов/ый** *a.* litmus; **л. лишай, л. мох** (bot.) orchilla weed (*Rocella tinctoria*); **—ая бумага** litmus paper.

**лаков/ый** *a.* lacquer; lacquered; varnish, varnished; **—ая камедь, —ая смола** lacquer resin; varnish resin; **—ая краска** lac dye; lake; varnish color, color varnish; **—ое дерево** lac tree; spec. lacquer tree (*Rhus vernicifera*); **—ое покрытие** coat of lacquer; coat of varnish.

**лако/красочный** *a.* paint and varnish; **—лента** *f.* varnished (insulation) tape.

**лаколь, лак-олифа** *f.* solution of polymerized and unsaturated hydrocarbons in solvent naphtha.

**лаконоска** *f.* (bot.) poke weed (*Phytolacca*).

**лако/образование** *n.* lacquer deposition (in oils); **—тканевый** *a.* cambric (insulation); **—тканевая лента** varnished tape; **—ткань** *f.* varnished cambric (or fabric).

**лакрим/атор** *m.* lacrimator, tear-producing substance; **—огенное масло** lacrimatory oil.

**лакри/ца** *f.*, **—чник** *m.*, **—чный** *a.* (bot.) licorice (*Glycyrrhiza glabra*).

**лакруазит** *m.* (min.) lacroixite.

**лаксативное средство** laxative.

**лаксит** *m.* (geol.) laxite, fragmental rocks.

**лаксманнит** *m.* (min.) laxmannite, vauquelinite.

**лакт—** *prefix* lact—, lacto— (milk); **—аза** *f.* lactase; **—альбумин** *m.* lactalbumin; **—ам, —ан** *m.* lactam,

**лактан; —амид** *m.* lactamide, 2-hydroxypropanamide; **—ариновая кислота** lactarinic acid; **—аровая кислота** lactaric acid (stearic acid); **—аровиолин** *m.* lactaroviolin; **—ат** *m.* lactate; **—ация** *f.*, **—ационный** *a.* lactation; **—ид** *m.* lactide; **—ил** *m.* lactyl; **—иловая кислота** lactylic acid; **—им** *m.* lactim; **—ин** *m.* lactin, lactose; lactim.

**лакто—** *prefix* lacto—; **—бацилла** *f.* lactobacillus; **—бациллин** *m.* lactobacillin; **—биоза** *f.* lactobiose, lactose; **—денсиметр, —метр** *m.* lactometer (milk hydrometer); **—за** *f.* lactose, milk sugar; **—крит** *m.* lactocrit; **—л** *m.* lactol, naphthyl lactate; **—лид** *m.* lactolide; **—лит** *m.* lactolite (a casein plastic); **—н** *m.*, **—ный** *a.* lactone; **—нитрил** *m.* lactonitrile; **—новая кислота** lactonic acid, galactonic acid; **—новая связь** lactonic linkage; **—прен** *m.* lactoprene; **—скоп** *m.* lactoscope; **—флавин** *m.* lactoflavin; **—хром** *m.* lactochrome.

**лакту/карий** *m.* lactucarium (juice of *Lactuca virosa*); **—кон** *m.* lactucon; **—церол** *m.* lactucerol; **—цин** *m.* lactucin.

**лакуна** *f.* (biol.) lacuna; **—рный** *a.* lacunar.

**лакцер/овая кислота** lacceroic acid, dotriacontanic acid; **—ол** *m.* laccerol.

**лакцин** *m.* laccin; **—овая кислота** laccinic acid.

**Лаланда элемент** (elec.) Lalande cell.

**лаллеманция** *f.* (bot.) lallemantia.

**лаль чанданум** *m.* red sandalwood.

**лама** *f.* (zool.) llama.

**ламантин** *m.* sea cow, manatee.

**Ламанш** the English Channel.

**ламберт** *m.* lambert (unit of brightness); **—ит** *m.* (min.) lambertite, uranophane.

**ламел/либранхиаты** *pl.* (zool.) lammellibranchs, pelecypods; **—лярный, —ьный** *a.* lamellar, lamellate, scale-like; **—ь** *m.* lamella, lamina; (elec.) commutator segment.

**ламинар/ия** *f.* (bot.) laminaria; **—ии** *pl.* Laminariaceae; **—ный** *a.* laminar, laminal; **—ный поток, —ное движение, —ное течение** laminar flow, streamline flow; —овая кислота laminaric acid.

ламиниров/ание *n.* lamination; —анный *a.* laminated, laminary, lamellar; —ать *v.* laminate, press into sheets.

Ламонта закон (phys.) Lamont's law.

лампа *f.* lamp; (elec.) bulb; (rad.) tube; л.-преобразователь *m.* converter tube; л.-час *m.* lamp-hour; tube-hour.

лампадит *m.* (min.) lampadite, cuprous manganese (a variety of wad).

лампов/щик *m.* lamp lighter, lamp trimmer; —ый *a.* lamp; —ая кислота lampic acid (obs.); —ая копоть, —ая сажа, —ая чернь lampblack (a carbon black); —ое стекло chimney (of kerosene lamp).

лампо/держатель *m.* lamp holder; tube holder; —испытатель *m.* tube tester; —час *see* лампа-час; —чка *f.* small lamp; (elec.) bulb.

лампрофир *m.* (petr.) lamprophyre.

ланадин *m.* lanadin.

ланаркит *m.* (min.) lanarkite.

ланациловый фиолетовый lanacyl violet.

ланберийский *a.* (geol.) Llanberis.

ланг/банит *m.* (min.) långbanite; —бейнит *m.* langbeinite; —ит *m.* langite.

лангобардский *a.* Lombard.

лангуст *m.*, —а *f.* (zool.) spiny lobster.

лангэнский ярус (geol.) Langhian stage.

Ланде коэффициент расщепления (phys.) Lande splitting factor; Л. фактор *g*-factor.

ландкарта *f.* map.

ландоверский *a.* (geol.) Llandovery.

Ландольта реакция Landolt's reaction.

Ландоре способ (met.) Landore process.

ландшафт *m.* landscape; district, region.

ландыш *m.* (bot.) lily of the valley (*Convallaria majalis*).

Ланжевена ион Langevin ion.

ланкаширский *a.* Lancashire; л. котел Lancashire boiler, double-flue boiler; л. кричный горн Lancashire hearth.

ланолин *m.*, —овый *a.* lanolin, hydrous wool fat.

лано/пальминовая кислота lanopalmic acid; —стерин *m.* lanosterol; —цериновая кислота lanoceric acid.

лансфордит *m.* (min.) lansfordite.

лантан *m.* lanthanum, La; окись —а lanthanum oxide; хлористый л. lanthanum chloride; —иды *pl.* lanthanides.

лантанин *m.* lantanine.

лантанит *m.* (min.) lanthanite.

лантановый *a.* lanthanum.

лантаноиды *see* лантаниды.

лантануровая кислота lantanuric acid.

лантопин *m.* lanthopine, lantol.

лангиновая кислота lanuginic acid.

ланцет *m.* (med.) lancet; —ник *m.* (zool.) lancelet; —овидный *a.* lanceolate, lanceolar, tapering.

лань *f.* (zool.) fallow, deer.

лап/а *f.* foot, paw; dovetail, tenon; lug; boss, claw; clamp, clutch; tooth (of cultivator); fluke (of anchor); л.-сковородень dovetail; сборка в —у dovetailing.

лапа/тин *m.* lapathin; —тиновая кислота lapathinic acid; —ховая кислота, —циновая кислота lapachoic acid; —хол *m.* lapachol.

лапилли *pl.* (geol.) lapilli (pieces of lava).

лапина *f.* (bot.) wing nut (*Pterocarya*).

лапис *m.* lunar caustic, fused silver nitrate; л.-лазули (min.) lapis lazuli (a mixture of lazurite, haüynite, etc.); л.-лазурь *see* лазурит.

лапк/а *f.* paw; draw vise, eccentric clamp or grip, toggle; tooth (of cultivator); —и *pl.* draw tongs.

Лапландия Lapland.

лапландский *a.* Laplandish, Lappish.

Лапласа преобразование (math.) Laplace transform.

лаплас/иан *m.* Laplacian, Laplacian operator; (nucl.) buckling; —овский *a.* Laplace, Laplacian.

лапорты *pl.* doors (of coke oven).

лаппаконит/ин *m.* lappaconitine; —овая кислота lappaconitic acid.

лаппинг-станок *m.* lapping machine.

лапсердак *m.* (text.) gabardine.

лапуга *f.* (bot.) rockweed (*Fucus*).

лапчат/ка *f.* (bot.) cinquefoil (*Potentilla*); корень —ки tormentil (root of *P. tormentilla*); —ый *a.* palmate, paw-shaped; (bot.) digitate; (zool.) web-footed; tooth (harrow).

лапша *f.* noodles.

**лар/амийский** *a.* (geol.) Laramie, Laramian (sands); **—дереллит** *m.* (min.) larderellite (an ammonium borate); **—дит** *m.* (min.) lardite, lardstone, agalmatolite.

**ларе/вой** *a.* chest, bin; **—к** *m.* stall; **—ц** *m.*, **—чный** *a.* small chest, trunk.

**лариксин** *m.*, **—овая кислота** larixine, larixinic acid.

**ларингит** *m.* (med.) laryngitis.

**ларицин/овая кислота** laricic acid; **—олевая кислота** laricinolic acid.

**ларморова прецессия** Larmor precession.

**ларнит** *m.* (min.) larnite (a calcium silicate).

**ларь** *m.* bin, chest; hopper; pit, cistern.

**ласк/а** *f.* caress, kindness; lap, scarf; (zool.) weasel; **сваривать в —у** *v.* lap-weld.

**ласковцы** *pl.* (bot.) hare's ear (*Bupleurum rotundifolium*).

**ласковый** *a.* affectionate; lap, scarf.

**ласт** *m.* (zool.) flipper, fin.

**ластик** *m.* eraser; (text.) lasting.

**ластов/енные, —невые** *pl.* (bot.) Asclepiadaceae; **—ень** *m.* swallowwort (*Asclepias* or *Cynanchum vincetoxicum*); **—ица** *f.* (aero.) gore; **—ица, —ичная трава** (bot.) celandine (*Chelidonium majus*); **—ник** *m.* cynanchum.

**ластоногие** *pl.* (zool.) Pinnipedia.

**ласточ/ка** *f.* (zool.) swallow; **соединение в —ку** dovetailing; **—кин камень** (min.) swallow stone; **—кин хвост** swallow tail, dovetail (joint); (min.) a gypsum crystal; **соединение в —кин хвост** dovetail, dovetailing; **—ник** *m.* (bot.) swallowwort (*Asclepias* or *Chelidonium*); (pharm.) vincetoxicum; (min.) swallow stone.

**лат.** *abbr.* (**латвийский**) Latvian.

**лата** *see* **латина**.

**латания** *f.* (bot.) latania.

**латать** *v.* patch, mend.

**латвийский** *a.* Latvian; **Латвия** Latvia.

**ЛатвССР** *abbr.* (**Латвийская Советская Социалистическая Республика**) Latvian Soviet Socialist Republic.

**латекс** *m.* latex; **—оподобный** *a.* latex-like, latex.

**латентный** *a.* latent, dormant.

**латеральный** *a.* lateral.

**латерит** *m.* (geol.) laterite (a weathered clay); **—изация** *f.* lateritization; **—изированные породы** laterites; **—иин** *m.* lateritiin; **—овый** *a.* lateritic.

**латина** *f.* lath, batten.

**латинский** *a.* Latin.

**латка** *f.* patch; earthen saucer, stew pan.

**л-атм** *abbr.* (**литро-атмосфера**) liter-atmosphere.

**латторфский** *a.* (geol.) Lattorfian.

**латук** *m.*, **—овый** *a.* (bot.) lettuce (*Lactuca*); **л.-ромэн** *m.* Romaine lettuce, Cos lettuce; **л.-салат** *m.* cultivated lettuce; **дикий л., ядовитый л.** wild lettuce (*L. virosa*); **—овая кислота** lactucic acid; **—овый опий** lactucarium.

**латунелитей/ная** *f.*, **—ный завод** brass foundry; **—щик** *m.* brass founder.

**латун/ирование** *n.* brass plating; **—ировать** *v.* brass-plate; **—ный** *a.* brass; **—ный припой** brass solder.

**латунолитейная** *see* **латунелитейная**.

**латунь** *f.* brass; **красная л.** red brass (a high-copper tombac).

**латынь** *f.* Latin.

**лаубанит** *m.* (min.) laubanite.

**лаудан/идин** *m.* laudanidine, tritopine; **—ин** *m.* laudanine; **—озин** *m.* laudanosine, N-methyltetrahydropapaverine.

**лаумонтит** *see* **ломонтит**.

**лаур/ан** *m.* laurane; **—елин** *m.* laureline; **—ен** *m.* laurene, pinene.

**лауренсит** *m.* (min.) lawrencite (found in meteoric iron).

**лаурентский** *a.* (geol.) Laurentian.

**лаур/ил** *m.*, **—иловый** *a.* lauryl; **хлористый л.** lauryl chloride; **—илен** *m.* laurylene; **—иловый спирт** lauryl alcohol, 1-dodecanol; **—ин** *m.* laurin, glyceryl laurate; **—иновая кислота** lauric acid, dodecanoic acid; **—иновый альдегид** lauric aldehyde, dodecanal; **—ит** *m.* (min.) laurite (ruthenium sulfide).

**лауро—** *prefix* lauro—; **—за** *f.* laurose; **—лен** *m.* laurolene; **—н** *m.* laurone, 12-tricosanone; **—ноловая кислота** lauronolic acid, laurolene-3-carboxylic acid; **—стеарин** *m.* laurostearin, laurin; —**тетанин** *m.* laurotetanine; —**церазин** *m.* laurocerasin.

**лаусонит** *m.* (min.) lawsonite.

**Лаута стан трио** Lauth three-high (rolling) mill; **Л. фиолетовый** Lauth's violet, thionine.

**лаут/аль** *m.* Lautal (an aluminum-copper-silicon alloy); —**арит** *m.*(min.) lautarite; —**ит** *m.* (min.) lautite.

**лауэграмма** *f.* Laue diffraction pattern, Laue photograph.

**лафет** *m.*, —**ный** *a.* carriage (of gun).

**лаять** *v.* bark.

**лгать** *v.* lie, tell a falsehood.

**ЛГУ** *abbr.* (Ленинградский государственный университет) Leningrad State University.

**ЛД** *abbr.* (летальная доза) lethal dose.

**леас** *m.* (geol.) Lias, Liassic; lias stone.

**лебеда** *f.* (bot.) orache, mountain spinach (*Atriplex*); goosefoot (*Chenopodium*); **белая л.** pigweed (*C. album*); **душистая л., мексиканская л.** Mexican tea (*C. ambrosioides*); **татарская л.** orache (*A. lacinatum*).

**лебедка** *f.* windlass, winch, hoist, jack.

**лебедовые** *pl.* (bot.) Chenopodiaceae.

**лебедочный** *a.* windlass, winch.

**лебедь** *m.* (zool.) swan.

**Лебеля-ванг Гоффа закон** Le Bel-van't Hoff's law.

**Леблана способ** Le Blanc process; **леблановская сода** Le Blanc soda.

**лебяжий** *a.* swan.

**лев** *m.* (zool.) lion.

**леван** *m.* levan.

**левант/ийский, —ский** *a.* levantine, eastern, oriental.

**левеит** *m.* (min.) löweite.

**Левенгерц** Löwenherz (name).

**левероид** *see* летероид.

**леверьерит** *m.* (min.) leverrierite (a hydrated aluminum silicate).

**левиафан** *m.* wool-washing machine.

**Левига способ** Löwig's process (for caustic soda).

**левигит** *m.* (min.) löwigite (probably same as alunite).

**лев/иин, —ин** *m.* (min.) levyne, levynite.

**левко—** *see* лейко—.

**левкой** *m.* (bot.) stock (*Matthiola*).

**лево, на л.** *adv.* left, to the left.

**лево—** *prefix* levo—, left; —**вращаю-**

**щий** *a.* levorotatory; —**мицетин** *m.* Levomycetin, chloramphenicol; —**ручной, —сторонний** *a.* left-handed.

**левулеза** *see* левулоза.

**левулин** *m.* levulin, fructosin; —**амид** *m.* levulinamide; —**овая кислота** levulinic acid, oxopentanoic acid; **соль —овой кислоты, —овокислая соль** levulinate; —**овый альдегид** levulinaldehyde, 4-oxopentonal.

**левулоза** *f.* levulose, fructose; —**н** *m.* levulosan, fructosan.

**левша** *m.* left-handed person.

**лев/ый** *a.* left, left-hand, counterclockwise, levo—; —**ая сторона** wrong side, reverse side (of material); —**ого направления** left-handed; —**ое вращение** counterclockwise rotation; (optics) levorotation; **с —ым ходом** left, left-handed (screw, etc.).

**лег** *past sing. of* лечь.

**легализ/ировать, —овать** *v.* legalize.

**легальн/о** *adv.* legally, lawfully; it is legal; —**ость** *f.* legality; —**ый** *a.* legal, lawful.

**леггорны** *pl.* leghorns (chickens).

**легенда** *f.* legend.

**легир/ование** *n.* (met.) alloying; —**ованный** *a.* alloyed, alloy; —**овать** *v.* alloy; —**ующий** *a.* alloying, alloy; —**ующий элемент** component (of alloy).

**легк/ий** *a.* light, light-weight; easy, simple; thin, slight; —**ое масло** light oil; —**ого типа** light-duty (machine).

**легко** *adv.* lightly, easily, readily; it is easy; **л. доступный** easily accessible, readily available; **л. растворимый** readily soluble, very soluble.

**легковесн/ость** *f.* lightness, light weight; —**ый** *a.* light, light-weight.

**легководяной** *a.* light-water.

**легковоспламеняющийся** *a.* readily inflammable, deflagrable.

**легк/ое** *n.* (anat.) lung; **воспаление —их** (med.) pneumonia.

**легко/зольный** *a.* giving light ash; —**кипящий** *a.* low-boiling, having a low boiling point; —**летучий** *a.* highly volatile; —**плавкий** *a.* fusible, easily fusible, easily melted, low-melting;

—плавкая вставка (elec.) fuse; —подвижный *a.* mobile; —растворимый *a.* readily soluble; —сть *f.* lightness, light weight; easiness, ease, facility; —суглинистый *a.* sandy loam; —усвояемый *a.* readily available; —ходовой *a.* smooth-running, smoothly operating, free-running, free.

легли *past pl. of* лечь.

легочн/ики, —ые *pl.*, —ые моллюски (zool.) Pulmonata; —ица *f.* (bot.) lungwort (*Pulmonaria officinalis*); —ый *a.* (med.) pulmonary, lung.

легум/елин *m.* legumelin; —ин *m.* legumin.

легч/ать *v.* lighten, grow lighter, abate; —е *comp. of* легкий, легко lighter; easier; more readily.

легший *past act. part. of* лечь.

лед *m.* ice; грунтовый л., донный л., почвенный л. ground ice, anchor ice.

лед. *abbr.* (ледяной) glacial; ЛЕД *abbr.* (лягушечья единица действия) (physiol.) frog unit.

ледгиллит *m.* (min.) leadhillite.

ледебурит *m.* (met.) ledeburite (cementite-austenite eutectic).

леден/еть *v.* freeze, congeal, turn to ice; —ец *m.* hard candy; —еющий, —ящий *a.* freezing; —ить *v.* freeze, chill, ice.

ледерин *m.* imitation leather.

ледиксантин *m.* ledixanthin.

ледник *m.* refrigerator, icebox; refrigerator car; icehouse; (geol.) glacier; —овый *a.* refrigerator; (geol.) glacial, glacier; —овый период (geol.) glacial period, ice age.

ледов/итый *a.* ice, icy; Л. океан Arctic Ocean; —ый *see* ледяной.

ледо/делательный завод ice plant; —дробилка *f.* ice crusher; —кол, —рез *m.* ice breaker; —мерный *a.* glacial (survey); —пад *m.* ice fall; —скат, —спуск *m.* ice chute; —став *m.* period of stable ice on open water; —стойкий *a.* sleetproof; —ход *m.* ice movement, ice flow, debacle.

ледуксит *m.* (min.) ledouxite (probably a form of mohawkite).

Ледюка эффект (phys.) Leduc effect.

ледян/ой *a.* ice, ice-cold, freezing; glacial; л. кабан, —ая голова ice block; л.

камень (min.) ice stone, cryolite; л. шпат (min.) ice spar, sanidine (a variety of orthoclase); —ая вода ice water; —ая гора iceberg; —ая крупа small hail; —ая сосулька icicle; —ые красители ice colors (azo dyes).

леер *m.* guard, rail; life line.

лежак *m.* bedstone.

лежалый *a.* not fresh, old, stale.

лежан *see* лежень.

Лежандра полином (math.) Legendre polynomial.

леж/ание *n.* lying, resting; —ать *v.* lie, rest; —ать на have bearing on; rest on.

лежа/чий, —щий *a.* lying, recumbent, horizontal; л. бок under side; л. в embedded; л. между interjacent; л. ниже underlying.

леж/ень *m.* foundation beam; ground plate; sleeper, tie; —ка *f.* ground plate; foot board; keeping quality; —невые дороги log roads; —няк *m.* bedstone (lower millstone).

лезвие *n.* edge, cutting edge, blade; bit; острое л. knife edge.

лезть *v.* climb, scale; intrude, interfere; (hair) come out, fall out.

лейас *see* леас.

лейденская банка (elec.) Leyden jar.

лейк— *prefix* leuc—.

лейка *f.* funnel; watering can, sprinkler; Leica (camera).

лейк/анилин *m.* leucaniline, methenyltrianiline; —анол *m.* Leukanol; —аурин *m.* leucaurine, triphenylolmethane; —ацен *m.* leucacene.

лейкемия *f.* (med.) leukemia.

лейко— *prefix* leuco—; —анилин *m.* leucoaniline, triaminotriphenylmethane; —дендрон *m.* (bot.) leucodendron; —дерма *f.* (med.) leucoderma, melanodermia; —дрин *m.* leucodrin, proteacin; —з *m.* (med.) leucosis; —зин *m.* leucosin; —индиго *n.* leucoindigo, indigo white; —кратовый *a.* (petr.) leucocratic; —ксен *m.* (min.) leucoxene (an alteration product of ilmenite); —лин *m.* leucoline, *i*-quinoline; —ма *f.* (med.) leucoma; —маин *m.* leucomaine.

лейкон *m.* leucone; —овая кислота leuconic acid.

**лейко/основание** *n.* leuco base; —**пения** *f.* (med.) leukopenia; —**пирит** *m.* (min.) leucopyrite (related to löllingite); —**розоловая кислота** leucorosolic acid, *o*-methylleucaurine; —**скоп** *m.* (optics) leucoscope; —**соединение** *n.* leuco compound; —**сфенит** *m.* (min.) leucosphenite; —**тионин** *m.* leucothionine, diamidothiodiphenylamine; —**троп** *m.* leucotrope; —**туровая кислота** leucoturic acid; —**фан** *m.* (min.) leucophane, leucophanite; —**феницит** *m.* (min.) leucophoenicite; —**фир** *m.* (petr.) leucophyre; —**хальцит** *m.* (min.) leucochalcite.

**лейкоцит** *m.* leucocyte, white blood corpuscle; —**оз** *m.* (med.) leucocytosis.

**лейна/-селитра** *f.* leuna saltpeter (ammonium nitrate-sulfate mixture); —**фос** *m.* diammophos-ammonium sulfate fertilizer.

**лейнер** *m.* liner.

**лейпцигская желть** Leipzig yellow, lead chromate.

**лейст/а** *f.* lath; —**овидный** *a.* lath-like.

**Лейстер** Leicester.

**лейте** *imp. of* **лить.**

**лейфит** *m.* (min.) leifite.

**лейхтенбергит** *m.* (min.) leuchtenbergite (a variety of clinochlore).

**лейц/ил** *m.* leucyl; —**иллейцин** *m.* leucyl leucine; —**ин** *m.*, —**иновый** *a.* leucine, aminoisocaproic acid; —**инамид** *m.* leucinamide; —**иновая кислота** leucic acid; —**инуровая кислота** leucinuric acid.

**лейцит** *m.* (min.) leucite, amphigène; —**ит** *m.* (petr.) leucitite (an alkali basalt); —**овый** *a.* leucitic, containing leucite; —**оэдр** *m.* (cryst.) leucitohedron.

**лейшмания** *f.* Leishmania (parasitic protozoa).

**лекаж** *m.* leakage.

**лекал/о** *n.* curve, French curve; mold, form, pattern, standard, gage; —**ьный** *a.* curve, mold; gaged; —**ьное дело** gage work; —**ьщик** *m.* gager, gage maker.

**леканор/ин** *m.* lecanorin; —**овая кислота** lecanoric acid, diorsellinic acid.

**лекарств/енный** *a.*, —**енное средство** medicinal; —**о** *n.* medicine, drug.

**Лекланше элемент** (elec.) Leclanché cell.

**леконтит** *m.* (min.) lecontite.

**лекпом** *m.* surgeon's assistant.

**лек/сикон** *m.* dictionary; —**тор** *m.* lecturer, speaker, professor; —**ция** *f.* lecture, discourse; **читать** —**ции** *v.* lecture.

**леллингит** *see* **лоллингит.**

**леме/х**, —**ш** *m.*, —**ховый** *a.* plowshare.

**Леминга способ** Laming process (for gas purification).

**лемма** *f.* (math., bot.) lemma.

**лемниската** *f.* (geom.) lemniscate.

**лемносская земля** (geol.) Lemnian earth (a variety of aluminous earth).

**лемонграсовое масло** lemongrass oil.

**лемпач** *m.* adobe.

**лен** *m.* (bot.) flax (*Linum*); **л.-моченец** water-retted flax; **л.-стланец** dew-retted flax; **л.-сырец** *m.* raw flax; **дикий л.** toadflax (*Linaria*).

**лен.** *abbr.* (**ленинградский**) Leningrad.

**ленгенбахит** *m.* (min.) lengenbachite.

**лензин** *m.* a white pigment (ground gypsum).

**лени/вец** *m.* (zool.) sloth; —**вец, —кс** *m.* idler, idle wheel; tightening wheel; —**во** *adv.* sluggishly, lazily; —**вый** *a.* sluggish, slow, lazy.

**ленинградский** *a.* Leningrad.

**лениться** *v.* be lazy, be idle.

**ленник** *see* **лен, дикий.**

**леновые** *pl.* (bot.) Linaceae.

**лент/а** *f.* tape, band, strip, ribbon, string, lace; belt; blade (of saw); (text.) sliver; **обматывать** —**ой** *v.* tape up.

**лентец** *m.* (zool.) tapeworm.

**ленто/вытяжная машина** (text.) drawing frame; —**обмоточный** *a.* taping; —**образный** *a.* ribbon, band-shaped; —**протяжный** *a.* tape-winding; feed; (telegraphy) paper-drive; —**ткацкий станок** (text.) ribbon loom.

**ленточн/ый** *a.* tape, band, belt; ribbon; conveyer-type, traveling-belt (dryer, etc.); **л. грохот** belt screen; **л. конвейер, л. транспортер** belt conveyer; **л. масштаб** tape measure; **л. рекордер** tape recorder; **л. тормоз** band brake; **л. червь**, —**ая глиста** (zool.) tapeworm; —**ая муфта** belt coupling;

—ая пила band saw; —ая подача belt feed; —ое железо strip iron.

Ленца закон (elec.) Lenz's law.

ленчик *m.* saddletree.

лень *f.* laziness, idleness.

леометр *m.* leometer, dynamic meter.

леон/гардит *m.* (min.) leonhardite (a variety of laumontite); —ит *m.* (min.) leonite.

леонтин *m.* leontin, caulosaponin.

леопард *m.* (zool.) leopard.

Леопольди печь (met.) Leopoldi furnace.

лепатиновая кислота lepathinic acid.

лепест/ковидный *a.* petal-shaped, petaliform; —ковый *a.* petal, petalous, petaled, petal-shaped; lobed; —ок *m.* petal; lobe.

лепешк/а *f.* press cake, tablet, lozenge; lump, slag, biscuit; —ообразный *a.* in tablet form; oblate.

лепид/ен *m.* lepidene, tetraphenylfuran; —ин *m.* lepidine, 4-methylquinoline.

лепидо— *prefix* lepido— (scale, flake); —крокит *m.* (min.) lepidocrocite (a dimorph of goethite); —лит *m.* lepidolite, lithia mica; —мелан *m.* lepidomelane (similar to iron-rich biotite mica); —н *m.* lepidone, hydroxylepidine; —феит *m.* (min.) lepidophaite, lampadite (a form of wad).

лепинин *m.* lepinine, 4-methyl quinine.

леп/ить *v.* model, sculpture; glue, stick together; —ка *f.* modeling; —кий *a.* sticky; —ной *a.* plastic; modeled; stucco (molding); —ная работа modeling.

леполит *m.* (min.) lepolite (a variety of anorthite feldspar).

лепр/а *f.* (med.) leprosy; —озный *a.* leprous; —озорий *m.* leper colony.

лептандр/ин *m.* leptandrin; —оид *m.* leptandroid.

лептинит *m.* (petr.) leptynite, granulite.

лептинол *m.* leptynol, palladous hydroxide.

лепто— *prefix* lepto— (small, weak, thin, fine); —клаз *m.* (min.) leptoclase, minor fracture; —метр *m.* leptometer (a viscosimeter); —н *m.* lepton (particle of small mass); —спироз *m.* (med.) leptospirosis; —хлорит *m.* (min.) leptochlorite.

лер *m.* (glass) lehr, annealing furnace.

лербахит *m.* (min.) lehrbachite.

лерз/ит *m.* (petr.) lherzite, hornblendite; —олит *m.* lherzolite (a variety of peridotite).

лерка *f.* die, screw-cutting die, thread chaser.

лес *m.* woods, forest; timber; вырубка —ов deforestation; —а *pl.* woodland, forests; scaffolding, scaffold trestle; supporting structure; —а, —ка *f.* fish line; —истый *a.* wooded, woody, timbered.

лесн. *abbr.* (лесничество) forestry.

лесни/к *m.*, —чий *a.* woodsman, forester, forest ranger; —на *f.* wild apple; —чество *n.* forestry.

лесн/ой *a.* wood, forest; lumber, timber; л. орех *see* лещина; л. склад lumber yard; —ая полоса tree belt; —ая шерсть a batting made from coniferous needles; —ое хозяйство forestry.

лесо— *prefix* wood, forest.

лесовод *m.* forester; —ственный *a.* forestry; —ство *n.* forestry, silviculture.

лесо/воз *m.* timber carrier; —возвращение *n.*, —возобновление *n.* reforestation; —вой *a.* wood, forest; —завод *m.* lumber mill, sawmill; —заготовка *f.* lumbering, logging; —защита *f.* forest protection; —инженерное дело forest engineering; —катка *f.* log roller; —материал *m.* lumber, timber.

лесопил/ка *f.*, —ьный завод sawmill.

лесо/питомник *m.* forest-tree nursery; —промышленник *m.* lumber man, lumber dealer; —руб *m.* wood cutter, lumberjack; —сека *f.* clearing; wood to be felled; —спуск *m.* timber slide, chute; —степной *a.*, —степь *f.* forest steppe; —сушилка *f.* lumber kiln; —таска *f.* log hauler; —технический *a.* wood technology; —устройство *n.* forest management; —химический *a.* wood chemical; —химия *f.* wood chemistry.

леспеде/за, —ца *f.* (bot.) lespedeza.

лесс *m.* (geol.) loess (wind-blown silt).

лессиров/ать *v.* glaze; scumble (painting); —ка *f.* glazing; scumbling.

лессовый *a.* (geol.) loess.

лестни/ца *f.*, —чный *a.* staircase; ladder;

(fire) escape; scale; движущаяся л. escalator; складная л. stepladder; —чатый столб H-pole; —чная жила (geol.) ladder vein.

лесхоз *m.* leskhoz, forestry farm; forestry.

лет *m.* flight, flying; на —у flying, on the wing, in flight.

леталь *f.*, —ный *a.* (med.) lethal.

летание *n.* flight, flying.

летарг/ический *a.* lethargic; —ия *f.* lethargy.

летат/ельный *a.* flying; л. аппарат, —ельные машины aircraft; —ь *v.* fly.

летероид *m.* leatheroid.

лететь *v.* fly; volatilize; hasten.

летига *f.* Indian summer.

летк/а *f.* (met.) tap, tap hole, tapping hole (of furnace); (foundry) gate; пробивать —у *v.* tap.

летн/ий *a.* summer, estival; *suffix* —year; —ик *m.* (bot.) annual.

летн/ый *a.* flight; —ое дело aeronautics.

лет/о *n.* summer; быть в —ах *v.* be up in years; ему пять лет he (or it) is five years old; средних лет middle-aged; —ом in the summer; —ование *n.* estivation; —овать *v.* pass the summer, estivate.

леток *m.* aperture.

летопис/ь *f.*, —ный *a.* chronicle, annals, yearbook, annual.

леторосль *f.* (bot.) shoot, sprout, sucker.

летосчисл/ение *n.* chronology; era; —и-тельный *a.* chronological.

леточная масса ball (of puddled iron).

леттсомит *m.* (min.) lettsomite, cyanotrichite.

летуч/есть *f.* volatility; —ий *a.* volatile; flying; —ая зола light ashes; —ая мышь (zool.) bat; —ие масла volatile oils; essential oils.

летучка *f.* leaflet, pamphlet, brochure.

летчик *m.* aviator, flyer, pilot; л.-наблю-датель aircraft observer.

летящий *a.* flying.

леунафос *see* лейнафос.

лехеровская система Lecher system.

лецидовая кислота lecidic acid.

лецит/ин *m.* lecithin; —ол *m.* lecithol; —опротеин *m.* lecithoprotein.

лечебн/ица *f.* hospital; —ый *a.* medical, medicinal, medicine.

леч/ение *n.* medical treatment; л. элек-тричеством electrotherapy; —енный *a.* treated; —ить *v.* treat, cure.

лечуха *f.* (bot.) sanicle (*Sanicula*).

лечь *see* ложиться.

Ле Шателье принцип Le Chatelier principle.

лещад/ь *m.* slab, flagstone; hearth block, hearth bottom, bottom, well (of blast furnace); bed, bed plate; —ная плита coping.

лещина *f.* (bot.) filbert (*Corylus avellana*).

лже— *prefix* pseudo—, false; —акация *f.* (bot.) false acacia (*Robinia pseud-acacia*); —апельсин *see* маклюра; —грибница *f.* (bot.) pseudomycelium; —ктыри *pl.* stiletto flies (*Therevidae*); —лиственница *f.* (bot.) golden larch (*Pseudolarix*); —тсуга *f.* pseudotsuga.

лживый *a.* false, lying, misleading.

ли *interrogative particle* whether, if (not translated).

лиана *f.* (bot.) liana.

либенерит *m.* (min.) liebenerite (a form of pinite or alteration product of nephelite).

либеральный *a.* liberal.

Либерия Liberia.

либермановская нитрозореакция Liebermann (nitroso) reaction (for phenols).

либетенит *m.* (min.) libethenite.

Либига охладитель Liebig condenser.

либигит *m.* (min.) liebigite, uranothallite.

либо *adv.* either, or; л. . . . л. either . . . or.

либоцедрен *m.* libocedrene.

либрация *f.* (astron., chem.) libration.

ливанский кедр (bot.) cedar of Lebanon (*Cedrus libani*).

ливеингит *m.* (min.) liveingite.

ливень *m.* shower, downpour, cloudburst.

ливер *m.*, —ный *a.* pluck (of animal); siphon, siphon tube; pump; crane.

Ливерпуль Liverpool.

ливийский *a.* Libyan.

ливингстонит *m.* (min.) livingstonite.

Ливия Libya.

ливневый *a.* shower; torrential (rain).

**ливший** *past act. part. of* **лить.**

**лига** *f.* league.

**лигамент** *m.* ligament.

**лигатур/а** *f.* (met.) alloy; (med.) ligature; **—ный** *a.* alloyed.

**лигнин** *m.*, **—овый** *a.* lignin; **—овая кислота** ligninic acid.

**лигнит** *m.* (min.) lignite, brown coal; **—овый** *a.* lignite, lignitic, lignitiferous.

**лигнификация** *f.* lignification, wood formation.

**лигно/за** *f.* lignose; **—лит** *m.* a plywood; **—н** *m.* lignone; **—стон** *m.* a laminated wood; **—сульфин**, **—сульфит** *m.* lignosulfin, lignosulfite; **—фоль** *m.* laminated birchwood; **—цериновая кислота** lignoceric acid, tetracosanoic acid.

**лигозин** *m.* lygosin, sodium lygosinate.

**лигроин** *m.* ligroin, solvent naphtha.

**лигустрин** *m.* ligustrin, syringin.

**лиддит** *m.* (expl.) lyddite.

**лидер** *m.* leader.

**лидийский камень** (min.) Lydian stone, touchstone (a variety of flinty jasper).

**лидит** *see* **лиддит; лидийский камень.**

**лидол** *m.* Lydol.

**Лидс** Leeds.

**лиды** *pl.* false webworms (*Lydidae*).

**лиеврит** *m.* (min.) lievrite, ilvaite, yenite.

**лижерьен** *m.* (geol.) Ligerian substage. **—лиз** *m. suffix* **—lysis.**

**лизальный камень** salt lick (for cattle).

**лизание** *n.* licking.

**лизариновая кислота** lizaric acid.

**лизатин** *m.* lysatine.

**лизаты** *pl.* lysates, products of lysis.

**лизать** *v.* lick.

**лизергиновая кислота** lysergic acid.

**лизи/генный** *a.* (bot.) lysigenous; **—дин** *m.* lysidine, methyldihydroimidazole; **—метр** *m.* lysimeter; **—н** *m.* lysine, 2,6-diaminohexanoic acid; lysin (cell-dissolving antibody); **—с** *m.* (med., biol.) lysis.

**лизнуть** *see* **лизать.**

**лизо/ген** *m.* lysogen; **—зим, —цим** *m.* lysozyme; **—л** *m.* Lysol (disinfectant); **—форм** *m.* lysoform; **—хлор** *m.* lysochlor.

**лизунец** *see* **лизальный камень.**

**ликаконитин** *m.* lycaconitine.

**ликвация** *f.* liquefaction; (met.) liquation, eliquation; segregation.

**ликвидамбра** *f.* (bot.) liquidambar.

**ликвид/атор** *m.* (aero.) destructor mechanism, exploder; **—ация** *f.*, **—ирование** *n.* liquidation; **—ировать** *v.* liquidate, put an end (to); **—ируемое имущество** assets.

**ликвидус** *m.* (met., etc.) liquidus.

**ликер** *m.*, **—ный** *a.* liqueur.

**лико/ктонин** *m.* lycoctonine; **—ктониновая кислота** lycoctoninic acid; **—маразмин** *m.* lycomarasmine; **—пен** *m.* lycopene; **—персицин** *m.* lycopersicin, tomatin; **—подиевые** *pl.* (bot.) Lycopodiaceae; **—подий** *m.* club moss (*Lycopodium*); lycopodium powder (spores of *Lycopodium clavatum*); **—подовая кислота** lycopodic acid; **—рин** *m.* lycorine, narcissine.

**ликс/оза** *f.* lyxose; **—оновая кислота** lyxonic acid; **—уроновая кислота** lyxuronic acid.

**лил** *past sing. of* **лить.**

**лилацин** *m.* lilacin, syringin.

**лилейн/ик** *m.* (bot.) day lily (*Hemerocallis*); **—ые** *pl.* Liliaceae; **—ый** *a.* lily.

**лили** *past pl. of* **лить.**

**лилианит** *m.* (min.) lillianite.

**лилипут** *m.* (min.) a small electric locomotive.

**лилия** *f.* (bot.) true lily (*Lilium*); (zool.) crinoid.

**лиловый** *a.* lilac, lilac-colored.

**лилол** *m.* lilole; **—идин** *m.* lilolidine, tetrahydrolilole.

**ЛИМ** *abbr.* (Ленинградский институт металлов) Leningrad Institute of Metals.

**лима** *see* **лайма.**

**лиман** *m.* estuary, firth.

**лимацид** *m.* limacide, slug poison.

**лимб** *m.* limb, dial, graduated circle.

**лимбургит** *m.* (petr.) limburgite.

**лиметт/а** *f.*, **—овый** *a.* (bot.) lime (*Citrus aurantifolia*); **—ин** *m.* limettin.

**лимит** *m.*, **—ировать** *v.* limit.

**лимниграф** *m.* limnograph, limnometer.

**лимнит** *m.* (min.) limnite (a yellow ocher).

**лимно—** *prefix* limno— (pool, marsh; fresh water); **—биотический** *a.* (zool.)

limnobiotic, living in fresh water; —логия *f.* limnology.

лимон *m.* (bot.) lemon (*Citrus limonia*); трехлисточковый л. trifoliate orange (*Poncirus trifoliata*); —ад *m.* lemonade.

лимон/ен *m.* limonene; —ин *m.* limonin; —ит *m.* (min.) limonite, brown hematite; —ник *m.* (bot.) schizandra.

лимонно/аммониевая соль ammonium citrate; —борнокислая соль borocitrate; —бутиловый эфир butyl citrate; —железная соль ferric citrate; —желтый *a.* lemon yellow; —калиевая соль potassium citrate; —кальциевая соль calcium citrate.

лимоннокисл/ый *a.* citric acid; citrate (of); л. натрий sodium citrate; —ая соль citrate; —ое железо iron citrate.

лимонно/магниевая соль magnesium citrate; —натриевая соль sodium citrate; —образный *a.* (bot.) lemonshaped, limoniform; —растворимый *a.* (fertilizer analysis) citrate-soluble; —свинцовая соль lead citrate; —этиловый эфир ethyl citrate.

лимонн/ый *a.* lemon; citric; л. куст (bot.) lemon verbena (*Lippia citriodora*); —ая кислота citric acid; соль —ой кислоты citrate; —ая корка lemon peel; —ая мята *see* мелисса; —ое дерево *see* лимон; —ое масло lemon oil.

лимская фасоль *see* лайма.

лимурит *m.* limurite (axinite contact rock).

лимф/а *f.* (physiol.) lymph; аденит *m.* (med.) lymphadenitis, inflammation of lymph glands; —атический *a.* lymphatic; —атический узел lymph node; —опения *f.* (med.) lymphopenia; —оцит *m.* lymphocyte.

линалил *m.,* —овый *a.* linalyl, linalool; —ацетат *m.,* —овый эфир уксусной кислоты linalyl acetate.

линалоевое масло linaloe oil.

линалоол *m.* linalool, coriandrol.

линамарин *m.* linamarin.

линарин *m.* linarin.

линарит *m.* (min.) linarite.

линдакерит *m.* (min.) lindackerite.

линдан *m.* Lindane (hexachlorocyclohexane insecticide).

Линде способ Linde process (for liquefaction of air).

линдохит *m.* lyndochite (thorium mineral of the euxenite group).

линеариз/ация *f.* linearization; —ировать, —овать *v.* linearize; —ирующий *a.* linearizing; linearity-control.

линевать *see* линовать.

линейка *f.* ruler, rule, straightedge; gage; подвижная счетная л. (math.) slide rule.

линейко— *prefix* linearly.

линейность *f.* linearity.

линейн/ый *a.* linear, lineal, line; л. корабль battleship; л. монтер, л. рабочий lineman; л. ускоритель linear accelerator; —ая мера linear measure; —ая молния forked lightning, streak; —ая потеря энергии linear stopping power.

линей/чатость *f.* lineation; —чатый *a.* linear; ruled; bright-line (spectra); —щик *m.* lineman.

линза *f.* lens.

линзообразный *a.* lenticular.

линзочки *pl.* seams.

линиевыбиратель *m.* (tel.) selecting switch.

линимент *m.* liniment.

линин *m.* linin, oxychromatin.

лин/ия *f.* line, mark; path, direction; (biol.) line, strain; line (2.540 mm.); —ии *pl.* lines; (flow) pattern.

линкор *m.* battleship.

линкруст *m.* Lincrust (a wall covering).

линнеит *m.* (min.) linnaeite, cobalt pyrite.

Линнея система (bot.) Linnaean classification.

линобатист *m.* (text.) lawn.

линов/альный *a.,* —ание *n.* ruling; —ан(н)ый *a.* ruled, lined; —ать *v.* rule, line, line off.

лино/зит *m.* (min.) linosite (a basaltic hornblende); —ксин *m.* linoxyn (solid, oxidized linseed oil).

линоле/ат *m.* —вокислая соль, соль —вой кислоты linoleate; —вая кислота linoleic acid, 9,12-octadecadienoic acid; —ин *m.* linolein; —новая кислота linolenic acid, 9,12,15-octadecatrienoic acid.

линолеум *m.* linoleum (floor covering).
лино/ловая кислота *see* линолевая кислота; —тип *m.* (typ.) linotype; linotype machine; —фир *m.* (petr.) linophyre; —фировый *a.* linophyric.
линтер *m.* (cotton) linter; linters; —ование *n.* lintering.
линузиновая кислота linusinic acid.
линь *m.* line, marline; tench (fish).
линька *f.* molting, shedding.
линюч/есть *f.* fugitiveness; —ий *a.* fugitive, fading (color).
лин/ялый *a.* faded, discolored; molted (bird); —яние *n.* fading; molting; —ять *v.* fade, lose color; molt; —яющий *a.* fading, fugitive, not fast.
лио— *prefix* lyo—; —сорпция *f.* lyosorption; —тропный *a.* lyotropic; —фильный *a.* lyophilic; —фобный *a.* lyophobic.
липа *f.* (bot.) linden, lime (*Tilia*).
липаза *f.* (physiol.) lipase.
липарит *m.* liparite, rhyolite (an aphanitic igneous rock).
лип/ид, —ин *m.* lipid, lipin.
липк/ий *a.* sticky, tacky, adhesive; —ость *f.* stickiness, tackiness, gumminess.
липник *m.* (bot.) hemp nettle (*Galeopsis*).
липнуть *v.* adhere, stick.
Липовитца сплав Lipowitz's alloy.
липов/ица *see* липа; —ые *pl.* (bot.) Tiliaceae; —ый *a.* linden, lime; —ое масло linden tree oil.
липо/ид *m.* lipoid (nitrogenous fat); —иодин *m.* lipoiodine, ethyl diiodobrassidate; —лиз *m.* lipolysis, cleavage of fat; —литический *a.* lipolytic, lipoclastic, fat-cleaving; —ма *f.* (med.) lipoma; —протеин *m.* lipoprotein; —фусцин *m.* lipofuscin; —хромовые пигменты lipochromes.
липучка *f.* (bot.) stickseed (*Lappula*).
лира *f.* lyre, harp; lira (money); (astron., anat.) lyra; (carpentry) apron.
лириодендрин *m.* liriodendrin.
лироконит *m.* (min.) liroconite.
лирообразный *a.* lyre-shaped, lyrate.
лис/а, —ица *f.* (zool.) fox; —ий *a.* fox, fox's; —ья нора (mil.) fox hole.
лисичка *f.* die, screw die, thread chaser.
лискеардит *m.* (min.) liskeardite.
лисохвост *m.* (bot.) foxtail (*Alopecurus*).

Лиссабон Lisbon.
Лиссажу фигуры (phys.) Lissajous figures.
лист *m.* leaf; blade; sheet, lamina, scale; foil; plate; в л. in folio; резина в —ах sheet rubber; —ва *f.* leaves, foliage.
лиственница *f.* (bot.) larch (*Larix*).
лиственничн/ый *a.* larch; л. гриб, —ая губка (bot.) purging agaric (*Polyporus officinalis*); л. сахар *see* мелецитоза.
лиственн/ый *a.* leaf, leafy, foliate; deciduous; —ое дерево greenwood.
листер *m.* lister (plow).
Листера способ Lyster flotation process.
листер/ный плуг *see* листер; —ование *n.* listering.
листик *m.* leaflet, little leaf, blade.
листо— *prefix* leaf, phyllo—, foli—; (met.) sheet, plate; —бит *m.* (met.) flattener; —блошка *f.* (zool.) psylla; —бойня *f.* (met.) flatting mill; —вальный *a.* sheeting; —вание *n.* (geol.) sheeting; —ватость *f.* lamination, foliation; fissility; —ватый *a.* leaf-like, foliate, foliated, scaly, laminated, lamellate, lamellar; —ватый излом foliated fracture; —ватая структура (geol.) book structure; —вертки *pl.* leaf roller moths (*Tortricidae*); —видный *a.* leaf-like, foliate, foliated, foliaceous; (met.) sheet, sheet-like; —вка *f.* leaflet; (bot.) follicle; parmelia (a lichen).
листов/ой *a.* leaf, foliated; sheet; lamellar, flake; л. конденсатор (elec.) plate condenser; л. материал (met.) sheet; л. металл sheet metal, sheet; metal foil; л. стан plate mill, sheet (rolling) mill; —ая заготовка sheet bar; —ая рама (elec.) plate frame; —ая резина sheet rubber; —ая рессора laminated spring, plate spring; —ая сварка sheet welding, plate welding; —ая сталь steel plate, sheet steel; —ая структура (geol.) book structure; —ая фибра fiberboard; —ая щетка (elec.) laminated brush; —ое золото gold leaf, gold foil; —ое стекло sheet glass.
листо/грызы *pl.* (zool.) leaf miners (*Tineoidea*); —еды *pl.* leaf beetles (*Chrysomelidae*); —загибочный *a.* (met.) plate-bending; —зелень *f.*

chlorophyll; —к *m.* leaflet, leaf; sheet; —колосник *m.* (bot.) phyllostachys; —ногие *pl.*, —ногие раки (zool.) Phyllopoda; —образный *a.* leaf-shaped, foliate; lamellar; —пад *m.*, —падение *n.* defoliation.

листоправ/ильный, —ный *a.* (met.) plate-straightening; л. станок, —ильная машина plate-straightening machine.

листо/прокатный валок (met.) plate roll; л. стан plate mill, sheet-rolling mill, flatting mill, laminating machine; —расположение *n.* (bot.) phyllotaxy; —резный станок (met.) shearing machine; —стебельные мхи (bot.) Musci; —чек *m.* leaflet, thin leaf; вторичный —чек (bot.) pinnule; —чный *a.* leaf, leaflet; —ядный *a.* browsing.

листья *pl. of* лист, leaves, foliage.

лисья *see* лисий.

лит. *abbr.* (литовский) Lithuanian.

—лит *m. suffix* —lyte; —lith (stone).

Литва Lithuania.

литейная *f.* (met.) foundry, casting shop, cast house.

литейн/ый *a.* (met.) foundry, founding, casting; л. двор casting bed; casting yard; л. завод, л. цех foundry, casting house; л. ковш foundry ladle, casting ladle; pouring ladle; л. кокс foundry coke; л. лом casting scrap, cast scrap; л. чугун foundry pig, foundry iron; —ая воронка pouring funnel; —ая канава, —ая яма casting pit, foundry pit; —ая модель casting pattern; —ая печь founding furnace; —ая форма mold, ingot mold; —ое дело founding, foundry work, casting.

литейщик *m.* foundry hand, founder; smelter; pourer, teemer, caster, molder.

литера *f.* (typ.) letter, type.

литератур/а *f.* literature; —ный *a.* literature, literary; —ная собственность copyright.

литиев/ый *a.* lithium; л. турмалин (min.) lithium tourmaline; —ая слюда lithia mica, lepidolite; —ая соль lithium salt.

лит/ий *m.* lithium, Li; гидроокись —ия

lithium hydroxide; карбонат —ия, углекислый л. lithium carbonate; окись —ия lithium oxide, lithia; хлористый л. lithium chloride.

лити/н, —он *m.* lithia, lithium oxide; едкий л. lithium hydroxide; —нистый *see* литиевый; —онит *m.* (min.) lithionite, lithia mica, lepidolite; —офорит *m.* lithiophorite (a lithium-containing psilomelane); —фицировать *v.* lithify.

литмоцидин *m.* litmocidin.

литник *m.* (foundry) gate, flow gate, pouring gate, sprue, pouring channel; jet; бассейн —а, —овая чаша pouring basin; круглый л. ball gate; —овый *a.* gate; pouring, teeming; —овый канал gate, casting conduit, pouring funnel.

лито— *prefix* litho— (stone, calculus).

литовский *a.* Lithuanian.

литогене/з, —зис *m.* lithogenesis, rock formation; —тический *a.* lithogenous, rock-building.

литограф *m.* lithographer; —ировать *v.* lithograph; —ический, —ский *a.* lithographic; —ия *f.* lithography.

литоид/ит *m.* (petr.) lithoidite (felsitic rhyolite); —ный *a.* lithoidal, stony.

лит/ой *a.* (foundry) cast; poured; molten; floated (asphalt); —ая сталь, —ое железо cast steel, ingot iron; —ые трубы pipe castings; в —ом виде as cast.

литоклаз *m.* (geol.) lithoclase.

литолог/ический *a.* lithologic; —ия *f.* lithology, petrology.

литопон *m.* lithopone (a mixture of zinc sulfide and barium sulfate).

литоральный *a.* littoral, coastal, shore.

литосфера *f.* (geol.) lithosphere.

литотомия *f.* (med.) lithotomy.

литофеллиновая кислота lithofellic acid.

лито/физа *f.* (petr.) lithophysa (a variety of spherulite); —фильный *a.* (geol.) lithophylic; (biol.) lithophilous.

литофон *see* литопон.

литохолевая кислота lithocholic acid.

литр *m.* liter (unit of volume).

лит-ра *abbr.* (литература) literature.

литраж *m.* displacement, capacity; volume in liters.

литров/ание *n.* refining; —анный *a.*

refined, purified; —ать *v.* refine, purify.

**литровый** *a.* liter.

**ЛитССР** *abbr.* (Литовская Советская Социалистическая Республика) Lithuanian Soviet Socialist Republic.

**лит/ый** *a.* poured; (met.) cast; —ь *v.* pour; found, cast, run, teem; —ься *v.* pour, run, flow.

**литье** *n.* founding, casting; cast, cast material; pouring; л. в песке sand casting; л. под давлением die casting; красное л. red brass or bronze; металлическое л. cast metal; стальное л. cast steel; steel casting.

**лифт** *m.*, —овый *a.* elevator, lift; pump; —ер *m.* lifter; elevator operator.

**лихва** *f.* interest, profit.

**лихен/идин** *m.* lichenidin; —ин *m.* lichenin, lichen starch; —иновая кислота lichenic acid (obs. term for fumaric acid); —иформин *m.* licheniformin; —оин *m.* lichenoin; —ол *m.* lichenol (ethyl ester of evernesic acid).

**лихе/стериновая кислота** lichesterinic acid; —строновая кислота lichestronic acid.

**лихозан** *m.* lichosan.

**лихорад/ить** *v.* be in a fever, have a fever, be feverish; —ка *f.* fever; —очник *m.*, —очная трава, —очное зелье (bot.) hedge hyssop (*Gratiola officinalis*); —очность *f.* feverishness; —очный *a.* feverish, febrile.

**лихтенбергова фигура** (elec.) Lichtenberg figure.

**лихтер** *m.* lighter, transport barge.

**ЛИХФ** *abbr.* (Ленинградский институт химической физики) Leningrad Institute of Chemical Physics.

**лицев/альный** *a.* facing; stripping; —ание *n.* facing; draw filing; stripping; —ать *v.* face; strip.

**лицев/ой** *a.* face, facial, front; personal (account); —ая отделка facing; —ая поверхность face; plane surface; —ая сторона face, front; right side (of material).

**лицемерный** *a.* hypocritical.

**лицендрат** *m.* litz, strand wire.

**лиценз/ионный** *a.*, —ия *f.* license.

**лицетол** *m.* lycetol, lupetazine tartrate.

**лицо** *n.* face, side; person; знать в л. *v.*

know by sight, recognize; на-л. present, ready.

**лицовка** *f.* smooth-cut file.

**личин/ка** *f.* larva, grub, maggot; земляная л. cutworm; —ник *m.* caterpillar (*Scorpiurus*); —очный *a.* larval; —очная стадия (pal.) immature instar, juvenile instar.

**личнев/ать** *see* **лицевать**; —ка *see* **лицевание**.

**лично** *adv.* personally, in person.

**личной** *a.* facial, face; smooth-cut (file).

**личн/ость** *f.* personality; person; удостоверение —ости identification card; —ый *a.* personal, individual, private, particular; —ый состав personnel.

**лишаевидный** *a.* resembling lichen; (med.) herpetic.

**лишай** *m.* (bot.) lichen; (med.) herpes, tetter; красильный л., лакмусовый л. (bot.) orchilla weed (*Rocella tinctoria*); морской л. alga, seaweed; опоясывающий л. (med.) shingles; стригущий л. (med.) ringworm; чешуйчатый л. (med.) psoriasis;—ники *pl.* (bot.) lichens.

**лишайный** *a.* (bot.) lichen; (med.) herpetic; л. крахмал *see* **лихенин**; л. сахар lichen sugar, erythrite.

**лишать** *v.* deprive (of), remove, eliminate, cut off; —ся *v.* be deprived (of), lose.

**лишек** *m.* surplus, excess.

**лиш/ение** *n.* deprivation, loss, forfeiture; —енный *a.* deprived (of), devoid; —ить *see* **лишать**.

**лишний** *a.* superfluous, unnecessary, excessive; spare, odd; overtime; л. раз once more, yet again.

**лишь** *adv.* only, but, even; as soon as, no sooner than; л. бы provided; л. только as soon as, no sooner than.

**лия** *pr. gerund of* **лить**.

**лияльная ложка** (foundry) casting ladle.

**лк** *abbr.* (люкс) lux.

**ЛКАО** *abbr.* (линейная комбинация атомных орбит) linear combination of atomic orbits, LCAO.

**ллан—** *see also under* **лан—**.

**лландейльский** *a.* (geol.) Llandeilian.

**лм** *abbr.* (люмен) lumen.

**лмб** *abbr.* (ламберт) lambert.

**л/мин** *abbr.* (литров в минуту) liters per minute.

**лм-с** *abbr.* (люмен-секунда) lumen-second; **лм-ч** *abbr.* (люмен-час) lumen-hour.

**ЛНИВИ** *abbr.* (Ленинградский научно-исследовательский ветеринарный институт) Leningrad Research Institute of Veterinary Science.

**л.н.с.** *abbr.* (линия наименьшего сопротивления) line of least resistance.

**лоангокопал/иновая кислота** loangocopalinic acid; **—овая кислота** loangocopalic acid.

**лоб** *m.* (anat.) forehead; front, face, crown, head.

**лобаровая кислота** lobaric acid.

**лобел/акрин** *m.* lobelacrin; **—идин** *m.* lobelidine; **—ин** *m.* lobeline, inflatine; **—иновая кислота** lobelic acid; **—ия** *f.* (bot.) lobelia; **—оид** *m.* lobeloid.

**лобзик** *m.* fret saw, scroll saw, jig saw.

**лобин/ин** *m.* lobinine; **—ол** *m.* lobinol.

**лобков/ый** *a.* (anat.) pubic; **—ая кость** pubis.

**лобненский** *a.* Lobnya (works).

**лобный** *a.* forehead, frontal.

**лобовина** *f.* forehead, frontal bone.

**лобов/ой** *a.* (anat.) forehead; frontal, front, face; head-on (impact); **л. коллектор** (elec.) vertical commutator; **л. молот** face hammer; slogging hammer; **л. станок, л. токарный станок** face lathe, facing lathe, surfacing lathe; **л. фонарь** headlight; **л. фрезер** facing cutter; **—ая доска** faceplate, face chuck (of lathe); **—ая обмотка** (elec.) evolute winding, end winding; **—ая поверхность** face; **—ая стенка** top cover (of cylinder); **—ое колесо** spur wheel; **—ое сопротивление** (aero.) head resistance, drag; **коэффициент —ого сопротивления** drag coefficient.

**лобогрейка** *f.* (agr.) reaper, harvester.

**лов** *m.* catching, capture.

**Лове волна** (seismology) Love wave.

**ловил/ьный** *a.* catching, catch; **л. инструмент** (min.) grab iron, grab; **л. колокол** socket; **—щик** *m.* catcher.

**ловит/ель** *m.* catch, stop; grab; catcher; **—ь** *v.* catch, seize, recover.

**—ловка** *f.* *suffix* catcher, trap.

**ловк/ий** *a.* clever, skilful; **—ость** *f.* cleverness, skill, knack, dexterity, craft.

**лов/ля** *f.* catching, capture, seizing, recovery; **—ушка** *f.* trap, snare, pitfall; (chem.) entrainment separator; **—чий** *a.* trap, catching.

**лог** *m.* ravine, valley, hollow; *suffix* **—логист.**

**логанин** *m.* loganin.

**логарифм** *m.* (math.) logarithm, log; **десятичный л.** common logarithm, Briggs' logarithm; **—ика** *f.* logarithmic curve; **—ировать** *v.* take the logarithm; **—ический** *a.* logarithmic; **—ическая линейка** slide rule.

**логи/ка** *f.* logic; **—чески, —чно** *adv.* logically; **—ческий, —чный** *a.* logical.

**—логия** *f.* *suffix* **—logy** (science, theory).

**логометр** *m.* (elec.) ratiometer (measurer of current ratio).

**лог-уошер** *m.* (min.) log washer.

**лодал** *m.* lodal (derivative of papaverine).

**Лодж-Мюиргеда когерер** (rad.) Lodge-Muirhead coherer.

**лод/ка** *f.*, **—очный** *a.* boat; (glass) debiteuse; **—очка** *f.* small boat; (analysis) boat, combustion boat; (bot.) cover slip.

**лодыж/ка** *f.*, **—ечный, —ный** *a.* ankle; cam, catch.

**ложа** *f.* (gun) stock.

**лож/бина** *f.* hollow, cavity; trough, ravine; **—бинка** *f.* little hollow; stria, minute channel; **—бистый** *a.* full of cavities, pitted; **—е** *n.* bed, channel (of river, cable, etc.), runway.

**ложеч/ка** *f.* small spoon; (anat.) pit of stomach; **—ник** *m.*, **—ница** *f.*, **—ный хрен, —ная трава** (bot.) spoonwort (*Cochlearia*); **—ный** *a.* spoon; shell (auger).

**ложиться** *v.* lie down.

**ложка** *f.* spoon; ladle; (foundry) sleeker, smoother.

**ложно** *adv.* falsely, false; *prefix* pseudo—; **—гусеница** *f.* larva resembling a caterpillar; **—кристаллический** *a.* pseudocrystalline; **—монашеский перец** (bot.) agnus castus; **—мучнистая роса** downy mildew (plant disease); **—ножка** *f.* (zool.) pseudopod; **—проволочники** *pl.* larvae of Tenebrionidae and Alleculidae; —**слоники** *pl.* fungus weevils (*Anthribidae*); —**щитовки** *pl.* soft scales (*Lecaniidae*).

**лож/ный** *a.* untrue, false, spurious; erroneous, fallacious; pseudo—; **л. вывод** fallacy; —**ь** *f.* falsehood, untruth.

**лоз/а** *f.* rod, branch, twig; (grape) vine; (bot.) osier willow (*Salix viminalis* or *S. triandra*); —**ник, —няк** *m.* willow bush; —**оподобный** *a.* vine-like; botryoidal, grape-like.

**лоипоновая кислота** loiponic acid.

**лойальный** *a.* loyal.

**Лока раствор** Locke's solution.

**локаин** *m.* locaine (dye).

**локал/изатор** *m.* localizer, finder, detector; —**изация** *f.* localization; —**изированный** *a.* localized; —**изировать** *v.* localize; —**ьный** *a.* local; autochthonous, indigenous.

**локановая кислота** locanic acid.

**локао** *n.,* —**новая кислота** locao, locaonic acid, Chinese green; —**за** *f.* locaose.

**локаут** *m.* lockout.

**локва** *f.* (bot.) loquat (*Eriobotrya japonica*).

**локомо/биль** *m.* locomobile, road locomotive, tractor; —**бильный** *a.* locomobile; portable; —**тив** *m.* locomotive.

**локон** *m.* lock (of hair); (geom.) witch.

**локот/ник** *m.* arm rest; —**ь** *m.,* —**ной** *a.* elbow; cubit, ell (measure).

**локсо/дрома** *f.* loxodrome, loxodromic curve, rhumb line (of sphere); —**клаз** *m.* (min.) loxoclase (a sodium-containing orthoclase).

**локтев/ой** *a.* elbow, ulnar; —**ая кость** (anat.) ulna.

**локус** *m.* (math.) locus.

**лоллингит** *m.* (min.) löllingite.

**лом** *m.* crowbar, bar; scrap, fragments, waste, debris; *suffix* —break; **металлический л.** scrap metal; —**аный** *a.* broken, fractured.

**ломать** *v.* break, break up, crush, fracture; demolish; quarry (stone); rack (one's brains); —**ся** *v.* break, get out of order.

**ломбардский** *a.* Lombard.

**ломик** *m.* small crowbar, pinch bar; pointed rabble.

**лом/ить** *v.* break; hurt, be painful; —**ка** *f.* breaking, demolishing; (stone) quarry.

**ломк/ий** *a.* brittle, friable, frangible, fragile, short; snap (bean); —**ость** *f.* brittleness, friability, frangibility, fragility; —**ость в холодном состоянии** cold shortness.

**ломов/ик** *m.,* —**ая лошадь** draft horse; —**ой** *a.* breaking; draft (horse).

**ломонос** *m.* (bot.) clematis.

**ломонтит** *m.* (min.) laumontite, leonhardite.

**лом/оть** *m.* slice, chunk; —**тик** *m.* slice.

**лонгволл** *see* **лонгуолл.**

**лонгифо/ловая кислота** longifolic acid; —**ровая кислота** longiforic acid.

**лонгуол/л** *m.,* —**ьный** *a.* (min.) longwall.

**лондонская глина** (geol.) London clay.

**лонжерон** *m.* (aero.) longeron; side member.

**лонный** *a.* (anat.) pubic.

**лопание** *n.* bursting, cracking, breaking.

**лопарский** *a.* Lappish.

**лопаст/ный** *a.* blade, vane, paddle; (biol.) laciniate, lobed; rotary (pump); —**ное колесо** rotor, impeller (of pump); —**ь** *f.* blade, vane, paddle; (biol.) lobe.

**лопат/а** *f.* shovel, spade; rabble; scraper, scoop; —**ить** *v.* spade, intermix; —**ка** *f.* small shovel, trowel; blade, paddle, vane (of turbine); (anat.) shoulder blade, scapula; —**ная работа** shoveling; —**оногие** *pl.* (zool.) tusk shells (*Scaphopoda*); —**очка** *f.* trowel; scoop, spatula; —**очный** *a.* shovel; scapular.

**лопаться** *v.* burst, crack, break, fracture, split, snap.

**лопинит** *m.* lopinit (suberose fossil coal).

**лопнуть** *see* **лопаться.**

**лополиты** *pl.* (geol.) lopoliths.

**лопу/х,** —**шник** *m.* (bot.) burdock (*Arctium* or *Lappa*).

**Лорана кислота** Laurent's acid, 1-naphthylamine-5-sulfonic acid.

**лоран/дит** *m.* (min.) lorandite (a member of the miargyrite group); —**скит** *m.* loranskite (similar to euxenite).

**лорантиловый спирт** loranthyl alcohol.

**лорензенит** *m.* (min.) lorenzenite.

лор/етин *m.* loretin, yatren; —етинат *m.* loretinate; —иодендрин *m.* loriodendrin.

лос/ий *a.* (zool.) elk; —ина *f.*, —иный *a.* chamois, buckskin.

лоск *m.* gloss, luster, polish, glaze.

лоскут, —ок *m.* shred, rag, scrap; flap; —ье *n.* rags.

лосн/истый *a.* glossy, sleek; —иться *v.* be glossy, lustrous, shiny; —ящийся *a.* glossy, shining, smooth.

лосос/ь *m.*, —ий, —иный *a.* (zool.) salmon.

лось *m.* elk (resembles American moose).

лот *m.* plumb line, plumb bob, bob; obs. unit of weight (12.797 g.).

Лотарингия Lorraine; лотарингский ярус (geol.) Lotharingian stage.

лотковый *a.* trough, tray, pan; л. классификатор launder-type classifier; л. транспортер pan conveyer.

лоткообразный *a.* trough-shaped.

лоток *m.* trough, tray, pan (for gold washing); (min.) launder; cradle; mold; hod; (ball bearing) race; chute; направляющий л. baffle; охлаждающий л. (glass) leer pan, lehr pan.

лото/с *m.* (bot.) lotus (*Nelumbo*); —флавин *m.* lotoflavine.

лоточный *see* лотковый.

лотрит *m.* (min.) lotrite.

лотузин *m.* lotusin.

лофин *m.* lophine, 2,4,5-triphenylimidazole.

лофофорин *m.* lophophorine, methoxyanhalonine.

лох *m.* (bot.) oleaster (*Elaeagnus*).

лохан/ка, —ь *f.*, —ный *a.* tub, basin; (anat.) pelvis.

лохм/атый *a.* shaggy, shaggy-haired; —отья *pl.* rags, tatters.

лохов/ой *a.* (bot.) oleaster; —ые *pl.* (bot.) Elaeagnaceae.

лохштейн *m.* jewel (bearing).

лоцман *m.*, —ский *a.* pilot.

лошадин/ый *a.* horse; —ая сила horsepower; —ая сила-час horsepower-hour.

лошадь *f.* horse, mare.

лошак *m.* hinny (similar to mule).

Лошмидта число Loschmidt number.

лош. сила *see* л.с.

лощен/ие *n.* glossing, polishing, burnishing, smoothing; glazing; —ый *a.* glossy, polished; glazed, calendered (paper).

лощил/ка *f.*, —о *n.* polisher, burnisher.

лощильный *a.* glossing, polishing, burnishing; glazing; л. зуб burnisher; л. пресс (paper) rolling press, calender.

лощина *f.* hollow, depression; ravine, gulch.

лощить *v.* gloss, polish, burnish, smooth; (paper) calender, glaze.

л.с., ЛС *abbr.* (лошадиная сила) horsepower.

л/сек *abbr.* (литров в секунду) liters per second.

Л-система *f.* laboratory system.

ЛСХА *abbr.* (Латвийская сельскохозяйственная академия) Latvian Agricultural Academy; ЛСХИ *abbr.* (Ленинградский сельскохозяйственный институт) Leningrad Agricultural Institute.

л.с.-ч *abbr.* (лошадиная сила-час) horsepower-hour.

лу— *see also under* лю—.

луаргол *m.* luargol.

луб *m.* bast, bast fiber.

лублинит *m.* (min.) lublinite (a fibrous variety of calcite).

лубо/вой *a.* bast, bast fiber; —еды *pl.* bark beetles (*Ipidae*); —к *m.*, —чный *a.* bast, bast fiber; (med.) splint.

лубрикатор *m.* lubricator.

лубяное волокно bast fiber.

луг *m.* meadow.

луговик *m.* (bot.) hairgrass (*Deschampsia* or *Aira*).

лугов/о— *prefix*, —ой *a.* meadow; prairie (dog); —ая руда (min.) meadow ore, bog iron ore (a spongy variety of limonite).

луда *f.* luda (a rocky littoral shoal or islet).

Лудвига явление Ludwig phenomenon, Soret's effect.

лудвигит *m.* (min.) ludwigite, ferroludwigite.

лудильн/ый *a.* (met.) tinning; л. завод, л. цех tinplating plant, tinplate works; —ая ванна tinning pot, tin pot.

луд/ильщик *m.* (met.) tinsmith, tinner; —ить *v.* tin, blanch (sheet iron).

лудламит *m.* (min.) ludlamite.

лудловские свиты (geol.) Ludlovian series, Ludlow beds.

Лудлума дуговая многоэлектродная печь Ludlum series-arc furnace.

лужа *f.* puddle, pool.

лужайка *f.* lawn, grass plot.

лужен/ие *n.* (met.) tinning, tinplating, blanching; —ый *a.* tinned, tinplated; —ое листовое железо tinplate.

лужица *f.* pool, puddle.

лузга *f.* husk, shell.

лузитанский *a.* (geol.) Lusitanian.

Луизиана, лузианский *a.* Louisiana.

лук *m.* bow; (bot.) onion (*Allium*); л.-порей leek (*A. porrum*); л.-резанец chives (*A. schoenoprasum*); л.-татарка Welsh onion (*A. fistulosum*); л.-чеснок *m.* garlic (*A. sativum*).

лука *f.* bend; saddle bow.

лукит *m.* (min.) luckite (a variety of melanterite).

луковиц/а *f.* (bot.) bulb; onion; —еносный *a.* bulb-bearing, bulbiferous; —еобразный *a.* bulb-shaped, bulbiform.

луковичн/ый *a.* bulb, bulbous; onion, alliaceous; —ое масло onion oil; —ое растение bulbous plant.

луко/возеленый *a.* leek-green; —вый *a.* onion; —образный *a.* bulb-shaped, bulbiform; arched, bow-shaped.

луксулианит *m.* (petr.) luxullianite (a tourmaline granite).

лукуллит *m.* (min.) lucullite (a black variety of marble).

лум— *see also under* люм—.

лумахель *see* люмахель.

луми— *see* люми—.

лумп *m.* lump sugar.

луна *f.* moon.

лунат/изм *m.* somnambulism, sleepwalking; —ик *m.* somnambulist, sleep-walker.

Лунге нитрометр Lunge nitrometer.

лунит *see* луннит.

лунк/а *f.* hole; (anat.) alveolus, socket; (geom.) lune; серебристая л. butterfly (*Phalera bucephala*); —окопатель *m.* hole digger.

луннит *m.* (min.) lunnite (probably same as pseudomalachite).

лунн/ый *a.* lunar, moon; л. камень (min.) moonstone (an opalescent variety of orthoclase or albite feldspar; also sometimes cut agates); —ое молоко agaric mineral.

луноч/ка *f.* (geom.) lune; (anat.) alveolus; —ный *a.* alveolar.

лупа *f.* magnifier, magnifying glass, lens; л. времени time magnifier.

лупа/нин *m.* lupanine; —ренол *m.* luparenol; —рон *m.* luparone.

лупе/оза *f.* lupeose; —ол *m.* lupeol; —тазин *m.* lupetazine, dimethylpiperazine; —тидин *m.* lupetidine, 2,6-dimethylpiperidine; —тидиновая кислота lupetidinic acid.

лупин *m.* (bot.) lupine (*Lupinus*); —идин *m.* lupinidine; —ин *m.* lupinin (glucoside); lupinine (alkaloid).

луп/ить *v.* peel, pare, strip; —иться *v.* peel, scale off, flake; —ление *n.* peeling, paring; —леный *a.* peeled, pared; flaked.

лупул/ин *m.*, —иновый *a.* lupulin; —иновая кислота lupulinic acid; —он *m.* lupulone.

лускач *m.* (corn) sheller.

луссатит *m.* (min.) lussatite (probably a form of tridymite).

лутеин *m.* lutein.

лутео— *prefix* luteo—; —л *m.* luteol (indicator); —лин *m.* luteolin, tetrahydroxyflavone; —соединение *n.*, —соль *f.* luteo compound, luteo salt; —стерон *m.* luteosterone, progesterone.

лутеций *see* лютеций.

лутецит *m.* (min.) lutecite (probably a fibrous form of chalcedony).

лутид/ин *m.* lutidine, dimethylpyridine; —иновая кислота lutidinic acid, 2,4-pyridinedicarboxylic acid; —он *m.* lutidone, 2,4-dimethyl-3-oxypyridine.

Луффа раствор Luff's reagent (for sugars).

луци/дол *m.* lucidol, benzoyl peroxide; —нит *m.* (min.) lucinite (identical with variscite); —фераза *f.* luciferase (enzyme); —ферин *m.* luciferin.

луцонит *m.* (min.) luzonite.

луч *m.* ray, beam, shaft (of light); path (in phase diagram); (biol.) arm; (zool.) ray; испускать —и *v.* radiate, emit rays; —евики *pl.* (zool.) Radiolaria.

**лучев/ой** *a.* ray, radial; —**ая болезнь** radiation sickness; —**ая кость** (anat.) radius; —**ое давление** radiation pressure.

**лучезвуковой** *a.* radiophonic.

**лучеиспуск/ание** *n.* radiation, radiant energy; irradiation; **поверхность** —**а-ния** radiating surface; —**ательный**, —**ающий** *a.* radiating; —**ательная способность** radiating power; —**ать** *v.* emit rays, radiate.

**луче/образный** *a.* ray-like, radial, radiating; —**образующий** *a.* beam-forming; —**поглощаемость** *f.*, **коэффициент** —**поглощения** immissivity.

**лучепреломл/ение** *n.* refraction, refringence, *see also* **преломление**; —**яющий** *a.* refractive.

**лучин/а** *f.*, —**ный** *a.* splinter, chip, shaving, turning, boring.

**лучисто/-волокнистый** *a.* (geol.) radiating columnar; —**сть** *f.* radiance, triboluminescence.

**лучист/ый** *a.* radiant, radial, radiating, radiated, in rays; **л. грибок** (bot.) actinomyces, ray fungus; **л. камень** (min.) asbestiform actinolite; amianthus; **л. разряд** (elec.) brush and spray discharge; —**ая руда** (min.) clinoclase, clinoclasite, aphanèse; —**ая теплота** heat of radiation, radiant heat; —**ые животные** (zool.) Radiata.

**лучить** *v.* spear (fish).

**лучицы** *pl.* (bot.) Characeae.

**луч/ковая пила** frame saw, hack saw; —**ок** *m.* frame (of saw).

**лучш/е** *comp. of* **хороший, хорошо**, better; **как можно л.** as well as possible; **тем л.** so much the better, all the better; —**ий** *a.* the best; the better; **к** —**ему** for the best.

**лущ/ение** *n.* shelling, husking, hulling; shallow plowing; —**еный** *a.* shelled, hulled; —**илка** *f.*, —**ильная машина** sheller, huller, hulling mill; —**ильник** *m.* shallow plow, surface plow; —**иль-ный** *a.* shelling; shell (beans); —**ить** *v.* shell, husk, hull.

**ЛХТИ** *abbr.* (Ленинградский химико-технологический институт) Leningrad Institute of Chemical Technology.

**лыж/а** *f.*, —**ный** *a.* ski, snowshoe; (elec.) collecting shoe.

**лыко** *n.* bast, bast fiber.

**лыс/еть** *v.* grow bald; —**ый** *a.* bald.

**ЛьвГУ** *abbr.* (Львовский государственный университет имени Ивана Фран-ко) Ivan Franko L'vov State University.

**львинки** *pl.* soldier flies (*Stratiomyiidae*).

**львиный** *a.* lion; **л. зев** (bot.) snapdragon (*Antirrhinum*); **л. зуб** dandelion (*Taraxacum dens-leonis*).

**льгот/а** *f.* privilege, exemption, advantage; —**ный** *a.* favorable; reduced (price).

**льд/а** *gen. of* **лед**; —**ина** *f.* cake of ice, block of ice, ice floe, ice float; —**инка** *f.* icicle; —**истый** *a.* icy.

**льдо—** *prefix* ice; —**генератор** *m.* ice producer; —**подобный** *a.* ice-like, icy; —**удалитель** *m.* deicer; —**хра-нилище** *n.* icehouse.

**льет** *pr. 3 sing. of* **лить**.

**льна** *gen. of* **лен**.

**льно—** *prefix* flax; —**водство** *n.* flax cultivation; —**вые** *see* **леновые**; —**мялка** *f.*, —**мяльная машина** scutcher; —**прядильня** *f.*, —**прядильная фабрика** flax mill, flax-spinning mill.

**льнуть** *v.* cling, stick, adhere (to).

**льнянка** *f.* (bot.) toadflax (*Linaria*).

**льнян/ой** *a.* flax, flaxen, linen; **л. жабрей** *see* **льнянка**; **л. холст** linen; —**ая кислота** linoleic acid; **соль** —**ой кислоты** linoleate; —**ая мука** linseed meal; —**ая олифа** boiled linseed oil, linseed oil varnish; —**ое масло** linseed oil, flaxseed oil; —**ое семя** linseed, flaxseed; —**ые жмыхи** linseed cake, oil cake.

**льняно/кислый** *a.* linoleic acid; linoleate (of); **л. кальций**, —**кальциевая соль** calcium linoleate; —**кислая соль** linoleate; —**масляная кислота** *see* **льняная кислота**.

**льюизит** *m.* (min.) lewisite; (mil.) lewisite, dichloroarsino-2-chloroethylene.

**Льюиса теория** Lewis theory.

**лью/т** *pr. 3 pl.*; —**щий** *pres. act. part. of* **лить**.

**лэмбовск/ий сдвиг**, —**ое смещение** (phys.) Lamb shift.

**Лэнгмюра теория** Langmuir theory.

**Любберса-Зиверта процесс** Lubbers-Sievert process (glass drawing).

**любезн/ость** *f.* kindness, courtesy; **—ый** *a.* courteous, obliging, polite.

**люберецкий песок** Lyubertsy sand.

**любимый** *a.* favorite.

**любисток** *m.*, **—овый корень** (bot.) lovage root (*Levisticum officinale*).

**любитель** *m.*, **—ский** *a.* amateur, fan.

**любить** *v.* like, love.

**любка** *f.* (bot.) an orchid (*Platanthera*).

**любоваться** *v.* admire.

**любовина** *f.* lean (beef).

**любовь** *f.* liking, love.

**любознательн/ость** *f.* curiosity, eagerness for knowledge; **—ый** *a.* curious, inquiring, eager to learn.

**любой** *a.* any; **л. ценой** at any price.

**любопыт/ный** *a.* curious, inquisitive; **—ство** *n.* curiosity.

**лювер** *m.* louver (ventilator).

**люд** *m.* people, nation; **—и** *pl.* people, men.

**Людерса линии** (met.) Lüders (flow) lines.

**людийский ярус** (geol.) Ludian stage.

**людный** *a.* crowded, thickly populated.

**люд/оед** *m.* cannibal; **—ский** *a.* human; **—ский материал** manpower.

**люизит** *see* **льюизит.**

**люк** *m.*, **—овый** *a.* manhole, hatch, trap door; **—овой** *m.* (min.) chute drawer.

**люкс** *m.* lux, meter-candle (unit of illumination).

**Люкса газовые весы** Lux gas balance

**люксембургский** *a.* Luxembourg.

**люксметр** *m.* luxmeter (photometer).

**люлька** *f.* cradle, cage; bucket; (foundry) ingot chair; (smoking) pipe.

**люмахель** *f.* (min.) lumachelle, shell marble, fire marble.

**люмен** *m.* lumen (unit of luminous flux); **л.-час** lumen-hour.

**люминал** *m.* Luminal, phenobarbital.

**люминесц/ентный** *a.* luminescent; fluorometric (method of uranium determination); scintillation (counter); **—ентное вещество** luminescent material, phosphor; **—енция** *f.* luminescence; **—ировать** *v.* luminesce; **—ирующий** *a.* luminescent.

**люми/ноген** *m.* phosphorogen; **—носкоп**

*m.* luminoscope (for analysis of uranium-containing minerals) **—нофлавин,** **—флавин** *m.* lumiflavin; **—нофор** *m.* (phys.) phosphor; (chem.) luminophore; **—стерин** *m.* lumisterol, irradiated ergosterol.

**люмнит** *m.* lumnite (shielding material).

**люнебургит** *m.* (min.) lüneburgite.

**люнет** *m.* lunette (opening); sighthole; (glass) linnet hole; support, rest; stay (of lathe); collar plate.

**люп/ин** *see* **лупин; —ус** *m.* lupus, tuberculosis of the skin.

**Люрмана шлаковая фурма** (met.) Lurmann front (of blast furnace).

**люстр/а** *f.*, **—овый** *a.* luster, chandelier.

**лютеин** *see* **лутеин.**

**лютеомицин** *m.* luteomycin.

**лютерная колонна** *a* continuous distillation column.

**лютетский ярус** (geol.) Lutetian stage.

**лютеций** *m.* lutecium, Lu.

**лютик** *m.* (bot.) crowfoot (*Ranunculus*); **—овые** *pl.* Ranunculaceae.

**люфа** *see* **люффа.**

**люфт** *m.* gap, clearance; slack, free play, backlash, freedom.

**люффа** *f.* (bot.) luffa.

**люцерн/а** *f.*, **—овый** *a.* (bot.) lucerne, alfalfa (*Medicago sativa*).

**люцит** *m.* Lucite (transparent plastic).

**лягут** *fut. 3 pl. of* **лечь.**

**лягуш/ка** *f.*, **—ечий** *a.* frog; (draw) tongs, draw vise, grip, toggle.

**лядвенец** *m.* (bot.) lotus; **рогатый л.** bird's foot trefoil (*Lotus corniculatus*).

**лядвея** *see* **ляжка.**

**лядник** *m.* (bot.) hierochloe.

**лядунка** *f.* cartridge pouch.

**ляжет** *fut. 3 sing. of* **лечь.**

**ляжка** *f.* thigh, haunch.

**лязг** *m.*, **—ать** *v.* clank, clang.

**Ляймана серия** (phys.) Lyman series.

**Ляме параметр** Lamé's constant.

**лямель** *see* **ламель.**

**Ляминга масса, лямингова масса** Laming's mass (for purifying gas).

**лям/ка** *f.*, **—очный** *a.* strap.

**ляпис** *see* **лапис; л.-лазурь** *see* **лазурит.**

**ляпсусы** *pl.* (typ.) corrigenda.

**лярд** *m.* lard; **—овое масло** lard oil.

**лятекс** *see* **латекс.**

**ляуданин** *see* **лауданин.**

# М

м *abbr.* (метр) meter; м² *abbr.* (квадратный метр) square meter; м³ *abbr.* (кубический метр) cubic meter; М code for molybdenum in steel mark; *abbr.* (металл) metal (in formula); (мега) mega; (молярный) molar (concentration); (число Маха) Mach number; М. *abbr.* (Москва) Moscow.

м- *see* мета—.

ма *abbr.* (миллиампер) milliampere.

маар *m.* maar (a type of volcanic crater).

мавриция *f.* (bot.) mauritia (palm).

магазин *m.*, —ный *a.* store; warehouse; (rifle) magazine; м. сопротивлений (elec.) resistance box; —ирование *n.* storing; —ка *f.*, —ная винтовка magazine rifle; —ный кран warehouse crane.

МАГАТЭ *abbr.* (Международное агенство по атомной энергии) International Agency on Atomic Energy.

магеллан/ова кора, —ская кора Winter's bark.

магента *f.* magenta, fuchsin, rosaniline hydrochloride.

магистр *m.* master (degree); м. наук Master of Science, M.S.

магистрал *m.* (met.) magistral (a roasted copper pyrites).

магистраль *f.* main line, trunk line, artery; (gas, water) main; —ный *a.* main, mainline; national, nationwide; —ная труба main.

магистрант *m.* undergraduate.

магический *a.* magic.

магма *f.* (geol.) magma, molten rock; (pharm.) magma (suspension); —тизм *m.* magmatism; —тический *a.* magma, magmatic.

магнал/ий, —иум *m.* magnalium (aluminum-copper-magnesium alloy); —ит *m.* magnalite (aluminum-magnesium alloy).

магнезиальн/ый *a.* magnesia, magnesian; м. цемент magnesian cement, Sorel's cement; —ая селитра (min.) nitromagnesite; —ые квасцы (min.) magnesia alum.

магнезио/феррит *m.* (min.) magnesiofer-rite, magnoferrite; —хромит *m.* magnesiochromite, picotite, chrome spinel.

магнезит *m.*, —ный, —овый *a.* (min.) magnesite; —овый шпат magnesite.

магнезия *f.* magnesia, magnesium oxide; белая м. magnesia alba, hydrated magnesium carbonate; водная м. magnesium hydroxide; жженая м. calcined magnesia; лимоннокислая м. citrate of magnesia, magnesium citrate; сернокислая м. magnesium sulfate.

магнетиз/ер *m.* magnetizer; —ирование *n.* magnetization; —ированный *a.* magnetized; —ировать *v.* magnetize; —м *m.* magnetism.

магнетит *m.*, —овый *a.* (min.) magnetite, magnetic iron ore.

магнет/ический *a.* magnetic; —о *n.* (elec.) magneto (generator); —ометр *m.* magnetometer; —он *m.* magneton (unit of magnetic moment); —офлекс *m.* Magnetoflex (copper-iron-nickel alloy); —рон *m.*, —ронный *a.* (thermionics) magnetron.

магниев/ый *a.* magnesium, magnesia, magnesian; м. известняк (min.) magnesian limestone, dolomitic limestone, dolomite; —ая лента magnesium ribbon; —ая слюда (min.) magnesium mica, phlogopite; —ая соль magnesium salt; —ые квасцы (min.) magnesia alum, pickeringite.

магн/ий *m.* magnesium, Mg; гидроокись —ия magnesium hydroxide; лимоннокислый м., цитрат —ия magnesium citrate; окись —ия magnesium oxide; сернокислый м., сульфат —ия magnesium sulfate; хлористый м. magnesium chloride.

магний/алкильное соединение magnesium alkyl compound; —бромэтил *m.* ethylmagnesium bromide; —галоидалкилы *pl.* alkylmagnesium halides; —органическое соединение organomagnesium compound; —органическая реакция Grignard reaction.

магнит *m.* magnet; брусковый м. magnetic bar, bar magnet; естественный м. (min.) natural magnet, lodestone, magnetic iron ore; **молекулярный м., элементарный м.** molecular magnet.

**магнит/изм** *m.* magnetism; **остаточный м.** (elec.) residual magnetism; remanence, retentivity; —**ит** *see* **магнетит**; —**ность** *f.* magnetizability.

**магнитн/ый** *a.* magnetic, magnet; **м. брусок** magnetic bar, bar magnet; **м. железняк** (min.) magnetic iron ore, magnetite; **м. колчедан** (min.) magnetic pyrites, pyrrhotite; **м. полюс** magnetic pole; **м. поток** magnetic flux; —**ая жесткость** magnetic rigidity; —**ая индукция** magnetic flux density; —**ая подвижность,** —**ое колебание** magnetic fluctuation, magnetic variation; —**ая проводимость** (elec.) permeance; —**ая проницаемость** permeability; —**ая сила** magnetic force; —**ая стрелка** magnetic needle, dipping needle; —**ая тяга** magnetic pull; —**ое отталкивание** magnetic repulsion; —**ое поле** magnetic field; **равнодействующее** —**ое поле** resultant magnetic field; —**ое притяжение** magnetic attraction; —**ое сопротивление** (elec.) magnetic resistance, reluctance; **удельное** —**ое сопротивление** (elec.) reluctivity.

**магнито**— *prefix* magneto—.

**Магнитогорск** Magnetogorsk.

**магнито/граф** *m.* magnetograph, recording magnetometer; —**движущая сила** magnetomotive force; —**держатель** *m.* magnet support, magnet cradle.

**магнитометр** *m.* magnetometer; —**ический** *a.* magnetometric; —**ия** *f.* magnetometry.

**магнито/оптика** *f.* magneto-optics; —**провод** *m.* (elec.) magnetic circuit; —**скоп** *m.* magnetoscope; —**стрикционный** *a.* magnetostrictive; —**стрикция** *f.* magnetostriction; —**теллурический** *a.* magnetotelluric; —**уловитель** *m.* magnetic detector; —**фон** *m.* magnetic (sound) recorder, tape recorder; magnetophone; —**фуга** *f.*, —**фугальная машина** an electric motor; —**химия** *f.* magnetochemistry.

**магнитоэлектричес/кий** *a.* magnetoelectric; —**кая машина** magneto; —**тво** *n.* magnetoelectricity.

**магнол/иевые** *pl.* (bot.) Magnoliaceae; —**ин** *m.* magnoline; —**ит** *m.* (min.) magnolite; —**ия** *f.* (bot.) magnolia; Magnolia metal (a lead-base alloy).

**магно/феррит** *m.* (min.) magnoferrite, magnesioferrite; —**хромит** *m.* magnochromite, magnesiochromite.

**Магнуса соль** Magnus salt, tetrammineplatinum(II) chloroplatinite.

**магогани** *see* **махогани.**

**мадаке, китайский** (bot.) a cane (*Phyllostachys pubescens*).

**мадар** *m.* mudar (bark of *Calotropis* root); —**албан** *m.* madaralban.

**Маделунга константа** (cryst.) Madelung's constant.

**мад/иевое масло** madia oil; —**ия** *f.* (bot.) melosa (*Madia sativa*).

**мадрепор/а** *f.* madrepore (coral); —**ит** *m.* (zool.) madreporite.

**мажет** *pr. 3 sing. of* **мазать.**

**мажеф** *m.* manganese ferric phosphate (corrosion inhibitor).

**мажор/итарный** *a.* majority; —**ный** *a.* major, greater.

**мажу/т** *pr. 3 pl. of* **мазать;** —**щий** *a.* greasing, smearing.

**мазание** *n.* greasing, smearing, daubing.

**мазанка** *f.* mud-walled hut; mud wall.

**мазанный** *a.* greased, smeared, daubed.

**маз/ать,** —**нуть** *v.* grease, smear, daub, apply; rub; —**собразный,** —**еподобный** *a.* pasty, greasy, salve-like; —**илка** *f.* brush; —**ка** *see* **мазание;** —**ня** *f.* smear, blur; —**ок** *m.* dab, stroke (of brush); smear; **метод** —**ков** smear technique.

**мазонит** *m.* Masonite (fiberboard).

**мазурий** *m.* (obs.) masurium, Ma (technetium, Tc).

**мазут** *m.* mazut, masut, black oil, petroleum residue; fuel oil.

**мазь** *f.* ointment, salve; grease, paste.

**маис** *m.*, —**овый** *a.* (bot.) maize, *see also* **кукуруза;** —**ин** *m.* maisin; —**овые** *pl.* (bot.) Maydeae; —**овый спирт** corn spirit, corn alcohol; —**овая каша** hominy, grits; —**овое масло** corn oil.

**май** *m.* May.

**майдан** *m.* tar pit; (market) square.

майеран *see* майоран.

майка *f.* (zool.) a beetle (*Meloe*).

Майн the Main (river).

майнцский *a.* (geol.) Mayencian.

майолика *f.* majolica (earthenware).

майонез *m.* mayonnaise.

майоран *m.* (bot.) marjoram (*Origanum*); —овое масло marjoram oil.

майский *a.* May.

майснеровский генератор Meissner oscillator.

майтландит *m.* maitlandite (uranium mineral).

майцена *f.* cornstarch.

мак *m.* (bot.) poppy (*Papaver*); м.-самосейка corn poppy (*P. rhoeas*); масличный м., опийный м., снотворный м. opium poppy (*P. somniferum*).

макадам *m.* macadam, macadam road, macadamized road; —изация *f.* macadamization.

мак/альный *a.* dipping; —ание *n.* dipping, dip; —аный *a.* dipped.

макароны *pl.* macaroni.

макассаровое масло Macassar oil.

макать *v.* dip, soak.

Мак Бэна центрифуга McBain centrifuge.

макет *m.* diorama; model, experimental model, mock-up.

макинтош *m.* mackintosh, raincoat.

Макки дистрибутор, Мак Ки д. (met.) McKee distributor.

Мак Кормика жатвенная машина (agr.) McCormick reaping machine.

маклейин *m.* macleyine, protopine.

Мак Леода манометр McLeod gage.

маклер *m.* broker, stockbroker; —ствовать *v.* job, be a broker.

Маклорена теорема (math.) Maclaurin's theorem.

маклюр/а *f.* (bot.) osage orange (*Maclura*); —ин *m.* maclurin, moringatannic acid.

макнуть *see* макать.

маковка *f.* crown, top, summit; poppy head; cupola.

маков/ые *pl.* (bot.) Papaveraceae; —ый *a.* poppy; —ая текстура (petr.) pelitic structure; —ое масло poppy seed oil.

макрель *f.* (zool.) mackerel.

макро— *prefix* macro—, macr— (long, large); broad-scale, large-scale; —возмущение *n.* broadscale perturbation; —графия *f.* macrography; —компонент *m.* macrocomponent; —концентрация *f.* macroscopic concentration; —коррозия *f.* macrocorrosion; —молекула *f.* macromolecule; —ось *f.* (cryst.) macroaxis; —пара *f.* macrocell; —пленка *f.* macrofilm; —сейсмический *a.* (geol.) macroseismic; —сейсмы *pl.* macroseisms; —система *f.* macrosystem.

макроскоп/ический *a.* macroscopic; over-all (reaction); (petr.) megascopic; —ия *f.* macroscopy.

макро/структура *f.* macrostructure; —течение *n.* broad-scale flow; —фаг *m.* (physiol.) macrophage; —филлин *m.* macrophylline; —фировый *a.* (geol.) macrophyric; —фотография *f.* macrophotography, enlarging; —фотоснимок *m.* enlargement; —частица *f.* macroparticle; —шлиф *m.* macrograph; large section; —элемент *m.* macrocell.

макс. *abbr.* (максимальный) maximum.

максвелл *m.* (elec.) maxwell (unit of magnetic flux); —метр *m.* maxwellmeter, fluxmeter; —овское распределение maxwellian distribution (of gas molecules).

максим/ально *adv.* at most, at a maximum; as much as possible; —альнодопустимый *a.* permissible; —альный *a.* maximum, highest, greatest, top; —альное значение, —ум *m.* maximum, highest quantity.

максит *m.* (min.) maxite (a variety of leadhillite).

максуэл *see* максвелл.

макулатура *f.* waste paper, spoilage.

макуха *f.* oil cake.

макушка *f.* crown, top, summit.

малабарское масло malabar tallow, piney tallow.

малайск/ий *a.* Malay; —ая камфора Malay camphor, *d*-borneol.

малакин *m.* malakin, salicylal-*p*-phenetidine.

малако— *prefix* malaco— (soft; mollusca); —зоология, —логия *f.* malacology, study of mollusks; —лит *m.*

(min.) malacolite (a variety of diopside pyroxene); —**метрия** *f.* determination of degree of softness of a semifluid; —**н** *m.* (min.) malacon (a variety of altered zircon).

**маламид** *m.* malamide, malic amide.

**маланга** *see* **мангарета.**

**мала/рин** *m.* malarin, acetophenone phenetidine; —**т** *m.* malate; —**тион,** —**тон** *m.* Malathion (insecticide).

**малахит** *m.,* —**овый** *a.* (min.) malachite, basic cupric carbonate; **зеленый м.** green malachite, malachite; **синий м.** blue malachite, azurite, chessylite; —**овый зеленый** malachite green, Victoria green (pigment).

**Малая Азия** Asia Minor.

**малдонит** *m.* (min.) maldonite (a native bismuth-gold alloy).

**малеат** *m.* maleate.

**малевать** *v.* paint roughly, whitewash.

**малеин—** *prefix* malein, male—; —**анил** *m.* maleinanil.

**малеиновокисл/ый** *a.* maleic acid; maleate (of); —**ая соль** maleate.

**малеинов/ый** *a.* maleic; **м. альдегид** maleic aldehyde, malealdehyde; **м. ангидрид** maleic anhydride; —**ая кислота** maleic acid, *cis*-butanedioic acid; **соль** —**ой кислоты** maleate.

**малейший** *a.* least, slightest.

**малек** *m.* young fish, fry.

**маленький** *a.* small, little.

**малигнит** *m.* malignite (a dark nepheline-syenite rock).

**малин/а** *f.,* —**ный** *a.* (bot.) raspberry (*Rubus*); spec. red raspberry (*Rubus idaeus*); **земляная м.** *see* **мамура;** —**ик** *m.* raspberry canes, raspberry garden; —**овка** *f.* (zool.) robin; —**овый** *a.* raspberry, crimson-colored.

**малк/а** *f.* bevel, bevel square, bevel protractor; **в** —**у** askew, obliquely.

**маллардит** *m.* (min.) mallardite.

**маллеин** *m.* (vet.) mallein; —**изация** *f.* malleinization, inoculation with mallein.

**мало** *adv.* little, few, not enough; **м. кто знает** few people know; **м. по малу** little by little, gradually, by degrees; *prefix* low, little; —**активный** *a.* low-activity; low-level; (nucl.) cold; —**ам-**перный *a.* (elec.) low-amperage, low-current; —**белковой** *a.* low-protein.

**малоберцов/ый** *a.* (anat.) peroneal, fibular; —**ая кость** fibula.

**маловажн/ость** *f.* insignificance; —**ый** *a.* insignificant, unimportant.

**маловат/о** *adv.,* —**ый** *a.* rather little.

**мало/ваттный** *a.* (elec.) low-watt; —**вероятный** *a.* scarcely probable, not very likely; —**габаритный** *a.* miniature, small-scale; —**головые** *pl.* (zool.) Microcephali; —**грамотный** *a.* illiterate; —**доступный** *a.* inaccessible.

**мал/ое** *n.* little; **без** —**ого** almost.

**малоемк/ий** *a.* low-capacity, small-size; —**остный** *a.* small-capacitance.

**малоземелье** *n.* shortage of arable land.

**малозеркальный чугун** white iron.

**малознач/ащий,** —**ительный,** —**ущий** *a.* insignificant, unimportant; —**ительность** *f.* insignificance, unimportance.

**мало/зольный** *a.* low-ash; —**известный** *a.* little-known; —**инерционный** *a.* quick-response; —**интенсивный** *a.* low-intensity; low (flux); —**калиберный** *a.* small-gage, small-bore; —**кормный** *a.* (biol.) oligotrophic; —**кровие** *n.* (med.) anemia; —**кровный** *a.* anemic.

**малол** *m.* malol, ursolic acid.

**малолегированный** *a.* (met.) low-alloy.

**малолетний** *a.* young, under age.

**маоловая кислота** *see* **малол.**

**мало/людный** *a.* sparsely populated, unfrequented; —**мерный** *a.* scanty, short; undersized; —**мощный** *a.* low-power, low-capacity, low-duty (machine); shallow (soil).

**малонамид** *m.* malonamide, propanediamide.

**малонаниловая кислота** malonanilic acid.

**малонаселенный** *a.* sparsely populated.

**малон/ат** *m.* malonate; —**ил** *m.* malonyl; **хлористый** —**ил** malonyl chloride; —**илмочевина** *f.* malonylurea, barbituric acid.

**малоново/бутиловый эфир, малонобутиловый эфир** butyl malonate;

—кальциевая соль calcium malonate; —кислый a. malonic acid; malonate (of) ;—кислый натрий, —натриевая соль sodium malonate; —кислая соль malonate; —метиловый эфир methyl malonate; —этиловый эфир ethyl malonate.

малоно/вый a. malonic; м. ангидрид malonic anhydride; м. эфир malonic ester, diethyl malonate; —вая кислота malonic acid, propanedioic acid; соль —вой кислоты malonate; —нитрил m. malononitrile, propanedinitrile.

мало/облученный a. slightly irradiated; —обогащенный a. slightly enriched; —опасный a. low-hazard; —опытный a. inexperienced, with little experience; —ответственный a. with few responsibilities; low-duty; —полярный a. of low polarity; —понятный a. abstruse, difficult to understand; —продуктивный a. inefficient, wasteful; —производительный a. low-output, unproductive; —процентный a. low-grade; —радиоактивный a. weakly radioactive; —развитый a. underdeveloped; —ресничные pl. (zool.) Oligotricha; —рослый a. stunted, undersized, dwarf

малороссийский a. Ukrainian.

Малороссия Little Russia, Ukraine.

мало/сернистый a. low-sulfur, low-sulfide; —сильный a. weak, feeble; —скоростной a. low-velocity, low-speed, low; —сольный a. freshly salted, freshly pickled; not very salty; —строчный a. low-definition, coarse.

малость f. littleness, smallness; trifle.

мало/углеродистый a. low-carbon; —употребительный a. rarely used; —фосфористый a. low-phosphorus; —ценный a. of small value, poor, inferior; lean (gas); —численный a. scanty, few; —чувствительный a. low-sensitivity; —шумный a. noiseless (typewriter); —щелочной a. low-alkali, containing little alkali; —щетинковые pl. (zool.) Oligochaeta.

малхит see мальхит.

малый a. little, small, low, minor; беско-

нечно м. infinitesimal; весьма м. minute.

мальв/а f. (bot.) mallow (Malva); —идин m. malvidin; —ин m. malvin; —овые pl. (bot.) Malvaceae.

мальдонит see малдонит.

мальк/и see малек; —овый a. of малек.

мальм m. (cer.) malm, washed clay; marl.

мальпигиевый a. (anat.) Malpighian.

мальта f. (geol.) maltha, mineral tar.

мальтаза f. maltase (enzyme).

мальтацит m. (min.) malthacite (a variety of fuller's earth).

мальтены pl. malthenes, petrolenes.

мальтийский крест Maltese cross.

мальтин m. maltine, extract of malt.

мальто— prefix malto—; —биоза f. maltobiose, maltose; —бионовая кислота maltobionic acid; —декстрин m. maltodextrin, amyloin; —за f. maltose, malt sugar; —новая кислота maltonic acid, d-gluconic acid.

мальхит m. malchite (dike rock of quartz-diorite aplite).

мальц-экстракт m. malt extract.

мальчик m. boy.

Малюса закон (phys.) Malus' law.

малютка f. pygmy.

маляр m. (house) painter; paper hanger.

маляр/ин see маларин; —ийный a. (med.) malarial; —ия f. malaria.

малярн/ый a. painter, house painter; —ое дело painting.

мамалыга f. hominy, grits.

маммеа f. (bot.) mammee tree (Mammea americana).

маммут-насос m. air lift.

мамонт m., —овый a. mammoth; —овое дерево big tree (Sequoia gigantea).

мамура f. (bot.) mamoura (Rubus arcticus).

мамут-насос see маммут-насос.

манацин m. manacine, vegetable mercury.

манган/ат m. manganate; —ин m., —иновый a. manganin (a manganese-nickel-copper alloy); —ит m. manganite; (min.) manganite, gray manganese ore.

мангано/аксинит m. (min.) manganoaxinite, manganiferous axinite; —за f. manganese carbonate fertilizer; —зит *m.* manganosite, manganese protoxide; —**кальцит** *m.* manganocalcite (a manganiferous variety of calcite); —**лит** *m.* manganolite (manganiferous rock); —**стибиит** *m.* (min.) manganostibiite; —**сферит** *m.* manganospherite (a variety of siderite); —**танталит** *m.* manganotantalite; —**филь** *m.* manganophyllite (a variety of biotite mica).

**мангарета** *f.* (bot.) yautia (*Xanthosoma*).

**мангеймское золото** Mannheim gold (a brass alloy).

**мангифер/а** *see* **манго;** —**ин** *m.* mangiferin, euxantogen.

**мангли** *see* **мангрова.**

**манго** *n.*, —**овое дерево** (bot.) mango (*Mangifera indica*).

**мангольд** *m.* (bot.) Swiss chard (*Beta vulgaris cicla*).

**мангост/ан** *m.* (bot.) mangosteen; —**ин** *m.* mangostin; mangosteen (pericarp of fruit of *Garcinia mangostana*).

**мангров/а** *f.*, —**ый** *a.* (bot.) mangrove (*Rhizophora*); —**ы** *pl.* Rhizophoraceae.

**мангуста** *f.* (zool.) mongoose.

**мангустан** *see* **мангостан.**

**мандарин** *m.* (bot.) mandarin (*Citrus nobilis, C. reticulata,* or *C. Unshiu* Marc.); mandarine, β-naphthol orange (dye); —**овое масло** mandarin oil, tangerine oil.

**мандат** *m.* mandate, warrant, order.

**мандельштейн** *m.* (petr.) almond rock, amygdaloid, amygdule.

**мандрагор/а** *f.* (bot.) mandrake (*Mandragora officinalis*); —**ин** *m.* mandragorine.

**манебахский закон** (cryst.) Manebach law.

**маневр** *m.*, —**енный** *a.* maneuver; —**енная способность**, —**енность** *f.* maneuverability; —**ирование** *n.* maneuvering; (railroad) switching, shunting; —**ировать** *v.* maneuver, manipulate, manage, work, operate; switch, shunt; —**овый** *a.* maneuvering; shunting.

**манекен** *m.* mannequin; model, mock-up.

**манер** *m.*, —**а** *f.* manner, way, form, fashion, method; —**а** *f.* (printing) stencil; **на м.** in the manner (of),

like; **таким** —**ом** in this fashion, in this way, thus; —**ы** *pl.* manners, behavior.

**манжета** *f.* cuff; flap, collar, sleeve; (pump) cup; blow-out patch (for tires).

**манжетка** *f.* (bot.) lady's mantle (*Alchemilla vulgaris*).

**манзат** *m.* manganese ethylene bisdithiocarbamate fungicide.

**маниакальный** *a.* maniacal.

**маникюр** *m.* manicure.

**манильская пенька** Manila hemp, abaca.

**маниок/а** *f.*, —**овый** *a.* (bot.) manioc, cassava (a group of *Euphorbiaceae*); spec. *Jatropha manihot;* —**овая мука** manioca starch, cassava.

**манипул/ирование** *n.*, —**яция** *f.* manipulation, handling, treatment; operation; (telegraphy) keying; —**ировать** *v.* manipulate, handle, treat; operate; —**ятор** *m.* manipulator; signaling key; operator; —**ятор ближнего действия** (nucl.) handler.

**манить** *v.* attract, lure.

**манифест/ация** *f.* manifestation; —**ировать** *v.* manifest, demonstrate.

**манифольд** *m.* manifold.

**маниха** *f.* slack tide, ebb tide.

**манихот** *m.* (bot.) manihot.

**мания** *f.* mania; **м. величия** megalomania; **м. преследования** persecution mania.

**манкировать** *v.* neglect, miss.

**манлийская эпоха** (geol.) Manlius epoch.

**манна** *f.* manna (dried saccharine exudation of *Fraxinus ornus*); —**н** *m.* mannan; —**я крупа** semolina.

**маннесмановский процесс** Mannesmann process (for rolling pipes).

**маннид** *m.* mannide.

**манник** *m.* manna grass (*Glyceria*).

**манни/л** *m.* mannyl; —**нотриоза** *f.* manninotriose; —**т**, —**тол** *m.* mannitol; **азотнокислый** —**т** mannitol nitrate, nitromannitol; —**тан** *m.* mannitan; —**тоза** *f.* mannitose, mannose.

**Манниха основание** Mannich base.

**манно/гептит** *m.* mannoheptitol, perseitol; —**гептоза** *f.* mannoheptose; —**за** *f.* mannose; —**зидострептомицин** *m.*

mannosidostreptomycin, streptomycin B; —лит *m.* mannolite, chloramine-T; —новая кислота mannonic acid; —сахарная кислота mannosaccharic acid; —триоза *f.* mannotriose.

**мано/вакуумметр** *m.* vacuum manometer, vacuum gage; —детандер *m.* pressure regulator; —метр *m.* manometer, pressure gage, gage; —метрический *a.* manometric, manometer.

**маноцитин** *m.* anticorrosive of wool fat and camphor oil.

**мансард/а** *f.* mansard, attic; mansard roof; —ный *a.* mansard; —ное помещение attic, garret.

**мантисса** *f.* (math.) mantissa.

**мантия** *f.* mantle.

**мануфактур/а** *f.*, —ный *a.* fabrics, dress goods; obs. textile mill.

**манчестер** *m.* (text.) velveteen; —ский коричневый Manchester brown, triamino-azo-benzene.

**Манчжурия** Manchuria.

**маншон** *m.* jacket.

**маразм** *m.* (med.) marasmus, progressive waste; —овая кислота marasmic acid.

**марантов/ые** *pl.* (bot.) Maranthaceae; —ый крахмал maranta, arrowroot.

**мараскин** *m.* maraschino (liqueur).

**марать** *v.* dirty, soil, smear; scribble.

**марашка** *f.* (typ.) turn, slur.

**марган/ец** *m.* manganese, Mn; гидрат закиси —ца manganous hydroxide; гидрат окиси —ца manganic hydroxide; двуокись —ца, перекись —ца manganese dioxide, manganese peroxide; закись —ца manganous oxide; соль закиси —ца manganous salt; закись-окись—ца manganomanganic oxide; окись —ца, черный м. manganic oxide, manganese (sesqui-) oxide; соль окиси —ца manganic salt; сернокислый м., сульфат —ца manganese sulfate; сернокислая закись —ца manganous sulfate; сернокислая окись —ца manganic sulfate; хлористый м. manganous chloride; хлорный м. manganic chloride.

**марган/о—** *prefix* mangano—; —цево— *see* марганцово—; —цевый *see* марганцовый.

**марганцовисто—** *prefix* mangano—,

manganous; —калиевая соль, —кислый калий potassium manganate; —кислый *a.* manganic acid; manganate (of); —кислая соль manganate; —синеродоводородная кислота manganocyanic acid.

**марганцовист/ый** *a.* manganous, manganese, manganiferous; м. ангидрид manganese trioxide; м. доломит (min.) mangandolomite; м. купорос manganous sulfate; м. шпат *see* марганцовый шпат; —ая кислота manganic acid; соль —ой кислоты manganate; —ая соль manganous salt; —ая сталь (met.) manganese steel; —ое железо (met.) ferromanganese.

**марганцово—** *prefix* mangani—, manganic, manganese; —калиевая соль, —кислый калий potassium permanganate; —кальциевая соль calcium permanganate; —кислый *a.* permanganic acid; permanganate (of); —кислая соль permanganate; —синеродоводородная кислота manganicyanic acid.

**марганцов/ый** *a.* manganic, manganese; м. ангидрид permanganic acid anhydride, manganese heptoxide; м. блеск (min.) manganese glance, alabandite; м. купорос manganese sulfate; м. пектолит (min.) manganpectolite; м. шпат (min.) manganese spar, rhodochrosite; rhodonite; м. эпидот (min.) manganese epidote, manganepidote, piedmontite; —ая кислота permanganic acid, соль —ой кислоты permanganate; —ая обманка (min.) manganese blende, mangan-blende, alabandite; —ая пена (min.) bog manganese, earthy manganese, wad; —ая соль manganic salt.

**маргарин** *m.* margarine (butter substitute); margarin (glyceryl ester of margaric acid).

**маргаринов/ый** *a.* margarine, margaric; —ая кислота margaric acid, heptadecanoic acid; соль —ой кислоты, —окислая соль margarate; —ое масло margarine oil.

**маргарит** *m.* (min.) margarite (a calcium aluminum silicate).

**маргаритка** *f.* (bot.) daisy (*Bellis*).

**маргаритовая кислота** margaritic acid.

**маргародит** *m.* (min.) margarodite (a variety of muscovite).

**маргарон** *m.* margaron, dihexadecyl ether.

**маргаросанит** *m.* (min.) margarosanite.

**маргиналии** *pl.* marginal notes.

**маргоз/ин** *m.* margosine; —**овая кислота** margosic acid; —**овое масло** margosa oil, oil of azedarach.

**марев/ые** *pl.* (bot.) Chenopodiaceae; —**ый** *a. of* **марь**; —**ое масло** ambrosia oil (from *Chenopodium ambrosioides*).

**мареграф** *see* **мареограф.**

**мареканит** *m.* (petr.) marekanite (a rhyolite perlite).

**марен/а** *f.*, —**овый** *a.* (bot.) madder (*Rubia*, spec. *R. tinctorum*); —**овые** *pl.* Rubiaceae.

**мареограф** *m.* tide gage, depth gage.

**мари** *pl.* mari (sparse larch forests with peat moss litter; shallow, often hummocky, bog; horizontal or sloping stretches with numerous small knolls or ridges with swampy patches between).

**мариалит** *m.* (min.) marialite (a variety of scapolite).

**маринов/ание** *n.* pickling, marinating; —**анный** *a.* pickled; —**ать** *v.* pickle.

**мариньяцит** *m.* (min.) marignacite (a variety of pyrochlore).

**Мариотта закон** (phys.) Mariotte's law.

**марипозит** *m.* (min.) mariposite (possibly same as alurgite mica).

**марка** *f.* stamp, mark, brand, make; quality, sort; (postage) stamp; (coal) rank; mark (money); **фабричная торговая м.** trademark, brand.

**марказит** *m.* (min.) marcasite, white iron pyrites, coxcomb pyrites; **гребенчатый м.** coxcomb pyrites; —**овый** *a.* marcasite, marcasitic.

**маркер** *m.*, —**ный** *a.* marker.

**маркизет** *m.* (text.) marquisette, voile.

**маркир/ованный** *a.* marked, stamped; labeled (molecule, etc.); —**овать** *v.* mark, stamp; gage; —**овка** *f.*, —**овочный**, —**ующий** *a.* marking, stamping; tagging, labeling; —**овщик** *m.*, —**ующий горизонт** marker.

**Марковникова правило** Markownikoff rule.

**Маркони когерер** (rad.) Marconi coherer.

**маркшейдер** *m.* mine surveyor, surveyor; —**ский** *a.* surveyor's, surveying; —**ский транспортир** surveyor's level; —**ская съемка** mine surveying; underground surveying.

**марлат** *see* **метоксихлор.**

**марлевый** *a.* gauze.

**марлит** *m.* (petr.) marlite, stony marl; —**овый** *a.* marlitic.

**марля** *f.* (med.) gauze.

**марматит** *m.* (min.) marmatite (ferriferous sphalerite).

**мармелад** *m.* fruit-paste candy.

**мармолит** *m.* (min.) marmolite (a foliated variety of serpentine).

**мародер** *m.* marauder, pillager.

**марокен** *m.* morocco (leather).

**марочный** *a.* stamp, mark.

**Марс** (astron.) Mars; —**а желть** Mars yellow (synthetic iron oxide); —**а печь** Mars furnace.

**марсельск/ий** *a.* Marseille; —**ое мыло** Marseille soap, Castile soap.

**марсово дерево** arbor Martis, iron tree (iron crystals).

**март** *m.* March.

**мартен** *see* **мартеновская печь;** —**зит** *see* **мартенсит;** —**ование** *n.* (met.) open-hearth refining.

**мартеновск/ий** *a.* (met.) Martin, Siemens-Martin, open-hearth; **м. передел, м. процесс** Martin process, Siemens-Martin process, open-hearth process; **м. цех** open-hearth plant; steel mill, steel works; —**ая печь** Martin furnace, open-hearth furnace; —**ая сталь** Martin steel, open-hearth steel.

**Мартенс-Гейн: твердость по** —**у** Martens-Heyn hardness.

**мартенсит** *m.* martensite (steel); —**овый** *a.* martensite, martensitic; —**овая сталь,** —**ная сталь** martensite steel.

**мартинит** *m.* (min.) martinite.

**мартит** *m.* (min.) martite, iron sesquioxide.

**мартышка** *f.* (zool.) marmoset.

**марцелин** *m.* (min.) marceline (impure braunite).

**марцесцин** *m.* marcescin.

**марципан** *m.* marchpane, marzipan.

**Марциуса желтый** Martius yellow (salt of 2,4-dinitro-1-naphthol).

**марш** *m.* march; flight (of stairs).
**Марша проба** Marsh test (for arsenic).
**маршанция** *f.* (bot.) marchantia.
**маршев** *see under* **Марша.**
**марши** *pl.* marsh, morass, swamp.
**маршировать** *v.* march.
**маршит** *m.* (min.) marshite (cuprous iodide).
**маршрут** *m.*, **—ный** *a.* route, itinerary, course.
**марь** *f.* mist; (bot.) goosefoot (*Chenopodium*); **белая м.** lamb's quarters, pigweed (*C. album*); **амброзиевая м., благовонная м., душистая м.** Mexican tea (*C. ambrosioides*).
**марьялит** *m.* (min.) marialite, dipyre (a variety of scapolite).
**марьянник** *m.* cow wheat (*Melampyrum*).
**маска** *f.* mask, disguise; face guard, face shield; **защитная м.** face guard.
**маска/гнин, —ньин** *m.* (min.) mascagnine, mascagnite (ammonium sulfate).
**маскелинит** *m.* (min.) maskelynite (related to labradorite feldspar).
**маскир/ованный** *a.* masked, camouflaged; concealed; **—овать** *v.* mask, disguise, camouflage; conceal, cover; **—овка** *f.* disguise, camouflage; concealment; **—овочный, —ующий** *a.* disguising, deceptive, camouflage; concealing.
**масксеть** *f.* (mil.) camouflage net.
**масленка** *f.* lubricator, oil can; lubricating valve; **ручная м.** oil can.
**маслен/ок** *see* **масляник**; **—ый** *see* **масляный.**
**маслин/а** *f.* olive; (bot.) *see* **масличное дерево; —ные** *see* **масличные.**
**маслить** *v.* oil, grease, lubricate.
**масличн/ость** *f.* percentage of oil; **—ые** *pl.* oil-producing plants; (bot.) Oleaceae; **—ый** *a.* oil, oil-yielding; olive; **—ая пальма** African oil palm (*Elaeis guineensis*); **—ое дерево** olive tree (*Olea europaea*).
**масло** *n.* oil; butter; **м. какао** cacao butter; **коровье м.** butter.
**маслобой/ка** *f.* churn (for butter); **—но-жировой** *a.* butter and fats; **—ный завод, —ня** *f.* oil mill; **—ный пресс, —ный станок** oil press; **—ное производство** oil manufacture; **—щик** *m.* oil manufacturer.

**масловыпускное отверстие** oil drain.
**маслодел/ие** *n.* butter making; **—ьный завод, —ьня** *f.* creamery.
**масло/емкость** *f.* oil absorption, oil number (of pigment); **—завод** *m.* creamery; oil mill; **—изготовитель** *m.* (butter) churn; **—мер** *m.*, **—мерное стекло** oil gage; **—непроницаемый** *a.* oiltight, oilproof, greaseproof; **—образный** *a.* oily, greasy; **—образующий** *a.* oil-forming, olefiant; **—отделитель** *m.* oil separator, oil catcher, oil expeller; **—отражатель** *m.* oil seal (for shaft), gland.
**маслоочиститель** *m.* oil purifier, oil filter; **—ный завод** oil refinery.
**масло/провод** *m.* oil pipeline, oil line; **—проводный** *a.* oil-piping; **—распределитель** *m.* oil distributor; **—растворимый** *a.* oil-soluble; **—родный** *a.* olefiant; **—сборник** *m.* drip pan, sump, oil collector.
**маслотта** *f.* ring pot.
**масло/указатель** *m.* oil gage; **—уловитель** *m.* drip pan, oil dish, oil catcher; **—фильтр** *m.* oil filter.
**масл/уха** *f.*, **—яник** *m.* (bot.) butter mushroom (*Boletus luteus*).
**маслянист/ость** *f.* oiliness; lubricity, lubricating property; ropiness (of wine); greasy pod (plant disease); **—ый** *a.* oily; butyrous, buttery; emulsive; ropy (wine); viscous; unctuous; **—ая взвесь** emulsion; **—ая смола** oleoresin.
**маслянка** *see* **масленка.**
**масляно/амиловый эфир** amyl butyrate; **—бутиловый эфир** butyl butyrate; **—кислый** *a.* butyric acid; butyrate (of); **—кислый кальций, —кальциевая соль** calcium butyrate; **—кислая соль** butyrate; **—кислое брожение** butyric (acid) fermentation; **—метиловый эфир** methyl butyrate.
**масляность** *f.* oiliness, greasiness, fatness.
**маслянoэтиловый эфир** ethyl butyrate.
**маслян/ый** *a.* oil, oily, greasy; butyrous, butyric; **м. альдегид** butyraldehyde, butanal; **м. ангидрид** butyric anhydride; **м. газ** oil gas; **м. лак** oil varnish; **м. туман** oil spray; **—ая заглушка, —ое уплотнение** oil seal; **—ая загрунтовка, —ая окраска** coat of

oil paint; —ая кислота butyric acid, butanoic acid; соль —ой кислоты butyrate; —ая краска oil paint, oil color; —ая пальма (bot.) oil palm (*Elaeis guineensis*).

масс/а *f.* mass, bulk, volume; heap; matter, substance, compound, composition; block; shoal, swarm; (paper) pulp; (cer.) body, paste; body (of casting); м. покоя, собственная м. (nucl.) rest mass; дефект —ы mass defect; единица —ы unit of mass, unit of measure; (nucl.) atomic mass unit, amu; закон действия масс law of mass action; испытание —ы bulk test; перенос —ы mass transfer.

массаж *m.*, —ный *a.* massage.

масс. ед. *abbr.* (массовая единица) mass unit; atomic mass unit.

массив *m.* solid mass, body; main part; block, group; large tract, area; shell (of furnace); (geol.) massif, mountain mass; лесной м. large forest; —ность *f.* massiveness, solidity; —ный *a.* massive, bulky, substantial, sturdy, heavy, compact; solid (tire, etc.).

массикот *m.* (min.) massicot, lead monoxide.

массиров/ание *n.* massaging; —ать *v.* massage, knead; mass, concentrate.

масскуит *m.* (sugar) massecuite.

массов/ый *a.* mass, bulk; м. продукт large-tonnage product; —ая единица (nucl.) atomic mass unit, amu; —ое изготовление, —ое производство mass production, assembly-line production, wholesale manufacture.

массои кора massoi bark.

массо/обмен *m.*, —обменный *a.*, —передача *f.* mass transfer.

масс-спектро/граф *m.* mass spectrograph; —метр *m.* mass spectrometer; —метрия *f.* mass spectrometry.

масс-эквивалент *m.* mass equivalent.

мастер *m.* master, skilled workman, expert; foreman; м.-беч master batch (of rubber); —ок *m.* trowel, smoother.

мастерск/ая *f.* workshop, shop; —ие *pl.* works; —ой *a.* skilful, workman-like.

мастерство *n.* skill, workmanship.

мастика *f.* mastic, gum mastic; putty, cement, composition; —тор *m.* masti-

cator (for rubber); —ция *f.* mastication.

мастико/вый *see* мастичный; —ловая кислота masticolic acid; —новая кислота masticonic acid.

мастикс *see* мастика.

мастит *m.* (med.) mastitis.

мастихин *m.* spatula.

мастицин *m.* masticin; —овая кислота masticinic acid.

мастичн/ый *a.* mastic; —ая замазка mastic cement; —ая фисташка (bot.) mastic tree (*Pistacia lentiscus*).

мастодонт *m.* (pal.) mastodon.

мастоидит *m.* (med.) mastoiditis.

масть *f.* color (of animal).

масштаб *m.*, —ный *a.* scale, gage, rule; rate; м. скольжения sliding scale; большого —a large-scale; в маленьком —е on a small scale; в уменьшенном —е scaled down; по —у to scale; сводить к определенному —у *v.* bring to scale; складной м. folding rule; чертить в —е *v.* draw to scale; —ная линейка scale, rule, measuring rule.

мат *m.* mat, mat finish; наводить м. *v.* mat, produce a mat finish; grind, frost (glass); наводка —а mat finishing, dull finishing; протрава для —а (met.) dull pickling; стравлять на м. *v.* dull, dull pickle.

матаи-резинол *m.* matairesinol.

мате *see* матэ.

математи/ка *f.* mathematics; —чески *adv.* mathematically; —ческий *a.* mathematical.

матереть *v.* harden, grow hard; grow, grow out.

материал *m.* material, goods, stock; data; fabric, cloth; сырой м. raw material; —изация *f.* materialization; —ьно *adv.* materially, physically; —ьный *a.* material, physical; mass (point).

материк *m.* continent, mainland; native soil; (geol.) matrix, gangue; (biol.) parent tissue; —овый *a.* continental; —овая порода (geol.) matrix, gangue; bedrock.

материнка *see* майоран, дикий.

материнск/ий *a.* maternal, mother; parent; —ая порода (geol.) matrix, gangue.

**материя** *f.* material, fabric; matter, substance; pus.

**матерка** *f.* (bot.) pistillate hemp.

**матерчатый** *a.* cloth, fabric.

**матерьял** *see* **материал.**

**матико** *n.* matico (dried leaf of *Piper angustifolium*).

**матильдит** *m.* (min.) matildite.

**матиров/ание** *n.*, **—ка** *f.* dull finish; producing dull finish; frosting (glass); **—анный** *a.* mat, dull; ground, frosted; **—ать** *v.* dull, deaden, tarnish; give a mat surface (to), produce a dull finish; grind, frost.

**Матиссена правило** (elec.) Mathiessen's rule.

**мати/ца** *f.*, **—чный** *a.* girder, main beam, tie-beam; templet.

**матка** *f.* (anat.) uterus, womb; (geol.) matrix; (zool.) dam, female parent; queen bee; (aircraft) carrier; master batch (of rubber); (text.) printing roller.

**матлокит** *m.* (min.) matlockite (lead chlorofluoride).

**матовопозолоченный** *a.* dead-gilded.

**матовость** *f.* dullness, deadness, dimness.

**матов/ый** *a.* dull, lusterless, tarnished, dead, mat, mat-finish; ground, frosted, etched (glass); (bot.) opaque; **м. блеск** dull finish, mat finish; **—ая краска** deadening color; **—ая отделка** dull finish; dull finishing; **—ая позолота** dead-gilding; **—ая протрава** (met.) pickle for giving a dull surface; **—ая электрическая лампочка** frosted bulb; **—ое золото** dead gold; **—ое место** dead spot.

**матонная трава** *see* **маточная трава.**

**маточник** *m.* mother liquor; master tap; lead screw; (bot.) ovary; (bot.) balm mint (*Melissa officinalis*); ostericum; dragonhead (*Dracocephalum moldavicum*).

**маточн/ый** *a.* mother; (anat.) womb, uterine; stock (pond); **м. лист** (met.) starting sheet; **м. метчик** master tap; **м. рассол, м. раствор** mother liquor; **м. чан** (vinegar) mother vat; **—ая порода** (geol.) matrix, gangue, ground mass; **—ая смесь** master batch (of rubber); **—ая трава** (bot.) feverfew

(*Pyrethrum parthenium*); **—ые рожки** (bot.) ergot (*Claviceps purpurea*).

**матрас** *m.* matrass (obs. term for distilling flask), separating flask.

**матрац** *m.*, **—ный** *a.* mattress, mat; **—евидная отдельность** (petr.) pillow structure, ellipsoid.

**матрикария** *f.* (bot.) German camomile (*Matricaria*).

**матрикул** *m.* matriculation certificate (obs.).

**матрин** *m.* matrine, isolupanine.

**матри/ца** *f.*, **—чный** *a.* matrix; (met.) die; (met.) starting sheet; **м.-образец** master die; **литье в —цах** die casting; **—цирование** *n.* matrixing; **—чная сталь** die steel.

**матрос** *m.* sailor, seaman.

**мать** *f.* mother; **м.-и-мачеха, м.-мачеха** (bot.) coltsfoot (*Tussilago farfara*).

**Матье функция** (math.) Mathieu's function.

**матэ** *n.* (bot.) maté, Paraguay tea (*Ilex paraguariensis*).

**мауерлат** *m.* wall plate.

**маун** *m.*, **—ный** *a.* (bot.) valerian (*Valeriana*).

**маухерит** *m.* (min.) maucherite.

**мауцелиит** *m.* (min.) mauzeliite (related to lewisite).

**МАФ** *abbr.* (**моноаммонийфосфат**) ammonium phosphate.

**мафи/ты** *pl.* (geol.) mafites, mafic minerals; **—ческий** *a.* mafic, ferromagnesian.

**мафурское сало** mafura tallow.

**мах** *m.* motion, move, stroke, wave; oscillation, vibration.

**Маха число** (phys.) Mach number.

**махагони** *see* **махогани.**

**махайрод** *m.* saber-toothed tiger.

**мах/альный** *a.*, **—ание** *n.* waving, brandishing, signaling; flapping (of wings); **—альщик** *m.* signal man, signaler.

**махать** *v.* wave, brandish, signal; beat, flap (wings).

**махаон** *m.* a swallow-tail butterfly (*Papilio machaon*).

**махе** *n.*, **Махе единица** Mache unit (of radioactivity).

**махилен** *m.* machilene.

**махнуть** *see* **махать.**

**махов/ик** *m.*, —**ое** *n.*, —**ой** *a.*, —**ое колесо** flywheel; **м.-регулятор** flywheel governor, shaft governor; **м.-ротор** flywheel rotor; **привод от** —**ика** flywheel drive; —**ичок** *m.* pilot wheel; knob; —**ой момент** flywheel moment, flywheel action, moment of gyration.

**махогани** *n.* mahogany (wood).

**махорка** *f.* (bot.) tobacco (*Nicotiana rustica*).

**махров/ость** *f.* (bot.) doubleness; —**ый** *a.* double-flowering, double.

**маца** *f.* unleavened bread, matzoth.

**мацер/атор** *m.* macerator; —**ация** *f.*, —**ирование** *n.* maceration; —**ировать** *v.* macerate, soak to a pulp.

**мациленовая кислота** macilenic acid.

**мацис** *m.*, —**овый** *a.* mace (spice).

**мац/они**, —**ун** *m.* a sour milk.

**мачт/а** *f.*, —**овый** *a.* mast, column, post, pole, tower, support; spar tree; —**овый** *a.* high-standing (timber); —**овая лампа** street lamp (on post); —**овое дерево** spar, sparwood; —**о-вый выключатель** (elec.) pole switch.

**маш** *m.* (bot.) bean (*Phaseolus mungo* or *P. aureus*).

**машет** *pr. 3 sing. of* **махать.**

**машин/а** *f.* machine, engine; —**ы** *pl.* machines, machinery; **м.-аналог** *m.* analog computer; **м. двигатель** engine, driving engine; **м.-орудие** power tool, machine tool; **опрыскивающая м.** sprayer; **паровая м.** steam engine; **составная м.** compound engine.

**машинальн/ость** *f.* mechanicalness; —**ый** *a.* mechanical, automatic.

**машин/изация** *f.* mechanization; —**ист** *m.* machine operator; mechanic; (railroad) engineer; —**истка** *f.* typist; —**ка** *f.* little machine; typewriter.

**машинн/ый** *a.* machine, engine; power (driven); mechanical; **м. журнал** logbook of machine performance; **м. зал**, —**ое отделение** machine room, machine shop, engine room; —**ое масло** machine oil, lubricating oil; —**ое оборудование** machinery, mechanical equipment; —**ое черчение** mechanical drawing; **обрабатывать** —**ым способом** *v.* machine.

**машино/писный** *a.* typewritten; —**пись** *f.* typing; —**поделочная сталь** structural steel (for machines); —**строение** *n.* machine building; mechanical engineering.

**машиностроитель** *m.* mechanic; mechanical engineer; —**ный** *a.* machine-building, machine-constructing; mechanical; —**ный завод** machine shop, machine works; —**ая промышленность** machine industry, machinery industry.

**машино-час** *m.* machine hour.

**машу/т** *pr. 3 pl.*; —**щий** *pr. act. part. of* **махать.**

**маюн** *m.* madjoun (liqueur).

**маяк** *m.* lighthouse, beacon, signal tower; (forestry) standard.

**маятник** *m.* pendulum, balance (of watch), bob; —**овый** *a.* pendulum, swing, floating; —**овый копер** impact tester; —**овая мешалка** balance agitator; —**овая опора** swing bearing; —**овая пила** swing saw.

**маятничек** *m.* small pendulum.

**мб** *abbr.* (**миллибар**) millibar; **м-б** *abbr.* (**масштаб**) scale; **м.б.** *abbr.* (**может быть**) perhaps.

**мбарн** *abbr.* (**миллибарн**) millibarn.

**мв** *abbr.* (**милливольт**) millivolt; **МВ** *abbr.* (**магнит вращение**) rotary magnet; **М/В** *abbr.* (**масло/вода**) oil-water emulsion, O/W.

**мвт** *abbr.* (**милливатт**) milliwatt; **Мвт** *see* **мгвт.**

**МВТУ** *abbr.* (**Московское высшее техническое училище**) Moscow Technical College.

**мг** *abbr.* (**миллиграмм**) milligram.

**мгвт** *abbr.* (**мегаватт**) megawatt; **мгвт-ч** *abbr.* (**мегаватт-час**) megawatt-hour.

**МГГ** *abbr.* (**Международный геофизический год**) International Geophysical Year.

**мггц** *abbr.* (**мегагерц**) megahertz, megacycles per second.

**мгдж** *abbr.* (**мегаджоуль**) megajoule.

**мгкал** *abbr.* (**мегакалория**) megacalorie.

**мгл/а** *f.* mist; —**истый** *a.* misty, hazy.

**мгн** *abbr.* (**миллигенри**) millihenry.

**мгновен/ие** *n.* instant, moment; —**но** *adv.* instantaneously, instantly; momentarily; —**но-критический** *a.*

prompt-critical; —ность *f.* instantaneousness; —ный *a.* instantaneous, prompt; momentary; —ного действия instantaneous.

мго *see* мо.

мгом *abbr.* (мегом) megohm.

МГРИ *abbr.* (Московский геологоразведочный институт им. С. Орджоникидзе) Moscow Geologic Prospecting Institute named for S. Ordzhonikidze.

МГУ *abbr.* (Московский государственный университет им. М.В. Ломоносов) Moscow State University named for M. V. Lomonosov.

Мгц *see* мггц.

м.д.с. *abbr.* (магнитодвижущая сила) magnetomotive force.

ме, МЕ *abbr.* (массовая единица) atomic mass unit.

меандр *m.* meander, winding; a feed unit; —ирующий, —ический *a.* meandering, winding.

мебель *f.* furniture; —ностолярная мастерская furniture factory.

Мебиуса способ (met.) Moebius process (of electrolytic refining).

меблиров/ать *v.* furnish; —ка *f.* furniture.

мег—, мега— *prefix* meg—, mega— (denoting a magnitude of $10^6$; large).

мегабар *m.* megabar (unit of pressure).

мегабромит *m.* (min.) megabromite (a variety of embolite).

мегаварметр *m.* (elec.) megavarmeter.

мега/ватт *m.* (elec.) megawatt; м.-час megawatt-hour; —вольт *m.* megavolt; —герц *m.* megahertz, megacycles per second; —джоуль *m.* megajoule; —дина *f.* megadyne.

мегакарпидин *m.* megacarpidine.

мегакюри *n.* (nucl.) megacurie.

мегаломания *f.* (med.) megalomania.

мега/метр *m.* megameter; —ом *see* мегом; —перм *m.* megaperm (nickel-iron-manganese alloy); —рад *m.* (nucl.) megarad; —резерфорд *m.* megarutherford; —рентген *m.* megaroentgen; —сейсмы *pl.* (geol.) megaseisms.

мегаскоп *m.* megascope; —ический *a.* megascopic, visible to the naked eye.

мега/фарада *f.* (elec.) megafarad, macrofarad; —фон *m.* megaphone; —цикл

*m.* (elec.) megacycle; —электронвольт *m.* megaelectron volt, million electron volt, mev; —эрг *see* мегэрг.

мег/гер *m.* (elec.) megger (for measuring insulation resistance); —ом *m.* megohm; —ометр *m.* megohmmeter; —омит *m.* megohmite (insulator); —эрг *m.* megerg.

мед— *abbr.* (медицинский) medical, medicinal.

мед *m.* honey; м.-самотек liquid honey; медицинский м. medicated honey, mellite.

медаль *f.* medal.

медведицы *pl.* tiger moths (*Arctiidae*).

медведка *f.* truck; die, stamp, hollow punch, punching machine, punch press; (zool.) mole cricket (*Gryllotalpa*).

медведь *m.* (zool.) bear.

медвеж/ий *a.* bear, ursine; м. виноград, —ья толокнянка, —ьи ягоды (bot.) bearberry (*Arctostaphylos uva ursi*); —ье ухо mullein (*Verbascum*); —ья лапа bear's breech (*Acanthus*); —ья трава lungwort (*Pulmonaria officinalis*).

медвяная роса *see* падь.

Медгиз *abbr.* (Государственное издательство медицинской литературы) State Medical Publishing House.

меде— *prefix* copper; —носный *a.* copper-bearing, cupriferous; —обжигательная печь copper furnace; —очистительный завод copper refinery; —плавильный завод copper works, copper smelter.

меджитит *m.* medjitite (a uranium mineral).

меди *gen. of* медь.

медиальный *a.* medial, middle.

медиан *m.*, —а *f.*, —ный *a.* median.

медик *m.* medical man, medical student.

медикамент *m.* medicine, medicinal, drug.

медико— *prefix* medico—, med—.

мединал *m.* Medinal, barbital sodium.

медист/о— *prefix* cupro—, cuprous, copper; —овисмутовый блеск (min.) wittichenite; —осинеродистый *a.* cuprocyanide (of); —ый *a.* cuprous, copper; cupriferous, copper-bearing; —ая сажа (met.) copper smoke, copper fumes; —ая соль cuprous salt.

**медиум** *m.* medium.

**медицин/а** *f.* medicine; —ский *a.* medical, medicinal; clinical (thermometer); —ская сестра trained nurse.

**медленн/о** *adv.* slowly; —одействующий *a.* slow, slow-acting; —ость *f.* slowness; —ый *a.* slow, sluggish.

**медлительн/ость** *f.* sluggishness; —ый *a.* sluggish, slow, tardy.

**медлить** *v.* be slow, delay.

**медляк** *m.* a beetle of the *Tenebrionidae* family.

**медн/ение** *n.* copper plating —ик *m.* coppersmith, brazier, brass worker; —ицкая *f.* copper smithy, copper shop.

**медно**— *prefix* cupri—, cupric, copper; —аммиачный шелк cuprammonium rayon; —винная кислота cupritartaric acid; —закисный *a.* cuprous oxide;—закисный выпрямитель copper oxide rectifier; —закисный элемент copper oxide cell; —кислый *a.* cupric acid; cuprate (of); —кислая соль cuprate; —котельная *f.*, —котельная мастерская copper smithy; —красный *a.* copper-colored.

**меднолитей/ная** *f.* copper foundry, brass foundry; —ный *a.* copper founding; —щик *m.* copper founder.

**медно/плавильный завод** copper works, copper smelter; —прокатный завод copper rolling mill; —серебряный блеск (min.) stromeyerite; —синеродистый *a.* cupricyanide (of); —цинковый элемент copper-zinc cell.

**медн/ый** *a.* cupric, copper; м. блеск (min.) copper glance, chalcocite; м. дождь (met.) copper rain; м. изумруд (min.) copper emerald, dioptase; м. колчедан (min.) copper pyrites, chalcopyrite, yellow copper ore; м. купорос blue vitriol, blue copperas, copper sulfate; м. уранит (min.) copper uranite; torbernite; м. цвет (min.) copper bloom (capillary cuprite); м. штейн (met.) copper matte, blue metal;—ая зелень copper rust, verdigris; (min.) chrysocolla; —ая изгарь, —ая окалина copper scale; —ая кислота cupric acid; соль —ой кислоты

cuprate; —ая лазурь (min.) azurite, azure stone, blue malachite; —ая пенка (met.) copper scum, copper froth; (min.) tyrolite; —ая руда copper ore; пестрая —ая руда (min.) variegated copper ore, peacock ore, bornite; —ая синь (min.) blue verditer, azurite; blue malachite; —ая смоляная руда (min.) copper pitch ore, chrysocolla; —ая фольга copper foil; —ая чернь (min.) melaconite, black copper oxide; tenorite; —ое индиго (min.) copper indigo, covellite; —ые квасцы copper alum; (pharm.) cuprum aluminatum, lapis divinus.

**медо**— *prefix* honey; nectar.

**медобслуживание** *n.* medical service.

**медов/ик**, —ник *m.* (bot.) hemp nettle (*Galeopsis*); —ка *f.* (zool.) apple psylla.

**медов/ый** *a.* honey; м. камень (min.) honeystone, mellite; м. уксус oxymel; —ая вода hydromel; —ая патока liquid honey; —ая трава *see* зверобой; —ое вино mead, mulse.

**медо/гонка** *f.* honey extractor; —нос *m.* nectariferous plant; —носный *a.* (bot.) nectariferous; honey (bee); —сбор *m.* yield of honey.

**мед/осмотр** *m.* medical inspection, medical examination; —персонал *m.* medical staff; —помощь *f.* medical assistance; —пункт *m.* medical station; —работник *m.* medical worker; —сантруд *m.* trade union of medical workers; —сестра *f.* nurse.

**медуз/а** *f.* (zool.) medusa, jellyfish; —овидный *a.* medusoid.

**медуллярный** *a.* (anat.) medullary.

**медун/ица** *f.* (bot.) lungwort (*Pulmonaria*); —ка *f.* medick (*Medicago*); lungwort (*Pulmonaria*); hemp nettle (*Geleopsis ladanum*).

**Медфак** *abbr.* (Медицинский факультет) Faculty of Medicine.

**мед/ь** *f.* copper, Cu; белая м. white copper, German silver (copper-nickel-zinc alloy); гидрат закиси —и cuprous hydroxide; гидрат окиси —и cupric hydroxide; двухлористая м. cupric chloride; желтая м. (met.) brass; жесть красной —и latten,

latten brass; закись —и cuprous oxide; соль закиси —и cuprous salt; красная м. (min.) cuprite, red copper ore; крецовая м. (met.) copper from waste; окись —и cupric oxide; соль окиси —и cupric salt; однохлористая м., полухлористая м. cuprous chloride; подовая м. (met.) copper bottoms, bottoms (cupriferous alloy); сернокислая м., сульфат —и copper sulfate; сернокислая закись —и cuprous sulfate; сернокислая окись —и cupric sulfate; углекислая м. copper carbonate; хлористая м. cuprous chloride; хлорная м. cupric chloride; черная м. (met.) black copper, coarse copper; (min.) black copper ore, melaconite; tenorite; черновая м. black copper; blister copper (high-grade crude copper).

медьсодержащий *a.* copper-bearing, cupriferous.

медяниц/а *f.* (zool.) psylla; —ы *pl.* jumping plant lice (*Psyllidae, Chermidae*).

медянк/а *f.* verdigris, green copper rust; smooth snake; —ового цвета verdigris-green, aeruginous.

меж—*prefix* inter—; *see also* между—.

межа *f.* boundary, landmark, bound, limit.

меж/атомный *a.* interatomic; —видовой *a.* interspecific, interspecies; —горный *a.* intermontane; —дендритовый *a.* interdendritic; —домолекулярный *a.* intermolecular; —доузельный, —доузловой *a.* internodal; (cryst.) interstitial; —доузлие *n.* internode; interstice.

между *prep. instr. and gen.* between, among; м. прочим by the way; м. тем meanwhile; м. тем как while, whereas.

между— *prefix* inter—, between; *see also under* меж—; —антный *a.* (instrumentation) interdee; —блочный *a.* interunit; —ведомственный *a.* interdepartmental; —венцовый зазор rim clearance; —городный *a.* interurban; intercity; (tel.) long-distance; —гранулярный, —зернистый *a.* intergranular; —железное пространство air gap, clearance;

—звездный *a.* (astron.) interstellar; —кристаллический *a.* intercrystalline; —ледниковый *a.* (geol.) interglacial; —лежащий *a.* intermediate; —молекулярный *a.* intermolecular.

международн/ый *a.* international, standard; —ое право international law.

между/осный *a.* interaxial; —полюсный *a.* interpolar; —путье *n.* track spacing; —реберный *a.* (anat.) intercostal; —речье *n.* interfluve, interfluvial area; —рядье *n.* distance between rows; —слойный *a.* interlayer, interlaminar; —строчный *a.* interlinear; —тропический *a.* intertropical; —узлие *n.* internode; interstice.

межев/ание *n.* surveying, land surveying, chorometry; —ать *v.* survey; fix boundaries; —ик *m.* surveyor; —ой *a.* surveying; boundary; —ой знак, —ой столб landmark, boundary mark.

межень *m.* low-water period (of river, etc.).

меж/звездный *a.* interstellar; —зернистый *a.* intergranular; —ионный *a.* inter-ion; —каскадный *a.* interstage; —клеточный *a.* (biol.) intercellular; —кристаллический *a.* intercrystalline; —ледниковый *a.* (geol.) interglacial; —молекулярный *a.* intermolecular; —осевое расстояние, —центровое расстояние center distance, center-to-center distance; —осный *a.* interaxial; —планетный *a.* interplanetary; —планетные сообщения astronautics; —плоскостной *a.* interplanar; —породное скрещивание (biol.) cross-breeding; —радиальный *a.* interradial; —расовый *a.* interracial; —реберный *a.* (anat.) intercostal; —сортовой *a.* intervarietal; —станционный *a.* (tel.) inter-office, interexchange; —трубный *a.* intertubular; —фазовый *a.* interphase; —формационный *a.* (geol.) interformational; —цеховой *a.* interdepartmental; —частичный *a.* interparticle; —челюстный *a.* (anat.) intermaxillary; —ядерный *a.* internuclear.

меза *f.* (geol.) mesa; plateau, terrace.

меза/коновая кислота mesaconic acid,

methylfumaric acid; —тон *m.* mesaton, phenylephrine hydrochloride.

**мезг/а** *f.*, —**овый** *a.* vegetable pulp.

**мездр/а** *f.* scrapings, shreds (of hide), glue stock; flesh side (of hide); (bot.) septum; —**ение** *n.* scraping, scouring (of hide); —**ина** *f.*, —**инный** *a.* flesh side, inner side; —**ить** *v.* scrape, scour; —**овый** *a.* hide; —**овый клей** hide glue, skin glue.

**мезембр/ен** *m.* mesembrene; —**ин** *m.* mesembrine.

**мезен/терий** *m.* (anat.) mesentery; —**терический** *a.* mesenteric; —**хима** *f.* (embryology) mesenchyme.

**мези/дин** *m.* mesidine, 2,4,6-trimethylaniline; —**тен** *m.* mesitene.

**мезитил** *m.*, —**овый** *a.* mesityl; **окись** —**а** mesityl oxide; **хлористый м.** mesityl chloride; —**ен** *m.* mesitylene; —**еновая кислота**, —**иновая кислота** mesitylenic acid, 3,5-xylic acid; —**овая кислота** mesitylic acid, trimethylglutaric lactam; —**овый спирт** *see* **мезитол.**

**мезитин** *m.*, —**овый** *a.* (min.) mesitine, mesitine spar (ferriferous magnesite).

**мезито/евая кислота** mesitoic acid, 2,4,6-trimethylbenzoic acid; —**л** *m.* mesitol, 2,4,6-trimethylphenol; —**оновая кислота** mesitonic acid, dimethyllevulinic acid.

**мезо**— *prefix* meso—, mes— (middle, intermediate); —**атом** *m.* mesonic atom; —**винная кислота** mesotartaric acid; —**глея** *f.* (biol.) mesoglea; —**дерма** *f.* (biol.) mesoderm; —**диалит** *m.* (min.) mesodialyte (ferruginous variety of eudialyte); —**зой,** —**зойская эра** (geol.) Mesozoic era; —**зона** *f.* mesozone; —**кратовый** *a.* (petr.) mesocratic.

**мезоксал/евая кислота** mesoxalic acid, oxopropanedioic acid; **соль** —**евой кислоты,** —**евокислая соль** mesoxalate; —**евокислый** *a.* mesoxalic acid; mesoxalate (of); —**ил** *m.* mesoxalyl.

**мезолит** *m.* (min.) mesolite (intermediate between natrolite and scolecite).

**мезомер** *m.* mesomer, meso-form; —**ия** *f.* mesomerism; —**ный** *a.* mesomeric.

**мезо/молекула** *f.* mesomolecule; —**н** *m.* (nucl.) meson; —**ний** *m.* mesonium (mu meson and electron system); —**ный** *a.* meson, mesonic; —**ный ливень** meson shower; —**положение** *n.* mesoposition; —**породы** *pl.* mesorocks, medium-colored rocks; —**рцин** *m.* mesorcinol; —**стазис** *m.* (petr.) mesostasis, basis, base; —**тан** *m.* mesotan, ericin; —**телий** *m.* (biol.) mesothelium; —**термальный** *a.* mesothermal; —**тип** *m.* (min.) mesotype (natrolite); —**торий** *m.* mesothorium, MsTh; —**трон** *m.* (nucl.) mesotron (obs. for mu meson); —**филл** *m.* (bot.) mesophyll; —**фит** *m.* (bot.) mesophyte.

**Мейгена реакция** (min.) Meigen's reaction.

**Мейдингера элемент** (elec.) Meidinger's cell.

**Мейера закон** Meyer's law, law of esterification.

**мейергофферит** *m.* (min.) meyerhofferite.

**меймацит** *m.* (min.) meymacite (alteration product of scheelite).

**мейоз** *m.* (biol.) meiosis.

**мейонит** *m.* (min.) meionite.

**мейотический** *a.* (biol.) meiotic.

**мекамин** *m.* mecamine, mecamylamine.

**меккский бальзам** Mecca balsam, balm of Gilead.

**мекон/идин** *m.* meconidin; —**ий** *m.* (zool.) meconium; —**ин** *m.* meconin, opianyl, 5,6-dimethoxyphthalide; —**иновая кислота** meconinic acid.

**меконовая кислота** meconic acid.

**мекоцианин** *m.* mecocyanin.

**Мексика** Mexico.

**мексиканский** *a.* Mexican.

**мел** *m.* chalk; (geol.) Cretaceous (period); *past sing. of* **мести; красный м.** red chalk, red bole; **осажденный м.** precipitated chalk; **отмученный м.** prepared chalk, whiting; **черный м.** slate black.

**мелаконит** *m.* (min.) melaconite, black copper oxide (a variety of tenorite).

**мелам** *m.* melam; —**ин** *m.* melamine, cyanuramide; —**пирин,** —**пирит** *m.* melampyrin, melampyritol, hexanehexol.

**меланжевый** *a.* mixed, blended; vari-colored.

**мелан/илин** *m.* melaniline; diphenyl guanidine; **—ин** *m.* (biol.) melanin.

**меланит** *m.* (min.) melanite (a black variety of andradite garnet); **—овый** *a.* melanite, melanitic.

**мелановая кислота** melanic acid; **м. слюда** (min.) stilpnomelane (in part).

**мелано/дерма** *f.* (med.) melanoderma, leucoderma; **—з** *m.* (med.) melanosis; **—кратовый** *a.* (petr.) melanocratic, dark-colored; **—флогит** *m.* (min.) melanophlogite (a form of tridymite); **—хальцит** *m.* (min.) melanochalcite; **—хроит** *m.* (min.) melanochroite, phoenicochroite; **—церит** *m.* (min.) melanocerite.

**мелан/терит** *m.* melanterite, mineral copperas; **—тигенин** *m.* melanthigenin; **—тин** *m.* melanthin; **—уровая кислота** melanuric acid, isocyanurmonoimide.

**меланхолия** *f.* (med.) melancholy.

**меласс/а** *f.*, **—овый** *a.* molasses; **—овая кислота** melassic acid.

**мелафир** *m.* melaphyre (a felsitic igneous rock).

**мелегет/а**, **—та** *f.*, **—ский перец** Melegueta pepper, grains of paradise, Guinea grains (seeds of *Amomum melegueta*).

**мелем** *m.* melem (amide of cyanuric acid).

**мелен** *m.* melene, triacontylene.

**мелен/ие** *n.* chalking; **—ый** *a.* chalked.

**мелет** *pr. 3 sing. of* **молоть.**

**мелетин** *m.* meletin, quercetin.

**мелеть** *v.* shoal, grow shallow.

**мелецитоза** *f.* melezitose, melicitose.

**мелеющий** *a.* shoaling, growing shallow.

**мели** *past pl. of* **мести.**

**мели/биоза** *f.* melibiase; **—биоза** *f.* melibiose, glucose-alpha-galactoside; **—бионовая кислота** melibionic acid; **—грин** *m.* meligrin; **—зитоза** *see* **мелецитоза.**

**мелилит** *m.* (min.) melilite.

**мелилотовая кислота** melilotic acid, hydroxyhydrocinnamic acid.

**мелинит** *m.* (expl.) melinite; (geol.) bole.

**мелинофан** *m.* (min.) melinophane, meliphanite.

**мелиор/ативный** *a.* meliorative; **—ация** *f.* melioration, amelioration, improvement, development; reclamation (of land); **—ировать** *v.* meliorate, ameliorate, improve, develop.

**мелис** *m.* granulated sugar.

**мелисс/а** *f.* (bot.) balm mint, balm (*Melissa officinalis*); **—ил** *m.* melissyl; **—иловый спирт**, **—ин** *m.*, **—овый спирт** melissyl alcohol, myricyl alcohol; **—иновая кислота** melissic acid; **—овое масло** melissa oil, balm oil.

**мелистый** *a.* shelvy, shoaling.

**мелите** *imp. of* **молоть.**

**мелит/оза**, **—риоза** *f.* melitose, raffinose.

**мелить** *v.* chalk.

**мелицитоза** *see* **мелецитоза.**

**мелкий** *a.* shallow, shoal; small, fine, finely divided, minute.

**мелко** *adv.* fine, in small particles; **—вкрапленный** *a.* disseminated (ore); **—водие**, **—водье** *n.* shoal water, shallow water; shoal; **—водный** *a.* shoal, shallow; **—волокнистый** *a.* fine-grained, close-grained; **—дисперсный** *a.* finely divided; **—зазубренный** *a.* crenulated, serrate; **—зем** *m.* melkozem, fine earth.

**мелкозернист/ость** *f.* fineness, fineness of grain, compact grain structure; **—ый** *a.* fine-grained, fine, compact-grained, close-grained.

**мелкозуб/ка** *f.* smooth-cut file, smooth file; **—чатый** *a.* denticulate; (biol.) crenulate; **—ый** *a.* close-toothed, fine-toothed.

**мелко/калиберный** *a.* small-bore; **—клетчатый** *a.* fine-mesh, close-mesh, close-weave; **—комковатый** *a.* crumbly (structure); **—кристаллический** *a.* fine-crystalline, finely crystalline; **—кусковой** *a.* small-sized, fine; **—лепестник** *m.* (bot.) fleabane (*Erigeron*); **—масштабный** *a.* small-scale; **—пористый** *a.* fine-pore, finely porous; **—распыленный** *a.* finely divided, finely pulverized; **—семянные** *pl.* (bot.) Microspermae; **—сидящий** *a.* shallow; **—слойный** *a.* fine-grain (wood); **—сопочник** *m.* area of low, rounded, isolated hills; **—сортное железо** light-section steel; **—сть**, **—та** *f.* shallowness; smallness, fineness;

—толченный *a.* finely ground, pulverized; —трещинный *a.* (cer.) crackle; —фокусный *a.* shallow-focus (earthquake); —ячеистый *a.* fine-mesh, close-mesh.

**меллас** *see* **меласса.**

**мелл/еин** *m.* mellein; —иктин *m.* (pharm.) methyllycaconitine hydroiodide.

**меллит** *m.* (min.) mellite, honeystone; (pharm.) mellite, medicated honey; —ен *m.* mellitene, hexamethylbenzene; —иловый спирт mellityl alcohol; —овая кислота mellitic acid, benzenehexacarboxylic acid; соль —овой кислоты, —овокислая соль mellitate.

**мелло/н** *m.* mellone, mellon (hydrocarbon); —новодородная кислота hydromellonic acid; —фановая кислота mellophanic acid.

**мелляса** *see* **меласса.**

**меловая** *f.* (rubber) compounding room.

**меловка** *f.* melovka (white clay produced by the action of organic acids).

**мелов/ой** *a.* chalk, chalky; м. период (geol.) Cretaceous period; —ая нитка chalk line; —ые свойства chalkiness.

**мелозирование** *n.* (met.) mellosing (pulverization process).

**мелонит** *m.* (min.) melonite, tellurnickel.

**мелочной** *a.* retail; м. торговец retailer.

**мелочн/ость** *f.* triviality, pettiness; —ый *a.* trivial, petty.

**мелоч/ь** *f.* trifle, detail; fines, smalls, shorts; рудная м. (min.) fines.

**мелубрин** *m.* melubrin.

**мель** *f.* shallow water, sandbank; сесть на м. *v.* run aground.

**Мельбурн** Melbourne.

**мельдолы голубой** meldola blue, naphthol blue (dye).

**мельдометр** *m.* meldometer (for determining melting points).

**мельк/ание** *n.* flashing, sparkling, flickering; —ать, —нуть *v.* flash, gleam, appear for an instant, flicker; —ом for a moment, in passing.

**мельник** *m.* miller.

**мельниковит** *m.* (min.) melnikovite (a modification of pyrite).

**мельни/ца** *f.* mill, grinder; м.-циклон cyclone mill; —чный *a.* mill, milling, grinding; —чный камень millstone.

**мельхиор** *m.*, —овый *a.* German silver, cupronickel (copper-zinc-nickel alloy).

**мельч/айший** *a.* smallest, finest, minute, almost imperceptible; —ать *v.* grow small, diminish in size; —е *comp. of* мелкий, мелко, finer, smaller; shallower; —ить *v.* make fine, pulverize, grind.

**мельштоф** *m.* (paper) flour, fines.

**мел/ют** *pr. 3 pl. of* молоть; —ющий *a.* grinding.

**меляс, —са** *see* **меласса.**

**мембран/а** *f.* membrane, film, diaphragm; угольная м. (acoustics) carbon microphone, carbon transmitter; —ный *a.* membrane, membranous, diaphragm; —ный насос diaphragm pump.

**меморандум** *m.* memorandum.

**мемуары** *pl.* memoirs.

**мена** *f.* exchange, barter.

**менаканит** *m.* (min.) menaccanite, ilmenite, titanic iron ore.

**менафтил** *m.* menaphthyl.

**менгадин** *m.* menhaden, mossbunker (fish); —овое масло menhaden oil.

**менгуз** *m.* mungoose (a German silver).

**менделе/вий** *m.* mendelevium, Md; —вит, —евит *m.* (min.) mendeleevite; —евский *a.* Mendelyeev.

**менделизм** *m.* (biol.) Mendelism.

**Менделя закон** Mendel's law.

**мендипит** *m.* (min.) mendipite.

**мендо/зит, —цит** *m.* (min.) mendozite (a variety of soda alum).

**менев/иенский ярус, —ский ярус** (geol.) Menevian substage.

**менегинит** *m.* (min.) meneghinite.

**менее** *comp. of* мало, less; м. всего least of all; тем не м. nevertheless, for all that.

**мензул/а** *f.* (surv.) plane table; —ьная съемка plane tabling.

**мензурка** *f.* graduate, graduated cylinder, measuring glass.

**мениант/ин** *m.* menyanthin, celastin; —ол *m.* menyanthol.

**менилит** *m.* (min.) menilite (a concretionary variety of opal).

**менингит** *m.* (med.) meningitis.

**мениск** *m.*, —овый *a.* meniscus; —овый визир meniscus sight, meniscus reader.

**менисперм/ин** *m.* menispermine; —**овая кислота** menispermic acid; —**оид** *m.* menispermoid.

**менов/ой** *a.* barter, exchange; —**ая торговля** barter, trade by exchange; —**ая ценность** exchange value.

**менструация** *f.* (physiol.) menstruation.

**мент/адиен** *m.* menthadiene; —**адиенон** *m.* menthadienone; —**ан** *m.* menthane, hexahydrocymene; —**андиол** *m.* menthanediol; —**анол** *m.* menthanol; —**анон** *m.* menthanone; —**ен** *m.* menthene.

**ментенер** *m.* road scraper.

**ментен/ол** *m.* menthenol; —**он** *m.* menthenone.

**ментил** *m.*, —**овый** *a.* menthyl; —**амин** *m.* menthylamine; —**овый спирт** menthanol; —**овый эфир валериановой кислоты** menthyl valerate.

**менто/л** *m.* menthol; —**ментен** *m.* menthomenthene; —**н** *m.* menthone, menthanone; —**нафталин** *see* **ментан.**

**ментор** *m.* educator, instructor; (genetics) mentor.

**меньш/е** *comp. of* **мало, малый** less, smaller; —**ий** *comp. of* **малый,** lesser smaller, minor, least; lower, inferior; —**инство** *n.* minority.

**меня** *gen. and acc. of* **я,** me.

**мен/яльный** *a.* change, exchange; —**ять** *v.* change, vary, shift, alternate; exchange, barter; —**яться** *v.* change, vary, shift, fluctuate; exchange; —**яющийся** *a.* changing, varying, variable, fluctuating, alternating, intermittent; live (load).

**мер/а** *f.* measure, dimension, size; standard, gage; degree, extent; **в** —**у** reasonably, sufficiently; **в значительной** —**е** largely, to a considerable extent; **не в** —**у, сверх** —**ы, через** —**у** excessively, immoderately; **единица** —**ы** unit of measure; **не знать** —**ы** *v.* be immoderate; **по** —**е** in proportion to, according to, according to the degree of; **по** —**е возможности** as far as possible; **по** —**е того как** in proportion to, as; **по большей** —**е** at most, at the utmost; **по крайней** —**е, по меньшей** —**е** at least, at any rate; **принимать** —**ы** *v.* take measures, provide, arrange; **соблюдать** —**ы** *v.*

keep within limits or bounds, restrict oneself.

**мербафен** *m.* merbaphen, novasurol.

**мергал** *m.* mergal (antisyphilitic).

**мергел/евание** *n.* marl application; —**евый, —истый, —ьный** *a.* (geol.) marl, marly, marlaceous; —**ь** *m.* marl.

**мережа** *f.* seine, drag net.

**мере/йный** *a.* (met.) blistered; (leather) grain; —**йчатый** *a.* grained.

**мерещиться** *v.* seem, appear dimly.

**мерея** *f.* (leather) grain.

**мерз/лость, —лота** *f.* frozen state; congelation, congealment; —**лота** *f.* frozen ground; frost; **вечная** —**лота** permafrost, perennially frozen ground; —**лотоведение** *n.* geocryology (study of frozen ground phenomena); —**лотомер** *m.* cryopedometer; —**лый** *a.* frozen, congealed, solidified; cryogenic; —**ляк** *m.* frozen turf; —**лятина** *f.* anything frozen (spec. food spoiled by freezing); —**нуть** *v.* freeze, congeal.

**мери—** *prefix* meri— (a part, a share; (chem.) parti—, partly).

**мериди/ан** *m.*, —**анный** *a.* meridian; —**ональный** *a.* meridian, meridional.

**мерило** *n.* standard, criterion, gage, measure, scale.

**меринос** *m.*, —**овый** *a.* merino (sheep or wool).

**мериодин** *m.* meriodin.

**меритель** *m.* measurer; —**ный** *a.* measuring; —**ная ножка** calipers.

**мерить** *v.* measure, gage.

**мерихинон** *m.* meriquinone.

**мерк/а** *f.* measure; **снимать** —**у** *v.* take the measure (of), measure.

**мерка/золил** *m.* Mercazole, methimazole; —**мин** *m.* β-mercaptoethylamine hydrochloride.

**меркантильный** *a.* mercantile, commercial.

**меркапт/ал, —аль** *m.* mercaptal, thioacetal; —**ан** *m.* mercaptan; ethyl mercaptan; —**ановая кислота** mercaptan acid; —**ид** *m.* mercaptide, metal mercaptan; —**о—** *prefix* mercapto— (indicating thiol group); —**ол** *m.* mercaptol; —**офенил** *m.* mercaptophenyl; —**офос** *m.* mercaptophos, Demeton (insecticide).

меркаторская проекция Mercator projection.

меркнуть *v.* darken, grow dim; fade.

меркуран *m.* an ethylmercuric chloride-hexachlorocyclohexane fungicide.

меркуриал/изм *m.* (med.) mercury poisoning; —ин *m.* mercurialine (supposedly methylamine); —ьный *a.* mercurial, mercury.

меркуриаммоний *m.* mercuriammonium, mercuric ammonium; хлористый м. mercuriammonium chloride; —ное соединение mercuriammonium compound.

меркуризация *f.* mercurization, mercuration.

Меркурий (astron.) Mercury.

меркури/метрия *f.* mercurimetry; —рование *see* меркуризация; —рованный *a.* mercurized, mercurated; —я желть king's yellow, arsenic trisulfide.

меркуроаммоний *m.* mercuroammonium, mercurous ammonium; хлористый м. mercuroammonium chloride; —ное соединение mercuroammonium compound.

меркуро/зал *m.* mercurosal; —л *m.* mercurol, mercury nucleinate; —фен *m.* mercurophen; —хром *m.* Mercurochrome.

меркурэтил *m.* diethylmercury.

мерлуш/ка *f.*, —ечий *a.* lambskin.

мермисы *pl.* nematode worms (*Mermithidae*).

мерн/ик *m.* measuring tank, calibrated tank; hopper; —ый *a.* measuring; measured, uniform, rhythmic, slow and regular; —ая линейка measuring rule; —ая цепь surveyor's chain.

меро— *prefix* mero—, mer— (part, fraction; (anat.) thigh); —дицеин *m.* merodicein; —ксен *m.* (min.) meroxene (a variety of biotite mica); —ксил *m.* meroxyl; —метр *m.* merometer (microscope for measuring short lengths); —морфный *a.* meromorphic, fractional; —планктон *m.* (zool.) meroplankton.

мероприятие *n.* measure, action; practice.

меро/скоп *see* мерометр; —стомовые *pl.* (zool.) Merostomata; —хинен *m.* meroquinene; —хром *m.* (cryst.)

merochrome; —эдрический *a.* merohedral.

мерсериз/ация *f.*, —ирование *n.* (text.) mercerization; —ированный *a.* mercerized; —ировать, —овать *v.* mercerize.

мертв/еть *v.* grow numb; —ец *m.* corpse; —ечина *f.* carrion, dead flesh; —оеды *pl.* carrion beetles (*Silphidae*).

мертв/ый *a.* dead; stagnant (water); dead-ripe; *m.* dead body, corpse; м. виток (elec.) idle turn; м. груз dead weight, dead load; м. ход free motion, play, backlash; —ая голова caput mortuum, colcothar; butterfly (*Acherontia atropos*); —ая точка, —ое положение dead point, dead center; —ое пространство dead space, dead spot.

мертель *m.* mortar.

мерц/ание *n.* flicker, glimmer, scintillation, shimmer, twinkling, gleam, flashing, blinking; —ательная клетка flame cell; —ать *v.* flicker, glimmer, shimmer, glitter, glint, gleam, flash, blink; —ающий *a.* flickering, glimmering, glittering, scintillating; —ающий свет glitter, gleam, glint; —ающий фотометр flicker photometer.

мер/ь *see* мера; —ять *see* мерить.

мес. *abbr.* (месяц) month.

месдоза *f.* dynamometer.

мес/иво *n.* mash; —илка *f.*, —ильная машина kneading machine, (rubber) masticator; —ильщик *m.* kneader; —ить *v.* knead, mix, work up, puddle (clay).

мескалин *m.* mescaline.

месниковатый песок (min.) gold-bearing sand with high clay content.

месонит *see* мазонит.

месселит *m.* (min.) messelite (possibly an alteration of anapaite).

месс/коффер *m.* measuring set; —ур *m.* dial gage.

мести *v.* sweep.

местком *abbr.* (местный комитет профсоюза) local trade-union committee.

местн/о *adv.* locally; —оанестезирующий *a.* local anesthetic; —ость *f.* locality, district, region, place; terrain, country, area; —ый *a.* local, regional; partial; domestic, native, indigenous, home; (biol.) endemic; country (rock); —ый житель native; —ый предмет landmark, feature (of terrain); —ое действие local action.

**мест/о** *n.* place, spot, locality, location, site, seat, position, point; space, room; situation, job; м. действия scene, scene of action; м. разрыва point of rupture; м. точек (math.) locus; —ами in certain places, here and there; трогаться с —а *v.* start; занять м. *v.* supersede, replace; иметь м. *v.* take place, occur; класть не на м. *v.* misplace, mislay; на —е on the spot, in situ; на вашем —е in your place; установка на м. positioning.

**место/жительство** *n.* residence;— нахождение *n.* location, position, site, spot, seat; occurrence; —положение *n.* location, locality, site, position, seat; situation; station; (bot.) habitat; —пребывание *n.* residence, dwelling place; seat, location; —расположение *n.* location, situation; —рождение *n.* birthplace; (geol.) layer, bed, deposit, formation; site; occurrence; (mother) lode; (coal) field; occurrence; (geol.) field map.

**месть** *f.* vengeance, revenge.

**меся/ц** *m.* month; moon; —чный *a.* monthly; lunar.

**мет—** *prefix* meth—, methyl.

**мета—** *prefix* meta—; в положении мета in the meta-position.

**метабиоз** *m.* (biol.) metabiosis.

**метабол/изм** *m.* (biol.) metabolism; —ит *m.* metabolite (product of metabolism); (petr.) metabolite (altered trachyte glass); —ический *a.* metabolic; —он *m.* (nucl.) metabolon.

**мета/брушит** *m.* (min.) metabrushite (probably identical with brushite); —ванадиевая кислота metavanadic acid; —винная кислота metatartaric acid; —вольтин *m.* (min.) metavoltine; —вольфрамовая кислота metatungstic acid; —галловая кислота metagallic acid; —геветтит *m.* (min.) metahewettite (similar to hewettite); —генез, —генезис *m.* (zool.) metagenesis; —дин *m.*, —динный *a.* (elec.) metadyne; —зоа *pl.* (zool.)

Metazoa; —зома *f.* (zool.) metasoma; —зоновая кислота metazonic acid, methazonic acid; —иодная кислота metaperiodic acid; —кремневая кислота metasilicic acid.

**метакриловая кислота** methacrylic acid.

**мета/кристалл** *m.* (petr.) metacryst, porphyroblast; —кролеин *m.* metacrolein; —ксит *m.* (min.) metaxite (a variety of fibrous serpentine); micaceous sandstone; —лепсия *f.* metalepsy, substitution; —лин *m.* metaline (lubricating alloy or compound).

**металл** *m.* metal; белый м. white metal, specif. antifriction metal; благородный м. noble metal; цветной м. nonferrous metal; черный м. ferrous metal.

**металлиз/атор** *m.* metal spray gun; —ация *f.*, —ирование *n.* metallization, metallic coating, plating; bonding (of metal parts); (min.) metallization, mineralization; —ация распылением pulverization (of a metal); —ированный, —ованный *a.* metallized; —ировать, —овать *v.* metallize, coat with metal, plate.

**металлист** *m.*, рабочий м. metal worker.

**металлическ/ий** *a.* metal, metallic; м. блеск (min.) metallic luster; —ая бумага metal foil; —ая изгарина, —ая окалина metallic ash; —ое полотно wire gauze; —ие изделия hardware.

**металличность** *f.* metallicity.

**металло—** *prefix* metallo—, metal; —вед *m.* metal scientist; —ведение *n.* science of metals, physical metallurgy; —видность *f.* metallicity; —видный *a.* metallic, metalline, metalliform; —гения *f.* (geol.) metallogeny.

**металлограф** *m.* metallographer; —ический *a.* metallographic; —ия *f.* metallography.

**металло/делательный завод** smeltery, metal works; —ид *m.* metalloid; non-metal; —искатель *m.* metal locator; —керамика *f.* metal ceramics, cermet; powder metallurgy; —магнитный *a.* metallomagnetic; —метр *m.* metallometer, metal tester;

—**метрический** *a.* metallometric; —**носный** *a.* metalliferous.

**металлообраб/атывающий** *a.*, —**отка** *f.* metal working; **м. станок** metal-working machine, metal-working lathe.

**металло/органический** *a.* metalloorganic, organometallic; —**очистительный** *a.* metal-refining; —**плавильная печь** smelter, smelting furnace; —**плавильный завод** smeltery; —**подобный** *a.* metallic, metalline, metal-like; —**подъемник** *m.* (foundry) riser (of mold); —**приемник** *m.* crucible, well, hearth (of furnace); —**пульверизатор** *m.* metal spray gun; —**рукав** *m.* flexible metal pipe or hose.

**металлосодержащ/ий** *a.* metal-containing, metalliferous; —**ая руда** metallic ore.

**металло/химия** *f.* chemistry of metals; —**хром** *m.* metallochrome; —**хромия** *f.* metallochromy, tinting of metal.

**металлург** *m.* metallurgist; **м.-сталеплавильщик** steel metallurgist, ferrous metallurgist; —**ический** *a.* metallurgic, metallurgical; —**ия** *f.* metallurgy.

**метальдегид** *m.* metaldehyde.

**метамер/ия** *f.* metamerism; —**ный** *a.* metameric.

**метаморф/изация** *f.* (geol.) metamorphization; —**изировать** *v.* metamorphize; —**изм** *m.* metamorphism; —**изованный** *a.* metamorphized, converted; —**ический**, —**ный** *a.* metamorphic; —**оз** *m.*, —**оза** *f.* (geol., biol.) metamorphosis.

**метамышьяковая кислота** meta-arsenic acid.

**метан** *m.* methane; —**ал**, —**аль** *m.* methanal, formaldehyde; —**амид** *m.* methanamide, formamide; —**дикарбоновая кислота** methanedicarboxylic acid, malonic acid.

**метание** *n.* throwing, flinging, tossing, projection; **м. икры** (zool.) spawning.

**метанил/иновая кислота**, —**овая кислота** metanilic acid, aniline-*m*-sulfonic acid; —**овый желтый** metanil yellow, metaniline yellow.

**метанный** *past pass. part. of* **метать.**

**метан/ный**, —**овый** *a.* methane; —**овая кислота** methanoic acid, formic acid;

—**оил** *m.* methanoyl, formoyl; —**окислородный** *a.* methane-oxygen; —**ол** *m.* methanol, methyl alcohol; —**ометр** *m.* methanometer; —**тиол** *m.* methanethiol, methyl mercaptan.

**метаоловянн/ая кислота** metastannic acid; **соль** —**ой кислоты**, —**окислая соль** metastannate.

**мета/плазма** *f.* (biol.) metaplasm; —**положение** *n.* meta-position; —**производное**, —**соединение** *n.* meta-derivative, meta-compound; —**сахарная кислота** metasaccharic acid; —**силикат** *m.* metasilicate; —**систокс** *m.* Meta-Systox (insecticide).

**метасомат/изм**, —**оз** *m.* (geol.) metasomatism, metasomatosis, replacement; —**ический** *a.* (geol., zool.) metasomatic.

**метастабильн/ость** *f.* metastability; —**ый** *a.* metastable.

**метаста/з**, —**зис** *m.* (med.) metastasis; (zool.) metastasis, metabolism; —**тический** *a.* metastatic.

**метастирол** *m.* metastyrene, metastyrolene.

**метасульфит** *m.* metasulfite, pyrosulfite.

**метасурьмян/ая кислота** metantimonic acid; **соль** —**ой кислоты**, —**окислая соль** metantimonate; —**истая кислота** metantimonious acid; **соль** —**истой кислоты**, —**истокислая соль** metantimonite.

**метательный** *a.* throwing, flinging, casting; missile; **м. снаряд** projectile.

**метаторбернит** *m.* (min.) metatorbernite.

**метать** *v.* throw, fling, cast, project; bring forth; **м. икру** (zool.) spawn.

**метаустойчивый** *a.* metastable.

**мета/фаза** *f.* (biol.) metaphase; —**фен** *m.* Metaphen, nitromersol; —**фенилен** *m.* metaphenylene; —**фос** *m.* metaphos, O,O-dimethyl-O-(4-nitrophenyl) thiophosphate (insecticide).

**метафосфорн/ая кислота** metaphosphoric acid; **соль** —**ой кислоты**, —**окислая соль** metaphosphate; —**о-натриевая соль** sodium metaphosphate.

**мета/хлорит** *m.* (min.) metachlorite (an

uncertain form of chlorite); —хроматический *a.* metachromatic; —цейнерит *m.* (min.) metazeunerite; —центр *m.* metacenter; —цид *m.* metacide (insecticide).

**метацетин** *m.* methacetin, *p*-methoxy acetanilide.

**метацимол** *m.* metacymene.

**метгемоглобин** *m.* methemoglobin.

**метебенол** *m.* methebenol.

**метелка** *f.* whisk broom, brush; (bot.) panicle.

**метеллаговая кислота** metellagic acid.

**метелоидин** *m.* meteloidine.

**метелочка** *f.* (elec.) brush.

**метель** *f.* snowstorm, drifting snow.

**метельчатый** *a.* (bot.) paniculate.

**метен** *m.* methene, methylene; —амин *m.* methenamine, hexamethylenetetramine.

**метение** *n.* sweeping.

**метенил** *m.*, —овый *a.* methenyl, methylidyne; хлористый м. methenyl chloride, chloroform.

**метенный** *past pass. part. of* мести.

**метенцикло—** *prefix* methenecyclo—.

**метео—** *abbr.* (метеорологический) meteorological; —аэробюллетень *m.* weather report.

**метеор** *m.* (astron.) meteor, bolide; —изм *m.* (med.) meteorism, flatulence; —ит *m.* (min.) meteorite, aerolite; —итный, —итовый *a.* meteoritic; —итное железо, —ическое железо meteoric iron, iron meteorite; —ический, —ный *a.* meteor, meteoric.

**метеорограф** *m.* (meteor.) meteorograph; —ический *a.* meteorographic; —ия *f.* meteorography.

**метеоролог** *m.* meteorologist; —ический *a.* meteorologic, meteorological; —ическая станция weather bureau; —ия *f.* meteorology.

**метеороподобный** *a.* meteor-like, meteoric.

**метео/служба** *f.* meteorological service; —станция *f.* weather bureau.

**метет** *pr. 3 sing. of* мести.

**метизация** *f.* (biol.) crossbreeding.

**метил** *m.* methyl; бензоат —а, бензойнокислый м. methyl benzoate; хлористый м. methyl chloride.

**метил/ал,** —аль *m.* methylal, dimethoxymethane; —амиловый эфир methyl amyl ether; —амин *m.* methylamine, aminomethane; —анилин *m.* methylaniline; —арсиновая кислота monomethylarsenic acid, arrhenic acid; —ат *m.* methylate, methoxide; —ацетат *m.* methyl acetate; —виолет *m.* methyl violet; —глиоксаль *m.* methylglyoxal, pyruvic aldehyde.

**метилен** *m.*, —овый *a.* methylene, methene; —сернокислый м., сульфат —а methylene sulfate; хлористый м. methylene chloride; —блау, —овая синь, —овая синька, —овый голубой methylene blue (thiazine dyestuff).

**метилиров/ание** *n.* methylation; —анный *a.* methylated; —ать *v.* methylate.

**метил/карбинол** *m.* methylcarbinol, ethanol; —каучук *m.* methyl rubber (polymer of dimethylbutadiene); —крахмал *m.* methyl starch.

**метиловый** *a.* methyl; м. альдегид methyl aldehyde, formaldehyde; м. спирт methyl alcohol, methanol; м. эфир methyl ether; м. эфир бензойной кислоты methyl benzoate; м. эфир серной кислоты methyl sulfate.

**метил/оранж** *m.* methyl orange (indicator); —рот *m.* methyl red; —стирол *m.* methylstyrene; —фениловый эфир methyl phenyl ether, anisole; —этилкетон *m.* methyl ethyl ketone.

**метин** *m.* methine, methylidyne; —он *m.* methinone.

**метион/ил** *m.* methionyl; —ин *m.* methionine, 2-amino-4-methylthiobutanoic acid; —овая кислота methionic acid, methanedisulfonic acid.

**метис** *m.* hybrid, halfbreed, mongrel.

**метистицин** *m.* methysticin, kavain; —овая кислота methysticinic acid.

**мет/ить** *v.* mark; label, tag (with tracers); aim (at), have in view; —ка *f.* mark, marking, sign; stamp, brand; (isotopic) label, tag, tracer.

**метк/ий** *a.* accurate; apt; —ость *f.* accuracy, exactness.

**метла** *f.* broom, brush.

**метлахская плитка** ceramic (floor) tile.

**метлица** *f.* (bot.) apera, spec. bent grass (*Apera spica venti*); (zool.) caddis fly.

**метод** *m.*, —а *f.* method, process, procedure, technique, way; **вносить м.** *v.* methodize; —**ика** *f.* method, methods; —**ика работы** procedure; —**ический,** —**ичный** *a.* methodical, orderly; continuous (furnace); —**ично** *adv.* methodically; —**ичность** *f.* methodicalness.

**метоксазин** *m.* metoxazine.

**метокси/бензальдегид** *m.* methoxybenzaldehyde; —**д** *see* **метилат;** —**л** *m.* methoxyl; —**хлор** *m.* methoxychlor (insecticide).

**метол** *m.* (phot.) Metol, *p*-methylaminophenol sulfate; —**еиновая кислота** metoleic acid.

**метон/ал** *m.* methonal; —**ий** *m.* methonium.

**метохинон** *m.* metoquinone.

**метоцин** *m.* metozine, antipyrine.

**метр** *m.* meter (unit of length); *suffix* —meter (instrument or means for measuring); **м.-свеча** meter-candle; **складной м.** folding rule; —**аж** *m.* meterage; measurement; metric area; length in meters.

**метрика** *f.* metrics; birth certificate.

**метрит** *m.* (med.) metritis.

**метрическ/ий** *a.* metric; *suffix* —metric, —metrical; —**ая выпись,** —**ое свидетельство** birth certificate; —**ая мера** metric system.

—**метрия** *f.* *suffix* —metry (measuring).

**метро** *see* **метрополитен.**

**метров/ой,** —**ый** *a.* meter, metric.

**метролог/ический** *a.* metrological; —**ия** *f.* metrology.

**метрон/овая кислота** methronic acid; —**ол** *m.* methronol.

**метроном** *m.* metronome.

**метропол/итен** *m.* subway, underground railway; —**ия** *f.* metropolis.

**метротонин** *m.* metrotonin (ergot substitute).

**метущий** *pr. act. part. of* **мести.**

**метчик** *m.* tap, screw tap; twist drill; (agr.) marker; **ловильный м.** (oil-well drilling) grab.

**Меуле реакция** Mäule reaction (for lignin).

**мефитический** *a.* mephitic, foul, noxious.

**мех** *m.* fur; bellows; water skin; **воздуходувный м.,** —**а** *pl.* bellows.

**мех**— *abbr.* (**механический**) mechanical.

**механайт** *m.* mechanite (a cast iron).

**механиз/атор** *m.* mechanic; —**ация** *f.* mechanization; **училище** —**ации** engineering school; —**ированный** *a.* mechanized, mechanically propelled; power; —**ировать** *v.* mechanize.

**механизм** *m.* mechanism, works, movement, gear; device; —**ер;** **подающий м.** feeder; —**ы** *pl.* machinery.

**механик** *m.* mechanic, operator; —**а** *f.* mechanics; mechanism, machinery.

**механически** *adv.* mechanically.

**механическ/ий** *a.* mechanical, machine, power-driven, power-operated; screen (analysis); **м. завод, м. цех,** —**ая мастерская** machine shop; **м. молот** power hammer; **м. момент** momentum; **м. насос** power pump; **м. состав** mechanical composition, texture (of soil); **м. станок** machine tool; —**ая отдача** mechanical efficiency (of engine); —**ая подача** mechanical feed; power feed; —**ая работа** mechanical work; —**ая смесь** mechanical mixture; —**ое оборудование** machinery; —**ое полное сопротивление** (acoustics) mechanical impedance; **с** —**им приводом** power-driven, power-operated.

**механопрочность** *f.* crushing strength (of soil).

**мехводитель** *m.* (mil.) tank driver.

**мехзатвор** *m.* slide fastener, zipper.

**мехов/ой** *a.* fur; bellows; —**щик** *m.* furrier.

**мехом** *abbr.* (**механический ом**) mechanical ohm.

**мехообразный** *a.* furry; bellows-type.

**мех/соединение** *n.* (mil.) mechanized unit; —**состав** *m.* mechanical composition, texture (of soil); —**часть** *f.* motorized unit.

**мецкалин** *m.* mescal (liqueur).

**меч** *m.* sword; —**евидный** *a.* sword-shaped, gladiate, ensiform (leaf).

**мечен/ие** *n.* labeling, tagging; —**ый** *a.* marked, branded; labeled (molecule); tagged, tracer (atom); **метод** —**ых элементов** tracer technique.

**мечеобразный** *see* **мечевидный.**

**мечет** *pr. 3 sing. of* **метать.**

**мечехвосты** *pl.* (zool.) Xiphosura.

**мечта** *f.* dream, hope; —**ть** *v.* dream.

**мечущий** *pr. act. part. of* **метать.**

**меш** *m.*, —**а** *f.* mesh (of screen), holes per linear inch.

**мешалка** *f.* mixer, agitator, stirrer, stirring rod; churn; **механическая м.** rabble; **стеклянная м.** stirring rod.

**меш/альный** *a.* mixing, stirring; —**ание** *n.* mixing, stirring, agitation; —**анка** *f.* mixture, mash (for livestock); —**ать** *v.* mix, stir, agitate; hinder, impede, interfere, be in the way (of); inhibit, prevent; clog, stop, encumber; disturb, confuse; —**ающий** *a.* mixing, stirring; interfering; inhibiting, preventing; —**ающее действие** interference.

**мешко/видный** *a.* sacculate; —**вина** *f.* sackcloth, burlap; —**насыпатель** *m.* bag filler.

**мешкотн/ость** *f.* sluggishness, slowness; —**ый** *a.* sluggish, slow, lingering.

**мешо/к** *m.*, —**чный** *a.* bag, sack; pocket; —**чек** *m.* little bag, kit; (biol.) follicle, utricle, saccule; —**чная ткань** burlap, sacking; —**чницы** *pl.* bagworm moths (*Psychidae*).

**МЖС** *abbr.* (машинно-животноводческая станция) machine and animal-breeding center.

**Ми рассеяние** (light) Mie scattering.

**миазис** *m.* (med.) myiasis.

**миазм/а** *f.*, —**ы** *pl.* miasma (noxious effluvium); —**атический** *a.* miasmatic.

**миальгия** *f.* (med.) myalgia.

**миаргирит** *m.* (min.) miargyrite.

**миаролитовый** *a.* (geol.) miarolitic.

**миарсенол** *m.* myarsenol, sulfarsphenamine.

**миаскит** *m.* (petr.) miascite, miaskite (biotitic nephelite-syenite).

**миастения** *f.* (med.) myasthenia, muscular debility.

**миг** *m.* moment, instant.

**миг/алка** *f.* flap valve; —**ание** *n.* blinking, flickering, flicker; —**атель** *m.*, —**ающий фонарь** blinker, flasher; —**ательный**, —**ающий** *a.* blinking, blinker, flickering; pulsed (beam; cyclotron); (zool.) nictitating (membrane).

**мигматит** *m.* migmatite (igneous-metamorphic rock).

**миграци/я** *f.*, —**онный** *a.* migration, travel; **скорость** —**и** migration velocity.

**мигрен/ь** *f.*, —**евый** *a.* (med.) migraine (headache); —**ин** *m.* migrainin.

**мигриров/авший** *a.* migrated, migratory; —**ание** *see* **миграция;** —**ать** *v.* migrate, travel.

**мидель** *m.* midship section.

**мидия** *f.* (zool.) mussel.

**мидриа/зин** *m.* Mydriasine; —**зис** *m.* (med.) mydriasis (dilatation of pupil); —**тин** *m.* mydriatine; —**тический** *a.*, —**тическое средство** mydriatic.

**мидрол** *m.* mydrol, midrol.

**миелин** *m.* (min.) myelin (a type of kaolin); (biol.) myelin; —**ит** *m.* (med.) myelitis.

**миерсит** *m.* (min.) miersite.

**мизгирь** *m.* (zool.) tarantula.

**мизерный** *a.* miserable, meager, scanty.

**мизинец** *m.* (anat.) the little finger; the little toe.

**мииаз** *see* **миазис.**

**мика/лекс** *m.* Mycalex (insulating material); —**лента** *f.* mica tape; —**нит** *m.*, —**нитовый** *a.* micanite (insulator).

**микарта** *f.* micarta (insulator).

**мико—** *prefix* myco—, myc— (fungus; (med.) mucus); —**з** *m.* (med.) mycosis; —**за** *f.* mycose; —**логия** *f.* (bot.) mycology; —**мицин** *m.* mycomycin; —**протеин** *m.* mycoprotein; —**риза** *f.* (bot.) mycorhiza; —**стерин** *m.* mycosterol; —**субтилин** *m.* mycosubtilin; —**трофный** *a.* (bot.) mycotrophic; —**феноловая кислота** mycophenolic acid; —**цидин** *m.* mycocidin.

**микрит** *m.* (geol.) micrite.

**микро—** *prefix* micro— (denoting a magnitude of $10^{-6}$); small, small-scale; microscopic; —**ампер** *m.* (elec.) microampere; —**анализ** *m.* microanalysis; —**афанитовый** *a.* (petr.) microaphanitic.

**микроб** *m.* microbe, bacterium.

**микробиология** *f.* microbiology.

**микробный** *a.* microbe, microbic.

**микро/бромит** *m.* (min.) microbromite (a variety of embolite); —**весы** *pl.*

microbalance; —включенный *a.* contained in microscopic foci; —волна *f.*, —волновый *a.* (rad.) microwave; —вольт *m.* (elec.) microvolt; —горелка *f.* microburner; —грамм *m.* microgram, gamma; —гранитный *a.* (petr.) microgranitic.

**микрограф** *m.* micrograph; —ический *a.* micrographic; —ия *f.* micrography.

**микро/гэс** *m.* small automatic hydroelectric power unit; —диорит *m.* (petr.) microdiorite (a fine-grained dioriteporphyry); —животное *n.* animalcule; —исследование *n.* microanalysis, microexamination; —калория *f.* ᵛmicrocalorie, small calorie; —климат *m.* (biol.) microclimate.

**микроклин** *m.* (min.) microcline (triclinic potash feldspar); зеленый **м.** amazon stone, amazonite, green feldspar; —пертит *m.* microclineperthite (a variety of perthite feldspar).

**микрококк** *m.* micrococcus (round bacterium); —ин *m.* micrococcin.

**микро/количество** *n.* microquantity, trace; —компонент *m.* microconstituent; —коррозия *f.* microcorrosion.

**микрокосм** *m.* microcosm; —ический *a.* microcosmic; —ическая соль microcosmic salt, sodium ammonium hydrogen phosphate.

**микрокристалл/ический** *a.* (min.) microcrystalline, cryptocrystalline; —ография *f.* microcrystallography.

**микро/крит** *m.* microcrith (obs. term for weight of hydrogen atom); —кулон *m.* (elec.) microcoulomb; —кюри *n.* (nucl.) microcurie.

**микролит** *m.* (min.) microlite (a calcium pyrotantalate); (geol.) microlith, microlite; —овый *a.* (geol.) microlitic, aphanitic.

**микро/литр** *m.* microliter, lambda; —м *see* **микроом;** —манометр *m.* micromanometer, micropressure gage; —масштаб *m.* microscale; —меритный *a.* micromeritic; —мерол *m.* micromerol (an alcohol); —метод *m.* micromethod.

**микрометр** *m.* micrometer, micrometer gage; —ический *a.* micrometer; —ия *f.* micrometry, measuring with a micrometer.

**микро/миллиметр** *m.* micromillimeter, millimicron; —мир *m.* microcosm; —мо *n.* (elec.) micromho; —моноспорин *m.* micromonosporin; —н *m.* micron ($10^{-3}$ mm.); —объемный *a.* microvolumetric; —ом *m.* (elec.) microhm; —омметр *m.* microhmmeter; —организм *m.* microorganism, microbe; —остатки *pl.* microfossils; —очковый *a.* microaugen.

**микропегматит** *m.* (petr.) micropegmatite, microscopic pegmatite; —овый *a.* micropegmatite, micrographic.

**микро/пертит** *m.* (petr.) microperthite (a variety of rock-making feldspar); —печь *f.* microfurnace; —пленка *f.* microfilm; —пористый *a.* microporous, millipore; —препарат *m.* (micros.) mount, slide; —реакция *f.* microreaction; —сегрегация *f.* microsegregation.

**микросейсм/ический** *a.* (geol.) microseismic; —ы *pl.* microseisms.

**микросекунд/а** *f.*, —ный *a.* microsecond.

**микроскладчатость** *f.* (geol.) microfoliation.

**микроскоп** *m.* microscope; —ический, —ичный *a.* microscopic, microscopical; —ичность *f.* microscopicity; —ия *f.* microscopy.

**микро/скрытокристаллический** *a.* microcryptocrystalline; —снимок *m.* micrograph; —сома *f.* (biol.) microsome; —соммит *m.* (min.) microsommite (near cancrinite); —спектроскоп *m.* microspectroscope.

**микроспор/а** *f.* (bot.) microspore; —идии *pl.* (zool.) Microsporidia.

**микро/структура** *f.* microstructure; —сферический *a.* microspheric; —сферулитовый *a.* (petr.) microspherulitic; —твердость *f.* microhardness; —текстил *m.* textile microscope.

**микротелефон** *m.*, —ная трубка microtelephone, hand set; —ный *a.* microtelephone, microtelephonic.

**микро/том** *m.* (micros.) microtome; —трон *m.* microtron, electron cyclotron; —удобрение *n.* trace-element fertilizer; —фаг *m.* (zool.) microphage; —фарада *f.* (elec.) microfarad.

**микрофельзит** *m.* (petr.) microfelsite (a

type of groundmass); —овый *a.* microfelsitic.

**микро/физика** *f.* microphysics; —фильма *f.* microfilm; —фировый *a.* microphyric; —флора *f.* (bot.) microflora; —флюидальный *a.* (petr.) microfluidal, having microscopic flow structure.

**микрофон** *m.,* —ная чашка microphone; —ный *a.* microphone, microphonic.

**микрофото/графирование** *n.* photomicrography; —графический *a.* photomicrographic; —графия *f.* photomicrography; photomicrograph; —снимок *m.* photomicrograph.

**микро/химический** *a.* microchemical; —химия *f.* microchemistry; —цефалия *f.* (med.) microcephaly; —цидин *m.* Microcidin, β-naphthol sodium; —цит *m.* (biol.) microcyte; —частица *f.* microparticle; —шлиф *m.* microsection; —штатив *m.* microscope stand; microstand; —элемент *m.* (elec.) microcell; (chem.) trace element; minor element.

**миксер** *m.* (met.) mixer, holding furnace.

**миксит** *m.* (min.) mixite.

**миксомицеты** *pl.* (bot.) Myxomycetes.

**мик/стура** *f.* (pharm.) mixture; —шер *m.* mixer.

**мил** *see* **миль.**

**мил/арит** *m.* (min.) milarite; —иарный *a.* miliary, like millet seeds; —лерит *m.* (min.) millerite, capillary pyrites; —леровский индекс (cryst.) Miller index.

**милли—** *prefix* milli— (one thousandth); —ампер *m.* (elec.) milliampere; —амперметр *m.* milliammeter.

**миллиард** *m.* milliard, *preferably* billion.

**милли/бар** *m.* millibar; —ватт *m.* (elec.) milliwatt; —вольт *m.* (elec.) millivolt; —генри *n.* millihenry; —грамм *m.* milligram; —кюри *n.* millicurie (unit of radioactivity); —литр *m.* milliliter; единица —массы millimass unit, mamu; —метр *m.* millimeter; —метровый *a.* graph (paper); —микрон *m.* millimicron; —моль *f.* millimole.

**миллион** *m.* million; —ный *a.* millionth.

**милли/рентген** *m.* milliroentgen; —секунда *f.* millisecond; —фот *m.*

milliphot; —эквивалент *m.* milliequivalent, milligram-equivalent.

**Миллона основание** Millon's base.

**милонит** *m.* (petr.) mylonite (a metamorphic schist).

**милори,** —евая синь *f.* Milori blue (iron blue pigment).

**милость** *f.* favor, kindness.

**милошит** *m.* (min.) miloschite (a type of chrome kaolin).

**милый** *a.* kind, pleasant.

**миль** *m.* mil (unit of length); *gen. pl. of* миля.

**мильбар** *m.* (met.) mill bar, flat bar.

**Мильвоки** Milwaukee.

**мильд/иу,** —ью *f.* (bot.) mildew.

**мильтон** *m.* (text.) melton.

**мил/я** *f.* mile; количество —ь, расстояние в —ях, число —ь mileage.

**мимеограф** *m.,* —ический *a.* mimeograph.

**мимет/езит,** —ит *m.* (min.) mimetesite; mimetite, lead chloroarsenate; —ический *a.* mimetic, imitative.

**мимикрия** *f.* (biol.) mimicry, camouflage.

**мимо** *adv. and prep. gen.* past, by; wide of (the mark); проходить м. *v.* by-pass; —ездом in passing by.

**мимоз/а** *f.* (bot.) mimosa; —овые *pl.* Mimosaceae.

**мимолетн/ость** *f.* transience; —ый *a.* transient, fugitive, passing, short-lived.

**мимоходом** *adv.* in passing, by the way, on the way.

**мин.** *abbr.* (минимум) minimum; (минута) minute.

**мина** *f.* mien, look, appearance, aspect; (mil.) mine; torpedo.

**минасрагрит** *m.* (min.) minasragrite.

**мингуетит** *m.* (min.) minguétite (member of chlorite group).

**миндал/евидный,** —еобразный *a.* almond-shaped, amygdaloidal; —евидная пустота (geol.) amygdule, geode; —евидные железы (anat.) tonsils; —ина *f.* almond; (geol.) amygdule, geode; tonsil; —каменный *a.* amygdaloidal.

**миндаль** *m.* (bot.) almond, almond tree (*Amygdalus communis*); земляной м. chufa (*Cyperus esculentus*); —ник *m.*

(geol.) amygdaloid; —ные *pl.* (bot.) Amygdalaceae.

миндальн/ый *a.* almond; м. камень (geol.) almond rock, amygdaloid, tonsillar concretion; amygdule; —ая кислота amygdalic acid; mandelic acid; —ое дерево *see* миндаль; —ое зерно almond kernel; —ое масло almond oil.

минер *m.* (zool., mil.) miner.

минераграф/ический *a.* (min.) mineragraphic, mineralographic; —ия *f.* mineragraphy, mineralography.

минерал *m.* mineral; удаление —ов (water purification) demineralizing process.

минерализ/атор *m.* (geol.) mineralizer; —ация *f.* mineralization; —ованный *a.* mineralized; —овать *v.* mineralize; petrify; —ующий *a.* mineralizing; —ующее средство mineralizer, mineralizing agent; —ующийся *a.* mineralizable.

минералит *m.* an asbestos cement.

минералог *m.* mineralogist; —ический *a.* mineralogical; —ия *f.* mineralogy.

минералография *f.* mineralography.

минеральн/ый *a.* mineral; м. воск mineral wax, ozokerite; м. деготь, —ая смола mineral tar, brea, maltha; —ая бель, —ая белая краска mineral white (barium or calcium sulfate); —ая вата slag cotton; —ая кислота mineral acid; —ая синь mineral blue, ground azurite; —ая чернь mineral black (ground graphite or graphitic slate); —ая шерсть rock wool; —ое масло mineral oil; —ые запасы mineral reserves, ore deposits.

минетта *f.* (min.) minette, oölitic iron ore.

миниатюр/изация *f.* miniaturization; —ный *a.* miniature, midget, micro—.

миний *see* миния.

миним/ал *m.* minim; —альный *a.* minimum, minimal, least, smallest; —изировать *v.* minimize; —етр *m.* minimeter (for measuring slight linear deviation); —етр-наездник *m.* straddle gage; —ум *m.* minimum.

минир/овать *v.* mine, undermine; —ующие мухи leaf-miner flies (*Agromyzidae*).

минист/ерство *n.* ministry; office, board, department; —р *m.* minister; Secretary.

миния *f.* minium, red lead (lead oxide).

минн/ый *a.* mine; torpedo; м. горн bursting chamber; м. заградитель mine layer; м. порох blasting powder; м. тральщик mine sweeper; —ое заграждение, —ое поле mine field.

миновать *v.* pass, elapse, run out; escape, elude, clear.

мино/вылавливатель *m.* torpedo catcher; —искатель *m.* mine detector; —мет mine thrower; torpedo tube; mortar; —носец *m.*, —носка *f.* torpedo boat, destroyer.

минор *m.* (math.) minor, minor determinant.

минувш/ее *n.* the past; —ий *a.* past.

минус *m.* (math.) minus; shortcoming; —овый *a.* minus; (elec.) negative.

минут/а *f.* minute; moment, instant; без 20 минут четыре twenty minutes to four (o'clock); три —ы пятого three minutes past four; в данную —у at the given moment, just now, for the moment; сию —у immediately, at once.

минутник *m.* a very fine abrasive powder.

минутн/ый *a.* minute; momentary; instantaneous; —ая стрелка minute hand.

минуть *see* миновать.

миньон *m.* (typ.) minion.

мио— *prefix* myo— (muscle); —ген *m.* myogen; —з, —зис *m.* (med.) miosis; —зин *m.* myosin; —зит *m.* (med.) myositis; —кард *m.* (anat.) myocardium; —кардит *m.* (med.) myocarditis; —ксантим *m.* myoxanthim; —логия *f.* myology, study of muscles; —пия *f.* myopia, nearsightedness; —тический *a.*, —тическое средство myotic.

миоцен *m.* (geol.) Miocene epoch; —овый *a.* Miocene.

миполам *m.* Mipolam (plastic).

мипор *m.* Mipor, microporous rubber.

мир *m.* world, universe; peace.

мирабель *m.* cherry plum (*Prunus cerasifera*).

**мирабилит** *m.* (min.) mirabilite, Glauber salt.

**мираж** *m.* mirage; candling (of eggs).

**мирбанов/ая эссенция, —ое масло** mirbane oil, nitrobenzene.

**мириа—** *prefix* myria— (denoting a magnitude of 10⁴); **—ватт** *m.* (elec.) myriawatt; **—да** *f.* myriad; **—литр** *m.* myrialiter; **—метр** *m.* myriameter.

**мирика** *f.* myrica, bayberry.

**мирист/амид** *m.* myristamide, tetradecanamide; **—икол** *m.* myristicol; **—ил** *m.*, **—иловый** *a.* myristyl; **—ин** *m.* myristin, glyceryl myristate; **—иновая кислота** myristic acid, tetradecanoic acid; **—ицин** *m.* myristicin, 5-methoxysafrole; **—ициновая кислота** myristicic acid; **—оловая кислота** myristoleic acid, tetradecenoic acid; **—он** *m.* myristone, myristic ketone.

**мирить** *v.* reconcile, mediate; **—ся** *v.* reconcile oneself (with), tolerate, put up (with), accept, make the best (of).

**мириц/етин** *m.* myricetin, hydroxyquercetin; **—етрин** *m.* myricetrin; **—ил** *m.* myricyl; **—иловый спирт** myricyl alcohol, melissyl alcohol; **—ин** *m.* myricin, myricyl palmitate.

**мирмекит** *m.* (petr.) myrmekite (intergrowth of quartz and silicic feldspar).

**мирмеко—** *prefix* myrmeco— (ant).

**мирн/о** *adv.* peacefully, quietly, without any disturbance; **—ый** *a.* peaceful, quiet, placid; **—ый договор** peace treaty.

**мироб/алан, — олан** *m.* myrobalan (dried fruits of *Terminalia chebula*).

**мировой** *a.* world; universal (time).

**мироздание** *n.* the universe, cosmos.

**мирозин** *m.* myrosin, myrosase.

**мирокс/ил** *m.* myroxyl; **—илиновая кислота** myroxylinic acid; **—ин** *m.* myroxin; **—окарпин** *m.* myroxocarpin.

**мироновая кислота** myronic acid.

**мироописание** *n.* cosmography.

**мирр** *m.*, **—а** *f.* myrrh (gum); **—ин** *m.* myrrhin (resin); **—овое дерево** (bot.) myrrh tree (*Balsamodendron myrrha*); **—овое масло** myrrh oil.

**мирт** *m.*, **—овый** *a.* (bot.) myrtle (*Myrtus*); **—енал** *m.* myrtenal, myrtenic aldehyde; **—еновая кислота** myr-tenic acid; **—енол** *m.* myrtenol; **—илин** *m.* myrtilin; **—иллидин** *m.* myrtillidin; **—иллин** *m.* myrtillin; **—овые** *pl.* (bot.) Myrtaceae; **—ол** *m.* myrtol (refined myrtle oil).

**мирцен** *m.* myrcene.

**МИС** *abbr.* (**машинноиспытательная станция**) Machine testing center.

**миси** *n.* (min.) misy, copiapite.

**миска** *f.* pan, basin, dish.

**миспикель** *m.* (min.) mispickel, arsenopyrite.

**миссия** *f.* mission, assignment.

**мист/ерия** *f.* mystery; **—ифицировать** *v.* mystify, puzzle.

**митил/ит** *m.* mytilitol, methylinositol; **—отоксин** *m.* mytilotoxin.

**митинг** *m.* meeting.

**миткал/ь** *m.*, **—евый, —ьный** *a.* (text.) calico; cambric.

**мито/з** *m.* (biol.) mitosis, karyokinesis; **—тический** *a.* mitotic.

**митра/версин** *m.* mitraversine; **—гинин** *m.* mitragynine, mitragyne.

**Митчелля грохот** Mitchell screen.

**миф** *m.* myth; **—ический** *a.* mythical.

**Мих/ельсона актинометр** Michelson actinometer; **—лера кетон** Michler ketone.

**мицел/ий** *m.* mycelium, mushroom "spawn"; **—ин** *m.* mycelin.

**мицелл/а** *f.* micelle; **—ярный** *a.* micellar; (bot.) mycelial, mycelian.

**миц/етин** *m.* mycetin; **—ето—** *prefix* myceto— (fungus); **—ин** *m.* *suffix* —mycin.

**миц/онит, —цонит** *m.* (min.) mizzonite, dipyre (a variety of scapolite).

**Мичелля подшипник** Michell bearing.

**мичуринское учение** (biol.) Mitchurinism.

**мишен/ный** *a.*, **—ь** *f.* target; **теория —и** (radiobiology) target theory, hit theory; **ток на —ь** target current.

**Мишера пипетка** (biol.) Miescher pipet.

**мишур/а** *f.* tinsel, spangle, shining platelet; metallic thread; Dutch metal; **—ный** *a.* tinsel.

**миэ—** *see* **мие—**.

**мк** *abbr.* (**микро—**) micro—; (**микрон**) micron; (**милликулон**) millicoulomb.

**мка** *abbr.* (**микроампер**) microampere.

**мкб** *abbr.* (**микробар**) microbar.

**мкв** *abbr.* (**микровольт**) microvolt.

**мквт** *abbr.* (**микроватт**) microwatt.

**мкг** *abbr.* (**микрограмм**) microgram.

**мкгн** *abbr.* (**микрогенри**) microhenry.

**мкк** *abbr.* (**микрокулон**) microcoulomb.

**мккюри** *abbr.* (**микрокюри**) microcurie.

**мкл** *abbr.* (**микролитр**) microliter.

**мкмк** *abbr.* (**микромикро**—) micro-micro—; **мкмкф** *abbr.* (**микромикро-фарада**) micromicrofarad.

**мком** *abbr.* (**микроом**) microhm.

**мкр** *abbr.* (**микрорентген**) microroentgen.

**МКРЕ** *abbr.* (**Международная комиссия по радиологическим единицам и измерениям**) International Commission on Radiological Units and Measurements, ICRU; **МКРЗ** *abbr.* (**Международная комиссия по радиологической защите**) International Commission on Radiological Protection, ICRP.

**мкс** *abbr.* (**максвелл**) maxwell; **МКС** *abbr.* (**метр-килограмм-секунда**) meter-kilogram-second, MKS (system of units).

**мксек** *abbr.* (**микросекунда**) microsecond.

**мкф** *abbr.* (**микрофарада**) microfarad; **МКФ** *abbr.* (**монокальцийфосфат**) monocalcium phosphate.

**мкюри** *abbr.* (**милликюри**) millicurie.

**мл** *abbr.* (**миллилитр**) milliliter; **Мл** *abbr.* (**моляльность**) molality (of a solution).

**младший** *a.* younger, junior (partner); *m.* the youngest.

**млеконосный** *a.* lactiferous, lacteal.

**млекопитающ/ее** *n.*, **м. животное** mammal; —**ий** *a.* mammalian.

**млечн/ик** *m.*, —**ый корень** (bot.) sea milkwort (*Glaux maritima*); —**ый** *a.* milk, milky, lactic, lacteal; *see also under* **молочный**; —**ый путь** (astron.) Milky Way; —**ый сок** milky juice; (bot.) latex; (physiol.) chyle.

**млн** *abbr.* (**миллион**) million.

**млрд** *abbr.* (**миллиард**) billion.

**млынок** *m.* grain blower and sorter.

**мм** *abbr.* (**миллиметр**) millimeter; **мм²** *abbr.* (**квадратный миллиметр**) square millimeter; **мм³** *abbr.* (**кубический миллиметр**) cubic millimeter.

**м.м.в.** *abbr.* (**максимальная молекуляр-ная влагоемкость**) maximum molecular water capacity.

**м/мин** *abbr.* (**метров в минуту**) meters per minute.

**ммк** *abbr.* (**миллимикро**—) millimicro—; (**миллимикрон**) millimicron.

**ммоль** *abbr.* (**миллимоль**) millimole.

**МН** *abbr.* (**магнитное насыщение**) magnetic saturation; **мн.** *abbr.* (**многие**) many; (**многолетний**) perennial; **мн. др.** *abbr.* (**многие другие**) many others.

**мне** *dat. of* **я**, me, to me.

**мнемо/ника**, —**техника** *f.* mnemonics; —**нический** *a.* mnemonic, memory; —**ническая схема** mimic flowsheet; (elec.) mimic bus.

**мнение** *n.* opinion, judgment.

**мнет** *pr. 3 sing. of* **мять**.

**мним/ый** *a.* supposed, imaginary, simulated; false; —**ая величина**, —**ое число** (math.) imaginary number; —**ое изображение** (optics) virtual image.

**мнить** *v.* think, imagine, suppose, be of the opinion; —**ся** seem, appear.

**МНК** *abbr.* (**мочевина-нитрат кальция**) calcium urea nitrate.

**многие** *pl.* many, a great many.

**много** *adv.* much, many, a great deal, considerably; **на м.** by far, much.

**много**— *prefix* poly—, multi—, many, multiple; —**адресный** *a.* multiple-address (system); —**актный** *a.* multi-event; —**амперный** *a.* heavy-current; —**анодный** *a.* multianode; —**арочный** *a.* multiple-arch; —**атомный** *a.* polyatomic; polyhydric (alcohol); —**бородковый** *a.* multiple (punch); —**брачный** *a.* (bot.) polygamous.

**многовалентн/ость** *f.* multivalence; —**ый** *a.* multivalent, polyvalent.

**много/вариантный** *a.* multivariant; —**вато** *adv.* a little too much; —**ваттный** *a.* (elec.) high-watt; —**вершинный** *a.* polyconic; —**витковый** *a.* (elec.) multiturn; —**водный** *a.* abounding in water; polyhydrate (compound); —**гнездный** *a.* (biol.) multilocular.

**многогранн/ик** *m.* (geom.) polyhedron; —**ый** *a.* polyhedral; varied, many-sided.

**много/групповой** *a.* multigroup; —**диапазонный** *a.* multirange; —**дырчатый** *a.* perforated.

**мног/ое** *n.* much; many things; **во —ом** in many respects.

**многожгутиковые** *pl.* (zool.) Polymastigina.

**многожильный** *a.* multiple-strand, multiple-wire, multiple (cord); multiple-core, compound (cable); **м. провод** cable wire.

**много/зажимный** *a.* multiterminal; —**зарядный** *a.* multicharge, highly charged; —**заходный** *a.* multiple-thread (screw); multiple (thread).

**много/звучный** *a.* polyphonic; —**знаменательность,** —**значительность** *f.* significance; —**знаменательный,** —**значительный** *a.* significant.

**многозначн/ость** *f.* multivalence, polyvalence; —**ый** *a.* multivalent, polyvalent; multiple-value; multiple-digit (number).

**много/зонный** *a.* multiregion; —**инерционный** *a.* multilag; —**камерный** *a.* multiple-chamber, multichambered, multicellular; (zool.) polythalamous; —**канальность** *f.* multichanneling; —**канальный** *a.* multichannel; —**каскадный** *a.* multistage; —**катодный** *a.* polycathode; —**кислотный** *a.* polyacid.

**многоклеточн/ые** *pl.* (zool.) Metazoa; —**ый** *a.* multicellular, many-celled.

**много/ковшовый** *a.* chain-bucket; —**колейный** *a.* multiple-track; —**колесный** *a.* multiple-impeller (pump); —**кольчатый** *a.* polycyclic; —**контактный** *a.* multiple-contact; —**корпусный** *a.* multiple, multiple-unit; multiple-effect (evaporator); multiple-furrow (plow); —**красочный** *a.* polychromatic, polychromic, many-colored.

**многократ** *m.* multiple; —**но** *adv.* repeatedly, over and over, many times; —**но отраженная волна** (seismology) multiple reflection; —**ность** *f.* frequency, multiplicity; —**ный** *a.* multiple, frequent, numerous, repeated, manifold, compound, multi—, multiplex, multistage; plural (scattering); —**ная связь** multiple bond.

**много/ламповый** *a.* multitube; —**лемешный** *a.* multiple, gang (plow); —**лепестковый** *a.* (bot.) many-petaled, polypetalous.

**многолет/ие** *n.* longevity, long life; —**ний** *a.* of several year's standing; (bot.) perennial; —**нее растение,** —**ник** *m.* (bot.) perennial.

**много/линейный** *a.* multicircuit; —**листник** *m.* multifoil; —**листный** *a.* many-leaved; (bot.) polyphyllous; —**лучевой** *a.* many-pronged; —**людный** *a.* populous, crowded; —**мерный** *a.* multidimensional; —**местный** *a.* multiseater, multiplace (plane); —**моторный** *a.* multiple-motor, multiengine; —**мужний** *a.* (bot.) polyandrous; —**накальный,** —**нитный** *a.* multifilament; —**направленный** *a.* multidirectional.

**многониточн/ый** *a.* multiple-thread, multiple; —**ая нарезка** multiple thread.

**много/ножка** *f.* (zool.) myriapod; **м.,** —**ножник** *m.* (bot.) polypody (*Polypodium*); —**обещающий** *a.* promising, hopeful; —**оборотный** *see* **многониточный.**

**многообраз/ие** *n.* diversity, variety, multiformity; —**ный** *a.* diverse, varied, multiform, manifold.

**много/опорный** *a.* multiple-seated (valve); —**основность** *f.* polybasicity; —**основный** *a.* polybasic; —**петлевый** *a.* multiple-loop; compound (cycle); —**пластинный,** —**пластинчатый** *a.* multiplate; —**плечий** *a.* multiple, multiple arm.

**многоплодников/ые** *pl.* (bot.) Polycarpicae; —**ый** *a.* polycarpic.

**много/подовый** *a.* multiple-hearth; —**полье** *n.* multiple-field crop rotation system; —**польный** *a.* multiple-field; —**полюсник** *m.* (elec. comm.) network; —**полюсный** *a.* multipolar, multipole; —**предельный** *a.* multirange; —**проводный** *a.* (elec.) multiple-wire, multiple (line); —**пролетный** *a.* multispan (bridge); —**пуансонный штамп** multiple die, gang die; —**разрезный** *a.* multisegment; —**раскосная решетка** multiple latticework.

**многорезцов/ые** *pl.* (zool.) Polyprotodontia; **—ый** *a.* multiblade, multicut, multicutting, multiple-tool.

**много/рожковый** *a.* multiple-jet; **—роты** *see* **многоусты**; **—рядный** *a.* multiple (riveting); polyserial; **—семенный** *a.* (bot.) polyspermous; **—сернистый** *a.* polysulfide (of); **—сеточный** *a.* multigrid; **—скоростной** *a.* multispeed, multiple-speed, multivelocity; **— сложный** *a.* complicated, complex, intricate; **—слойный** *a.* multilayer, multiple (belting), multiwall (bag); **—сочный** *a.* succulent; **—срезный** *a.* multiple-shear.

**многосторонн/ий** *a.* (geom.) polygonal, multilateral; many-sided, versatile; multi—; **—ость** *f.* versatility, variety.

**много/стрендовая цепь** multiple-strand chain; **—ступенчатый** *a.* multistage, multiple-stage, multistep, multiple-phase, compound; **—тигельная печь** multiple-crucible furnace; **—томный** *a.* voluminous, extensive; **—тоннажный** *a.* large-tonnage; **—точечный** *a.* multiple-point; multiple-projection (weld); **—точие** *n.* dotted line; **—трубный** *a.* multitubular.

**многоугольн/ик** *m.* (geom.) polygon; **—ый** *a.* polygonal.

**многоусты** *pl.* (zool.) Polystomeae.

**многофазн/ый** *a.* (elec.) polyphase, multiphase; **м. кабель** compound cable; **—ая обмотка** multicoil winding.

**много/факторный** *a.* multiple-factor, complex; **—формность** *f.* polymorphism.

**многоходов/ой** *a.* multipass, multiplepass; multiple-thread, multithread (screw); **м. червяк** helical gear; **—ая резьба** multiple thread.

**многохромосомность** *f.* (biol.) polyploid.

**многоцветн/ица** *f.* butterfly (*Vanessa polychloros*); **—ость** *f.* polychromy; **—ый** *a.* polychromatic, polychrome, multicolored, iridescent; (bot.) multiflorous.

**много/целевой** *a.* multipurpose; **—цилиндровый** *a.* multicylinder; **—частичный** *a.* many-particle; many-body (forces); **—частотный** *a.* multifrequency; **—черпаковый** *a.* chain-and-bucket (excavator).

**многочисленн/ость** *f.* multiplicity; **—ый** *a.* multiple, numerous, manifold.

**многочлен** *m.* (math.) polynomial; **—ный** *a.* polynomial, multinomial.

**много/шамот** *m.* (cer.) ware containing a high percentage of chamotte; **— шкальный** *a.* multiscale; multirange; **—шкальный (измерительный) прибор** multimeter; **—шпиндельный** *a.* multiple-spindle, gang (drill); **— штемпельный пресс** multiple die, gang die; **—щетниковые** *pl.* (zool.) Polychaeta; **—элементный** *a.* multiple-unit; **—этажный** *a.* many-storied, multistage, multiple-stage; **—ядерный** *a.* polynuclear, polynucleate; polymorphonuclear (leucocyte); **—ядность** *f.* (med., zool.) polyphagia; **—ярусный** *a.* multistage, multiplestage.

**многояч/еистый** *a.* multicellular; **— ейковый** *a.* multicell, multiple-cell; **—ейный** *a.* multichambered, multiple-chamber.

**множественн/ость** *f.* plurality, multiplicity; **—ый** *a.* plural, multiple.

**множество** *n.* great number, multitude, numbers; mass; set (of numbers).

**множ/имое** *n.* (math.) multiplicand; **—итель** *m.* multiplier, multiple, factor; **общий —итель** common multiple; **разложение на —ители** factorization; **—ительная машина** duplicating machine; **—ить** *v.* multiply.

**мной, мною** *instr. of* **я**, by me.

**мн/ут** *pr. 3 pl.;* **—ущий** *pr. act. part.;* **—я** *pr. gerund of* **мять**.

**мо** *n.* (elec.) mho (unit of conductance); **МО** *abbr.* (молекулярная орбита) molecular orbit; (магнит отбоя) release magnet.

**мобилиз/ация** *f.,* **—ационный** *a.* mobilization; **—ировать** *v.* mobilize.

**мобильн/ость** *f.* mobility; **—ый** *a.* mobile.

**мовеин** *m.* mauveine, Aniline Purple.

**мовр/а** *f.* mowrah (seeds of *Bassia butyraceae*); **—авая кислота** mowric acid; **—агениновая кислота** mowrageninic acid; **—агеновая кислота** mowragenic acid; **—ин** *m.* mowrin.

**мог** *past sing. of* **мочь**, could.

**могар** *m.* Italian millet (*Setaria italica* var. *mogharicum*).

**могаукит** *m.* (min.) mohawkite (near domeykite).

**могер** *m.* mohair.

**могил/а** *f.*, **—ьный** *a.* grave, tomb; **—ьник** *see* гармала; **—ьщик** *m.* burying beetle (*Necrophorus*).

**могли** *past pl. of* мочь, could.

**мого** *n.* (geol.) Moho (strata between earth's crust and mantle).

**могу** *1 pr. sing. of* мочь; **—т** they can; **—честь** *f.* strength; **—чий** *a.* strong, vigorous, powerful; **—щественный** *a.* potent, powerful, strong; **—щество** *n.* potency, power, might; **—щий** *a.* powerful, strong; he who can.

**могший** *past act. part. of* мочь.

**мода** *f.* style, fashion; (statistics) mode; **—льный** *a.* modal.

**моделир/ование** *n.* operation with models, miniature-scale operation; modeling; simulation; **—овать** *v.* model, simulate; **—ующая (вычислительная) машина**, **—ующее устройство** analog computer; simulator.

**модел/ь** *f.*, **—ьный** *a.* mock-up, model; pattern, shape, form, standard; make, type; **испытание на —ях** mock-up testing; **м.-эталон** *m.* master pattern; **—ьер**, **—ьщик** *m.* modeler, model maker; pattern maker; **—ьная** *f.*, **—ьностолярная мастерская** pattern shop; **—ьная доска**, **—ьная плита** molding board; **—ьное дело** pattern making.

**модератор** *m.* (mach.) moderator, speed regulator.

**модерниз/ация** *f.* modernization; **—ировать** *v.* modernize.

**модильон** *m.* modillion (a bracket).

**модифи/катор** *m.* modifier, transformer; **—кация** *f.* modification, modified version; **—цировать** *v.* modify.

**модный** *a.* fashionable, stylish.

**модулир/ование** *n.* modulation; **—ованный** *a.* modulated; **—овать** *v.* modulate; **—ометр** *m.* modulation meter; **—ующийся** *a.* modular.

**модуль** *m.* (math.) modulus, coefficient; (bath or liquor) ratio; module, standard; module (of gear); **м. сдвига** shear modulus; **м. упругости** modu-lus of elasticity; **объемный м.** bulk modulus; **—ный** *a.* module, modular; **—ная резьба** worm thread; **—ная фреза** gear cutter.

**модуля/тор** *m.* (rad.) modulator; **—ция** *f.*, **—ционный** *a.* modulation.

**модус** *m.* modus, mode of procedure.

**мое/т** *pr. 3 sing. of* мыть; **—чный** *a.* washing, wash (water); **—чная машина** washing machine, washer.

**мож/а** *pr. gerund;* **—ет** *pr. 3 sing. of* мочь, he can.

**можжевеловые** *pl.* (bot.) Juniperoideae.

**можжевелов/ый** *a.* juniper; **м. спирт** (pharm.) spirit of juniper; Holland gin; **—ая водка**, **—ая настойка** Holland gin; **—ая кислота** juniperic acid, 16-hydroxyhexadecanoic acid; **—ая смола** juniper tar, cade oil; gum juniper (sandarac); **—ое масло** juniper oil; **пригорелое —ое масло** cade oil, juniper tar.

**можжевельн/ик** *m.*, **—ый** *a.* (bot.) juniper (*Juniperus communis*).

**можно** *v.* it is possible, one may, one can.

**мозазавр** *m.* (pal.) Mosasaurus.

**мозаи/ка** *f.* mosaic; **набирать —ку** *v.* inlay; **—чный** *a.* mosaic, inlaid; tile (floor); **—чная структура** mosaic structure.

**мозандрит** *m.* (min.) mosandrite (near johnstrupite).

**мозг** *m.* brain; (anat.) cerebrum; marrow (of bone); **воспаление —а** (med.) cephalitis; **спинной м.** spinal cord.

**мозглый** *see* промозглый.

**мозгов/атый** *a.* pithy; **—ина** *f.* (bot.) pith; pulp.

**мозгов/ой** *a.* brain, cerebral; myeloid; medullary; **—ая кислота** cerebric acid; **—ая кость** marrow bone; **—ая тыква** (bot.) vegetable marrow; **—ое вещество** medullary substance; **мягкая —ая оболочка** (anat.) pia mater; **твердая —ая оболочка** (anat.) dura mater.

**мозезит** *m.* (min.) mosesite.

**мозжечок** *m.* cerebellum, little brain.

**мозжить** *v.* split, cleave.

**Мозли закон** (phys.) Moseley's law.

**мозол/истый** *a.* callous; **—ь** *f.*, **—ьный** *a.* corn, callosity.

**МОИП** *abbr.* (Московское общество

испытателей природы) Moscow Society of Naturalists.

**мой** *a.* my, mine.

**мойка** *f.* washing; washing machine, washer.

**мокайа масло** mocaya oil (from kernels of *Acrocomia scelerocarpa*).

**мокко** *m.*, **кофе м.** mocha (coffee).

**мокну/ть** *v.* become wet, get soaked; soak, steep; **—щий** *a.* soaking; weeping (eczema).

**мокра** *f.* sprinkling brush.

**мокрец** *m.* (vet.) malanders (eczema); **—ы** *pl.* biting midges (*Heleidae*).

**мокрица** *f.* (zool.) wood louse; (bot.) chickweed (*Stellaria media*).

**мокро** *adv.* wet; **м.-сухой** *a.* wet and dry; **—ватый** *a.* wettish, moist; **—воздушный** *a.* wet-air; **—воздушный насос** water-jet air pump.

**мокр/ота** *f.* wet, wetness, moisture, humidity; phlegm, mucus, sputum; **—отный** *a.* mucous; **—ый** *a.* wet, moist, damp; **—ым путем** by the wet process; **анализ —ым путем** wet analysis.

**мол** *m.* pier, jetty, breakwater, dam.

**мол.** *abbr.* (молекулярный) molecular.

**мол. в.** *abbr.* (молекулярный вес) molecular weight.

**молдавит** *m.* (petr.) moldavite, bottle-stone.

**МолдССР** *abbr.* (Молдавская Советская Социалистическая Республика) Moldavian Socialist Soviet Republic.

**молевой** *a.* moth.

**молекул/а** *f.* molecule; **м.-донор** *m.* donor molecule; **—ярность** *f.* molecularity.

**молекулярн/ый** *a.* molecular, molar; **м. вес** molecular weight; **м. раствор** molecular solution; **—ая сила** molecular force; **—ая теплоемкость** molecular heat; **—ая частота** molecular frequency; **—ая электропроводность** molecular conductivity, molal conductivity; **—ое притяжение** molecular attraction.

**молелистовертки** *see* **моли-листовертки.**

**молескин** *m.* (text.) moleskin.

**молеточина** *f.* moth hole (in cloth).

**моли** *gen. and pl. of* **моль; настоящие м.** clothes moths, etc. (*Tineidae*);

**м.-листовертки** *pl.* Glyphipterygidae; **м.-малютки** *pl.* Nepticulid moths (*Nepticulidae*); **м.-пестрянки** *pl.* leaf blotch miners, etc. (*Gracilariidae*).

**молибдат** *m.* molybdate.

**молибден** *m.* molybdenum, Мо; **двуокись —а** molybdenum dioxide; **окись —а** molybdenum oxide, specif. molybdenum monoxide; **хлористый м.** molybdenum chloride; **—ил** *m.* molybdenyl; **хлористый —ил** molybdenyl chloride.

**молибденист/ый** *a.* molybdenum, molybdenous; **—ая соль** molybdenous salt; **—ая сталь** molybdenum steel; **—ое железо** ferromolybdenum.

**молибден/ит** *m.* (min.) molybdenite; **—о—** *prefix* molybdeno—, molybdenum.

**молибденово/аммониевая соль** ammonium molybdate; **—кальциевая соль, —кислый кальций** calcium molybdate; **—кислый** *a.* molybdic acid; molybdate (of); **—кислая соль** molybdate; **—свинцовистая соль** lead molybdate.

**молибденов/ый** *a.* molybdenum, molybdic; **м. ангидрид** molybdic anhydride, molybdenum trioxide; **м. блеск, —ая обманка** (min.) molybdenite, molybdenum blende; **—ая кислота** molybdic acid; **соль —ой кислоты** molybdate; **—ая охра** (min.) molybdic ocher, molybdite, ferrimolybdite; **—ая соль** molybdic salt, molybdenum salt; **—ая сталь** molybdenum steel.

**молибденосвинцовистая соль** *see* **молибденовосвинцовистая соль.**

**молибдит** *m.* (min.) molybdite.

**молибдо/менит** *m.* (min.) molybdomenite (lead selenite); **—содалит** *m.* molybdosodalite (a variety of sodalite); **—филлит** *m.* molybdophyllite.

**молизация** *f.* molization, formation of molecules (from ions, etc.).

**молизит** *m.* (min.) molysite (ferric chloride).

**Молиша проба** Molisch test.

**моллеруп** *m.* mechanical plunger lubricator.

**моллюск** *m.* (zool.) mollusk; shell fish; **—овидные, —ообразные** *pl.* Molluscoidea; **—овидный** *a.* molluscoid, molluscoidal; —**овый** *a.* molluscous, mollusk.

**молн/еотвод** *m.* lightning rod, lightning conductor; —**иевидный** *a.* lightning-like; —**иеносный** *a.* quick as lightning.

**молния** *f.* lightning; **зигзагобразная м., линейная м.** forked lightning, lightning stroke; **расплывчатая м., сплошная м.** sheet lightning; **четочная м.** beaded lightning; **шаровидная м.** globe lightning, ball lightning.

**молод/ежь** *f.* youth, young people; —**еть** *v.* grow young again, be rejuvenated; —**ило** *n.* (bot.) house leek (*Sempervivum*); —**ить** *v.* make young again, rejuvenate; —**ка** *f.* pullet; —**няк** *m.* underbrush, undergrowth; young stock; younger generation; —**ой** *a.* young, youthful, immature; green, raw, unseasoned; —**ость** *f.* youth, youthfulness; —**ь** *f.* (zool.) young ones, brood; young fish, fingerlings, fry.

**моложавый** *a.* young-looking, youngish.

**моложе** *comp. of* **молодой**, younger.

**молозиво** *n.* (med.) colostrum.

**молокан** *m.* (bot.) lettuce (*Lactuca*); mulgedium; —**ка** *see* **молочай**.

**молоки** *pl.* soft roe, milt (of fish).

**молок/о** *n.* milk; **выделение** —**а** lactation.

**молоко/гонный** *a.* milk-producing, lactiferous; —**мер** *m.* measuring pail; —**подобный** *a.* milk-like, lacteal, lactescent; **содержащий** *a.* lactiferous, containing milk.

**молот** *m.* large hammer; **ковка** —**ом, обработка** —**ом** hammer forging; **удар** —**ом** hammer blow.

**молот/илка** *f.* (agr.) threshing machine, thresher; (corn) sheller; —**ильный** *a.* threshing; shelling; —**ить** *v.* thresh; shell.

**молотков/ый** *a.* hammer; **м. перфоратор** hammer drill; —**ая мельница** hammer mill.

**молото/боина** *f.*, —**вая окалина** (met.) forge scale, hammer scale, scale; hearth cinder; —**вая** *f.* forge shop; —**вище** *n.* hammer handle; —**вой** *a.* hammer; percussive (welding).

**молото/к** *m.* hammer; mallet; **м.-ручник**

hand hammer; —**чек** *m.* little hammer; clapper (of bell); —**чковый, —чный** *a.* hammer.

**молот/ый** *a.* milled, ground; —**ь** *v.* mill, grind, stamp (ore); —**ьба** *f.* (agr.) threshing.

**молочай,** —**ник** *m.* (bot.) spurge (*Euphorbia*); —**ная камедь** euphorbium (resin); —**ные** *pl.* Euphorbiaceae.

**молочн/ая** *f.* dairy; milk house; —**ик** *m.* milkman, dairyman; milk can.

**молочно/аммониевая соль** ammonium lactate; —**белый** *a.* milk-white; —**железистая соль** ferrous lactate; —**железная соль** ferric lactate; —**кальциевая соль,** —**кислый кальций** calcium lactate; —**кислый** *a.* lactic acid; lactate (of); —**кислый ряд** lactic acid series; —**кислая соль** lactate; —**кислое брожение** lactic fermentation; —**магниевая соль** magnesium lactate; —**натриевая соль** sodium lactate; —**ртутистая соль** mercurous lactate; —**ртутная соль** mercuric lactate; —**серебряная соль** silver lactate.

**молочность** *f.* milkiness, lactescence.

**молочнофосфорно/кальциевая соль,** —**кислыйкальций** calcium lactophosphate; —**кислая соль** lactophosphate.

**молочноцинковая соль** zinc lactate.

**молочн/ый** *a.* milk, lactic; milk-white, milky, lacteal, lactescent; dairy (cattle); butter (fat); mammary (gland); **м. ангидрид** lactic anhydride; **м. камень** (min.) galactite (a variety of natrolite); **м. сахар** milk sugar, lactose; **м. сепаратор** cream separator; —**ая кислота** lactic acid, 2-hydroxypropanoic acid; **соль** —**ой кислоты,** —**ая соль** lactate; —**ая трава** *see* **молочай;** —**ое стекло** milky glass, opal glass; —**ое тельцо** milk globule, fat globule in milk.

**молуранит** *m.* (min.) moluranite.

**молча** *adv.* silently; —**ливый** *a.* silent, uncommunicative, tacit; —**ние** *n.* silence; —**ть** *v.* keep silent; —**щий** *a.* silent; idle.

**моль** *f.* (zool.) moth; *m.* (chem.) mole, gram-molecule.

**мольберт** *m.* easel.

**мольдавит** *see* **молдавит.**

**мол/ьный** *a.* mole, molar; **—ьная дляо** mole fraction; **—ьная концентрация** molar concentration; **—яльность** *f.* molality (moles per 1000 g. of solvent); **—яльный** *a.* molal.

**моляр** *m.* (anat.) molar.

**молярность** *f.* molarity (moles per liter of solution).

**молярн/ый** *a.* molar, gram-molecular; molal; **м. вес** gram-molecular weight, molal weight; **м. зуб** (anat.) molar; **м. объем** gram-molecular volume, molal volume; **м. раствор** molar solution; **—ая доля** mole fraction; **—ая концентрация** molarity.

**мом** *abbr.* (миллиом) milliohm; **Мом** *abbr.* (мегом) megohm.

**момент** *m.* moment; momentum; torque; feature, point; *look for idioms under more descriptive words, e.g.,* **инерции, момент** moment of inertia; **механический м.** momentum.

**моментальн/о** *adv.* instantly, at once, immediately; **—ый** *a.* instantaneous; (phot.) snap(shot); **—ого действия** instantaneous, immediate.

**моменто/мер** *m.* torque meter; **—скоп** *m.* (mach.) ignition tester.

**монаднок** *m.* (geol.) monadnock.

**монады** *pl.* (zool.) Monadina.

**мон/амид** *m.* monamide; **—амин** *m.* monamine; **—арда** *f.*, **—ардовый** *a.* *a.* (bot.) horsemint (*Monarda*); **—ардин** *m.* monardin.

**монах** *m.* monk; (geol.) pinnacle.

**монацетин** *m.* monoacetin, glyceryl monoacetate.

**монацит** *m.*, **—овый** *a.* (min.) monazite.

**монашенка** *f.* moth (*Porthetria monacha*); mantis (*Lymantria monacha*).

**монгеймит** *m.* (min.) monheimite (a variety of smithsonite).

**монгольский** *a.* Mongolian.

**монгумовая кислота** mongumic acid.

**Монда газ** Mond gas, semi-water gas.

**мондамин** *m.* mondamin (a corn-starch).

**монез/ин** *m.* monesin; **кора —ия** monesia bark (of *Chrysophyllum glyciphloeum*).

**монель-металл, Монеля сплав** Monel metal (a nickel-copper-iron alloy).

**монета** *f.* coin.

**монетит** *m.* (min.) monetite.

**монетный** *a.* monetary, coin; troy (weight); **м. двор** mint; **м. пресс** coining stamp.

**монж/у, —ю, —юс** *m.* montejus, air lift; (sugar) juice pump.

**монимолит** *m.* (min.) monimolite.

**монит** *m.* (min.) monite (a variety of collophanite).

**монитор** *m.* monitor; (min.) monitor, hydraulic jet; flaxseed cleaning plant.

**монмориллонит** *see* **монтмориллонит.**

**моно—** *prefix* mono— (one, single); **—аммоний** *m.* monoammonium; **—атомный** *a.* monatomic; monovalent; **—ацетат** *m.* monoacetate; **—ацетин** *see* **монацетин; —блок** *m.* monoblock.

**монобром—** *prefix* monobrom—, monobromo—; **—камфора** *f.* monobromated camphor; **—уксусная кислота** monobromoacetic acid.

**моно/генный** *a.* monogenetic; (biol.) asexual; **—гидрат** *m.* monohydrate; **—графия** *f.* monograph; **—за** *f.* monose; monosaccharide.

**моноиод—** *prefix* monoiod—, monoiodo—.

**моно/калий** *m.* monopotassium; **—карбоновая кислота** monocarboxylic acid; **—кись** *f.* monoxide.

**моноклин/аль** *m.*, **—альная складка** (geol.) monocline, monoclinal fold; **—альный** *a.* monoclinal; **—ический, —ный** *a.* (cryst.) monoclinic.

**монококк** *m.* (aero.) monocoque.

**монокристалл** *m.*, **—ический** *a.* single-crystal.

**монокультура** *f.* one-crop system.

**монокулярный** *a.* monocular, one-eyed.

**монолит** *m.* monolith; core sample (of soil); **—ный, —овый** *a.* monolithic.

**моном** *m.* (math.) monomial.

**мономагний** *m.* monomagnesium.

**мономер** *m.* monomer; **—ность** *f.* monomerism; **—ный** *a.* monomeric.

**монометаллический** *a.* monometallic.

**монометил** *m.*, **—овый** *a.* monomethyl.

**мономолекулярный** *a.* monomolecular; **м. слой** monomolecular layer, monolayer.

**моно/надсерная кислота** permonosulfuric acid, Caro's acid; **—окись** *see* **монокись.**

**моноплан** *m.* (aero.) monoplane.

**моноплегия** *f.* (med.) monoplegia.

**монопол/изация** *f.* monopolization; **—изировать** *v.* monopolize; **—ия** *f.* monopoly; **—ь** *m.* monopole; **—ьный** *a.* monopolistic, exclusive; **—ярный** *a.* monopolar.

**монопропил** *m.,* **—овый** *a.* monopropyl.

**монорельс** *m.,* **—овый** *a.* monorail.

**моносахарид** *m.* monosaccharide.

**монотип** *m.* (typ.) monotype; **—ный** *a.* monotypic; **—ный сплав** monotype metal (a lead-antimony-tin alloy).

**монотонн/ость** *f.* monotony; **—ый** *a.* monotonous; (math.) monotonic, monotone (function).

**монотроп/изм** *m.,* **—ия** *f.* monotropism; **—ный** *a.* monotropic.

**монофилетический** *a.* (biol.) monophyletic.

**моно/фракс** *m.* monofrax (refractory material); **—хлор—** *prefix* monochlor—, monochloro—; **—хлоруксусная кислота** monochloroacetic acid; **—хорд** *m.* (phys.) monochord; **—хроматизация** *f.* monochromatization; **—хроматический** *a.* monochromatic; **—хроматор** *m.* monochromator (a spectroscope); **—циклический** *a.* monocyclic; **—энергетический** *a.* monoenergetic.

**моноэтил** *m.,* **—овый** *a.* monoethyl.

**монпа/нсье, —сье** *n.* drops, lozenges.

**Монреаль** Montreal.

**монроэнский подъярус** (geol.) Monroan or Monroe substage.

**монтаж** *m.* assembling, assembly, setting up, putting together, erection, installation, mounting, fitting, rigging; adjustment, arrangement; **м. проводов** (elec.) wiring; **м. трубопровода** pipe laying; **—ная** *f.* assembly room; (cinematography) clipping room.

**монтажн/ик** *see* **монтер; —ый** *a.* assembly, assembling, erecting, fitting; **—ый цех, —ая мастерская** assembly room; fitting shop; **—ая схема** (elec.) wiring diagram, hook-up.

**монтан/а-воск, —вакс** *m.,* **—ский воск** montan wax; **—иловый спирт** montanyl alcohol, nonacosanol; **—ин** *m.* montanin (hydrofluosilicic acid disin-

fectant); **—ит** *m.* (min.) montanite (a bismuth tellurate); **—овая кислота** montanic acid; **—селитра** *f.* ammonium sulfate-nitrate; **—ский слой** (geol.) Montanan subdivision.

**монтебразит** *m.* (min.) montebrasite (a variety of amblygonite).

**монтеж/у, —ю** *see* **монжу.**

**Монте-Карло метод** (nucl.) Monte-Carlo method.

**монтер** *m.* assembler, erector, mounter, rigger; adjuster; (engine) fitter; repairman, mechanic; **—ский** *a.* fitter's; lineman's; tool (case).

**монтжюс** *see* **монжу.**

**монтиров/ание** *n.,* **—ка** *f.* assembly, assembling, erection, mounting, connecting up; **—анный** *a.* assembled, erected, mounted; **—ать** *v.* assemble, erect, mount, install, arrange, fit, fit up, build up, rig up.

**монт/ицеллит, —ичеллит** *m.* (min.) monticellite (a member of the chrysolite group); **—мориллонит** *m.* montmorillonite (a clay mineral); **—ройдит** *m.* montroydite (a native mercuric oxide).

**Монтье синий** Monthier's blue.

**монумент** *m.* monument; **—альный** *a.* monumental.

**монцонит** *m.* monzonite (an igneous rock); **—овый** *a.* monzonitic.

**мончикит** *m.* monchiquite (a porphyritic silicate rock).

**Монье свод** Monier's arch.

**Моора фильтрпресс** Moore filter press.

**Мооса шкала** *see* **Моса шкала.**

**МОП** *abbr.* (Международное общество почвоведов) International Society of Soil Scientists.

**мор** *m.* pestilence, plague.

**Мора литр** Mohr liter; **М. соль** Mohr's salt, ferrous ammonium sulfate (hexahydrate).

**мораль** *f.* morals, ethics; **—ный** *a.* moral, ethical; mental; **—ное состояние** morale.

**морг** *m.* morgue; unit of land measurement (approx. 0.5 hectares).

**Моргана уравнение** Morgan equation.

**морганит** *m.* (min.) morganite (a variety of beryl).

**моргать** *v.* blink.

**морда** *f.* muzzle, snout.

**морденит** *m.* (min.) mordenite.

**мордовник** *m.* (bot.) globe thistle (*Echinops*).

**мор/е** *n.* sea; —ем by sea, by water; к —ю seaward; удаленный от —я inland; —еведение *n.* oceanography.

**морен/а** *f.* (geol.) moraine; —ный *a.* morainic.

**моренозит** *m.* (min.) morenosite (a nickel sulfate).

**мореные изделия** (cer.) unglazed fumed earthenware.

**море/плавание** *n.* navigation, seafaring; —плаватель *m.* navigator, seaman; —плавательный *a.* nautical; —ходность *f.* seaworthiness; —ходный *a.* nautical, seafaring, seagoing; —ходство *n.* navigation.

**морж** *m.*, —овый *a.* (zool.) walrus.

**Морзе азбука** Morse code.

**морил/ка** *f.* (wood) stain; (dyeing) mordant; specimen jar, insect-killing jar; (sericulture) stoving room; водяная **м.** mordant based on water; —ьный *a.* mordant; stoving, stifling.

**морин** *m.* morin, pentahydroxyflavone; —га *f.* (bot.) moringa; —гадубильная кислота —одубильная кислота moringatannic acid; —дин *m.* morindin; —довое масло ben oil; —дон *m.* morindone.

**морион** *m.* (min.) morion (a variety of smoky quartz).

**морить** *v.* starve, exhaust; exterminate, kill; fume; stain (wood).

**морков/ник** *m.*, —ный *a.*, —ь *f.* carrot (*Daucus carota*).

**моров/ой** *a.* pestilential; —ая язва, —ое поветрие pestilence, plague.

**морожен/ица** *f.* ice cream freezer; —ое *n.* ice cream.

**мороз** *m.* frost; frosted finish; наводить **м.** *v.* frost, apply a frosted finish; —илка *f.* freezer; refrigerator; —ить *v.* freeze, congeal, chill; —ник *m.* (bot.) hellebore (*Helleborus*); —ный *a.* frosty, frost; —обоина, —овина *f.* (geol.) frost cleft, frost fissure; (bot.) frost crack; —обой *m.* winterkilling.

**морозостойк/ий** *a.* frostproof, winterproof; antifreeze, non-freezing; —ость *f.* resistance to frost.

**морос/ить** *v.* drizzle; —ь, —ящий дождь drizzle, light rain.

**морошка** *f.* (bot.) cloudberry (*Rubus chamaemorus*); красная м. *see* мамура.

**морру/а** *f.* morrhua (codfish); —ин *m.* morrhuin; —иновая кислота morrhuic acid; —ол *m.* morrhuol.

**морс** *m.* cranberry juice.

**морск/ой** *a.* sea, marine, maritime; nautical; naval; м. ангел monkfish; м. воробей lumpfish; м. жолудь (zool.) barnacle; м. клей marine glue; м. конек (zool.) sea horse; м. лук (bot.) squill (*Scilla maritima*); м. мох *see* ирландский мох; м. сухарь hardtack, ship's biscuit; м. флот merchant marine; м. шелк byssus silk; м. шлам sea ooze; —ая болезнь seasickness; —ая вода sea water; —ая звезда (zool.) starfish; —ая капуста *see* катран; —ая пенка (min.) sea foam, meerschaum, sepiolite; —ая свинка (zool.) guinea pig; —ая свинья (zool.) porpoise; —ая синь marine blue; —ая трава (bot.) grass wrack (*Zostera marina*); —ие лилии (zool.) sea lilies (*Crinoidea*); —им путем by sea; —ое ухо, —ое ушко (zool.) abalone.

**мортир/а** *f.* (mil.) mortar; —ка *f.* rifle grenade discharger.

**морф/енол** *m.* morphenol; —ий, —ин *m.*, —иновый *a.* morphine; серно-кислый —ин, сульфат —ина morphine sulfate; хлористоводородный —ин morphine hydrochloride; —инизм *m.* (med.) morphinism; —инист *m.* morphine addict; —иновый *a.* morphine; —ол *m.* morphol, 3,4-phenanthrenediol; —олин *m.* morpholine.

**морфолог** *m.* morphologist; —ический *a.* morphological; —ия *f.* morphology.

**морфотроп/изм** *m.* (cryst.) morphotropism; —ия *f.* morphotropy; —ный *a.* morphotropic.

**морфохинон** *m.* morphoquinone.

**морщ/ина** *f.* wrinkle, crease, fold, pucker; —инистый *a.* wrinkled, creased; rugose; —ить *v.* wrinkle, pucker, gather, contract, crinkle, crumple; corrugate; —иться *v.* shrivel.

**моряк** *m.* sailor, seaman.

**морянка** *see* **томлянка.**

**Моса шкала твердости** (min.) Mohs hardness scale.

**москатель** *f.*, **—ный товар** commercial chemicals such as paints, oils, glues; chandlery.

**Москва** Moscow.

**москит** *m.*, **—ный** *a.* (zool.) mosquito, gnat.

**московск/ий** *a.* Moscow; **—ое стекло** (min.) Muscovy glass, common mica.

**мослен** *m.* moslene.

**моссит** *m.* (min.) mossite (a variety of tapiolite).

**мост** *m.* bridge; **м.-транспортер** transporter bridge; **наводить м.** *v.* bridge.

**мостик** *m.* little bridge, bridge deck, staging; cross bar; (elec.) bridge; cross link (in polymer); **соединение —ом** (elec.) bridge joint; **—овый** *a.* bridge, bridging; cross linkage.

**мост/ить** *v.* pave; **—овая** *f.* pavement, roadway.

**мостов/ой** *a.* bridge; pavement; **м. кран** bridge crane, overhead crane; **м. переход** (elec.) bridge transition; **—ые весы** platform scales, weigh bridge; platform balance; counter scales.

**мосток** *m.*, **рабочий м.** footpath.

**мостостроение** *n.* bridge building.

**МОСХОС** *abbr.* (Московская областная сельскохозяйственная опытная станция) Moscow Regional Agricultural Experiment Station.

**мот/алка** *f.* reeler, reel, winder, coiler, coiling machine; (film) rewinder; **—альница** *f.* reel, winder; **—альный** *a.* reeling, winding; **—анный** *a.* wound, coiled; **—ать** *v.* reel, wind, coil; shake, wag; waste; **—аться** *v.* dangle, hang loose; hurry about.

**мотив** *m.* motive, reason, cause, ground; **—ировать** *v.* motivate; justify; **—ировка** *f.* motivation, motives, reason, justification.

**мотил** *m.* antiknock motor fuel containing high percentage of iron pentacarbonyl.

**мотнуть** *see* **мотать.**

**мото—** *prefix* motor, power; mechanical.

**мотовил/о** *n.* reel, reeling frame, swift, coiler; **—ьный** *a.* reeling.

**моток** *m.* skein, hank, bundle, cut; link.

**мотолин** *m.* antiknock motor fuel containing 0.1% iron pentacarbonyl.

**мото/лодка** *f.* motorboat; **—лопата** *f.* power shovel, excavator; **—мех** *m.* (mil.) mechanized forces; **—механизированный** *a.* mechanized; **—пехота** *f.* motorized infantry; **—пила** *f.* power saw; **—помпа** *f.* motor-operated pump.

**мотор** *m.* motor; motorcar, automobile; **м.-вентилятор** blower, blowing engine; blast engine; **м.-генератор** (elec.) dynamo; motor generator; **—изация** *f.* motorization; **—изованный** *a.* motorized; **—ный** *a.* motor; **—ный вагон** (railroad) motorcar; **—остроительный** *a.* motor-building; **—чик** *m.* little motor.

**мототерапия** *f.* exercise therapy.

**мото/цикл, —циклет** *m.* motorcycle; **—шина** *f.* motorcycle tire.

**моттрамит** *m.* (min.) mottramite (a cuprous variety of descloizite).

**моты/га** *f.* hoe, mattock; scraper, scraping tool; pick, pickax; **—жить** *v.* hoe.

**мотыл/ек** *m.* moth, butterfly; **кукурузный м., стеблевой м.** European corn borer (*Pyrausta nubilalis*); **—ица** *f.* bee moth; **—ь** *m.* crank, handle; mosquito larva; moth, butterfly.

**мотылько/вые** *pl.* (bot.) Papilionaceae; **—вый** *a.* butterfly-shaped, papilionaceous; **—образный** *a.* butterfly-shaped, butterfly.

**мофетта** *f.* (geol.) mofette (gas emanation); noxious gas, spec. choke damp.

**мох** *m.* (bot.) moss; **белый м.** *see* **торфяной мох; земляной м., змеиный м., ползучий м.** *see* **плаун.**

**мохиловый спирт** mochyl alcohol.

**мохнатый** *a.* hairy, shaggy, woolly, long-napped; Turkish (towel); (bot.) pilose.

**мохо/видный** *a.* mossy; **—вик** *m.* capercaillie (a grouse); (bot.) mushroom (*Boletus circinans*); (min.) *see* **моховой агат.**

**моховой** *a.* moss, mossy; **м. агат** (min.) moss agate, mocha stone (a variety of agate quartz); **м. торф** (geol.) moss peat, bog peat.

**мохокэн** *m.* (geol.) Mohawkian series.

**мохообразные** *pl.* (bot.) Bryophyta.

**моцион** *m.* exercise.

**моч/а** *f.* urine; анализ —и uranalysis; выделение —и urinary secretion.

**мочажина** *see* мочежина.

**мочал/ина** *f.* filament, string; —ить *v.* separate into fibers; —о *n.* soaked bast, fiber.

**мочевин/а** *f.* urea, carbamide; **азотнокислая м.**, **нитрат** —ы urea nitrate; —оформальдегидная смола ureaformaldehyde resin.

**мочевоаммониевая соль** ammonium urate.

**мочев/ой** *a.* urine, urinary; м. песок, —ые камни (med.) gravel; м. пузырь (anat.) bladder; —ая кислота uric acid, trioxypurine; соль—ой кислоты urate.

**мочево/калиевая соль**, —кислый калий potassium urate; —кислый *a.* uric acid; urate (of); —кислая соль urate; кислая —кислая соль biurate, acid urate; —натриевая соль sodium urate.

**мочегонн/ый** *a.*, —ое средство diuretic.

**мочежина** *f.* mochezhina (land permanently wet from outflow of underground water).

**мочеизнурение** *n.* (med.) diabetes.

**мочеиспуск/ание** *n.* urination; —ательный *a.* urinating; —ательный канал (anat.) urethra.

**мочекислый** *see* мочевокислый.

**мочен/ие** *n.* wetting, soaking, steeping, maceration; retting (fiber); —ый *a.* wetted, soaked, steeped.

**мочеполовой** *a.* urogenital, urinogenital; venereal (disease).

**мочеточник** *m.* (anat.) ureter.

**мочильный** *a.* wetting, steeping, soaking.

**мочина** *see* жидовская вишня.

**мочить** *v.* wet, moisten, soak, steep, drench, macerate; ret (fiber); —ся *v.* get wet; urinate.

**мочк/а** *f.* wetting, soaking, maceration; filament, thread, fiber; lobe (of ear); —оватый *a.* fibrous, filamentous.

**мочь** *v.* be able; *f.* strength, might, power; может быть perhaps, maybe; не может быть it is impossible.

**мошенничество** *n.* swindle, fraud.

**мошк/а** *f.* midge, gnat; (glass) seeds; —и *pl.* buffalo gnats, black flies (*Simuliidae*); —ара *f.* swarm of midges; moths.

**мош/на** *f.* pouch, bag, purse; —онка *f.* (anat.) scrotum;—оночный *a.* scrotal.

**мощен/ие** *n.* paving; —ый *a.* paved.

**мощност/ь** *f.* power, horsepower; force, vigor, might; potency; (dose) rate; duty (of engine), efficiency, output, capacity; (geol.) width (of vein); thickness, magnitude; м. в лошадиных силах horsepower; м. установки plant capacity; большой —и highpower, high-duty; коэффициент —и (elec.) power factor; кривая —и power curve; малой —и low-power, low-duty; отбор —и, отъем —и (mach.) power take-off, p.t.o.; переданная м., подведенная м., поглощенная м., сообщенная м. power input; полной —ью full power.

**мощн/ый** *a.* powerful, vigorous, energetic; high-power, high-duty, heavyduty, heavy (machine); thick, sturdy; —ая лампа (rad.) power tube, output tube.

**мощь** *f.* power, vigor, strength; воздушная м. air power.

**мо/ют** *pr. 3 pl. of* мыть; —ющий *a.*, —я *adv.* washing; —ющая способность detergency; —ющее средство detergent, cleansing agent.

**МПВО** *abbr.* (местная противовоздушная оборона) local anti-aircraft defense.

**мпз** *abbr.* (миллипуаз) millipoise.

**МПП** *abbr.* (Министерство пищевой промышленности) Ministry of the Food Industry.

**мпуаз** *see* мпз.

**мр** *abbr.* (миллирентген) milliroentgen.

**мрак** *m.* darkness, gloom, obscurity.

**мрамор** *m.*, —ный *a.* (min.) marble; пестрый м., разноцветный м. variegated marble; под м. marbled (surface); —ная доска marble slab; —ная мука marble flour; —овидный, —оподобный *a.* marble-like, marbly, marbled, marmoreal, marmoric.

**мрачный** *a.* gloomy, dark, dismal, dim.

**мрезерфорд** *abbr.* (миллирезерфорд) millirutherford.

**мсб** *abbr.* (миллистильб) millistilb.

**мсек** *abbr.* (миллисекунда) millisecond; **м/сек** *abbr.* (метров в секунду) meters per second.

**мстить** *v.* revenge oneself.

**МСХ** *abbr.* (Министерство сельского хозяйства) Ministry of Agriculture; **МСХЖ** *abbr.* (Международный сельскохозяйственный журнал) International Agricultural Magazine.

**МТМ** *abbr.* (машинно-тракторная мастерская) machine and tractor repair shop.

**МТР** *abbr.* (магнитный термоядерный реактор) magnetic thermonuclear reactor.

**МТС** *abbr.* (машинотракторная станция) machine and tractor service station; (метр-тонна-секунда) meter-ton-second; (междугородная телефонная станция) long-distance exchange.

**муар** *m.* moire, watered fabric; moiré, watered effect; wrinkle finish; (old chem.) black, ethiops; **наводить м.,** **—ировать** *v.* water, moiré (fabric); **—овый** *a.* moiré.

**Муассана способ** (met.) Moissan process.

**муассанит** *m.* (min.) moissanite (natural silicon carbide).

**мудар** *see* **мадар; —овая кислота** mudaric acid.

**мудрен/о** *adv.* ingeniously, subtly; it is difficult; **не м., что, нет —ого, что** no wonder that; **—ый** *a.* ingenious, clever; difficult, abstruse, complicated.

**мудр/ец** *m.* sage; **—о** *adv.* wisely, cleverly; **—ость** *f.* wisdom; **зуб —ости** wisdom tooth; **—ый** *a.* wise, sage.

**муж** *m.* husband; **—еский** *see* **мужской.**

**мужественн/ость** *f.* masculinity; **—ый** *a.* masculine, manful, manly, virile.

**мужик** *m.* peasant, countryman.

**муж/ской** *a.* masculine, male; **—чина** *m.* man.

**музарин** *m.* musarin.

**музей** *m.,* **—ный** *a.* museum.

**музыка** *f.* music.

**мук/а** *f.* flour, meal; suffering, torment, pain; **—оед** *m.* grain beetle.

**муко/ид** *m.* mucoid; **—лактоновая кислота** mucolactonic acid.

**мукомол** *m.* miller; **—ьный** *a.* milling, grinding; **—ьный постав, —ьная мельница, —ьня** *f.* flour mill.

**муко/новая кислота** muconic acid, 2,4-hexadienedioic acid; **—рин** *m.* mucorin (a plant mold protein); **—хлоровая кислота** mucochloric acid.

**мукуновое масло** mucuna oil.

**мул** *m.* (zool.) mule.

**мулат** *m.,* **—ка** *f.* mulatto.

**мулл/ит** *m.* mullite (aluminum silicate refractory); **—ицит** *m.* (min.) mullicite (a variety of vivianite).

**муль** *m.* (dyeing) mull madder.

**мульда** *f.* (met.) mold, charging box, pan, basin; (geol.) trough, syncline.

**мульденпресс** *m.* (text.) cylinder press.

**мульти—** *prefix* multi—, poly—; *see also* **много—; —вариантный** *a.* multivariant; **—вибратор** *m.* (elec.) multivibrator; **—граф** *m.* (typ.) multigraph; **—план** *m.* (aero.) multiplane; **—плексная обмотка** (elec.) multiplex winding; **—плет** *m.* (phys.) multiplet; **—плетность** *f.* multiplicity.

**мультиплика/тор** *m.* (phys.) multiplier, intensifier; (gas pressure) booster; metering pump; duplicating machine; multiple-lens camera; **—ция** *f.,* **—ционный** *a.* multiplication.

**мульти/ротация** *f.* multirotation, mutarotation; **—циклон** *m.* multicyclone (dust extractor).

**мультиполь** *m.,* **—ный** *a.* multipole; **—ность** *f.* multipolarity.

**мульч/а** *f.,* **—ировать** *v.* mulch; **—бумага** *f.* mulching paper; **—ер** *m.* mulcher; **—ирование** *n.* mulching.

**мулэн** *m.* (geol.) moulin.

**муляж** *m.* modeling, molding, casting.

**муметалл** *m.* Mu Metal (a nickel-iron-copper-manganese alloy).

**муми/фикация** *f.* mummification; **—фицированный** *a.* mummified; **—фицировать** *v.* mummify; **—я** *f.* mummy; colcothar, Prussian red, rouge.

**мундир** *m.* uniform; **картофель в —е** potato cooked in jacket.

**мундшту/к** *m.,* **—чный** *a.* bit, mouthpiece; nozzle, jet, spout, tip; (extrusion) die; spinneret (for rayon).

**муниципальн/ый** *a.* municipal; **—ые предприятия** public utilities.

**Мунтца металл, мунцевая латунь, мунцметалл** Muntz metal, Muntz bronze (a copper-zinc alloy).

**мурава** *f.* grass; (cer.) glaze, glazing, enamel; **свинцовая м.** glazier's lead.

**муравей** *m.* (zool.) ant; **белый м.** termite (*Isoptera*); **—ник** *m.* ant hill.

**мурав/ить** *v.* (cer.) glaze; **—ление** *n.* glazing; vitrification; **—леный** *a.* glazed; vitrified.

**муравье/д** *m.* (zool.) anteater; **—жук** *m.* ant beetle (*Thanasimus formicarius*).

**муравьино/аммониевая соль** ammonium formate; **—бутиловый эфир** butyl formate; **—кислый** *a.* formic acid; formate (of); **—кислый натрий, —натриевая соль** sodium formate; **—кислая соль** formate; **—этиловый эфир** ethyl formate.

**муравьин/ый** *a.* (zool.) ant; formic; **м. альдегид** formaldehyde, methanal; **м. лев** (zool.) ant lion; **—ая кислота** formic acid, methanoic acid; **соль —ой кислоты** formate.

**мурашка** *f.* small ant.

**мурашник** *m.* (petr.) myrmekite.

**мурекс/ан** *m.* murexan, uramil; **—ид** *m.* murexide, ammonium purpurate; **—идная проба** (med.) murexide test (for uric acid).

**муррайин** *m.* murrayine.

**мурчисонит** *m.* (min.) murchisonite (a variety of orthoclase feldspar).

**мусивн/ый** *a.* mosaic; **—ое золото** mosaic gold (stannic sulfide pigment or a copper-zinc alloy); **—ое серебро** mosaic silver (a tin-bismuth amalgam).

**мускарин** *m.* muscarine; **действие —а** (med.) muscarinic action.

**мускат** *m.* nutmeg; muscatel (wine); muscadine (grape).

**мускатн/ый** *a.* nutmeg; muscatel (wine); **м. бальзам, жирное —ое масло** nutmeg butter; **м. орех** nutmeg; **м. цвет** mace; **—ая дыня** (bot.) muskmelon (*Cucumis melo*); **—ое дерево** (bot.) nutmeg (*Myristica fragrans*); **—ое масло** nutmeg oil; myristica oil; mace oil.

**мусковит** *m.* (min.) muscovite, potash mica, common mica.

**мускон** *m.* muscone, muskine.

**мускул** *m.* (anat.) muscle; **—атура** *f.* muscles, sinews; **—истость** *f.* muscularity; **—истый** *a.* muscular; **—ьный** *a.* muscle, muscular.

**мускус** *m.*, **—ный** *a.* musk, deer musk; **м.-амбрет** musk seed, ambrette; **кабардинский м., русский м., сибирский м.** cabardine musk; **—ный корень** musk root, sumbul (dried root of *Ferula sumbul*); **—ный овцебык** musk ox.

**муслин** *m.* (text.) muslin.

**мусор** *m.*, **—ный** *a.* dust, rubbish, trash, debris, refuse, sweepings; garbage; fines; **—ить** *v.* litter; **—ный ящик** dust bin; **—ная горловина** mud hole (of boiler); **—осжигатель** *m.*, **—осжигательная печь** incinerator; **—осжигательная установка** incinerator, garbage disposal plant; **—щик** *m.* scavenger.

**муссивный** *see* **мусивный**.

**муссон** *m.*, **—ный** *a.* monsoon, trade wind.

**муст** *m.* must (of grapes).

**мустанг** *m.* (zool.) mustang.

**мутаза** *f.* mutase.

**мута/нт** *m.*, **—нтный** *a.* (biol.) mutant; **—ротация** *f.* mutarotation (of sugar solutions); **—тор** *m.* mutator; **—ционный** *a.*, **—ция** *f.* mutation.

**мут/ить** *v.* disturb, make turbid, make muddy, stir up; **—иться, —неть** *v.* grow turbid, get muddy, get cloudy.

**Мутмана жидкость** Muthmann liquid, acetylene tetrabromide.

**мутманнит** *m.* (min.) muthmannite (a silver-gold telluride).

**мутн/ость** *f.* turbidity, muddiness, cloudiness; **—ый** *a.* turbid, thick, muddy, cloudy, hazy.

**мутов/ка** *f.* churn staff, beater; (biol.) verticil, whorl; **—чатый** *a.* verticillate, whorled.

**мутуализм** *m.* (biol.) mutualism, symbiosis.

**муть** *f.* turbidity, suspension, cloud; mud, sludge, slime, sediment.

**муфель** *m.*, **—ный** *a.* muffle; **—ная печь** muffle furnace; **—ные краски** (cer.) muffle colors.

**муфлон** *m.* mouflon (wild sheep).

**муфт/а** *f.*, **—овый** *a.* muff; clutch; coupling, connecting piece, connection, sleeve, sleeve pipe, union (for pipes); junction box (for cables); socket, socket joint; **м. подшипника** bearing sleeve; **м. сцепления, зубчатая м., кулачная м.** clutch, clutch coupling; **м. с нарезкой** screw socket; **глухая м.** closed coupling; **соединение —ой, —овое соединение** muff coupling, box coupling, sleeve joint, socket joint; **соединительная м.** coupling box; **стяжная винтовая м.** turnbuckle; **—овая труба** sleeve pipe.

**муфточка** *f.* small coupling, socket, sleeve.

**мух/а** *f.* (zool.) fly; **настоящие —и** Muscidae; **—и-сирфиды** *pl.* flower flies, hover flies (*Syrphidae*); **—и-цветочницы** *pl.* Anthomyid flies (*Anthomyiidae*); **—оловка** *f.* fly trap; (bot.) Venus' flytrap (*Dionaea muscipula*); flycatcher (bird); **—оловный** *a.* flycatching; **—омор** *m.*, **—оморный** *a.* (bot.) fly agaric (*Amanita muscaria*).

**мухортый** *a.* brown, bay.

**муцедин** *m.* mucedin.

**муцин** *m.*, **—овый** *a.* mucin.

**муч/ение** *n.* suffering, torment, pain, agony; **—ительный** *a.* acutely painful, poignant; **—ить** *v.* torture, worry, bother, torment.

**мучнист/оросяные грибы** (bot.) the powdery mildews (*Erysiphaceae*); **—ость** *f.* mealiness; **—ые** *pl.* (bot.) farinose plants; **—ый** *a.* mealy, floury, farinaceous; **—ая роса** powdery mildew; **ложная —ая роса** false mildew, downy mildew; **—ое вещество** farinaceous substance.

**мучн/ой** *a.* meal, flour, mealy, farinaceous; **—ая роса** *see* **мучнистая роса.**

**Мушета сталь** Mushet (self-hardening) steel.

**муш/иный** *a.* (zool.) fly; **—ка** *f.* little fly, midge, gnat; (pharm.) cantharides; sight, aim.

**мушкель** *m.* mallet, wooden hammer.

**мушкетовит** *m.* (min.) muschketowite (magnetite after hematite).

**мушмула, германская м.** (bot.) medlar (*Mespilus germanica*).

**мф** *abbr.* (миллифот) milliphot; (миллифарада) millifarad.

**МФТИ** *abbr.* (Московский физикотехнический институт) Moscow Institute of Physics and Technology.

**мхи** *pl. of* **мох,** (bot.) Bryophyta.

**МХТИ** *abbr.* (Московский химико-технологический институт) Moscow Chemico-Technological Institute.

**м/ч, м/час** *abbr.* (метров в час) meters per hour.

**мчать** *v.* rush; **—ся** *v.* hurry, rush.

**мшанк/а** *f.* (bot.) pearlweed, pearlwort (*Sagina*); **—и** *pl.* (zool.) Bryozoa; **голоротые —и** (zool.) Gymnolaemata; **покрыторотые —и** Phylactolaemata.

**мшистый** *a.* mossy, moss-grown; cottony.

**мы** *pron.* we.

**мывший** *past act. part. of* **мыть.**

**мыз/а** *f.*, **—ный** *a.* farm, farmstead.

**мык/ание** *n.* rippling (of flax); **—аница** *f.* rippling comb; **—ать** *v.* ripple, hackle.

**мыл** *past sing. of* **мыть.**

**мыл/ение** *n.* soaping, lathering; **—енный** *a.* soaped, lathered; **—истый** *a.* soapy; **—ить** *v.* soap, lather; **—кий** *a.* soapy, freely lathering; **—кость** *f.* soapiness.

**мыло** *n.* soap; lather; **горное м.** (min.) saponite; **зеленое м.** soft soap, potash soap.

**мыловар** *m.* soap boiler, soap manufacturer; **—ение** *n.* soap boiling, soap manufacture; **—енный завод, —ня** *f.* soap works, soap factory; **—енный котел, —ный котел** soap boiler, soap kettle; **—ный** *a.* soap-boiling, soap.

**мылов/ка** *see* **мыльный камень; —ник** *see* **мыльное дерево; кора —ника** *see* **мыльная кора.**

**мылонафт** *m.* naphthenate soap.

**мыльник** *see* **мыльнянка.**

**мыльн/ый** *a.* soap, soapy, saponaceous; **м. камень** (min.) soapstone, steatite, massive talc; **м. клей** soap glue, soap paste; (paper) soap size; **м. корень** soaproot; **м. орешник, м. ягодник, —ое дерево** (bot.) soapbark tree, quillai (*Quillaja saponaria*); **м. спирт** (pharm.) spirit of soap (alcoholic soap solution); —ая вода soap water, soapsuds; —ая кора soapbark, quillaia bark; —ая пена soapsuds, lather.

**мыльнянка** *f.* (bot.) soap plant, spec. saponaria; **лекарственная м.** soapwort (*Saponaria officinalis*).

**мыс** *m.* (geol.) cape, promontory, cusp; **М. Горн** Cape Horn; **М. Доброй Надежды** Cape of Good Hope.

**мысл/енный** *a.* mental; imaginary, ideal; —**имый** *a.* thinkable, conceivable; —**ить** *v.* think, conceive.

**мысль** *f.* thought, idea, notion, conception; **ему пришло на м.** it occurred to him; **наводить на м., подавать м.** *v.* suggest, give an idea.

**мыслящий** *a.* thinking, intellectual.

**мыт** *m.* (vet.) strangles; (poultry) molt; —**иться** *v.* molt.

**мытник** *m.* (bot.) wood betony (*Pedicularis*).

**мыт/ый** *a.* washed; —**ь** *v.* wash; —**ье** *n.* washing.

**мышатник** *m.* (bot.) thermopsis.

**мышей** *m.* bristly foxtail grass (*Setaria*); **м. брица** foxtail millet (*S. viridis*).

**мышеловка** *f.* mousetrap.

**мышечный** *a.* muscle, muscular.

**мыш/ий, —иный** *a.* mouse, mouse's; **м. горошек** (bot.) cow vetch (*Vicia cracca*).

**мышленный** *past pass. part. of* **мыслить.**

**мышца** *f.* (anat.) muscle.

**мышь** *f.* mouse; **летучая м.** bat; **м.-полевка** *f.* field mouse.

**мышьяк** *m.* arsenic, As; **белый м.** white arsenic (arsenous oxide); **двусернистый м., красный м.** arsenic disulfide, red arsenic; **желтый м., трехсернистый м.** yellow arsenic, arsenic trisulfide; **окись —а, пятиокись —а** arsenic oxide, arsenic pentoxide; **сернистый м., пятисернистый м.** arsenic sulfide, arsenic pentasulfide; **хлористый м.** arsenous chloride, arsenic trichloride; **хлорный м.** arsenic pentachloride.

**мышьяковисто/калиевая соль** potassium arsenite; —**кальциевая соль, —кислый кальций** calcium arsenite; —**кислый** *a.* arsenous acid; arsenite (of); —**кислая соль** arsenite; —**магниевая соль** magnesium arsenite;

—**медистая соль** cuprous arsenite; —**медная соль** cupric arsenite; —**свинцовистая соль** lead arsenite.

**мышьяковист/ый** *a.* arsenic, arsenous, arsenical, arsenide (of); **м. ангидрид** arsenous acid anhydride, arsenous oxide, arsenic trioxide; **м. водород** hydrogen arsenide, arsine; **м. колчедан** *see* **мышьяковый колчедан; м. никель** nickel arsenide; **м. свинец** lead arsenide; **м. цинк** zinc arsenide; —**ая кислота** arsenous acid; **соль —ой кислоты** arsenite; **хлорангидрид —ой кислоты** arsenyl chloride.

**мышьяково/аммониевая соль** ammonium arsenate; —**железистая накипь** (min.) pitticite, scorodite; —**железистая соль** ferrous arsenate; —**кальциевая соль, —кислый кальций** calcium arsenate; —**кислый** *a.* arsenic acid; arsenate (of); —**кислая соль** arsenate; **кислая —кислая соль** biarsenate; —**кобальтовая соль** cobalt arsenate; —**медная соль** cupric arsenate, copper arsenate; —**натриевая соль** sodium arsenate; —**свинцовистая соль** lead arsenate.

**мышьяков/ый** *a.* arsenic, arsenical; **м. ангидрид** arsenic pentoxide; **м. колчедан** (min.) arsenical pyrites, arsenopyrite, mispickel; **м. цвет** (min.) arsenic bloom, arsenolite; —**ая кислота** arsenic acid; **соль —ой кислоты** arsenate.

**мыщел/ковый** *a.* (anat.) condyloid; —**ок** *m.* condyle.

**МЭБ** *abbr.* (**Международное эпизоотическое бюро**) International Epizootic Bureau.

**Мэв** *abbr.* (**мегаэлектрон-вольт**) million electron-volts, Mev.

**мэкв, м.-экв.** *abbr.* (**миллиэквивалент**) milliequivalent; **мэкв/л** *abbr.* (**миллиэквивалентов на литр**) milliequivalents per liter.

**мэнджэк** *m.* manjak (natural bitumen).

**мэр** *m.* mayor.

**МЭТИ** *abbr.* (**Московский электротехнический институт**) Moscow Electro-Technical Institute.

**Мэя соль** May's salt (double salt of benzene-diazonium chloride and antimony trichloride).

**мю** *n.* mu (μ).

**мюллерово стекло** (min.) Müller's glass, yalite (a variety of opal).

**мюль** *m.*, **—ная машина** (text.) mule; **—щица** *f.* mule spinner.

**мю-мезон** *m.* (nucl.) mu-meson, muon.

**Мюнке насос** Muencke (filter) pump.

**Мюнхен** Munich.

**мюон** *see* **мю-мезон.**

**мюрг** *m.* (min.) unit of resistance to ventilation.

**мюскардина** *f.* a fungus disease of insects.

**мягк/ий** *a.* soft, mild, smooth, mellow, pliant, supple; clement (weather); **—ая вода** soft water; **—ая прослойка** pad.

**мягко** *adv.* softly, mildly; **—кожие** *pl.* (zool.) Malacodermata; **—сть** *f.* softness, pliability; (meteor.) clemency; **—телки** *pl.* predaceous beetles (*Cantharididae*); **—телые** *pl.* (zool.) mollusks; **—телый** *a.* soft-bodied; **—тянутый** *a.* soft-drawn.

**мягок** *m.* (min.) nontronite (a variety of chloropal).

**мягч/е** *comp. of* **мягкий, мягко,** softer, more softly; **—ение** *n.* softening; **—итель** *m.*, **—ительное средство** softener, softening agent; plasticizer; (pharm.) emollient, demulcent; **—ительный** *a.* softening; plasticizing; (pharm.) mitigant, lenitive, emollient, demulcent; **—ить** *v.* soften.

**мязга** *see* **мезга.**

**мяздра** *see* **мездра.**

**мякин/а** *f.* chaff, husk; **—ный** *a.* chaff, chaffy; (bot.) paleaceous; **—ная оболочка** hull.

**мяк/иш** *m.* crumb (soft part of bread); **—лый** *a.* soft, pulpy, flabby; **—нуть** *v.* soften, grow pulpy; **—оть** *f.*, **—отный** *a.* pulp, flesh (of fruit).

**мял** *past sing. of* **мять.**

**мял/ица, —ка** *f.*, **—о** *n.* brake (for fiber); **—ка** *f.* crusher, crushing mill, pulper;

**—ьно-трепальная машина** breaker and scutcher; **—ьный** *a. suffix* (fiber) breaking; crushing.

**мяс/истый** *a.* fleshy, meaty, pulpy (fruit); **—истая сторона** flesh side, rough side (of leather).

**мясни́га** *f.* myasniga (viscous clay in an auriferous placer).

**мясник** *m.* butcher.

**мясника** *see* **мясни́га.**

**мясной** *a.* meat; beef (cattle); **м. клей** sarcocolla; **м. сахар** inositol.

**мясо** *n.* meat, flesh; pulp (of fruit); **дикое м.** (med.) proud flesh; **—ведение** *n.* meat science; **—комбинат** *m.* meat-packing plant.

**мясомолочн/ая кислота** sarcolactic acid, *p*-lactic acid; **соль —ой кислоты, —окислая соль** sarcolactate.

**мясо/рубка** *f.* meat grinder, meat chopper; **—хладобойня** *f.* packing house.

**мята** *f.* (bot.) mint (*Mentha*); **английская м., перечная м.** peppermint (*M. piperita*); **зеленая м.** spearmint (*M. viridis*).

**мятеж** *m.* mutiny, revolt, rebellion.

**мятель** *see* **метель.**

**мятина** *f.* hollow, dent, nick.

**мятлик** *m.* (bot.) meadow grass (*Poa*); **луговой м.** Kentucky blue grass (*Poa pratensis*).

**мятлица** *f.* sunflower moth.

**мятн/ый** *a.* mint, peppermint; **—ая камфора** peppermint camphor, menthol; **—ое масло** peppermint oil.

**мятый** *a.* rumpled, crumpled, crumbled (microstructure of metal); exhaust (steam).

**мять** *v.* rumple, crumple, crease; brake, break (fiber); work up, knead (clay); dip (leather); throttle (steam); **—е** *n.* rumpling; breaking.

**мяук/ать, —нуть** *v.* mew (of cat).

**мяч** *m.* ball.

# Н

**н** *abbr.* (**нормальный**) normal; (**ньютон**) newton; **н.** *abbr.* (**нормальность**) normality; **Н** code for nickel in steel mark.

**на** *prep. acc. to indicate motion; prepos.*

*to indicate location;* at, by, on, upon; in, into; for, per; over, to, toward; **на 10%** by 10%; **на 360°** through 360°; **на вес** by weight, in weight; **на другой день** next day; **на единицу** per unit; **на заказ** to order; **на запад** to the west, westward; **на зиму** for the winter; **на куски** to pieces, into pieces; **на полном ходу** at full speed; **на фут короче** a foot shorter; **на что?** what for? why?

**на—** *prefix used before verbs to denote completed action;* onto, toward.

**набав/ить, —лять** *v.* add, increase, raise; **—ка** *f.* increase; **—ленный** *a.* increased.

**набат** *m.* alarm, alarm bell.

**набег** *m.* raid, invasion; incursion.

**набе/гание** *n.* running against, running on; creeping, climb (of belt); flowing in; **—гать, —жать** *v.* run against, hit, strike; creep, climb; run in, flow in; fold (cloth); **—гающий** *a.* leading; creeping, climbing; inflowing.

**набело** *adv.* clean, fair; **переписанное н.** clean copy.

**набережная** *f.* embankment, quay.

**набив/ание** *n.,* **—ка** *f.* filling, filler, stuffing, packing, gasket; padding, lining; tamping, stamping, ramming; (text.) printing; **с —кой** packed; **—ать** *v.* fill, stuff, pack; pad, line; tamp, stamp (in), ram; (text.) print; nail on; raise (price); **—аться битком** crowd, jam.

**набивн/ой** *a.* tamped, rammed; (text.) printed, printing; **н. под** rammed bottom lining (of furnace); **—ая футеровка** rammed lining; **—ые доски** print stamps, engraving plates.

**набивочн/ый** *a.,* **н. материал** packing, stuffing, padding; **—ая камера** stuffing box; **—ое кольцо** gasket.

**набирать** *v.* collect, gather, accumulate; (typ.) compose, set up; dial (a number); contract (workers); pick up (speed); **—ся** *v.* collect, gather, get together.

**набит/ый** *a.* packed, padded; **—ь** *see* **набивать.**

**набла** *f.* (math.) nabla (Hamiltonian operator).

**наблюдаемый** *a.* observable.

**наблюдатель** *m.* observer, spectator; overseer, supervisor; lookout, spotter; surveyor; **—ность** *f.* keenness of observation; **—ный** *a.* observant; observation; supervisory; **—ный**

**пункт** observation post, lookout.

**наблюд/ать** *v.* observe, watch, survey; supervise, superintend, control; inspect; spot; **—ающий** *a.* observing; supervisory; **—ение** *n.* observation; supervision, superintendence, control; inspection; **—енный** *a.* observed.

**набой/ка** *f.* packing, stuffing; printed cloth; lining, facing, fettling (of furnace, etc.); heel tap; **—ник** *m.* stick; calking iron, calking tool; **—ный цех** (text.) printery; **—чатый** *a.* print; **—щик** *m.* printer.

**набок** *adv.* on one side, sideways.

**набольший** *a.* principal, superior, first; *m.* head, chief.

**набор** *m.* collection, assembly, outfit, kit, set (of tools); bank (of cells); (typ.) composing, typesetting; gage (of wire); (tel.) dialing; **н. высоты** climb (of plane); **—ка** *f.* gathering, assembly; **—ная** *f.* (typ.) typesetting room.

**наборн/ый** *a.* composition, typesetting; veneering; **—ая линейка** typesetting rule; **—ая машина** typesetting machine, typesetter; **—ая работа** inlaid work.

**наборщик** *m.* compositor, typesetter.

**набранный** *a.* collected, gathered; (typ.) composed, set up.

**набрасыв/ание** *n.* throwing on; sketching; **—ать** *v.* throw on; sketch, draw, outline; **—аться** *v.* fall on, attack.

**набрать** *see* **набирать.**

**набрести** *v.* come across, meet.

**наброс/анный** *a.* thrown on; sketched, outlined; **—ать, —ить** *see* **набрасывать; —ка** *f.* (geol.) talus; **—ок** *m.* sketch, rough drawing, layout, draft, rough copy.

**набух/аемость** *f.* swelling ability; swelling; **—ание** *n.* swelling; **—ать, —нуть** *v.* swell; **—ший** *a.* swollen.

**набыль** *f.* (geol.) thrust.

**навал** *m.,* **—ка** *f.* loading, heaping; **—ом** in bulk; **—ивать, —ить** *v.* heap up, pile, accumulate; fill, load, charge; **—иваться, —иться** *v.* fall on, lean; bend; **—оотбойщик** *m.* miner who cuts ore or coal and loads it on conveyor; **—очная машина** loading machine.

**навальцованный** *a.* rolled on.

**навар** *m.* broth; scum; shoulder, boss, built-up metal; **—енный** *a.* cooked; welded (on), deposited, built up; faced, tipped; fused (hearth bottom); **—енный сталью** steel-faced, steel-tipped; **—ивать**, **—ить** *v.* cook in quantities; brew; weld (on), build up (metal); face, tip; **—ивать сталью** edge, face or overlay with steel; **—ка** *f.* weld bead; welding (on), building up (metal); boss, shoulder; **—ка пода**, **—ка подины** burning in, sintering, fettling (furnace with refractory material); **—ной** *a.* weld, welded; covered with scum; **—ной под** sintered hearth bottom.

**наващивать** *v.* wax, coat with wax.

**навевать** *v.* drift, heap up, blow together; stack, load; roll on.

**наведаться** *see* **наведываться.**

**наведен/ие** *n.* leading, guiding; bringing on; application; (elec., etc.) induction; **н. лоска** polishing, varnishing; **н. справок** making inquiries; **—ный** *a.* led, guided, directed; brought on; induced.

**наведываться** *v.* visit; inquire about.

**навеки** *adv.* forever.

**наверно**, **—е** *adv.* certainly, surely; of course; for certain.

**навернут/ый** *a.* turned on, twisted on; screwed on; **—ь** *see* **навертывать.**

**наверст/ать**, **—ывать** *v.* make up, catch up; compensate; **—ывание** *n.* making up; recovery; compensation.

**наверт/ка** *f.* twisting, winding; **—ный** *a.* twist; screw (cap); **—ное сверло** common bit, flat drill; **—ывать** *v.* turn on, twist around, wind; screw on.

**наверх** *adv.* upward, up, upstairs; **—у** *adv.* above, aloft, at the top (of), upstairs.

**навес** *m.* shed, hangar; awning; (geol.) overhang; **ледяной н.** hanging glacier.

**навес/ить** *see* **навешивать**; **—ка** *f.* hanging; suspension, dispersion; weighed portion, batch; hinge; fitting, mounting; **—ной** *a.* hinged; attached, inserted; mounted, tractor-mounted; **—ная петля** hinge; **—ный** *a.* of **навес**; curved (trajectory), high-angle (fire).

**навести** *see* **наводить.**

**навестить** *see* **навещать.**

**навесу** *adv.* hanging, overhanging; in suspension.

**наветренный** *a.* windward, exposed to the wind.

**навеш/ать**, **—ивать** *v.* hang up, suspend; mount; **—енный** *a.* hung, suspended.

**навещать** *v.* visit, see.

**навеять** *see* **навевать.**

**навзничь** *adv.* backwards, on one's back.

**навив/альный**, **—ной**, **—очный** *a.* winding, coiling; **—ание** *n.*, **—ка** *f.* winding on, rolling on; **—ать** *v.* wind, wind on, roll on, reel, reel in, coil; spool; stack; **—аться** *v.* climb (of belt).

**навига/тор** *m.* navigator; **—ция** *f.* navigation.

**навин/тить**, **—чивать** *v.* screw on; **—ченный** *a.* screwed on; **—чивающийся** *a.* screw-on, screw, screwing.

**навис/ание** *n.* hanging over, impendence; **—ать**, **—нуть** *v.* hang over, overhang, impend; **—ающий** *a.* overhanging, pendant; **—лый**, **—ший** *a.* overhanging, impending; threatening.

**навит/ый** *a.* wound on, rolled on; **—ь** *see* **навивать.**

**навле/кать**, **—чь** *v.* bring on, cause, incur.

**навод/ить** *v.* direct, point (at), aim (at), set, sight (a telescope); lead, guide; bring on, apply; (elec., etc.) induce; make (inquiries); **н. глянец** gloss, glaze; **—ка** *f.* directing, pointing, aiming, setting, sighting, laying, laying on; foil (of mirror).

**наводн/ение** *n.* flood, inundation, submersion, overflow; **заливать —ением**, **—ить**, **—ять** *v.* swamp, flood, inundate, submerge, overflow, deluge.

**наводорож/енный** *a.* hydrogenated; **—ивание** *n.* hydrogenation; hydrogen absorption (by metals).

**наводчик** *m.* gunner, sighter.

**наводящий** *a.* directing, aiming; bringing on; (elec.) inducing; leading (question).

**навоз** *m.*, **—ный** *a.* manure, dung; **н.-сыпец** *m.* pulverized manure; **—ить** *v.* bring, carry, convey; manure, dung; **—ник** *m.* dung beetle; (bot.)

coprinus; **кукурузный** **—ник** beetle (*Pentodon idiota*); **—ный червь** muckworm; **—ная жижа** liquid manure; **—оразбрасыватель** *m.* manure spreader.

**навой** *m.*, **—ный** *a.* (text.) weaver's beam.

**наволок** *m.* (geol.) overthrust folding.

**наволока** *f.* pillowcase.

**навор/ачивать, —отить** *v.* pile up, heap up, roll on.

**навощ/енный** *a.* cerated, waxed; **—ить** *see* **наващивать.**

**навряд, —ли** *adv.* hardly, scarcely.

**навсегда** *adv.* forever; **раз н.** once for all.

**навстречу** *adv.* toward; **итти н.** *v.* meet.

**—навтика** *f. suffix* —nautics.

**навыворот** *adv.* wrong side out, inside out.

**навык** *m.* habit, practice, experience; **практический н.** skill.

**навылет** *adv.* through, right through.

**навьюч/ивать, —ить** *v.* load, burden.

**навяз/ать** *see* **навязывать; —ной** *a.* tied on; knitted on.

**навязнуть** *v.* stick, cling.

**навязчив/ость** *f.* intrusion, importunity; **—ый** *a.* obtrusive; fixed (idea).

**навязывать** *v.* attach, fasten, tie on; impose, obtrude, press (advice); **—ся** *v.* intrude, thrust oneself (upon).

**нагар** *m.* scale, deposit (of carbon); snuff; **—ообразование** *n.* scale formation (in motors).

**нагартов/ка** *f.* (met.) cold hardening, cold working; **—ывать** *v.* ball up, gather (soil).

**нагель** *m.* pin, dowel, peg.

**нагельфлю** *n.* (petr.) nagelfluh, gompholite, pudding stone.

**нагиагит** *m.* (min.) nagyagite.

**нагиб/ание** *n.* bending, bowing down; **—ать** *v.* bend, bow down.

**наглазник** *m.* eyeshade; blinker.

**наглухо** *adv.* hermetically, tightly; permanently.

**нагляди/о** *adv.* graphically; by ocular demonstration; **—ый** *a.* graphic, descriptive; visual; obvious; object (lesson); injection (well).

**нагнать** *see* **нагонять.**

**нагнет** *m.* (vet.) gall, sore.

**нагнет/ание** *n.* pressing, squeezing,

forcing, delivering, injecting; **камера —ания** discharge chamber; **ход —ания** pressure stroke; **—атель** *m.* blower, (force) pump; (mach.) supercharger.

**нагнетательн/ый** *a.* pressure, force, delivery; **н. клапан** pressure valve, delivery valve; **н. насос** force pump, pressure pump; **н. рукав** pressure hose; **н. трубопровод** pressure line; delivery conduit; **—ая труба** rising pipe, ascending pipe, stand pipe; delivery pipe; **—ое сопло** discharge nozzle.

**нагнет/ать** *v.* force, press, squeeze; deliver, feed, pump; **—ающий** *a.* forcing, pressing, pressure; *see also* **нагнетательный; —енный** *a.* forced, pressed.

**нагноение** *n.* fester, suppuration; **вызвать н.** *v.* fester.

**нагнут/ый** *a.* bent; **—ь** *see* **нагибать.**

**нагодки** *pl.* (bot.) marigold (*Calendula officinalis*).

**нагой** *a.* naked, nude, bare, uncovered.

**наголо** *adv.* bare; entirely.

**наголовник** *m.* head, cap.

**нагонять** *v.* overtake, come up (with); cause; drive on, drive together, fit; distil (a given quantity).

**нагораживать** *v.* pile up, stack up; divide into compartments.

**нагорный** *a.* upland, highland, raised; mountainous, high (land).

**нагородить** *see* **нагораживать.**

**нагорье** *n.* upland, highlands.

**нагота** *f.* bareness, nakedness.

**нагот/авливать, —овить, —овлять** *v.* prepare, make ready (in quantity); store, stock up; **—ове** *adv.* ready, in readiness, on call; **стоящий —ове** *a.* standby.

**награ/да** *f.*, **—дной, —дный** *a.* reward, recompense, remuneration; premium; **—дить, —ждать** *v.* reward, recompense, remunerate; **—дные** *pl.* bonus; **—ждение** *n.* reward, remuneration; **—жденный** *a.* rewarded.

**нагребать** *v.* rake together.

**нагрев** *m.*, **—ание** *n.* heating (up), warming (up); **поверхность —а** heating surface; **степень —а** temperature; **—атель** *m.* heater.

нагревательн/ый *a.* heating; preheating (torch); **н. змеевик** heating coil; **н. колодец** (met.) soaking pit, pit furnace; **н. прибор** heater; **—ая печь** heat-treatment furnace, heating furnace; (met.) soaking pit; **—ая плита** hot plate; **—ая проволока** (elec.) heating wire, hot wire.

нагре/вать, **—ть** *v.* heat, warm; **—вающий** *a.* heating, warming; **—тый** *a.* heated.

нагромо/ждать, **—здить** *v.* pile, pile up, accumulate, build up; **—ждение** *n.* pile, piling, heaping, packing; **—жденный** *a.* piled, heaped.

нагрубо *adv.* rough, roughly.

нагрудник *m.* breastplate.

нагру/жаемость *f.* load capacity; **—жать, —зить** *v.* load, charge; **—жающий** *a.* loading, charging; **—женный** *a.* loaded, charged; supporting (surface).

нагрузк/а *f.* load, loading, charge; weight; lading, shipment, freight; **—и** *pl.* stress; **н. на разрыв** tensile stress; **н. по жидкости** liquid rate; **н. по отношению к мощности** power loading (pounds per horsepower); **без —и** empty; **высшая н., наибольшая н.** peak load, maximum load; **допускаемая н., допустимая н.** load capacity, load-carrying capacity; permissible load; **емкость —и** (elec.) load capacity; **колебание —и** (elec.) load variations, fluctuation of load; **коэффициент —и** load factor; **плотность —и** (elec.) charging density; **полная н.** full load; full-time job.

нагруз/очный *a.* load, loading, charge; **н. ток** (elec.) load current; **—чик** *m.* loader.

нагрянуть *v.* take by surprise, come unawares (upon); happen suddenly, occur unexpectedly.

нагул *m.* pasturing; fattening (of livestock).

над *prep. instr.* above, over, on, upon.

над— *prefix* over—, super—, hyper—, epi—, above; per— (acid, salt).

надав/ить, **—ливать** *v.* press, squeeze, contract.

надазотная кислота pernitric acid.

надбав/ить, **—лять** *v.* add, increase; **—ка** *f.* increase, rise; bonus; outbidding; **—ленный** *a.* increased, raised; **—очный** *a.* additional.

надбензойная кислота perbenzoic acid.

надбори/ая кислота perboric acid; **соль —ой кислоты, —окислая соль** perborate; **—окислый** *a.* perboric acid; perborate (of); **—окислый магний, —омагниевая соль** magnesium perborate.

надвесный *a.* overhung, overhanging.

надви/г *m.* thrust; (geol.) overthrust, overthrust folding; **крутой н.** (geol.) upthrust; **—гать, —нуть** *v.* move up, move against, move upon, push on, thrust; **—гаться** *v.* approach, draw near, come on; (geol.) overthrust; **—гающийся** *a.* approaching, impending, imminent.

надводный *a.* above-water, emergent.

надвое *adv.* in two, in half; ambiguously.

надворн/ый *a.* outdoor, yard; **—ое строение** outbuilding, outhouse.

надгибать *v.* bend, fold.

надглоточный узел brain (of insect).

надгортанник *m.* (anat.) epiglottis.

надда/вать, **—ть** *v.* add, superadd; **н. скорость** increase speed, accelerate; **—ча** *f.* addition; outbidding.

наддув *m.* pressure charging, pressure feed, pressurization.

надев/ание *n.* putting on; **—ать** *v.* put on, slip on, don; gear, harness.

надежда *f.* hope, expectation.

надежн/ость *f.* safety, security, reliability, dependability; **—ый** *a.* safe, secure, sure, reliable, dependable, trustworthy.

надел *m.* share, portion; plot (of land).

наделать *v.* make in large quantity, produce in mass; cause.

надел/ение *n.* dispensation, allotment, consignment; **—ить, —ять** *v.* impart, dispense, allot, consign.

надельфейль *m.* needle file.

надет/ый *a.* put on, slipped on; **—ь** *see* **надевать.**

надеяться *v.* hope (for), look forward (to), rely (upon), have confidence (in).

наджелезно/кислая соль perferrate; **—синеродоводородная кислота** perferricyanic acid.

**надземный** *a.* overground, above ground; overhead, aerial; elevated (railroad).

**надзир/атель** *m.* inspector, supervisor, superintendent, overseer; **—атель-ство** *n.* supervision, overseeing; **—ать** *v.* supervise, superintend, inspect, control.

**надзор** *m.* supervision, superintendence, inspection, control; servicing.

**надир** *m.* nadir, lowest possible point.

**надир/ание** *n.* (text.) raising; **—ать** *v.* tear up; raise.

**надкалывать** *v.* pierce slightly, prick; split slightly, cleave.

**надкислота** *f.* per acid.

**над/кожица, —кожница** *f.* (biol.) epidermis; cuticle; **—коленная кость** (anat.) patella.

**надколоть** *see* **надкалывать.**

**надкости/ая плева, —ица** *f.* (anat.) periosteum; **воспаление —ицы** (med.) periostitis.

**надкритический** *a.* supercritical, above-critical.

**надкрылье** *n.* (zool.) elytron, wing sheath.

**надламывать** *v.* break partly, crack.

**надлеж/ать** *v.* be necessary; want, need; **—ит это сделать** it must be done.

**надлежащ/ий** *a.* proper, fit, due, expedient; **н. размер** correct size; **—им образом** properly, suitably.

**надлом** *m.* fracture, break; **—ать, —ить** *see* **надламывать; —ленный** *a.* partly broken, cracked.

**надмасляная кислота** perbutyric acid.

**надмуравьиная кислота** performic acid.

**на-днях** *adv.* before long, one of these days; lately, the other day.

**надо** *v.* it is necessary; *prep.*, *see* **над; ему н.** he must, he needs.

**надобн/ость** *f.* necessity, requirement, need, want; **иметь н.** *v.* require, need; **нет —ости** there is no need; **—ый** *a.* necessary, requisite; useful.

**надое/дать, —сть** *v.* bore, annoy, worry, bother; **—дливый** *a.* irksome, tiresome, tedious.

**надой** *m.* milk yield.

**надолбы** *pl.* (mil.) obstacle, post.

**надолго** *adv.* for a long time, for long.

**надорвать** *see* **надрывать.**

**надорит** *m.* (min.) nadorite.

**надосновный** *a.* superbasic.

**надотряд** *m.* (biol.) super-order.

**надпил** *m.* saw cut, notch; **—ивать, —ить** *v.* saw a little, notch.

**надпис/анный** *a.* inscribed; **—ать, —ывать** *v.* inscribe, superscribe; letter; **—ь** *f.* inscription, superscription, superscript; notice; legend.

**надпочечн/ик** *m.*, **—ая железа** (anat.) adrenal gland; **—ый** *a.* adrenal, suprarenal.

**надпропионовая кислота** perpropionic acid.

**надрез** *m.* cut, incision, notch, gash, tap (on tree); **—анный** *a.* cut, notched, tapped; **—ать, —ывать** *v.* cut (into), incise, make an incision, notch, tap.

**надрениевая кислота** perrhenic acid.

**надруб/ать, —ить** *v.* mark, notch.

**надрыв** *m.* slight tear, rupture, strain, overstraining; **—ать** *v.* begin to tear, rupture, lacerate.

**надсекать** *v.* make cuts, make incisions, notch, gash.

**надсемейство** *n.* (biol.) superfamily.

**надсерн/ая кислота** persulfuric acid; **соль —ой кислоты, —окислая соль** persulfate; **—оаммониевая соль** ammonium persulfate; **—окислый** *a.* persulfuric acid; persulfate (of); **—окислый натрий, —онатриевая соль** sodium persulfate; **—ый ангидрид** sulfur heptoxide.

**надсечь** *see* **надсекать.**

**надсинхронный** *a.* hypersynchronous.

**надслуховой** *a.* supersonic, ultraphonic.

**надсм/атривать** *v.* supervise, look after, control, inspect; **—отр** *m.* control, supervision; inspection; **—отрщик** *m.* supervisor, overseer.

**надсоль** *f.* persalt.

**надстав/ить, —лять** *v.* piece, add on, lengthen; **—ка** *f.* extension, extension piece, extension arm; adapter; **кольцевая —ка** extension ring; **—ленный** *a.* added on, lengthened, extended; **—ной** *a.* extension; **—ная труба** adapter.

**надстр/аивать, —оить** *v.* build on, build a superstructure; **—ойка** *f.* superstructure; superstruction, building on.

**надстрочный** *a.* superlinear.

надсульфоновая кислота persulfonic acid.

надтепловой *a.* epithermal, above-thermal.

надтиоугольн/ая кислота perthiocarbonic acid; соль —ой кислоты, —окислая соль perthiocarbonate.

надтональный *a.* supersonic.

надув/ание *n.* inflation; —ать *v.* inflate, blow up, distend, fill (with air); cheat; —аться *v.* inflate, swell, puff up; —ная подушка air cushion.

надугольн/ая кислота percarbonic acid; соль —ой кислоты, —окислая соль percarbonate; —окислый *a.* percarbonic acid; percarbonate (of).

надуксусн/ая кислота peracetic acid; соль —ой кислоты, —окислая соль peracetate; —окислый *a.* peracetic acid; peracetate (of).

надум/анный *a.* farfetched, exaggerated; —ать, —ывать *v.* devise; —аться, —ываться make up one's mind, decide.

надут/ый *a.* inflated, blown up, bloated; (bot.) torous; —ь *see* надувать.

надуш/енный *a.* perfumed, scented; —ить *v.* perfume, scent; fumigate.

надфиль *m.* needle file.

надфосфорная кислота perphosphoric acid.

надхромовая кислота perchromic acid.

надчерепная оболочка (anat.) pericranium.

наедине *adv.* in private, privately, alone.

наезд *m.* incursion; quick visit.

наездник *m.* ichneumon wasp; rider (of analytical balance); —и *pl.* Ichneumonidae.

наезж/ание *n.* running into, striking; interference; —ать *v.* run into, strike, hit.

наем *m.* hire, rent, employment; брать в н. *v.* rent (from); сдавать в н. *v.* rent (to), let; —ный *a.* hired.

наехать *see* наезжать.

нажат/ие *n.* pressing, pressure, depression; —ый *a.* pressed down; reaped, harvested; —ь *see* нажимать, нажинать.

наждак *m.* emery (impure corundum).

наждачн/ый *a.* emery; н. круг, —ое точило emery wheel, emery cutter,

emery grinder; н. порошок emery dust; н. холст, —ая шкура, —ое полотно emery cloth; —ая лента emery belt.

нажива *f.* gain, profit; —ть *v.* gain, profit, acquire, get; contract (disease).

нажив/ка *f.* bait (for fish); —лять *v.* bait.

нажим *m.* push, thrust, pressure, stress; clamp, pinchcock; —ать *v.* push, press, force (against), depress, contract; clamp, pinch; —ающее усилие tension, pressure.

нажимн/ой *a.* pressure; clamp, clamping; н. валик printing roller; pressure roll; н. винт clamping screw; adjusting screw; н. стержень push bar, press rod; —ая кнопка (elec.) push button; —ая планка cleat; —ая пружина pressure spring; —ая скоба dog clamp; —ое приспособление printing device; clamp.

нажимчик *m.* stuffing box.

нажинать *v.* harvest, reap.

нажировка *f.* (agr.) fattening.

наз. *abbr.* (называемый) called; (называется) is called.

назад *adv.* back, backwards; брать н., отводить н. *v.* back up, retract; взгляд н. retrospect; год тому н. a year ago; движение н. return; ход н. reverse running, backing; return stroke (of piston).

назв/ание *n.* name, designation; title; —анный *a.* named, called; —ать *see* называть.

назем *m.* dung, manure.

наземн/ый *a.* land, terrestrial, ground; superficial; н. предмет landmark; —ая вода surface water; —ая подготовка (aero.) ground training; —ая порода (geol.) surface rock, supercrust rock.

назначать *v.* appoint, name, assign, allot, set, fix; quote (price).

назначен/ие *n.* appointment, assignment; designation; purpose, destination; fixing (of price); место —ия destination; общего —ия general purpose, general duty; особого —ия special purpose; станция —ия receiving station, receiving end.

назнач/енный *a.* appointed, assigned, set, designated; —ить *see* назначать.

**назовем** *fut. 1 pl. of* **называть.**

**назойливый** *a.* importunate, insistent.

**назре/вание** *n.* ripening, maturing; —**вать**, —**ть** *v.* ripen, mature; be preparing, be about to happen; gather head (of abscess); —**вающий** *a.* ripening; gathering; —**лый** *a.* ripe, mature.

**назубок** *m.* file.

**назубр/енный** *a.* indented, notched, nicked; —**ивать**, —**ить** *v.* indent, make indentations, notch, nick; learn by rote.

**назыв/аемый** *a.* named, called; **так н.** so-called; —**ать** *v.* name, call, designate, term, qualify (as), describe.

**наи—** *prefix* the most; —**более** *adv.* the most, utmost; above all; —**больший** *a.* the greatest, maximum, extreme, peak; —**больший размер** overall dimension.

**наивный** *a.* naive, simple.

**наивыгоднейший** *a.* most advantageous, most favorable, best.

**наивысший** *a.* highest, maximum, ceiling.

**наизнанку** *adv.* inside out, wrong side out.

**наизусть** *adv.* by heart, by rote.

**наил/ивание** *n.* silt deposition; —**ок** *m.* warp (sediment deposited by water); **с —ком** warp (soil or land).

**наилучш/ий** *a.* the best; —**им образом** in the best way possible, to the best advantage.

**наименее** *adv.* the least; less.

**наименов/ание** *n.* name, denomination; item; **привести к одному —анию** *v.* (math.) reduce to one denomination; —**ать** *v.* name, denominate.

**наименьший** *a.* the least, minimum.

**наирит** *m.* Nairit, chloroprene rubber (equivalent to neoprene).

**наискось** *adv.* on the slant, obliquely, skew; **располагать н.** *v.* skew.

**наихудший** *a.* the worst.

**най/денный** *a.* found; —**ти** *see* **находить.**

**наказ** *m.* order; instructions; —**ание** *n.* punishment, penalty; —**анный** *a.* punished; —**ать**, —**ывать** *v.* punish.

**накал** *m.* incandescence, intense heat, white heat, red heat, glow; **батарея —a** filament battery; **белый н.** white heat, incandescence; **напряжение —a** (elec.) filament voltage; **нить —a** filament; **ток —a** filament current.

**накаленн/ость** *f.* heat, incandescence; —**ый** *a.* incandescent, glowing.

**накалив/ание** *n.* heating, incandescence, glowing; **н. добела** incandescence, white heat; **лампа —ания** incandescent lamp, filament lamp; —**ать** *v.* heat, incandesce; —**ать добела** bring to white heat; —**ать докрасна** bring to red heat; —**аться** *v.* incandesce, get hot, glow; —**ающийся** *a.* incandescent.

**накалить** *see* **накаливать.**

**накалывать** *v.* prick; split, break; pin on.

**накалять** *see* **накаливать.**

**накануне** *adv.* the day before, on the eve (of); **н. вечером** on the previous night.

**накапать** *see* **накапывать.**

**накаплив/ать** *see* **накоплять;** —**ающий** *a.* accumulating; —**ающий счетчик** (computers) accumulator.

**накапывать** *v.* pour by drops, drop on; dig, dig up.

**накат** *m.* subflooring; sand bank; scab (on rolled material); —**анный** *a.* rolled on; —**ать**, —**ить** *see* **накатывать.**

**накатина** *f.* joist, girder.

**накат/ка** *f.* knurl, knurling tool; knurling, milling; **винт с —кой** knurled screw, milled screw; —**ная машина** knurling machine, knurling tool; —**очный валик** (rubber) batch-off roll.

**накатчик** *m.* roller, cloth roller.

**накатыв/ание** *n.* rolling on; knurling, milling; —**ать** *v.* roll, roll on, smooth with rollers; knurl, mill; —**ающее колесо** knurling wheel, milling wheel.

**накач/ать**, —**ивать** *v.* pump, pump up, inflate; feed; —**енный** *a.* pumped up, inflated; **туго —енный** fully inflated, full; —**ивание** *n.* pumping, inflation.

**накерн/ивание** *n.* prick-punching; —**ивать**, —**ить** *v.* prick-punch, center-punch, center, mark (with center punch), make an indentation.

**накид/ать**, —**ывать** *v.* throw on, cast on; —**ка** *f.* throwing on; cover, mantle, cloak; increase (in price).

**накип/ать, —еть** *v.* form by boiling, be incrusted; **—елый** *a.* formed by boiling, incrusted; **—еобразование** *n.* scale formation (on boilers); **—еочиститель** *m.* scaler; **—ной** *a.* **—ь** *f.*, scum; scale, boiler scale, incrustation; deposit, sediment, sinter.

**накладка** *f.* facing, cover plate, lap; strap; (geol.) overlap, superposition.

**накладная** *f.* (com.) invoice; bill of lading.

**накладн/ой** *a.* laid on, put on, superposed, applied; **н. металл** metal plating, metal coating; **—ое золото** gold plate; **—ое серебро** silver plate; **—ые расходы** overhead expense, overhead cost, overhead; **—ый** *a.* unprofitable, disadvantageous.

**накладыв/аемый, —ающийся** *a.* superposable; **—ание** *n.* laying on, superimposing, superposition; plating, coating; **—ать** *v.* lay on, put on, superimpose, superpose, apply, coat, plate; apply (tool); telescope; **—ать сверху** superimpose.

**наклёвываться** *v.* begin sprouting.

**накле/ивание** *n.,* **—йка** *f.* gluing, pasting; **—ивать, —ить** *v.* glue, paste (on); **—йка** *f.* label, sticker; patch.

**наклеп** *m.* riveting; (met.) cold hardening, cold working, hammer hardening; **—анный** *a.* riveted; cold-worked; **—ывать** *v.* rivet.

**наклон** *m.* slope, incline, inclination; slant, pitch, gradient, grade; tilt; **—ение** *n.* inclination, dip, tilting, pitch; **магнитное —ение** magnetic inclination, magnetic dip; **стрелка —ения** (geol.) dip needle, dipping compass; **угол —ения** angle of dip, angle of inclination; **—енный** *a.* inclined, dip; **—ить** *see* **наклонять.**

**наклонн/о** *adv.* obliquely, slantingly, aslant; **—ость** *f.* inclination, leaning, tendency, bent, propensity, proclivity; obliquity; **—ый** *a.* inclined, sloping, slanted, slanting, tilting, oblique; **—ый желоб, —ая эстакада** chute; **—ая линия** incline.

**наклон/омер** *m.* tiltmeter; **—яемый, —яющийся** *a.* inclinable; **—ять** *v.* incline, slant, slope, lean, tilt, tip;

depress, decline; **—яться** *v.* slope, incline, lean, lean over.

**наков/альня** *f.* anvil; **стул —альни, чубан —альни** anvil block; **—анный** *a.* forged on; **—ать, —ывать** *v.* forge on.

**накожн/ый** *a.* cutaneous, skin; **—ая болезнь** skin disease, dermatitis.

**накол** *m.* pinholes.

**наколенник** *m.* (anat.) kneecap, patella.

**накол/оть** *see* **накалывать; —юшка** *f.* awl.

**наконец** *adv.* at last, at length, finally.

**наконечник** *m.* tip, point; nozzle, spout, mouth, mouthpiece, nipple; adapter; head, cap; (arrow) head; terminal, clip; tag; ferrule; (pole) shoe.

**накоп/итель** *m.* accumulator; storing device; tank; **—ить, —лять** *v.* accumulate, gather, get together, heap up, store (up), stock up; **—ляться** *v.* gather, aggregate; be accumulated; **—ление** *n.* accumulation, agglomeration; storage; build-up, pile-up; **коэффициент —ления** build-up factor; **—ленный** *a.* accumulated, cumulative; stored; **—ляющийся** *a.* cumulative.

**накоротко: замкнуть н.** *v.* short, short-circuit.

**накрененный** *a.* lopsided.

**накрепко** *adv.* firmly, fast, tightly.

**накрест** *adv.* cross, crosswise.

**накрит** *m.* nacrite (a kaolin mineral).

**накрой** *m.* lap, lap joint, overlapping.

**накры/вание** *n.* covering; **—вать, —ть** *v.* cover; **—тый** *a.* covered.

**нактоуз** *m.* binnacle (of compass).

**накуп/ать, —ить** *v.* buy, buy up, purchase.

**налагать** *v.* impose, inflict, lay on, put on, superimpose.

**нала/дить, —живать** *v.* put right, fix, mend, repair; set, adjust, tune up; align; make ready; **—дка** *f.,* **—живание** *n.* fixing, repairing; adjusting, tuning up; **—женный** *a.* fixed, repaired; set, adjusted, tuned up.

**налево** *adv.* to the left, left, on the left hand; **брать н.** *v.* turn left.

**налег/ание** *n.* superposition, juxtaposition; (transgressive) overlap; **—ать** *v.* overlie; lean on; apply oneself.

**налед/енелый** *a.* iced, covered with ice; **—енеть** *v.* get covered with ice, freeze over; **—ь** *m.* layer of ice.

**налеп/ить, —лять** *v.* stick on, glue on.

**налет** *m.* deposit, incrustation, coating; bloom, tarnish, film; efflorescence; frost; raid, inroad; sudden attack, onslaught (of insects); swoop (of bird); **влажный н.** condensed moisture, condensate, "sweat"; **—ать** *v.* fly (on, against); strike, rebound; **—ающий** *a.* incident, impinging, bombarding (particle).

**налив** *m.* pouring in, infusion; ripening (of fruit); forming (of grain); sap, juice; **—ание** *n.* pouring in, filling; **—ать** *v.* pour in, fill, fill up; introduce; **—аться** *v.* fill with juice, ripen; be poured in, run in; **—ка** *f.* pouring in, infusion; fruit liqueur.

**наливн/ой** *a.* pouring, filling; molded; juicy (fruit); liquid (cargo); inlet (pipe); overshot (wheel); **—ое отверстие** inlet, filling hole; **—ое судно** tanker.

**налим** *m.* burbot, eelpout (fish).

**налип/ать, —нуть** *v.* stick, adhere.

**налит/ый** *a.* poured in, filled; **—ь** *see* **наливать.**

**налицо** *adv.* present, ready.

**наличие** *n.* presence.

**наличник** *m.* doorcase; window frame; (anvil) plate, cover plate; (zool.) clypeus.

**наличн/ость** *f.,* **—ые** *pl.* cash, ready money; **в —ости** present, ready, on hand, available.

**наличный** *a.* present, on hand, available; effective; **н. расчет** cash payment; **н. состав** personnel.

**наловчиться** *v.* become dextrous, become skilful.

**налог** *m.,* **—овый** *a.* tax, assessment; **облагать —ом** *v.* tax, assess; **—овый инспектор** assessor; **—ообложение** *n.* taxation; **—оплательщик** *m.* taxpayer.

**наложен/ие** *n.* laying on, imposition; superposition, superimposing, overlap; **—ный** *a.* laid on, superimposed.

**наложить** *see* **налагать, накладывать.**

**нальчикин** *m.* nalchikin, clay from the Nalchik region.

**нам** *dat. of* **мы,** us, to us, for us.

**намагни/тить, —чивать** *v.* magnetize; **—чение, —чивание** *n.,* **—чивающий** *a.* magnetization, magnetizing; **—ченность** *f.* magnetization, intensity of magnetization; **—ченный** *a.* magnetized; **—чиваемость** *f.* magnetizability; **—чиваемый, —чивающийся** *a.* magnetizable; **коэффициент —чивания** coefficient of magnetization; **кривая —чивания** magnetization curve; **—чивающее устройство** magnetizer.

**намаз/анный** *a.* smeared, daubed, coated; **—ать, —ывать** *v.* smear, daub, coat, cover; **—ка** *f.* smearing; filler; **—ная пластина** pasted plate (in storage cell).

**намасл/енный** *a.* greased, oiled; **—ивание** *n.* greasing, oiling, lubrication; **—ивать, —ить** *v.* grease, oil, lubricate.

**наматыв/ание** *n.* winding, reeling; **—ать** *v.* wind, reel, coil; **—ающий** *a.* winding, reeling, coiling; take-up (reel).

**намачив/ание** *n.* wetting, moistening; soaking, steeping; **—ать** *v.* wet, moisten; soak, steep, macerate.

**намек** *m.* hint, allusion, insinuation; **—ать, —нуть** *v.* hint, insinuate, allude (to), suggest, indicate.

**намер/еваться** *v.* intend, propose, design, consider; **—ение** *n.* intention, purpose, design; **—енный** *a.* intentional, deliberate.

**намер/ивать, —ить** *v.* measure.

**намертво** *adv.* dead; **обжигать н.** *v.* deadburn; **обожженный н.** deadburned.

**намерять** *see* **намеривать.**

**намет** *m.* shed; thread, string; drift.

**наметать** *v.* drift, sweep up.

**наметить** *see* **намечать.**

**наметка** *f.* casting net; basting; rough draft; measuring rod.

**намеч/ать** *v.* mark; plan, project, contemplate, have in view; set (a course); **—енный** *a.* marked; planned, projected; designated, set (course).

**нами** *instr. of* **мы,** by us, us.

**наминать** *v.* knead, work.

**намного** *adv.* by far.

**намок/ать, —нуть** v. become wet, get wet; **—ший** a. wet, soaked.

**намолот** m. grain yield.

**намордник** m. muzzle.

**намот/анный** a. wound, coiled; **—ать** see **наматывать; —ка** f. winding, coil; **—очный** a. winding; **—очная машина** coil-winding machine; reeling machine.

**намоч/енный** a. wet, wetted; soaked, steeped; **—ить** see **намачивать.**

**намыв** m. (geol.) alluvium, alluvion; **—ание** n. alluviation, deposition; **—ать** v. deposit; pan out (gold); **—ной** a. alluvial; **—ной слой** alluvium, alluvial soil; **—ная коса** spit, bar.

**намыл/енный** a. soaped, lathered; **—ивать, —ить** v. soap, lather.

**намыть** see **намывать.**

**намять** see **наминать.**

**нандинин** m. nandinine.

**нанес/ение** n. bringing on, infliction; application (of paint); drawing, plotting; heaping, drifting; **—енный** a. a. brought; applied; drawn, plotted; entered (on chart); inscribed, etched; **—ти** see **наносить.**

**на-нет: сойти н.** v. come to nothing.

**нанизывать** v. thread, string.

**наниматель** m. employer; tenant, lessee.

**нанимать** v. hire, engage, employ; rent; **—ся** v. apply for work; be hired.

**нано—** prefix nano— (indicating a magnitude of $10^{-9}$); **—ампер** m. (elec.) nanoampere.

**нанос** m. (geol.) alluvium, alluvion, deposition, accretion (of soil), float, blanket, drift; **—ы** pl. detritus, debris; **—итель** m. draftsman; **—ить** v. bring; heap, drift; aggrade; deposit; build up (layers); apply, coat; plot, draw, map; insert.

**наносн/ый** a. (geol.) alluvial, drift; alien, superficial; **н. слой, —ая земля, —ое отложение** alluvium, alluvion.

**нанофарада** f. (elec.) nanofarad.

**нанофин** m. Nanofin, 2,6-dimethyl-piperidine hydrochloride.

**нансук** m. (text.) nainsook.

**нантокит** m. (min.) nantokite (cuprous chloride).

**нанят/ой** a. hired; rented; **—ь** see **нанимать.**

**наоборот** adv. contrary, inversely, the wrong way; on the contrary, on the other hand; **и н.** and vice versa.

**наобум** adv. at random, without thinking.

**наоткос** adv. aslant, slantwise, obliquely.

**наотрез** adv. flatly, point-blank.

**напад** m., **—ение** n. attack, invasion; infestation; **—ать** v. attack, invade; infest; find fault (with), criticize.

**напа/ивать** v. solder on, fuse on, seal on; **—йка** f. soldering on, building up (metal); soldered piece.

**напаковка** f. filling, packing.

**напарье** n. auger, screw drill, drill; countersink.

**напасть** see **нападать.**

**напая/нный** a. soldered on, welded on; **—ть** see **напаивать.**

**напеллин** m. napelline, benzaconine.

**наперво** adv. first (of all).

**наперебой** see **наперерыв.**

**наперевес** adv. atilt, tilting.

**наперед** adv. in advance, beforehand; first.

**напере/кор** adv. in defiance (of), in opposition (to); **—рез** adv. across (path of travel); **—рыв** adv. vying (with each other); one after the other.

**напереть** see **напирать.**

**наперечет: знать н.** v. know every item from memory.

**наперст/ковый** a., **—ок** m., **—очный** a. thimble; **—очная трава, —янка** f. (bot.) foxglove, digitalis (Digitalis purpurea).

**напечат/анный** a. printed, published; **—ать** v. print, publish.

**напил/ок, —ьник** m. file.

**напирать** v. press, depress.

**напис/анный** a. written; **—ать** v. write, write down; paint.

**напит/анный** a. impregnated, saturated; **—ать** see **напитывать.**

**напиток** m. drink, beverage; liquor.

**напитыв/ание** n. saturation, impregnation; satiation; **—ать** v. saturate, impregnate, soak, steep; satiate.

**наплав/ить, —ливать, —лять** v. fuse, melt, smelt; fuse on, build up (layers of metal); float (wood); **—ка** f. beading, weld seam; (metal) surfacing; **—ление** n. building up (by welding); —**ленный** *a.* fused on, built up (metal), deposited.

**наплав/ной, —очный** *a.* fused; floating (bridge, etc.); surfacing (alloy); **н. материал** (welding) filler; **н. металл** welding metal.

**напластов/ание, —ывание** *n.* (geol.) stratification, deposition, layer; overlap; —**ания** *pl.* strata, rock beds; —**анный** *a.* stratified, arranged in layers; superposed, superimposed; —**ывать** *v.* (geol.) deposit sediments; superimpose; overlap; —**ываться** *v.* stratify.

**наплодить** *v.* bring forth, produce; —**ся** *v.* multiply.

**наплы/в** *m.* influx, abundance; excrescence (on trees); beading; —**вать, —ть** *v.* float, drift; —**вной** *a.* floating; (geol.) alluvial; —**вной слой** alluvium.

**наповал** *adv.* on the spot, outright.

**наподобие** *adv.* like, similarly (to), in like manner.

**наполеонит** *m.* (petr.) napoleonite, corsite (an orbicular diorite).

**наполнен/ие** *n.* filling, packing, stuffing; admission; inflation; (cement) aggregate; **коэффициент —ия** (mech.) volumetric efficiency, coefficient of admission; —**ность** *f.* fullness; inflation; —**ный** *a.* filled, full; inflated.

**наполнитель** *m.* filler, filling; feeder, charger; —**ный** *a.* filling; feeding, charging.

**наполн/ить, —ять** *v.* fill, fill up, charge; impregnate; inflate (with gas); —**яющий** *a.* filling, charging.

**наполовину** *adv.* half, by halves, semi—.

**напольный** *a.* low-ground, ground-type; outdoor.

**напом/инание** *n.* reminding, reminder; —**инать, —нить** *v.* remind, recall, put in mind, suggest; —**инающий** *a.* reminding, reminiscent.

**напор** *m.* pressure, thrust, head, pressure head; —**истый** *a.* energetic; pushing.

**напорн/ый** *a.* pressure, force, delivery; **н. бак** header, supply tank; **н. клапан** pressure valve; **н. насос** force pump, pressure pump; **н. столб** delivery head; **н. трубопровод** delivery conduit; — **ая труба** rising pipe, stand

pipe (of pump); —**ое сопло** discharge nozzle.

**напоследок** *adv.* in the end, in conclusion.

**напр.** *abbr.* (**например**) for example.

**направ/итель** *m.* guide; —**ительный** *a.* guiding, directing; —**ительные тельца** (biol.) polar bodies; —**ить** *see* **направлять; —ка** *f.* adjustment, setting.

**направлен/ие** *n.* direction; trend; tendency, leaning; bearing, set; alignment; course, route; guidance, guiding; specialization; **переменить н. *v.*** reverse; **по —ию** in the direction (of), toward, with; —**ный** *a.* directed, set; directional (correlation, etc.); direct (current); —**ный внутрь** inward; —**ная связь** directional bond.

**направлять** *v.* direct, guide, lead; aim, set, adjust; refer; —**ся** *v.* head (for).

**направляющая** *f.* guide, rail, runner, slide.

**направляющ/ий** *a.* guiding, guide, directive, directing, director; control, controlling, regulating; leading, leader; pilot, piloting; **н. аппарат** distributor; deflector; **н. брус** guide bar, slide bar; **н. винт** set screw, adjusting screw; **н. лист** baffle plate, deflector; **н. лоток** baffle; **н. ролик, н. шкив** guide, guide pulley, idle pulley, idler; **н. стержень** steering bar, guide; **н. экран** baffle; —**ая колодка** guide shoe; —**ая линейка, —ая тяга** guide bar, guide rod; —**ая поверхность** sliding track, slide; —**ая проводка** (rolling) guard; —**ая сила** controlling force; —**ая стена** deflecting wall; —**ее колесо** idle wheel, idler; steering wheel; —**ее острие** guide pivot; —**ее поле** (nucl.) guide field; —**ее устройство** guide device.

**направо** *adv.* to the right, right, on the right hand; **брать н.** *v.* turn right.

**напрасн/о** *adv.* in vain, to no purpose, uselessly; **не н.** to some purpose, not in vain; —**ый** *a.* useless, vain, purposeless.

**напрашиваться** *v.* thrust oneself (upon); ask (for); suggest itself.

**например** *adv.* for example, for instance; **так н.** for instance; thus.

**напрокат** *adv.* on hire, for hire.

**напрол/ет, —ом** *adv.* through, through and through; **итти н.** *v.* break through, pierce; stop at nothing.

**напроситься** *see* **напрашиваться.**

**напротив** *prep. gen.* opposite, counter, facing, across; *adv.* on the contrary, in contrast; on the other hand.

**напрягать** *v.* strain, tax, force.

**напряжен/ие** *n.* tension, pressure, stress; exertion, effort; (elec.) voltage; **н. в якоре** armature voltage; **н. от кручения, н. при кручении** torsional stress; **н. от сдвига, н. при сдвиге, н. сдвига** shear stress; **н. печи** furnace voltage; **н. при разрыве** breaking stress; **н. разложения** decomposition voltage; **н. тока** voltage; **н. топочного пространства** heat liberated (by fuel) per cubic meter per hour; **без —ия** (elec.) dead; **внутреннее н. в отливке** casting stress; **высокого —ия** (elec.) high-tension; high-pressure; **проводка высокого —ия** high-tension line; **механическое н.** mechanical stress; **низкого —ия** low-tension; low-pressure; **проводка низкого —ия** low-tension line; **ограничитель —ия** (elec.) circuit breaker; **повышать н.** *v.* (elec.) boost; **под —ием** (elec.) live, charged; **постоянного —ия** constant-voltage; constant-pressure; **динамо постоянного —ия** constant-voltage dynamo; **ряд —ий** electromotive series; **температурное н., тепловое н.** thermal stress; **узел —ия** (elec.) potential node; **уравнивающее н.** compensating voltage; equalizing pressure; **чрезмерное н.** overstrain.

**напряженн/о** *adv.* tensely, under tension; **—ость** *f.* intensity, strength; tension; strain; **—ость поля** (elec.) field intensity; **—ый** *a.* tense, strained, taut; intense, intensive; stressed; **—ое состояние** stress.

**напрямик** *adv.* straight; point-blank.

**напугать** *v.* frighten, scare.

**напульсник** *m.* wristlet.

**напус/к** *m.* letting in, admitting, filling (with); flooding; irrigation; lap, lap joint, lapping, overlap, overlapping; projection; **в н.** *adv.* lap, overlapping; **полив —ком** (agr.) flooding; **сросток в н.** lap joint; **—кать, —тить** *v.* let in, admit, run in, fill (with); lap, overlap; **—кной** *a.* let in, admitted; assumed, put on; overlapping.

**напут/анный** *a.* confused, entangled; **—ать, —ывать** *v.* confuse, entangle, make a mess (of).

**напух/ание** *n.* swelling; **—ать, —нуть** *v.* swell.

**напущенный** *a.* let in, admitted, run in; overlapped.

**напыл/енный** *a.* spray-coated; **—ивать, —ить** *v.* raise dust; spray, dust; (electron microscopy) sputter, shadow; **—ьник** *m.* dust screen.

**напышенный** *a.* inflated, pompous.

**нар—** *abbr.* (**народный**) the people's.

**наравне** *adv.* on a level (with), flush (with), on a par (with), on an equal footing, just as, like; **итти н. с** *v.* keep pace with.

**наральник** *m.* tip, point (of cultivator).

**нараст/ание** *n.* growth, growing, rise; accumulation, building up; increment; (min.) accretion; **коэффициент —ания** growth factor; **—ать, —и** *v.* grow on, be formed on; increase, accumulate; **—ающий** *a.* incremental; **—ить** *see* **наращивать.**

**нарасхват** *adv.* in great demand.

**наращ/ение, —ивание** *n.* growing, increment, accretion, accumulation; graft, grafting; building up, plating (with metal); **—енный** *a.* accumulated; **—ивать** *v.* accumulate; cultivate, grow, raise; graft, join; build up, plate.

**наргол** *m.* nargol, silver nucleinate.

**нард** *m.*, **—овый** *a.* (bot.) spikenard (*Aralia racemosa*); citronella grass (*Cymbopogon nardus*).

**нарез** *see* **нарезка; —ание** *n.* cutting; **—ание резьбы** cutting thread, threading; **—анный** *a.* cut, threaded; **—ать** *see* **нарезывать.**

**нарезк/а** *f.* cut, incision, indentation; cutting, threading; thread (of screw), worm; rifling; **винт с правой —ой** right-handed screw.

**нарез/ной** *a.* cut, threaded; rifled; **н. канал** rifled bore; **—ывать** *v.* cut; thread (screw), chase; rifle; shape.

**наринг/енин** *m.* naringenin, 4,5,7-trihydroxyflavanone; **—ин** *m.* naringin.

**нарисов/анный** *a.* drawn, sketched; **—ать, —ывать** *v.* draw, sketch.

**нарифл/ение** *n.* rifle, rifling, grooving; (min.) rifle; **—енный** *a.* rifled, grooved; **—ять** *v.* rifle, groove.

**нарицательный** *a.* nominal; denominate (number).

**наркоз** *m.* (med.) narcosis.

**нарколан** *m.* Narcolan, tribromoethanol.

**нарком—** *obs. abbr.* (народный комиссариат) The People's Commissariat (of).

**наркоман** *m.* drug addict.

**наркотиз/ация** *f.* narcotization; **—ировать, —овать** *v.* narcotize; **—м** *m.* narcotism; **—ование** *n.* narcotizing, narcotization; **—ованный** *a.* narcotized; **—ующий** *a.* narcotizing.

**наркот/ик** *m.* narcotist; drug; **—ин** *m.* narcotine, opianine; **—ический** *a.*, **—ическое средство** narcotic.

**народ** *m.* people, nation; **—ный** *a.* popular, people's, national, public; **—ная сеть** national network; **—ное здравие** public health; **—ное хозяйство** national economy; **—онаселение** *n.* population; **—осчисление** *n.* census.

**нарост** *m.* excrescence, growth, outgrowth; tuber, tubercle; knot, node (on tree); wart; **—ить** *see* **наращивать.**

**нароч/итый** *a.* intentional, deliberate, studied; **—но** *adv.* on purpose, purposely, intentionally; **—ный** *a.* intentional; *m.* express messenger; **с —ным** by express, by messenger.

**нарпит** *abbr.* (народное питание) Department of Public Nutrition.

**нарсарсукит** *m.* (min.) narsarsukite.

**нарт/а** *f.*, **—ы** *pl.* sledge.

**наруб/ать, —ить** *v.* cut, chop; **—ка** *f.* cut, incision, notch.

**наружн/о** *adv.* externally; apparently; **—ость** *f.* exterior, outward aspect, appearance; **—ый** *a.* external, exterior, outer, outside; surface; extraneous; outdoor; male (thread); **—ый размер** outside measurement.

**наружу** *adv.* out, outside, outwards.

**наручники** *pl.* handcuffs.

**наруш/ать, —ить** *v.* break, infringe, transgress, violate; disturb, upset, disrupt; **—ение** *n.* breaking, breach, infringement, infraction, violation; disturbance, dislocation; (phys.) perturbation; **—енный** *a.* broken, infringed; disturbed, upset, disrupted; **—итель** *m.* transgressor, violator.

**нар. х-во** *abbr.* (народное хозяйство) national economy.

**нарц/еин** *m.* narceine; **—еоновая кислота** narceonic acid; **—ил** *m.* narcyl, ethylnarceine hydrochloride; **—илен** *m.* narcylene (pure acetylene gas); **—исс** *m.* (bot.) narcissus; **—иссин** *m.* narcissine; **—иссовые** *pl.* (bot.) Amaryllidaceae.

**нарыв** *m.* abscess, boil; **—ание** *n.* suppuration, gathering, festering; **—ники** *pl.* blister beetles (*Meloidae*).

**нарывн/ой, —ый** *a.* abscess; blister-producing, vesicant; **н. газ** vesicant gas; **—ое средство** vesicant, vesicatory.

**наряд** *m.* order; (mil.) detail.

**наряду** *adv.* side by side, equally (to), on a level (with), together (with).

**нас** *gen., prepos., acc. of* **мы,** us.

**насад/ить** *see* **насаждать, насаживать; —ка** *f.* putting on, setting, fitting on; filling, packing (of column); nozzle; cap, capping, headpiece; hood; building up (of metal); built-up part; adapter, attachment; fin (of drum dryer); bed (of demineralizer); checker, checkered brickwork (of regenerator); (agr.) planting; **башня без —ки** packless tower; **башня с —кой** packed tower; **заполнять —кой** *v.* pack; **—очный** *a. of* **насадка;** packed; **—очная колонна** packed column.

**насажд/ать** *v.* plant, set; spread, propagate; **—ение** *n.* planting; **—енный** *a.* planted, set.

**насаж/енный** *a.* put on, set; built up; planted; **—ивать** *v.* put on, fit, fit on, fit over, slip over, set, mount; plant.

**наседать** *v.* press; settle on.

**насек/альный** *a.*, **—ание** *n.* cutting, incising, notching; frosting, hatching (steel); (text.) embossing; **—альщик** *m.* cutter; **—ать** *v.* notch, incise, slit, scratch; frost, hatch; damaskeen (with gold, silver); emboss.

**насеком/ое** *n.* insect; **н.-вредитель** *m.*

insect pest; —ые *pl.* Hexapoda; порошок от —ых insect powder, insecticide; —оядные *pl.* Insectivora; —оядный *a.* insectivorous, insecteating.

насел/ение *n.* population; —ить, —ять *v.* populate; inhabit.

насеч/енный *a.* cut, incised; frosted, hatched (steel); —ка *f.* incision, notch; cut (of file); (text.) embossing; (med.) scarification.

насиживать *v.* sit on (eggs), hatch, brood.

насилу *adv.* hardly, with difficulty.

насильно *adv.* by force, under compulsion.

наскакивать *v.* run against, strike, collide (with), smash (into).

насквозь *adv.* through, right through, to the core; проходить н. *v.* penetrate, pierce.

наскокнуть *see* наскакивать.

насколько *adv.* how much? for how much? to what extent? as far as.

наскоро *adv.* hastily, hurriedly.

наскочить *see* наскакивать.

наслаив/ание *n.* stratification, stratifying, bedding; arranging in layers; superposition, overlapping, covering with a layer; —ать *v.* stratify, arrange in layers, laminate; superpose, overlap, add; —аться *v.* (geol.) stratify, deposit sediments.

наслед/ие *n.* legacy, inheritance; —ник *m.* heir; legatee; —ование *n.* inheritance, succession; —овать *v.* inherit, succeed (to); —ственность *f.* (biol.) heredity; —ственный *a.* hereditary; —ство *n.* heritage, inheritance, legacy; —уемость *f.* (biol.) hereditivity.

наслоен/ие *n.* stratification, lamination; (geol.) stratum, layer; —ный *a.* stratified, laminated, arranged in layers; superposed, covered with a layer.

насморк *m.* (med.) cold, head cold.

насол/енный *a.* salted, pickled; —ить *v.* salt, pickle.

насонит *m.* (min.) nasonite (related to ganomalite).

насос *m.*, —ный *a.* pump; н.-лягушка diaphragm pump; н.-мамут air lift; н.-смеситель *m.* pump-mixer; высота

всасывания —а, высота подачи —а lift of pump; подавать —ом *v.* pump, pump up; —ная станция waterworks.

наспех *adv.* hurriedly.

наспиртов/анный *a.* alcoholized; —анное вино brandy; —ывание *n.* alcoholization; —ывать *v.* alcoholize.

Нассау Nassau.

наст *m.* frozen snow crust.

наст. *abbr.* (настоящий) real, true.

наставать *v.* approach, come (of time).

наставительный *a.* instructive, edifying.

настав/ить *v.* set up (in quantity); piece, put a piece on, extend, join; instruct, teach, direct, admonish; —ка *f.* extension, extension rod, extension arm; adapter.

наставл/ение *n.* direction, instruction, teaching; —ять *see* наставить.

наставн/ой *a.* set on, added, pieced; —ая труба extension pipe; adapter; —ое основание extension base.

настаив/ание *n.* digesting, digestion, infusing, infusion, steeping; persistence, insisting; —ать *v.* digest, infuse, steep; persist, insist, urge, press; —ать на том, что insist that; —ающий *a.* digesting, infusing, steeping; insisting, insistent.

настал/енный *a.* steel-faced; —ивание *n.* steel facing; —ивать *v.* steel, plate with steel, edge with steel, point with steel.

настать *see* наставать.

настежь *adv.* open, wide open.

настенный *a.* wall, attached to the wall; н. ворот bracket winch, wall windlass; н. кран wall bracket crane; н. подшипник bracket bearing.

настиг/ать, —нуть *v.* overtake, catch up, reach.

настил *m.* floor, flooring; deck, bridging; frame; trestles; layer; половой н. flooring; —ать *v.* lay, plank, pave (with); bridge (over); —ка *f.*, —очный *a.* laying; boarding, planking; flooring.

настильная траектория flat trajectory.

настичь *see* настигать.

настлать *see* настилать.

настоенный *see* настоянный.

настой *m.* infusion, tincture, extract;

н. на травах herb infusion; —ка *f.* liqueur; (pharm.) tincture, infusion.

настойчив/ость *f.* persistence, insistence; urgency; —ый *a.* persistent, insistent, unremitting; urgent, pressing.

настолько *adv.* so; so far, thus far, so much; н., насколько as much as.

настольный *a.* table, desk; bench (lathe); reference (book).

настороже *adv.* on the alert, on the lookout.

настоян/ие *n.* insistence, persistence; по его —ию at his urgent request.

настоянный *a.* infused, steeped, digested.

настоятельн/ость *f.* urgency, insistence; —ый *a.* urgent, pressing, insistent.

настоять *see* настаивать.

настоящ/ий *a.* real, actual, genuine, natural, regular, true; present, current; в —ее время at present, now, nowadays.

настраив/аемый *a.* adjustable; —ание *see* настройка; —ать *v.* adjust, align, tune, tune up, tool (machine); build (on), construct; incite, instigate; —ать на станцию (rad.) tune in; —аться *v.* become adjusted; —ающий *a.* adjusting, tuning; —ающая катушка (rad.) syntonizing coil.

настриг *m.* clip (of wool).

настроение *n.* frame of mind, humor, mood.

настро/енный *a.* adjusted, tuned; tooled (machine); built (on), constructed, added (on); —ечный *a.* tuning; —ечное устройство tuner; —ить *see* настраивать.

настройка *f.* adjustment, tuning, setting; superstructure; superstruction; н. на станцию (rad.) tuning in.

наступ/ать, —ить *v.* come, approach (of time); advance; set in (of reaction); tread on, step on; —ающий *a.* approaching, advancing; —ление *n.* coming, approach; advance, onset, attack.

настуран *m.* (min.) uraninite, pitchblende.

настурц/ий *m.*, —ия *f.* (bot.) nasturtium (*Tropaeolum*).

настыль *f.* (met.) crust, incrustation, accretion, bear, sow; scum (on molten metal).

насухо *adv.* dry.

насущный *a.* daily; urgent.

насчет *prep. gen.* of, about, concerning, as regards, with regard to.

насчит/ать, —ывать *v.* count, number, reckon; —ываться *v.* be counted; there are.

насып *m.* hopper, feed bin; —ать *v.* put, fill, pour (grain); —ка *f.* filling.

насыпн/ой *a.* filled, poured; н. вес bulk density; н. груз bulk cargo; —ая дорога causeway.

насыпь *f.* bank, embankment, terrace, mound; dam, dike; fill, filling; causeway; груз —ю bulk freight; грузить —ю *v.* load in bulk.

насы/тимый, —щаемый, —щающийся *a.* saturable; —тить, —щать *v.* saturate, impregnate; satiate, satisfy; —щаться *v.* become saturated; —щаемость *f.* saturability, capacity for saturation; —щающий *a.* saturating; —щающее средство saturator.

насыщен/ие *n.* saturation, impregnation; satiation; давление —ия saturation pressure; предел —ия, точка —ия saturation point; —ность *f.* saturation, impregnation; —ный *a.* saturated, impregnated; satiated, satisfied; —ный раствор saturated solution.

наталкиваться *v.* come across, strike, meet.

наталоин *m.* nataloin.

наталивать *v.* heat intensely; melt.

натачивать *v.* sharpen; turn (on lathe).

натек *m.* leakage; (geol.) sinter, incrustation; stalactite; (surface coatings) sag, run; —ание *n.* inleakage; —ать *v.* flow into, run in; leak; accumulate.

нательный *a.* (worn) next to the skin.

натер/еть *see* натирать; —тый *a.* rubbed; grated.

натечка *f.* fine-calibrated orifice.

натечные отложения (geol.) sinter.

натечь *see* натекать.

натир/ание *n.*, —ка *f.* rubbing, touching, touch; grating; ointment, unguent; —ать *v.* rub, touch; grate.

натиск *m.* inrush, rush; impression.

наткнут/ый *a.* driven in, set out; —ь *see* натыкать.

натолкнуться *see* наталкиваться.

натопить *see* натапливать.

наточить *see* натачивать.

натощак *adv.* on an empty stomach.

натр *m.* soda (sodium oxide); едкий н. caustic soda, sodium hydroxide; кристаллический углекислый н. soda crystals (sodium carbonate); серно-кислый н. sodium sulfate.

натрав/ить, —ливать *v.* set (on), set (at), instigate, incite.

натриево-водяной *a.* sodium-to-water (heat exchanger).

натриев/ый *a.* sodium, soda, *see also* натронный; н. полевой шпат (min.) soda feldspar, albite; —ая бронза sodium bronze (a sodium tungstate); —ая селитра Chile saltpeter, sodium nitrate; —ая соль sodium salt; —ое растворимое стекло water glass, sodium silicate; —ые квасцы soda alum, aluminum sodium sulfate.

натриекальциевое стекло soda lime glass.

натр/ий *m.* sodium, Na; бромистый н. sodium bromide; гидрат окиси —ия, гидроокись —ия sodium hydroxide; двухромовокислый н. sodium bichromate; едкий н. *see* натр, едкий; окись —ия sodium oxide; перекись —ия sodium peroxide; сернистый н. sodium sulfide; сернокислый н., сульфат —ия sodium sulfate; уксусно-кислый н. sodium acetate; хлорид —ия, хлористый н. sodium chloride, common salt.

натрий/амид *m.* sodamide, sodium amide; —аммоний *m.* sodium ammonium; —ацетоуксусный эфир sodio-acetoacetic ester; -натриевый *a.* sodium-to-sodium (heat exchanger).

натристый *see* натриевый, натронный.

натро/борокальцит *m.* (min.) natroborocalcite, ulexite, boronatrocalcite; —вый *see* натриевый; —кальцит *m.* (min.) natrocalcite, gaylussite; —лит *m.* (min.) natrolite (a zeolite).

натронн/ый *a.* soda; н. щелок soda lye, liquid caustic soda, caustic soda solution; —ая известь soda lime (sodium hydroxide mixed with lime); —ая селитра Chile saltpeter, sodium nitrate; —ое мыло hard soap (soap made with soda); —ое озеро soda lake; —ое стекло soda glass; —ые квасцы *see* натриевые квасцы.

натро/филит *m.* (min.) natrophilite (near triphylite); —хальцит *m.* (min.) natrochalcite.

натрус/ить *v.* sprinkle; —ка *f.* sprinkling.

натрясти *v.* scatter, let fall; shake, jolt.

Наттерера прибор Natterer's apparatus (for preparing carbon dioxide).

нату/га *f.* effort, strain; —женный *a.* stretched, strained; —живать, —жить *v.* stretch, strain, tighten; —живаться, —житься *v.* make an effort, strain.

натур/а *f.* nature, character; измерение в —е actual measurement; платить —ой *v.* pay in kind; по —е by nature, naturally; —ализация *f.* naturalization; —алист *m.* naturalist.

натуральн/о *adv.* naturally; —ость *f.* naturalness; —ый *a.* natural; real; virgin (wool); crude (rubber).

натурный *a.* full-scale.

натуроза *f.* a grape product (glucose substitute).

натуроплата *f.* payment in kind, payment in produce.

натыкать *v.* drive in, stick in, set out; —ся *v.* strike, run against, stumble over.

натяг *m.* tightness; interference, obstruction; clearance (of roll).

натягив/ание *n.* pulling, tightening (up); stringing (wire); —ать *v.* stretch, tighten, draw up, pull up, string; fix, fasten; —ающий *a.* tightening, pulling, drawing; —ающее усилие tensile strength, tensile stress.

натяжен/ие *n.* tension, strain; pull, pulling, pull-up, tightening; н. поверхности, поверхностное н. surface tension; сила —ия tensile strength, tensile stress; степень —ия tautness, tightness.

натяжн/ой *a.* tightening, tension, strain; stretching; pull; н. болт adjuster bolt, draw-in bolt; strain pin; н. винт tightening screw; н. выключатель (elec.) pull switch; н. груз counter-weight; н. зажим strain clamp; н. прибор, —ое приспособление tightening device; stretcher, stretching device; **н. ролик** tension roller; **н. шкив** tension pulley; **н. стержень** tension rod; **н. трос** guy rope; stretching wire; **—ая пружина** draw spring; **—ая чека** tightening key; wedge bolt.

**натянут/ость** *f.* tension, tenseness; tightness; **—ый** *a.* tense, tight, drawn; **—ь** *see* натягивать.

**наугад** *adv.* by guesswork, by rule of thumb, haphazardly, at random.

**науглерож/енный** *a.* carbonized; (met.) carburized; **—енная сталь** carburized steel, cement steel; **—ивание** *n.* carbonization, carbonizing; carburization, carburizing; **—ивание поверхности** surface carburization, case carburization; **—иватель** *m.* carburetor; carburizer; **—ивать** *v.* carbonize; carburize; **—ивающий** *a.* carbonizing; carburizing.

**наугольн/ик** *m.* square, bevel, corner iron; **—ый** *a.* angular; corner.

**наудачу** *adv.* at a venture, haphazardly.

**наука** *f.* knowledge, science; **академия наук** academy of sciences.

**науманит** *m.* (min.) naumannite (silver-lead selenide).

**наутилоиды** *pl.* (zool.) Nautiloidea.

**науч/ать, —ить** *v.* teach, instruct, direct; **—аться, —иться** *v.* learn.

**научно** *adv.* scientifically.

**научноисследовательск/ая работа** scientific research work, research; **—ий институт** research institute.

**научный** *a.* scientific.

**наушник** *m.* ear muff, ear cap; headphone.

**нафт—** *prefix* naphth—, naphtho—; **—а** *see* нефть; **—азарин** *m.* naphthazarine, alizarin black; **—ал—** *prefix* naphthal—, naphthalene.

**нафтал/ан** *m.* naphthalane, decahydronaphthalene; **—ат** *m.*, **соль —евой кислоты** naphthalate; **—евая кислота, —овая кислота** naphthalic acid, naphthalenedicarboxylic acid; **—евый ангидрид** naphthalic anhydride; **—изировать** *v.* naphthalize, enrich with naphthalene; **—ин** *m.*, **—иновый** *a.* naphthalene; **—индиол** *m.* naphthalenediol, dihydroxynaphthalene; **—иновый желтый** naphthalene yellow, dinitro-α-naphthol;

**—ол** *m.* naphthalol, naphthyl salicylate.

**нафт/альдегид** *m.* naphthaldehyde, naphthalenecarbonal; **—амид** *m.* naphthamide, naphthalenecarbonamide; **—амин** *m.* naphthamine, hexamethyleneamine; **—ан** *m.* naphthane; **—антрацен** *m.* naphthanthracene, benzanthrene.

**нафтацен** *m.* naphthacene; **—хинон** *m.* naphthacenequinone.

**нафтен** *m.* naphthene (a cycloparaffin); **—ат** *m.* naphthenate; **—ил** *m.* naphthenyl, naphthylmethylidyne; **—овая кислота** naphthenic acid (mixture of cycloparaffin acids).

**нафтил** *m.*, **—овый** *a.* naphthyl; **—амин** *m.* naphthylamine; **—ен** *m.*, **—еновый** *a.* naphthylene; **—иден** *m.* naphthylidene; **—овый спирт** naphthyl alcohol, naphthol; **—овый эфир** naphthyl ether; **—овый эфир уксусной кислоты** naphthyl acetate.

**нафти/оновая кислота** naphthionic acid; **—ридин** *m.* naphthyridine, 1,7-benzodiazine.

**нафто—** *prefix* naphtho—; **—ил** *m.* naphthoyl.

**нафтойн/ая кислота** naphthoic acid, naphthalenecarboxylic acid; **—ый альдегид** naphthoic aldehyde, naphthyl aldehyde.

**нафто/кси—** *prefix* naphthoxy—; **—кумарин** *m.* naphthocoumarin.

**нафтол** *m.*, **—овый** *a.* naphthol, naphthyl alcohol; **—ат** *m.* naphtholate; **—овый голубой** naphthol blue, Meldola Blue.

**нафтонитрил** *m.* naphthonitrile, naphthyl cyanide.

**нафтохин/альдин** *m.* naphthoquinaldine; **—гидрон** *m.* naphthoquinhydrone; **—оксалин** *m.* naphthoquinoxaline, 1,4-naphthisodiazine; **—олин** *m.* naphthoquinoline; **—он** *m.* naphthoquinone.

**нахлестк/а** *f.* lap, lap joint, overlap, overlapping; **в —у** *adv.* lap, overlapping; **сваривать в —у** *v.* lap-weld; **сшивка в —у** lap joint.

**нахлестыв/ание** *n.* lapping, overlapping; **—ать** *v.* lap, overlap.

**нахлынуть** *v.* rush, flood.

**находить** *v.* find, locate, come upon, strike (ore deposit), detect; determine, arrive at (solution), develop; —**ся** *v.* be, occur, exist; be found; —**ся под** underlie.

**находка** *f.* find, finding; windfall, godsend.

**находчив/ость** *f.* resourcefulness, readiness; —**ый** *a.* resourceful.

**находящий** *a.* finding; —**ся** *a.* being, occurring; —**ся под** underlying.

**нахождение** *n.* finding, locating, detecting; being, occurrence; calculation.

**наце/дить,** —**живать** *v.* decant.

**нацел/ивание** *n.* aiming, pointing; —**иваться,** —**иться** *v.* aim (at).

**нацело** *adv.* completely.

**нацеп/ить,** —**лять** *v.* attach, fasten, hook on.

**национал/изация** *f.* nationalization; —**изировать** *v.* nationalize; —**ьность** *f.* nationality; —**ьный** *a.* national.

**нация** *f.* nation, people.

**нач.** *abbr.* (**начальный**) initial; **нач**— *abbr.* (**начальник**) head, chief.

**начавший** *past act. part. of* **начинать.**

**начал/о** *n.* beginning, start, outbreak, inception, commencement; origin, origination, source; (math.) principle, basis; —**а** *pl.* principles, elements (of subject); **н. уменьшения пламени** point at which the flame begins to die down; **брать н.** *v.* spring, rise (from), originate; **быть под** —**ом** *v.* be in subordination (to); **вести н., давать н.** *v.* originate; **действующее н.** primary nutrient; **на кредитных** —**ах** on credit basis; **положить н.** *v.* initiate.

**начальник** *m.* head, chief, superior; **н. станции** station master.

**начальн/ый** *a.* initial, original, first; starter; elementary, rudimentary; primary (school); **н. угол** angle of impulsion; —**ая тарелка** feed plate; —**ая точка** origin, source; starting point.

**начальство** *n.* authorities, chiefs, superiors; —**вать** *v.* command.

**начат/ки** *pl.* rudiments, elements; —**ый** *a.* started; —**ь** *see* **начинать.**

**начерно** *adv.* rough, roughly, coarse, coarsely; in draft form; **обделка н.**

rough finishing, rough finish, roughing; **обрабатывать н.** *v.* rough-finish, rough, rough out; **обработанный н.** rough-finished, unfinished; **шлифовать н.** *v.* rough-grind, grind coarse.

**начерп/ать,** —**ывать** *v.* scoop up.

**начер/тание** *n.* sketch, outline, plan; —**тательный** *a.* graphic; descriptive (geometry); —**тить,** —**чивать** *v.* draw, trace, outline, draft; —**ченный** *a.* traced, outlined.

**начес/ать,** —**ывать** *v.* card (wool); hackle (fiber); raise (fabric).

**начет** *m.* deficit, fine for deficit; —**истый** *a.* expensive, disadvantageous.

**начин/ание** *n.* beginning, start; undertaking; —**атель** *m.* originator, initiator, author; —**ать** *v.* begin, start, initiate, set in; set up, undertake; —**ать действия** start operations; **успешно** —**ать** make a good start; —**ающий** *m.* a beginner, novice; *a.* beginning, initial; —**ающийся** *a.* incipient.

**начинка** *f.* stuffing, filling.

**начисл/ение** *n.* charge, charging; counting, reckoning up; —**ить,** —**ять** *v.* charge; ascribe; count, count up, reckon up, enumerate; pay down.

**начистить** *see* **начищать.**

**начисто** *adv.* cleanly, clean; thoroughly, flatly, definitely; cold (drawn); **обрабатывать н.** *v.* finish, finish off.

**начитанный** *a.* well-read.

**начищать** *v.* clean; peel, shell; brush, rub up, polish.

**начн/ет** *fut. 3 sing.;* —**ите** *imp. of* **начинать.**

**начхоз** *abbr.* (**начальник хозяйственного управления**) Head of the Economic Department.

**наш** *a.* our, ours.

**нашатыр/ный спирт** aqua ammonia, ammonium hydroxide; —**ь** *m.* sal ammoniac, ammonium chloride.

**нашел** *past sing. of* **находить.**

**нашествие** *n.* (biol.) invasion.

**наш/ивать,** —**ить** *v.* sew on; sew (in quantity); —**ивной** *a.* sewed on, attached.

**нащупыватель** *m.* feeler, feeler mechanism.

**наэгит** *m.* (min.) naegite (a radioactive zirconium silicate).

**наэлектризов/ание** *n.* electrification; **—анный** *a.* electrified; **—ать, —ывать** *v.* electrify.

**наяд/а** *f.* (bot.) naiad (*Naias*); (zool.) naiad; **—овые** *pl.* (bot.) Naiadaceae.

**н.в.э.** *abbr.* (нормальный водородный эквивалент) normal hydrogen equivalent.

**нгайовая камфора** ngai camphor, *l*-borneol.

**не** *adv.* not, no, none; *prefix* un—, in—, non—, mis—, dis—; **—автоматический** *a.* non-automatic, manual; **—аддитивный** *a.* non-additive; **—адэкватный** *a.* inadequate, insufficient.

**неактив/ированный** *a.* non-activated; **—ность** *f.* inactivity; **—ный** *a.* inactive, passive, inert; idle.

**неаполитанский** *a.* Naples; **н. желтый** Naples yellow (lead antimonate); **н. красный** Naples red.

**Неаполь** Naples.

**неароматический** *a.* non-aromatic.

**небалии** *pl.* (zool.) Nebaliacea.

**небеленый** *a.* unbleached, crude, raw.

**небесн/оголубой** *a.* sky-blue; **—ый** *a.* sky, celestial; **—ые светила, —ые тела** heavenly bodies, celestial bodies.

**неблагоприятный** *a.* unfavorable, disadvantageous, adverse.

**неблагородный** *a.* ignoble, base (metal).

**небн/ый** *a.* (anat.) palate, palatal; **—ая занавеска** velum palatinum; **—ые кости** palatine bones.

**небо** *n.* sky, heaven, firmament; crown (of furnace); (anat.) palate.

**небольш/ой** *a.* small, little, low; **сто с —им** one hundred odd.

**небо/склон** *m.* horizon; sky; **—скреб** *m.* skyscraper, tall building.

**небрежн/ость** *f.* carelessness, negligence; **—ый** *a.* careless, negligent, slipshod, lax.

**небуларин** *m.* nebularin.

**небулярный** *a.* nebular.

**небывалый** *a.* unprecedented.

**небытие** *n.* non-existence.

**небьющийся** *a.* unbreakable, safety (glass).

**невадит** *m.* (petr.) nevadite (a rhyolite).

**неважн/о** *adv.* insignificantly; poorly, indifferently; it is not important; **это н.** it does not matter; **—ый** *a.* unimportant, insignificant; poor, indifferent.

**невед/ение** *n.* ignorance; **—омо** *adv.* without knowing; **—омый** *a.* unknown, unfamiliar.

**невежливый** *a.* impolite, discourteous.

**невейка** *f.* unwinnowed, ground grain.

**невеликий** *a.* not great, small.

**неверн/о** *adv.* incorrectly, wrong; **н. рассчитать** *v.* miscalculate; **—ость** *f.* inaccuracy; **—ый** *a.* inaccurate, incorrect, wrong; untrue, false, mis—; **—ый нуль** (elec.) false zero.

**невероятн/о** *adv.* incredibly; it is improbable; **—ость** *f.* incredibility; improbability; **—ый** *a.* incredible, unbelievable, inconceivable; improbable, unlikely.

**невесом/ость** *f.* imponderability; zero gravity, weightlessness; **—ый** *a.* imponderable, without weight; trace.

**невзгода** *f.* misfortune.

**невзирая** *see* несмотря.

**невз/орвавшийся** *a.* unexploded; **н. снаряд** dud; **—рываемый, —рывчатый** *a.* non-explosive.

**невианскит** *m.* (min.) nevyanskite (a variety of iridosmine).

**невидимый** *a.* invisible.

**невинный** *a.* innocent, not guilty.

**невихревой** *a.* irrotational, non-circuital.

**невменяемый** *a.* irresponsible.

**невнимательный** *a.* inattentive, absent-minded.

**невнятный** *a.* unintelligible.

**невод** *m.* seine, sweep net, casting net.

**неводный** *a.* non-aqueous; anhydrous.

**неводостойкий** *a.* hydrolabile.

**невозбужденный** *a.* unexcited.

**невозделанный** *a.* raw, crude, untreated; virgin (soil), unworked, uncultivated.

**невозможн/о** *adv.* impossibly; it is impossible; **—ость** *f.* impossibility; **—ый** *a.* impossible.

**невозмущенный** *a.* unperturbed.

**невол/ить** *v.* force, compel; **—ьный** *a.* involuntary, unintentional; **—я** *f.* bondage; necessity.

**невооруженный** *a.* unarmed; unaided, naked (eye).

**невоспламеняющийся** *a.* incombustible, non-combustible; safety (film).

**невоспри/имчивость** *f.* non-susceptibility; **—имчивый, —нимающий** *a.* unsusceptible, non-susceptible.

**невосстановленный** *a.* unreduced.

**невостребованный** *a.* unrequired; unclaimed.

**невпопад** *adv.* inopportunely, out of place, irrelevantly.

**невр—** *prefix* neur—, neuro— (nerve), *see also* **нейр—**; **—алгический** *a.* (med.) neuralgic; **—алгия** *f.* neuralgia; **—астения** *f.* neurasthenia.

**невращающийся** *a.* irrotational, non-rotatory.

**неври/лемма** *f.* (anat.) neurilemma; **—т** *m.* (med.) neuritis.

**невро—** *prefix* neuro— (nerve); **—з** *m.* (med.) neurosis; **—зный** *a.* neurotic; **—лог** *m.* neurologist; **—логия** *f.* neurology; **—ма** *f.* neuroma; **—н** *m.* neuron, nerve cell; **—патология** *f.* neuropathology; **—тический** *a.* neurotic.

**невставленный** *a.* unmounted, loose.

**невыводимый** *a.* indelible (ink).

**невыгод/а** *f.* disadvantage; **—но** *adv.* disadvantageously, unprofitably; it is not profitable; **—ный** *a.* disadvantageous, unprofitable, uneconomical; **ставить в —ное положение** *v.* place at a disadvantage, handicap.

**невыделанный** *a.* raw, crude, unfinished; undressed (hide).

**невыдыхающийся** *a.* non-volatile.

**невызревший** *a.* unripened, softwood (cutting).

**невымывающийся** *a.* indelible (stain); fast (dye).

**невыполн/ение** *n.* non-performance, non-fulfillment, failure; **—имость** *f.* impracticability; **—имый** *a.* impracticable.

**невысокий** *a.* not high, low.

**невысыхающий** *a.* non-drying (oils).

**невыцветающий** *a.* non-fading, fast (dye).

**невыясненный** *a.* unexplained, obscure.

**негармонический** *a.* (math.) anharmonic.

**негасимый** *a.* unquenchable; non-slaking (lime).

**негатив** *m.* (phot.) negative.

**негативн/ость** *f.* negativeness; **—ый** *a.* negative; **—ая пластина** (phot.) negative plate; **—ое изображение** negative image, negative.

**негатрон** *m.* negatron (vacuum tube); (nucl.) negative electron.

**негашеный** *a.* unslaked, quick (lime).

**негде** *adv.* there is no room, there is no place, there is nowhere (to).

**негермет/изированный** *a.* unsealed; **—ический, —ичный** *a.* non-hermetic, leaking;**—ичность** *f.* leaking, seepage.

**негибк/ий** *a.* inflexible, stiff, rigid; **—ость** *f.* inflexibility, stiffness, rigidity.

**негигиенический** *a.* unsanitary.

**негладкий** *a.* uneven, rough, jagged.

**неглазурованный** *a.* unglazed.

**негласный** *a.* secret; private.

**негли жировать** *v.* neglect; be careless.

**неглубокий** *a.* not deep, shallow.

**неги/ючее дерево, —ой дерево** (bot.) yew (*Taxus baccata*); **—иючка** *f.* yew (*Taxus*); arbor vitae (*Thuja occidentalis*); **—иющий** *a.* rotproof, imputrescible.

**негнущийся** *a.* unbending, inflexible, rigid.

**негодн/ость** *f.* unfitness, unsuitability; worthlessness; **приходить в н.** *v.* get out of order; become useless; **—ый** *a.* unsuitable, unfit, improper, useless, worthless; refuse, waste; faulty.

**негомогенный** *a.* non-homogeneous, heterogeneous.

**негорюч/есть** *f.* incombustibility; **—ий** *a.* incombustible, non-combustible, non-burning, fire-resistant.

**неготовый** *a.* not ready, unprepared.

**негоциант** *m.* merchant, wholesale dealer.

**негр** *m.* negro.

**негранёный** *a.* rough, uncut (jewel).

**негр/итянский** *a.* negro; **—ообразный** *a.* negroid.

**негустой** *a.* thin, watery.

**нед—** *prefix* sub—, below; un—.

**недавн/ий** *a.* recent, late, new; **—о** *adv.* recently, lately, of late.

**недалек/ий** *a.* near, not far; **—о** *adv.* near, near at hand, not far.

**недаром** *adv.* not in vain, not without reason; no wonder.

**недвиж/имость** *f.* immovability; real estate; **—имости** *pl.* immovables; real estate; **—имый** *a.* immovable, immobile, motionless; **—ущийся** *a.* stationary.

**недействителен** (bank notation on check) insufficient funds, overdrawn.

**недействительн/ость** *f.* ineffectiveness, inefficiency; invalidity; **—ый** *a.* ineffective, inefficient, inoperative; inefficacious (medicine); invalid, null and void; **делать —ым** *v.* invalidate, nullify, cancel, neutralize.

**недействующий** *a.* inactive, passive, inert; non-operating, idle.

**неделим/ость** *f.* indivisibility; **—ый** *a.* indivisible.

**неделовой** *a.* unbusinesslike.

**недел/ьный** *a.* week, weekly; **—я** *f.* week.

**неделящийся** *a.* (nucl.) non-fissionable.

**недержание** *n.* non-retention, irretention.

**недетонирующий** *a.* antiknock (gasoline); non-knocking.

**недеформированный** *a.* undistorted.

**недеятельн/ость** *f.* inactivity, inertness, passivity; ineffectiveness, inefficiency; **—ый** *a.* inactive, inert, passive; inoperative, idle; dormant; indolent.

**недислоцированный** *a.* undisturbed.

**недо—** *prefix* under—, incompletely.

**недобор** *m.* remainder, arrears.

**недовар/енный** *a.* insufficiently cooked; parboiled; **—ивать, —ить** *v.* parboil.

**недоверчивый** *a.* suspicious, distrustful.

**недове/с** *m.* short weight, underweight; **—шивать** *v.* give short weight.

**недовозбужденный** *a.* underexcited.

**недоволь/ный** *a.* discontent, displeased, dissatisfied; **—ство** *n.* discontent, dissatisfaction.

**недовыполнение** *n.* underfulfillment.

**недовыработка** *f.* underproduction.

**недоглядеть** *v.* overlook, miss; neglect, not see after.

**недогрев** *m.* underheating.

**недогрузка** *f.* underloading, underload.

**недодача** *f.* deficiency in delivery.

**недоделанный** *a.* unfinished, incomplete.

**недодержка** *f.* (phot.) underexposure.

**недож/игать** *v.* (cer.) underfire; **—женый** *a.* underfired; incompletely roasted; incompletely burned.

**недозамедленный** *a.* unmoderated.

**недозрелый** *a.* unripe, immature, green.

**недоимка** *f.* arrears.

**недоказанный** *a.* unproved, not demonstrated.

**недокал** *m.* underheating.

**недокись** *f.* suboxide.

**недоконченный** *a.* unfinished, incomplete.

**недокорм** *m.* underfeeding.

**недолго** *adv.* for a short period, briefly; **—вечный** *a.* short-lived, transient.

**недолет** *m.* falling short; undershot.

**недоли/вать, —ть** *v.* fill short of the top.

**недомер** *m.* short measure; offsize; **—ивать** *v.* give short measure.

**недомес** *m.* undermixing.

**недомогание** *n.* poor health.

**недомол** *m.* undermilling, undergrinding.

**недомолвка** *f.* reservation, omission.

**недоно/сок** *m.* miscarriage; abortion; **—шенный** *a.* premature.

**недоокисленный** *a.* incompletely oxidized.

**недооцен/ивать** *v.* underestimate, underrate, undervalue; **—ка** *f.* underestimation, underestimate, underrating.

**недопал** *m.* incompletely burned material; (cooking) green butts.

**недополучение** *n.* deficiency.

**недопроизводство** *n.* underproduction.

**недопустим/ость** *f.* inadmissibility; **—ый** *a.* inadmissible, intolerable, not to be put up with.

**недопущение** *n.* non-admission; banning.

**недоразвитый** *a.* underdeveloped, rudimentary.

**недоразумение** *n.* misunderstanding.

**недорогой** *a.* inexpensive, cheap.

**недород** *m.* crop failure, poor crop.

**недосланный** *a.* short-shipped.

**недосмотр** *m.* oversight, slip, error; **—еть** *see* **недоглядеть.**

**недосол** *m.* insufficient salting.

**недоста/вать** *v.* be wanting, be insufficient, fall short, run short, lack, miss; **ему не —ет** he lacks, he is short (of).

**недостат/ок** *m.* deficiency, shortage, lack, scarcity; defect, fault, blemish, flaw, imperfection; disadvantage, drawback, shortcoming; **из-за —ка**

for lack of, for want of; **иметь н.** *v.* have the disadvantage; be short, want, lack, need.

**недостаточн/о** *adv.* insufficiently; it is insufficient; **—ость** *f.* insufficiency, inadequacy, inefficiency; shortage, deficiency; imperfection; **—ый** *a.* insufficient, inadequate, under—, meager, deficient, poor; defective, faulty, imperfect, inefficient; **—ое питание** malnutrition; **быть —ым** *v.* fall short.

**недоста/ть** *see* **недоставать; —ча** *f.* deficiency, shortage, lack; **—ющий** *a.* deficient, lacking, missing.

**недостижим/ость** *f.* inaccessibility; **—ый** *a.* inaccessible, unattainable.

**недостоверный** *a.* doubtful, uncertain; unauthentic.

**недостроенн/ость** *f.* incompleteness (of electron levels); **—ый** *a.* unfinished, incomplete.

**недоступн/ость** *f.* inaccessibility; unavailability; **—ый** *a.* inaccessible, unapproachable, impenetrable, impervious; unavailable; prohibitive (cost).

**недосчит/аться, —ываться** *v.* find a deficit, find something missing.

**недосыщенный** *a.* unsaturated, incompletely saturated.

**недосягаем/ость** *f.* unattainability; **—ый** *a.* unattainable; unrivaled, unequaled.

**недотрога** *f.* (bot.) touch-me-not (*Impatiens*).

**недоум/евать** *v.* be perplexed, be at a loss, not be able to understand; **—ение** *n.* perplexity, quandary; **—енный** *a.* perplexed, puzzled, baffled.

**недохват** *m.*, **—ка** *f.* shortage, deficiency.

**недочет** *m.* deficiency, deficit; shortcoming, defect.

**недра** *pl.* bosom, depths, interior (of the earth); midst; **богатства недр** mineral wealth; **охрана недр** conservation of mineral resources.

**недубленный** *a.* untanned, raw (hide).

**неду/г** *m.* illness, ailment, sickness; **—жный** *a.* ailing, infirm, sick.

**недурной** *a.* not bad.

**недюжинный** *a.* remarkable, unusual, exceptional, outstanding.

**неестественный** *a.* unnatural, abnormal.

**нежелательн/ость** *f.* undesirability; **—ый** *a.* undesirable, objectionable; (rad., etc.) parasitic.

**нежелезный** *a.* (met.) non-ferrous.

**нежели** *conj.* than.

**нежестк/ий** *a.* flexible, not rigid; loose; soft (water); **—о соединенный** loosely connected, loosely attached, loose.

**нежилой** *a.* uninhabited, non-residential.

**нежн/ость** *f.* gentleness, delicacy, tenderness, softness; **—ый** *a.* gentle, delicate, tender, soft, frail.

**незабудка** *f.* (bot.) forget-me-not (*Myosotis*).

**незавершенный** *a.* unfinished.

**независим/о** *adv.* independently; **н. от** regardless of, disregarding; **—ость** *f.* independence; freedom (of movement); **—ый** *a.* independent, individual, self-contained, separate, insulated, isolated; foreign (body); **—ая переменная** (math.) independent variable.

**незагруженный** *a.* unloaded, uncharged; idle (machine).

**незагрязненн/ость** *f.* non-contamination, purity; **—ый** *a.* uncontaminated, pure.

**незадемпфированный** *a.* (phys.) undamped.

**незадолго** *adv.* shortly, not long (before).

**незаземленный** *a.* (elec.) ungrounded.

**незакаленный** *a.* (met.) untempered, soft.

**незаклиненный** *a.* unfastened, loose.

**незаконн/ость** *f.* illegality; **—ый** *a.* illegal, unlawful.

**незаконченный** *a.* unfinished, incomplete.

**незакреплени/ость** *f.* looseness; **—ый** *a.* loose, unfastened, unmounted; loose-running, mobile, floating.

**незамедленный** *a.* (nucl.) unmoderated.

**незаменим/ость** *f.* irreplaceability; indispensability; **—ый** *a.* irreplaceable, not interchangeable; indispensable.

**незамерзающ/ий** *a.* non-freezing; **н. раствор, —ая жидкость** antifreeze (for motors).

**незаметн/о** *adv.* unnoticeably, imperceptibly; it is not noticeable; **—ый** *a.* unnoticeable, imperceptible, inconspicuous.

**незамещенный** *a.* unsubstituted.

**незамкнут/ый** *a.* unlocked, open; **—ая цепь** (elec.) open circuit.

**незанятый** *a.* unoccupied, idle, free, available; vacant, unfilled.

**незаполненный** *a.* unfilled, not filled, blank.

**незаразный** *a.* non-contagious.

**незаращение** *n.* (med.) aplasia.

**незаряженный** *a.* uncharged, unloaded.

**незасоренный** *a.* unobstructed, clear; weed-free (garden).

**незатейливый** *a.* plain, simple.

**незатухающий** *a.* continuous, sustained, undamped.

**незаурядный** *a.* superior, above average.

**незачем** *adv.* unnecessarily; there is no need.

**незащищенный** *a.* unprotected, unsheltered, exposed; (nucl.) unshielded.

**нездоровый** *a.* unwholesome, unsanitary; sick, unwell; **—ье** *n.* ill health.

**незеркальный** *a.* non-reflecting.

**незнакомый** *a.* unknown, unfamiliar, strange.

**незнание** *n.* ignorance, lack of knowledge.

**незначимость** *f.* insignificance.

**незначительн/ость** *f.* insignificance; **—ый** *a.* insignificant, negligible, trivial, imperceptible; small, little, low.

**незрел/ость** *f.* immaturity, greenness (of fruit); **—ый** *a.* immature, unripe, green.

**незыблем/ость** *f.* firmness, steadiness, immovability; **—ый** *a.* firm, steady, secure, stable, immovable; hard-and-fast (rule).

**неидеальный** *a.* imperfect.

**неизбежн/о** *adv.* inevitably, of necessity, by the nature of things; **—ость** *f.* inevitability, imminence; **—ый** *a.* inevitable, imminent, unavoidable.

**неизведанный** *a.* unknown, untried.

**неизвестн/о** *adv.* it is unknown, it is not known; **—ое** *n.* the unknown; unknown quantity; **—ость** *f.* uncertainty, ignorance; obscurity; **быть в —ости** *v.* be uncertain, be ignorant (of); **—ый** *a.* unknown, uncertain, obscure **—ое число** unknown quantity.

**неизгладим/ость** *f.* indelibility; **—ый** *a.* indelible, ineffaceable.

**неизданный** *a.* unpublished.

**неизлечим/ость** *f.* incurability; **—ый** *a.* incurable, irremediable.

**неизлучающий** *a.* non-radiating.

**неизменн/ость** *f.* invariability, changelessness, inalterability, immutability; **—ый** *a.* invariable, unchangeable, unalterable, immutable; constant, fixed, permanent, stable, stationary; unfailing.

**неизменяем/ость** *f.* inalterability, stability; **н. на** resistance (to); **—ый** *a.* unalterable, immutable, permanent, constant.

**неизмеримый** *a.* immeasurable, bottomless, fathomless.

**неизолированный** *a.* non-insulated, bare (wire).

**неизотропн/ость** *f.* anisotropy, anisotropism; **—ый** *a.* anisotropic.

**неимен/ие** *n.* lack, want; **за —ием, по —ию** for want (of), for lack (of).

**неименованный** *a.* indeterminate, abstract.

**неион/изирующий** *a.* non-ionizing; **—ный, —огенный** *a.* non-ionic.

**неискаженный** *a.* undistorted, distortion-free.

**неискрящийся** *a.* non-sparking, sparkless, free from sparks; (elec.) non-arcing.

**неискусный** *a.* inexperienced, inexpert, unskilled.

**неисполн/ение** *n.* non-performance, non-fulfillment; **—имость** *f.* impracticability; **—имый** *a.* impracticable.

**неисправн/ость** *f.* inaccuracy; disrepair, faultiness, fault, trouble, defect; **—ый** *a.* inaccurate, incorrect, improper, unsatisfactory; in bad repair, out of order, damaged, faulty, defective.

**неиспробованный** *a.* untested, untried.

**неиспровергающий** *a.* subversive.

**неиспытанный** *a.* untested, untried.

**неиссякаемый** *a.* inexhaustible.

**неистощим/ость** *f.* inexhaustibility; **—ый** *a.* inexhaustible.

**неисцелимый** *see* **неизлечимый**.

**неисчерпаемый** *a.* inexhaustible.

**неисчислимый** *a.* innumerable, countless.

**нейбергский голубой** Neuberg blue (copper blue and Chinese blue); **н. эфир**

Neuberg ester (a hexose monophosphate).

**нейблау** *m.* new blue (dye).

**нейвидский голубой** Neuwied blue, Bremen blue, blue copper carbonate.

**Нейгофа диаграмма** Neuhoff diagram.

**нейдорфит** *m.* (min.) neudorfite (a resinous hydrocarbon).

**нейзильбер** *m.*, **—овый** *a.* German silver, argentan (copper-zinc-nickel alloy).

**нейлон** *m.*, **—овый** *a.* nylon.

**Неймана закон** Neumann's law.

**нейр—** *prefix* neur—, neuro— (nerve); *see also* **невр—**; **—идин** *m.* neuridin; **—ин** *m.* neurine, amantine; **—один** *m.* neurodin, acetyl-*p*-hydroxyphenylurethan; neurodine (a ptomaine); **—озин** *m.* neurosin, calcium glycerophosphate; **—он** *m.* neuron, nerve cell; **—онал** *m.* neuronal, diethylbromacetamide.

**нейтр.** *abbr.* (**нейтральный**) neutral; (**нейтрон, нейтронный**) neutron.

**нейтрализ/атор** *m.* neutralizer; **—ационный** *a.*, **—ация** *f.* neutralization; **—ованный** *a.* neutralized; **—овать** *v.* neutralize; counteract; **—ующий** *a.* neutralizing; **—ующее средство** neutralizing agent, neutralizer.

**нейтралитет** *m.* neutrality.

**нейтраль** *f.* neutral main; (elec.) neutral, neutral conductor, middle conductor.

**нейтрально** *adv.* neutrally; **—сть** *f.* neutrality.

**нейтральн/ый** *a.* neutral; indifferent, inert; **н. газ** inert gas; **н. пояс** neutral zone; **н. раствор** neutral solution; **—ая реакция** neutral reaction.

**нейтральтинт** *m.* neutral tint (a mineral black).

**нейтрин/ный** *a.*, **—о** *n.* (nucl.) neutrino.

**нейтродин** *m.*, **—ный, —овый** *a.* (rad.) neutrodyne (a high-frequency amplifier).

**нейтрон** *m.*, **—ный** *a.* (nucl.) neutron; **на быстрых —ах** fast-neutron (cycle); fast (reactor, fission); **на медленных —ах** slow; **поток —ов, —ный поток** neutron flux; **—ограмма** *f.* neutron diffraction pattern; **—ограф** *m.* neutron diffraction camera; **—ография** *f.* neutron diffraction study; neutron

scattering; **—одефицитный** *a.* neutron-deficient; **—озахватывающий** *a.* noutron-capture; **—онепроницаемый** *a.* neutron-tight.

**нейтр-ция** *abbr.* (**нейтрализация**).

**нейуротропин** *m.* new urotropine.

**некаль** *m.* Nekal, sodium dibutylnaphthalenesulfonate.

**некальцинированный** *a.* uncalcined, unroasted, raw.

**некаптированный** *a.* wild (oil well).

**неквалифицированный** *a.* unqualified; unskilled (labor).

**неквантов/анный, —ый** *a.* unquantized.

**некий** *a.* one, some, a certain.

**некк** *m.* (geol.) neck, plug.

**неклен** *m.* (bot.) box elder (*Acer negundo*).

**некоаксиальный** *a.* misaligned.

**некогда: мне н.** I have no time; *adv.* formerly, once.

**некогерентн/ость** *f.* (phys.) incoherence; **—ый** *a.* incoherent.

**некомпетентн/ость** *f.* incompetence; **—ый** *a.* incompetent.

**некомплект** *m.* shortage, deficiency.

**некондиционный** *a.* non-standard, substandard; non-grade (grain).

**некоптящий** *a.* sootless (flame), non-smoking.

**некорневое питание** (agr.) foliar feeding, spray feeding; **н. удобрение** leaf-feeding spray.

**некорродир/уемый** *a.* non-corrodible, corrosion-resistant; **—ующий** *a.* non-corroding, non-rusting, stainless.

**некоторый** *a.* some, certain.

**некро—** *prefix* necro— (dead); **—биоз** *m.* (med.) necrobiosis; **—з** *m.* (med.) necrosis; **—лог** *m.* obituary; **—тический** *a.* necrotic.

**нек-рый** *abbr.* (**некоторый**) some, certain.

**некстати** *adv.* inopportunely, untimely, irrelevantly.

**нектар** *m.* (bot.) nectar; **—ин** *m.* nectarine; **—ник** *m.* nectary.

**некто** *pron.* somebody, someone.

**нектон** *m.* (zool.) nekton.

**нектрия** *f.* coral spot (plant disease).

**некуда** *adv.* nowhere, there is nowhere (to).

**нелегированный** *a.* (met.) unalloyed, pure, plain.

**нелеп/ость** *f.* absurdity; **—ый** *a.* absurd, preposterous; incongruous.

**нелетучий** *a.* non-volatile, fixed.

**нелинейн/ость** *f.* non-linearity; **—ый** *a.* non-linear.

**неловкий** *a.* awkward, clumsy.

**неломкий** *a.* (met.) tenacious, tough, unbreakable.

**нельзя** *v.* it is impossible, it is prohibited.

**нем.** *abbr.* (**немецкий**) German.

**немагнитный** *a.* non-magnetic.

**немалит** *m.* (min.) nemalite (a variety of brucite).

**немал/о** *adv.* much, many; **—оважный** *a.* important; **—ый** *a.* fairly big.

**немато—** *prefix* (biol.) nemato— (thread; nematode); **—бластический** *a.* (petr.) nematoblastic; **—ды** *pl.* (zool.) nematodes (*Nematoda*).

**немафилит** *m.* (min.) nemaphyllite (a variety of serpentine).

**нембутал** *m.* Nembutal, pentobarbital sodium.

**немедленн/о** *adv.* immediately, instantly, directly, at once, without delay; **—ый** *a.* immediate, instantaneous, prompt, fast.

**немезонный** *a.* (nucl.) non-mesonic.

**немертины** *pl.* ribbon worms (*Nemertinea*).

**неметалл** *m.* non-metal; metalloid; **—ический** *a.* non-metallic.

**неметь** *v.* grow numb, grow torpid.

**немецк/ий** *a.* German; **н. куб** (dyeing) soda vat; **—ая цепь** long-link chain; **—ое золото** Manheim gold (a brass alloy); **—ое серебро** German silver, nickel silver.

**неминуем/ость** *f.* inevitability, unavoidability; **—ый** *a.* inevitable, unavoidable, inescapable; impending.

**немки** *pl.* velvet ants (*Mutillidae*).

**немног/ие** *pl.* a few, few, not many; **—о** *adv.* little, somewhat; some, few, some few; **—ое** *n.* little; **—очисленность** *f.* fewness, scarcity.

**немой** *a.* dumb, mute; silent; outline (map); (geol.) unfossiliferous; *m.* mute.

**немонохроматический** *a.* polychromatic.

**немонтированный** *a.* unmounted; unassembled.

**немота** *f.* dumbness, muteness.

**немотин** *m.* nemotin; **—овая кислота** nemotinic acid.

**немо/чь, —щь** *f.* illness, infirmity; **бледная н.** (med.) chlorosis; **—щный** *a.* infirm, weak, feeble; (math.) nilpotent.

**немыслимый** *a.* unthinkable, impossible.

**ненагруженный** *a.* unloaded, empty, idle.

**ненадежн/ость** *f.* unreliability, insecurity; **—ый** *a.* unreliable, insecure, unsafe, untrustworthy.

**ненадкевит** *m.* (min.) nenadkevite (a uranium silicate).

**ненадлежащий** *a.* undue, excessive.

**ненадобн/ость** *f.* uselessness; **за —остью** being useless; **—ый** *a.* useless.

**ненадолго** *adv.* for a short time, not for long.

**ненаполненный** *a.* unadulterated, pure.

**ненапряженный** *a.* relaxed; without tension; (elec.) dead.

**ненарушенный** *a.* undisturbed, unbroken.

**ненаст/ный** *a.* rainy, bad; **—ье** *n.* bad weather.

**ненастоящий** *a.* not geniune, pseudo—, false.

**ненастроенный** *a.* untuned, unadjusted.

**ненасытн/ость** *f.* insatiability; **—ый** *a.* insatiable.

**ненасыщ/ающийся** *a.* unsaturable; **—енность** *f.* non-saturation, unsaturated state; **—енный** *a.* unsaturated.

**ненатянут/ость** *f.* looseness, slack; **—ый** *a.* loose, slack.

**неноздреватый** *a.* non-porous, dense, compact.

**ненормальный** *a.* abnormal; insane.

**ненужн/о** *adv.* unnecessarily; it is unnecessary; **—ый** *a.* unnecessary, useless, needless, waste.

**ненулевой** *a.* non-zero.

**нео—** *prefix* neo— (new, recent); **—арсфенамин** *m.* neoarsphenamine.

**необделанный** *a.* unfinished, rough.

**необитаемый** *a.* uninhabited.

**необнаруживаемый** *a.* undetectable.

**необогащенный** *a.* (met.) unconcentrated, undressed, crude (ore).

**необожженный** *a.* unburnt, unroasted, raw (ore); (cer.) unfired.

**необозначенный** *a.* not indicated.

**необозрим/ость** *f.* vastness, immensity; **—ый** *a.* vast, immense, boundless.

**необоснованный** *a.* groundless, baseless, unfounded, without proof.

**необработанный** *a.* untreated, unrefined, crude, raw; unfinished, rough; **н. материал** rough stock; raw material.

**необратим/ость** *f.* irreversibility; **—ый** *a.* irreversible, non-reversible.

**необруцин** *m.* neobrucine.

**необученный** *a.* untrained, unskilled.

**необходим/о** *adv.* necessarily; it is necessary; **—ое** *n.* requisite, necessaries; **—ость** *f.* necessity, need, indispensability; **вызвать —ость** *v.* necessitate; **по —ости** of necessity.

**необходим/ый** *a.* necessary, needed, required, requisite, indispensable, essential, imperative; **делать —ым** *v.* necessitate; **заранее н.** prerequisite; **крайне н.** urgent, imperative.

**необшитый** *a.* unlined, unfaced.

**необъявленный** *a.* (tel.) unlisted.

**необъясним/о** *adv.* inexplicably; it is inexplicable; **—ость** *f.* inexplicability; **—ый** *a.* inexplicable, unaccountable.

**необъятный** *a.* immense, unbounded.

**необыкновенн/о** *adv.* unusually; it is unusual; **—ость** *f.* unusualness, singularity; **—ый** *a.* unusual, singular, uncommon, rare, extraordinary.

**необыч/айный, —ный** *see* **необыкновенный.**

**необязательный** *a.* not obligatory, optional.

**нео/гексан** *m.* neohexane, 2,2-dimethylbutane; **—ген** *m.* (geol.) Neogene system; Neogen (a copper-base alloy); **—генез** *m.* (biol.) neogenesis, regeneration; **—генный** *a.* (geol.) Neogenic.

**неограниченн/о** *adv.* unreservedly, without restriction, indefinitely; **—ый** *a.* unrestricted, unbounded, indefinite, unlimited, absolute; unheard-of (yield).

**неодевон** *m.* (geol.) Neodevonian period.

**неодим, —ий** *m.* neodymium, Nd; **окись —ия** neodymium oxide, neodymia; **хлористый н.** neodymium chloride.

**неодинаковый** *a.* different, not uniform.

**неоднозначн/ость** *f.* ambiguity; **—ый** *a.* ambiguous.

**неодно/именный** *a.* unlike, opposite;

dissimilar; **—кратный** *a.* repeated, reiterated; **—образный** *a.* irregular.

**неоднородн/ость** *f.* heterogeneity; discontinuity; **—ый** *a.* heterogeneous, non-homogeneous, non-uniform.

**неодревесневший** *a.* softwood.

**неожиданн/о** *adv.* unexpectedly, suddenly; **—ость** *f.* suddenness, surprise; **—ый** *a.* sudden, surprising, unexpected.

**неозвученный** *a.* silent (moving picture).

**неозин** *m.* neosine.

**неозой** *m.* (geol.) Neozoic group, Cenozoic group; **—ский** *a.* Neozoic, Cenozoic.

**неозон** *m.* Neozone, phenylnaphthylamine.

**неокаин** *m.* neocaine, procaine.

**неокисл/енный** *a.* unoxidized; **—яемость** *f.* non-oxidizability, inoxidizability; **—яемый, —яющийся** *a.* non-oxidizable, inoxidizable; **—яющий** *a.* non-oxidizing.

**неоком** *m.* (geol.) Neocomian stage.

**неокончательный** *a.* inconclusive, not final.

**неоконченный** *a.* unfinished, incomplete, imperfect.

**неокрашенный** *a.* colorless; unpainted, unfinished.

**нео/лактоза** *f.* neolactose; **—лин** *m.* Neolin, benzathine penicillin G.

**неолит** *m.* (geol.) Neolithic stage; **—ический** *a.* Neolithic, stone age; **—ический век** Neolithic stage.

**неомерпин** *m.* neomerpin (detergent).

**неомицин** *m.* neomycin.

**неоморфоз** *m.* (zool.) neomorphosis.

**неомыляющийся** *a.* non-saponifying, unsaponifiable.

**неон** *m.* neon, Ne.

**неонал** *m.* Neonal, butethal.

**неонов/ый** *a.* neon; **—ая лампа, —ая трубка** neon tube, neon light.

**неопадающий** *a.* (bot.) not deciduous.

**нео/палеозойский** *a.* (geol.) Neopaleozoic; **—пентан** *m.* neopentane; **—пин** *m.* neopine.

**неопис/анный** *a.* not yet described; **—уемый** *a.* indescribable.

**неоплазма** *f.* (med.) neoplasm.

**неопределенн/о** *adv.* indefinitely; it is not definite; **—ость** *f.* indefiniteness, uncertainty; ambiguity; **принцип** **—ости** (quantum mechanics) indeterminacy principle, uncertainty principle; **—ый** *a.* indefinite, uncertain, vague, indeterminate (function); undefined, undetermined.

**неопределимый** *a.* undefinable, indeterminate.

**неопрен** *m.*, **—овый** *a.* neoprene, duprene (synthetic chloroprene rubber).

**неопробованный** *a.* untested, untried.

**неопровержим/ость** *f.* irrefutability; **—ый** *a.* irrefutable, indisputable, incontestable, incontrovertible, undeniable.

**неопытн/ость** *f.* inexperience; **—ый** *a.* inexperienced, unpracticed, unskilled.

**неорганизованн/ость** *f.* lack of organization; **—ый** *a.* disorganized.

**неорганическ/ий** *a.* inorganic; **—ое соединение** inorganic compound.

**неориентированный** *a.* unoriented.

**неосальварсан** *m.* neosalvarsan, neoarsphenamine.

**неосведомленность** *f.* lack of information, scanty information.

**неосевой** *a.* off-axis.

**неоседающий** *a.* non-settling.

**неослабный** *a.* unremitting.

**неоснователь/о** *adv.* groundlessly, without foundation; **—ость** *f.* groundlessness, lack of foundation; **—ый** *a.* groundless, unfounded; superficial.

**неоспоримый** *see* **неопровержимый.**

**неостаток** *m.* non-residue.

**неосторожн/о** *adv.* carelessly; **—ость** *f.* carelessness, negligence; **—ый** *a.* careless, negligent, unwary.

**неосуществим/ость** *f.* impracticability; **—ый** *a.* impracticable, not feasible.

**неосязаем/ость** *f.* intangibility; **—ый** *a.* intangible, imperceptible, impalpable.

**неотвратимый** *a.* inevitable.

**неотделанный** *a.* unfinished, rough; uncut (stone); raw.

**неотделимый** *a.* inseparable.

**неотип** *m.* (min.) neotype, alstonite, barytocalcite.

**неоткуда** *adv.* from nowhere.

**неотложн/ость** *f.* urgency; **—ый** *a.* urgent, pressing, imperative.

**неотлучный** *a.* always present, permanent, continuous.

**неотожженный** *a.* unannealed, crude, raw.

**неотокит** *m.* (min.) neotocite (usually an alteration product of rhodonite).

**неотпущенный** *a.* (met.) untempered.

**неотравленный** *a.* unpoisoned; (nucl.) uncontaminated, clean.

**неотражающий** *a.* non-reflective.

**неотразимый** *a.* irresistible; insurmountable.

**неотстоявшийся** *a.* unsettled, turbid.

**неотступный** *a.* importunate, urgent, persistent.

**неотчетливый** *a.* indistinct, vague.

**неотъемлемый** *a.* inherent.

**неохотный** *a.* unwilling, reluctant.

**неоцен** *m.* (geol.) Neocene.

**неоценимый** *a.* inestimable, invaluable.

**неоцидин** *m.* neocidin.

**неоцинкованный** *a.* (met.) ungalvanized.

**неочищенный** *a.* unpurified, unrefined, untreated, crude, raw.

**неощутимый** *a.* impalpable, imperceptible, inappreciable.

**непалин** *m.* nepalin.

**непарнокопытный** *a.* (zool.) perissodactyl.

**непарный** *a.* odd, unpaired, unmatched.

**непахучий** *a.* odorless.

**непер** *m.* (elec.) neper (unit of attenuation).

**непере/гружающийся** *a.* antisaturation (amplifier); **—носный** *a.* non-portable, stationary; **—ходный** *a.* intransitive (relation).

**непериодич/еский** *a.* non-periodical, acyclic; **—ность** *f.* aperiodicity.

**неперов** *a.* (math.) Napier, Napierian; **—о число** Napier number; **—ы логарифмы** natural logarithms.

**непищевой** *a.* inedible.

**неплав/кий, —ящийся** *a.* infusible; **—кость** *f.* infusibility.

**неплатеж** *m.* non-payment, default.

**неплодо/родие** *n.* sterility; **—родный, —творный** *a.* sterile, barren, dead (soil).

**неплотн/ость** *f.* looseness; leakiness, leakage; **—ый** *a.* loose, not compact; low-density; leaky, leaking; unsound.

**неповоротимый** *a.* irrotational, non-rotatory.

**неповрежденный** *a.* unimpaired, intact, sound.

**непогашеный** *a.* unslaked, quick (lime).

**непоглощающий** *a.* non-absorbing.

**непогода** *f.* bad weather, stormy weather.

**неподалеку** *adv.* near, not far.

**неподатной** *a.* exempt from tax (or duty), tax-free, duty-free.

**неподвижн/о** *adv.* without moving; immovably, securely; **—ость** *f.* immovability, immobility; **—ый** *a.* immobile, immovable, stationary, fixed; tight, rigid; motionless, resting, at rest, standing, quiescent; stagnant; (elec.) static; dead (center); **—ая точка** point of rest; fulcrum; pause.

**неподдельный** *a.* unadulterated, pure; genuine, real, authentic.

**неподеленный** *a.* unshared.

**неподин** *m.* nepodin.

**неподлежащий** *a.* not subject (to), not liable (to), exempt (from), free (from).

**неподменим/ость** *f.* non-interchangeability; **система —ости** non-interchangeable system; **—ый** *a.* non-interchangeable.

**неподобный** *a.* dissimilar, unlike.

**неподражаемый** *a.* inimitable.

**неподходящий** *a.* unsuitable, unsuited, inappropriate, inadequate, unfitted.

**непозволительный** *a.* not permissible, not to be permitted, inadmissable.

**непоколебим/ость** *f.* firmness; **—ый** *a.* firm, unyielding, immovable.

**непокрытый** *a.* uncoated, uncovered, plain.

**неполадка** *f.* shutdown, failure; maladjustment, trouble, kink, disturbance.

**неполно** *adv.* incompletely; **—зубые** *pl.* (zool.) Edentata; **—мерный** *a.* short, scanty; **—та** *f.* incompleteness, imperfection.

**неполн/ый** *a.* incomplete, partial; short (measure); light (load); imperfect, defective.

**неполовозрелый** *a.* (biol.) immature.

**неполяр/изованный** *a.* non-polarized; **—ный** *a.* non-polar.

**непомерный** *a.* exorbitant, excessive.

**непонят/но** *adv.* incomprehensibly; it is incomprehensible; **—ность** *f.* incomprehensibility; **—ный** *a.* incomprehensible, unintelligible, obscure; **—ый** *a.* misunderstood, not properly understood.

**непоправимый** *a.* irreparable.

**непористый** *a.* non-porous, compact, dense.

**непорченный** *a.* unspoiled, sound.

**непорядок** *m.* disorder, chaos, confusion.

**непосильный** *a.* excessive; too difficult.

**непоследовательн/о** *adv.* inconsistently, not in order; **—ость** *f.* inconsistency, inconsequence; **—ый** *a.* inconsistent, inconsequent, irrelevant, irregular, non-consecutive.

**непосредственн/о** *adv.* immediately, directly, next; **—ость** *f.* immediateness; spontaneity; **—ый** *a.* immediate, direct; spontaneous; **—ый нагрев** direct heating; **—ого действия** direct-action.

**непостижим/ость** *f.* incomprehensibility, inscrutability; **—ый** *a.* incomprehensible, impenetrable, inscrutable.

**непостоян/ный** *a.* inconstant, not constant, unstable, unsteady, unsettled, changeable, variable; **—ство** *n.* inconstancy, instability, variability, mobility.

**непохожий** *a.* dissimilar, unlike.

**непочатый** *a.* entire, untouched, not begun.

**непоявление** *n.* non-appearance, failure.

**неправильно** *adv.* incorrectly; it is incorrect, it is not correct; **—сть** *f.* incorrectness, inaccuracy; irregularity.

**неправильн/ый** *a.* incorrect, inaccurate, untrue, false, wrong; mal—; defective; irregular, erratic; **н. подход** wrong approach; **—ая дробь** (math.) improper fraction; **—ая работа** malfunction; **—ая форма** irregular shape; **—ое сращение** (med.) vicious union; **—ое употребление** misuse; **—ое употребление термина** misnomer.

**неправоспособн/ость** *f.* incompetence; **—ый** *a.* incompetent, disqualified.

**неправ/ота** *f.* wrongness; **—ый** *a.* wrong, unjust.

**непрактичн/ость** *f.* impracticability; —ый *a.* impracticable.

**непревзойденный** *a.* unsurpassed, second to none, supreme.

**непредвиденный** *a.* unforeseen, unlooked for, unexpected.

**непредельн/ый** *a.* unlimited, unbound; (chem.) unsaturated; —ое соединение unsaturated compound.

**непредохраненный** *a.* unprotected; (elec.) not provided with a fuse.

**непреклонный** *a.* inflexible, unbending, rigid.

**непреложн/ость** *f.* immutability; —ый *a.* immutable, unalterable.

**непременн/о** *adv.* without fail, for certain, by all means; necessarily; —ый *a.* unfailing, certain; indispensable, imperative.

**непререкаемый** *a.* unquestionable.

**непрерывно** *adv.* uninterruptedly, without interruption, continuously; —действующий *a.* continuous; —поточное производство continuous production; continuous operation; —сть *f.* continuity, persistence; (phys.) continuum.

**непрерывн/ый** *a.* uninterrupted, continuous, unbroken, constant, ceaseless, incessant; н. ряд unbroken series, succession; —ая дробь (math.) continued fraction; —ая работа, —ое производство continuous operation; —ого действия continuous, continuous-motion.

**непрестанный** *a.* unceasing, ceaseless.

**непреходящий** *a.* permanent.

**неприбыльный** *a.* unprofitable, profitless.

**непривар** *m.* non-fusion (of welded metals); cold welding.

**неприветливый** *a.* unfriendly, ungracious.

**неприводимый** *a.* irreducible.

**непривычный** *a.* unaccustomed, unusual.

**непригодный** *a.* unfit, useless, ineffective, unsuitable.

**неприемлемый** *a.* unsuitable, unacceptable.

**неприкрепленный** *a.* unattached, loose, free.

**неприкрытый** *a.* uncovered, unprotected.

**неприменим/ость** *f.* inapplicability; irrelevance; —ый *a.* inapplicable, impracticable; irrelevant.

**неприметный** *a.* imperceptible, indiscernible.

**непримиримый** *a.* irreconcilable; implacable.

**непринужденный** *a.* unconstrained, free.

**непринятие** *n.* non-acceptance, rejection, refusal.

**неприспособляем/ость** *f.* inadaptability; —ый *a.* inadaptable, inapplicable.

**неприступн/ость** *f.* inaccessibility; —ый *a.* inaccessible, impregnable.

**неприученный** *a.* untrained.

**неприхотливый** *a.* simple, unpretentious.

**неприятельский** *a.* unfriendly, hostile.

**неприятн/ость** *f.* unpleasantness, trouble, annoyance, nuisance; —ый *a.* unpleasant, troublesome, disagreeable.

**непрободенный** *a.* imperforated, imperforate.

**непробудный** *a.* sound (sleep).

**непровар** *m.* non-fusion (of welded metals); incomplete melting (of glass batch).

**непровод/ник** *m.* non-conductor; —ящий *a.* non-conducting.

**непродолжительн/ый** *a.* short, brief; intermittent, discontinuous; в —ом времени before long, shortly, soon.

**непроезжий** *a.* impassable.

**непрозрачн/ость** *f.* opacity; —ый *a.* opaque, non-transparent, impervious; cloudy (liquid).

**непроизводительн/ость** *f.* unproductiveness, barrenness; —ый *a.* unproductive, barren, poor (land).

**непроизвольн/о** *adv.* involuntarily, unintentionally; —ый *a.* involuntary, unintentional; —ое движение involuntary movement, reflex.

**непрокалывающийся** *a.* punctureproof.

**непромокаем/ость** *f.* impermeability, imperviousness (to moisture); —ый *a.* impermeable, non-wettable, waterproof, watertight; делать —ым *v.* waterproof.

**непромышленный** *a.* unprofitable; non-industrial, non-commercial.

**непроницаем/ость** *f.* impermeability,

impenetrability, tightness; (optics) opacity; —ый *a.* impermeable, impervious, impenetrable, tight; —ый для воздуха airtight; —ый для дождя rainproof.

**непропитанный** *a.* unimpregnated.

**непропорциональн/о** *adv.* disproportionately, out of proportion; —ость *f.* disproportion, disproportionality; —ый *a.* disproportionate, out of proportion.

**непропускающий** *a.* impervious, tight.

**непрореагировавший** *a.* unreacted.

**непростительный** *a.* inexcusable, unjustifiable.

**непросушенный** *a.* unseasoned, undried.

**непротив/ление** *n.* non-resistance, acquiescence; —оречивость *f.* consistency.

**непроходим/ость** *f.* impassability, impenetrability; —ый *a.* impassable, impenetrable, impervious.

**непрочный** *a.* unstable, labile; flimsy, insecure, not solid, unreliable; fugitive (color); perishable (food).

**непроявление** *n.* (phot.) non-development; failure to appear.

**непрямой** *a.* indirect.

**Нептун** (astron.) Neptune.

**нептун/изм** *m.* (geol.) neptunism, neptunian theory; —ий *m.* neptunium, Np; —ит *m.* (min.) neptunite; —ический *a.* (geol.) neptunic, neptunian; —овый голубой Neptune blue.

**непуит** *m.* (min.) nepouite.

**неработающий** *a.* idle, standing, inoperative, non-operating.

**нерабоч/ий** *a.* idle, not working, inactive, inoperative; off (position); —ее время idle time, time off.

**неравенство** *n.* inequality, disparity.

**неравнобокий** *a.* unequal-sided, scalene.

**неравновесный** *a.* non-equilibrium.

**неравногранн/ик** *m.* (cryst.) scalenohedron; —ый *a.* scalenohedral.

**неравномерн/о** *adv.* irregularly, not uniformly; —ость *f.* irregularity, nonuniformity, inequality, discontinuity; коэффициент —ости (illum.) variation factor; —ый *a.* irregular, erratic, uneven, not uniform, discontinuous, disproportionate, unequal.

**неравн/осторонний** *a.* (geom.) scalene, having unequal sides; —оценный *a.*

non-equivalent; heterodynamic; —ый *a.* unequal, uneven.

**нерад/ение** *n.*, —ивость *f.* negligence, carelessness; —ивый *a.* negligent.

**неразбавленный** *a.* undiluted, concentrated; raw (alcoholic beverage).

**неразборчивый** *a.* illegible, undecipherable; undiscriminating.

**неразделимый** *a.* indivisible, inseparable.

**нераздельно кипящий** *a.* azeotropic.

**нераздельн/ость** *f.* inseparability, indivisibility; —ый *a.* inseparable, indivisible; unseparated, undivided; —ая часть integral part.

**неразлагаем/ый** *a.* undecomposable, simple; indivisible; —ое вещество element.

**неразличимый** *a.* indiscernible, indistinguishable, undecipherable.

**неразлож/енный**, —ившийся *a.* undecomposed; —имый *see* неразлагаемый.

**неразрезной** *a.* continuous, solid.

**неразреш/енный** *a.* unauthorized; forbidden; unresolved; —имый *a.* insoluble (problem).

**неразрушим/ость** *f.* indestructibility; —ый *a.* indestructible.

**неразрывн/о** *adv.* inseparably; —ость *f.* indissolubility; continuity; —ый *a.* indissoluble; continuous.

**неразъед/аемый**, —ающийся *a.* non-corrodible, corrosion-resistant; —ающий *a.* non-corroding, non-corrosive.

**неразъемный** *a.* non-detachable, solid, permanent.

**нерал** *m.* neral, citral b.

**нераскисленный** *a.* unreduced.

**нерасплавленный** *a.* unfused, unmelted.

**нерасплывающийся** *a.* non-deliquescent.

**нераспознаваемый** *a.* undecipherable.

**нераствор/енный** *a.* undissolved; —имость *f.* insolubility; —имый *a.* insoluble.

**нерасчетлив/ость** *f.* extravagance, wastefulness; —ый *a.* extravagant, wasteful, not economical.

**нерасчлененный** *a.* whole; undifferentiated.

**нерациональный** *a.* irrational.

**нерв** *m.* nerve; —ация *f.* (bot.) nervation, venation; —ничать *v.* be nervous;

—но *adv.* nervously; —нобольной *m.* neurotic; —ность *f.* nervousness.

нервн/ый *a.* nervous, nerve; н. узел (anat.) ganglion; н. центр nerve center; —ая ткань nerve tissue; —ое волокно nerve fiber, axon.

нервозность *see* нервность.

нервон *m.* nervon; —овая кислота nervonic acid, selacholeic acid.

нервюра *f.* wing rib, rib (of airplane, etc.).

нереагирующий *a.* non-reacting.

нереверс/ивный *a.* non-reversing; —ируемый *a.* non-reversible.

нерегулярный *a.* irregular, sporadic.

нередко *adv.* not seldom, often.

нерезкий *a.* soft (sound).

нерелятивистский *a.* non-relativistic.

нерентабельный *a.* unprofitable.

нерест *m.*, —овый *a.* (zool.) spawning; —иться *v.* spawn.

нерешительн/ость *f.* indecision, indetermination, irresolution; быть в —ости, проявлять н. *v.* hesitate; —ый *a.* undecided, indecisive, irresolute, dubious.

нержавеющ/ий *a.* non-rusting, rustproof, rust-resisting, non-corrosive, stainless; —ая сталь stainless steel.

нери/антин *m.* nerianthin; —ин *m.* neriin; —олин *m.* neriolin; —товый *a.* (geol.) neritic.

нерка *f.* (zool.) red salmon.

Нернста лампа (elec.) Nernst lamp.

неровн/о *adv.* unevenly, roughly, irregularly; —ость *f.* unevenness, roughness, irregularity, wrinkle; inequality; —ый *a.* uneven, rough, irregular, rugged, ragged, jagged; bumpy; unequal; odd (number); irregular (pulse).

нерол *m.* nerol; —идол *m.* nerolidol, peruviol; —иевая камфора neroli camphor; —иевое масло neroli oil (oil of bitter orange flowers); —ин *m.* nerolin.

неротативный *see* неповоротимый.

нерудные ископаемые non-metallic minerals, rock products.

нерушимый *a.* inviolable, indestructible.

нес *past sing. of* нести.

несбыточн/ость *f.* impossibility of realization; —ый *a.* unrealizable, unachievable, impossible.

несварение *n.* indigestion.

несведущий *a.* inexpert, unskilled.

несвежий *a.* not fresh, stale, old.

несветящийся *a.* non-luminous (flame).

несвободный *a.* restricted, bound, not free; combined (element).

несвоевременн/ость *f.* inopportuneness; —ый *a.* inopportune, untimely, ill-timed.

несвойственный *a.* not characteristic (of), unnatural, extrinsic, inappropriate.

несвязанный *a.* uncombined, free, available; unbound, loose; unbonded.

несвязн/ость *f.* incoherence; —ый *a.* incoherent, disconnected.

несгибающийся *a.* inflexible, rigid.

несгор/аемость *f.* incombustibility; —аемый *a.* incombustible, non-combustible, fireproof, refractory; —аемый шкаф, —аемый ящик safe, strongbox; —ающий *a.* incombustible, non-burning; —евший *a.* unburned.

несгущаемый *a.* non-condensable.

несдавливаемый *see* несжимаемый.

несение *n.* performance (of duties).

нес/енный *a.* carried; —ет *pr. 3 sing. of* нести.

несжимаем/ость *f.* incompressibility; —ый *a.* incompressible, non-condensable.

несимметр/ический, —ичный *a.* unsymmetrical, asymmetrical, asymmetric, unbalanced; irregular; —ия, —ичность *f.* dissymetry, asymmetry, lack of symmetry.

несинусоидальный *a.* (elec.) non-sinusoidal (wave), distorted.

несинхронный *a.* asynchronous, non-synchronous.

несите *imp. of* нести.

неск. *abbr.* (несколько) several.

несквегонит *m.* (min.) nesquehonite.

несквозной *a.* blind (passage).

нескладчатый *a.* (geol.) not folded, unfolded.

нескользящий *a.* non-skidding, non-skid, skidproof, antiskid, non-slip.

несколько *adv.* somewhat, rather; some, few, several.

нескончаемый *a.* endless, interminable.

нескоропортящийся *a.* non-perishable.

**несли** *past pl. of* **нести.**

**несложн/о** *adv.* simply; —**ость** *f.* simplicity; —**ый** *a.* simple.

**неслоистый** *a.* unstratified.

**неслы/ханный** *a.* unheard of; —**шный** *a.* inaudible.

**несмачиваемый** *a.* non-wettable.

**несменяем/ость** *f.* irremovability; —**ый** *a.* irremovable, non-detachable.

**несмесимость** *see* **несмешиваемость.**

**несметный** *a.* infinite, innumerable.

**несмеш/анный** *a.* unmixed, unblended; —**иваемость** *f.* immiscibility; —**иваемый, —ивающийся** *a.* immiscible, non-miscible.

**несминаемый** *a.* crease-resistant, wrinkle proof.

**несмотря на** in spite of, notwithstanding, regardless of; **н. на это** in spite of this, nevertheless.

**несмываемый** *a.* indelible; permanent (finish).

**несоблюдение** *n.* non-observance, infringement (of patent law).

**несобранный** *a.* unassembled, dismantled; ungathered.

**несобственный** *a.* improper (integral).

**несовершеннолетний** *a.* minor, under age.

**несовершен/ный** *a.* imperfect, defective; incomplete, inadequate, deficient (number); —**ство** *n.* imperfection, irregularity.

**несовме/стимость, —стность** *f.* incompatibility, inconsistency; —**стимый, —стный** *a.* incompatible, inconsistent, incongrous; —**щение** *n.* non-registration (of colors).

**несовпадение** *n.* non-coincidence, disagreement, discrepancy, variance; misalignment (of axis); (electron.) anticoincidence.

**несоглас/ие** *n.* disagreement, variance, difference, unconformity; **н., —ное напластование** (geol.) unconformity; —**но** *adv.* in disagreement (with), at variance (with); —**ность** *f.* disagreement; —**ный** *a.* disagreeing, differing; (geol.) unconformable; —**ованность** *f.* inconsistency, disagreement, mismatching.

**несодержащий** *a.* not containing; **н. хлора** chlorine-free.

**несоизмеримый** *a.* incommensurable.

**несокрушимый** *a.* firm, steady; indestructible, invincible.

**несомненн/о** *adv.* undoubtedly, no doubt, certainly, decidedly, assuredly; —**ый** *a.* doubtless, indubitable, definite, absolute.

**несообразн/ость** *f.* incompatibility, incongruity, absurdity; —**ый** *a.* incompatible, incongrous (with), absurd.

**несоответств/енный, —ующий** *a.* conflicting, incongruous, contrary, inappropriate, inadequate, inexpedient, undue; —**ие** *n.* non-correspondence, conflicting, non-conformity, discrepancy, disparity, inadequacy; misfit.

**несопряженный** *a.* disconnected.

**несоразмерн/ость** *f.* disproportion; incommensurability; —**ый** *a.* disproportionate; incommensurable.

**несортированный** *a.* unsorted, run-of-mine, run-of-mill.

**несостоявшийся** *a.* not taken place.

**несостоятельн/ость** *f.* incompetence, unfitness; insolvency; —**ый** *a.* incompetent, unfit; insolvent.

**несохранение** *n.* non-conservation.

**неспаренный** *a.* unpaired.

**неспасаемый** *a.* non-recoverable, expendable.

**неспекающийся** *a.* non-caking, non-sintering.

**неспециал/ист** *m.* layman; —**ьный** *a.* general-purpose, non-specialized, universal.

**неcподручный** *a.* inconvenient, unhandy.

**неспокойный** *a.* restless, erratic.

**неспособн/ость** *f.* incapacity, inability, inaptitude, failure; —**ый** *a.* incapable, unable, inapt, unfit, inadequate.

**несправедливый** *a.* unfair, unjust, wrong.

**несрабатывание** *n.* non-operation.

**несравн/енный, —имый** *a.* incomparable, matchless, perfect.

**несродный** *a.* heterogeneous; uncongenial.

**несслеров реактив** Nessler reagent.

**нестабил/изированный** *a.* unstabilized; —**ьность** *f.* instability, unstable state; —**ьный** *a.* unstable.

**нестандартный** *a.* non-standard, irregular; optional (equipment).

**нестареющий** *a.* non-aging.

**нестационарный** *a.* transient, transitional; unsteady; portable.

**нестерпимый** *a.* unendurable, intolerable.

**нести** *v.* carry, bear; suffer, sustain, incur (losses); smell, reek (of); lay (eggs).

**нестираемый** *a.* indelible (ink, stain).

**нестись** *v.* rush (along); be carried, drift; lay eggs.

**нестойк/ий** *a.* unstable; —**ость** *f.* instability; **коэффициент** —**ости** instability constant.

**нестроевой** *a.* (mil.) non-combatant.

**нестройный** *a.* discordant; disordered.

**несуразный** *a.* incoherent, absurd; irregular; awkward.

**несут** *pr. 3 pl. of* **нести.**

**несущая** *f.* carrier.

**несущественный** *a.* unessential, unimportant, immaterial.

**несущ/ий** *a.* bearing, supporting, carrying, carrier; **н. элемент** carrier; —**ая волна** (rad.) carrier wave; —**ая ось** supporting axle; —**ая поверхность** supporting surface, bearing surface, face; —**ая способность** supporting power; carrying capacity; buoyancy; —**ая частота** (elec.) carrier frequency; —**ее устройство** carrier.

**несход/имость** *f.* divergence; —**имый** *a.* divergent; —**ный** *a.* dissimilar, unlike, diverse; —**ство** *n.* dissimilarity, difference, discrepancy.

**несцементированный** *a.* loose (rock).

**несчаст/ливый, —ный** *a.* unlucky, unfortunate; —**ный случай** accident, mishap; —**ье** *n.* misfortune, accident, disaster, ill luck; **к —ью, по —ью** unfortunately.

**несчетный** *a.* innumerable, countless, incalculable, numberless.

**несший** *past act. part. of* **нести.**

**несъедобный** *a.* inedible.

**неся** *pr. gerund of* **нести.**

**несяк** *m.* floeberg, floe.

**нет** no; there is not, there are no.

**нетвердый** *a.* unsteady, shaky; soft.

**нетекучий** *a.* stagnant (water).

**нетель** *f.* heifer.

**нетемнеющий** *a.* non-darkening; non-browning (glass).

**нетеплопроводный** *a.* non-heat-conducting, impervious to heat.

**нетерпение** *n.* impatience, restlessness.

**нетопырь** *m.* (zool.) bat.

**неточн/о** *adv.* not exactly, incorrectly, inaccurately; —**ость** *f.* incorrectness, inaccuracy, error, discrepancy; —**ый** *a.* inexact, incorrect, inaccurate.

**нетребовательный** *a.* not exacting, unpretentious, modest.

**нетронутый** *a.* untouched, intact, whole.

**нетропсин** *m.* netropsin.

**нетто** *adv.* (com.) net.

**неубедительный** *a.* unconvincing, inconclusive.

**неуверенн/ость** *f.* uncertainty; —**ый** *a.* uncertain, unsure.

**неувяд/аемый** *a.* unfading; —**анка** *f.* (bot.) everlasting flowers (*Gnaphalium*).

**неувязка** *f.* discrepancy; lack of co-ordination.

**неугасимый** *a.* inextinguishable, unquenchable.

**неугрожаем/ость** *f.* safety; —**ый** *a.* safe.

**неудач/а** *f.* failure, lack of success; **потерпеть —у** *v.* meet with failure, fail; —**но** *adv.* unsuccessfully; —**ный** *a.* unsuccessful, unfortunate, unlucky.

**неудержимый** *a.* uncontrollable.

**неудобн/о** *adv.* inconveniently; it is inconvenient; —**ый** *a.* inconvenient, unhandy, awkward; unproductive (land).

**неудобо/варимый** *a.* indigestible; —**исполнимый** *a.* impracticable; —**понятный** *a.* unintelligible; —**проходимый** *a.* impassable; —**читаемый** *a.* illegible.

**неудобство** *n.* inconvenience, discomfort; drawback, difficulty, disadvantage.

**неудовлетвор/енность** *f.* dissatisfaction; —**енный** *a.* dissatisfied; —**ительный** *a.* unsatisfactory, insufficient, inadequate, imperfect.

**неужели** *adv.* is it possible? indeed?

**неузнаваемый** *a.* unrecognizable.

**неуклонный** *a.* steady, steadfast; infallible.

**неуклюж/есть** *f.* clumsiness, awkwardness; —**ий** *a.* clumsy, awkward.

**неукоснительный** *a.* strict, unfailing.

**неулавливаемый** *a.* inappreciable, imperceptible.

**неулетучивающийся** *a.* non-volatile, fixed.

**неуловимый** *a.* elusive, impossible to catch; inappreciable.

**неуме/лый** *a.* ignorant; unskilful; —**ние** *n.* ignorance; lack of skill.

**неумеренн/о** *adv.* immoderately, in excess; —**ый** *a.* immoderate, excessive.

**неуместный** *a.* misplaced, out of place, irrelevant, uncalled for, superfluous.

**неумышленный** *a.* unintentional, inadvertent.

**неуничтожаем/ость** *f.* indestructibility; —**ый** *a.* indestructible.

**неуплата** *f.* non-payment.

**неуплотняем/ость** *f.* incompressibility; —**ый** *a.* incompressible, uncondensable.

**неупорядоченный** *a.* disordered.

**неупотреб/ительный** *a.* not in use, not used, unused, unpracticed, unusual; —**ление** *n.* disuse.

**неуправляемый** *a.* unguided, random.

**неупругий** *a.* inelastic, rigid.

**неуравновешенный** *a.* unbalanced, out of balance, out of alignment.

**неурожай** *m.* (agr.) crop failure, poor crop.

**неурочный** *a.* unseasonable, undue.

**неусвояемый** *a.* unassimilable; unavailable.

**неусиленный** *a.* non-reinforced.

**неуспе/х** *m.* failure, lack of success; —**шный** *a.* unsuccessful.

**неустанный** *a.* relentless, tireless.

**неустанов/ившийся** *a.* unsettled, unsteady, irregular, interrupted; transient, transitional; **н. режим** transient; —**ленный** *a.* unestablished; unmounted.

**неустойка** *f.* forfeit, penalty.

**неустойчив/ость** *f.* instability, unsteadiness, fluctuation; —**ый** *a.* unstable, labile; unsteady, fluctuating, shifting; precarious (position).

**неустройство** *n.* disorder, disorganization, lack of organization.

**неутолимый** *a.* unquenchable, insatiable.

**неуч/итываемый** *a.* negligible; —**тенный** *a.* unaccounted for.

**неуязвимый** *a.* invulnerable.

**нефелин** *m.* (min.) nepheline, nephelite; —**ит** *m.* (petr.) nephelinite (an alkalic basalt); —**овый** *a.* nepheline, nephelinic.

**нефелометр** *m.* nephelometer, turbidimeter; —**ический** *a.* nephelometric, turbidimetric (analysis).

**нефильтрованный** *a.* unfiltered.

**нефоскоп** *m.* (meteor.) nephoscope.

**нефр**— *prefix* nephr— (kidney).

**нефранкированный** *a.* unstamped.

**нефр/идий** *m.* (zool.) nephridium; —**ин** *m.* nephrine; —**ит** *m.* (min.) nephrite, jade; (med.) nephritis; —**итный,** —**итовый** *a.* nephritic; —**о**— *prefix* nephro— (kidney); —**оз** *m.* (med.) nephrosis.

**нефте**— *prefix* petroleum; —**база** *f.* petroleum-product storage and distribution center; —**вать** *v.* petrolize, treat with petroleum; —**водяное зеркало** (geol.) oil-water table.

**нефте/гиль,** —**дегиль** *m.* (min.) neftgil, neftdegil (related to zietrisikite).

**нефте/добывающий** *a.* petroleum-extracting, petroleum (industry); —**добыча** *f.* petroleum output; —**заводский** *a.* refinery; —**наливное судно** tanker, tank ship; —**носность** *f.* petroleum content; —**носный** *a.* oil-bearing, petroliferous; —**носный район** oil field; —**очистительный завод,** —**перегонный завод,** —**перерабатывающий завод** petroleum refinery, oil refinery; —**очистка** *f.* petroleum refining; —**переработчик** *m.* petroleum refiner; —**провод** *m.* pipeline, oil pipe; —**продукты** *pl.* petroleum products, petroleum derivatives; —**промысловое дело,** —**промышленность** *f.,* —**промышленный** *a.* petroleum industry, oil industry; —**топливо** *n.* fuel oil; —**химический** *a.,* —**химический продукт** petrochemical, petroleum chemical; —**хранилище** *n.* oil tank.

**Нефт. хоз.** *abbr.* (**Нефтяное хозяйство**) Petroleum Economy (journal).

**нефть** *f.* petroleum; **сырая н.** crude oil.

**нефтян/ик** *m.* oilman; petroleum specialist; —**ка** *f.* gasoline engine.

**нефтян/ой** *a.* petroleum, oil; **н. гудрон**

petroleum asphalt; **н. двигатель** petroleum (oil) engine, gasoline engine, gas engine; **н. источник, —ая скважина** oil well; **н. эфир** petroleum ether; **—ое месторождение** oil field; **—ое топливо** fuel oil; **—ые остатки** petroleum residue, mazut.

**нехват/ать** *see* **недоставать; —ка** *f.* shortage, deficiency, scarcity, lack, short weight; (chromosome) deletion.

**неходовой** *a.* unmarketable.

**нехороший** *a.* bad, poor, low (yield).

**нецелесообразн/о** *adv.* not to the purpose; **—ый** *a.* unsuitable.

**нецентр/альный** *a.* off-center, side; noncentral; **—ированный** *a.* eccentric.

**нециклический** *a.* acyclic.

**нечаянн/о** *adv.* unexpectedly, accidentally, by accident; **—ость** *f.* unexpectedness; unforeseen accident; **—ый** *a.* unexpected, inadvertent, unintentional.

**нечего, нечему:** there is nothing (to); **н. и говорить, что** it goes without saying that; **больше н.** nothing more; no more; **нечему удивляться** it is no wonder.

**нечет** *m.* odd number.

**нечеткий** *a.* illegible, undecipherable.

**нечет/о-нечетный** *a.* odd-odd; **—о-четный** *a.* odd-even; **—ый** *a.* odd, uneven (number).

**нечисто** *adv.* not cleanly; **—кровный** *a.* half-breed; **—та** *f.* dirtiness, impurity; **—ты** *pl.* impurities; sewage.

**нечистый** *a.* unclean, impure.

**нечленораздельный** *a.* inarticulate.

**нечто** *pron.* something, somewhat.

**нечувствительн/ость** *f.* lack of sensitivity, insensitivity; **время —ости** (instruments) dead time; **—ый** *a.* insensitive, insensible, unsusceptible.

**нешлакующийся** *a.* non-clinkering.

**неэконом/ичный, —ный** *a.* uneconomical, wasteful.

**неэластичн/ость** *f.* inelasticity, rigidity, stiffness; **—ый** *a.* inelastic, rigid.

**неэффективный** *a.* ineffective, inefficient.

**неявка** *f.* non-appearance, absence.

**неявная функция** (math.) implicit function.

**неядовитый** *a.* non-toxic, non-poisonous.

**неясн/о** *adv.* vaguely; it is not clear; **—ость** *f.* vagueness, obscurity, confusion; **—ый** *a.* vague, obscure, indistinct, blurred, hazy, nebulous, foggy, turbid; confused, not clear.

**ни** *conj.* neither, nor; **ни . . . ни** neither . . . nor; **ни за что** not for anything; **ни один** none, no one, nobody; **чтобы ни случилось** whatever may happen.

**НИ** *abbr.* (научный институт) scientific institute; (научно-исследовательский институт) research institute; **н.-и.** *abbr.* (научноисследовательский) scientific-research.

**ниагарск/ий** *a.* Niagara, Niagara Falls; **н. голубой** Niagara Blue, Trypan Blue; **—ая свита** (geol.) Niagarian series.

**ниамский жир** niam fat.

**ниаулиевое масло** niaouli oil (from leaves of *Melaleuca viridiflora*).

**ниацин** *m.* niacin, nicotinic acid.

**нива** *f.* (corn) field; arable land.

**ниваловая кислота** nivalic acid.

**нивация** *f.* (geol.) nivation (effect of névé).

**нивелир** *m.*, **—ующее приспособление** level, leveling instrument; **—ная рейка, —очная рейка** leveling rod, level rod; **—ование** *n.*, **—овка** *f.* leveling, grading; **—овать** *v.* level, grade; **—овочный** *a.* leveling; level; **—овщик** *m.* leveler; **—ующий** *a.* leveling.

**нивенит** *m.* (min.) nivenite (a variety of uraninite).

**нивяник** *m.* oxeye daisy (*Leucanthemum*).

**нигде** *adv.* nowhere.

**нигерицин** *m.* nigericin.

**нигеровое масло** nigerseed oil (from seeds of *Guizotia oleifera*).

**нигони формация** (geol.) Negaunee formation.

**нигр/анилин** *see* **нигрозин; —изин** *m.* nigrisine (dye); **—ин** *m.* (min.) nigrine (a ferriferous variety of rutile); **—ит** *m.* (elec.) nigrite (insulator); nigrite (a natural asphalt); **—озин** *m.* nigrosine, aniline black; **—ол** *m.* nigrol (a heavy, unpurified lubricating oil); **—ометр** *m.* nigrometer (for carbon blacks); **—оспороз** *m.* Nigrospora infection (of plants); —отовая кислота nigrotic acid.

**Нидерландская Индия** Dutch East Indies.

**нидерландский** *a.* Netherland, Dutch.

**Нидерланды** Netherlands.

**Ниецкого правило** Nietzki's rule (of dye colors).

**ниже** *comp. of* низкий, низко, lower; *prep. gen.* below, beneath, under; —изложенный *a.* given below, set forth below; —кипящий *a.* lower-boiling; —лежащий *a.* underlying; —означенный *see* нижеупомянутый; —подписавшийся *a.* the undersigned; —приведенный *a.* stated below, cited below.

**нижеследующ/ий** *a.* following, next; сказал —ee said as follows.

**нижеупомянутый** *a.* mentioned below.

**Нижне-Тагильский завод** Nizhne Tagilski works.

**нижнечелюстный** *a.* (anat.) mandibular.

**нижн/ий** *a.* lower, bottom, inferior, under; **Н.-Новгород** Nizhni-Novgorod; **н. привод** underneath drive; **н. слой** substratum, bottom layer; **н. этаж** ground floor; —яя тяга downdraft; —яя часть, —ик *m.* bottom part, bottom section, bottom.

**низ** *m.* bottom, base, lowest part; (geol.) lowest bed of formation; *prefix* down, downward.

**низать** *v.* string, thread.

**низбегающий** *a.* running down, decursive, decurrent.

**низведение** *n.* bringing down.

**низвер/гать,** —гнуть *v.* precipitate, throw down; —жение *n.* precipitation, throwing down.

**низ/вести,** —водить *v.* bring down.

**низин** *m.* nisin.

**низин/а** *f.,* —ный *a.* lowland, floodplain, low place, flat.

**низк/ий** *a.* low; base; deep (sound); котел —ого давления low-pressure boiler.

**низко** *adv.* low; —вольтный *a.* (elec.) low-voltage; —вязкий *a.* low-viscosity; —калорийный *a.* low-calorie; —кипящий *a.* low-boiling; —легированный *a.* low-alloy; —молекулярный *a.* low-molecular; —оборотный

*a.* slow-speed; —омный *a.* (elec.) low-resistance.

**низкопробн/ость** *f.* inferior quality; —ый *a.* poor-quality, base, base-alloy.

**низко/проходный фильтр** (elec.) low-pass filter; —процентный *a.* low-percentage, low-grade, inferior; —сортный *a.* poor-quality, low-grade; —температурный *a.* low-temperature; —углеродистый *a.* low-carbon; —фонный *a.* low-background (counter); —частотный *a.* low-frequency; —энергетический *a.* low-energy.

**низменн/ость** *f.* lowness; lowland, depression; —ый *a.* low, low-lying, callow.

**НИЗМИР** *abbr.* (Научно-исследовательский институт земного магнетизма, ионосферы и распространения радиоволн) Scientific Research Institute of Earth Magnetism, Ionosphere and Distribution of Radio Waves.

**низов/ой** *a.* bottom, sedimentary (fermentation); lowland, situated downstream; —ье *n.* lower river, lower reaches (of river); в —ьях down stream.

**низ/ость** *f.* lowness, baseness; —ший *comp. of* низкий, lower, inferior; lowest; net; —ы *pl. of* низ; —ь *f.* low place.

**НИИ** *abbr.* (научно-исследовательский институт) scientific research institute; **НИИГА** *abbr.* (Научно-исследовательский институт геологии Арктики) Scientific Research Institute of the Geology of the Arctic; **НИИПМ** *abbr.* (научно-исследовательский институт пластических Масс) Scientific Research Institute of Plastics; **НИИТН** *abbr.* (научно-исследовательский институт технического нормирования) Scientific Institute of Technical Standardization.

**никак** *adv.* by no means, in no way; —ой *a.* no, not any, none.

**никалой** *m.* Nicaloi (iron-nickel alloy).

**никеле—** *prefix* nickeli—, nickelic, nickel.

**никелевосурьмяный блеск** (min.) ullmannite.

**никелев/ый** *a.* nickel; **н. блеск** (min.)

nickel glance, gersdorffite; **н. гимнит** (min.) nickel gymnite, genthite; **н. изумруд** (min.) emerald nickel, zaratite; **н. купорос** nickel vitriol, nickel sulfate; **—ая жесть** nickel sheet, nickel plate; **—ая соль** nickel salt (usually nickelous salt); **—ое железо** (met.) ferronickel; **—ые цветы** (min.) nickel bloom, annabergite, hydrous nickel arsenate.

**никелесинеродоводородная кислота** nickelicyanic acid.

**никелин** *m.*, **—овый** *a.* (met.) nickeline (a nickel alloy); (min.) *see* **никколит.**

**никелиров/ание** *n.*, **—ка** *f.* (met.) nickel plating; **—анный** *a.* nickel-plated; **—ать** *v.* nickel-plate.

**никелисто—** *prefix* nickelo—, nickelous, nickel; **—синеродоводородная кислота** nickelocyanic acid.

**никелит** *see* **никколит.**

**никел/ь** *m.* nickel, Ni; **азотнокислый н., азотнокислая закись —я** nickel(ous) nitrate; **бромистый н.** nickel bromide, nickelous bromide; **гидрат закиси —я** nickelous hydroxide; **гидрат окиси —я** nickelic hydroxide; **зеленый гидрат —я** hydrous nickelous hydroxide; **закись —я** nickelous oxide, nickel monoxide; **соль закиси —я** nickelous salt; **карбонил —я** nickel carbonyl (gas); **молибденистый н.** nickel-molybdenum; **окись —я** nickelic oxide, nickel tetroxide; **соединение окиси —я** nickelic compound; **сернокислый н.** nickel sulfate; **хлористый н.** nickel chloride, nickelous chloride.

**никель/аммоний** *m.* nickel ammonium; **сернокислый н.** nickel ammonium sulfate; **—шпейс** *m.* (met.) nickel speiss; **—штейн** *m.* (met.) nickel matte.

**никкель** *see* **никель.**

**никколит** *m.* (min.) niccolite, copper nickel, arsenical nickel.

**никогда** *adv.* never.

**никодуст** *m.* lime-nicotine sulfate insecticide.

**никоим образом** *adv.* by no means, in no way; not at all.

**николаит** *m.* (min.) nicolayite.

**николин** *m.* nicoline.

**николь** *see* **Николя призма.**

**Никольсона гидрометр** Nicholson hydrometer; **Н. голубой** Nicholson Blue (dye).

**никольсонит** *m.* (min.) nicholsonite (a variety of aragonite).

**Николя призма** Nicol's prism, nicol (for polariscope).

**никот/еин** *m.* nicoteine; **—еллин** *m.* nicotelline; **—ианин** *m.* nicotianine.

**никотин** *m.* nicotine; **сернокислый н.** nicotine sulfate; **—овый** *a.* nicotine, nicotinic; **—овая кислота** nicotinic acid, 2-pyridinecarboxylic acid.

**никр/ал** *m.* Nicral (aluminum alloy); **—осилал** *m.* Nicrosilal (chrome-nickel cast iron).

**никт—**, **—и—** *prefix* nyct—, nycti— (night); **—алопия** *f.* (med.) nyctalopia, night blindness.

**никто** *pron.* nobody, no one, none.

**никуда** *adv.* nowhere, in no direction; **это н. не годится** this is no good.

**НИКФИ** *abbr.* (Научно-исследовательский кино-фото институт) Motion Picture and Photography Scientific Research Institute.

**Нил** Nile (river).

**Ниландера реактив** Nylander reagent.

**нильский** *a.* Nile.

**нимало** *see* **нисколько.**

**нимф/а** *f.* (zool.) nymph; **—алиды** *pl.* Nymphalidae; **—ея** *f.* (bot.) water lily (*Nymphaea*).

**нингидрин** *m.*, **—ный** *a.* ninhydrin.

**ниобат** *m.* niobate, columbate.

**ниобиев/ый** *a.* niobium; **н. ангидрид** niobic anhydride, niobium pentoxide; **—ая кислота** niobic acid, columbic acid; **соль —ой кислоты, —окислая соль** niobate, columbate.

**ниоб/ий** *m.* niobium, Nb; **закись —ия** niobium monoxide; **окись —ия** niobium tetroxide.

**ниобит** *m.* (min.) niobite, columbite.

**ниобовое масло** niobe oil, methyl benzoate.

**ниоткуда** *adv.* from nowhere.

**нипагин** *m.* Nipagin, ethyl- or methyl-*p*-hydroxybenzoate.

**нипекотовая кислота** nipecotic acid, 3-piperidinecarboxylic acid.

**нипермаг** *m.* Nipermag (iron-nickel-aluminum-titanium alloy).

**ниппель** *m.* nipple, sleeve, adapter.

**нирван/ин** *m.* nirvanine; **—ол** *m.* nirvanol.

**нирезист** *m.* Ni-Resist (heat-resistant iron alloy).

**НИРП** *abbr.* (Научный институт резиновой промышленности) Scientific Institute of the Rubber Industry.

**нисколько** *adv.* not at all, not in the least; **н. не меньше** none the less.

**ниспровергающий** *a.* subversive.

**нистагм, —ус** *m.* (med.) nystagmus.

**нисходить** *v.* descend, go down.

**нисходя/щий** *a.* descending, downward, down, downcast; (med., meteor.) catabatic; (bot.) decursive; **н. дымоход** downtake; **н. канал** (min.) downcast shaft, downcast; **н. сброс** (geol.) downcast side, downthrow; **н. холодильник** condenser set for distillation; **—ая труба** drain pipe, waste pipe; **—ее скольжение** downslide.

**нисхождение** *n.* descent.

**ниталь** *m.* nital (pickling reagent).

**нитбанк** *m.* riveting stock.

**ните/видный, —образный** *a.* threadlike, filar, filiform, capillary, filament, filamentary; straight-chain (molecule); **—вод, —водитель, —проводник** *m.* twine guide; (text.) thread guide; **—ловка** *f.* thread picker, thread extractor; **—образные черви** (zool.) thread-worms; **—резка** *f.* thread cutter.

**нитка** *f.* thread, fiber, filament.

**НИТО** *abbr.* (Научное инженерное техническое общество) Scientific Engineering and Technical Society.

**нитон** *m.* niton, Nt, Radon, Rn.

**ниточ/ка** *f.* little thread, thread, filament; **—ник** *m.* (text.) thread board; **—ный** *a.* thread, filar.

**нитр—** *prefix* nitr—, nitro—; **—агин** *m.* nitragin (bacterial fertilizer); **—азин** *m.* nitrazine; **—алой, —аллой** *m.* Nitralloy (chromium-aluminum steel); **—амид** *m.* nitramide; **—амин** *m.* nitramine, tetranitromethylaniline; **—амино—** *prefix* nitramino—.

**нитранил/ид** *m.* nitroanilide, diazobenzolic acid; **—ин** *m.* nitraniline;

**—овая кислота** nitranilic acid.

**нитрат** *m.*, **—ный** *a.* nitrate; **н. калия** potassium nitrate; **—ин** *m.* (min.) nitratine, sodium nitrate; **—ные бактерии** nitro-bacteria.

**нитрато—** *prefix* nitrato—; **—р** *m.* nitrator.

**нитраци/я** *f.*, **—онный** *a.* nitration, nitrating; **—онная смесь** nitrating mixture.

**нитр/ен** *m.* nitrene; **—ид** *m.* nitride; **—ил** *m.* nitrile, cyanide; nitroxyl, nitro group; **—ило—** *prefix* nitrilo—; **—иловый, —ильный** *a.* nitrile; **—ильная группа** nitrile group; **—ин** *m.* nitrine.

**нитрир/ование** *n.* nitration; (met.) nitriding, nitride casehardening; **—ованный** *a.* nitrated; nitrided; **—овать** *v.* nitrate; nitride, caseharden (with nitrogen); **—ующий** *a.* nitrating; nitriding; **—ующее средство** nitrating agent.

**нитрит** *m.* nitrite; **н. натрия** sodium nitrite; **—о—** *prefix* nitrito—.

**нитрифи/кация** *f.* nitrification; **—цировать** *v.* nitrify; **—цируемый, —цирующийся** *a.* nitrifiable; **—цирующий** *a.* nitrifying.

**нитро—** *prefix* nitro—; **—амин** *m.* nitroamine, nitramine; **—антрацен** *m.* nitroanthracene, nitrososanthrone; **—бактерии** *pl.* nitro-bacteria; **—бенз—** *prefix* nitrobenz—; **—бензол** *m.* nitrobenzene.

**нитров/альная смесь** nitrating mixture; **—ание** *see* **нитрирование; —анный** *a.* nitrated; nitrided; **—ать** *v.* nitrate; nitrify; nitride.

**нитро/винная кислота** nitrotartaric acid; **—глауберит** *m.* (min.) nitroglauberite (probably a mixture of darapskite and soda niter); **—глицерин** *m.* (expl.) nitroglycerin, **—группа** *f.* nitro group, nitroxyl; **—желатин** *m.* (expl.) nitrogelatin, gelatin dynamite.

**нитроза** *f.* nitrose (solution of nitrosyl sulfuric acid in sulfuric acid); **—мин** *m.* nitrosamine; **—т** *m.* nitrosate.

**нитрозил** *m.*, **—овый** *a.* nitrosyl; **серно-кислый н.** nitrosyl sulfate, nitrososulfuric acid; **—овая кислота** nitrosylic acid (hyponitrous acid); **—серная кислота** nitrosylsulfuric acid.

**нитроз/ирование** *n.* nitrosation; —**ит** *m.* nitrosite; —**ный** *a.* nitrose.

**нитрозо**— *prefix* nitroso—; —**амин** *m.* nitrosoamine; —**бензол** *m.* nitrosobenzene; —**вый голубой** nitroso blue; —**группа** *f.* nitroso group; —**краски** *pl.* nitroso dyes; —**ность** *f.* nitrosity; —**соединение** *n.* nitroso compound; —**толуол** *m.* nitrosotoluene; —**этан** *m.* nitrosoethane.

**нитро/ил** *m.* nitroyl; —**кальцит** *m.* (min.) nitrocalcite, hydrous calcium nitrate; —**кислота** *f.* nitro acid.

**нитроклетчат/ка** *f.*, —**очный** *a.* nitrocellulose; —**очный шелк** nitrocellulose rayon.

**нитро/краски** *pl.* nitro dyes; —**крахмал** *m.* (expl.) nitro starch, starch nitrate; —**ксил** *m.* nitroxyl; —**л** *m.* nitrol; —**лак** *m.* nitrocellulose varnish (or lacquer); —**овая кислота** nitrolic acid; —**магнезит** *m.* (min.) nitromagnesite, hydrous magnesium nitrate; —**маннит** *m.* (expl.) nitromannite, mannitol nitrate; —**метан** *m.* nitromethane; —**метр** *m.* nitrometer.

**нитрон** *m.* nitron; **азотнокислый н.**, **нитрат** —a nitron nitrate.

**нитро/нафталин** *m.* nitronaphthalene; —**новая кислота** nitronic acid; —**пленка** *f.* nitrate film; —**производные** *pl.* nitro derivatives, nitro compounds.

**нитропруссид** *m.* nitroprusside; —**водородная кислота** nitroprussic acid; —**ный натрий** sodium nitroprusside.

**нитро/серная кислота** nitrosulfuric acid; —**смолы** *pl.* nitro resins; —**соединение, —тело** *n.* nitro compound; —**спорин** *m.* nitrosporin; —**стирол** *m.* nitrostyrene; —**сульфоновая кислота** nitrosulfonic acid, nitrosyl sulfuric acid; —**толуол** *m.* nitrotoluene; —**уретан** *m.* nitrourethan; —**фенол** *m.* nitrophenol; —**форм** *m.* nitroform, trinitromethane; —**фоска** *see* **азофоска**; —**фталевая кислота** nitrophthalic acid; —**целлюлоза** *f.*, —**целлюлозный** *a.* nitrocellulose; —**шелк** *m.* nitrocellulose rayon; —**этан** *m.* nitroethane.

**нитрующ/ий** *a.* nitrating; nitrifying;

(met.) nitriding; —**ая кислота** nitrating acid; —**ийся** *a.* nitratable; nitrifiable; nitridable.

**нитчат/ка** *f.* (bot.) hairweed (*Conferva*); —**ки** *pl.* (zool.) Filarioidea; —**ый** *a.* thread, filar; (bot.) confervoid.

**нить** *f.*, —**яный** *a.* thread, filament, fiber; (med.) suture; —**яный крест** cross-hairs (of microscope).

**НИУИФ** *abbr.* (Научный институт по удобрениям и инсектофунгисидам) Scientific Institute of Fertilizers and Insecticides and Fungicides; **НИУИФ-1** an ethylmercury phosphate fungicide; **НИУИФ-2** *see* **гранозан**; **НИУИФ-100** *see* **паратион**.

**ни/фе** (geol.) Ni-Fe (nickel-iron core of earth); —**хром** *m.* Nichrome (a nickel-chromium-iron alloy).

**Ницца** Nice.

**ничего** *gen. of* **ничто**, nothing, not anything; it does not matter.

**ничей** *a.* nobody's, belonging to nobody.

**ничто** *pron.* nothing; **н. иное как** nothing less than, nothing but.

**ничтож/ество** *n.* nonentity; —**но** *adv.* insignificantly; —**ность** *f.* insignificance; —**ный** *a.* insignificant, meaningless; slight, faint, negligible, infinitesimal; —**ное количество** trace.

**ничуть** *see* **нисколько**.

**ниша** *f.* niche, recess, housing.

**нищ/ета** *f.* poverty; —**ий** *a.* poor; *m.* beggar, pauper.

**НК** *abbr.* (натуральный каучук) natural rubber.

**нм³** *abbr.* (м³ пересчитанный на нормальные условия) normal cubic meter.

**нмт** *abbr.* (нижняя мертвая точка) lower dead center.

**но** *conj.* but; yet.

**нобелий** *m.* nobelium, No.

**новаин** *m.* novain, carnitine.

**новакулит** *m.* novaculite (a bedded cherty rock).

**нов/альгин** *m.* Novalgin; —**арган** *m.* Novargan (a silver proteinate); —**арсенол** *m.* Neodiarsenol, neoarsphenamine; —**аспирин** *m.* Novaspirin, salicitrin; —**асурол** *m.* Novasurol, merbaphen; —**асекит** *see* **новачекит**.

**новатор** *m.* innovator; —**ство** *n.* innovations.

**нов/атофан** *m.* Novatophan, neocinchophen; —**атропин** *m.* Novatropin, homoatropine methyl bromide; —**ачекит** *m.* novacekite (uranium mineral).

**Новая Гвинея** New Guinea; **Н. Зеландия** New Zealand.

**новейший** *a.* newest, modern, most recent.

**новизна** *f.* novelty, newness; innovation.

**новин/а** *see* **новь;** —**ка** *f.* novelty.

**новичок** *m.* novice, beginner, apprentice.

**ново** *adv.* newly; recently, just; *prefix* neo—, new, newly; —**введение** *n.* innovation, novelty.

**новозеландский лен** (bot.) New Zealand hemp (*Phormium tenax*).

**новоизобретенный** *a.* newly invented, recent.

**новокаин** *m.* Novocaine, procaine hydrochloride; —**амид** *m.* Novocainamid, procaine amide hydrochloride.

**новокрылые** *pl.* (zool.) Neoptera.

**новола/ки, —чные смолы** *pl.* Novolaks, novolacs (soluble phenol-formaldehyde resins).

**новолуние** *n.* new moon.

**новоль** *m.* a drying oil (for paints).

**новообразован/ие** *n.* (med.) neoplasm, new growth; regeneration; —**ный** *a.* (geol.) neogenic, neogene.

**ново/прибывший** *a.* newly come; *m.* newcomer; —**рожденный** *a.* newborn.

**новосадка** *f.* novosadka (salt deposited in a lake during one season).

**новостройка** *f.* new buildings, erection of new factories and plants.

**новость** *f.* news.

**новотельный** *a.* newly calved.

**новоциллин** *m.* procaine salt of penicillin.

**новшество** *n.* innovation, novelty.

**новый** *a.* new, novel, modern, recent, fresh; **н. голубой** New Blue; **Н. Орлеан** New Orleans.

**новь** *f.* (agr.) virgin soil, fresh land.

**ног/а** *f.* leg; foot; stand, brace; **на твердую —у** on a sure footing; —**ие** *pl. suffix* (zool.) —poda.

**ноголистник** *m.* (bot.) duck's foot (*Podo-*

*phyllum*); —**а смола** podophyllin (resin).

**ногоплодник** *m.* (bot.) podocarpus.

**ногот/ки** *pl.*, **аптечный —ок** (bot.) marigold (*Calendula*).

**ноготь** *m.* nail (on hand or foot).

**ногохвостки** *pl.* (zool.) Collembola.

**ногтоеда** *f.* (med.) whitlow, felon.

**ноет** *pr. 3 sing. of* **ныть.**

**нож** *m.* knife, blade; —**евка** *see* **ножовка.**

**ножев/ой** *a.* knife; **н. клинок** knife blade; **н. патрон,** —**ая головка** cutter block; **н. товар** cutlery; **н. штамп** shearing die; —**ая опора** knife edge, knife-edge bearing.

**ножк/а** *f.* small foot; leg; shank, stem; (bot.) stalk, pedicle; jaw (of measuring instrument); (mech.) shoe; arm, tine (of tuning fork); **черная н.** wirestem (plant disease); —**и** *pl. suffix* (zool.) —poda.

**ножницы** *pl.* scissors, shears, cutter.

**ножн/ой** *a.* foot, pedal; **н. привод** foot drive; **с —ым приводом** driven by foot, pedal-operated; **н. рычаг** pedal; **н. тормоз** foot brake.

**ножны** *pl.* case, sheath, scabbard.

**ножов/ка** *f.*, —**очный** *a.* hand saw; hack saw; **машинная н.,** —**очный станок** power hack saw; —**очный напилок** knife file; —**очное полотно** hacksaw blade.

**ножовый** *see* **ножевой.**

**ноздреват/ость** *f.* porosity, sponginess; —**ый** *a.* porous, spongy; blown, blistered; —**ая отливка** casting with blowholes, porous casting.

**ноздрица** *f.* (bot.) agaric.

**ноздря** *f.*, —**ной** *a.* nostril.

**нозеан** *m.*, —**овый** *a.* (min.) nosean, noselite (near haüynite); —**ит** *m.* (petr.) noseanite (an alkali basalt).

**нозематоз** *m.* Nosema infection of bees or silkworms.

**нозология** *f.* nosology (classification of diseases).

**нозофен** *m.* Nosophen, iodophthalein.

**нокард/амин** *m.* nocardamine; —**ин** *m.* nocardin.

**ноктал** *m.* Noctal, Nostal.

**нолит** *m.* (min.) nohlite.

**ноль** *m.*, —**ный** *a.* zero; naught, cipher; —**ный уступ** (min.) lower level.

**номенклатур/а** *f.*, **—ный** *a.* nomenclature; list, range.

**номер** *m.* number; issue, copy (of journal); size, gage (of wire), mesh (of screen), count (of yarn); item; **—ник** *see* **нумерник; —ный** *a.* number, numerical; **—ное сверло** wire drill; **—овать** *see* **нумеровать; —ок** *m.* tally; **—онабиратель** *m.* (tel.) dial.

**номинал** *m.* rating; nominal value.

**номинальн/ый** *a.* nominal; rated; **н. параметр** rating factor; **н. режим** (mach.) duty; **н. ток** current rating; **—ая мощность** (elec.) rated output, rated capacity, power rating; **—ая стоимость** face value, par value.

**номо/грамма** *f.* nomogram, nomograph, chart; **—графия** *f.* nomography.

**нона/декан** *m.* nonadecane; **—деканон** *m.* nonadecanone, dinonyl ketone; **—дециловый спирт** nondecyl alcohol, nonadecanol; **—козан** *m.* nonacosane.

**нонан** *m.* nonane; **—диол** *m.* nonanediol; **—овая кислота** nonanoic acid, pelargonic acid; **—оил** *m.* nonanoyl; **—ол** *m.* nonanol; **—он** *m.* nonanone.

**нонвариантный** *a.* non-variant.

**нон/дециловая кислота** nonadecylic acid, nonadecanoic acid; **—ен** *m.* nonene, nonylene.

**нонил** *m.* nonyl; **синеродистый н.** nonyl cyanide, caprinitrile; **—ен** *m.* nonylene, nonene; **—еновая кислота** nonylenic acid; **—овая кислота** nonylic acid, pelargonic acid; **—овый альдегид** nonyl aldehyde, pelargonaldehyde; **—овый спирт** nonyl alcohol.

**нонин** *m.* nonine, *n*-heptylacetylene.

**нониус** *m.* nonius, vernier.

**ноноза** *f.* nonose (a monosaccharide with 9 carbon atoms).

**нонпарель** *f.* (typ.) nonpareil.

**нонтронит** *m.* (min.) nontronite.

**нооткатин** *m.* nootkatin.

**нопин/ен** *m.* nopinene, beta-pinene; **—овая кислота** nopinic acid.

**нор—** *prefix* nor—.

**нора** *f.* burrow, hole.

**норатропин** *m.* noratropine.

**норв.** *abbr.* (норвежский) Norwegian.

**Норвегия** Norway.

**норвежск/ий** *a.* Norwegian; **—ая селит-** ра Norwegian saltpeter, calcium nitrate.

**нор/гваяксмоляная кислота** norguaiaretic acid; **—гераниевая кислота** norgeranic acid; **—гомокамфорная кислота** norhomocamphoric acid.

**норд** *m.* north; north wind.

**нордгаузенск/ая серная кислота, —ое купоросное масло** Nordhausen acid, fuming sulfuric acid, oleum.

**норденшельдин** *m.* (min.) nordenskiöldine (a calcium-tin borate).

**нордмаркит** *m.* (min.) nordmarkite (a variety of staurolite); (petr.) nordmarkite (a sodic variety of syenite).

**норит** *m.* (petr.) norite (a variety of gabbro); Norite (a purified charcoal).

**норичник** *m.* (bot.) figwort (*Scrophularia*); **—овые** *pl.* Scrophulariaceae.

**нория** *f.* bucket conveyer; irrigating wheel.

**норка** *see* **нора;** (zool.) mink.

**норкамф/ан** *m.* norcamphane, 1,2,2-bicycloheptane; **—анил** *m.* norcamphanyl; **—ора** *f.* norcamphor; **—орная кислота** norcamphoric acid.

**нор/карен** *m.* norcarene, bicycloheptene; **—лейцин** *m.* norleucine, glycoleucine.

**норм.** *abbr.* (нормальный) normal.

**норм** *m.*, **—а** *f.* norm, standard; rate; quota; **—ы** *pl.* standard specifications.

**нормализ/ация** *f.* normalization, standardization; (met.) normalizing; **комитет по —ации** standard specification board; **—ованный** *a.* standardized; **—овать** *v.* normalize, standardize.

**нормаль** *m.* normal, standard, standard specifications; **—ность** *f.* normality.

**нормальн/ый** *a.* normal, standard, regular, conventional; rated; neutral (salt); **н. раствор** normal solution; **н. термометр** standard thermometer; **—ая величина** normal; rating; **—ые технические условия** standard specifications.

**норматив** *m.*, **—ный** *a.* norm; **—ный состав** (petr.) norm.

**нормиров/ание** *n.*, **—ка** *f.* rate fixing; rationing; (agr.) thinning; normalization; **—анный** *a.* fixed, set; **—ать** *v.* normalize, standardize; ration.

**норов** *m.* custom, habit.

норпин/ан *m.* norpinane, 1,1,3-bicyclo-heptane; —овая кислота norpinic acid.

норсульфазол *m.* norsulfazole, sulfa-thiazole.

Нортона теорема (elec.) Norton's theorem.

нортроп/ан *m.* nortropane, 2,3-dihy-dronortropidine; —ен, —идин *m.* nortropene, nortropidine; —инон *m.* nortropinone.

Нортрупа печь (elec.) Northrup furnace.

нортупит *m.* (min.) northupite.

нос *m.* nose; point, forepart; horn (of anvil); (geol.) headland, promontory, point; lip (for pouring); prow (of boat); —ик *m.* little nose; tip; bill; spout.

носил/ки *pl.* handbarrow; stretcher, litter; skids; —очный *m.* stretcher bearer; —ьный *a.* carrying; —ьщик *m.* carrier, porter; stretcher bearer.

носител/ь *m.* bearer, carrier; без —я carrier-free; н. бацилл (med.) carrier.

носить *v.* carry, bear; wear; —ся *v.* wear; float, ride, be borne.

носка *f.* carrying, bearing; wear, wearing.

носк/ий *a.* durable, lasting, strong; —ость *f.* durability, wearing qualities.

—носный *suffix a.* bearing, containing; —iferous.

носов/ой *a.* nose, nasal; (naut.) bow, fore; —ая качка pitching.

носок *m.* spout, nozzle; point, bill; (pouring) lip; toe (of shoe); sock.

носорог *m.* (zool.) rhinoceros.

нософен *see* нозофен.

ностоковые *pl.* (bot.) Nostocaceae.

НОТ *abbr.* (научная организация труда) Scientific Organization of Labor.

нота *f.* note.

нотализин *m.* notalysin.

нотариус *m.* notary public.

нотатин *m.* notatin.

нот/ация *f.* notation; —ификация *f.* notification.

ноцерин *m.* (min.) nocerine, nocerite.

ночевать *v.* spend the night, sleep.

ноч/ецветные *pl.* (bot.) Nyctaginaceae; —ецветный *a.* night-blooming; —ницы *pl.* owlet or cutworm moths (*Noctuidae*).

ночной *a.* nightly, night, nocturnal.

ноч/ь *f.* night; за н. during the night; по —ам at night, nights; —ью at night.

нош/а *f.* load, burden; kit; —ение *n.* carrying; wearing.

ною/т *pr. 3 pl.;* —щий *pr. act. part. of* ныть.

ноябрь *m.* November.

НПИ *abbr.* (Новочеркасский политехнический институт) Novocherkassk Polytechnical Institute.

НР *abbr.* (нормаль) standard (specification).

нрав *m.* disposition, temper; —иться *v.* please; ему не —ится he does not like.

НСА *abbr.* (нитросульфат аммония) ammonium nitrosulfate.

НТО *abbr.* (научно-технический отдел) Scientific Technical Department, Technological Department; НТС *abbr.* (научно-технический совет) Scientific Technical Council, Technological Council.

нубук *m.* buffed-grain leather.

нуг *m.* (bot.) guizotia.

нуга *f.* nougat.

нудный *a.* tedious.

нудовая кислота nudic acid.

нужд/а *f.* need, necessity, want; без —ы unnecessarily, needlessly; —аться *v.* need, require, want, be in want (of), lack; —ающийся *a.* needing, needy, destitute.

нужный *a.* necessary, requisite, needful.

НУК *abbr.* (α-нафталуксусная кислота α-naphthaleneacetic acid.

нукле/аза *f.* nuclease (enzyme); —арный *a.* nuclear.

нуклеин *m.*, —овый *a.* nuclein; —овая кислота nucleinic acid, nucleic acid.

нуклео/альбумин *m.* nucleoalbumin; —ген *m.* nucleogen; —зид *m.* nucleoside; —зин *m.* nucleosin; —н *see* нуклон; —ника *f.* nucleonics; —протеин *m.* nucleoprotein; —тид *m.* nucleotide; —фильность *f.* nucleophilicity.

нукл/еус *m.* nucleus; queen cell (of bees); —ид *m.* nuclide (a species of atom); —он *m.* nucleon, nuclear particle; —онный *a.* nucleon, nucleonic.

нукс вомика *f.* nux vomica (dried seeds of *Strychnos nux vomica*).

**нулев/ой** *a.* zero, neutral; **н. метод** zero method; **н. отсчет** zero reading; **н. провод** (elec.) neutral conductor, middle conductor; neutral wire; **—ая мощность, —ая энергия** zero power, zero-point energy; **—ая отметка, —ая черта, —ое деление** zero mark; **—ая поверхность** (surv.) datum level; **—ая точка** zero point, zero; (elec.) neutral point; dead center; **смещение —ой точки** zero creep; **—ое сопротивление** (elec.) neutral point resistance.

**нуллипор/а** *f.* (bot.) nullipore (*Corallina officinalis*); **—овый** *a.* nullipore, nulliporous.

**нул/ь** *m.* zero; **настройка на н.** zero adjustment; **отличный от —я** non-vanishing.

**нуме/аит, —ит** *m.* (min.) noumeite, garnierite.

**нумер** *see* **номер; —атор** *m.* numerator, numbering machine; annunciator, indicator; **—ация** *f.*, **—ование** *n.* numeration, numbering; quantization; **—ник** *m.*, **—ная доска** gage plate, wire gage plate; **—ной аппарат** indicator; **—ованный** *a.* numbered; **—овать** *v.* number; index.

**нуммулит** *m.* (zool.) nummulite; **—овый** *a.* (geol.) nummulitic; **—овый известняк** Nummulite limestone.

**нунатаки** *pl.* (geol.) nunataks.

**Нупа твердость** (met.) Knoop hardness.

**нут** *m.* (bot.) chick-pea (*Cicer arietinum*).

**нутация** *f.* nutation.

**нутре/вики** *pl.* (bot.) Gastromycetes; **—ц** *m.* (med.) cryptorchid.

**нутрия** *f.* (zool.) nutria; coypu fur.

**нутро** *n.* inside, interior.

**нутроза** *f.* nutrose (sodium caseinate).

**нутромер, н.-калибр** *m.* inside calipers, inside micrometer.

**нутря/к** *m.* inner fat; **—ной** *a.* internal, inner, inward.

**нутталлиоз** *m.* (vet.) nuttalliosis.

**нутч, н.-фильтр** *m.* Nutsch filter, suction filter.

**нуфарин** *m.* nupharine.

**нуцин** *m.* nucin, juglone.

**нуч** *see* **нутч.**

**НЧ** *abbr.* (низкочастотный) low-frequency; **Н. Ч.** *abbr.* (низкая частота) low frequency.

**ныл** *past sing. of* **ныть.**

**ныне** *adv.* now, at present; **—шний** *a.* present, of the present time, modern.

**ныр/яло** *n.* ram, plunger; **—яние** *n.* diving, plunging, dip, pitching motion, galloping motion; **—ять** *v.* dive, plunge, dip, pitch; **—яющий** *a.* diving, plunging, dipping.

**ныть** *v.* ache.

**Нью** New (in geographic names).

**ньюарская свита** (geol.) Newark system.

**ньюбериит** *m.* (min.) newburyite.

**ньютон** *m.* newton (unit of force).

**Ньютона сплав, Н. металл** Newton's alloy (a bismuth-lead-tin alloy); **Н. цветные кольца** (phys.) Newton's rings.

**ньютон/ианский, —овский, —овый** *a.* Newton, Newtonian; **—ит** *m.* (min.) newtonite (probably same as alunite).

**Ньюфаундленд** Newfoundland.

**Н.Э.** *abbr.* (нашей эры) A.D. (year).

**нэк** *m.* (geol.) neck, chimney; strait.

**нэпер** *see* **непер.**

**ню—** *see also* **нью—.**

**нюрнбергская зелень** Nuremberg Green (pigment); **н. фиолетовая** Nuremberg Violet (manganic phosphate).

**нюх** *m.* scent; **—ание** *n.* smelling; **—ательный** *a.* smelling; **—ательный табак** snuff; **—ать** *v.* smell, sniff.

**няша** *f.* soil humus.

# О

**о** *prep. acc.* against; *prepos.* about, concerning, on, upon, of; **о—** *prefix* circum—, about, around; **о.** *abbr.* (область) oblast, region; (общество) society; (остров) island; (очень) very.

**оазис** *m.* oasis.

**об** *see* **о; об—** *see* **о—; об.** *abbr.* (оборот) revolution; (объемный) volume, volumetric; **об.** % *abbr.* (объемный процент) per cent by volume.

**оба** *a.* both.

**обагр/енный** *a.* bloodstained; **—ить, —ять** *v.* stain with blood, imbrue; redden.

обанкротиться *v.* go bankrupt.

оббо́рка *f.* (min.) knocking down loose rock from ceiling.

об.в. *see* об. вес; ОБВ *abbr.* (Всесоюзное общество по борьбе с вредителями сельского хозяйства) All-Union Society for Control of Agricultural Pests.

обва́л *m.* crumbling, falling, caving in, collapse; landslide, slide, avalanche; —ивать, —ить *v.* crumble, knock down, cave in; heap around; —иваться, —иться crumble, fall, cave in; —ившийся *a.* caved in, fallen.

обвалование *n.* embankment; damming up.

обвар/ивать, —ить *v.* scald; —ка *f.* scalding; shoulder, collar, seam.

обвевать *v.* winnow, fan.

обведение *n.* enclosing, encircling, surrounding; outline, contour.

обвер/нуть, —теть, —тывать *v.* wrap up, bind up, envelop; entwine, twist around; —тка *f.* wrapping; sheath; (corn) husk.

обвес *m.* false weight.

об. вес *abbr.* (объемный вес) density.

обвести *see* обводить.

обветренный *a.* weather-beaten, weathered; wind-blown.

обветш/алый *a.* dilapidated, worn out, decrepit; obsolete, old; —ание *n.* dilapidation, aging.

обвеять *see* обвевать.

обвив/ать, —аться *v.* wind around, twist around; —ка *f.* winding around.

обвин/ение *n.* accusation, charge, indictment; —итель *m.* accuser, prosecutor; —ить, —ять *v.* accuse, charge (with); —яемый *m.* the accused, defendant.

обвислый *a.* flabby, drooping, hanging.

обвить *see* обвивать.

обвод *m.*, —ка *f.* enclosing, surrounding; outlining, outline; by-pass; —ить *v.* lead around; encircle, surround, encompass; outline, contour.

обводн/ение *n.* flooding, inundation; irrigation; —ить *v.* irrigate, flood, supply with water.

обводн/ый *a.* encircling, surrounding; leading around; by-pass; о. канал, о. провод by-pass, by-pass canal, by-pass conduit; о. штифт guide pin; —ая стена encircling wall, enclosure.

обводнять *see* обводнить.

обвойник *m.* (bot.) periploca, spec. silk vine (*Periploca graeca*).

обвол/акивать, —очь *v.* wrap, envelop, cover, coat; drag around.

обвяз/ать, —ывать *v.* bind, tie, bandage; hoop (barrel); —ка *f.* binding, bandage; liner; brace, framework; —очный *a.* binding, fastening; —ь *f.* frame; hoop.

обгар *m.* combustion loss.

обгладывать *v.* pick off, gnaw; browse.

обгон/ные выработки (min.) by-passes, detour shafts; —ять *v.* outstrip, outdistance, pass, overtake.

обгор/ание *n.* charring, scorching; —ать, —еть *v.* char, scorch; burn around; —елый *a.* charred, scorched, burnt.

обда/вать, —ть *v.* scald; drench, pour over.

обдел/ать, —ывать *v.* work, fashion, form; polish, finish; dress (leather); set (jewels); —ка *f.* working, fashioning, shaping; jacketing.

обдир/ать *v.* bark, peel, strip; skin, flay, rip off; hull, shell (corn); rough, rough out; —ка *f.* stripping; skinning; hulling, shelling; roughing, chipping; abrasion; —ный *see* обдирочный.

обдирочн/ый *a.* stripping; shelling; abrasive; о. камень abrasive; о. постав huller, hulling mill, sheller; о. резец roughing tool; —ая машина stripping machine; —ая шкурка coarse emery cloth; —ая шлифовка rough grinding.

обдув/ать *v.* blow off, blow out; —ка *f.* blow out, steam-blast cleaning.

обдум/анно *adv.* with careful planning, deliberately; —анный *a.* well-planned, carefully thought out; —ать, —ывать *v.* consider, think over, weigh.

обдуть *see* обдувать.

обе *see* оба.

обег/ать *v.* run around, run past, by-pass; circulate; —ающий *a.* by-pass; circulating.

обед *m.* dinner; —ать *v.* dine.

обедн/евший, —елый *a.* poor, impoverished; —ение *n.* impoverishment, exhaustion, depletion; stripping; —енный *a.* impoverished, depleted; stripped; underfit (river); —еть *v.*

grow poor, become depleted; —**ять** *v.* impoverish, deplete; strip; —**яющий** *a.* stripping (column).

**обез**— *prefix* be—, de—.

**обезболив/ание** *n.* anesthetization; —**ать** *v.* anesthetize; —**ающее сред-ство** anesthetic.

**обезвкусить** *v.* deprive of flavor.

**обезводить** *v.* dehydrate.

**обезводоро/дить** *v.* dehydrogenate; —**жение** *n.* dehydrogenation.

**обезвоженный** *a.* dehydrated; anhydrous.

**обезвожив/ание** *n.* dehydration, desiccation; —**атель** *m.* dehydrator, desiccator; —**ать** *v.* dehydrate; —**аться** *v.* be dehydrated, become anhydrous; —**ающий** *a.* dehydrating; —**ающий реактив**, —**ающее средство** dehydrating agent, dehydrant.

**обезволашивание** *n.* depilation, unhairing (of hides).

**обезвре/дить**, —**живать** *v.* render harmless.

**обезгажив/ание** *n.* degasification, degassing; (vacuum system) outgassing; deaeration; —**ать** *v.* degas; outgas.

**обезглавливание** *n.* decapitation.

**обезжир/енный** *a.* degreased, freed from fat; skim (milk); (text.) scoured; —**ивание** *n.* degreasing, fat extraction; scouring; —**иватель** *m.*, —**и-вающее средство** degreasing agent, degreaser, scouring agent; —**ивать**, —**ить** *v.* degrease, extract the fat, skim off the fat; scour; —**ивающий** *a.* degreasing; scouring; —**ивающее мыло** scouring soap.

**обеззара/женный** *a.* disinfected, antiseptic, sterile; —**живание** *n.* disinfection; —**живать**, —**зить** *v.* disinfect, sterilize; (nucl.) decontaminate; —**живающий** *a.* disinfecting, disinfectant, germicidal; decontaminating; —**живающее средство** disinfectant, germicide.

**обеззол/енный** *a.* decalcified; —**ивание** *n.* decalcification; —**ивать** *v.* decalcify, delime.

**обезил/ивание**, —**ование** *n.* desilting, desliming.

**обезлес/енный** *a.* cleared (land); —**ить** *v.* clear, cut down forests, deforest.

**обезлиствление** *n.* defoliation.

**обезличка** *f.* lack of responsibility (for entrusted tools, etc.).

**обезмедивание** *n.* decoppering, copper extraction.

**обезметилировать** *v.* demethylate.

**обезобра/живать**, —**зить** *v.* mutilate, disfigure, deform, cripple.

**обезопасить** *v.* secure (against).

**обезоружив/ание** *n.* disarmament; —**ать** *v.* disarm.

**обезрепеивающая машина** (agr.) burr extractor.

**обезуглерож/енный** *a.* decarbonized; —**ивание** *n.* decarbonization, decarbonizing; —**ивать** *v.* decarbonize; decarburize.

**обезыливание** *see* обезиливание.

**обезьян/а** *f.* (zool.) monkey, ape; —**ий** *a.* simian.

**обелиск** *m.* obelisk, spine, needle.

**об'ем** *see* объем.

**обепин** *m.* aubepine, anisaldehyde.

**обер**— *prefix* chief.

**обер/егать**, —**ечь** *v.* guard, defend, protect, preserve.

**обернут/ый** *a.* wrapped, enveloped; —**ь** *see* обертывать.

**обертка** *f.* wrapper, wrapping, envelope, cover, casing, jacket, sheath; liner.

**обертон** *m.* overtone.

**оберточный** *a.* wrapping, casing; packing (material).

**обертух** *m.* (paper) overfelt.

**обертыв/ать** *v.* wrap up, envelop, cover; —**аться** *v.* be wrapped; turn, turn around; —**ающий** *a.* wrapping, enveloping.

**обес**— *prefix* de—; *see also* обез—; —**клеивание** *n.* degumming; —**кров-ливание** *n.* bleeding; —**парафиниро-вание** *n.* deparaffination.

**обеспеч/ение** *n.* security, guarantee, warrant, provision; —**енный** *a.* secure, well provided (for); —**ивать**, —**ить** *v.* secure, make sure (of), guarantee, warrant, provide; —**и-вающий** *a.* guaranteeing; safety.

**обеспло/дить** *v.* sterilize, make barren; —**жение** *n.* sterilization.

**обеспылив/ание** *n.* dust removal, dust elimination; —**атель** *m.* dust remover;

—ать *v.* remove dust, settle dust; —ающее масло dust-laying oil.

обессахарив/ание *n.* sugar extraction; —ать *v.* extract sugar.

обес/свинцевание *n.* deleading, lead extraction; —серебрение *n.* extraction of silver (from lead ores); desilverization (of alloys).

обессер/ение, —ивание *n.* desulfurization, desulfurizing; —енный *a.* desulfurized; —иватель *m.* desulfurizer, sulfur remover; —ивать *v.* desulfurize, free from sulfur, eliminate sulfur; —ивающий *a.* desulfurizing, sulfur-removing.

обессил/еть *v.* become weak, become feeble, lose strength; —ивать, —ить *v.* weaken, make weak.

обессмолив/ание *n.* resin extraction, de-resination; detarring; —ать *v.* extract resin, deresinate, deresinify; detar.

обессолив/ание *n.* salt elimination; desalinization (of water); —ать *v.* free from salt.

обессталив/ание *n.* (met.) softening; —ать *v.* soften.

обесточ/енный *a.* (elec.) dead; de-energized; —ивать, —ить *v.* disconnect, cut off current; de-energize.

обесфосфор/енный *a.* dephosphorized; —ивание *n.* dephosphorization; —ивать *v.* dephosphorize, free of phosphorus.

обесфторенный *a.* defluorinated.

обесцветить *see* обесцвечивать.

обесцвеч/енный *a.* decolorized, bleached; discolored; —ивание *n.* decolorization; discoloration; —ивать *v.* decolorize, bleach; discolor; —ивающий *a.* decolorizing; discoloring; —ивающее средство decolorant, decolorizing agent.

обесцен/ение, —ивание *n.* depreciation; —енный *a.* depreciated; —ивать, —ить *v.* depreciate, underrate; lessen the value (of).

обесцинкование *n.* (met.) dezincing, zinc extraction.

обечайка *f.* shell (of boiler or kiln).

обещ/ание *n.* promise, word; —ать *v.* promise.

обжаловать *v.* appeal a case.

обжар/ивать, —ить *v.* roast, brown, sear (meat); —ка *f.* searing.

обжат/ие *n.* squeezing, pressing, wringing out; (rolling) reduction, reduction in area; cobbing, breaking down; степень —ия shrinkage (in rolling); —ый *a.* squeezed, pressed; —ь *see* обжимать.

обжечь *see* обжигать.

обжиг *m.* burning, roasting, calcining, calcination; firing, annealing, kilning.

обжигаем/ость *f.* calcinability; —ый *a.* calcinable; —ая руда ore to be roasted.

обжиган/ие *n.* burning, roasting, calcining, calcination; firing, annealing; baking; о. глазури (cer.) glaze baking; полное о. dead roasting.

обжиг/ательный *a.* roasting, calcining; annealing; о. газ gas from roasting; —ательная печь, —овая печь kiln, fire kiln, roasting kiln, roaster, roasting furnace; —ательная установка roasting plant; (nucl.) calciner; —ать *v.* roast, calcine; burn, burn off, scorch; anneal, kiln; fire; bake.

обжим *m.*, —ка *f.* squeezing, pressing, compression, shortening; (met.) shingling; upsetting; set die (for rivets), shape die; —ать *v.* squeeze, press, wring out; (met.) shingle; upset, swage; (rolling) cog, reduce; —ной, —ный, —очный *a.* squeezing, pressing; shingling; reducing, cogging; —ный пресс shingling press; —ный стан roughing mill; cogging mill; —ные валки shingling rolls; reducing rolls; cogging mill; —ные щипцы crimper.

обжорливый *a.* gluttonous, greedy.

обзав/едение *n.* providing (with); acquisition; —естись, —одиться *v.* provide oneself (with), acquire.

обзол/енный *a.* calcined, incinerated, reduced to ashes; (foundry) ashed (molds); —ивание *n.* calcination, incineration; combustion; ashing; —ивать, —ить *v.* calcine, incinerate, reduce to ashes; ash.

обзольный *a.* dull-edged.

обзор *m.*, —ный *a.* survey, review, synopsis, summary, outline; field of vision, coverage; о. печати press review; краткий о. abstract, résumé.

**обив/ать** *v.* cover, upholster; nail around; **—ка** *f.* upholstery; casing.

**оби/да** *f.* insult, offense, injury; **нанести —ду, —деть, —жать** *v.* offend, insult, hurt; **—женный** *a.* offended, hurt.

**обилие** *n.* abundance, copiousness, plenty.

**обильный** *a.* abundant, plentiful, copious, ample, liberal, profuse, rich, generous; heavy (dose); flood (lubrication).

**обир/ание** *n.* gathering, picking (of fruit); **—ать** *v.* gather, pick.

**обит/аемый** *a.* inhabited, habitable; **—атель** *m.* inhabitant, inmate; **—ать** *v.* inhabit, dwell, reside, live (in).

**обит/ый** *a.* upholstered, padded, covered; **—ь** *see* **обивать.**

**обиход** *m.* custom, habit; **выйти из —а** *v.* become obsolete; **—ный** *a.* daily, for everyday use, necessary.

**обкалывать** *v.* pin, prick around; break, cleave around.

**обкап/ать, —ывать** *v.* sprinkle over, let drops fall (on), spray.

**обкармливать** *v.* overfeed.

**обкат/ание** *n.*, **—ка** *f.* rolling; burnishing; spinning (of rivet head); **—ать, —ывать** *v.* roll; burnish; spin; run in; *see also* **окачивать; —ить** *see* **окачивать.**

**обкачивать** *see* **окачивать.**

**обкла/дка** *f.*, **—дывание** *n.* facing (with brick, etc.), lining, covering, coating; (capacitor) plate; **—дывать, —сть** *v.* face, line, cover, incrust, lay (around); tax.

**обклеивать** *see* **оклеивать.**

**обколоть** *see* **обкалывать.**

**обкорнать** *v.* cut, clip.

**обл.** *abbr.* **(область)** district, region, field; **обл—** *abbr.* **(областной)** district, regional.

**облаг/аемость** *f.* taxability; **—аемый** *a.*, **—аемый налогом** taxable, assessable; **—ать** *v.* impose (a tax).

**облагоражив/ание** *n.* improvement; refining; cultivation (of plants); **—ать** *v.* improve; purify, refine; cultivate; ennoble; enrich; (text.) finish, dress.

**облад/ание** *n.* possession; **—атель** *m.* possessor, owner, master, proprietor; **—ать** *v.* possess, own.

**облако** *n.* cloud; **—мер** *m.* ceiling-height indicator.

**обламывать** *v.* break, chip, chip off; truncate.

**област/ной** *a.* district, regional, territorial, provincial; **—ь** *f.* region, sphere, area, zone, field, domain; range, band; district, territory.

**облатка** *f.* wafer; capsule.

**облачн/ость** *f.* cloudiness; **—ый** *a.* cloudy, overcast; clouded, nebulous; ceiling (light); **—ое знамя** banner cloud.

**облег/ать** *v.* encircle, encompass; **—ающий** *a.* encircling, encompassing; outlining, close.

**облегч/ать, —ить** *v.* relieve, alleviate, lighten, ease, ease up, facilitate; **—ающий** *a.* relieving, alleviating; **—ение** *n.* relief, alleviation, lightening, easing, facilitation; **—енный** *a.* relieved, alleviated, lightened, eased, facilitated; **—енного типа** light-duty (machine).

**обледен/елый** *a.* iced, icy; **—ение** *n.* icing, formation of ice, freezing; **—еть** *v.* ice over, become covered with ice, freeze.

**облез/ать, —ть** *v.* peel, come off, grow bare, shed; **—лый** *a.* shabby, bare.

**облек/ание** *n.* veiling; **—ать** *v.* clothe, put on; invest.

**облеп/ить, —лять** *v.* stick around, glue around; **—иха** *f.* (bot.) sea buckthorn (*Hippophae*, spec. *H. rhamnoides*).

**облесение** *n.* afforestation.

**облет** *m.* trial flight; **—ать, —еть** *v.* fly around; fly off (of leaves).

**облеч/ение** *n.* investment with power; **—енный** *a.* invested (with); **—енный доверием** entrusted (with); **—ь** *see* **облекать.**

**облив/ание** *n.* pouring over; **—ать** *v.* pour over, drench, douse; cast around; **—ка** *f.* (cer.) glazing; **—ной** *a.* wet, drenched; glazed.

**облигаци/я** *f.*, **—онный** *a.* bond.

**облиз/ать, —ывать** *v.* lick.

**облик** *m.* face, figure, appearance; (min.) habit.

**облип/ать, —нуть** *v.* stick all around.

**облиств/ение, —ление** *n.* foliation, leafing, leaf formation; **—ленность** *f.*

foliage, leafage; —ленный *a.* leafy, verdant.

облитерация *f.* obliteration.

облит/ый *a.* drenched, covered (with a liquid); —ь *see* обливать.

облицевать *see* облицовывать.

облицов/анный *a.* faced, lined, coated; о. свинцом lead-lined; —ка *f.*, —очный *a.* facing, lining, coat, coating, covering, jacketing, casing; (met.) fettling; finish; —очный камень ashlar; —ывать *v.* face, line, coat, cover; fettle.

облич/ать, —ить *v.* discover, reveal, display; expose; convict.

обличический *a.* oblique.

облог *m.* fallow, lea, meadow.

облож/ение *n.* taxation, assessment, imposition; laying around, edging; —енный *a.* taxed; faced, covered (with); surrounded, edged; coated (tongue); —ить *see* обкладывать.

обложка *f.* wrapper; cover (of book).

обложной *a.* steady, continuous (rain).

облой *m.* fin, seam, projection.

облом/анный *a.* broken off; truncated; —ать, —ить *see* обламывать.

облом/ок *m.* broken piece, fragment, splinter, chip; —ки *pl.* rubble, scrap, debris; (geol.) detritus, rock waste; в —ках (petr.) brecciated; —очный, —чатый *a.* rubbly; (petr.) brecciated, breccia-like; (geol.) detrital, clastic, fragmental.

облуп *m.* rhizina root rot.

облуп/ить, —ливать, —лять *v.* peel, strip, decorticate; shell, hull; —ленный *a.* peeled, stripped, pared; shelled, hulled; —ливание *n.* peeling off, stripping; shelling, hulling.

облуч/атель *m.* irradiator, irradiating unit; —ать *v.* irradiate, expose (to rays); —ение *n.* irradiation, exposure; анализ до —ения prebombardment analysis; мощность —ения radiation power; —енный *a.* irradiated.

облыс/евший *a.* bald; —еть *v.* get bald, grow bald.

обмаз/анный *a.* smeared, greased, coated; —ать, —ывать *v.* smear, grease, daub, apply a coat (of); putty; —ка *f.*, —ывание *n.* smearing,

greasing, coating, coat; putty, lute, luting, plastering.

обмак/ивать, —нуть *v.* dip, steep.

обман *m.* fraud, deceit; illusion; о. зрения optical illusion.

обманка *f.* (min.) blende; spec. zinc blende.

обман/ный *a.* fraudulent; misleading; —уть, —ывать *v.* deceive, mislead; —чивость *f.* fallacy, illusion; —чивый *a.* deceptive, delusive, illusory.

обмасливание *n.* oiling, lubricating.

обматыв/ание *see* обмотка; —ать *v.* wind, wind around, coil, wrap around, tape, encircle, wrap, sheathe, cover.

обмах/ивать, —нуть *v.* brush away; fan.

обмачивать *v.* steep, dip, soak, wet.

обмеднен/ие *see* омеднение; —ный *see* омедненный.

обмел/ение *n.* shoaling; —еть *v.* shoal, grow shallow.

обмен *m.*, —а *f.* exchange, interchange, change; barter; (physiol.) metabolism; (elec. comm.) traffic; (meteor.) austausch; о. веществ metabolism; болезни —а веществ metabolic diseases; о. теплоты heat exchange, heat transfer; реакция —а, —ная реакция, —ное взаимодействие exchange reaction; —ивать, —ять *v.* exchange, interchange; —ник *m.* exchanger, interchanger; —но-связанный *a.* exchangeable (catalysts); —ный *a.* exchange; metabolic; double (decomposition); converted, composite (wave); —ная способность exchange capacity.

обмер *m.* measurement, measuring; —енный *a.* measured.

обмерз/ать, —нуть *v.* freeze around, get frostbitten.

обмер/ивать, —ить, —ять *v.* measure.

обмерший *a.* stunned, dazed.

обмет/ать, —ывать *v.* sweep, dust; overcast, overstitch.

об/мин. *abbr.* (число оборотов в минуту) revolutions per minute, r.p.m.

обмин/ать *v.* press down, trample down; —ка *f.* pressing down, pressing.

обмок/ать, —нуть *v.* get wet through, get soaked, get drenched.

обмол/ачивание *n.*, —от *m.* (agr.)

threshing; —ачивать, —отить *v.* thresh; —оченный *a.* threshed.

обмор/аживать, —озить *v.* freeze.

обморок *m.* faint, syncope; падать в о. *v.* faint, lose consciousness.

обмотанн/ый *a.* wound, coiled, wrapped, covered, taped; о. провод, —ая проволока (elec.) covered wire, insulated wire.

обмот/ать *see* обматывать; —ка *f.*, —очный *a.* winding, coiling, covering, wrapping, taping; cover, sheath, tape; (elec.) winding; коэффициент —ки, —очный коэффициент (elec.) winding factor; (mach.) differential factor; —ки *pl.* windings; puttees, leggings; —очный *a. suffix* —wound.

обмочить *see* обмачивать.

обмундиров/ать, —ывать *v.* equip, provide with equipment, fit out.

обмуров/анный *a.* brick-lined, bricked; —ка *f.* brickwork, masonry, outer brick or metal walls (for boilers), covering, casing, lining (of furnace); —ывать *v.* wall up, brick, line (with brick, etc.).

обмыв/ание *n.* washing; —ать *v.* wash.

обмылив/аемость *see* омыляемость; —ание *see* омыление; —ать *see* омылять.

обмыть *see* обмывать.

обмять *see* обминать.

обнадеж/ивать, —ить *v.* give hope, reassure, encourage.

обнаж/ать, —ить *v.* bare, lay bare, uncover, strip; reveal, disclose; —аться, —иться *v.* become exposed, appear; (geol.) crop out, outcrop; —ение *n.* baring, uncovering, exposure; erosion; outcrop (of rock); —енный *a.* bare, uncovered, exposed, naked; eroded; outcropped; —енная порода (geol.) outcrop, basset.

обнарод/ование *n.* publication; —овать, —ывать *v.* publish, promulgate.

обнаруж/ение, —ивание *n.* uncovering, discovery, finding, disclosure, detection; development, appearance; display; —енный *a.* uncovered, discovered, located, exposed; —ивать, —ить *v.* uncover, discover, disclose, detect, reveal, identify, find, trace, locate; develop, display; —иваться

*v.* develop, appear; —итель *m.* detector, finder; —ительный *a.* detector, warning.

обн/ашивать, —ести *see* обносить; —есение *n.* carrying around; enclosing (with); —есение стеной walling in.

обнимать *v.* embrace, hug, envelop, include.

обнищалый *a.* impoverished.

обнов/итель *m.* restorer, regenerator; —ить, —лять *v.* restore, renovate, renew; —ление *n.* restoration, renovation, renewal, rejuvenation; innovation, change; —ленный *a.* restored, renewed; —ляемость *f.* renewability; interchangeability; —ляемый *a.* renewable.

обносить *v.* carry around; enclose, surround, encompass; wall in, fence; rail in, rail off.

обнять *see* обнимать.

обо *see* о; обо— *see* о—.

обобрать *see* обирать.

обобщ/ать *v.* generalize, draw inferences, theorize; correlate (data); —ение *n.* generalization; correlation; —енный *a.* generalized; —ествление *n.* collectivization, socialization; —ествленный *a.* collectivized, socialized.

обогатительн/ый *a.* enriching; (met.) concentration, dressing; —ая установка, —ая фабрика concentration plant, concentrating mill, dressing plant; —ая часть enriching section (of column).

обога/тить, —щать *v.* enrich; (met.) concentrate, dress, beneficiate; —щение *n.* enriching, enrichment; concentration, dressing, beneficiation; коэффициент —щения (nucl.) enrichment factor; —щенный *a.* enriched, concentrated, dressed, beneficiated; —щенный продукт concentrate.

обогн/анный *a.* outdistanced, passed; —ать *see* обгонять.

обогнуть *see* огибать.

обогр/ев *m.*, —вание *n.* warming, heating; —ватель *m.* heater; —евать, —еть *v.* warm, heat; —етый *a.* warmed, heated.

обод *m.*, —ковый, —очный *a.* rim (of

wheel); hoop, ring; —ок *m.* rim; ring, circle; —очная кишка (anat.) colon.

ободрать *v.* strip, tear off, rip off.

ободр/ить, —ять *v.* encourage, inspire; —яться *v.* take courage; —яющий *a.* encouraging, promising.

обоеполый *a.* bisexual; (bot.) monoecious.

обожженный *a.* burnt, calcined, roasted; окончательно о. dead-burned.

обоз *m.* train, transport, convoy.

обознач/ать, —ить *v.* mark, label, denote, designate, define, characterize; mean, represent; детально о. specify; —ающий *a.* denoting, designating; —ение *n.* mark, marking, denotation, designation, specification; sign, symbol, indication; index, criterion, characteristic; система —ения nomenclature; —енный *a.* marked, designated, specified.

обозная лошадь draft horse.

обозр/еватель *m.* reviewer; —евать, —еть *v.* review, survey, inspect; —ение *n.* review, survey, sketch, news.

обои *pl.* wallpaper; *a.* both.

обой *m.* windfall (fruit).

обойденный *a.* by-passed.

обойка *f.* huller; scourer, polisher; upholstering.

обойма *f.* (iron) ring, band, girdle, yoke, clip; о. катания (ball bearing) race.

обойный *a.* upholstery; wallpaper.

обой/ти *see* обходить; —тись *see* обходиться; все —дется everything will be all right.

обойщик *m.* upholsterer; paper hanger.

оболван/ивать, —ить *v.* (foundry) roughhew, rough-work, rough out.

оболовый *a.* obolus.

оболонь *f.* (bot.) alburnum, sapwood.

оболоч/ечный, —ный *a.* shell; —ка *f.*, —ковый *a.* film, coat, coating; envelope, cover, sheath; shell (of nucleus); case, casing, sheathing; capsule; (gas) blanket; (anat.) membrane; (nucl.) jacket, can; (seismology) mantle; покрытие —кой filming (over); jacketing, canning; с резиновой —кой rubber-covered; —ники *pl.* (zool.) Tunicata; —ное строение shell structure (of nucleus); —ь *v.* wrap around.

обон/яние *n.* smell, sense of smell; органы —яния olfactory organs; —ятельный *a.* olfactory; —ять *v.* smell.

обор *m.* (text.) coarse abb; refuse clinker.

оборачивать *v.* turn; change, transform.

оборв/анный *a.* torn, broken, cut short; broken (line); —ать *see* обрывать.

оборка *f.* flounce, trimming.

оборон/а *f.* defense; —ительный *a.* defense, defensive, defended; быть в —ительном положении *v.* be on the defensive; —ить, —ять *v.* defend.

оборот *m.* revolution, rotation, turn; (com.) turnover; convolution; direction; жиклер быстрых —ов accelerating nozzle; на —е on the reverse, on the back; пускать в о. *v.* circulate, put into circulation; работающий на полных —ах running at full power; сбавить —ы *v.* slow down (engine); счетчик —ов speedometer; увеличить —ы *v.* accelerate (engine); число —ов rotation speed; число —ов в минуту revolutions per minute, r.p.m.

оборотистый *a.* resourceful, clever.

оборотить *see* оборачивать.

оборотливый *see* оборотистый.

оборотн/ый *a.* reverse, back, reversible; circulating; working (capital); о. котел Scotch boiler, marine boiler; —ая вода (paper) return water, white water; —ая сторона reverse side, wrong side.

оборудов/ание *n.* fitting, outfitting, outfit, equipment; instrumentation; plant; arrangement, system; appliance, contrivance, facility; о. паром steam working, steam driving; —ать *v.* equip, fit out; arrange.

обоснов/ание *n.* basis, ground; —анный *a.* valid, sound; well-founded; —ать, —ывать *v.* ground, prove, substantiate.

обособ/ить, —лять *v.* keep apart, isolate, insulate; —иться, —ляться *v.* keep separate; —ление *n.* separation, isolation, insulation; —ленность *f.* apartness; individualization; isolation, insulation; —ленный *a.* individual, single; detached; isolated, insulated.

**обостр/ение** *n.* aggravation, sharpening, accentuation; (med.) exacerbation; **—енный** *a.* aggravated, strained; **—ить, —ять** *v.* aggravate, increase; exasperate; **—иться, —яться** *v.* become aggravated, become strained; **—яющий** *a.* peaking (circuit).

**обочина** *f.* shoulder (of road), curb.

**обоюд/но** *adv.* mutually, reciprocally; *prefix, see* **обоюдо—; —ность** *f.* mutuality, reciprocity; **—ный** *a.* mutual, reciprocal; **—овогнутый** *a.* concavo-concave, biconcave; **—овыпуклый** *a.* convexo-convex, biconvex; **—оострый** *a.* double-edged.

**обр.** *abbr.* (образец) sample, specimen.

**обрабатываем/ость** *f.* workability, processability; machinability; **о. на станках** machinability; **—ый** *a.* workable, processable; machinable; **—ый предмет, —ое изделие** workpiece.

**обрабатыв/ание** *see* **обработка; —ать** *v.* work, process, treat; machine, tool, finish, mill; develop, elaborate; interpret (data); fashion, adapt; manufacture; (agr.) cultivate, till; **—ать на станке, —ать резанием** machine, tool; **—ающий** *a.* working, processing, treating; machining; process (industry).

**обработанный** *a.* worked, processed, treated; machined, tooled; finished, dressed, trimmed; cultivated (field); **о. на станке, механически о.** machined, tooled; **о. начисто** finished, finished off.

**обработать** *see* **обрабатывать.**

**обработк/а** *f.* working, processing, treating, treatment; machining, tooling, milling; manufacture, preparation; conditioning; adaptation; refining; dressing (of ore); cultivation (of field); (statistical, etc.) analysis; **о. на станках, механическая о.** machining, tooling, finishing; **допуск на —у** machining allowance; **площадь —и** (agr.) area under cultivation; **подвергать механической —и, подвергать холодной —и** *v.* machine, tool.

**обравн/ивать, —ять** *v.* level, even up, trim.

**образ** *m.* shape, form; manner, way; im-

age; **о. действия** behavior; procedure; **о. мыслей** trend of thought, viewpoint, attitude; **каким —ом** how, in what manner; **некоторым —ом** in a way, after a fashion, somehow; **никоим —ом** by no means; **таким —ом** thus, in this way.

**образ/ец** *m.* specimen, sample, model, example, test piece, copy; pattern, shape, form, type; standard, original; **выбор —ца, забор —ца, отбор —цов** sampling; **сделать по —цу** *v.* duplicate, pattern (after).

**образный** *a.* descriptive; *suffix* **—shaped, —formed, —form, —oid; о. камень** (min.) figure stone, agalmatolite.

**образов/авшийся** *see* **образованный; —ание** *n.* education, instruction; formation, production; evolution, generation (of gas, heat); origination, development; organization; *suffix* **—genesis; —ание осадка** precipitation; **высшее —ание** higher education, college education; **среднее —ание** secondary education; **момент —ания, состояние —ания** nascent state; **в момент —ания** nascent, in the nascent state; **—анность** *f.* education; **—анный** *a.* educated; formed; produced; evolved, generated (gas, heat).

**образов/ательный** *a.* educational; **—ать, —ывать** *v.* instruct, teach, educate; form, produce; evolve, generate (gas, heat); organize, establish, construct; constitute, make up; **—аться, —ываться** *v.* be educated; form, develop, originate.

**образующ/ая** *f.* (math.) generatrix; **—ий** *a.* forming, producing, generating; **—ийся при этом продукт** the resulting product.

**образцов/ый** *a.* sample, model, exemplary, classical, standard, master, original; **о. инструмент, о. прибор** standard instrument, calibrating instrument; **о. калибр** check gage; **—ая гиря** standard weight; **—ая мера** standard measure, standard; **—ая монета** proof coin; **—ое сопротивление** calibration resistance; comparison rheostat.

**образчик** *m.* sample, specimen, pattern.

**обрамл/ение** *n.* framing, framework; **—енный** *a.* framed; **—ивать, —ять** *v.* frame.

**обраст/ание** *n.* overgrowing; **—ать, —и** *v.* overgrow (with).

**обрат** *m.* skimmed milk; usable waste.

**обрати/мость** *f.*, **о. хода** reversibility; **—мый** *a.* reversible; **—ть** *see* **обращать.**

**обратно** *adv.* back, inversely, conversely, reversibly, counter—; **о. действующий** retroactive; **о. пропорциональный** inversely proportional; **о. текущий** flowing back, returning (liquid), reflux; **итти о.** *v.* return, retrace one's steps.

**обратно/идущий** *a.* retrogressive; returning; **—ступенчатый** *a.* step-back (welding).

**обратн/ый** *a.* reverse, return, back, backward; counter, opposite, converse, inverse, inverted; **о. ом** (elec.) reciprocal ohm, mho; **о. поток** reflux; **о. преобразователь** (elec.) inverter; **о. пропуск, о. проход** (rolling) return path; **о. удар** kick, kickback, recoil; backfire (of motor); **о. удар пламени** flashback; **дать о. удар** *v.* kick back; **о. ход** return, return motion, reverse running, backing; back stroke (of piston); **дать о. ход** *v.* reverse, back, back up; **—ого хода** reverse (lever, etc.); **сообщение —ого хода** reversing; **с —ым ходом** reversing, reversible; **о. холодильник** reflux condenser; **о. час** (nucl.) inverse hour, inhour (measure of reactivity); **—ая величина, —ая дробь** (math.) reciprocal; **—ая вспышка** backfire, flashback; **—ая конденсация** retrograde condensation; **—ая пропорциональность** inverse ratio; **—ая реакция** back reaction; **—ая связь, —ое питание** feedback; **цепь —ой связи** feedback circuit; **—ая сторона** wrong side, reverse; **—ое влияние, —ое действие** reaction, retroaction; **имеющий —ое действие** retroactive; **—ое движение** return movement, back stroke (of piston); **—ое добывание, —ое получение** recovery (from waste); **—ое течение** reflux; **—ого направления** reverse; **—ой**

**почтой** by return mail; **на —ом пути** on the way back, while returning.

**обращать** *v.* turn, change, convert, transform; reduce; reverse; invert (sugar); circulate; pay (attention); **—ся** *v.* turn, rotate; return, revert; circulate; apply, appeal, turn (to); handle, manipulate, treat; **—ся плохо** maltreat, treat badly.

**обращающий** *a.* reversing; **—ся** *a.* rotating; circulating.

**обращен/ие** *n.* revolution, rotation, turn; circulation; application, appeal; treatment, usage, handling, manipulation, care (for); conversion, reduction; reversal; inversion; **изъять из —ия** *v.* withdraw from circulation; **пустить в о.** *v.* issue, circulate, put in circulation; **температура —ия** transition point.

**обращенный** *a.* turned (to), exposed, facing; reversed; inverse, inverted; invert (sugar).

**обрез** *m.* cut, edge; (typ.) size; bevel; a short-barreled rifle; **в о.** only just enough, barely enough; **—ание** *n.*, **—ка** *f.* cutting, clipping, trimming, pruning (trees); cut-off; (med.) circumcision; **—анный** *a.* cut off; **—атель** *m.* chopper; **—ать** *v.* cut, clip, crop, trim, prune; (cryst.) truncate.

**обрезн/ой** *a.* cut, cut-off, trimming; **о. станок** trimmer; **о. штамп** trimming dies; **—ая пила** rip saw.

**обрез/ок** *m.* piece, cut, length; **—ки** *pl.* pieces, shearings, clippings, shreds, scraps, waste, debris; scrap (iron).

**обрезыв/ание** *see* **обрезание; —ать** *see* **обрезать.**

**обремен/ение** *n.* overloading, burdening, clogging; **—ительность** *f.* burdensomeness; **—ительный** *a.* burdensome, burdening, overwhelming, heavy; **—ить, —ять** *v.* burden, overburden, overload, encumber, overtax, overdo.

**обре/сти, —тать** *v.* find, discover; **—тение** *n.* finding, discovery; **—тенный** *a.* found, discovered.

**обрешет/ина** *f.* joist; **—ка** *f.* lathing, lattice, bracing; crate; **—ник** *m.* lathing; **переплет —ника** latticework.

**обрив/ание** *n.* shaving; **—ать** *v.* shave.

**обрисов/ать, —ывать** v. sketch, outline; **—ка** f. sketch, outline, outlining.

**обрить** see **обривать.**

**обронить** v. drop, let fall, lose.

**обросший** a. overgrown (with).

**обруб/ать, —ить** v. cut round, trim off, clip, prune (trees); chip off, knock off; **—ка** f. trimming, pruning; chipping; **—ленный** a. cut, trimmed, pruned; **—ная, —очная** f., **—очный цех** (foundry) cleaning room, cleaning shop; **—ок** m. block, trunk, stump; lump, piece; **—ки** pl. scrap, chippings; **—очный** a. cutting, trimming; chipping; **—щик** m. (foundry) cleaner.

**обруч** m. hoop, ring, band, collar, clamp; **наколачивать о.** v. hoop (a barrel); **—ник** m. hoop maker; cooper; **—ное железо** hoop iron, band iron.

**обруш/ать, —ивать, —ить** v. demolish, destroy; attack; knock down, cave in; **—аться, —иваться, —иться** v. crumble, fall, break down, cave in, collapse; **—ение, —ивание** n. crumbling, falling, collapsing, collapse; hulling (of grain); **—енный** a. fallen, collapsed, caved in.

**обрыв** m. steep, precipice, cliff, bluff, escarpment, scarp; (chain) termination; breaking away, break (in wire); **—ание** n. breaking, tearing; **—ать** v. break, tear; pluck, pick, tear off; intercept, cut off; dig around; **—аться** v. break, tear; fall; be plucked, be picked.

**обрывист/ость** f. steepness, abruptness; **—ый** a. steep, abrupt, precipitous.

**обрывок** m. scrap; bit; patch.

**обрызг/ать, —ивать** v. sprinkle, spray, wet, moisten; **—ивание** n. sprinkling, spraying, spray, wetting, moistening.

**обрыскать** v. search everywhere, hunt.

**обрыт/ый** a. dug up; **—ь** v. dig around, dig up.

**обса/дить, —живать** v. plant (around); **—дка** f., **—живание** n. planting; compression, shortening, upsetting; **—дная труба** (min.) drive pipe, casing pipe; **—дочный** a. drive; **—женный** a. planted; cased (well).

**обсахаривать** v. sugar, candy.

**обсе/вать, —ивать** v. sow, plant; **—вка** f. chaff, siftings.

**об/сек.** abbr. (число оборотов в секунду) revolutions per second.

**обсекать** see **отсекать, обрубать.**

**обсемен/ение** n. sowing, seeding; **—ить, —ять** v. sow, seed, plant; **—иться** v. go to seed.

**обсерва/тория** f., **—торский** a. observatory; **—ционный** a. observation; observatory; **—ция** f. observation.

**обсея/нный** a. sown, planted; **—ть** see **обсеивать.**

**обсидиан** m. (petr.) obsidian, volcanic glass, rhyolite glass; **—иты** pl. obsidianites, obsidian pebbles.

**об/ск.** see **об/сек.**

**обскабливать** v. scrub, scour, scrape off.

**обследов/ание** n. inspection, examination; **—ать** v. inspect, examine, explore.

**обслужив/аемый район** service zone; **—ание** n. service, servicing, maintenance, care, attendance, tending, **—ание** n. service, servicing, maintenance, care, attendance, tending, attention, handling; accommodation; **—ать** v. service, maintain, care (for), attend (to), handle; accommodate (with); **—ающий** a. serving, servicing; attending; auxiliary; m. attendant, man in charge; **—ающий персонал** attendants; **—ающее лицо** attendant, service man.

**обсохнуть** see **обсыхать.**

**обстав/ить, —ливать, —лять** v. set, put, place around; furnish.

**обстановка** f. furniture, furnishings; setting, arrangement; circumstances, conditions, situation.

**обстоятель/но** adv. thoroughly, in detail; **—ный** a. circumstantial, detailed; thorough, reliable; **—ство** n. circumstance, case.

**обстоять** v. be, get on.

**обстрагивать** see **обстругать.**

**обстраив/ание** n. building; **—ать** v. build, build around, construct.

**обстрел** m. fire, firing, bombardment; **—ивать** v. fire on, bombard.

**обстри/гать, —чь** v. cut, crop, shear.

**обстро/гать** see **обстругать; —жка** see **обстругивание.**

**обстроить** see **обстраивать.**

**обструг/ать, —ивать** v. plane, smooth

off, trim; —**ивание** *n.* planing, trimming.

**обструк/тивный** *a.* obstructive; —**ция** *f.* obstruction, obstacle.

**обсужд/ать, обсудить** *v.* consider, discuss, dispute; —**ение** *n.* consideration, discussion, dispute; **предмет** —**ения** topic of discussion, point at issue, the issue.

**обсуш/ивать,** —**ить** *v.* dry.

**обсчит/аться,** —**ываться** *v.* miscalculate, miscount.

**обсып/ать** *v.* strew, sprinkle, powder, dust; —**ка** *f.* sprinkling, dusting.

**обсыхать** *v.* dry, get dry, dry up.

**обтаивать** *v.* thaw, melt around.

**обтачив/ание** *n.* turning (on lathe), machining, rounding off; —**ать** *v.* turn, machine, round off; erode.

**обтаять** *see* **обтаивать.**

**обтек/аемый** *a.* streamline, streamlined; **о. контур,** —**аемая форма, линия** —**ания** streamline; —**аемая поверхность** (aero.) fairing; —**ание** *n.* flowing around, passing around; —**атель** *m.* deflector; shield; streamlined unit; (aero.) fairing; —**ать** *v.* flow around, by-pass, circumvent; —**ающий** *a.* circumvent, flowing around.

**обтереть** *see* **обтирать.**

**обтес/анный** *a.* rough-hewn, squared; dressed, trimmed; **грубо о.** rough-finished; —**ать,** —**ывать** *v.* rough-hew, rough-work, chip, square; dress, trim; —**ка** *f.,* —**ывание** *n.* rough-hewing, squaring; dressing, trimming.

**обтирать** *v.* wipe, dry; polish, grind, abrade.

**обточ/енный** *a.* turned (on lathe), machined, rounded off; —**ить** *see* **обтачивать;** —**ка** *f.* turning, machining, rounding off; dressing, cleaning off, facing; —**ка вторец,** —**ка торцов, лобовая** —**ка** facing.

**обтреп/анный** *a.* worn out, frayed; —**ать,** —**ывать** *v.* wear out, fray; swingle (flax); —**аться,** —**ываться** *v.* get worn, fray, become ragged.

**обтузатовая кислота** obtusatic acid.

**обтюр/атор** *m.,* —**аторный** *a.* obturator, seal, cut-off; baffle plate, shield;

diaphragm, stop; (cinema) shutter; —**ация** *f.* obturation, sealing.

**обтя/гивать,** —**нуть** *v.* stretch, cover; —**жка** *f.* stretching, covering, jacketing, coating; **в** —**жку** tight-fitting, close; —**нутый** *a.* stretched, covered.

**обув/ать** *v.* provide with shoes; —**ной** *a.* shoe; —**щик** *m.* shoemaker; —**ь** *f.* footwear, shoes.

**обугл/енный** *a.* carbonized, charred; —**ероживание** *n.* carbonization; (met.) carburization, carburizing; —**иваемый** *a.* carbonizable; —**ивание** *n.* carbonization, charring; —**ивать,** —**ить** *v.* carbonize, char; —**ивающий** *a.* carbonizing; —**ивающийся** *a.* carbonizing, carbonizable.

**обуж/ение** *n.* narrowing, making narrow, tightening; —**енный** *a.* narrowed, narrow, tight; —**ивать** *v.* narrow, make narrow, make tight, tighten.

**обуза** *f.* burden, encumbrance, difficulty.

**обузд/ание,** —**ывание** *n.* repression, restraint, checking; —**ать,** —**ывать** *v.* repress, restrain, keep in check, check, curb, keep in hand; get the better (of).

**обузить** *see* **обуживать.**

**обуревать** *v.* agitate, shake.

**обуслов/ить,** —**ливать** *v.* specify, stipulate, make conditions; cause; determine; —**иться,** —**ливаться** *v.* be stipulated, depend (on), be explained (by); —**ленный** *a.* specified, stipulated, dependent (on), conditional; explained, determined (by).

**обутин** *m.* obutin.

**обут/ый** *a.* shod; —**ь** *see* **обувать.**

**обух** *m.* butt, head (of axe); back, back edge.

**обуч/ать,** —**ить** *v.* teach, instruct, train; —**аться** *v.* be taught, learn; —**ение** *n.* teaching, instruction, training; —**енный** *a.* taught, trained, skilful.

**обуш/ек,** —**ок** *m.* back, back edge; pick with detachable point; eye bolt.

**обхаживать** *see* **обходить.**

**обхват** *m.* circumference, compass; perimeter; clasping, engagement; **угол** —**а** angle of contact; —**ить,** —**ывать** *v.* embrace, clasp, girth, surround, envelop.

**обход** *m.* by-pass, diversion; passing around; alternate route; round (of patrol, etc.); circumvention, evasion (of law); **в о.** in a roundabout way, indirectly.

**обходить** *v.* visit, make the rounds; by-pass; deprive (of); **—ся** *v.* cost, come to; treat; get used (to); **—ся без** do without, dispense with.

**обходн/ый** *a.* roundabout, circuitous, alternate, indirect; by-pass; **о. канал** by-pass canal, by-pass; **о. путь** detour; **о. способ** makeshift; indirect method; **—ые выработки** (min.) by-passes, detour shafts.

**обчесть** *see* **обсчитаться.**

**обчи/стить, —щать** *v.* clean, scour, clear.

**обшив/ание** *n.,* **—ка** *f.,* **—очный** *a.* facing, lining, sheathing, sheath, casing, covering, sheeting, coating, jacket, shell; paneling, wainscot, veneering, trimming, planking, planks, boarding, lathing; **—ать** *v.* face, line, plank, sheathe; coat; sew around, edge, border; **—очный лист,** **—очное железо** cover plate, shell.

**обширн/ость** *f.* spaciousness, bigness, vastness, expanse, latitude, field; **—ый** *a.* spacious, big, vast, broad, wide, ample, voluminous; comprehensive.

**обшит/ый** *a.* faced, covered, lined, paneled, trimmed; **о. сталью** steel-plated; **—ь** *see* **обшивать.**

**обшкур/ивать, —ить** *v.* grind, polish (with emery cloth).

**обшлаг** *m.* cuff.

**общаться** *v.* associate, mix (with).

**обще—** *prefix* general, generally, widely.

**общедоступн/ость** *f.* accessibility; popularity; **—ый** *a.* accessible; popular.

**обще/житие** *n.* home, asylum; hostel, boarding house; **—известный** *a.* well-known, popular; **—народный** *a.* general, public; **—образовательный** *a.* general instruction.

**общеполезн/ость** *f.* universal utility, world-wide use; **—ый** *a.* generally useful, universally beneficial.

**общепонятн/ость** *f.* obviousness, clarity; **—ый** *a.* obvious, clear, evident, apparent.

**общепринятый** *a.* generally accepted,

universal, world-wide, standard, current.

**общесоюзный** *a.* All-Union.

**общественн/ый** *a.* social, public, common; **—ая гигиена** public health.

**общество** *n.* society; association, company; **—ведение** *n.* social science.

**общеупотребительный** *a.* general use, commonly used, customary.

**общ/ий** *a.* general, common, public; total, aggregate, overall (length); joint, mutual; miscellaneous; **о. делитель** (math.) common divisor; **о. итог,** **—ая сумма** total sum, sum total, total; lump sum; **о. остаток** total residue; **—ая мощность** unit capacity; total capacity; **—ая реакция** (biol.) systemic reaction; **—ее место** generality, commonplace; **—ее свойство рода** generic feature, peculiarity, property; **—ее число** total number; **в —ем** on the whole, in general.

**общин/а** *f.* community, society; **—ный** *a.* communal, common.

**общность** *f.* community.

**объедать** *v.* eat around, corrode; **—ся** *v.* overeat.

**объедин/ение** *n.* union, joining, amalgamation, consolidation; society, association; **—енный** *a.* united, joint; associate; **—ить, —ять** *v.* unite, join, unify; assemble; associate; **—яться** *v.* unite, incorporate.

**объедки** *pl.* food scraps, leftovers.

**объез/д** *m.* circuit, round, roundabout way, detour; **—дить, —жать** *v.* go around, detour; **—жий путь** detour.

**объект** *m.* object, item; substance; objective.

**объектив** *m.* (optics) objective.

**объективн/ость** *f.* objectivity; **—ый** *a.* objective, unbiased, unprejudiced.

**объем** *m.* volume, size, bulk, space, capacity, contents; compass, extent, amplitude; **в процентах —а** per cent by volume, volume per cent; **измеритель —а** volumenometer; **испытание на о.** (nucl.) bulk test; **коэффициент —а** volumetric efficiency; **кубический о.** capacity; **прирост —а** increase in volume, expansion; **сокращение —а**

decrease in volume, shrinkage; **соотношение —ов** volume ratio; **увеличиваться в —е** v. expand; **удельный о.** specific volume.

**объем/истый** a. voluminous, bulky, unwieldy; **—лющая** f. (elec. comm.) envelope; **—лющий** a. enveloping, convolute; **—но** adv. volumetrically; in volume; **—ноцентрированный** a. (cryst.) body-centered.

**объемн/ый** a. volume, volumetric; **о. анализ** volumetric analysis; **о. вес** weight by volume; volumetric weight; **о. заряд** (thermionics) space charge; **о. процент** per cent by volume, volume per cent; **—ая волна** (seismology) body wave; **—ая доза** (nucl.) volume dose, integral dose; **—ая плотность** density by volume, volume density; **—ая производительность, полезное —ое действие** volumetric efficiency; **—ая скорость** space velocity; **—ая часть** part by volume; **—ое количество** volume; **—ое отношение** volume ratio; **—ое число** specific volume.

**объемометр** m. volumenometer.

**объехать** see **объезжать.**

**объизвествл/ение** n. calcification, lime deposition; **—енный** a. calcified; **—ять** v. calcify.

**объяв/итель** m. advertiser; announcer; **—ить, —лять** v. advertise, announce; state, notify, declare; **—ление** n. advertisement, announcement; statement; bill, poster, notice; **дать —ление** v. advertise; **доска для —лений** bulletin board.

**объярь** f. moire, watered silk.

**объясн/ение** n. explanation, comment, legend (of diagram); **—ить, —ять** v. explain, elucidate, demonstrate, clear up; **—имый** a. explicable; **—ительный** a. explanatory.

**обыденн/ость** f. commonness, usualness; **—ый** a. common, usual, everyday.

**обызвест/вление** n. calcification; **—влять** v. calcify; **—кование** n. calcitization; (agr.) liming.

**обыкновен/ие** n. habit, custom, way; **он имел о.** he used to, he would, he was accustomed to; **по —ию** as usual, in the usual manner, according to habit.

**обыкновенн/о** adv. usually, habitually, ordinarily, as a rule; **как о.** as usual; **—ый** a. usual, habitual, customary, normal; ordinary, simple, plain; (biol.) common (*vulgaris*).

**обыск** m., **—ать, —ивать** v. search.

**обыскрывание** n. sparking.

**обычай** m. custom, usage, use, habit.

**обычн/о** adv. usually, generally; **—ый** a. usual, habitual, normal, regular; ordinary, common, plain; (biol.) common (*vulgaris*); **—ого типа** conventional, conventional type.

**ОБЭ** abbr. (**относительная биологическая эффективность**) relative biological effectiveness (of radiation), RBE.

**обязанн/ость** f. duty, obligation, charge; **—ый** a. obligated, under obligation, indebted; **он обязан** he must, he has (to), it is his duty.

**обязатель/но** adv. without fail, surely, certainly; **—ный** a. obligatory, compulsory; **—ство** n. obligation, bond, engagement, contract, guarantee.

**обяз/ать, —ывать** v. bind, oblige, engage; **—аться, —ываться** v. bind, engage, pledge oneself.

**ов** abbr. (**отравляющие вещества**) toxic agents, poisons; **о-в** abbr. (**остров**) island; **ОВ** abbr. (**окислительно-восстановительный**) oxidation-reduction.

**овал** m. oval.

**овалевое масло** owala oil.

**овалогубцы** pl. roundnose pliers.

**овальн/о-токарный станок** lathe for oval pieces; **—ый** a. oval.

**овариальный** a. (biol.) ovarian.

**овер/драйв** m. (automobile) overdrive; **—шот** m. (oil-well drilling) overshot.

**овес** m. (bot.) oats (*Avena*).

**овеч/ий** a. sheep, ovine; **о. жиропот** wool grease; **о. копытный жир** sheep's-foot oil; **—ка** f. ewe lamb; mushroom (*Boletus piperatus*).

**овин** m., **—ный** a. barn, drying barn.

**овицид** m. ovicide (egg-killing insecticide).

**овлад/евать, —еть** v. seize, take possession (of); master; **—ение** n. seizing; mastering.

**о-во** abbr. (**общество**) society.

**ово—** *prefix.* (biol.) ovo— (ovum, egg cell); **—генез** *m.* ovogenesis.

**овод** *m.* (zool.) gadfly.

**оводн/ение** *n.* irrigation; soaking, steeping; hydration; **—ять** *v.* irrigate; soak, steep; hydrate.

**овод/** *pl.*, **—носоглоточные —ы** bot flies (*Oestridae*).

**ово/клор, —тран** *m.* Ovotran (miticide); **—скоп** *m.* (egg) candling device; **—флавин** *m.* ovoflavin, vitamin $B_2$.

**овощ** *m.*, **—ной** *a.* vegetable; **—евод** *m.* vegetable grower; **—еводство** *n.* vegetable growing; **—еводческий** *a.* truck (farm).

**ОВП** *abbr.* (окислительно-восстановительный потенциал) oxidation-reduction potential, redox potential.

**овра/г** *m.*, **—жный** *a.* gully, ravine, gulch; **—жек** *m.* (zool.) gopher; **—жистый** *a.* gullied; **—жность** *f.* extent of gully formation; degree to which area is subjected to gullying; **—жный песок** pit sand.

**ОВС** *abbr.* (окислительно-восстановительная среда) oxidation-reduction medium.

**овс/ец** *m.* (bot.) perennial oat (*Avenastrum*); **—овые** *pl.* (bot.) Aveneae.

**овсю/г, —жный** *a.* (bot.) wild oat (*Avena fatua*); **—жница** *f.* wild oat separator.

**овсяниц/а** *f.* (bot.) fescue, fescue grass (*Festuca*); **—евые** *pl.* Festuceae.

**овсян/ка** *f.* oatmeal; (zool.) bunting; **—ый** *a.* oat; **—ая мука** oatmeal.

**овуляция** *f.* (physiol.) ovulation.

**овц/а** *f.* sheep, ewe; **—ебык** *m.* ox; **—евод** *m.* sheep breeder; **—еводство** *n.* sheep raising; **—ематка** *f.* ewe.

**овч/ар** *m.* shepherd; **—арка** *f.* sheep dog; **—арник** *m.*, **—арня** *f.* sheep pen; **—ина** *f.* sheepskin.

**Огайо** Ohio.

**огар/ок** *m.* cinder, ash; (met.) calcine; candle end; **водочный о., кислотный о.** niter cake, sodium bisulfate; **—ки** *pl.* cinders, esp. pyrite cinders; skimmings, scoria, discarded metal (of electrode).

**огболт** *m.* eye bolt, toggle bolt, eye ring.

**огиб/ание** *n.* rounding; diffraction (of waves; **—ать** *v.* round; bend round;

**—ающая** *f.* (math.; elec. comm.) envelope.

**огива** *f.* (statistics) ogive.

**ОГИЗ** *abbr.* (Объединение государственных издательств) Unified State Publishing House.

**оглавл/ение** *n.* table of contents, index; **—енный** *a.* indexed; **—ять** *v.* index, prepare the table of contents.

**огла/дить, —живать** *v.* smooth out.

**оглазур/ивать, —ить** *v.* glaze.

**огланлинский** *a.* Oglanly (Turkmen SSR).

**огла/сить, —шать** *v.* publish, announce; **—ска** *f.* publicity; **—шение** *n.* publicizing.

**оглеен/ие** *n.* gleying; **—ный** *a.* gleyed; **—ная почва** gley soil.

**оглинение** *n.* argillization; claying (of soil).

**оглобля** *f.* shaft.

**оглох/лый, —ший** *a.* grown deaf; **—нуть** *v.* get deaf.

**оглум** *m.* (med.) hydrocephalus.

**оглуш/ать, —ить** *v.* deafen, stun, stupefy; **—енный** *a.* deafened, stunned, dazed; **—ительный** *a.* deafening, stunning.

**огля/деть, —дывать, —нуть** *v.* look around, examine; **—дка** *f.* looking back; mistake, oversight.

**огне—** *prefix* pyro—, fire; **—видный** *a.* fire-like; (geol.) igneous, plutonic; **—вик** *m.* firestone; flint; (med.) anthrax; **—вица** *f.* fever; (bot.) pellitory of Spain (*Anacyclus pyrethrum*); **—вки** *pl.* pyralid or snout moths (*Pyralididae*).

**огнев/ой** *a.* fire; (geol.) pyrogenous, igneous; **о. ход, —ая труба** flue, flame flue; **—ая камера, —ая коробка, —ое пространство** firebox; fireplace; heating space; combustion chamber; **—ая рафинировка** pyrorefining, refining with fire; **—ые работы** (min.) firing.

**огнегаситель** *m.*, **—ный прибор** fire extinguisher; **—ный** *a.* fire-extinguishing.

**огне/дышащая гора** (geol.) volcano; **—задерживающий** *a.* fire-retardant; **—защитный** *a.* fireproof, fireproofing; **—ины** *pl.* (min.) firing.

**огнемет** *m.* (mil.) flame thrower, flame gun, flame projector; —**ный** *a.* flame-throwing; fire-throwing, igneous.

**огненно/водный** *a.* (geol.) igneo-aqueous; —**жидкий** *a.* molten, fused, liquid at a high temperature; —**красный** *a.* red hot.

**огненный** *a.* fire, igneous.

**огнеопасн/ость** *f.* inflammability, fire risk, fire hazard; —**ый** *a.* inflammable, subject to fire risk, apt to catch fire.

**огне/постоянный** *a.* fire-resistant, heat-stable; —**припасы** *pl.* (mil.) ammunition; —**проводный шнур** fuse; —**родный** *a.* (geol.) pyrogenous, igneous.

**огнестойк/ий** *a.* fire-resistant; —**ость** *f.* resistance to fire.

**огнестрельн/ый** *a.* firing; —**ое оружие** firearm, firearms; —**ые припасы** ammunition.

**огнетрубный котел** fire-tube boiler.

**огнетушитель** *m.*, —**ный прибор**, —**ное средство** fire extinguisher; —**ный** *a.* fire-extinguishing.

**огнеупор** *m.* refractory material; —**ность** *f.* refractoriness, resistance to fire, fire-proofness.

**огнеупорн/ый** *a.* fireproof, refractory; **о. кирпич** firebrick, refractory brick; **о. материал**, —**ое тело** refractory material; —**ая глина** fire clay, refractory clay; —**ая набойка**, —**ая футеровка** refractory lining; brasque, steep.

**огниво** *n.* flint, flintstone; chert.

**оговорка** *f.* reservation, stipulation.

**огол/енный** *a.* uncovered, exposed, bare; —**ить** *v.* uncover, strip, denude, bare.

**оголовье** *n.* headband.

**оголять** *see* **оголить**.

**огонек** *m.* little fire, light; (bot.) globe flower (*Trollius asiaticus*).

**огонь** *m.* fire; light; **поддерживать о.** *v.* stoke; **полный о.** full fire, full heat; **разводить о.** *v.* fire up, kindle.

**огораживать** *v.* enclose, fence, rail in.

**огород** *m.*, —**ный** *a.* garden, truck garden, kitchen garden; —**ить** *see* **огораживать**; —**ник** *m.* gardener; —**ничество** *n.* gardening, vegetable raising.

**огорч/ать**, —**ить** *v.* distress, vex, annoy; —**ение** *n.* distress, vexation, concern, annoyance, chagrin; —**енный** *a.* distressed, concerned; —**ительный** *a.* distressing, irritating.

**огра** *f.* Ogra (Soviet thermonuclear mirror machine).

**ограда** *f.* fence, fencing, enclosure, wall.

**оградитель** *m.* protector, guard; —**ный** *a.* protecting, guard; enclosing; —**ный щит** guard, fender.

**огражд/ать**, **оградить** *v.* defend, guard; enclose, fence; —**ающий** *a.* safety, security; enclosing; —**ение** *n.* guard, guarding, guardrail, safeguard, protection, safety device; enclosing, enclosure, fencing, barrier; locking.

**ограничен/ие** *n.* limitation, restriction, termination; —**ность** *f.* limitedness, scantiness; —**ный** *a.* limited, bounded, finite, restricted, circumscriptive, confined, restrained, bound, narrow.

**ограничив/ать** *v.* limit, set limits, set boundaries, circumscribe, confine, restrain, restrict, narrow; terminate; —**аться** *v.* confine (oneself); —**ающийся** *a.* confined, restricted.

**ограничител/ь** *m.*, **о. хода** catch, stop, stopping device, arresting device; limiter; **о. импульсов, цепь —я импульсов** (instrumentation) clipping circuit; **постоянная времени —я** clipping time; —**ьный** *a.* stopping, arresting; restricting, limiting, stringent.

**ограничить** *see* **ограничивать**.

**огребать** *v.* rake round.

**огревать** *see* **обогревать**.

**огрести** *see* **огребать**.

**огреть** *see* **обогревать**.

**огрех** *m.* blemish, flaw; gap.

**огромн/ость** *f.* enormousness, vastness, bigness; —**ый** *a.* enormous, vast, big, huge, immense, mammoth, bulky.

**огруб/елый** *a.* coarse; —**ить** *v.* roughen; desensitize.

**огузок** *m.* buttock, rump.

**огул/ом** *adv.* wholesale, in a lump; —**ьный** *a.* groundless, unfounded; indiscriminate.

**огур/ец** *m.*, —**ечный** *a.* (bot.) cucumber (*Cucumis sativus*); **морской о.** (zool.)

sea cucumber; —**ечник,** —**ечная трава** *see* **бурачник.**

**одабривать** *see* **одобрить.**

**одаренный** *a.* talented, gifted.

**одевать** *v.* dress; put on, coat, cover.

**одежавель** *see* **жавелева вода.**

**одежда** *f.* clothes, clothing; jacket, lining, insulation; revetment; pavement, surfacing, topping, top dressing (of road).

**одеколон** *m.* eau de Cologne.

**оделять** *v.* give, present, endow (with).

**одеревенение** *n.* lignification.

**одеревян/елость** *f.* stiffening, hardening; —**еть** *v.* grow stiff.

**одерж/ать,** —**ивать** *v.* gain, win; **о. верх** overcome, get the upper hand, get the advantage (of).

**одержимый** *a.* possessed, obsessed (by), seized, overcome; afflicted (with).

**одернованный** *a.* turfed.

**одесский** *a.* Odessa.

**одет/ый** *a.* dressed, clad, coated; —**ь** *see* **одевать.**

**одеяло** *n.* blanket, quilt.

**од/ин** *m., a., pron.,* —**на** *f.,* —**но** *n.* one; a certain; a, an; alone, only, single; **о. другого** one another, each other; **о. за другим** one after another, one by one; **о. на о.** face to face; confidentially, in private; —**но и тоже** one and the same thing, it is all the same; **все до** —**ного** everyone, to the last man; **по** —**ному** one by one, singly.

**одинаков/о** *adv.* in like manner, alike, equally; —**ость** *f.* sameness, identity, equality, uniformity; —**ый** *a.* same, the same, identical, duplicate, equal.

**одинарный** *a.* single; single-thickness, single-ply.

**одиннадцати/плоскостной** *a.* (cryst.) hendecahedral; —**угольник** *m.* (geom.) hendecagon; —**угольный** *a.* hendecagonal.

**одиннадцат/ый** *a.* eleventh; —**ь** eleven.

**одинокий** *a.* single, solitary, unique, only.

**одиноч/ество** *n.* solitude, isolation; —**ный** *a.* solitary, single, separate, self-contained.

**одиозный** *a.* odious, repulsive, offensive.

**одич/алый** *a.* wild; —**ать** *v.* grow wild.

**одна** *see* **один.**

**однажды** *adv.* once, one day.

**однако** *conj.* but, however, nevertheless, yet, still.

**одно** *see* **один;** *prefix* one, mono—, uni—, single; —**атомный** *a.* monatomic; monohydric (alcohol); —**бромистый** *a.* monobromide (of); —**бромистая камфора** monobromated camphor; —**валентность** *f.* univalence; —**валентный** *a.* univalent; —**вариантный** *a.* monovariant; univariant; —**витковый** *a.* (elec.) single-turn, single-coil; —**водный гидрат** monohydrate.

**одновременн/о** *adv.* simultaneously, at the same time; **существовать о.** *v.* coexist; —**ость** *f.* simultaneousness, synchronism, coincidence; —**ый** *a.* simultaneous, synchronous, isochronous.

**одно/главый** *a.* one-headed, monocephalous; —**гнездный** *a.* one-celled, unicellular, unilocular; —**горбый** *a.* single-humped; —**групповой** *a.* one-group; —**декадный** *a.* one-digit decimal; —**диапазонный** *a.* single-band; —**дневка** *f.* May fly, ephemerid; —**дневный** *a.* one-day.

**однодольн/ые** *pl.* (bot.) monocotyledons; —**ый** *a.* monocotyledonous.

**одно/домный** *a.* (bot.) monoecious; —**дуантный** *a.* one-dee (cyclotron); —**желобчатый** *a.* single-groove; —**жильный** *a.* single-core, single (cable); —**замещенные** *pl.* monosubstitution products, mono-derivatives; —**замещенный фосфат кальция** monocalcium phosphate; —**зарядный** *a.* single-charged.

**однозаходн/ый** *a.* single-cut (screw); —**ая резьба** single thread.

**однозвучный** *a.* monotonous.

**однозернянка** *f.* (bot.) einkorn (*Triticum monococcum*).

**однознач/ащий** *a.* synonymous, identical; —**ный** *a.* well-defined, unambiguous, unequivocal, clear; single-valued (function, etc.); —**ное число** simple number, digit.

**одно/именный** *a.* like, similar, analogous, of the same kind; —**калиберный** *a.* of the same caliber; —**калиевый** *a.* monopotassium; —**камерный** *a.* unilocular; (zool.) monothalamous;

single-stage; —канальный *a.* single-channel; —каскадный *a.* single-stage, single-step; —катушечный *a.* single-coil; —качественный *a.* (math.) isomorphic; —квантовый *a.* one-quantum; —керновый *a.* unipivot (instrument); —кислотный *a.* monoacid; —клапанный *a.* single-valved, one-valve.

одноклеточн/ые *pl.* one-celled animals; —ый *a.* one-celled, unicellular.

одно/клетьевой прокатный стан single-stand (rolling) mill; —клиномерный *a.* monoclinic; —колейный *a.* single-gage, single-track (railroad); one-way (street); —коленчатый *a.* single-jointed, one-jointed; —колонный *a.* single-column; —кольчатый *a.* monocyclic; —контурный *a.* single-circuit; —копытный *a.* (zool.) solid-ungulate, whole-hoofed; —корпусный *a.* single-unit; single-effect (evaporator); single hull (ship); —красочный *see* одноцветный.

однократн/о *adv.* once, one time; —ый *a.* single, single-stage; once through; —ого действия single-acting.

одно/кристальный *a.* single-crystal; —крылый *a.* single-blade; one-winged; —ламповый *a.* (rad.) single-tube; —летки *pl.* (bot.) seedlings.

однолетн/ий *a.* one-year, yearly, annual; —ее растение, —ик *m.* (bot.) annual.

одно/линейный *a.* unilinear, one-line; —листный *a.* monophyllous; —лопастный *a.* unilobed, single-lobed; —лучевая щель (pal.) monolete markings; —мастный *a.* monochrome, one-color; —мерный *a.* unidimensional; —местный *a.* single-position; single-seater (plane, car); —молекулярный *a.* monomolecular; —моторный *a.* single-motor; —направленный *a.* unidirectional; (math.) unicursal; —натриевый *a.* monosodium; —нитный, —ниточный *a.* unifilar; —ниточный, —оборотный *a.* single-cut, single-thread (screw).

однообраз/ие *n.* monotony, equality; similarity, uniformity; —ный *a.* monotonous, alike, equal; monotonic (function).

одно-однозначный *a.* one-to-one.

одноокись *f.* monoxide.

однооснови/ый *a.* monobasic; —ая кислота monobasic acid; —ая карбоновая кислота monocarboxylic acid.

одноосн/ость *f.* (cryst.) uniaxiality; —ый *a.* uniaxial, monoaxial; (biol.) uniaxial, haplocaulescent.

одно/палубный *a.* single-deck; —пальцевой *a.* fingertip (control); —пламенный *a.* single-flame; —подовая печь single-hearth furnace; —полосный *a.* single-band; —полупериодный *a.* half-wave (circuit); —полый *a.* unisexual.

однополюсн/ость *f.* unipolarity; —ый *a.* unipolar, one-poled, single-pole; (elec.) unipolar, monopolar; single-throw (switch).

одно/породный *a.* monogenetic; —поточный *a.* single-flow; —преломляющий *a.* singly refracting; —проводный *a.* single-wire; —проволочный *a.* unifilar; —проходные *pl.* (zool.) Monotremata; —путный *a.* single-line, single-track (railroad); one-way (street); —разовый *a.* single, one-time; —разрядный *a.* one-column, single-digit (adder); —реданный *a.* (aero.) single-step; —рельсовый *a.* monorail.

однородни/ость *f.* homogeneity, homogeneousness, uniformity, unity, similarity; evenness (of fibers); —ый *a.* homogeneous, uniform, similar, of the same kind.

однорядный *a.* single-row, one-row, uniserial, unilinear, single.

односеменодольн/ые *pl.* (bot.) monocotyledons; —ый *a.* monocotyledonous.

одно/семянный *a.* one-seeded, monospermous; —сернистый *a.* monosulfide (of); —слойный *a.* single-layer, single-ply, one-ply; —срезный *a.* single-shear; —станинный *a.* openside (machine); overhanging (hammer); —створчатый *a.* univalve; —стоечный *a.* single-column; (aero.) single-bay; open-side (machine); overhanging (hammer); —сторонний *a.* unilateral, one-sided, single-ended, single; one-way, unidirectional; openside (machine); prejudiced, biased;

—**ступенчатый** *a.* single-stage, single-step; simple (process); —**суставный** *a.* single-jointed, one-jointed; —**тактный** *a.* single-cycle.

**однотес** *m.* plank nail.

**одно/типичный** *a.* monotypic; —**трубный** *a.* tubeless (tire); —**угольный** *a.* one-angled; —**ударный** *a.* single-stroke; —**утробный** *a.* (biol.) monodelphian; —**фазный** *a.* single-phase, monophase, uniphase; —**хлористый** *a.* monochloride (of); —**ходовой** *a.* single-pass, one-pass, straight-through (flow); single-thread (screw); —**цветный** *a.* monochromatic, one-colored; —**центровый** *a.* concentric; —**цепный** *a.* single-chain; (elec.) single-circuit; —**цилиндровый** *a.* single-cylinder; —**частичный** *a.* one-particle, single-particle; —**частотный** *a.* single-frequency.

**одночлен** *m.*, —**ный** *a.* (math.) monomial.

**одно/шахтный** *a.* single-shaft; —**шерстный** *a.* identically colored (animals); —**шкивный привод** single-pulley drive; —**шпиндельный автомат** automatic single-mandrel lathe; —**этажный** *a.* single-stage, single-deck, one-story; —**ядерный** *a.* mononuclear, uninucleate; —**якорный** *a.* (elec.) single-armature; —**ярусный** *a.* single-stage; —**ячейковый** *a.* unicellular.

**одобр/ение** *n.* approval; —**енный** *a.* approved, sanctioned, favored; —**ительный** *a.* approving; —**ить**, —**ять** *v.* approve, indorse, favor, sanction.

**одол/евать**, —**еть** *v.* overcome, surmount, master, conquer; overrun.

**одолж/ение** *n.* favor, service; loan; —**ать**, —**ить** *v.* lend, loan.

**одомашн/ивать**, —**ить** *v.* tame, domesticate.

**одометр** *m.* odometer, distance gage.

**одонто**—*prefix* odonto— (tooth); —**граф** *m.* (mach.) odontograph; —**лит** *m.* odontolite (a type of fossil bone); —**логия** *f.* odontology.

**одор/ант** *m.* odorant; malodorant; —**изация** *f.* imparting odor (to gases); —**иметрия** *f.* odorometry; —**ин** *m.* odorin.

**одревесн/евать** *v.* lignify, become wood;

—**евший** *a.* hardwood; —**ение** *n.* lignification.

**одряхление** *n.* aging.

**одубина** *f.* tan waste.

**одуванчик** *m.* (bot.) dandelion (*Taraxacum officinale*).

**одум/аться**, —**ываться** *v.* think better of it, reconsider, change one's mind.

**одур/елый** *a.* stupid, stupefied; —**еть** *v.* grow stupid, get dizzy; —**манить** *v.* stupefy; —**ь** *f.* stupor; **сонная** —**ь** (bot.) belladonna (*Atropa belladonna*); —**ять** *v.* stupefy; —**яющий** *a.* stupefying.

**одутловатый** *a.* puffy, bloated.

**одышка** *f.* shortness of breath, panting; (med.) dyspnea, labored breathing.

**Оже эффект** (phys.) Auger effect.

**ожелезнение** *n.* iron accumulation (in soil).

**оже-переход** (phys.) Auger transition.

**ожеребиться** *v.* foal.

**ожерелье** *n.* necklace.

**ожечь** *see* **обжигать.**

**оживальный** *a.* ogival.

**ожив/ать** *v.* revive, regain consciousness; —**ить,** —**лять** *v.* revive; animate, enliven; clear, brighten, freshen (color); —**ка** *f.* reviving, regeneration, vivification; —**ление** *n.* revival, revivification, resuscitation, regeneration, vivification; liveliness, animation; —**ленный** *a.* revived, vitalized; lively, animated.

**ожигать** *see* **обжигать.**

**ожид/аемость** *f.* expectancy; —**аемый** *a.* expectant; —**аемый срок службы** (mach.) life expectancy; —**ание** *n.* expectation, waiting; expectancy, anticipation; **в** —**ании** pending; **обмануть о.** *v.* disappoint, come short of one's expectations; —**ать** *v.* expect, wait (for); anticipate.

**ожиж/атель** *m.* liquefier; —**ать** *v.* liquefy; —**ающий** *a.* liquefying; —**ающийся** *a.* liquefiable; —**ение** *n.* liquefying, liquefaction (of gas); (met.) thinning; liquation; destructive hydrogenation (of coal).

**ожика** *f.* (bot.) wood rush (*Luzula*).

**ожина** *f.* European dewberry (*Rubus caesius*).

**ожир/ение** *n.* obesity, corpulence; (med.)

adiposity; —**енный** *a.* fat; oily; —**еть** *v.* get fat.

**ожог** *m.* burn, scald; blight (of plants).

**оз** *m.* (geol.) os, esker.

**оз.** *abbr.* (озеро) lake; (озимь) winter crop.

**озабо/тить,** —**чивать** *v.* occupy, busy; —**титься,** —**чиваться** attend (to), take care (of); —**ченность** *f.* preoccupation, anxiety, concern; —**ченный** *a.* preoccupied, anxious, concerned, troubled.

**озаглав/ить,** —**ливать** *v.* entitle; —**ленный** *a.* entitled.

**озадач/енный** *a.* perplexed, puzzled; —**ивать,** —**ить** *v.* perplex, puzzle.

**озазон** *m.* osazone, diphenyl hydrazone.

**озамин** *m.* ozamin, benzopurpurin.

**озаннит** *m.* (min.) osannite (a soda-amphibole near riebeckite).

**озарить** *see* озарять.

**озаркит** *m.* (min.) ozarkite (a variety of thomsonite).

**озарять** *v.* illuminate, lighten, irradiate; dawn.

**озвереть** *v.* become wild, become primitive.

**озвуч/енный** *a.* sound (moving picture); sonicated, exposed to sonic waves; —**ивание** *n.* sonication; —**ивать,** —**ить** *v.* sonicate.

**оздор/авливать,** —**овить,** —**овлять** *v.* improve sanitary conditions; renew, sweeten (air); —**овление** *n.* sanitation.

**озеленять** *v.* plant with trees.

**озерненность** *f.* grain content in ear.

**озерно-речной** *a.* (geol.) fluvio-lacustrine.

**озерн/ый** *a.* lake, lacustrine; —**ая руда** (min.) lake (iron) ore, bog iron ore.

**озеро** *n.* lake; —**ведение** *n.* (biol.) limnology.

**озим/ые** *pl.* winter crops; —**ый** *a.* winter; —**ь** *f.* winter crop.

**озираться** *v.* look around, observe.

**озиритин** *m.* osyritin.

**ознаком/ить,** —**лять** *v.* acquaint (with); show around; —**иться,** —**ляться** *v.* become acquainted, become familiar (with); —**ление** *n.* acquaintance, knowledge.

**ознаменов/ание** *n.* sign; **в о.** in honor (of), to mark the occasion; —**ать,** —**ывать** *v.* signalize, mark.

**означ/ать** *v.* mean, stand (for), denote, indicate, imply; —**енный** *see* вышеозначенный.

**озноб** *m.* shivering, chill; (med.) rigor.

**озобензол** *m.* ozobenzene.

**озокерит** *m.* (min.) ozocerite, ozokerite, mineral wax (in part), fossil wax.

**озоление** *n.* calcination; combustion; **анализ мокрым** —**м** wet assaying; **анализ сухим** —**м** blow-pipe analysis.

**озолотить** *v.* gild.

**озолять** *see* обзоливать.

**озон** *m.* ozone; —**атор** *m.,* —**изатор** ozonizer; —**ация,** —**изация** *f.* ozonization, ozonation; —**ид** *m.* ozonide; —**идация** *f.* ozonidation, conversion to an ozonide.

**озониоз** *m.* Texas root rot.

**озониров/ание** *n.* ozonization; —**анный** *a.* ozonized; —**ать** *v.* ozonize.

**озонная бумага** ozone test paper.

**озонолиз** *m.* ozonolysis.

**озонометр** *m.* ozonometer; —**ический** *a.* ozonometric; —**ия** *f.* ozonometry.

**озоноскоп** *m.* ozonoscope.

**озотетразон** *m.* ozotetrazone.

**ОЗРА** *abbr.* (отдел защиты растений) plant protection division.

**озы** *pl.* (geol.) osar (*pl. of* os), eskers.

**оид/иум** *m.,* —**ии** *pl.* (bot.) oidium; powdery mildew.

**ОИЯИ** *abbr.* (Объединенный институт ядерных исследований) United Institute of Nuclear Research.

**ойкокристалл** *m.* (petr.) oikocryst.

**ойльдаг** *m.* Oildag (lubricant).

**ойтиковое масло** oiticica oil.

**ок.** *abbr.* (около) approximately; (океан) ocean.

**оказание** *n.* showing, rendering.

**оказ/ать** *v.* show, render, pay; exert (pressure); —**аться** *v.* find oneself, appear, occur; prove to be; —**ывается** it appears (that), it is found (that), it turns out (that).

**оказия** *f.* opportunity.

**оказывать** *see* оказать.

**окайм/ить,** —**лять** *v.* border, edge, flange; —**ление** *n.* bordering, edging, flange, burr; **светлое** —**ление** halo, halation; —**ленный** *a.* edged.

**окалина** *f.* (hearth) cinder, sinter,

clinker; scale; slag, dross; (casting) skin.

**окалывать** *v.* break round, split round.

**окамен/евать, —еть, —ять** *v.* (geol.) petrify, be petrified; harden, fossilize; **—елость** *f.* petrifaction, petrification; fossil; **руководящая —елость** guide fossil, index fossil; **—елый** *a.* petrified; fossil, petrous; silicified; **—ение** *n.* petrifaction, petrification; lithification; fossilization; silicification; **—слости** *pl.* fossil soil.

**окантов/ать, —ывать** *v.* frame.

**оканчивать** *v.* finish, end, terminate; **—ся** *v.* come to an end, end, terminate.

**окапывать** *see* **обкапывать**.

**окарбоначивание** *n.* carbonate accumulation (in soils).

**окармливать** *see* **обкармливать**.

**окатанность** *f.* toughness.

**окатанный** *a.* rolled; rounded; nodulized.

**ока/тить, —чивать** *v.* pour over, drench, sluice.

**окашивать** *v.* mow around.

**океан** *m.* ocean; **—ический, —ский** *a.* ocean, oceanic; **—ичность** *f.* (meteor.) oceanity; **—ография** *f.* oceanography.

**окенит** *m.* (min.) okenite (a zeolite).

**окилен/ие** *n.* (biol.) carina; **—ный** *a.* carinate, carinated, keel-shaped; **—ная складка** (geol.) carinate fold, isoclinal fold.

**окис/ание** *see* **окисление**; **—ать** *see* **окиснуть**; **—ел** *see* **окись**; **—и** *pl. and gen. of* **окись**.

**окислен/ие** *n.* oxidation; acidification, souring; **продукт —ия** oxidation product; **—ность** *f.* state of oxidation; **—ный** *a.* oxidized; acidified, soured.

**окислитель** *m.* oxidizing agent, oxidant; acidifier; **—но-восстановительный** *a.* reduction-oxidation, redox; **—ный** *a.* oxidizing; acidifying.

**окисл/ить, —ять** *v.* oxidize; acidify, sour; **—иться, —яться** *v.* oxidize, be oxidized; become sour, turn sour; **—ость** *f.* acidity; **—ый** *a.* acid; **—яемость** *f.* oxidizability; **—яемый**, **—яющийся** *a.* oxidizable; acidifiable; **—яющий** *a.* oxidizing; acidifying; **—яющее средство** oxidizing agent; acidifier.

**окисн/о-ртутный** *a.* mercury-mercurous oxide (electrode); **—уть** *v.* oxidize; turn sour; **—ый** *a.* oxide; **—ая соль** higher or **—ic** salt; **—ое покрытие** oxide coating, oxide film.

**окис/ь** *f.* oxide (higher or **—ic** oxide); **о. железа** ferric oxide; **азотнокислая о. железа** ferric nitrate; **лимоннокислая о. железа** ferric citrate; **о. меди** cupric oxide; **сернокислая о. меди** cupric sulfate; **о. углерода** carbon monoxide; **безводная о.** anhydride; **водная о., гидрат —и** hydroxide.

**окклю/дирование** *n.*, **—зия** *f.* occlusion (of gas or liquid); **—дированный** *a.* occluded; **—дировать** *v.* occlude.

**оккуп/ация** *f.* occupation; **—ированный** *a.* occupied; **—ировать** *v.* occupy.

**Оклагома, оклагомский** *a.* Oklahoma.

**оклад** *m.* tax; salary, pay.

**окладка** *f.* lining.

**окладной** *a.* tax, rate.

**окле/ивать** *v.* glue around; **—йка** *f.* gluing; clarification (of fruit juices).

**окно** *n.* window; opening, rift; aperture; (anat.) fenestra.

**оков/анный** *a.* iron-bound; **—ать, —ывать** *v.* bind with iron; iron, chain; **—ка** *f.* binding (with iron); fittings, ironwork; **—ы** *pl.* irons, chains.

**околачивать** *v.* hammer round, beat down.

**около** *prep. gen. and adv.* near, toward; around, about, by; approximately; *prefix* near, para—, peri—; circum—; **—горизонтальный** *a.* circumhorizontal; **—зенитный** *a.* circumzenithal; **—плодие** *n.*, **—плодник, —семянник** *m.* (bot.) pericarp, seed vessel; **—плодный** *a.* fetal (fluid); **—полюсный, —полярный** *a.* (astron.) circumpolar.

**околосерд/ечный** *a.* (anat.) pericardial; **—ечная оболочка, —ие** *n.* pericardium.

**около/ушная железа** (anat.) parotid gland; **—цветник** *m.* (bot.) perianth; **—щитовидная железа** parathyroid gland.

**окольный** *a.* roundabout, indirect, tortuous; oblique (electron); **о. путь** indirect route; detour.

**оконечн/ик** *m.* terminator; **—ость** *f.*

extremity, end, tip, tail; —ый *a.* terminal, end.

**оконн/ица** *f.* window frame; —ый *a.* window; —ый переплет, —ая рама sash; —ое стекло window pane.

**оконопа/тить, —чивать** *v.* calk, stop up.

**оконтурив/ание** *n.* (min.) mapping (boundaries of deposits); —ать *v.* outline.

**оконце** *n.* little window.

**окончание** *n.* end, ending, completion, finishing, termination, conclusion, consummation, closing, expiration.

**окончательн/о** *adv.* finally, definitely; again; о. обработанный finished, completely finished; —ый *a.* final, finishing, closing, definitive; —ая отделка finishing, finishing work, finishing touch.

**окончат/ый** *a.* fenestrated, having apertures; —ое отверстие (anat.) fenestra.

**оконч/енный** *a.* finished, completed; —ивающий *a.* terminating; —ить *v.* finish, complete.

**окоп** *m.* trench.

**окопник** *m.* (bot.) comfrey (*Symphytum*).

**окопный** *a.* trench.

**окорачивать** *v.* shorten, curtail, crop.

**окор/енный** *a.* barked; —ивать *v.* bark, peel, scrape, strip; —ка *f.* barking.

**окорм** *m.* overfeeding; —ить *v.* overfeed.

**окорн/ать** *v.* cut, clip, cut too short; —ик *m.* spudder.

**окорок** *m.* ham; leg of mutton.

**окоротит** *see* окорачивать.

**окорочный** *a.* bark-stripping.

**окорчевка** *f.* uprooting.

**окор/щик** *m.* barker; —ять *v.* bark, peel.

**окосить** *see* окашивать.

**окостен/евать, —еть** *v.* (biol.) ossify; harden; —елость *f.* ossification; hardness; stiffness, numbness; —елый *a.* ossified; hardened, stiff; —ение *n.* ossification, bone formation.

**окот** *m.* lambing.

**окочен/евший, —елый** *a.* numb, stiff; —еть *v.* get numb, grow stiff.

**окош/ечко, —ко** *n.* little window, aperture; —ечный *see* оконный.

**окр.** *abbr.* (округ) district.

**окраина** *f.* outskirts; margin.

**окрасить** *see* окрашивать.

**окра/ска** *f.* color, coloration, tint; pigmentation; dyeing; painting, staining; ненормальная о., неправильная о., плохая о. off color, off shade; —шенный *a.* colored, tinted; dyed; painted, stained.

**окрашив/аемость** *f.* colorability; —аемый *a.* colorable; —ание *n.* coloring, coloration, tinting, pigmentation; dyeing; painting, staining; tinge, tint; —ать *v.* color, tint; dye; paint, stain; —ать в красный цвет dye red; paint red; —ающий *a.* coloring; dyeing; painting; —ающее средство pigment.

**окремн/евать** *v.* silicify; —ение *n.* silicification; silication; —енный *a.* silicified.

**окрести/ость** *f.,* —ости *pl.* neighborhood, vicinity, environs, surroundings; —ый *a.* neighboring, adjacent.

**окристаллизовать, —ся** *v.* crystallize.

**окровавленный** *a.* blood-stained, bloody.

**окроп/ить, —лять** *v.* sprinkle, spray.

**округ** *m.* district, region; circuit, circle.

**округлен/ие** *n.* rounding, rounding off, making round; —но *adv.* round; in round numbers; —ность *f.* roundness.

**округленноугловат/ость** *f.* subangularity; —ый *a.* subangular.

**округл/енный** *a.* rounded, rounded off (figure), blunt; —ить, —ять *v.* round, round off; —ость *f.* roundness; circle; curve; —оугловатость *see* округленноугловатость; —ый *a.* round, rounded, curved; orbicular, spherical.

**окруж/ать, —ить** *v.* surround, encircle, enclose, envelop, embrace, encompass; —ающий *a.* surrounding, encircling, circumjacent, circumfluent; environmental; —ающая среда environment; —ение *n.* surrounding, encircling, enclosing; surroundings, environment, vicinity; —енный *a.* surrounded.

**окружн/ость** *f.* circumference, periphery, circle; circuit; surrounding region, neighborhood, district; сила на —ости circumferential force; скорость на —ости, —ая скорость peripheral speed; —ый *a*. circumferential, peripheral, circling; surrounding; district.

оксаз/идин *m*. oxazidine; —ин *m*., —иновый *a*. oxazine; —иновые краски oxazine dyes; —ол *m*., —оловый *a*. oxazole; —олидин *m*. oxazolidine; —олин *m*. oxazoline, ethylene urea; —он *m*. oxazone.

оксал/амид *m*. oxalamide, oxamide; —анилид *m*. oxalanilide, oxanilide; —ат *m*. oxalate; —ен *m*. oxalene; —ил *m*. oxalyl; —илмочевина *f*. oxalyl urea.

оксалур/амид *m*. oxaluramide, oxamic acid ureide; —овая кислота oxaluric acid, oxalic monoureide.

оксам/ид *m*. oxamide, ethanediamide; —ил *m*. oxamyl; —иновая кислота, —овая кислота oxamic acid; соль —иновой кислоты, —иновокислая соль oxamate; —иновокислый *a*. oxamic acid; oxamate (of); —иновометиловый эфир methyl oxamate.

оксан *m*., —овый *a*. oxirane, ethylene oxide; —илид *m*. oxanilide; —иловая кислота oxanilic acid, phenyloxamic acid.

оксантр/анол *m*. oxanthranol, anthrahydroquinone; —ол, —он *m*. oxanthrol, oxanthrone.

оксафор *m*. oxaphore (50% oxycamphor solution).

Оксениуса теория баров (geol.) Ochsenius' bar theory.

окси— *prefix* oxy—; (more frequently) hydroxy—; —азокраски *pl*. hydroxyazo dyes; —азосоединение *n*. hydroxyazo compound; oxyazo compound; —альдегид *m*. hydroxyaldehyde; —амид *m*. oxamide, hydroxamide; —амино— *prefix* hydroxyamino—; —аммиак *m*. oxyammonia, hydroxylamine; —ацетиленовая сварка oxyacetylene welding; —ацетон *m*. hydroxyacetone, 1-hydroxy-2-propanone; —бензойная кислота hydroxybenzoic acid; —газ *m*. oxygen gas; —гемоглобин *m*. oxyhemoglobin, hematoglobulin; —гидрохинон *m*. hydroxyhydroquinone, 1,2,4-trihydroxybenzene.

оксид *see* окись; —аза *f*. oxidase (oxidizing enzyme); —атор *m*. oxidant;

—ационит *m*. oxidation product; —ация *f*. oxidation; —иметрия *f*. oxidimetry.

оксидиров/ание *n*., —ка *f*. oxidation; (met.) oxide coating; —анный *a*. oxidized; —ать *v*. oxidize.

оксидифтериновая кислота hydroxydiphtheric acid.

оксид/меонит *m*. (min.) oxide-meionite; —ная пленка oxide film.

оксиженная соль tin tetrachloride, stannic chloride.

окси/карбоновая кислота hydroxycarboxylic acid; —керченит *m*. (min.) oxykertschenite (a hydrated ferric phosphate); —кетон *m*. hydroxy ketone; —кислота *f*. hydroxy acid; —коричная кислота hydroxycinnamic acid, coumaric acid; —лактон *m*. oxylactone; —ликвит *m*. (expl.) oxyliquit (chiefly liquid air); —лит *m*. a sodium peroxide preparation for producing oxygen; —льные производные oxyl compounds (such as methoxyl, phenoxyl).

оксим *m*. oxime.

оксимасляная кислота hydroxybutyric acid.

оксимель *m*. oxymel (medicated honey).

оксиметил *m*. hydroxymethyl, oxymethyl; —ен *m*. oxymethylene, formaldehyde.

оксим/ид *m*. oximide; —идо— *prefix* oximido—, isonitroso—; —идосоединение *n*. oximido compound; —ирование *n*. formation of oximes.

оксиндол *m*. oxindol, 2-ketoindoline.

оксинон *m*. oxynone, 2,4-diaminodiphenylamine.

окси/олеиновая кислота hydroxyoleic acid, ricinoleic acid; —пропионовая кислота hydroxypropionic acid, lactic acid; —ран *m*. oxirane; —соединение *n*. oxy compound, hydroxy compound; —стрептомицин *m*. hydroxystreptomycin; —сульфид *m*. oxysulfide; —уксусная кислота hydroxyacetic acid, glycocollic acid.

оксиуро/вые *pl*. pinworms (*Oxyuridae*); —з *m*. (med.) oxyuriasis.

окси/хинолин *m*. hydroxyquinoline; —хинон *m*. hydroxyquinone; —циан *m*. oxycyanogen; —этил *see* оксэтил;

—янтарная кислота hydroxysuccinic acid, malic acid.

**оксод** *see* **оксилит.**

**оксозон** *m.* oxozone; —**ид** *m.* oxozonide.

**оксоль** *m.* a drying oil (for paints).

**оксон/иевый** *a.* oxonium; —**иевое соединение,** —**ий** *m.* oxonium compound; —**ит** *m.* (expl.) oxonite (picric acid dissolved in nitric acid).

**оксфордск/ий** *a.* Oxford; **о. отстойник** Oxford settler; **о. ярус** (geol.) Oxfordian stage; —**ая глина** (geol.) Oxford clay (an Upper Jurassic blue marine clay); —**ая единица** Oxford unit, Florey unit (for penicillin).

**оксэтил** *m.* ethoxy, hydroxyethyl, ethylol.

**окт**—, —**а**— *prefix* oct—, octa— (eight); —**ава** *f.* octave; —**агон** *m.* (geom.) octagon.

**октадекан** *m.* octadecane; —**овая кислота** octadecanoic acid, stearic acid; —**ол** *m.* octadecanol, octadecyl alcohol.

**окта/деценовая кислота** octadecenic acid; —**децил** *m.*, —**дециловый** *a.* octadecyl; —**диен** *m.* octadiene, conylene.

**октальдегид** *see* **октиловый альдегид.**

**окта/льный** *a.* octal, scale-of-eight; —**метил** *m.* octamethyl pyrophosphoramide (insecticide); —**н** *m.* octane; —**нафтен** *m.* octanaphthene.

**октан/овая кислота** octanoic acid, caprylic acid; —**овое число** octane number, octane rating (of gasoline); —**ол** *m.* octanol, octyl alcohol; —**он** *m.* octanone.

**окта/нт** *m.* octant; —**хлор** *see* **хлордан.**

**октаэдр** *m.* (cryst.) octahedron; —**ит** *m.* (min.) octahedrite, anatase; —**ический** *a.* octahedral.

**окт/ен** *m.* octene, caprylene; —**ет** *m.* octet (group of 8 valence electrons).

**октиббенит** *m.* (min.) octibbenite (an iron-nickel alloy).

**октил** *m.*, —**овый** *a.* octyl; **хлористый о.** octyl chloride; —**амин** *m.* octylamine; —**ен** *m.* octylene, octene; —**еновая кислота** octylenic acid; —**овая кислота** octylic acid, caprylic acid; —**овый альдегид** octyl aldehyde, caprylic aldehyde; —**овый**

**спирт** octyl alcohol, octanol; —**овый эфир уксусной кислоты** octyl acetate.

**октин** *m.* octyne, octine, hexylacetylene.

**окто**— *prefix* octo—; —**д** *m.* (thermionics) octode; —**за** *f.* octose.

**октэстрол** *m.* Ocestrol, benzestrol.

**октябрь** *m.* October.

**окуба воск** ocuba wax.

**окукляться** *v.* (zool.) pupate.

**окулиров/анный** *a.* inoculated; budded, grafted; —**ать** *v.* inoculate; bud, graft; —**ка** *f.* inoculation; budding, grafting.

**окулист** *m.* oculist.

**окультур/енный** *a.* continuously cultivated; —**ивание** *n.* cultivation.

**окулянт** *m.* (bot.) grafted bud sprout.

**окуляр** *m.* ocular, eyepiece (of microscope); eye glass; —**ный** *a.* ocular.

**окун/ание** *n.* dipping, plunging, immersing; —**ать,** —**уть** *v.* dip, plunge, immerse, steep; —**уться** *v.* dip, plunge.

**окунь** *m.* (zool.) perch; **морской о.** bass.

**окуп/аемость** *f.* profit, return; —**ать** *v.* pay, warrant; —**аться** *v.* pay (for itself), be worth.

**окургузить** *v.* curtail.

**окур/енный** *a.* fumigated; smoke-cured, smoked; —**ивание** *n.* fumigation; curing, smoking; —**ивать,** —**ить** *v.* fumigate, disinfect; cure, smoke; —**ивающий** *a.* fumigating; smoking; —**ивающее средство** fumigant.

**окускование** *n.* lumping, clotting; sintering, caking.

**окут/анный** *a.* wrapped, enveloped; —**ать,** —**ывать** *v.* wrap up, envelop, blanket.

**окуч/ивать** *v.* (agr.) hill; —**ник** *m.* hiller.

**окшар** *m.* white pigment (white lead and lead sulfate).

**оладья** *f.* pancake.

**олафит** *m.* (min.) olafite (a variety of albite feldspar).

**олеандр** *m.* (bot.) oleander (*Nerium oleander*); —**ин** *m.* oleandrin.

**олеа/нол** *m.* oleanol; —**ноловая кислота** oleanolic acid; —**т** *m.* oleate.

**оледен/елый** *a.* frozen, congealed, iced, covered with ice; —**ение,** —**ие** *n.* freezing; (geol.) glaciation; —**еть** *v.*

freeze, congeal, be covered with ice; glaciate.

**олеин** *m.* olein (glyceride of oleic acid); oleine (mixture of fatty acids).

**олеиново/калиевая соль, —кислый калий** potassium oleate; **—кислый** *a.* oleic acid; oleate (of); **—кислая соль** oleate; **—натриевая соль** sodium oleate.

**олеинов/ый** *a.* olein, oleic; **о. ряд** oleic series; **—ая кислота** oleic acid, 9-octadecenoic acid; **соль —ой кислоты** oleate.

**олен/ий** *a.* deer, cervine; **о. лишай** (bot.) reindeer moss (*Cladonia rangiferina*); **о. рог, спирт —ьего рога** hartshorn, spirit of hartshorn (ammonia water); **соль —ьего рога** hartshorn salt (ammonium carbamate); **о. язык** (bot.) hart's tongue (*Scolopendrium*); **—ьи рога** antlers; **—ья кожа** buckskin; **—ина** *f.* venison; deerskin; **—ка** *f.* (zool.) chafer, *spec.* rose chafer; **—ь** *m.* (zool.) deer.

**олео—** *prefix* oleo—, oil; **—графия** *f.* oleography; **—маргарин** *m.* oleomargarine, margarine; **—метр** *m.* oleometer, oil hydrometer; **—нафт** *m.* a lubricating oil; **—стеарин** *m.* oleostearin, beef stearin.

**олеум** *m.* oleum, fuming sulfuric acid.

**олефин** *m.*, **—овый** *a.* olefin.

**олибанум** *m.* olibanum, frankincense.

**олив/а** *f.* (bot.) olive; **—енит** *m.* (min.) olivenite, wood copper; **—еторовая кислота** olivetoric acid; **—ил** *m.* olivil (gum principle from olive tree); **—ин** *m.*, **—иновый** *a.* (min.) olivine, chrysolite.

**оливков/о-зеленый** *a.* olive green, olive-colored; **—ый** *a.* olive, olive-colored; **—ое дерево** *see* масличное дерево; **—ое масло** olive oil.

**олиго—** *prefix* oligo— [few, scant; (med.) deficiency]; **—клаз** *m.* (min.) oligoclase (a plagioclase feldspar); **—новый шпат** oligon spar, oligonite (a manganiferous siderite); **—сахарид** *m.* oligosaccharide.

**олигоцен** *m.*, **—овые слои** (geol.) Oligocene (epoch); **—овый** *a.* Oligocene.

**олиф/а** *f.* drying oil (a boiled linseed or hempseed oil), paint vehicle; **—ить** *v.* treat with drying oil.

**олицетвор/ить, —ять** *v.* personify.

**олов/о** *n.* tin, Sn; **гидрат закиси —а** stannous hydroxide; **гидрат окиси —а** stannic hydroxide; **двуокись —а, окись —а** tin dioxide, stannic oxide; **двусернистое о.** tin bisulfide, stannic sulfide; **двухлористое о., хлористое о.** stannous chloride; **закись —а, одноокись —а** stannous oxide, tin monoxide; **соль закиси —а** stannous salt; **соль окиси —а** stannic salt; **листовое о.** tin foil; **односернистое о., сернистое о.** stannous sulfide; **сернокислая закись —а** stannous sulfate; **сернокислая окись —а** stannic sulfate; **хлорное о., четыреххлористое о.** stannic chloride, tin tetrachloride; **основное хлорное о.** stannic oxychloride.

**олово/водород** *m.* stannic hydride; **—носный, —содержащий** *a.* tin-bearing, stanniferous; **—плавильный завод** (met.) tin smelter, tin works.

**оловянисто/кислый** *a.* stannous acid; stannite (of); **о. натрий, —натриевая соль** sodium stannite; **—кислая соль** stannite.

**оловянист/ый** *a.* stannous, tin; **—ая кислота** stannous acid, stannous hydroxide; **соль —ой кислоты** stannite; **—ая соль** stannous salt.

**оловянно/кислый** *a.* stannic acid; stannate (of); **о. натрий, —натриевая соль** sodium stannate; **—кислая соль** stannate; **—фтористый калий** potassium fluostannate; **—фтороводородная кислота** fluostannic acid; **—хлористый аммоний** ammonium chlorostannate; **—хлороводородная кислота** chlorostannic acid.

**оловянн/ый** *a.* stannic, tin; **о. ангидрид** stannic anhydride, stannic oxide; **о. камень** (min.) tinstone, tin ore, cassiterite; **о. колчедан** (min.) tin pyrites, stannite; **о. пепель, —ая зола** tin ash, stannic oxide; **—ая бумага, —ая фольга** tin foil; **—ая кислота** stannic acid; **соль —ой кислоты** stannate; **—ая посуда** tinware; **—ая протрава** tin mordant, tin liquor; **—ая соль** stannic salt; **—ая**

чума "tin pest" (allotropic transformation); —ое дерево dendritic crystals of tin; —ое масло butter of tin, stannic chloride.

олометр *m.* holometer, altitude gage.

ольдгамит *m.* (min.) oldhamite (meteoric calcium sulfide).

ольпидий *m.* (bot.) a fungus (*Olpidium*).

ольслайминг *m.* all-sliming (of ore).

ольфактометрия *f.* olfactometry, odorimetry.

ольх/а *f.*, —овый *a.* (bot.) alder, alder tree (*Alnus*); —овник *m.* alder grove; —овый уголь alderwood charcoal.

ом *m.* ohm (unit of electrical resistance); Ома закон Ohm's law; —ад *m.* ohmad (unit of resistance).

омар *m.* (zool.) lobster.

омброметр *m.* ombrometer, rain gage.

омгаз *m.* an enriched water gas.

омег *see* омел.

омега *f.* omega (ω); водяная о. (bot.) water fennel (*Oenanthe phellandrium*).

омедн/ение *n.* coppering, copper plating; —енный *a.* copper-plated, copper-clad; —ивать, —ять *v.* copper, copper plate, clad with copper.

оме/жник *m.* (bot.) water hemlock (*Cicuta maculata*); water dropwort (*Oenanthe*); —л *m.* poison hemlock (herb) (*Conium maculatum*).

омел/а *f.* (bot.) mistletoe (*Viscum*); —овые *pl.* Loranthaceae.

ОМЕН *abbr.* (отделение математических и естественных наук) Division of Mathematical and Natural Sciences.

омертв/елость *f.* stiffness, numbness; —елый *a.* stiff, numb; (med.) necrotic; —ение *n.* (med.) necrosis, gangrene; —еть *v.* grow stiff, grow numb; become gangrenous, mortify.

омет *m.* stack.

омическ/ий *a.* (elec.) ohmic; —ое сопротивление resistance.

омлет *m.* omelet.

омметр *m.* (elec.) ohmmeter.

омнибус *m.* bus.

омов/ский, —ый *see* омический.

омол/аживать, —одить *v.* rejuvenate; —ожение *n.* rejuvenation; —оженный *a.* rejuvenated.

ОМПА *see* октаметил.

омрач/ать, —ить *v.* obscure, darken, cloud; —енный *a.* obscured, darkened, clouded.

омут *m.* pool.

омфацит *m.* (min.) omphacite (a variety of hedenbergite pyroxene).

омшаник *m.* vegetable cellar; apiary house.

омыв/аемый *a.* washed, reached (by stream, etc.); —ать *v.* wash; flow (over, around).

омыл/ение, —ивание *n.* saponification; число —ения saponification number; —ивающий *a.* saponifying; —ивающее средство saponifying agent, saponifier; —яемость *f.* saponifiability; —яемый, —яющийся *a.* saponifiable; —ять, —яться *v.* saponify; hydrolyze.

он *pron.* he; —а she.

онагриковые *pl.* (bot.) Onagraceae.

оназот *m.* a spongy ebonite.

онгстрема единица *see* ангстрем.

ондатра *f.* (zool.) muskrat.

ондограф *m.* (elec.) ondograph.

ондул/ировать *v.* undulate; —ятор *m.* (elec.) undulator.

онегит *m.* (min.) onegite (a variety of goethite).

онем/елость *f.* numbness; dumbness; —елый *a.* numb; dumb; —еть *v.* grow numb; become dumb, lose one's speech.

Онзагера уравнение Onsager equation.

они *pron.* they.

ониевый *a.* onium (compound).

они/кс *m.* (min.) onyx (a cryptocrystalline variety of quartz); —хит *m.* onychite, onyx marble, Oriental alabaster.

онихия *f.* (med.) onychia.

онкограф *m.* (med.) oncograph.

онкози/метр *m.* (met.) oncosimeter; —н *m.* (min.) oncosine (a variety of cryptocrystalline hydro-mica).

онколог *m.* (med.) oncologist, tumor specialist; —ия *f.* oncology.

онколь *m.*, —ный счет (com.) on call, current account.

онкотический *a.* (med.) oncotic, swelling.

оно *pron.* it.

ОНО *abbr.* (Отдел народного образования) Board of National Education.

оно/кол *m.* onocol, onocerin; —нетин *m.* ononetin; —нид *m.* ononid (from root of *Ononis spinosa*); —нин *m.* ononin; —фрит *m.* (min.) onofrite (mercury sulfoselenide); —церин *m.* onocerin, onocol.

ОНТИ *abbr.* (Объединенное научно-техническое издательство) United Technological Publishers, United Scientific-Technical Publishers.

онтоген/ез *m.*, —ия *f.* (biol.) ontogenesis, ontogeny, development; —етический *a.* ontogenetic.

онхоцеркоз *m.* (vet.) onchocerciasis, Onchocerca infestation.

оо— *prefix* оö— (egg); —генез *m.* (biol.) oogenesis.

оолит *m.*, —овый известняк (min.) oölite, oölitic limestone (a variety of granular calcite); —овый *a.* oölitic, like fish roe.

оомицеты *pl.* (bot.) Oömycetes.

ООН *abbr.* (Организация Объединенных Наций) United Nations Organization, UNO.

оофор/ин *m.* oöphorin; —ит *m.* (med.) oophoritis.

оп. *abbr.* (опытный) experimental.

ОП-7, ОП-10 emulsifiers and wetting agents of the alkyl phenol-ethylene oxide type.

опад/ание, —ение *n.* falling off; —ать *v.* fall off; collapse; go down, subside (of swelling); —ающий *a.* (bot.) deciduous.

опаздыв/ание *n.* lateness, delay, retardation; —ать *v.* be late, come too late; be slow (of clock).

опаивать *v.* solder.

опак *m.* opaque, opacity; white kaolin; dishware of fine kaolin; —овый *a.* opaque; (bot.) dull.

опал *m.* (min.) opal (an amorphous form of silica); благородный о. precious opal; водянистый о. water opal, hydrophane; огненный о. fire opal; печенковый о. liver opal, menilite.

опаленный *a.* singed, burned.

опалесц/енция *f.* opalescence; —ировать *v.* opalesce; —ирующий *a.* opalescent.

опалив/ание *n.* singeing, burning; —ать *v.* singe, burn, sear, scorch.

опалин *m.* opaline (glass), fusible porcelain, milky glass.

опалить *see* опаливать.

опало/вый *a.* opal, opaline, opalescent; —вая матка (min.) opal matrix; —вое стекло opal glass; —подобный *a.* opal-like, opaline.

опалуб/ить *v.* sheathe, incase, jacket; —ка *f.* sheathing, casing, lining; cement mold or form; —очные работы preparation of cement molds.

опалывать *v.* weed around, hoe around.

опалять *see* опаливать.

опар/а *f.*, —ный *a.* leavened dough; (dyeing, tanning) bran drench, bran steep.

опас/аться *v.* fear, apprehend; —ение *n.* fear, apprehension, misgiving; с —кой, —ливо *adv.* warily, cautiously; —ливость *f.* wariness, caution, circumspection; —ливый *a.* wary, cautious, watchful, guarded.

опасн/о *adv.* dangerously; it is dangerous; —ость *f.* danger, risk, hazard; вне —ости out of danger, safe, secure; зона —ости danger zone; коэффициент —ости danger coefficient; —ый *a.* dangerous, unsafe, hazardous; —ое сечение cross section of beam, etc., under great stress.

опасть *see* опадать.

опахал/о *n.*, —ьный *a.* fan, vane.

опах/ать, —ивать *v.* plow around, plow; fan.

опацит *m.* (petr.) opacite (microscopic grains).

опаять *v.* solder.

опека *f.* custody.

опенер *m.* opener.

опенок *m.* (bot.) armillaria.

оперативно-производственное планирование schedule planning (of plant operations).

оперативн/ый *a.* operative, operations; —ая сводка summary of operations.

оператор *m.* operator; (med.) surgeon.

операц/ионный *a.* operation, operating; о. год fiscal year; о. стол (med.) operating table; —ионная доска (elec.) switchboard; —ия *f.* operation, working; сделать —ию *v.* perform an operation, operate.

опере/дить, —жать *v.* lead, outstrip,

leave behind; anticipate; —жающий
*a.* leading; —жающий угол, угол
—жения angle of advance; (elec.)
angle of lead; —жение *n.* leading,
lead, outstripping, outrunning; advance, advancing; anticipation; (rolling) forward flow; —жение на leading
by.
оперен/ие, —ье *n.* feathering, feathers,
plumage; tail group (of airplanes);
—ный *a.* feathered, fledged.
опереться *see* опираться.
оперирован/ание *n.* operation, operating;
—ать *v.* operate; work, perform, do.
опермент *m.* (min.) orpiment, arsenic
trisulfide.
оперяться *v.* feather.
опечат/ать, —ывать *v.* seal, seal up.
опечатка *f.* erratum, misprint, error.
опеченение *n.* (med.) hepatization.
опиа/нил *m.* opianyl, meconine; —нин
*m.* opianine; narcotine; —новая кислота opianic acid, 5,6-dimethoxyphthalaldehydic acid; —т *m.* opiate,
narcotic; —товый *a.* opiatic, narcotic.
опивки *pl.* dregs, sediment.
опиевый *see* опийный.
опизометр *m.* (surv.) opisometer, map
measurer.
опий *m.*, —ный *a.* opium.
опил/ивание *n.*, —овка *f.* filing; —ивать,
—ить *v.* file; —ки *pl.* (met.) filings,
turnings; (wood) sawdust; —овочный
*a.* filing; —очный *a.* sawdust.
опиомания *f.* (med.) opiumism.
опирать *v.* rest, push; —ся *v.* rest (on),
lean (against), have bearing (on).
опис/ание *n.* description, account, report; —анный *a.* described; circumscribed; —ательный *a.* descriptive;
—ать, —ывать *v.* describe, depict,
set forth, report; circumscribe; —ка *f.*
clerical error, slip of the pen.
опись *f.* list, catalog, schedule; inventory.
опиум *see* опий.
оправл/ение *n.* fusion, fusing; glazing;
fire-polishing (of glass); (welding)
flashing off; sweating (of refractory
material); сварка —ением flash welding; —енный *a.* fused; —ивать,
—ять *v.* fuse, fuse on; —иваться,
—яться *v.* (welding) flash off; sweat.

опла/та *f.* payment, remuneration;
—тить, —чивать *v.* pay, remunerate;
settle (account); —ченный *a.* paid,
postpaid; с —ченным ответом prepaid; —чиваемый *a.* paying, stipendiary; хорошо —чиваемый well
paid, profitable.
оплеснев/елый *a.* moldy, musty; —еть
*v.* become moldy, get musty.
оплет/ать, оплести *v.* entwine, braid;
—енный *a.* braided, covered, insulated (wire); —енная бутыль basket-
covered carboy; —ка *f.*, —очный *a.*
braiding (of electric wires), covering;
basket.
оплешиветь *v.* grow bald.
оплодотвор/ение *n.* impregnation, fecundation; fertilization; —итель *m.*
(bot.) fertilizer, pollinator; —ить,
—ять *v.* impregnate, fecundate; fertilize.
оплот *m.* bulwark, stronghold.
оплошать *v.* make a mistake, fail.
оплы/вать, —ть *v.* circumnavigate;
welter; о. жиром grow fat; —вина *f.*
mudflow.
опобальзам *m.* opobalsam, Mecca balsam.
опове/ститель *m.*, —стительное устройство signal device; annunciator;
—щать *v.* inform, notify, advise, let
know; —щение *n.* announcement;
reporting, warning.
оподзол/енный *a.* podsolized (soil);
—ивание *n.* podsolization.
опоек *m.* calf leather, calfskin.
опозд/ание *n.* being late, tardiness,
delay; —ать *see* опаздывать.
опозн/авательный *a.* identification,
recognition; —авать *v.* identify, recognize, spot; —ание *n.* identification.
опой *m.* (vet.) rheumatic pododermatitis.
опойковый *a.* calfskin.
опока *f.* (foundry) flask, mold box, mold
frame, casting box; *pl.* (petr.) opoka,
gaize; литье в —х flask casting.
ополаскива/ние *n.* rinsing; —ть *v.* rinse,
wash.
ополз/ание *n.* creep, creeping, sliding;
—ать *v.* creep, slide, slip; —ень *m.*
landslide, slide, earth creep; —невая
почва soil creep.
ополос/кать, —нуть *see* ополаскивать.

**ополоть** *see* **опалывать.**

**опопанакс** *m.* (bot.) opopanax (*Opopanax chironium*); **—овая смола** opopanax (resin); **—овое масло** opopanax oil.

**опор: во весь о.** at full speed.

**опор/а** *f.* bearing, support, rest, carrier, fulcrum, prop, foot, footing; bracket, mount; pole, pillar, buttress, abutment (of arch); **катковая о.** roller bearing; **клиновидная о., ножевидная о., призматическая о.** knife edge; **точка —ы** point of rest; bearing; fulcrum, prop.

**опоражнив/ание** *n.* emptying, evacuation, discharging, discharge, draining, dumping; deflation; **—ать** *v.* empty, evacuate, discharge, drain, dump; deflate.

**опорн/ый** *a.* bearing, supporting; index, guide, reference, key; marker (horizon); research (well); exploratory (drillhole); **о. изолятор** bracket insulator; **о. подшипник** journal bearing, supporting bearing; **о. фланец** bearing flange; **—ая балка** supporting beam; **—ая конструкция** supporting structure; **—ая плита** bearing disk, step; foundation plate, bed plate; **—ая площадь, —ая поверхность** bearing, bearing surface, seat; **—ая призма** fulcrum; knife edge; **—ая подушка** support, cushioning; **—ая свая** bridge pile; **—ая стойка** support, stand; **—ая точка** reference point; **—ое давление** bearing pressure; counterpressure; **—ое кольцо** supporting ring, ring support; bracket rim (of furnace); **—ое трение** friction of rest, static friction.

**опорожн/ение** *see* опоражнивание; **—енный** *a.* emptied, evacuated, clear; **—ить, —ять** *see* опоражнивать.

**опороситься** *v.* farrow, have a litter.

**опоссум** *m.* (zool.) opossum.

**опочное литье** (foundry) flask casting, box casting.

**опояс/ать, —ывать** *v.* encircle, girdle, span.

**оппанол** *m.* Oppanol (a synthetic polyisobutylene rubber).

**Оппенгеймера-Филлипса процесс** (nucl.) Oppenheimer-Phillips process.

**оппо/зитный** *a.* opposite, contrary; **—зиция** *f.* opposition; **—нировать** *v.* oppose.

**оправа** *f.* instrument case, case, holder; mounting, setting (for gem); rim (of glasses); mandrel.

**оправд/ание** *n.* excuse, justification; **—ательный** *a.* justificatory, exonerative; **—ательный документ** voucher; **—ать, —ывать** *v.* excuse, justify, exculpate, vindicate; acquit; **—аться, —ываться** *v.* justify oneself; pay, be worth while.

**оправить** *see* **оправлять.**

**оправка** *f.* mandrel, arbor (of lathe); (met.) mandrel; (riveting) drift; straightening device (for pipes); setting, mounting.

**оправлять** *v.* set right, arrange; set, mount; **—ся** *v.* recover, recuperate.

**оправочный** *a.* setting, mounting; mandrel; **о. электрод** (elec.) contact bar (of resistance welding machine).

**опрашивать** *v.* question, examine.

**определение** *n.* determination, identification; detection, finding, location; definition; decision; appointment; computation, calculation, estimation; analysis; test; **о. весовым способом** gravimetric determination; **о. объемным способом** volumetric determination.

**определенн/о** *adv.* definitely, positively, absolutely; **—ость** *f.* definiteness; **—ый** *a.* determined; definite, specific, fixed, certain, given; distinct, sharp, concrete, absolute; **за —ое время** in a unit of time.

**определ/имый** *a.* determinable, definable; **—итель** *m.* finder, locator, detector; guide, index, key; analyzer; determinative tables; (math.) determinant; **—ить, —ять** *v.* determine, establish, ascertain, identify, define, distinguish; detect, locate; specify, fix; allot, settle, assign, appoint; **—ить количественно** determine quantitatively, analyze.

**опресн/ение** *n.* distillation (of salt water); demineralization; decreasing salinity (of soil); **—итель** *m.* distiller; **—ить, —ять** *v.* distil.

**опрессов/анный** *a.* molded, pressed, press-fitted; pressurized; **—ка** *f.*,

—ывание *n.* molding, pressing; pressurization; —ывать *v.* mold, press; pressurize.

опробковение *n.* (bot.) suberization; corking (plant disease).

опробов/ание *n.* trying out, sampling; testing; assaying, assay; —атель *m.* sampler; —ательный *a.* sampling; testing.

опровер/гание, —ганье *n.* refuting, disproving; —гать, —гнуть *v.* refute, disprove, dispute; —жение *n.* refutation, disproof, countercheck, denial.

опрокидыв/ание *n.* turning over, upsetting, tipping, dumping, tilting; reversal (of phase); схема —ания (elec. comm.) flip-flop; —атель *m.* dumper, tipper, tipple, kick-up, trip, tripper; (foundry) ingot chair; —ать *v.* overthrow, overturn, turn over, upset, tip over, tip, dump, trip, tilt, invert; reverse; —аться *v.* tip over, capsize; —ающий, —ающийся *a.* tipping, tilting, dumping, dump; —ающий момент overturning moment, tilting moment; leverage; —ающаяся вагонетка dump car, dumper.

опрокинут/ый *a.* overturned, turned over, upset, tipped, tilted, dumped, inverted; reversed; —ь *see* опрокидывать.

опрос *m.* inquiry, interrogation; question; —ный *a.* interrogatory, inquiry; answering; —ный лист form, questionnaire; —чик *m.* interrogator.

опротестование *n.* (com.) complaint, claim.

опрыс/канный *a.* sprayed, sprinkled; —кивание *n.* spraying, sprinkling; —киватель *m.* sprayer, spray pump; —кивать, —нуть *v.* spray, sprinkle, wet, moisten; —кивающий *a.* spraying, spray.

опрятный *a.* neat, clean, orderly.

опсон/изация *f.* (bact.) opsonization; —ин *m.* opsonin; —ический *a.* opsonic.

оп. ст. *abbr.* (опытная станция) experiment station.

оптик *m.* optician; —a *f.* optics.

оптимальный *a.* optimum, best, most favorable.

оптиметр *m.* optical measuring device for very fine linear dimensions.

оптимум *m.* optimum, the best, ideal.

оптически *adv.* optically.

оптическ/ий *a.* optic, optical, visual; о. обман optical illusion; —ая деятельность optical activity, optical rotation, opticity; —ая напряженность *f.* optical power; —ая ось (cryst.) optic axis; угол —их осей (min.) optic axial angle; optic angle; —ое стекло optical glass; lens; —ое явление optical phenomenon.

оптичность *see* оптическая деятельность.

опто/вик *m.* wholesale dealer; (text). converter; —вый *a.*, —м *adv.* wholesale; торгующий —м wholesaler.

опто/техника *f.* technical optics; —фон *m.* optophone; —хин *m.* optochine, ethylhydrocupreine.

опубликов/ание *n.* publication; —анный *a.* published, issued; —ать, —ывать *v.* publish, make public, issue.

опудривание *n.* powdering, dusting; ashing (molds).

опунция *f.* (bot.) opuntia.

опуск *m.* omission; —ание *n.* letting down, lowering, dropping, drop, descent, sinking, settling; plunging, downstroke (of piston); (geol.) subsidence; глубина —ания descent, drop; —ать *v.* let down, lower, immerse, sink; drop, omit; deposit (coin); —аться *v.* descend, sink, subside, drop down, cave in; —ающийся *a.* lowering, descending; —ной *a.* lowering, drop; —ная труба downcomer.

опуст/еть *v.* become empty; —евший, —елый *a.* empty, deserted, desolate.

опуст/ившийся *a.* sunken, submerged; —ить *see* опускать.

опустош/ать *v.* destroy, lay waste; —ение *n.* destruction, devastation; —ительный *a.* destructive.

опух/ание *n.*, —оль *f.* swelling, tumor; —ать, —нуть *v.* swell, intumesce; —лый, —ший *a.* swollen, distended, puffed up.

опущен/ие *n.* omission; letting down lowering; (med.) prolapse; —ный *a.*

omitted; lowered, dropped, depressed, sunk.

**опыл/ение** *n.* (bot.) pollination; **—енный** *a.* pollinated; dusted; **—ивание** *n.* (agr.) dusting; **—иватель** *m.* duster; **—ивать** *v.* dust; **—итель** *m.* pollinator; duster; **—ять** *v.* pollinate.

**опыт** *m.* experiment, test; experience, practice; **о. на замерзание** freezing test; **в пределах ошибок —а** in the range of experimental error; **делать —ы, производить —ы** *v.* experiment, conduct experiments, carry out experiments; **на —е** experimentally; in practice; **—ничество** *n.* experimentation, experimental work.

**опытн/о** *adv.* expertly; experimentally; **о.-заводский** *a.* pilot-plant; **о.-показательный** *a.* experimental-demonstrative; **—ость** *f.* experience, proficiency; **—ый** *a.* experienced, practiced, expert, competent, skilful; experimental; empirical (formula, etc.); pilot (plant); **—ая станция** experiment station; **—ное дело** experimentation; **—ым путем** experimentally, by experimentation.

**опьян/ение** *n.* intoxication; **—енный** *a.* intoxicated; **—еть** *v.* become intoxicated; **—яющий** *a.* intoxicating; **—яющее средство** intoxicant.

**опять** *adv.* again, once more.

**оральный** *a.* oral.

**оранг-утан** *m.* (zool.) orang-outang.

**оранж/ад** *m.* orangeade; **—ево-желтый** *a.* orange-yellow; **—евый** *a.* orange-colored, orange.

**оранжер/ея** *f.*, **—ейный** *a.* greenhouse, hothouse, conservatory.

**оранжит** *m.* (min.) orangite (a variety of thorite).

**орби/кулярный** *a.* (bot.) orbicular, circular; (petr.) orbicular, spheroidal; **—та** *f.* orbit; **—тальный** *a.* orbital; planetary.

**орвиллит** *m.* (min.) orvillite (a variety of altered zircon).

**орг.** *abbr.* (**органический**) organic.

**орган** *m.* organ, member; device, tool, instrument; element, unit; institution, department; (executive) body; **—ы управления** controls.

**организ/ационный** *a.*, **—ация** *f.* organ-

ization, management; **—м** *m.* organism; **—ованность** *f.* discipline; **—ованный** *a.* organized, managed, arranged; **—овать, —овывать** *v.* organize, manage, arrange; **—оваться, —овываться** *v.* organize, get organized.

**органическ/и** *adv.* organically; **о. присущий** *a.* intrinsic; **—ий** *a.* organic; **—ое соединение** organic compound; **—ое тело** organism.

**орган/ный** *a.* organ, organpipe; **—ная крепь, —ка** *f.* (min.) organpipe supporting structure.

**органо—** *prefix* organo—, organic; **—ген** *m.* organogen; **—графический** *a.* (biol.) organographic; **—графия** *f.* organography, descriptive organology; **—золь** *m.* organosol; **—логический** *a.* organologic; **—логия** *f.* organology; **—терапия** *f.* organotherapy.

**ордер** *m.* (com.) order.

**ординальный** *a.* ordinal (number).

**ординар** *m.* zero water level, normal water level.

**ординарный** *a.* ordinary, common; single, plain.

**ордината** *f.* (math.) ordinate.

**ординатор** *m.* hospital physician; intern.

**ордович** *m.* (geol.) Ordovician (period).

**оребренный** *a.* finned.

**орегонензин** *m.* oregonensin.

**ореид** *m.* a copper-zinc alloy.

**орексин** *m.* orexin, phenzoline.

**орел** *m.* (zool.) eagle.

**оре/ллин** *m.* orellin; **—одафен** *m.* oreodaphene; **—одафнол** *m.* oreodaphnol.

**ореол** *m.* aureole, corona, halo, halation.

**орех** *m.*, **—овый** *a.* nut; spec. walnut (*Juglans*); **американский о., бразильский о.** Brazil nut (*Bertholletia excelsa*); **лесной о.** *see* **орешник; серый о.** butternut (*J. cinerea*); **черный о.** black walnut (*J. nigra*); **—овобурый** *a.* nut-brown; **—овые** *pl.* Juglandaceae; **—отворки** *pl.* gall wasps (*Cynipidae*).

**орешек** *m.* little nut; nut coal, chestnut coal; **мелкий о.** pea coal.

**орешко/вый** *a.* nut; **о. уголь** nut coal, chestnut coal; **—вая кислота** gallic acid; —дубильная кислота tannic acid.

орешник *m.* nut tree; spec. filbert (*Corylus avellana*); (min.) coarse-grain ore; nut coal; мелкий о. pea coal, pea-grade coal; —овые *see* ореховые.

орибатиды *pl.* mites (*Oribatidae*).

оригинал *m.* original.

оригинальн/о *adv.* originally; peculiarly; —ость *f.* originality, singularity; —ый *a.* original, singular, peculiar, eccentric.

оригинатор *m.* originator.

ориентация *f.* orientation; (geol.) attitude (of beds).

ориентир *m.* orienting point, guiding line; indicator; landmark; о.-буссоль declinometer; естественный о. landmark.

ориентиров/ание *n.*, —ка *f.* orientation; —анный *a.* oriented; —ать *v.* orient, direct; —аться *v.* get one's bearings, orientate; —очный *a.* approximate, rough, tentative (plan).

оризацидин *m.* oryzacidin.

ориктогнозия *f.* oryctognosy, descriptive mineralogy.

орисканский ярус (geol.) Oriskany stage.

Оркла способ a pyritic smelting process.

орлеан *m.* orlean, annatto (dye from *Bixa orellana*); —овые *pl.* (bot.) Bixaceae.

орлец *m.* (min.) rhodonite.

орлики *pl.* (bot.) aquilegia.

орлин/ый *a.* aquiline; eagle; о. камень (min.) eaglestone, aetite (a form of ironstone); —ое дерево (bot.) eagle wood (*Aquilaria agallocha*).

ормозин *m.* ormosine; —ин *m.* ormosinine.

орнамент *m.*, —ировать *v.* ornament; —альный, —ный *a.* ornamental, decorative; —ация *f.* ornamentation, decoration.

орнитин *m.* ornithine, 2,5-diaminopentanoic acid.

орнито— *prefix* ornitho— (bird); —логия *f.* ornithology.

орнитоптер *m.* (aero.) ornithopter.

орнитуровая кислота ornithuric acid.

ороген/езис *m.* (geol.) orogenesis, orogeny; —ический *a.* orogenic.

орограф/ический *a.* (geol.) orographic, mountain; —ия *f.* orography.

орология *f.* (geol.) orology, orography.

оропон *m.* leather softener and decalcifier.

ороситель *m.* irrigator, sprinkler; irrigating ditch; (met.) feeder; —ный *a.* irrigating, irrigation; sprinkling, trickling, spray; —ный аппарат sprinkler, sprayer; —ного типа trickle (dissolver).

орош/атель *m.* irrigator; —ать, оросить *v.* irrigate, sprinkle, shower, spray; —ающий *a.* irrigating, sprinkling; —ающая вода irrigation water; trickling water; —ение *n.* irrigation, sprinkling, trickling, spraying; (distillation) reflux; liquid rate; —енный *a.* irrigated, sprinkled.

Орса прибор Orsat apparatus (for gas analysis).

орс/еин *m.* orcein; —ейлин ,—еллин *m.*, —еллиновый *a.* orsellin, orseillin; —ейль, —ель *m.* orseille, orsel, orchil (coloring material); —еллевая кислота, —еллиновая кислота orsellinic acid, orsellic acid.

орсин, —ол *m.* orcinol, methylresorcinol.

орсудан *m.* orsudan.

орт *m.* (min.) crosscut, cross drift.

ортзанд *m.* ortsand (sand containing calcium carbonate).

ортизон *m.* ortizon, hyperol.

ортит *m.* (min.) orthite, allanite.

орто— *prefix* ortho—; в положении орто in the ortho position; —аминобензойная кислота orthoaminobenzoic acid; —борная кислота orthoboric acid; —бромит *m.* (min.) orthobromite (a variety of embolite).

ортовая система (min.) crosscut method.

орто/водород *m.* (nucl.) ortho hydrogen; —гелий *m.* ortho helium; —генез *m.* (biol.) orthogenesis; —гнейс *m.* (petr.) orthogneiss (a gneissic igneous rock); —гональный *a.* orthogonal, right-angled; —дома *f.* (cryst.) orthodome (monoclinic system); —донтия *f.* (med.) orthodontics; —кислота *f.* ortho acid.

ортоклаз *m.*, —овый *a.* (min.) orthoclase (monoclinic potassium feldspar).

**орто/кластический** *a.* orthoclastic; **—коричная кислота** orthocinnamic acid; **—кремневая кислота** orthosilicic acid; **соль —кремневой кислоты, —кремневокислая соль** orthosilicate; **—муравьиная кислота** orthoformic acid; **—мышьяковая кислота** orthoarsenic acid; **—мышьяковистая кислота** orthoarsenious acid; **—ник** *m.* Orthonik (iron-nickel alloy); **—ноль** *m.* Orthonol (iron-nickel alloy); **—ось** *f.* (cryst.) orthoaxis, ortho-diagonal.

**ортопед/ический** *a.* (med.) orthopedic, orthopedical; **—ия** *f.* orthopedics.

**орто/положение** *n.* ortho position; **—ромбический** *a.* (cryst.) orthorhombic, rhombic, prismatic; **—серная кислота** orthosulfuric acid; **—силикат** *m.* orthosilicate; **—скопический** *a.* orthoscopic; **—скопия** *f.* orthoscopy; **—соединение** *n.* ortho compound; **—сурьмяная кислота** orthoantimonic acid; **—сурьмянистая кислота** orthoantimonious acid.

**ортотест** *m.* measurer.

**орто/угольная кислота** orthocarbonic acid; **—уксусная кислота** orthoacetic acid; **—фировый** *a.* orthophyric; **—форм** *m.* orthoform.

**ортофосфорн/ая кислота** orthophosphoric acid; **соль —ой кислоты, —окислая соль** orthophosphate.

**орто/фталевая кислота** *o*-phthalic acid; **—хлорит** *m.* (min.) orthochlorite; **—хроматический** *a.* (phot.) orthochromatic; **—центр** *m.* (geom.) orthocenter; **—цимол** *m. o-cymene*.

**ортштейн** *m.* (geol.) ortstein, iron pan (a variety of hardpan).

**оруден/елость** *f.* (min.) protore; **—елый** *a.* (geol.) mineralized; **—ение** *n.* mineralization.

**оруд/ие** *n.* instrument, tool; (mil.) gun, cannon, armament; **—ийный** *a.* gun.

**орудовать** *v.* manage, handle, run.

**оружейн/ый** *a.* gun, armament; **о. завод, —я** *f.* arsenal, armory; **о. мастер, —ик** *m.* gunsmith, armorer.

**оружие** *n.* weapon; *pl.* arms.

**орфол** *m.* orphol, bismuth naphtholate.

**Орфорда способ** Orford process (for copper-nickel separation).

**орхид/ея** *f.* (bot.) orchid (*Orchis*); **—ные** *pl.* Orchidaceae.

**орцеин** *see* **орсеин.**

**орясина** *f.* long rod, pole.

**ОС-20** a non-ionic surface-active agent (condensation product of octodecyl alcohol and ethylene oxide).

**ос/а** *f.* wasp; **—ы** *pl.* Vespidae; **—ы блестянки** cuckoo wasps (*Chrysididae*).

**осада** *f.* siege.

**осадитель** *m.* precipitator, precipitant, precipitating agent; settler; **—ный** *a.* precipitation, precipitating; settling; **—ный аппарат** precipitator; settler; **—ный чан** settling tank.

**осадить** *see* **осаждать, осаживать.**

**осад/ка** *f.* settling, settlement, setting, set; sagging, sag; sinking, immersion; sedimentation; shortening, upsetting; pressurizing (of fuel jacket); **—ок** *m.* residue, dregs, tails; sediment, mud, sludge; deposit, deposition, precipitate, precipitation; **—ки** *pl.* rainfall, precipitation; (acid) sludge; (radioactive) fall-out; **атмосферные —ки** rainfall; **выпадение —ка** precipitation; **давать —ок** *v.* deposit; precipitate; **количество —ков, сумма —ков** rainfall, amount of precipitation; **—комер** *m.* precipitation gage, rain gage.

**осадочн/ый** *a.* settling; precipitation; sedimentary; upsetting; sludge (superphosphate); **о. бассейн, о. чан** precipitation tank; sedimentation tank, settling tank; **о. чехол** (geol.) sedimentary mantle; **—ая ванна** plating bath; **—ая машина** upsetting machine, upsetter; jolt-ramming machine; **—ые породы** (geol.) sedimentary rock; **—ые кольца** Liesegang rings.

**осаждаем/ость** *f.* precipitability; sedimentation capacity; **—ый** *a.* precipitable.

**осаждать** *v.* precipitate, deposit, settle, settle out, separate out; upset; (mil.) lay siege; **—ся** *v.* precipitate (out), settle out, fall out, be deposited.

**осаждающ/ий** *a.* precipitating, settling; **о. реактив, —ее средство** precipitant, precipitating agent; coagulant; **—ее**

**влияние** precipitating action; —**ийся** *a.* precipitating, settling; precipitable.

**осажден/ие** *n.* precipitation, precipitating, settling out, settling, deposition, sedimentation; precipitate, deposit, sediment; condensation; (concentration) jigging; (met.) plating, coating, coat; —**ный** *a.* precipitated, settled, deposited; plated; sedimentary.

**осажив/ание** *n.* pressing back; upsetting, jumping up; clenching, clinching (of rivet); —**ать** *v.* press back; upset, jump up; clench, clinch; tap, jolt, settle; —**ающая машина** jolting machine, jolt ramming machine.

**осарсол** *m.* Osarsol, acetarsone.

**осахарив/ание** *n.* saccharification; sugaring, candying; —**ать** *v.* saccharify; sugar, candy.

**осваив/ание** *n.* familiarization; —**ать** *v.* familiarize; assimilate; master, cope (with); develop (land); accept, tolerate; —**аться** *v.* become familiar (with), get used (to); —**аться с климатом** become acclimated.

**осведом/итель** *m.* informer; (rad.) commentator; —**ительный** *a.* informative; —**ить,** —**лять** *v.* inform; —**иться,** —**ляться** *v.* inquire, ask about, question; —**ление** *n.* inquiry, information; —**ленность** *f.* information, knowledge; —**ленный** *a.* informed, well-informed.

**освеж/ать,** —**ить** *v.* refresh, freshen, air; regenerate, renew; —**ающий,** —**ительный** *a.* refreshing; —**ение** *n.* refreshment; renewal; —**енный** *a.* refreshed; renewed, strengthened.

**осветитель** *m.* illuminator; condenser (of microscope).

**осветительн/ый** *a.* illuminating, illumination, lighting; —**ая арматура,** —**ые приборы** (elec.) fixtures; —**ая ракета** (aero.) flare; —**аи сеть** lighting system, lighting network; —**ая способность** illuminating value; —**ое масло** illuminating oil, lamp oil; —**ое средство** illuminant.

**осветить** *see* **освещать.**

**осветл/ение** *n.* clarification; purification; brightening effect (of detergents); (glass) fining, plaining; thinning (of trees); —**енный** *a.* clarified, cleared; purified; —**итель** *m.* clarifier, clarifying agent; —**ять** *v.* clarify, clear; purify.

**освещ/ать** *v.* light, illuminate, throw light upon, irradiate; expose (to light); —**ающая бомба** (aero.) pilot bomb; —**ение** *n.* light, lighting, illumination; (phot.) exposure; —**енность** *f.* illuminance, illumination; exposure (to light); **коэффициент естественной** —**енности** daylight factor; —**енный** *a.* illuminated, lighted, lit.

**освидетельствов/ание** *n.* examination; —**ать** *v.* examine, inspect, survey.

**освинцов/ание** *n.* treating with lead; lead plating, lead lining; —**анный** *a.* lead-plated, lead-lined; —**ать,** —**ывать** *v.* lead, treat with lead, lead-plate.

**освободит/ельный** *a.* liberating, freeing; —**ь** *see* **освобождать.**

**освобожд/ать** *v.* free, set free, release, liberate; disengage, unlock; rid (of), eliminate, clear; relieve; exempt; loose, loosen, ease; —**ающий** *a.* setting free, liberating, releasing; —**ающий механизм** release.

**освобожден/ие** *n.* setting free, liberation, release; riddance, elimination; exemption; **о. от серы** elimination of sulfur, desulfurization; —**ный** *a.* freed, liberated, released; exempt.

**осво/ение** *n.* mastering, coping (with); assimilation; acceptance; (industrial) adoption; —**енный** *a.* assimilated; —**ить** *see* **осваивать.**

**осев/ой** *a.* axial; axle; **о. канал** (elec.) axial duct; **о. подшипник** axle bearing; —**ая втулка** axle bed; —**ая шайба** axle tree; —**ая шейка** axle journal; —**ое давление** end thrust.

**осевший** *a.* precipitated, settled, deposited.

**оседаем/ость** *f.* precipitability; —**ый** *a.* precipitable.

**осед/ание** *n.* settling, settlement, sinking, lowering, subsidence, subsiding, depression; sag, sagging, yielding (of wall), collapse; settling, precipitation; (radioactive) fall-out; shrinkage, shrinking; —**ать** *v.* settle, settle down, sink, subside; sag, yield, collapse;

set; precipitate; —**ающий** *a.* settling, sinking, subsiding; sagging, yielding.

**оседлый** *a.* settled (population).

**осейдженская свита** (geol.) Osagian series.

**осел** *m.* (zool.) ass.

**осело/к** *m.*, —**чный** *a.* whetstone, grindstone, hone.

**осемен/ение** *n.* sowing, seeding, planting; fertilization, pollination; (zool.) insemination; —**ить**, —**ять** *v.* sow, seed, plant; fertilize.

**осен/не-зимний** *a.* autumn-winter; —**ний** *a.*, —**ь** *f.* autumn, fall; —**ник**, —**ница** *see* **безвременник.**

**осеребр/ить**, —**ять** *v.* silver, silver-plate.

**осер/енный** *a.* sulfured, fumigated with sulfur; —**нение** *n.* sulfuring; —**нять** *v.* sulfur, fumigate with sulfur.

**осе/симметричный** *a.* axisymmetric; —**токарный станок** shafting lathe.

**осетр** *m.*, —**овый** *a.* (zool.) sturgeon; —**ина** *f.*, —**инный** *a.* sturgeon meat.

**осеченный** *a.* truncated, shortened.

**осечка** *f.* miss, misfire.

**оси** *pl.* of **ось**, axes; *see also under* **ось.**

**осили/вать**, —**ть** *v.* overcome, get the better (of), prevail (upon).

**осин/а** *f.*, —**овое дерево**, —**овый** *a.* (bot.) asp, aspen (*Populus tremula*); —**овик** *m.* aspen mushroom (*Boletus rufus*).

**осиный** *a.* wasp.

**оскабливать** *v.* scrape.

**оскоблить** *see* **оскабливать.**

**оскол/ок** *m.*, —**очный** *a.* splinter, sliver, fragment, chip, scale; —**ки** *pl.* chippings, debris; —**ки деления** (nucl.) fission fragments; **разрыв на** —**ки** fragmentation; —**очный элемент** fission product; —**очная бомба** splinter bomb.

**оскоп/ить**, —**лять** *v.* castrate; —**ление** *n.* castration.

**оскорб/ительный** *a.* offensive; —**ить**, —**лять** *v.* offend, insult; —**ление** *n.* offense, insult; —**ленный** *a.* offended, insulted.

**оскре/бать**, —**сти**, —**сть** *v.* scrape off; —**бки** *pl.* scrapings.

**оскуд/евание**, —**ение** *n.* impoverishment; —**евать**, —**еть** *v.* become poor, become impoverished; grow scarce, die off; —**евший**, —**елый** *a.* scanty.

**ослаб/евание** *n.* weakening; —**евать**, —**еть** *v.* weaken, become weak; diminish, decrease, abate, fade away, decline, lull, slacken; loosen, work loose, become slack; —**евший**, —**е-лый** *a.* weakened, weak, feeble; loose; —**итель** *m.* (phys.) attenuator; (phot.) reducer; —**ить** *see* **ослаблять.**

**ослабл/ение** *n.* weakening; dilution; attenuation, reduction, decrease, abatement; relaxation, loosening, slackening, slack, laxity; reducing, reduction (of negatives); **коэффициент** —**ения** (nucl.) attenuation factor; **слой двухкратного** —**ения**, **слой половинного** —**ения** (nucl.) half-thickness, half-value layer; —**енный** *a.* weakened; attenuated, reduced, decreased; loose, lax, relaxed; —**ять** *v.* weaken; dilute; attenuate, reduce, decrease, abate; reduce (a negative); loosen, get loose, unfasten; relax, slacken, ease, ease up; —**яющий** *a.* weakening; loosening; —**яющий раствор** (phot.) reducer; —**яющее средство** diluent.

**ослаб/нувший**, —**ший** *a.* weakened, weak; loose, slack; —**нуть** *see* **ослабевать.**

**осланцевание** *n.* (min.) settling coal dust with powdered slate.

**осленок** *m.* foal (of donkey).

**ослепительный** *a.* blinding, glaring, dazzling; **о. свет** glare.

**ослеп/ить**, —**лять** *v.* blind, dazzle; —**ление** *n.* blinding; going blind; —**ленный** *a.* blinded, dazzled; —**нуть** *v.* go blind.

**ослиз/лый** *a.* slimy; —**нение** *n.* sliming; gelatinization.

**ослик, водяной** (zool.) asellus.

**ослинник** *m.* evening primrose (*Oenothera*).

**ослиный** *a.* asinine, ass.

**осложн/ение** *n.* complication; —**енный** *a.* complicated, complex; —**ить**, —**ять** *v.* complicate.

**ослышаться** *v.* hear incorrectly.

**осмазом** *m.* osmazome.

**осмалива/ние** *n.* resinification; pitching; tarring; —**ать** *v.* resinify, convert into resin; pitch, tar; —**аться** *v.* resinify, become resinous; gum (of oil).

**осмат** *m.* osmate.

**осматривать** *v.* examine, look over, inspect, survey; search.

**осмеливаться** *v.* take the liberty, dare.

**осмелит** *m.* (min.) osmelite, pectolite.

**осмелиться** *see* осмеливаться.

**осмие/вый** *a.* osmium, osmic; **о. анги-дрид** osmic anhydride, osmium tetroxide; **о. сплав** osmium alloy; **—вая кислота** osmic acid; **соль —вой кислоты, —вокислая соль** osmate; **—хлористый аммоний** ammonium chlorosmate.

**осм/ий** *m.* osmium, Os; **закись —ия** osmious oxide, osmium monoxide; **иридистый о., —иридий, —истый иридий** (min.) osmiridium, iridosmine; **окись —ия** osmic oxide, osmium dioxide; **хлористый о.** osmious chloride, osmium dichloride; **хлорный о.** osmic chloride, osmium tetrachloride; **—истый** *a.* osmium, osmious.

**осмоз** *see* осмос; **—ировать** *v.* osmose, subject to osmosis.

**осмол** *m.* tar-impregnated wood; **—ение, —ка** *see* осмаливание; **—енный** *a.* resinified; pitched, tarred; **—ять** *see* осмаливать.

**осмометр** *m.* osmometer.

**осмондит** *m.* (met.) osmondite (iron carbide in alpha iron).

**осмо/с** *m.* osmosis; **—тически** *adv.* by osmosis; **—тический** *a.* osmotic; **—тическое давление** osmotic pressure.

**осмотр** *m.* examination, inspection; survey, review, search; **—еть** *see* осматривать.

**осмотрительн/ость** *f.* discretion, circumspection; **—ый** *a.* cautious, circumspect.

**осмотрщик** *m.* examiner, inspector.

**Осмунда печь** (met.) Osmund furnace.

**осмысл/енный** *a.* intelligent; **—ить** *v.* comprehend.

**осн.** *abbr.* (основанный) based.

**осна/стить, —щивать** *v.* rig, fit out; **—стка** *f.*, **—щение** *n.* rigging, fitting out, equipment; **—стка приборами** instrumentation.

**основ/а** *f.* base, basis, foundation; base (of alloy); origin, starting point; framework, backing; principle, element; (met.) starting sheet; (text.) warp; **—ы** *pl.* fundamentals; **на урановой —е** uranium-base (alloy, etc.); **набирать —у** *v.* (text.) warp.

**основан/ие** *n.* foundation, basis, base, foothold, stand; (chem.) base; principle; origin, starting point; founding, establishment; motive, reason; **ион —ия** basic ion; **лежать в —ии** *v.* underlie; **на —ии** on the basis of; **—ный** *a.* based.

**основатель** *m.* founder, establisher; **—но** *adv.* fully, thoroughly, soundly, firmly; **—ность** *f.* soundness; **—ный** *a.* solid, well-grounded, thorough, firm.

**основать** *see* основывать.

**основн/ой** *a.* fundamental, basic, principal, essential, chief, main, primary, staple; ultimate; primary (color); base (metal); ground, normalized (state of nucleus, etc.); flat (rate); prime (cost); **о. конус** base cone; **о. пласт, —ая жила** (min.) mother lode, source vein; **—ая** *a. see also under* основный; **—ая масса** bulk; matrix; **—ая плита** foundation plate, bed plate; **—ая плоскость** (cryst.) basal plane, basal face; **—ая реакция** main reaction; **—ая сила** fundamental force; **—ое значение** primary meaning; **—ое количество** bulk; **—ое правило** fundamental rule; **в —ом** basically, mainly, principally.

**основность** *f.* basicity, alkalinity.

**основн/ый** *a.* basic, alkaline; sub— (salt); **о. силикат** subsilicate; **—ая соль углекислоты** subcarbonate; **—ая уксусномедная соль** cupric subacetate, basic cupric acetate.

**основопол/агающий** *a.* basic; **—ожник** *m.* founder, initiator, establisher.

**основывать** *v.* found, establish, set up, constitute, erect; **—ся** *v.* be based (on).

**Осоавиахим** *abbr.* (Общество друзей обороны и авиа-химического строительства) Society for Promotion of Self-Defense and Aero-Chemical Industry.

**особенно** *adv.* especially, particularly, specifically, unusually.

**особенност/ь** *f.* peculiarity, singularity, specialty, feature, special feature, characteristic, property; **в —и** in particular, particularly, especially; **главная о.** chief characteristic; **характерная о.** characteristic, characteristic property.

**особенный** *a.* special, singular, peculiar, particular, specific.

**особняк** *m.* detached house.

**особо** *adv.* apart, separately; extra; **—чувствительный** *a.* hypersensitive.

**особый** *a.* peculiar, singular; particular, special, specific; separate.

**особь** *f.* individual, specimen; (biol.) species.

**осоед** *m.* (zool.) honey buzzard.

**осозн/авать, —ать** *v.* realize, perceive.

**осок/а** *f.,* **—овый** *a.* (bot.) sedge (*Carex*); **—овые** *pl.* Cyperaceae; **—овый** *a.* meadow (bog).

**осокорь** *f.* black poplar (*Populus nigra*).

**осолаживание** *n.* malting, adding malt.

**осолод/евать** *v.* solodize (soil); **—елый** *a.* solodized; **—ение** *n.* solodization.

**осолон/цевание** *n.* salinization (of soils); solonetzization, alkalization; **—чакование** *n.* salinization; development of solonchak.

**осот** *m.* (bot.) thistle; spec. sow thistle (*Sonchus*); **огородный о.** sow thistle (*Sonchus oleraceus*); **розовый о.** Canada thistle (*Cirsium arvense*).

**осочник** *see* **осока.**

**осп/а** *f.* (med.) smallpox, variola; **ветреная о.** chicken pox; **натуральная о.** smallpox; **прививать —у** *v.* vaccinate; **телячья о.** cow pox.

**оспаривать** *v.* dispute, contend, question.

**оспенн/ый** *a.* variolous, variolate; (petr.) variolitic; **о. камень** (petr.) variolite; pearl diabase (spherulitic basalt glass); **—ая коррозия** (met.) pitting.

**оспина** *f.* pock mark.

**оспиртованный** *a.* alcoholized.

**осповидн/ый** *a.* pock-marked; **—ое разъедание** (met.) pitting.

**осповрив/ание** *n.,* **—ательный** *a.* (med.) vaccination.

**осреднен/ие** *n.* averaging; **—ный** *a.* averaged.

**оссеин** *m.* ossein, collagen.

**ост** *m.* east.

**ОСТ** *abbr.* (общесоюзный стандарт) All-Union Standard.

**остав/аться** *v.* remain, be left over; stay, stop; **—ить, —лять** *v.* leave, abandon, desert, quit; lay down; **—ить за собой** reserve; **—ить у себя** keep, retain; **—ление** *n.* leaving, abandonment; **—ленный** *a.* left.

**осталив/ание** *n.* (met.) steeling; conversion into steel, acieration; electroplating with iron; **—ать** *v.* steel; convert to steel.

**остальн/ой** *a.* remaining, residual; **—ые** *pl.* the rest; **в —ом** as to the rest, in other respects.

**останавлив/ать** *v.* stop, discontinue, close, shut down, put out of service; check, arrest; stunt (growth); **быстро о.** (nucl.) scram; **—ающий** *a.* stopping; **—ающее приспособление** stopping device, stop, arrester.

**останец** *m.* (geol.) residual mountain, butte, mesa; residual outcrop (of soil).

**останов** *m.* stop, stop piece, checking device, detent, detainer; **—ившийся** *a.* stopped, at rest; **—ить** *see* **останавливать; —иться на** *v.* decide (on); **—ка** *f.* stop, stopping, standstill, halt, cessation, shutting down, shutdown; stagnation; intermission, pause; disturbance, interruption; **аварийная —ка, быстрая —ка** (nucl.) scram, emergency shutdown; **процедура —ки** shut down procedure; **—ленный** *a.* stopped, standing; **—очный** *a.* stopping, stop, check.

**остат/ок** *m.* residue, remainder, remnant; surplus, balance, the rest; (chem.) radical, group; **—ки** *pl.* scraps, leftovers, fragments, remnants, refuse, waste, bottoms, residues.

**остаточн/ый** *a.* residual; after—; remanent (magnetization); **явление —ого магнетизма** remanence; magnetic after-effect; **—ая теплота** after-heat; **—ое напряжение** residual stress; (elec.) residual voltage.

**остаться** *see* **остаться.**

**остающийся** *a.* residual, remaining; permanent, lasting, durable, stable; persistent; staying, stopping.

**Оствальда закон** Ostwald (dilution) law.

**остеклов/ание, —ывание** *n.* vitrification; **—анный** *a.* vitrified, fused, glazed; **—ать, —ывать** *v.* vitrify, glaze; **—аться, —ываться** become vitreous, become glassy, vitrify.

**остеклян/елый** *a.* vitreous, glassy; **—еть** *v.* vitrify, become vitreous, become glassy.

**остео—** *prefix* osteo— (bone); **—генный** *a.* osteogenic, bone-forming; **—идный** *a.* osteoid; **—лит** *m.* (min.) osteolite, earthy apatite; **—логия** *f.* (anat.) osteology; **—миелит** *m.* (med.) osteomyelitis; **—саркома** *f.* osteosarcoma; **—склероз** *m.* osteosclerosis; **—тропный** *a.* osteotropic; **—тропное вещество, —фил** *m.*, **—фильный изотоп** (radiobiology) bone seeker; **—фильный** *a.* bone-seeking.

**остер/егание** *n.* warning, admonition; **—егать, —ечь** *v.* warn, caution; **—егаться** *v.* be careful, be on guard, take heed.

**Ост-Индия** East Indies.

**ост-индский** *a.* East Indian; **о. злак** (bot.) cus-cus grass, vetiver (*Andropogon muraticus* or *Vetiveria zizanoides*).

**остировать** *v.* standardize (to All-Union standard).

**остистый** *a.* (bot.) awned, bearded.

**остит** *m.* osteitis, inflammation of bone.

**остов** *m.* skeleton, framework, frame, shell, hull, body, casing; core (of atom or ion).

**остойчивость** *f.* (mech.) stability.

**остол** *m.* osthole.

**остолбен/елый** *a.* stupefied, numb; **—ение** *n.* stupor, stupefaction, daze, torpor.

**осторожн/о** *adv.* carefully, with care, cautiously, gently; **—ость** *f.* care, caution, precaution, heed; **—ый** *a.* careful, cautious, delicate (adjustment).

**остракоды** *pl.* (zool.) Ostracoda.

**остреастерин** *m.* ostreasterol.

**острее** *see* **острие.**

**острение** *n.* pointing, sharpening.

**острец** *m.* (bot.) sedge (*Carex caespitosa*).

**остригать** *v.* shear, cut, crop.

**остр/ие** *n.* edge, point, cutting point (of tool); peak, cusp; pivot; **разряд с —ия** (elec.) point discharge.

**остриженный** *a.* cropped, sheared, cut.

**острийный** *a.* point; peak; **о. счетчик** *see* **Гейгера счетчик.**

**острить** *v.* sharpen, whet; point.

**острица** *f.* pinworm (*Oxyuris vermicularis; Enterobius v.*); (bot.) asperugo.

**остричь** *see* **остригать.**

**остро** *adv.* sharply.

**остров** *m.* island; **—ной** *a.* insular, island; **—ок** *m.* islet.

**острога** *f.* spear, harpoon.

**острогать** *v.* plane, pare down.

**острогубцы** *pl.* cutting pliers, nippers.

**острозаразный** *a.* highly contagious.

**остроконечный** *a.* sharp, acute, acicular, pointed, fine-pointed, tapered, tapering; (bot.) cuspidate; peaked (wave); ridged, gable (roof).

**острол** *m.* ostrole.

**остролист, —ник** *m.* (bot.) holly (*Ilex*).

**остро/лодочник** *m.* (bot.) oxytropis; **—лучевой** *a.* pencil-beam; **—направленный** *a.* narrow, pointed; pencil (beam).

**остроносый** *a.* pointed, sharp, tapered; **о. напилок** taper file.

**остропестро** *n.* milk thistle (*Silybum marianum*).

**остропить** *v.* strop.

**острота** *f.* sharpness, acuteness, fineness, keenness (of blade), pungency (of taste).

**остро/угольный** *a.* acute-angled; acute (triangle); **—фокусный** *a.* sharp-focused.

**оструктур/енный** *a.* aggregated, structurized (soil); **—ивать** *v.* aggregate, structurize.

**острутин** *m.* ostruthin.

**остр/ый** *a.* sharp, keen, fine, edged, pointed, acicular; (geom.; med.) acute; strong, pungent (taste), acrid (odor); live (steam); **о. конец** point; **—як** *m.* point (of arrow); ramp (of rail).

**остудить** *see* **остужать.**

**остуднев/ание** *n.* gelatinization; **—ать** *v.* gelatinize, gelate.

**остуж/ать** *v.* cool, chill; **—енный** *a.* cooled; **—ивание** *n.* cooling, chilling.

**осты/вать, —нуть, —ть** *v.* cool, cool off, get cold; **—вший** *a.* cooled, cold, congealed.

**ость** *f.* (bot.) awn, beard; coarse wool; (anat.) spine.

**осу/дить, —ждать** *v.* criticize, blame, censure; condemn, convict; **—ждение** *n.* blame, censure; conviction; **—жденный** *a.* condemned.

**осумкование** *n.* (biol.) encystment.

**осунуться** *v.* become gaunt-looking.

**осуш/аемая площадь** drainage area; **—ать, —ивать** *v.* dry, desiccate; drain (land); **—ение** *n.* drying; drainage, reclamation (of land); **—енный** *a.* dried, dry; drained, reclaimed.

**осушитель** *m.*, **—ное средство** drier, drying agent, desiccant, siccative; **—ный** *a.* drying, desiccating; draining, drainage.

**осуш/ить** *see* **осушать; —ка** *see* **осушение.**

**осуществ/имость** *f.* feasibility, practicability; **—имый** *a.* feasible, practicable, realizable; **—ить, —лять** *v.* realize, accomplish, carry out, bring about, put into practice; **—ление** *n.* realization, accomplishment, achievement, actuality; **—ленный** *a.* realized, accomplished.

**осцилл/атор, —ятор** *m.* oscillator; **—ирование** *n.*, **—яция** *f.* oscillation; **—ограмма** *f.* oscillogram; **—ограф** *m.* oscillograph; **—ометр** *m.* oscillometer; **—оскоп** *m.* oscilloscope.

**осцин** *m.* oscine, scopoline.

**осы** *pl. of* **оса.**

**осып/ание** *n.* falling down, crumbling; shedding (of leaves); shattering (of grain); sprinkling, dusting; **—анный** *a.* fallen, crumbled; sprinkled, dusted, strewn; **—ать** *v.* sprinkle, dust, strew (with); heap; **—аться** *v.* fall, crumble, slip (down); **—ь** *f.* mound; earthwork slope; (geol.) talus, scree, rock waste.

**ос/ь** *f.* axis; axle, shaft, spindle, pin, pivot; (biol.) rachis; **о. вращения** spinning axis, pivotal axis, pivot; **боковая о., побочная о.** (cryst.)

secondary axis; **имеющий общую о., совпадающий —ями** coaxial; **малая о., мнимая о.** (math.) secondary axis; **на одной —и** in line (with), in alignment (with), aligned; **по —и** axially, endwise.

**осьми—** *see* **восьми—.**

**осьминог** *m.* (zool.) octopus.

**осяз/аемость** *f.* tangibility; **—аемый** *a.* tangible, tactile; **—ание** *n.* touch, sense of touch, feel; **—ательный** *a.* tactile, palpable; sensitive; **—ать** *v.* touch, feel.

**от** *prep. gen.* from, off, out of, of, for; **от и до** from point to point; **день ото дня** from day to day.

**от—** *prefix* de—, ab—, away from.

**отава** *f.* aftermath.

**отавит** *m.* (min.) otavite (a basic cadmium carbonate).

**отаплив/ание** *n.* heating, warming; firing; **—ать** *v.* heat, warm; fire.

**отаптывать** *v.* tread down, trample.

**отара** *f.* flock.

**отбав/ить, —лять** *v.* decrease, diminish, take away, subtract; **—ка** *f.*, **—ление** *n.* decrease, diminution, taking away, subtraction.

**отбел** *m.* (met.) formation of cementite on surface of cast iron.

**отбеленный** *a.* whitened, bleached, decolorized; (met.) refined; (foundry) chilled.

**отбелив/ание** *n.* whitening, bleaching, bleaching out, blanching, decolorizing; brightening effect (of detergent); (met.) refining; (foundry) chilling; **—ательный, —ающий** *a.* bleaching; refining; **—ательный горн** refining furnace, refinery; **—ать** *v.* whiten, bleach, blanch, decolorize; refine; chill; **—ающий реагент** bleaching agent, bleach; **—ающая земля** bleaching clay; fuller's earth.

**отбел/ить** *see* **отбеливать; —ка** *see* **отбеливание; —ьная** *f.* bleachery; **—ьщик** *m.* bleacher.

**отбензинивание** *n.* separation of light benzine fraction from gasoline.

**отбив** *m.*, **—ание** *n.*, **—ка** *f.* repelling, repulsion, warding off; beating off; **—ать** *v.* repel, ward off, drive away;

beat off, strike off; fag, beat (fiber); —ать запах deodorize.

**отбир/ание** *n.* taking away, withdrawal; selecting, picking, sorting; —**ать** *v.* take away, confiscate; remove, withdraw; take (samples); select, pick, sort, sort out, cull; bevel (edge).

**отбит/ие** *see* **отбивание;** —**ь** *see* **отбивать.**

**отблеск** *m.* reflection, gleam.

**отбликовать** *v.* tarnish, grow dull.

**отбой** *m.* repelling, repulsion, repulse; stop; cushioning (in hammer); (hydraulics) apron; backsweep (of waves); ringing (of signal); (tel.) ring-off; (mil.) retreat; **о. паром** steam cushioning; **дать о.** *v.* (tel.) ring off; —**ка** *f.* (min.) breaking, breaking down, cutting.

**отбойный** *a.* repelling, recoil; guard; (tel.) supervisory, clearing; ring-off; (min.) breaking, cutting; **о. молоток** (min.) pneumatic drill.

**отбойщик** *m.* (min.) breaker, cutter.

**отбор** *m.* selection, choice; sampling; picking, separating, sorting; (biol.) breeding; recovery (of core); (power) take-off; (isotope separation) outgoing materials; **о. образцов, о. проб** sampling; **правило** —**a** (nucl.) selection rule; —**ка** *f.* molding plane; —**ник** *m.* separator, sorter; sifter; sampler; —**ный** *a.* choice, select, the best; picked, screened (ore).

**отбортов/ка** *f.,* —**ывать** *v.* flange, crimp, crease.

**отбраковщик** *m.* quality checker.

**отбрасыв/ание** *n.* throwing away, rejection, discarding; repulsion; kick, kicking up; spattering; centrifuging; —**ать** *v.* throw away, throw back, reject, discard; reflect; repel, repulse, drive back; kick; spatter; centrifuge.

**отбро/с** *m.* residue, waste product, rejected material; deflection; —**сы** *pl.* waste, refuse, garbage, sweepings, scrap; (min.) tailings, tails; dross; —**сы производства** industrial waste; —**санный,** —**шенный** *a.* thrown away, discarded, rejected; —**сать,** —**сить** *see* **отбрасывать;** —**сный** *a.* waste.

**отбы/вать,** —**ть** *v.* depart, set off; —**тие** *n.* departure.

**отвал** *m.* bank, terrace (of open-cut mine); tails, tailings; spent material; dump, dumping ground; moldboard (of plow); **о. пород** tailings heap, refuse dump, refuse ore.

**отвалив/ание** *n.* banking, heaping; pushing away; dumping; —**ать** *v.* bank, heap; push away; dump; —**аться** *v.* fall off, come off.

**отвалообразов/ание** *n.* piling; —**атель** *m.* swing chute.

**отвальный** *a.* dump, waste; banking; **о. плуг** terracer, terracing plow, blade grader.

**отвар** *m.* decoction, tea, broth; —**ивание** *n.* boiling, cooking, digesting; decocting; —**ивать,** —**ить** *v.* boil, digest; decoct; (text.) scour; —**ной,** —**ный** *a.* boiled, digested.

**отведен/ие** *n.* removal, elimination, drawing off, carrying off; —**ный** *a.* removed, drawn off, drained off:

**отвезти** *see* **отвозить.**

**отверг/ать,** —**нуть** *v.* reject, refuse, repudiate; repel; —**нутый** *a.* rejected.

**отверд/евание,** —**ение** *n.* hardening, congealing, setting, solidification; —**евать,** —**еть** *v.* harden, grow hard, congeal, set, solidify; —**елость** *f.* hardness, callousness; stiffness; —**елый** *a.* hardened, callous; —**ить** *see* **отверждать.**

**отвержд/ать** *v.* consolidate, strengthen; —**ение** *see* **отвердевание;** —**енный** *a.* consolidated, strengthened.

**отвернуть** *see* **отвертывать.**

**отверст/ие** *n.* opening, aperture, hole, perforation, mesh (of screen); orifice, mouth, vent, passage, inlet, outlet, port; break, gap; bore; span (of bridge); **сто** —**ий на 1 дм.** 100-mesh.

**отверт/ка** *f.* screw driver; —**ывать** *v.* unscrew, screw off; open (faucet, valve); unfasten; turn off, turn back, avert; —**ываться** *v.* be unscrewed; open; turn away (from).

**отвес** *m.* plumb, plumb line, plumb bob, plummet, bob, perpendicular; **груз** —**a** bob; **свинцовый о.** plumb line; —**ить** *see* **отвешивать.**

**отвесн/о** *adv.* sheer, plumb, perpendicular; —**ость** *f.* perpendicularity, verticality, steepness; —**ый** *a*. perpendicular, vertical, upright, plumb; sheer, precipitous; —**ый берег** bluff; —**ая доска** plumb rule.

**отвести** *see* **отводить.**

**ответ** *m*. answer, reply, response.

**ответвитель** *m*. coupler.

**ответвительн/ый** *a*. branching, distributing; **о. зажим** branch terminal; —**ая коробка** (elec.) distributing box, distributor.

**ответвить** *see* **ответвлять.**

**ответвлен/ие** *n*. branching, branch, parting, arm, offset, offshoot; branch pipe; side drain; derivation, tapping, tap, take-off; spur line; (elec.) shunting, shunt; **сделать о.** *v*. branch off; —**ный** *a*. branched, branch; —**ный провод,** —**ная цепь** (elec.) shunt circuit, derived circuit; branch circuit.

**ответвл/ять** *v*. branch off, turn off; take off, tap; (elec.) shunt; —**яться** *v*. branch out, bifurcate; —**яющий** *a*. branching.

**ответ/ить** *see* **отвечать;** —**ный** *a*. reply, answering, in answer; reciprocal, return.

**ответств/енность** *f*. responsibility, liability; —**енный** *a*. responsible, liable (for), answerable (for); —**овать** *v*. make a reply, reply, answer; be responsible (for).

**ответчик** *m*. (law) defendant.

**отвечать** *v*. answer, reply, respond; correspond (with); **о. перед** be responsible to.

**отвеш/енный** *a*. weighed out, weighed off; —**ивание** *n*. weighing, weighing out; —**ивать** *v*. weigh, weigh out; plumb, make vertical.

**отвин/тить,** —**чивать** *v*. screw off, unscrew, dismantle, take down; —**титься,** —**чиваться** *v*. unscrew, get loose, work loose, —**ченный** *a*. unscrewed; —**чивание** *n*. screwing off, unscrewing, dismantling; loosening.

**отвис/ать,** —**нуть** *v*. hang down, sag.

**отвле/кать,** —**чь** *v*. distract, divert; draw off; —**каться** *v*. digress; —**кающий** *a*. distracting; —**чение** *n*. distraction, diversion; digression; abstraction; discharge, removal; —**чен-** **ный** *a*. abstract (quantity); distracted; removed.

**отвод** *m*. branch, branch pipe, offset; bend, elbow; tap, drain, outlet, runoff, by-pass flue; tapping, drawing off, take-off; withdrawal, extraction, removal, discharge, elimination (of heat); diversion; (patent) claim; allotment, distribution; **делать о.** *v*. object, take exception (to).

**отвод/имый** *a*. outgoing, exit; withdrawable; —**итель** *m*. outlet; baffle; —**ить** *v*. lead away, lead off, carry off, derive, draw off, extract, remove, drain off, discharge, run off; take aside, divert, deflect; (elec.) shunt; drive back (water); —**ить назад** run back; —**ка** *f*. (belt) shifter, shifting device; —**ник тока** (elec.) brush.

**отводный** *a*. branch; outlet, drain; **о. канал** diverter, diversion cut, spillway; **о. кран** drain cock, drain; **о. мундштук** deflecting nozzle.

**отвод/ок** *m*. layer, cutting (of plant); **разводить** —**ками** *v*. layer.

**отводящ/ий** *a*. deflecting, diverting, diversion; discharge, outlet; abductor (muscle); **о. канал** offtake; **о. патрубок** outlet branch; **о. трубопровод** drain pipe, drain; —**ая труба** exhaust pipe, exhaust.

**отвозить** *v*. transport, take away.

**отвол/акивать,** —**очь** *v*. drag away.

**отворачивать** *see* **отвертывать, отворотить.**

**отворить** *see* **отворять.**

**отворот** *m*. flange, fold; —**ы** *pl*. flaps; tops (of boots); —**ить** *v*. turn up; turn away, turn aside, avert.

**отворять** *v*. open.

**отвра/тительный** *a*. disgusting, abominable; —**тить,** —**щать** *v*. disgust; avert, turn away, ward off; —**щение** *n*. disgust, aversion, distaste, repulsion.

**отв./см²** *abbr*. (**отверстий в сите на 1 см²**) openings/cm² in screen.

**отвык/ать,** —**нуть** *v*. get out of the habit, lose the habit, be out of practice.

**отвяз/ать,** —**ывать** *v*. untie, unbind, unfasten, loose, loosen, disengage.

**отгиб** *m*. fold; —**ание** *n*. bending (aside),

deflection; diffraction; snapping off; turning back; unbending, straightening; —**ать** *v.* bend aside, deflect; bend off, snap off; turn back, turn down, fold; unbend, straighten.

**отгов/аривать,** —**орить** *v.* dissuade; —**ариваться** *v.* excuse oneself; —**орка** *f.* pretext, pretense, excuse.

**отгон** *m.* distillate; distilling off; —**ка** *f.* driving off, elimination; distillation; —**ять** *v.* drive off, drive away, drive out, eliminate, remove; distill, distill off; drive back, repel.

**отгор/аживать,** —**одить** *v.* partition off, fence off, shut off; —**оженный** *a.* partitioned, fenced off, shut off, cut off, stopped; —**оженное место** enclosure.

**отгре/бать,** —**сти** *v.* rake off, rake away, scrape.

**отгру/жать,** —**зить** *v.* unload; —**зка** *f.* unloading; shipping.

**отдаваемый** *a.* output.

**отдавать** *v.* give away; deliver, yield, give off, lose; smell (of); give back, return, restore; recoil, rebound, reverberate; loosen (bolt), unfasten, slacken, unscrew, turn back; **о. назад** give back, return; recoil, kick back; —**ся** *v.* devote oneself (to); resound, ring, echo.

**отдав/ить,** —**ливать** *v.* squeeze, crush.

**отдален/ие** *n.,* —**ность** *f.* remoteness, distance; removal; **в** —**ии** at a distance; distant, remote; —**ный** *a.* distant, remote, far.

**отдал/ить,** —**ять** *v.* move off; estrange, alienate; postpone.

**отда/нный** *a.* given back, returned; given off, yielded; —**ть** *see* **отдавать.**

**отдач/а** *f.* efficiency, performance (of machine); delivery, output, yield; evolution, emission (of heat); extraction (of oil); giving back, return; recoil, kick (of gun), rebound, repercussion, kicking up, spring back, springiness; deflection (of structure or machine); payment (of debt); **коэффициент** —**и** efficiency; (elec.) output coefficient, specific torque coefficient; **кривая** —**и** efficiency curve; **промышленная о.** efficiency; **удельная о.** (elec.) specific output; **частица** —**и** (nucl.) recoil particle.

**отдел** *m.* section, division, branch, department; class; step, stage; (geol.) formation, series.

**отдел/анный** *a.* finished, dressed, trimmed; —**анная поверхность** finish; —**ать** *see* **отделывать.**

**отделен/ие** *n.* division, branch, department, section, compartment, partition; separation, separating out, isolation, segregation; evolution, emission; precipitation; recovery (from waste); cutting, cleaving, severance; detaching, detachment; —**ный** *a.* separated, segregated, eliminated, isolated; detached; —**ный осаждением** precipitated out.

**отдел/ившийся** *a.* separated, loosened; —**имость** *f.* separability; —**имый** *a.* separable; detachable; —**итель** *m.* separator, divider; eliminator; —**ительный** *a.* separating; —**ить** *see* **отделять.**

**отдел/ка** *f.* finishing, finish, dressing, cleaning, trimming; setting (of gem); structure; **о. начисто** polishing; —**очная** *f.* finishing shop.

**отделочный** *a.* finishing, cleaning, trimming; **о. инструмент** smoothing tool; **о. калибр** planishing pass.

**отделывать** *v.* finish, finish off, dress, clean, cleanse, trim; work up, fashion; align, adjust.

**отдельно** *adv.* separately, apart; **о. расположенный,** **о. стоящий** independent, separate, detached.

**отдельност/ь** *f.* individuality; (geol.) cleavage, parting, rift, jointing; structure; (structural) unit; **в** —**и** separately.

**отдел/ьный** *a.* separate, discrete, individual; detached, independent, isolated, single; partial, divided; —**ять** *v.* separate, separate out, extract; single out, isolate, segregate; divide, part; partition; sever, cut off, detach, disengage; drive off, eliminate, liberate, free; pick, sort (ore); clear, clarify (liquid); analyze.

**отдер/гивание** *n.* drawing back, jerking back; —**гивать,** —**нуть** *v.* draw back, withdraw, jerk back.

**отдир/ание** *n.* tearing off, peeling; —**ать** *v.* tear off, rip off, peel off, skin.

**отдохнуть** *see* **отдыхать.**

**отдубина** *f.* tan waste, spent tanbark.

**отдувать** *v.* blow off.

**отдулина** *f.* bulge, bulging.

**отдуть** *see* **отдувать.**

**отдушина** *f.* air hole, air vent, air drain (in mold), air funnel, ventilator; hole, draft hole, vent, vent hole.

**отдых** *m.* rest, repose, recreation, relaxation; **—ать** *v.* rest.

**отек** *m.* (med.) edema, dropsy; sag (of surface coating); **о. легких** (med.) emphysema; **—ать** *v.* swell, inflate; flow off, run; **—лый, —ший** *a.* swollen.

**отел** *m.* calving; **—иться** *v.* calve.

**отель** *m.* hotel.

**отенит** *see* **отунит.**

**отепл/ение** *n.* warming; heat insulation; **—ять** *v.* warm, heat.

**отереть** *see* **обтирать.**

**отесывать** *see* **обтесывать.**

**оте/ц** *m.* father; **—ческий** *a.* paternal.

**отечеств/енный** *a.* native, home; **—енная промышленность** domestic (Soviet) industry; **—о** *n.* fatherland, native country.

**отеч/ный** *a.* (med.) edematous; **—ь** *see* **отекать.**

**отжат/ый** *a.* squeezed out, pressed out; detached; **—ь** *see* **отжимать.**

**отжечь** *see* **отжигать.**

**отжив/ать** *v.* become obsolete; **—ающий** *a.* obsolescent; **—ший** *a.* obsolete.

**отжиг** *m.*, **—ание** *n.*, **—ательный** *a.* annealing; **—ать** *v.* anneal; burn off, roast.

**отжим/ание** *n.* squeezing, squeezing out, pressing out; centrifuging; **—ать** *v.* squeeze out, press out, force out; wring out; centrifuge; **—аться** *v.* be squeezed out; become detached, get loose; **—ка** *f.*, **—ная машина** centrifuge, centrifugal, centrifugal machine; squeezer; wringing machine, wringer; **—ки** *pl.* scrap.

**отжить** *see* **отживать.**

**отзвук** *m.* repercussion, echo.

**отзейгерованный** *a.* (met.) liquated, melted out; **о. свинец** liquation lead.

**отзыв** *m.* testimonial, reference; review; response; report, echo; **—ать** *v.* call away, take aside, summon back,

recall; revoke, countermand; **—аться** respond; echo; **—ающийся** *a.* resonant; **—чивость** *f.* response, effect; responsiveness (of instrument); **—чивый** *a.* responsive, sympathetic.

**отиатр** *m.* (med.) ear specialist; **—ия** *f.* otiatrics.

**отирать** *see* **обтирать.**

**отит** *m.* otitis, inflammation of ear.

**отказ** *m.* refusal, denial, rejection; non-operation; failure (of current, etc.); **о. в действии, о. в работе** failure, breakdown (of machine); **до —а** to the limit; **полный до —а** as full as possible, filled to the top, heaping full; **—ать, —ывать** *v.* refuse, reject, deny; renounce; **—аться, —ываться** *v.* refuse; give up, renounce; **—аться действовать** fail, break down, get out of order.

**откалыв/ание** *n.* breaking off, splitting off, detaching; spalling, splintering; exfoliation; **—ать** *v.* break off, split off, cleave, cut off, chop off; detach, separate, exfoliate; unfasten, unpin; **—аться** *v.* split off, chip, spall.

**откапыв/ание** *n.* exhumation; **—ать** *v.* exhume, dig up, disinter, unearth.

**откармлив/ание** *n.* fattening; **—ать** *v.* fatten, feed up.

**откат** *m.* recoil (of arms); rolling back, backsweep (of waves); **—ать** *v.* roll back, roll away.

**откатить** *see* **откатывать.**

**откат/ка** *f.* (min.) haulage; **—ной мост** drawbridge, pull-back bridge; **—очный** *a.* hauling, delivery; **—чик** *m.* hauler, drawer, driver.

**откатыв/ание** *n.* rolling off, wheeling off; **—ать** *v.* roll off, wheel off; (min.) haul; **—аться** *v.* roll off; recoil (of gun).

**откач/анный** *a.* evacuated; **—ать, —ивать** *v.* pump out, evacuate, exhaust; **—ка** *f.* pumping (out), evacuation; **—ной** *a.* exhaust.

**откашливать** *v.* cough up, expectorate.

**отокваска** *f.* steep, drench.

**откидн/ой** *a.* reversible; folding back, folding, collapsible; throw-over, drop, flap, hinged; tipping, dumping; **о. болт** swing bolt; **о. клапан** flap valve; **—ое сопло** deflecting nozzle.

отки/дывать, —нуть *v.* throw off, throw away; tilt.

откисл/енный *a.* deacidified, freed of acid, neutralized; —ить *v.* deacidify, neutralize.

откладыв/ание *n.* putting off, postponing; laying aside, putting aside; —ать *v.* put off, postpone, defer, delay, shelve (a project, etc.); adjourn, call off; put aside, set aside, put away, reserve, put by, lay up; settle, deposit, precipitate; plot (curve), lay off.

отклеи/вать, —ть *v.* take off, remove, unglue, degum; —ваться, —ться *v.* unglue, come loose.

отклонен/ие *n.* deflection, declination, divergence, diversion, digression, deviation, aberration; variation, discrepancy, departure, error; oscillation; tilt; о. шага difference in pitch; предел —ия play; сила —ия deflecting force; угол —ия angle of deflection; angle of deviation; —ный *a.* deflected, divergent.

отклон/итель *m.*, —яющее устройство, —яющий аппарат deflector; —ить, —ять *v.* turn aside, decline, deflect, divert, deviate, alter (direction); avert; derive; —иться, —яться *v.* decline, deflect, divert, deviate, digress, swerve, diverge, depart; slant, tilt; —яющий *a.* deflecting, deflection, diverting; beam-deflection (tube); —яющая сила deflecting force; —яющийся *a.* divergent, deviating.

отключ/аемый *a.* detachable; —ать, —ить *v.* detach, isolate, disconnect, switch off, cut off; —ающий *a.* cut-off; —ение *n.* detachment, isolation, disconnecting, switching off, cutting off; —енный *a.* detached, disconnected, switched off, dead (wire).

откованный *a.* forged.

отколот/ый *a.* split off, cleaved; —ь *see* откалывать.

откопать *see* откапывать.

откорм *m.* fattening; —ить *v.* fatten.

откос *m.* slant, slope, side slope, declivity, inclination, dip; bank; с —ом sloped; угол естественного —а angle of rest, angle of repose.

откреп/ить, —лять *v.* untie, unfasten, loosen.

откровенн/ость *f.* frankness; —ый *a.* frank, outspoken.

откру/тить, —чивать *v.* untwist, unscrew, open (faucet, valve).

открыв/аемый *a.* detectable; —ание *n.* opening; —атель *m.* opener; —ать *v.* open, uncover, reveal, disclose, discover, detect; turn on (faucet, valve); clear (a path); unlock; —аться *v.* open.

открытие *n.* opening; disclosure, discovery, invention; detection.

открытка *f.* post card.

открыто *adv.* openly, publicly; —плодные *pl.* (bot.) Discomycetes.

открыт/ый *a.* open, exposed; clear (path); straightforward, outspoken; о. разрез open-cut mine; —ое письмо post card; —ые работы open-cut mining, open-pit mining; на —ом воздухе, под —ым небом in the open, outdoors.

открыть *see* открывать.

откуда *adv.* from where? from which, whence, where from; о.-либо, о.-ни wherever from; о.-нибудь from somewhere or other; о. следует whence it follows.

откуп *m.* lease; —ать, —ить *v.* take on lease; —аться, —иться *v.* pay off.

откупор/енный *a.* uncorked, unstopped, unstoppered, uncapped, unsealed, opened; —ивать, —ить *v.* uncork, unstop, uncap, unseal, open; —ка *f.* opening.

отлаг/ательство *n.* delay, procrastination; —ать *v.* delay, put off; lay aside, set aside; —аться *v.* separate, settle out, precipitate, deposit.

отламывать *v.* break off, chip off.

отлеж/аться, —иваться *v.* rest; lie around; —ка *f.* resting; wetting off, softening; —ь *f.* sediment, deposit.

отлеп/ить, —ливать, —лять *v.* take off, unglue; mold, fashion.

отлет *m.* flying away, take-off; —ать, —еть *v.* fly away, fly off, take off.

отлив *m.* reflux, return flow, discharge; ebb, low tide; hue, play (of colors); о. цветов iridescence, opalescence; прилив и о. ebb and flow; с —ом iridescent, opalescent, chatoyant;

—**аемость** *f.* flowability (of molten metal).

**отливать** *v.* found, cast; pour, decant, pour off; ebb; **о. всеми цветами радуги** iridesce, be iridescent.

**отливка** *f.* founding, casting, molding; cast, cast material, ingot; pouring off, decanting; **о. в почве** casting in the open; **бронзовая о.** cast bronze; **bronze casting; чугунная о.** cast iron.

**отливн/ой** *a.* founded, cast, molded; founding, casting; decanting; **о. канал** delivery channel (of valve); —**ая печь** founding furnace; —**ая рама** casting frame, casting box; —**ая струя** discharge jet; —**ая труба** delivery pipe (of pump); discharge pipe.

**отливо/к** *m.* cast, casting; —**чный** *a.* casting.

**отлип** *m.* tackiness, tack (of surface coatings); —**ание** *n.* ungluing, peeling off, loosening; —**ать,** —**нуть** *v.* unglue, peel off, come off, become detached.

**отлит/ый** *a.* cast, founded; poured off, decanted; —**ое отверстие** core hole; **в** —**ом виде** as cast; —**ь** *see* **отливать.**

**отлич/ать** *v.* distinguish, discriminate, discern; —**аться,** —**иться** *v.* differ, be distinguished (by), be characterized (by); surpass, outdo, excel; —**ие** *n.* difference, distinction; contrast; nature, variety; **в** —**ии от** in contrast to, unlike.

**отличительн/ый** *a.* distinctive, distinguishing, characteristic, peculiar, special; **о. знак** distinctive mark, distinction; **о. признак** distinguishing feature, feature, characteristic; —**ая черта** characteristic.

**отлич/ить** *see* **отличать;** —**ный** *a.* excellent, perfect; different, distinct (from).

**отлог** *m.* inclination, slope; —**ий** *a.* sloping, shelving, gentle (climb); —**о** *adv.* at a slope; —**о спускаться** *v.* slope, slant, shelve; —**ость** *f.* slope, sloping, declivity.

**отлож/ение** *n.* precipitation, precipitate, sediment; (geol.) deposit, deposition, sedimentation, blanket, incrustation; laying aside, postponing; —**енный** *a.* precipitated, deposited; put off, post-

poned; —**ившийся** *a.* precipitated, deposited, settled; —**ить** *see* **откладывать, отлагать.**

**отлом/ать,** —**ить** *see* **отламывать;** —**ка** *f.* (glass) cracking off; —**очный** *a.* cracking, breaking off; —**очное железо** (glass) cracking ring.

**отлупляться** *v.* scale off, peel, exfoliate.

**отлуч/ать,** —**ить** *v.* remove, withdraw; —**аться,** —**иться** *v.* absent oneself, be absent; —**ка** *f.* absence.

**отмаз/ать,** —**ывать** *v.* finish greasing; unlute.

**отмарывание** *n.* mark off (staining of adjacent white material in dye-fastness tests).

**отматывать** *v.* wind off, unwind.

**отмачивать** *v.* soak, soak off; ret.

**отмежев/ать,** —**ывать** *v.* measure off, survey, mark off, draw a boundary.

**отмель** *f.* bank, shoal, shoal water, shallow, shelf, flat.

**отмен/а** *f.* abolition, abolishment; revocation, annulment, countermand; —**енный** *a.* cancelled; —**ить** *v.* abolish; revoke, annul, cancel, countermand.

**отменный** *a.* superior, excellent.

**отменять** *see* **отменить.**

**отмерз/ать,** —**нуть** *v.* freeze off; thaw; —**лый** *a.* frozen (off); thawed out.

**отмер/ивание** *n.* measuring off; —**ивать,** —**ить,** —**ять** *v.* measure off, mark off.

**отме/сти,** —**тать** *v.* sweep away.

**отмет/ина** *f.* mark, marking, notch, nick; —**ить** *see* **отмечать;** —**ка** *f.* mark, notch, marker; sign, indication, index, criterion; label; marking; —**чик** *m.* marker; —**чик времени** timer.

**отмеч/ать** *v.* mark, mark down, record, register, note; take (readings); label; plot; —**ающий** *a.* recording, registering; —**ающий автоматически** self-recording; —**енный** *a.* marked, recorded, registered; plotted.

**отминать** *v.* knead, work.

**отмир/ание** *n.* dying off, necrosis, atrophy; disappearance (of species); —**ать** *v.* die off; disappear; —**ающий** *a.* moribund; rudimentary.

**отмок/ать,** —**нуть** *v.* soak off.

**отмол/ачивать,** —**отить** *v.* (agr.) thresh.

отмор/аживание *n.* freezing, frostbite; —аживать, —озить *v.* freeze, freeze off, be frostbitten; —оженный *a.* frozen, frostbitten.

отмотать *see* отматывать.

отмоч/енный *a.* soaked (off); —ить *v.* soak (off); —ка *f.* soaking.

отмуч/енный *a.* elutriated, purified by washing and decantation, clarified; sedimentary; —ивание *n.* elutriation, clarification; —ивать, —ить *v.* elutriate, wash, clarify, levigate; (min.) buddle.

отмыв/ание *n.,* —ка *f.* washing off; —ать *v.* wash off, wash out.

отмык/ание *n.* unlocking, opening; —ать *v.* unlock, open.

отмылив/ание *n.* rinsing; —ать *v.* rinse, free from soap, cleanse from soap.

отмыт/ый *a.* washed, washed off, washed out; —ь *see* отмывать.

отмычка *f.* skeleton key, master key.

отмяк/лость *f.* softening; —лый, —ший *a.* softened, soft, grown soft; —нуть *v.* soften, grow soft.

отмять *see* отминать.

ОТН *abbr.* (отделение технических наук) Division of Technical Sciences.

отн. ед. *abbr.* (относительная единица) relative unit.

отнес/енный *a.* referred; carried away; —ти, —ть *see* относить.

отнимать *v.* take away, confiscate; cut off, amputate; —ся *v.* be taken away; be paralyzed, lose the use (of).

отнога *f.* (bot.) aerial root.

относ *m.* delivery; deviation.

относительн/о *adv.* comparatively, relatively; *prep. gen.* relative to, regarding, with regard to, concerning, with reference to; —ость *f.* relativity, relativeness; relation; теория —ости theory of relativity; —ый *a.* relative, comparative; —ая ошибка, —ая погрешность relative error, percentage error; —ое отверстие aperture ratio, *f*-number (of lens).

относ/ить *v.* take, deliver; carry away; refer; deviate; о. к direct; attribute to; —иться *v.* relate, concern, pertain, belong; refer; report; treat, behave (toward), act; —ящийся *a.* concerning, pertaining; acting.

отношен/ие *n.* relation, relationship, connection; (math.) ratio, proportion; attitude, behavior; reference; rate; о. числа нейтронов и протонов neutron-proton ratio; в —ии in regard (to), in respect (to); в других —иях in other respects, otherwise; во всех —иях in all respects, in every respect; весовое о. ratio by weight; закон кратных —ий law of multiple proportions; закон постоянства весовых —ий law of combining weights; иметь о. *v.* pertain (to), concern, apply, affect; не имеющий —ия unrelated, not pertinent, beside the point; обратное о. inverse ratio; по —ию as regards, concerning.

отныне *adv.* henceforth, henceforward.

отнюдь *adv.* by no means, not at all.

отнят/ие *n.* taking away, removal, elimination; о. фосфора dephosphorization; —ый *a.* taken away, removed, eliminated; —ь *see* отнимать.

ото *see* от.

ото— *prefix* oto— (ear).

отобит *m.* otobite (from otoba wax).

отображ/ать *v.* reflect, represent; —ение *n.* reflection, representation; (mirror) transformation; —енный *a.* reflected.

отобрать *see* отбирать.

отовсюду *adv.* from everywhere.

отогн/анный *a.* driven off; distilled; —ать *see* отгонять.

отогнут/ый *a.* bent back, recurved; —ь *see* отгибать.

отогре/вание *n.* warming; —вать, —ть *v.* warm, take the chill off.

отодви/гание *n.* removing, moving away, drawing back; —гать, —нуть *v.* remove, move away, move aside, draw back; —гаться, —нуться *v.* draw aside.

отодрать *see* отдирать.

отождеств/ить, —лять *v.* identify; —ление *n.* identification.

отожженный *a.* annealed.

отойти *see* отходить.

отолит *m.* (zool.) otolith, ear stone; —ический, —овый *a.* otolithic.

отология *f.* (med.) otology.

отомкнут/ый *a.* unlocked, open; —ь *see* отмыкать.

**отомстить** *v.* revenge; avenge.

**отоп/ительный** *a.* heating, heat; **—и-тельная нагрузка** (elec.) heating load; **—ить** *see* **отапливать.**

**отоплен/ие** *n.* heating; **водяное о.** hot-water heating (system); **воздушное о.** hot-air heating; **паровое о.** steam heat; **—ный** *a.* heated.

**отопре/вать, —ть** *v.* become damp or soft after thawing out; come off from heat or damp.

**оторв/анный** *a.* torn, torn off, severed; **—ать** *see* **отрывать; —аться** *v.* tear oneself away from; lose contact (with).

**оторочка** *f.* edge, edging, border; (geol.) fringe.

**оторфование** *n.* peat formation.

**отослать** *see* **отсылать.**

**отощ/авший, —алый** *a.* lean, emaciated; **—ать** *v.* grow lean, become emaciated; **—ающий материал** (cer.) non-plastic material; **—ение** *n.* (cer.) grog addition; **—енный** *a.* lean (coal).

**отпад/ать** *v.* fall off, drop off; become superfluous; **—ающий** *a.* falling, dropping; (bot.) deciduous; **—ение** *n.* falling off, falling away, dropping.

**отпа/ивать** *v.* unsolder; seal off; **—йка** *f.* unsoldering.

**отпалка** *f.* firing, blasting.

**отпар/ивание** *n.* steaming; **—ивать, —ить** *v.* steam; **—ный** *a.* steaming; stripping (column).

**отпарывать** *v.* rip, rip off, rip out.

**отпасть** *see* **отпадать.**

**отпая/нный** *a.* sealed off; **—ть** *see* **отпаивать.**

**отпереть** *see* **отпирать.**

**отпечат/ание, —ывание** *n.* printing; imprint, impression; **—анный** *a.* printed; imprinted, stamped; **—ать, —ывать** *v.* print; type; imprint, impress, stamp; **—аться, —ываться** *v.* leave an impression (upon); **—ок** *m.* print; impression, imprint, stamp, seal; **цветной —ок** color print.

**отпилить** *v.* saw off.

**отпир/ание** *n.* unlocking; **—ать** *v.* unlock, open, unfasten, unbolt; trigger; **—ающий** *a.* unlocking; trigger.

**отпла/та** *f.* repayment, return; **в —ту** in return; **—тить, —чивать** *v.* repay;

recompense, reward, reciprocate.

**отполировать** *v.* polish off.

**отпор** *m.* repulse, resistance; rebuff.

**отпороть** *see* **отпарывать.**

**отпот/евание** *n.* sweating, sweat, dew, condensate; **—евать, —еть** *v.* sweat, perspire, be covered with moisture; **—елый** *a.* covered with sweat.

**отправитель** *m.* transmitter, sender; shipper; originator, initiator; **—ный** *a.* transmitting, transmission.

**отправ/ить, —лять** *v.* send, transmit, forward, dispatch; ship, consign (goods); perform (duties); **—ляться** *v.* set off, set forth, depart, proceed; **—ка** *f.* sending, dispatching, forwarding; shipment, conveyance; **—ление** *n.* sending, shipping; transmitting, transmission; departure, start; performance (of duties); functioning, function; **место —ления, точка —ления** starting point; point of origin, source; **—ленный** *a.* sent, shipped.

**отправн/ой** *a.* starting; **—ая точка** starting point, origin.

**отпрессованный** *a.* pressed, squeezed (out).

**отпрыг/ивать, —нуть** *v.* jump aside; rebound, recoil, spring back.

**отпрыск** *m.* spur, branch; (bot.) shoot, sprout, sucker; descendant.

**отпрягать** *v.* unharness, unhitch.

**отпрянуть** *v.* rebound, recoil, spring back.

**отпрячь** *see* **отпрягать.**

**отпус/к** *m.* holiday, leave (of absence), furlough; issue, distribution; (met.) tempering, drawing; **о. в масле** oil tempering; **о. на синий цвет** blue annealing; **высокий о.** high-temperature tempering; **низкий о.** low-temperature tempering; **—кание** *n.* letting go, dismissing; release, drop-out; slackening, loosening; (met.) tempering; **—кать, —тить** *v.* let go, dismiss, release, give leave; slacken, unfasten, loosen, ease; unscrew; allow to expand; supply; (met.) temper, draw; **—кной** *a.* dismissive; releasing; release (spring); tempering.

**отпущенный** *a.* dismissed, released; slackened, loosened; (met.) tempered.

**отраб/атывать, —отать** *v.* finish one's

work, finish off; —**отавший, —отанный** *a.* worked out, used up, exhausted, depleted, spent (solution);
waste, stripped, exhaust (gas); —**от-
анная жидкость** spent liquor, discharge liquor.

**отрав/а** *f.* poison, toxin; —**ить, —лять**
*v.* poison; —**ление** *n.* poisoning, toxic
effect; contamination; —**ленный** *a.*
poisoned; contaminated; —**ляющий**
*a.* toxic; contaminating; —**ляющее
вещество** toxin; contaminant; (nucl.)
denaturant.

**отрадный** *a.* comforting, gratifying.

**отраж/аемость** *f.* reflectivity; —**атель**
*m.* reflector; deflector; extractor (of
gun).

**отражательн/ый** *a.* reflecting, reverberatory; deflecting, baffle; **о. козырек, о.
лист, о. свод, о. щиток, —ая
заслонка, —ая плита** deflector, deflector plate, deflecting plate, baffle,
baffle plate; **о. телескоп** reflecting
telescope; —**ая печь** (met.) reverberatory furnace; —**ая способность** reflecting power, reflectivity; (nucl.)
albedo; reflectance.

**отраж/ать** *v.* reflect, mirror, reverberate;
indicate; rebound; repel, repulse,
ward off; iridesce; echo (sound);
—**аться** *v.* reflect, reverberate; rebound, impinge; echo; —**ающий** *a.*
reflecting, reverberatory; deflecting;
iridescent; —**ающее сопло** deflecting
nozzle.

**отражен/ие** *n.* reflection, reverberation;
image; repercussion, rebound, impingement; repulsion; echoing (of
sound); —**ный** *a.* reflected, reverber-
ated; —**ный звук** echo.

**отразить** *see* **отражать.**

**отрапортовать** *v.* report.

**отра/сль** *f.* branch; field; (bot.) sprout,
shoot, sucker; —**стать, —сти** *v.* grow,
sprout; —**стить, —щивать** *v.* let
grow; tap; —**щивание** *n.* letting
grow; tapping.

**отрегулиров/ание** *n.* adjustment; —**анный** *a.* adjusted, set; —**ать** *v.* adjust,
set.

**отрез** *m.* cut, edge of a cut; piece; (plow)
share; —**ание** *n.*, —**ка** *f.*, —**ывание**
*n.* cutting, cutting off, severing,

severance; —**анный** *a.* cut, cut off,
severed; —**ать, —ывать** *v.* cut (off),
clip, sever; —**ной** *a.* cut-off, cutting;
shearing (die); —**ок** *m.* piece, length,
stretch, distance; section; fragment,
remnant; (geom.) segment; —**ки** *pl.*
fragments, remnants; scrap; —**очный**
*a.* shear.

**отрекаться** *v.* deny, repudiate, renounce.

**отрекомендовать** *v.* introduce (someone).

**отречься** *see* **отрекаться.**

**отреш/ать, —ить** *v.* dismiss.

**отриц/ание** *n.* negation, denial; negative; —**ательно** *adv.* negatively;
adversely; —**ательный** *a.* negative;
deleterious, unfavorable; —**ательный
ток** (elec.) negative current; —**ателья-
ная сторона** disadvantage, drawback; —**ать** *v.* negate, deny, contradict.

**отрог** *m.* spur, branch; **горный о.** (geol.)
spur.

**отрост/ок** *m.* sprout, shoot, sprig, off-
shoot, branch, side arm; outlet, tap;
prolongation, extension; (plant) cutting; (biol.) appendage, process;
(med.) appendix; (geol.) apophysis.

**отруб** *m.* holding; butt; —**ать, —ить** *v.*
chop off, cut off, clip.

**отруби** *pl.* bran, siftings.

**отрубное долото** chipping chisel.

**отруб/ной, —ный, —яной** *a.* bran.

**отрыв** *m.*, —**ание** *n.* break, break-off,
breaking away, tear; detachment,
removal; (aero.) take-off; **зажигание
на о.** make-and-break ignition; —**ать**
*v.* break off, break away, tear away;
dig up, unearth, disinter, excavate;
—**аться** *v.* break off, break away,
tear away, come off; (aero.) take off;
—**ающая сила** pull.

**отрывист/ость** *f.* abruptness, suddenness, jerkiness; —**ый** *a.* abrupt,
sudden, jerky.

**отрыв/ное приспособление** (elec.) con-
tact-breaking device; —**ок** *m.* fragment, piece; excerpt; —**очный** *a.*
fragmental, fragmentary; interrupted.

**отры/гание** *n.* regurgitation; —**гать,
—гивать, —гнуть** *v.* regurgitate;
belch; —**жка** *f.* belching, eructation.

**отрыть** *v.* dig up, excavate.

**отря/д** *m.* (biol.) order; division, brigade;

—дить, —жать *v.* detach, appoint, order.

отря/сать, —сти, —хивать, —хнуть *v.* shake off.

отса/дить, —живать *v.* (agr.) layer; transplant; (min.) jig; —дка *f.* transplanting; jigging; —док *m.* transplanted plant; layer, cutting (of plant); —дочный *a.* jigging, jig; —дочный чан buddle; —дочная машина jigging machine, jigger, jig.

отсалив/ание *n.* salting out; —ать *v.* salt out.

отсасыв/ание *n.* drawing off, suction; —атель *m.* suction pump; —ать *v.* suck off, draw off (by suction); filter by suction; press dry; —ающий *a.* suction; outgoing, outlet; —ающий вентилятор suction fan, exhaust fan; —ающий колокол suction hood, exhaust hood.

отсве/т *m.* reflection, sheen; —чивание *n.* brilliancy, glare; reflection; —чивать *v.* reflect; shine, gleam.

отсев *m.* sifting; selection; siftings, screenings, residue; —ание *n.* sifting; —ать *v.* sift, screen; choose, select, cull.

отседать *v.* settle, precipitate.

отсеивание *see* отсевание.

отсек *m.* compartment, cubicle, part, section; —ание *n.* splitting off, cleaving; interception, cutting off; —ательный, —ающий *a.* intercepting, cutting off; cut-off (valve); —ать *v.* split off, cleave; cut off, intercept, chop off, detach.

отсеч/ение *n.*, —ка *f.* cutting off, interception; cut-off, closing; —енный *a.* split off; cut off, intercepted; closed; —ь *see* отсекать.

отсеять *see* отсевать.

отсиненный *a.* blued.

отсифонив/ание *n.* siphoning off; —ать *v.* siphon off.

отскаблив/ание *n.* scraping off; —ать *v.* scrape off.

отск/акивание *n.*, —ок *m.* recoil, rebound, kick, spring back, jumping back; breaking away, peeling off, coming off; —акивать, —очить *v.* recoil, rebound, kick, spring back,

jump back, bounce; jump off, jump aside; break away, peel off, come off.

отскре/бать, —сти *v.* scrape off, scrub off; —бки *pl.* scrapings.

отсл/аивание, —оение *n.*, —ойка *f.* scaling, peeling, exfoliation; stripping; —аиваться, —оиться *v.* scale (off), come off in scales, peel off, flake, exfoliate; —оенный *a.* scaled, exfoliated.

отслуж/ивать, —ить *v.* serve (one's or its) time.

отсоединение *n.* disconnecting, isolation.

отсортиров/ание *n.*, —ка *f.* sorting, sorting out, picking; rejection; —анный *a.* sorted, picked; rejected; —ать, —ывать *v.* sort, sort out, pick; reject.

отсос/анный *a.* drawn off, sucked off, filtered by suction; —ать *see* отсасывать; —ный *a.* suction; —ная склянка filter flask.

отсохнуть *see* отсыхать.

отсроч/енный *a.* delayed; —ивать, —ить *v.* postpone, put off, delay, defer; —ка *f.* postponement, delay, deferment, adjournment; respite.

отстав/ание *n.* lag, lagging, creep; delay, retardation; loosening, peeling, exfoliation; arrears; о. фаз phase lag; промежуток —ания time lag; угол —ания (elec.) angle of lag; —ать *v.* lag, fall behind; creep; be slow (of clock); come off, come loose, peel, exfoliate.

отстав/ить, —лять *v.* set aside, remove; dismiss, discharge; —ка *f.*, —ление *n.* setting aside, removal; dismissal; resignation, retirement; в —ке retired; подавать в —ку *v.* retire, resign; —ной *a.* retired.

отстаив/ание *n.* standing, settling, clearing, clarification; —ать *v.* let stand, settle, allow to settle, clarify; deposit, precipitate; fight, defend; assert (one's rights); —аться *v.* settle, precipitate.

отстал/ость *f.* backwardness; arrears; —ый *a.* backward, retarded; out of date, outdated.

отстать *see* отставать.

отстающий *a.* lagging, slow.

отстег/ивать, —нуть *v.* unfasten, unhook, unbutton.

отстир/ать, —ывать *v.* wash off, wash out, launder out.

отстой *m.* sediment, dregs, bottoms, residue, sludge, deposit; period of settling; —ник *m.* settler, settling tank; sedimentation tank; elutriator; (sugar) clarifier; mud drum; (automobile) sump.

отстойн/ый *a.* settling; о. бак, о. бассейн, о. резервуар, о. чан settler, settling tank; clarifying tank, separating tank; sedimentation tank; —ая колба decanting flask.

отсто/ять *see* отстаивать; —ящий *a.* distant, remote.

отстраивать *v.* build up.

отстран/ение *n.* putting aside; removal, elimination, discharge, dismissal; —ить, —ять *v.* put aside, push aside, set aside, drive back; discharge, dismiss.

отстри/гать, —чь *v.* cut off, clip, shear.

отстро/ить *see* отстраивать; —йка *f.* building up; —йка от (rad.) tuning out.

отстук/ать, —ивать *v.* tick off, tap off.

отступ/ать, —ить *v.* fall back, give way, withdraw, recede, retreat; digress, depart; —ающий *a.* receding; retrograde; divergent; —ление *n.* falling back, withdrawal, recession, retreat, regression, retrogression; departure, deviation, variation, divergence; —ный *a.* receding, retreating.

отсутств/ие *n.* absence, freedom (from); deficiency; быть в —ии, —овать *v.* be absent; —ующий *a.* absent.

отсчет *m.,* —ный *a.* reading; count; metering; о. на нуль, о. от нуля zero reading; о. показаний reading; производить о., сделать о. *v.* take a reading; прямого —а, с непосредственным —ом direct-reading; система —а frame of reference; reading system; точка —а reference point.

отсчит/анный *a.* read off; counted off, reckoned; —ать, —ывать *v.* read, read off, take a reading; count off, reckon; —ывание *n.* reading, reading off; counting off, reckoning.

отсылать *v.* send off, dispatch, post; refer (to); remit (money).

отсыпать *v.* pour off (dry material).

отсыр/елый *a.* damp, dampened; —ение *n.* damping; —еть *v.* grow damp, get wet, become moist.

отсыхать *v.* dry out, dry up; dry off.

отсюда *adv.* from here, hence.

оттаив/ание *n.* thawing, thawing out, defrosting; —ать *v.* thaw, thaw out, defrost, melt away.

отталкив/ание *n.* repulsion; сила —ания, —ательная сила, —ающая сила repulsive force; —ать *v.* repel, push away, drive back, resist.

оттартать *v.* bail, bail out.

оттаскивать *v.* drag away, pull aside.

оттачив/ание *n.* sharpening, whetting, pointing; —ать *v.* sharpen, whet, point.

оттащить *see* оттаскивать.

отта/янный *a.* thawed out, defrosted; —ять *see* оттаивать.

оттвейлерские слои (geol.) Ottweilian series.

оттен/ок *m.* shade, shading, hue, tinge, tint, tone; —ять *v.* shade, tint, graduate.

оттепель *f.* thaw; стоит о. it is thawing.

оттереть *see* оттирать.

оттесн/ить, —ять *v.* drive back, force back.

оттирать *v.* rub out, rub away, abrade; wipe away.

оттиск *m.* impression, imprint; indentation, dent; print, copy; printing.

оттитровать *v.* titrate back, back-titrate.

Отто цикл Otto cycle (of engine).

оттого *adv.* therefore, therefrom.

отток *m.* outflow, efflux; flow-off, run-off.

оттолкнуть *see* отталкивать.

оттопыр/ивать, —ить, —иваться, —иться *v.* bristle up, stick out, bulge out.

оттормаживать *v.* release the brake.

отточ/енный *a.* sharpened, sharp, edged, pointed; —ить *see* оттачивать.

оттрелит *m.* (min.) ottrelite, chloritoid.

оттуда *adv.* from there, therefrom.

оттягать *v.* gain by lawsuit.

оттягив/ание *n.* drawing off; (met.) drawing out; clarification (of liquid); spanning; delaying, prolonging; —ать

**v.** draw off, divert; draw out; clarify; delay, prolong, extend, procrastinate; span; —**ать молотом** hammer out; —**ающий** *a.* drawing out; —**ающая пружина** release spring.

**оттяжка** *f.* delay, procrastination; drawing out, pointing (of wire); span, span rope, guy rope, guy, stay, strut, brace.

**оття/жной** *a.* drawing out; **о. винт** set screw, adjusting screw; **о. изолятор** (elec.) shackle insulator; **о. трос** guy rope, guy; —**нутый** *a.* drawn (out); —**нуть** *see* **оттягивать.**

**отуман/ивать,** —**ить** *v.* fog, cover with fog; confuse.

**отунит** *m.* (min.) autunite (a calcium-uranium phosphate).

**отуп/евший** *a.* torpid, dull; —**ение** *n.* torpor, stupor; —**еть** *v.* sink into torpor, become dull.

**отучать** *v.* break (a habit), unteach.

**отфильтров/анный** *a.* filtered; —**ать,** —**ывать** *v.* filter, filter off, filter out.

**отфлан/жированный,** —**цованный** *a.* flanged.

**отформов/ать,** —**ывать** *v.* model, mold, shape.

**отхарк/ать,** —**ивать,** —**нуть** *v.* expectorate; —**ивающее средство** (med.) expectorant.

**отхлынуть** *v.* rush back.

**отход** *m.* setting off, departure, start; withdrawal, removal; drop-out; —**ы** *pl.* waste, waste products, refuse; by-product; (min.) tailings, tails; siftings, screenings; bottoms; —**ить** *v.* go off, leave, depart, withdraw; branch out; fall back.

**отходни/к** *m.* seasonal migratory worker; nightman; —**чество** *n.* seasonal migratory work.

**отходящий** *a.* outgoing, exit, waste; **о. газ** waste gas, flue gas, exhaust gas.

**отхожий** *a.* separated; **о. промысел** seasonal work, migratory work.

**отцве/сти,** —**тать** *v.* finish blossoming.

**отцеживать** *v.* strain off, filter; —**ся** *v.* filter, pass through.

**отцеп/ить,** —**лять** *v.* unhook, uncouple, unhitch, detach, release, disengage; —**ка** *f.* uncoupling; —**ляемый** *a.* detachable.

**отцовский** *a.* paternal.

**отчаиваться** *v.* despair, lose courage.

**отчал/ивать,** —**ить** *v.* put off, push off.

**отчасти** *adv.* partly, in part, partially.

**отчаян/ие** *n.* despair; —**ный** *a.* desperate.

**отчего** *adv.* why, for what reason.

**отчерк/ивать,** —**нуть** *v.* mark off.

**отчет** *m.* account, report, record; —**ы** *pl.* proceedings; **отдавать о.** *v.* account (for).

**отчетлив/ость** *f.* clearness, distinctness; precision; —**ый** *a.* clear, distinct, sharp.

**отчетн/ость** *f.* accounts; bookkeeping; —**ый** *a.* account; report; current, accountable; fiscal (year); under review, under consideration.

**отчисл/ение** *n.* reckoning off; deduction; —**ить,** —**ять** *v.* reckon off; deduct.

**отчистить** *see* **отчищать.**

**отчит/ать,** —**ывать** *v.* finish reading; rebuke; —**аться,** —**ываться** *v.* report.

**отчищ/ать** *v.* clean off, scour; free (from), purify; —**енный** *a.* cleaned; purified.

**отчужд/ать,** —**ить** *v.* alienate, estrange; —**ение** *n.* alienation; exclusion; **полоса** —**ения** right of way.

**отшвыр/енный** *a.* rejected; —**ивать,** —**нуть,** —**ять** *v.* throw away, reject.

**отшиб/ать,** —**ить** *v.* strike off, knock off.

**отшитый** *a.* boxed off.

**отшлаков/ать,** —**ывать** *v.* (met.) tap off slag, clear from slag or dross.

**отшлифов/анный** *a.* ground, polished; —**ать,** —**ывать** *v.* grind, polish up.

**отшнуров/ание,** —**ывание** *n.* pinch, constriction; contraction, shrinkage; —**анный** *a.* pinched; —**ать** *v.* pinch, constrict.

**отштукатур/енный** *a.* plastered; —**ивать,** —**ить** *v.* plaster.

**отщем/ить,** —**лять** *v.* pinch off.

**отщеп/ить,** —**лять** *v.* chip off, split off; detach, separate; —**иться,** —**ляться** *v.* split off, come off; —**ление** *n.* splitting off, cleavage; spallation; detachment, detaching, separation; —**ленный** *a.* split off; detached, separated.

**отщип/ать,** —**нуть,** —**ывать** *v.* pinch off.

отъедин/ение *n.* disconnecting, switching off; —ять *v.* disconnect, switch off.

отъезд/д *m.* departure, leaving, setting off; —жать *v.* drive off, depart.

отъем *m.* removal, take-off; tripper (of conveyer); о. мощности power take-off, p.t.o.; —ный *a.* removable, detachable.

отыск/ание *n.* finding, localization; —ать, —ивать *v.* seek, search for, look for; find, detect, discover; —аться, —иваться *v.* be sought; be found; —ивание *n.* searching, looking.

отяго/тительный *a.* burdensome; —щать *v.* burden, aggravate.

отяжел/евший *a.* heavy; —ение *n.* growing heavy; (text.) weighting; —еть *v.* become heavy, grow heavy; —ить, —ять *v.* (text.) weight.

Оуена процесс Owen (flotation) process.

ОУСХ *abbr.* (Областное управление сельского хозяйства) Regional Department of Agriculture.

офелиевая кислота ophelic acid.

офикальцит *see* офиолит.

офиоксилин *m.* ophioxylin.

офиолит *m.* (min.) ophiolite, ophicalcite; serpentine; —овый *a.* ophiolitic.

офиотоксин *m.* ophiotoxin.

офит *m.* (petr.) ophite (a diabase basalt); —овый *a.* ophitic, diabasic, lath-shaped.

офиуры *pl.* (zool.) Ophiuroidea.

офицер *m.* officer.

официальный *a.* official, formal.

официоз *m.* semiofficial publication; —ный *a.* semiofficial.

офлюсование *n.* fluxing.

оформл/ение *n.* appearance, design; shaping; official registration, putting into official form; —ять *v.* shape, mold; design; register officially, make official; draw up (documents).

офорт *m.* etching; aqua fortis, nitric acid.

офсет *m.* offset; —ная печать offset printing.

офтальм/ический *a.* ophthalmic; —ия *f.* (med.) ophthalmia; —о— *prefix* ophthalmo— (eyes); —ология *f.* ophthalmology; —оскоп *m.* ophthalmoscope.

оффицинальн/ый *a.* officinal, medicinal; —ые травы medicinal herbs.

оффретит *m.* (min.) offretite (a potash zeolite).

охапка *f.* bunch, bundle, armful, arm load.

охарактеризовать *v.* characterize, determine.

охва/т *m.* reach, range, coverage, compass, scope, girth; envelopment; overlapping; —тить, —тывать *v.* embrace, hug, envelop, encompass; —тываемый *a.* male (contact); —тывающий *a.* female (contact); —ченный *a.* embraced, enveloped, encompassed, seized.

охвостье *n.* tailings, tails.

охлад/евать, —еть *v.* become cool; become indifferent (to).

охладитель *m.* cooler, refrigerator; condenser; coolant, cooling agent, refrigerant; (met.) quenching medium, quenching compound; обратный о. reflux condenser; —ный *a.* cooling; —ная коробка (met.) chill box, chill mold, cooler; —ная смесь freezing mixture.

охла/дить, —ждать *v.* cool, chill, reduce the temperature (of), refrigerate; condense (steam); —ждаться *v.* cool, grow cool, cool off, get cold; —ждаемый *a.* cooled; —ждаемый водой water-cooled.

охлаждающ/ий *a.* cooling, chilling, freezing, refrigerating, refrigerant; condensing; о. прибор cooler, refrigerator; о. цилиндр condenser; —ая жидкость coolant; —ая колонна cooling tower; —ая смесь freezing mixture; —ая среда cooling medium; —ее вещество, —ее средство cooling agent, coolant, refrigerant; (met.) quenching compound; —ее пространство condensation chamber.

охлажден/ие *n.* cooling, chilling, refrigeration; condensation; искусственное о. air conditioning; поверхность —ия cooling surface; condensing surface; пространство —ия cooling jacket; condensation chamber; с водяным —ием water-cooled; с воздушным —ием air-cooled; система —ия cooling system; точка —ия freezing point.

охлажденный *a.* cooled, chilled, refrigerated; condensed; резко о. chilled.

**охлоп/ок** *m.* stuffing; **—ки** *pl.* waste.

**ОХН** *abbr.* (отделение химических наук) Division of Chemical Sciences.

**охолостить** *v.* castrate.

**охот/а** *f.* desire, will, inclination; hunt; (vet.) rut; **о. у него отпала** he no longer wanted (to); **отбивать —у** *v.* discourage; **—иться** *v.* hunt; **—ник** *m.* hunter; volunteer; **—но** *adv.* willingly.

**охра** *f.* ocher (usually impure iron oxide); **бурая о.** (min.) brown iron ocher, ocherous limonite; **желтая о.** yellow ocher, ocherous goethite or limonite; **золотистая о.** golden ocher; spruce ocher; **красная о.** red iron ocher, ocherous hematite; **черная о.** black ocher, wad, bog manganese ore.

**охран/а** *f.* guard, escort, custody; conservation, preservation; (labor) protection; **—ение** *n.* guarding, keeping; security; (mil.) outpost; **—ительный, —ный** *a.* protective, guard; preservative; **—ительное приспособление** guard; safety device; **—ное кольцо** guard ring (an auxiliary electrode); **—ить, —ять** *v.* guard, keep watch (over); preserve.

**охренный** *see* охристый.

**охрип/лость** *f.* hoarseness; **—лый, —ший** *a.* hoarse; **—нуть** *v.* get hoarse.

**охр/истый, —овый** *a.* ocherous, ocher-colored; **—истая земля** (min.) ocherous earth, yellow ocher; **—ить** *v.* paint with ocher.

**охрометь** *v.* grow lame.

**охроподобный** *a.* ochroid, ocherous, ocher-colored.

**охрупчивание** *n.* (met.) embrittlement.

**охряной** *see* охристый.

**оцеживать** *v.* strain, filter.

**оцеллярный** *a.* (petr.) ocellar (structure).

**оцелот** *m.* (zool.) ocelot.

**оцен/ивать, —ить, —ять** *v.* appraise, estimate, rate, value, evaluate, price, gage, grade; appreciate; **—ка** *f.* evaluation, appraisal; estimate, estimation, analysis, study; rating, rate; definition, determination; appreciation; **—очный** *a.* appraisable; **—щик** *m.* appraiser, estimator, evaluator.

**оцепен/елость** *f.*, **—ение** *n.* numbness, torpor; **—елый** *a.* numb, torpid;

**—еть** *v.* grow numb, become torpid.

**оцеп/ить, —лять** *v.* surround, encompass; **—ление** *n.* surrounding, encompassing.

**оцимен** *m.* ocimene, 2,6-dimethyl-1,5,7-octatriene.

**оцинков/ание** *n.*, **—ка** *f.*, **—ывание** *n.* zincing, zinc plating, galvanizing, galvanization; **—анный** *a.* zinc-plated, galvanized; **—анное железо** galvanized iron; **—ать, —ывать** *v.* zinc, zinc-plate, coat with zinc, galvanize; **—щик** *m.* galvanizer.

**оч.** *abbr.* (очень) very; **ОЧ** *abbr.* (октановое число) octane number.

**очаг** *m.* hearth, fireplace; refining furnace; focus, seat, location; source, origin; (magma) chamber; focus (of earthquake).

**очажное стекло** glass that has run down into the hearth.

**очанка** *f.* (bot.) eyebright (*Euphrasia*).

**очаровательный** *a.* charming.

**очевид/ец** *m.* eyewitness, witness; **—но** *adv.* apparently, evidently, obviously; it is obvious; **—ность** *f.* evidence, obviousness; reality, tangibility; **—ный** *a.* evident, obvious, apparent, manifest, clear.

**очекан/ивание** *n.* calking; chiseling; **—ивать, —ить** *v.* calk; chisel around, carve around.

**очень** *adv.* very, greatly, highly, much.

**очеред/ной** *a.* in turn, next; routine; **—ность** *f.* sequence; **—ь** *f.* turn, course; line, queue; (mil.) salvo; **в первую —ь** primarily, first; **по —и** in turn.

**очерк** *m.* outline, sketch, essay; synopsis, abridgment; tabulation.

**очерств/елый** *a.* hard, stale (bread); **—еть** *v.* harden, grow stale.

**очер/тание** *n.* outline, contour, configuration, circumscription, form, profile; **—тить, —чивать** *v.* trace, outline, draw a line, describe, define.

**очес** *m.* combings, waste; noil (of hair or fiber); (peat) dust; **—ать, —ывать** *v.* comb; deseed (flax, etc.); **—ки** *pl.* combings, waste; (silk) floss.

**очехловка** *f.* jacketing, canning.

**очечный** *a.* eyeglass, spectacles.

**очин/ивать, —ить** *v.* sharpen (pencil).

**очиститель** *m.* purifier, cleaner, cleanser; (gas) scrubber; separator; rectifier; (nucl.) decontaminator, scavenger.

**очистительн/ый** *a.* purifying, cleaning; (nucl.) decontaminating; **о. аппарат** purifier; rectifier; **о. бак** (sugar) clarifier, clearing pan; **о. завод, —ая установка** purifying plant; refinery; **—ое средство** purifying agent, purifier; cleanser, detergent; decontaminant.

**очист/ить** *v.* clean, cleanse; purify, refine; clarify, clear; clear away, clear off, scrape off; rectify; scrub (gas); (nucl.) decontaminate; (met.) scour, pickle; **—ка** *f.* cleaning, cleansing; purifying, purification, refining; rectification; clarification; clearing; clearing off, scraping off; trimming; scouring, pickling; (concentration) separation; cleaning unit; (nucl.) decontamination, scavenging; **—ки** *pl.* siftings, screenings; peelings; **мокрая —ка** scrubbing (of gas); **показатель —ки** decontamination index; **—ная** *f.* cleaning room; **—ной** *a.* cleaning.

**очиток** *m.* (bot.) stonecrop (*Sedum*).

**очищ/ать** *see* **очистить; —ающий** *a.* purifying, cleaning; sweeping (electrode); **—ающее средство** purifying agent, purifier; **—ение** *see* **очистка; —енный** *a.* purified, cleaned; refined; clarified; (nucl.) decontaminated.

**очки** *pl.* glasses, spectacles; eyepiece; (protective) goggles.

**очко** *n.* point; eye; mesh (of screen).

**очковать** *see* **прививать.**

**очков/ый** *a.* eyeglass, spectacle; **о. гнейс** augen gneiss (a lenticulated metamorphic rock); **—ая змея** (zool.) cobra; **—ая печь** spectacle furnace; **—ая текстура** (petr.) augen texture.

**очной** *see* **очный.**

**очнуться** *v.* recover, regain consciousness.

**очн/ый** *a.* ocular, eye; **о. корень** (bot.) valerian (*Valeriana*); **о. цвет** (bot.) pimpernel (*Anagallis arvensis*); **—ая**

**трава, жабная —ая помощь** (bot.) eyebright (*Euphrasia officinalis*).

**очувств/ление** *n.* sensitization, activation; **—оваться** *v.* regain consciousness.

**очутиться** *v.* appear, find oneself.

**ошвартов/ать, —ить** *v.* lash, moor.

**ошев** *m.* (glass) calcar, fritting furnace.

**ошейник** *m.* collar; (mech.) bush.

**ошелом/ить, —лять** *v.* stupefy, stun.

**ошелудиветь** *v.* grow scabby, get mangy.

**ошиб/аться, —иться** *v.* make a mistake, err; **—ка** *f.* mistake, error, inaccuracy, blunder, oversight, fault; **—ка в расчете** miscalculation; **—ка при отсчете** error in reading, reading error; **—ка счета** miscount; **по —ке, —очно** *adv.* by mistake, erroneously; **—очность** *f.* fallibility; inaccuracy; **—очный** *a.* mistaken, wrong, erroneous, inaccurate, incorrect, faulty.

**ошиновка** *f.* (elec.) leads.

**оширенный** *a.* broadened, extended.

**ошлаков/ание** *n.* (met.) slagging, formation of slag, scorification, clinkering; **—анный** *a.* scorified; **—атель** *m.* scorifier; **—ать, —ывать** *v.* slag, form slag, scorify, clinker; **—аться, —ываться** *v.* slag, form slag or clinker.

**ошпар/енный** *a.* scalded; **—ивание** *n.* scalding; **—ивать, —ить** *v.* scald.

**оштрафов/ать, —ывать** *v.* fine.

**оштукатур/енный** *a.* plastered; **—ивание** *n.* plastering; **—ить** *v.* plaster.

**ощелачив/ание** *n.* alkalization, alkalizing; **—ать** *v.* alkalize.

**ощуп/ание, —ывание** *n.* feeling, probing, sounding; **—ывать** *v.* feel, probe, sound.

**ощупь** *f.* touch, feel; **на о.** to the touch.

**ощу/тимый, —щаемый** *a.* sensible, perceptible, appreciable, apparent; **—тительность** *f.* perceptibility; **—тительный** *a.* perceptible, tangible, palpable, appreciable; **—тить, —щать** *v.* feel, perceive; **—щение** *n.* feeling, feel, perception, sensation.

# П

**п.** *abbr.* (поле) field; (правый) right-hand, clockwise; (пуд) pood; (пункт) point.

**ПАБК** *abbr.* (парааминобензойная кислота) *p*-aminobenzoic acid, PABA.

**пава** *f.* (zool.) peahen.

**павиан** *m.* (zool.) baboon.

**павил/ион, —ьон** *m.* pavilion.

**павинол** *m.* a leather substitute.

**павлин** *m.* (zool.) peacock; **—ий, —ный, —овый** *a.* peacock, pavonin; **—ий глаз** peacock butterfly (*Vanessa*); **—ово-голубой** *a.* peacock blue; **—о-глазки** *pl.* giant silkworm moths (*Saturniidae*); **—ья руда** (min.) peacock ore, bornite, purple copper ore.

**павлит** *see* **паулит.**

**павловния** *f.* (bot.) paulownia.

**паводо/к** *m.*, **—чный** *a.* flood, high water, freshet.

**ПАГ** *abbr.* (парааминогиппуровая кислота) *p*-aminohippuric acid.

**пагинация** *f.* (typ.) pagination.

**пагод/ит** *m.*, **—овый камень** (min.) pagodite, pagoda stone, agalmatolite; **—овый** *a.* pagoda.

**паголенок** *m.* leg (of stocking).

**пагубный** *a.* pernicious, noxious, destructive, fatal.

**падалица** *f.* windfall, fallen fruit.

**падаль** *f.* carrion.

**пад/ать** *v.* fall, drop, decrease, diminish, decline, dip; **—ающий** *a.* falling, dropping; (geol.) dipping; impinging, incident (rays, etc.); incoming (particle); shooting (star); drop (hammer).

**падеж** *m.* murrain, cattle plague; (grammar) case.

**паден/ие** *n.* fall, decrease, diminution, reduction, lowering, depression, drop (in pressure, etc.); incidence (of rays); (geol.) dip; gradient (of curve), slant, slope, descent, incline, inclination, grade; precipitation; collapse; **высота —ия** drop height; **сброс по —ию** (geol.) dip fault; **угол —ия** angle of incidence; (geol.) angle of dip.

**падзол** *m.* tannery waste (fertilizer).

**падкий** *a.* inclined having a weakness (for), susceptible (to).

**падуб** *m.* (bot.) holly (*Ilex*).

**пад/учая** *f.*, **п. болезнь** (med.) epilepsy; **—учий** *a.* falling; **—ший** *a.* fallen; **—ь** *f.* honeydew (from aphids).

**паев/ой, —ый** *a.* portion, part; share; (chem.) equivalent, equivalent-weight.

**паек** *m.* allowance, ration.

**пажёный** *a.* grooved.

**пажитник** *m.* (bot.) trigonella.

**пажит/ный** *a.*, **—ь** *f.* pasture.

**ПАЗ** *abbr.* (противоатомная защита) antinuclear defense.

**паз** *m.* groove, mortise, slot, rabbet, channel, channeling, flute; recess, notch; (welding) gap; **—ить, —овать** *v.* groove, mortise; join by tenon and mortise; **—ник** *m.* grooving plane, groover; (bot.) cat's-ear (*Hypochaeris*); **—ный** *a.* grooved, slotted; **—овик** *m.* notching tool; boaster, drove chisel (for masonry); **—овочный** *a.* grooving, mortising.

**пазов/ый** *a.* groove, mortise, slot; **п. нож, п. резец** grooving tool, grooving iron, groove-cutting chisel, slotting tool; **—ая фреза** slot mill.

**пазуха** *f.* bosom; (anat.) sinus; (bot.) axil.

**па/й** *m.* part, portion; share, interest; (chem.) equivalent, equivalent weight, combining weight; **вес —я** weight equivalent; **электрохимические —и** electrochemical equivalents.

**пайза** *f.* (bot.) Japanese millet (*Echinochloa frumentacea*).

**пайка** *f.* soldering, solder; seal.

**пайлер** *m.* (rolling) piler.

**пайрекс-трубки** *see* **пирекс-трубки.**

**пайсбергит** *m.* (min.) paisbergite (a variety of rhodonite).

**пайтин** *m.* paytine.

**пайщик** *m.* shareholder, partner.

**пак** *m.* pack; pack ice.

**пакгауз** *m.* warehouse, bonded warehouse, storehouse; stores.

**пакеляж** *see* **накляж.**

**пакер** *m.* (oil-well drilling) packer.

**пакет** *m.*, **—ный** *a.* packet, package, parcel, pack, bale; (met.) fagot, pile;

(mach.) block; (registered) letter; прокатка —ами (met.) pack rolling.

пакетиров/ание *n.*, —ка *f.* packing, baling; (met.) piling, fagoting; —анный *a.* packed, baled; fagoted (iron); —ать *v.* pack, bale; fagot, pile; —очный *a.* packing, baling; fagoting.

пакетн/ый *a. of* пакет; —ая прокатка (met.) pack rolling; —ая связка fagot, pile; —ое железо fagot iron.

паклун *m.* (bot.) germander (*Teucrium*).

пакля *f.* tow, oakum, fiber packing.

пакляж *m.* stone base (of pavement).

пакляный *a.* tow, oakum.

паков/ание *n.* packing, baling; —ать *v.* pack, bale; —очный *a.* packing, baling; (met.) fagoting, fagot bundling; —ый *a.* pack; —ый лед pack ice.

пакт *m.* pact, agreement.

пакфонг *m.* (met.) packfong, paktong, German silver, nickel silver.

пал *m.* ridge; (mach.) pawl; forest burning; *past sing. of* падать.

палагонит *m.* (petr.) palagonite (basalt glass); —овый *a.* palagonite, palagonitic.

палата *f.* chamber, board; (hospital) ward; bureau (of weights and measures).

палатин/ит *m.* (petr.) palatinite (a diabase rock); —овый красный Palatin Red (dye); —ол *m.* palatinol; —охромовый черный Palatinchrome Black.

палатка *f.* tent; stall, stand.

палахеит *m.* (min.) palacheite (same as botryogen).

палевый *a.* pale yellow, straw-colored.

пален/ие *n.* burning, singeing; firing, discharging, blasting; —ый *a.* burned, singed, scorched.

палео— *prefix* paleo— (old, ancient; early, primitive); —ботаника *f.* paleobotany, study of fossil plants; —ген *m.* (geol.) Paleogene (period of Cenozoic era); —зой *m.*, —зойская эра (geol.) Paleozoic era; —зойский *a.* Paleozoic; —лит *m.* paleolith; —литический *a.* paleolithic; —магнитный *a.* paleomagnetic; —нтолог *m.* paleontologist; —нтология *f.* paleontology; —тропический *a.* (bot.)

paleotropic; —цен *m.*, —ценовый период (geol.) Paleocene period.

палетка *f.* transparent graph paper.

пал/ец *m.* finger; (crank)pin, pin, peg; cam, cog, tooth, catch; guard; lifter; (zool.) digit; большой п. thumb; big toe; отпечаток —ьца fingerprint.

пали *past pl. of* падать.

паликурин *m.* palicourine.

палильн/ый *a.* burning, singeing; firing, blasting; —ая машина (min.) blasting machine, battery.

палимпсестовая структура (geol.) palimpsest structure.

палингенезис *m.* (geol., zool.) palingenesis.

палинологический *a.* palynological.

палинспастический *a.* palinspastic.

палисад *m.*, —ный *a.* palisade; —ник *m.* small front garden.

палис/андровое дерево, —сандровое дерево (bot.) rose wood, pallisander wood (*Jacaranda brasiliana*).

палит *m.* palite, chloromethyl chloroformate (poison gas).

палитра *f.* palette.

палить *v.* burn, scorch, singe; fire, discharge, shoot.

палка *f.* stick, cane; segment.

палладиев/ый *a.* palladic, palladium; —ая кислота palladic acid; —ая чернь palladium black.

палладизированный *see* палладированный.

паллад/ий *m.* palladium, Pd; азотнокислый п., азотнокислая закись —ия palladium nitrate, palladous nitrate; бромистый п. palladium bromide, palladous bromide; водородистый п. palladium hydride; гидрат закиси —ия palladium hydroxide, palladous hydroxide; двуокись —ия, окись —ия palladium oxide, palladic oxide; двухлористый п., хлористый п. palladium chloride, palladous chloride; закись —ия, одноокись —ия palladous oxide, palladium monoxide; соль закиси —ия palladous salt; соль окиси —ия palladic salt; хлорный п. palladic chloride, palladium tetrachloride.

палладированный *a.* palladized, palladium-coated, palladium-plated.

палладист/ый *a.* palladous, palladium; —ая соль palladous salt.

паллас *m.* (met.) pallas (gold-palladium-platinum alloy); —ит *m.* (petr.) pallasite, Pallas iron (ultrabasic rock).

паллет *m.*, —а *f.* pallet.

паллиатив *m.*, —ный *a.* palliative.

палочк/а *f.* small stick; (bact.) bacillus; в —ах stick; —ообразный *a.* bacillary, rod-shaped.

палочн/ик *m.* (bot.) reed mace (*Typha*); —ики *pl.* (zool.) walking sticks, etc. (*Phasmidae*); —ый *a.* stick; —ая трава *see* ежа.

палтрейбиловый спирт paltreubyl alcohol.

палтус *m.* (zool.) halibut.

палуб/а *f.*, —ный *a.* deck.

палудрин *m.* Paludrine (hydrochloride), chlorguanide hydrochloride.

палыгорскит *m.* (min.) mountain leather, mountain cork (a variety of asbestos).

пальба *f.* firing; cannonade.

пальм/а *f.* (bot.) palm, palm tree; —ы *pl.* Palmaceae; —арозовое масло palmarosa oil, geranium oil; —атин *m.* palmatine; —еллин *m.* palmellin.

пальмер *m.* micrometer calipers, micrometer gage.

пальмерит *m.* (min.) palmerite.

пальмер-фосфат *m.* a phosphate fertilizer.

пальметка *see* пальмер.

пальмиерит *m.* (min.) palmierite.

пальмитат *m.* palmitate, hexadecanoate.

пальмитил *m.* palmityl; хлористый п. palmityl chloride; —овый спирт palmityl alcohol, cetyl alcohol.

пальмитин *m.* palmitin, tripalmitin; —овокислый *a.* palmitic acid; palmitate (of); —овый *a.* palmitin, palmitic; —овый ангидрид palmitic anhydride;—овая кислота palmitic acid, hexadecanoic acid; соль —овой кислоты, —овокислая соль palmitate.

пальмито/левая кислота, —ловая кислота palmitolic acid, 7-hexadecynoic acid; —н *m.* palmitone, 16-hentriacontanone; —нитрил *m.* palmitonitrile, hexadecanenitrile.

пальмо/вые *pl.* (bot.) Palmaceae; —вый *a.* palm; —керновое масло, —ядерное масло palm (kernel) oil.

пальник *m.* blasting cap, cap.

пальп/ация *f.* (med.) palpation; —ировать *v.* palpate.

пальто *n.* overcoat, coat.

паль/цевидный, —цеобразный *a.* finger, fingered, digitate; —цевой *a.* finger; pin; finger-action (tool); end (milling cutter); —чатовидный *a.* digitiform; —чатонервный *a.* (bot.) digitinervate, palminerved; —чатораздельный *a.* (bot.) palmatipartite;—чатый *a.* finger, prong, pin; (bot.) palmate; —чатая трава Bermuda grass (*Cynodon dactylon*).

пальщик *m.* firer, blaster, discharger.

Паля-Кнорра синтез Paal-Knorr synthesis (of pyrrole derivatives).

палящий *a.* burning, scorching, singeing.

пампасы *pl.* pampas.

пампельмус *m.* (bot.) shaddock (*Citrus maxima*).

памфлет *m.* pamphlet.

памят/ливость *f.* retentive memory; —ливый *a.* having a retentive memory; —ник *m.* monument, memorial; —ный *a.* memorable; —ная записка memorandum; —уя *gerund* remembering, bearing in mind; —ь *f.* memory, recollection; storage (of data); восстанавливать в —и *v.* recollect, remember; объем —и storage capacity; заучить на —ь *v.* memorize.

паназа *f.* panase.

панакон *m.* panacon.

панама *f.* Panama bark, quillaia bark.

панамериканский *a.* Pan-American.

панамский *a.* Panama.

панариций *m.* (vet.) panaris, felon, whitlow.

панацея *f.* panacea.

панбархат *m.* (text.) panne.

пандажметр *m.* (min.) pendage meter, dip meter.

пандан *m.* (bot.) screw pine (*Pandanus*); —усовые *pl.* Pandanaceae.

пандем/ический *a.* (med.) pandemic; —ия *f.* pandemia.

пандермит *m.* (min.) pandermite, priceite.

пандус *m.* ramp (for cars, people).

панель *f.*, —ный *a.* panel, wainscot; (switch) board; footway, sidewalk;

обшивать —ю v. panel; —ная обшивка paneling, wainscoting.

панзоотический a. (vet.) panzootic.

панидиоморфный a. (petr.) panidiomorphic.

паника f. panic, fear, fright.

паникулатин m. paniculatine.

панкластит m. (expl.) panclastite.

панкреа/с m., —тическая железа (anat.) pancreas; —тин m. pancreatin; pancreatic juice; —тит m. (med.) pancreatitis; —тический a. pancreatic.

панно n. (wall) panel.

паноген m. Panogen (insecticide).

панорам/а f. panorama; —ирование n. (phot.) panning; panorama; scanning; —ировать v. pan; scan; —ный a. panorama, panoramic.

пансион m. boarding house; boarding school; board and lodging; —ер m. boarder.

пантал m. Pantal (aluminum alloy).

пантеле/граф m. (elec. comm.) pantelegraph; —графия f. pantelegraphy, facsimile telegraphy; —фон m. pantelephone, microtelephone.

пантера f. (zool.) panther.

панто— prefix panto—, pan—; —граф m. pantograph; —логия f. pantology; —метр m. pantometer; —морфизм m. (cryst.) pantomorphism; —пон m. Pantopon (mixture of hydrochlorides of opium alkaloids); —скоп m. pantoscope, panoramic camera; —теновая кислота pantothenic acid, vitamin $B_5$; —цид m. Pantocid, halazone.

панхроматический a. (phot.) panchromatic.

панцирн/оголовые pl. (zool.) Stegocephalia; —ые pl. (zool.) Dinoflagellata.

панцир/ный a. armorclad, armored, iron-clad; —ная плита armor plate; —ь m. armor, shell; в медном —е copperclad.

панцитопения f. (physiol.) pancytopenia.

папавер/альдин m. papaveraldine; —амин m. papaveramine; —ин m. papaverine; —иновая кислота papaveric acid, rhoeadic acid; —инол m. papaverinol (a hydroxy-papaverine); —олин m. papaveroline.

папа/ин m., —йотин m. papain, papayotin, vegetable pepsin; —йя f. (bot.) papaya (Carica papaya).

папиллярный a. (biol.) papillary, papillose.

папинов котел Papin's digester.

папирос/а f., —ный a. cigarette; —ная бумага tissue paper; cigarette paper.

папирус m. papyrus (paper); —ный a. papyrus, papyraceous.

папк/а f., —овый a. portfolio; cardboard, pasteboard, millboard, board; (roofing) paper; pulp.

пап-машина f. constructionboard machine, millboard machine.

папоротник m. (bot.) fern; лесной п., мужской п., черный п. male fern (Dryopteris filix-mas); водные —и Hydropteridineae; настоящие —и Polypodiaceae.

папоротнико/вые pl. (bot.) Filicales; Polypodiaceae; —вый a. fern; ferny; —образные pl. Pteridophyta; —семянные pl. Pteridospermae.

папорть see папоротник, мужской.

паппатачи, лихорадка (med.) phlebotomus fever.

паприк/а f., —овый a. paprika.

папула f. (med.) papule.

папье-маше n. papier-maché.

пар m. steam, vapor; (agr.) fallow; gen. pl. of пара; —ы pl. vapor; fumes; водяной п. steam; water vapor; давление —а, упругость —a vapor pressure; обрабатывать —ом v. steam; очищать —ами v. fumigate; перегонка —ом steam distillation; плотность —a vapor density; поднять —ы v. fire up (boiler), raise steam; полным —ом full steam, full power; продутый —ом steam-treated; расход —a steam consumption; температура образования —a vaporization point.

пар/а f. pair, couple, dyad; п. сил (mech.) couple; без —ы unpaired, odd; образование —ы (nucl.) pair production.

пара— prefix para—; в положении пара in the para position; —аминофенол m. p-aminophenol; —бановая кислота parabanic acid, oxalylurea.

парабол/а *f.* (geom.) parabola; —ический *a.* parabolic; —оид *m.* paraboloid.

пара/вивианит *m.* (min.) paravivianite (a variety of vivianite); —винная кислота paratartaric acid, racemic acid; —водород *m.* para hydrogen.

парагвайский *a.* Paraguay; п. чай Paraguay tea, mate (leaves); п. чайный куст (bot.) Paraguay tea, mate (*Ilex paraguariensis*).

пара/гелий *m.* para helium; —генезис *m.* (min.) paragenesis; —генетический *a.* paragenetic; —гнейс *m.* (petr.) paragneiss; —гонит *m.* (min.) paragonite (a variety of mica); —гопеит *m.* (min.) parahopeite (a hydrous zinc phosphate).

параграф *m.* paragraph, section, clause.

парад *m.* parade, show.

парадиазин *m.* paradiazine, pyrazine; —дихлорбензол *m.* paradichlorobenzene.

парадн/ый *a.* for show; gala; front, main; —ое испытание trials (of power plant) under optimum conditions.

парадокс *m.* paradox; —альный *a.* paradoxical.

парадоксит *m.* (min.) paradoxite (a variety of orthoclase).

паразит *m.* parasite; parasitic oscillation; (bot.) epiphyte; (mech.) idler wheel, idle gear, idler; —ы *pl.* vermin; —арный, —ический, —ный, —овый, —оподобный *a.* parasitic; idle; spurious, stray; —изм *m.* (biol.) parasitism; —ный ток (elec.) eddy current; —ная потеря (elec.) parasitic loss; —ная шестерня idle gear, idler gear, intermediate gear; —ное колесо idler wheel, idler; —оубивающий *a.* parasiticidal; —оубивающее средство parasiticide.

пара/каучук *m.* Para rubber; —клаз *m. m.* (geol.) paraclase, fault; —коновая кислота paraconic acid; —красный *m.* Para Red (dye); —ксантин *m.* paraxanthine, 1,7-dimethylxanthine; —ксилол *m.* *p*-xylene; —лауриопит *m.* (min.) paralaurionite (same as rafaelite).

парали/затор *m.* inhibitor; —зованный *a.* paralyzed, paralytic; —зовать,

поражать —чом *v.* paralyze; —тик *m.*, —чный *a.* paralytic; —чная трава (bot.) bryony (*Bryonia*).

параллак/с *m.* parallax; —сный, —тический *a.* parallactic, parallax.

параллел/епипед *m.* (geom.) parallelepiped; —изм *m.* parallelism; —о-грамм *m.* parallelogram.

параллель *f.* parallel; проводить п. *v.* draw a parallel; contrast, compare; —но *adv.* parallel (with); (elec.) in parallel; —но-последовательно *adv.* (elec.) in parallel-series; —ность *f.* parallelism.

параллельн/ый *a.* parallel; collateral; cocurrent (flow); п. контур, —ая цепь (elec.) parallel circuit; —ое включение, —ое соединение (elec.) connection in parallel; гравировать —ыми линиями *v.* hatch, shade; с —ыми пластинами parallel-plate.

пар/альдегид *m.* paraldehyde (trimer of acetaldehyde); —альдол *m.* paraldol (dimer of aldol); —алюминит *m.* (min.) paraluminite (near aluminite).

парамагн/етизм *m.* paramagnetism; —етик *m.* paramagnet; —итный *a.* paramagnetic; —итное тело paramagnetic body, paramagnetic.

параметр *m.* (math.) parameter; —ы *pl.* parameters, variables; conditions; п. кривизны buckling; —ит *m.* (med.) parametritis;—ический *a.* parametric.

парамецин *m.* paramecin.

парамид *m.* paramide, mellimide.

парамолочная кислота paralactic acid, sarcolactic acid.

параморф/изм *m.* (min.) paramorphism; —ный *a.* paramorphic; —оз *m.*, —оза *f.* paramorph (crystal).

парангон *m.* paragon; flawless gem.

паранитро/анилин *m.* *p*-nitroaniline; —толуол *m.* *p*-nitrotoluene.

парано/йя, —я *f.* (med.) paranoia.

парантез *m.* parenthesis.

парапет *m.* parapet, breastwork.

пара/положение *n.* para position; —розоловая кислота pararosolic acid, aurine; —сахариновая кислота parasaccharic acid; —сепиолит *m.* (min.) parasepiolite (a fibrous variety of sepiolite); —стильбит *m.* (min.) parastilbite (a variety of epistilbite);

—такамит *m.* (min.) paratacamite (a twinned atacamite); —тион *m.* Parathion (insecticide); —тирин *m.* Parathyrin (extract of parathyroid gland).

**паратиф** *m.* (med.) paratyphoid.

**паратон** *m.* an additive for lubricant oils.

**парафиз** *m.* (biol.) paraphysis.

**парафин** *m.* paraffin; paraffin wax; **жидкий п.** liquid paraffin, petrolatum; **сырой п.** crude paraffin; paraffin scale; **твердый п.** paraffin wax.

**парафин/изация** *f.* paraffinization; —и-**рованный** *a.* paraffined; waxed with paraffin; —**ировать** *v.* paraffin, paraffinize; —**исто-смолистая нефть** paraffin-asphalt petroleum; —**истый**, —**овый** *a.* paraffin; —**истая нефть** paraffin-base petroleum; —**овая кислота** paraffinic acid; —**овое масло** paraffin oil.

**парафировать** *v.* initial.

**пара/форм**, —**формальдегид** *m.* paraformaldehyde, paraform; —**фталевая кислота** *p*-phthalic acid, terephthalic acid; —**хинон** *m.* paraquinone; —**хлортолуол** *m.* *p*-chlorotoluene; —**хор** *m.* parachor (expression of molecular volume); —**центрический** *a.* (math.) paracentric, paracentrical; —**циан** *m.* paracyanogen; —**цимол** *m.* *p*-cymene.

**парашют** *m.*, —**ный** *a.* parachute; —**ист** *m.* parachutist.

**паращитовидная железа** (anat.) parathyroid gland.

**парволин** *m.* parvoline.

**паргазит** *m.* (min.) pargasite (green-blue hornblende).

**паргел/ий** *m.* parhelion, mock sun; —**ический** *a.* parhelic.

**парез** *m.* (med.) paresis, incomplete paralysis.

**парейр/ин** *m.* pareirine, pereirine; —**ы корень** pareira (dried root of *Chondrodendron tomentosum*).

**парен/ие** *n.* steaming, stewing; flight, soaring.

**паренхима** *f.* (biol.) parenchyma; —**тоз-ный** *a.* parenchymatous; —**тозные черви** (zool.) Parenchymata.

**пареный** *a.* steamed, stewed.

**парень** *m.* young man, fellow.

**пари** *n.*, **держать п.** *v.* bet, wager.

**париан** *see* **паросский фарфор**; —**ит** *m.* (min.) parianite (a variety of asphaltum).

**паридин** *m.* paridin.

**париетальный** *a.* (biol.) parietal.

**париет/ин** *m.* parietin, physcion; —**овая кислота** parietic acid, chrysophanic acid.

**Париж** Paris.

**парижск/ий** *a.* Paris, Parisian; **п. желтый** Paris yellow, lead chromate; —**ая зелень** Paris green (insecticide); —**ая лазурь**, —**ая синь** Paris blue, ferric ferrocyanide.

**паризит** *m.* (min.) parisite (a fluocarbonate of cerium metals).

**парик** *m.* wig; —**махер** *m.* barber; —**махерская** *f.* barbershop; hairdresser's; —**овое дерево** (bot.) Venice sumac (*Rhus cotinus*).

**парилл/ин** *m.*, —**овая кислота** parillin, parillic acid.

**парильня** *see* **парная**.

**паринаровая кислота** parinaric acid.

**парировать** *v.* parry, counter.

**паритет** *m.* parity, equality; **на —ных началах с** on a par with, equal to.

**парить** *v.* steam, stew; soar, hover.

**парицин** *m.* paricine.

**парк** *m.* park, yard; (railroad) stock; fleet (of trucks); **п. подвижного состава** rolling stock; **п. путей** switch yard; **мостовой п.** bridging train.

**паркеризация** *f.* parkerizing, parkerization (rustproofing process).

**паркесирование** *see* **Паркса способ**.

**паркет** *m.*, —**ный** *a.* parquet; parquet floor.

**паркин** *m.* parkine.

**парковый** *a.* park.

**Паркса способ** Parkes process (for refining argentous lead).

**парламент** *m.* parliament.

**парлифт** *m.* steam lift (for liquids).

**пармы** *pl.* parmy (low, wooded ridges flanking the Ural Mountains).

**парная** *f.* steam room.

**парник** *m.* hotbed, seed bed; **в —е under glass**; **холодный п.** coldframe; —**о-вый** *a.* hotbed, hothouse (plants).

**парной** *a.* fresh, new; warm.

**парно/копытные** *pl.* (zool.) Artiodactyla; **—листник** *m.* (bot.) bean caper (*Zygophyllum*); **—листные** *pl.* (bot.) Zygophyllaceae; **—перистый, —перистосложный** *a.* (bot.) paripinnate, abruptly pinnate; **—усые** *pl.* (zool.) Antennata.

**парн/ый** *a.* twin, pair, sister; dual; (bot.) twin; conjugate (leaves); fuming, fumy, steaming; **—ая деталь** mate.

**паро—** *prefix* steam; vapor; (agr.) fallow; **—вание** *n.* fallowing; **—вик** *m.* boiler; **—вичная** *f.* boiler house, boiler room; **—вичный** *a.* steam; boiler; **—водяной** *a.* steam-and-water; **—воз** *m.*, **—возный** *a.* locomotive, steam engine; **—воздушный** *a.* exhaust (passage); **—возостроительный завод** locomotive factory, engine works.

**паров/ой** *a.* steam, steam-driven; vapor, vaporous; (agr.) fallow; **п. котел** boiler; **—ая машина** steam engine; **—ая мельница** power mill; **—ая пробка** vapor lock; **—ая сила** steam power; **—ое отопление** steam heat.

**паро/впуск** *m.*, **—впускная труба** steam admission pipe; **—выпускной** *a.* exhaust; **—выпускная труба** exhaust pipe, exhaust; **—генератор** *m.* steam generator, boiler; **—гидравлический** *a.* steam-hydraulic; **—динамо** *n.*, **—динамомашина** *f.* steam dynamo, steam-driven generator; **—запорный** *a.* steam cut-off; **—запорное приспособление** cut-off device, cut-off.

**пароксизм** *m.* paroxysm, fit.

**паром** *m.* ferry, ferryboat; *instr. of* **пар**; **подвесной п.** transporter bridge.

**паро/мер, —метр** *m.* steam meter, steam flow meter; vaporimeter; **—непроницаемый** *a.* vaportight; steamproof.

**парообработ/ка** *f.* fallow tillage; **—ник** *m.* weeder.

**парообраз/ный** *a.* vaporous, in vapor form; steamlike; **—ование** *n.* formation of steam, steam generation, steam production; evaporation, vaporization; volatilization; **теплота —ования** heat of evaporation.

**парообразователь** *m.*, **—ный прибор** steam generator, boiler; evaporator, vaporizer; **—ный** *a.* steam-generating,

steam-producing; **—ная способность** evaporative capacity.

**паро/осушитель** *m.* steam dryer; **—отвод** *m.*, **—отводная труба** steam discharge pipe, steam exhaust, exhaust pipe; **—отделитель** *m.* steam separator.

**пароотсек/атель** *m.* steam cut-off valve; **—ающее приспособление** steam cut-off device, steam cut-off.

**пароочиститель** *m.* field cultivator.

**паро/перегреватель** *m.* steam superheater; **—пескоструйный аппарат** steam sand blast, steam sand blaster; **—подвод** *m.* steam supply; **—приводная труба** steam supply pipe, steam supply line; **—провод** *m.*, **—проводная труба** steam pipe, steam supply line.

**паропроизвод/ительность** *f.* evaporative value; (boiler) rating; **—ительный** *a.* steam-producing; evaporating; **—ительная способность** evaporative capacity; **—ство** *n.* generation of steam.

**парораспредел/ение** *n.* steam distribution; **—итель** *m.* steam distributor, steam header; **—ительная труба** steam-distributing pipe, steam supply line.

**парораспыл/ение** *n.* steam atomization; **—итель** *m.* steam atomizer.

**паро/сборник** *m.* steam collector; dome (of boiler); **—светный** *a.* vapor-discharge; **—силовая установка** steam power plant; **—собиратель** *m.* steam collector; steam header; **—содержание** *n.* steam content; vapor content.

**паросский** *a.* Parian; **п. мрамор** Parian marble (a marble from Paros); **п. фарфор** (cer.) Parian porcelain.

**паростойкий** *a.* vaporproof.

**пароструйн/ый** *a.* steam-jet; **п. распылитель** steam-jet atomizer, steam-jet sprayer; **—ое сопло** steam-jet nozzle.

**паросушитель** *m.* steam dryer.

**паротит** *m.* (med.) parotitis.

**паро/турбина** *f.* steam turbine; **—фазный** *a.* vapor-phase.

**пароход** *m.*, **—ный** *a.* steamboat, steamship, steamer; **—ная труба** smoke stack; **—ство** *n.* steam navigation; steamship company.

пароэлектроцентраль *m.* steam power plant.

Парра аппарат Parr apparatus (for carbon determination).

Парри колошниковый затвор Parry cup and cone arrangement.

парсек *m.* (astron.) parsec (unit of measure).

парсонсит *m.* parsonsite (uranium mineral).

партено— *prefix* (biol.) partheno— (asexual); —генез *m.* parthenogenesis.

партизанская война guerilla warfare.

партийный *a.* party, communist.

партиний *m.* (met.) partinium (an aluminum-tungsten alloy).

партия *f.* party, group, crew; (com.) parcel, consignment, lot, set; batch, cut (of flax).

партнер *m.* partner.

парус *m.* sail, canvas; fan (of windmill); (bot.) vane; —ина *f.*, —инный, —и-новый *a.* canvas, duck; tarpaulin; —ить *v.* sail; —ник *m.* sailboat; sail maker; sailfish; —ники *pl.* (zool.) swallow tails (*Papilionidae*); —ный *a.* canvas, sail.

парфюмер *m.* perfumer; —изация *f.* imparting odor (to gas); —ия *f.*, —ный *a.* perfumery; —ное искусство perfumery; —ное производство perfume manufacture; —ные изделия, —ные товары perfumes, perfumery.

парфюмировать *v.* perfume, scent.

парц. *abbr.* (парциальный) partial.

парцелл/а *f.* parcel; —ировать *v.* parcel (out), allot; —яция *f.* parceling.

парциальн/ый *a.* partial, fractional, divided; —ая волна partial wave.

парч/а *f.*, —евая ткань (text.) brocade; —евой, —евый *a.* brocade, brocaded.

парш/а *f.* mange, scab; —иветь *v.* grow mangy; —ивый *a.* mangy, scabby.

пары *pl.* of пар; *gen. and pl. of* пара.

парящий *a.* steaming, steamy; soaring.

пасе/ка *f.*, —чный *a.* apiary, beehive; —чник *m.* bee keeper.

пасик *m.* round drive belt.

ПАСК *abbr.* (парааминосалициловая кислота) *p*-aminosalicylic acid.

Паскаля закон Pascal's law.

пасквиль *m.* libel; —ный *a.* libelous.

паскоит *m.* (min.) pascoite.

паслен *m.* (bot.) nightshade (*Solanum*); черный п. deadly nightshade (*Solanum nigrum*); —овые *pl.* Solanaceae.

пасмурн/ость *f.* mist, haze; gloominess, gloomy weather; —ый *a.* cloudy, dull, overcast; gloomy, dismal.

пасока *f.* (bot.) bleeding sap.

паспал/ум, —юм *m.* (bot.) paspalum.

паспарту *n.* passe-partout, mount; master key.

паспорт *m.*, —ный *a.* passport, pass; record; (mach.) rating plate, name plate; заводский п., —ная дощечка rating plate; —изация *f.* rating; conditioning.

пасс *m.* pass; —аж *m.*, —ажный *a.* passage; —ажир *m.*, —ажирский *a.* passenger.

пассаметр *m.* indicating snap gage (for outside measurements).

пассат *m.*, —ный ветер tradewind.

пассатижи *pl.* combination cutting and twisting pliers.

пассет *m.* bubble cap (in distillation or absorption tower).

пассив *m.* (com.) liabilities.

пассив/ация, —изация *f.*, —ирование *n.* (met.) passivation, passivating, inhibition of corrosion; —ированный *a.* passivated, passive; —ировать *v.* passivate; —ирующий *a.* passivating.

пассивноплавающий *a.* (zool.) planktonic.

пассивн/ость *f.*, —ое состояние passivity, inertness; —ый *a.* passive, inert.

пассиметр *m.* indicating plug gage.

пассир *m.*, —ный *a.* cow dung.

пассифлора *f.* (bot.) passiflora.

паста *f.* paste.

пастбище *n.* pasture, pasture ground.

паства *f.* flock, herd; pasture.

пастель *f.*, —ный *a.*, —ный карандаш pastel, crayon, —ные краски pastel colors, crayons.

пастериз/атор *m.* pasteurizer; —ация *f.*, —ование *n.* pasteurization; —о-ванный *a.* pasteurized; —овать *v.* pasteurize.

пастернак *m.* (bot.) parsnip (*Pastinaca sativa*).

пастеровский *a.* Pasteur.

пасти *v.* tend, herd, shepherd; pasture.

пастила *f.* fruit candy; lozenge, pastille.

пастилаж *m.* (cer.) ornamentation in relief.

пастиров/ание *n.* pasting; —анный *a.* pasted; —ать *v.* paste.

пастись *v.* graze.

пастозный *a.* pasty, doughlike, flabby.

пастух *m.* herdsman, cowherd, swineherd, shepherd; (electric) fence.

пастушья сумка, п. трава (bot.) shepherd's purse (*Capsella bursa pastoris*).

пасть *f.* mouth (of animal); trap, snare; *v. see* падать.

пастьба *f.* pasturage, grazing.

пасын/кование *n.* (agr.) sucker removal; —ок *m.* sucker, side shoot.

пасьма *f.* (text.) cut; lea; skein.

пасюк *m.* Norway rat.

пат. *abbr.* (патент) patent; (патогенный) pathogenic; (патология) pathology.

патент *m.* patent; бюро —ов, учреждение по выдаче —ов patent office; владелец —а patentee; заявлять п. *v.* patent, apply for a patent; описание —а patent specification.

патент/ирование, —ование *n.* patenting; (met.) patenting (hardening steel in lead); —никель *m.* copper-nickel alloy resembling constantan; —ный *a.* patent, patented; —ованный *a.* patented; —ованный голубой patent blue; —ованная желть patent yellow, mineral yellow; —овать *v.* patent.

Патера способ Patera process (for extracting silver from its ores).

патерностер *m.* a continuously operating elevator.

патефон *m.*, —ный *a.* phonograph.

патин/а *f.* patina (metal oxide film); —ирование *n.* covering with patina; —ировать *v.* cover with patina; —ирующая краска greening lacquer.

патиссон *m.* scallop squash (*Cucurbita pepo condensa*).

—патия *f. suffix* —pathy.

пато— *prefix* patho—, pathological; —генез *m.* pathogenesis; —генный *a.* pathogenic.

патока *f.* syrup; molasses; сахарная п.

syrup; черная п. molasses.

патолог *m.* pathologist; —ический *a.* pathologic; —ия *f.* pathology.

паточный *a.* syrupy; molasses; п. песок brown sugar.

патриотичный *a.* patriotic.

патрон *m.*, —ный *a.* chuck (of drill, lathe), holder, holding device, hold; case, shell; extractor thimble; (elec.) receptacle; (lamp) socket; (mil.) cartridge; pattern, stencil; patron; п.-пальник *m.* igniter; зажимной п. chuck; плавкий п. (elec.) cartridge fuse; полный п. (molding) core barrel.

патронит *m.* (min.) patronite (a vanadium sulfide).

патронник *m.* cartridge chamber.

патронн/ый *a. of* патрон; п. завод ammunition factory; п. захват socket tool; п. ключ socket wrench; п. предохранитель, —ая трубка (elec.) cartridge fuse; п. пункт ammunition distributing point; п. станок, п. токарный станок chucking lathe, chucking machine; —ая гильза cartridge case; —ая муфта sleeve coupling, coupling sleeve.

патронташ *m.* cartridge belt.

патрубок *m.* nipple, nozzle, outlet; socket, sleeve, connection, connecting piece, connecting pipe; branch pipe; (thermometer) boss.

патруль *m.*, —ный *a.* patrol.

Паттинсона белила Pattinson's white (pigment); П. процесс Pattinson process (for separating silver from lead).

паттинсониров/ание *n.* (met.) pattinsonization; —ать *v.* pattinsonize, apply Pattinson process.

патулин *m.* patulin, clavacin (antibiotic).

пауза *f.* pause, break, interval, intermission, rest; blank.

паук *m.* (zool., mech.) spider; compressed-air distributor; distillation "pig" (fraction distributor); —и *pl.* (zool.) Araneae; —овидный, —о-образный *a.* spiderlike; arachnoid, cobweblike; —ообразные *pl.* (zool.) Arachnida; —ообразная опора (mech.) spider.

**Паули принцип** (quantum mechanics) Pauli (exclusion) principle; **П. реакция** Pauly reaction (for proteins).

**паулиния** *f.* (bot.) paullinia.

**паундаль** *m.* poundal (unit of force).

**пауроподовые** *pl.* (zool.) Pauropoda.

**паутина** *f.* cobweb, web.

**пауцин** *m.* paucine.

**паучок** *m.* little spider; (mech.) spider collar.

**паушальный** *a.* total, lump (sum).

**пах** *m.* (anat.) groin.

**паха/рь** *m.* plowman; —**ть** *v.* plow, till.

**пахи**— *prefix* pachy— (thick); —**дермия** *f.* (med.) pachydermia; —**дермы** *pl.* (zool.) pachyderms; —**карпин** *m.* pachycarpine; —**тена** *f.* (biol.) pachytene.

**пахнолит** *m.* (min.) pachnolite (an alteration product of cryolite).

**пахнуть** *v.* smell, reek (of).

**паховой** *a.* (anat.) groin, inguinal.

**пахот/а** *f.* tillage, plowing; arable land; —**нопригодный, —носпособный** *a.* arable, tillable; —**ный** *a.* arable, tillable; top (soil).

**пахт/а** *f.* buttermilk; —**алка** *f.* churn; —**анье** *n.* churning; buttermilk; —**ать** *v.* churn.

**пахуч/есть** *f.* fragrance, scent, odoriferousness; —**ий** *a.* fragrant, sweet-scented, odoriferous, redolent; —**ий колосок** (bot.) sweet-scented vernal grass (*Anthoxanthum odoratum*); —**ее вещество** perfume, scent; —**ка** *f.* (bot.) woodruff (*Asperula odorata*); wild basil (*Calamintha* or *Clinopodium vulgare*); savory (*Satureia*).

**пациент** *m.* patient.

**пачечный** *a.* bundle, bundling; (met.) fagoting, fagot bundling.

**пачиниевы тельца** (anat.) Pacinian corpuscles.

**пачка** *f.* pack, packet, parcel, batch, block; (met.) fagot, pile, stack; (stratigraphy) member.

**пачк/ание** *n.* soiling, contamination; —**ать** *v.* soil, contaminate, dirty.

**Пачука чан** Pachuca tank (pulp agitator).

**пачул/ен** *m.* patchoulene; —**и** *pl.*, —**ь** *f.*, —**иевый** *a.* (bot.) patchouli (*Pogostemon patchouli*); —**иевый спирт** patchouli alcohol; —**ин** *m.* patchoulin.

**Пашена ряд** Paschen series (of spectrum lines).

**паш/енный** *a.* plowed, tilled; —**ет** *pr. 3 sing. of* **пахать**; —**ня** *f.* plowed field.

**паштет** *m.* meat pie.

**пашущий** *a.* plowing.

**паюсный** *a.* pressed (caviar).

**паяльник** *m.* soldering iron, soldering bit.

**паяльн/ый** *a.* soldering; **п. свинец** lead solder; —**ая вода** soldering fluid (solution of zinc chloride); —**ая горелка, —ая лампа, —ая трубка** blowpipe; blow torch, torch; —**ая кислота** soldering acid; —**ая печь** soldering furnace.

**пая/льщик** *m.* solderer, tinsmith; —**ние** *n.* soldering; —**ть** *v.* solder.

**ПВД** *abbr.* (**прямоточный воздушно-реактивный двигатель**) ramjet-engine.

**ПВЛ** *abbr.* (**повальное воспаление легких**) epidemic pneumonia.

**ПВМ** *abbr.* (**прессовыдувная машина**) (glass) press and blow machine.

**ПВНО** *abbr.* closed-cup flash-point apparatus (flame-heated); **ПВНЭ** *abbr.* closed-cup flash-point apparatus (electrically heated).

**ПВО** *abbr.* (**противовоздушная оборона**) anti-aircraft defense.

**пг** *abbr.* (**пикограмм**) micromicrogram.

**ПД** *abbr.* (**поршневой двигатель**) piston engine.

**ПДБ** *abbr.* (**парадихлорбензол**) para-dichlorobenzene.

**ПДК** *abbr.* (**предельно допустимая концентрация**) maximum permissible concentration.

**пеан** *m.* (med.) Pean's forceps, clamp forceps.

**небрина** *f.* pébrine (silkworm disease).

**пегамоид** *m.* pegamoid (artificial leather); pegamoid (an aluminum paint).

**пеганин** *m.* peganine, vasicine (insecticide).

**пеганит** *m.* (min.) peganite, variscite.

**пегель/мессер** *m.*, —**ная установка** transmission level meter.

**пегий** *a.* dappled, spotted, mottled.

**пегмат/изация** *f.* (geol.) pegmatization; —**ит** *m.* (petr.) pegmatite, giant granite; —**итовый** *a.* pegmatitic; —**оидный** *a.* pegmatoid.

**педагог** *m.* teacher, pedagogue.

**педал/ь** *m.*, **—ьный** *a.* pedal, foot lever, treadle; **от —и, с —ьным приводом** pedal-driven; **тормоз с —ью** foot brake; **—ьный привод** pedal drive; **—ьная передача** pedal gear; **—ьное коромысло** foot lever, pedal.

**педантичный** *a.* pedantic, punctilious.

**педиальный** *a.* (cryst.) pedial.

**педиатр** *m.* (med.) pediatrician; **—ический** *a.* pediatric; **—ия** *f.* pediatrics.

**педикулез** *m.* pediculosis, infestation with lice.

**педометр** *m.* (surv.) pedometer.

**пезиза** *f.* (bot.) a manure mushroom (*Peziza vesiculosa*).

**пейзаж** *m.* landscape.

**пейте** *imp. of* **пить.**

**пейцеданин** *m.* peucedanin, imperatorin.

**пек** *m.* pitch (distillation residue); peck (measure); *past sing. of* **печь.**

**пекан** *m.* (bot.) pecan (*Carya olivaeformis*).

**пекар/ный** *a.* baking; **п. порошок** baking powder; **—ня** *f.* bakery; **—ь** *m.* baker.

**Пекин** Peking.

**Пекле число** Peclet number.

**пеклеван/ка** *f.*, **—ная мука** fine quality rye flour; **—ник** *m.* rye bread.

**пекл/и** *past pl. of* **печь; —о** *n.* scorching heat.

**пект/аза** *f.* pectase; **—ат** *m.* pectate; **—енин** *m.* pectenine; **—изация** *f.* pectization, gelatinization, jellification; **—изировать** *v.* pectize, gelatinize.

**пектин** *m.* pectin; **—аза** *f.* pectinase; **—овая кислота** pectic acid; **соль —овой кислоты, —овокислая соль** pectate; **—овокислый** *a.* pectic acid; pectate (of); **—овые вещества** pectins; **—оза** *f.* pectinose, arabinose.

**пекто/за** *f.* pectose; **—зиновая кислота** pectosinic acid; **—зовый** *a.* pectose, pectosic; **—лиз** *m.* pectolysis.

**пектолит** *m.* (min.) pectolite.

**пек/ут** *pr. 3 pl. of* **печь; —ущий** *a.* baking, roasting; **—ший** *past act. part. of* **печь.**

**пелаг/ит** *m.* (min.) pelagite (deep-sea manganese nodules); **—ический** *a.* pelagic, pelagian, deep-sea.

**пеларгон** *m.* pelargone, 9-heptadecanone; **—ат** *m.* pelargonate; **—идин** *m.* pelargonidin; **—ий** *m.*, **—ия** *f.* (bot.) pelargonium; **—ил** *m.* pelargonyl; **хлористый —ил** pelargonyl chloride; **—ин** *m.* pelargonin, pelargonidin glucoside.

**пеларгоново/кислый** *a.* pelargonic acid; pelargonate (of); **—кислая соль** pelargonate; **—этиловый эфир** ethyl pelargonate.

**пеларгонов/ый** *a.* pelargone, pelargonic; **п. альдегид** pelargonaldehyde, nonanal; **—ая кислота** pelargonic acid, nonylic acid; **соль —ой кислоты** pelargonate.

**Пеле волосы** (min.) Pélé's hair (a fibrous, basaltic glass).

**пелейский** *a.* peléan (eruption).

**пелена** *f.* shroud; (bot.) hymenium; **—ть** *v.* swaddle, wrap.

**пеленг** *m.*, **—овый** *a.* bearing, direction; **—атор** *m.* (rad.) direction finder; **—ация** *f.*, **—ирование** *n.* direction finding; **—овать** *v.* set, bear, take a course.

**пеленка** *f.* diaper, swaddling cloth.

**пелециподы** *pl.* (zool.) Pelecypoda.

**Пелиго соль** Peligot salt(probably potassium chlorochromate).

**пеликан** *m.* (zool.) pelican.

**пелит** *m.* (geol.) pelite (fine clay sediment); **—овый** *a.* pelitic, clay; **—овая почва** pelitic soil, fine clay soil.

**пеллагра** *f.* (med.) pellagra.

**пеллет/иерин, —ьерин** *m.* pelletierine, punicine; **—иериновая кислота** pelletieric acid.

**пеллидол** *m.* pellidol.

**пелликула** *f.* pellicle, scum, film.

**пеллотин** *m.* pellotine.

**пелькомпас** *m.* azimuth compass.

**Пельтона колесо** Pelton wheel (a water turbine).

**пельтуровый ярус** (geol.) Peltura stage.

**Пельтье коэффициент** (elec.) Peltier coefficient; **П. явление** Peltier effect.

**пелюшка** *f.* maple pea (*Pisum arvense*).

**пелядь** *f.* whitefish.

**пемз/а** *f.*, **—овый** *a.* pumice, pumice stone (volcanic froth); **—обетон** *m.* pumice cement; **—овать** *v.* pumice, polish with pumice; **—овидный** *a.*

pumiceous; —**овка** *f.* pumicing, polishing with pumice.

**пен/а** *f.* foam, froth; suds, lather; scum, skimmings, dross; **образование —ы** (flotation) frothing; foaming.

**пенавар, п.-пулу** *see* **пенгавар-джамби.**

**пенал** *m.* pencil box, pen case; (isotope) can.

**пенгавар-джамби** *n.* pengawar djambi, golden moss.

**пенджабский ярус** (geol.) Penjabian stage.

**пенеплен** *m.* (geol.) peneplain.

**пенетр/ация** *f.* penetration; —**ометр** *m.* penetrometer; —**ометрия** *f.* penetrometry.

**пение** *n.* singing.

**пенизетум** *see* **пеннизетум.**

**пенис** *m.* (anat.) penis.

**пенист/ость** *f.* foaminess, frothiness; effervescence; —**ый** *a.* foamy, frothy; effervescent; froth (fermentation); —**ый известняк, —ый шпат, —ая земля** (min.) sparry aphrite, foaming earth, foam spar (a form of calcite); —**ый камень** foamstone.

**пенить** *v.* make foam, churn up; —**ся** *v.* foam, froth; effervesce, bubble.

**пеницилл/ин** *m.* penicillin; —**иназа** *f.* penicillinase; —**оиновая кислота** penicilloic acid.

**пенка** *f.* foam, froth, scum, skimmings.

**пенкатит** *m.* (min.) pencatite (mixture of calcite and brucite).

**пеннизетум** *m.* (bot.) pennisetum.

**пеннин, —ит** *m.* (min.) penninite, pennine (a chlorite).

**пеннирояловое масло** pennyroyal oil.

**пенницы** *pl.* spittle insects, etc. (*Cercopidae*).

**пеннон** *m.* pennone, tetramethyl pentanone.

**пенн/ый** *a.* foam, foamy, froth, frothy; —**ая флотация** froth flotation; —**ое число** lather value (of detergent).

**пено—** *prefix* foam, froth; —**аккумуляторная станция** foam-manufacturing plant (for fighting oil-well fires); —**бетон** *m.* cellular concrete; —**гаситель** *m.* antifoaming agent; —**гасительный** *a.* fire-extinguishing (with foam); —**генератор** *m.* foam generator, foam producer.

**пенообраз/ный** *a.* foamy, frothy; —**ователь** *m.*, —**ующее вещество** foaming agent, frothing agent; (flotation) frother; —**ующий** *a.* froth-forming.

**пено/отделитель** *m.* skimmer; —**стекло** *n.* cellular glass, foam glass; —**стойкость** *f.* froth resistance.

**пенсильванский** *a.* Pennsylvania, Pennsylvanian; **п. отдел** (geol.) Pennsylvanian epoch.

**пенсия** *f.* pension.

**пента—** *prefix* penta—, five-; —**бром—** *prefix* pentabrom—, pentabromo—; —**бромобензол** *m.* pentabromobenzene; —**гон** *m.* (geom.) pentagon; —**гональный** *a.* pentagonal; —**грамма** *f.* pentagram; —**грид** *m.* (thermionics) pentagrid, heptode; —**гридпреобразователь частоты** pentagrid converter.

**пентада** *f.* pentad, five-day period.

**пентадекан** *m.* pentadecane; —**овая кислота** pentadecanoic acid, *n*-pentadecylic acid; —**ол** *m.* pentadecanol, pentadecyl alcohol; —**он** *m.* pentadecanone.

**пента/децил** *m.* pentadecyl; —**диен** *m.* pentadiene; —**диенон** *m.* pentadienone, divinyl ketone; —**дный** *a.* pentad; five-day; —**зил** *m.* pentazyl; —**зин** *m.* pentazine; —**зол** *m.* pentasol (mixture of amyl alcohols); —**карбонил железа** iron pentacarbonyl; —**козан** *m.* pentacosane; —**козановая кислота** pentacosanic acid, cerebronic acid; —**л** *m.* pental, trimethylethylene.

**пентаметил** *m.* pentamethyl; —**ен** *m.* pentamethylene, cyclopentane.

**пентамин** *m.* pentamine, azamethonium bromide.

**пентан** *m.* pentane; —**диол** *m.* pentanediol; —**ол** *m.* pentanol, amyl alcohol; —**он** *m.* pentanone.

**пента/сульфид** *m.* pentasulfide; —**тионовая кислота** pentathionic acid; —**хлор—** *prefix* pentachlor—, pentachloro—; —**хлорбензол** *m.* pentachlorobenzene; —**циклический** *a.* pentacyclic, five-membered.

**пентаэдр** *m.* pentahedron; —**ический** *a.* pentahedral.

пента/эритрит *m.* pentaerythritol, pentaerythrite; —этил *m.* pentaethyl.

пентен *m.* pentene, amylene; —ил *m.* pentenyl; —овая кислота pentenic acid, pentenoic acid; —ол *m.* pentenol.

пентиазолин *m.* penthiazoline.

пентил *m.* pentyl, amyl; —ен *m.* pentylene, pentadiene; —овый спирт pentyl alcohol, amyl alcohol.

пент/ин *m.* pentyne; —иофен, —иофуран *m.* penthiophene, penthiofuran; —ит *m.* pentitol (pentahydric alcohol).

пентландит *m.* (min.) pentlandite (an iron-nickel sulfide).

пентод *m.* pentode (electron tube).

пенто/за *f.* pentose; —зан *m.* pentosan (gum or resin); —ксил *m.* pentoxyl, 5-hydroxymethyl-4-methyluracil; —ксим *m.* pentoxime; —н *m.* pentone; —новая кислота pentonic acid.

пенфильдит *m.* (min.) penfieldite (an oxychloride of lead).

пень *m.* stump (of tree).

пеньк/а *f.* hemp; —овый *a.* hemp, hempen; —опрядильня *f.* hemp mill.

пен/я *f.*, брать —ю *v.* fine; —ять *v.* reproach, blame.

пенящийся *a.* frothing, frothy, foaming, foamy; effervescent, sparkling (wine).

пеон *m.* (bot.) peony (*Paeonia*); —ин *m.* peonin, aurine; peonine (alkaloid from *Paeonia officinalis*); —ол *m.* peonol.

пепел *m.* ashes, cinder, cinders; —истый *a.* ashen; —ица *f.* powdery mildew (plant disease); —ьница *f.* ash tray; —ьно-серый *a.* ash-gray; —ьный *a.* ash, ashen, cinereous.

пеперин *m.* (min.) peperino, leucite tuff.

пепермент *m.* peppermint.

пеп/син *m.* pepsin (enzyme); растительный п. vegetable pepsin, papain; —синовый *a.* peptic, pepsin; —синовое вино essence of pepsin; —тид *m.* peptide.

пептиз/атор *m.* peptizator; —ация *f.* peptization; —ировать *v.* peptize, bring into colloidal solution; convert into a sol; —ованный *a.* peptized.

пептоли/з *m.* peptolysis, peptone hydrolysis; —тический *a.* peptolytic.

пептон *m.* peptone; —изация *f.* peptonization; —изировать *v.* peptonize, change to peptone; —изующий *a.* peptonizing; —овый *a.* peptone, peptonic.

пептотоксин *m.* peptotoxine.

пер *past sing. of* переть.

пер. *abbr.* (перевод) translation; (период) period, cycle; (периодический) periodic; batch.

пер— *prefix* per—; —бензойная кислота perbenzoic acid; —борат *m.* perborate.

перв. *abbr.* (первичный) primary.

первейший *a.* very first; first-rate.

первенство *n.* priority, precedence, pre-eminence; иметь право на п., —вать *v.* take precedence.

первитин *m.* Pervitin, methamphetamine.

первично *adv.* primarily, initially, first; —бескрылые *pl.* (zool.) Apterygota, Apterygogenea; —монадные *pl.* (zool.) Protomonadina; —полостные черви (zool.) Nemathelminthes; —ротые *pl.* (zool.) Protostomia; —трахейные *pl.* (zool.) Prototracheata.

первичный *a.* primary, initial, first, original, fundamental; parent; virgin (neutron); п. амин primary amine; п. материал raw material; п. спирт primary alcohol.

перво— *prefix* first, primary; —бытный *a.* primitive, primeval, original; —гон *m.* first runnings; —звери *pl.* (zool.) Prototheria; —зданный *a.* protoplastic; (geol.) primitive, primary; —источник *m.* primary source, origin; —классный *a.* first-class, first-rate; —курсник *m.* freshman (student).

первоначальн/ый *a.* elementary, primary, primitive, primeval, primordial; original, initial; incipient; п. материал, —ое вещество parent substance; raw material.

первообраз *m.* protoplast, original; —ный *a.* protoplastic, original; —ование *n.* incipience, inception, beginning.

перво/основа *f.* fundamental principle; —очередный *a.* first, most important; —причина *f.* original cause, origin, source.

**первород/ный** *a.* first born; original; **—ство** *n.* primogeniture.

**перворожденный** *see* **первородный.**

**перво/сортный** *a.* top-grade, first-rate, of the best quality; **—степенный** *a.* paramount, foremost, chief.

**первоцвет** *m.* (bot.) primrose (*Primula*); **желтый п.** cowslip (*P. officinalis*); **—никовые, —ные, —овые** *pl.* Primulaceae.

**перв/ый** *a.* first; chief, main; former; raw, starting (material); **—ая помощь** first aid; **—ым делом** first of all; **в п. раз** the first time; **во —ых** in the first place, to begin with.

**перга** *f.* bee bread.

**пергамент** *m.*, **—ный** *a.* parchment; **—ирование** *n.* parchmentizing.

**пергамин** *m.* pergamyn (an artificial parchment paper).

**пергидроль** *m.* Perhydrol.

**пере—***prefix* afresh, again, anew, once more, re—; over, super—; out—; inter—; trans—, across; back and forth; **—амидирование** *n.* transamidation; **—аминирование** *n.* transamination; **—балтывание** *n.* agitation, thorough mixing.

**перебе/г** *m.*, **—гание** *n.* running over, crossing; overrunning; **—гать, —жать** *v.* run over, cross; overrun; **—жки** *pl.* bounds.

**перебив/ать** *v.* interrupt; break up; beat again; nail in another place; **—аться** *v.* be interrupted, be broken; **—ка** *f.* reupholstering.

**перебирать** *v.* sort out, look over; **—ся** *v.* move (to another place); cross.

**перебить** *see* **перебивать.**

**перебой** *m.* intermission, interruption, stop, delay, standstill, stagnation; trouble, failure, disturbance; missing (of motor); **давать п.** *v.* fail; miss (of motor); **пульс с —ями** intermittent pulse.

**перебор** *m.* excess, surplus receipts; gear; cone pulley mechanism; **—ка** *f.* sorting; looking over, overhauling, overhaul; bulkhead, partition, diaphragm, web, wall, baffle; (typ.) resetting; **тарелка с —ками** baffle plate; **—ная коробка** gear box.

**перебрасывать** *v.* throw over; transfer.

**перебрать** *see* **перебирать.**

**перебродить** *v.* overferment; ferment.

**перебро/с** *m.* throw-over, change-over, transfer; splashing over; surge (of gas); (elec. comm.) flip-flop; (geol.) overthrust; **—сать, —сить** *see* **перебрасывать; —ска** *f.* throwing over; transfer; rehandling; **—шенный** *a.* thrown over; transferred; overthrust.

**перевал** *m.* passing, crossing; (mountain) pass; skimmer, dam, damstone (of blast furnace); (min.) cave-in; **—ка** *f.* rolling; roll changing.

**перевар/енный** *a.* overdone, overcooked; digested; **—ивание** *n.* digestion; **—ивать, —ить** *v.* overcook, boil to excess; digest; **—имый** *a.* digestible; **—ка** *f.* overcuring (of varnish).

**перевезти** *see* **перевозить.**

**перевер/нутый** *a.* upset, turned over, inverted, reverse; **—нуть, —тывать** *v.* upset, turn over, invert, trip; reverse; rabble, stir.

**перевес** *m.* overweight, overbalance; preponderance; advantage; **п. в его пользу** the odds are in his favor; **иметь п.** *v.* overbalance; **—ить** *see* **перевешивать.**

**перевести** *see* **переводить.**

**перевешив/ать** *v.* weigh again; outbalance, overbalance, outweigh, preponderate; overcome; **—аться** *v.* lean over; overhang; **—ающий** *a.* preponderant; top-heavy.

**перевив/ать** *v.* entwine; interweave, intertwine; **—ной** *see* **перевитой.**

**перевис/ать, —нуть** *v.* overhang.

**перевит/ый** *a.* entwined, interwoven, intertwined; **—ь** *see* **перевивать.**

**перевод** *m.* transfer, change-over, shifting, shift; conversion, reduction; recalculation; translation, interpretation; (money) order; **таблица для —а** conversion table; **устный п.** interpretation; **—имый** *a.* transferable; convertible; translatable.

**переводина** *f.* crossbeam, joist.

**переводить** *v.* transfer, change over, change, switch over, shift; carry over, convey; convert, reduce; translate, interpret; remit (money); **—ся** *v.* be transferred; die out.

**переводка** *f.* shifter.

**переводник** *m.* adapter.

**переводн/ой, —ый** *a.* transfer, shift, shifting, switch; conversion; translation; reversing; **п. вексель** (com.) draft; **п. коэффициент, п. множитель** conversion factor, reduction factor; **п. коэффициент, —ое число** (chem.) transference number, transport number; **п. механизм** shifter; **п. рельс** switch rail; **—ая бумага** carbon paper; **—ая картина** decalcomania; **—ая надпись** (com.) indorsement; **—ая таблица, —ая шкала** conversion table; **—ая труба** by-pass pipe.

**переводчик** *m.* translator; interpreter.

**перевоз** *see* **перевозка.**

**перевозбужден/ие** *n.* (elec.) overexcitation; **—ный** *a.* overexcited.

**перевоз/имый** *a.* transportable; **—ить** *v.* convey, carry, cart, move, transfer, transport; **—ка** *f.* conveyance, conveying, carting, hauling, transfer, transport, transportation; **при —ке** in transit; **—ный, —очный** *a.* transporting; **—очная тележка** delivery car; **—чик** *m.* carrier.

**перевор/ачиватель** *m.* (hay) tedder; **—ачивать, —отить** *see* **перевертывать; —от** *m.* upheaval, revolution; turnover; (geol.) cataclysm.

**перевыпас** *m.* overgrazing.

**перевыполн/ение** *n.* overfulfillment, surpassing; **—ять** *v.* surpass, exceed.

**перевяз/ать, —ывать** *v.* bind, tie up, bandage, dress; **—ка** *f.*, **—очный** *a.* binding, dressing, bandage; bond; ligature; **—очный материал** dressing; **—очный пункт** dressing station; **—очная вата** sterile cotton; **—ь** *f.* (mil.) shoulder belt; (med.) sling.

**перегар** *m.* combustion product; (sod) decomposition.

**перегиб** *m.* bend, fold; twist, curl, kink, recurvature; crest; discontinuity; **п. кривой** (math.) inflection; **—ать** *v.* bend, fold, twist, kink; **—ный** *a.* (math.) inflectional.

**перегн/анный** *a.* distilled; **—ать** *see* **перегонять.**

**перегной** *m.* humus, mulch, compost; **—но—** *prefix* humus.

**перегнут/ый** *a.* folded; **—ь** *see* **перегибать.**

**перегов/аривать, —орить** *v.* talk over, discuss; **—ор** *m.* conversation; (tel.) call; **—оры** *pl.* negotiations; **вести —оры** *v.* negotiate; **—орный** *a.* negotiatory; (tel.) call; telephone (booth); **—орный пункт** call office.

**перегон** *m.* distillate, distillation product; stage; (railroad) run.

**перегонк/а** *f.* distillation; fractionation; driving over; sublimation; **п. в пустоте** vacuum distillation; **п. водяным паром** steam distillation; **вторичная п.** rerun; **дробная п.** fractional distillation; **продукт —и** distillation product, distillate; **сухая п.** dry distillation, destructive distillation.

**перегон/ный, —очный** *a.* distillation, distilling, distilled; **п. завод** distillery; **п. куб** still; **—ная колонна** distillation column, fractioning column; **—щик** *m.* distiller; **—яемость** *f.* distillability; **—яемый** *a.* distillable; **—ять** *v.* distill, drive over; sublimate; outspeed, outstrip, outrun, pass, surpass; drive (cattle); (text.) wind, spool.

**перегораживать** *v.* partition.

**перегор/ание** *n.* combustion, burning, burning through, burning out; **—ать, —еть** *v.* burn, burn through, burn out; blow out (of fuse); **—елый** *a.* burnt out.

**перегород/ить** *see* **перегораживать; —ка** *f.* partition, barrier, screen, wall, dividing wall, diaphragm, membrane; compartment, closure; baffle, baffle plate, bridge, deflector; (biol.) septum; **—очный** *a.* partition; dividing; septal.

**переграждать** *v.* lock.

**перегранич/ивать, —ить** *v.* fix other limits, change the boundaries.

**перегребать** *v.* rake over.

**перегрев** *m.* superheat, overheat, excess heat, superheating, overheating; **местный п.** hot spot; **—ание** *n.* superheating, overheating; **—атель** *m.* superheater; **—ать** *v.* superheat, overheat; heat again.

**перегрест/и, —ь** *see* **перегребать.**

**перегрет/ый** *a.* superheated, overheated;

(met.) over-refined; dry (copper);
—ое место hot spot; —ь *see* пере-
гревать.

**перегруж/аемость** *f.* overload capacity;
—ать, —ивать *v.* overload, overburden, overwork, strain, force (a
machine); surcharge, overcharge;
transship, transfer a load, handle;
—енность *f.* overload, overwork;
—енный *a.* overloaded, overladen,
overweighed; overworked.

**перегруз/ить** *see* перегружать; —ка *f.*
overload, overloading, excess weight,
excess load; surcharge, overcharging;
overwork, straining (of machine);
transshipment, reshipment, rehandling, handling, reloading, transfer;
—ной *a.* transshipped; —очный *a.*
transport, transfer; loading.

**перегруппиров/анный** *a.* rearranged;
—ка *f.* rearrangement, regrouping;
—ывать *v.* rearrange, regroup.

**перегу/стить**, —щать *v.* make too thick,
thicken too much.

**перед** *prep. instr.* before, in front of;
against; to; *m.* front, forepart.

**передав/аемый** *a.* transferable; negotiable; —ать *v.* transmit, transfer,
pass on, relay, convey, give, impart,
give over, turn over (duties), deliver,
hand; report, communicate; broadcast; refer, remit; —аться *v.* be transmitted, be passed on; (med.) be
catching, be contagious, be caught.

**передавливать** *v.* convey by pressure.

**перед/анный** *a.* transmitted, conveyed;
—аточность *f.* transmissibility.

**передаточн/ый** *a.* transmitting, transmission, transmissive, transfer, conveying, carrier; driving; intermediary; п. вагон, —ая тележка transfer
car; п. вал countershaft; п. кран transfer crane; п. механизм driving gear,
drive; communicator; п. путь delivery line; п. ремень driving belt; п.
стержень transmission lever; п. червяк worm conveyer, screw conveyer;
—ая волна transmission wave; —ое
колесо carrier; —ое отношение, —ое
число gear ratio; (illum.) transmission ratio; ratio; —ые рычаги transmission gear.

**передатчик** *m.* transmitter, transferrer,

carrier; (elec. comm.) transmitter,
transmitting station, sending set,
sender; п. кислорода oxygen carrier;
п. тепла heat transmitter, heat
conductor.

**передать** *see* передавать.

**передач/а** *f.* transmission, transmittal,
transfer, transferring; passage, conveyance, delivering, delivery, sending; communication; gear, gearing,
driving gear, gear ratio; drive, driving;
assignation, assignment; п. энергии
energy transfer; power transmission;
балансирная п. transmission by
rocking lever; большая п. high gear
ratio; винтовая п., червячная п.
worm gear; высота единицы —и
height of transfer unit, HTU (of
packed column); колесная п. gearing;
коробка передач gear box, transmission; вал коробки передач transmission shaft; малая п. low gear
ratio; первая п. low gear; цепная п.
chain drive.

**передающ/ий** *a.* transmitting, sending;
п. аппарат transmitter; —ее приспособление carrier; gearing.

**передвигать** *v.* move, stir, shift, slip,
slide; —ся *v.* move, travel.

**передвигающий** *a.* moving, shifting; п.
магнит feed magnet; п. механизм
thrust gear; п. стержень push rod.

**передвиж/ение** *n.*, —ка *f.* travel, progression, moving, movement, locomo-
tion, traction; removal, transfer,
transportation; shifting; (bot.) trans-
location; средства —ений means of
transportation.

**передвижн/ой** *a.* traveling, mobile, movable, portable; sliding, adjustable;
shifting, displaceable; п. ковш (foundry) ladle car; п. кран traveling crane,
traveler; —ая лестница escalator;
—ая платформа elevator car.

**передвинуть** *see* передвигать.

**передел** *m.* conversion; process stage;
(met.) reduction; repartition, re-
allotment; —ка *f.* alteration, remodeling, repairs; —ать, —ывать *v.*
alter, remodel, remake; convert,
change; —очный чугун, —ьный
чугун cast iron for steel manufacture.

**передерж/ать**, —ивать *v.* hold over,

keep too long; (phot.) overexpose; —ка *f.* overexposure.

**передне—** *prefix* pro—, before; front; —грудка *f.* (zool.) prosternum; — грудь *f.* (zool.) prothorax; —жаберные *pl.* (zool.) Prosobranchia; —коренной зуб (anat.) bicuspid; —навесной *a.* front-mounted.

**передн/ий** *a.* front, fore, anterior, forward, leading, leader; п. план foreground; п. ход forward running; —яя грань face (of tool); —яя сторона, —яя часть front, forepart; —ее стекло (automobile) windshield.

**передн/ик** *m.* apron; —яя *f.* entrance hall, lobby, vestibule, antechamber.

**передо** *see* перед.

**передовер/енный договор** subcontract; —ить, —ять *v.* subcontract.

**передов/ица** *f.*, —ая статья leading article, editorial; —ой *a.* forward, advanced, leading, foremost, fore, front.

**передок** *m.* forecarriage; front (of carriage); vamp (of shoe).

**передув/ать** *v.* overblow; —ка *f.* overblowing; (met.) afterblow.

**передум/ать, —ывать** *v.* think over, change one's mind.

**передутый** *a.* overblown.

**переды/хать** *v.* stop and rest; —шка *f.* respite, rest.

**пере/езд** *m.* passage, crossing, transit; moving; —езжать, —ехать *v.* cross, come over; move; run over; —езжающий *a.* mobile.

**пережать** *see* пережимать.

**пережев/ать, —ывать** *v.* chew again, ruminate; masticate, chew well.

**переж/ечь** *see* пережигать; —женный *a.* burnt, burned, overroasted.

**пережив/ание** *n.* experience; survival; —ать *v.* experience; survive, outlast.

**пережиг/ание** *n.* combustion, burning, calcination, roasting; —ать *v.* burn, calcine, roast.

**пережим** *m.* narrowing, contraction; reduced width; distortion; bending; nick; —ать *v.* pinch; press; press over again, squeeze again; —ный баллон intermediate vessel.

**пережит/ок** *m.* survival; —ь *see* переживать.

**пережог** *m.* overheating; burn-out; (met.) burning; hot spot (of furnace shell).

**перезаря/д** *m.* overcharge; recharge; —дить, —жать *v.* overcharge; recharge, reload; —дка *f.* overcharging, supercharging; overloading; recharging, reloading; charge exchange.

**перезимовать** *v.* winter, hibernate.

**перез/ол** *m.* perezol (indicator); —он *m.* perezon, pipitzahoic acid.

**перезре/вать, —ть** *v.* get too ripe, over-ripen; —лый *a.* overripe, overmature.

**переизвесткование** *n.* overliming (of soil).

**переиздавать** *v.* reissue.

**переирин** *m.* pereirine.

**перейти** *see* переходить.

**перекал** *m.* overheating; (met.) over-tempering; —енный *a.* overheated, burnt; —ивать, —ить *v.* overheat, make red hot; overtemper; —ьная печь (glass) calcar.

**перекармливать** *v.* overfeed.

**перекат** *m.* thunderclap, rolling (of thunder); sandbank; —и-поле *n.* (bot.) tumbleweed; —ить, —ывать *v.* roll over, turn over; reroll; —ный *a.* (geol.) erratic.

**перекач/ать, —ивать** *v.* pump over, transfer.

**перекашив/ание** *n.* distortion, buckling, warping, twisting, torsion; —ать *v.* warp, twist, bend, slant, cant; mow, mow again; —аться *v.* twist, distort, run out of true, get out of alignment.

**перекид/ать** *see* перекидывать; —ка *f.* throwing over; overhead span (of wire); rehandling, transfer.

**перекидн/ой** *a.* reversing, reversible; tipping, dumping; knife (switch); (elec. comm.) flip-flop; п. клапан butterfly valve; п. механизм tumbler; п. рычаг reverse lever; —ая схема flip-flop; —ое устройство reversing gear, reversing device.

**переки/дывать, —нуть** *v.* turn over; throw over, fling over; span.

**перекип/ать, —еть** *v.* boil over.

**перекис/ать, —нуть** *v.* turn sour; —ление *n.* overacidification; peroxidation, overoxidation; —ленный *a.*

overacidified, too acid, too sour; peroxidized, overoxidized; —лить, —лять *v.* acidify to excess, overacidify; peroxidize, overoxidize; — ная соль persalt; —ное число peroxide number.

перекись *f.* peroxide; п. водорода hydrogen peroxide.

переклад *m.* cross bar; —ина *f.* crossbeam, cross bar, tie beam, joist, brace; slat, rung (of ladder); spar; transom; —ывать *v.* interlay; reset, relay, transpose.

переклассификация *f.* reclassification.

переклейка *f.* plywood; regluing.

переключ/аемый *a.* reversible; exchangeable; —атель *m.* (elec.) switch, throw-over switch, change-over switch, reverser; —атель газа periodic gas feeder (for raising oil from well); —ать *v.* (elec.) switch, switch over, shift, change over, commutate, throw over (switch); —ающий *a.* switching, throw-over, changeover; reversing; —ающий механизм switch gear; —ающийся *a.* shifting.

переключен/ие *n.* (elec.) switching, change-over, changing over, changing, commutation; shifting; reversing, reversion; п. скоростей gear shifting; педаль —ия shift pedal; рычаг —ия shift lever; —ный *a.* switched, changed over, shifted.

переключить *see* переключать.

перекомпаундирован/ие *n.* (elec.) overcompounding; —ный *a.* overcompounded, heavily compounded.

перекомпенсировать *v.* overcompensate.

переконструирование *n.* reconstruction, remodeling, redesigning.

перекоп *m.* cross ditch, canal.

перекорм *m.* overfeeding; —ить *v.* overfeed.

переко/с *m.* curving, bending, skewing; slant, angularity; bias, misalignment; (door) jamb; —сить *see* перекашивать; —шенный *a.* warped, twisted, crooked, skew; out of alignment.

перекра/сить *v.* redye, dye another color; repaint; —шенный *a.* redyed; repainted.

перекрест *m.* (biophysics) crossing over; —ие *n.* cross lines; —ить *see* пере-

крещивать; —но *adv.* cross (pollinated, etc.); —ноопыляемый, —ноопыляющийся *a.* cross-pollinated; —но-слоистый *a.* cross-bedded; — ный *a.* cross, crossing, crossed; —ные члены cross terms; —ок *m.* crossing, crossroads, crossover; —ье *n.* crosshair; cross.

перекрещ/енный *a.* crossed; —ивание *n.* crossing, intersecting; —ивать *v.* cross (over), intersect; transpose; rename; —иваться *v.* cross, intersect; —ивающийся *a.* crossing, intersecting, crisscross; гравировать —ивающимися линиями *v.* crosshatch.

перекристаллиз/ация *f.* recrystallization; —ованный *a.* recrystallized; —овать *v.* recrystallize.

перекруч/енный *a.* twisted, skew; —ивание *n.* twisting, distortion; —ивать *v.* twist, skew, distort.

перекрыв/ание *n.* overlapping, overlap, lap; —ать *v.* overlap, lap, imbricate, superimpose; span, bridge over; shut off (valve); —ающий *a.* overlapping, covering; —ающий ряд, —ающая плита coping; —ающие породы (min.) overburden.

перекрыт/ие *n.* overlapping, overlap, lap; duplication; coverage, covering, cover; span; sparkover, arcover, flashover; ceiling; roof; floor; коэффициент —ия period of contact; —ый *a.* overlapped; covered, bridged, spanned; crossed (belt); coped (joint).

перекрыш/а, —ка *f.* overlap, overlapping, lap, imbrication; ceiling, cover.

перекуп/ной *a.* second-hand, used; — щик *m.* second-hand dealer.

перекурка *f.* distillation.

перелагать *see* перекладывать.

переламывать *v.* break to pieces, break in two, crush; fracture.

перелеска *see* печеночница.

перелет *m.* flight, passage; transmigration (of birds); —ать, —еть *v.* fly across; —ный *a.* migratory.

перелив *m.* overflow; —ание *n.* overflow, overflowing; pouring over, decantation; (blood) transfusion; —ать *v.* pour over, decant; transfuse; (foundry) recast; —аться *v.* overflow, run over; iridesce (of colors); —а-ющий *a.*, —ающий цветами радуги iridescent, opalescent; —ка *f.* (foundry) recasting.

**переливн/ой** *a.* pouring; overflow; (foundry) recast, recasting; **п. ствол** overflow lip; —ая труба overflow, overflow pipe; —ое отверстие overflow, outlet.

**переливчат/ость** *f.* iridescence; —ый *a.* iridescent, chatoyant, opalescent.

**перелист/ать,** —ывать *v.* turn over (pages), look through, scan.

**перелит/ый** *a.* poured over, decanted; (foundry) recast; —ь *see* **переливать.**

**перелицованный** *a.* turned over, turned, reversed.

**перелов** *m.* overfishing.

**перелог** *m.* (agr.) fallow.

**перелож/ение** *n.* transposition; —енный *a.* transposed; —ить *see* **перекладывать.**

**перелой** *m.* (med.) gonorrhea.

**перелом** *m.* break, discontinuity; crisis, change; sudden transition; (med.) fracture; —ать *see* **переламывать.**

**перелопачивание** *n.* shoveling, shoveling up, digging up; scooping.

**перем.** *abbr.* (переменный) alternating.

**перемагни/тить,** —чивать *v.* reverse the magnetism; —чение, —чивание *n.* magnetic (polarity) reversal.

**перематыв/ание** *n.* rewinding; (text.) reeling; —ать *v.* rewind; reel.

**перемеж/аться** *v.* intermit, be interrupted; alternate; —ающийся *a.* intermittent, alternate; intermediate; interbedded; (elec.) alternating.

**перемен/а** *f.* change, alteration, mutation, transformation; alternation; interval; move, shift; **п. движения, п. направления, п. хода** reversal, reversing; поддающийся —е alterable; рычаг —ы хода reversing lever, reverse lever; —ить *see* **переменять;** —ная *f.* (math.) variable.

**переменно** *adv.* alternately; **п. действующий** alternating; **п.-возвратное движение** reciprocal motion; **п.-полярный** *a.* (elec.) heteropolar; —е *n.* (math.) variable.

**переменность** *f.* variability, change-ability, mutability, unsteadiness, instability.

**переменн/ый** *a.* variable, varying, changeable, interchangeable, alternative; alternate; (elec.) alternating; **п. клапан** intercepting valve; **п. ток** (elec.) alternating current; **генератор** —ого тока alternator; —ая величина (math.) variable; —ая нагрузка live load; мотор с —ым ходом reversible engine.

**переменчив/ость** *see* **переменность;** —ый *a.* variable, changeable, alterable, inconstant, unstable, shifting.

**переменять** *v.* vary, change, alter, transform; shift; exchange, interchange; **п. направление** reverse; —ся *v.* change; exchange; take turns.

**переместит/ельный** *a.* transposing, transposable; (math.) commutative; —ь *see* **перемещать.**

**перемет** *m.* seine, net.

**переметилирование** *n.* transmethylation.

**перемеш/анный** *a.* mixed, stirred; mixed up, confused; —ать, —ивать *v.* mix, stir, rabble; intermingle, intermix, blend, intersperse; mix up, confuse; —ивание *n.* mixing, stirring, agitation; intermixing, interspersion; confusion.

**перемещ/аемость** *f.* movability; transportability; —аемый *a.* movable, mobile; transportable; —ать *v.* transpose, transfer, transport, move, shift, displace, shuffle; convey, drive; —ать вперед advance; —аться *v.* move, slip, slide, migrate, travel; —ающий *a.* moving, motive; —ающийся *a.* moving, movable, mobile, adjusting, sliding; traversing, shifting, heaving (sand); migratory, traveling.

**перемещен/ие** *n.* transfer, transference, translation, transposition, change of positions; shift, shifting, moving, movement, motion, travel, migration; transportation, hauling, haulage, conveying, conveyance; displacement, dislocation; adjustment, sliding; (math.) permutation; —ный *a.* transferred, shifted, moved; dislocated.

**переминать** *v.* knead, work.

**перемирие** *n.* truce, armistice.

**перемок/ать, —нуть** v. get wet.

**перемол** m. grinding, grist; **—оть** v. grind over.

**перемонтаж** m. remounting; rewiring.

**перемотка** f. rewinding, rewind.

**перемы/вать, —ть** v. wash up; wash again, rewash; rework.

**перемычка** f. crosspiece, tie plate, bridge, connector; dam, dike, bulkhead; seal; coffer, cofferdam; groove.

**перемятый** a. deformed.

**перенапр/ечься, —ягать** v. overstrain; **—яжение** n. overstrain, overexertion; (mech.) overstress; (elec.) overvoltage, excess voltage.

**перенаселенн/ость** f. overpopulation; **—ый** a. overpopulated, congested.

**перенастройка** f. change-over; retuning.

**перенасыщ/ать** v. supersaturate; **—ение** n. supersaturation; **—енный** a. supersaturated.

**перенес/ение** n. transference, transportation, removal; postponement; endurance, bearing; **—ти** see **переносить.**

**перенимать** v. imitate; intercept, catch; take over.

**перенормиров/анный** a. renormalized; **—ка** f. renormalization.

**перенос** m. transfer, transport, transportation; transmission; migration (of ions); transposition (of a term); **п. вещества, п. массы** mass transfer; **п. тепла** heat transfer; **единица —а** transfer unit (of column); **постоянная —ов** migration constant (of ions); **уравнение —a** transport equation; **число —a** transport number, transference number; **чистый п.** (isotopes separation) net transport; **—имый** a. transferable; bearable, endurable; contagious, infectious (disease); **—имый по воздуху** airborne.

**переноситель** m. carrier; transferrer, transporter, transmitter, means of transmission; **п. галогена** halogenating agent.

**перенос/ить** v. transfer, carry over, carry, convey, take, transmit, transport, relay, shift; (math.) transpose; endure, bear, stand; undergo (operation); **—ица** f. (anat.) bridge of nose; **—ка** see **перенесение; —ный** a.

transferable, transportable, portable, movable, moving, removable; applicable; figurative; translational; **в —ном смысле** figuratively.

**переноспор/овые** pl. (bot.) Perenosporaceae; **—оз** m. mold caused by perenospora.

**переносчик** m. (disease) carrier.

**перенумерация** f. relabeling (of coordinates).

**перенять** see **перенимать.**

**переоблучение** n. overirradiation, overexposure (to radiation).

**переоборудов/ание** n. re-equipment; reconstruction, remodeling; **—ать** v. reequip; reconstruct, remodel.

**переокисл/ение** n. peroxidation; **—ять** v. peroxidize, overoxidize.

**переориентация** f. reorientation; flipping (of spins).

**переосаждать** v. reprecipitate.

**переотклонение** n. overshooting, overswing.

**переотливка** f. (foundry) recasting.

**переотложение** n. redeposition.

**переохлажден/ие** n. supercooling; **—ный** a. supercooled, undercooled.

**переоцен/ивать, —ить** v. overestimate, overrate; revalue; outbid; **—ка** f. overestimation; revaluation.

**перепад** m. jump, drop (in pressure, temperature); (met.) skimmer.

**перепа/ивать** v. resolder; **—йка** f. resoldering.

**перепалзывать** v. crawl over, creep over.

**перепар/енный** a. oversteamed, stewed; **—ивать, —ить** v. oversteam, overstew.

**перепачкать** v. soil, dirty.

**перепаять** see **перепаивать.**

**перепекать** v. overbake.

**перепел** m., **—иный, —очный** a. (zool.) quail; **—очная калючка, —очная трава** (bot.) thistle (*Carduus nutans*).

**перепечат/ать, —ывать** v. reprint; type; **—ка** f. reprint, reprinting.

**перепечь** see **перепекать.**

**перепис/ать, —ывать** v. copy, rewrite; type, transcribe (shorthand notes); make a list (of); **—ываться** v. correspond; **—ка** f. copying; typing, transcription; correspondence; **—чик**

*m.* copyist; typist; —ь *f.* census; inventory.

**переплав/ить,** —лять *v.* remelt; (met.) smelt, refound, recast; float; —ка *f.,* —ление *n.* remelting, refusion, melting; smelting, refounding; —ленный *a.* remelted, melted; smelted.

**перепла/та** *f.* surplus payment; —тить, —чивать *v.* overpay, pay too much.

**переплет** *m.* (book) binding, cover; (chair) caning; lacing; transom (of door), casement; в матерчатом —е bound in cloth; крышка —a board.

**переплет/ать** *v.* interweave; bind (a book); cane (chair); —аться *v.* interweave, intertwine, interlace, interlock; —ающийся *a.* interwoven, interlaced, interlocked; —ение *n.* interweaving, interdigitation, interlacing, interlocking.

**переплет/ная** *f.* bindery; —ный *a.* bookbinding, binding; —ное дело bookbinding; —чик *m.* bookbinder.

**переполз/ание** *n.* creeping, creeping over; —ать, —ти *see* **перепалзывать.**

**переполн/ение** *n.* overfilling, repletion; overflowing; —енный *a.* overfull, overcrowded, overflowing; —ить, —ять *v.* overfill; overflow; —иться, —яться *v.* get too full, brim over, overflow.

**переполюсовать** *v.* reverse the polarity, change the poles.

**перепон/ка** *f.* membrane, film, web, webbing, diaphragm, lamella; —чатокрылые *pl.* (zool.) Hymenoptera; —чатый *a.* membranous, webbed.

**перепортить** *v.* spoil, ruin.

**переправ/а** *f.* passage, crossing, portage, ferry; —ить, —лять *v.* convey; relay, cross over; ferry; revise, correct.

**перепре/вать,** —ть *v.* stew too much; rot (of leaves, etc.).

**перепремник** *m.* (elec. comm.) transducer.

**перепроизводство** *n.* overproduction.

**перепроявленный** *a.* (phot.) overdeveloped.

**перепус/к** *m.* by-pass; —кать, —тить *v.* let across, let go across; let flow too much, let go too much; —кной *a.* by-pass; passage; —кной канал by-

pass, passageway, spillway; —кной клапан by-pass, by-pass valve, release valve; —кная труба overflow pipe, overflow.

**перепут/ать,** —ывать *v.* entangle; confuse; —ье *n.* crossroads, parting of the ways.

**перер.** *abbr.* (**переработанный**).

**перераб/атывать,** —отать *v.* work over, treat, digest; reprocess; make over, remake, revise; work overtime; п. на convert to; —отанный *a.* worked over, treated, digested; made over, converted; refabricated (fuel); —отка *f.* working over, treatment, digestion; reprocessing; recovery; conversion; remaking, redesigning; overtime work; потери при —отке reprocessing loss.

**переразрядить** *v.* (elec.) run down.

**перераспредел/ение** *n.* redistribution; (chem.) disproportionation; —ять *v.* redistribute.

**перераст/ать,** —и *v.* overgrow; develop, grow (into); outgrow.

**перерасход** *m.* overexpenditure; overexertion; (com.) overdraft; —овать *v.* spend too much; overdraw.

**перерегулирование** *n.* overcontrol; overshooting, overswing.

**перерез** *m.* crosscut; на п. at right angles; —ать, —ывать *v.* crosscut, cut, intersect; —ывающий *a.* intersecting; transverse.

**перереш/ать,** —ить *v.* change one's mind, alter one's decision; solve.

**перержав/елый** *a.* rusted; —еть *v.* get rusty, become covered with rust.

**переро/д** *m.* (agr.) degenerative crop; —дить, —ждать *v.* regenerate; revive; —диться, —ждаться *v.* be regenerated; degenerate; —ждение *n.* regeneration, palingenesis; degeneration.

**переросший** *a.* overgrown.

**перерыв** *m.* interruption, break, discontinuity, disturbance; gap, pause, stop, interval, intermission, rest period; с —ами intermittent, interrupted; пользование с —ами intermittent use.

**переса/дить,** —живать *v.* transplant, replant; graft; transship, transfer;

—дка *f.* transplanting; transfer (on trip); —женный *a.* transplanted.

**переса́ливать** *v.* oversalt.

**пересверли́ть** *v.* redrill, rebore.

**пересе́в** *m.* reseeding; —ать *v.* reseed, sow over again.

**пересе́к/ать** *v.* intersect, intercept, cross, cut; traverse; interlace; —а́ться *v.* cross, intersect; —а́ющий *a.* crossing, intersecting; transverse (axis); —а́ющая ли́ния (geom.) secant; —а́ющийся *a.* intersecting; interlaced; concurrent (forces); —а́ющееся строе́ние interlaced structure.

**пересе́л/е́нческий** *a.* migrant (population); —и́ть, —я́ть *v.* transplant, move; —и́ться, —я́ться *v.* migrate, move.

**пересе́ч/е́ние** *n.* intersection, crossing, crossover, traversal; traverse; interlacing; ме́сто —е́ния, то́чка —е́ния point of intersection, point of interception, crossing point; —е́нный *a.* intercepted, crossed; broken (terrain); —ь *see* пересека́ть.

**пересини́ть** *v.* give a bluish tint; make too blue.

**переск/а́кать, —а́кивать** *v.* jump over; skip, omit; —а́кивание *n.*, —о́к *m.* jump, jump-over, jumping over; skipping, omitting; transfer, transition, passage; —а́кивание и́скр sparking over; —а́кивающий *a.* jumping over.

**переслаи́в/а́ние** *n.* (geol.) interstratification, interbedding; layers, beds; —а́ть, —а́ться *v.* interstratify; —а́ющийся *a.* interstratified, interbedded.

**пересла́ть** *see* пересыла́ть.

**пересло/и́ть** *see* переслаи́вать; —йка *f.* stratification.

**пересм/а́тривать, —отре́ть** *v.* look over, review; re-examine, revise; reconsider; —о́тр *m.* inspection, overhauling; review; revision; reconsideration; —о́тренный *a.* inspected, overhauled; reviewed; revised.

**пересн/има́ть, —я́ть** *v.* rent again; (phot.) copy; rephotograph, take over.

**пересо́х/нуть** *see* пересыха́ть; —ший *a.* dried out, dry, parched.

**переспе́/ва́ть, —ть** *v.* overripen, get

too ripe; —лый *a.* overripe; (met.) over-refined; dry (copper).

**перестава́ть** *v.* cease, stop, discontinue.

**перестав/ить, —ля́ть** *v.* transpose, rearrange, change the order, change the position, reset, readjust, regulate; —ля́емый *a.* adjustable; —но́й *a.* adjustable; reversible.

**переста́иваться** *v.* stand too long.

**перестан/а́вливать** *see* переста́вить; —о́вка *f.* transposition, rearrangement, displacement, change, inversion; exchange, interchange; readjustment, regulation; (math.) permutation; у́гол —о́вки angle of displacement.

**перестано́вочный** *a.* adjustable; п. винт set screw, adjusting screw; п. рыча́г reverse lever, reversing lever.

**переста́ть** *see* перестава́ть.

**пересто́/й** *m.* overripe crop; overmature wood; —йный *a.* overripe, overmature (forest); —я́лый *a.* kept too long; —я́ться *see* переста́иваться.

**перестра́ивать** *v.* rebuild, reconstruct; reorganize, change over.

**перестро/е́ние** *n.* reorganization; —енный *a.* reorganized; rebuilt; —ить *see* перестра́ивать; —йка *f.* reorganization, rearrangement; retuning; rebuilding.

**пересту́п** *see* переступе́нь.

**переступа́ть** *v.* cross, step over; overstep, exceed; transgress.

**переступе́нь** *m.* (bot.) bryony (*Bryonia*).

**переступи́ть** *see* переступа́ть.

**пересульфи́рование** *n.* sulfur transfer.

**пересу́ш/ивать, —и́ть** *v.* dry too much, overdry, parch.

**пересчёт** *m.*, —ный *a.* conversion, translation; recalculation; scaling; counting; п. на два scale of two; двои́чный п. binary scaling; коэффицие́нт —а scaling factor; conversion factor; при —е на on conversion to; табли́ца —а, табли́ца для —а conversion table; —ка *f.* scaler, scaling circuit; —ный прибо́р, —ная устано́вка, —ное устро́йство (radiation counting) scaler, scaling unit; counter (of electric pulses); —ная схе́ма scaler, scaling circuit; counter system; кольцева́я —ная схе́ма ring scaler; —чик *m.* register, director; translator.

**пересчит/анный** *a.* converted; recounted; —**ать,** —**ывать** *v.* convert; recount, count over; recalculate; scale; —**ываемый** *a.* countable; —**ывание** *n.* conversion; recounting, counting over, repeated counting.

**пересыл/атель** *m.* sender; —**ать** *v.* send, forward; transport, convey; remit (money); —**ать по почте** forward; —**ка** *f.* forwarding; remittance.

**пересып/ание** *n.* interspersion; overfilling; —**ать** *v.* intersperse; pour over; pour too much, overfill.

**пересыхать** *v.* dry; parch, dry to excess.

**пересыщ/ать** *v.* supersaturate; surfeit; —**ение** *n.* supersaturation; satiety; —**енный** *a.* supersaturated; surfeited.

**переталкив/ать** *v.* push over, move over; —**ающий питатель** reciprocating feed.

**перетапливать** *v.* heat to excess, overheat; melt again, remelt.

**перетачивать** *v.* resharpen, regrind.

**перетек/ание** *n.* overflowing, overflow; —**ать** *v.* overflow, flow over.

**перетереть** *see* **перетирать.**

**перетечь** *see* **перетекать.**

**перетир/ание** *n.* wearing, grinding; —**ать** *v.* wear, grind; rub over, rub through; —**аться** *v.* wear by friction, wear through, rub through.

**переток** *m.* (elec.) overcurrent.

**перетолк/ать,** —**нуть** *see* **переталкивать.**

**перетолков/ание** *n.* interpretation; misinterpretation; —**ать,** —**ывать** *v.* discuss a matter; misinterpret.

**перетопки** *pl.* dregs.

**переточка** *f.* regrinding; sharpening.

**переть** *v.* press, push, thrust.

**перетя/гивать,** —**нуть** *v.* outweigh, overbalance; prevail, win over; draw, tighten; stretch again; —**жка** *f.* bank; intake; pumping over; constriction, drawn-out portion (of tube); neck, sausage-type instability (in a plasma column); —**нутость** *f.* contraction, tightness; —**нутый** *a.* tightened.

**переувлажненный** *a.* water-logged.

**переуглероживание** *n.* (met.) supercarburization, excessive carburization; recarburization.

**переулок** *m.* lane, alley.

**переуспокоение** *n.* overdamping.

**переустр/аивать** *v.* rebuild; reorganize; —**ойство** *n.* rebuilding, reconstruction; reorganization.

**переуступ/аемый** *a.* negotiable; —**ать,** —**ить** *v.* cede, give up; recede.

**переутом/ить,** —**лять** *v.* overfatigue, overwork; —**ление** *n.* overfatigue, overwork, overexertion, overstrain; —**ленный** *a.* overfatigued, overworked, overstrained, overwrought (nerves).

**переучет** *see* **учет;** **п. векселя** discount.

**переформиров/ание** *n.,* —**ка** *f.* re-forming.

**переформулировать** *v.* reformulate.

**перефосфорилирование** *n.* transphosphorylation.

**перехват** *m.* interception; constriction; intake; (zool.) cervical sinus; —**ать,** —**ить,** —**ывать** *v.* intercept; overshoot the mark; —**чик** *m.* interceptor; —**ывание** *n.* interception; (med.) strangulation, constriction.

**перехлорированный** *a.* after-chlorinated.

**переход** *m.,* —**ка** *f.* transition, passing over, passing, conversion; transfer, passage, crossing, migration (of ions); exchange (of places), switching; blending, shading (of colors); **точка** —**а** transition point; —**ить** *v.* pass, pass over, go over, be converted, change, turn (into); develop, proceed; cross; shunt.

**переходн/ый** *a.* transitional, transition, transient, passing, intermediate, connecting, crossover; circulatory; reversible; (math.) transitive (group, relation); **п. комплекс** intermediate complex; **п. оттенок** transition color; **п. процесс,** —**ое состояние,** —**ое явление** (elec.) transient; **п. фитинг,** —**ая втулка,** —**ая муфта** adapter, coupling, reducer, reducing bush; —**ая кривая** transition curve; —**ая полоса** transition zone; —**ая стадия** intermediate stage, transition stage; —**ая труба** reducing pipe, reducer; —**ое колено** bridge piece; —**ое положение** transitional position, transition; —**ое равновесие** transient (radioactive) equilibrium; —**ое сопротивление** intermediate resistance; —**ое состояние** transition state.

**переходящий** *a.* transitory, transient; changing (into), passing over; erratic.

**пер/ец** *m.* (bot.) pepper (*Piper*); **английский п., ямайский п.** *see* **пимент**; **водяной п.** water pepper, smartweed (*Polygonum hydropiper*); **дикий п.** wild pepper, mezereon (*Daphne mezereum*); **душистый п.** tarragon (*Artemisia dracunculus*); **зерно —ца** peppercorn; **испанский п., стручковый п.** red pepper, cayenne pepper, Spanish pepper (condiment); **обыкновенный п., черный п.** black pepper (*Piper nigrum*); **огородный п.** common garden pepper (*Capsicum annuum*).

**переце/дить, —живать** *v.* refilter.

**перечень** *m.* list, catalog; schedule, inventory; sum, total.

**перечерк/ать, —ивать, —нуть** *v.* strike out, draw lines across.

**перечесть** *see* **пересчитывать.**

**перечисл/ение** *n.* enumeration; translation, transfer; **—ить, —ять** *v.* enumerate, list; transfer.

**перечистить** *see* **перечищать.**

**перечит/ать, —ывать** *v.* reread; revise.

**перечищать** *v.* clean up; clean again, scour again.

**перечневый** *a.* abridged, brief.

**перечник** *m.* (bot.) candytuft (*Iberis*).

**перечн/ые** *pl.* (bot.) Piperaceae; **—ый** *a.* pepper, peppery; **—ая трава** peppergrass (*Lepidium*).

**перешеек** *m.* isthmus, neck (of land); vent.

**перешиб** *m.* fracture; **—ать, —ить** *v.* fracture, break.

**перешивать** *v.* alter.

**переэтерификация** *f.* ester interchange.

**переяр/ка** *f.*, **—ок** *m.* yearling.

**пери—** *prefix* peri— (round); **—анций** *m.* (bot.) perianth; **—блема** *f.* (bot.) periblem; **—гелий** *m.* (astron.) perihelion; **—дерма** *f.* (bot.) periderm; **—дий** *m.* (bot.) peridium.

**перидот** *m.* (min.) peridot (a gem variety of olivine); **—ит** *m.* peridotite (an igneous rock).

**перикард, —ий** *m.* (anat.) pericardium; **—ит** *m.* (med.) pericarditis; **—ический** *a.* pericardial, pericardiac.

**перикарпий** *m.* (bot.) pericarp.

**перикл/аз** *m.* (min.) periclase (magnesi-um oxide); **—ин** *m.* (min.) pericline (a variety of albite); **—инальный** *a.* pericline, periclinal.

**перила** *f.* handrail, railing, rail, guard rail, bar, barrier, parapet.

**перилен** *m.* perylene; **—хинон** *m.* perylenequinone.

**перилл/а** *f.* (bot.) perilla (*Perilla ocimoides*); **—овый** *a.* perilla; perillic; **—овый альдегид** perillaldehyde; **—овый спирт** perillic alcohol; **—овая кислота** perillic acid.

**перимагматический** *a.* perimagmatic.

**периметр** *m.* (geom.) perimeter.

**перимид/ил** *m.* perimidyl; **—ин** *m.* perimidine.

**периморфоза** *f.* (min.) perimorph.

**перинафто—** *prefix* perinaphtho—.

**периней** *m.* (anat.) perineum.

**период** *m.* period, phase, stage; age; interval; (operating) cycle; (lattice) spacing, pitch; spell (of weather); **измеритель —а** (nucl.) period meter.

**периодат** *m.* periodate.

**периодика** *f.* periodicals.

**периодическ/ий** *a.* periodical, recurrent; alternating, intermittent; batch (process); **п. закон** periodic law, Mendeleyev's law; **—ая дробь** (math.) repeating decimal, circulating decimal; **—ая печать** periodicals; **—ая система** periodic system (of elements); **—ого действия** batch, batch-operated.

**период/ичность** *f.* periodicity; batch nature, non-continuity; (feed) rate; **—ограмма** *f.* periodogram; **—ообразователь** *m.* frequency changer.

**периост** *m.* (anat.) periosteum; **—ит** *m.* (med.) periostitis.

**периплазм/а** *f.* (bot.) periplasm; **—одий** *m.* periplasmodium.

**перипло/генин** *m.* periplogenin; **—цин** *m.* periplocin.

**перископ** *m.* periscope, altiscope; **оконный п.** altiscope; **—ический** *a.* periscopic; **—ические стекла** periscopic lenses.

**перисперм** *m.* (bot.) perisperm.

**перистальт/ика** *f.* (physiol.) peristalsis; (med.) peristaltics; **—ин** *m.* peristaltin; **—ический** *a.* peristaltic, compressive; **—ическое сокращение** peristalsis.

перистерит *m.* (min.) peristerite (a variety of albite).

перисто— *prefix* feather; (bot.) penni—, pinnately; —жаберные *pl.* (zool.) Pterobranchia; —кучевое облако cirrocumulus, mackerel sky; —листый *a.* (bot.) pinnate, feather-leaved; —лопастный *a.* (bot.) pinnately lobed.

перистом *m.* (biol.) peristome.

перисто/нервный *a.* (bot.) penninervate; —образный *a.* featherlike; cirriform (cloud); —слоистое облако cirrostratus; —сть *f.* plumosity.

перист/ый *a.* feather, feathery; (biol.) plumose, feathered; pinnate, featherlike; п. агат (min.) feather agate; п. глет feathers of litharge; —ое облако high cloud, cirrus; —ое строение feathered structure.

перитекти/ка *f.*, —ческий *a.* (met.) peritectic.

перитеций *m.* (bot.) perithecium.

перитонит *m.* (med.) peritonitis.

перифер/ийный, —ический *a.* peripheral, circumferential; outlying (district); —ия *f.* periphery, circumference; outlying district.

перицикл *m.* (bot.) pericycle; —ический *a.* pericyclic; —окамфан *m.* pericyclo-camphane.

перицит *m.* (biol.) pericyte.

перка *f.* bit, flat bit, cutter, drill point; drill, flat drill.

перкал/ь *m.*, —евый *a.* (text.) percale.

перкамфорная кислота percamphoric acid.

Перкина реакция Perkin's reaction.

перкислота *see* надкислота.

перкнит *m.* (petr.) perknite.

перков/ый *a.* bit, flat bit; drill; —ое сверло flat drill.

перкол/ировать *v.* percolate; —ирующий *a.* percolating; —ятор *m.* percolator; —яция *f.*, —яционный *a.* percolation.

перку/ссионный *a.*, —ссия *f.* percussion; —тировать *v.* percuss.

перл *m.* pearl, bead; (typ.) pearl (5 points).

перламутр *m.* mother-of-pearl, nacre; —енница *f.* (zool.) a butterfly (*Argynnis pahia*); —овый *a.* pearly, nacreous.

перлатолиновая кислота perlatolinic acid.

перл/аш *m.* pearl ash (a potassium carbonate); —вейс *m.* pearl white (white lead).

перли *past pl. of* переть.

перлинь *m.* hawser, tow line.

перлит *m.* (min.) perlite (a volcanic glass); (met.) perlite; —ный, —овый *a.* perlitic, spherulitic; —ный чугун perlite iron; —ообразный *a.* pearl-shaped, bead-shaped.

перлов/ица *f.* pearl shell; (zool.) pearl oyster; —ник *m.* (bot.) melica.

перлов/ый *a.* pearl; п. камень (min.) pearl stone, perlite; п. шелк (text.) ardassine; —ая крупа pearl barley.

перлполимеризация *f.* pearl polymerization.

перлюстрация *f.* censoring of letters.

пермаллой *m.* Permalloy (a nickel-iron alloy).

перманганат *m.* permanganate; п. калия potassium permanganate.

перманентн/ость *f.* permanence, permanency; —ый *a.* permanent, lasting; —ая белая permanent white, precipitated barium sulfate.

перманит *m.* Permanite (nickel-iron alloy).

пермеаметр *m.* permeameter (for measuring magnetic permeability).

перм/ендюр *m.* Permendur (iron-cobalt alloy); —енорм *m.* Permenorm (iron-nickel alloy); —ет *m.* Permet (copper-cobalt-nickel alloy).

пер/мин *abbr.* (периодов в минуту) cycles per minute.

перминвар *m.* Perminvar (alloy of Permalloy type).

пермиссивный *a.* permissive.

пермский *a.* (geol.) Permian, Permic; п. период Permian epoch.

пермут/ация *f.*, —ирование *n.* permutation; transmutation; Permutit process; —ит *m.* permutite (artificial zeolite); —итный процесс Permutit process (for water purification).

пермь *see* пермский период.

пернамбуков/ый каучук pernambuco rubber; —ое дерево (dyeing) pernambuco, Lima wood, Nicaragua wood.

**пернатый** *a.* feathered.

**перициозный** *a.* (med.) pernicious.

**Перно печь** Pernot furnace (for steel).

**Перо лампа** Pérot (mercury-vapor) lamp.

**перо** *n.* feather; pen; fin (of fish); **п. рондо** lettering pen; **вечное п.** fountain pen; **—видный** *a.* feather-like, plumaceous; **—вое сверло** pointed drill.

**перовскит** *m.* (min.) perovskite.

**пероксид** *m.* peroxide; **—аза** *f.* peroxidase; **—ол** *m.* peroxydol, sodium perborate.

**перонин** *m.* peronine, benzylmorphine hydrochloride.

**перочинный ножик** penknife, pocket-knife.

**перпендикуляр** *m.* perpendicular; **—но** *adv.* perpendicularly, perpendicular (to); **—ность** *f.* perpendicularity; **—ный** *a.* perpendicular.

**перпетуум мобиле** perpetual motion.

**Перрина уравнение** Perrin equation.

**Перринса метод** (met.) Perrins rolling process.

**перрон** *m.* railroad platform.

**персеит** *m.* perseite, perseitol.

**пер/сек** *abbr.* (периодов в секунду) cycles per second.

**перс/елоза** *f.* perseulose; **—ея** *f.* (bot.) persea; **приятнейшая —ея** avocado (*Persea americana*).

**персидск/ий** *a.* Persian, Iranian; **П. Залив** Persian Gulf; **п. порошок** pyrethrum dust; **—ая камедь** sagapenum (gum resin from *Ferula persica*).

**персик** *m.*, **—овый** *a.* (bot.) peach (*Persica vulgaris*); **—о** *n.* peach brandy.

**персилит** *m.* (min.) percylite (a lead-copper oxychloride).

**персио** *n.* persio, cudbear, orchil (coloring material).

**персистентность** *f.* persistence.

**Персо раствор** Persoz solution (of basic zinc chloride).

**персона** *f.* person, personage; **—л** *m.* personnel, staff; **—льный** *a.* personal.

**перспекс** *m.* Perspex (plastic).

**перспектив/а** *f.* perspective; prospect, outlook, aspect; **—ный** *a.* perspective; promising; long-term (plan).

**перстневидный** *a.* ring-shaped; (anat.) cricoid.

**персульф/ат** *m.* persulfate; **—ид** *m.* persulfide.

**пертинакс** *m.* Pertinax (a bakelite board).

**пертио—** *prefix* perthio—.

**пертит** *m.* (min.) perthite (a variety of feldspar); **—овый, —оподобный** *a.* perthitic.

**пертурбаци/онный** *a.*, **—я** *f.* perturbation, disturbance; **п. ток** stream of disturbances.

**перуанск/ий** *a.* Peruvian; **п. бальзам** Peru balsam, Indian balsam; **—ое серебро** a kind of German silver.

**перув/ианский** *see* **перуанский**; **—ин** *m.* peruvin, cinnamic alcohol; **—иол** *m.* peruviol, nerolidol; **—ит** *m.* (min.) peruvite (same as matildite).

**перу/ген** *m.* perugen, synthetic Peru balsam; **—ол** *m.* peruol, benzyl benzoate.

**перфокарта** *f.* punch card.

**перфор/атор** *m.* perforator, punch, puncher; punch-card machine; drill, drilling machine, boring machine; **вращательный п.** drill; **—ация** *f.*, **—ирование** *n.* perforation, punching; drilling, boring; **—ированный** *a.* perforated, punched; drilled, bored; **—ировать** *v.* perforate, punch; drill, bore; **—ирующий** *a.* perforating; **—ирующая коррозия** pitting.

**перхлор/ат** *m.* perchlorate; **—ид** *m.* perchloride; **—овинил** *m.* chlorinated polyvinyl chloride; **—этан** *m.* perchloroethane, hexachloroethane; **—этилен** *m.* perchloroethylene, tetrachloroethylene.

**перхота** *f.* dryness of the throat.

**перхоть** *f.* dandruff.

**перцилит** *see* **персилит**.

**перцов/ка** *f.* pepper brandy; **—ое дерево** (bot.) agnus castus.

**перчат/ка** *f.*, **—очный** *a.* glove; **—очный бокс**, **—очная камера** (nucl.) glove box.

**перчинка** *f.* peppercorn.

**перчить** *v.* pepper, season with pepper.

**пер/ышко** *n.* little feather; **—ья** *pl.* of **перо**; **—янка** *f.* fin.

**пес** *m.* dog, hound; **—ец** *m.* polar fox; **—ий** *a.* canine, dog; **—ий язык** (bot.)

hound's tongue (*Cynoglossum offici-nale*).

**пескарь** *m.* (zool.) gudgeon.

**пески** *pl.* of **песок**; sand desert, sand plain; bank of river.

**песко/вание** *n.* sanding (of soil); —**ватый** *a.* sandy, rather sandy; —**дувка** *f.*, —**дувная машина,** —**дувный** *a.* sandblast; —**жил** *m.* (zool.) lugworm; —**ловка** *f.* sand trap; —**люб** *m.* (bot.) ammophila; —**мет** *m.* (foundry) sand slinger; —**отделитель** *m.* sand separator, sand trap; —**рой** *m.* (zool.) sand eel; fossorial wasp.

**пескоструй** *m.* sandblast, sandblast machine; —**ный** *a.* sandblast; —**ная очистка** sandblasting, sandblast cleaning.

**песко/сушилка** *f.* sand dryer, sand-drying oven; —**черпалка** *f.* sand dredger.

**пес/ок** *m.* sand; gravel; **отливка в —ке** (foundry) sand casting.

**песоч/ина** *f.* sand hole; —**ница** *f.* sand box; sanding apparatus; (paper) riffler, sand trap.

**песочн/ый** *a.* sand, sandy; **п. корень** *see* осока, **песочная**; **п. насос** sand pump, sludger; **п. фильтр** sand filter, gravel filter; —**ая бумага,** —**ая шкурка** sandpaper; —**ая ванна** sand bath; —**ая раковина** sand hole (in casting); —**ые часы** hourglass; **отливка в —ой форме** (foundry) sand casting.

**пессарий** *m.* (med.) pessary.

**пест** *m.* pestle, beater, rammer; —**ик** *m.* pestle, pounder; (bot.) pistil; —**иковый** *a.* (bot.) pistillate, pistillary; —**ичные** *pl.* pistillate plants.

**пестовник** *m.* (bot.) horsetail (*Equisetum*).

**пестовой молот** drop hammer.

**пестокс** *m.* Pestox (insecticide).

**пестр/еть** *v.* appear variegated; —**ить** *v.* variegate; —**о** *adv.* variegatedly; —**оватый** *a.* somewhat variegated; —**окрылки** *pl.* fruit flies (*Trypetidae*); —**олистный** *a.* having variegated leaves; —**ополье** *n.* irregular sowing; —**ота** *f.* variegation; —**уха** *f.* salmon trout; —**ушка** *f.* brook trout, rainbow trout; —**ый** *a.* variegated, parti-

colored, mottled, blended; iridescent; —**яки** *pl.* checkered beetles (*Cleridae*); —**янки** *pl.* (zool.) Zygaenidae.

**пестрятка** *f.* parr (young salmon).

**песчаник** *m.*, —**овый** *a.* (petr.) sandstone.

**песчанистый** *a.* sandy, arenaceous.

**песчанка** *f.* (zool.) sand eel; (bot.) sandwort (*Arenaria*).

**песчано—** *prefix* sand; —**струйный** *see* пескоструйный.

**песчан/ый** *a.* sandy, sand, gritty, gravelly; *see also* песочный; —**ая буря** sandstorm; —**ая коса** sandbar.

**песчинка** *f.* grit, particle of sand.

**песья вишня** (bot.) physalis.

**петалит** *m.* (min.) petalite.

**петарда** *f.* petard; firecracker.

**петель/ка** *f.* eyelet, mesh; —**ный** *a.* loop; —**чатый** *a.* netted, mesh; —**чатая структура** (min.) mesh structure, net structure, lattice structure.

**петзит** *m.* (min.) petzite (a silver-gold telluride).

**Пети** *see under* Дюлонг и Пти.

**петигреновое масло** petitgrain oil (from *Citrus bigaradia*).

**петинка** *f.* (text.) hank.

**петиотизовать** *v.* petiotize (wines).

**петит** *m.* (typ.) brevier (8 points).

**петиция** *f.* petition.

**петле/вание** *n.* (met.) looping; —**видный** *a.* loop, loop-shaped.

**петлев/ой** *a.* loop; hinge; **п. стан** (met.) loop mill, looping mill; **п. бельгийский стан** Belgian mill; —**ая обмотка** (elec.) lap winding.

**петлеобразн/ый** *a.* loop, loop-shaped; —**ая обмотка** (elec.) lap winding.

**петли/стый** *a.* loop, looped; —**ца** *f.* buttonhole.

**петл/я** *f.* loop, kink; noose, slip knot; mesh (of net); eye; hinge (of door); (elec.) loop; collar; **внутренняя мертвая п.** inside loop; **закрытая п., замкнутая п.** closed loop; **на —ях** hinged; **соединение —ей** clasp joint.

**Петри чашка** Petri dish.

**петро—** *prefix* petro—, stone, rock.

**петров крест** (bot.) toothwort (*Lathraea*).

**петроген/езис** *m.* (petr.) petrogenesis; —**етический** *a.* petrogenetic; —**ия** *f.* petrogeny.

петрограф *m.* (petr.) petrographer; —
ический *a.* petrographic, petrograph-
ical; —ия *f.* petrography.
Петрозаводск Petrozavodsk.
петрол/ат, —атум *m.* petrolatum; —ейный *a.*, —еум *m.* petroleum; —ейный
эфир petroleum ether, ligroin; —ен
*m.* petrolene, asphalt; malthene;
—ин *m.* petroline (a paraffin).
петрология *f.* petrology, lithology.
петроль *m.* petrol (British term for gasoline); petroleum ether.
Петропавловск Petropavlovsk.
петро/селиновая кислота petroselinic
acid, petroselic acid; —силан *m.*
petrosilane.
петросилекс *m.* (petr.) petrosilex;
felsite.
петросилиевая трава *see* петрушка.
петроцен *m.* petrocene.
петруш/ка *f.* ,—ечный *a.* (bot.) parsley
(*Petroselinum sativum*); болотная п.
marsh parsley (*Peucedanum palustre*).
петр. эф. *abbr.* (петролейный эфир).
петтикот *m.* (elec.) petticoat.
петун/ин *m.* petunine; —ия *f.* (bot.)
petunia.
петух *m.* rooster, cock.
петуш/ий, —иный *a.* rooster, cock; п.
гребешок (bot.) cockscomb (*Celosia
cristata*); —иный гребень cockscomb;
—ки *pl.* (bot.) iris; —ник *m.* (bot.)
hemp nettle (*Galeopsis*); —ок *m.*
cockerel; weathercock; (elec.) riser,
commutator riser, commutator lug;
—ье просо barn grass (*Echinochloa
crus-galli*).
петь *v.* sing.
пехмановские красители Pechmann
dyes.
пехота *f.* (mil.) infantry.
пецица *f.* (bot.) peziza.
печальный *a.* sad, grievous, mournful.
печат/ание *n.* printing; imprint; sealing;
—анный *a.* printed; —ать *v.* print;
type; stamp, seal, imprint, impress;
—ающий *a.* printing; —ка *f.* signet,
seal; —ник *m.* printer.
печатн/ый *a.* printed; stamped, sealed,
marked; п. лист quire; п. станок
printing press; —ая краска printing
ink.

печат/ня *f.* printery, printing office; —ь
*f.* seal, stamp; press; print, printing;
выйти из —и *v.* come out, be fresh
from the press; золотая —ь *see*
гидрастис; накладывать —ь *v.*
stamp; —ывать *see* печатать.
печен/ие *n.* baking; порошок для —ия
baking powder.
печенка *see* печень.
печенков/ый *a.* hepatic; *see also* пече-
ночный; п. колчедан (min.) liver
pyrites; hepatic pyrite, marcasite;
п. опал (min.) liver opal, menilite;
—ая руда (min.) liver ore (a variety
of cuprite or of cinnabar).
печенный *a.* baked, roasted.
печеночн/ик *m.*, —ица *f.*, —ый мох
(bot.) liverwort (*Hepatica triloba*);
—ики *pl.* Hepaticae; —ый *a.* hepatic,
liver; —ый сахар liver sugar, glycogen; —ая ворвань fish-liver oil, spec.
cod-liver oil.
печеный *a.* baked, roasted.
печень *f.* (anat.) liver.
печенье *n.* pastry; cookies, etc.
печерица *see* шампиньон.
печи *see under* печь.
печка *see* печь.
печкоуступная система (min.) stoping.
печн/ой *a.* furnace, stove; coke-oven
(coke); п. агрегат furnace unit; п. газ
furnace gas; п. камень ovenstone; п.
сок, п. шлак furnace slag, slag; —ая
стяжка furnace draft connection;
—ая труба chimney, flue; —ое
стекло glass that has run down into
the hearth.
печ/ь *f.* furnace, kiln, oven, stove; *v.*
bake, roast; п.-компаунд combination (coke) oven; п. с мешалкой
rabble furnace; п. сопротивления
resistance furnace; высушенный в
—и kiln-dried; продуктивность —и,
производительность —и furnace output; работа —и, ход —и furnace
operation.
пешеход *m.*, —ный *a.* pedestrian; —ный
мост footbridge.
пеш/ий *a.* pedestrian; —ком *adv.* on
foot; итти —ком *v.* walk.
пещер/а *f.* cave, cavern; —истый *a.*
cavernous; —ный *a.* cave; —ная
вода interstitial water.

**ПЖР** *abbr.* (плотномер жидкости радио-активный) radioactive fluid densitometer.

**пз** *abbr.* (пьеза) pièze; (пуаз) poise.

**пи** (math.) pi, $\pi$.

**пиазин** *m.* piazine, pyrazine.

**пиазотиол** *m.* piazothiole.

**пиасава** *f.* palm fibers for rope.

**пиаселенол** *m.* piaselenole, isobenzo-selenodiazole.

**пиаузит** *m.* (min.) piauzite (an asphaltoid substance).

**пивал/ил** *m.* pivalyl; **хлористый п.** pivalyl chloride; **—иновая кислота** pivalic acid, trimethylacetic acid.

**пивн/ой** *a.* beer; brewer's (yeast); **—ая гуща** brewer's grains, spent malt.

**пиво** *n.* beer; ale; **варить п.** *v.* brew.

**пивовар** *m.* (beer) brewer; **—ение** *n.* brewing; **—енный, —ный** *a.* brewing; **—енный завод, —ня** *f.* brewery; **—ничать** *v.* brew, brew beer or ale.

**пивший** *past act. part. of* **пить.**

**пигмей** *m.* pygmy, dwarf.

**пигмент** *m.* pigment; **—ация** *f.* pigmentation; **—ированный** *a.* pigmented, colored; **—ировать** *v.* pigment, color; **—ный** *a.* pigment, pigmentary.

**пигмолит** *m.* pigmolite (dome-like magma massif resembling a fist).

**пид** *abbr.* (прямоточный испаритель-дефлегматор) air-separating apparatus.

**пиджак** *m.* coat, jacket.

**пидин** *m.* pydine.

**пиезо—** *see* **пьезо—.**

**пие/лит** *m.* (med.) pyelitis; **—ло—** *prefix* pyelo— (pelvis); **—мия** *f.* (med.) pyemia.

**пижма** *f.* (bot.) tansy (*Tanacetum vulgare*).

**пизанг** *see* **банан.**

**пиз/анит** *m.* (min.) pisanite (an iron-copper sulfate); **—олит** *m.* pisolite, peastone (a form of limestone); **—олитовый, —олитоподобный** *a.* pisolitic, pea-like.

**пиин** *m.* pyin.

**пик** *m.* peak, pinnacle, cusp, crest; spike.

**пика** *f.* pike, lance, spear; slice bar, straight poker (for furnace).

**пика/ковая кислота** picacic acid; **—мар** *m.* picamar, propylpyrogallol dimethyl ether.

**пикап** *m.* pickup (truck).

**пике** *n.* (text.) piqué; (aero.) dive.

**пикелевание** *n.* (leather) pickling.

**пикер** *m.* picker.

**пикет** *m.* picket; stake, peg; **—аж** *m.* (min.) staking out, marking out; **—ажная книжка** field book; **—ирование** *n.* picketing.

**пикир/ование** *n.* (aero.) diving, nose dive; **вывод из —ования** pull-out; **—ованный** *a.* transplanted; **—овать** *v.* dive; prick out, single; **—овка** *f.* transplanting; **—ующий** *a.* diving, dive (bomber).

**пиккер** *m.* picker.

**пиккерингит** *m.* (min.) pickeringite, magnesia alum.

**пикн—** *see* **пикно—.**

**пикнит** *m.* (min.) pycnite (a variety of topaz).

**пикно—** *prefix* pycno— (dense, close, compact); **—метр** *m.* pycnometer, specific gravity flask; **—троп** *m.* (min.) pycnotrope (near serpentine); **—хлорит** *m.* (min.) pycnochlorite.

**пико—** *prefix* pico—, micromicro— (denoting a magnitude of $10^{-12}$).

**пиков/ый** *a.* peak; **—ая нагрузка** peak load; **—ое острие** spear point.

**пикол/ил** *m.* picolyl; **—ин** *m.* picoline, methylpyridine; **—иновая кислота** picolinic acid, 2-pyridinecarboxylic acid.

**пикотаж** *m.* making mine tubing water-tight with wedges.

**пикотит** *m.* (min.) picotite, chrome spinel.

**пикофарада** *f.* (elec.) picofarad, micro-microfarad.

**пикразмин** *m.* picrasmin.

**пикраль** *m.* picral (pickling reagent).

**пикрам/ид** *m.* picramide, 2,4,6-trinitro-aniline; **—иновая кислота** picramic acid, 2-amino-4,6-dinitrophenol; **—нин** *m.* picramnine.

**пикр/ат** *m.* picrate; **—атол** *m.* picratol, silver picrate; **—ил** *m.* picryl; **—ин** *m.* picrin.

**пикринов/ая кислота** picric acid, tri-nitrophenol; **соль —ой кислоты, —окислая соль** picrate; **—оаммони-евая соль, —окислый аммоний** ammonium picrate; **—окислый** *a.* picric acid; picrate (of); —ый порох (expl.) picric powder.

пикрит *m.* (petr.) picrite (a variety of peridotite).

пикро— *prefix* picro—; —аконитин *m.* picroaconitine; —амозит *m.* (min.) picroamosite (a variety of amphibole); —змин *see* пикросмин; —ильменит *m.* (min.) picroilmenite (a magnesian ilmenite); —кармин *m.* picrocarmine.

пикрол *m.* picrol; —ит *m.* (min.) picrolite (a variety of serpentine); —ихениновая кислота picrolicheninic acid; —оновая кислота picrolonic acid.

пикро/мерит *m.* (min.) picromerite; —мицин *m.* pikromycin, picromycin; —подофиллин *m.* picropodophyllin; —смин *m.* (min.) picrosmine (a magnesium metasilicate); —тефроит *m.* (min.) picrotephroite (a variety of tephroite).

пикротин *m.* picrotin; —овая кислота picrotinic acid.

пикротитанит *m.* (min.) picrotitanite (a magnesian variety of ilmenite).

пикротоксин *m.* picrotoxin; —ин *m.* picrotoxinin; —иновая кислота picrotoxininic acid; —овая кислота picrotoxinic acid.

пикро/тон *m.* picrotone; —фармаколит *m.* (min.) picropharmacolite.

пиктограмма *f.* (statistics) pictogram.

пикули *pl.* pickles.

пикульник *m.*, желтый п. (bot.) hemp nettle (*Galeopsis*).

пикша *f.* (zool.) haddock.

пил *past sing. of* пить.

ПИЛ *abbr.* (прибор для измерения липкости почвы) soil adhesiveness meter.

пила *f.* saw; file; п.-ножевка hack saw; п. одноручка hand saw; двуручная п. cross-cut saw; круглая п. circular saw, disk saw; продольная п. rip saw.

пилав *m.* pilau, stewed rice.

пила-рыба *f.* saw fish.

пиленгас *m.* mullet (fish).

пилен/ие *n.* sawing; filing; —ый *a.* sawed; filed; lump (sugar).

пили *past pl. of* пить.

пилиганин *m.* piliganine.

пилигримовый стан *see* пильгер-стан.

пилильный *a.* sawing, saw; filing.

пилильщик *m.* saw fly; п.-ткачи *pl.* web-spinning sawflies (*Pamphiliidae*); настоящие —и sawflies (*Tenthredinidae*); хвойные —и conifer sawflies (*Diprionidae*).

пилить *v.* saw; file.

пил/ка *f.* sawing; filing; fret saw; file; —овочник *m.* saw log.

пилозин *m.* pilosine; —ин *m.* pilosinine.

пилокарп/идин *m.* pilocarpidine; —ин *m.* pilocarpine; —иновая кислота pilocarpic acid; —ус *m.* (bot.) pilocarpus.

пило/материал *m.* lumber; —машина *f.* power saw.

пилон *m.* pylon, tower.

пило/насекательный станок file cutter, file-sharpening machine; —образный *a.* saw-like, saw-tooth, serrate, notched.

пилоповая кислота pilopic acid.

пилорама *f.* saw frame.

пилорический *a.* (anat., zool.) pyloric.

пилоруб *m.* file cutter.

пилот *m.* pilot; —аж *m.* pilotage.

пилотакситовый *a.* (petr.) pilotaxitic.

пилотировать *v.* pilot.

пилохвост *m.* dogfish.

пилоцерин *m.* pilocerine.

пильбарит *m.* (min.) pilbarite.

пильгер-стан *m.* pilger mill (for pipes).

пильн/ый *a.* sawing, saw; file; lump (sugar); п. мастер saw-sharpener; file cutter; п. станок bench saw; filing machine; —ая лента saw blade; —ая трава (bot.) sawwort (*Serratula* or *Saussurea*).

пильпеля *m.* pilpelya (mud volcano in Transcaucasia).

пиль/чатозубчатый *a.* (bot.) dentatoserrate; —чатолистный *a.* serrate-leaved; —чатый *a.* saw-like, saw-tooth, serrate, notched; —щик *m.* sawyer.

пилэ *n.* crushed sugar.

пилюл/ька *f.* pilule, little pill, pellet; —ьный *a.* pill; —я *f.* pill, pellet, capsule, globule.

пилястр *m.*, —а *f.* pilaster, column.

пимар/иновая кислота pimarinic acid; —овая кислота pimaric acid.

пи-мезон *m.* (nucl.) pi-meson, pion.

**пимелин/кетон** *m.* pimelic ketone, cyclohexanone; **—овая кислота** pimelic acid, heptanedioic acid; **соль —овой кислоты, —овокислая соль** pimelate.

**пимелит** *m.* (min.) pimelite.

**пимент** *m.*, **—овый** *a.* pimento, allspice (condiment); **—овая кислота** pimentic acid; **—овое масло** pimento oil, allspice oil.

**пимпинеллин** *m.* pimpinellin.

**пин— prefix** pin—; **—абиетиновая кислота** pinabietic acid.

**пинавердол** *m.* pinaverdol (dye).

**пинагор** *m.* (zool.) lump-fish.

**пинакиолит** *m.* (min.) pinakiolite, manganludwigite.

**пинакоид** *m.* (cryst.) pinacoid, pinakoid; **—альный** *a.* pinacoidal, pinacoid.

**пин/акол, —акон** *m.* pinacol, 2,3-dimethyl-2,3-butanediol; **—аколил** *m.* pinacolyl; **—аколиловый спирт** pinacolyl alcohol; **—аколин** *m.* pinacolin, 3,3-dimethyl-2-butanone; pinacoline; **—альдегид** *m.* pinaldehyde; **—ан** *m.* pinane, bicyclo-(2:4)-heptane; **—астровая кислота** pinastric acid; **—ацианол** *m.* pinacyanol.

**пингвин** *m.* (zool.) penguin; pinguin, alantol.

**пинеарезен** *m.* pinearesene.

**пинен** *m.* pinene; **хлористоводородный п.** pinene hydrochloride.

**пинеоловая кислота** pineolic acid.

**пининовая кислота** pininic acid.

**пиниолы** *pl.* pine nuts.

**пинипикрин** *m.* pinipicrin.

**пинит** *m.* pinitol, cyclohexanepentol; (min.) pinite (an alteration product).

**пиния** *f.* Italian stone pine (*Pinus pinea*).

**пинк** *m.* (cer.) pink (tin and chromium oxides); **—зальц** *m.* pink salt, ammonium stannic chloride.

**пинноит** *m.* (min.) pinnoite (a magnesium borate).

**пино/вая кислота** pinic acid; **—камфорная кислота** pinocamphoric acid.

**пинол** *m.* pinol, pine camphor; **—ен** *m.* pinolene; **—ин** *m.* pinoline, rosin spirit;**—ит** *m.* (petr.) pinolite (carbonate slate or phyllite); **—овая кислота** pinolic acid.

**пиноль** *m.* tail spindle.

**пинон** *m.*, **—овый** *a.* pinone, 6-oxypinol; **—овая кислота** pinonic acid.

**пино/резинол** *m.* pinoresinol; **—товое масло** pinot oil.

**пинселин** *m.* pinselin.

**пинта** *f.* pint (measure).

**пинтадоит** *m.* (min.) pintadoite (a hydrous calcium vanadate encrustation).

**пинц/ет** *m.* pincers, nippers, forceps, tweezers; **—етка** *f.* forceps, tweezers; **—ировка** *f.* pinching (tops of plants).

**пинч-эффект** *m.* pinch effect.

**пиньола** *f.* pine nut.

**пио— prefix** pyo— (pus); **—генный** *a.* (med.) pyogenic; **—зин** *m.* pyosin; **—ксантин** *m.* pyoxanthin; **—ктанин** *m.* pyoctanin, dahlia violet; **—липовая кислота** pyolipic acid; **—луен** *m.* pyoluene.

**пион** *m.* (bot.) peony (*Paeonia*); (nucl.) pi-meson, pion.

**пионер** *m.* pioneer.

**пионефроз** *m.* (med.) pyonephrosis.

**пионовый** *a.* peony.

**пиорея** *f.* (med.) pyorrhea.

**пиоскоп** *m.* pioscope (for estimating fat content of milk).

**пио-соединение** *n.* pyo, pyo substance (antibiotic from *Pseudomonas pyocyanea*).

**пиотин** *m.* (min.) piotine, saponite.

**пиоцианин** *m.* pyocyanin, cyopin.

**пипеколин** *m.* pipecoline, methyl piperidine; **—овая кислота** pipecolinic acid, piperidine-N-carboxylic acid.

**пипер/азидин, —азин** *m.* piperazidine, piperazine, diethylene diamine; **—амид** *m.* piperamide, piperic acid amide.

**пиперид/ил** *m.* piperidyl; **—ин** *m.*, **—иновый** *a.* piperidine, hexahydropyridine; **—иниевые соединения** piperidinium compounds; **—инкарбоновая кислота** piperidinecarboxylic acid, nipecotic acid; **—овая кислота** piperidic acid, gamma-aminobutyric acid.

**пипер/ил** *m.* piperyl; **—илгидразин** *m.* piperylhydrazine, piperidylamine; **—илен** *m.* piperylene, pentadiene; **—ин** *m.* piperine, piperylpiperidine; **—иновая кислота** piperic acid; **—итон** *m.* piperitone; **—олидин** *m.* piperolidine, octahydropyrrocoline; —онал *m.* piperonal, heliotropin.

**пиперонил** *m.* piperonyl, 3,4-methylenedioxyphenyl (Soviet nomenclature); —иден *m.* piperonylidene; —овая кислота piperonylic acid, heliotropic acid; —овый спирт piperonyl alcohol.

**пипетка** *f.* pipette, pipet; п. на полное выпускание a pipet delivering a single definite amount without a graduated scale; transfer pipet.

**пипи/тзаоин,** —цагоин *m.* pipitzahoin; —тзаоиновая кислота pipitzahoic acid, perezon.

**пир**— *prefix* pyr—, pyro— (fire, heat); —азин *m.* pyrazine, paradiazine; —азино— *prefix* pyrazino—.

**пиразол** *m.,* —овый *a.* pyrazole, 1,2-diazole; —идин *m.* pyrazolidine, tetrahydropyrazole; —идон *m.* pyrazolidone, ketopyrazolidine; —ил *m.* pyrazolyl; —ин *m.* pyrazoline, dihydropyrazole; —ол *m.* pyrazolol; —он *m.,* —оновый *a.* pyrazolone, ketopyrazoline.

**пираконитин** *m.* pyraconitine.

**пираллолит** *m.* (min.) pyrallolite (decomposition product of pyroxene).

**пирамида** *f.* pyramid; —льный *a.* pyramidal, tapered; —льный куб tetrahexahedron.

**пирамидон** *m.* Pyramidon, aminopyrine.

**пиран** *m.* pyran.

**Пирани манометр** Pirani (hot-wire) gage.

**пиран/ил** *m.* pyranyl; —оза *f.* pyranose; —ол *m.* pyranol, sodium acetyl salicylate; —ометр *m.* pyranometer (for measuring radiation); —тин *m.* pyrantin, phenosuccin; —трен *m.* pyranthrene.

**пираргирит** *m.* (min.) pyrargyrite, ruby silver ore.

**пирацен** *m.* pyracene.

**пиргелиометр** *m.* (meteor.) pyrheliometer.

**пиргеометр** *m.* pyrgeometer (for determining earth's radiation).

**пирекс-трубки** *pl.* Pyrex (glass) tubes.

**пирен** *m.* pyrene, benzo[*def*]-phenanthrene.

**Пиренеи** the Pyrenees.

**пиренейский** *a.* Pyrenean.

**пиреновая кислота** pyrenic acid.

**пиреноид** *m.* (bot.) pyrenoid.

**пиренол** *m.* pyrenol, sodium thymol benzoate.

**пиреномицеты** *pl.* (bot.) Pyrenomycetes.

**пиренхинон** *m.* pyrenquinone.

**пиретол** *m.* solution of 1% pyrethrin in alcohol.

**пиретр/ин** *m.* pyrethrin; —он *m.* pyrethrone; —оновая кислота pyrethronic acid; —ум *m.* (bot.) pyrethrum.

**пирибол** *m.* (petr.) pyribole (a contraction of the names pyroxene and amphibole).

**пиридаз/ин** *m.* pyridazine, 1,2-diazine; —инон *m.* pyridazinone; —он *m.* pyridazone, 3-ketopyridazine.

**пиридил** *m.* pyridyl; —иден *m.* pyridylidene.

**пиридин** *m.,* —овый *a.* pyridine; —дикарбоновая кислота pyridinedicarboxylic acid; —карбоновая кислота pyridinecarboxylic acid; —овые основания pyridine bases.

**пиридо/ксал** *m.* pyridoxal, pyridoxine 4-aldehyde; —ксин *m.* pyridoxine, vitamin $B_6$; —л *m.* pyridol, hydroxypyridine; —н *m.* pyridone, ketopyridine; —пиридин *m.* pyridopyridine, 1,5-benzodiazine; —хинолин *m.* pyridoquinoline.

**пиримид/ил** *m.* pyrimidyl; —ин *m.* pyrimidine, 1,3-diazine; —он *m.* pyrimidone, dihydroketopyrimidine.

**пиринд/ан** *m.* pyrindane; —ин *m.* pyrindine; —оксиловая кислота pyrindoxylic acid; —ол *m.* pyrindol, 2,4-pyrrolopyridine.

**пирит** *m.* (min.) pyrite, fool's gold (iron sulfide); pyrites; —изация *f.* pyritization, conversion to pyrite; —изировать *v.* pyritize; —ный, —овый *a.* pyritic; —ная плавка (met.) pyritic smelting; —ные огарки pyrite cinders.

**пирито/ид,** —эдр *m.* (cryst.) pyritoid, pyritohedron, pentagonal dodecahedron; —логия *f.* pyritology; —подобный *a.* pyritiform, resembling pyrite; —содержащий *a.* pyritiferous, containing pyrite; —эдрический *a.* pyritohedral.

**пиро**— *prefix* pyro— (fire, heat); —аурит

*m.* (min.) pyroaurite; —**белонит** *m.*
(min.) pyrobelonite (a basic vanadate
of manganese and lead); —**бензол** *m.*
pyrobenzol (mixture of benzene,
toluene, etc.); —**битум** *m.* (min.) pyro-
bitumen (a form of natural hydrocarbon); —**борная кислота** pyroboric
acid; **соль**—**борной кислоты** pyrobor-
ate; —**ванадиевая кислота** pyro-
vanadic acid.

**пировин/ная кислота** pyrotartaric acid,
uvic acid; **соль**—**ной кислоты** pyro-
tartrate; —**оградная кислота** pyro-
racemic acid, pyruvic acid.

**пирог** *m.* pie; mass, cake.

**пирогалло**— *prefix* pyrogallo—; —**вая
кислота,** —**л** *m.* pyrogallic acid,
pyrogallol; **соль**—**вой кислоты** pyrogallate.

**пирогелит** *m.* (min.) pyrogelite (a colloidal form of pyrite).

**пироген/ация,** —**изация** *see* **пиролиз;**
—**етический,** —**ный,** —**овый** *a.* pyrogenic, pyrogenous, igneous; —**ная
реакция** pyrogenic reaction; —**овые
краски** pyrogen dyes, sulfur dyes.

**пирограф** *m.* pyrograph; —**ия** *f.* pyrog-
raphy.

**пиродин** *m.* pyrodin, acetylphenylhydrazine.

**пирожное** *n.* pastry.

**пиро/замок** *m.* (rockets) separation
charge; —**запал** *m.* cartridge igniter,
squib; —**заряд** *m.* explosive charge.

**пиро/зин** *m.* pyrosin, erythrosin; —**ка-
техин** *m.* pyrocatechol, 1,2-benzene-
diol; —**керам** *m.* Pyroceram (microcrystalline glass); —**кислота** *f.* pyro
acid; —**кластический** *a.* (petr.) pyro-
clastic; —**колл** *m.* pyrocoll; —**кол-
лодий** *m.* collodion, nitrocellulose;
—**коман** *m.* pyrocomane, 1,4-pyrone;
—**коменовая кислота** pyrocomenic
acid; —**кремневая кислота** pyrosilic-
ic acid.

**пироксен** *m.* (min.) pyroxene; —**ит** *m.*
(petr.) pyroxenite; —**овый** *a.* pyroxene, pyroxenic.

**пироксилин** *m.,* —**овый** *a.* (expl.) pyroxylin, soluble guncotton, nitrocellulose.

**пироксмангит** *m.* (min.) pyroxmangite
(a manganese pyroxene).

**пирол** *see* **пиррол.**

**пиро/лигнит** *m.* pyrolignite; —**лиз** *m.*
pyrolysis, decomposition by heat;
—**логия** *f.* pyrology, blowpipe analysis; —**лузит,** —**люзит** *m.* (min.)
pyrolusite (a manganese dioxide);
—**магнетизм** *m.* pyromagnetism;
—**магнитный** *a.* pyromagnetic; —
**меллитовая кислота** pyromellitic acid; —**металлургия** *f.* pyrometallurgy;
—**метаморфизм** *m.* (geol.) pyrometa-
morphism; —**метр** *m.* pyrometer;
—**метрический** *a.* pyrometric, high-
temperature; —**метрия** *f.* pyrometry.

**пироморф/ит** *m.* (min.) pyromorphite,
green lead ore; —**ный** *a.* pyromorph-
ous.

**пиромышьяков/ая кислота** pyroarsenic
acid, diarsenous acid; **соль**—**ой кислоты** pyroarsenate.

**пирон** *m.* pyrone; pin, dowel.

**пиронафт** *m.* a high ignition-tempera-
ture kerosene for lighthouse lamps.

**пирон/дикарбоновая кислота** pyronedicarboxylic acid, chelidonic acid;
—**ин** *m.* pyronine (a red aniline dye);
—**карбоновая кислота** pyronecar-
boxylic acid; —**он** *m.* pyronone.

**пироп** *m.* (min.) pyrope, magnesium-
aluminum garnet.

**пиропатрон** *m.* flare cartridge; (expl.)
powder charge.

**пирописсит** *m.* pyropissite (an earthy,
friable, coaly mineral).

**пироплазмоз** *m.* (vet.) piroplasmosis,
babesiosis.

**пироретин** *m.* pyroretin, pyroretinite (a
variety of coal resin).

**пиросвеча** *f.* cartridge igniter.

**пиросерн/ая кислота** pyrosulfuric acid,
disulfuric acid; **соль**—**ой кислоты,**
—**окислая соль** pyrosulfate; **хлорангидрид**—**ой кислоты** pyrosulfuryl
chloride; —**истая кислота** pyrosul-
furous acid; **соль**—**истой кислоты,**
—**истокислая соль** pyrosulfite; —**и-
стокалиевая соль** potassium pyrosulfite; —**окалиевая соль** potassium
pyrosulfate.

**пироскоп** *m.* Seger (pyrometric) cone.

**пирослизев/ая кислота** pyromucic acid,
furan-2-carboxylic acid; **соль**—**ой**

кислоты, —окислая соль pyromucate.

пиро/смалит *m.* (min.) pyrosmalite; —стат *m.* pyrostat, high-temperature thermostat; —стильпнит *m.* (min.) pyrostilpnite (a variety of pyrargyrite).

пиросульф/ат *m.* pyrosulfate; —ит *m.* pyrosulfite; —урил *m.* pyrosulfuryl.

пиросурьмян/ая кислота pyroantimonic acid; соль —ой кислоты, —окислая соль pyroantimonate; —онатриевая соль sodium pyroantimonate.

пиросфера *f.* (geol.) pyrosphere, barysphere.

пиротехни/ка *f.* pyrotechnics; —ческий *a.* pyrotechnic, pyrotechnical; —ческие изделия fireworks.

пироукеусн/ая кислота pyroligneous acid, pyracetic acid; соль —ой кислоты, —окислая соль pyrolignite; —окальциевая соль calcium pyrolignite.

пирофан *m.* (min.) pyrophane (a variety of opal); —ит *m.* (min.) pyrophanite (manganese titanate).

пирофиллит *m.* (min.) pyrophyllite; pencilstone.

пирофор *m.* pyrophorus (spontaneously ignitable substance); —ный *a.* pyrophoric.

пирофосф/ат *m.* pyrophosphate; —ит *m.* pyrophosphite; —орил *m.* pyrophosphoryl; —орит *m.* pyrophosphorite.

пирофосфор/истая кислота pyrophosphorous acid; соль —истой кислоты, —истокислая соль pyrophosphite; —ная кислота pyrophosphoric acid; соль —ной кислоты, —нокислая соль pyrophosphate; —нокислый *a.* pyrophosphoric acid; pyrophosphate (of); —нокислый натрий, —нонатриевая соль sodium pyrophosphate.

пиро/химия *f.* pyrochemistry; —хинин *m.* pyroquinone; —хлор *m.* (min.) pyrochlore; —хроит *m.* (min.) pyrochroite (a manganous hydroxide); —хромат *m.* pyrochromate, dichromate.

пироэлектричес/кий *a.* pyroelectric; —тво *n.* (cryst.) pyroelectricity, thermal deformation.

пиррил *m.* pyrryl; —ен *m.* pyrrylene.

пиррит *m.* (min.) pyrrhite (probably a niobate related to pyrochlore).

пирро— *prefix* pyrro—; pyrrho—; —диазол *m.* pyrrodiazole; —ил *m.* pyrroyl; хлористый —ил pyrroyl chloride; —колин *m.* pyrrocoline, 8-pyrrolopyridine.

пиррол *m.*, —овый *a.* pyrrole, azole; pyrrhol; —енин *m.* pyrrolenine; —идил *m.* pyrrolidyl; —идин *m.* pyrrolidine, tetrahydropyrrole; —идон *m.* pyrrolidone; —илен *m.* pyrrolylene, 1,3-butadiene; —ин *m.* pyrroline, dihydropyrrole; —овая кислота pyrrolic acid; —овая синь pyrrole blue; —оиндол *m.* pyrroloindol; —он *m.* pyrrolone; —охинолин *m.* pyrroloquinoline; —рот *m.* pyrrole red.

пирро/тин, —тит *m.* (min.) pyrrhotine, pyrrhotite, magnetic pyrite; —триазол *m.* pyrrotriazole.

пирс *m.* (naut.) pier.

Пирса печь Pearce (turret) furnace (for sulfide ores).

пирсинг-процесс *m.* piercing, roll-piercing process; стан пирсинг piercing mill.

Пирсона коэффициент Pearson's coefficient.

пирссонит *m.* (min.) pirssonite.

пируво/вая кислота *see* пировиноградная кислота; —нитрил *m.* pyruvonitrile, 2-oxopropanenitrile.

пирхинакридин *m.* pyrquinacridine.

пирцеит *m.* (min.) pearceite (an arsenical variety of polybasite).

писание *n.* writing.

писанит *see* пизанит.

писанный *a.* written.

писасфальт *m.* (min.) pissasphalt (a natural bitumen).

пис/атель *m.* writer, author; —ательство *n.* writing, literary profession, authorship; —ать *v.* write; type.

писк *m.* squeak; peep, chirp.

пискарь *see* пескарь.

писк/ливый, —лявый *a.* squeaky, squeaking; —нуть *see* пищать; —отня *f.* squeaking; peeping, chirping.

писолит *see* пизолит.

пистаколовая кислота pistacolic acid.

**пистац/иарезен** *m.* pistaciaresene; **—ин** *m.* pistacin; **—иновая кислота** pistacic acid; **—иноловая кислота** pistacinolic acid; **—ит** *m.* (min.) pistacite, epidote.

**пистолет** *m.*, **—ный** *a.* pistol; **—ная труба** (met.) pistol pipe, tuyère (of hot-blast furnace).

**пистомезит** *m.* (min.) pistomesite (a variety of magnesite-siderite).

**пистон** *m.* (percussion) cap, blasting cap; piston.

**писцид/ин** *m.* piscidin; **—иновая кислота** piscidic acid; **—ия** *f.* piscidia, Jamaica dogwood (bark of *Piscidia erythrina*).

**писцикультура** *see* рыбоводство.

**писчая бумага** writing paper, stationery.

**писчебумажн/ый** *a.* stationery; **п. товар** stationery, writing paper; **—ая фабрика** paper mill.

**письмен/а** *pl.* characters, letters; **—но** *adv.* in writing, by letter.

**письменн/ый** *a.* writing, written; (petr.) graphic; **п. стол** desk; **п. теллур, —ое золото** (min.) graphic tellurium, graphic gold (crystals of sylvanite); **—ая руда** (min.) graphic ore, sylvanite; **—ые принадлежности** stationery.

**письмо** *n.* letter; writing; **—водитель** *m.* clerk; **—водство** *n.* clerical work; **—носец** *m.* mailman, mail carrier.

**питаемый** *a.* fed.

**питан/ие** *n.* feeding, feed; supply, delivery; power supply; loading, charging; nourishment, nutrition; alimentation; recharge (of ground water); **блок —ия, источник —ия, пак —ия** (elec. comm.) power pack; **линия —ия** feed line; **недостаточность —ия** malnutrition; **обратное п.** feedback; **продукты —ия** foodstuffs; **резервуар —ия** feed tank; **с двойным —ием** dual-feed; **химия —ия** food chemistry.

**питатель** *m.* feeder; **—ность** *f.* food value, nutritiousness.

**питательн/ый** *a.* feed, feeding; nourishing, nutritious, food; (anat.) alimentary; **п. кран** feed cock; **п. насос** feed pump; **п. прибор** feed apparatus, feeder; **п. провод, —ая линия** (elec.)

feeder; **п. танк** feed tank, supply tank; **п. штуцер, —ое сопло** feed nozzle; **—ая вода** feed water; **—ая полоса, —ая шина** (elec.) feeder busbar; **—ая среда** (bact.) culture medium; **—ая труба** feed pipe, supply pipe; **—ая установка** source; **—ая ценность** food value; **—ое вещество, —ое средство** nutriment, nutrient, food; **—ое опрыскивание** foliage spraying (with fertilizer); **—ые соки** (bot.) sap.

**пит/ать** *v.* feed, deliver, supply; nourish; maintain; **—аться** *v.* feed (on), live (on); **—ающий** *a.* feeding, feed; nourishing; power supply; **—ающий механизм** feed mechanism, feeder; **—ающий провод** (elec.) power lead; **—ающая труба** feed pipe, feed line, supply pipe.

**питекантроп** *m.* Pithecanthropus (primitive man).

**питкарлодер** *m.* (min.) pit car loader.

**Пито трубка** Pitot tube, Pitot's gage.

**питометр** *m.* (hydraulics) pitometer.

**питомник** *m.* (agr.) nursery.

**питон** *m.* (zool.) python.

**питтакол** *m.* pittacol, eupittonic acid.

**питтинг** *m.* pitting (corrosion).

**питтинговая руда** (min.) a variety of pitchblende.

**питтицит** *m.* (min.) pitticite (an alteration product from arsenopyrite).

**питуитрин** *m.* Pituitrin, posterior pituitary extract.

**питч** *m.* pitch (of gear); **—евая резьба** worm thread; **—евое зубчатое колесо** pitch gear.

**Питчера насос** Pitcher pump.

**пить** *v.* drink; **—е** *n.* drink, beverage; drinking; **годный для —я** potable, drinkable; **—евая вода** drinking water.

**Пифагора теорема** (geom.) Pythagorean proposition.

**пи-фотомезон** *m.* (nucl.) photo-pion.

**пихта** *f.* (bot.) fir (*Abies*).

**пихтов/ые** *pl.* (bot.) Abietaceae; **—ый** *a* fir; **—ое масло** pine oil.

**пихурим, бобы п.** pichurim beans (seeds of *Nectandra pichurim*).

**пице/ановое кольцо** picean nucleus,

*gem*-dimethylcyclobutane ring; —a-**пимаровая кислота** picea-pimaric acid; —**ин** *m.* picein; —**н** *m.* picene, dibenzo(*a,i*)phenanthrene; —**нкетон** *m.* picene ketone; —**новая кислота** picenic acid; —**нхинон** *m.* picenequinone; —**озид** *m.* piceoside, salinigrin, ameliaroside.

**пицилен** *m.* picylene, picene fluorene.

**пицит** *m.* (min.) picite, pizite (probably borickite).

**Пичи процесс** Peachey (vulcanization) process.

**пич-пайн** *m.* (bot.) pitch pine, yellow pine (*Pinus australis*).

**Пише испаритель** Piché evaporimeter.

**пишет** *pr. 3 sing. of* **писать.**

**пишущ/ий** *a.* writing; —**ая машинка** typewriter; —**ее колесо** printing wheel; —**ее перо** recording pen.

**пищ/а** *f.* food, nourishment, nutriment; **годный в** —**у** edible.

**пищать** *v.* squeak, peep, cheep.

**пищевар/ение** *n.* digestion; **плохое п.** indigestion; **расстройство** —**ения** dyspepsia; —**ительный** *a.* digestive, peptic; alimentary (canal).

**пищевик** *m.* worker in food industry.

**пищев/од** *m.* (anat.) esophagus; —**ой** *a.* alimentary, nutritive; —**ой сок** (physiol.) chyle; —**ая кашица** chyme; —**ые продукты** foodstuffs.

**пищепром.** *abbr.* (**пищевая промышленность**) food industry.

**пищик** *m.* buzzer, ticker; (car) horn.

**пиэ**— *see under* **пие—.**

**пиявк/а** *f.* (zool.) leech; —**и** *pl.* Hirudinea.

**пл.** *abbr.* (**плавление**) melting; (**площадь**) area.

**плав** *m.* melt.

**плав/ание,** —**анье** *n.* swimming, floating; navigation; voyage, trip; —**ательный,** —**ающий** *a.* swimming, floating, natatorial; —**ать** *v.* swim, float; navigate, sail; —**ающий кварц** (petr.) floatstone; —**ающий реактор** (nucl.) swimming-pool reactor.

**плавень** *m.* flux, fusing agent.

**плавик** *m.*, —**овый шпат** (min.) fluorspar, fluorite; —**овый** *a.* fluoric; —**овая кислота** hydrofluoric acid; **соль** —**овой кислоты** fluoride.

**плавильник** *see* **плавильный тигель.**

**плавильн/ый** *a.* melting; (met.) smelting; **п. горн** smelting hearth; **п. горшок, п. тигель** crucible, melting pot; **п. жар** fusion temperature; **п. завод,** —**я** *f.* foundry, smelter, smeltery, smelting works; **п. журнал** (met.) charge book; —**ая печь** smelting furnace, smelter; —**ая трубочка** melting tube.

**плавильщик** *m.* founder, smelter.

**плавить** *v.* melt, fuse; (met.) smelt; —**ся** *v.* melt, fuse; blow out (of fuse).

**плавка** *see* **плавление.**

**плавк/ий** *a.* fusible, meltable, liquefiable; (met.) smeltable; **п. камень** (min.) mizzonite, dipyre; **п. предохранитель, п. штепсель,** —**ая вставка,** —**ая пробка** (elec.) fuse; —**ая проволока** (elec.) fuse wire, fuse; —**ость** *f.* fusibility.

**плавлен/ие** *n.* fusion, melting, liquefaction; (met.) smelting, smelting process, liquation; **сырое п.** ore smelting; **температура** —**ия, точка** —**ия** melting point; **теплота** —**ия** heat of fusion.

**плавленый** *a.* fused, melted; smelted, liquated; **п. кварц** fused quartz glass.

**плавни** *pl.* flooded areas; plavni (lower reaches of some Russian rivers covered with reeds and trees).

**плавник** *m.* fin (of fish); driftwood.

**плавн/о** *adv.* smoothly; —**орегулируемый** *a.* continuously adjustable, continuously variable; —**ость** *f.* smoothness, evenness, facility; —**ый** *a.* smooth, even.

**плавочный** *see* **плавильный.**

**плавун** *see* **плаун;** —**цы** *pl.* predaceous diving beetles (*Dytiscidae*).

**плавуч/есть** *f.* flotage, buoyancy; —**ий** *a.* floating.

**плавь** *f.* steel pig, pig iron for steel making.

**плавящий** *a.* melting; smelting.

**плаги/ат** *m.* plagiarism, plagiarizing; —**ировать** *v.* plagiarize.

**плагио**— *prefix* plagio—, slanting, oblique; —**гранит** *m.* (petr.) plagiogranite (plagioclase granite).

**плагиоклаз** *m.* (min.) plagioclase, albite-anorthite feldspars; —**овый** *a.* plagioclastic.

**плагионит** *m.* (min.) plagionite.

**плазм/а** *f.*, **—енный** *a.* (biol.) plasma; (min.) plasma (a form of quartz); **физика —ы, —енная физика** plasma physics; **—аген** *m.* (biol.) plasmagene; **—атические** *pl.* (zool.) Plasmadroma; **—атический** *a.* plasmic, plasmatic; **—енный сгусток** plasmoid; **—енный шнур** (nucl.) plasma column, pinch.

**плазмо—** *prefix* plasmo—, plasma; **—гамия** *f.* (biol.) plasmogamy; **—дий** *m.* (biol.) plasmodium; **—ид** *m.* plasmoid; **—лиз** *m.* plasmolysis; **—хин** *m.* Plasmochin, pamaquine naphthoate; **—цит** *m.* plasmocyte.

**плакат** *m.*, **—ный** *a.* placard, poster, bill; **—ная краска** lithographic color.

**плакать** *v.* weep, cry, shed tears.

**плакиров/ание** *n.*, **—ка** *f.* (met.) cladding, plating; **—анный** *a.* clad, plated; **—ать** *v.* clad; (agr.) sod.

**плакун-трава** *f.* (bot.) purple loosestrife (*Lythrum salicaria*).

**плакуч/ий** *a.* weeping, pendant; **—ая ива** weeping willow (*Salix babylonica*).

**пламегаситель** *m.* (mil.) flash hider.

**пламен/еть** *v.* flame, blaze; **—ник** *m.* torch; (bot.) phlox; **—нокрасный** *a.* fiery red; **—но-фотометрический** *a.* flame-photometric.

**пламенн/ый** *a.* flaming, flame; warm (color); bituminous (coal); **п. порог** fire bridge; **—ая печь** flame furnace, reverberatory furnace; **—ая труба** flue.

**плам/ень** *m.*, **—я** *n.* flame, fire, blaze; **выбрасывание —ени** flareback; **—естойкий** *a.* flameproof.

**план** *m.* plan, scheme, proposal, project; design; layout; draft; device; schedule; plane, surface; **генеральный п.** State economic production plan; **задний п.** background; **общий п.** general layout; **передний п.** foreground; **составлять п.** *v.* plan, design.

**плангерд** *m.* (min.) racking table.

**планер** *m.* (aero.) glider, glider plane.

**планерит** *m.* (min.) planerite (probably identical with coeruleolactite).

**планерный полет** (aero.) gliding.

**планет** *m.* (agr.) cultivator.

**планет/а** *f.* planet; **—арий** *m.* planetarium; **—арный, —ный** *a.* planet, plane-tary, planetesimal; **—арный механизм, —арная передача** planetary gear, planet differential; **—оид** *m.* planetoid.

**планзифтер** *m.* plansifter (sorting screen).

**планиметр** *m.* (geom.) planimeter; **—ировать** *v.* measure with a planimeter; **—ирующий индикатор** integrating indicator; **—ический** *a.* planimetric; **—ия** *f.* planimetry, mensuration of plane surfaces; plane geometry.

**планир** *m.* bar, rod; leveler.

**планиров/ание** *n.* planning, designing, laying out; systematization; leveling, smoothing, planing; (aero.) gliding, glide, soaring; sizing (paper); **—ать** *v.* plan, design; systematize; level, smooth, plane; glide, soar; size (paper); **—ка** *f.* planning; (paper) size, glue water.

**планисфера** *f.* planisphere.

**планицкий лигнит** (min.) black hornblende, common hornblende.

**планка** *f.* plank, lath, strip; cleat; (mach.) gib; baffle, baffle plate.

**Планка постоянная** Planck's constant.

**планкообразный** *a.* (cryst.) lath-shaped.

**планктон** *m.* (biol.) plankton; **—ный** *a.* planktonic.

**планов/ик** *m.* planner; **—о-предупредительный ремонт** preventive maintenance; **—ость** *f.* development according to plan; **—ый** *a.* planned, systematic; **—ое хозяйство** planned economy.

**планозигота** *f.* (bot.) planozygote, motile zygote.

**планозол** *m.* planosol (group of soils).

**планомерн/ость** *f.* development according to plan; **—ый** *a.* systematic.

**плано/феррит** *m.* (min.) planoferrite (a hydrous ferric sulfate); **—фировый** *a.* (petr.) planophyric.

**плантагиновая кислота** plantagic acid.

**планта/ж** *m.*, **—жный** *a.* deep plowing, trenching; **—тор** *m.* planter, grower; **—ция** *f.* plantation; field.

**Планте аккумулятор** (elec.) Planté accumulator.

**плантеноловая кислота** plantenolic acid.

**планхеит** *m.* (min.) plancheite.

**планчатый** *a.* plank, lath, strip.

**планшайба** *f.* chuck, faceplate (of lathe).

**планшет** *m.* topographic map; (surv.) plane table, drawing board, plotting board; **п.-преобразователь** *m.* conversion table; **—ная доска** plotting board; **—ная съемка** plane tabling.

**пласт** *m.* layer, sheet; (geol.) stratum, bed, seam, shelf (of rock), blanket; wafer; furrow; **—ы** *pl.* strata; **п.-проводник** (geol.) rider.

**пластбетон** *m.* plastic concrete.

**пластидный** *a.* (bot.) plastid.

**пластик/а** *f.* plastic art; plastic surgery; **—и** *pl.* plastics; **—ат** *m.* masticated rubber; plasticized resin; **—атор** *m.* masticator; **—ация** *f.* mastication, rolling (of rubber).

**пластилин** *m.* modeling clay.

**пластин/а** *f.*, **—ка** *f.* plate, tablet, lamina, flake, flakelet, leaf; membrane; blade; (phonograph) record; (blood) platelet; **—ы** *pl.* (battery) grid; **листовая п.** (bot.) blade, lamina; **метод —ок** plate count; **резина в —ах** sheet rubber.

**пластинн/иковые** *pl.* (bot.) Agaricaceae; **—ый** *a.* plate, laminar.

**пластино/жаберные** *pl.* (zool.) Elasmobranchii; **—образный** *a.* plate-like, lamellar, lamelliform, tabular; **—чка** *f.* lamella, flakelet; **—чница** *f.* (bot.) laminaria.

**пластинчато/жаберные** *pl.* (zool.) Lamellibranchia; **—сть** *f.* lamination; **—у-сые** *pl.* lamellicorn beetles (*Scarabaeidae*).

**пластинчат/ый** *a.* lamellar, lamellate, laminar, laminated, foliated, scaly, flaky, flaked; plate, plate-type; plate-like, tabular; sheet, sheet-like; finned; gill (fungi); apron (conveyer); **п. конденсатор** plate condenser; **п. подогреватель** baffle feed heater; **—ая отдельность** lamination; **—ая слюда** sheet mica; **—ая структура** slaty structure, lamination.

**пластифи/катор** *m.* plasticizer; softener; **—цированный** *a.* plasticized; masticated (rubber).

**пластич/еский, —ный** *a.* plastic, moldable, pliable; soft (clay, rubber); **—е-ская земля, —ная глина** plastic clay; **—еская обработка** shaping, molding;

**—еское последействие** relaxation; **—ность** *f.* plasticity, pliability; ductility.

**пласткожа** *f.* an artificial leather.

**пластмасс/а** *f.*, **—овый** *a.* plastic, composition material; **—ы** *pl.* plastics.

**пластов/ой, —ый** *a.* stratified, sheet, layer; (geol.) formation; stratal (water); **—ые залежи** (geol.) blanket deposits.

**пластогамия** *f.* (biol.) plastogamy.

**пласто/мер, —метр** *m.* plastometer (for measuring plasticity).

**пластообразный** *a.* sheet, sheet-like.

**пластыр/ь** *m.*, **—ный** *a.* plaster, patch; **английский п.** court plaster, sticking plaster; **вытяжной п.** blistering plaster; **клейкий п., липкий п., свинцовый п.** adhesive plaster.

**плата** *f.* pay, salary, wages; charge, fee.

**платан** *m.* (bot.) plane tree (*Platanus*); **—овые** *pl.* Platanaceae.

**платеж** *m.* payment; **наложенным —ом** cash on delivery, C.O.D.; **расписка в —е** receipt; **—еспособность** *f.* paying capacity.

**плательщик** *m.* payer.

**ПЛАТИН** *abbr.* (Институт по изучению платины и других благородных металлов) Institute for the Study of Platinum and Other Precious Metals.

**платин/а** *f.* platinum, Pt; **гидрат закиси —ы** platinous hydroxide; **гидрат окиси —ы** platinic hydroxide; **двуокись —ы, окись —ы** platinum dioxide, platinic oxide; **двухлористая п., хлористая п.** platinum dichloride, platinous chloride; **закись —ы, одноокись —ы** platinous oxide, platinum monoxide; **соль закиси —ы** platinous salt; **соль окиси —ы** platinic salt; **иридистая п.** (min.) platiniridium; **нашатырная п.** ammonium chloroplatinate; **хлорная п., четыреххлористая п.** platinic chloride, platinum tetrachloride.

**платин/ат** *m.* platinate; **—иак** *m.* complex compound of platinum (especially with ammonia).

**платиниров/ание** *n.*, **—ка** *f.* platinization, platinum plating; **—анный** *a.* platinized, platinum-plated; **—анный асбест** platinized asbestos (catalyst);

—**ать** v. platinize, plate with platinum, coat with platinum.

**платинисто**— prefix platino—, platinous; —**родановодородная кислота** thiocyanoplatinous acid.

**платинистосинерод/истый натрий** sodium platinocyanide; —**оводородная кислота** platinocyanic acid, cyanoplatinous acid; **соль** —**оводородной кислоты** platinocyanide, cyanoplatinite.

**платинистохлор/истый натрий** sodium platinochloride; —**оводородная кислота** chloroplatinous acid; **соль**—**оводородной кислоты** chloroplatinite, platinochloride.

**платинистый** a. platinous, platinum.

**платинит** m. (min.) platynite; (met.) platinite (a ferronickel alloy).

**платино**— prefix platini—, platinic.

**платиново/кислый** a. platinic acid; platinate (of); —**кислая соль** platinate; —**синеродистая кислота** see **платиносинеродоводородная кислота.**

**платинов/ый** a. platinic, platinum; **п. лист,** —**ая пластинка** platinum foil; —**ая кислота** platinic acid; **соль** —**ой кислоты** platinate; —**ая лодочка** platinum boat (for analysis); —**ая проволока** platinum wire; —**ая сетка** platinum gauze; —**ая чернь** platinum black.

**платино/ид** m. platinoid (a copper-base alloy); —**подобный** a. platinoid, like platinum; —**родановодородная кислота** thiocyanoplatinic acid; —**селеносинеродоводородная кислота** selenocyanoplatinic acid; —**сернистый** a. sulfoplatinate (of); —**синеродоводородная кислота** platinicyanic acid, cyanoplatinic acid; —**содержащий** a. platinum-containing, platiniferous.

**платинохлор/истоводородная кислота,** —**оводородная кислота** chloroplatinic acid; **соль** —**истоводородной кислоты** chloroplatinate, platinichloride; —**истый** a. chloroplatinate (of), platinichloride (of); —**истый натрий** sodium platinichloride.

**платить** v. pay.

**плати/филлин** m. platyphilline; —**цефалия** f. (anat.) platycephaly.

**Платнера процесс** (met.) Plattner's process (for gold extraction).

**платнерит** m. (min.) plattnerite (a lead dioxide).

**платный** a. requiring payment; paying; toll.

**плато** n. plateau, table land; —**базальт** m. plateau basalt.

**платок** m. handkerchief, kerchief.

**платтнерит** see **платнерит.**

**платформ/а** f., —**енный** a. platform, stage; flatcar; —**енный** a. platform-like.

**платье** n. clothes, dress, clothing.

**плаун** m., —**ный,** —**овый** a. (bot.) club moss (Lycopodium); **булавовидный п.** common club moss (L. clavatum); —**ы,** —**овые** pl. Lycopodiaceae; —**ный порошок,** —**овое семя** see **ликоподий.**

**плафон** m., —**ный** a. ceiling.

**плаха** f. block, chunk, log.

**плацдарм** m. (mil.) area of concentration.

**плацента** f. (biol.) placenta.

**плачевный** a. lamentable, deplorable; sad.

**плаш/ка** f., —**ечный** a. die, screw die, cutting die, cutter; chuck, jaw (of chuck); (pal.) tooth; **сгибающая п.** bending block; —**ечный метчик** master tap.

**плашкоут** m. pontoon, lighter.

**плашмя** adv. flatwise, flat, prone.

**плащ** m. cloak, mantle; (rain) coat.

**плебисцит** m. plebiscite; referendum.

**плева** f. membrane, film, coat, pellicle; (bot.) aril.

**плев/ание** n. spitting; spluttering (of arc); —**ать** v. spit; splutter.

**плевел** m., —**ьный** a. rye grass (Lolium); **одуряющий п., опьяняющий п.** darnel (L. temulentum).

**плевок** m. spittle; (med.) sputum.

**плевр/а** f. (anat.) pleura; **воспаление** —**ы,** —**ит** m. (med.) pleurisy; —**итный** a. pleuritic; —**о**—prefix pleuro— (rib, side); —**опневмония** f. pleuro-pneumonia.

**плед** m. rug; plaid.

**плезанский ярус** (geol.) Plaisancian stage.

плезио/завр *m.* plesiosaurus, plesiosaur (fossil reptile); —морфизм *m.* (cryst.) plesiomorphism, isogonism.

плейасы *pl.* (geol.) playas (shallow aridland lakes).

плейон *m.* (meteor.) pleion.

плейохазий *m.* (bot.) pleiochasium.

плейро/мутилин *m.* pleuromutilin; —тин *m.* pleurotin.

плейстон *m.* pleuston, free-floating plants.

плейстоцен *m.*, —овая эпоха (geol.) Pleistocene (Glacial epoch); —овый *a.* Pleistocene, Pleistocenic.

плекси/гласс *m.* Plexiglas (acrylate or methacrylate resin); —гум *m.* Plexigum (plastic).

плектенхима *f.* (bot.) plectenchyma.

плел *past sing. of* плести.

плем/енной *a.* breeding; pedigreed (livestock); —хоз *abbr.* (племенное хозяйство) pedigreed stock farm; breeding of pedigreed stock; —я *n.* tribe, race; breed; generation.

плен *m.* captivity, bondage.

плена *f.* flaw, rack; blister; scab (in casting), scale, skin, shell; spangle.

пленарный *a.* plenary, complete, absolute.

пленистая полоса (met.) blister bar.

пленк/а *f.* film, layer, pellicle, coating; tarnish; skimmings, scum, dross; (phot.) film; коэффициент —и film coefficient (of heat or mass transfer); —одержатель *m.* (phot.) film holder; —ообразователь *m.* film-forming material.

пленн/ик *m.*, —ый *a.* captive, prisoner.

пленочный *a.* film, pellicular; п. дозиметр film badge (for detecting radiation exposure).

пленчатоцветные *pl.* glumaceous plants.

пленчатый *a.* filmy; laminated, scaly.

плео— *prefix* pleo—, pleio— (more); —морфизм *m.* (cryst.) pleomorphism; —морфный *a.* pleomorphic, occurring in more than one form; —наст *m.* (min.) pleonaste, ceylonite, iron magnesia spinel; —псидовая кислота pleopsidic acid.

плеохрои/зм *m.* (cryst.) pleochroism; —ческий, —чный *a.* pleochroic, pleochromatic; —чные кольца, —ч-ные оболочки (min.) pleochroic halos.

плерома *f.* (bot.) plerome.

плес *m.* reach, stretch of water.

плесень *f.* mold, must; mildew; головчатая п. (bot.) mold (*Mucor mucedo*).

плеск *m.* splash, splatter; —ание *n.* splashing; —ать *v.* splash, splatter.

плесне/велый *a.* moldy, stale; —веть, —ть *v.* mold, grow moldy, get musty; effloresce; —вой *a.* mold; —вые грибки mold, mold fungus.

плеснуть *see* плескать.

Плесси зелень Plessy's green, chromic phosphate.

плессиметр *m.* (med.) plessimeter, pleximeter.

плессит *m.* (min.) plessite (a variety of meteoric iron).

плести *v.* braid, plait; spin; weave, wattle; net; twine.

плетен/ие, —ье *n.* network, plexus; net, netting, fencing; braiding, plaiting, weaving; wickerwork, basketwork, wattle; —ка *f.* plexus, network; mat; braid; basket; —ый *a.* woven, wicker; mesh; —ь *m.* wattle; net, fencing.

плет/ет *pr. 3 sing. of* плести; —ущий *a.* braiding; weaving; —ь *f.* vine, runner.

плечев/ой *a.* shoulder, humeral; brachial; —ая кость (anat.) humerus.

плеченогие *pl.* (zool.) Brachiopoda.

плечо *n.* shoulder; (anat.) humerus; (lever) arm; leg (of cathode).

плеши/вый *a.* hairless, bald; —на *f.* bare place; lapse.

плеяд/а *f.* pleiad (group of isotopes); —ен *m.* pleiadene.

плиенсбахский *a.* (geol.) Pliensbachian.

пликативн/ый *a.* plicative, plicate, plicated, folded, plaited; —ая дислокация (geol.) folding.

пликатовая кислота plicatic acid.

плиниан *m.* (min.) arsenical pyrites.

плиниевский *a.* plinian (eruption).

плинт, —ус *m.* plinth, skirting, base, base molding, baseboard.

плиодинатрон *m.* (rad.) pliodynatron.

плиоцен *m.*, —овая эпоха (geol.) Pliocene (epoch); —овый *a.* Pliocene.

плис *m.* (text.) plush, velveteen.

плит/а *f.* plate, slab, tile; flag, flagstone; range, stove; (continental) platform;

—ка *f.* slab, cake, block; tile; scale, flake; hot plate; —ка-калибр gage block.

плитко/ватый *a.* laminated; —образный *a.* plate-like, tabular; —образная обмотка (elec.) batch winding.

плитный *see* плиточный.

плитняк *m.*, —овый *a.* flag, flagstone; plate coal; —овая структура platy structure.

плито/ломня *f.* quarry; —образный *a.* plate-like, tabular, slab-shaped.

плит/очный *a.* plate, laminated; cake, brick; apron, slat (conveyor); п. пресс slab-molding machine; —чатый *a.* (geol.) platy.

плица *f.* shoe, cleat; float; bailing device; (wheel) paddle.

пловец *m.* swimmer; floater.

пловуч/есть *f.* floatability, floatage, buoyancy; —ий *a.* floating, buoyant.

плод *m.* fruit, offspring; (med.) fetus; —ить *v.* procreate, produce; —иться *v.* multiply, breed; spawn; —ник *m.* (bot.) pistil; *suffix* —carp; —ный *a.* *suffix* —carpous.

плодо— *prefix* fruit.

плодов/итость *f.* fruitfulness, fertility; —итый *a.* fruitful, fertile, prolific, productive; —од *m.* fruit grower; —одство *n.* fruit growing; —ый *a.* fruit; —ый сахар fruit sugar, fructose.

плодо/жорка, яблонная lesser apple worm; codling moth; —жорки *pl.* tortricids (*Tortricidae*); Laspeyresiinae; —корм *m.* mast (nuts collectively); —листик *m.* (bot.) carpel; —ножка *f.* (bot.) fruit stem; —носить *v.* bear fruit; —носный *a.* fertile, productive, prolific; rich (soil); —носящий *a.*, —ношение *n.* fruit bearing; —образование *n.* fruit formation, fructification; —овощеводство *n.* fruit and vegetable growing.

плодород/ие *n.*, —ность *f.* fertility, productivity; (diminishing) return; —ный *a.* fertile, productive, prolific; rich (soil).

плодо/смен *m.*, —сменная система (agr.) crop rotation; —сниматель *m.* fruit picker; —сушилка *f.* fruit dryer; —творный *a.* fruitful; —хранилище

*n.* fruit storage (place); —ядный *a.* fruit-eating, frugivorous.

плоду/ха, —шка *f.* fruit bud, fruit spur.

пло/ение *n.* folding, plaiting; —еный *a.* folded, plicated, plaited; —идия, —идность *f.* *suffix* —ploidy; —ить *v.* fold, plait.

плойчат/ость *f.* (geol.) plication, folding, contortion; —ый *a.* plicated, folded together, contorted.

пломб/а *f.* stamp, seal; (dental) filling, inlay; —ир *m.* ice cream containing chocolate, nuts, fruit; —ирная масса sealing compound.

пломбиров/ание *n.*, —ка *f.* stamping, sealing; filling (dental cavity); —анный *a.* stamped, sealed; filled; —ать *v.* stamp, seal; fill.

плоск/ий *a.* flat, plane, horizontal; flush; —ая поверхность plane surface, plane.

плоско *adv.* flatly, flat, on a plane; —бимсовое железо, —бульбовое железо flat-bulb iron; —бокорезы *pl.* sidecutting pliers; —вогнутый *a.* planoconcave; —выпуклый *a.* planoconvex; —горье *n.* plateau, table land; —губцы *pl.* flat-nosed pliers, flat pliers, pliers; —донный *a.* flat-bottomed; —звенная цепь flat-link chain; —компаундированный *a.* (elec.) flat-compounded, level-compounded; —параллельный *a.* planeparallel; parallel-plate (electrode); —стной *a.* plane, planar; —стность *f.* planeness, smoothness, levelness.

плоскост/ь *f.* plane, surface, level, flatness; pad, sheet; face, facet (of crystal); п. пола floor line; геометрия на —и plane geometry.

плоско/телки *pl.* flat bark beetles (*Cucujidae*); —шлифовальный станок surface-grinding machine, surface grinder; —шляпный *a.* flat-headed (nail).

плот *m.* raft, float.

плотва *f.* roach (fish).

плотик *m.* (min.) bed (of placer).

плотина *f.* dam, dike, lock, embankment, barrage; causeway.

плотн. *abbr.* (плотность) density.

плотни/к *m.* carpenter; —чать *v.* carpenter, do carpentry work; —чество *n.* carpentry; —чий *a.* carpenter's.

плотно *adv.* tightly, closely, close; consistently; п. лежащий, п. пригнанный, п. прилегающий snug, tight; —зернистый *a.* close-grained, compact; —кустовой *a.* bunch-forming; —лежащий *a.* dense, close; —мер, —стемер *m.* densimeter, density meter, density gage.

плотность *f.* density, thickness, consistency; massiveness, solidity, compactness, impenetrability, tightness; close weave (of cloth); п. паров vapor density; поверхностная п. surface density.

плотноупакованный *a.* close-packed, densely packed.

плотн/ый *a.* dense, thick, consistent, solid, compact, close, thickset; sound, hard, tough; tight, leakproof; closely woven (cloth); (min.) massive, close-grained; —ое строение close texture.

плотоядн/ый *a.* (zool.) carnivorous, flesh-eating; —ое животное carnivore.

плох/о *adv.* bad, badly, poorly, ill; —оватый *a.* rather bad, rather poor; —ой *a.* bad, poor, mal—; —ая настройка, —ое приспособление maladjustment.

плошка *f.* earthen saucer; lampion.

площад/ка *f.* platform, stand, stage, gallery, floor; plateau (of graph); terrace; landing; —ь *f.* area, surface, space, section; square; единица —и unit of area; по —и areal.

площица *f.* (zool.) crab louse.

плувиометр *see* плювиометр.

плуг *m.* plow; п.-канавокопатель *m.* trenching plow; п.-сеялка *f.* drill plow; —арь, —атарь *m.* plowman.

плумб/агин *m.* plumbagin, methyljuglone; —аго *n.* plumbago, native graphite; —ан *m.* plumbane; —ат *m.* plumbate; —ит *m.*, —итный *a.* plumbite.

плумбо/гуммит *m.* (min.) plumbogummite; —кальцит *m.* plumbocalcite (a variety of calcite); —куприт *m.* plumbocuprite, cuproplumbite; —манганит *m.* plumbomanganite; —ниобит *m.* plumboniobate; —феррит *m.* plumboferrite.

плумиер/ин *m.* plumierin, asonidin;

plumierine (alkaloid from *Plumiera acutifolia*); —овая кислота plumieric acid.

плумозит *m.* (min.) plumosite.

плунжер *m.*, —ный *a.* plunger, ram, piston; насос с —ом, —ный насос plunger pump, piston pump; —ный поршень plunger, piston.

плутон/иевый *a.*, —ий *m.* plutonium, Pu; —изм *m.* (geol.) plutonic theory; —ил *m.* plutonyl; —ический *a.* plutonic, intrusive, deep-seated; —ическая порода plutonic rock.

плыв/ет *pr. 3 sing. of* плыть; —ун *m.*, —учий песок quicksand, running sand; —учесть *f.* deliquescence; —учий *a.* deliquescent, flowing; quick, running (rock).

плыть *v.* navigate; float, swim; run (of melted candle).

плювиальный *a.* pluvial, rain.

плювио— *prefix* pluvio—, rain; —граф *m.* pluviograph, recording rain gage; —метр *m.* pluviometer, rain gage; —метрический *a.* pluviometric.

плюмб— *see* плумб—.

плюмерицин *m.* plumericin.

плюнуть *see* плевать.

плюр *m.* onionskin (paper).

плюс *m.* (math.) plus; advantage.

плюск/а *f.* (bot.) cupule; —оносные *pl.* Cupuliferae.

плюсна *f.* (anat.) metatarsus.

плюсов/ать *v.* impregnate (with); (text.) pad; —ка *f.* padding machine (or mangle).

плюсовой *a.* plus, positive.

плюш *m.* plush, velour.

плющ *m.*, —евый *a.* (bot.) ivy (*Hedera*); moonseed (*Menispermum*); —елистный *a.* ivy-leaved.

плющ/ение *n.* laminating, flattening; spreading, upsetting; —енный *a.* laminated, flattened; —илка *f.* crusher, roller.

плющильн/ый *a.* laminating, flattening; upsetting; п. молот planing hammer, flatter; п. станок, —я *f.* flatting mill, rolling mill; —ая машина planing machine; upsetting machine, upsetter.

плющ/ильщик *m.* flattener, laminator; planisher; —ить *v.* flatten, laminate, even out, roll, spread; compress, mash, planish; bruise, crush.

**пляж** *m.* beach.

**пляска св. Вита** (med.) St. Vitus dance.

**п.н.** *abbr.* (порядковый номер) ordinal number; index number.

**пневмати/к** *m.* pneumatic tire; **—ка** *f.* pneumatics; **—ческий** *a.* pneumatic; air; **—ческий лифт** air lift; **—ческий перфоратор** pneumatic drill; **—ческий элеватор** blower.

**пневмато—** *prefix* pneumato— (air); **—лиз** *m.* (geol.) pneumatolysis; **—литовый** *a.* pneumatolytic; **—логия** *f.* (phys.) pneumatology, pneumatics.

**пневмеркатор** *m.* pneumatic (liquid-level) gage.

**пневмо-** *prefix* pneumo— (lung); pneumatic; **—бетон** *m.* Gunite (pressure-applied cement); **—датчик** *m.* pressure gage, pressure pickup; **—кокк** *m.* (bact.) pneumococcus; **—кониоз** *m.* (med.) pneumoconiosis; **—костюм** *m.* pneumatic suit; **—механический** *a.* pneumatic; **—нический** *a.* (med.) pneumonic; **—ния** *f.* pneumonia; **—почта** *f.,* **контейнер —почты** (pneumatic) rabbit, shuttle; **—реле** *n.* air relay; **—торакс** *m.* (med.) pneumothorax; **—транспортер** *m.* blower, pneumatic conveyer.

**пнеймо—** *see* **пневмо—**.

**по** *prep. dat.* on, by, at, over, through, in, to, according to, conforming to; at the rate of; **по. дороге** on the way, in passing; **по капле** drop by drop; **по Кариусу** by the Carius method; according to Carius; **по масштабу** to scale; **по нашему** by our method; in our opinion; **по этому образцу** after this model; **судить по** *v.* judge by; *prep. acc.* as far as, up to, to, till; **с 1920 по 1928 г.** from 1920 to 1928; *prep. prepos.* on, after; for; **по рассмотрении** on examination; **диаграмма по времени** time diagram.

**по—** *prefix* with verbs signifying action which is weak or continues for a short or unknown length of time, usually translated as "a little"; *prefix* with adjectives and adverbs meaning "somewhat more, as possible," for example: **поинтереснее** somewhat more interesting; as interesting as possible; *prefix* with certain adverbs meaning "in," for example: **по-английски** in English; **говорить по английски** *v.* speak English.

**побагроветь** *v.* become purple.

**побалтывать** *v.* shake from time to time, agitate periodically.

**побег** *m.* escape, flight; (bot.) shoot, sprout, sucker, runner, trailer; scion, graft; **—ать** *v.* run (a little).

**побеговьюн** *m.* a leaf roller moth (*Evetria*); **п.-смолевщик** *m.* Evetria resinella.

**победа** *f.* victory, conquest.

**победит** *m.* Pobedit (tungsten-cobalt-carbon-titanium alloy).

**побед/итель** *m.* winner, victor; **—ить** *see* **побеждать**; **—ный** *a.* victorious, triumphant.

**побежал/ость** *f.* (met., min.) iridescence, iridescent tarnish; **цвет —ости, —ый цвет** (met.) temper color.

**побежать** *v.* run; start to run.

**побеждать** *v.* conquer, overcome, get the better (of).

**побежка** *f.* pace, gait (of horse).

**побел/еть** *v.* grow white, turn pale, blanch; **—ить** *v.* whiten, whitewash; **—ка** *f.* whitening, whitewashing.

**побережье** *n.* shore, coast, littoral.

**побит/ость** *f.* bruise (of produce); **—ый** *a.* bruised; beaten; **—ь** *v.* bruise; beat.

**побледнеть** *v.* turn pale.

**поблекл/увший** *a.* tarnished, dull; **—уть** *v.* tarnish, dull, fade; (bot.) wither.

**поблизости** *adv.* near, near at hand.

**побол/ее, —ьше** *comp. of* **большой, много,** larger; more.

**поборник** *m.* advocate, supporter.

**побороть** *v.* overcome, conquer, subdue.

**побочн/ый** *a.* secondary, side, by—, subsidiary, subordinate, incidental; indirect; accessory, collateral, supplementary, adjoining; false, spurious; **п. продукт** by-product; **п. процесс, —ая реакция** side reaction, secondary reaction, simultaneous reaction; **п. путь** (railroad) siding; **п. счет** spurious count; **—ая валентность** auxiliary valence, secondary valence; **—ая ось** (cryst.) secondary axis; **—ое**

**действие** secondary action; —ое производство side line.

**побудитель** m. stimulus; —ный a. stimulating, inciting, impellent; —ная причина incentive.

**побудить** see **побуждать**.

**побужд/аемый** a. stimulated, impelled; prompted (by); —ать v. stimulate, impel, instigate, spur, induce, urge; —ающий a. stimulating, impelling, impellent; —ение n. stimulation, prompting; motive, incentive, impulse.

**побурение** n. damping off (of seedlings); Rhizoctonia disease; root browning; russeting (of fruit).

**побыв/ать** v. visit, be for a while, stay for a while; —ка f. leave of absence, (mil.) furlough; на —ку on leave.

**побыть** v. stay for a time.

**п-ов** abbr. (**полуостров**) peninsula.

**повагонный груз** carload.

**повадка** f. habit, custom.

**повал/енный** a. thrown down, downed; tipped over, overturned; felled (tree); —ить v. throw down, overthrow; tip over, overturn; go or come in hordes; —иться v. be thrown down, fall; —ка f. (vet.) epidemic pneumonia; в —ку huddled together, crowded.

**повальн/о** adv. without exception, all; —ый a. general, epidemic.

**повар** m. cook; —енный a. culinary, cooking; —енная соль common salt, sodium chloride.

**поведение** n. conduct, behavior; procedure; п. по времени time behavior.

**повеллит** m. (min.) powellite.

**повер/енный** m. attorney, lawyer, agent; —ить v. believe, credit; —ка f. checking, check, verification; control, control test; (math.) proof; (mil.) roll call.

**повернут/ый** a. turned; —ь see **поверты-вать**.

**поверочн/ый** a. checking, check, verifying; п. анализ check analysis; —ая проба umpire assay; —ое испытание check test; aptitude test.

**повертыв/ание** n. turning; —ать v. turn around; —аться v. turn, turn around; —аться кругом face about.

**поверх** prep. gen. over, above.

**поверхностно** adv. superficially, on the surface; п.-активные вещества surface-active agents; —сть f. superficiality.

**поверхностн/ый** a. surface, superficial; exposed (wire); п. разряд (elec.) surface discharge; п. сток (geol.) surface discharge; —ая закалка (met.) case hardening; —ая плотность surface density, areal density; —ое напряжение, —ое натяжение surface tension; —ое обнажение (geol.) surface exposure, erosion; —ое унавоживание (agr.) top dressing.

**поверхност/ь** f. surface, area, plane; (water) table; п. нагрева heating surface; п. соприкосновения contact surface; п. трения rubbing surface, surface in contact; выход слоя на п. (geol.) outcrop; нагрузка на единицу —и load per unit area; охлаждаемый с —и surface-cooled; сожжение под —ью submerged combustion.

**повер/ье** n. belief, superstition; —ять v. trust, entrust; verify, check.

**повесить** v. hang, hang up, suspend.

**повести** v. lead, conduct.

**повестка** f. notice, summons, subpoena; п. дня agenda.

**поветрие** n. epidemic, infection.

**повеять** v. begin to blow.

**повив** m. lay (of cable); —ать v. twine.

**повидать** v. see; —ся v. see, have an interview (with).

**по-видимому** adv. seemingly, apparently, evidently; it seems, it appears.

**повидло** n. fruit paste; (apple) butter.

**повили/ка**, —ца f., —чный a. (bot.) dodder (Cuscuta, spec. C. europaea).

**повинн/ость** f. duty, obligation, compulsory service; —ый a. guilty.

**повинов/аться** v. obey, comply (with); —ение n. obedience, compliance.

**повис/ать**, —нуть v. hang, droop, be suspended; —лый a. hanging, drooping.

**повитель** m. (bot.) bindweed (Polygonum convolvulus).

**повить** see **повивать**.

**повлечь** v. involve, entail, necessitate, occasion.

**повлиять** v. influence.

**повод** *m.* halter, rein; occasion, reason, ground, cause; **давать п.** cause, occasion, give rise (to); **по —у** in connection (with), apropos (of).

**поводка** *f.* distortion, deformation, warping, buckling.

**повод/ковый** *a.,* **—ок** *m.* carrier, guide; dog, lathe carrier; tenon, tongue; **п. патрон** carrier plate, catch plate; **—ковая рамка** tool-bar frame.

**повозка** *f.* vehicle, conveyance, cart, wagon, car, lorry.

**повой** *m.* (bot.) glorybind (*Calystegia*); **подстенный п.** wall pellitory (*Parietaria officinalis*); **—ник, —ничек** *m.* waterwort (*Elatine*).

**Поволжье** land along the Volga.

**поворачив/ание** *n.* turning, slewing; **—ать** *v.* turn, turn round, swing, swivel, slew; turn over, tilt; divert, turn aside; (elec.) reverse; *see also* **повертывать;** **—ать на себя** pull; **—ать от себя** push; **—аться** *v.* turn, swing, swivel; rotate, work, run; **—ающийся** *a.* swinging, swivel; rotating, running; reversible.

**поворот** *m.* turn, turning, bend, winding, detour; steering; swinging, slewing; reversal; **муфта —а** steering clutch; **ось —а** pivot axis; **угол —а** deflection angle; **—ить** *see* **повертывать, поворачивать.**

**поворотлив/ость** *f.* handiness, agility; **—ый** *a.* handy, maneuverable, agile.

**поворотн/ый** *a.* turning, steering; rotating, rotatable, rotary, revolving, revolvable; swing, swivel, tilting, pivoted, slewing, slewable; reversing, reversible; hinged, articulated; **п. изомеризм** rotational isomerism; **п. кран** slewing crane, swing crane; **п. круг, —ая площадка** turntable, turnplate; **п. мост** swing bridge; **—ая головка** swivel head.

**повре/дить, —ждать** *v.* injure, damage, do harm (to), impair; **—ждаться** *v.* be injured, get damaged, get out of order; **—ждение** *n.* injury, damage, harm, hurt, impairment, breakage, accident, disturbance; defect; **—ждение нейтронами** neutron-induced damage; **—жденный** *a.* injured, damaged, faulty, defective.

**повременн/о** *adv.* at times, periodically; **—ый** *a.* periodical, periodic; **—ое издание** periodical.

**повседневн/о** *adv.,* **—ый** *a.* daily, every day.

**повсеместн/о** *adv.* universally, generally, everywhere; **—ый** *a.* universal, general.

**повсюду** *adv.* everywhere, throughout.

**повтор/ение** *n.* repetition, recurrence, iteration, reiteration; **—итель** *m.* repeater; (cathode) follower; **—ительный** *a.* reiterative, repeating; **—ить** *see* **повторять.**

**повторн/о** *adv.* repeatedly, over again, once more; **—о-кратковременный** *a.* intermittent; **—ый** *a.* repeated, repetitive, reiterated, re—; several, multiple, duplicate; **—ое замерзание** refreezing.

**повтор/яемость** *f.* recurrence, frequency; **—ять** *v.* repeat, reiterate; **—яться** *v.* recur; repeat, be repeated; **—яющийся** *a.* recurrent, reiterative, repeating.

**повысит/ель** *see* **трансформатор-повыситель;** **—ельный** *a.* increasing, boosting; (elec.) step-up; **—ь** *see* **повышать.**

**повыш/ать** *v.* raise, increase, heighten; promote, advance, boost; (elec.) step up; **—аться** *v.* rise, increase; **—ающий** *a.* (elec.) step-up; **—е** *comp. of* **высокий, высоко,** somewhat higher, somewhat taller; above; **—ение** *n.* rise, rising, increase, boost; elevation; (elec.) stepping up; **—енный** *a.* raised, increased; stepped up; **—енного типа** advanced.

**повяз/ать, —ывать** *v.* tie, bind; **—ка** *f.* band, bandage, sling.

**пог.** *abbr.* (**погонный**) linear, running.

**поган/ка** *f.* (bot.) toadstool; **—ый** *a.* unclean, impure, bad; garbage (can).

**пога/сание** *n.* extinction, extinguishment; **—сать, —снуть** *v.* go out, be extinguished; **—сить, —шать** *v.* extinguish, put out, quench; darken; pay off, liquidate, clear off (debt); **—сший** *a.* extinguished; extinct; **—шение** *n.* extinction, extinguishment; payment; **—шенный** *a.* extinguished, out; quenched; slaked; paid off.

погиб/ать, —нуть v. perish, be lost;
—ель f. ruin, destruction; —ельный
a. ruinous, fatal, pernicious; —ший a.
lost, ruined, perished.

поглотитель m. absorber, absorption apparatus; absorbent; sorbent; —ный
a. absorbing, absorption, absorbent;
sorptive; —ная башня absorption
tower; —ная способность absorptive
power; sorptive power; —ное вещество absorbent.

поглотить see поглощать.

поглощаем/ость f. absorbability; absorptivity; —ый a. absorbable.

поглощ/ательный, —ающий a. absorbing, absorbent, absorptive; sorbent;
—ательная способность, способность —ать absorptive power, absorptivity; —ать v. absorb, suck up,
swallow up, take up, pick up, consume, engulf; capture (neutrons);
—аться v. be absorbed, merge;
—ающее средство absorbent;
sorbent.

поглощен/ие n. absorption; sorption;
input, consumption (of power); коэффициент —ия absorption coefficient;
сила —ия absorptive power; —ный
a. absorbed, taken up.

поглубже compr. of глубокий, глубоко,
somewhat deeper.

погляд/еть v. look, see; —ывать v. look
from time to time.

погнать v. drive.

погну/вшийся a. bent, sagged; —ть v.
bend, curve.

поговорить v. talk (of), discuss.

погода f. weather.

погодить v. wait a little.

погодн/о adv. annually, yearly, per year;
—ый a. annual, yearly.

погодо/стойкий, —устойчивый a.
weatherproof.

поголовн/о adv. without exception, all,
one by one; —ый a. general.

поголовье n. livestock.

погон m. distillate, fraction; голова —а,
первый п. first runnings.

погонн/ый a. linear, length; п. вес weight
of one linear unit (of cable, etc.); п.
метр running meter; —ая мера linear
measure.

погор/ать, —еть v. burn, burn out, be

burned out; —елый a. burned out.

пограничн/ый a. boundary, bordering;
п. слой boundary layer; —ая линия
boundary line; demarcation line;
—ая область border zone.

погреб m. cellar; (powder) magazine;
(geol.) crystal-lined vug in a vein.

погреб/ать v. inter, bury; —енный a.
interred, buried.

погремок m. rattle; (bot.) yellow rattle
(*Alectorolophus* or *Rhinanthus*).

погреш/ать, —ить v. err, make mistakes; —имость f. fallibility; —имый
a. fallible.

погрешност/ь f. error, mistake; defect;
абсолютная п. отсчета accuracy of
reading; величина —и, значение —и
magnitude of error, extent of error.

погруб/елый a. roughened, coarse, grown
hard; —еть v. roughen, grow hard.

погруж/аемый a. submergible, submersible; immersion, immersed; —ать v.
plunge, dip, immerse, submerge, bury,
embed, sink; load; —аться v. plunge;
dip, sink (into), submerge, merge;
cave in; —ающийся a. plunging,
sinking, merging; —ение n. plunging,
dipping, insertion; sinking, immersion, submersion, merging, mergence;
лак наносимый —ением dipping
varnish; —енность f. submergence;
—енный a. plunged, immersed, submerged, sunk, buried; swimming-pool
(nuclear reactor); —енный в масло
oil-immersed; —ной a. immersion,
immersible.

погруз/ившийся a. sunken, buried;
—ить see погружать; —ка f. loading,
shipping, freight handling; —очно-
разгрузочный a. handling.

погрузочн/ый a. loading; п. желоб loading chute; п. пункт landing point;
—ая установка handling equipment,
loading equipment.

погрузчик m. loader.

погуб/ить, —лять v. ruin, destroy.

под m. hearth, bottom, sole (of
furnace).

под prep. acc. and instr. under; in imitation of; to, toward, near; п. гору
down hill; п. землей underground;
п. красное дерево in imitation of
mahogany; п. рукой near at hand; п.

**40° северной широты** in latitude 40° north.

**под—** *prefix* sub—, hypo—; *with verbs indicating* under, up to, close; *also* up, *as in* подсчитать *v.* count up.

**подав/аемый** *a.* fed, supplied; **—атель** *m.* feeder; server.

**подавать** *v.* give, present; supply, convey, feed; serve, hand; submit, hand in (application); set (an example); **—ся** *v.* draw, move; give way, yield.

**подав/итель** *m.* suppressor; attenuator (of oscillation); (flotation) depressant, depressing agent; **—ить, —лять** *v.* suppress, crush, overwhelm, smother; quench; depress; **—иться** *v.* choke; **—ление** *n.* suppression, repression; quenching; depression; **—ленный** *a.* suppressed; depressed; **—ляющий** *a.* suppressing; overwhelming (majority).

**подагр/а** *f.* (med.) podagra, gout; **—ический** *a.* podagric, gouty.

**подазотистая кислота** *see* азотноватистая кислота.

**подальше** *compr. of* далекий, далеко, somewhat farther on.

**подар/ить** *v.* give, present, bestow; **—ок** *m.* gift, present, donation.

**податель** *m.* bearer, petitioner, suppliant.

**податлив/ость** *f.* pliability, pliancy, yielding; (acous.) compliance; **—ый** *a.* pliable, pliant, yielding.

**подать** *see* подавать; *f.* tax, assessment.

**подач/а** *f.* giving, presenting; supply, feed, feeding, introduction (of reagent), delivery, delivering, conveyance, admission, inflow, input; motion, travel, approach; **п. воздуха** air feed, air supply; **высота —и** lift (of pump); **коробка подач** gear box; feed unit, feeder; **механизм —и** (illumination) feed mechanism; **объем —и** delivery volume (of pump); **с автоматической —ей** self-feeding; **стокер с нижней —ей** underfeed stoker.

**подающ/ий** *a.* feeding, feed, conveying, supply, delivery (pump, pipe); **п. барабан** feed roller; **п. конвейер, п. транспортер** feed, feeder; **п. механизм** feeding mechanism, feeder; **п.**

---

червяк worm conveyor, screw conveyer; **—ая лента** feed belt, loading belt; **—ая труба** supply pipe, feed pipe, delivery pipe.

**подбаб/ник** *m.* driving cap (for pipe); **—ок** *m.* follower.

**подбав/ить, —лять** *v.* add; **—ка** *f.* adding, addition.

**подбадривать** *v.* encourage; **—ся** *v.* take heart.

**подбалка** *f.* bolster, support.

**подбалтывать** *v.* beat in, mix in.

**подбарабанье** *n.* (mech.) concave.

**подбе/гать, —жать** *v.* run up to.

**подбел** *m.* (bot.) butterbur (*Petasites*); andromeda.

**подбел/ивание** *n.*, **—ка** *f.* whitening, bleaching; (calico) branning; **—ивать, —ить** *v.* whiten, bleach.

**подбив/ать** *v.* line, pad; beat under, drive under; nail up; instigate; disable (a gun); **—ка** *f.* lining, padding; driving under; nailing up.

**подбир/ание** *n.* gathering, picking up; selection; **—ать** *v.* gather, pick up; select, assort, match, fit, blend (colors); **—аться** *v.* be selected; steal up to.

**подбить** *see* подбивать.

**подбой** *m.* lining; (min.) cutting; **—ка** *f.* swage, bottom swage; beater, packer; **—щик** *m.* (min.) cutter.

**подболт/ать** *see* подбалтывать; **—ка** *f.* thickening; beaten-up substance.

**подбор** *m.* selection, matching; assortment, set; breeding; **метод —а** trial-and-error method; **на п.** selected, chosen, matched, assorted; **—ка** *f.* set, selection; planks between beams of ceiling.

**подбородок** *m.* chin.

**подборщик** *m.* picker, collector.

**подбр/асывать, —осить** *v.* throw up, throw under; leave, abandon.

**подбрюшник** *m.* support (for boiler).

**подбурочный шпур** (blasting) block hole.

**подбутка** *f.* inferior concrete.

**подвал** *m.* basement, cellar.

**подвал/ивать, —ить** *v.* throw, heap up; roll under.

**подвальный** *a.* cellar, basement; **п. этаж** basement.

подвар/ивать, —ить v. boil while adding new ingredients; weld on, solder on.

подведен/ие n. supply, feeding; —ный a. led up to, conducted, fed, supplied.

подведомственный a. in charge (of); within the jurisdiction (of).

подверг/ать, —нуть v. subject, submit, treat (with), expose (to); п. гидролизу hydrolyze; п. действию treat; expose to the action (of); п. действию света expose to light; п. испытанию test, experiment (with); —аться, —нуться v. be subjected, undergo; be exposed (to); incur.

подвержен/ие n. subjection; п. изгибу bending load; —ность f. susceptibility; liability; —ный a. subjected (to), exposed; subject, liable (to).

подвер/нуть, —теть, —тывать v. screw, tighten; tuck in, slip under, thrust under, turn under; —тываться v. slip under, fall under; turn up, appear; —тывание n. screwing, tightening.

подвес m. suspension, suspension device, carrier arm, hanger (in furnace); точка —a point of support; —ить see подвешивать; —ка f. suspension, hanging; suspension support, suspension arm, suspended span, suspender, hanger, bracket; top strut assembly; ear, lug; countershaft, communicator; система —ок supporting structure.

подвесн/ой, —ый a. suspension, suspended, hanging, hanger, supporting; overhead, overhung, aerial; underslung; swinging, pendant; mounted, attached; outboard (motor); п. конвейер trolley conveyer, overhead conveyer; п. мост suspension bridge; —ая дорога ropeway, overhead trolley, aerial trolley; —ая дуга bracket rim (of furnace); —ая железная дорога suspension railroad; —ая кривая (math.) catenary; —ая рессора supporting spring; —ая система supporting structure; (parachute) harness; —ая стенка breastwall; —ые леса suspended scaffolds.

подвести see подводить.

подветренный a. lee, leeward.

подвеш/енный a. suspended, pendent,

perched; —енная порода (geol.) perched rock; —ивание n. suspension, hanging; —ивать v. suspend, hang, hang up.

подвздошн/ый a. (anat.) iliac; —ая кость ilium.

подвиг m. exploit, feat.

подвигать v. move on, advance, push, promote; —ся v. move on, advance, draw up, make progress, get ahead; —ся вперед progress, get ahead.

подвид m. subspecies.

подвижка f. movement, shift; (tectonics) shove; (ore) adjustment.

подвижн/ой, —ый a. mobile, movable, moving; portable, transportable; migratory; traveling, sliding, traversing; loose, free; active, lively, live; п. вес sliding weight; п. контакт (elec.) sliding contact; п. кран traveling crane; п. масштаб, —ая шкала sliding scale; п. состав (railroad) rolling stock; п. центр live center; —ая счетная таблица sliding scale; —ая щека swing jaw (of crusher); —ое равновесие dynamic equilibrium; —ое топливо (nucl.) circulating fissionable material; —ость f. mobility, maneuverability; liveliness; portability; availability (of nutrients); —ость ионов ionic mobility.

подвинтить see подвинчивать.

подвинуть see подвигать.

подвинчивать v. screw up, tighten.

подвисание n. holdup (in distillation).

подвод m. supply, delivery, feed, admission; feed line; (elec.) lead, feeder; cross support, undersetter, underpinning prop; п. тепла heat supply; линия —а (elec.) supply main, feeder.

подвода f. wagon, cart.

подводим/ый a. fed, supplied; п. воздух air supply; —ая мощность (elec.) power input, input.

подвод/ить v. lead up to; feed, supply; place under; —ка f. leading in, leading up to; delivery, service; feed, supply.

подводн/ый a. subaqueous; submarine; submerged, sunk, sunken; underwater (explosion); (bot.) submersed; —ая лодка submarine, U-boat; —ая

**мина** depth charge; —**ое течение** undercurrent.

**подводчик** *m.* feeder.

**подводящ/ий** *a.* leading in, conveying, supply, delivery, feeding; **п. канал** feeder; **п. механизм** feeding mechanism, feeder; admission gear; **п. патрубок** inlet branch; **п. провод** (elec.) supply main, feeder; —**ая труба** feed pipe, delivery pipe, inlet pipe; —**ее сопло** distributing nozzle, feed nozzle.

**по-двое** *adv.* in pairs, two at a time.

**подвоз** *m.* supply; transport, transportation, hauling, conveyance; —**ить** *v.* bring, carry; transport.

**подвой** *m.* (bot.) wilding; (agr.) stock.

**подволока** *f.* ceiling.

**подвор/ачивать**, —**отить** *v.* turn under.

**подвох** *m.* trap, snare, trick.

**подвулканизация** *f.* (rubber) scorching; precure.

**подвяз/ать**, —**ывать** *v.* bind, tie up; —**ка** *f.* suspender, garter; —**ывание** *n.* binding, tying; —**ь** *f.* cording, binding.

**подвяливать** *v.* (cer.) sour.

**подгаечник** *m.* lock nut.

**подгибать** *v.* turn in, bend under.

**подгн/ивать**, —**ить** *v.* start decaying, rot slightly; —**оить** *v.* rot, decay.

**подголовок** *m.* neck.

**подгон** *m.* (bot.) second growth.

**подгонка** *f.* adjustment, fitting.

**подгонообразование** *n.* sprouting.

**подгонщик** *m.* beater.

**подгонять** *v.* hurry, urge on, speed up; drive on; adapt, suit, adjust, fit; **п. под один размер** reduce to one size.

**подгор/ание** *n.* scorching, burning; —**ать**, —**еть** *v.* scorch, burn, be burned; catch fire; —**елый** *a.* scorched, burnt.

**подгоризонт** *m.* subhorizon.

**подгорный** *a.* at the foot of a mountain.

**подгородный** *a.* near a city, suburban.

**под-гору** *adv.* downhill.

**подгорье** *n.* foothills.

**подготовитель** *m.* preparator; —**ный** *a.* preparatory, preliminary; roughing (mill); —**ная работа** preliminary work, development work, development.

**подготов/ить**, —**лять** *v.* prepare, get ready, make ready; prime (engine); train; —**ка** *f.*, —**ление** *n.* preparation; training; **без** —**ки** off-hand, impromptu; untrained; —**ленность** *f.* preparedness; —**ленный** *a.* prepared.

**подгре/бать**, —**сти** *v.* rake up, scrape up.

**подгруздь** *m.* (bot.) mushroom (*Agaricus scrobiculatus*).

**подгруппа** *f.* subgroup, subunit.

**поддавать** *v.* add, increase; reinforce; subdue, subjugate; —**ся** *v.* give in, yield; give way, break down; be open (to suggestion).

**поддан/ный** *m.* subject, citizen; —**ство** *n.* citizenship.

**поддать** *see* **поддавать.**

**поддающийся** *a.* yielding (to); conformable; **п. мытью** washable; **п. обработке** machinable; **не п. анализу** unanalyzable.

**поддвиг** *m.* (geol.) underthrust.

**поддел/ать**, —**ывать** *v.* forge, falsify; counterfeit; adulterate; —**ка** *f.* imitation, counterfeit; adulteration; adulterant; —**ывание** *n.* imitation, counterfeiting; adulteration; —**ьный** *a.* counterfeit, forged (signature); artificial, false, dummy; adulterated, impure; —**ьная кожа** artificial leather.

**поддерж/ание** *n.*, —**ка** *f.* support, prop, rest, holder; supporting, sustaining, maintenance, keeping, upkeep; backing; —**ать**, —**ивать** *v.* support, prop up, hold up, hold, bear, carry; sustain, keep; maintain, keep up, feed; advocate, second, back up, favor; —**иваемый** *a.* supported, sustained; —**ивающий** *a.* supporting, carrying, carrier; —**ивающее устройство** carrier.

**поддиапазон** *m.* subrange, sub-band.

**поддир** *m.* (min.) a long cutting wedge.

**поддоменник** *m.* bottom (of blast furnace).

**поддон**, —**ок** *m.* tray, pan, drip pan; pallet; (foundry) bottom plate.

**поддуб/ица** *f.* oak-forest soil; —**овик** *m.* mushroom (*Boletus pachypurus*).

**подду/вало** *n.* ash pit (of furnace); —**вание** *n.* blowing; heave; (min.) creeping; —**вать**, —**ть** *v.* blow, blow under.

**подействовать** *v.* act, have an effect (on); work, operate.

подел/енный *a.* shared, distributed; —ить, —иться *v.* share.

поделка *f.* odd work, job.

поденк/а *f.* may fly; —и *pl.* Ephemeroptera.

поден/но *adv.* daily, by the day; —ный *a.* daily, day; —ная работа, —щина *f.* day labor; —щик *m.* day laborer; —щина *f.* day labor.

подергив/ание *n.* twitching, jerking, jerk; —ать *v.* pull (at), jerk (at).

подерж/ание *n.* holding, keeping; взять на п. *v.* borrow; дать на п. *v.* lend; —анный *a.* secondhand, used; kept, held; —ать *v.* hold for some time, keep for a while.

подернуться *v.* be covered (with).

подешев/еть *v.* get cheaper, become less expensive; —ле *adv.* somewhat cheaper; as cheaply as possible.

поджар/енный *a.* roasted; fried; —ивание *n.* roasting; frying; —иватель *m.* toaster (for bread); —ивать, —ить *v.* roast (a little); toast; fry; broil.

поджарый *a.* lean, thin, emaciated.

поджать *see* поджимать.

поджелудочн/ый *a.* below the stomach; —ая железа (anat.) pancreas; —ая область epigastrium.

поджечь *see* поджигать.

поджигать *v.* heal, be healing.

поджиг *m.* ignition; —ание *n.* ignition, firing; —атель *m.* incendiary; —ательство *n.* incendiarism; —ать *v.* set on fire, set fire (to); light, kindle; —ающий *a.* incendiary.

поджидать *v.* wait (for), watch (for).

поджилки *pl.* (anat.) hamstring, tendon, hough, hock.

поджимать *v.* draw in, tighten, adjust.

поджить *see* поживать.

поджог *m.* setting fire (to); (law) arson.

подзаголовок *m.* subtitle, subhead.

подзаря/дить, —жать *v.* (elec.) give an additional charge, recharge; replenish; —дка *f.* additional charge, recharging; replenishing.

подзатылок *m.* nape of neck.

подзащитный *a.* entrusted (to), under the care (of); *m.* client (of lawyer).

подзвуковой *a.* (acous.) subsonic.

подзем/елье *n.* cave, vault; —ельный *see* подземный; —ка *f.* subway.

подземн/ый *a.* underground, subterranean, subsurface; buried; ground (water); п. толчок, п. удар earthquake shock; п. ход subway, tunnel; —ая вода ground water; —ая железная дорога subway (train).

подзимний *a.* late fall, early winter.

подзол *m.* podzol (soil); —изация *f.* podzolization; —истоглеевый *a.* podzolized gley (soil); —истый *a.* podzolic.

подзорн/ая труба telescope, field glass; —ое стекло sight glass.

подзывать *v.* call up, call over.

подизвестк覆истый *a.* subcalcareous.

подинтегральная функция (math.) integrand.

подины *pl.* fettlings (of open-hearth furnace).

подкалывать *v.* split, cleave, break (a little); pin up.

подкапывать *v.* undermine, dig under.

подкараул/ивать, —ить *see* подстерегать.

подкармливать *v.* feed up, fatten.

подкасательная *f.* (geom.) subtangent.

подкат/ать, —ить, —ывать *v.* roll up, drive up; roll under; —аться, —иться, —ываться *v.* roll under, be rolled under; —чик *m.* (min.) drawer.

подкач/ивать *v.* pump (up to); —ивающий *a.* booster (pump); —ка *f.* pumping.

подкашивать *v.* mow, mow down.

подква/сить, —шивать *v.* put ferment (into), inoculate with ferment; acidulate.

подки/дать, —дывать, —нуть *see* подбрасывать.

подкисл/ение *n.* acidification; acidulation; —енный *a.* acidified, acidulous; —ять *v.* acidify; acidulate; —яющий *a.* acidifying.

подклад/ка *f.* lining, backing; packing, strip, washer; block; —ки *pl.* blocking; —ной *a.* put under, laid under, underneath, backing; —очный *a.* lining; —ывание *n.* putting under; —ывать *v.* put under, lay under, pad, line.

подкласс *m.* subclass.

подкле/ивание *n.*, —йка *f.* pasting,

gluing; —ивать, —ить *v.* paste, glue under.

подклинивать *v.* wedge up, block up, shim.

подключать *v.* (elec.) switch (in or on).

подключичный *a.* (anat.) subclavian.

подков/а *f.*, —ный *a.* horseshoe; —анный *a.* shod; —ать *v.* shoe; —ообразный *a.* horseshoe-shaped; horseshoe (magnet).

подкожн/ый *a.* under the skin; (med.) hypodermic, subcutaneous; —ая клетчатка hypodermic tissue; —ое впрыскивание hypodermic injection.

подколен/ный *a.* (anat.) popliteal; —ок *m.* hamstring, tendon; shank.

подколоть *see* подкалывать.

подкомиссия *f.* subcommittee.

подконтрольный *a.* under control.

подкоп *m.* mine, undermining; underhand practice; вести п., подводить п. *see* подкапывать; —ный *a.* undermining.

подкоренн/ая величина, —ое количество, —ое число (math.) radicand.

подкорковые пузыри (casting) blisters beneath the crust.

подкорм/ить *v.* feed up, fatten; —ка *f.* feeding; top dressing; liquid fertilization; (mineral) supplements, supplementary feeding; —щик *m.* plant feeder; fertilizer spreader.

подкоровой *a.* (geol.) subcrustal.

подкос *m.* strut, brace, angle brace, prop.

подкра/сить, —шивать *v.* tint, color, retouch.

подкреп/ить, —лять *v.* fortify, strengthen, reinforce; support; —ление *n.* fortification, reinforcement; —ляющий *a.* fortifying, strengthening, reinforcing; invigorating; supporting, sustaining, nourishing, wholesome.

подкритич/еский *a.* subcritical; below-critical (temperature, etc.); —ность *f.* subcriticality.

подкрыл/ок *m.* flap, wing flap; —ьцовый *a.* (anat.) axillary.

подкупать *v.* bribe, buy over, buy off.

подкуривать *v.* smoke; fumigate.

подладанник *m.* (bot.) rock rose parasite (*Cytinus*).

подла/дить, —живать *v.* fit, suit, adapt.

подламывать, —ся *v.* break, crack, split.

подлап/ок *m.* corbel, bracket; —ки *pl.* blocking.

подле *prep. gen.* near, by, beside, by the side of, side by side.

подледниковый *a.* (geol.) subglacial.

подлеж/ать *v.* depend (on), be subject (to), be under the jurisdiction (of); —ащий *a.* subject, liable; applicable, relevant; —ащий уплате payable.

подлез/ать, —ть *v.* creep under, get under.

подлесник *m.* (bot.) sanicle (*Sanicula*).

подлесок *m.* underbrush, undergrowth.

подлет/ать, —еть *v.* fly up to.

подлив/ать *v.* pour to, pour more, add a little; —ка *f.* sauce, gravy; —ное колесо undershot wheel.

подлинн/ик *m.* original, first draft; —о *adv.* in truth, really, authentically; —ость *f.* authenticity; —ый *a.* authentic, original, real, genuine, true.

подлить *see* подливать.

подложечный *a.* (anat.) substernal.

подлож/ить *see* подкладывать; —ка *f.* foundation, support; base, base layer, backing; substrate; (acous.) core; на —ке backed (emulsion).

подложный *a.* false, counterfeit.

подлом/ать, —ить *see* подламывать.

подлопаточный *a.* (anat.) subscapular.

подлунный *a.* sublunar, terrestrial.

подлый *a.* ignoble, base, mean.

подмагничив/ание *n.* magnetic biasing; —ать *v.* bias; magnetize.

подмаз/ать, —ывать *v.* grease, oil; smear; paint; —ка *f.* greasing, oiling; first coat (of paint).

подмаренник *m.* (bot.) bedstraw (*Galium*).

подмастерье *m.* apprentice, assistant.

подмачивать *v.* wet, moisten, damp.

подмен *m.*, —а *f.* substitute, substitution; —енный, —ный *a.* substituted, substitute; —ивать, —ить *v.* substitute, exchange, replace.

подмерз/ать, —нуть *v.* freeze (a little), get frostbitten; —лый *a.* slightly frozen, frostbitten.

подмести *v.* sweep up.

подмесь *f.* adulteration, admixture; (biol.) rogue.

подметать *see* подмести, подметывать.

подметить *see* подмечать.

подметка *f.* sole (of shoe).

подметывать *v.* baste, tack.

подмеч/ать *v.* notice, observe; —енный *a.* noted, observed.

подмеш/анный *a.* mixed, not pure, adulterated; —ать, —ивать *v.* mix (in), adulterate.

подминать *v.* tread, trample (on).

подмножество *n.* (math.) subset.

подмодельная плита (foundry) bottom board.

подмок/ать, —нуть *v.* get wet.

подмор/аживать, —озить *v.* freeze; —оженный *a.* frozen, frostbitten.

подмост/и,—ки *pl.* scaffoldings, scaffold, trestle, stage, supporting structure.

подмоч/енный *a.* wet, moistened, damp; —ить *see* подмачивать.

подмы/в *m.*, —вание *n.* washing, scouring; washing away; —вать, —ть *v.* wash up; wash away, undermine, undercut; —тый *a.* washed; washed away, undermined.

подмыш/ечный *a.* (anat.) axillary; —ечная ямка, —ка *f.* axilla, armpit; —ку under one's arms.

подмять *see* подминать.

поднадзорный *a.* under observation.

поднаковальн/ик *m.*, —я *f.* anvil bed, anvil block, anvil stand.

поднасадочный свод rider arch (of regenerator).

подначальный *a.* subordinate.

поднес/ти *see* подносить; —ущая *f.* (elec. comm.) subcarrier.

подним/ание *n.* raising, lifting, hoisting; —ать *v.* raise, lift, hoist; get up (steam), turn up (flame); (elec.) step up; break, plow (new land); —аться *v.* rise, go up, climb, ascend, emerge; —ающий *a.* raising, lifting, hoisting; —ающая мышца (anat.) elevator; —ающийся *a.* rising, ascending.

поднов/ить, —лять *v.* renovate, renew, refresh, repair, alter; —ление *n.* renovation; —ленный *a.* renovated.

поднож/ие *n.* foot (of hill, etc.), pedestal; —ка *f.* step, footboard, running board (of automobile); —ный *a.* underfoot; —ный корм green fodder, pasture.

поднормаль *m.* (math.) subnormal.

поднос *m.* tray; —ить *v.* offer, present, bring up to, carry up to, bring into contact.

поднутр/ение *n.* undercutting, undercut; угол —ения undercut; —енный *a.* undercut; —ять *v.* undercut, recess.

поднят/ие *n.* rise, rising, ascent, lift, upheaval, elevation; (geol.) upheaval; uplift; reclamation (of land); —ый *a.* raised, hoisted; cocked; —ь *see* поднимать.

подоб/ать *v.* suit, be worthy (of); —ающий *a.* due, proper.

подоб/ие *n.* similarity, similitude, likeness, resemblance, equality, comparison; по —ию in the image (of), resembling; теория —ия similarity theory, similitude theory.

подобласть *f.* (zool.) phylum.

подобн/о *adv.*, —ым образом similarly, in like manner, likewise; п. тому как just as; —ый *a.* similar, like, equal, congruent; *suffix* —like, —oid, similar to, resembling; ничего —ого nothing of the kind.

подоболочка *f.* subshell (of electrons).

подобр/анный *a.* gathered, picked; assorted, matched, selected; плохо п. ill-assorted; —ать *see* подбирать.

подов/ый *a.* hearth, bottom; п. материал (met.) bottoms; п. шлак hearth cinder, slag; —ая печь, —ая топка hearth furnace; —ая плита hearth plate.

подогн/анный *a.* adjusted; —ать *see* подгонять.

подогнуть *see* подгибать.

подогрев *m.*, —ание *n.* warming up, heating; preheating; booster heating; ток —а (elec.) heater current; —атель *m.* heater; preheater; reboiler (of distillation unit); —ательный *a.* heating; preheating; —ательная печь preheating furnace; —ать *v.* warm up, heat up; preheat.

подогрет/ый *a.* warmed up, heated; preheated; —ь *see* подогревать.

пододви/гать, —нуть *v.* push up.

подождать *v.* wait (for).

подозвать *see* подзывать.

подозре/вать *v.* suspect, doubt, mistrust; —ние *n.* suspicion, distrust.

подозрительн/о *adv.* suspiciously, with suspicion; it is suspicious; —ость *f.* suspiciousness; —ый *a.* suspicious.

подойник *m.* milk pail.

подойти *see* подходить.

подокарп/иновая кислота podocarpic acid; —ус *m.* (bot.) Japan yew (*Podocarpus*).

подоконн/ик *m.*, —ый *a.* window sill, sill.

подолгу *adv.* for a considerable time.

подолит *m.* (min.) podolite (probably identical with dahllite).

подонки *pl.* sediment, residue, dregs, refuse, waste.

подопр/евать, —еть *v.* rot, spoil from dampness.

подопытный *a.* tentative, experimental, test.

подорвать *see* подрывать.

подорешник *m.* (bot.) wild nard, asara-bacca (*Asarum europaeum*).

подорожать *v.* become more expensive.

подорожник *m.* (bot.) plantain (*Plantago*); —овые *pl.* Plantaginaceae.

подорожный *a.* along the road.

подосиновик *m.* (bot.) aspen mushroom (*Boletus rufus*).

подостлать *see* подстилать.

под/отдел *m.* subdivision, subsection, branch; —отряд *m.* suborder.

подотчетн/ость *f.* accountability; —ый *a.* accountable (to).

подофилл *m.* (bot.) Podophyllum; —ин *m.* podophyllin (resin); —овая кислота podophyllic acid; —отоксин *m.* podophyllotoxin.

подохнуть *v.* die, die off (of animals).

подоходный налог income tax.

подошв/а *f.*, —енный *a.* sole, bottom, underside; foot (of slope), base.

подпадать *v.* fall under.

подпаивать *v.* solder up.

подпалзывать *v.* creep under, crawl under.

подпал/ивать, —ить *v.* singe, scorch; —ина *f.* scorched place, burn.

подпасть *see* подпадать.

подпахотный *a.* sub-soil.

подпаять *see* подпаивать.

подпекать *v.* bake brown, bake longer.

подпер/еть *see* подпирать; —тый *a.* propped, supported.

подпестичный *a.* (bot.) hypogynous.

подпечь *see* подпекать.

подпил/ивать, —ить *v.* saw; file; —ок *m.* file.

подпир/ание *n.* propping, supporting; —ать *v.* prop up, support, bear, steady, stiffen, sustain; —ающий *a.* supporting.

подпис/авшийся *a.* signatory; —ание, —ывание *n.* signing; subscription; —ать, —ывать *v.* sign; —аться, —ываться *v.* sign; subscribe (for); —ка *f.* signature; subscription; —ной *a.* signed; subscribed; —чик *m.* subscriber.

подпись *f.* signature; subscript; за —ю signed (by), bearing the signature (of).

подпит/ка *f.*, —ывание *n.* make-up; feed maintenance; water-level maintenance in boiler; field current, magnetization current; —очный *a.* make-up (water, etc.); —ывать *v.* make up.

подпласток *m.* substratum.

подплы/вать, —ть *v.* swim up to, float up to.

подповерхностный *a.* subsurface.

подполз/ать, —ти *see* подпалзывать.

подполь/е *n.* cellar under the floor; —ный *a.* under the floor; underground.

подпор *m.* head, backwater; hydrostatic head; raising of water; affluent (of river).

подпор/а, —ка *f.* prop, support, brace, strut, stay; stand; foundation, pillar, buttress; bracket, rest, bearer; scaffolding; packing, chock, wedge, block; —ная стена bulkhead.

подпорядок *m.* suborder.

подпочв/а *f.* subsoil, undersoil, substratum; —енный *a.* subsoil, subsurface, subterranean; ground, underground (water).

подправ/ить, —лять *v.* correct, rectify.

подпрыг/ивание *n.* jumping, hopping, springing; —ивать, —нуть *v.* jump up, hop, bounce, spring.

подпус/кать, —тить *v.* admit, let; allow to approach.

подпушок *m.* linter, fuzz.

подпятник *m.* step bearing, bearing (for vertical axis); jamb; кольцевой п. collar bearing, collar step bearing;

**шариковый п.** ball thrust bearing, ball bearing.

**подравн/ивать, —ять** v. level, make even, fit together, trim.

**подраж/ание** n. imitation; **—атель** m. imitator; **—ательный** a. imitative; **—ать** v. imitate, follow.

**подраздел** m. subsection; **—ение** n. subdivision, section; **—енный** a. subdivided, divided; graduated; split (winding); **—ить, —ять** v. subdivide, divide, classify, class; **—ительная доска** distributing board.

**подразумев/аемое** n. inference; **—ание** n. implication; **—ать** v. imply, mean; **—аться** v. be implied.

**подраст/ать, —и** v. grow up; **—ающее поколение** rising generation.

**подреберный** a. subcostal, under the ribs.

**подрегулиров/ание** n., **—ка** f. adjustment, readjustment; **—ать** v. adjust, readjust.

**под ред.** abbr. (под редакцией) edited by.

**подрез/ание, —ывание** n., **—ка** f. cutting, trimming, pruning (trees); undercutting; **—анный** a. cut, trimmed, pruned; undercut; **—ать, —ывать** v. cut, clip, trim, prune; undercut; **—ной** a. cutting, trimming; undercutting; **—ной резец** recessing tool, undercutting tool.

**подрессор/енный** a. supported on springs, spring-mounted, cushioned; **—ивание** n. cushioning; **—ивать** v. mount on springs, set on springs.

**подрешет/ина** f. counterlathing; **—ка** f. sublattice.

**подрисов/ать, —ывать** v. touch up, retouch (photograph, drawing).

**подробн/о** adv. in detail, at length; **—** **ость** f. detail; **вдаваться в —ости** v. go into details; **—ый** a. detailed, minute, circumstantial; comprehensive; **—ый перечень, —ое обозначение, —ое определение** specification.

**подровнять** see **подравнивать.**

**подрод** m. subgenus.

**подрост** m. seedlings, seedling growth; regrowth; **—ок** m. youngster, youth; **труд —ков** juvenile labor.

**подруб/ать, —ить** v. hew, hack, tap, make incisions; **—ка** f. hewing, hackling, tapping, cutting.

**подрудок** m. (min.) smalls, fines, slack.

**подружить** v. make friends (with).

**подрусловый** a. under a river bed; underground (river or stream).

**подручник** m. arm rest.

**подручный** a. handy, available; improvised; m. apprentice, assistant, helper.

**подрыв** m. injury, detriment, harm.

**подрыв/ать, подрыть** v. dig down, undermine, sap; explode, blast, blow up; **—ной** a. blasting; **—ной заряд** blast, blasting charge; **—ные работы** blasting, demolition work.

**подря/д** adv. one after the other, in succession, without interruption; m. contract; **несколько дней п.** several days running; **—дить, —жать** v. hire, contract; **—дная работа** contract work; **—дчик** m. contractor.

**подсаживать** v. add, recharge; set out, plant (in addition or in place of).

**подсасывать** v. draw under, drain.

**подсачивать** v. tap, gash (trees).

**подсборка** f. subassembly.

**подсвекольник** m. beetroot, pigweed (*Amaranthus retroflexus*).

**подсве/тка** f. bias lighting; **—чивающий** a. brightening; intensifier; **—чник** m. candlestick.

**подсвита** f. member.

**подсев** m. undersowing; additional sowing; **—ать** v. sow more; **—ок** m. (min.) smalls, fines, slack.

**подсед** m. (bot.) sprout; (vet.) scratches.

**подсекать** see **подрубать.**

**подсекция** f. subsection, subdivision.

**подсемейство** n. subfamily.

**подсемядольное колено** (bot.) hypocotyl.

**подсернистонатриевая соль** sodium hydrosulfite.

**подсеточная вода** (paper) tray water.

**подсеч/ка** f. cutting, incision, tapping; cutter; **место —ки** incision; **—ь** see **подрубать.**

**подсеять** see **подсевать.**

**подсин/ивание** n. bluing; **—ивать, —** **ить** v. blue, use bluing.

**подсинхронный** a. hyposynchronous.

**подсистема** f. subsystem.

**подскабливать** v. scrape; rub off, erase.

**подскакив/ание** n. jumping up, springing up; **—ать** v. jump up, spring up.

**подскоблить** see **подскабливать.**

подско/кнуть, —чить see подскакивать.

подскре/бать, —сти v. scrape.

подслаивание n. subcoating, undercoating.

подслащ/ать, —ивать, подсластить v. sweeten, edulcorate; —енный a. sweetened; —ивание n. sweetening.

подслеповатый a. having poor sight.

подслой m. substratum, sublayer; coating.

подслушивать v. listen in, intercept.

подсмол/ок m., —ьная вода tar water.

подснежн/ик m. (bot.) snowdrop (Galanthus); —ый a. under the snow.

подсобн/ый a. secondary, by—; auxiliary; branch (works); utility (building); servo (motor); п. материал intermediate; п. продукт secondary product, by-product.

подсов/ать, —ывать v. push under.

подсознательный a. subconscious.

подсол/евой a. (geol.) subsalt; —енный a. salted; —ить v. salt, add some salt.

подсолн/ечник m., масличный п. (bot.) sunflower (Helianthus annuus); —ечный a. sunflower; subsolar; —ечное масло sunflower oil; —ух m. sunflower seeds.

подсос m. inflow, inleakage; —ать see подсасывать; —ный a. inflow; suckling (animal).

подсостояние n. substate.

подсохнуть see подсыхать.

подсоч/ка f., —ный a. gashing, tapping (of trees).

подспорье n. help, assistance, aid.

подстав/ить, —лять v. place under; (math.) substitute; lift up, hold up; —ка f. support, prop, brace, strut, stay; stand, base, rest, bracket, bearer, fulcrum; socket; chock, block; —ной a. false; —очный a. supporting.

подстанов/ить, —лять v. substitute; —ка f., —ление n. substitution.

подстанция f. substation.

подстволок m. (min.) sump, pit.

подстег/ать, —ивать v. pad, line.

подстелить see подстилать.

подстенный a. wall.

подстенок m. buttress, prop.

подстенье n. foundation.

подстере/гать, —чь v. be on the lookout (for), be on the watch.

подстил/ать v. lay, strew (under); —ающий a. under (layer); underlying, subjacent; —ающая порода (geol.) basement rock, bedrock; —ка f.,—очный a. litter, bedding; flooring.

подсторожить see подстерегать.

подстрекатель m. instigator.

подстрел/ина f. angle brace; —ьник m. cross bar.

подстри/гание n. cutting, shearing, clipping, cropping; trimming, pruning; —гать, —чь v. cut, shear, clip, crop; trim, prune (trees); —женный a. cut, shorn, clipped, trimmed.

подстройка f. fine tuning; alignment.

подстрочное примечание footnote.

подступ m. approach, advance; access; —ать, —ить v. approach, advance, come near.

подсудн/ость f. cognizance; jurisdiction; —ый a. under the jurisdiction (of).

подсунуть see подсовывать.

подсуш/ивать, —ить v. dry a little.

подсч/ет m. calculation, computation, determination, rating; tabulation; производить п. v. calculate, figure out; —итать, —итывать v. calculate, count up, reckon, compute, estimate; tabulate.

подсыпать v. add, fill.

подсых/ание n. drying; —ать v. get dry, get a little drier.

подтаивать v. thaw, melt.

подталкив/атель m. plunger, ram; push rod; —ать v. push, shove; —ающий a. pushing, actuating.

подтангенс m. (geom.) subtangent.

подтапливать v. heat a little.

подтаск/ать, —ивать v. drag up to.

подтачив/ание n. sharpening; gnawing, boring (of worms); (geol.) erosion; —ать v. sharpen, give an edge (to); gnaw, bore; erode.

подтащить see подтаскивать.

подтаять see подтаивать.

подтвержд/ать, подтвердить v. confirm, corroborate, verify, bear witness; —ение n. confirmation; —енный a. confirmed, corroborated, verified.

подтек m., —ание n. inflow; (med.) bruise, suffusion (of blood); —ать v. flow under, leak; —ающий a. leaking.

**подтепловой** *a.* subthermal.

**подтечь** *see* **подтекать.**

**подтип** *m.* subtype.

**подток** *m.* inflow, seepage.

**подтолкнуть** *see* **подталкивать.**

**подтональный** *a.* (acous.) subsonic, sub-audio.

**подтопить** *see* **подтапливать.**

**подтопление** *n.* rise (of ground water).

**подточ/енный** *a.* sharpened; gnawed, eaten (by worms); (geol.) eroded; **п. червями** worm-eaten; **—ить** *see* **подтачивать; —ка** *f.* sharpening; recess, groove.

**подтропический** *a.* subtropical.

**подтынник** *m.* (bot.) polypody (*Polypodium*).

**подтя/гивать, —нуть** *v.* pull, draw up, tighten, screw up; reset, adjust (bearing); **—гиваться** *v.* pull oneself together; pull oneself up; catch up; **—жка** *f.* drawing up, tightening; **—жки** *pl.* suspenders.

**подувать** *v.* blow a little.

**подуклонка** *f.* canting, sloping, inclination.

**подум/авши** *adv.* on second thought; **—ать** *v.* reflect, consider; think; **—ывать** *v.* think (of), contemplate.

**подуровень** *m.* sublevel.

**подуры** *pl.* snow fleas, springtails (*Poduridae*).

**подуть** *see* **подувать.**

**подуч/ать, —ивать, —ить** *v.* instruct, teach; **—иться** *v.* learn.

**подуш/ечка** *f.* cushion; **—ечницы** *pl.* scale insects (*Coccidae*); **—ечный** *a.,* **—ка** *f.* cushion, pillow, pad; bearing; bearer, chock, block; (gas) blanket; (distillation) carrier liquid, chaser; **—ечный слой** cushion, padding; **—ечная отдельность, —ечная структура** pillow structure (of lavas); **—ковидный, —кообразный** *a.* pillowlike, pillow.

**подферменн/ик** *m.,* **—ый камень** foundation stone.

**подхват** *m.* cross support; catching up, picking up; pickup; **реакция —а** (nucl.) pickup reaction, pickup; **—ить, —ывать** *v.* take up, catch up, snatch up, pick up; **—цы** *pl.* tongs; forceps, tweezers; **—чик** *m.* pickup.

**подход** *m.* manner, way; approach, drawing near; **—ы** *pl.* access, approaches; **—ить** *v.* approach, come near, draw near, arrive (at); fit, match up, match, suit; **—ный** *a.* approach; **—ящий** *a.* suitable, fitting, appropriate, adequate, proper (to occasion), expedient, pertinent, advantageous; approaching, incoming.

**подцве/тить, —чать, —чивать** *v.* dye, color, paint; tint, shade.

**подцеп/ить, —ливать, —лять** *v.* hook, hook up; pick up, catch.

**подчас** *adv.* sometimes, at times.

**подчекан/енный** *a.* calked; **—ивать, —ить** *v.* calk; **—ивающий** *a.* calking.

**подчелюстной** *a.* (anat.) submaxillary.

**подчерк/ивание** *n.* underlining, emphasis, accentuation, stress; **—ивать, —нуть** *v.* underline, underscore; stress, emphasize, point out.

**подчин/ение** *n.* subordination, compliance; **—енность** *f.* subordination, dependence; **—енный** *a.* subordinate, inferior; **—ить, —ять** *v.* subordinate, subdue, conquer, subject; **—иться, —яться** *v.* be subordinated; submit, obey, comply, conform, acquiesce, give way.

**подчистить** *see* **подчищать.**

**подчитчик** *m.* (typ.) copy holder.

**подчищать** *v.* clean, erase, rub out; trim.

**подчревный** *a.* (anat.) hypogastric.

**подшабр/ивать, —ить** *v.* scrape, scrape up.

**подшашка** *f.* (min.) sprag, gib.

**подшив/ать** *v.* sew underneath; line; file (papers); **—ка** *f.* lining; filing.

**подшипник** *m.,* **—овый** *a.* bearing, bush, bushing, collar; chock; **п. на камнях** jeweled bearing; **шариковый п.** ball bearing; **—овый щит** bearing housing.

**подшить** *see* **подшивать.**

**подшлифовывать** *v.* grind, polish up.

**подщелачив/ание** *n.* alkalization; **—ать** *v.* alkalize, make alkaline.

**подъезд** *m.* approach, access; porch, entrance, steps; **—ной, —ный** *a.* approach; **—ная аллея** driveway.

**подъезжать** *v.* drive up, approach.

**подъем** *m.* lift, ascent, rise, uplift; hoisting, lifting, raising, elevation;

(mech.) pitch; lever, hand screw, jack; development; (aero.) climb, climbing, taking off; telescope (of lift truck); **высота** —a lift; —**ка** *f.* hoisting, hauling up; —**ник** *m.* hoist, lift, elevator; —**ник-крючок** (foundry) lifting hook; —**но-транспортный** *a.* hoisting and transport.

**подъемн/ый** *a.* lifting, hoisting, raising; swing; traveling (expenses); **п. ворот,** —**ая лебедка** hoisting winch; **п. кран** crane, jenny, derrick; **п. механизм** hoisting mechanism, hoist; **п. мост** drawbridge; **п. противовес** sash weight (of window); **п. стол** lifting platform, lift; —**ая башня** derrick tower; —**ая вагонетка** lift truck, telescoping truck; —**ая заслонка** drop door; —**ая машина** elevator, lift; —**ая мощность,** —**ая сила** supporting power, carrying capacity, lifting force, lifting capacity; (aero.) lift; buoyancy; leverage; **коэффициент** —**ой силы** (aero.) lift coefficient; —**ая таль** hoisting tackle, lifting tackle; —**ая труба** uptaking pipe, riser; —**ое орошение** overhead irrigation; —**ое приспособление,** —**ое устройство** lifting device, hoisting equipment, hoist, crane.

**подъемщик** *m.* lifter.

**подъехать** *see* **подъезжать.**

**подъязычный** *a.* (anat.) sublingual.

**подъярус** *m.* (geol.) substage.

**подымать** *see* **поднимать.**

**подынтегральная функция** (math.) integrand.

**подыск/ать,** —**ивать** *v.* search, seek, try to find, look for something suitable.

**подытож/ивание** *n.* summation; —**и-вать,** —**ить** *v.* sum up, add up, total.

**подышать** *v.* breathe.

**подэтажный штрек** (min.) subdrift.

**поедать** *v.* eat up, devour.

**поезд** *m.* train; —**ить** *v.* travel (a little); —**ка** *f.* trip, journey, voyage; —**ограф** *m.* railway traffic recording apparatus.

**поемный** *a.* flooded, inundated (land).

**поение** *n.* watering (of stock).

**поехать** *v.* go; slide, glide.

**пожалов/ание** *n.* granting; award; —**ать** *v.* grant, confer, present.

**пожалуй** *adv.* maybe, perhaps, very

likely; —**ста** *adv.* please, kindly.

**пожар** *m.* fire, conflagration; **опасность** —a fire risk, fire hazard.

**пожарить** *v.* roast, fry.

**пожарище** *n.* site after a fire.

**пожар/ный** *a.* fire; *m.* fireman; **п. кран** fire plug, fire hydrant; **п. насос,** —**ная машина** fire engine; —**ная опасность** *f.* fire hazard; inflammability.

**пожат/ие** *n.* pressing, squeezing, clasp; —**ь** *see* **пожимать, пожинать.**

**пожелать** *v.* wish.

**пожелт/евший** *a.* yellowed; —**еть** *v.* yellow, get yellow.

**пожертвование** *n.* donation, gift.

**пожива** *f.* gain, profit.

**поживать** *v.* live; feel (well or ill).

**пожив/иться,** —**ляться** *v.* profit (by).

**пожиже** *comp. of* **жидкий, жидко,** thinner, more dilute, weaker.

**пожизненн/ый** *a.* life, lifelong; —**ая рента** annuity.

**пожилой** *a.* middle-aged, elderly.

**пожимать** *v.* press, squeeze.

**пожинать** *v.* reap, harvest.

**пожить** *v.* live, stay.

**пожнивный** *a.* after-harvest.

**поза** *f.* pose, posture, attitude.

**позаботиться** *v.* look after, take care (of), provide (for).

**позавчера** *adv.* the day before yesterday.

**позади** *adv.* behind, back; *prep. gen.* behind.

**позапрошлый** *a.* last but one; **п. год** the year before last.

**позвать** *v.* call, summon.

**позвол/ение** *n.* permission, leave; —**енный** *a.* permitted, allowed; —**ительный** *a.* permissible; —**ить,** —**ять** *v.* permit, allow, let, give leave; make possible; —**яющий** *a.* permitting, permissive.

**позвонить** *v.* ring; (tel.) call up.

**позвонок** *m.* (anat.) vertebra.

**позвоночн/ик** *m.* (anat.) spine, backbone; —**ые,** —**ые животные** (zool.) vertebrates; —**ый** *a.* vertebral; (zool.) vertebrate; —**ый столб** spine, spinal column.

**поздн/ее** *comp. of* **поздно,** later; —**ей-ший** *a.* last, latest, posterior; recent; —**еспелый** *a.* late-ripening; late;

—ий *a.* late, tardy, retarded; —о *adv.* late; —овато *adv.* rather late.

**поздороветь** *v.* become healthy, improve.

**поздрав/ительный** *a.* congratulatory, complimentary; —ить, —лять *v.* congratulate; —ление *n.* congratulation.

**позеленеть** *v.* turn green.

**позем** *m.* manure.

**поземельный** *a.* land, territorial.

**позём/ка** *f.*, —ок *m.* drifting snow.

**позже** *see* позднее.

**позитив** *m.*, —ный *a.*, —ное изображение (phot.) positive image, positive.

**позитрон** *m.*, —ный *a.* positron, positive electron; —ий *m.* positronium.

**позици/я** *f.*, —онный *a.* position, attitude; item (of specification, estimate); —онная война trench fighting.

**позн/аваемость** *f.* perceptivity; —аваемый *a.* cognizable; —авание, —ание *n.* perception, knowledge; conception; —авательный *a.* cognitive; —авать, —ать *v.* know, perceive.

**позоло/та** *f.* gilding, gilt, gold-plating, gold leaf; —тить *v.* gild; —ченный *a.* gilded, gilt, gold-plated.

**позонный** *a.* zone.

**позор** *m.* disgrace, dishonor; —ный *a.* disgraceful, dishonorable, shameful.

**позумент** *m.* trimming, galloon, braid; —ировать *v.* trim.

**позыв** *m.* inclination, urge.

**позывн/ой** *a.* (rad.) call; —ые *pl.* call letters, station identification letters.

**поилка** *f.* fountain; drinking bowl (for stock).

**поимен/но** *adv.* by name; —ный *a.* nominal; —овать *v.* nominate, designate.

**поимка** *f.* catching, capture, seizure.

**по-иному** *adv.* otherwise.

**поиск** *m.*, —овый *a.* search, searching; —и *pl.* search, hunt, quest, pursuit; research; (min.) prospecting, exploration; —ать *v.* seek, search; explore; —овый *a.*, —овая работа prospecting.

**поистине** *adv.* indeed, in truth.

**поить** *v.* give to drink, water (animals).

**пойкилит** *m.* (min.) poikilite (same as bornite); —овый *a.* (petr.) poikilitic.

**пойло** *n.* swill, mash; hogwash.

**пойма** *f.* bottom land, floodplain.

**пойм/анный** *a.* caught, captured; —ать *v.* catch, capture, catch hold (of), seize, trap.

**пойменный** *a.* tidal (marsh); river (terrace).

**пойнт** *m.* (min.) point (pointed steam pipe for thawing ground).

**пойти** *v.* go; come.

**пок** *see* бакаут.

**пока** *conj.* while, so long as, till, until, for the present, as yet; п. что for the time being, meanwhile.

**показ** *m.* show, demonstration, exhibition; на п. for show, on display.

**показание** *n.* reading; indication; showing, exhibiting; (law) deposition, testimony, evidence; affidavit; давать п. *v.* bear witness, testify, depose; замечать п. *v.* take a reading.

**показатель** *m.* indicator, pointer; property, characteristic; rate; (math.) exponent, index; п. качества, качественный п. qualitative index; п. преломления index of refraction; п. степени (math.) exponent, power; это —но it is significant; —ный *a.* exponential; significative; demonstrative, representative, model; —ная функция (math.) exponential; —ное хозяйство model farm.

**показ/ать**, —ывать *v.* show, exhibit, demonstrate, display, set forth; direct, instruct, show how; reveal, disclose; denote, indicate, register; (law) depose, bear witness, testify; —аться *v.* seem, appear, emerge, show itself; —ной *a.* display; —ывание *n.* showing, exhibiting; —ывающий прибор indicator.

**покамест** *see* пока.

**покат/ить** *v.* roll, set rolling; —о *adv.* slopingly, at a slope; —ость *f.* slope, declivity, descent, inclination, grade, pitch; —ый *a.* slope, sloping, slanting, inclining, declivous; (min.) plagihedral; —ый настил chute; —ое место grade.

**покач/ать** *v.* swing, shake a little; pump (a little); —ивание *n.* swinging, tilting; pumping; —ивать *v.* keep swinging lightly; —нуть *v.* shake, unsettle; tilt.

**поки/дать, —нуть** v. forsake, abandon, quit, desert, leave, vacate; **—нутый** a. deserted, vacated; desolate.

**покип/еть** v. boil for a while; **—ятить** v. boil for a while, let boil for a while.

**поклажа** f. load, freight; putting, placing.

**поклон** m. greeting, salute; regards.

**поков/ать** v. forge; **—ка** f. forging; forged piece; **—ки** pl. forge work.

**покоиться** v. rest, lie, repose.

**пок/ой** m. rest, quiet, peace, repose, standstill; state of rest; (bot.) dormancy; (hospital) room; **в —ое** at rest; **масса —оя, масса в состоянии —оя** (nucl.) rest mass; **на —ое** in seclusion, retired; **находящийся в —ое** at rest, idle; **оставить в —ое** v. let alone, let be; **период —оя** quiescent stage; **положение —оя** (mach.) position of rest; **состояние —оя** state of rest; dormant state; **в состоянии —оя** at rest; (bot.) dormant; **точка —оя** point of rest; fulcrum; pause; **трения —оя, трение в —ое** static friction; **угол —оя** angle of repose; **энергия—оя** potential energy.

**покойн/ик** m. corpse; the deceased; **—ицкая** f. mortuary; **—о** adv. quietly, peacefully, restfully; **—ый** a. quiet, calm, peaceful, restful, comfortable; m. deceased, late.

**поколебаться** v. hesitate, waver.

**поколение** n. generation.

**покор/ение** n. subjugation, conquest; **—ить** see **покорять.**

**покормить** v. feed.

**покорн/ость** f. obedience; **—ый** a. submissive, obedient, acquiescent.

**покороб/ившийся, —ленный** a. warped, buckled; **—ить** v. warp, bend.

**покороче** compr. of **коротко,** somewhat shorter.

**покорять** v. subdue; **—ся** v. submit, yield, give in, surrender, aquiesce.

**покос** m., **—ный** a. hay field; haying season; hay-making, mowing; **второй п.** aftermath; **—ившийся** a. lopsided; **—ить** v. slope, slant; mow.

**покошенный** a. slanted, sloping; mowed.

**покоя** gen. of **покой.**

**покоящийся** a. quiescent.

**покрас/ить** v. paint, dye, color; **—ка** f. painting, dyeing; coat (of paint).

**покрасн/евший** a. reddened; **—еть** v. redden, get red.

**покров** m. cover; sheet; mantle, sheath, sheathing; coating, coat (of paint); (lava) bed, flow; **кожный п.** (anat.) integument; **листовой п.** foliage; **твердый п.** (biol.) crust, incrustation.

**покровитель** m. patron, sponsor; **—ственный** a. protective; **—ство** n. patronage, protection, support, sponsorship; **—ствовать** v. patronize, protect; sponsor, support, promote.

**покровн/ый** a. cover, covering; (biol.) integumentary; **—ая залежь** (geol.) blanket deposit; **—ое стекло, —ое стеклышко** (micros.) cover glass; **—ые растения** (agr.) cover crop.

**покрой** m. style, shape, cut.

**покромка** f. selvage.

**покрыв/ало** n. cover, spread, blanket; veil; **—альце** n. (bot.) involucre; **—ание** n. covering, coating, incrustation; **—ать** v. cover; roof, house, shelter; cap; sheathe, envelop, blanket; overspread, overlay, apply, coat, plate (with metal), deposit; overcrust; span, bridge; wipe out (deficit); **—ать лаком** varnish; **—ающий** a. covering; cap (rock); **—ающий слой** coating, coat.

**покрытие** n. covering, coating; (met.) plating, cladding; layer, film, deposit; blanket; insulation (of wire); payment, discharge (of debts, etc.).

**покрыто/жаберные** pl. (zool.) Tectibranchia; **—семенные, —семянные** pl. (bot.) Angiospermae; **—семянный** a. angiospermous.

**покрыт/ый** a. covered, coated, plated; insulated (wire); paid (debt); **п. медью** copper-plated; **—ь** see **покрывать.**

**покрыш/ка** f., **—ечный** a. covering, cover, lid, cap; hood, mantle, jacketing, case; tire tread, casing; **—ечный камень** coping stone.

**покупатель** m. buyer, purchaser; customer, client; **—ный** a. purchasing.

**покуп/ать** v. buy, purchase; **—ка** f. buying, purchasing; purchase; **—ной** a. purchased, bought.

**покусать** v. bite, sting (all over).

**покуситься** see **покушаться.**

**покушать** *v.* eat.

**покуш/аться** *v.* attempt (crime); encroach (on); **—ение** *n.* attempt.

**пол** *m.* floor, ground; sex; **настилать п.** *v.* floor; **сцепление с —ом** (biol.) sex linkage.

**пол—** *see* **полу—**.

**пол.** *abbr.* (**половина**) half.

**пола** *f.* skirt, flap.

**полаг/ать** *v.* think, deem, reckon, suppose, assume, imagine; count, expect; **—ается** it is usual, it is the custom; **—ают** it is assumed, it is claimed; **положим** let us assume; **—аться на** *v.* rely on, depend on; **—ающийся** *a.* due.

**поладить** *v.* come to an understanding, come to terms, agree.

**полб/а** *f.*, **п. спельта** (bot.) spelt (*Triticum spelta*); **воложская п., двузерная п.** emmer (*T. dicoccum*); **—овидный** *a.* speltoid.

**пол/века** *m.* half a century; **—года** *m.* half a year; **—день** *m.* noon, midday, meridian; **—дня** *f.*, **—дневный** *a.* half day; **—дюжины** *f.* half a dozen, six.

**пол/е** *n.* field, ground; margin (of book); brim (of hat); **коэффициент —я** (elec.) field-form factor; **теория —я** field theory; **заметки на —ях** marginal notes.

**полеви/ца** *f.* (bot.) bent grass, red top (*Agrostis*); **—цевые** *pl.* Agrostideae; **—чка** *f.* love grass (*Eragrostis*).

**полевка** *f.* field mouse; meadow mouse, vole; (bot.) myagrum.

**полевод** *m.* field-crop grower; **—ство** *n.* field-crop cultivation.

**полевой** *a.* field; (bot.) arvensis, campestris, agrarius, agrestis, arvalis; **п. камень** (petr.) adinole; petrosilex; **п. шпат** (min.) feldspar.

**полевошпатовый** *a.* (min.) feldspar, feldspathic,

**полег/ание** *n.* lodging, beating down (of grain crop); **—ать** *v.* lodge, beat down; **—аться** *v.* fall; **—лый** *a.* lodged, downed, fallen.

**полег/оньку** *adv.* by easy stages; **—че** *comp. of* **легкий, легко,** somewhat easier.

**полежать** *v.* lie for a while.

**полезащитный** *a.* field-protecting, windbreak.

**полезно** *adv.* usefully; **—сть** *f.* usefulness, utility.

**полезн/ый** *a.* useful, helpful, beneficial, serviceable; available; active, effective; profitable; **п. груз** net load; (aero.) useful load; **п. ток** useful current; **—ая емкость** useful capacity; **—ая лошадиная сила** effective horsepower, actual horsepower, working horsepower; **—ая мощность** (elec.) useful power, useful output; net power; **удельная —ая мощность** specific output; **—ая работа** useful work; efficiency, effect, useful effect; **—ое действие** efficiency, effect, useful effect; duty (of machine); **коэффициент —ого действия** efficiency, performance.

**полей** *m.* (bot.) pennyroyal (*Mentha pulegium*).

**полемизировать** *v.* controvert, dispute.

**поленика** *f.* arctic bramble (*Rubus arcticus*).

**поленница** *f.* stack.

**полено** *n.* log, billet, chump.

**полесье** *n.* wooded district, forest area; polessie (vast alluvial plain).

**полет** *m.* flight; **—ы** *pl.* flying; **п.-соло** solo flight; **высота —a** flying altitude; **длина —a** range (as of a water jet); **—еть** *v.* fly off, take flight, take off.

**полз/ание** *n.* creeping, crawling, sliding; **—ать,** **—ти** *v.* creep, crawl, slide.

**ползун** *m.* slide block, slide bar, slider, slide, runner, slipper, shoe, guide shoe; crosshead (of engine); **—ок** *m.* (elec.) sliding contact, slider; carrier (of lathe).

**ползучесть** *f.* creeping; (met.) creep; **удельная п.** creep rate.

**ползуч/ий** *a.* creeping, crawling; viscous; slow (fever); **п. кран** crawler crane; **—ая деформация** (met.) creep; **—ая скорость** creepage, rate of creepage (of electrolytes); **—ее растение** vine.

**ползучка** *see* **плаун.**

**ползушка** *see* **ползун.**

**ползущий** *a.* creeping; (biol.) benthic, benthonic.

**поли—** *prefix* poly—, many, multiple; **—адельфит** *m.* (min.) polyadelphite (a manganese garnet); —аза *f.* polyase; —алкил— *prefix* polyalkyl—.

**полианит** *m.* (min.) polianite (related to pyrolusite).

**поли/аргирит** *m.* (min.) polyargyrite (a silver-antimony sulfide); —**атомный** *a.* polyatomic; polyhydric (alcohol); —**базит** *m.* (min.) polybasite.

**полив** *m.* watering, irrigation.

**полива** *f.* glaze, glazing, enamel.

**поливал/ка** *f.* watering can; —**ьщик** *m.* sprinkler, irrigator.

**поливариантный** *a.* polyvariant.

**поливать** *v.* water, irrigate; sprinkle, shower, pour on, wet.

**поливинилов/ый спирт** polyvinyl alcohol; —**ые смолы** polyvinyl resins.

**полив/ка** *f.*, —**очный** *a.* watering, irrigation; spraying, wetting; —**очная жидкость** cooling mixture, cooling liquid, coolant; —**ной** *a.* irrigated; requiring irrigation.

**поли/галин** *m.*, —**галовая кислота** polygalin, polygalic acid; —**галит** *m.* (min.) polyhalite; —**галогениды,** — **галоидные соединения** polyhalides; —**гамический** *a.* (biol.) polygamous; —**гексоза** *f.* polyhexose; —**ген** *m.* (biol.) polygene; —**генный** *a.* polygenetic, polygenous, polygenic; — **глюкин** *m.* polyglucin, dextran.

**полигон** *m.* (geom.) polygon; artillery range, firing ground; —**альный** *a.* polygonal; —**ин** *m.* polygonin.

**полиграф** *m.* polygraph (copying machine); **пушистый п.** a bark beetle (*Polygraphus poligraphus*); —**ический** *a.* polygraphic; —**ическая промышленность** printing trade; —**ия** *f.* polygraphy.

**поли/дериваты** *pl.* poly derivatives; —**димит** *m.* (min.) polydymite, nickel-linnaeite; —**ен** *m.* polyene; —**карпический** *a.* (bot.) polycarpic; —**кислота** *f.* poly acid; —**конденсация** *f.* condensation polymerization; —**коричная кислота** polycinnamic acid;—**краз** *m.* (min.) polycrase (related to euxenite); —**кремневая кислота** polysilicic acid; —**кристалл** *m.*, —**кристаллический** *a.* polycrystal; —**ксен** *m.* polyxen (an old synonym for platinum); —**литионит**

*m.* (min.) polylithionite (a lithium mica).

**полимент** *m.* gilding size, gold size.

**полимер** *m.*, —**ное соединение** polymer; —**изат** *m.* polymerization product; —**изация** *f.* polymerization; —**изованный** *a.* polymerized; —**изовать,** —**изоваться** *v.* polymerize; —**ия** *f.* polymerism; —**ный** *a.* polymeric.

**поли/метилен** *m.* polymethylene; —**метр** *m.* polymeter; —**мигнит** *m.* (min.) polymignite;—**миксин** *m.* polymyxin; —**мнит** *m.* polymnite (a dendritic stone).

**полиморф** *m.* polymorph; —**изм** *m.* polymorphism; —**ический,** —**ный** *a.* polymorphous, polymorphic.

**полиневрит** *m.* (med.) polyneuritis.

**полином** *m.*, —**иальный** *a.* (math.) polynomial.

**полин/ялый** *a.* faded, discolored; —**ять** *v.* fade, lose color.

**полиоза** *f.* polyose, polysaccharose.

**полиокси—** *prefix* polyoxy—.

**полиомиелит** *m.* (med.) poliomyelitis.

**полип** *m.* (zool.) polyp; (med.) polypus.

**поли/пентоза** *f.* polypentose; —**пептид** *m.* polypeptide; —**пептин** *m.* polypeptin, circulin; —**плоид** *m.* (biol.) polyploid;—**пняк** *m.* (zool.) polypary; —**подий** *m.* (bot.) polypody (*Polypodium*).

**полипо/медузы** *pl.* (zool.) Polypomedusae; —**образный** *a.* polypoid, polypous.

**полипор/еновая кислота** polyporenic acid; —**ин** *m.* polyporin.

**поли/прен** *m.* polyprene (pure rubber polymer); —**решетка** *f.* composite lattice.

**полирит** *m.* Polirit (abrasive powder containing cerium oxide).

**полировально-шлифовальный станок** honing machine.

**полировальн/ый** *a.* polishing, buffing, burnishing; **п. материал** polish; **п. станок** buffing machine; —**ая бумага** sandpaper; —**ая жидкость** liquid polish; —**ая работа** polishing, buffing.

**полиров/ание** *n.* polishing, buffing, burnishing; —**анный** *a.* polished, burnished; plate (glass); —**ать** *v.* polish, buff, burnish, brighten; —**ка** *f.*

polishing, buffing; etching (with acid); polish, gloss, finish; —**ник,** —**щик** *m.* polisher, burnisher; burnishing stick; —**очная** *f.* polishing room, polishing department; —**очный** *a.* polishing, buffing, burnishing.

**полирующий** *a.* polishing; —**ся** *a.* capable of taking on a polish.

**полис** *m.* policy.

**поли/сахарид** *m.* polysaccharide; —**симметрия** *f.* (min.) polysymmetry; —**соль** *f.* poly salt.

**полиспаст** *m.* polyspast, compound pulley; **крановый п.** crane pulley, crane block.

**поли/стиктин** *m.* polystictin; —**стирол** *m.* polystyrene; —**стихин** *m.* polystichin; —**стихинол** *m.* polystichinol; —**стихоцитрин** *m.* polystichocitrin; —**сульфид** *m.* polysulfide.

**политаппарат** *m.* political administration.

**политерпен** *m.* polyterpene.

**политехни/зация** *f.* introduction of polytechnic education; —**зм** *m.* system of polytechnic education; —**ка** *f.* polytechnics, polytechnology; —**кум** *m.* polytechnic, polytechnic school; —**ческий** *a.* polytechnic, polytechnical.

**политика** *f.* politics; policy.

**поли/тионовая кислота** polythionic acid; —**типный** *a.* polytypic, polytypal.

**политический** *a.* political.

**политой обжиг** (cer.) glost firing.

**политроп/а** *f.,* —**ическая кривая,** —**ная кривая** polytropic curve; —**ический,** —**ный** *a.* polytropic; —**ическое сжатие** polytropic compression; —**ия** *f.* polytropy (a form of polymorphism).

**политура** *f.* polish; varnish; pressboard.

**поли/урия** *f.* (med.) polyuria; —**фаг** *m.* (zool.) polyphage; —**фагия** *f.* polyphagy; —**фенол** *m.* polyphenol; —**филетический** *a.* polyphyletic, convergent.

**полихлор/винил** *m.* polyvinyl chloride; —**ид** *m.* polychloride; —**ированный** *a.* polychlorinated; —**опрен** *m.* polychloroprene.

**полихроизм** *m.* (cryst.) polychroism, pleochroism.

**полихром** *m.* polychrom, esculin; —**атический** *a.* polychromatic, polychromic, multicolored; —**ия** *f.* polychromy; —**овая кислота** polychromic acid.

**полицейский** *a.* police; *m.* policeman.

**поли/циклический** *a.* polycyclic, polynucleated; —**цитемия** *f.* (med.) polycythemia.

**полиция** *f.* police (force).

**поли/эдр** *m.* (geom.) polyhedron; —**эдрический** *a.* polyhedral; —**энергетический** *a.* polyenergetic, heteroenergetic; —**этилен** *m.* polyethylene; —**эфир** *m.,* —**эфирный** *a.* polyester; polyether; —**эфирные смолы** polyester resins;—**ядерный** *a.* polynuclear.

**полк** *m.* (mil.) regiment.

**полка** *f.* shelf, rack; bordering; weeding.

**поллантин** *m.* pollantin (hay-fever antitoxin.)

**поллопас** *m.* Pollopas (synthetic resin).

**поллу/кс,** —**цит** *m.* (min.) pollucite.

**поллюция** *f.* (med.) pollution, spermatorrhea.

**пол/месяца** *f.* half a month; —**минуты** *f.* half a minute.

**полнейший** *a.* fullest, utmost, sheer, utter.

**полнеть** *v.* grow stout, gain weight.

**полно** *adv.* full, completely; *prefix* holo—; —**ватый** *a.* rather full; —**весный** *a.* full-weight; —**габаритный** *a.* full-sized; —**гранник** *m.* (cryst.) holohedron; —**гранный** *a.* holohedral;—**кристаллический** *a.* (petr.) holocrystalline.

**полнокров/ие** *n.* (med.) plethora; —**ный** *a.* full-blooded; (med.) plethoric.

**полно/мочие** *n.* authority, power; (law) proxy; —**осный** *a.* (cryst.) holoaxial; —**правный** *a.* competent; —**размерный** *a.* full-scale.

**полностью** *adv.* completely, totally, fully, utterly; at length, at full length.

**полнота** *f.* fullness; absoluteness, completeness; amplitude; volume (of sound).

**полноценный** *a.* full-value, rich.

**полночь** *f.* midnight.

**полн/ый** *a.* full, complete, absolute; total, gross, overall; solid; stout; deep (sound); high (speed); **п. вес** gross weight; (chem.) combining weight; **п. излучатель** ideal black body; **п. размер** overall dimension; **—ое орошение** (distillation) total reflux; **в —ой мере** fully, completely.

**пол-оборота** *m.* half turn.

**полова** *f.* chaff.

**половик** *m.* mat, floor mat.

**половин/а** *f.* half; **п. на —у** half and half; **п. третьего** half past two (o'clock); **в —у** half as much; **на —у** half, in half; **—ка** *f.*, **—ный** *a.* half; **—ник** *m.* semibeam, semigirder, cantilever; **—чатый** *a.* halved, half, half and half, split; folding; mottled (iron).

**половица** *f.* floor board.

**половодье** *n.* high water; flood time.

**полов/озрелый** *a.* (biol.) adult, mature; **—ой** *a.* sex, sexual, reproductive; floor; **—ая зрелость** puberty; **—ая способность** (physiol.) potency.

**полог** *m.* canopy, cover.

**полог/ий** *a.* slanting, sloping; **п. откос** flat slope; **—ость** *f.* slope, declivity.

**полодув** *m.* chaff fan, chaff blower.

**положение** *n.* position, situation, location, locality, place; state, condition, status, aspect; circumstances, case; stand, conclusion, assumption; **не меняя п.** without disturbing.

**положим** *see* **полагать.**

**положительно** *adv.* positively; decidedly; **—сть** *f.* positiveness.

**положительн/ый** *a.* positive, plus; affirmative; favorable; absolute; **п. знак** (math.) plus, positive sign; **п. ток** (elec.) positive current; **—ое качество** feature, advantage.

**положить** *see* **полагать, класть.**

**полоз** *m.* runner, slide; **—ья** *pl.* runners, slide.

**полозок** *m.* (foundry) sleeker, smoother.

**полок** *m.* loading platform with a charging hole.

**полольн/ик** *m.* hoe; weeding harrow, cultivator; **—ый** *a.* weeding.

**полом/ать** *v.* break, break down; **—ка** *f.* breakdown, breaking down, accident; fracture; rupture.

**полоний** *m.* polonium, Po.

**полос/а** *f.* band; strip, stripe, border; streak; zone, belt; stretch, width;

rail; (cutter) bar; (typ.) page; **п. частот** frequency band; **проводить —ы** *v.* streak; **—атик** *m.* rorqual, finback whale; **—атый** *a.* band; striped, ribbed, striated, streaky; **—атый спектр** band spectrum; **—атое сложение** (geol.) banded structure; **—ка** *f.* band, strip, streak; (biol.) stria.

**полоск/ание** *n.* rinse, rinsing; wash; **—ательный** *a.* rinsing; **—ать** *v.* rinse; gargle (throat); **—ун** *m.* raccoon.

**полос/но-заграждающий** *a.* band-elimination; **—ной, —ный, —овой** *a.* band, strip, bar (metal); **—ной фильтр** (phot.) banded filter; **—нопропускающий** *a.* band-pass; **—нуть** *v.* slash; **—овать** *v.* (met.) make into bars; **—овой спектр** band spectrum; **—овое железо** (flat) bar iron.

**полост/ной** *a.* cavity, cavity-type; **—ь** *f.* hollow, cavity, void; recess, housing, chamber; (cer.) nodule.

**полосчат/ость** *f.* banding, striation; streak (plant disease); **—ый** *a.* banded, banding, striped, streaky, striated; ribbon; lamellar, laminated; **—ая руда** band ore, banded ore.

**полотенце** *n.* towel.

**полотнище** *n.* width, breadth; panel; blade (of saw).

**полотн/о** *n.* linen; (text.) card web; (saw) blade; (railroad) bed; roadbed, roadway; **—яный** *a.* linen.

**полоть** *v.* weed; **—е** *n.* weeding, hoeing.

**полочный** *a.* shelf, shelved; tray (dryer); multiple-hearth (reactor).

**полпути: на п.** halfway.

**пол-сотни** half a hundred, fifty.

**полстина** *f.* (text.) lap.

**полстить** *v.* felt, mat.

**полтора** one and a half, sesqui—; **—ста** a hundred and fifty.

**полу—** *prefix* semi—, demi—, hemi—, half—.

**полуавтомат** *m.* semiautomatic device or machine; **—ический** *a.* semiautomatic.

**полу/антрацит** *m.* semianthracite; **—бархат** *m.* velveteen; **—битуминозный** *a.* semibituminous; **—бочка** *f.* (aero.) half roll; **—валик** *m.* bead;

—**вар** *m.* pitch and tar; —**вареный** *a.* half-cooked, half-digested; soupled (silk); —**ватт** *m.* (elec.) half watt; —**витковый** *a.* half-turn; —**влажный** *a.* semihumid; —**водяной газ** semi-water gas.

**полуволн/а** *f.*, —**овой** *a.* half-wave; **потенциал** —**ы** half-wave potential; —**истый** *a.* (met.) semicorrugated, partly corrugated.

**полу/вращающийся** *a.* semirotatory; —**выведения, период** (nucl.) half-life, half-value period; —**гайка** *f.* half nut; —**гидрат** *m.* semihydrate.

**полугод/ие** *n.* half year; —**ичный, —о-вой** *a.* semiannual, biennial; —**оваль-ный** *a.* half a year old, six months old.

**полугоризонтальный** *a.* inclined, sloping.

**полугранн/ик** *m.* (cryst.) hemihedron; —**ый** *a.* hemihedral.

**полугусеничный** *a.* half-track.

**полуда** *f.* tin, tin plate; tinning.

**полуденный** *a.* midday, noontide, meridian, meridional.

**полу/диаметр** *m.* radius; —**дистанцион-ный** *a.* semiremote; —**дневный** *see* **полдневный**; —**домна** *f.* (met.) low-blast furnace; —**жесткий** *a.* semirigid; —**жесткокрылые** *pl.* (zool.) Hemiptera; —**жидкий** *a.* semiliquid, semi-fluid; —**заводский** *a.* pilot plant; —**закрытый** *a.* semienclosed; —**за-сушливый** *a.* semiarid; —**защищен-ный** *a.* semiprotected; —**зонтик** *m.* (bot.) cyme; —**зонтиковый, —зон-тичный** *a.* cymose;—**известковистый** *a.* semicalcareous; —**карда** *f.* (text.) card breaker; —**кардан** *m.* semi-cardan joint; —**кислый** *a.* semiacid; —**клевер** *m.* (bot.) yellow trefoil (*Medicago lupulina*).

**полукокс** *m.* semicoke; —**ование** *n.* semi-coking, low-temperature carbonization.

**полу/комплект** *m.* subassembly; —**коро-нирующий разряд** (dielectrics) semi-corona discharge; —**котельное желе-зо** (met.) thick plate, boiler plate; —**кристаллический** *a.* semicrystal-line; **продувка** —**крицы** (met.) first refining.

**полукруг** *m.* semicircle; —**лый** *a.* semi-circular; semispherical, half-round; (bot.) cup-shaped.

**полу/лежать** *v.* recline; —**летальный** *a.* semilethal; —**лунный** *a.* half-moon, crescent-shaped, crescent; —**мера** *f.* *f.* half measure; palliative; —**металл** *m.* semimetal; —**металлический** *a.* (min.) submetallic; —**навесной** *a.* semimounted; —**нержавеющий** *a.* (met.) semistainless; —**непрерывный** *a.* semicontinuous; —**непроницаемый** *a.* semitight.

**полуночный** *a.* midnight; northern.

**полу/обмена, период** (chem.) half-time of exchange; —**оборот** *m.* half turn; **на** —**оборот** halfway around; —**обработанный** *a.* semifinished; semiprocessed; —**окатанность** *f.* subangularity; —**окружность** *f.* semi-circumference, semicircle; —**опал** *m.* (min.) semiopal, common opal; —**осевая шестерня** differential side gear.

**полуостров** *m.* peninsula.

**полу/ось** *f.* semiaxis; —**отделанный** *a.* semifinished, rough-finished; unfin-ished (furniture); —**открытый** *a.* semienclosed; —**параболический** *a.* semiparabolic; —**паралич** *m.* (med.) hemiplegia; —**перекрестный** *a.* quar-tertwist (belt); —**переменный** *a.* semivariable;—**период** *m.* half period, half-cycle; semioscillation; (nucl.) half-life; —**период распада** half-life; —**период реакции обмена** (chem.) half-time of exchange; —**пиритная плавка** (met.) semipyritic smelting; —**подкисленный** *a.* semiacidified; —**полба** *f.* (bot.) emmer (*Triticum dicoccum*); —**портальный кран** semi-gantry crane; —**потайная головка** (met.) button head; —**призма** *f.* (cryst.) hemiprism; —**прицеп** *m.* semitrailer.

**полупровод/ник** *m.*, —**никовый** *a.* (elec.) semiconductor; —**никовый триод, —никовый усилитель** transistor; —**ящий** *a.* semiconducting.

**полу/продукт** *m.* half-finished product, semifinished material, intermediate product; —**прозрачный** *a.* semitrans-parent, translucent; —**проницаемый**

*a.* semipermeable; —просвечивающий *a.* semitranslucent; —пространство *n.* half space; —прямая *f.* (math.) half line; —пустынный *a.* semiarid; —пустыня *f.* semiarid land, near desert; —равнина *f.* rolling country; —размах *m.* semispan, amplitude; —разрез *m.* semisectional view; —раковистый *a.* subconchoidal; —распад *m.* (nucl.) half-decay, half-disintegration; период —распада half-life; —расплавленный *a.* semifused, semi-molten.

**полусварить** *v.* parboil, partially boil.

**полусвет** *see* **полутень.**

**полусернист/ый** *a.* sesquisulfide (of); (—ous) sulfide; —ая медь cuprous sulfide; —ое соединение sesquisulfide.

**полу/смертельный** *a.* half-lethal; —смола *f.* resinoid; —спекшийся *a.* semisintered, partly caked; —сталь *f.* (met.) semisteel.

**полустанок** *m.* small station, flag station.

**полу/стационарный** *a.* semiportable; —сток *m.* semiflow; —стык *m.* half joint; —суперфосфат *m.* semisuperphosphate; —суточный *a.* semidiurnal; —сухой *a.* semiarid; moist; —сфера *f.* hemisphere; —сферический *a.* hemispherical; —тарифный *a.* half-rate; —твердый *a.* semisolid; medium hard; —теневой *a.*, —тень *f.* (optics) penumbra; —толщина *f.* half-thickness; —тоновый *a.* half-tone.

**полутора—** *prefix* sesqui—; —окись *f.* sesquioxide.

**полуторно—** *prefix* sesqui—; —сернистый *a.* sesquisulfide (of); —углекислая соль sesquicarbonate; —угленатриевая соль sodium sesquicarbonate; —хлористый *a.* sesquichloride (of); —хромовокислая соль sesquichromate.

**полуторн/ый** *a.* one and one half; sesqui—; —ая окись sesquioxide; —ая соль sesquisalt; —ая углекислая соль sesquicarbonate.

**полу/травеллер** *m.* semi-gantry crane; —трубчатый *a.* semitubular; —угловатость *f.* (geol.) subangularity; —угловатый *a.* subangular; —фабрикат *m.* semifinished product,

semimanufactured product, intermediate product; —фарфор *m.* semiporcelain; —форма *f.* half mold.

**полухлорист/ый** *a.* sesquichloride (of); (—ous) chloride; —ая медь cuprous chloride; —ая сера sulfur monochloride; —ое олово stannous chloride.

**полу/целлюлоза** *f.* hemicellulose; —целый *a.* half-integral; half-integer (momentum); —целое число half-integer; —центр *m.* half center; —циркуль *m.* semicircle.

**получаем/ый** *a.* resulting, resultant; received; —ая энергия (elec.) input.

**получасовой** *a.* half hourly.

**получ/атель** *m.* recipient, assignee; —ать *v.* receive, obtain, get, secure; derive, extract; produce, generate; take in; gain, win; —ать обратно recover, get back; —аться *v.* be received; result; —аться в результате result, ensue, be the consequence.

**получен/ие** *n.* receipt, reception, receiving, getting, obtaining; derivation, extraction; production, output, crop; generation; п. вновь, обратное п. recovery; —ный *a.* received, obtained, resulting.

**получистый** *a.* semifinished; partly contaminated.

**получить** *see* **получать.**

**получше** *comp. of* **хороший, хорошо,** somewhat better.

**полу/шар** *m.*, —шарие *n.* hemisphere; —ширина *f.* half width; half thickness (of absorber).

**полушник** *m.* (bot.) quillwort (*Isoetes*).

**полушубок** *m.* short sheepskin coat.

**полу/элемент** *m.* (elec.) half cell; —эмпирический *a.* semiempirical.

**пол/фунта** *m.* half a pound; —часа *m.* half an hour.

**пол/ый** *a.* hollow, tubular; bare, uncovered, open; —ая вена (anat.) vena cava; —ая вода high water in spring, spring freshets.

**полын/ь** *f.*, —ный *a.* (bot.) wormwood (*Artemisia*); горькая п. common wormwood (*A. absinthium*); обыкновенная п. mugwort (*A. vulgaris*); —ная водка, —новка *f.* absinthe (liqueur); —ное масло oil of wormwood.

**полынья** *f.* polynia (area of open water in ice).

**полыхать** *v.* blaze.

**польдер** *m.* polder, low fertile land.

**польз/а** *f.* use, good, profit, benefit, advantage; **извлекать—у из** *v.* benefit by.

**пользов/ание** *n.* use; treatment, cure; **—ать** *v.* treat, doctor, attend (to); **—аться** *v.* make use (of), put to use, employ, profit (by).

**польский** *a.* Polish; **Польша** Poland.

**полюс** *m.* pole, terminal; **переключатель —ов** (elec.) pole changer, pole-changing switch; **поверхность —а** polar surface; **шаг —ов** (elec.) pole pitch.

**полюсн/ый** *a.* polar, pole; **п. башмак, п. наконечник** (elec.) pole shoe, pole piece; **п. зажим** pole terminal; **п. магнитный поток** polar flux; **п. стержень** contact bar; **п. шаг, —ое деление** pole pitch.

**полюсо/магнитный** *a.* (min.) polarmagnetic; **—определитель** *m.* (elec.) polarity indicator.

**поля** *gen. and pl. of* **поле.**

**поляк** *m.* Pole, Polish citizen.

**поляна** *f.* forest glade.

**поляра** *f.* (math.) polar.

**поляриз/атор** *m.*, **—ационная призма** (optics) polarizer; **—ационный** *a.*, **—ация** *f.*, **—ование** *n.* polarization, polarizing; **—ируемый, —уемый, —ующийся** *a.* polarizable; **—ованный** *a.* polarized; **—овать** *v.* polarize; **—ующий** *a.* polarizing.

**поляри/метр** *m.* (optics) polarimeter; **—скоп** *m.* polariscope; **—метрия** *f.* polarimetry; **—скопия** *f.* polariscopy.

**полярность** *f.* polarity.

**полярн/ый** *a.* polar; arctic; **п. пояс** frigid zone; **—ая звезда** North Star, Polaris; **—ая ось** (cryst.) polar axis; **—ая связь** polar bond; **—ое сияние** aurora polaris, aurora; **—ое соединение** polar compound.

**поляро/графический** *a.* (electroanalysis) polarographic; **—графия** *f.* polarography, polarographic analysis; **—ид** *m.* Polaroid (light-polarizing material).

**пом—** *abbr.* (**помощник**) assistant.

**помад/а** *f.* pomade, salve, ointment; **—ить** *v.* put on salve, grease.

**помаз/ать, —ывать** *v.* anoint, smear, apply; oil, grease; **—ок** *m.* (foundry) bosh, swab.

**помарка** *f.* blot, blur.

**помело** *n.* hearth broom.

**поменьше** *comp. of* **мало, малый,** somewhat smaller, less, a little less.

**поменяться** *v.* exchange.

**померанец** *m.* (bot.) bitter orange (*Citrus aurantium*).

**померанцев/ые** *pl.* (bot.) Aurantiaceae; **—ый** *a.* bitter orange, orange; **—ая горькая, —ая корка** Sevilla orange, curacao orange, bitter orange peel; **—ое дерево** osage orange (*Maclura*); **—ое масло** bitter orange oil.

**померз/лый** *a.* frostbitten; **—нуть** *v.* be frostbitten; be killed by frost.

**померкл/ый** *a.* dimmed, tarnished; **—нуть** *v.* grow dim, get tarnished; be eclipsed, disappear.

**поместительн/ость** *f.* roominess; **—ый** *a.* capacious, roomy, spacious.

**поместить** *see* **помещать.**

**поместн/о** *adv.* locally, by places, by countries; **—ый** *a.* local.

**поместье** *n.* domain; land.

**помесь** *f.* cross, cross-breed, hybrid; adulteration.

**помесячн/о** *adv.* per month, once a month; **—ый** *a.* monthly.

**помет** *m.* dung, excrement, droppings, manure; litter, brood.

**помет/ить** *see* **помечать; —ка** *f.* mark, note.

**помех/а** *f.* interference, disturbance, hindrance, impediment, obstacle; difficulty, trouble, kink; **—и** *pl.* (rad.) interference, static, noise; **атмосферные —и** (rad.) static; **служить —ой** *v.* hinder, stand in the way, impede; **создавать —и** *v.* disturb, perturb; **—остойкий, —оустойчивый** *a.* noiseproof, staticproof; anti-jamming, interference-free; **—офильтр** *m.* noise filter.

**помеч/ать** *v.* mark, label; date; **—енный** *a.* marked, labeled.

**помеш/анный** *a.* mad, insane; *m.* madman, maniac; **—ательство** *n.* madness, mania; **—ать** *v.* mix, stir, agitate; be in the way, prevent (from); **—аться** *v.* be obsessed (by); go mad;

—**ивание** *n.* mixing, stirring, agitation; —**ивать** *v.* stir occasionally.

**помещать** *v.* place, put, set, install, insert; set up, establish, locate; accommodate, arrange; (com.) invest; —**ся** *v.* be placed (in), sit, rest, fit.

**помещение** *n.* room, space, compartment, chamber; premises, place, accommodation; putting, setting, installation, insertion; (com.) investment.

**помещик** *m.* landowner, landlord.

**помидор** *m.* tomato (*Lycopersicum esculentum*).

**помимо** *adv.* apart; besides, except; unknown (to), without a person's knowledge; **п. того** moreover.

**поминать** *v.* mention.

**поминутно** *adv.* every minute.

**помириться с** *v.* be reconciled to.

**помнить** *v.* remember, keep in mind.

**помногу** *adv.* much, in large quantities.

**помнож/ать**, —**ить** *v.* multiply; —**ение** *n.* multiplication; —**енный** *a.* multiplied.

**помогать** *v.* help, assist, aid; relieve, ease; favor, promote.

**по-моему** *adv.* in my opinion; in my way.

**помо/и** *pl.* slops, swill; —**йная яма** sink, drain pit; —**йница** *f.* wash hole; (min.) lade hole, drain.

**помокнуть** *v.* soak for a time.

**помол** *m.* grist; milling, grinding; (paper) beating.

**помолог** *m.* (agr.) pomologist; —**ия** *f.* pomology.

**помоложе** *comp.* of **молодой**, somewhat younger.

**помор/ский** *a.* seashore, coast; —**ье** *n.* seashore, coast, coastal region.

**помост** *m.* raised platform, stage, dais, gallery, scaffold, bridging.

**помоха** *f.* pomokha (haze of dust from deflation over chernozem).

**помочь** *see* **помогать.**

**помощ/ник** *m.* helper, assistant; —**ь** *f.* help, assistance, aid; relief; favor, service; —**ью, при —и, с —ью** with the help (of), by means (of); **оказать —ь, подавать —ь** *v.* help, assist; **первая —ь, скорая —ь** first aid.

**помпа** *f.* pump; —**ж** *m.* pumpage.

**помпейский красный** Pompey red, ferric oxide.

**помпельмус** *see* **грейпфрут.**

**помут/ить** *v.* make turbid; —**иться** *v.* become turbid, get cloudy; get dim, blear; blur; —**нение** *n.* turbidity, cloudiness; dimness, blur; —**нение воздуха** atmospheric turbidity; **испытание на —нение** cloud test; **точка —нения** (petroleum) cloud point.

**помыл/ивать**, —**ить** *v.* soap, lather; —**ки** *pl.* suds, lather.

**помы/сел**, —**сл** *m.* thought, idea, notion, intention, inclination; —**слить**, —**шлять** *v.* think (of), intend, design; —**шление** *n.* thought, idea.

**помянуть** *see* **поминать.**

**помятый** *a.* crumpled, bent, dented.

**понадобиться** *v.* be necessary.

**понапрасну** *adv.* in vain.

**по-настоящему** *adv.* in earnest; in the right way, properly.

**по-нашему** *adv.* in our opinion; in our way, according to our custom.

**пондеромоторное притяжение** (elec.) pondermotive force.

**поневоле** *adv.* against one's will, by force, perforce, necessarily.

**понедельн/ик** *m.* Monday; —**о** *adv.*, —**ый** *a.* weekly, per week.

**по-немецки** *adv.* in German; **говорить п.** *v.* speak German.

**понемногу** *adv.* little by little, gradually.

**понести** *v.* carry; conceive.

**понижать** *v.* reduce, lower, let down, relieve (pressure); depress (a constant); (elec.) step down; —**ся** *v.* fall, go down, drop, lower, diminish.

**понижающий** *a.* reducing, depressing (constant); (elec.) step-down; **п. трансформатор** step-down transformer; —**ся** *a.* falling, dropping, downward.

**пониже** *comp.* of **низкий, низко**, somewhat lower, a little below; —**ние** *n.* reduction, lowering, drop (in pressure, temperature), decrease, fall, falling down, subsiding, settling; depression (of constant); (elec.) stepping down; **период —ния** period of decline; —**нный** *a.* reduced, lowered, depressed.

**понизит/ель** *m.* reducer; *see also* транс-
форматор-понизитель; **п. твердости**
softening solution for boring in rock;
—**ельный** *a.* reducing; (elec.) step-
down; —**ельный редуктор** reduction
gear; —**ь** *see* **понижать**.

**поник/ать**, —**нуть** *v.* droop, wilt.

**поним/ание** *n.* understanding, comprehension, conception; sense, intelligence; —**ать** *v.* understand, comprehend, realize, recognize; grasp, seize;
penetrate; gather.

**понит** *m.* (min.) ponite (a ferriferous
rhodochrosite).

**по-новому** *adv.* in a new way.

**понор** *m.* (geol.) sink hole, sink, swallow
hole.

**понос** *m.* (med.) diarrhea, dysentery.

**поношенный** *a.* shabby, threadbare,
worn.

**понравиться** *v.* appeal (to).

**понселет** *m.* poncelet, Poncelet wheel
(undershot wheel).

**понсировка** *f.* rubbing with pumice.

**понсо** *n.* ponceaux (a group of dyes).

**понт** *m.* bridge (in oil well).

**понтианак** *m.* pontianac (copal-type
resin).

**понтический** *a.* (geol.) Pontiac.

**понтия** *f.* (glass) pontil, punty.

**понтол** *m.* pontol (alcohol denaturant).

**понтон** *m.*, —**ный** *a.* pontoon; —**ный
кран** floating crane.

**понтоп** *m.* Pontop (rubberized cloth).

**понудитель** *m.* compeller; —**ный** *a.*
compelling, coercive, impellent.

**пону/дить**, —**ждать** *v.* compel, force,
drive, impel, urge, press; —**ждение**
*n.* compulsion, coercion.

**понукать** *v.* drive on, urge on, spur.

**понур** *m.* front part of dam spillway.

**поныне** *adv.* until now, up to the present.

**понырь** *f.* couch grass (*Triticum repens*).

**понят/ие** *n.* conception, idea; —**ливость**
*f.* understanding, comprehension; —
**но** *adv.* clearly, plainly, intelligibly;
naturally, of course; —**ность** *f.* clearness, intelligibility; —**ный** *a.* clear,
intelligible, comprehensible, understandable, apparent; —**ый** *a.* understood; —**ь** *see* **понимать**.

**поодаль** *adv.* at some distance, removed.

**поодиночке** *adv.* one by one, singly.

**поопалит** *see* **пуналит**.

**по-отрядно** *adv.* (aero.) by flights.

**поотсыреть** *v.* grow slightly damp.

**поочередн/о, по очереди** *adv.* by turns,
alternately; —**ый** *a.* alternate.

**поощр/ение** *n.* encouragement, incentive; promotion; —**ительный** *a.* encouraging, stimulating, inspiring; —
**ить**, —**ять** *v.* encourage, stimulate,
excite, spur, incite, promote, favor,
advance.

**попад/ание** *n.* hit; entry; —**ать** *v.* hit,
strike, get into; fall; **как попало**
carelessly, anyhow, haphazardly; **куда попало** at random, anywhere;
—**аться** *v.* get into, be caught, fall
into.

**попарно** *adv.* in pairs; **связывать п.** *v.*
couple.

**попасть** *see* **попадать**.

**поперек** *adv.* across, crosswise; at right
angles to; **разрезание п.** cross-cutting.

**попеременн/о** *adv.* by turns, in turn,
alternately; **п.-возвратное движение**
alternate motion, reciprocating motion; —**ый** *a.* alternate; alternative.

**попереч/ина** *f.* cross beam, cross bar,
cross tie, cross piece, cross arm, tie
beam; crosshead (of engine); boom,
jib (of crane); —**ка** *f.* crosscut saw;
—**ник** *m.* diameter; girth; cross section; —**но** *adv.* transversely; —**норо-
тые** *pl.* (zool.) Plagiostomi, Selachii;
—**но-строгальный станок** shaper,
horizontal shaping machine.

**попереч/ый** *a.* transverse, cross, dia-
metrical; cross-sectional; lateral; **п.
анкер** cross tie; **п. разрез**, —**ое сечение** cross section; **площадь** —**ого
сечения** sectional area; —**ая балка**,
—**ая связь** *see* **поперечина**; —**ая
пила** crosscut saw; —**ая распорка**
cross piece; —**ая связь** crosslink;
**образование** —**ых связей** crosslinking,
crosslinkage; —**ая сила** transverse
force, shearing force; —**ое расширение** lateral expansion; —**ое ребро**
tie; —**ые нити ткани** (text.) weft;
—**ые схватки** cross bracing; **в** —**ом
направлении** across.

**поперхнуться** *v.* choke.

**попеч/ение** *n.* care, solicitude; —**итель**
*m.* trustee, guardian.

**поплав/ковый, —очный** *a.* floating, float; **п. клапан** float valve, ball valve; **п. кран** ball cock; **п. шар** ball float; **—ковая камера** float chamber (of carburetor); **—ок** *m.* float, buoy; (aero.) pontoon; **уровень —ка** float level.

**поплатиться** *v.* pay, have to pay (for).

**поплевка** *f.* (zool.) fly (*Musca vomitoria*).

**поплин** *m.* (text.) poplin.

**поповник** *m.* (bot.) ox-eye daisy (*Chrysanthemum leucanthemum*).

**пополам** *adv.* in two, in half, by halves; **делить п.** *v.* divide in two, halve.

**поползушка** *f.* (elec.) shoe, slide contact.

**пополн/ение** *n.* supplement; replenishment, enrichment, addition, completing; reinforcement, replacement; **—итель** *m.* replenisher; **—ить, —ять** *v.* supplement, add, fill up, refill, replenish; enrich, widen, enlarge.

**пополу/дни** *adv.* in the afternoon, post meridiem (р.м.); **—ночи** *adv.* after midnight, ante meridiem (а.м.).

**по-польски** *adv.* in Polish; (speak) Polish.

**попона** *f.* (horse) blanket.

**попортить** *v.* spoil.

**поправ/имый** *a.* remediable, corrigible, repairable; **—ить, —лять** *v.* correct, rectify; repair, mend, readjust, put in order; **—иться, —ляться** *v.* recover, get better, improve; correct oneself; **—ка** *f.* correction, rectification; allowance; modification, alteration, amendment; repair, repairing, readjustment; recovery (from illness); **—ка на** correction for; **—ка на запаздывание** lag correction; **коэффициент —ки, —очный множитель** correction factor; **—ление** *n.* correction; recovery; **—очный** *a.* correction.

**по-прежнему** *adv.* as before, as usual.

**попрек/ать, —нуть** *v.* reproach, reprove.

**поприще** *n.* area, field; profession, course.

**попробовать** *see* **пробовать.**

**попросту** *adv.* simply.

**попрыск/ать, —ивать** *v.* sprinkle.

**попугай** *m.* (zool.) parrot.

**популин** *m.* populin, salicin benzoate.

**популяр/изация** *f.* popularization; **—и-зировать** *v.* popularize; **—ность** *f.* popularity; **—ный** *a.* popular.

**популяция** *f.* (biol.) population.

**попус/кать, —тительствовать, —тить** *v.* suffer, let, permit, allow; **—тительство** *n.* sufferance, toleration.

**попут/ник** *see* **подорожник; —но** *adv.* in passing, by the way; incidentally; **—ный** *a.* passing; by-product (manufacture); fair (wind); running (commentary); **—ная добыча** (met.) side recovery; **—чик** *m.* fellow traveler.

**попущение** *n.* sufferance, permission.

**попыт/ать, —аться** *v.* try, attempt, undertake; **—ка** *f.* trial, attempt, endeavor, venture.

**пора** *f.* pore.

**пор/а** *f.* time, season, period; it is time (to); **п. итти** it is time to go; **давно п.** it is high time; **—ой, —ою** from time to time, now and then, occasionally; **вечерней —ой** in the evening; **глухая п.** slack season, off season; **до —ы** up to a certain time; **до —ы до времени** up to a given moment; **до каких пор** how long? until when? **до сих пор** until now, hitherto; **до тех пор, пока** until; **с тех пор** since then, since that day; **с этих пор** hence, in future, from now on.

**поработать** *v.* work (for a certain time).

**порабощение** *n.* enslavement, subjugation.

**поравнять** *v.* equate, make equal; **—ся** *v.* equal; come up to.

**пораж/ать** *v.* strike; surprise, astonish; **—аться** *v.* be surprised; **—ающий** *a.* harmful, injurious; **—ение** *n.* blow; defeat; (med.) affection, disease; **—енный** *a.* surprised, astonished; struck; affected; infested (with pests).

**пораз—** *double prefix for verbs, see under* **раз—, рас—.**

**поразительн/о** *adv.* wonderfully, astonishingly; it is remarkable; **—ость** *f.* strikingness; **—ый** *a.* wonderful, astonishing, striking.

**поразить** *see* **поражать.**

**поран/ение** *n.* wound; **—енный** *a.* wounded; **—ить** *v.* wound.

**пораньше** *adv.* as early as possible.

**порас—** *see* **пораз—.**

**пораст/ать, —и** *v.* grow over (with).

**порв/анный** *a.* torn, broken; —**ать** *v.* tear, break.

**поребрик** *m.* border, border stone.

**пореде́лый** *a.* grown thinner.

**порез** *m.* cut, slash, wound; —**ать** *v.* cut; —**ная трава** *see* **поречник.**

**порей** *m.* (bot.) leek (*Allium porrum*).

**поречник** *m.* (bot.) athamanta; mountain parsley (*Peucedanum oreoselinum*).

**пореч/ный** *a.* riverside; —**ье** *n.* river country.

**порист/ость** *f.* porosity; —**ый** *a.* porous, spongy, blown, vesicular, cellular, pitted; timely, ready; —**ая масса** porous material; —**ая перепонка,** —**ая стенка** porous diaphragm.

**пориц/ание** *n.* blame, censure; —**ать** *v.* blame, censure, reprove.

**поркупайн** *m.* porcupine.

**поровну** *adv.* equally, in equal parts.

**поровняться** *see* **поравняться.**

**поровый** *a.* pore; interstitial (water).

**порог** *m.* threshold; cut-off; baffle, baffle plate, dam, altar (of furnace); **топочный п.** baffle; —**и реки** rapids.

**порогамия** *f.* (bot.) porogamy.

**порогов/ый** *a.* threshold; cut-off; baffle; **п. вход** cut-off input; —**ая величина,** —**ое значение** threshold value, threshold; —**ая энергия** threshold energy, threshold.

**пород/а** *f.* breed, stock, race, strain, species, variety, kind; (geol.) rock; **безрудная п., пустая п.** barren rock, overburden, waste rock, rubbish, debris; **горная п.** rock; **п.-коллектор** *m.* container-rock, reservoir rock.

**породиновый** *a.* porodic, amorphous.

**породистый** *a.* thoroughbred, pedigreed.

**породо/образующий** *a.* rock-forming; —**составляющие** *pl.* rock constituents.

**порождать** *v.* produce, generate, engender, give rise (to); breed, give birth (to).

**порожистый** *a.* full of rapids.

**порожн/ий** *a.* empty; **п. ход** (mach.) idling, running without load; —**як** *m.* empty (car); —**яком** *adv.* empty.

**порозность** *see* **пористость.**

**порознь** *adv.* separately, asunder, apart, severally; **вместе и п.** all and sundry.

**порой** *see under* **пора.**

**порок** *m.* flaw, blemish, defect, imperfection, fault, unsound spot; vice, crime; taint (in heredity).

**порометр** *m.* porosimeter.

**порос/енок** *m.* young pig; —**иться** *v.* farrow.

**поросл/ь** *f.* verdure, shoots; —**и** *pl.* scrub, brush, undergrowth.

**порост** *m.* (bot.) sea weed (*Fucus*).

**поросший** *a.* overgrown (with).

**порося/та** *pl.* young pigs; —**чий** *a.* pig.

**пороть** *v.* rip, undo.

**порох** *m.*, —**овой** *a.* powder, gunpowder; **бездымный п.** smokeless powder; **пироксилиновый п., хлопчатобумажный п.** pyroxylin, guncotton; **черный п.** gunpowder; —**овидный** *a.* powdery, powdered; —**овница** *f.* powder flask; —**острельная работа** blasting.

**пороч/ить** *v.* defame, discredit; —**ный** *a.* defective, faulty; fallacious; depraved; vicious (circle).

**порош/ечный** *a.* powder, powdered; —**инка** *f.* grain of powder, grain of dust.

**порошко/ватый,** —**видный,** —**образный** *a.* powdery, powder-like, powdered, pulverulent; **металлургия** —**образных металлов** powder metallurgy.

**порошок** *m.* powder; **п. от насекомых** insect powder, insecticide.

**порою** *see under* **пора.**

**порпе/зит,** —**цит** *m.* (min.) porpezite, palladium gold.

**порпорино** *n.* (met.) porporino (imitation of gold); porporino, hemato-porphyrin.

**порсугели** *pl.* porsugeli (coneless mud volcanos).

**порт** *m.* port, harbor; porthole.

**порт.** *abbr.* (**португальский**) Portuguese.

**портал** *m.* portal, doorway; gantry (of crane); —**ьно-фрезерный станок** plano-milling machine; —**ьный** *a.* portal, doorway; gantry (crane).

**портативн/ость** *f.* portability; —**ый** *a.* portable, handy.

**портвейн** *m.* port (wine).

**портер** *m.*, —**ный** *a.* porter (beer); —**ная приправа** porter-wort.

**портик** *m.* portico.

**портить** *v.* spoil, damage, waste, impair;

—ся *v.* spoil, be damaged, get out of order; decay, rot.

**портландский** *a.* (geol.) Portland; **п. цемент** Portland cement.

**портн/ой** *m.* tailor; —**яжная мышца** (anat.) sartorius.

**портов/ый** *a.* port, harbor; **п. грузчик** longshoreman; —**ые деньги** harbor dues.

**Порто-Рико** Puerto Rico.

**портостат** *m.* (aero.) portostat.

**порто-франко** *n.* free port.

**портплед** *m.* hold-all, carry-all.

**портрет** *m.* portrait.

**портсигар** *m.* cigar or cigarette case.

**Портсмут** Portsmouth.

**Португалия** Portugal.

**португальск/ий** *a.* Portuguese; —**ое масло** Portugal oil, sweet orange flower oil.

**портулак** *m.* (bot.) purslane (*Portulaca oleracea*); —**овые** *pl.* Portulacaceae.

**портфель** *m.* portfolio, briefcase.

**портьера** *f.* curtain.

**портящийся** *a.* putrefying, decaying, perishable.

**порубежный** *see* **пограничный.**

**порубка** *f.* cutting down, felling; illegal felling of timber.

**порука** *f.* surety, pledge, security, guarantee, bail; **круговая п.** mutual responsibility.

**по-русски** *adv.* in Russian; (speak) Russian.

**поручать** *v.* commission, commit, entrust (with), charge (with).

**поручейник** *m.* (bot.) water parsnip (*Sium*).

**поручение** *n.* commission, charge; mission, errand; message.

**поруч/ень** *m.* handrail, guardrail; handle; **ременный п.** hand strap; —**ни** *pl.* railing.

**поручит/ель** *m.* guarantor, bondsman; —**ельство** *n.* guarantee, bond, bail; —**ь** *see* **поручать.**

**поручневая скоба** handle.

**порфиновое кольцо** porphin ring.

**порфир** *m.* (petr.) porphyry.

**порфира** *m.* purple; *f.* (bot.) porphyra.

**порфир/изация** *f.* porphyrization, pulverization; —**ин** *m.* porphyrin (decomposition product of hematin); porphyrine (alkaloid from *Alstonia*

*constricta*); —**ит** *m.* (petr.) porphyrite; —**ический,** —**овый** *a.* porphyritic; purple; —**област** *m.* porphyroblast; —**областический** *a.* porphyroblastic; —**овая кислота** porphyric acid, euxanthone; —**овидный,** —**оподобный** *a.* (petr.) porphyritic, porphyraceous; —**оид** *m.* porphyroid (a metamorphic rock); —**оксин** *m.* porphyroxine.

**порхать** *v.* flap, flutter.

**порцелланит** *m.* (petr.) porcellanite, porcelain jasper.

**порционн/о** *adv.* in portions, in batches, in small amounts; —**о-периодического действия** repeated-batch (dryer); —**ый** *a.* portion, batch, lot; —**ое испытание** batch testing.

**порция** *f.* portion, batch, lot.

**порч/а** *f.* damage, injury, breakage, waste; spoiling, putrefaction; deterioration, wear and tear; getting out of order, trouble; defect, flaw; —**енный** *a.* damaged, injured; spoiled, putrefied, decomposed, tainted (meat).

**поршень** *m.* piston, plunger (of pump).

**поршнев/ой,** —**ый** *a.* piston; **п. насос** piston pump; **п. палец** piston pin; **п. пресс** power press; **п. привод** piston drive; **п. стержень, п. шток** piston rod; —**ая машина** reciprocating engine; —**ое кольцо** piston ring; —**ое парораспределение** piston valve gear.

**порыв** *m.* gust (of wind), puff, fit, inrush; **в —, под влиянием** —a on impulse; —**истость** *f.* gustiness; —**истый** *a.* gusty, violent, impetuous; percussive; jerky, irregular.

**порыж/евший,** —**елый** *a.* grown rust-colored, reddish, brownish.

**порядков/ый** *a.* ordinal; **п. номер,** —**ое число** ordinal number; number in a series, spec. atomic number; —**ое числительное** ordinal.

**поряд/ок** *m.* order, rank; form; sequence, series, succession, course, arrangement; (biol.) order; (shut-down or start-up) procedure; **п. величины** order of magnitude; **п. реакции** order of reaction; **в полном** —**ке** in running order; **величина** —**ка** magnitude of the order (of); **изменение** —**ка** rearrangement; **на два п.** by a factor of

10²; не в —ке out of order, irregular; обыкновенным —ком ordinarily; по —ку in order, in succession, one after the other; делать по —ку *v.* proceed in order, do things systematically; приводить в п. *v.* set in order, set right, arrange, adjust; смотреть за —ком *v.* keep order; это в —ке вещей that is as it should be, that is normal.

порядочн/о *adv.* a good deal; pretty well; honestly; —ый *a.* honest, respectable, decent; sizable, considerable (price).

посад *m.* suburb.

посадить *v.* set down; make one sit down; (agr.) plant.

посадк/а *f.* setting, fitting, fit; (agr.) planting; (aero.) landing; checkered brickwork; (min.) artificial caving in of roof; глухая п., тугая п. tight fit, close fit; итти на —у *v.* make a landing, land; ячейка —и checker opening.

посадочн/ый *a.* setting; (aero.) landing; (agr.) planting; п. круг (aero.) circle marker; —ая машина machine for caving in roof of mine; —ая площадка landing field; —ое приспособление landing gear.

посасывать *v.* suck a little, draw in at intervals.

посатижы *pl.* gas (pipe) pliers.

посвеж/елый *a.* grown fresh, fresh; —еть *v.* grow fresh, get fresh.

посвет/ить *v.* give some light; —леть *v.* grow light.

по-своему *adv.* in one's own way.

посвящ/ать, посвятить *v.* devote, give up (to); dedicate; —ение *n.* devotion; dedication; —енный *a.* devoted; dedicated.

посев *m.* sowing, seeding, planting; inoculation; young crop; seed; —ать *v.* sow, plant; —ной *a.* sowing; seed; (bot.) sown, common (*sativus*); —ной материал, —ные семена seed.

посед/евший, —елый *a.* grown gray, gray; —еть *v.* grow gray, get gray hair.

поселен/ец *m.* settler; —ие *n.* settlement.

посел/ить, —ять *v.* settle, colonize, establish; —иться, —яться *v.* settle, take up residence; —ок *m.* settlement, small village.

посеребр/ение *n.* silver plating; —енный *a.* silver-plated, silvered; —ить *v.* silver-plate, silver.

посереди, —не *adv.* in the middle.

посереть *v.* grow gray.

посетит/ель *m.* visitor; —ь *see* посещать.

посещ/аемость *f.* attendance; —аемый *a.* frequented, visited; —ать *v.* frequent, visit; —ение *n.* visit.

посе/янный *a.* sowed, planted; —ять *v.* sow, plant.

посидеть *v.* sit for a while.

посильный *a.* within one's powers, feasible.

посин/елый *a.* gone blue, turned blue; —еть *v.* get blue, turn blue; —ить *v.* blue, color blue.

поскользнуться *v.* slip.

поскольку *adv.* in so far as, inasmuch as, as, since; п. . . . постольку just as . . . so.

поскон/ник *m.* (bot.) hemp agrimony (*Eupatorium cannabinum*); —ный *a.* hemp, hempen; —ь *f.* staminate hemp.

поскорее *comp.* of скоро, faster, more quickly.

поскре/бки *pl.* scrapings; —сти *v.* scrape a little.

послабление *n.* slackening, indulgence.

послабляющее *n.* laxative.

послан/ие *n.* sending; message; —ник *m.* ambassador; —ный *a.* sent.

послать *see* посылать.

послаще *comp.* of сладкий, сладко, sweeter.

после *prep. gen. and adv.* after, afterwards, later, subsequently, since, another time; п. чего whereupon; *prefix* post—, after, subsequent, additional, supplementary, secondary; —военный *a.* postwar.

послед *m.* remainder, rest; (med.) afterbirth; (anat.) placenta; —ки *pl.* remainder, residue, leavings.

последействие *n.* secondary action, reaction; aftereffect, residual effect.

последн/ий *a.* last, closing, finishing, final, conclusive; recent; *m.* the latter; в п. раз for the last time; в —ее время for some time past; за —ее время lately, recently.

последование *n.* following.

**последователь** *m.* follower; —**но** *adv.* in succession, in sequence, in turn, one after another; (elec.) in series; —**но-параллельный** *a.* (elec.) series-parallel; —**ность** *f.* sequence, succession, series, order, coherence, continuity; graduation; (wave, pulse) train; —**ность во времени** distribution in time; —**ность операции** flow sheet.

**последовательн/ый** *a.* successive, consecutive, sequential; gradual, step-by-step; straight-line (welding); consistent, coherent, systematic; (elec.) series, in series; **п. порядок** consecutive order, sequence, succession; **п. распад** (nucl.) series decay; —**ая обмотка** (elec.) series winding; —**ая цепь** series circuit; —**ое деление** consecutive indexing; —**ое соединение** series connection, connection in series.

**послед/ствие** *n.* consequence, result, aftereffect; —**ствия** *pl.* effect; —**ующий** *a.* following, subsequent, ensuing, posterior; (math.) consequent; —**ующая обработка** aftertreatment.

**после/завтра** *adv.* day after tomorrow; —**импульс** *m.* afterpulse; —**ледниковый** *a.* (geol.) postglacial; —**охладитель** *m.* aftercooler, recooler; —**очиститель** *m.* repurifier; —**полуденный** *a.* afternoon; —**родовой** *a.* postnatal.

**послесвечен/ие** *n.* afterglow; persistence; **с —ием** persistent (phosphor); **с длительным —ием** long-persistence, long-lag; **с коротким —ием** short-persistence, rapid-decay.

**после/словие** *n.* concluding remarks; —**теплота** *f.* afterheat; —**третичный** *a.* (geol.) post-Tertiary; —**ускорение** *n.*, —**ускоряющий** *a.* postacceleration; —**фокусировка** *f.* secondary focusing.

**пословица** *f.* proverb.

**послойн/о** *adv.*, —**ый** *a.* in layers; lit-par-lit; —**ое движение** laminar flow, viscous flow, streamline flow.

**послужить** *v.* serve for a while, work for a while.

**послуш/ание** *n.* obedience; —**ать** *v.* listen; —**ный** *a.* obedient, manageable, governable, responsive.

**посматривать** *v.* glance at occasionally, observe from time to time.

**посменно** *adv.* by turns, alternately, in shifts.

**посмертный** *a.* posthumous.

**посметь** *v.* dare.

**поснимать** *v.* take off.

**пособие** *n.* help, assistance, relief; manual, textbook; school supplies.

**посодействовать** *v.* help, assist, promote.

**посол** *m.* ambassador; corning, pickling.

**посолить** *v.* salt.

**пососать** *see* посасывать.

**посотенно** *adv.* by hundreds, by the hundred.

**посп/евать,** —**еть** *v.* ripen, grow ripe; be ready, arrive in time; keep up, keep pace (with); **п. за** keep up with.

**поспешн/о** *adv.* hastily, hurriedly, in a hurry, promptly; —**ость** *f.* hurry, haste, speed; —**ый** *a.* hasty, hurried, prompt.

**посреди** *adv.* in the middle, among; —**не** in the middle.

**посредни/к** *m.* negotiator, intermediary, agent; broker, middleman; umpire, arbitrator; —**ческий** *a.* intercessory, interceding, intervening; —**чество** *n.* intervention; agency.

**посредственн/ость** *f.* mediocrity; —**ый** *a.* mediocre, fair.

**посредство** *n.* means, agency, medium; —**м** by means of, through; —**м которого** by means of which, whereby; —**м этого** thereby; **через п.** by, through, thanks to, owing to.

**посредствующий** *a.* intermediate.

**пост** *m.* post, station; (bench) mark; (diet) fast.

**пост.** *abbr.* (**постоянный**) constant.

**постав** *m.* (text.) loom; mill, huller; set of millstones; **мельница на три —а** a mill with three sets of millstones.

**поставить** *v.* put, place, set; erect, set up, raise; regulate; conduct (experiment).

**постав/ка** *f.* supplying, delivering, delivery; procurement; —**ки** *pl.* supplies; —**ленный** *a.* placed, set; —**лять** *v.* supply, furnish, deliver; —**щик** *m.* contractor, supplier, outfitter; maker.

**постамент** *m.* pedestal, base, support.

**постановить** *see* **постановлять.**

**постановка** *f.* erection, raising; statement, formulation; organization (of work, etc.); putting (a question); arrangement, set-up; (anat.) base.

**постановл/ение** *n.* decision, resolution, decree; —**ять** *v.* decide, fix, stipulate, establish, decree.

**постар/евший,** —**елый** *a.* grown old, aged; —**еть** *v.* get old, age.

**по-старому** *adv.* as of old, as before.

**постатейно** *adv.* by paragraphs, clause by clause.

**постел/ить** *see* **постилать;** —**ь** *f.*, —**ьный** *a.* bed; (geol.) bed; bottom, sole.

**постенн/ица** *f.* (bot.) pellitory (*Parietaria*); —**ый** *a.* (biol.) parietal.

**постепенно** *adv.* gradually, by degrees, little by little, by stages, in steps, stepwise; —**сть** *f.* gradualness, graduation, gradation; course.

**постепенн/ый** *a.* gradual, progressive, step-by-step; fractional (crystallization); **п. переход** gradation.

**постеречь** *see* **стеречь.**

**пости/гать,** —**гнуть** *v.* understand, comprehend, grasp; strike, overtake, reach; —**жение** *n.* understanding, comprehension; —**жимый** *a.* understandable, comprehensible, conceivable.

**постил/ать** *v.* spread, lay; —**ка** *f.* spreading, laying, covering; litter, bed.

**постичь** *see* **постигать.**

**постлать** *see* **постилать.**

**пости/чать** *v.*, —**ый** *a.* fast; —**ое масло** vegetable oil.

**постольку** *adv.* in so far as, inasmuch as.

**посторонн/ий** *a.* strange, foreign, alien, outside, extraneous; *m.* stranger, outsider, bystander; —**ее включение,** —**яя примесь** foreign matter, foreign substance, contaminant, impurity.

**постоянн/ая** *f.* constant; —**о** *adv.* constantly, continually, always, permanently; uniformly; —**о кипящий** *a.* constant-boiling; —**о-направленный** *a.* constant (field).

**постоянн/ый** *a.* constant, invariable, steady, uniform; stable, permanent, fixed, stationary, dead (center); perpetual, persistent, lasting, continuous;

**п. белый,** —**ые белила** permanent white, precipitated barium sulfate; **п. магнит** permanent magnet; **п. ток** (elec.) direct current; **двигатель** —**ого тока** direct-current motor, d. c. motor; —**ая величина** constant; —**ая точка** fixed point; —**ое напряжение** (elec.) direct-current voltage; **генератор** —**ого напряжения** constant-voltage generator; **ускоритель** —**ого напряжения** constant-potential accelerator.

**постоянств/о** *n.* constancy, stability, steadiness, uniformity; continuity, continuance, persistence; **п. отношений** constant proportions; **закон** —**а состава** law of definite proportions.

**постоять** *v.* stand for a while.

**постплиоценовая эпоха** (geol.) Post-Pliocene epoch.

**пострад/авший** *a.* having suffered; having undergone; *m.* victim; —**ать** *v.* suffer, come to harm; undergo.

**постраничный** *a.* per page, paginal, for every page.

**постро/ение** *n.* construction; building up, synthesis; structure; (curve) plot; (mil.) formation; **п. потока** flux plot; **масштаб** —**ения** plotting scale; —**енный** *a.* constructed, built; composite; plotted (against); —**ечный** *a.* building; —**ить** *v.* build; build up, synthesize; plot (curve); —**йка** *f.* building, structure, construction.

**постромка** *f.* trace (of harness).

**построчный** *a.* by the line.

**постскриптум** *m.* postscript.

**постукив/ание** *n.* light knocking, rapping; (med.) percussion; —**ать** *v.* knock, rap, tap.

**постул/ат** *m.* postulate, hypothesis; —**ировать** *v.* postulate, assume.

**поступание** *see* **поступление.**

**поступательно-возвратн/ый** *a.* reciprocating; —**ое движение** reciprocation, alternating motion.

**поступательн/ый** *a.* progressive, forward, advancing; step (function); —**ое движение** forward motion, advance, headway; translation; —**ое сгущение** livering (of paint).

**поступ/ать,** —**ить** *v.* act, deal, treat;

behave, conduct oneself, proceed, do; enter, go in, be admitted; enlist; —a-ющий *a.* entering, incoming; feeding (into); —ление *n.* entrance, entering, entry, arrival, admission, ingress, intake, inflow; return, receipt (of profits); enlistment; —ок *m.* action, act, step; conduct, behavior; procedure.

**постучать** *v.* knock, tap.

**постэмбриональный** *a.* (med.) post-embryonic, fetal.

**посуд/а** *f.* dishware, dish; **глиняная п.** earthenware; **фарфоровая п.** china-ware; —ина *f.* vessel, jar.

**посудный** *a.* dish, plate.

**посуточн/о** *adv.,* —ый *a.* per day, per diem, daily, every 24 hours.

**посыл/атель** *m.* sender, transmitter; —ать *v.* send, mail, post; —ка *f.* sending, consignment; parcel, package; (elec. comm.) sample; errand; —ьный *m.* messenger.

**посып/ание** *n.,* —ка *f.* strewing, sprinkling, dusting; —анный *a.* sprinkled, powdered, dusted; —ать *v.* strew, sprinkle, powder, dust; pour (dry substance).

**посяг/ание** *n.,* —ательство *n.* encroachment, infringement; —ать, —нуть *v.* encroach, infringe; attempt; —а-ющий *a.* encroaching, infringing.

**пот** *m.* perspiration, sweat; suint, yolk (of wool); **весь в —у** covered with perspiration; **обливаться —ом** *v.* be wet with perspiration.

**потазот** *m.* a potassium-ammonium chloride fertilizer.

**потайн/ой** *a.* secret, hidden; sunk, countersunk, flush; —ая головка countersunk head.

**поталь** *m.* (met.) Dutch gold, brass leaf.

**потамо—** *prefix* potamo—, river; —метр *m.* (elec.) potamometer (current meter).

**потассий** *see* **калий.**

**поташ** *m.* potash, potassium carbonate; **едкий п., каустический п.** caustic potash, potassium hydroxide; —ник *m.* Russian thistle (*Salsola kali*); —ный *a.* potash, potassic.

**потем/ки** *pl.* darkness, obscurity; —нев-ший *a.* grown dark, dim; —нение *n.*

darkening, dimness, dullness; —неть *v.* darken, grow dark, become dark.

**потение** *n.* perspiration, sweating.

**потенциал** *m.,* —ьный *a.* (elec.) potential; **п. нулевого заряда** electrocapillary maximum; **падение —а** potential drop; **разность —ов, скачок —а** potential difference; —ьная яма (nucl.) potential well; —ьность *f.* potentiality.

**потенциометр** *m.* (elec.) potentiometer; —ический *a.* potentiometric (titration, etc.); —ический датчик resistive transducer.

**потенц/ировать** *v.* (math.) raise to a higher power; —ия *f.* potency.

**потепление** *n.* warming up, rise in temperature.

**потерп/евший** *a.* having suffered, having undergone; *m.* victim, sufferer; —еть *v.* suffer, undergo, endure.

**потертый** *a.* old, worn.

**потер/я** *f.* loss, disappearance, waste, escape (of gas, etc.); (mil.) casualty; —и *pl.* loss, losses; **п. на рассеивание** dispersion loss, loss by dispersion; **п. на трение** friction loss, loss due to friction; **п. от излучения** radiation loss; **п. при пуске** starting loss; —и в меди (elec.) copper losses; —и вследствие поглощения absorption loss.

**потер/явший** *a.* having lost; —янный *a.* lost; —ять *v.* lose, mislay.

**потеть** *v.* perspire, sweat; become covered with condensate.

**потихоньку** *adv.* little by little, slowly; noiselessly, silently.

**пот/ливость** *f.* tendency to perspire; —ливый *a.* having a tendency to perspire, perspiring readily; —ный *a.* perspiring, damp with perspiration, sweaty.

**потов/ой, —ый** *a.* sweat, perspiration; **п. воск** yolk wax, wax from suint; **п. жир** suint, yolk (of wool).

**потогонн/ый** *a.* sweat-inducing, sudorific, diaphoretic; sweatshop (system); —ое средство sudorific, diaphoretic.

**поток** *m.* stream, current, torrent, flow, flux; (nucl.) flux; run, race, duct; **высокого —а** high-flux; **линия —а** streamline; **магнитный п.** magnetic flux; **обратный п.** reflux; **отношение**

—ов flux ratio; **скорость** —a flow rate; **скос** —a (aero.) downwash; —**ообразный** a. torrential; —**осцепление** (elec.) linkage.

**потолкоуступн/ый** a. overhead; —**ая выемка** (min.) overhand stoping.

**потоло/к** m. ceiling; crown (of furnace); —**чина** f. (min.) block of untouched ore; —**чный** a. ceiling, overhead.

**потом** adv. then, next, subsequently, later on, afterwards, after this.

**потомок** m. descendant, offspring.

**потомств/енный** a. hereditary; —**о** n. posterity, descendants, progeny; race.

**потому** adv. therefore, consequently; **п. что** because, on account of.

**потон/увший** a. drowned, sunk, sunken, submerged; —**уть** v. be drowned, sink, go down.

**потоп** m. flood, inundation, deluge; —**ить**, —**лять** v. sink, drown, submerge, immerse; —**ление** n. sinking, drowning, submersion, immersion; —**ленность** f. submergence; —**ленный** a. drowned, submerged, immersed.

**потор/апливать**, —**опить** v. hasten, hurry, push, speed up.

**поточить** v. sharpen a little, sharpen.

**поточн/ый** a. of **поток**; —**ая система** continuous operation; —**о-массовое производство** continuous mass production.

**потребитель** m. consumer, customer; —**ная стоимость** costs; —**ский** a. consumers'; cooperative (store).

**потребить** see **потреблять**.

**потребл/ение** n. consumption, use, expenditure; **п. в ваттах** (elec.) watt consumption; **п. силы** power consumption; —**яемая мощность** (elec.) input; —**ять** v. consume, use, expend; —**яться** v. be consumed, be used.

**потребн/ость** f. necessity, need, requirement, demand, want; —**ый** a. necessary, needful; —**ое количество** demand.

**потребовать** v. demand, request.

**потрепанный** a. shabby, tattered.

**потрескив/ание** n. crackling, crepitation, decrepitation; —**ать** v. crackle, crepitate, decrepitate; —**ающий** a. crackling.

**потрещать** see **потрескивать**.

**потро/ха** pl. bowels, intestines; —**шить** v. disembowel, gut, eviscerate.

**потряс/ающий** a. tremendous, staggering, stupendous; startling; —**ение** n. shock; disturbance, commotion.

**потускн/евший**, —**елый** a. tarnished, dull; dim; —**ение** n. tarnishing; fogging, clouding; —**еть** v. tarnish; fog, cloud.

**потух/ание** n. extinction; —**ать**, —**нуть** v. be extinguished, go out; —**ший** a. extinct, out.

**потушить** v. extinguish, put out; slake.

**Потье реактивное сопротивление** (elec.) Potier's reactance.

**потя/гивание** n. pulling, pull; —**гивать**, —**нуть** v. pull (occasionally); draw in, inhale.

**поубавить** v. lessen, diminish.

**поундаль** see **паундаль**.

**поурочн/ая плата** piecework pay; —**о** adv. by the job, by the piece.

**поутру** adv. in the morning.

**поучительный** a. instructive.

**по-французски** adv. in French; (speak) French.

**ПОХ** abbr. (Промышленность органической химии) Industrial Organic Chemistry (journal).

**похвал/а** f. praise, commendation; —**ить** v. praise.

**поход** m. expedition, trip; march; campaign; overweight.

**походить** v. resemble, look like, bear resemblance; walk a little.

**походн/ый** a. camp, camping; field (kitchen); —**ая установка** temporary plant; —**ое движение** march.

**похож/е** adv. like; **п. на** it looks like; —**ий** a. like, similar, resembling.

**похолодание** n. cooling off, getting colder.

**поцарапать** v. scratch, mar.

**поцелуй** m. kiss.

**почасно** adv. hourly, by the hour.

**початко/видный** a. (bot.) spadiciform, spadiceous; —**вый** a. spadiceous; —**дробилка** f. cob crusher; —**обрыватель**, —**срыватель** m. (corn) picker; —**отделитель** m. picker-husker; —**цветные** pl. (bot.) Spadiciflorae.

**початок** m. (bot.) spadix; (corn) cob;

(text.) cop; —**чный** *a.* spadiceous; cob; cop.

**почаще** *comp. of* **часто,** more often, more frequently.

**почв.** *abbr.* (**почвоведение**) soil science; (**почвенный**) soil, pedological.

**почв/а** *f.,* —**енный** *a.* soil, ground, earth, land; —**енная вода** ground water.

**почвенно**— *prefix* soil.

**почв. компл.** *abbr.* (**почвенный комплекс**) soil complex; (**комплексность почв**) soil heterogeneity.

**почво/вед** *m.* soil scientist, pedologist; —**ведение** *n.* soil science; —**грунт** *m.* ground; —**закрепляющий** *a.* soil-conserving; —**истощающий** *a.* soil-depleting; —**обрабатывающая машина** cultivator; —**образующий** *a.* soil-forming; —**покровный** *a.* ground-cover; —**углубитель** *m.* (agr.) subsoil plow, deep plow; —**углубление** *n.* subsoil plowing; —**уплотнитель** *m.* packer; —**уступная система** (min.) underhand stoping; —**утомление** *n.* soil depletion; —**фреза** *f.* rototiller.

**почем** *adv.* how much? what is the price? **п. он знает** how does he know?

**почему** *adv.* why; **п.-то** for some reason or other; **вот п.** that is why.

**почерк** *m.* handwriting.

**почерн/евший,** —**елый** *a.* blackened, grown black; —**ение** *n.* blackening, growing black; (phot.) density; **плотность** —**ения** density; —**еть** *v.* grow black, get black; —**ить** *v.* blacken, make black.

**почерп/ать,** —**нуть** *v.* draw up, fetch, get.

**почесть** *f.* honors; respect, esteem.

**почет** *m.* honor, respect, esteem; —**ный** *a.* honorable, honorary, complimentary.

**почечка** *f.* (biol.) gemmule, small bud.

**почечник** *m.* (min.) jade (a form of nephrite).

**почечн/ый** *a.* kidney, renal, nephritic; **п. камень** (min.) nephrite (a form of amphibole, jade in part); (med.) kidney stone; —**ое сало** suet.

**почечуй** *m.* (med.) hemorrhoids, piles; **п.,** —**ник** *m.* (bot.) peachwort (*Polygonum persicaria*); —**ный** *a.* hemorrhoidal.

**почин** *m.* beginning; initiative; —**ать** *v.* begin; broach, tap (barrel).

**почин/ить,** *v.* mend, repair; —**ка** *f.* mending, repairing, repair.

**починок** *m.* clearing, cleared field.

**почин/очная мастерская** repair shop; —**ять** *see* **починить.**

**почитать** *v.* read a little; honor, respect, look up to; consider.

**почище** *comp. of* **чисто, чистый,** cleaner.

**поч/ка** *f.* (bot.) bud; (min.) druse, nodule; (anat.) kidney; **воспаление** —**ек** (med.) nephritis; **осадок** —**ками** (geol.) nodular deposit.

**почко/вание** *n.* (bot.) budding, gemmation, gemmulation; —**ватый,** —**видный,** —**образный** *a.* kidney-shaped, reniform, nodular; —**ваться** *v.* bud; —**видная руда** kidney ore (a reniform hematite); —**вый** *a.* bud, gemmate; —**носный** *a.* gemmiferous, gemmate.

**почленно** *adv.* (math.) termwise.

**почт/а** *f.* mail, post; post office; (nucl.) rabbit; **по** —**е** by mail; —**альон** *m.* mailman, postman; —**амт** *m.* post office.

**почтен/ие** *n.* respect, esteem, consideration, honor; —**ный** *a.* respectable, honorable; considerable.

**почти, п.-что** *adv.* nearly, almost, at the point (of); *prefix* near—, almost; quasi—; **п.-равнина** *f.* (geol.) peneplain.

**почтов/ый** *a.* mail, post, postal, postage; carrier (pigeon); **п. штемпель** postmark; —**ая марка** stamp; —**ое отделение** post office.

**пошат/ать,** —**нуть,** —**ывать** *v.* push, rock slightly.

**пошлин/а** *f.* duty, customs, tax; royalty; **оплаченный** —**ой** duty paid.

**поштучн/о** *adv.,* —**ый** *a.* by the piece, piecemeal, by the job; —**ая плата** piecework pay.

**пощуп/ать,** —**ывать** *v.* feel, handle.

**поэтажный** *a.* floor, story; per floor.

**поэтому** *adv. and conj.* therefore, that is why, consequently.

**поющий** *a.* singing, humming.

**появ/иться,** —**ляться** *v.* appear, make its appearance, show itself, emerge, originate; —**ление** *n.* appearance, emergence, emersion, advent; **—ляющийся** *a.* appearing, emerging, forthcoming.

**по            яр/ок** *m.*, **—ковый** *a.* felt, lamb's wool.

**пояс** *m.* belt, band; zone, region; flange, collar, hoop; boom (of bridge, arch); **—ковый** *a.* (zool.) clitellar.

**поясн/ение** *n.* explanation, elucidation; **—ительный** *a.* explanatory; **—ить** *see* **пояснять.**

**поясни/ца** *f.* (anat.) small of the back; **—чный** *a.* lumbar.

**поясн/ый** *a.* belt; zone, zonal; boom (of bridge, arch); **п. лист, —ая накладка** flange plate.

**пояснять** *v.* explain, expound, comment, illustrate.

**пояс/овое строение** (geol.) girdle fabric; **—ок** *m.* little belt; collar; band, strap; (zool.) clitellum.

**п/п** *abbr.* (**по порядку**) in sequence; serial number.

**ППК** *abbr.* (**почвенный поглощающий комплекс**) soil absorbing complex.

**п.п.п.** *abbr.* (**потери при прокаливании**) calcination loss.

**пр.** *abbr.* (**прочее, прочий**), the rest; **и пр.** and so on, etc.

**пра—** *prefix* great—.

**прабанговая кислота** prabangic acid.

**правд/а** *f.* truth, verity; **—ивость** *f.* truthfulness, veracity; **—ивый** *a.* truthful, veracious, honest.

**правдоподоб/ие** *n.* probability, likelihood, plausibility; **—ный** *a.* probable, likely, plausible.

**правил/о** *n.* rule, maxim, principle; regulation, specification; guide bar, reversing rod; straightedge; (mil.) traversing handpsike; *obs.* helm, rudder; **—а** *pl.* instructions; specifications; **поставить себе за п.** *v.* make it one's rule.

**правильно** *adv.* right, accurately, correctly, properly; **—сть** *f.* accuracy, correctness; regularity, basic pattern.

**правильн/ый** *a.* accurate, correct, proper; true; normal, sound, regular, legitimate; straightening; **п. многоугольник** rectilineal polygon; **п. раствор** regular solution; **п. станок** straightener;**—ая доска** straightedge, ruler; **—ая дробь** (math.) proper

fraction;**—ая машина** leveler, leveling machine; straightening machine; **—ая плита** dressing plate.

**правитель** *m.* ruler, administrator, manager; **п. дел** head clerk; **—ство** *n.*, **—ственный** *a.* government; **—ствующий** *a.* ruling, governing.

**прав/ить** *v.* govern, rule, manage, direct, guide, administer; drive (car); correct; straighten, dress, trim; **—ка** *f.* correcting; straightening, dressing, trimming, leveling; setting.

**правление** *n.* government; direction, administration, management; board, board of directors.

**прав/о** *n.* right; privilege; law; claim; *adv.* really, truly, indeed; **п. прохода** right of way; **доктор прав** doctor of laws (degree); **по —у** rightfully, legally; **поплатиться —ом** *v.* forfeit (the right); **предъявлять —а** *v.* lay claim, assert one's claims (to).

**право/вед** *m.* lawyer; **—ведение** *n.* jurisprudence; science of law; **—вой** *a.* law, right; lawful, rightful.

**правовращающ/ий** *a.* (light) dextrorotatory; **—ее соединение** dextrorotatory compound, dextro-compound.

**право/мерный** *a.* rightful; lawful; **—мочие** *n.* competence; **—мочный** *a.* competent; **—нарушение** *n.* infringement of the law, breaking of a law; **—писание** *n.* orthography, spelling.

**правоспособн/ость** *f.* capacity; **—ый** *a.* capable, competent.

**право/судие** *n.* justice; **—та** *f.* justice, legitimacy, lawfulness; integrity.

**прав/ый** *a.* right, righthand, clockwise, dextro—; right, rightful; **—ая винная кислота** dextrotartaric acid; **—ая молочная кислота** dextrolactic acid; **быть —ым** *v.* be right; **на —ую сторону** to the right, on the right hand.

**правящ/ий** *a.* governing, ruling, managing; **—ая власть** controlling authority.

**Прага** Prague.

**праздн/ик** *m.*, **—ичный** *a.* holiday; **—овать** *v.* celebrate; **—ость** *f.* idleness, inactivity; **—ый** *a.* idle, inactive.

**празем** *m.* (min.) prase (a variety of chalcedony).

**празеодим, —ий** *m.*, **—иевый** *a.* praseodymium, Pr; **окись —ия** praseodymium oxide; **сернокислый п.** praseodymium sulfate; **хлористый п.** praseodymium chloride; **—иевая земля** praseodymia, praseodymium trioxide.

**празеолит** *m.* (min.) praseolite (an alteration product of cordierite).

**празер** *see* **празем.**

**практик** *m.* practical person; skilled worker;—a *f.* practice; training; **на —е** in practice; **—ант** *m.* probationer; trainee; **—овать, —оваться** *v.* practice; **—ум** *m.* practical course, laboratory course; practical work; laboratory manual; **—ующий** *a.* practicing.

**практич/еский, —ный** *a.* practical, useful; **—ность** *f.* practicalness, practicality, usefulness.

**Прандтля число** Prandtl number.

**прат/енсол** *m.* pratensol; **—ол** *m.* pratol (a hydroxymethoxyflavone).

**прах** *m.* dust, earth, ashes, ruin.

**прачечн/ая** *f.*, **—ое заведение** laundry.

**пращ/а** *f.*, **—евой** *a.* sling.

**пр-во** *abbr.* (правительство) government.

**пре—** *prefix* very, most; *prefix with verbs* sur—, over—.

**пребы/вание** *n.* stay, residence; **—вать, —ть** *v.* stay, reside; continue, remain.

**превалировать** *v.* prevail, predominate.

**превен/тер** *m.* (oil-well drilling) preventer; **—тивный** *a.* preventive; **—ция** *f.* prevention.

**превзой/денный** *a.* surpassed; **не п.** unsurpassed, unequaled, unrivaled; **—ти** *see* **превосходить.**

**превозмо/гать, —чь** *v.* overcome, master.

**превосход/ить, —ствовать** *v.* surpass, excel, outdo, top, exceed; **п. числом** outnumber; **—но** *adv.* excellently, superiorly; **—ный** *a.* excellent, superior, first-class, splendid; **—ство** *n.* excellence, superiority, preeminence; preponderance; advantage.

**превращ/имый** *see* **превращаемый; —ить** *see* **превращать.**

**превратн/о** *adv.* wrongly; **п. истолковать** *v.* misinterpret, misunderstand; **—ый** *a.* wrong; changeful.

**превращ/аемый** *a.* convertible, trans-

formable; **—ать** *v.* convert, transform, change, turn (into), alter; (math.) reduce; **—аться** *v.* be converted, change, turn, become, pass over, pass into, go over (to another form).

**превращен/ие** *n.* conversion, transformation, change, transmutation (of elements); inversion (of sugar); **реакция —ия** conversion reaction, conversion; **точка —ия** transition point, critical point; **—ный** *a.* converted, transformed, changed; **—ный сахар** invert sugar.

**превысить** *see* **превышать.**

**превыш/ать** *v.* exceed, surpass, outdo, go beyond, excel; **—ение** *n.* excess, exceeding, surpassing.

**прегн/ан** *m.* pregnane; **—анолон** *m.* pregnanolone; **—ен** *m.* pregnene.

**прегра/да** *f.* obstacle, obstruction, barrier, bar, barricade, impediment; interception; fender; **действие —ды** (phys.) screening effect; **—дить, —ждать** *v.* obstruct, block up, impede, bar; intercept, interrupt; **—ждать доступ** seal (off); **—ждающий** *a.* obstructing, blocking up; intercepting; **—ждение** *n.* obstruction, blocking up; interception.

**преграттит** *m.* (min.) pregrattite (a variety of muscovite).

**пред** *see* **перед;** *prefix* pre—.

**пред—** *abbr.* (председатель) chairman.

**предавать** *v.* betray, give up.

**предаззит** *m.* (min.) predazzite (mixture of calcite and brucite).

**преданн/ость** *f.* devotion, attachment, loyalty; **—ый** *a.* devoted, attached, loyal.

**предат/ельский** *a.* treacherous; **—ь** *see* **предавать.**

**предацит** *see* **предаззит.**

**предварен/ие** *n.* forewarning; precedence; advance, lead; **п. впуска** preadmission; **угол —ия** (elec.) angle of lead.

**предварительн/о** *adv.* preliminarily, first; pre—, fore—; **п. охлаждать** *v.* precool; **п. сжатый** precompressed; **—ый** *a.* preliminary, previous, pre—; **—ое нагревание** preheating.

**предвар/ить, —ять** *v.* warn, forewarn; precede, anticipate, forestall.

**предвест/ить, предвещать** *v.* predict, foretell; forerun; **—ник** *m.* forerunner, sign, indication.

**предвзят/ый** *a.* preconceived; **—ое мнение** preconception, prejudice.

**предвид/ение** *n.* foresight; **—еть** *v.* foresee, visualize, forecast; **—еться** *v.* be foreseen, be in view; **—имый** *a.* predictable.

**предвкушение** *n.* anticipation, expectation.

**предводительство** *n.* leadership; **—вать** *v.* lead, command.

**предвосхи/тить, —щать** *v.* anticipate; **—щение** *n.* anticipation.

**предгор/ный** *a.* piedmont; **—ье** *n.* foothills.

**предел** *m.* limit, bound, boundary, end, termination, limitation; capacity, extent, compass; point; **—ы** *pl.* range; margin (of error); **—ы колебания температуры** temperature range; **п. насыщения** saturation point; **п. прочности** strength; **п. регулировки** range of adjustment; **п. скорости** speed limit; **в —ах от 30 до 40 from 30 to 40; в —ах года** within a year; **в температурных —ах** in the temperature range; **выходить за —ы** *v.* exceed; **достигать —а** *v.* range; attain; **за —ы** outside of, beyond; **критический п.** critical limit, breaking-down point; **критические —ы** critical range; **положить п., ставить п.** *v.* limit, terminate.

**предельно-допустимый** *a.* permissible.

**предельн/ый** *a.* limiting, limit, boundary, threshold; extreme, terminal, end; maximum, ultimate, full, overall (dimension); (chem.) saturated; **п. срок** deadline; **п. углеводород** saturated hydrocarbon; **п. угол** critical angle; **—ая величина** threshold value, threshold; **—ая кривая** limiting curve, limit curve; **—ая линия** boundary line, boundary, border; **—ая плоскость** (cryst.) end plane, base; **—ая поверхность** boundary surface, surface of contact, interface; **—ая скоба** limit gage; **—ая скорость** speed limit; (aero.) terminal velocity; maximum speed; (distillation) flooding velocity; **—ая точка** end point; **—ая упругость** perfect elasticity; **—ое напряжение** breaking point; pressure limit; **—ое напряжение сдвига** yield value; **—ое положение** end position; **—ое соединение** saturated compound; **—ое сопротивление разрыву, —ое сопротивление излому** breaking point; **—ое состояние** limiting state; **точка —ого значения** yield point.

**преджелудок** *m.* (zool.) rumen; gizzard (of insects).

**предзнаменов/ать, —ывать** *v.* foreshadow, forebode, portend.

**предилекция** *f.* predilection, partiality (for).

**предисловие** *n.* preface, foreword, introduction; **служить —м** *v.* preface.

**предкамера** *f.* antechamber, precombustion chamber.

**предлагать** *v.* offer, propose, put forward, propound, suggest.

**предлежание** *n.* (med.) presentation (of fetus).

**предлог** *m.* pretext, pretence; (grammar) preposition.

**предложение** *n.* offer, proposal, proposition, suggestion; (com.) supply; (grammar) sentence, clause; **делать п.** *v.* propose; **спрос и п.** supply and demand.

**предложит/ельный** *a.* propositional; **—ь** *see* предлагать.

**предместье** *n.* suburb, outskirts.

**предмет** *m.* subject, topic; object; (com.) article, commodity, item; piece of work; **п. потребления, п. широкого потребления** commodity; **на п.** for.

**предметность** *f.* objectivity.

**предметный** *a.* object, objective; **п. столик** (microscope) stage, stand; **п. урок** object lesson; **—ное стекло** (microscope) slide; **—одержатель** *m.* (microscope) stage, stand; slide, mount.

**предназнач/ать, —ить** *v.* intend, reserve (for); designate, set aside, earmark (for); **—ение** *n.* destination, design.

**преднамерен/ие** *n.*, **—ность** *f.* premeditation, forethought; **—но** *adv.* on purpose, by design; **—ный** *a.* premeditated, aforethought, preconceived.

**предначерт/ание** *n.* outline, plan, design; **—ать, —ывать** *v.* outline in advance.

**предок** *m.* progenitor, ancestor, predecessor.

**предоминирующий** *a.* predominant.

**предоплата** *f.* prepayment.

**предопредел/ить, —ять** *v.* predetermine.

**предостав/ить, —лять** *v.* leave, submit; let, allow; **—ление** *n.* leaving, submitting, giving.

**предостере/гать, —чь** *v.* warn, caution, admonish, put on guard; **—жение** *n.* warning, caution, notice.

**предосторожност/ь** *f.* precaution, safeguard; **мера —и** precautionary measure, precaution; **принимать —и** *v.* take precautions.

**предотвра/тить, —щать** *v.* prevent, avoid, avert, ward off, obviate; **—щаемый** *a.* preventable; **—щение** *n.* prevention, precluding; averting, warding off.

**предохранен/ие** *n.* protection, security; (mach.) safety device; preservation, conservation; prevention; **—ный** *a.* protected, shielded; preserved.

**предохранитель** *m.* protector, safety device, safety catch, safety stop, safety lock; guard, safeguard; preserver, preservative; (elec.) fuse, cutout; **п. от обледенения** (aero.) deicer; **свинцовый п.** (elec.) lead fuse.

**предохранительн/ый** *a.* protective, protecting, protection; safety, security, guard; preservative; precautionary (measures); (med.) prophylactic, preventive; (nucl.) shut-off, scram (rod); **п. клапан** safety valve; **п. кожух** (nucl.) shield; **п. штепсель, —ая вставка, —ая пробка** (elec.) fuse; **п. щит** (mach.) fender, guard; **—ая коробка** (elec.) fuse box; **—ая маска** face guard; **—ая плита** baffle plate; screen; **—ая проволока** (elec.) fuse wire; **—ая трубка** safety tube; **—ое приспособление** safeguard; **—ое средство** preservative; (med.) prophylactic; **—ое устройство** precaution; protector, safety device.

**предохран/ить, —ять** *v.* protect, guard, keep safe, insulate (from); prevent; preserve, conserve; **—яющий** *see* **предохранительный.**

**предпис/ание** *n.* order, regulation, instruction, direction, injunction, prescription; **согласно —анию** by order; **—анный** *a.* prescribed, specified; **—ать, —ывать** *v.* prescribe, order, decree; instruct, direct; assign.

**предпламенный** *a.* pre-ignition.

**предплата** *f.* prepayment.

**предплеч/ие, —ье** *n.* (anat.) forearm.

**предплюсна** *f.* (anat.) tarsus.

**предполаг/аемый** *a.* supposed, reputed, conjectural, probable, prospective; **—ать** *v.* suppose, surmise, conjecture, presume, assume; propose, contemplate; **предположим, что** let us suppose that, if we assume that; **—аться** *v.* be supposed, be assumed; **—ая** assuming.

**предполож/ение** *n.* supposition, surmise, hypothesis, assumption; **—енный** *a.* supposed, assumed; proposed; **—ительно** *adv.* supposedly, presumably, hypothetically; **—ительный** *a.* hypothetical, conjectural; **—ить** *see* **предполагать.**

**предполярный** *a.* subarctic.

**предпосевной** *a.* presowing.

**предпоследний** *a.* penultimate, last but one.

**предпосылка** *f.* premise, prerequisite; reason, ground.

**предпоч/есть, —итать** *v.* prefer, like better, choose; **—тение** *n.* preference.

**предпочтительн/о** *adv.* preferably, in preference, rather; **—ость** *f.* preferableness; **—ый** *a.* preferable.

**предприимчив/ость** *f.* enterprise; **—ый** *a.* enterprising.

**предприн/иматель** *m.* industrialist, owner (of a firm or business); employer; **—имать, —ять** *v.* undertake.

**предприятие** *n.* undertaking, enterprise; concern, business; plant; **п.-тень** (mil.) skeleton factory, standby plant.

**предпряжа** *f.* coarse linen.

**предпрямокрылые** *pl.* (zool.) Protorthoptera.

**предраспол/агать, —ожить** *v.* predispose; **—ожение** *n.* predisposition;

(med.) diathesis; —оженный *a.* predisposed.

предраспределительный *a.* predistributing.

предрассудок *m.* prejudice.

предреш/ать, —ить *v.* predetermine, decide beforehand; foreclose.

предротовой *a.* (anat.) preoral.

председатель *m.* chairman; president; speaker; —ствовать *v.* preside, be the chairman; —ствующий *a.* presiding; *m.* chairman.

предсердие *n.* (anat.) auricle (of the heart).

предсказ/ание *n.* prophecy, prediction, forecast; п. погоды weather forecast; —ать, —ывать *v.* prophesy, predict, foretell.

представитель *m.* representative; example; —ность *f.* presence; —ный *a.* imposing, impressive; —ство *n.* representation.

представ/ить *see* представлять; —ление *n.* presentation, exhibition; introduction; concept, idea, notion; representation; —ленный *a.* presented, introduced; represented.

представлять *v.* present, offer, introduce, submit (plan); represent, describe; п. себе imagine, visualize; п. собой be, represent; —ся *v.* be presented; pretend; seem.

представительная железа (anat.) prostate gland.

предстать *v.* appear, come before.

предсто/ять *v.* be imminent; have (to); ему —ит пойти he has to go; ему —ят he faces (difficulties); —ящее *n.* (math.) coefficient; —ящий *a.* future.

предтопок *m.* precombustion chamber, preliminary chamber (of furnace).

предубежд/ать *v.* prejudice; —ение *n.* prejudice; —енный *a.* prejudiced, biased.

предуведом/ить, —лять *v.* inform beforehand, notify, advise; —ление *n.* notification, notice, forewarning.

предугад/ать, —ывать *v.* predict, foresee.

предузловой *a.* antenodal.

предумышленный *see* преднамеренный.

предупредительн/ый *a.* preventive, precautionary; courteous, attentive; п.

сигнал warning, warning signal; —ая мера, —ое средство preventive.

предупредить *see* предупреждать.

предупрежд/аемый *a.* preventable; —ать *v.* prevent; forestall, anticipate; notify, tell beforehand; warn, caution (against); —ающий *a.* preventing; warning; —ение *n.* prevention; warning; —енный *a.* prevented; warned.

предусилитель *m.* preamplifier; preliminary intensifier.

предускорение *n.* preacceleration.

предусматривать *see* предусмотреть.

предусмотр/енный *a.* provided (for), specified; —еть *v.* provide (for), specify, foresee; —ительность *f.* foresight, prevision, forethought, prudence; —ительный *a.* foreseeing, long-sighted, prudent.

предустановленный *a.* predetermined, preestablished.

предхолодильник *m.* precooler; preliminary condenser, precondenser.

предшеств/енник *m.* predecessor, forerunner, precursor; —ие, —ование *n.* precedence, antecedence, priority; —овавший *a.* preceding, antecedent, foregoing, prior; —овать *v.* precede, forego, forerun; —ующий *a.* preceding, precedent, antecedent, foregoing, prior, previous, older.

предъявител/ь *m.* bearer; на —я payable to bearer; —ьный *a.* presenting.

предъяв/ить, —лять *v.* produce, present, set forth; —ление *n.* producing, presentation; по —лению on presentation, at sight.

предыдущий *a.* preceding, foregoing, previous, former.

предыонизация *f.* pre-ionization.

предыск/ание *n.* preselection; —атель *m.* preselector.

предыстория *f.* previous history.

предэкспоненциальный *a.* pre-exponential.

преем/ник *m.* successor; —ственность *f.* continuity, succession; —ственный *a.* successive.

прежде *adv.* before, previously, formerly, heretofore; *prep. gen.* before; п. всего first of all, to begin with; п. чем before, prior to, previous to.

**преждевременн/ость** *f.* prematurity; —**ый** *a.* premature, early, untimely.

**прежн/ий** *a.* previous, preceding, prior, former, earlier; по —**ему** as before.

**презентация** *f.* presentation.

**презерва/тив** *m.* preservative; —**ция** *f.* preservation.

**президент** *m.* president.

**презрение** *n.* contempt.

**преизбыток** *m.* superabundance, excess.

**преим.** *abbr.* (преимущественно).

**преимуществ/енно** *adv.*, по —**у** in preference, pre-eminently; mostly, principally, chiefly, mainly, for the most part; —**енный** *a.* primary; preferred; —**енное право** preference; pre-emption; —**о** *n.* advantage; preference; seniority; odds.

**преисполн/енный** *a.* full, filled; —**ить, —ять** *v.* fill.

**прейскурант** *m.* price list, price current.

**прекословие** *n.* contradiction.

**прекрасн/о** *adv.* excellently, very well; —**ый** *a.* excellent, fine.

**прекра/тить, —щать** *v.* discontinue, cease, stop, put a stop (to), terminate, finish, end, break off, cut off, suspend; shut down; —**титься, —щаться** *v.* come to an end, cease, stop, be stopped; die away (of oscillation); —**щение** *n.* discontinuance, cessation, ceasing, stopping, stop, finishing, cutting off; closing down, shutting down; полное —**щение действия** deadlock; —**щенный** *a.* discontinued, stopped, finished, cut off; shut down.

**прелом/имый** *see* преломляемый; —**итель** *m.* refractor; —**ить** *see* преломлять.

**преломлен/ие** *n.* breaking; (phys.) refraction; двойное **п.** (cryst.) double refraction, birefringence; измеритель —**ия** refractometer; коэффициент —**ия, показатель —ия** index of refraction, refractive index; —**ный** *a.* refracted.

**преломл/яемость** *f.* refractability, refractivity, refrangibility; —**яемый** *a.* refractable, refrangible; —**ять** *v.* break; refract; diffract, deflect; —**яться** *v.* be broken; be refracted, deflect; —**яющий** *a.* refracting, refractive.

**прел/ый** *a.* rotten; —**ь** *f.* rot, mold.

**премиальный** *a.* premium; bonus.

**преминуть: не п.** *v.* not to fail.

**премиров/анный** *a.* prize; rewarded; —**ать** *v.* award a prize or bonus.

**премия** *f.* premium, prize, bonus.

**пренебре/гаемый, —жимый, —жимо малый** *a.* negligible; —**гать, —чь** *v.* neglect; disregard, ignore, discard, omit; —**гая** *adv.* disregarding, barring; —**жение** *n.* neglect, disregard; disdain; —**жительный** *a.* neglectful; disdainful.

**прение** *n.* rotting; sweating; stewing.

**пренит** *m.* (min.) prehnite; —**ен, —ол** *m.* prehnitene, prehnitol, 1,2,3,4-tetramethylbenzene; —**иловая кислота** prehnitilic acid, 2,3,4-trimethylbenzoic acid; —**овая кислота** prehnitic acid, 1,2,3,4-benzenetetracarboxylic acid.

**прения** *pl.* debate; discussion.

**пренол** *m.* prenol, 3-methyl-2-buten-1-ol.

**преоблад/ание** *n.* predominance, prevalence; —**ать** *v.* predominate, dominate, prevail; —**ающий** *a.* predominant, dominant, prevailing, preponderant.

**преобра/жать, —зить** *v.* transform, change; —**жающая** *f.* (math.) transform.

**преобразов/ание** *n.* conversion, transformation; reorganization, reform, alteration; variation; regeneration; (math.) transform; —**анный** *a.* converted, transformed; —**анная функция** (math.) transform; —**атель** *m.* converter, transformer; regenerator; (elec. comm.) transducer; —**атель фаз** phase transformer; —**ательный** *a.* converting, transforming, transformation; —**ать, —ывать** *v.* convert, transform, change, turn (into), modify, alter; regenerate; transpose (equation, etc.); reorganize, reform; —**ать в** reduce to (in a diagram).

**преодол/евание, —ение** *n.* overcoming, surmounting; —**евать, —еть** *v.* overcome, surmount, get over; —**имый** *a.* superable, surmountable.

**препарат** *m.* preparation, compound; (micros.) specimen; —**ивный** *a.* preparative; —**ивная соль, —ная соль**

preparing salt (sodium stannate); —одержатель *m.* mounting screen (in electron microscope).

препариров/ать *v.* prepare, make; —ка *f.* preparation.

препод/аватель *m.* teacher, instructor; —авательский *a.* teacher's, teaching; —авать, —ать *v.* teach, instruct, lecture.

преподн/есение *n.* presentation; —ести, —осить *v.* present, offer, bring up to.

препоруч/ать, —ить *v.* entrust, commit; —ение *n.* entrusting, commission.

препрово/дительный *see* сопроводительный; —дить, —ждать *v.* forward, send, dispatch, convey.

препятств/ие *n.* obstacle, impediment, difficulty, obstruction, barrier, hindrance, drawback, check, stop; —о-вать *v.* prevent, stop, inhibit, obstruct, hinder, impede, interfere, interrupt; oppose, cross.

прерв/анный *a.* discontinuous, interrupted, cut off; —ать *see* прерывать.

прерия *f.* prairie.

прерогатива *f.* prerogative.

прерыв *m.,* —ание *n.* interruption, interception, breaking, break, cutting off; discontinuity; —атель *m.* interrupter; (instruments) chopper; (elec.) breaker, contact breaker; cut-out; —ать *v.* interrupt, intercept; stop, discontinue, break off, cut short; break, chop; (elec.) break contact; —ающий *a.* interrupting, intercepting; breaking; disruptive; —ающийся *a.* intermittent, discontinuous.

прерыв/истость, —ность *f.* discontinuity, brokenness; —истый, —ный, —чатый *a.* discontinuous, non-continuous, broken, interrupted, intermittent; gusty (wind); broken (line); —ного действия intermittent.

пресе/кать, —чь *v.* suppress, interrupt, cut short, cut off; —чение *n.* interruption, cutting off.

прескверный *a.* very bad.

преслед/ование *n.* pursuing, pursuit, chasing, persecution; —овать *v.* pursue, follow; persecute; institute (proceedings against); —ующий *a.* pursuing.

пресмык/аться *v.* creep, crawl; —ающиеся *pl.* (zool.) reptiles.

пресн/оводность *f.* freshness (of water); —оводный *a.* fresh-water, limnetic; —ость *f.* freshness; insipidity, flatness (of taste); —ый *a.* fresh; insipid, flat, unflavored; unleavened (bread).

пресс *m.* press, punch, punching machine; (hay) baler; гидравлический п. hydraulic press; п.-котел *m.* autoclave press; п.-масленка *f.* pressure lubricator; п.-подборщик *m.* (agr.) pickup baler; —а *f.* press (relating to newspapers, etc.); —борд *m.* pressboard; —материал *m.,* —овочная композиция molding composition.

прессов/альный *a.* press, pressing; п. инструмент pressing tool, pressing die; —альщик *m.* presser; —ание *n.,* —ка *f.* pressing, compression, squeezing, extrusion; —анный *a.* pressed, compressed, squeezed, extruded; compacted (powder);—анный картон pressboard; —ать *v.* press, compress, squeeze, extrude; —щик *m.* presser; —ыдувная машина (glass) press and blow machine.

пресс-папье *n.* paperweight.

пресс/порошок *m.* molding powder; —уемый *a.* pressed, extruded; extrudable; —ующий *a.* pressing, press; —фильтр *m.* press filter; —форма *f.* mold; —шпан *m.* pressboard.

престабитоль *m.* Prestabitol (detergent).

престарелый *a.* very old, ancient.

престиж *m.* prestige.

престометр *m.* prestometer (for measuring thickness and diameter); fluid gage.

преступ/ать, —ить *v.* transgress, overstep, pass; —ление *n.* crime, offense; —ник *m.,* —ный *a.* criminal.

пресы/тить, —щать *v.* satiate; supersaturate; surcharge.

пресыщен/ие *n.* satiation; supersaturation; —ность *f.* satiety, surfeit; —ный *a.* satiated; supersatured.

прет *pr.* 3 *sing.* of переть.

претвор/ить, —ять *v.* transform, change, transmute.

претен/довать *v.* pretend, claim, lay claim (to); —зия *f.* pretension, claim; grievance.

**претерп/евать, —еть** *v.* undergo, bear, endure.

**преть** *v.* sweat, stew; rot.

**преувелич/ение** *n.* exaggeration, overstatement; **—енный** *a.* exaggerated; **—ивать, —ить** *v.* exaggerate, overstate.

**преуменьш/ать, —ить** *v.* minimize, understate; **—ение** *n.* understatement; **—енный** *a.* minimal.

**преуспе/вать, —ть** *v.* succeed, prosper.

**преференциальный** *a.* preferential.

**преход/ить** *v.* pass; **—ящий** *a.* passing, transient, temporary.

**прецедент** *m.* precedent.

**прецесс/ировать** *v.* precess; **—ия** *f.* precession.

**прецизионн/ость** *f.* precision, accuracy; **—ый** *a.* precision.

**преципит/ат** *m.* precipitate; spec. dicalcium phosphate (fertilizer); **белый п.** white precipitate, ammoniated mercury, mercuriammonium chloride; **—ация** *f.* precipitation; **—ин** *m.* precipitin.

**прешпан** *m.* pressboard.

**при** *prep. prepos.* in the time of, during; in, at, by, near; in the presence of; about, with; attached, affiliated with; **п. анализе** on analysis; **п. всем том** in spite of all that; **п. заводе** at the plant; **п. малярии** in case of malaria, when suffering from malaria; **п. нагревании** upon heating, on heating; **п. нем** in his presence; **п. помешивании** on mixing; with mixing; **п сем** herewith; **напряжение п. сжатии** compression stress; **п. условии** under the condition (that); **п. цифре** followed by a figure; **п. этом** besides, in addition to this, moreover; at the same time, simultaneously; in this case, here; **состоять п.** *v.* be attached to.

**при—** *prefix* ad—, toward; at, in the region of, in the vicinity of.

**Приамурье** Amur river region.

**прианодный** *a.* anolyte (layer).

**прибав/ить, —лять** *v.* add, increase, augment; **п. на огонь** for; **—иться, —ляться** *v.* increase; be added; **—ка** *f.*, **—ление** *n.* increase, addition, supplement, annex, appendix; allowance; (com.) bonus; **—ляемое** *n.*

(math.) addend; **—очный** *a.* additional; after—; **—очная стоимость** surplus value.

**прибалтийский** *a.* Baltic.

**прибег/ать, —нуть** *v.* have recourse (to), resort (to), apply (to).

**прибе/гать, —жать** *v.* run (to), run up (to); **—жище** *n.* refuge, retreat, haven.

**прибере/гать, —чь** *v.* reserve, keep, preserve.

**прибив/ание** *n.*, **—ка** *f.* fastening, nailing (on); **—ать** *v.* fasten, nail (on).

**прибирать** *v.* put in order, straighten out.

**прибит/ый** *a.* fastened, nailed (on); lodged, knocked down (grain); **—ь** *see* **прибивать.**

**прибл.** *abbr.* (приблизительно) approximately.

**приближ/ать** *v.* draw nearer, approximate, approach; **—аться** *v.* draw near, approximate, approach, converge; **—ающийся** *a.* approaching, forthcoming.

**приближен/ие** *n.* approach, approaching, drawing near, approximation; **—ность** *f.* nearness, proximity; **—ный** *a.* approximate, rough; close; **—ный метод** method of approximation.

**приблизительн/о** *adv.* approximately; **—ость** *f.* approximateness; approximation; **—ый** *a.* approximate, rough.

**приблизить** *see* **приближать.**

**прибой** *m.* surf, breakers.

**прибол/тить, —чивать** *v.* bolt on; **—ченный** *a.* bolted, bolted on.

**прибор** *m.* apparatus, instrument, implement, device, appliance; set, outfit; gear; **—er, —or; п. для испытаний, испытательный п.** tester; **погрешность —a** instrumental error; **установка —ов** instrumentation; **—ная доска** instrument panel; **—остроение** *n.* instrument making, instrument engineering.

**прибортовой** *a.* near the side of (a boat, basin, mountain).

**прибр/анный** *a.* put in order, arranged; **—ать** *see* **прибирать.**

**прибрежный** *a.* littoral, coastal; riparian.

**прибыв/ание** *n.* increase, rise, rising;

—**ать** *v.* increase, rise (of water); arrive, come, flow.

**прибыль** *f.* profit, gain, benefit, returns; increase, rise; (foundry) head, deadhead, lost head, shrinkage head; —**но** *adv.* profitably; —**ный** *a.* profitable, gainful, commercial; —**ный конец** (foundry) deadhead.

**прибыт/ие** *n.* arrival; —**ь** *see* прибывать.

**привал** *m.* halt; —**ивать**, —**ить** *v.* lean, rest (against); heap up, pile up.

**привар** *m.*, —**ивание** *n.* sticking; —**енный** *a.* welded; —**ивать**, —**ить** *v.* boil more, boil in addition; weld (on); —**ка** *f.* welding; —**ной** *a.* welded, welding.

**приварок** *m.* victuals.

**приведение** *n.* bringing; adduction, adducing; (math.) reduction; setting (in motion); putting (in order).

**приведенн/ый** *a.* corrected; reduced; brought; referred; quoted; presented; п. центр reduction point; —**ая вязкость** reduced viscosity; —**ая чувствительность** factor of merit (of measuring instruments); —**ое давление** reduced pressure.

**привезти** *see* привозить.

**приверженн/ость** *f.* adherence, attachment; —**ый** *a.* attached; devoted.

**привер/нуть**, —**теть**, —**тывать**, —**чивать** *v.* screw, tighten, clamp; —**тный** *a.* screwed on, screw.

**привес** *m.* overweight; gain, increase in weight; —**ить** *see* привешивать; —**ка** *f.*, —**ок** *m.* pendant.

**привести** *see* приводить.

**привет** *m.* welcome; regards; —**ствовать** *v.* greet, welcome.

**привешивать** *v.* append, hang, suspend.

**привив/ание** *n.*, —**ка** *f.* (bot.) grafting; (cryst.) inoculation, seeding; (med.) inoculation; vaccination; —**ать** *v.* graft; inoculate; vaccinate; —**аться** *v.* be grafted; take; —**ок** *m.* graft; —**очный** *a.* grafting; inoculative, inoculating; —**очный воск** grafting wax.

**привидениевые** *pl.* (zool.) Phasmodea.

**привилег/ированный** *a.* privileged, licensed; —**ия** *f.* privilege, license, patent; royalty.

**привин/тить**, —**чивать** *v.* screw on;

—**ченный** *a.* screwed on; —**чивание** *n.* screwing on.

**привит/ие** *see* прививка; —**ый** *a.* grafted; graft (polymer); —**ь** *see* прививать.

**привкус** *m.* taste, aftertaste.

**привле/кательный** *a.* attractive; —**кать**, —**чь** *v.* attract, draw, pull; —**каться** *v.* be attracted, be drawn; —**чение** *n.* attraction, drawing, pulling.

**привн/ести**, —**осить** *v.* introduce; —**ос** *m.* introduction, addition.

**привод** *m.* bringing; driving gear, drive, drive mechanism, actuator; **паровой** п. steam drive; **передача** —**ом** driving gear; gear transmission; **ременный** п. belt drive; с —**ом** driven by; с —**ом от мотора** motor-operated; с механическим —**ом** power-driven, power-operated; с ручным —**ом** hand-operated, hand-driven; **червячный** п. worm gear.

**приводимый** *a.* driven; reducible; cited (as an example); п. мотором motor-operated, motor-driven.

**приводить** *v.* bring, lead; drive; reduce; adduce, bring forward, present; quote, cite; (physiol.) adduct; set (in motion); put (in practice); п. к общему знаменателю (math.) reduce to a common denominator; п. к тому, что mean, signify that; —**ся** *v.* be brought; be corrected; be reduced (to); be led; chance, happen.

**приводка** *f.* (printing) registration.

**приводн/ой** *a.* driving, drive; power driven, power-operated; supply; п. вал driving shaft, drive shaft; п. механизм driving gear; п. насос power pump; п. ремень driving belt; п. шкив driver, driving pulley; —**ая цепь** sprocket chain, chain drive; —**ое колесо** driving wheel, driver.

**приводящ/ий** *a.* bringing, leading; driving; reducing; (physiol.) adducent, adducting; —**ая мышца** (anat.) adductor.

**привоз** *m.* bringing, supply; import, importation; —**ить** *v.* bring, convey; import; —**ной**, —**ный** *a.* imported; brought from another place.

**привой** *m.* (bot.) graft, scion.

**приворотень** *see* пижма.

**привратник** *m.* gate keeper; (elec.) door opener; porter, janitor; (anat.) pylorus.

**привы/кание** *n.* getting accustomed, acclimatization; habituation; **—кать, —кнуть** *v.* get accustomed (to), become used (to); become acclimated; **—чка** *f.* habit, custom, practice; **—чный** *a.* habitual, customary, usual.

**привяз/анный** *a.* tied, attached; **—ать, —ывать** *v.* tie, bind, fasten, attach; **—ка** *f.* tying; **—ь** *f.* tie, string, rope.

**пригар** *m.* (foundry) loam or sand crust picked up on casting, pickup.

**пригво/ждать, —здить** *v.* nail to; **—ждение** *n.* nailing.

**пригибать** *v.* bend, bow.

**пригла/дить, —живать** *v.* smooth, make smooth, slick.

**пригла/сить, —шать** *v.* invite, ask, bid; **—шение** *n.* invitation.

**приглуш/ать, —ить** *v.* damp down, choke (fire); muffle, deaden (sound).

**пригляд/еть, —ывать** *v.* look after; **—ываться** *v.* look attentively (at), scrutinize.

**пригн/анность** *f.* matching, fitting together; **—анный** *a.* matched, fitted, adjusted; **—анная деталь** mate; **быть —анным к** *v.* be fitted to, fit; **—ать** *see* **пригонять.**

**пригнуть** *see* **пригибать.**

**приговор** *m.* sentence, verdict, decision.

**пригод/иться** *v.* be of use, be useful, stand one in good stead; **—ность** *f.* usefulness, fitness, suitableness, serviceability, adaptability; **—ный** *a.* useful, fit, suitable, adaptable, applicable, adequate, good (for).

**приголовок** *m.* first runnings.

**пригон/ка** *f.* fitting, fitting together, jointing; adjusting, adjustment, alignment; reseating (valve); **п. вновь** readjustment; **п. частей** assembling; **плотная п.** tight fit; **—очный** *a.* adjusting; **—щик** *m.* fitter, adjuster; **—ять** *v.* fit, fit on, fit in, work in, join, joint; adjust, adapt; reseat (a valve).

**пригор/ание** *n.* scorching, burning; sticking; **—ать, —еть** *v.* scorch, burn; **—елый** *a.* scorched, burnt;

empyreumatic, tarry; **—елое масло** empyreumatic oil.

**пригород** *m.* suburb; **—ный** *a.* suburban; (tel.) local.

**пригорок** *m.* hillock, knoll, elevation.

**пригоршня** *f.* handful.

**приготов/ительный** *a.* preparatory; *suffix* processing; **—ить, —лять** *v.* prepare, make ready, provide, arrange; **—иться, —ляться** *v.* be prepared; prepare, get ready; be in preparation; **—ление** *n.* preparation, production; arrangement; **—ленный** *a.* prepared; **—ленный на** made with.

**пригре/вать, —ть** *v.* warm.

**пригрозить** *v.* threaten, menace.

**придавать** *v.* give, add, confer, lend, impart; attach, adjoin; **п. лоск** polish.

**придав/ить, —ливать** *v.* press, squeeze; **—ленный** *a.* pressed, squeezed.

**придан/ие** *n.* giving, imparting; **—ный** *a.* given, added, imparted; attached.

**прида/ток** *m.* appendage, addition, supplement; (anat.) appendix, hypophysis; **—точный** *a.* additional, accessory; (bot.) adventive; **—ть** *see* **придавать; —ча** *f.* addition.

**придви/гать, —нуть** *v.* move near, push; **—гаться, —нуться** *v.* draw near, approach; **—жной винт** set screw, adjusting screw.

**придел/ать, —ывать** *v.* attach, join; put; adapt, fit.

**придерж/анный** *a.* held, clamped; **—ать, —ивать** *v.* hold, hold down, hold back; **—аться, —иваться** *v.* hold (to), keep (to), adhere (to), follow, confine oneself (to); **—ка** *f.* stripper, stripping device.

**придираться** *v.* find fault (with).

**придонный** *a.* (biol.) bottom-dwelling, demersal.

**придорожн/ик** *m.* (bot.) ageratum; **—ый** *a.* roadside, wayside; **—ая игла** (bot.) jujube (*Zizyphus jujube*).

**придраться** *see* **придираться.**

**придум/ать, —ывать** *v.* devise, concoct, fabricate, develop, invent, find.

**приез/д** *m.* arrival, coming; **—жать** *v.* arrive, come; **—жающий** *a.* arriving; *m.* newcomer, visitor; **—жий** *a.* on tour; *m.* non-resident, newcomer, visitor.

**прием** *m.* reception, receiving, acceptance; admission, intake; mode, way, method, procedure, method of procedure, process; dose (of medicine); *suffix* practice, method; —ы *pl.* procedure; в несколько —ов in stages, by series; первого —а primary; сила —а (rad.) receptivity.

**прием/истость** *f.* pickup (of motor); —ка *f.* reception, acceptance, adoption; inspection; —лемость *f.* acceptability; —лемый *a.* acceptable, admissible.

**приемн/ая** *f.* anteroom, hall, reception room; —ик *m.* receiver, receiving vessel, collector, receptacle, container, vessel, flask, tank, reservoir; hopper; (elec.) transducer; (radiation) detector; feeder (of machine gun).

**приемн/ый** *a.* reception, receiving, collecting, take-up; adopted; *see also under* приемочный; п. валец, п. ролик drawing-in roller, take-in roller; п. желоб pouring gate, hopper; п. калибр purchase inspection gage; п. клапан suction valve (of pump, etc.); п. покой dispensary, casualty ward; —ая воронка charging hopper, feed hopper, hopper; —ая камера suction chamber (of pump); —ое отверстие intake, inlet; —ое сопло combining nozzle, mixing nozzle; —ое устройство intake; —ые часы consultation hours, office hours.

**приемо/передаточный** *a.* (rad.) two-way; —передатчик *m.* transceiver; —указатель *m.* finder; —чно-техническое испытание warranty test.

**приемочн/ый** *a.* reception, acceptance; *see also* приемный; п. акт inspection certificate, acceptance certificate; —ое испытание acceptance test, official test; —ое клеймо acceptance stamp.

**приемщик** *m.* receiver, inspector.

**приехать** *see* приезжать.

**прижать** *see* прижимать.

**прижечь** *see* прижигать.

**приживаться** *v.* get accustomed to a place, acclimatize, take root.

**прижиг/ание** *n.* searing, cauterization; —ательный *a.* (med.) caustic; —ать *v.* sear, cauterize, scorch; —ающий *a.* searing, cauterizing, caustic; —ающее средство caustic.

**прижизненный** *a.* in one's lifetime.

**прижим** *m.* clip; —ание *n.* pressing, squeezing; tightening, clamping; —ать *v.* press, squeeze; tighten, clamp, screw; —ающий *a.* pressing, squeezing; tightening, clamping; —ающая сила pressing force, pressure.

**прижимн/ой** *a.* pressing, tightening, clamp; п. болт clamp bolt; п. контакт (elec.) rubbing contact; —ая планка clamp, cleat.

**прижиться** *see* приживаться.

**приз** *m.* prize.

**призв/ание** *n.* vocation, calling; —анный *a.* called (to); —ать *see* призывать.

**приземистый** *a.* thickset, squat, stocky.

**призем/ление** *n.* (aero.) landing; —литься *v.* land; touch the ground; —ной *a.* surface, near the ground.

**призма** *f.* prism; —тин *m.* (min.) prismatine.

**призматическ/ий** *a.* prismatic; —ая опора knife edge, knife-edge bearing, blade bearing, fulcrum bearing; —ое преломление prismatic refraction.

**призм/атоид** *m.* (geom.) prismatoid; —енный *a.* prism, prismatic; —оид *m.*, —оидный *a.* prismoid; —ообразный *a.* prismoid, prismoidal.

**признавать** *v.* acknowledge, recognize, admit, own; —ся *v.* be acknowledged; confess, admit.

**признак** *m.* sign, indication, symptom, mark, index, criterion; feature, characteristic, attribute; vestige, trace; служить —ом *v.* indicate, denote.

**призн/ание** *n.* acknowledgement, recognition, acceptance; —анный *a.* acknowledged; —ательный *a.* grateful, thankful; —ать *see* признавать; надо —аться, что it must be admitted that.

**призовой** *a.* prize.

**призонный болт** templet bolt, tight-fitting bolt; п. штифт set pin, steady pin.

**призор** *m.* care, protection.

**призра/к** *m.* specter, phantom; illusion; —чный *a.* illusory, unreal.

**призыв** *m.* conscription; call, appeal;

—ать *v.* call; call up, draft, conscript; —ной *m.* draftee.

**прииск** *m.* mine, placer; —ание *n.* finding; **бюро по —анию работы** employment office; —ать *v.* find; —ивать *v.* look for, seek.

**прийти** *see* **приходить.**

**приказ** *m.* order, command, injunction; **чек —у** (com.) order check, check to person's order; —ание *n.* order, command, summons; direction, instruction; —ать, —ывать *v.* order, command, bid; direct, instruct.

**прикалывать** *v.* pin, fasten with a pin.

**приканчивать** *v.* finish.

**прикасаться** *v.* touch, abut, adjoin.

**прикат/ить** *see* **прикатывать;** —ка *f.* stitching.

**прикатодный** *a.* at the cathode, cathodic; catholyte (layer).

**прикатывать** *v.* roll, roll up (to); pack (soil).

**приклад** *m.* rifle butt; (text.) trimmings.

**прикладн/ой** *a.* applied; —ая химия applied chemistry.

**прикладыв/ание** *n.* application; —ать *v.* apply; add, annex, affix, join; enclose; —ать к apply to; impress upon.

**прикле/енный** *a.* glued, pasted (on); —ивание *n.,* —йка *f.* gluing, pasting, sticking; —ивать, —ить *v.* glue, paste, attach, stick; —иваться, —иться *v.* be glued to; stick, adhere.

**приклеп/ать,** —ывать *v.* rivet (to).

**приклинок** *m.* (mach.) gib.

**приклон/ить,** —ять *v.* lay, incline.

**приключ/ать** *v.* (elec.) connect up; —аться, —иться *v.* happen, occur; —ение *n.* adventure; (elec.) connection.

**приков/ать,** —ывать *v.* forge (to); chain; rivet (attention).

**прикол/ачивать,** —отить *v.* nail, fasten with nails.

**приколоть** *see* **прикалывать.**

**прикомандиров/ать,** —ывать *v.* (mil.) attach.

**прикончить** *see* **приканчивать.**

**прикопка** *f.* heeling (of plants).

**прикорнев/ой** *a.* radical; at the roots; —ая зона rhizosphere.

**прикосновен/ие** *n.* touch, touching, contact; **точка —ия** point of contact; —ность *f.* contiguity, proximity;

participation, implication; —ный *a.* adjacent, adjoining; implicated (in).

**прикоснуться** *see* **прикасаться.**

**прикра/сить,** —шивать *v.* embellish, adorn.

**прикреп/итель** *m.* fastener; —ить, —лять *v.* fasten, attach, fix, affix, secure, anchor, connect; —ление *n.* fastening, fixture; —ленный *a.* fastened, attached, adherent; (zool.) sessile, sedentary.

**прикру/тить,** —чивать *v.* tie, bind, fasten; turn down, tighten.

**прикры/вать,** —ть *v.* cover, screen, shelter, protect; throttle (valve); —тие *n.* cover, screen, protection; housing; escort, convoy; throttling; —тый *a.* covered, protected; throttled.

**прикуп/ать,** —ить *v.* buy more, make an additional purchase; —ка *f.* additional purchase; —ной *a.* bought in addition.

**прикус** *m.* (odontology) bite, occlusion; **неправильный п.** malocclusion; —ка *f.* (vet.) air swallowing.

**прилавок** *m.* counter, store counter.

**прилагать** *see* **прикладывать.**

**прила/дить,** —живать *v.* fit, adapt, adjust; —дка *f.,* —живание *n.* fitting.

**прилег/ать** *v.* adjoin, be adjacent (to), abut, butt (against), border; **плотно п. к** fit; —ающий *a.* adjoining, adjacent, contiguous, neighboring, abutting.

**прилежание** *n.* diligence, industry, application.

**прилежащий** *a.* adjacent, adjoining, contiguous; **п. угол** angle of contact.

**прилежный** *a.* diligent, industrious.

**прилеп/ить,** —лять *v.* stick, glue, attach (to).

**прилет** *m.* arrival, coming (by flight); —ать, —еть *v.* arrive, come; —ный *a.* migratory (birds).

**прилив** *m.* influx, flow; congestion (of blood); tide, high tide, high water; rib, tongue, boss, lug; cleat; **волна —а** tidal wave; —ать *v.* flow (to); rush (of blood); pour in, run in, add more (liquid); —ающий *a.* inflowing, affluent; —ообразующий *a.* tide-generating; —чик *m.* boss, rib, fillet.

прилип/аемость *f.* adherence; —ала *f.* remora (sucking fish); —ание *n.* adhesion, adherence, sticking, attachment; —атель *m.* (insecticides) sticker; —ать, —нуть *v.* adhere, stick, cling, agglutinate, cohere; be communicated (of disease); —ший *a.* adhesive, adherent; stuck.

прилистник *m.* (bot.) stipule.

прилит/ый *a.* poured (to), added, run in; (foundry) cast on; —ь *see* приливать.

приличный *a.* decent, proper.

прилож/ение *n.* application; enclosure; appendix, supplement, addition, annex; точка —ения point of application; —енный *a.* applied; —ить *see* прикладывать.

прим *m.* (math., etc.) prime.

прим. *abbr.* (примечание) note.

примавера *see* махогани, белое.

приман/ивать *v.* bait, lure, attract; —ка *f.* bait; decoy.

примат *m.* pre-eminence.

приматы *pl.* (zool.) Primates.

примачивать *v.* bathe, moisten, wet.

прим/вераза *f.* primverase; —верин *m.* primverin; —еверин *m.* primeverin; —евероза *f.* primeverose.

примен/ение *n.* application, use, employment, utilization, adaptation; —енный *a.* applied, employed, utilized, adapted; —имость, —яемость *f.* applicability, adaptability; —имый *a.* applicable, usable, adaptable, practicable, appropriate; available; —ительный *a.* applicable; conformable, suitable; —ить, —ять *v.* apply, employ, use, adapt, practice, put in practice; —иться, —яться *v.* be applied; adapt oneself, conform (to).

пример *m.* example, model, sample, instance; по —у in imitation of; подавать п. *v.* set an example; приводить в п. *v.* cite as an example, illustrate (with).

примерз/ание *n.* freezing on, adhesion by freezing; —ать, —нуть *v.* freeze (on, to, together); —лый *a.* frozen.

пример/ивание *n.*, —ка *f.* trying on, fitting; —ивать, —ить *v.* try on, fit.

примерн/о *adv.* exemplarily, as an example; approximately, say; —ый *a.* exemplary; approximate.

примерять *see* примеривать.

примесь *f.* admixture, addition, ingredient; foreign body, foreign matter, impurity, contaminant; adulteration, contamination; (met.) alloy; побочная п., посторонняя п., случайная п. secondary constituent; impurity, foreign matter; с —ю impure.

примет *fut. 3 sing.* of принимать.

примет/а *f.* sign, indication, mark, index, criterion, characteristic; —ы *pl.* description, distinctive marks; —ить *see* примечать; —ливый *a.* observant; —но *adv.* perceptibly; —ный *a.* perceptible, visible; conspicuous.

приметывать *v.* tack, stitch (to).

примеч/ание *n.* note, annotation, comment, remark; footnote; снабжать —аниями *v.* annotate; —ательность *f.* notability, noteworthiness; —ательный *a.* notable, noteworthy, remarkable; —ать *v.* perceive, notice, take notice (of), observe.

примеш/ивание *n.* admixing, addition, introduction; impurity; —ать, —ивать *v.* admix, add, introduce; (met.) alloy.

приминать *v.* trample down, crush, flatten, pack.

примир/ительный *a.* conciliatory; —ить, —ять *v.* reconcile; —иться, —яться *v.* reconcile oneself (to).

примите *imp.* of принимать.

примитив *m.* primitive; —ный *a.* primitive, early; simple, rough.

примкнуть *see* примыкать.

примоина *f.* (geol.) alluvium, river silt.

примордиальный *a.* primordial, initial, original.

примор/ский *a.* maritime; seaside; п. порт seaport; —ье *n.* seaside, seashore, shore.

примоч/ить *see* примачивать; —ка *f.* wash, lotion, fomentation.

прим. ред. *abbr.* (примечание редактора) editor's note.

примул/а *f.* (bot.) primrose (*Primula*); —аверин *m.* primulaverin; —ин *m.*, —иновый *a.* primulin; —ит *m.* primulite (a sugar).

примус *m.* Primus (a Swedish stove).

примут *fut. 3 pl.* of принимать.

примык/ать *v.* adjoin, abut, border

(upon); join; fix; —**ающий** *a*. adjoining, adjacent, abutting.

**примят/ый** *a*. trampled, treaded, crushed, packed (soil); —**ь** *see* **приминать.**

**принадлеж/ать** *v*. belong, pertain (to), appertain; —**ность** *f*. belonging, affiliation; appurtenance; appliance, implement, gadget, fixture, fitting; accessory, attachment, part; —**ности** *pl*. outfit, equipment; tackle; mountings, parts; **по** —**ности** to the owner; to the proper quarter.

**принайтовать** *v*. lash.

**принести** *see* **приносить.**

**приним/ать** *v*. take, receive, accept, admit; assume, put on, take on, take up (a position); adopt; inspect (merchandise); **п. за** mistake for; **п. на себя** assume, take upon oneself; —**аться** *v*. be received; begin, set about, set to, get started; be assumed; take root, take (of a plant).

**приноготовник** *m*. (bot.) whitlow-wort (*Paronychia*).

**приносить** *v*. bring; bring in, return, bear, yield.

**принудит/ельно** *adv*. compulsorily; —**ельный** *a*. compulsory, forced, coercive; positive; —**ь** *see* **принуждать.**

**принужд/ать** *v*. oblige, constrain, force, compel, impel; —**ение** *n*. constraint, forcing, compulsion, coercion; —**енно** *adv*. constrainedly, by force; —**енный** *a*. constrained, forced.

**принцип** *m*. principle; mode (of operation); **в** —**е** as a matter of principle; theoretically; **из** —**а,** —**иально** *adv*. on principle; —**ал** *m*. principal; —**иальный** *a*. principle; —**иальная схема** line diagram.

**принцметалл** *m*. Prince's metal (a zinc-copper brass).

**принят/ие** *n*. reception, acceptance, admission, adoption, assumption; —**ый** *a*. accepted, admitted, assumed;—**о** it is assumed, it is taken for granted; **это не** —**о** it is not done, it is not the custom; —**ь** *see* **принимать.**

**приобре/сти,** —**тать** *v*. acquire, gain, obtain, get, take on; buy, purchase; —**тание** *n*. acquirement, acquisition, gaining, obtaining; purchase; —**тение**

*n*. acquisition; —**тенный** *a*. acquired.

**приобщ/ать,** —**ить** *v*. unite, join, aggregate; —**ение** *n*. uniting, junction.

**приовражный** *a*. gully control (planting).

**приорит** *m*. (min.) priorite.

**приоритет** *m*. priority.

**приостан/авливать,** —**овить** *v*. stop, cease, suspend; —**овка** *f*. stopping, stoppage, cessation; stop, pause, rest; cutting off, turning off; **период** —**овки** down time (of plant, etc.); —**овленный** *a*. stopped, closed, closed down.

**приотвор/ить,** —**ять** *v*. open slightly, crack.

**припад/ать** *v*. fall down; fall, press (against); —**ок** *m*. fit, attack, paroxysm.

**припаив/аемый** *a*. solderable; —**ание** *n*. soldering; —**ать** *v*. solder, fix on.

**припай** *m*. land floe.

**припайка** *see* **припаивание.**

**припал/енный** *a*. burnt, singed; —**ить** *v*. burn, singe, scorch.

**припар/ивать,** —**ить** *v*. steam, poultice, foment; —**ка** *f*. poultice, cataplasm.

**припас** *m*. store, supply, provision; (cer.) kiln furniture; —**ы** *pl*. supplies, provisions, victuals; —**ать** *v*. lay up, store.

**припасов/анный** *a*. fitted; —**ка** *f*. fitting; alignment.

**припасти** *see* **припасать.**

**припасть** *see* **припадать.**

**припа/янный** *a*. soldered; —**ять** *see* **припаивать.**

**припе/к** *m*. surplus (in weight of bread on baking); (sun) burn; —**кать,** —**чь** *v*. bake too long; be hot, parch.

**припис/ать,** —**ывать** *v*. add (writing); attach, register; ascribe, attribute, put down (to), impute; assign (a value); —**ка** *f*. postscript; attaching, registration; —**ывание** *n*. adding; attribution, imputation.

**припла/та** *f*. additional payment; —**тить,** —**чивать** *v*. pay more, pay in addition.

**приплод** *m*. issue, offspring; —**ный скот** breeding cattle, breeding stock.

**приплы/вать,** —**ть** *v*. come up, swim up, float up.

**приплю/снуть,** —**щивать** *v*. flatten.

приподн/имать, —ять *v.* raise a little, take up; —ятие *n.*, —ятость *f.* elevation; —ятый *a.* raised a little; (geol.) upheaved, raised.

припой *m.* solder; крепкий п. brazing solder; слабый п. soft solder.

приполярный *a.* circumpolar.

припом/инание *n.* remembering, recollection; —инать, —нить, —януть *v.* remember, recollect, recall.

припосадочный *a.* preplanting, starter.

приправ/а *f.* seasoning, condiment; — ить, —лять *v.* season, flavor; (typ.) make ready; —ка *f.* making ready.

припудрив/ание *n.* (foundry) dusting; —ать *v.* dust, sprinkle.

припуск *m.* allowance, margin; п. на allowance for; п. на усадку shrinkage allowance; оставлять п. *v.* allow (for).

припус/кать, —тить *v.* couple, pair; add; let in, admit; let out (in sewing).

припух/ать, —нуть *v.* swell a little; —лость *f.* swelling, intumescence; —лый *a.* swollen, puffed up.

припыл *m.*, —ивающее вещество (foundry) parting medium; powder, dust; —ивание *n.* powdering, dusting (molds).

прираб/атывать *v.* earn extra; —атываться, —отаться *v.* work in, run in (of bearing); —отавшийся *a.* worn in.

приравнивать *v.* level, adjust, adapt; equate; set (to zero, etc.); compare (with).

прира/стать, —сти *v.* adhere; grow, increase, accrue; —стить, —щать *v.* make adhere, attach; increase; —щение *n.* increment, increase, gain.

прирез/ать, —ывать *v.* cut, fit, fit in; measure in; —ной *a.* cut.

приречный *a.* riparian, riverain.

прировнять *see* приравнивать.

природ/а *f.* nature; испытатель —ы naturalist; по —е by nature.

природн/ый *a.* natural, inborn, innate, inherent, intrinsic, indigenous, native, in the native state; crude, raw; п. газ natural gas; п. житель native; —ая сила natural agent.

природовед/ение *n.* natural history, natural science; —ческий *a.* natural history, naturalistic.

прирожденный *a.* inborn, innate, native.

прирос/т *m.* growth, increment, increase, gain; accretion; —ток *m.* excrescence, growth; —ший к grown fast to.

прирубежный *a.* frontier, border.

прируч/ать, —ить *v.* domesticate, tame.

Приса формула (elec.) Preece's formula.

присад/ка *f.* addition, supplement, admixture; additive; (met.) aftercharge, aftercharging; —очный *a.* additional; —очный пруток welding rod; —очный элемент (elec.) addition agent; alloy; —очное устройство adjusting device.

присажив/ание *n.* addition, introduction; —ать *v.* add, introduce, fill up.

присасыв/ание *n.* sucking, suction, indraft; —ать *v.* suck, pull, draw in; —аться *v.* attach itself by suction, stick, adhere; —ающий *a.* sucking.

присваивать *v.* appropriate, adopt, assume; award, give, confer.

присводовый *a.* crest.

присво/ение *n.* appropriation; awarding, conferment; —ить *see* присваивать.

прискорбие *n.* sorrow, distress, regret.

прислон/енный *a.* recumbent, leaning; —ить, —ять *v.* lean (against).

прислу/га *f.* servant; service, attendance; attendants; (mil.) crew; —живать *v.* serve, attend.

прислуш/аться, —иваться *v.* listen (for).

присматривать *v.* look (for); п. за look after, keep an eye on, attend; supervise, oversee (work); —ся *v.* examine, scrutinize.

присмотр *m.* looking after, care, attendance; superintendence, supervision; —еть *see* присматривать.

присовокуп/ительный *a.* additional; — ить, —лять *v.* add, annex, append; —ление *n.* addition.

присоединен/ие *n.* addition, annexation, joining; (elec.) connection, contact; продукт —ия addition compound; продукт —ия брома bromine addition product; реакция —ия addition, addition reaction; —ный *a.* added, joined; augmented; associated, connected.

присоедин/ить, —ять *v.* add, join, adjoin, annex, attach, incorporate;

(elec.) connect, connect up; —ю-
щийся *a.* additive; joining, adjoining.
присос/аться *v.* adhere, attach oneself
(to); —ка *f.* (biol.) sucker, sucking
disk.
присохнуть *see* присыхать.
приспе/вать, —ть *v.* approach, come.
приспос/абливать, —обить *see* приспособлять.
приспособл/ение *n.* adaptation, adjustment, fitting, accommodation, arrangement; device, appliance, apparatus, contrivance, gadget, attachment, accessory, fixture; equipment,
outfit; —енный *a.* adjusted, suited,
fitted, adapted; —яемость *f.* adaptability; —яемый *a.* adjustable, adaptable, applicable.
приспособлять *v.* adapt, fit, adjust,
suit, accommodate, arrange; —ся *v.*
adapt oneself, get accustomed (to).
пристав/ание *n.* adhesion, clinging,
sticking; —ать *v.* adhere, cling, stick;
join, side; worry, annoy.
пристав/ить, —лять *v.* set, put, lean;
appoint; —ка *f.* attachment, attached
piece; adapter; (grammar) prefix;
—ной *a.* added, attached; —ная
лестница lean-to ladder; —ший *a.*
adherent.
пристальный *a.* fixed, intent, steady
(gaze).
пристанище *n.* refuge, shelter, asylum.
пристань *f.* landing, wharf, pier, quay.
прист/ать *see* приставать; —ающий *a.*
adhering, adhesive, sticking; tenacious.
пристенный *a.* boundary (layer).
пристимерин *m.* pristimerin.
Пристлея кольца (elec.) Priestley's
rings.
пристраивать *v.* add to a building;
settle, establish; —ся *v.* be added, be
attached; find a place.
пристрастный *a.* partial, prejudiced.
пристрел/ивать *v.* target (firearms);
—ка *f.* adjustment, fire for adjustment; —очная пуля tracer bullet;
—очная стрельба fire for adjustment.
пристро/енный *a.* added on, built on;
—ить *see* пристраивать; —йка *f.*
lean-to, shed, addition (to building),
annex.

приступ *m.* fit, attack, paroxysm; as-
sault; access; beginning; к нему нет
—а he is inaccessible; —ание *n.*
beginning, entering upon; —ать,
—ить *v.* approach; set about, enter
upon, begin, start, proceed.
прису/дить, —ждать *v.* adjudge, award;
sentence, condemn; confer (a degree);
—ждение *n.* awarding, conferment;
sentencing.
присутственн/ое место office; —ые часы office hours.
присутств/ие *n.* presence, occurrence;
attendance; office; —овать *v.* be
present, attend, assist; —ующий *a.*
present, attending, attendant, assist-
ing.
присуч/ивание *n.* twisting together,
piecing (of thread); —ивать, —ить
*v.* twist together, twist on.
присущ/ий *a.* inherent, innate, intrinsic,
indigenous; —ность *f.* inherence.
присылать *v.* send.
присып/ать *v.* add, pour more; sprinkle;
—ка *f.* sprinkling, powdering; powder; —ки *pl.* prisypki [crystals or
fragments of crystals accumulated
on the top face(s) of a larger crystal].
присыхать *v.* adhere (in drying).
прися/га *f.* oath; —гать, —гнуть *v.*
take oath, swear; —жный *m.* juror;
суд —жных jury.
притаптывать *v.* tread down, crush,
pack.
прита/скивать, —щить *v.* bring, drag
in.
притворить *see* притворять.
притвор/ный *a.* pretended, simulated;
—ство *n.* pretense, simulation.
притворять *v.* shut, close.
притворяться *v.* pretend, simulate.
притворяшки *pl.* serricorn beetles (*Pti-
nidae*).
притек/ать *v.* flow (to), run; —ающий *a.*
flowing, incoming.
притереть *see* притирать.
притерт/ый *a.* ground, ground in,
ground down; ground-glass (stopper);
wiped; —ое стекло ground glass.
притес/ать, —ывать *v.* adjust, cut to fit.
притир *m.* lap; —ание, —анье *n.* grinding; fitting in; rubbing; cosmetic,
rouge; —ать *v.* grind, lap; rub; fit;

reset (valve); —ка *f.* grinding, regrinding, abrading, abrasion, lapping,
attrition; fitting; reseating (valve);
—очный стан lapping machine.
**приткнуть** *see* **притыкать.**
**приток** *m.* tributary (of river), affluent;
influx, inflow, affluence; delivery,
admission, intake, feed, supply (of air).
**притол/ка, —ока** *f.* lintel (of door).
**притом** *adv.* besides, moreover.
**притоптать** *see* **притаптывать.**
**приточный** *a.* tributary.
**притр/агиваться, —онуться** *v.* touch.
**притти** *see* **приходить.**
**притуп/ить, —лять** *v.* blunt, dull,
deaden; (cryst.) truncate; —ление *n.*
blunting, dulling; truncation; —ленный *a.* blunted, dulled; truncated.
**притык** *m.* joint; abutment, end; **сваривать в п.** *v.* butt-weld; **сросток в п.**
butt joint; —ать *v.* stick, fasten (to);
stop up; —аться *v.* touch, push; join.
**притяг/ательный** *a.* attractive; —ивать
*v.* attract, draw to itself; screw up,
tighten.
**притяжен/ие** *n.* attraction, gravitation;
**сила —ия** attraction, attractive
force, pull; gravity; —женность *f.*
gravity.
**притяз/ание** *n.* pretension, claim; —а-
тельный *a.* exacting, exigent; —ать
*v.* pretend, lay claim (to).
**притянут/ый** *a.* pulled, attracted;
screwed up, tightened; —ь *see*
**притягивать.**
**приумнож/ать, —ить** *v.* increase, augment, multiply; —ение *n.* augmentation, multiplication.
**приуроч/енный** *a.* confined (to); —и-
вать, —ить *v.* confine; time, coordinate, relate, adapt.
**приуч/ать, —ить** *v.* accustom, train;
acclimatize; —аться, —иться *v.* get
accustomed; —ение, —ивание *n.*
accustoming, training, schooling.
**прификс** *m.* fixed price, set price.
**прифлянцованный** *a.* flange-mounted.
**прифугов/ка** *f.* joint, jointing; —ывать
*v.* joint.
**прихват/ить, —ывать** *v.* catch, seize,
tack, hold; pinch, injure slightly;
—ка *f.* tack weld, temporary weld;
clamp; **сварка с —ками** tack weld.

**приход** *m.* coming, arrival, advent; income; receipt; —ить *v.* come, arrive;
—ить в себя recover consciousness;
—иться *v.* fit; be; be obliged to, have
to; exert, be exerted (of pressure);
ему —ится he has to, he must; —но-
расходная книга account book; —
ный *a.* coming, arriving; income (tax);
receipt (book); —ящий *a.* arriving,
incoming; day, non-resident (pupil).
**прихожая** *f.* entrance, anteroom, lobby.
**прицветник** *m.* (bot.) bract; **вторичный
п.** bractlet.
**прицеит** *m.* (min.) priceite.
**прицел** *m.* aim, taking aim; sight (of gun);
—ивание *n.* aiming, sighting; —и-
ваться, —иться *v.* aim, take aim,
sight.
**прицельн/ый** *a.* sighting; **п. барабан**
range dial; **п. хомутик** rear-sight
slide; —ая колодка rear-sight bed;
—ая линия line of aim; —ые при-
способления sights.
**прицеп** *m.* trailer; hook; —ить, —лять
*v.* hook, hitch, connect; (railroad)
couple; —ка *f.* hooking, hitching;
trailer; (bot.) tendril, cirrus; —ление
*n.* hooking, hitching, connecting;
coupling; —ленный *a.* hooked, connected; coupled; adherent, attached;
—ной *a.* trailer, pull-type; —ной
вагон, —ная тележка trailer; —щик
*m.* plow operator.
**причал** *m.* hawser, mooring rope; —ивание *n.* mooring; —ивать, —ить *v.*
moor, make fast; —ка *f.* alignment
rope (for building wall).
**причастный** *a.* participating (in), implicated, involved, concerned.
**причека** *f.* gib.
**причем** *conj.* while, during which, whereupon; **п. известно, что** it being
known that.
**причесывать** *v.* comb, brush.
**причин/а** *f.* reason, cause, source, origin,
principle; **п. ошибки** source of error;
**по —е** because (of), by reason (of),
owing (to), on account (of); **служить
—ой** *v.* cause, be the cause (of).
**причин/ение** *n.* causing; —енный *a.*
caused; —ить, —ять *v.* cause, occasion, do; —ность *f.*, —ная связь
causality; —ный *a.* causal, causative.

**причисл/ение** *n.* reckoning; addition; attaching; **—ить, —ять** *v.* reckon, number, rank; add; attach.

**причитывать** *v.* add; **—ся** *v.* be due.

**пришабр/енный** *a.* scraped; **п. к** scraped to fit; **—ивание** *n.* scraping off; **—ивать, —ить** *v.* scrape, scour; fit.

**приш/ивать, —ить** *v.* sew on.

**пришлифов/анный** *a.* ground, ground down, ground in; **—ка** *f.* (mach.) seating.

**пришлось** *past of* **приходиться.**

**прищем/ить, —лять** *v.* pinch, catch, jam.

**прищеп** *m.* (bot.) graft.

**прищипывание** *n.* pinching (plant tops).

**приют** *m.* shelter, refuge, asylum; **—ить** *v.* shelter, give refuge.

**прият/ель** *m.* friend; **—ный** *a.* agreeable, pleasant.

**про** *prep. acc.* of, about; for.

**про—** *prefix* per—, through, past; *with verbs to indicate action over a definite period, or completed or thorough action.*

**проактиномицин** *m.* proactinomycin.

**проб/а** *f.* trial, test, experiment; test sample, sample, specimen; analysis; (met.) assay; purity (of gold); standard; **п. на тест for; п. на разрядку** (elec.) discharge test; **п. нагреванием** heat test; **брать —у** *v.* sample, take a sample; **взять на —у** *v.* sample; take on trial; **взятие —ы, отбор —ы** sampling; **золото 96-й —ы** pure gold; **метод проб** trial-and-error method; **рудная п.** assay; **серебро высокой —ы** sterling silver.

**пробанить** *v.* brush out (flues).

**пробег** *m.* run, mileage; running through, flow, passage; race; (phys.) range, path; **п. поглощения** (nucl.) attenuation length; **время —а** running time; **длина —а** range, reach, scope; path length (of particle); **средняя длина свободного —а** mean free path; **испытание —ом** road test; **разброс —ов** range straggling; **соотношение п.-энергия** range-energy relation; **спектр —ов** range spectrum; **число миль —а на** miles per (gallon, etc.).

**пробе/гать, —жать** *v.* run, run through, run over, pass over, skim.

**пробегать** *v.* run for a while.

**пробежно-ионизационный** *a.* range-ionization.

**пробел** *m.* gap, blank; spacing, interval; (biol.) lacuna; (zool.) hiatus; **восполнять —ы** *v.* fill in the gaps; **—ьный** *a.* spacing.

**пробив/ание** *n.* piercing, punching, puncture; clearing (pipe); (elec.) breakdown; **—ать** *v.* make a hole in, pierce, punch, puncture, perforate; breach, break through, go through; force open, clear; **—ать дорогу** open a way; **—аться** *v.* break through, force one's way; **—ающий** *a.* piercing, punching, puncturing; (elec.) disruptive.

**пробивн/ой** *a.* piercing, punching, puncturing; break-through; (elec.) disruptive; **п. разряд** (elec.) disruptive discharge; **п. станок** punch, puncher; **—ое действие** penetrating power (of bullet); **—ое напряжение** (elec.) disruptive voltage; breakdown voltage.

**пробирать** *v.* reprimand; go through; **—ся** *v.* get through, make one's way.

**пробир/ер** *see* **пробирщик; —ка** *f.* test tube.

**пробирн/ый** *a.* test, testing; (met.) assay, assaying; **п. камень** touchstone, basanite, Lydian stone (for testing gold and silver); **п. металл** test metal; **п. разновес** assay weights; **п. цилиндр, —ая склянка** test tube; **—ая игла** touch needle; **—ая палатка** assay office; **—ая печь** assay furnace; **—ая чашечка** (met.) cupel; **—ое искусство** assaying; **—ое клеймо** hallmark, assay mark; **—ые весы** assay balance.

**пробирщик** *m.* assayer, tester.

**пробит/ие** *n.* breaching, piercing; **—ый** *a.* pierced, perforated, punched, punctured; cleared; **—ь** *see* **пробивать.**

**пробк/а** *f.* cork, stopper, plug; tap; plug gage, internal gage; block, lock (in pipe); (vapor) lock; bottleneck; **сварка —ой** plug welding; **—овидный** *a.* suberiform, suberose.

**пробков/ый** *a.* cork, cork-like, suberose; stopper, plug; **п. дуб, —ое дерево** (bot.) cork oak (*Quercus suber*); **п. уголь** burnt cork; **—ая кислота** suberic acid, octanedioic acid; **соль —ой кислоты, —окислая соль** suberate; **—ое вещество** suberin.

**проблема** *f.* problem; crux (of matter); —**тика** *f.* problems; —**тический,** —**тичный** *a.* problematic.

**проблес/к** *m.* gleam, flash, ray of light, spark; —**ковый** *a.* flashing, intermittent; —**нуть** *v.* gleam, flash.

**пробник** *m.* sampler, sampling tube; test rod, trial rod; probe; (sugar) proof stick; try cock, gage cock.

**пробн/ый** *a.* experimental, test, tentative; proof; **п. брусок** test piece, specimen; **п. груз** test load; **п. камень** *see* **пробирный камень; п. ковш, п. уполовник** (met.) assay spoon; **п. кран** test cock, try cock, gage cock; **п. лист** proof sheet; **п. оттиск** proof; **п. спирт** proof spirit; **п. шурф** (min.) test pit; **п. экземпляр** specimen; —**ая полоса** test strip; —**ая протолочка** mill run, mill test; —**ая страница** proof page; —**ая штанга** (met.) trial rod, test rod; —**ое давление** test pressure; —**ое золото** standard gold; —**ое предложение** tentative proposal; —**ое серебро** standard silver.

**пробов/ание** *n.* trying, testing; tasting; —**ать** *v.* try, test, sample; (met.) assay; attempt, endeavor; taste.

**пробод/ать** *v.* pierce, gore; —**ение** *n.* (med.) perforation.

**пробоина** *f.* hole, gap, rift; eruption.

**проб/ой** *m.* cramp iron; puncture, rupture, disruption; irruption; breakthrough; (elec.) breakdown; flashover, spark-over; **напряжение** —**оя** breakdown voltage; **потенциал** —**оя** breakdown potential; —**ойник,** —**ойчик** *m.* punch, puncher, hollow punch, piercer, drift; mandrel.

**пробо/отбиратель,** —**отборник** *m.* sampler.

**пробор/ка** *f.* (text.) drawing-in; —**ный станок** drawing-in frame.

**пробочн/ик** *m.* corkscrew; —**ый** *a.* cork, suberose; plug; *see also* **пробковый;** —**ая сварка** plug welding.

**пробраться** *see* **пробираться.**

**пробродить** *v.* ferment.

**пробу/дить** —**ждать** *v.* waken, rouse; —**диться,** —**ждаться** *v.* wake up.

**пробуксовка** *f.* slip, slipping, skidding, spinning.

**пробурав/ить,** —**ливать** *v.* bore, perfo-

rate, broach; —**ливание** *n.* boring.

**пробщик** *m.* sampler.

**пробыть** *v.* stay, remain.

**пров.** *abbr.* (провинция) province.

**провал** *m.* downfall; valley, trough; dip (of curve); cave-in; dip; gap, (air) pocket; failure; —**иваться,** —**иться** *v.* fall through, collapse, break down; fail; —**ьный** *a.* downcomer; —**ьная тарелка** (distillation) grid plate.

**прованское масло** olive oil (high grade).

**провар** *m.* (welding) penetration; (glass) complete melting; —**ивание** *n.* boiling; —**ивать,** —**ить** *v.* boil thoroughly.

**проватернашивать** *v.* level up.

**провевать** *v.* winnow; blow.

**проведать** *see* **проведывать.**

**проведен/ие** *n.* leading, conducting; construction, building, laying; installation; carrying out, execution; passing; drawing (a line); **порядок** —**ия** procedure; —**ный** *a.* carried out, accomplished.

**проведывать** *v.* find out, learn; visit.

**провезти** *see* **провозить.**

**провеивать** *v.* (agr.) winnow.

**провентилировать** *v.* ventilate, air, aerate.

**провер/ить** *see* **проверять;** —**ка** *f.* verification, checking, check up, follow-up; (math.) proof, check; examination, inspection, testing.

**провернуть** *v.* crank (motor); work out (problem); *see also* **провертеть.**

**проверочн/ый** *a.* verifying, checking, test, control; calibrating (instrument); —**ая установка** calibrating equipment.

**проверт/еть,** —**ывать** *v.* bore, perforate, pierce.

**провер/яемый** *a.* under examination, under consideration; —**ять** *v.* verify, check, calibrate; examine, test, inspect; audit; —**яющий** *m.* inspector, checker.

**провес** *m.* wrong weight; weighed portion, given weight; slack, sag, sagging, dip (of wire); —**стрела** —**a** deflection, sag, dip; —**ить** *see* **провешивать.**

**провести** *see* **проводить.**

**проветр/иваемый** *a.* ventilated; —**ивание** *n.* ventilation, airing, aeration;

—ивать, —ить *v.* ventilate, air, aerate.

провешив/ание *n.* marking a direction (with stakes, etc.); **п. линии** alignment; —ать *v.* plumb, make vertical; align; stake out; weigh inaccurately; dry in the open, air.

прове/янный *a.* (agr.) winnowed; —ять *v.* winnow; blow.

провиант *m.* provisions, victuals.

провизия *f.* provisions, food; provision.

провизор *m.* pharmacist, druggist.

провизорный *a.* provisional, temporary; preliminary.

провиниться *v.* be guilty (of), transgress, make a slip.

провинц/иальный *a.* provincial; —ия *f.* province.

провис/ание *n.* sag, sagging, slackening; —ать *v.* sag, deflect; —еть *v.* hang (for some time); —ший *a.* sagged, slack.

провитамин *m.*, —ный *a.* provitamin, vitamin precursor.

провод *m.* conductor, (conducting) wire, cable; duct; **п. с пущенным током** (elec.) live wire; **п.-рельс** contact rail, conductor rail; **вводной п., подводящий п.** (elec.) lead; **монтировать —а** *v.* wire; **прокладка —ов** wiring; **по прямому —у** by direct contact.

проводим/ость *f.* conductivity, conduction; conductance; admittance (of servo system); **активная п., ваттная п.** (elec.) conductance; **удельная п.** conductivity; —ый *a.* conducted; in progress.

проводить *v.* lead, conduct; (elec.) conduct, carry; carry out (reaction); lay out, mark; lay, construct (road); drive (tunnel); install (piping, etc.); draw, trace (line); spend, pass (time); develop (idea).

проводк/а *f.* (elec.) wiring, wiring system; line, main, conduit; **п. труб** pipe laying; **схема —и** wiring diagram.

проводник *m.*, —овый *a.* guide, conductor; vehicle (of infection); (railroad) guard; (min.) streak; **п. звука** sound conductor; **п. под током** (elec.) current-carrying conductor.

провод/ность *see* проводимость; —ный *a.* conducting; wire; —одержатель

*m.* hanger; —ящий *a.* conducting, conveying, carrying; —ящий под (met.) hearth contact; —ящая жила conductor; —ящая поверхность conducting surface.

провожать *v.* accompany, escort, convoy.

провоз *m.* conveying, carting, transport; **стоимость —а** freight charge; —ить *v.* convey, transport, carry; —оспособность *f.* capacity (of railroad).

проволок/а *f.* wire; —ообразный *a.* wire-shaped, filiform.

проволоч/ка *f.* little wire; procrastination, delay; —ник *m.* wireworm; spec. click beetle larva; —ники *pl.* click beetles (*Elateridae*).

проволочно/-волочильный станок wire-drawing bench; —канатный *a.* wire-rope; —канатная дорога wire ropeway, overhead railway; —намоточный станок wire-coiling machine; —прокатный стан rod mill, rod-rolling mill.

проволочн/ый *a.* wire; **п. калибр** wire gage; **п. штаг, —ая оттяжка** guy wire; —ая сетка, —ая ткань, —ое сито wire gauze, wire screen, wire mesh; —ая сеть wire netting, fencing; —ая спираль coil; —ые изделия wirework.

проворачивать *v.* pull (a belt).

провор/ный *a.* quick, prompt, alert, adroit; —ство *n.* quickness, adroitness.

провоцировать *v.* provoke; induce.

провял/ивать, —ить *v.* dry in the open air, sun-dry, jerk.

прогад/ать, —ывать *v.* miscalculate.

прогалина *f.* clearing, gap (in woods).

прогар *m.* burnout; —ина *f.* burnt place, burn; —ная доска, —ный лист baffle, baffle plate.

прогест/ерон *m.* progesterone, luteal hormone; —ин *m.* Progestin.

прогиб *m.* caving in, break; sag, sagging, deflection, depression, buckling, flexure, camber; (geol.) downwarp; **линия —а** line of deflection (of shaft); **передовой п.** foredeep; **стрела —а** deflection, camber, depth of camber, depth of curvature, sagging, sag; —ание *n.* deflection, sagging; —ать *v.* deflect; —аться *v.* deflect, sag, give, yield, collapse, cave in; —омер *m.* deflectometer.

проглатыв/ание *n.* swallowing; —ать, проглотить *v.* swallow.

прогляд/еть, —ывать *v.* overlook, miss.

прогля/дывать, —нуть *v.* appear, show; look through.

прогнать *see* прогонять.

прогн/ивание *n.* rotting through; —ивать, —ить *v.* rot through.

прогно/з *m.* forecast; (med.) prognosis; ставить п., —зировать *v.* predict, forecast, prognosticate; —зирование *n.* predicting, forecasting; —зист *m.* forecaster; —стика *f.* prognostication; —стический *a.* prognostic; forecast, forecasting.

прогнуться *see* прогибаться.

прогон *m.* drive, run; girder, boxbeam, bearer, span; —ы *pl.*, —ные, —ные деньги traveling expenses; —ка *f.* die, screw die; —ять *v.* drive away, drive off; dismiss; pass (current, etc.).

прогор/ание *n.* burning through; burnout; —ать, —еть *v.* burn through, burn down; go bankrupt; —елый *a.* burnt through.

прогорк/ание *n.* turning rancid; rancidity; —ловатый *a.* somewhat rancid; —лость *f.* rancidity; —лый *a.* rancid, rank; —нуть *v.* get rancid.

прогорчить *v.* make extremely bitter.

программ/а *f.* program, schedule, course; curriculum (of studies); —ирующее приспособление programmer; —ное реле cycle timer.

прогрев *m.* initial heating, warm-up; heating through; —ание *n.* heating, warming up; —ать *v.* heat, warm up, warm thoroughly.

прогресс *m.* progress, development, evolution; —ивно *adv.* progressively, gradually, by degrees, little by little; —ивный, —ирующий *a.* progressive, progressing, gradual; —ировать *v.* progress; —ия *f.* (math.) progression.

прогреть *see* прогревать.

прогрохоченный *a.* screened.

продав/ать *v.* sell; —ец *m.* salesman.

продав/ить, —ливать *v.* press down, press through, punch; —ливание *n.* punching.

прода/вщик *see* продавец; —жа *f.* sale,

selling; в —же for sale, on sale; пустить в —жу *v.* put on the market, market; —жный *a.* selling, sales; commercial.

продалбливать *v.* chisel through, make a hole in.

продать *see* продавать.

продви/гать, —нуть *v.* move forward, push forward, impel; —гаться, —нуться *v.* advance, move forward, get on, make way; —жение *n.* advancement, advance, progress, headway; feed.

продев/ание *n.* passing through, threading; —ать *v.* pass through, put through, run through, insert; thread.

продел/ать, —ывать *v.* do, perform, make; —ывание *n.* doing, performing.

продергивать *v.* jerk through, thread; (agr.) thin.

продерж/ать, —ивать *v.* keep, hold, detain; —аться, —иваться *v.* hold out.

продернуть *see* продергивать.

продеть *see* продевать.

продешевить *v.* sell too cheaply.

продиктовать *v.* dictate.

продиффундировавш/ий *a.* diffused; —ее вещество diffusate, dialyzate.

продком *abbr.* (продовольственный комитет) food supply committee.

продл/ение *n.* prolongation, extension; —ить *v.* prolong, lengthen, extend; —иться *v.* be prolonged, last a long time, draw out.

продовольств/енный *a.* supply, provision; п. склад supply depot; —ие *n.* supply, supply of provisions, provisioning; provisions, food; subsistence.

продолбить *see* продалбливать.

продолговат/ость *f.* oblong form; —ый *a.* oblong; prolate, extended; elongated; —ый мозг (anat.) medulla oblongata.

продолж/ать *v.* continue, go on, go ahead, proceed; carry on, pursue, persist; resume; prolong; extend; elongate, lengthen, broaden; —аться *v.* continue, last; be prolonged, be extended; —ение *n.* continuation, continuance; prolongation, extension; protraction; sequel; duration, course, space (of time), interval; resumption, в —ение in the course (of), during, throughout.

продолжительн/ость f. continuance, duration, length, period, time, cycle; endurance; п. действия, п. жизни life; п. работы, полезная п. службы useful life, life; полет на п. endurance flight; —ый a. continuous, lasting, prolonged, long, of long duration, long-term; на —ое время for a long time.

продолжить see продолжать.

продольно adv. longitudinally, lengthwise; п.-сверлильный станок slot drill; п.-строгальный станок planing machine, planer; п.-тангенциальное коробление bow warp; п.-токарный станок long-bed lathe; п.-фрезерный станок plano-milling machine.

продольн/ый a. longitudinal, lengthwise, linear; drawn out; rip (saw); п. разрез, —ое сечение axial section, longitudinal section; —ое изменение linear deformation; в —ом направлении lengthwise; —ые нити ткани (text.) warp.

продор/аживать v. groove; —оженный a. grooved, channeled.

продром m., —альное явление (med.) prodrome, premonitory symptom.

продуб/ить v. tan; —ленный a. tanned.

продувало n. ashpit.

продув/ание n., —ка f. blowing through, blowing off, blow-out; scavenging (of gases); purging, purge, drainage; —ательный, —ной see продувочный; —ать v. blow through, blow off, blow out; scavenge, remove, exhaust (gases); bubble through.

продувочн/ый a. blow-through, blow-off; п. воздух scavenging air; п. клапан blow-through valve, blow valve, blow-off valve, drain valve; п. кран drain cock, scum cock; п. насос scavenging pump, scavenger pump; п. прибор bellows; —ая труба blow-off pipe, blast pipe.

продукт m. product, commodity, item; побочный п. by-product.

продуктивн/о adv. productively, efficiently, with good results; —ость f. productivity, efficiency; —ый a. productive, producing, efficient.

продуктовый магазин grocery store.

продукц/ия f. production, productive capacity, output, manufacture; product; количество —ии output.

продум/ать, —ывать v. think out, reason out, think over.

продут/ый a. blown, blown through, blown out; —ь see продувать.

продух m., —a f. air hole.

продуц/ент m. producer; —ирующий a. producing, productive.

продушина f. air hole, vent.

продыряв/ить, —ливать v. pierce, punch, perforate; —иться, —ливаться v. become full of holes, tear, wear through; —ленный a. pierced, perforated.

проед/ать v. eat away, corrode; —енный a. corroded.

проез/д m. passage; thoroughfare, way; —дом in transit; passing through; —дная плата fare; —жать v. pass, drive through; —жая дорога public road, thoroughfare, highway.

проект m. project, plan, layout, scheme, design; составлять п. v. plan, devise; —ант see проектировщик; —ивность f. (math.) projectivity; —ивный a. projective.

проектиров/ание n., —ка f. projecting, projection, designing, planning; —ать v. project, design, plan, engineer; —щик m. projector, planner, designer.

проектно-расчетный a. preliminary estimation.

проектн/ый a. project, plan; —ая величина (elec.) rating; —ая мощность (elec.) rated capacity; —ая нагрузка load rating; —ая схема layout.

проектор m. projector.

проекц/ионный a., —ия f. projection; п. аппарат, п. фонарь projector; п. окуляр projection eyepiece.

проем m. aperture, opening, embrasure.

проесть see проедать.

проехать see проезжать.

прожар/енный a. thoroughly roasted; fried; —ивать, —ить v. roast thoroughly; fry.

прождать v. wait.

прожект/ер m. projector, planner; —ор m. projector, searchlight; (electron) gun.

**прожелть** *f.* yellowish tint.

**прожечь** *see* **прожигать.**

**проживать** *v.* live, reside, stay; spend (money).

**проживление** *n.* refining.

**прожиг/ание** *n.* burning through; jetting (of well); **—ать** *v.* burn through.

**прожил/ка** *f.*, **—ок** *m.* vein, veinlet, fiber, filament; (geol.) streak, lead-vein, apophysis; **—ки** *pl.* filaments, fibers; streaks.

**прожим/ание** *n.* squeezing through, trickling, dropping; **—аться** *v.* squeeze through, trickle, drop.

**прожир/енный** *a.* greased, tallowed; **—овать** *v.* grease, tallow.

**прожит/ие** *n.*, **—ок** *m.* living, livelihood; **—очный** *a.* living; **—ь** *see* **проживать.**

**прожорливый** *a.* voracious.

**прозама** *f.* (foundry) mixer.

**прозвенеть** *v.* ring.

**прозвучать** *v.* sound, be heard.

**прозевать** *v.* miss, let slip.

**прозектор** *m.* prosector, anatomist's assistant.

**прозенхима** *f.* (bot.) prosenchyma.

**прозерин** *m.* proserine, neostigmine.

**прозодежда** *f.* work clothes.

**прозол** *m.* prosol; **—аннеловая кислота** prosolannelic acid.

**прозопит** *m.* (min.) prosopite.

**прозор** *m.* space, gap.

**прозрачн/ость** *f.* transparency; **—ый** *a.* transparent, clear; obvious; (biol.) hyaline; **—ый холст** tracing cloth; **делаться —ым** *v.* clear, become clear, clarify.

**прозре/вать, —ть** *v.* recover one's sight; see through.

**проигр/а** *f.* flight (of bees); **—ать, —ывать** *v.* lose, lose out; play back (record); **—ывание** *n.* losing; play-back; **—ыватель** *m.* record player; **—ыш** *m.* loss, failure; **коэффициент —ыша** disadvantage factor.

**произведен/ие** *n.* production, work, composition; origination; (math.) product; **п. растворимости** solubility product; **—ный** *a.* produced, manufactured; generated; derived.

**произвести** *see* **производить.**

**произ-во** *abbr.* (производство) production.

**производимый** *a.* producible.

**производитель** *m.* producer, generator; manufacturer, maker; grower; (breeding) sire; **п. газа** gas producer; **п. работ** works superintendent.

**производительн/ость** *f.* productivity, productiveness, productive capacity, output, yield, delivery, discharge (of pump); capacity, efficiency, effect, performance, duty (of machine); (elec.) rating; **п. труда** output per man-hour; operating efficiency (of a plant); **—ый** *a.* productive, efficient.

**производить** *v.* produce, make, manufacture; create, originate; exert (pressure); generate (gas); derive; effect, perform, do; promote; **п. опыты** carry out experiments, experiment.

**производн/ая** *f.* (math.) derivative; **брать —ую** *v.* derive; **—ое** *n.* (chem.) derivative; **—ые** *pl.* derivatives; **—ый** *a.* derivative, derived; **—ая единица** derived unit.

**производственн/ик** *m.* industrial worker, production worker; **—о-технический** *a.* industrial-engineering.

**производственн/ый** *a.* industrial, manufacturing, production; **п. контроль** plant supervision; **п. метод** industrial method, method of manufacture; **п. совет** work council; **—ая единица** production unit; **—ая мощность** productive capacity; **—ая практика** industrial practice; **—ая стоимость** cost of production, operating cost; **—ые условия** working conditions.

**производств/о** *n.* production, preparation, manufacture, manufacturing, making; generation; industry; derivation; execution, effecting; factory, works; **издержки —а** cost of production; **своего —а** of domestic make.

**производящий** *a.* producing, forming, yielding, generating; productive; producer; **—ся** *a.* being produced, in process, in progress.

**произвольн/о** *adv.* arbitrarily, voluntarily; it is a matter of judgment; **—ый** *a.* arbitrary, voluntary; **—ая постоянная** arbitrary constant.

**произн/ести, —осить** *v.* pronounce, utter; make (a speech); **—ошение** *n.* pronunciation, utterance.

**произойти** *see* **происходить.**

**произраст/ание** *n.* growth, growing, springing (up); vegetation; —**ать,** —**и** *v.* grow, spring up.

**происте/кать,** —**чь** *v.* result, ensue, spring (from); —**кающий** *a.* resulting, resultant.

**происходить** *v.* come (from), emanate, proceed, result, spring, arise, originate, be derived; descend, issue, stem (from); happen, occur, take place, be in progress, come about, come to pass.

**происхождение** *n.* origin, genesis, parentage, descent; derivation, extraction; emanation; **п. видов** (biol.) origin of species; **п. элементов** nucleogenesis.

**происшествие** *n.* incident, occurrence, event; accident, emergency.

**пройденный** *a.* passed, run through, looked over.

**пройма** *f.* opening, aperture, hole.

**пройти** *see* **проходить.**

**прок** *m.* use, benefit; **заготовлять в п.** *v.* cure (food); **запасать в п.** *v.* store.

**прока/женный** *a.* (med.) leprous; *m.* leper; —**за** *f.* leprosy.

**прокаин** *m.* procaine, Novocaine.

**прокал/енный** *a.* calcined, roasted; —**иваемость** *f.* hardenability (of steel); —**ивание** *n.* calcination, roasting; —**ивать,** —**ить** *v.* calcine, roast, bake, fire; harden.

**прокалыват/ельный станок** puncturing machine, punch; —**ь** *v.* puncture, prick, pierce.

**прокамбий** *m.* (bot.) procambium.

**прокапывать** *v.* dig across, dig through.

**прокармливать** *v.* keep, feed.

**прокат** *m.* hire; release (of motion picture); (met.) drawn-out iron, rolled iron; —**анный** *a.* rolled; —**анное листовое железо** laminated sheet iron, rolled iron; **в —анном виде** as rolled; —**ать,** —**ить** *see* **прокатывать;** —**ка** *see* **прокатывание.**

**прокатн/ый** *a.* rolling, rolled; hired, on hire, let out on hire; **п. валок** roller; **п. завод, п. стан** rolling mill, mill; **п. материал** rolled stock, mill bar; —**ая окалина** mill scale; mill cinder; —**ое железо** rolled iron.

**прокат/чик** *m.* roller, rolling mill oper-

ator; —**ывание** *n.* rolling, flattening, lamination; —**ывать** *v.* roll, mill, flatten, laminate, draw out.

**прокач/ивать** *v.* pump through; —**ка** *f.* injection.

**проква/сить,** —**шивать** *v.* sour thoroughly; leaven (bread); —**шенный** *a.* leavened.

**прокип/ать,** —**еть** *v.* boil thoroughly; —**ятить** *v.* boil thoroughly, let boil thoroughly; —**яченный** *a.* boiled.

**прокис/ать,** —**нуть** *v.* sour, turn sour, turn; —**лый,** —**ший** *a.* sour, rancid.

**прокладка** *f.* packing, stuffing, padding, pad, cushion, lining, strip, layer; interlayer, intermediate layer; spacer, distance piece; separator (of battery); washer, gasket, bearing disk; laying, breaking (of road, etc.); plotting (of course); **п. подшипника** bearing gasket; **п. трубопровода** pipe laying.

**проклад/ной,** —**очный** *a.* packing, stuffing, lining; gasket; **п. скобель** bearing scraper; —**ная шайба** bearing disk; —**ное кольцо** gasket (ring).

**прокладывать** *v.* lay, lay out, lay off; run (a wire, etc.); break (a road); drive (a tunnel); interlay; **п. путь** pave the way.

**прокле/ивание** *n.,* —**йка** *f.* pasting, gluing; sizing; —**ивать,** —**ить** *v.* paste, glue; size.

**проков/анный** *a.* forged, hammered; —**ка** *f.* (welding) peening; —**ывать** *v.* forge, hammer.

**проковыр/ивать,** —**ять** *v.* pick through, pick a hole in.

**прокол** *m.* prick, pricking, puncture; —**ка** *f.* pricking, puncturing, piercing; —**оть** *see* **прокалывать.**

**прокопать** *see* **прокапывать.**

**прокопт/елый** *a.* smoked; fumigated; —**еть** *v.* get permeated with smoke, be smoked; —**ить** *v.* smoke; fumigate.

**прокорм** *m.* nourishment, sustenance; —**ить** *see* **прокармливать.**

**прокра/сить,** —**шивать** *v.* paint or dye (thoroughly).

**проксимальный** *a.* proximal.

**прокур/атура** *f.* procurator's office; —**ор** *m.* procurator, agent.

**пролагать** *see* **прокладывать.**

**пролазный** *a.* access, for access.

пролактин *m.* prolactin, mammotropin.

проламин *m.* prolamine, gliadin.

проламывать *v.* break, fracture; break through, cut open; —ся *v.* break through.

пролан *m.* prolan (hormone).

пролегать *v.* lie (of road).

пролежень *m.* (med.) bedsore.

пролез/ать, —ть *v.* get through, crawl through.

пролес/ка *f.* (bot.) squill (*Scilla*); mercury (*Mercurialis*); —ник *m.* mercury.

пролет *m.* flight; span, arch, spacing, bay, aperture, opening; aisle, runway; flight of stairs; transit (of electron); **п. в свету** span (of bridge, etc.); **время** —a transit time; **по времени** —a time of flight (spectrometer); **угол** —a transit angle.

пролетарский *a.* proletarian.

пролет/ать, —еть *v.* fly past, fly through; —ный *a. of* пролет; —ная трубка flight-path tube, drift tube.

пролив *m.* strait, sound, narrow.

пролив/ать *v.* shed, spill; (foundry) cast on; —ной дождь downpour.

прол/ил *m.* prolyl; —ин *m.* proline, 2-pyrrolidinecarboxylic acid.

пролит/ие *n.* shedding, spilling; —ый *a.* spilled; —ь *see* проливать.

пролиферация *f.* (biol.) proliferation.

пролож/енный *a.* laid; sandwiched; —ить *see* прокладывать.

пролом *m.* breach, gap, break, split, eruption; —анный *a.* breached, broken; —ать, —ить *see* проламывать; —ник *m.* (bot.) rock jasmine (*Androsace*).

пролонг/ация *f.* prolongation; —ировать *v.* prolong.

пролювий *m.* (geol.) slopewash, colluvium.

пром. *abbr.* (промышленность) industry; пром., пром— *abbr.* (промышленный) industrial.

промаз/анный *a.* greased, smeared; —ать *v.* grease, smear.

промалывать *see* молоть.

промасл/енный *a.* oiled, oil; —ивать, —ить *v.* oil, treat with oil; grease.

промах *m.* miss, fault; blunder, slip, oversight, failure; —иваться, —нуть-ся *v.* miss, miss the mark, miss one's aim.

промачив/ать *v.* wet thoroughly, drench, soak, steep; —ающий *a.* soaking.

промбанк *abbr.* (промышленный банк) industrial bank.

промедление *n.* delay.

промежность *f.* (anat.) perineum.

промежуток *m.* interval, space, stretch, distance, gap, clearance, play; span; intermediate space, interspace; interstice; time interval, period, pause; **п. времени** period, stretch of time, interval.

промежуточн/ый *a.* intermediate, interjacent, interstitial; compound (nucleus); **п. вал** communicator; **п. воздушный холодильник** air-cooled intercooler; **п. горизонт, п. штрех** (min.) counter-level; **п. продукт** intermediate product, intermediate; —ая часть, —ое кольцо, —ое тело spacer; —ая шестерня intermediate gear, idler gear, idler; —ое пространство interspace; —ое тело spacer (of turbine).

промелькнуть *v.* flash by, flash past.

промен *m.* exchange, barter; rate of exchange; —ивать, —ять *v.* exchange, barter.

промер *m.* measurement, measuring; error in measurement.

промерз/ание *n.* freezing; **линия** —ания frost line; —ать, —нуть *v.* freeze through; —лый *a.* frozen.

промер/ивать, —ить, —ять *v.* measure, survey; make a mistake in measurement; —ный *a.* measure, measuring.

прометий *m.* promethium, Pm.

промешивать *v.* mix thoroughly, stir up.

промил/ле *adv.* pro mille, parts per thousand; —ь *f.* one thousandth.

проминать *v.* knead thoroughly, work.

промкооперация *f.* producers' cooperation.

промозглый *a.* damp, dank (weather); stagnant (air).

промои *pl.* wash water; —на *f.* water hole, washout, washed-out hollow.

промок/ание *n.* permeation, wetting; —ательная бумага blotting paper; —ать, —нуть *v.* get wet, get soaked, be permeated, be wetted; blot (of ink); —ший *a.* wet, soaked, permeated.

промол/ачивать,—отить *v.* (agr.) thresh.

промораживать *v.* freeze through.

**Пром. орг. х.** *see* **ПОХ.**

промороз/ить *see* промораживать; —ка *f.* promorozka (natural freezing of the ground during the sinking of a pit in a water-bearing horizon).

промо/тирование *n.*, —ция *f.* promotion; —тировать *v.* promote; —тор *m.* (catalyst) promoter, activator, accelerator.

промочить *see* промачивать.

промпродукт *abbr.* (промежуточный продукт) intermediate product.

пром-сть *abbr.* (промышленность) industry.

пром/товары *abbr.* (промышленные товары) manufactured goods; —фин-план *abbr.* (промышленный финансовый план) industrial and financial plan.

промчаться *v.* fly past, rush past.

промыв *m.* washout, channel; —алка *f.* washer; wash bottle; —альщик руды (min.) jigger, jig, jigging machine; —ание *n.* washing, scrubbing (gas); irrigation; —ание для ран lotion; —атель *m.* washer, purifier, scrubber.

промывательн/ый *a.* washing; **п. мутильный чан, п. чан,** —ая кадь washing tub, washing tank; (min.) dolly tub; —ая склянка wash bottle.

промыв/ать *v.* wash, rinse; scrub (gas); jig (ore); pan out (gold dust); syringe (wound); —истый песок auriferous sand containing a large quantity of pebbles; —ка *f.* washing, flushing, rinsing; leaching operation (of soil); (met.) ore washer, spec. log washer.

промывн/ой *a.* washing, flushing, rinsing; scrubbing (column); *see also* промывательный; **п. барабан,** —ая бочка, —ое корыто log washer (for ore); **п. лучок** mud hole, hand hole (in boiler); —ая ванна (text.) scouring liquor; —ая вода wash water; —ая колба wash bottle.

промывочный *see* промывательный, промывной.

промыс/ел *m.* trade, business, profession; **горный п.** mining; **золотые** —лы gold fields; **соляной п.** salt mine or mining.

промысло/ведение *n.* technology; —вый *a.* industrial; craft; —вое свидетельство license.

промыт/ый *a.* washed, flushed, rinsed; —ь *see* промывать.

промышленн/ик *m.* manufacturer; industrialist; —ость *f.* industry; **тяжелая** —ость heavy industry.

промышленн/ый *a.* industrial, commercial; **п. кпд** practical efficiency; **п. округ** industrial district; —ая руда pay ore; в —ом масштабе on an industrial scale, industrially.

промять *see* проминать.

пронашивать *v.* wear out, wear through.

пронести *see* проносить.

пронз/ать, —ить *v.* pierce, run through, spear, transfix; —ительный *a.* piercing, sharp, shrill, acute.

прониз/ать, —ывать *v.* pierce, perforate; permeate; thread.

проник/ание, —новение *n.* penetration, permeation, impregnation, infiltration, infusion, pervasion; **двойники** —новения (cryst.) penetration twins; —ать *v.* penetrate, permeate, impregnate, pervade, infiltrate, filter through, percolate; sink, work (into), bore, pierce, pass through; —ать взаимно interpenetrate; —аться *v.* penetrate; be filled (with), be impregnated; —ающий *a.* penetrating, thorough.

проникнут/ый *a.* penetrated, permeated; —ь *see* проникать.

проницаем/ость *f.* penetrability, penetrance, permeability, perviousness, porosity; transmittancy; **вероятность** —ости penetration probability, transmission coefficient; **магнитная п.** permeability; —ый *a.* penetrable, permeable, pervious; passable.

прониц/ание *n.* permeation; —ательность *f.* penetration, understanding, clear-sightedness; penetrability; —ательный *a.* penetrating; —ать *see* проникать.

проносить *v.* be carried, carry (along, past, through); (med.) have loose bowels; —ся *v.* rush (along, past, through).

проношенный *a.* threadbare, worn out, worn through.

прообраз *m.* prototype, standard; type,

symbol, sign; **быть —ом** v. figure, prefigure; indicate.

**пропавший** a. missing, lost, hopeless.

**пропаганда** f. propaganda.

**пропадать** v. be lost, vanish, disappear.

**пропа/диен** m. propadiene, dimethylenemethane; **—езин** m. propaesin, propyl p-aminobenzoate.

**пропажа** f. loss; lost article, missing object.

**пропаз/ить** v. mortise, groove; **—ованный** a. mortised, grooved, slotted.

**пропаланин** m. propalanine, aminobutyric acid.

**пропалывать** v. cultivate, weed.

**пропан** m. propane; **—ал, —аль** m. propanal, propionic aldehyde; **—дикислота, —диовая кислота** propanedioic acid, malonic acid; **—диол** m. propanediol, dihydroxypropane; **—овая кислота** propanoic acid, propionic acid; **—ол** m. propanol, propyl alcohol; **—он** m. propanone, acetone.

**пропаргил** m. propargyl; **—овая кислота** propargylic acid, propiolic acid; **соль —овой кислоты, —овокислая соль** propargylate; **—овый спирт** propargyl alcohol, propynol; **—овый эфир уксусной кислоты** propargyl acetate.

**пропар/ивание** n., **—ка** f. steaming, spec. low-temperature steaming; **—иватель** m. (dairy) steamer, sterilizer; **—ивать** v. steam, steam out; **—ина** f. proparina (open space in ice produced by subaqueous springs); **—очный котел** steam tank, autoclave.

**пропасть** see **пропадать**; f. precipice, abyss, gulf.

**пропа/хивать** v. plow (through); **—шка** f. (thorough) plowing; **—шник** m. furrow plow; cultivator.

**пропащий** a. ruined, lost.

**пропедевт/ика** f. preliminary instruction; **—ический** a. preparatory.

**пропеллер** m., **—ный** a. propeller, airscrew, fan, impeller (of flotation machine); **—ная мешалка** agitator mixer.

**пропен** m. propene, propylene; **—ал, —аль** m. propenal, acrolein; **—ил** m., **—иловый** a. propenyl; **—илиден** m. propenylidene; **—ол** m. propenol, allyl alcohol.

**пропептон** m. propeptone, hemialbumose.

**пропил** m. kerf, saw cut, cut, groove, gash, notch; **делать —ы** v. kerf.

**пропил** m. propyl; **хлористый п.** propyl chloride; **—амин** m. propylamine; **—бензол** m. propylbenzene.

**пропилен** m. propylene, propene; **окись —а** propylene oxide, propene oxide; **хлористый п.** propylene chloride, 1,2-dichloropropane; **—гликол** m. propylene glycol, propanediol.

**пропиливать** v. saw through.

**пропилиден** m. propylidene.

**пропилит** m. (petr.) propylite; **—изация** f. propylitization; **—овый** a. propylite, propylitic.

**пропилить** see **пропиливать**.

**пропиловый** a. propyl; **п. спирт** propyl alcohol, propanol; **п. эфир бензойной кислоты** propyl benzoate; **п. эфир уксусной кислоты** propyl acetate.

**проп/ин** m. propyne, allylene; **—инал, —иналь** m., **—иновый альдегид** propynal, propioaldehyde; **—иновая кислота, —иоловая кислота** propynoic acid, propiolic acid; **соль —иоловой кислоты, —иоловокислая соль** propiolate; **—инол** m. propynol, propargyl alcohol; **—иолил** m. propiolyl; **—иоловый** a. propiolic; **—иоловый спирт** propiolic alcohol.

**пропион** m. propione, 3-pentanone; **—ат** m. propionate; **—ил** m. propionyl; **хлористый —ил** propionyl chloride.

**пропионитрил** m. propionitrile, ethyl cyanide.

**пропионово/кислый** a. propionic acid; propionate (of); **п. натрий, —натриевая соль** sodium propionate; **—кислая соль** propionate; **—этиловый эфир** ethyl propionate.

**пропионов/ый** a. propionic; **п. альдегид** propionic aldehyde, propionaldehyde; **п. ангидрид** propionic anhydride, propionyl oxide; **—ая кислота** propionic acid, propanoic acid; **соль —ой кислоты** propionate.

**пропиофенон** m. propiophenone.

**пропис/ать, —ывать** v. prescribe, order; register, enter, record; **—ка** f. visa; inscription, entry; omission; **—ной**

**a.** capital (letter); common (truth); —ю (figures written out) in words.

**пропитание** *n.* subsistence, livelihood.

**пропитанн/ость** *f.* impregnation; —ый *a.* impregnated, permeated, saturated, treated; **дважды** —ый compound impregnated, compound.

**пропит/ать,** —ывать *v.* impregnate, saturate, imbue, soak, steep, treat; preserve (wood); —ка *f.,* —ывание *n.* impregnation, saturation, soaking, steeping, treatment; transfusion; — очный, —ывающий *a.* impregnating.

**проплав/ить,** —лять *v.* fuse, melt; — ленный *a.* fused, melted.

**пропласток** *m.* (geol.) seam, streak, intercalation, interstratification.

**проплы/вать,** —ть *v.* swim (past, along, through), float.

**проповедывать** *v.* preach, hold forth; advise, recommend.

**пропокси—** *prefix* propoxy—.

**прополаскив/ание** *n.* rinsing, flushing; —ать *v.* rinse, flush.

**прополз/ать,** —ти *v.* creep, crawl (past, through).

**прополис** *m.* propolis, bee glue.

**прополосканный** *a.* rinsed, flushed.

**пропонал** *m.* proponal, di-*iso*-propyl-barbituric acid.

**пропорциональн/о** *adv.* proportionally, in proportion; **среднее** —ое mean proportion; —ость *f.* proportionality, proportionateness, proportion; **обратная** —ость inverse proportion, inverse ratio; —ый *a.* proportional, proportionate, in proportion; —ая **область** (nucl.) proportional region.

**пропорция** *f.* proportion, ratio; degree, rate; **п. флегмы** reflux ratio.

**пропотевание** *n.* transudation.

**пропс** *m.* prop; —ы *pl.* props.

**пропуск** *m.* pass, permit; admission, passing, passage; omission, lapse, miss; blank, gap; idle stroke (of piston); leak, leaking; **п. в зажигании** misfire; **за один п.** in one operation; **регулирование** —ами hit and miss governing.

**пропускан/ие** *n.* passing, passage; (illum., elec. comm.) transmission; bubbling (gas); **п. через фильтр** filtration; **схема** —ия (computers, etc.) gating circuit, gate.

**пропускать** *v.* pass, let pass, pass through, pass over, conduct; omit, miss, skip; leak, drop through; filter; **п. мимо** by-pass; **п. над** pass over.

**пропуск/ающий** *a.* passing, allowing passage, conducting, carrying; —ющая **схема** *see* **пропускания, схема;** —ной *a.* permeable; allowing passage; —ная **бумага** filter paper; blotting paper; —ная **способность** throughput; capacity (of pipe); output (of conveyer); traffic capacity; permeability.

**пропу/стить** *see* **пропускать;** —щенный *a.* passed through; filtered.

**прораб** *m.* foreman, engineer in charge.

**прораб/атывать,** —отать *v.* work through; —отка *f.* working up (of a question); purification by electrolysis.

**прора/стание,** —щивание *n.* intergrowth; (bot.) germination, sprouting; **двойник** —стания (cryst.) penetration twin; **щель** —стания (pal.) germinal aperture, haptotypic features; —стать, —сти *v.* intergrow; appear, germinate, sprout, shoot (up); —стающий *a.* germinating; —щивать *v.* let germinate.

**прорвать** *see* **прорывать.**

**прореагиров/авший** *a.* reacted; converted; —ать *v.* react.

**прорежив/ание** *n.* thinning (of trees, plants); —ать *v.* thin.

**прорез** *m.* slot, slit, groove; notch, recess, cut, nick; perforation, aperture; section; —анный *a.* slotted, slit; notched, cut; —ать *see* **прорезывать.**

**прорезин/енный** *a.* rubberized, rubber-treated; —ивание *n.,* —ка *f.* rubberizing; —ивать, —ить *v.* rubberize, treat with rubber, coat with rubber.

**прорезная пила** fret saw; **п. трава** (bot.) mountain parsley (*Peucedanum oreoselinum*); **п. фреза** slitting cutter.

**прорезывать** *v.* cut through, slit, slot, notch; **п. канавки, п. пазы** chase.

**прорезь** *see* **прорез.**

**прореха** *f.* hole, slit, tear; lapse, gap.

**проржав/евший** *a.* eaten away by rust, rusted through; —еть *v.* rust through.

**прорис** *m.* tracing; **—овать, —овывать** *v.* trace.

**проросший** *a.* intergrown, interpenetrating.

**пророческий** *a.* prophetic.

**прорубь** *f.* ice hole.

**прорыв** *m.* breach, break, break through, gap; inrush; outbreak, outburst, rupture, eruption, blowout; (geol.) fault; **полный п.** breakdown; **—ать** *v.* break through; tear, rupture; dig through; **—аться** *v.* burst open, shoot forth; **—ка** *f.* thinning.

**просад/ка** *f.* sag; **—очный** *a.* sagged.

**просал/ивание** *n.* greasing; **—ивать, —ить** *v.* grease.

**просаливать** *v.* corn; salt down.

**просапогенин** *m.* prosapogenin.

**просасыв/ание** *n.* suction, drawing through, draft; **—ать** *v.* draw through; suck through; filter; **—аться** *v.* be drawn through; infiltrate.

**просачив/ание** *n.* soaking; infiltration, permeation; percolation; oozing, exudation, seepage, leakage, leaking, escape, escaping; **—аться** *v.* soak, impregnate; infiltrate, filter through, percolate; ooze, ooze through, exude, seep, leak, escape; **—ающийся** *a.* percolating; leaking.

**просверл/енный** *a.* drilled, perforated; **—ивание** *n.* drilling, boring, perforation; **—ивать, —ить** *v.* drill, bore, perforate, pierce.

**просвет** *m.* clearance, opening, clear gap, gap, chink; (anat.) lumen.

**просветит/ельный** *a.* instructive, enlightening, elucidative; **—ь** *see* **просвещать.**

**просветл/ение** *n.* (med.) lucid interval; **—еть** *v.* clear up, clarify; **—ить, —ять** *v.* clear, clarify.

**просвечив/аемость** *f.* translucence; **—ание** *n.* translucence; radioscopy; X-raying; **—ать** *v.* be translucent; X-ray, examine with X-rays; **—аться** *v.* be X-rayed; **—ающий** *a.* translucent, diaphanous, transparent; (micros.) transmitting, transmission-type.

**просвещ/ать** *v.* enlighten, instruct, teach, educate; **—ение** *n.* instruction, education; **—енный** *a.* educated, intellectual, informed; expert (opinion).

**просвир/няк** *m.,* **—ки** *pl.* (bot.) mallow (*Malva*); **—чатый** *a.* malvaceous.

**просе/в** *m.* undersize (ore, etc.); gap (in sowing); **—вальный** *a.,* **—ивание** *n.,* **—ивающий** *a.* screening, sifting, bolting, riddling; **—вальщик** *m.* screener; **—ивать** *v.* screen, sift, bolt, riddle, sieve.

**просек** *m.* (min.) crosscut, cut-through, cross-hole, breakoff, break-through; **—а** *f.* clearing; **—ать** *v.* cut through.

**просело/к** *m.,* **—чная дорога** country road, dirt road, side road.

**просеренный** *a.* fumigated with sulfur.

**просеч/ка** *f.* break-through, gap; **—ь** *see* **просекать.**

**просе/янный** *a.* screened, sifted, riddled; **—ять** *see* **просеивать.**

**просин/ить** *v.* blue; **—ь** *f.* bluish color.

**проситель** *m.* applicant, petitioner; **—ный** *a.* petitionary, supplicatory.

**просить** *v.* ask, request, solicit; sue; intercede; **—ся** *v.* ask.

**просиять** *v.* brighten up, shine through, irradiate.

**проскабливать** *v.* scrape through.

**проскак/ивать, —нуть** *v.* jump, spring, slip (in, past, through), get through.

**проскальзыв/ание** *m.* slipping, slip, slippage (past, through); **—ать** *v.* slip (past, through).

**проскоблить** *see* **проскабливать.**

**проскок** *m.* passage; getting through; breakthrough (in ion exchange); **—нуть** *see* **проскакивать.**

**проскользнуть** *see* **проскальзывать.**

**проскочить** *see* **проскакивать.**

**проскре/бать, —сти** *v.* scrub thoroughly; scrub through.

**прослав/иться, —ляться** *v.* become famous; **—ленный** *a.* famous, celebrated.

**прослаивать** *v.* sandwich, insert (between); interlay, interstratify, interbed.

**проследить** *see* **прослеживать.**

**проследовать** *v.* pass (through, by).

**прослеживать** *v.* trace, track, follow.

**просло/ек** *m.* layer, band, seam, streak; **—енный** *a.* interstratified, interbedded; **—ить** *see* **прослаивать.**

**прослой** *m.,* **—ка** *f.* layer, sheet, lamina; padding, stuffing; interlayer; (geol.)

seam, streak; intercalation, interstratification.

**просмаливать** *v.* tar, coat with tar, impregnate with tar; treat with resin.

**просматривать** *v.* look through, look over, glance over, scan; overlook, miss.

**просмол/ение** *n.* tarring, treating with tar; treating with resin; —**енный** *a.* tarred; treated with resin; friction (tape); —**ить** *see* **просмаливать.**

**просмотр** *m.* survey, review; scanning; omission, oversight, blunder; —**енный** *a.* reviewed; revised, checked, looked over, examined; —**енное и исправленное издание** revised edition; —**еть** *see* **просматривать.**

**просо** *n.* (bot.) panic grass (*Panicum*), spec. millet (*P. miliaceum*); **итальянское п.** foxtail millet (*Setaria italica*); **культурное п.** millet (*P. miliaceum*); **куриное п.** barnyard millet (*Echinochloa crus-galli*); **негритянское п.** pearl millet (*Pennisetum typhoideum*); —**видный** *a.* miliary, like millet seeds.

**просовывать** *v.* push through, shove through, force through, extrude.

**просовые** *pl.* (bot.) Paniceae.

**просол/енный** *a.* salted, preserved in salt; salt-impregnated; corned (beef); —**ить** *see* **просаливать.**

**прососать** *see* **просасывать.**

**просох/нуть** *v.* get dry, dry out; —**ший** *a.* dried.

**просочиться** *see* **просачиваться.**

**проспект** *m.* prospectus, pamphlet; avenue.

**проспектор** *m.* (min.) prospector.

**просроч/енный** *a.* overdue; —**ивать, —ить** *v.* be overdue; hold over, delay; —**ка** *f.* delay, expiration (of term).

**простаивать** *v.* stand.

**простат/а** *f.,* —**ическая железа** (anat.) prostate (gland); —**ит** *m.* (med.) prostatitis.

**простейш/ий** *a.* the simplest; —**ие** *pl.,* —**ие животные** (zool.) Protozoa.

**простенок** *m.* pier, separating wall.

**простереть** *see* **простирать.**

**простетический** *a.* prosthetic (group).

**простир/ание** *n.* stretch, extension, spreading, spread; (geol.) course,

strike, trend; **п. пластов** direction of strata; —**ать** *v.* stretch, extend, reach (out); launder; —**аться** *v.* stretch, reach, range, spread, extend; (geol.) trend, run.

**простительный** *a.* pardonable, justifiable.

**просто** *adv.* simply, plainly; merely, just.

**прост/ой** *a.* simple, ordinary, common, plain, single; bare, mere; flat (rate); *m.* standstill, inactivity, idle period, lost time; —**ое вещество, —ое тело** element; —**ое число** (math.) prime number; **иметь п.** *v.* be inactive, remain idle.

**простокваша** *f.* sour milk, clabber.

**простор** *m.* spaciousness, ampleness, roominess, scope; —**ный** *a.* spacious, ample, roomy, capacious, open; spatial, steric.

**простота** *f.* simplicity.

**простоять** *see* **простаивать.**

**постранн/о** *adv.* extensively; at length, in detail; —**ость** *f.* extensiveness; verbosity; —**ый** *a.* extensive, expansive, vast, ample, spacious.

**пространственн/о-однородный** *a.* spatially homogeneous; —**оподобный** *a.* space-like; —**ый** *a.* space, spatial, steric, three-dimensional; solid (angle); directional (quantization); —**ый заряд** (thermionics) space charge; —**ая изомерия** stereoisomerism; —**ая решетка** (cryst.) space lattice; —**ая формула** spatial formula; —**ая химия** stereochemistry; —**ое затруднение, —ое препятствие** steric hindrance; —**ое размещение** spacing.

**пространств/о** *n.* space, spacing, expanse, scope, extent, range, amplitude; field, area; room, volume; distance; **на широком —е** over a widespread area.

**прострация** *f.* prostration, exhaustion.

**прострел** *m.* (radiation) streaming, leakage; channeling; (med.) lumbago; (bot.) anemone; pasque flower (*Pulsatilla*); **п.-трава** *f.,* —**ьная трава** (bot.) aconite (*Aconitum*); —**ивание** *n.* shooting through; cleaning, blowing (condenser tubes); —**ивать, —ить** *v.* shoot through; —**ка** *f.* shooting.

просту/да *f.* cold, chill; —диться, — жаться *v.* catch cold; —дный *a.* catarrhal.

простукивать *v.* rap, tap.

проступ/ать, —ить *v.* show, protrude; pass through, step through.

проступок *m.* fault; misdemeanor.

простыня *f.* sheet.

просунуть *see* просовывать.

просуш/енный *a.* dried; —ивание *n.*, —ка *f.* drying, desiccating, dehumidifying; —ивать, —ить *v.* dry, dry thoroughly, kiln-dry, desiccate.

просуществовать *v.* exist.

просч/ет *m.* error in counting; countdown, counting loss; checking; —итать, —итывать *v.* check; count; —итаться, —итываться *v.* make an error in counting; miscalculate.

просыпать *v.* spill; —ся *v.* wake up, awaken, rouse; be spilled.

просыхать *v.* dry, get dry.

просьб/а *f.* request, petition, application; обращаться с —ой *v.* ask, request.

просяновский *a.* Prosyanaya.

просяной *a.* (bot.) millet.

протагон *m.* protagon.

протактин/иды *pl.* protactinides; —ий *m.* protactinium, Pa.

проталина *f.* (geol.) thawed patch.

проталкив/ание *n.* pushing (through); —ать *v.* push, press, force (through).

протальбиновая кислота protalbinic acid.

протамин *m.* protamine (simple protein).

протапливать *v.* heat (occasionally).

протаптывать *v.* beat (a path).

протарг/ил *m.* protargyl, protyle; —ол *m.* Protargol.

протаре *m.* a calcium arsenite seed disinfectant.

протаскивать *v.* drag through, pull through, run (cable).

протачивать *v.* sharpen; turn (on lathe); eat, gnaw through, bore (of worm).

протащить *see* протаскивать.

протеаза *f.* protease, proteolytic enzyme.

протежировать *v.* protect, favor.

протез *m.*, —ирование *n.* (med.) prosthesis; —ный *a.* prosthetic.

протеид *m.* proteide (protein); —ин *m.* proteidin.

протеин *m.*, —овый *a.* protein; —овая кислота proteic acid; соль —овой кислоты proteinate; —овое вещество protein substance, protein.

протейные *pl.* (bot.) Proteaceae.

протек/ание *n.* flow, flowing; passing; course; —ать *v.* flow past, pass, run through; leak; elapse; proceed, take place; —ать нормально *v.* take a normal course.

протектор *m.*, —ный *a.* protector, protective device; (tire) tread.

протекция *f.* protection, favor.

протеоли/з *m.* proteolysis; —тический *a.* proteolytic, proteoclastic, protein-splitting.

протереть *see* протирать.

протерозой *m.*, —ская эра (geol.) Proterozoic era.

протертый *a.* worn, threadbare.

протест *m.* protest, complaint; —овать *v.* protest, complain.

протеч/ная бумага filter paper; —ь *see* протекать.

против *adv. and prep. gen.* opposite; against, versus; counter; contrary; to; as compared to, in comparison with; за и п. pro and con; стоящий п. facing.

противень *m.* drip pan; griddle; tray.

противиться *v.* oppose, resist, object (to).

противн/ик *m.* adversary, opponent, enemy; —о *adv.* contrary, against; disgustingly, repulsively; —ый *a.* opposed, contrary, adverse; alien; disgusting, repugnant; в —ом случае otherwise.

противо— *prefix* counter—, anti—; —атомный *a.* antinuclear; —борствовать *v.* oppose, resist, fight; —вес *m.* counterweight, counterbalance, balance weight, counterpoise; equipoise; —вирусный *a.* (med.) antiviral; —включение *n.* (elec.) opposition, balancing; —воздушная оборона (mil.) anti-aircraft defense; —воспалительный *a.* (med.) antiphlogistic.

противогаз *m.*, —овый шлем gas mask; —овый *a.* gasproof, antigas.

противоглистный *a.* vermifuge, anthelmintic.

противогнилостн/ость *f.* asepsis; resistance to rotting; **—ый** *a.* aseptic; resistant to rotting; preservative; **—ое средство** preservative.

противогрибковый *a.* fungicidal.

противодавление *n.* counterpressure, back pressure, resistance.

противодейств/ие *n.* counteraction, reaction, resistance, counterforce, opposing force; **оказывать п.** *v.* counteract; **—овать** *v.* counteract, react (against); oppose, resist; cross; destroy; **—ующий** *a.* counteractive, reactive; opposing, antagonistic; reactionary; **—ующая сила** counterforce, opposing force, thrust.

противо/детонирующий *a.* antiknock; **—естественный** *a.* unnatural; **—желчный** *a.* (med.) antibilious; **—законный** *a.* illegal; **—замерзающий состав** antifreeze; **—зобовое средство** (med.) antistrumatic; **—ион** *m.* counterion, gegenion; **—кашлевый** *a.* antitussive, cough (remedy); **—коагулирующее средство** anticoagulant, anticoagulin; **—кражная сигнализация** burglar alarm; **—лежащий** *a.* lying opposite, opposite.

противолихорадочн/ый *a.* antifebrile; **—ое средство** febrifuge, antipyretic.

противо/ломотный *a.* (med.) antiarthritic; **—микробный** *a.* antimicrobic; **—накипное средство** boiler compound; **—намагнитить** *v.* backmagnetize; **—нитный** *a.* counterfilar; **—обледенитель** *m.* (aero.) deicer; **—окислитель** *m.* antioxidant; **—опухолевый** *a.* (med.) antineoplastic, antitumorigenic; **—параллельный** *a.* (geom.) antiparallel.

противопожарн/ый *a.* fireproof; firefighting; **—ая техника** fire prevention.

противо/показание *n.* (med.) contraindication; **—полагать** *see* противопоставить.

противополож/ение *n.* contrast, antithesis, contradistinction; **—ить** *see* противопоставить; **—но** *adv.* contrarily, contrariwise, in contrast, oppositely; **—ное** *n.* the contrary, the reverse, counterpart; **—ность** *f.* opposition, contrast; **в —ность** on the contrary,

in contrast (with); **прямая —ность** the exact opposite (to); **—ный** *a.* contrary, opposite, opposed, contradictory, reverse, inverse; counter—; different; **диаметрально —ный** antipodal.

противопостав/ить, **—лять** *v.* oppose, contrast, set against, set off; object; **в —лении** versus.

противо/пыльный *a.* dustproof, dusttight; **—рвотный** *a.* (med.) antiemetic; **—регулирование** *n.* counterregulation.

противореч/иво *adv.* in contradiction; **—ивый** *a.* contradictory, inconsistent; **—ие** *n.* contradiction, conflict, inconsistency, discrepancy, variance; **—ить** *v.* contradict; cross, interfere.

противосамолетный *a.* antiaircraft.

противосифилитический *a.* antisyphilitic.

противосовпадение *n.* (detectors) anticoincidence.

противосредство *n.* remedy, antidote.

противостаритель *m.* age resistor, antioxidant; **—ные свойства** aging properties.

противосто/яние *n.* resistance; (astron.) opposition; **—ять** *v.* resist, oppose, withstand, face; **—ящий** *a.* opposed, resisting; opposite.

противосудорожн/ый *a.*, **—ое средство** antispasmodic.

противо/сумеречный *a.* anticrepuscular; **—сыростный** *a.* dampproof, moisture-resistant; **—танковый** *a.* (mil.) antitank; **—течение** *n.* counterflow; **—ток** *m.*, **—точный** *a.* countercurrent, counterflow; reflux; **—угон** *m.*, **—угонный** *a.* anticreeper; **—фаза** *f.* antiphase, opposite phase; **—фоновый** *a.* antibackground; antihum.

противохимическ/ий *a.* (mil.) antigas; **—ая оборона** gas defense.

противо/цинготный *a.* antiscorbutic; **—электродвижущий** *a.* counterelectromotive; **—ядие** *n.* antidote; **—ядный** *a.* antidotal.

протий *m.* protium (light hydrogen isotope).

протир/ать *v.* rub, rub through; **—очная машина** triturator.

**протис/кать, —кивать, —нуть** v. press, squeeze (through, past).

**протисты** pl. (biol.) Protista.

**проткнуть** see **протыкать.**

**прото—** prefix proto— (first); **—актиний** m. protactinium, Pa; **—анемонин** m. protoanemonin; **—вератрин** m. protoveratrine; **—генный** a. protogenic; **—гин** m., **—гиновый** a. protogine (old name for a variety of igneous rock); **—зои** pl. (zool.) Protozoa.

**проток** m. canal, channel, tube; throat, neck (of glass furnace); (anat.) duct.

**протокатех/овая кислота** protocatechuic acid, 3,4-dihydroxybenzoic acid; **—ол** m. protocatechol.

**протокла/з** m. protoclase (a sedimentary rock); **—стический** a. protoclastic.

**протококк/и** pl., **—овые зеленые водоросли** (bot.) Protococcaceae.

**протококовая кислота** protococcaic acid.

**протокол** m. minutes, proceedings, official report, record; **—ы** pl. transactions, proceedings; **—ировать** v. record.

**протокурарин** m. protocurarine.

**протолихестериновая кислота** protolichesteric acid.

**протолк/ать, —нуть** see **проталкивать.**

**протолоч/ка** f. grinding, crushing; **—ь** v. grind, pulverize; break, crush.

**протон** m. proton; **—ный** a. proton, protonic.

**протонефть** f. protopetroleum.

**протопин** m. protopine, fumarine.

**протопить** see **протапливать.**

**протоплазм/а** f. (biol.) protoplasm; **—енный** a. protoplasmic.

**протопласт** m. protoplast.

**протопорфирин** m. protoporphyrin.

**протоптать** see **протаптывать.**

**проторенный** a. beaten, well-trodden.

**прототип** m. prototype.

**прототроп/ия** f. prototropy (proton or hydrogen migration); **—ный** a. prototropic.

**протоцетраровая кислота** protocetraric acid.

**протоцилиаты** pl. (zool.) Protociliata.

**проточ/енный** a. sharpened; eaten, gnawed, bored; **п. червями** wormeaten; **—ить** see **протачивать.**

**проточн/ость** f. flow, flowage; **—ый** a. flowing, flow, flow-type, flow-through; circulating, continuous (stream); running (water); production (line); **—ый счетчик** flow-type counter.

**протрав/а** f. (dyeing) mordant; (met.) pickle, pickling, dip; **красная п.** (dyeing) red liquor; **—итель** m. (seed) disinfectant; **—ка** f. mordanting; pickling; **поверхностная —ка** (met.) passivation; **—ленный** a. treated with a mordant; pickled; etched; pitted; stained (wood); **—ливание** n. mordanting; pickling, dipping, scouring, cleansing, corroding off; etching; (seed) treatment, disinfection; **—ливатель** m. disinfecting apparatus; **—ливать, —лять** v. treat with mordant, mordant; pickle, dip, scour, corrode off; etch; stain (wood); treat, disinfect; **—ляющий** a. corrosive; **—ный** a. mordant; **—ные краски** mordant dyes; **—очная ванна** pickling bath.

**протромбин** m. prothrombin.

**протрузия** f. protrusion.

**протуберанц** m. protuberance.

**протух/лость** f. putrescence; **—лый, —ший** a. putrid, rotten; **—нуть** v. become putrid, putrefy.

**протык/алка** f. pricker; **—альник** m. skewer; **—ать** v. prick through, pierce.

**протычка** f. pricker.

**протягив/ание** n. drawing, pulling through; broaching (holes); **—ать** v. draw out, stretch, extend; pull through; broach; prolong; reach out; **—аться** v. extend, stretch out; last.

**протяжен/ие** n. extent, stretch, expanse; spread, expansion, extension, elongation; range, amplitude; field; dimension, length; run; **п. времени** duration; **большое п.** expanse; **—ность** f. expansion, extension, spread; extent, length.

**протяж/ка** f. drawing; broach (for machining holes); **—ной станок** broaching machine, broaching lathe; **—ность** f. lengthiness; **—ный** a. lengthy, lasting, slow.

**протянут/ый** a. stretched, extended; pulled through; prolonged; **—ь** see **протягивать.**

**Проута гипотеза** Prout hypothesis.

**проушина** *f.* lug, ear, eye, staple.

**проф—** *abbr.* (профессиональный) professional; trade; (профсоюзный) trade union; **проф.** *abbr.* (профессор) professor.

**профаза** *f.* (biol.) prophase.

**профан** *m.* layman.

**профдвижение** *n.* trade unionism.

**профермент** *m.* proenzyme, zymogen.

**профессионал** *m.* professional; **—ьный** *a.* professional, trade; occupational (disease, hazard); **—ьный союз** trade union.

**професс/ия** *f.* profession, occupation, trade, business, function; **—ор** *m.* professor; **—орство** *n.* professorship; **—ура** *f.* professorate; professorship.

**профетин** *m.* prophetin.

**профилакт/ика** *f.* prophylaxis, preventive treatment; preventive measure; (mach.) preventive maintenance; **—ический** *a.* prophylactic; preventive, protective; **—ический осмотр** preventive maintenance; **—ическая мера, —ическое средство** prophylactic, preventive; **—орий** *m.* dispensary; (mach.) preventive maintenance building.

**профилиров/ание** *n.* profiling, shaping, designing of construction lines; **—анный** *a.* profiled, profile, shaped; **—анный валок** grooved roll; **—ать** *v.* profile, cut a profile, shape.

**профиль** *m.* profile, outline, contour, lines, design, shape; section, cross section, side view; elevation; section iron; **п.-каландр** profiling calendar; **поперечный п.** cross section, transverse section; **продольный п.** longitudinal section; **сложный п.** irregular outline.

**профильн/ый** *a.* profile, contour; shaped, section-shaped, section; **п. каландр** *see* **профиль-каландр**; **п. прибор** profiling instrument, edging instrument; **п. резец** forming cutter, form tool, shaping tool; **п. фрезер** profile cutter; **—ая проекция** end view; **—ое железо** profile iron, section iron, structural iron.

**профильтров/анный** *a.* filtered through;

**—ать, —ывать** *v.* filter (through).

**профит** *m.* profit.

**про/флавин** *m.* proflavine, 3,6- diaminoacridine; **—форетин** *m.* prophoretin.

**профрезированный** *a.* milled.

**проф/союз** *abbr.* (профессиональный союз) trade union; **—школа** *abbr.* (профессиональная школа) trade school.

**прохаживать** *see* **проходить**.

**прохлад/а** *f.* coolness, freshness; **—ительный** *a.* cooling, refreshing; refrigerating; **—ить** *see* **прохлаждать**; **—но** *adv.* coolly; it is cool; **—ность** *f.* coolness, freshness; **—ный** *a.* cool, fresh.

**прохлорит** *m.* (min.) prochlorite (ripidolite in part).

**проход** *m.* passage, passageway, conduit, canal; pass; passing, passing through; thoroughfare; lane, aisle, way; gate; aperture, opening, orifice; (anat.) duct, meatus; **за один п.** in one operation, per pass; **задний п.** (anat.) anus, vent.

**проходим/ость** *f.* permeability, penetrability; passability; **—ый** *a.* permeable, pervious; passable, navigable.

**проходить** *v.* pass, be over, terminate, expire, elapse; go through, run through, pass through, move through; cover (distance); sink (a shaft); **п. сквозь, п. через** penetrate, permeate, pass through.

**проход/ка** *f.* cutting; (min.) sinking (of shaft); **—ник** *m.* long-eye auger; **—ной** *a.* going through, straight through, through, straightway; **—ческий** *a.* sinking; **—ящий** *a.* passing, going through; transient.

**прохож/дение** *n.* passage, passing, crossing, going through, running through, flow; transmission; path; **—ий** *a.* passing; *m.* passerby.

**процарапать** *v.* scratch through.

**процвет/ание** *n.* prosperity; **—ающий** *a.* prosperous, flourishing.

**процедить** *see* **процеживать**.

**процедура** *f.* procedure.

**процежив/ание** *n.* filtration, straining; **—ать** *v.* filter, strain.

**процент** *m.* per cent, percentage; interest rate; **п. влажности** moisture content; в весовых—ах, весовой п. per cent by weight; **содержание в —ах** percentage, content; **число —ов, —ы** percentage; **—ность** *f.* percentage; degree.

**процентн/ый** *a.* per cent, percentage; **—ая квантиля** percentile; **—ое начисление** interest charge; **—ое отношение** percentage; **—ое отношение по весу** per cent by weight; **—ое отношение по объему** per cent by volume; **—ое содержание** percentage, per cent, content.

**процесс** *m.* process, operation; procedure; lawsuit, litigation; **п. производства** course of production; industrial process.

**процессия** *f.* procession.

**прочес** *m.* fleece; **—анный** *a.* hackled (flax); **—ать** *see* **прочесывать.**

**прочесть** *see* **прочитать.**

**прочесыв/ание** *n.* combing; hackling (of flax); **—ать** *v.* comb; hackle.

**проч/ий** *a.* other, rest, remaining; **—ие принадлежности** sundry accessories; **и —ее** and so on, et cetera; **и все —ее** and all the rest of it; **между —им** by the way; **между —ими** among the rest, among others.

**прочист/ить** *see* **прочищать; —ка** *f.* scouring, cleansing; (med.) purging.

**прочит/ать, —ывать** *v.* read through, peruse; scan.

**прочить** *v.* intend (for).

**прочищ/ать** *v.* scour, clean, cleanse thoroughly; (med.) purge; **—аться** *v.* clear up; **—ающий** *a.* cleaning; purging; **—ение** *see* **прочистка.**

**прочно** *adv.* firmly, stably, securely.

**прочност/ь** *f.* stability, firmness, sturdiness, solidity, substantiality; reliability, safety; durability, strength, tenacity, toughness, endurance, lasting quality, permanence; **п. конструкции** structural strength; **п. на изгиб** bending strength, transverse strength; **п. на износ** resistance to wear; **п. на кручение** torsional strength; **п. на разрыв, предел —и на растяжение** tensile strength; **п. на сдвиг, п. на срез** shearing strength; **п. на удар** resistance to impact; **запас —и,**

коэффициент **—и** safety factor, safety margin; **испытание на п.** endurance test; **предел —и** strength; **предел —и на сжатие** compression strength.

**прочн/ый** *a.* stable, sturdy, rugged, tough, substantial, solid; durable, strong, wear-resisting; lasting, permanent; fast (color); **—ое основание** stable foundation.

**прочтение** *n.* reading.

**прочь** *adv.* away, off; **он не п.** he is not averse (to), he has no objection (to).

**прошедш/ее** *n.* the past; **—ий** *a.* past, previous; having passed.

**прошеллаченный** *a.* shellacked.

**прошение** *n.* application, petition.

**прошеств/ие** *n.* lapse, expiration, end; **по —ии** on expiration (of).

**прошив/ать** *v.* sew, stitch; pierce; broach; (med.) suture; **—ень** *m.* punch, drift; (met.) mandrel; **—ка** *f.* piercing; broaching; broach, broaching bit, reamer.

**прошив/ной, —очный** *a.* piercing; broaching; **п. стан** piercing mill; **п. станок** broaching machine, broaching lathe.

**прошить** *see* **прошивать.**

**прошлифов/очный станок** honing machine; **—ывание** *n.* honing; polishing; **—ывать** *v.* hone; polish.

**прошлогодний** *a.* last year's.

**прошл/ое** *n.* the past; **—ый** *a.* past, former; last (year, month, etc.).

**прощальный** *a.* farewell, parting.

**прощать** *v.* pardon, excuse, overlook; **—ся** *v.* be excused; take one's leave.

**проще** *comp. of* **просто, простой,** easier, simpler.

**прощение** *n.* pardon, forgiveness.

**прощуп/ать, —ывать** *v.* feel; probe; **—ывание** *n.* probing.

**проэктировать** *see* **проектировать.**

**проэнзим** *m.* proenzyme, zymogen.

**проявит/ель** *m.* (phot.) developer; **—ельный** *a.* developing; **—ь** *see* **проявлять.**

**проявл/ение** *n.* manifestation, display, exhibition, show; (phot.) development; **—енный** *a.* manifested, shown; developed; **—ять** *v.* manifest, display, show, exhibit, exert, give rise (to);

develop; —яться *v.* develop, come through, appear.

проясн/ение *n.* clearing; точка —ения clear point; —еть, —ивать, —ить *v.* clear up, brighten; —ить, —ять *v.* clear, make clear, clarify; elucidate, explain; —яться *v.* clear up.

пруд *m.*, —овой *a.* pond, reservoir; —ить *v.* dam; —овик *m.* pond snail; —ок *m.* pool, puddle.

пружин/а *f.* spring, coil; п.-волосок hairspring; главная п. mainspring; —е-ние *n.* spring, springing; —ить *v.* spring, have a spring (in), be elastic, yield; —ность *f.* springiness, elasticity.

пружинн/ый *a.* spring; п. арретир, —ая упорка stop spring; п. крюк snap hook; п. стопор spring lock.

пружинодержатель *m.* spring hold, spring support.

пружиняш/ий *a.* springy, springing, elastic; —ая способность springiness, elasticity; —ее кольцо snap ring.

прулауразин *m.* prulaurasin; —овая кислота prulaurasic acid.

пруназ/а *f.* prunase; —ин *m.* prunasin; —иновая кислота prunasic acid.

прун/етол *m.* prunetol, genistein; —озин *m.* prunosin; —ол *m.* prunol, ursolic acid.

прус, —ик *m.* a locust (*Calliptamus*); —ак *m.* cockroach; —сак *m.* German cockroach.

Пруссия Prussia.

прусск/ий *a.* Prussian; п. красный Prussian red, colcothar; —ая голубая, —ая лазурь Prussian blue; —ие белила ceruse, white lead.

Пруста закон Proust's law, law of constant proportions.

прустит *m.* (min.) proustite, ruby silver ore.

прут *m.* rod, stick, twig, switch; *pr. 3 pl. of* переть; —ик *m.* twig.

прутков/ый *a.* rod, rod-shaped; —ое железо rod iron, wire rod.

прутняк *m.* (bot.) kochia (spec. *K. prostrata*); agnus castus.

пруток *m.* bar, rod; rung (of ladder).

прутяной *a.* osier.

прыг/ание *n.* jumping, skipping, jerking; —ать, —нуть *v.* jump, leap, spring, bound, skip, jerk; knock (of valve); —ун *m.* hopper, jumper.

прыжок *m.* jump, leap, spring, bound.

прыс/калка *f.* sprayer, syringe; —кание *n.* spraying; —кать, —нуть *v.* spray.

прыщ, —ик *m.* pimple, acne; (med.) pustule; —еватый *a.* pimpled; pustular.

прюнель *f.* prunelle (dried plum); (text.) prunella.

пряд/ево *n.* tow; —ение *n.* spinning; ручного —ения homespun; —еный *a.* spun; —ет *pr. 3 sing. of* прясть.

прядиль/ный *a.* spinning; textile; п. раствор spinning solution; п. станок spinning loom; —ные насосики (rayon) spinnerets; —ня *f.* spinning mill; —щик *m.* spinner.

пряд/ут *pr. 3 pl. of* прясть; —ущий *a.* spinning; —ь *f.* strand, yarn; ply.

пряжа *f.* yarn, thread; (bot.) maidenhair (*Adiantum capillus veneris*).

пряж/ка *f.*, —ечный *a.* buckle, clasp.

пряжный *see* прядильный.

прял *past sing. of* прясть; —ка *f.* spinning wheel.

прям/ая *f.* straight line; на одной —ой с, по одной —ой с in line with; —изна *f.* straightness; —иком *adv.* cross country; —ило *n.* parallel motion; —ить *v.* straighten (out, up).

прямо *adv.* straight, directly; immediately.

прямо— *prefix* straight, rect—, recti—; —бортная покрышка beadless tire; —гонный *a.* directly distilled; —дей-ствующий *a.* direct-acting, direct; —звенная цепь straight-link chain.

прям/ой *a.* straight, direct, through; straightforward; upright, erect; right (angle); forward (reaction); roman (type); reef (knot); sheer (waste); п. голубой Direct Sky Blue (dye); п. удар (nucl.) knock-on impact; п. ход forward stroke; —ое действие direct action, direct effect; —ое уравнение linear equation; —ым путем directly; под —ым углом at right angles.

прямокрылые *pl.* (zool.) Orthoptera.

прямолинейно *adv.* rectilinearly; straight-forwardly; п.-возвратный *a.* reciprocating, moving to and fro.

прямолинейн/ость *f.* rectilinearity; —ый

*a.* rectilinear, straight, straight-line, linear.

**прямослойн/ость** *f.* straight grain (of wood); **—ый** *a.* straight-grained.

**прямо/сторонний** *a.* straight-sided; **—струйный** *a.* direct-spray, direct-jet; **—та** *f.* straightness, rectitude.

**прямоточн/ость** *f.* direct flow, straight-through feed; **—ый** *a.* direct-flow; uniflow; concurrent; once-through; single-pass (boiler); **—ый воздушно-реактивный двигатель** ram-jet engine.

**прямоугольн/ик** *m.* rectangle, square; **—ый** *a.* right-angled, rectangular, quadrate, square; orthogonal; right (triangle); **—ая кромка** straightedge.

**прямо/частотный** *a.* straight-line frequency; **—шовные** *pl.*, **—шовные мухи** straight-seamed flies (*Orthorrhapha*).

**прян/ость** *f.*, **—ое вещество** spice, condiment; **—ый** *a.* spicy; rich (food).

**прясть** *v.* spin.

**прят/ание** *n.* hiding; **—анный** *a.* hidden; **—ать** *v.* hide, conceal, cover; secrete.

**пряха** *f.* spinner.

**пряч/ет** *pr. 3 sing. of* **прятать**; **—ущий** *a.* hiding.

**пс** code for "killed" in steel mark; *abbr.* self potential; **ПС** *see* **профсоюз**.

**псаммит** *m.* psammite (a dendrital sedimentary rock); **—овый** *a.* psammitic, made up of sand-like particles.

**псевдо—** *prefix* pseudo—, pseud—; **—аконитин** *m.* pseudoaconitine; **—апатит** *m.* (min.) pseudoapatite; **—брукит** *m.* (min.) pseudobrookite; **—гранат** *m.* (min.) pseudogarnet; **—жиженный** *see* **псевдоожиженный**; **—изомерия** *f.* pseudoisomerism; **—индил** *m.* pseudoindyl; **—кислота** *f.* pseudo acid.

**псевдокристалл** *m.* pseudocrystal; **—ический** *a.* pseudocrystalline.

**псевдо/кумидин** *m.* pseudocumidine, 2,4,5-trimethylaniline; **—кумол** *m.* pseudocumene; **—лейцит** *m.* (min.) pseudoleucite (a variety of leucite); **—мерия** *f.* pseudomerism.

**псевдоморф** *m.* (cryst.) pseudomorph; **—ия** *f.* pseudomorphy; **—ный** *a.* pseudomorphous; **—оза** *f.* pseudomorphosis.

**псевдо/мочевая кислота** pseudouric acid; **—ожижение** *n.* fluidization; **—ожиженный** *a.* fluidized, quasi-liquid; **—ожиженный слой** fluidized bed; **—основание** *n.* pseudo base; **—равновесие** *n.* pseudo-equilibrium; **—раствор** *m.* pseudo solution, colloidal suspension or emulsion; **—родановодород, —сульфоциан** *m.* pseudothiocyanogen; **—симметрия** *f.* (cryst.) pseudosymmetry; **—соединение** *n.* pseudo compound; **—сфера** *f.*, **—шар** *m.* (geom.) pseudosphere; **—тройной** *a.* pseudoternary; **—фит** *m.* (min.) pseudophite (a variety of penninite); **—холестен** *m.* pseudocholestene; **—чума** *f.* pseudopest (poultry disease).

**псефит** *m.* (petr.) psephite; **—овый** *a.* psephitic, made up of pebbles.

**псикаин** *m.* psicaine, *d-psi*-cocaine bitartrate.

**псиллов/ая кислота** psyllic acid, psyllostearylic acid; **—ый спирт** psillic alcohol, psyllostearyl alcohol.

**псиломелан** *m.* (min.) psilomelane (a hydrated manganese oxide).

**пситтацинит** *m.* (min.) psittacinite (a variety of descloizite).

**психиатр** *m.* psychiatrist; **—ический** *a.* psychiatric; **—ия** *f.* psychiatry.

**психи/ка** *f.* psychics; psychology; **—чески** *adv.* mentally (ill); **—ческий** *a.* psychic; **—ческое расстройство** *see* **психоз**.

**психо—** *prefix* psycho—, psychological; **—анализ** *m.* psychoanalysis; **—генезис** *m.* psychogenesis; **—з** *m.* psychosis.

**психозойская эра** (geol.) Psychozoic era.

**психолог** *m.* psychologist; **—ический** *a.* psychological; **—ия** *f.* psychology.

**психо/невроз** *m.* psychoneurosis; **—пат** *m.* psychopath; **—патия** *f.* psychopathy; **—патология** *f.* psychopathology; **—терапия** *f.* psychotherapy; **—трин** *m.* psychotrine; **—физиология** *f.* psychophysiology, psychic physiology.

**психрометр** *m.* (meteor.) psychrometer; **—ический** *a.* psychrometric.

**псориаз** *m.* (med.) psoriasis.

**псоромовая кислота** psoromic acid.

**птеригоспермин** *m.* pterygospermin.

**птериновая кислота** pteroic acid.

**птеро—** *prefix* ptero— (wing); **—дактил** *m.* (pal.) pterodactyl; **—завр** *m.* pterosaur; **—карпин** *m.* pterocarpin; **—малиды** *pl.* (zool.) Pteromalidae.

**Пти** *see under* Дюлонг и Пти.

**птиал/аза** *f.*, **—ин** *m.* ptyalase, ptyalin, salivary amylase.

**птигматовый** *a.* ptygmatic (folds in metamorphic rocks).

**птилолит** *m.* ptilolite (a zeolitic mineral).

**птихотисовое масло** ptychotis oil, oil of ajowan.

**птиц/а** *f.* bird; poultry, fowl; **домашняя п.** poultry; **—евод** *m.* poultry farmer; **—еводство** *n.* poultry farming; aviculture; **—еводческая ферма, —е-ферма** *f.* poultry farm; **—емлечник** *m.* (bot.) star of Bethlehem (*Ornithogalum*).

**птич/ий** *a.* bird; **п. клей** bird lime; **—ья гречиха** *see* спорыш; **вид с —ьего полета** birdseye view.

**птич/ка** *f.* little bird; tick; **ставить —ки** *v.* tick off, mark off; **—ник** *m.* aviary; poultry house, chicken coop.

**ПТО** *abbr.* (противотанковая оборона) antitank defense.

**птоз, —ис** *m.* (med.) ptosis.

**птомаин** *m.* ptomaine.

**ПТЭ** *abbr.* (Приборы и техника эксперимента) Instruments and Experimental Techniques (journal).

**пуаз** *m.* poise (unit of viscosity).

**Пуазейля закон** Poiseuille's law.

**пуансон** *m.* point; punch, die, stamp; plunger; **—одержатель** *m.* punch holder; die stock.

**Пуассона коэффициент** Poisson's ratio.

**пуберул/овая кислота** puberulic acid; **—оновая кислота** puberulonic acid.

**публик/а** *f.* public; **—ация** *f.* publication; advertisement; **—овать** *v.* publish; advertise, announce.

**публичн/о** *adv.* publicly, in public; **—ость** *f.* publicity; **—ый** *a.* public, common, open; **—ая продажа** auction.

**пуга** *f.* air pocket (in egg).

**пуг/ать, —нуть** *v.* frighten, scare; appall; **—ливый** *a.* fearful, timid.

**пугов/ица** *f.*, **—ичный** *a.* button, stud; **—ичный транспортер** (min.) a type of apron conveyer; **—ка** *f.* head, knob; button; sleeker.

**пуговник** *m.* a weed (*Centaurea scabiosa*).

**пуд** *m.* (obs.) pood (36 pounds).

**пуддинг** *m.*, **—овый камень** (petr.) pudding stone (a conglomerate).

**пудельбарс** *m.* (met.) puddle bar.

**пудинг** *m.* pudding; **—овый камень** *see* пуддинг.

**пудлинговальн/ый** *a.* (met.) puddling, puddle; **п. прут** puddle stick; **п. цех, —я** *f.* puddling works.

**пудлингов/ание** *n.* (met.) puddling; **—ать** *v.* puddle; **—щик** *m.* puddler.

**пудлингов/ый** *a.* (met.) puddling, puddled; **—ая заготовка** puddle bar; **—ая крица** puddle ball; **—ая печь** puddling furnace; **—ое железо** puddled iron; **—ые шлаки** puddling slag.

**пудовый** *a.* of пуд.

**пудожский камень** (min.) calcareous tufa, calcareous sinter.

**пудр/а** *f.* powder; **—ение** *n.* dusting; **—ет** *m.* poudrette (fertilizer from dried and powdered excrement); **—илка** *f.* duster.

**пузанок** *m.* shad (fish).

**пузыр/евидный** *a.* (bot.) bladder-like, utricular; **—ек** *m.* bubble, blister; bead; (biol.) vesicle, vacuole; phial, vial; **—еногие** *pl.* (zool.) thrips (*Physopoda, Thysanoptera*); **—еплодник, —чатник** *m.* (bot.) ninebark (*Physocarpus*); **—истость** *see* пузырчатость; **—истый** *see* пузырчатый; **—иться** *v.* bubble, blister; **—ник** *m.* (bot.) colutea; **—ница, —чатка** *f.* (bot.) bladderwort (*Utricularia*); **—чатковые** *pl.* Lentibulariaceae.

**пузырчат/ость** *f.* vesiculation; (met.) blistered condition; (bot.) pustule; **—ый** *a.* bubbly; (biol.) vesicular; blistered, containing blisters, porous; **—ая медь** blister copper (a high-grade crude copper); **—ая сталь** blister steel; **—ые поры** vesicular cavities.

**пузырь** *m.*, **—ковый** *a.* bubble, blister, air hole, blow hole; (anat.) bladder; (biol.) cyst; pocket, sac; **выделять**

—ки *v.* bubble, effervesce; —ковая камера bubble chamber.

пук *m.* bunch, tuft; faggot, truss.

пукатеин *m.* pukateine.

пулег/ановая кислота puleganic acid; —еновая кислота pulegenic acid; —еноловая кислота pulegenolic acid; —енон *m.* pulegenone; —ол *m.* pulegol, 3-menthenol; —он *m.* pulegone.

пулемет *m.*, —ный *a.* machine gun; —чик *m.* machine gunner, gunner.

пуленен *m.* pulenene.

пуленепроницаемый *a.* bulletproof.

пуленон *m.* pulenone.

пуллинг-мачта (oil-well drilling) a substitute for a derrick.

пульвериз/атор *m.* pulverizer; atomizer, sprayer, nebulizer; —ационный *a.* *a.* pulverization, pulverizing; atomizing, spraying; jet (pump); —ация *f.*, —ирование *n.* pulverization; atomization, spraying; —ированный, —ованный *a.* pulverized, reduced to a powder, pulverulent; atomized, sprayed; —ировать, —овать *v.* pulverize, reduce to a powder; atomize, spray.

пульвинов/ая кислота pulvinic acid; соль —ой кислоты, —окислая соль pulvinate.

пульзометр *see* пульсометр.

пульман *m.* (railroad) Pullman car.

пульмотор *m.* pulmotor.

пульп/а *f.* (paper; min.) pulp; slurry; —ер, —ообразователь *m.* pulper, pulping machine; —овидный *a.* pulpy; —омер *m.* pulp density meter; —оотделяющий *a.* depulping.

пульс *m.* pulse; частота —a pulse rate.

пульс/атор *m.* pulsator; (elec.) pulser; (min.) pulsator jig; —ация *f.*, —ирование *n.* pulsation; ripple; fluctuation; flutter; surging; —ировать *v.* pulse, pulsate; —ирующий *a.* pulsating, pulsatory; variable, intermittent; —ометр *m.* pulsometer, vacuum pump.

пульс-реле *n.* (elec.) relay-interrupter.

пульт *m.* desk; stand; panel, board.

пульхериновая кислота pulcheric acid.

пуля *f.* bullet, ball, shot; pellet.

пуляр/да, —ка *f.* spayed hen.

пумил/ин *m.* pumiline (from pine oil); —он *m.* pumilone.

пумпаж *m.* irregular running of turbo-machine.

пуналит *m.* (min.) poonahlite, scolecite.

пуниц/ин *m.* punicine, pelletierine; —овая кислота punicic acid.

пункт *m.* point, spot, locality; article, paragraph, item, clause; (med.) dispensary; (observation) post; (service) station, center; конечный п. end point.

пунктир *m.* dotted line; stipple; п. точка-тире, осевой п., фигурный п. dot-and-dash line; точечный п. dotted line.

пунктирн/ый *a.* dotted, punctuate; dotting (needle); prick (wheel); spot (welding); —ая линия dotted line, broken line.

пунктиров/альное колесико pricking wheel, prick wheel; —анный *a.* dotted; stippled; —ать *v.* dot, prick, point; stipple; —ка *f.* dotting; stippling.

пунктуальн/о *adv.* punctually, on the minute, in good time; —ость *f.* punctuality, exactness, accuracy; —ый *a.* punctual, precise.

пунсон *see* пуансон; symbol.

пунцовый *a.* crimson.

пунш *m.*, —евый *a.* punch (drink).

пунширов/ание *n.* punching; —ать *v.* punch, stamp.

пуня *f.* hay barn.

пуп *see* пупок.

пупавка *f.* (bot.) camomile (*Anthemis*).

пупин/изация *f.* (elec. comm.) pupinization, coil loading; шаг —изации coil spacing; —изированный *a.* coil-loaded; —овская катушка Pupin coil, loading coil.

пупо/видный *a.* umbilicate; —вина *f.* (anat.) umbilical cord; funicle; —к *m.* navel, umbilicus; водяной —к (bot.) marsh pennywort (*Cotyledon umbilicus*); —чный *a.* umbilical.

пупыр/ышек, —ь *m.* pimple, fever blister; (med.) papule.

пурбекский *a.* (geol.) Purbeckian.

пурга *f.* snowstorm, blizzard.

пург/атин *m.* —атол *m.* purgatin, purgatol, anthrapurpurin diacetate; —иновая кислота purgic acid.

**пурин** *m.* purine; —**овое основание** purine base; —**он** *m.* purinone, hypoxanthine.

**пурка** *f.* grain tester.

**пуро/н** *m.* purone; —**тионин** *m.* purothionin.

**пурпур** *m.* purple, spec. Tyrian purple.

**пурпур/а** *f.* (med.) purpura; —**ат** *m.* purpurate; —**есоединение** *n.* purpureo compound; —**ин** *m.* purpurin, trihydroxyanthraquinone; —**ит** *m.* (min.) purpurite.

**пурпурно—, пурпурово—** *prefix* purple.

**пурпур/ный,** —**овый** *a.* purple; —**ная руда** (min.) purple ore; blue billy; —**овая кислота** purpuric acid; **соль** —**овой кислоты,** —**овокислая соль** purpurate; —**овокислый аммоний** ammonium purpurate; **хлористый** —**окобальтиак** purpureocobaltichloride, chloropentammine cobaltichloride; —**оксантен** *m.* purpuroxanthene, xanthopurpurin; —**оксантовая кислота** purpuroxanthic acid; —**сульфоновая кислота** sulfopurpuric acid.

**пуррон** *m.* purrone, euxanthone.

**пуск** *m.,* —**ание** *n.* permission, letting; starting, start-up; triggering; **п. в ход** setting in motion, starting up, starting; **положение** —**а** starting position; —**ание ростков** (bot.) sprouting; —**атель** *m.* starter.

**пускать** *v.* let, allow, permit; turn on (water, gas); run, set in motion, start up (machine); put (into service); strike, take (root), put forth, sprout, shoot, bud; spin; spread (rumor); —**ся** *v.* be started; start, set out.

**пусков/ой** *a.* starting, start-up, trigger; actuating; **п. прибор,** —**ое устройство** starter; trigger; —**ая рукоятка** starting crank, crank; —**ая схема** starting trigger.

**пустеть** *v.* empty; become empty.

**пустить** *see* **пускать.**

**пуст/о** *adv.* empty, emptily; —**оватый** *a.* rather empty; —**ой** *a.* empty, void; hollow; vacant (building); blank, bare; (min.) barren, dead; vain, futile; —**ой узел** (cryst.) vacancy; —**ая порода** *see under* **порода;** —**ое место** blank; —**ое пространство**

vacuum; void; —**ота** *f.* emptiness, void, vacuum; hollow, cavity, blow hole (in casting); blankness; (cryst.) vacancy; **в** —**оте** in a vacuum.

**пустотел/ость** *f.* hollowness; —**ый** *a.* hollow; **отливать** —**ым, отливать** —**ую вещь** *v.* cast hollow.

**пустоти/ость** *f.* hollowness; vacuum; —**ый** *a.* hollow; vacuum; void (effect).

**пустоцвет** *m.* (bot.) sterile flower.

**пустошь** *f.* waste land, barren land.

**пустоягодник** *m.* strawberry clover (*Trifolium fragiferum*).

**пустул/а** *f.* (med.) pustule; —**езный** *a.* pustulous, pustular.

**пустын/ный** *a.* desert, arid; **п. загар, п. лак, п. налет, лак** —**и** (geol.) desert varnish; —**я** *f.* desert, waste, barrens, badlands; wilderness.

**пустырник** *m.* (bot.) water fennel, (*Oenanthe phellandrium*); mother wort (*Leonurus*).

**пустырь** *f.* vacant land; waste land.

**пусть** *v.* let, permit; suppose (that); **п. будет** let it be.

**пустя/к** *m.* trifle; —**шность** *f.* triviality, nothingness; —**шный** *a.* trifling, trivial.

**пусьера** *f.* blue powder (a zinc dust).

**пут/аница** *f.* confusion, tangle, maze; mix-up; —**анный** *a.* confused, tangled; confusing; —**ать** *v.* confuse, tangle; hobble.

**путевка** *f.* pass, permit.

**путевод/итель** *m.* guidebook, guide, itinerary; —**ный** *a.* guide, serving as guide.

**путевой** *a.* traveling, itinerary; track; road; **п. кран** crane truck; **п. струг** road grader.

**путе/ец** *m.* student of the Institute of Ways and Means of Communication; (obs.) railroad engineer; —**мер** *m.* pedometer; —**передвигатель** *m.* (railroad) track-moving machine; —**перевод** *m.* viaduct; —**рихтовщик** *m.* track liner; —**укладочная машина** track-laying machine.

**путешеств/енник** *m.* traveler; —**ие** *n.* travel, journey, trip; voyage; —**овать** *v.* travel.

**путресцин** *m.* putrescine, 1,4-butanediamine.

**пут/ь** *m.* way, road, route, course, path; (nucl.) track; journey; railroad track; race, runway, passage; means, method; **п. направления, п. прохождения** path, course; **п. подвоза** supply line; **—ем** by means of, by way of, through, via; **мокрым —ем** by the wet method; **разделение мокрым —ем** wet separation; **сухим —ем** by the dry method; by land; **разделение сухим —ем** dry separation; **на ложном —и** on the wrong track; **на обратном —и** on the way back; **на пол —и** halfway, midway; **обычный п.** usual course; **перехватить на —и** *v.* intercept; **сбиться с —и** *v.* lose one's way, stray.

**пух** *m.* down, fluff, fuzz, floss.

**пухиин** *m.* puchiin.

**пух/лый** *a.* bulky; plump; **—нуть** *v.* swell.

**пухо/вый** *a.* downy, fluffy; **—еды** *pl.* chewing lice, bird lice (*Mallophaga*).

**пуццолан** *m.*, **—а** *f.*, **—овая земля** (petr.) pozzuolana (a leucitic tuff); **—овый** *a.* pozzuolanic; **—овый цемент** pozzuolanic cement, trass cement.

**пучек** *see* **пучок.**

**пучение** *n.* swelling, heaving.

**пучина** *f.* gulf; the deep.

**пучить** *v.* swell, raise, inflate, distend; **—ся** *v.* swell, rise, heave.

**пучко/вание** *n.* bunching; **—ватель** *m.* buncher; **—ватый** *a.* (bot.) fascicular; **—видный** *a.* clustered, tufted; **—видный слой** (anat.) zona fasciculata; **—вый** *a.* cluster, sheaf; **—жаберный** *a.* (zool.) lophobranchiate.

**пучность** *f.* (phys.) antinode, loop.

**пучок** *m.* cluster, tuft, bunch, bundle, sheaf, pile, nest; wisp; (bot.) fascicle; pencil (of rays); (rad., nucl., etc.) beam; **п. проводов** (elec.) multiwire conductor.

**пушеный** *a.* fiberized (asbestos).

**пушер** *m.* pusher, ram.

**пушерит** *m.* (min.) pucherite (a bismuth vanadate).

**пушечн/ый** *a.* gun, cannon; **п. металл, —ая бронза** gun metal (a copper-tin or zinc alloy); **п. порох** gunpowder; **п. станок** gun carriage; **—ое мясо** (mil.) cannon fodder.

**пушилка** *f.* (leather) beam.

**пуш/инка** *f.* particle of fluff or fuzz; flake, floc; **—истость** *f.* fluffiness; **—истый** *a.* fluffy, downy, fleecy, cottony.

**пушица** *f.* cotton grass (*Eriophorum*).

**пушка** *f.* cannon, gun; bomb, irradiation unit.

**пушн/ина** *f.* fur; **—ой** *a.* fur, fur-bearing; **—ой товар** furs, peltry.

**пушок** *see* **пух;** (bot.) bloom, down, pubescence.

**пушонка** *f.* slaked lime, calcium hydroxide; **асбестовая п.** flaked asbestos.

**пушпул/л** *m.*, **—ьный** *a.* (rad.) push pull.

**пуща** *f.* dense forest.

**пуэрперальный** *a.* (med.) puerperal.

**пф** *abbr.* (**пикофарада**) picofarad, micro-microfarad.

**Пфунда серия** Pfund series (of spectrum lines).

**пфейфка** *f.* tube, pipe.

**ПХД** *abbr.* (**полихлориды бензола**) benzene polychlorides (insecticide and fungicide).

**ПХО** *abbr.* (**противохимическая оборона**) antigas defense.

**ПХФ** *abbr.* (**пентахлорфенол**) pentachlorophenol.

**п. ч.** *abbr.* (**потому что**) because; **ПЧ** *abbr.* (**промежуточная частота**) intermediate frequency.

**пчел/а** *f.* bee, honeybee; **—ы, —иные** *pl.* Apidae; **—иный** *a.* bee; **—иный воск** beeswax; **—иный волк** *see* **филант; —иная смазка** propolis; **—оводство** *n.* apiculture, bee keeping; **—ожук** *m.* (zool.) *Trichodes apiarus*; **—ьник** *m.* apiary.

**пшеница** *f.* (bot.) wheat (*Triticum*); **п. двузернянка** emmer (*T. dicoccum*); **п. однозернянка** einkorn (*T. monococcum*); **английская п.** poulard wheat (*T. turgidum*); **карликовая п.** club wheat (*T. compactum*); **мягкая п.** wheat (*T. vulgare*); **польская п.** Polish wheat (*T. polonicum*); **твердая п.** durum wheat (*T. durum*).

**пшеничка** *f.* maize, corn.

**пшеничный** *a.* wheat.

**пшен/о** *n.*, **—ный** *a.* millet (grain).

**Пшорр: синтез по —у** Pschorr synthesis (for phenanthrene).

**пыж** *m.*, **—овый** *a.* wadding, wad (in gun); (min.) stemming; **—ить** *v.* wad; **—иться** *v.* puff up, bristle.

**пыл** *m.* flame, blaze, heat, fire; **—ание** *n.* flaming, blazing; **—ать** *v.* flame, blaze; glow; **—ающий** *a.* flaming, blazing.

**пыле/ватый** *a.* dusty, dust-like; silty (soil); **—видный, —образный** *a.* pulverulent, pulverized, powdered; dust, dust-like, dusty; **—вой** *a.* dust; dust-borne (infection); **—высасыватель** *m.* dust remover; **—защищенный** *a.* dustproof; **—ловка** *f.* dust catcher, filter; **—мер** *m.* (meteor.) dust counter; **—непроницаемый** *a.* dustproof, dust-tight; **—образование** *n.* dust formation; **—осадитель** *m.* dust extractor; **центробежный —осадитель** cyclone; **—осадительная камера, —отстойная камера** dust-collecting chamber; **—осадочная камера, —отстойная камера** dust-removing compartment; **—отделитель** *m.* dust separator, dust remover; **—отсасывающий** *a.* dust-removing; **—очиститель** *m.* dust remover; **—приготовление** *n.* preparation of pulverized coal; **—собиратель** *m.* dust collector; **—содержание** *n.* dust content.

**пылесос** *m.* vacuum cleaner; dust collector, dust-collecting fan; **—ное устройство** vacuum attachment; dust-removing attachment.

**пыле/стойкий** *a.* dustproof; **—угольная мельница** coal-pulverizing mill; **—удаление** *n.* dust removal, elimination of dust; **—улавливание** *n.* dust collecting, elimination of dust.

**пылеуловитель** *m.* dust catcher, dust collector, dust trap; **—ный** *a.* dust-catching, dust-collecting.

**пыл/инка** *f.* dust particle, mote; **—ить** *v.* raise dust; **—иться** *v.* get dusty.

**пыль** *f.* dust, powder; spray; (soils) silt; **—ник** *m.* dust coat, smock; (bot.) anther; **—ность** *f.* dustiness; pulverulence; **—ный** *a.* dusty, dust-laden (air); pulverulent, powdery; **—ная буря** duststorm; **—ца** *f.*, **—цевой** *a.* (bot.) pollen; **—цееды** *pl.* comb-claw beetles (*Alleculidae*).

**пырей** *m.*, **ползучий п.** couch grass, quack grass (*Agropyron repens*).

**пытать** *v.* attempt; (met.) assay; **—ся** *v.* attempt, try, endeavor.

**пытлив/ость** *f.* searchingness, keenness, acuteness; **—ый** *a.* searching, keen, acute; curious, inquisitive.

**пыхтеть** *v.* pant, puff.

**пышать** *see* вспыхнуть.

**пышка** *f.* doughnut, bun.

**пышный** *a.* luxurious (vegetation).

**пьедестал** *m.* pedestal, stand, base.

**пьеза** *f.* pièze (unit of pressure).

**пьезо—** *prefix* piezo— (pressure); piezoelectric; **—диффузия** *f.* pressure diffusion; **—кварц** *m.* (rad.) piezoelectric crystal; **—кристаллизация** *f.* (geol.) piezocrystallization; **—метр** *m.* piezometer, pressure gage; **—метрический** *a.* piezometric; **—тропный** *a.* piezotropic; **—химия** *f.* piezochemistry.

**пьезоэлектричес/кий** *a.* piezoelectric; **—тво** *n.* piezoelectricity.

**пьемонтит** *m.* (min.) piedmontite.

**пь/ет** *pr. 3 sing.*; **—ют** *pr. 3 pl.* of **пить**; **—ющий** *a.* drinking.

**пьявица** *f.* leaf beetle (*Lema melanopus*).

**пьявки** *see* пиявки.

**пьян/еть** *v.* get intoxicated; **—ить** *v.* intoxicate; **—ица** *f.*, **—ая ягода** (bot.) bog bilberry (*Vaccinium uliginosum*); **—ый** *a.* intoxicated; **—ый хлеб** bread made of contaminated grain.

**пэ-аш** *p*H (hydrogen ion concentration).

**Пэджа явление** (elec.) Page effect.

**пюпитр** *m.* desk, reading stand.

**пюре** *n.* puree, soup.

**пяд/еницы** *pl.* measuring worm moths (*Geometridae*); **—ень, —ь** *f.* span; stretch.

**пясть** *f.* (anat.) metacarpus.

**пят/а** *f.* heel; abutment (of arch), base, foot; pin, pivot, pivot journal; **п. свода** skewback; **шарнир в —е** pivot hinge.

**пятер/ичный** *a.* fivefold, quintuple; **—ной** *a.* consisting of five parts, quinary, quinquepartite; **—о** five.

**пяти—** *prefix* penta—, quinque—, five; **—атомный** *a.* pentatomic; **—бромистый** *a.* pentabromide (of).

**пятивалентн/ость** *f.* pentavalence; **—ый** *a.* pentavalent.

**пятиводный гидрат** pentahydrate.

**Пятигорск** Piatigorsk.

**пятигранн/ик** *m.* (geom.) pentahedron; **—ый** *a.* pentahedral.

**пяти/десятый** *a.* fiftieth; **—дневка** *f.* five-day period; **—замещенные** *pl.* pentaderivatives, penta-substitution products.

**пятизначн/ый** *a.* five-unit; **—ое число** a number of five ciphers.

**пятикант** *m.* ashlar.

**пяти/карбонил железа** iron pentacarbonyl; **—кольчатый** *a.* pentacyclic, five-membered; **—кратный** *a.* fivefold, quintuple.

**пятилет/ие** *n.* five-year period; **—ка** *f.* Five-Year Plan; **—ний** *a.* five-year, five-year-old.

**пяти/листник** *m.* (bot.) cinquefoil (*Potentilla*); **—месячный** *a.* five-month; **—мужие, —мужство** *n.* (bot.) pentandria; **—мужний** *a.* pentandrian; **—нормальный** *a.* fifth normal; **—окись** *f.* pentoxide; **—основной** *a.* pentabasic; **—полье** *n.*. **—польная система** (agr.) five-field crop rotation; **—сернистый** *a.* pentasulfide (of); **—слойная фанера** five-ply veneer; **—сотлетний** *a.* quincentenary.

**пятисторонн/ий** *a.* (geom.) pentahedral; **—ик** *m.* pentahedron.

**пяти/тысячный** *a.* five-thousandth; **—тычинковый** *a.* (bot.) pentandrous.

**пятиться** *v.* back, move back.

**пятиугольн/ик** *m.* (geom.) pentagon; **—ый** *a.* pentagonal.

**пяти/устки** *pl.* (zool.) Pentastomida; **—фазный** *a.* five-phase; **—фтористый** *a.* pentafluoride (of); **—хлористый** *a.* pentachloride (of); **—членный** *a.* five-membered; **—электродный** *a.* five-electrode (tube).

**пятка** *f.* heel; anvil, sole.

**пятнадцат/икратный** *a.* fifteenfold; **—ый** *a.* fifteenth; **—ь** fifteen.

**пятнать** *v.* spot, stain, blot.

**пятнист/ость** *f.* spottiness, mottling, patch-work; (electrochem.) spotting out; blight, spot, blotch (plant disease); **—ый** *a.* spotty, spotted, mottled, speckled, dappled, stained; (biol.) punctate; maculose (structure).

**пятница** *f.* Friday.

**пятн/о** *n.* spot, stain, blotch, dab, patch, smear, blur; blot, blemish; **выводить —а** *v.* remove stains; **покрытый —ами** mottled, speckled, spotted; **—о-выводящее средство** stain remover, cleaner; **—оцветник** *m.* (bot.) para cress (*Spilanthes oleracea*); **—ышко** *n.* speckle, speck, small stain, small spot, freckle.

**пятов/ой, —ый** *a.* heel; base; pivot; abutment (stone); **п. шарнир** pivot hinge.

**пяточн/ый** *a.* heel; **—ая кость** (anat.) calcaneus.

**пят/ый** *a.* fifth; **—ая часть** fifth, one fifth.

**пять** five; **—десят** fifty; **—сот** five hundred.

# Р

**р.** *abbr.* (разрез) section; (резкий) sharp; (река) river; (рентген) roentgen; (род) genus; (рубль) ruble; (ряд) series; **Р** code for boron in steel mark.

**раб** *m.* slave, bondsman.

**рабарберон** *m.* rhabarberon.

**рабатка** *f.* border (of plants).

**рабдионит** *m.* (min.) rabdionite (an impure psilomelane).

**рабдит** *m.* (zool., med.) rhabditis.

**рабдо/лит** *m.* (zool.) rhabdolith; **—мома** *f.* (med.) rhabdomyoma; **—писсит** *m.* (min.) rhabdopissite; **—фан** *m.* (min.) rhabdophane, rhabdophanite, scovillite.

**рабелаизин** *m.* rabelaisin.

**рабеншварц** *m.* jet black; **сажа р.** vine black.

**рабкооп** *abbr.* (рабочий кооператив) workers' cooperative store.

**работ/а** *f.* work, labor, task, job; employment; service (of equipment), duty, performance (of machine); working, running, operation; procedure; **—ы** *pl.* work, operations; **р. вылета, р. выхода** work function (of electron); **р. на изгиб** bending strain; **р. на**

**срез** shear strain; **в —е** at work, in operation; **быть в —е** *v.* work, operate, be in operation; **загонять —ой** *v.* overwork; **режим —ы** procedure; operating conditions; **стоимость —ы** cost of operation; **условия —ы** operating conditions, working conditions; **ход —ы** operation.

**работ/ать** *v.* work, labor, toil; (mach.) run, operate, be in operation, function; **не р.** be idle; be out of order; **—ающий** *a.* working, at work; running, operating, functioning; acting; in gear.

**работни/к** *m.* worker, workman, laborer, hand; **—ца** *f.* workwoman.

**работодатель** *m.* employer.

**работоспособн/ость** *f.* efficiency, effect; (rubber) fatigue life; **—ый** *a.* efficient.

**рабоч/ий** *a.* work, working, worker, labor; running, operating, functioning; effective; actuating; active; process (solution); live (steam); *m.* worker, workman, laborer, employee; operator; **р.-пудлинговщик** *m.* (met.) puddler; **р. вопрос** labor question, labor problem; **р. груз** working load, net load; useful load; **р. костюм** overalls, work clothes; **р. листок** time card, time sheet; **р. механизм** operating mechanism; **р. период** operating cycle, cycle of operation; **р. предел** effective range; **р. процесс** operation, procedure; operating conditions; **р. ход** course of work; working stroke, impulse stroke; (aero.) power stroke; forward motion; **р. шкив** drive pulley; **р. элемент, —ая часть** working piece; **—ая бригада** operating crew; **—ая жидкость** pressure fluid (of hydraulic press); **—ая колоша кокса** coke per charge; **—ая нагрузка** operating load; **—ая площадь** effective area; **—ая поверхность** effective area; supporting surface; **—ая производительность** working capacity, operating capacity; **—ая сила** labor, manpower; **—ая смена** shift, operating crew; **—ая смесь** air-fuel mixture (for internal combustion engine); **—ая сторона** drive side; **—ая функция выхода** work function (of electron); **—ая характеристика** perform-

ance (of machine); **—ее вещество** agent; **—ее время** operating period; running time (of machine); **—ее давление** working pressure, effective pressure; **—ее колесо** rotor, runner (of turbine), impeller; **—ее место** operator's position; **—ее положение** working position, on-position; **—ее пространство** combustion space (of furnace); **—ее состояние** working order; **—ие руки** labor; **в —их условиях** under working conditions, in operation.

**рабочком** *m.* workers' committee.

**рабсила** *f.* manpower, labor.

**рабство** *n.* slavery.

**рабфак** *abbr.* (рабочий факультет) Workers' Faculty, Workers' High School; **—овец** *m.* student of Workers' Faculty.

**равен/дук, —тух** *m.* (text.) duck.

**равенство** *n.* equality, parity; congruence; (chem.) equation.

**равизоновое масло** ravison oil, Black Sea rape oil.

**равн/ение** *n.* leveling, equalization; **—ина** *f.* plain, flatland, flat country, lowland; **—итель** *m.* leveler, smoother; (paper) dandy roll; **—о** *adv.* equally, alike.

**равно—** *prefix* equi—, iso—, homo—; **—бедренный** *a.* (geom.) isosceles; **—великий** *a.* equidimensional; **—вероятный** *a.* equally probable.

**равновес/ие** *n.* equilibrium, balance, equibalance, equipoise; **отношение —ия** equilibrium ratio; **подвижное р., химическое р.** chemical equilibrium; **приводить в р.** *v.* balance, equilibrate; **состояние —ия** state of equilibrium; **—ный** *a.* equilibrium; equiponderant.

**равновременн/ость** *f.* isochronism; **—ый** *a.* isochronous.

**равнодействующ/ая** *f.*, **—ая сила** resultant, equivalent force; **—ий** *a.* equal, equally effective; resultant.

**равноденств/енный** *a.* equinox, equinoctial; equatorial; **—ие** *n.*, **точка —ия** equinox.

**равнодушный** *a.* indifferent, unconcerned.

**равнозернист/ость** *f.* even-grained texture; **—ый** *a.* even-grained.

**равнознач/ность** *f.* equivalence; **—ный** *a.* equivalent; **—ущий** *a.* equivalent, synonymous; iso—, equi—, homo—.

**равнокрылые** *pl.* termites (*Isoptera*); **р. хоботные** (zool.) Homoptera.

**равномерн/о** *adv.* uniformly, evenly; **—ость** *f.* uniformity, evenness, steadiness; proportionality, equality; **—ый** *a.* uniform, even, steady; proportional, equal; (math.) isometric.

**равно/мощный** *a.* equipollent, equivalent; **—мускульный** *a.* (zool.) isomyarian; **—направленный** *a.* (elec.) rectified, unidirected; of like orientation; **—ногие** *pl.* (zool.) Isopoda; **—образие** *n.* homorphism; **—осный** *a.* equiaxial; **—отстоящий** *a.* equidistant, equally spaced; **коэффициент —падаемости** settling ratio; **—площадный** *a.* equal-area; **—потенциальный** *a.* equipotential; **—приливный** *a.* cotidal; **—распределение** *n.* equipartition.

**равнореснични/ые** *pl.* (zool.) Holotricha; **—ый** *a.* holotrichous.

**равносил/ие** *n.* equipollence, equivalence; **—ьный** *a.* equipollent, equivalent.

**равно/сторонний** *a.* (geom.) equilateral; **—сть** *f.* equality; **—та** *f.* evenness; **—температурный** *a.* isothermal; **—угольный** *a.* equiangular; isogonal (transformation); **—фазный** *a.* equiphase.

**равноценн/ость** *f.* equivalence; parity; **—ый** *a.* equivalent.

**равночисленн/ость** *f.* equality in number; **—ый** *a.* equal in number.

**равноэнергетический** *a.* equal-energy.

**равн/ый** *a.* equal, alike, similar, like, congruent; **—ым образом** equally, to the same extent; **ему нет —ого** he has no equal, he has no match.

**равнять** *v.* equalize, equate; even, smooth, level, flatten; compare; **—ся** *v.* be equalized; compare (to).

**рагит** *m.* (min.) rhagite.

**рад** *a.* glad; *m.* rad (unit of absorbed energy); *abbr.* (**радиан**) radian.

**радар** *m.*, **—ный** *a.* radar (radio detec-

tion and location).

**ради** *prep. gen.* for the sake of, for, on account of; **р. чего** why, what for?

**радиально** *adv.* radially; **р. расходиться** *v.* radiate, diverge; **—волокнистый, —столбчатый** *a.* radial-columnar, divergent-columnar; **—лучистая структура** (cryst.) divergent structure, radiation; **—ребристый** *a.* (pal.) radially striated; **—сверлильный станок** radial drill, radial drilling machine.

**радиальный** *a.* radial; **р. подшипник** radial bearing, journal bearing.

**ради/ан** *m.* (geom.) radian; **—ант** *m.* radiant; **—атор** *m.* radiator, emitter; **—ационно-химический** *a.* radiation-chemistry; radiochemical; **—ационный** *a.* radiation, radiative; solar (thermometer); **—ационный захват** (nucl.) radiative capture; **—ационная вулканизация, —ационное сшивание** radiative crosslinking; **—ация** *f.* radiation; **—ировать** *v.* radiate.

**рад/ий** *m.* radium, Ra; **излучение —ия, эманация —ия** radium emanation, radon; **лечение лучами —ия** radium therapy; **хлористый р.** radium chloride; **—ийсодержащий** *a.* radium-bearing, radium-containing.

**радикал** *m.* radical; **знак —а** (math.) radical sign; **кислотный р.** acid radical.

**радикальн/ость** *f.* radicalness; efficiency, completeness; **—ый** *a.* radical; efficient, complete; **—ое количество** (math.) radical.

**радикула** *f.* (bot.) radicle.

**радио** *n.* radio; *prefix* radio—, radio; radiation, radioactive; radium; **—автограф** *see* **авторадиограф.**

**радиоактив/ация** *f.* radioactivation; **—ировать** *v.* radioactivate; **—ность** *f.* radioactivity; **—ный** *a.* radioactive, active; **—ный ряд, —ное семейство** radioactive series; **—ный углерод** radiocarbon; **—ный элемент** radioelement; **—ные осадки** fallout.

**радио/актиний** *m.* radioactinium, RaAc; **—аппарат** *m.* radio (receiving) set.

**радиобиолог** *m.* radiobiologist; —**ический** *a.* radiobiological; —**ия** *f.* radiobiology.

**радио/вещание** *n.*, —**вещательный** *a.* broadcast, broadcasting; —**взрыватель** *m.* radio detonator, radio fuse; —**вождение** *n.* radio aids to navigation; —**волна** *f.* radio wave; **частота** —**волн** radio frequency; —**высотомер** *m.* sound-ranging altimeter; —**вышка** *f.* radio tower; —**генный** *a.* radiogenic; —**гониометр** *m.* direction finder; —**грамма** *f.* radiogram, radio message; röntgenogram.

**радиограф** *m.*, —**ировать** *v.* radiograph; —**ический** *a.* radiographic; —**ия** *f.* radiography, X-ray photography; radiograph.

**радио/дефектоскопия** *f.* X-ray defectoscopy, radiographic inspection; —**диагностика** *f.* X-ray diagnostics; —**зонд** *m.*, —**зондовый** *a.* (meteor.) radiosonde; —**излучение** *n.* radio emission, radio waves; —**изотоп** *m.* radioisotope, radioactive isotope; —**индуцированный** *a.* radiation-induced; —**источник** *m.* radiation source; —**коллоид** *m.* radiocolloid; —**компас** *m.* radio compass, direction finder; —**лампа** *f.* (rad.) tube; —**ларии** *see* **радиолярии**; —**лечение** *n.* radiotherapy; —**лиз** *m.* radiolysis, radiolytic decomposition.

**радиолит** *m.* radiolite (a fossil pelecypod); —**овый** *a.* radiolitic; radiolytic.

**радиолог** *m.* (med.) radiologist; —**ический** *a.* radiological; —**ия** *f.* radiology; **медицинская** —**ия** nuclear medicine.

**радиолок/атор** *m.* radar (device); —**ационный** *a.* radar, radiolocation; —**ационная установка,** —**ационная станция** radar; —**ация** *f.* radar (radio detection and ranging), radiolocation, radio position finding.

**радио/лот** *m.* sound-ranging altimeter; —**луч** *m.* radio beam; —**любитель** *m.* radio amateur; —**люминесцентный** *a.* radioluminescent.

**радиоляр/иевый** *a.* radiolarian; **р. ил** (geol.) radiolarian ooze; —**ии** *pl.* (zool.) Radiolaria.

**радио/маркер** *m.* marker beacon; —**мач-**

**та** *f.* radio mast; —**маяк** *m.* radio-range beacon, equisignal beacon.

**радиометалл** *m.* Radiometal (alloy of Permalloy type); —**ография** *f.* radiometallography.

**радиометр** *m.* radiometer; —**ист** *m.* radar operator; radio operator; —**ический** *a.* radiometric; —**ия** *f.* radiometry.

**радио/мутация** *f.* radiomutation; —**обмен** *m.* radio traffic; —**обнаружение** *n.* radio detection; —**отправитель** *m.* radio transmitter, transmitting set.

**радиопеленг** *m.*, —**ация** *f.* (radio) direction finding, radio bearing; —**атор** *m.* direction finder.

**радио/передатчик** *m.* transmitter; —**передача** *f.* transmission, broadcasting; **станция** —**подслушивания** radio-intercept station; —**прием** *m.* radio reception; —**приемник** *m.* receiver, receiving set; —**разведка** *f.* prospecting by location of radioactive elements; —**резистентность** *f.* radioresistance; —**свечение** *n.* radioluminescence; —**свинец** *m.* radiolead; radium G, PbRa; —**связь** *f.* radio communication; —**сенсибилизация** *f.* radiosensitization; —**сеть** *f.* radio network; antenna.

**радиоскоп** *m.* radioscope; —**ический** *a.* radioscopic; —**ия** *f.* radioscopy, detection of radioactive substances.

**радио/снимок** *m.* radiograph; —**сопровождение** *n.* radio tracking; —**станция** *f.* radio station; —**стерилизация** *f.* radiation sterilization; —**стойкость** *f.* radioresistance.

**радиотелеграф/ировать** *v.* radiotelegraph; —**ист** *m.* wireless operator; —**ия** *f.* radiotelegraphy, wireless telegraphy.

**радиотерап/евт** *m.* radiotherapist; —**евтический** *a.* radiotherapeutic; —**ия** *f.* radiotherapy, radiation therapy.

**радио/техника** *f.*, —**технический** *a.* radio engineering; —**тин** *m.* (min.) radiotine.

**радиотокс/емия** *f.* radiation sickness; —**икология** *f.* radiotoxicology; —**ичность** *f.* radiotoxicity.

**радио/тор** *m.* radiothor, radioactive indicator; **—торий** *m.* radiothorium, RaTh; **—трансляция** *f.* rebroadcasting; **—узел** *m.* radio broadcasting and receiving unit; **—управление** *n.* radio control.

**радиоусилитель** *m.* radio amplifier; **—ная лампа** amplifying tube.

**радио/установка** *f.* radio, radio set; **—устойчивость** *f.* radioresistance; **—физика** *f.* radiophysics; **—фикация** *f.* establishment of radio communication facilities; **—фон** *m.* radiophone.

**радиохим/ик** *m.* radiochemist; **—икали** *pl.* radiochemicals; **—ический** *a.* radiochemical; **—ия** *f.* radiochemistry, chemistry of radioactive elements.

**радио/центр** *m.* radio center, union of individual radio stations; **—частота** *f.*, **—частотный** *a.* radio-frequency; **—чувствительность** *f.* radiosensitivity; **-шар-зонд** *m.* radio sounding balloon; **—элемент** *m.* radioelement, radioactive element; **—эхо** *n.* radio echo.

**рад/ируемый** *a.* radioed; **—ист** *m.* radio operator.

**радиус** *m.* radius; **р.-вектор** radius vector; **р. действия** range.

**радовать** *v.* gladden, rejoice.

**радон** *m.* radon, Rn, radium emanation.

**радостный** *a.* glad, joyous.

**рад/сек** *abbr.* (**радианов в секунду**) radians per second.

**радуг/а** *f.* rainbow; **переливающий всеми цветами —и** iridescent.

**радужница** *f.* a leaf beetle (*Donacia*).

**радужно/зеленый** *a.* iridescent green; **—синий** *a.* iridescent blue; **—сть** *f.* iridescence.

**радужн/ый** *a.* rainbow, rainbow-hued, iridescent, opalescent; **р. агат** (min.) rainbow agate; **—ая оболочка** (anat.) iris; **отливать —ыми красками** *v.* iridesce, opalesce.

**радушный** *a.* cordial, genial.

**раз** *adv.* once, one time; *m.* time; one; **р. навсегда** once for all; **—ом** at once, at a stroke; **все —ом** simultaneously, all together; **в другой р.** some other time, another time; **еще р.** once more, again; **за р.** at once, at one go; **много**

**р.** repeatedly, many times, often; **не р.** more than once; **пять р. по шестнадцать** five times sixteen; **этот р.** this time.

**раз—** *prefix* un—, dis—; away, off; *with verbs to indicate intensified action, division into parts, cessation of action or reversal of action.*

**разб.** *abbr.* (**разбавленный**) dilute.

**разбав/итель** *m.* diluent; **—ить, —лять** *v.* dilute; thin, rarefy (gas); **—ление** *n.* dilution; rarefaction; **закон —ления** dilution law; **—ленный** *a.* diluted, dilute, weak (solution); rare, thin.

**разбаланс** *m.* unbalance.

**разбаливаться** *v.* start aching.

**разбалластование** *n.* (aero.) lightening, unloading.

**разбалтывать** *v.* stir, shake up, agitate.

**разбе/г** *m.* starting, warming up, acceleration, racing (of motor); (aero.) run; momentum; **—гаться, —жаться** *v.* get started, warm up; gather momentum; disperse.

**разбив/ать** *v.* break, smash, fracture; parcel, divide, split; lay out, mark off, peg out (line), space; align; defeat; **—ка** *f.* division, splitting; laying out, layout, marking off; (mach.) dismantling, taking apart; **в —ку** retail; haphazardly; (typ.) spaced out; **—ной** *a.* separable; **—очный** *a.* marking, spacing; **—очный колышек** peg stake; **—чивый** *a.* brittle, frangible.

**разбинтов/ать, —ывать** *v.* unbind, remove (bandage).

**разбир/аемый** *a.* in question, under discussion; **—ание** *n.* examination, discussion; taking to pieces; **—ательство** *n.* examination, discussion; (law) trial, court examination.

**разбирать** *v.* take to pieces, take apart, dismantle, strip, break up, disjoint, knock down, take down, dismount; pull down (building); unpack; dispute, discuss, analyze; sort, pick, choose; make out, decipher; **р. дело** (law) try a case; **—ся** *v.* discriminate.

**разбит/ость** *f.* breakdown; **—ый** *a.* broken; **—ь** *see* **разбивать**.

**разблокировать** *v.* unlock.

**разбогатеть** *v.* get rich, acquire wealth, become prosperous; **р. внезапно** boom.

**разбойнич/еский,** **—ий** *a.* pirate, bandit.

**разболеться** *see* **разбаливаться.**

**разболт/анный** *a.* stirred, shaken up, loose; **—ать** *see* **разбалтывать.**

**разболчивать** *v.* unbolt.

**разбор** *m.* choice, selection; analysis, examination (of problem); review, criticism (of book); **р. дела** (law) trial; **без —а** without distinction, indiscriminately; **одного —а** of the same stamp.

**разбор/ка** *f.* taking apart, dismantling (machine); demolishing, wrecking; separation, sorting, picking (of ore); **—ный** *a.* collapsible, dismountable, separable, sectional; knockdown (column).

**разборчив/о** *adv.* clearly, plainly; **—ость** *f.* intelligibility; **—ый** *a.* clear, legible; discriminating, fastidious, fussy.

**разбрасыв/ание** *n.* scattering, scattering effect, dispersing, strewing, broadcasting (seed); spreading, distribution (of fertilizer); **—атель** *m.* disperser; spreader, distributor; sower, broadcaster; **—ать** *v.* scatter, disperse, throw about, strew; **—аться** *v.* lack singleness of purpose, be aimless; **—ающий** *a.* scattering, dispersing.

**разбрестись** *v.* straggle, disperse.

**разброд** *m.* disorder.

**разброс** *m.* scatter, scattering; spread, spreading; broadcasting; (statistics, etc.) straggling; **р. по углам** angle spread; **случайный р.** straggling; **случайный р. пробега** range straggling; **—анность** *f.* dispersion; disconnectedness; **—анный** *a.* dispersed; disconnected; strewn, scattered; spread; loose (cargo); **—ать** *see* **разбрасывать;** **—ный посев** (agr.) broadcasting.

**разбрызг/анный** *a.* sprayed, sprinkled, spattered; **—ивание** *n.* spraying, sprinkling, spattering, splashing, spurting; **охлаждение —иванием** spray cooling; **—иватель** *m.* sprayer, sprinkler; atomizer, pulverizer; **—и-**

**вать** *v.* spray, sprinkle; atomize, pulverize; spatter, splash.

**разбрызгивающ/ий** *a.* spraying, sprinkling; atomizing; spattering; **—ее кольцо** spray ring; **—ее сопло** spray nozzle.

**разбур/ав** *m.* countersink; **—ивание** *n.* (min.) drilling out; **—овка** *f.* counterbore, counterboring.

**разбух/ание** *n.* swelling, distension, inflation; **—ать,** **—нуть** *v.* swell, distend, inflate, expand; **—ший** *a.* swollen.

**развал** *m.* disorganization, collapse, breakdown; break-up, split (of nucleus); razval (disintegrated blocks piled up on mountain slopes); **—енный** *a.* collapsed, broken down; loose (cargo); **—ивать,** **—ить** *v.* undo, unmake; pull down, demolish; break up, split; **—иваться,** **—иться** *v.* fall, go to pieces, collapse; **—ина** *f.* ruin, wreck; **—ины** *pl.* ruins, debris.

**развальцов/анный** *a.* rolled out, laminated, expanded; **—ка** *f.* rolling out, lamination, expansion; **—ывать** *v.* roll out, laminate, expand.

**развар/енный,** **—ной** *a.* cooked to a pulp; **—ивать,** **—ить** *v.* cook to shreds, boil to a pulp.

**разве** *adv.* perhaps; if, save, unless; is that so?

**развев/ание** *n.* blowing, scattering; weathering; deflation (wind action); **—ать** *v.* blow, scatter.

**развед/анный** *a.* explored, investigated, tested; **—ать** *see* **разведывать.**

**разведен/ие** *n.* dilution (of liquids); thinning, rarefaction (of gas); (brewing) attenuation; parting, disunion; breeding (of stock), cultivation (of plants), propagation, culture (of bacteria); **р. в себе, чистолинейное р.** (biol.) autosexing; **—ный** *a.* diluted, dilute; thin, rare, rarefied; separated; pulled up (bridge); bred, cultivated.

**разведк/а** *f.* search, exploration; survey, surveying; reconnaissance; intelligence; (min.) prospecting; **предварительная р.** reconnaissance; **производить —у** *v.* reconnoiter; prospect.

**разведочно-эксплоатационная скважина** exploratory well; test pit.

**разведочн/ый** *a.* exploring; (min.) prospecting; **—ая выработка, —ая работа** prospecting; **—ая скважина** test well; test pit; wildcat well.

**разведчик** *m.* (min.) prospector, scout.

**разведыв/ание** *n.,* **—ательный** *a.* searching, exploring; reconnaissance; (min.) prospecting; **—ать** *v.* investigate, explore; inquire (about); scout, reconnoiter; prospect; exploit.

**развезти** *see* **развозить.**

**развериться** *v.* get out of true, get out of alignment.

**развернут/ый** *a.* unfolded, developed; **—ь** *see* **развертывать.**

**разверст/ать, —ывать** *v.* divide, distribute, allot; **—ка** *f.* division, distribution, allotment.

**развертк/а** *f.* unfolding, evolvement, development, presentation; unrolling, unwrapping; reaming, broaching; reamer, broach bit, broach; evolute (of curve); (telev., etc.) scanning; scan; resolution, analysis; **отделка отверстия —ой** reaming; **р. пучка ионов** ion beam scanning; **генератор —и** (cathode-ray tubes) time-base generator; **ось —и** timing axis, time base.

**развертыв/ание** *n.* opening, unwrapping, unrolling, unfolding, development, evolution; (telev., etc.) scanning; rectification (of curve); reaming; running down (of clock spring); **—атель** *m.,* **—ающее устройство** scanner; **—ать** *v.* open, unwrap, unroll, spread, expand, unfold, develop, display, evolve; unwind, uncoil, unfurl; scan, analyze; ream, broach; (geom.) show three-dimensional body on a plane; **—аться** *v.* expand, develop; come out (of leaves).

**развес** *m.* weighing; **на р.** by weight.

**развесистый** *a.* spreading, branched, branchy, ramose, ramous.

**развес/ить** *see* **развешивать; —ка** *see* **развес; —ной** *a.* sold loose by weight; **—очная** *f.* (rubber) compounding room; **—очный** *a.* weighing.

**развести** *see* **разводить.**

**разветвит/ель** *m.* bifurcating device, splitter; **—ься** *see* **разветвляться.**

**разветвл/ение** *n.* branching, ramification, bifurcation, subdivision, split-

ting up; fringing; branch, fork; **—ен-ный** *a.* branched, branch, ramified, forked; tapped off; **—ять** *v.* branch, branch out, ramify; tap; **—яться** *v.* branch, branch out, fork.

**развехованный** *a.* marked.

**развешивать** *v.* weigh out; suspend, hang up.

**развеять** *see* **развевать.**

**развив/аемый** *a.* generated; developed, evolved (theory); **—аемая мощность** output (of machine); **—ание** *n.* development, generation; **—ать** *v.* develop, generate, evolve; amplify, build up; untwist, unwind, wind off; **—ать скорость** accelerate; **—аться** *v.* develop, grow; unfold, evolve.

**развил/ина** *f.* fork, yoke, crotch; forking, bifurcation, divarication; **—истый** *a.* forked, furcate; **—ка** *f.* fork; **в —ку** Y-shaped.

**развин/тить, —чивать** *v.* unscrew, screw off, unfasten, loosen; **—ченный** *a.* unscrewed, unfastened, loose; **—чивание** *n.* unscrewing, unfastening, loosening.

**развит/ие** *n.* development, growth, progress, evolution; spread; distribution; **—ый** *a.* developed, evolved; **—ь** *see* **развивать.**

**развле/кать, —чь** *v.* amuse, entertain, divert; **—каться** *v.* be distracted.

**развод** *m.* separation, divorce; **—ы** *pl.* design, arabesque; stains.

**развод/ить** *v.* dilute (liquids); thin, rarefy (gas); breed, propagate, spread; raise, cultivate; separate, divorce; pull up (bridge); set (teeth of saw); get up, raise (steam); light (a fire); **—иться** *v.* breed, multiply; **—ка** *f.* separation; swinging up (of bridge); saw set.

**разводн/ой** *a.* separating; **р. ключ** monkey wrench; **р. мост** drawbridge, swing bridge, bascule; **—ая чека, —ая шпилька** split cotter.

**развоз/ить** *v.* convey, transport, carry; **—ка** *f.* conveyance, transport.

**разволновать** *v.* agitate, excite, stir up, move; **—ся** *v.* get agitated, get excited; palpitate.

**разворачив/ание** *n.* unwrapping, unfolding; turning; **—ать** *v.* unwrap, unfold, unroll; upset, shatter, destroy; crack, split; **—аться** v. turn around.

**развор/от** m. turn; **—отить** see **разворачивать**; **—оченный** a. unwrapped, unfolded; destroyed; separated.

**разворошить** v. scatter (about), spread.

**развьюч/ивать, —ить** v. unload, unpack.

**развяз/ать, —ывать** v. untie, unbind, undo, unfasten, loosen; **—аться, —ываться** v. undo, get untied, come loose; **—ка** f. outcome, issue; uncoupling; bypass; **—ный** a. forward, fast, free and easy; **—ывание** n. untying, uncoupling, unfastening; **—ывающий** a. uncoupling.

**разгад/ать, —ывать** v. guess, puzzle out.

**разгар** m. climax, highest point; height (of season); **в полном —е** in full swing.

**разгиб/ание** n. unbending, straightening; **—ать** v. unbend, straighten; smooth out; **—аться** v. straighten, straighten up, straighten out; **—ающий** a. straightening; **—ающая мышца** (anat.) extensor.

**разгла/дить, —живать** v. smooth, smooth out, press, iron; (met.) planish; **—женный** a. smoothed, pressed, ironed; planished; **—живание** n. smoothing, pressing, ironing; planishing.

**разгла/сить, —шать** v. spread, proclaim, publish; **—ска** f. publicity, notoriety; **—шение** n. spreading, publishing.

**разгляд/еть, —ывать** v. view, examine, scrutinize, consider.

**разгов/аривать** v. talk, speak; **—ор** m. talk, conversation; **—орная будка** telephone booth; **—орный пункт** telephone station.

**разгон** m., **—ный** a. run, start; racing, speeding up, acceleration; take-off run, launching; runaway; dispersal, dispersion; (typ.) spacing; **—ка** f. distillation, fractional distillation; **—ный молот** chasing hammer; **—ная скорость** (mach.) runaway speed; **—ять** v. distill; drive away, dispel, dissipate, disperse, scatter; speed up, accelerate, race; (typ.) space; **—яться** v. pick up speed.

**разгораживать** v. take down a fence; fence; divide off, separate.

**разгор/аться, —еться** v. begin to burn, start burning, leap into flames.

**разгородить** see **разгораживать**.

**разгоряченный** a. heated.

**разгранич/ение** n. demarcation; черта **—ения, —ивающая линия** line of demarcation, boundary line; **—енный** a. delimited, bound, defined, demarcated; **—ивать, —ить** v. delimit, fix the limit (of), fix the boundaries, bound.

**разграф/ить, —лять** v. rule, draw lines; **—ление** n. ruling.

**разгре/бать, —сти** v. rake.

**разгром** m. destruction; **—ить** v. destroy, ruin, shatter, devastate, waste.

**разгруж/атель** m. discharger; **—ать** v. discharge, unload, dump; relieve; **—ающий** a. discharging, unloading, dumping; relieving; **—енный** a. discharged, unloaded, dumped; relieved.

**разгруз/ить** see **разгружать**; **—ка** f. discharging, discharge, unloading, dumping, emptying; clearing, removing (weight), throwing off (load); easing, relieving, relief; **—очный** a. discharging, discharge, unloading, dumping.

**разгруппирование** n. debunching.

**разд.** abbr. (**раздел**) section.

**раздав/ание** n. distribution, dispensation; **—ать** v. distribute, dispense, deal out; spread, widen, expand, open out, flare; **—аться** v. be distributed; be paid, be conferred, be granted; expand, grow wider, flare; be heard, resound.

**раздав/ить, —ливать** v. crush, smash; **—ленный** a. crushed; **—ливание** n. crushing, smashing, mashing.

**раздаивание** n. (agr.) increasing milk yield.

**раздалбливать** v. hollow out, groove.

**раздат/очный** a. distributing; **—очная ведомость** pay roll; **—чик** m. distributor; **—ь** see **раздавать**.

**раздача** f. distribution, allotment; delivery, presentation; spread, expansion.

**раздваивать** v. bifurcate, split; **—ся** v. bifurcate, fork; split off, break down.

**раздвиг** m., **—ание** n. opening, release, separation; extension, expansion; **—**

ать v. open, separate, draw apart; extend, expand; —аться v. move apart; telescope.

раздвижка f. separation, moving apart, parting.

раздвижн/ой a. extensible, extension-type, expansible, expanding, tele-scopic, telescope; р. калибр slide gage; р. ключ monkey wrench; —ая муфта expansion clutch; disengaging coupling; —ое соединение telescope (coupling).

раздвинут/ый a. separated, drawn apart; extended; —ь see раздвигать.

раздвоен/ие n. bifurcation, furcation, branching; forking, fork; (biol.) dichotomy; breaking down, splitting off; —ный a. forked, furcate, bifurcate, split; broken down; swallow (tail).

раздвойникование n. untwinning.

раздев/ание n. undressing; (foundry) stripping; —ать v. undress; strip.

раздел m. division, allotment; section, class; граница —а (seismology) discontinuity; линия —а, линия —ения line of demarcation, dividing line, boundary line; плоскость —а division plane; поверхность —а interface; (phase) contact area; surface of separation; —ать see разделывать; —ение n. division, dividing, separation, partition; (assaying) parting; distribution; classing, indexing; cleaving, cleavage, fission, splitting; segregation (of genes; losses, etc.); (sex) differentiation; деление труда division of labor; коэффициент —ения separation factor; (distillation) relative volatility; точка —ения separation point; —енный a. divided, parted; classed, graded; slotted (brush); —ившийся a. separated; fissioned, divided.

разделим/ость f. divisibility, separability; —ый a. divisible, separable; analyzable.

разделитель m. separator, separating agent; divider; spacer; (assaying) parting agent; —ный a. separating; dividing, partitioning; partition (chromatography); fractionating; —ный сосуд separating vessel, parting

vessel; —ная стенка partition; (regenerator) tongue; —ное средство separating agent; parting agent.

разделить see разделять.

разделка f. dressing, preparing.

разделывать v. do; finish; dress; р. под make in imitation of; —ся с be done with, be through with, part with.

раздельно/лепестный a. (bot.) choripetalous; —полый a. (biol.) dioecious.

раздельный a. divided, separate, distinct, discrete; split (bearing).

раздел/ять v. divide, part, separate, split; partition; sever, dismember, disjoint, dissociate; disintegrate; analyze; pick, sort (ore); share, distribute; —яться v. divide, split, branch; —яющий a. dividing, separating; —яющее приспособление divider, separator.

раздер/гать, —гивать, —нуть v. pull apart, shred.

раздеть see раздевать.

раздир/альный a., —ание n. tearing, shredding; —альная машина (text.) disintegrator, shredder; —ать v. tear, lacerate; shred; dismember; tear open, open; —ающий a. tearing, lacerating; shredding.

раздой see раздаивание.

раздолбить see раздалбливать.

раздрабливать see раздробить.

раздраж/ать, —ить v. irritate, annoy, exasperate; stimulate; —ающий a. irritating, acrid; —ение n. irritation; stimulation; —итель m. (biol.) stimulus; —ительный a. irritable.

раздроб/ить, —лять v. break to pieces, shatter, disintegrate, crush, grind, comminute; (math.) reduce; —иться, —ляться v. fall to pieces, crumble away; be parceled out; —ление n. breaking to pieces, breaking up, shattering, disintegration, crushing; fractionation; parceling (of land); —ленный a. broken, shattered, crushed, granulated; —ляющий a. crushing, grinding; —ляющее приспособление crusher.

раздув m. bulge; —альный a. blowing, inflating; —альный мех bellows; —ание n. blowing, inflation; swelling, bulging, thickening; —ать v. blow, inflate, distend; fan, blow away, disperse; —**аться** *v.* blow up, inflate, swell.

**раздулка** *f.* (bot.) water fennel, horsebane (*Oenanthe phellandrium*).

**раздум/ать** *v.* change one's mind; —**ывать** *v.* hesitate; —**ье** *n.* hesitation.

**раздут/ость** *f.* inflation, swelling, dilation, distention, bulge; —**ый** *a.* inflated, swollen, bulging; —**ь** *see* **раздувать.**

**разевать** *v.* gape, open wide.

**разжать** *see* **разжимать.**

**разжев/ать**, —**ывать** *v.* masticate, chew; —**ывание** *n.* mastication, chewing.

**разжечь** *see* **разжигать.**

**разжиг/ание** *n.* kindling, firing, starting up (furnace); —**ать** *v.* kindle, fire, start up; excite, stimulate; —**аться** *v.* catch fire, blaze up.

**разжиж/аемый** *a.* capable of dilution; liquefiable, liquescent; —**ать** *v.* dilute (liquids); thin, rarefy (gas); liquefy; —**ающий** *a.* diluting; rarefying; liquefying; —**ающее вещество**, —**итель** *m.* diluent; —**ение** *n.* dilution; thinning, rarefaction; liquefaction; —**енность** *f.* fluidity, liquid state; —**енный** *a.* diluted, dilute; thin, rare; —**итель** *m.* thinner, diluent.

**разжим/ание** *n.* unclasping, opening, releasing, release; —**ать** *v.* unclasp, open, release, unfasten, unclamp; —**аться** *v.* come loose.

**разжиреть** *v.* grow fat.

**раззенков/ка** *f.* counterbore, countersink, reamer, rose bit; —**ывать** *v.* ream, ream out.

**разинуть** *see* **разевать.**

**разительный** *a.* striking, impressive.

**разить** *v.* smell, reek (of); beat, strike, hit.

**разлаг/аемый** *a.* decomposable; analyzable; —**ать** *v.* decompose, dissociate, separate; analyze, resolve; disorganize; (math.) expand; —**аться** *v.* decompose, disintegrate, break up, break down, separate; dissolve; decay, putrefy, rot; —**ающий** *a.* decomposing; —**ающее средство** decomposing agent; —**ающийся** *a.* decomposing; decomposable; analyzable.

**разла/д** *m.* discord, dissension; disorder;

—**диться**, —**живаться** *v.* go wrong, take a bad turn, fail.

**разламыв/ание** *n.* breaking, fracture; wrecking (of building); —**ать** *v.* break, fracture; break up, chip; break open, force open; wreck, pull down (building).

**разлез/аться**, —**ться** *v.* come apart, tear, ravel out.

**разлет** *m.* dispersion, scattering; **угол** —**а** angle of divergence; —**аться**, —**еться** *v.* fly apart, fly (to pieces), scatter; come apart, disintegrate.

**разлив** *m.* overflow, inundation, flood; irruption; spread (of surface coatings); —**ание** *n.* pouring out, filling; diffusion; —**ать** *v.* pour, pour out; spill; bottle, fill; (foundry) teem; diffuse; —**аться** *v.* overflow, spill; —**ающийся** *a.* overflowing, spilling, flowing; —**ка** *f.* pouring; bottling, filling; (foundry) teeming, casting; cast; —**о-укупорочный** *a.* bottling and capping.

**разливочн/ый** *a.* pouring; (foundry) teeming, casting; **р. ковш** teeming ladle, feeding ladle; **р. кран** ladle crane; **р. стакан** casting nozzle; —**ая машина** casting machine; bottling machine; —**ая яма** teeming hole.

**разлинзование** *n.* (geol.) boudinage.

**разлинов/ать**, —**ывать** *v.* rule, make lines.

**разлистов/ание** *n.* foliation cleavage; —**анный** *a.* foliated, leaf-like, laminated; —**ать** *v.* foliate.

**разлит/ие** *n.* pouring; overflow, inundation; irruption; —**ый** *a.* poured; spilled; (foundry) cast; —**ь** *see* **разливать.**

**различ/ать**, —**ить** *v.* discern, distinguish, discriminate; —**аться** *v.* differ, be unlike, be distinguished; —**ение** *n.* distinction, discrimination; —**ие** *n.* distinction, difference, diversity, discrepancy; variety; —**имый** *a.* discernible; —**итель** *m.* discriminator; —**ительно** *adv.* in contra-distinction (to); —**ительный** *a.* distinctive.

**различн/о** *adv.* differently; —**ость** *f.* difference, unlikeness; —**ый** *a.* different, unlike, dissimilar, distinct, varied, diverse; —**ый по существу** essentially different.

**разложен/ие** *n.* decomposition, disintegration, separation, dissociation, splitting, splitting up, breaking down (into); analysis, resolution; disorganization; putrefaction, decay, rotting; (telev.) scanning; **р. (в ряд)** (math.) expansion; **гнилостное р.** wet rot; **двойное р., обменное р.** double decomposition; **продукт —ия** decomposition or dissociation product.

**разлож/енный** *a.* decomposed, dissociated; analyzed; laid out; (math.) expanded; **—ившийся** *a.* putrefied, putrid, rotten; **—имость** *f.* decomposability; **—имый** *a.* decomposable, dissociable, separable; analyzable; **—ить** *see* **разлагать, раскладывать.**

**разлом** *m.* break, fracture; rupture, abruption; **—ать, —ить** *see* **разламывать.**

**разлуч/ать, —ить** *v.* sever, separate, part, disunite; **—ение** *n.* severance, separation.

**размагни/тить, —чивать** *v.* demagnetize; **—чение, —чивание** *n.* demagnetization.

**размаз/анный** *a.* smeared (out); **—ать, —ывать** *v.* smear, spread; blur; **—ывание** *n.* smearing.

**размалыв/аемость** *f.* grindability; **—аемый** *a.* grindable; **—ание** *n.* grinding, crushing; **—ать** *v.* grind, crush, break up, mill; (paper) beat.

**размасл/ивать, —ить** *v.* oil, treat with oil.

**разматыв/ание** *n.* unwinding, unreeling; **—ать, —аться** *v.* unwind, unreel, reel off, uncoil, unroll, pay out, run off.

**размах** *m.* swing, sweep, stroke; spread, span (of wings); range, scope, amplitude (of pendulum); (mech.) throw; **—ивание** *n.* swinging; **—ивать, —нуть** *v.* swing, sway.

**размачив/ание** *n.* soaking, steeping, saturation, wetting, maceration; **—ать** *v.* soak, steep, saturate, wet, macerate, soften; ret (flax, hemp).

**размежев/ание** *n.* demarcation, delimitation; **—ать, —ывать** *v.* mark limits, bound; **—аться, —ываться** *v.* fix the boundaries.

**размельч/ать, —ить** *v.* grind, crush, break up, disintegrate, pulverize; **—аться, —иться** *v.* break up, disintegrate; **—ение** *n.* grinding, crushing, disintegration; **—енный** *a.* crushed, disintegrated.

**размен** *m.,* **—ный** *a.* exchange, change; **—ная валюта** exchangeable value; **—ная монета** small coin, change.

**размер** *m.* dimension, size, gage, caliber; rate; quantity, amount; yield; grade (of particles); **по —у** to size; **не по —у** offsize; **точно по —у** to specifications; **полный р.** full size, finished size.

**размер/ение, —ивание** *n.* measuring, measurement; **—ивать, —ить, —ять** *v.* measure off, measure out, proportion; **—ность** *f.* dimension, dimensions; dimensionality; scale; **уравнение —ности** (math.) dimensional equation; **—ный** *a.* dimensional.

**размести** *see* **разметывать.**

**разместить** *see* **размещать.**

**разметать** *see* **разметывать.**

**размет/ить** *see* **размечать; —ка** *f.* marking, marking out, laying out, setting.

**разметочн/о-сверлильный станок, —ый станок** jig borer, high-precision marking and boring machine; **—ый** *a.* marking, layout; **—ая плита** layout block.

**разметчик** *m.* marker, tracer, surface gage.

**разметывать** *v.* toss, scatter, disperse, spread about; sweep away.

**размеч/ать** *v.* mark, mark off, mark out, lay off, lay out; trace; graduate (a vessel); locate, space; annotate; **—енный** *a.* marked, marked out.

**размеш/анный** *a.* stirred, mixed, blended; **—ать, —ивать** *v.* stir, mix, blend thoroughly; knead (clay); churn; **—ивание** *n.,* **—ивающий** *a.* stirring, agitating, mixing, blending; kneading.

**размещ/ать** *v.* dispose, distribute, set, place, allocate; mount; rank; **—ение** *n.* disposition, disposal, distribution, placement, allocation; order, arrangement, position, spacing; (math.) permutation; **—енный** *a.* distributed, allocated; arranged, set.

**разминать** *v.* crumble, pulverize; knead.

**размин/овка** *f.* (railroad) by-pass, siding; **—уться** *v.* pass each other, cross each other (of letters).

**размнож/ать, —ить** *v.* multiply; propagate; manifold (manuscript); **—аться** *v.* breed, propagate; spawn (of fish); **—ающий** *a.* fertile (medium); **—ение** *n.* multiplication, propagation, reproduction, duplication, increase; (nucl.) breeding (of fuel); **—ение делением** (biol.) fission; **коэффициент —ения** multiplication factor; **—итель** *see* **реактор-размножитель**.

**размол** *m.* grist, grind; grinding, pulverization; milling; (paper) beating; **—оспособность** *f.* crushability, grindability; **—отый** *a.* crushed, ground, pulverized; **—оть** *see* **размалывать**.

**размор/аживать, —озить** *v.* thaw out, defrost.

**размот/ать** *see* **разматывать**; **—ка** *see* **разматывание**.

**размочал/ивать, —ить** *v.* separate into filaments, shred.

**размоч/енный** *a.* soaked, steeped, macerated; **—ить** *see* **размачивать**; **—ка** *see* **размачивание**.

**размыв** *m.*, **—ание** *n.* scouring, washing; (geol.) washout, erosion; **—атель** *m.* scourer; **—ать** *v.* scour, wash away, wash off, hollow out; erode.

**размык/ание** *n.* (elec.) breaking, break, disconnection; interruption (of circuit); **—атель** *m.* breaker, release; **—ать** *v.* open, unlock, unfasten; break, interrupt, disconnect, turn off; **—ающий** *a.* releasing, release; breaking, disconnecting; trip (hook).

**размыслить** *see* **размышлять**.

**размыт/ие** *n.* erosion; blow-up (of beam); disassembly (of plasma); **—ый** *a.* washed out, eroded; diffuse; **—ь** *see* **размывать**.

**размышлять** *v.* reflect, consider, speculate.

**размягч/ать, —ить** *v.* soften; soak (until soft); **—ающий** *a.* softening; (pharm.) emollient; **—ающее средство** softening agent; emollient; **—ение** *n.* softening; (med.) malacia, morbid softening; **температура —ения, точка —ения** softening point; **—итель** *m.* softener; plasticizer.

**размяк/ать, —нуть** *v.* soften, become sodden.

**размят/ие** *n.* crumbling, pulverizing; kneading; (geol.) shearing; **—ый** *a.* crumbled; kneaded; sheared; **—ь** *see* **разминать**.

**разнес/енный** *a.* dispersed; spaced; **—ти** *see* **разносить**.

**разнимать** *v.* part, separate, dismember, disjoint, tear apart; take apart, take to pieces, dismantle, dismount.

**разн/иться** *v.* differ, vary, be unlike; **—ица** *f.* difference, distinction, contrast; **—о** *adv.* differently, diversely, variously.

**разно—** *prefix* different, hetero—.

**разновес** *m.* set of weights.

**разновидн/ость** *f.* variety; **—ый** *a.* various, diverse, multiform, of different form; (biol.) variant.

**разновременн/ость** *f.* diversification; difference in time; **коэффициент —ости** (elec.) diversity factor; **—ый** *a.* alternative; at different times; not contemporary.

**разноглас/ие** *n.*, **—ица** *f.* discord, difference of opinion, variance, discrepancу; **—ный** *a.* discordant, conflicting.

**разное** *n.* variety, miscellany.

**разно/зернистый** *a.* (petr.) consertal, sutured; **—значащий** *a.* of different meaning; **—именный** *a.* of different names, of different kinds, unlike, opposite; (elec.) of opposite charge; **—калиберный** *a.* different-caliber, different-sized; **—лепестка** *f.* (bot.) candytuft (*Iberis*); **—листный** *a.* (bot.) heterophyllous; **—мастный** *a.* different-colored; **—мыслие** *n.* difference of opinion, disagreement.

**разнообраз/ие** *n.* variety, diversity, range; multiplicity; **—ить** *v.* vary, diversify; **—ный** *a.* various, diverse, variegated; miscellaneous.

**разно/племенный** *a.* of different races, of different stock; **—полый** *a.* of different sexes; **—ресничные** *pl.* (zool.) Heterotricha; **—ресничный** *a.* heterotrichous.

**разнореч/ивый** *a.* contradictory, inconsistent; **—ие** *n.* contradiction; **—ить** *v.* contradict oneself, be inconsistent.

**разнородн/ость** *f.* heterogeneity; difference in kind; **—ый** *a.* heterogeneous, mixed, hybrid, unlike, different, dissimilar, diversified, various, manifold.

**разнос** *m.*, **—ка** *f.* bearing about, carrying about, delivery; dispersion; racing, overspeeding; (min.) open-cut mine, open pit, strip pit, quarry; **—ить** *v.* carry, carry around, convey, deliver; disperse, scatter; **щеку разнесло** the cheek is swollen; **—иться** *v.* spread; resound; **—ная скорость** runaway speed (of machine).

**разносол** *m.* sauce, etc., for food; **—ы** *pl.* all kinds of pickles, mixed pickles.

**разностеномер** *m.* pipe-thickness gage.

**разностный** *a.* difference, different; (elec.) differential.

**разносторонн/ий** *a.* many-sided, resourceful; (geom.) scalene, scalenous; **—ость** *f.* resourcefulness; miscellaneousness, multiplicity.

**разность** *f.* variety, diversity, difference; (math.) difference.

**разносчик** *m.* vector, carrier (of disease).

**разно/травье** *n.* mixed grass; **—усые** *pl.* (zool.) Heterocera; **—форменность** *f.* heteromorphism; **—цветный** *a.* many-colored, multi-colored, varicolored, variegated, polychromatic; **—центренность** *f.* eccentricity; **—чтение** *n.* variant reading; **—шерстный** *a.* different-colored (animals).

**разнузданный** *a.* unruly, uncontrollable.

**разный** *a.* different, unlike, diverse, various, miscellaneous.

**разнять** *see* **разнимать.**

**разоблачение** *n.* disclosure, exposure.

**разобр/анный** *a.* dismantled, broken up; picked, screened (ore); **—ать** *see* **разбирать.**

**разобщ/ать** *v.* separate, dissociate, disconnect, uncouple, disengage, throw out of gear; **—ающий** *a.* dissociative, disconnecting, disengaging, releasing; cut-out; **—ающий механизм** releasing device, release; **—ение** *n.* separation, disjunction, disconnecting, uncoupling, release; interruption, disturbance; **—енность** *f.* disconnection; **—енный** *a.* disconnected, disengaged, released; separate, discrete; (phys.) insulated.

**разобщитель** *m.* disconnector; **—ный** *a.* disconnecting, releasing; **—ный механизм** releasing device, release.

**разобщить** *see* **разобщать.**

**разовой** *a.* single, for one application.

**разогн/ание** *n.* dispersion, scattering; **—анный** *a.* dispersed, scattered; staggered, alternating; **—ать** *see* **разгонять.**

**разогнуть** *see* **разгибать.**

**разогре/в** *m.* initial heating, warm-up, heat-up; firing (of furnace); **—вание** *n.* warming up; evolution of heat (from reaction); **—вать, —ть** *v.* warm up; **—ваться** *v.* warm up, get warm; **—тый** *a.* warmed up, heated.

**разодр/анный** *a.* torn, tattered; **—ать** *see* **раздирать.**

**разойтись** *see* **расходиться.**

**разомкнут/ый** *a.* open, clear; (elec.) disconnected, broken, interrupted; **—ая цепь** open circuit; **—ь** *see* **размыкать.**

**разорв/анно—** *prefix* fracto—; **—анный** *a.* torn; (geol.) faulted; **—ать** *see* **разрывать.**

**разор/ение** *n.* ruin, destruction; **—енный** *a.* ruined, destroyed; **—ительный** *a.* ruinous, destructive, wasteful; **—ить** *see* **разорять.**

**разоруж/ать** *v.* disarm; dismantle; **—ение** *n.* disarmament; dismantling.

**разорять** *v.* ruin, destroy, spoil, waste.

**разослать** *see* **рассылать.**

**разостлать** *see* **расстилать.**

**разотравление** *n.* removal of poisoning.

**разочаров/ание** *n.*, **—анность** *f.* disappointment; **—анный** *a.* disappointed; **—ать, —ывать** *v.* disappoint.

**разрабатыв/аемый** *a.* workable, exploitable, capable of development; **р. на** worked for; **—ание** *see* **разработка; —ать** *v.* develop, work out (method), elaborate; exploit, work (a mine); cultivate (soil); treat, process; **—аться** *v.* be developed, develop, evolve.

**разработ/анный** *a.* developed; exploited, worked (mine); cultivated (soil); treated, processed; **—ать** *see* **разрабатывать; —ка** *f.* development, elaboration; exploitation, working, mining; cultivation; treatment, processing; dressing (of ore); **заслуживающий** —ки workable, worth exploiting; **открытая** —ка open-cut mining, open-pit mining; —чик *m.* developer.

**разравнивать** *v.* level, smooth out.

**разра/жать,** —зить *v.* break, shatter, destroy; —жаться, —зиться *v.* break out, burst, explode.

**разраст/ание** *n.* growth, expansion; —аться, —ись *v.* grow, expand, widen.

**разрегулиров/анность** *f.* misalignment; —анный *a.* misaligned, maladjusted; —ка *f.* misalignment, maladjustment.

**разре/дить,** —жать *v.* rarefy, thin, evacuate, exhaust; —жающий *a.* vacuum (pump).

**разрежен/ие** *n.* rarefaction, rarefying, thinning; exhaustion (of air), evacuation; vacuum; negative pressure; **камера** —ия vacuum space; —ность *f.* rarefaction, rarity, thinness, tenuity; —ный *a.* rarefied; exhausted, evacuated; —ное **пространство** vacuum; **сушилка с** —ным **пространством** vacuum dryer.

**разреживать** *see* **разредить.**

**разрез** *m.* cut, slit, gash, slash, rip; profile, section, cross section, cutaway view, plan; (min.) pit; layer; **в р.** contrary; **вид в** —е sectional view, cut-away view; **горизонтальный р.** plan; —ать *see* **разрезывать;** —нозубчатый *a.* (biol.) incisely dentate.

**разрезн/ой** *a.* slit, slitted, split, gapped, cut; sectional, laminated; (bot.) laciniate; detached (foundation); rip (saw); —ая **балка** flitch beam, sandwich beam; —ая **горелка** slot burner, wing burner.

**разрезыв/ание** *n.* cutting, slitting; —ать *v.* cut, slit, rip; snip.

**разреш/ать** *v.* permit, allow, authorize; solve (problem), clear up; resolve; —ающий *a.* permitting; resolving; —ающее **время, время** —ения resolving time (of counter); —ающая **способность** resolving power, resolution; —ающая **способность** по **времени** time resolution; —ение *n.* permission, permit, authorization,

grant, license; solution (of problem), settlement (of question); resolution; **функция** —ения resolution function; —енный *a.* permitted, permissible, authorized, licensed; allowed (spectrum, etc.); resolved.

**разрешим/ость** *f.* solvability; —ый *a.* solvable, capable of solution.

**разрешит/ельный** *a.* absolutory, absolving; permitting, permissive; —ельное **свидетельство** license; —ь *see* **разрешать.**

**разрисов/ать,** —ывать *v.* ornament, decorate; —ка *f.* painting, decoration.

**разровнять** *see* **разравнивать.**

**разрозн/енно** *adv.* singly, separately; —енный *a.* disconnected, separate; —ивать, —ить *v.* disconnect, separate; break (a set of books, etc.).

**разруб/ание** *n.* chopping, cleaving, slashing, cutting; —ать, —ить *v.* chop, cleave, slash, cut.

**разруха** *f.* ruin, collapse, devastation.

**разруш/ать** *v.* demolish, wreck, blow up, destroy, ruin; crush, break down; corrode, attack; erode; —аться *v.* go to ruin, collapse; decompose, decay, disintegrate; —ающий *a.* destructive, devastating, disruptive; —ающая **нагрузка** breaking load; —ающее **напряжение** breaking point.

**разрушен/ие** *n.* destruction, demolition, wrecking; ruin, collapse, failure, breakdown, disintegration; rupture, shattering, crushing; disaggregation (of soil); (med.) caries, decay; **р. пены** lather collapse, foam breakage; **предел** —ия breaking point; —ный *a.* destroyed, ruined; decayed, rotten, crumbling (rock).

**разруш/ившийся** *a.* decayed, crumbled, loosened; —ительный *a.* destructive, subversive, fatal; —ить *see* **разрушать.**

**разрыв** *m.* rupture, break, breach; fracture, fissure, crack, gap, void, space; severance, breaking, breaking off, disruption, discontinuity, interruption, disturbance; tearing, shredding; burst, bursting, explosion, blow-out (of tire); (astrophysics) burst; (min.) fracturing; (heart) failure; laceration (of perineum); shear (of wind); (geol.)

fault; **зажигание** —ом make-and-break ignition; **испытание на р.** tensile test, tensile strength test; **крепость на р., прочность на р., сопротивление** —y tensile strength, tenacity, toughness; **модуль** —a (met.) modulus of rupture.

**разрыв/ание** *n.* tearing, rupturing, breaking; —**ать** *v.* tear, lacerate; break, disrupt; dig up, unearth, excavate; —**аться** *v.* tear, rupture, crack; explode, burst; —**ающий** *a.* tearing, rupturing; disrupting; rifting, splitting, cleaving; —**ающая нагрузка** breaking load; —**ающее усилие** tensile force.

**разрывн/ой** *a.* tearing, breaking; discontinuous; **р. заряд** bursting charge; **р. снаряд** explosive shell; —**ая втулка** split boss; —**ая мощность** (elec.) breaking capacity, rupturing capacity; —**ая пуля** dumdum (bullet); —**ая сила** explosive force; —**ая трубка** fuse; —**ое усилие** breaking load; —**ость** *f.* discontinuity.

**разрывомер** *m.* gap meter.

**разрыв-трава** *f.* (bot.) saxifrage (*Saxifraga*).

**разрывчатый** *a.* disconnected; *see also* **разрывной.**

**разрыт/ый** *a.* dug up, excavated; —**ь** *v.* dig up, unearth, excavate.

**разрыхл/ение** *n.* breaking up, loosening, disintegration; mellowing (of soil); aeration; —**итель** *m.* scarifier; (text.) opener; —**ить,** —**ять** *v.* break up, loosen, stir up; hoe, mellow; aerate; —**иться,** —**яться** *v.* separate, disintegrate; —**яющий** *a.* disintegrating; antibonding (electron level).

**разряд** *m.* class, category, division, sort; (elec.) discharge; **р. высокой частоты** high-frequency discharge; **первого** —**a** first-class; **темный р., тихий р., тлеющий р.** (dielectrics) silent discharge, corona; —**итель** *m.* discharger; —**ить** *see* **разряжать.**

**разрядк/а** *f.* discharging, discharge; deexcitation; (typ.) spacing; **набирать в** —**y** *v.* space.

**разрядн/ик** *m.* (elec.) discharger; discharging rod, (lightning) arrester; spark gap; —**ый** *a.* discharging, discharge; —**ый контур** discharge circuit; —**ая емкость,** —**ая мощность** discharge capacity.

**разряж/ать** *v.* unload, discharge; (elec.) discharge; —**ающийся** *a.* discharging; —**ение** *n.* discharging, discharge, unloading.

**разсол** *see* **рассол.**

**разуб/едить,** —**еждать** *v.* dissuade.

**разубожив/ание** *n.* impoverishment, depletion, exhaustion, working out (of ore); —**ать** *v.* impoverish, deplete, exhaust, work out; dilute.

**разуголка** *f.* cornerpiece.

**разузна/вание** *n.* inquiry, investigation; —**вать,** —**ть** *v.* inquire, investigate, get information.

**разукра/сить,** —**шивать** *v.* decorate.

**разукрупн/ение** *n.* dividing into smaller units, subdivision; comminution; —**ить** *v.* subdivide; comminute.

**разум** *m.* reason, intelligence, mind: —**ение** *n.* understanding; **по моему** —**нию** to my mind, as I understand it; —**еть** *v.* understand, comprehend; —**еется** it is understood; certainly, of course; **само собой** —**еется** it stands to reason, it is obvious.

**разумн/ость** *f.* reasonableness, reliability, soundness; —**ый** *a.* reasonable, intelligent, responsible.

**разупорядоч/ение** *n.* disorder, disordering; (biol.) randomization; —**енный** *a.* disordered; randomized; —**ивать** *v.* disorder; randomize; —**ный** *a.* disordered, disorderly.

**разупрочнение** *n.* softening, weakening; (met.) recrystallization by process annealing.

**разуч/ивать,** —**ить** *v.* learn, study; practice; —**иваться,** —**иться** *v.* forget, unlearn.

**расцепить** *see* **расцепить.**

**разъед/аемость** *f.* corrodibility; —**аемый** *a.* corrodible; —**ание,** —**ение** *n.* corrosion, attack, eating away, pitting; (geol.) erosion; —**ать** *v.* corrode, attack, eat away, pit; erode; —**ающий** *a.* corroding, corrosive, caustic; erosive; —**ающее вещество** corrosive; —**енный** *a.* corroded, attacked, pitted; eroded.

**разъединен/ие** *n.* disunion, disjunction,

dissociation, separation, unfastening, severing, releasing, release; (elec.) disconnection, breaking, interruption; **—ный** *a.* disconnected, disengaged, out of gear; separate, discrete.

**разъедин/итель** *m.* (elec.) disconnecting switch, cut-out switch, breaking device; **—ительное реле** cut-off relay; **—ить, —ять** *v.* separate, detach, dissociate, disjoint, unlink, sever, release, disengage, throw out of gear; (elec.) disconnect, break; **—яющий** *a.* dissociative, separating; disconnecting, cut-off; releasing, disengaging; trip (hook).

**разъез/д** *m.* departure, going away, separation; (railroad) siding; **—дной путь** shunt; **—жать** *v.* ride around, go around; **—жаться** *v.* break up, separate, move apart; miss one another; fray, go to pieces, unravel.

**разъем** *m.* joint; **—ный** *a.* divided, split, detached; detachable, separable, dismountable; disengaging, release; **—ный подшипник** split bearing.

**разъесть** *see* **разъедать.**

**разъехаться** *see* **разъезжаться.**

**разъясн/ение** *n.* explanation, interpretation; **—ительный** *a.* explanatory; **—ить, —ять** *v.* explain, make clear, expound.

**разыск/ание, —ивание** *n.* research, search, inquiry, investigation; **—ать** *v.* find, discover; **—аться** *v.* be found, be discovered, turn up; **—ивать** *v.* search, look for, hunt for, trace, investigate.

**рай—** *abbr.* (районный) regional.

**райграс** *m.* (bot.) rye grass (*Lolium*); **английский р.** cultivated rye grass (*L. perenne*); **итальянский р.** Italian rye grass (*L. italicum*); **французский р.** oat grass (*Arrhenatherum*).

**рай/дерево** *n.* (bot.) Venice sumac (*Rhus cotinus*);—**ка** *f.* paradise apple (*Malus sylvestris paradisiaca*).

**райком** *m.* district committee.

**раймовка** *f.* residual slag in zinc distillation.

**раймондит** *m.* (min.) raimondite (probably identical with jarosite).

**райоленье** *n.* trenching.

**район** *m.* district, region, area, zone, field, locality; **—ирование** *n.* regionalization, zoning, division into zones; laying out, breaking up (area); **—ный** *a.* district, regional.

**райсемхоз** *m.* district seed-raising farm.

**райск/ий** *a.* paradise; **р. цвет** (bot.) flower fence (*Poinciana*); **—ое дерево** *see* **банан; —ие зерна** grains of paradise (seeds of *Amomum melegueta*).

**Райта прибор** Wright's meter.

**рак** *m.* (zool.) crayfish; (med., plant pathology) cancer; (astron.) Cancer; **р.-отшельник** *m.* hermit crab; **—ом** crabwise, sideways.

**ракель** *m.* (printing) doctor, wiper.

**ракет/а** *f.* rocket; flare; (tennis) racket; **р.-аэроплан, —оплан** *m.* rocket aircraft; **р.-парашют** parachute flare; **посадочная р.** (aero.) flare; **—ный** *a.* rocket, rocket-borne.

**ракит/а** *f.* (bot.) crack willow (*Salix fragilis*); goat willow (*S. caprea*); **—ник** *m.* willow osier; (bot.) broom (*Cytisus*).

**ракля** *f.* (calico printing) doctor, knife for removing paint.

**раковидный** *a.* (med.) cancerous.

**раковин/а** *f.*, **—ный** *a.* shell; sink, basin; vesicle; (met.) blister, bubble, air hole, blow hole, cavity, flaw; **ушная р.** (anat.) helix; **—ный шелк** Byssus silk; **—ные амебы** (zool.) Testacea; **—ообразный** *a.* shell-like, conchoidal.

**раковистость** *f.* (met.) blistered condition.

**раковистый** *a.* shell, shelly, shell-like, conchoidal (structure); (met.) blistered, containing blisters, blown; (bot.) mytiliform; **р. излом** conchoidal fracture; **р. мергель** (geol.) shell marl.

**раков/ый** *a.* (zool.) crayfish; (med.) cancerous; **—ые глазки, —ые жерновки** crab's eyes (seeds of *Abrus precatorius*).

**раком** *see under* **рак.**

**ракообразн/ые** *pl.* (zool.) Crustacea; **—ый** *a.* crustacean; (med.) cancerous; **—ая опухоль** cancerous tumor.

**ракоустойчив/ость** *f.* resistance to cancer; **—ый** *a.* cancer-resistant.

**ракурс** *m.* foreshortening (in a drawing).

**ракуша** *f.* hempseed husk.

**ракуш/ечник** *m.* ,—**ечниковый** *a.* (petr.) coquina, shell rock; —**ка** *f.* (zool.) mussel; —**ковые** *pl.* (zool.) Ostracoda; —**ник** *m.* crag (shell and sand rock).

**ральстонит** *m.* (min.) ralstonite.

**рама** *f.* frame, casing; chassis, carriage; bed plate; rack; (hotbed) sash.

**рамалиновая кислота** ramalinic acid.

**раман/овский** *a.* Raman; —**спектр** *m.* Raman spectrum.

**рамеалин** *m.* ramealin.

**рамен** *see* **ромашка.**

**рамень** *f.* forest border.

**рамзаит** *m.* (min.) ramsayite.

**Рамзай-Юнга**   **уравнение**   Ramsay-Young equation.

**рами** *f.* (bot.) ramie (*Boehmeria*); **пряжа р.** ramie yarn.

**рамигеновая кислота** ramigenic acid.

**рамификация** *f.* ramification, branching.

**рамка** *see* **рама.**

**раммельсбергит** *m.* (min.) rammelsbergite (a nickel diarsenide).

**рамн/аза** *f.* rhamnase; —**егин** *m.* rhamnegin; —**етин** *m.* rhamnetin.

**рамни/когенол** *m.* rhamnicogenol; —**козид** *m.* rhamnicoside; —**н** *m.* rhamnin; —**ноза** *f.* rhamninose; —**т** *m.* rhamnitol.

**рамно/глюкозид** *m.* rhamnoglucoside; —**за** *f.* rhamnose; —**зид** *m.* rhamnoside; —**ксантин** *m.* rhamnoxanthin, frangulin; —**л** *m.* rhamnol; —**новая кислота** rhamnonic acid; —**флуорин** *m.* rhamnofluorin.

**рам/ный,** —**очный** *a.* frame; chassis; plate and frame (filterpress).

**рампа** *f.* ramp; footlight.

**рамул/иоспороз** *m.* Ramulispora infection (of plants); —**ярноз** *m.* leaf spot (caused by Ramularia).

**РАН** *abbr.* (**Российская академия наук**) Russian Academy of Sciences.

**рана** *f.* wound, cut.

**ранаректор** *m.* automatic gas analyzer.

**ранг** *m.* (math.) rank (of a matrix).

**рангиформовая кислота** rangiformic acid.

**ранговый** *a. of* **ранг.**

**ранданит** *m.* (min.) randanite, kieselguhr.

**рандбалка** *f.* reinforced-concrete girder.

**рандит** *see* **ураноталит.**

**Рандольфа процесс** (met.) Randolph process (for copper refining).

**ранее** *see* **раньше.**

**ранен/ие** *see* **рана;** —**ый** *a.* wounded.

**ранет** *m.* rennet (kind of apple).

**ранец** *m.* knapsack, pack, kit, satchel.

**ранит** *m.* (min.) ranite (similar to hydronephelite).

**ранить** *v.* wound, cut.

**Ранкина формула** Rankine's formula.

**ранкинит** *m.* (min.) rankinite.

**раннеспел/ость** *f.* early maturity; —**ый** *a.* early, early-ripening.

**ранний** *a.* early, previous.

**ранник** *m.* polypody root.

**рано** *adv.* early, at an early hour, soon; —**вато** *adv.* rather early, rather soon;—**опадающий** *a.* (bot.) caducous.

**рант** *m.* welt, boss.

**ранцевый** *a.* knapsack (sprayer).

**раньше** *compr. of* **ранний, рано** earlier, sooner; before, formerly, prior; **как можно р.** as soon as possible.

**рапа** *f.* natural brine, saline water.

**рапакиви** *n.* (petr.) Rapakivi granite.

**рапин** *m.* rapine; —**овая кислота** rapinic acid, rapic acid.

**рапира** *f.* rapier, foil.

**рапонт/ик,** —**ин** *m.* (bot.) rhubarb (*Rheum rhaponticum*); —**ицин** *m.* rhaponticin.

**рапорт** *m.* report, account; —**овать** *v.* report, give an account.

**раппа-киви** *see* **рапакиви.**

**раппорт** *m.* (text.) pattern repeat.

**рапс** *m.* (bot.) rape (*Brassica napus*); —**овое масло** rape oil, rapeseed oil.

**рапунцель** *m.* corn salad (*Valerianella olitorea*); rampion (*Campanula rapunculus*).

**раритет** *m.* rarity, curiosity.

**рас—** *see* **раз—.**

**раса** *f.* race, breed.

**раскаленн/ость** *f.* incandescence, glow; **р. добела** incandescence, white heat; **р. докрасна** red heat; —**ый** *a.* incandescent, glowing, red hot; —**ая нить** (elec., thermionics) filament.

**раскал/ивать,** —**ить** *v.* incandesce, bring to red heat; —**иваться,** —**иться** *v.* get hot, begin to glow.

**раскалываем/ость** *f.* cleavability, cleavage; —**ый** *a.* cleavable.

**раскалыв/ание** *n.* cleaving, cleavage, splitting, cracking; separation, division, cutting; (nucl.) spallation; **—ать** *v.* cleave, split, split up, split off, crack, rift, fissure; slit, cut off; **—аться** *v.* cleave, split, crack; **—ающийся** *a.* cleavable, scissile, fissile; cleaving, splitting, rifting; **—ающийся пластами** fissile.

**раскалять** *see* **раскаливать.**

**раскапывать** *v.* dig out, excavate, unearth.

**раскармливать** *v.* fatten.

**раскат/ать, —ывать** *v.* roll out, flatten, laminate; unroll; **—ить** *v.* set rolling; **—ка** *f.*, **—ывание** *n.* rolling, flattening, flattening out, lamination, expansion; unrolling.

**раскач/ать, —ивать** *v.* swing, set swinging; shake, loosen; **—иваться** *v.* sway, swing, oscillate; loosen, get rickety; **—ивание** *n.* swinging, swaying, oscillation, vibration; loosening.

**расквартировать** *v.* house, quarter.

**раскид/ать, —ывать** *see* **разбрасывать; —истый** *a.* branchy; scattered; **—ной** *a.* unfolding, folding, collapsible; **—ывание** *n.* spreading, scattering; unfolding.

**раскинут/ый** *a.* spread, extended; **—ь** *v.* spread, extend; pitch (a tent); **—ь умом** consider.

**раскисл/ение** *n.* deoxidation, reduction; **—енный** *a.* deoxidized, reduced; **—итель** *m.*, **—ительное вещество, —яющее средство** deoxidizing agent, reducing agent, reducer; **—ительный, —яющий** *a.* deoxidizing, reducing; **—ить, —ять** *v.* deoxidize, reduce.

**расклад/ка** *f.* division, distribution, allotment; **—очный** *a.* distributing; **—очная машина** (text.) spreader; **—ывать** *v.* spread, lay out; build (a fire).

**расклеи/вать, —ть** *v.* unglue; post, stick up, placard.

**расклеп/ать, —ывать** *v.* unrivet, unclench; rivet, clench; spread, jump up, upset; **—ывание** *n.* unriveting; riveting, clenching; jumping up, upsetting.

**расклин/ивание** *n.* cleavage, splitting; **—ивать, —ить** *v.* cleave, split; unwedge, loosen; wedge, fasten with wedges; **—ивающий** *a.* cleaving; disjoining (pressure).

**расков/ать, —ывать** *v.* hammer out, malleate, flatten, draw out; jump up, upset, jump, jolt; unshoe (a horse); unchain, unfetter; **—аться** *v.* lose a shoe; (met.) expand; **—ка** *f.* hammering out, flattening, spreading; upsetting; **испытание на —ку** hammer test.

**раскол** *m.* cleft, crack; **—ачивание** *n.* (molding) rapping; breaking to pieces; **—ачивать** *v.* rap; break to pieces; stretch on a last (shoes); **—ка** *f.* chopping, splitting.

**расколот** *m.* (min.) bunton (timbers); **—ить** *see* **расколачивать; —ый** *a.* split, split apart, cleaved; **—ь** *see* **раскалывать.**

**расколыхать** *v.* rock, set rocking.

**раскомпенсация** *f.* decompensation, loss of compensation.

**расконоп/атить, —ачивать** *v.* uncalk.

**раскоп/ать** *see* **раскапывать; —ка** *f.* digging, excavation.

**раскормить** *see* **раскармливать.**

**раскос** *m.* cross stay, angle brace, diagonal, diagonal strut, strut, truss, prop; **—ина** *f.* cross bar; angular iron; **—ная система** latticework; **—ость** *f.* slant.

**раскрас/ить** *see* **раскрашивать; —ка** *f.* painting, coloring, coloration.

**раскрасн/евшийся** *a.* red, crimson; **—еться** *v.* redden, get red.

**раскраш/енный** *a.* painted, colored; **—ивание** *n.* painting, coloring; **—ивать** *v.* paint, color.

**раскрой** *m.* laying out (patterns for stamping forms out of plate).

**раскромс/анный** *a.* shredded, cut to pieces; **—ать** *v.* shred, cut to pieces.

**раскрош/енный** *a.* crumbled, broken; **—ить** *v.* crumble, break into small pieces, crush; **—иться** *v.* crumble, fall apart, disintegrate.

**раскру/тить, —чивать** *v.* untwine, untwist, unwind, disentangle; **—титься, —чиваться** *v.* untwist, get untwisted, uncoil; **—тка** *f.* (turbine) overspeeding; **—чивание** *n.* untwisting, back twist.

**раскрыв/ать** v. uncover, open, reveal, disclose, expose; **—ающийся** a. opening; hinged.

**раскрылка** f. may disease (of bees).

**раскрыт/ие** n. uncovering, opening; disclosure, exposure; mouth; evaluation; (math.) expansion; **—ый** a. open; disclosed, exposed; **—ь** see **раскрывать.**

**раскряжевка** f. (min.) crosscutting.

**раскуп/ать, —ить** v. buy up; **—аться** v. be bought up, sell.

**раскупор/ивать, —ить** v. open, uncork, unseal; **—ка** f. uncorking, unsealing.

**раскут/ать, —ывать** v. uncover, unwrap.

**расовый** a. race, racial.

**расп.** abbr. (распад) decomposition, disintegration.

**распавшийся** a. disintegrated, crumbled.

**распад** m., **—ение** n. decomposition, dissociation, disruption, breaking up; separation, falling to pieces, disintegration; resolution; ruin, downfall, destruction; (nucl.) decay; **продукты —а** decomposition products; **ряд —ов, цепочка —ов** (nucl.) chain decay, series disintegration; **скорость —а** disintegration rate; **теплота —а** heat of dissociation; **—аться** v. decompose, break down; crumble, disintegrate, break up, separate into; **—ающийся** a. decomposing; disintegrating.

**распа/ивание** n., **—йка** f. unsoldering; **—ивать** v. unsolder.

**распаков/ать, —ывать** v. unpack, undo; **—ка** f. unpacking.

**распалубка** f. vaulting cell.

**распар** m. bosh, body (of blast furnace).

**распар/енный** a. steamed, softened; **—ивание** n. steaming; (med.) fomentation; **—ивать, —ить** v. steam, soften, stew.

**распасться** see **распадаться.**

**распах/ать** v. plow up, till; **—ивание** n. plowing up; **—ивать** v. plow up; open wide; **—нуть** v. open wide, throw open.

**распаш/ка** f. plowing; **—ник** m. ridging plow, furrower.

**распа/янный** a. unsoldered; **—ять** see **распаивать.**

**распереть** see **распирать.**

**распечат/ать, —ывать** v. open, unseal, break the seal; unlute; **—ывание** n. opening, unsealing.

**распил** m. cut, saw cut, gash; **—енный** a. sawed; **—ивание** n., **—ка** f., **—овка** f. sawing; **—ивать, —ить** v. saw.

**распирать** v. bulge out, push apart.

**расписание** n. time table, schedule.

**расписать** see **расписывать.**

**расписка** f. receipt, voucher; **обратная р.** advice of delivery.

**расписывать** v. describe, depict; paint; **—ся** v. sign, acknowledge receipt (of).

**распит** m. (min.) raspite (a lead tungstate).

**расплав** m. fusion; melt; **—ить, —ливать, —лять** v. melt, fuse, liquefy; (met.) smelt; **—ливаться** v. melt, fuse, liquefy, run; **—ка** f., **—ление —ливание** n. melting, fusion; smelting; **—ленный** a. melted, molten, fused; melted out, extracted; smelted; **—ленный металл** smelt; **—ленная масса** melt, molten mass, fusion.

**распланиров/ать, —ывать** v. plan out, lay out, mark out; **—ка** f. layout.

**распласт/ать, —ывать** v. spread, flatten, stretch; split into layers; **—ывание** n. spreading, flattening; splitting.

**распла/та** f. pay, payment, settling (of accounts); **—титься, —чиваться** v. v. pay, settle (with).

**расплеск/ать, —ивать** v. spill, splash, spatter.

**распле/сти, —сть, —тать** v. untwist, unplait, unbraid; **—тание** n. untwisting, unplaiting.

**распло/д** m. breeding, reproduction; breed; brood; **—дить, —жать** v. breed, propagate; **—диться** v. breed, multiply.

**расплыв/ание** n. spreading, running, deliquescence; **—аться** v. spread, run, melt, dissolve, deliquesce; **—ающийся** a. deliquescent.

**расплывчат/ость** f. diffuseness, indistinctness; **—ый** a. diffuse, indistinct, dim.

**расплыться** see **расплываться.**

**расплю/снуть, —щивать, —щить** v. hammer out, beat, flatten (out);

widen, broaden; rivet; —**щиваться**
v. mushroom; —**щенный** a. hammered out, flattened, laminated; —**щивание** n. hammering, flattening, lamination.

**расп/мин** abbr. (**распадов в минуту**) disintegrations per minute.

**распозн/авание, —ание** n. discernment, distinction, discrimination, perception, knowledge, recognition; —**а-вать, —ать** v. discern, distinguish, discriminate, recognize; (med.) diagnose; —**ающий** a. discerning, discriminative.

**располаг/аемый** a. available; —**ать** v. dispose, place, set, arrange, lay out, locate, situate; incline (to); intend; **р. временем** have time (for); —**ающий** a. conducive (to).

**располз/аться, —тись** v. tear, ravel, go to pieces, deteriorate; crawl apart.

**расположен** see **расположенный**.

**расположен/ие** n. disposition, disposal, arrangement, layout, distribution, spacing, grouping, order; pattern, design; (phys.) geometry, configuration; situation, location, locality, exposure (of building); inclination, tendency; **р. местности** lay of the land; **р. цифр в виде диаграммы** tabulation; **общее р.** general layout; **схема —ия** layout.

**расположенный** a. disposed, inclined, having a tendency; situated, located; **правильно р.** in position.

**расположить** see **располагать**.

**распор** m. thrust; —**ка** f. cross bar, cross bracing, brace, strut, tie beam, tie rod, stay rod; spacer, distance piece.

**распор/ный, —очный** a. thrust, brace; distance (ring, tube, etc.); **р. болт** distance bolt, expansion stay bolt, stay bolt; **р. винт** clamp screw; **р. зажим** distance terminal; —**ная балка** brace; —**ная поперечина** tie bar, cross bar.

**распорядитель** m. manager, director; —**ность** f. good management, control, efficiency, activity; **отсутствие —ности** mismanagement; —**ный** a. efficient, capable, active, administrative, control.

**распоря/диться, —жаться** v. dispose

(of), do, deal (with); order; —**док** m. order, standing order, arrangement, method.

**распоряжен/ие** n. disposition, disposal, arrangement, order; ordinance, edict, decree; **в —ии** at the disposal (of), at hand, available; **отдать р.** v. give orders, leave instructions; **управление —ия** (nucl.) configuration control.

**расправ/ить, —лять** v. straighten; set right; —**иться, —ляться** v. obtain satisfaction (from); —**ление** n. straightening, smoothing; setting right; (text.) tentering, stretching.

**распределен/ие** n. distribution, dispensation, assignment, allocation, allotment, division, apportionment; assessment (of tax); spreading, dispersion, diffusion, dissemination; pattern; **р. во времени** time distribution; **р. выхода по массам** yield-mass distribution; **р. по массам** mass distribution; **коэффициент —ия** distribution ratio; partition coefficient; **р. фаз** phase distribution; —**ный** a. distributed, divided; **тонко —ный** finely divided.

**распределитель** m. distributor; spreader; manifold; **р.-щит** switchboard.

**распределительн/ый** a. distributing, distributive; regulating, control; partition (chromatography); **р. вал** camshaft; countershaft; **р. диск, р. кулак** cam; **р. клапан** regulating valve; **р. круг** distributing plate, distributor plate; **р. пункт** distributing center; **р. щит, —ая доска, —ая таблица** (elec.) switchboard, distribution board, panel; (automobile) dashboard; **р. щиток** dashboard; —**ая коробка** (elec.) distributing box, switch box; —**ая магистраль** (elec.) distributing main, distributor; —**ая полоса, —ая шина** (elec.) distributing busbar; —**ая сеть** distributing network, distributing system.

**распредел/ить, —ять** v. distribute, assign, allot, apportion; sort; disperse, disseminate; —**яющий** a. distributing.

**распредщит** m. distributing board.

**распрод/авать, —ать** v. sell out, auction off; —**аваться** v. sell, have a market; —**ажа** f. sale, auction.

**распрост/ереть, —ирать** *v.* stretch out, extend, spread, widen.

**распространен/ие** *n.* propagation; expansion, spreading, spread, dissemination, distribution; extension, dilation; enlargement, amplification; diffusion, emission; convection (of heat); circulation; occurrence; **постоянная —ия** (elec. comm.) propagation constant; **функция —ия** propagator; **—ность** *f.* prevalence, extent, rate of occurrence; abundance (of isotopes, etc.); **—ный** *a.* prevailing, prevalent, common, widespread, abundant, controlling (influence, etc.); **широко —ный** widespread.

**распростран/итель** *m.* vector, spreader (of disease); **—ить, —ять** *v.* circulate, spread, broadcast, propagate; disseminate, disperse, diffuse, radiate, emit; **—иться, —яться** *v.* spread, expand, broaden, extend, branch out; propagate; radiate, emit; pervade; be circulated abroad; persist.

**распрыск/ать, —ивать** *v.* spray, sprinkle.

**распрягать** *v.* unharness.

**распрям/ить, —лять** *v.* straighten, unbend; set upright; **—иться, —ляться** *v.* straighten out; **—ление** *n.* straightening, unbending.

**распрячь** *see* **распрягать.**

**расп/сек** *abbr.* (**разпадов в секунду**) disintegrations per second.

**распус/кание** *n.* melting, running, deliquescence; (bot.) opening, blossoming, blooming; **—кать, —тить** *v.* melt, liquefy, deliquesce; let go, undo, untie, relax; disperse, diffuse; unravel; discharge (employees); **—каться** *v.* dissolve, melt; become lax; become unraveled; (bot.) open; **—кающийся** *a.* deliquescent.

**распут/ать, —ывать** *v.* disentangle, unravel, untwine.

**распух/ание** *n.* swelling, inflation; intumescence; **—ать** *v.* swell, inflate, bulge, expand; **—ающий** *a.* swelling; intumescent; **—ший** *a.* swollen, inflated, tumid.

**распушиться** *v.* become fluffy.

**распущенный** *a.* loose, relaxed; undisciplined; untied, undone; open (blossom).

**распыл/ение, —ивание** *n.* atomization, spraying; diffusion, dispersion; pulverization; (agr.) dusting; (thermionics) sputtering; **—енный** *a.* atomized, sprayed; pulverized, pulverulent, divided, powdered; **тонко —енный** finely divided; **—енное масло** oil spray; **—ивающий абсорбер** spray chamber.

**распылитель** *m.* atomizer, sprayer, pulverizer, diffuser; (agr.) duster; **—ный** *a.* spray; **—ное сопло** spray nozzle.

**распыл/ить, —ять** *v.* spray, atomize, diffuse; pulverize, powder; (thermionics) sputter; **—иться, —яться** *v.* disperse, scatter; be pulverized, turn to dust; **—янный** *see* **распыленный; —яющий** *a.* spray, spraying; pulverizing; **—яющее сопло** spray nozzle.

**расса/да** *f.* seedling, sprout; **—дить, —живать** *v.* plant, transplant, set out; seat; **—дка** *f.,* **—живание** *n.* planting; **—дник** *m.* nursery; seedbed; hotbed; breeding farm; **—допосадочный** *a.* transplanting.

**рассасыв/ание** *n.* resorption; (med.) resolution; **—ать** *v.* resorb, reabsorb; **—аться** *v.* resolve.

**рассверлив/ание** *n.* boring, drilling; **—ать** *v.* bore, bore out, drill.

**рассвет** *m.* dawn, daybreak; **на —е** at dawn, at daybreak; **—ать** *v.* dawn.

**рассев** *m.* sowing; dissemination; screening, separation (of powders); sifter; **—ать** *see* **рассеивать.**

**расседаться** *v.* crack, chap.

**рассеив/ание** *n.* dispersal, dispersion, scattering, dissipation, diffusion; (agr.) sowing; **—атель** *m.* diffuser, scatterer, scattering material; **—ать** *v.* disperse, scatter, dissipate, diffuse, disseminate, dispel; (agr.) sow; leak, diverge, stray; **—аться** *v.* scatter, dissipate; diverge.

**рассеивающ/ий** *a.* dispersion, dispersive, dispersing; diffusion, diffusing, scattering; **р. фотометр** dispersion photometer; **—ая способность** dispersibility; (electrolysis) throwing power.

**рассек/ание** *n.* cleaving; dissection; **—атель** *m.* dissector; **—ать** *v.* cleave; dissect.

**расселение** n. settlement.

**расселина** f. split, cleft, rift, crack.

**Расселя-Сондерса связь** (nucl.) Russell-Saunders coupling.

**рассесть** see **рассаживать**; **—ся** see also **расседаться.**

**рассеч/ение** n. dissection; **—ка** f. cutting, breaking (of circuit); (min.) crosscut; **в—ку** (elec.) in series; **—ь** see **рассекать.**

**рассеян/ие** n. dispersion, dissemination, dissipation, diffusion, scattering, scattering effect; (elec.) leakage, leak; (magnetic) leakage; degradation (of energy); scattering (of particle); **р. света** light scattering; **р. тепла** heat dissipation; **комбинационное р.** Raman effect; **коэффициент —ия** dispersion factor; circle coefficient (of electric motor); **коэффициент магнитного —ия** leakage coefficient; **мощность —ия** dissipated power; **обратное р.** (nucl.) back scatter, back scattering; **—нопористый** a. (bot.) diffuse-porous; **—ный** a. dispersed, disseminated, dissipated, diffused, scattered; sprinkled, strewn; sparse; distracted, absentminded; erratic (value); trace (element); **—ный обратно** back-scattered; **—ный свет** diffuse light, scattered light.

**рассеять** see **рассеивать.**

**рассказ/ать, —ывать** v. tell.

**расслаб/евать, —еть, —нуть** v. grow weak, weaken suddenly; **—ить, —лять** v. weaken; **—ление** n. weakening, depression, prostration; relaxation; **—ленность** f. (med.) asthenia; **—ленный** a. weakened, prostrate; slack.

**расслаив/ание** n. stratification, lamination, foliation, cleavage, separation, exfoliation, scaling; phase separation, segregation, demixing; **—ать** v. divide into layers, stratify, exfoliate, flake; **—аться** v. exfoliate, peel off; **—ающий стол** buddle (for ore concentration).

**рассланц/евание** n., **—овка** f. (geol.) schist formation, shearing; **—ованный** a. sheared.

**расследов/ание** n. investigation, inquiry, examination; (law) inquest; **—ать** v. investigate, inquire, look into.

**расслоен/ие** see **расслаивание**; **—ный** a. stratified, laminated.

**расслоина** f. spill.

**рассло/ить** see **расслаивать**; **—йка** f. separation into layers, separation into flakes, lamination; (geol.) strata.

**рассматрив/аемый** a. in question, under consideration; **—ание** n. examination; consideration; **—ать** v. examine, inspect, look at, observe, study, investigate, analyze; overhaul; discuss, consider.

**рассмотр/ение** n. examination, inspection, investigation; consideration; treatment; **направлять на р.** v. refer, submit (to); **представлять на р.** v. submit for consideration; **—еть** see **рассматривать.**

**рассогласован/ие** n. disagreement, mismatch; **угол —ия** displacement angle.

**рассол** m., **—ьный** a. pickle, brine; (mother) liquor; **—ение** n. desalinization (of soil); **—одение** n. desolodization; **—оносная зона** (geol.) zone of sediment rocks over salt deposit; **—онцевание** n. desolonetzization, dealkalinization.

**рассортиров/ать, —ывать** v. sort out, classify.

**рассох/а** f. forked tree, bifurcated stem; **—нуться** see **рассыхаться**; **—шийся** a. cracked, split (from dryness).

**расспр/ашивание** n. questioning, inquiry; **—ашивать, —осить** v. question, inquire, interrogate; **—ос** m. question, inquiry, interrogation.

**рассроч/ивать, —ить** v. authorize deferred payment; **—ка** f. instalment, part payment; **в —ку** on the instalment plan; **уплата в —ку** instalment.

**расстав/ание** n. parting, separation; **—аться** v. part, separate, leave.

**расстав/ить, —лять** v. place, set, dispose, arrange, put in proper order.

**расстан/авливать, —овить** v. place, arrange; **—овка** f. arrangement, order, disposition, spacing.

**расстаться** see **расставаться.**

**расстег/ивать, —нуть** v. unfasten, unbuckle, unclasp, unhook.

**расстеклов/ание, —ывание** n. devitrification; **—анный** a. devitrified; **—анный обсидиан** (min.) devitrified obsidian, apobsidian; —ывать *v.* devitrify.

**расстил** *m.* spreading; —ание *n.*, —ка *f.* spreading, strewing; unfolding; —ать, —аться *v.* spread, strew; unfold, extend.

**расстопоривание** *n.* unlocking, release.

**расстоян/ие** *n.* distance, way, space, spacing, interval; **р. между электродами** electrode spacing; **на —ии** distant, at a distance, remote; **на одинаковом —ии** at regular intervals, regularly spaced; **на равном —ии** equally spaced, equidistant; **перевозка на дальнее р.** long-distance transportation; **управление на —ии** remote control.

**расстраивать** *v.* unbalance, unsettle, disorganize, disturb, disrupt, derange, disarrange; disconcert, upset, perturb; (rad.) detune; —ся *v.* become upset; get out of tune.

**расстрел** *m.* execution, shooting down; (min.) bunton; —ять *v.* shoot down.

**расстро/енный** *a.* disorganized; upset, disturbed; unbalanced (mind); —ить *see* **расстраивать**; —йка *f.* detuning; frequency difference.

**расстройство** *n.* disorder, disorganization, confusion, derangement, disturbance, disruption; **р. желудка** (med.) indigestion; **р. хода** breakdown, trouble.

**рассудительн/ость** *f.* common sense, reasonableness; —ый *a.* reasonable.

**рассуд/ить** *see* **рассуждать**; —ок *m.* reason, understanding, mind, sense; —очно *adv.* rationally; —очность *f.* rationality; —очный *a.* rational.

**рассужд/ать** *v.* reason, discuss, argue, debate; —ение *n.* reasoning; discussion, discourse.

**рассунуть** *see* **рассовывать.**

**рассуч/ивать, —ить** *v.* untwine, untwist.

**рассчит/анный** *a.* calculated, computed; —ать, —ывать *v.* calculate, compute, figure out; reckon (on), expect, depend, count (on); design; dismiss, discharge, pay off; —ывать на calculate for; depend on; —аться, —ываться *v.* settle (with), obtain satisfaction; defray (expenses); —ывающий *a.* expectant.

**рассыл/ание** *n.*, —ка *f.* distribution; —ать *v.* distribute; send about, send around; —ьный *m.* messenger, delivery man.

**рассып/ание** *n.*, —ка *f.* strewing, scattering; —анный *a.* scattered; loose (cargo); —ать *v.* scatter, disperse, diffuse; intersperse; spill; —аться *v.* crumble, crumble away, disintegrate, molder; spill; —ной *a.* loose; **в —ную** dispersedly; loose, loosely.

**рассыпчат/ость** *f.* friability; —ый *a.* friable, crumbly, powdery, arenaceous.

**рассыхаться** *v.* dry, dry out, parch.

**Раст:** по —у by Rast's method (molecular-weight determination).

**растаивать** *v.* thaw, melt.

**расталкивать** *v.* push apart.

**растаплив/ание** *n.* lighting, kindling, firing; melting, liquefaction; (met.) smelting; —ать *v.* light, kindle, fire up; melt, fuse, liquefy; smelt.

**растаптывать** *v.* crush, trample, tread down; wear out (shoes).

**растачивать** *v.* bore, bore out.

**раста/явший** *a.* melted, thawed out; —ять *see* **растаивать.**

**раствор** *m.* solution; liquor, bath; paste; suspension; (clay) mortar; aperture, opening, span (of vise); **давление —а** solution pressure; **напряжение —а,** **упругость —а** solution tension; solution pressure; **твердый р.** solid solution; **угол —а** aperture angle.

**растворен/ие** *n.* solution, dissolving; diffusion (of metals in each other); —ный *a.* dissolved; —ное вещество solute.

**растворим/ое** *n.* solute; —ость *f.* solubility; deliquescence; —ый *a.* soluble; liquefiable; —ый в воде water-soluble; —ый легко —ый readily soluble.

**раствор/итель** *m.* solvent; dissolver (apparatus); —ить, —ять *v.* dissolve; open, unfasten; —иться, —яться *v.* dissolve, be dissolved; open, be opened; —омешалка *f.* cement (or mortar) mixer; —яемый *a.* undergoing solution, being dissolved, dissolving; soluble.

**растворяющ/ий** *a.* dissolving, solvent; —ая способность solvent action;

—ее вещество, —ее средство solvent;
—ийся *a.* dissolving; soluble.

**растек/ание** *n.* spreading; —**атель** *m.*
spreading agent, wetting agent; —
**аться** *v.* spread, spill, run.

**растел** *m.* calving.

**растение** *n.* plant; **р.-индикатор** *m.*
plant indicator, soil-testing crop;
**р.-краситель** *m.* dye crop; **р.-хозяин**
*m.* host plant; —**вод** *m.* plant grower;
—**водство** *n.* plant growing; —**питатель** *m.* plant feeder.

**растеребить** *v.* dishevel, tear to pieces.

**растереть** *see* **растирать.**

**растертый** *a.* ground (powder); rubbed.

**растер/янный** *a.* lost, perplexed, confused; —**яться** *v.* be at a loss, be
disconcerted.

**растечься** *see* **растекаться.**

**расти** *v.* grow, increase; —**льня** *f.*
germinator.

**растинон** *m.* Rastinon, tolbutamide.

**растир/аемый** *a.* pulverizable, friable;
—**ание** *n.* pulverization, grinding,
trituration; attrition, rubbing, massage; —**ательный** *a.* pulverizing,
grinding; rubbing; —**ать** *v.* pulverize,
grind, triturate, comminute, crush;
rub up (paint); rub, massage.

**растис/кивать,** —**нуть** *v.* push apart,
burst open; unclench.

**растительно/-животный** *a.* vegetoani-
mal; —**сть** *f.* vegetation, verdure,
green; flora; —**ядный** *a.* (zool.)
herbivorous; —**ядное животное**
herbivore.

**растительн/ый** *a.* plant, vegetable,
phyto—; **р. жир** vegetable fat; **р.
казеин** vegetable casein, legumin; **р.
краситель,** —**ая краска** plant pigment; vegetable color, vegetable dye;
**р. клей** gum, mucilage; —**ая вытяжка** vegetable extract; —**ая земля**
vegetable mold, humus; —**ая кислота**
vegetable acid; —**ая слизь** mucilage;
—**ая смола** vegetable resin; —**ая химия** plant chemistry, phytochemistry;
—**ое волокно** vegetable fiber, plant
fiber; —**ое масло** vegetable oil.

**растить** *v.* grow, raise, breed.

**растолк/ать,** —**нуть** *see* **расталкивать.**

**растолков/ать,** —**ывать** *v.* interpret,
explain, expound; —**ывание** *n.* interpretation, explanation.

**растолочь** *v.* pound, grind, pulverize,
crush.

**растоп/ить,** —**лять** *see* **растапливать;**
—**ка** *f.* kindling, firing; melting;
—**ление** *see* **растапливание;** —**ленный** *a.* kindled, fired; melted, molten.

**растоптать** *see* **растаптывать.**

**растопыр/енный** *a.* bristling; (bot.)
divaricate; —**ивать,** —**ить** *v.* spread
wide, straddle; —**иваться,** —**иться**
*v.* bulge out; bristle.

**растор/гать,** —**нуть** *v.* cancel, break.

**расторжение** *n.* cancellation, dissolution.

**растормаживать** *v.* release the brake.

**расторопша** *f.* milk thistle (*Silybum*).

**расточ** *see* **расточка.**

**расточ/ать,** —**ить** *v.* dissipate, waste;
—**ение** *n.* waste, wasting; —**ительность** *f.* wastefulness; —**ительный**
*a.* wasteful, extravagant.

**расточ/ка** *f.* bore, boring; —**ный** *a.*
boring; —**ный станок** borer, boring
machine; —**ная оправка** boring bar.

**растрав/ить,** —**ливать,** —**лять** *v.* irritate; corrode, destroy with caustics;
—**ление,** —**ливание** *n.* irritation;
corrosion.

**растра/та** *f.* spending, waste; embezzle-
ment; —**тить,** —**чивать** *v.* spend,
waste, squander; embezzle.

**растревож/ивать,** —**ить** *v.* alarm, perturb, disturb.

**растрепать** *v.* tatter, fray.

**растрес/каться,** —**киваться,** —**нуться**
*v.* crack, burst, split; decrepitate,
crackle; disintegrate; —**кивание** *n.*
cracking, bursting, splitting, fissuring;
decrepitation; disintegration; (biol.)
dehiscence, bursting open; (nucl.)
spallation; (masonry) spalling; **осколок** —**кивания** spallation fragment;
—**кивающийся** *a.* cracking, splitting,
rifting; friable.

**раструб** *m.* funnel, funnel-shaped opening, trumpet, bell, bell mouth, mouth;
cone, cone bottom (of tank); socket
(of pipe); **с** —**ом** bell-mouthed;
**соединение** —**ом** bell-and-spigot,
spigot and socket joint (of pipes).

**растру/сить,** —**шивать** *v.* scatter, strew.

**растряс/ать,** —**ти,** —**ывать** *v.* strew,

scatter; shake up; **—ение, —ывание** *n.,* **—ка** *f.* scattering; shaking up.

**растушев/ать, —ывать** *v.* shade, stipple, level (color).

**растущий** *a.* growing, rising.

**растягив/аемый** *a.* stretching, stretchable; **—ание** *n.* stretching, extending, lengthening, protraction; **—ать** *v.* stretch, extend, lengthen, elongate, distend, expand; sprain, strain (muscle); **—аться** *v.* stretch, give, extend, expand.

**растягивающ/ий** *a.* stretching; **р. механизм** stretcher; **—ая нагрузка** tension; **—ая сила, —ее усилие** tension, tensile force, tensile stress; tractive force, pull.

**растяжен/ие** *n.* stretching, stretch, elongation, extension, expansion, dilation, dilatation; pull; tension; strain, sprain (of muscle); **прочность на р., сопротивление —ию** tensile strength, tenacity; **сила —ия** tensile force, tension.

**растяжим/ость** *f.* stretchability, tensility, elasticity; extensibility, extensiveness, expansibility, expansiveness; (met.) ductility; **—ый** *a.* stretchable, tensile, elastic; extensible, extensive, expansive; ductile.

**растяж/ка** *f.* stretching, extending; tension member; **в —ку** at full length; **—ной** *a.* stretching, extension; **—ной болт** expansion bolt.

**растянут/ость** *f.* lengthiness; **—ый** *a.* stretched, stretched out, elongated, distended, expanded; lengthy, dragged out; **—ь** *see* **растягивать.**

**расфасов/ать, —ывать** *v.* bag, pack, package; **—ка** *f.* bagging, packing.

**расфокусиров/анный** *a.* defocused, out of focus; **—ка** *f.* defocusing; debunching (of electrons).

**расформиров/ание** *n.* dissolution, breaking up; **—ать, —ывать** *v.* dissolve, break up, separate.

**расхвал/ивать, —ить** *v.* praise.

**расхляб/анность** *f.* looseness, shakiness; **—анный** *a.* loose, slack, unstrung; **—аться** *v.* get loose, work loose, get slack; get shaky; need tightening, require tuning up.

**расход** *m.* expense, expenditure, outlay,

disbursement; flow rate; discharge (of water); delivery (of pump); consumption, input; span (of vise); **р. энергии** power consumption.

**расход/имость** *f.* divergence; **—иться** *v.* part, break up, go separate ways, diverge (of lines); differ (in opinion), disagree; radiate (of heat); drop away; be spent.

**расходник** *m.* (bot.) quillwort (*Isoetes*).

**расходн/ый** *a.* expense, expenditure; **р. бак** service tank; **—ое отверстие** delivery outlet (of pump, etc.).

**расходов/ание** *n.* expenditure, consumption; **—ать** *v.* spend, consume, use up.

**расходомер** *m.* flow meter, meter; **—ный** *a.* flow-measuring.

**расходящийся** *a.* divergent, diverging.

**расхождение** *n.* divergence, separation, coming apart, gaping (of joints), space; deviation, disagreement, discrepancy.

**расхолаживание** *n.* shut-down cooling (of reactor).

**расцве/сти, —тать** *v.* bloom, open, come into flower; **—т** *m.,* **—тание** *n.* bloom, blossoming, opening.

**расцве/тить, —чивать** *v.* tint, tone; **—тка** *f.* tinting, toning, coloring, shading; tint, hue; **—чение, —чивание** *n.* tinting, coloring.

**расцен/ивание** *n.* estimation, evaluation, appraisal; **—ивать, —ить** *v.* estimate, evaluate, appraise, value; assess, tariff; **—ка** *f.* estimation, estimate, quotation, evaluation, appraisal; tariff; cost sheet; **—ок** *m.* rate of wages; **—очный** *a.* valuation; **—очная ведомость** cost sheet; **—щик** *m.* assessor.

**расцеп, —итель** *m.,* **—ляющее приспособление** trip, release; **—ить, —лять** *v.* unhook, unlink, uncouple, disconnect, shut off; trip, release, disengage, throw out (clutch); **—ка** *f.* release, release catch; **—ление** *n.* unhooking, unlinking, uncoupling, disconnecting, release; **механизм —ления** release gear; **—ленный** *a.* unhooked, disconnected, disengaged, out of gear; **—ляющий** *a.* disconnecting, disengaging, releasing; **—ляющий механизм** releasing mechanism, trip mechanism; —ной *a*. detachable, disengageable.

расчал/ивать, —ить *v*. brace, guy; —ка *f*. bracing, (aero.) bracing wire; tension member.

расчекан/ивать, —ить *v*. calk, tighten (seam); —ка *f*. calking.

расчер/тить, —чивать *v*. trace, line, delineate.

расчес/анный *a*. combed; carded (flax); —ать *see* расчесывать; —ка *f*. comb.

расчесть *see* рассчитывать.

расчесыв/ание *n*. combing; carding, hackling (of flax); —ать *v*. comb; card, hackle; scratch, scratch up (the skin).

расчет *m*. calculation, computation, estimation, estimate; sizing (of equipment); account, reckoning; design; economy, saving; dismissal (from work); р. мощности capacity rating; входить в р. *v*. be taken into consideration; не принимаемый в р. negligible; нет —а it is not worth; по моему —у to my mind, in my estimation; принять в р. *v*. take into consideration, take into account, allow (for).

расчетлив/ость *f*. economy, thrift; —ый *a*. economical, careful, calculating.

расчетн/ый *a*. calculating, calculated, estimated, rated (capacity); pay (day); р. пролет effective span; —ая величина (elec.) rating; —ая длина gage length (of sample); —ая мощность nominal output, rated output.

расчетчик *m*. calculator, estimator; designer.

расчисл/ение *n*. calculation, computation, reckoning; —ить, —ять *v*. calculate, compute, reckon, figure out.

расчист/ить *see* расчищать; —ка *f*. clearing, eradication.

расчит/ать, —ывать *v*. calculate, compute; rate (at).

расчищ/ать *v*. clear, clear away, free from obstruction; —ение *n*. clearing; —енный *a*. cleared, freed, open.

расчлен/ение *n*. separation, disjunction, breaking up, disintegration; dissection; (math.) differentiation; —енный *a*. separated, disjointed; dissected; —ить, —ять *v*. separate, break up;

disarticulate, dismember, disjoint; analyze, dissect.

расшат/анность *f*. shakiness, instability; —анный *a*. loose, shaky, unstable, rickety; —ать, —ывать *v*. shake loose, loosen; shatter, upset (nerves); —аться, —ываться *v*. get loosened, get loose; go to pieces; —ывание *n*. loosening.

расшив/ать *v*. (masonry) point; —ка *f*. pointing; bracing.

расширен/ие *n*. expansion, widening, broadening, dilation, spreading, extension, elongation; enlargement, amplification, development; dilatation (of the heart); коэффициент —ия coefficient of expansion; машина с —ием пара expansion engine; —ный *a*. expanded, widened, dilated, enlarged; extensive.

расширитель *m*. dilator, widener, expander, extender; (elec.) expander; reamer; bead tool (for wood turning).

расширительн/ый *a*. expanding, widening, broadening; expansion (tank); р. болт expansion bolt; р. вентиль expansion valve; —ая трубка extension tube; —ое сопло expanding nozzle.

расшир/ить, —ять *v*. expand, widen, broaden, dilate, extend, elongate; enlarge, amplify; р. скважину ream; —яемость *f*. expansibility, extensibility, dilatability; —яемый *a*. expansible, extensible, expansive, dilatant, dilatable; —яющий *a*. expanding, dilating; reaming; —яющийся *a*. expansible, extensible, dilatable; expanding, spreading out.

расшифров/ать, —ывать *v*. decipher, decode, interpret; expand (abbreviation); —ка *f*. deciphering, interpretation.

расшлихтовка *f*. (text.) desizing.

расщел/иваться, —иться *v*. crack, split; —ина *f*. crack, split, chink, cleft, fissure, crevice, crevasse, interstice.

расщеп *m*. split, scissure, fissure; —итель *m*. (atom) smasher; —ить *see* расщеплять.

расщеплен/ие *n*. splitting, splitting up, fission, division, separation, resolution (into), parting, cleavage, cleaving, foliation, lamination, splintering; break-up, disintegration (of nucleus); (nucl.) spallation; (biol.) segmentation; **р. жира** lipolysis; **продукт —ия** cleavage product, fission product.

**расщепленно—** *prefix* schizo— (division, cleavage); **—ногие** *pl.* (zool.) Schizopoda.

**расщепл/енный** *a.* split, cleaved, cloven; **—яемость** *f.* cleavability, cleavage; fissionability; **—яемый** *a.* cleavable; fissionable; **—ять** *v.* split, split up, break down, decompose; slit, cleave, rend, fissure, crack, foliate, laminate; splinter, chip; **—яться** *v.* split, split up, break down, disintegrate; cleave, crack; splinter, shatter; **—яющийся** *a.* cleavable, scissile; fissionable; splintery (fracture).

**расщепывание** *see* **расщепление.**

**расщип/ать, —ывать** *v.* unravel, pick apart, shred.

**ратан/ин** *m.* rhatanin, angelin; **—ия** *f.* (bot.) rhatany (*Krameria triandra*); **—овая кислота** rhatanic acid, krameric acid; **—одубильная кислота** rhatania-tannic acid, kramerio-tannic acid.

**ратин** *m.* (text.) ratteen.

**ратит** *m.* (min.) rathite.

**ратифи/кация** *f.* ratification; **—цировать** *v.* ratify, validate.

**ратовкит** *m.* (min.) ratofkite (a fluorite).

**раувит** *m.* (min.) rauvite.

**раувольфия** *f.* (bot.) Rauwolfia.

**Рауля закон** Raoult's law.

**рафан/ин** *m.* raphanin; **—ол** *m.* raphanol.

**рафаэлит** *m.* (min.) rafaelite (a vanadiferous asphaltum).

**рафинад** *m.* refined (lump) sugar.

**рафинадный** *a.* refining; **р. завод** refinery.

**рафиназа** *f.* raffinase.

**рафин/ация** *see* **рафинирование; —ер** *m.* refiner; (paper) refiner, perfecting machine.

**рафиниров/альщик** *m.* refiner; **—ание** *n.*, **—ка** *f.* refining, purification; **—анный** *a.* refined, purified; **—ать** *v.* refine, purify; make refined lump sugar; **—очный** *a.* refining; **—очный завод** refinery.

**рафиноза** *f.* raffinose, melitose.

**рафия** *f.* (bot.) raffia palm (*Raphia ruffia*).

**раффинат** *m.* (solvent extraction) raffinate.

**раффинирование** *see* **рафинирование.**

**раффлез/иевые** *pl.* (bot.) Rafflesiaceae; **—ия** *f.* patma-wort (*Rafflesia arnoldi*).

**рахит, —изм** *m.* (med.) rickets; **—ик** *m.* sufferer from rickets; rickets patient; **—ический** *a.* rachitic, rickets.

**рацем/изация** *f.*, **—изирование** *n.* racemization; **—ический** *a.* racemic; **—ическая кислота** racemic acid, paratartaric acid; **—ия** *f.* racemism.

**рацион** *m.* ration, allowance.

**рационализ/атор** *m.* innovator; **—аторский** *a.* efficiency; **—аторское предложение** innovation; **—ация** *f.* rationalization; industrial efficiency; **—ировать** *v.* rationalize; innovate.

**рациональн/ость** *f.* rationality, reasonableness; efficiency; **—ый** *a.* rational, reasonable; efficient, expedient; **—ая формула** rational formula; **—ое число** rational number.

**рация** *f.* radio station.

**рачий** *a.* crayfish.

**рачка** *f.* ratchet, click; ratchet drill; **сверлильная р.** ratchet drill.

**рачь/и глаза, р. жерновки** *see* **раковые глазки; —я шейка** (bot.) snakeweed (*Polygonum bistorta*).

**Рашига кольца** Raschig (packing) rings.

**рашкуль** *m.* charcoal pencil.

**рашпиль** *m.* rasp, rasp file; grater.

**ращение квасцов** roching (crystallization) of alum.

**рвал** *past sing. of* **рвать.**

**рван/ина** *f.* fissure, crack, flaw; scab; **—уть** *v.* draw, pull, jerk; **—ь** *f.* rags; (tech.) clamp; **—ый** *a.* ragged, broken.

**рват/ель** *m.* (min.) core lifter, core extractor; **—ь** *v.* tear, lacerate; sever; pull, pick, gather; vomit; **—ься** *v.* tear, wear out; break, snap, burst.

**рвет** *pr. 3 sing. of* **рвать.**

**рвота** *f.* vomiting; (met.) flaw.

**рвотн/ый** *a.* emetic; **р. камень** tartar emetic, antimonyl potassium tartrate; **р. корень** ipecac root, ipecacuanha; **р. орех** nux vomica (seeds of *Strychnos nux-vomica*); **—ое зелье** (bot.) Indian

tobacco (*Lobelia inflata*); —ое средство emetic.

**рву/т** *pr. 3 pl. of* **рвать;** —**щий** *a.*
tearing; breaking (stress).

**РГА** *abbr.* (реакция гемагглютинации)
hemagglutination reaction.

**рд** *abbr.* (резерфорд) rutherford; **РД**
*abbr.* (ракетный двигатель) rocket
engine.

**рде/лый** *a.* red; —**ние** *n.* redness, glow.

**рдест,** —**ник** *m.* pond weed (*Potamo-
geton*); —**овые** *pl.* Zannichel-
liaceae.

**рде/ть,** —**ться** *v.* redden, glow; —**ющий**
*a.* glowing.

**ре** *n.* rhe (unit of viscosity).

**ре—** *prefix* re—, back, again.

**реабилит/ация** *f.* rehabilitation; —**ировать** *v.* rehabilitate.

**реагенин** *m.* rhoeagenine.

**реагент** *m.* reagent.

**реагир/ование** *n.* reacting, reaction;
**скорость** —**ования** responsiveness
(of instruments); —**ованный** *a.* reacted; —**овать** *v.* react; respond;
—**ующий** *a.* reacting, reactive; responsive (to); **быстро** —**ующий** sensitive; **не** —**ующий** non-reacting, non-
reactive.

**реад/ин** *m.* rhoeadine; —**овая кислота**
rhoeadic acid, papaveric acid.

**реактан/с,** —**ц** *m.* (elec.) reactance.

**реактив** *m.* reagent, agent; **р. на группу**
group reagent; agent;—**ация** *f.* reactivation; —**ность** *f.* reactivity; (elec.)
reactance.

**реактивн/ый** *a.* reactive, reaction, reagent; (aero.) jet; (elec.) reactive; **р.
раствор** reagent solution; **р. ток**
(elec.) reactive current; **р. цилиндр,**
—**ая трубка** test tube; —**ая бумага**
reagent paper, test paper; —**ая
катушка** (elec.) reactor, reactance
coil, choking coil, inductance coil;
—**ая сила** jet power; —**ая склянка**
reagent bottle; —**ая турбина** reaction
turbine; —**ое напряжение** (elec.)
reactive voltage; —**ое сопротивление**
(elec.) reactance, reactive resistance;
—**ое средство** reagent.

**реактиметр** *m.* reactimeter (reactivity
meter).

**реактор** *m.,* —**ный** *a.* reaction vessel;

(nucl.) reactor; (elec.) reactor, reactance coil; **р. на тепловых нейтронах,
тепловой р.** thermal reactor; **р.-
двигатель** *m.* propulsion reactor;
**р.-конвертер** *m.* converter; **р.-размно-
житель** *m.* breeder; —**остроение** *n.*
reactor engineering, reactor construction.

**реакционн/оспособность** *f.,* —**ая способность** reactivity; —**оспособный**
*a.* reactive; —**ый** *a.* reaction; *see also*
**реактивный.**

**реакц/ия** *f.* reaction; (instruments) response; (elec.) reactance; **р. на реакцию для; р. на крахмал** starch reaction; **р. почвы** soil reaction, pH;
**интенсивность** —**ии, скорость** —**ии**
rate of reaction, reaction rate; **конец**
—**ии** end point; **подвергнуть** —**ии**
*v.* react; **полоса** —**ии** period of
reaction; reaction zone; **продукты**
—**ии** reaction products; **сильная р.**
vigorous reaction.

**реал** *m.* (typ.) composing frame, rack.

**реализ/ация** *f.* realization; —**ировать,**
—**овать** *v.* realize.

**реалист** *m.* realist; —**ический** *a.* realistic.

**реальгар** *m.* (min.) realgar.

**реальн/ость** *f.* reality; —**ый** *a.* real,
tangible, concrete; workable, practicable.

**реаэрация** *f.* reaeration.

**ребенок** *m.* child, infant.

**реберный** *a.* rib, costal.

**реборда** *f.* flange, collar rim (of pulley).

**ребристо/призматический** *a.* angular-
prismatic; —**сть** *f.* ribbing; —**тубу-
лярный** *a.* fin-tube (heater, heat-
exchanger).

**ребрист/ый** *a.* ribbed, costate, costal;
finned, corrugated; (geol.) mullion,
rodding (structure); **р. нагреватель**
radiator; **р. охладитель** fin cooler;
—**ая труба** grilled tube.

**ребр/о** *n.* rib, fin; edge, verge; (geol.)
riffle; **краевое р.** (pal.) marginal frill;
—**а** *pl.* ribbing; **р.-спица** spoke-rib;
—**ом** edgewise; **обмотка** —**ом** (elec.)
edgewise winding; **поставить** —**ом**
*v.* stand edgewise, up-edge; **поставить вопрос** —**ом** *v.* ask a direct
question; **ложные** —**а** (anat.) false
ribs; **нижние** —**а** (anat.) short ribs.

**ребровик** *m.* rebrovik (vertical shale bedrock underneath a placer).

**рев** *m.* howling.

**ревдинскит** *m.* (min.) revdinskite (a nickel silicate).

**ревен/ный** *a.* rhubarb; —**одубильная кислота** rhubarb tannin, rheotannic acid.

**ревень** *m.* (bot.) rhubarb (*Rheum*); **овощной р., понтический р., черенковый р.** rhapontic rhubarb (*R. rhaponticum*).

**ревербер** *m.* reverberator; reverberatory furnace; reflecting lamp; —**ационный** *a.*, —**ация** *f.* reverberation; —**ировать** *v.* reverberate; —**ный** *a.* reverberatory (furnace); —**ометр** *m.* reverberometer.

**реверс** *m.* reverse, reversing gear; (elec.) reverser; rundown (of nuclear reactor); —**ер** *see* **реверсор.**

**реверсивн/ость** *f.* reversibility; —**ый** *a.* reversing, reversible; —**ый клапан** reversing valve; —**ый механизм** reversing gear; —**ая коробка** reversing gear box, return gear box; —**ая муфта,** —**ая фрикционная муфта** reversing clutch.

**реверс/ирование** *n.* reversing, reversal, reversion; —**ированный** *a.* reversed; —**ировать,** —**овать** *v.* reverse; —**ируемость** *f.* reversibility; —**ируемый** *a.* reversible; —**ирующий** *a.* reversing, reverse; —**ирующее приспособление,** —**ор** *m.* reverser; —**ия** *f.* reversion, throwback; reversal (of direction).

**ревертекс** *m.* Revertex (concentrated latex).

**ревивиф/айер** *m.* revivifier; - **-икация** *f.* revivification, reactivation.

**ревиз/ионный** *a.* revisionary, revisory; —**ия** *f.* revision, examination, inspection; census (of population); —**овать** *v.* examine, inspect, audit; test; —**ор** *m.* inspector, auditor.

**ревмат/изм** *m.* (med.) rheumatism; —**ик** *m.,* —**ический** *a.* rheumatic.

**револьвер** *m.* revolver; (micros.) nosepiece.

**револьверно-токарный автомат** automatic turret lathe; **р.-т. станок** turret lathe, capstan lathe.

**револьверн/ый** *a.* revolving; revolver; **р. станок** turret lathe; —**ая головка** turret, capstan (of lathe); monitor.

**революц/ионизировать** *v.* revolutionize; —**ионный** *a.* revolutionary; —**ия** *f.* revolution.

**регенерат** *m.* reclaim, reclaimed rubber; —**ивный** *a.* regenerative, regeneration; —**ивная печь** regenerative furnace; —**ор** *m.* regenerator.

**регенер/ация** *f.,* —**ирование** *n.* regeneration, recovery; reclaiming (of rubber); reprocessing (of fuel); revivification, reactivation; —**ированный** *a.* regenerated, recovered, restored; reclaimed; —**ировать** *v.* regenerate, recover, restore; reclaim; reprocess.

**региональный** *a.* regional, district; local (anesthetic).

**регистр** *m.,* —**овой** *a.* register, list; damper; —**атор** *m.* registrar, recorder; recording system; (nucl.) monitor; —**атура** *f.* registry, registration office; —**ационный** *a.,* —**ация** *f.,* —**ирование** *n.* registration, recording, record; **карта** —**ации** recording chart; —**ировать** *v.* register, record, file; —**ирующий,** —**ующий** *a.* registering, recording; graphic; —**ирующий прибор** recorder, self-recording device.

**регламент** *m.* regulation, rule, order, standing order; **согласно** —**у** in order; —**ация** *f.* regulation; —**ированный** *a.* regulated; —**ировать** *v.* regulate.

**реголит** *m.* (geol.) regolith.

**реградировать** *v.* regrade.

**регресс** *m.* regress, regression, return, retrogression, retrogradation; (astron.) regression; —**ивный** *a.* regressive, retrograde; —**ировать** *v.* regress, retrogress, turn back; —**ия** *f.* regression.

**регулиров/ание** *n.,* —**ка** *f.* regulation, control, governing; arrangement, setting, adjustment, tuning (of engine); **р. изменением концентрации** concentration control; —**ка механизма** gear adjustment; —**анный** *a.* regulated, adjusted; —**ать** *v.* regulate, control, govern, gage; set, adjust, tune.

**регулировочн/ый** *a.* regulating, adjusting; *see also* **регулирующий**; **р. винт** regulating screw; **р. реостат** (elec.) rheostatic controller; **—ое сопротивление** (elec.) regulating resistance; rheostat, regulator.

**регулируемый** *a.* regulatable, adjustable; regulated, controlled.

**регулирующ/ий** *a.* regulating, regulator, controlling, control, governing, adjusting; **р. болт** adjuster bolt; **р. клапан** regulator valve, throttle valve, throttle; **р. стержень** regulating rod (of nuclear reactor); **—ее приспособление** control device, adjustment device, adjuster; governor; **—ийся** *a.* adjustable; controlled (by); **—ийся упор** adjustable stop.

**регулус** *m.* (met.) regulus.

**регулы** *pl.* (physiol.) menses, menstruation.

**регулярн/о** *adv.* regularly; **—ость** *f.* regularity, order; **—ый** *a.* regular, routine.

**регулятор** *m.*, **—ный** *a.* regulator, controller; adjuster; governor (of steam engine); **шаровой р.** ball governor.

**регуляционное окно** (min.) window for control of ventilation.

**ред.** *abbr.* (редактор) editor; (редакция) editorial office.

**редак/тировать** *v.* edit, revise; **—тор** *m.* editor; **—тор-издатель** *m.* publisher; **главный —тор** editor-in-chief; **—торский**, **—ционный** *a.* editorial; **—ция** *f.* editorial office; editorship; editing.

**реддингит** *m.* (min.) reddingite.

**редечный** *a.* radish.

**редингтонит** *m.* (min.) redingtonite (a hydrous chromium sulfate).

**редис** *m.*, **—ка** *f.* garden radish (*Raphanus sativus* var. *radicula*).

**редистилляция** *f.* redistillation, rerun.

**редк/ий** *a.* rare, uncommon, infrequent, scarce, sparse; drift (ice); loosely woven (cloth); **—ая вещь** curiosity, rarity; **—ие земли** rare earths.

**редко** *adv.* rarely, seldom; **—ватый** *a.* rather rare; **—зазубренный** *a.* (bot.) remotely serrate; **—земельный** *a.* rare-earth; **—лесье** *n.* thin forest; **—сть** *f.* rarity, rareness, infrequency.

**реднин/а** *f.*, **—ный** *a.* sack canvas, burlap.

**редокс** *m.* redox, reduction-oxidation; (geol.) redox potential.

**редрутит** *m.* (min.) redruthite, chalcocite, copper glance.

**редуктаза** *f.* reductase (reducing enzyme).

**редукто—** *prefix* reducto—.

**редуктор** *m.* reducer, reducing agent; reductor (apparatus); (mech.) reducer; reducing gear; reducing valve; decelerator (of motor); **р.-трансформатор** (elec.) step-down transformer.

**редукци/онный** *a.*, **—я** *f.* reduction, reducing; **р. вентиль**, **р. клапан** reducer, reducing valve, pressure regulator.

**редуцир/ование** *n.* reduction; **—ованный** *a.* reduced; vestigial (structure); **—овать** *v.* reduce; **—ующий** *a.* reducing; **—ующий фермент** reductase; **—ующая способность** reducing power.

**редька** *f.* (bot.) radish (*Raphanus*); **дикая р.**, **полевая р.** jointed charlock (*R. raphanistrum*).

**редюсинг** *m.* reducing.

**реестр** *m.* register, list, catalog, record.

**реет** *pr. 3 sing. of* **реять**.

**реечн/ый** *a.* rack; **р. классификатор** (ore concentration) rake classifier; **р. стан** *see* **протяжной станок**; **—ая передача** rack and pinion, rack and pinion gear.

**режектор** *m.* rejector.

**режет** *pr. 3 sing. of* **резать**.

**режим** *m.* regime, system, practice, method, process; regulation, management, handling; normal operation, regular running; behavior; mode (of operation); (operating) conditions; cycle; rate; schedule; (med.) regimen, diet; **р. запуска** start-up conditions; **р. при заряде** charging load; **р. работы** routine, procedure; operating conditions; (mach.) performance, duty; **с легким —ом** light-duty; **работа в критическом —е** critical operation (*good example of absorbed meaning*).

**режуха** *see* **резуха**.

**режут** *pr. 3 pl. of* **резать**.

режущ/ий *a.* cutting; **р. инструмент** cutting tool, cutter; **—ая кромка, —ее ребро** cutting edge, tool edge, blade; lip (of drill); **хорошо р.** keen.

ре/жьте *imp. of* **резать**; **—з** *m.* cut.

резазурин *m.* resazurin, diazoresorcinol.

рез/ак *m.* cutter, chopper, chopping knife; plowshare, colter; lip (of scoop shovel); torch, cutting torch; (bot.) falcaria; sedge (*Carex gracilis*); prionitis; **—алка** *f.* cutter.

рез/альгин *m.* resalgin, antipyreticin; **—альдол** *m.* resaldol.

рез/альная машина cutting machine, guillotine; **—анец** *see* **шнит-лук**; **—ание** *n.* cutting; **—ан(н)ый** *a.* cut; **—ать** *v.* cut, slice, slit; slaughter, butcher; **—ать по меди** engrave on copper.

резацетофенон *m.* resacetophenone, 2,4-dihydroxyacetophenone.

резачок *m.* bit, point, tip.

резбаниит *m.* (min.) rezbanyite.

резед/а *f.* (bot.) mignonette (*Reseda*); **душистая р.** mignonette (*R. odorata*); **желтоватая р., —акрасильная церва** weld (*R. luteola*); **—овые** *pl.* Resedaceae; **—овый** *a.* mignonette, resedaceous.

резен *m.* resene.

резерв *m.* reserve; (calico) resist, reserve; drainage canal; dump hole; **—ы** *pl.* reserves; **—аж** *m.* (calico; cer.) reserving; **—ация** *f.*, **—ирование** *n.* reservation; **—ный** *a.* reserve, spare, standby, emergency, subsidiary; **—ная установка** emergency service.

резервуар *m.*, **—ный** *a.* reservoir, receiver, receptacle, container, basin, cistern, tank, vessel, well; **р.-хранилище** *n.* storage tank; **емкость —а** tankage.

резерпин *m.* reserpine.

резерфорд *m.* (nucl.) rutherford (unit of decay rate); **—ин, —ит** *m.* rutherfordite (uranium mineral); **—овский** *a.* Rutherford.

резец *m.* cutter, cutting tool; knife, draw knife, blade, chisel; (drill) bit; colter (of plow); tool; incisor (front tooth).

резиден/т *m.* resident; **—ция** *f.* residence.

резильянс *m.* resilience.

резина *f.* (cured) rubber; elastic, rubber band; **искусственная р.** synthetic rubber.

резин/амин *m.* resinamine; **—ат** *m.* resinate; **—ен** *m.* resinene; **—еон** *m.* resineon; **—ирование** *n.* (wine) treatment with resin; **—ит** *m.* (min.) resinite, pitch stone; a synthetic Thiokol rubber.

резинка *f.* elastic, rubber band; eraser.

резинов/ый *a.* rubber; **р. клей** rubber cement; **р. рукав, р. шланг** rubber hose; **—ая прокладка** rubber lining, rubber gasket; **—ая трубка** rubber tubing; **—ое дерево** *see* **каучуковое дерево.**

резино/ид *m.* resinoid; **—л** *m.* resinol; **—ловая кислота** resinolic acid.

резиносмеситель *m.* rubber mixer.

резинотаннол *m.* resinotannol.

резинщик *m.* worker in rubber industry, rubber technician.

резиньяция *f.* resignation.

резист/ер, **—ор** *m.* (elec.) resistor, resistance; **—ивность** *f.* (elec.) resistivity, specific resistance; **—ивный** *a.* resistive, resistance; **—ивная катушка** (elec.) resistance coil; **—ин** *m.* a copper-manganese-iron alloy; **—омицин** *m.* resistomycin.

резит *m.* resite, C-stage resin.

резка *f.* cutting, cutting off, severing, severance, clipping.

резк/ий *a.* abrupt, sudden; brisk; hard; shrill, sharp, piercing (sound); pungent, acrid; **—о** *adv.* sharply, abruptly; clearly (defined); **—ость** *f.* sharpness, abruptness; definition; shrillness.

резн/ой *a.* cut, carved, fretted; **—ая работа** carving; **—я** *f.* slaughter, butchery.

резо— *prefix* reso— (resorcinol); **—л** *m.* resol, A-stage resin.

резольвент/а *f.*, **—ный** *a.* resolvent.

резольн/ый *a.* resol; **—ые смолы** resols.

резолюция *f.* resolution, decision.

резон/анс *m.* (acous.) resonance; **—сный** *a.* resonant; resonance; **—атор** *m.* resonator; **—аторного типа** cavity-type (accelerator); **—ировать** *v.* resonate; **—ирующий** *a.* resonating, resonant.

резонный *a.* reasonable, rational, sensible.

**резорб/тивный** *a.* resorptive; **—ция** *f.* resorption.

**резоруфин** *m.* resorufin, oxyphenazone.

**резорб/тивный** *a.* resorptive; **—ция** *f.* resorption.

**резоруфин** *m.* resorufin, oxyphenazone.

**резорцил** *m.* resorcyl; **—альгин** *m.* resorcylalgin, antipyrine resorcylate.

**резорцилово/бензиловый эфир** benzyl resorcylate; **—кислый** *a.* resorcylic acid; resorcylate (of); **—кислая соль** resorcylate.

**резорцилов/ый** *a.* resorcyl; **—ая кислота** resorcylic acid, dihydroxybenzoic acid; **соль —ой кислоты** resorcylate.

**резорцин** *m.*, **—овый** *a.*, **—ол** *m.* resorcin, resorcinol, 3-hydroxyphenol; **—изм** *m.* resorcin poisoning; **—овый голубой** resorcin blue (microchemical stain).

**резорцит,** **—ол** *m.* resorcitol, 1,3-quinitol.

**резо/флавин** *m.* resoflavin (dye); **—цианин** *m.* resocyanine.

**результат** *m.* result, consequence, outcome, effect; yield; product; corollary; (foregone) conclusion; **—ом этого было** the result was (that); **в —е** as a result, in consequence; **иметь —ом** *v.* result (in), give rise (to); **—ный** *a.* resulting, resultant.

**результирующий** *a.* resulting, resultant; net (efficiency, transport, leakage, etc.).

**резу/ха** *f.* (bot.) rock cress (*Arabis*); **—шка** *f.* a cress (*Arabidopsis*).

**резце—** *prefix* cutter, tool; **—державка** *f.*, **—держатель** *m.* cutter holder, tool holder, tool clamp, tool block; tool box.

**резцов/ый** *a.* tool, cutter; **—ая коробка** tool box.

**резче** *compr. of* **резкий, резко**; sharper; more sharply.

**резчик** *m.* cutter, engraver, carver.

**резь** *f.* (med.) colic.

**резьб/а** *f.* carving, engraving; thread (of screw); **нарезать —у** *v.* thread.

**резьбов/ой** *a.* thread, threading, threaded; **р. гребец, р. резец, —ая гребенка** threading tool, thread cutter, thread chaser, chasing tool; **р. калибр** thread gage; **р. фрезер** thread-milling cutter; **—ые часы** thread indicator.

**резьбо/мер** *m.* thread gage, screw pitch gage; **—накатный станок** thread-generating machine; **—нарезной станок** screw-cutting machine, screw-cutting lathe; **—указатель** *m.* thread indicator; **—фрезерный станок** thread-milling machine; **—шлифовальный станок** thread-grinding machine.

**резюм/е** *n.* résumé, summary; **—ировать** *v.* summarize, sum up.

**реин** *m.*, **—овая кислота** rhein, rheic acid; **—овый** *a.* rhein, rheic; **—оловая кислота** rheinolic acid.

**рейб/ал,** **—ол,** **—ор** *m.* reamer, broach.

**рейд** *m.* raid; (naut.) roadstead, road.

**рейдер** *m.* rider.

**рейк/а** *f.* rod, lath, batten, cleat; edging; straightedge, rule; (mach.) rack; **мерная р.** surveying rod; **передача зубчатой —ой** rack and pinion, rack and pinion gear; **скреплять —ами** *v.* batten; **—онарезной станок** rack-cutting machine.

**Реймера-Тимана реакция** Reimer-Tiemann reaction.

**Рейн** the Rhine.

**Рейнеке соль** Reinecke salt, ammonium tetrathiocyanodiammonochromate.

**рейнит** *m.* (min.) reinite (probably a pseudomorph after scheelite).

**Рейнольдса число** Reynolds number.

**рейнский** *a.* Rhine, Rhenish.

**рейс** *m.* passage, voyage.

**Рейса микрофон** Reis microphone.

**рейсм/ас,** **—ус** *m.* scribing block, surface gage; marking gage; shifting gage.

**рейссит** *m.* (min.) reissite (a variety of apistilbite).

**рейс/федер** *m.* drawing pen, pen; pencil holder; **—шина** *f.* T-square.

**рейтер** *m.* rider (of analytical balance).

**рейхардит** *m.* (min.) reichardite (a variety of epsomite).

**рейхблей** *m.* rich (argentiferous) lead.

**Рейхерт-Мейссля число** (butter analysis) Reichert-Meissl number.

**рейхс—** *prefix* Reichs—.

**рек/а** *f.* river, stream; **р.-захватчик** pirate river; **вверх по —е** upstream.

**рекалесценция** *f.* (met.) recalescence.

**рекапитуляция** *f.* (biol.) recapitulation.

**рекарбюриз/атор** *m.* (met.) recarburizer,

recarbonizer; —ация *f.* recarburiza-tion, recarbonization; —ировать *v.* recarburize, recarbonize.

реквиз/ировать *v.*, —иция *f.*, —ицион-ный *a.* requisition.

реклам/а *f.* advertisement; publicity; —ация *f.* reclamation, protest, com-plaint; claim; —ировать *v.* advertise; make a claim; —ный *a.* advertising; publicity; —одатель *m.* advertiser.

рекогносцировка *f.* reconnaissance, re-connoitering, preliminary survey.

рекомбин/атор *m.* recombiner; —ацион-ный *a.*, —ация *f.* recombination; —ировать *v.* recombine.

рекоменд/ательный *a.* recommendation, recommending; —ация *f.* recommen-dation, introduction, reference; —о-ванный *a.* recommended, introduced; —овать *v.* recommend, introduce; —уемый *a.* tentative; —уется it is recommended, it is advisable.

реконстру/ировать *v.* reconstruct, re-build, remodel, renovate, restore, modernize; —ктивный *a.* reconstruc-tive; —кция *f.* reconstruction, restoration, rearrangement, modern-ization.

реконцентрация *f.* reconcentration.

рекорд *m.* record; —ер *m.* recorder; —ный *a.* record, record-breaking; —смен *m.* record holder.

рекреация *f.* recreation.

рекристаллизация *f.* recrystallization.

рекрут *m.* (mil.) recruit.

рекс *m.* Rex (abrasive).

рексит *m.* rhexite (a form of dynamite).

ректифи/кат *m.* rectified spirit; —катор *m.*, —кационный прибор rectifier; —кационный *a.* rectification; frac-tionating; —кационная колонна fractionating column; —кация *f.*, —цирование *n.* rectification, redis-tillation; fractionation, fractional dis-tillation; (geom.) rectification; —ко-ванный, —цированный *a.* rectified, redistilled; fractionated; —ковать, —цировать *v.* rectify, redistill, purify by repeated distillation; frac-tionate.

ректор *m.* rector, head (of university).

ректорит *m.* (min.) rectorite.

рекупер/ативный *a.* recuperative, regen-

erative; recovery; —атор *m.* recuper-ator, regenerator; recovery unit; —ация *f.* recuperation, regeneration; recovery; —ированный *a.* recuper-ated, regenerated, restored; re-covered; —ировать *v.* recuperate, regenerate, restore; recover.

рекуррентный *a.* recurrent, recurring.

релакс/ационный *a.*, —ация *f.* relaxa-tion; —ин *m.* relaxin (a hormone).

реле *n.* (elec.) relay; р. времени timer; р.-клопфер sounding relay, relaying sounder; р.-повторитель repeating relay; включающее р. relay switch.

релеевский *a.* Rayleigh (scattering, etc.).

релейн/ый *a.* relay; discontinuous-type; —ая защита relaying.

реликт *m.* relict; —овый *a.* relic, relict (structure); connate (waters); cliff (dwelling).

релит *m.* a tungsten carbide composi-tion.

релуктанц *m.* (elec.) reluctance.

рельеф *m.* relief, contour, raised work; topography; boss; форма —а topo-graphic form; —но *adv.* in relief; —ность *f.* relief; —ный *a.* relief, em-bossed, raised, prominent; —ная карта relief map.

рельс *m.* rail, track, runway.

рельсо— *prefix* rail; —балочный стан rail-structural mill; —балочный про-катный стан rail-rolling mill, rail mill.

рельсовый *a.* rail, track; р. калибр, р. ручей (rolling) rail pass; р. костыль rail spike; р. путь track; р. стык rail joint, rail bond.

рельсо/выпрямитель *m.* rail straighten-er; —гибочный пресс rail-bending press; —отделочный стан rail-finish-ing mill; —правильная машина rail-straightening machine; —прокатный стан rail mill, rail-rolling mill; —сверлильный станок rail-drilling machine.

релэ *see* реле.

релюктанц *see* релуктанц.

реляксатор *see* релаксатор.

релятив/изм *m.*, —ность *f.* relativity; —истский *a.* relativistic, relativity; —истское уравнение массы relativ-istic mass equation; —ный *a.* relative.

**ремалой** *m.* Remaloy (iron-molybdenum-cobalt alloy).

**реманентн/ость** *f.* (elec.) remanence, retentivity; —**ый** *a.* remanent.

**ременн/ый** *a.* belt, strap; leather; **р. привод,** —**ая передача** belt drive; **от** —**ого привода, с** —**ым приводом** belt-driven.

**ремень** *m.* belt, strap, leather band; **приводной р.** driving belt, belting.

**ремерит** *m.* (min.) roemerite.

**ремесленн/ик** *m.* workman, craftsman, artisan; —**ичество** *n.* workmanship; —**ый** *a.* trade, industrial; —**ое училище** trade school.

**ремесло** *n.* trade, craft, handicraft.

**ремесса** *f.* (com.) remittance.

**ремешок** *m.* little belt, strap.

**ремиджии кора** cuprea bark (of *Remijia* species).

**ремиз/а,** —**ка** *f.,* —**ный** *a.,* —**ная нить** (text.) heald, heddle.

**ремингтонит** *m.* (min.) remingtonite (a hydrated cobalt carbonate).

**реми/ссия** *f.* (com.; med.) remission; —**тировать** *v.* remit.

**ремне—** *prefix* belt; —**надеватель,** —**отводчик** *m.* belt shifter, shifting fork.

**ремнец** *m.* (zool.) ligula.

**ремнецветные** *pl.* (bot.) Loranthaceae.

**ремн/и** *pl. of* **ремень;** —**я** *gen. of* **ремень.**

**ремонт** *m.* repair, repair work, repairing, reconditioning; upkeep, maintenance; **р. и уход** care and maintenance; **в** —**е, при** —**е** under repair; **капитальный р.** overhaul; **текущий р.** maintenance; —**антный** *a.* perpetual; (bot.) everbearing, everblooming; —**ина** *f.* (min.) temporary supporting structure.

**ремонтиров/ание** *n.* repairing, repair, reconditioning, overhauling; —**ать** *v.* repair, recondition, overhaul, refit, remount; **капитально** —**ать** overhaul.

**ремонтн/ый** *a.* repair; **р. пункт,** —**ая станция** service station; **р. слесарь** repairman; **р. цех** repair shop.

**реморкер** *m.* hauling truck, truck.

**рему** *n.* (aero.) remou (local atmospheric disturbances).

**ренания-фосфат** *m.* Rhenania-phosphate.

**ренардит** *m.* renardite (uranium mineral).

**рендзина** *f.* rendzina (group of soils).

**рениев/ый** *a.* rhenium; **р. ангидрид** rhenium heptaoxide; —**ая кислота** rhenic acid; **соль** —**ой кислоты,** —**о-кислая соль** rhenate.

**рен/ий** *m.* rhenium, Re; **двуокись** —**ия** rhenium dioxide; **хлористый р.** rhenium chloride; —**истый ангидрид** rhenium trioxide.

**ренит** *m.* (min.) rhoenite.

**Ренкина** *see* **Ранкина.**

**ренклод** *m.* (bot.) greengage (kind of plum).

**ренн/аза** *f.,* —**ин** *m.* rennin, rennase.

**ренод** *m.* renode valve.

**реноме** *n.* fame, reputation, name.

**рента** *f.* rent; annuity.

**рентабельн/о** *adv.* profitably; **it is profitable, it is economical;** —**ость** *f.* profitableness, earning capacity; —**ый** *a.* profitable, commercial.

**рентген** *m.* roentgen (unit of X-ray radiation); **р. в ткане** tissue roentgen; **биологический эквивалент** —**а, биологический р.-эквивалент** roentgen equivalent, man (rem); **р.-кубический сантиметр** roentgens per cubic centimeter; **р.-эквивалент** *m.* roentgen equivalent; **физический р.-эквивалент** roentgen equivalent, physical (rep).

**Рентгена лучи** Roentgen rays, X-rays.

**рентгениз/ация** *f.* X-raying; —**ировать** *v.* X-ray; (med.) treat with X-rays.

**рентгенметр** *m.* roentgen meter.

**рентгено—** *prefix* Roentgen, X-ray; —**вский,** —**вый** *a.* roentgen, X-ray; —**вский анализ** roentgen-ray analysis, X-ray (diffraction) analysis; —**вский снимок,** —**грамма** roentgenogram, X-ray photograph; X-ray (diffraction) pattern; —**вские лучи** roentgen rays, X-rays; **подвергать действию** —**вских лучей** *v.* X-ray.

**рентгенограф** *m.* roentgenograph, X-ray photograph; —**ический** *a.* roentgenographic, X-ray diffraction; —**ическое исследование** (met.) X-ray examination; —**ия** *f.* roentgenography, X-ray radiography, X-ray diffraction analysis.

**рентгено/дефектоскопия** *f.* X-ray flaw detection; **—диагностика** *f.* X-ray diagnosis.

**рентгенолог/ический** *a.* roentgenologic, X-ray; **р. анализ** X-ray analysis; **—ия** *f.* roentgenology.

**рентгено/метр** *m.* roentgenometer; **—скоп** *m.* roentgenoscope, fluoroscope; **—скопия** *f.* roentgenoscopy, radioscopy, X-ray examination; **—снимок** *m.* roentgenogram, X-ray photograph; **—спектральный** *a.* X-ray spectral; **—структурный** *a.* X-ray diffraction; **—терапия** *f.* X-ray therapy; **—техник** *m.* X-ray technician; **—техника** *f.* X-ray technology.

**рентген-эквивалент** *see under* **рентген.**

**рео—** *prefix* rheo— (current; flow).

**реодорант** *m.* (rubber) reodorant.

**рео/дубильная кислота** rheotannic acid, rhubarb tannin; **—ид** *m.* rheoid; **—лавер** *m.*, **—мойка** *f.* (min.) rheolaveur; **—логия** *f.* rheology; **—метр** *m.* rheometer, flow meter.

**Реомюра термометр** Réaumur thermometer.

**реорганиз/ация** *f.* reorganization; **—о-вать** *v.* reorganize.

**рео/скоп** *m.* (elec.) rheoscope, current detector; **—сплав** *m.* high-resistivity alloy; **—стан** *m.* rheostan (alloy for rheostats).

**реостат** *m.* (elec.) rheostat; **р. возбуждения** field rheostat; **—ный** *a.* rheostat, rheostatic; **—ный пуск** rheostatic starter.

**рео/стрикция** *f.* (elec.) rheostriction, pinch effect; **—тан** *m.*, **—тановый** *a.* rheotan (copper-zinc-manganese alloy); **—том** *m.* (elec.) rheotome (current breaker); **—тропный** *a.* (biol.) rheotropic; **—хора** *m.* rheochord, slide wire; **—хризин** *m.* rheochrysin.

**репа** *f.* (bot.) turnip (*Brassica rapa*).

**репей** *m.*, **—ник** *m.*, **—ный** *a.* (bot.) bur; burdock (*Arctium lappa*); **—ник, —ничек** *m.* agrimony (*Agrimonia*); **—ница** *f.* a butterfly (*Pyrameis cardui*).

**репеллент** *m.* repellent.

**репер** *m.* reference point; (surv.) datum mark, datum point, bench mark; bench; **—ный** *a.* reference, reference

point; datum, bench; **—ный знак** bench mark; **—ная кривая** calibration curve; **—ная точка** reference point.

**репетировать** *v.* rehearse; tutor, coach.

**репешок** *see* **репейничек.**

**репка** *f.* carline thistle (*Carlina vulgaris*).

**репленишер** *m.* replenisher.

**реплика** *f.* (micros.) replica.

**репница** *f.* cabbage butterfly (*Pieris rapae*).

**репное масло** *see* **репсовое масло.**

**репорт/аж** *m.* reporting; **—ер** *m.* reporter, representative of the press.

**репперит** *m.* (min.) roepperite (a variety of tephroite).

**репрезент/ант** *m.*, **—ативный** *a.* representative.

**репресс/ивный** *a.* repressive; **—ия** *f.* repression.

**репроду/ктивный** *a.* reproductive; **—к-тор** *m.* reproducer; (rad.) loudspeaker; **—кция** *f.* reproduction; **—цент** *m.* reproducer; **—цировать** *v.* reproduce.

**репс** *m.* (text.) repp; (bot.) *see* **рапс.**

**репсов/ый** *a.* rape, rapeseed; **р. жмых** rapeseed cake; **—ое масло** rapeseed oil, rape oil, colza oil.

**рептилия** *f.* (zool.) reptile.

**репульпатор** *m.* (flotation) repulping machine.

**репульсионный** *a.* repulsion.

**репутация** *f.* reputation, name, character.

**репчатый** *a.* turnip-like.

**репяшок** *m.* weed (*Caucalis daucoides*).

**Рерига трубка** Röhrig tube (for fat extraction).

**ресивер** *m.* receiver.

**ресконтро** *n.* (com.) ledger.

**Реслера процесс** (met.) Roesler process.

**ресмус** *see* **рейсмус.**

**ресни/тчатый** *a.* (biol.) ciliate; (anat.) ciliary; **—ца** *f.* eyelash; (biol.) cilium.

**реснични/ые** *pl.* (zool.) Ciliophora; **—ый** *a.* eyelash, ciliary; (biol.) ciliate; **—ые черви** (zool.) Turbellaria.

**ресорб/ировать** *v.* resorb, reabsorb; **—ция** *f.* resorption, reabsorption.

**респектабельный** *a.* respectable.

**респира/тор** *m.* (med.) respirator, inhaler, mouthpiece; **—аторный** *a.* respiratory; **—ция** *f.* respiration.

**республика** *f.* republic, commonwealth.

**рессор/а** *f.*, **—ный** *a.* spring; **—ная державка** spring support.

**реставр/ация** *f.*, **—ирование** *n.* restoration, renovation; **—ированный** *a.* restored, renovated, repaired; **—ировать** *v.* restore, renovate, repair, mend.

**рестант** *m.* residue, remainder.

**реституция** *f.* (biol.) restitution, regeneration.

**ресторан** *m.* restaurant.

**ресургентный** *a.* resurgent.

**ресурс** *m.* resource.

**ретен** *m.* retene, methylisopropylphenanthrene.

**ретикул/ин** *m.* reticulin; **—иновый, —ярный** *a.* reticular, net-like.

**ретин/а** *f.* (anat.) retina; **—алит** *m.* (min.) retinalite (a variety of massive serpentine); **—ит** *m.* retinite (related to fossil amber); (med.) retinitis; **—ол** *m.* retinol, rosin oil; retinol, vitamin A.

**ретиров/аться** *v.* retreat, retire, withdraw; **—ка** *f.* withdrawal.

**ретовина** *f.* rot.

**реторт/а** *f.*, **—ный** *a.* retort; (met.) converter; **—ный уголь** retort carbon; **—ная печь** retort furnace; **—ообразный** *a.* retort-shaped; converter-shaped.

**ретрансляционный** *a.* relay.

**ретрансмиттер** *m.* retransmitter.

**ретро—** *prefix* retro— (back, backward; behind; retrograde); **—активность** *f.* retroaction; retroactivity; **—активный** *a.* retroactive; **—вакцина** *f.* (med.) retrovaccine; **—градация, — градность** *f.* retrogradation; **—градный** *a.* retrograde; **—грессивный** *a.* retrogressive.

**ретронецин** *m.* retronecine; **—овая кислота** retronecinic acid.

**ретроспек/тивный** *a.* retrospective; **— ция** *f.* retrospection.

**ретрофлексия** *f.* retroflexion.

**ретуш/ирование** *n.*, **—ь** *f.* retouching; **—ировать** *v.* retouch.

**реумэмодин** *m.* rheum-emodin.

**реутилизация** *f.* re-using.

**реф.** *abbr.* (**реферат**) abstract.

**рефер/ат** *m.* abstract; reference; paper, report; **—ендум** *m.* referendum; **— ент** *m.* reader, reviewer; **—енция** *f.* reference; **—ировать** *v.* read a paper; review.

**рефлек/с** *m.*, **—сный** *a.* reflex; **—сия** *f.* reflection, reflex action; **—тивный** *a.* reflective, reflex; **—тирующий** *a.* reflecting; **—тометр** *m.* reflectometer; **—тор** *m.* reflector, mirror; reverberator; (med.) speculum; **—торный** *a.* reflector; reflex.

**рефлюкс** *m.* (fractional distillation) reflux, bottoms.

**реформ/а** *f.* reform, amendment; **—ировать** *v.* reform, amend; **—ирующий** *a.* reformative, reforming; **—фосфат** *m.* reform phosphate, neutral phosphate.

**рефракс** *m.* refrax (refractory material).

**рефракт/ометр** *m.* (light) refractometer; **—ометрическая разница** refractivity intercept; **—ор** *m.* refractor; **—орный** *a.* refractor; refracting.

**рефракци/я** *f.*, **—онный** *a.* refraction.

**рефри/гератор, —жератор** *m.* refrigerator; condenser, cooler; **—жерация** *f.* refrigeration.

**рефулер** *m.*, **—ный насос** dredging pump, hydraulic dredge.

**рецбаниит** *see* **резбаниит**.

**реценз/ент** *m.* critic, reviewer; **—ировать** *v.* criticize, review; **—ия** *f.* review.

**рецеп/т** *m.* prescription; recipe; formula; **—тивный** *a.* receptive; **—тированный** *a.* formulated; **—тор** *m.* receptor, sense organ; **—тура** *f.* prescribing, filling out prescriptions; **—турщик** *m.* (rubber) compounder; **—ция** *f.* reception.

**рецессивный** *a.* (biol.) recessive.

**рецидив** *m.* relapse, setback.

**реципиент** *m.* recipient; receiver, reservoir, container.

**реципрокный** *a.* reciprocal.

**рециркул/ировать** *v.* recirculate, recycle; **—яция** *f.* recycling.

**речевой** *a.* speech; vocal.

**реч/ка** *f.* small river; **—никоватый песок** gold-bearing sand with a predominance of pebbles; **—ной** *a.* river, riverine, fluvial.

**реч/ь** *f.* speech, address; **органы —и** vocal organs.

**реш/ать** *v.* decide, determine, conclude, settle, fix; work out, solve (problem); **—аться** *v.* decide, determine, resolve, make up one's mind; **—ающий** *a.* decisive, determining, determinative, conclusive; **—ающий фактор** determinant.

**решен/ие** *n.* decision, determination, resolution; working, solution (of problem); pronouncement, judgment, verdict, vote; **—ный** *a.* determined; solved.

**решетина** *f.* lath.

**решетить** *v.* sift, sieve, riddle, screen, bolt.

**решетк/а** *f.* lattice; grating, grate, grill, grid; framework; checker, network; fencing; cascade; **постоянная —и** (cryst.) lattice constant; **—ообразный** *a.* lattice-like, lattice.

**решет/ник** *m.* lathing; **—ный** *a.,* **—о** *n.* screen, sieve; **—очный** *a.* screen; network.

**решетчат/ый** *a.* grate, grill, grid; screen; meshed; lattice, latticed; skeleton; (bot.) clathrate; **р. барабан** revolving screen; **р. колосник** grid bar, grid; **р. люк** grating; **р. столб** girder pole; **—ая балка,** **—ая ферма** lattice girder; **—ая жесть** perforated sheet; **—ая конструкция** lattice structure; latticework, lattice girder construction; framework; **—ая пластина** (elec.) grid plate; **—ая система** framework; **—ая структура** lattice structure, mesh structure.

**решимость** *f.* resoluteness, resolution.

**решительн/о** *adv.* resolutely, determinedly, absolutely; **—ость** *f.* resolution, determination, decision, decisiveness, firmness; **—ый** *a.* resolute, determined, decisive, resolved; categorical; deciding, crucial; drastic (measures).

**решить** *see* **решать.**

**решот/ка** *see* **решетка; —чатый** *see* **решетчатый.**

**решофер** *m.* preheater; reheater.

**рештак** *m.* (min.) chute, shoot; trough.

**реэкстра/гирование** *n.,* **—кция** *f.* re-extraction; **—гировать** *v.* re-extract.

**ре/ющий** *a.* soaring; rushing; **—ять** *v.* soar, hover; float, rush, be carried along; flow.

**ржа** *f.* rust; (agr.) smut.

**ржав/еть** *v.* rust, corrode; **—ление** *n.* rusting, corrosion; **—ленный** *a.* rusted, corroded; **—окрасный** *a.* rust-red, rusty-red; **—осерый** *a.* grey ferruginous (soil); **—ость** *f.* rustiness.

**ржавчин/а** *f.* rust; blight, rust, spec. wheat mildew (*Puccinia graminis*); **—ные грибы** rust fungi (*Uredinales*); **—оустойчивый** *a.* rust-resistant.

**ржавый** *a.* rusty, rusted, corroded.

**рж/аной** *a.* rye; **—и** *gen. of* **рожь.**

**РЖХим** *abbr.* (**Реферативный Журнал, Химия**) Chemical Abstract Journal.

**Р.З.** *abbr.* (**редкие земли**) rare earths.

**риас** *m.* (geol.) ria.

**рибекит** *m.* (min.) riebeckite.

**рибоз/а** *f.* ribose; **—офосфат** *m.* ribose phosphate.

**рибойлер** *m.* reboiler (of fractionating unit).

**рибо/новая кислота** ribonic acid; **—нуклеиновая кислота** ribonucleic acid, RNA; **—флавин** *m.* riboflavin, vitamin $B_2$.

**рибулозофосфат** *m.* ribulose phosphate.

**риванол** *m.* Rivanol, ethodin.

**ривотит** *m.* (min.) rivotite.

**Ривса процесс** Reeves process.

**рига** *f.* threshing barn, barn.

**ригель** *m.* cross bar, collar beam.

**ригидность** *f.* rigidity.

**риголен** *m.* rhigolene (most volatile fraction of petroleum).

**ригор/изм** *m.,* **—истичность** *f.* rigor, rigidity.

**ридберг** *m.* rydberg (spectroscopic unit).

**Ридберга постоянная** (nucl.) Rydberg constant.

**Риза процесс** (met.) Reese river process (of pan amalgamation).

**ризо—** *prefix* rhizo— (root); **—бацидин** *m.* rhizobacidin; **—ид** *m.* (bot.) rhizoid; **—карпиновая кислота** rhizocarpinic acid; **—карповая кислота** rhizocarpic acid; **—ктониоз** *m.,* **—ктония** *f.* rhizoctonia disease (of plants); **—мастигины** *pl.* (zool.) Rhizomastigina; **—ниновая кислота** rhizoninic acid; **—новая кислота** rhizonic acid;

—поды *pl.* (zool.) Rhizopoda; —холевая кислота rhizocholic acid.

**ризьюинг** *m.* (min.) resuing (method of stoping).

**риккардит** *m.* (min.) rickardite (a copper telluride).

**риккетс/ии** *pl.* Rickettsia (microorganisms); —иоз *m.* rickettsiosis, rickettsial disease.

**рикошет** *m.* ricochet, rebounding, rebound; **делать р.,** —**ировать** *v.* ricochet, rebound; —ом on the rebound; —ный *a.* rebounding.

**рилинг-машина** *f.* (text.) reeling machine.

**Рим** Rome.

**рима** *f.* tenter, stretcher.

**риманово пространство** (math.) Riemannian space, elliptic space.

**римоцидин** *m.* rimocidin.

**римск/ий** *a.* Roman; —ая свеча (pyrotechnics) Roman candle.

**ринантин** *m.* rhinantin.

**ринит** *m.* (med.) rhinitis.

**ринкит** *m.* (min.) rinkite.

**ринманов зеленый** Rinmann's green (cobalt zincate).

**риннеит** *m.* (min.) rinneite.

**рино—** *prefix* rhino— (nose); —**логия** *f.* (med.) rhinology; —**склерома** *f.* rhinoscleroma; —**скоп** *m.* rhinoscope.

**Ринхим** *abbr.* (**Российский институт прикладной химии**) Russian Institute of Applied Chemistry.

**ринхо/спориоз** *m.* rhynchosporium disease (of plants); —**цефал** *m.* (zool.) rhynchocephalian.

**риолит** *m.* rhyolite (an igneous rock); —**овый** *a.* rhyolite, rhyolitic.

**рипидолит** *m.* (min.) ripidolite.

**риппер** *m.* ripper.

**рис** *m.* (bot.) rice (*Oryza sativa*); **канадский р.** wild rice (*Zizania aquatica*).

**рис.** *abbr.* (**рисунок**) figure, illustration.

**рисайклинг** *m.* recycling.

**рисберма** *f.* (hydraulic engineering) apron.

**риск** *m.* risk, hazard.

**риска** *f.* graduation line; groove, channel.

**риск/нуть,** —**овать** *v.* risk, hazard, venture; —**ованность** *f.* riskiness; —**ованный** *a.* risky, hazardous.

**рисов/альный** *a.* drawing; —**альное**

—**перо** lettering pen; —**ание** *n.* drawing, designing; —**ать** *v.* draw, design; depict.

**рисо/видка** *f.* mountain rice (*Oryzopsis*); —**водство** *n.* rice growing; —**вые** *pl.* (bot.) Oryzeae; —**вый** *a.* rice; —**завод** *m.,* —**рушка** *f.* rice mill.

**рисский век** (geol.) Rissian stage.

**рисунок** *m.* drawing, illustration, figure, diagram; representation; cut; draft; sketch; design, pattern, markings.

**ритизма** *f.* tar spot (plant disease).

**ритм** *m.,* —**ика** *f.* rhythm; swinging; —**ический,** —**ичный** *a.* rhythmic; —**ично** *adv.* rhythmically; —**ичность** *f.* rhythmicality, evenness.

**ритрон** *m.* retron (a gamma-ray spectrometer).

**риттингерит** *m.* (min.) rittingerite (same as xanthoconite).

**Ритца уравнение** Ritz formula.

**риф** *m.* reef, ledge, shelf.

**рифайнер** *m.* (rubber) refiner.

**рифельная сталь** cutting steel.

**рифл/евать,** —**ить** *v.* channel, rib, groove, flute, corrugate, crimp; —**ение** *n.* channeling, grooving, fluting, corrugation; —**еный** *a.* channeled, grooved, fluted, corrugated, ribbed, riffled; checkered (metal plate); —**уар** *m.* riffle file, riffler; —**я** *f.* riffle, groove, flute; —**и** *pl.* fluting.

**рифо/вый** *a.* reef; —**генный** *a.* (geol.) of reef origin; —**образующий** *a.* reef-building.

**риформинг** *m.* (petroleum cracking) reforming.

**рифт** *m.* groove.

**рифтали** *pl.* reeftackle.

**рифтов/ать** *v.* groove, flute, corrugate, crimp; —**очный станок** riffling machine.

**Рихтера закон** Richter's law.

**рихтерит** *m.* (min.) richterite (a variety of amphibole).

**рихтовальн/ый** *a.* straightening; **р. станок, р. штамп** straightener; leveling machine; —**ая линейка** straightedge, ruler; —**ая плита** adjusting plate.

**рихтов/ать** *v.* straighten, level; dress; —**ка** *f.* straightening; —**очный** *see* **рихтовальный.**

**рицин** *m.* ricin; —**ат** *m.* ricinate, ricinoleate; —**ин** *m.* ricinine; —**иновая кислота** ricininic acid; —**овокислый** *see* **рициноловокислый.**

**рицинов/ый** *a.* ricin, ricinic; castor; —**ая кислота** *see* **рициноловая кислота;** —**ое масло** castor oil.

**рицинолев/ая кислота** ricinoleic acid, ricinic acid; **соль** —**ой кислоты,** —**окислая соль** ricinoleate; —**окислый** *a.* ricinoleic acid; ricinoleate (of); —**онатриевая соль** sodium ricinoleate.

**рицино/леин** *m.* ricinolein, glyceryl ricinoleate; —**ловая кислота** *see* **рициноловая кислота;** —**стеароловая кислота** ricinostearolic acid.

**рицинус** *m.* (bot.) castor plant (*Ricinus*); **семена** —**а** castor oil beans.

**рицинэлаидин** *m.* ricinelaidin; —**овая кислота** ricinelaidic acid.

**рицовка** *f.* scored line (to facilitate bending).

**Рича теорема** Reech's theorem.

**ричардсоновый голубой** Richardson blue.

**ричмондские слои** (geol.) Richmond subdivision.

**Рише газ** Riché gas (from wood distillation).

**ришеллит** *m.* (min.) richellite.

**ришта** *f.* parasitic worm (*Filaria medinensis*).

**РИЯИ** *abbr.* (**радиоактивные изотопы и ядерные излучения**) radioactive isotopes and nuclear radiations.

**р-н** *abbr.* (**район**) area, region.

**РНК** *abbr.* (**рибонуклеиновая кислота**) ribonucleic acid.

**РНР** *abbr.* (**Румынская Народная Республика**) Rumanian People's Republic.

**робин** *m.* robin (from bark of *Robinia pseudacacia*); —**ин** *m.* robinin; —**оза** *f.* robinose.

**роблингит** *m.* (min.) roeblingite.

**робот** *m.* robot, automatic device.

**робурит** *m.* (expl.) roburite.

**ров** *m.* ditch, pit, trench, moat, dike.

**ровит** *see* **раувит.**

**ровнитель** *see* **равнитель.**

**ровница** *f.* (text.) roving, slubbing.

**ровно** *adv.* just, exactly, equally; smoothly, steadily, uniformly; **р. в семь** at seven o'clock sharp.

**ровн/ость** *f.* equality; uniformity; evenness, flatness, smoothness; —**ый** *a.* equal; uniform, steady; even, flat, level, plane; —**я** equal, an equal; —**ять** *see* **равнять.**

**рог** *m.* horn; antler; beak (of anvil); **обугленный р.** horn charcoal.

**рогатик** *m.* (bot.) clavaria.

**рогатка** *f.* turnpike; obstacle.

**рогатый** *a.* horned; **р. скот** cattle.

**рогач** *m.* stag beetle; (bot.) weed (*Ceratocarpus*); —**и** *pl.* (zool.) Lucanidae; —**ка** *f.* (bot.) hedge mustard (*Sisymbrium sinapistrum*).

**роговидный** *a.* horn-shaped, corniculate, cornute; **р. выступ** horn.

**роговик** *m.* (petr.) hornstone, chert (an impure flint or chalcedony); —**овый** *a.* hornstone; horny; chert, cherty; (geol.) Corniferous; —**овая порода** (petr.) hornfels (a type of silicified shale).

**рогови/на** *f.* horn; —**ца** *f.* (anat.) cornea.

**рогов/ой** *a.* horn, horny, corneous; **р. гравий** (petr.) chert gravel; **р. камень** (petr.) hornstone, chert; **р. каучук** ebonite, hard rubber; **р. порфир** (petr.) hornstone porphyry; **р. свинец** (min.) horn lead, lead chloride; —**ая мука** horn meal; —**ая обманка** (min.) hornblende (a variety of amphibole); —**ая оболочка** (anat.) cornea; —**ая ткань** (anat.) horny tissue; —**ое вещество** keratin; —**ое серебро** (min.) horn silver, cerargyrite.

**роговообманков/ый** *a.* (min.) hornblende; **р. сланец** (petr.) hornblende schist; —**ая порода** (petr.) hornblendite (an igneous rock).

**рогож/а** *f.* matting, mat; bast; —**ка** *f.* coarse canvas.

**рогоз** *m.* (bot.) reed mace, cat-tail flag (*Typha*); —**овые** *pl.* Typhaceae.

**рого/листн/ик** *m.* (bot.) hornwort (*Ceratophyllum*); —**ые** *pl.* Ceratophyllaceae.

**рого/образный** *a.* horn-shaped, horn-type; horny; (bot.) corniform; —**хвосты** *pl.* (zool.) horntails (*Siricidae*).

**рогул/ька,** —**я** *f.* fork, splitting; (text.) flyer.

**род** *m.* family, origin, race, species, stock, descent; generation; (biol.) genus; variety, sort, type, kind, nature; (grammar) gender; *suffix* (chem.) —gen; **р. действия** method of operation; type of action; **в некотором —e** in some way; **что-то в этом —e** something to that effect.

**Рода реакция** Rhode test (for proteins).

**род/аллин** *m.* rhodalline, allyl sulfocarbamide; **—амин** *m.* rhodamine, 4-keto-2-thiothiazolidine.

**родаммоний** *m.* rhodammonium; **хлористый р.** rhodammonium chloride, rhodium ammonium chloride.

**родан** *m.* thiocyanogen; **—ид** *m.* thiocyanate.

**роданизирование** *n.* (met.) rhodanizing, rhodium plating.

**роданин** *m.*, **—овая кислота** rhodanine, rhodanic acid.

**роданистоводородная кислота** *see* **родановодородная кислота.**

**роданист/ый** *a.* thiocyanate, sulfocyanate (of); **р. алюминий** aluminum thiocyanate; **р. аммоний** ammonium thiocyanate; **—ая кислота** *see* **родановодородная кислота; —ая соль** thiocyanate, sulfocyanate; **—ое железо** ferrous thiocyanate; **—ое соединение** thiocyanogen compound.

**роданкалий** *m.* potassium thiocyanate.

**родано—** *prefix* thiocyano—.

**родановодород** *m.*, **—ная кислота** thiocyanic acid, sulfocyanic acid; **соль —ной кислоты** thiocyanate; **—ный** *a.* thiocyanate (of).

**роданов/ый** *a.* thiocyanate, sulfocyanate (of); **—ая кислота** *see* **родановодородная кислота; —ая ртуть** mercuric thiocyanate, mercuric sulfocyanide; **—ое железо** ferric thiocyanate.

**роданцен** *m.* rhodacene.

**Родезия** Rhodesia.

**роде/ит** *m.* rhodeite, rhodeol; **—оза** *f.* rhodeose; **—оретин** *m.* rhodeoretin, convolvulin.

**роджерсит** *m.* (min.) rogersite (alteration product of samarskite).

**родиев/ый** *a.* rhodium; **—ая соль** rhodium salt; **—ая чернь** rhodium black (catalyst).

**родиен** *m.* rhodiene.

**родизит** *m.* (min.) rhodizite (a calcium borate).

**родизоновая кислота** rhodizonic acid.

**род/ий** *m.* rhodium, Rh; **двуокись —ия** rhodium dioxide; **закись —ия** rhodium monoxide; **окись —ия** rhodium oxide; **полуторная окись —ия** rhodium sesquioxide; **сернокислый р., сульфат —ия** rhodium sulfate; **хлористый р.** rhodium dichloride; **хлорный р.** rhodium chloride, rhodium trichloride.

**родильн/ый** *a.* (med.) confinement, birth; **—ая горячка** puerperal fever.

**родим** *m.* rhodime, 2-thiozolimine.

**роди/мый** *a.* native, natal; **—мое пятно** birthmark, mole; **—на** *f.* native country.

**родинал** *m.* rhodinal, cintronellal; Rodinal, *p*-aminophenol.

**родин/овая кислота** rhodinic acid; **—ол** *m.* rhodinol, 2,6-dimethyloctene-2-ol.

**родирование** *n.* (met.) rhodium plating.

**роди/стый** *a.* rhodium; **—стое золото, —т** *m.* (min.) rhodium gold, rhodite.

**родит/ель** *m.* parent, father; **—ели** *pl.* parents; **—ельский** *a.* parental, paternal; **—ь** *see* **рождать.**

**родицит** *see* **родизит.**

**родичи** *pl.* parents.

**родник** *m.*, **—овый** *a.* spring, source.

**родн/ой** *a.* natal; own; **—я** *f.* relations.

**родовибрен** *m.* rhodovibrene, rhodopurpurin.

**родов/ой** *a.* ancestral, racial; generic; **—ое название** generic name.

**родовспомогательный** *a.* (med.) obstetric.

**рододендр/ин** *m.* rhododendrin; **—ол** *m.* rhododendrol; **—он** *m.* (bot.) rhododendron.

**родо/дубильная кислота** rhodotannic acid; **—ксантин** *m.* rhodoxanthin, thujorhodin; **—л** *m.* rhodol, metol; **—лит** *m.* (min.) rhodolite (a variety of garnet).

**родолия** *f.* Australian lady beetle (*Rodolia cardinalis*).

**родомицин** *m.* rhodomycin.

**родоначальн/ик** *m.* ancestor, forefather; **—ый** *a.* ancestral; parental.

**родо/нит** *m.* (min.) rhodonite, manganese spar (manganese silicate); **—псин** *m.*

rhodopsin, visual purple; —пурпурин *m.* rhodopurpurin, rhodovibrene.

Родос Rhodes.

родослов/ие *n.*, —ная *f.* genealogy, pedigree; —ный *a.* genealogical, pedigree.

родосское дерево *see* розовое дерево.

родо/тилит *m.* (min.) rhodotilite (same as inesite); —филлит *m.* rhodophyllite (a variety of penninite); —хрозит *m.* rhodochrosite (manganese carbonate).

родств/енник *m.* relative, kinsman; —енность *f.* relation; —енный *a.* related, relative, akin (to), allied; —енное разведение inbreeding; —о *n.* relationship, relation, kinship, propinquity; affinity, alliance; (petr.) consanguinity; parentage; в —е related.

родузит *m.* (min.) rhodusite (an asbestos-like variety of glaucophane).

родулин *m.* rhoduline (aniline dye).

роды *pl.* childbirth, confinement.

роение *n.* swarming (of bees).

роет *pr. 3 sing. of* рыть.

рожа *f.* (med.) erysipelas.

рож/авшая *a.* parous, having borne one or more children; —ать *see* рождать.

рожд/аемость *f.* birth rate; breeding, propagation; —ать *v.* bear, give birth, bring forth; —аться *v.* be born; breed; —ающийся *a.* being born; nascent.

рожден/ие *n.* birth; delivery; production; origination; до —ия prenatal; место —ия birthplace; статистика —ий vital statistics; —ный *a.* born; originated.

рожечник *m.* (bot.) carob bean, St. John's bread (*Ceratonia siliqua*).

рожист/ый *a.* (med.) erysipelatous, erysipelous; —ое воспаление erysipelas.

рожков/ый *a.* horn-type, pronged; —ое дерево *see* рожечник.

рож/ок *m.* little horn; (gas) burner, jet; catch, prong; horn, siren; socket (of lamp); —ки *pl.* (zool.) antennae, feelers; horns; —ки, маточные —ки, черные —ки ergot (of rye); сахарный р., сладкий р. *see* рожечник.

рожь *f.* (bot.) rye (*Secale cereale*); горная

р. wild rye (*S. montanum*); индийская р. wild flax (*Camelina sativa*).

роза *f.* (bot.) rose (*Rosa*).

Роза процесс *see* Розе процесс.

роза/гинин *m.* rosaginin; —зит *m.* (min.) rosasite (a variety of zinciferous malachite); —нилин *m.* rosaniline; —нные *pl.* (bot.) Rosaceae; —риум *m.* rosary, rose garden.

розвязь *f.* (agr.) mowed (unbound) grain.

Розе процесс (met.) Rose process (for gold); Р. сплав Rose metal, Rose's metal (a bismuth-lead-tin alloy).

роз/еин *m.* rosein; —елит *m.* (min.) roselite; —еллан *m.* rosellane (same as rosite); —енбушит *m.* rosenbuschite (near pectolite).

Розен/стила зелень Rosensthiel's green, barium manganate; —штейна способ Rosenstein process (for hydrochloric acid).

розеомицин *m.* roseomycin.

розет/ирование *n.* (met.) making rosette copper; conversion into rosettes or disks; —ировать *v.* make rosette copper; —ка *f.* rosette; (elec.) socket; контактная —ка plug socket; —ная медь rosette copper, rose copper; —очная болезнь rosette (plant disease); —очность *f.* rosetting, rosette character.

розин/дон *m.* rosindone, rosindulone; —дулин *m.* rosinduline (aniline dye); —ол *m.* rosinol, retinol.

розит *m.* (min.) rosite, decomposed anorthite; a form of pinite.

розлив *m.* pouring; bottling.

розмарин *m.* (bot.) rosemary (*Rosmarinus officinalis*); дикий р. wild rosemary, Labrador tea (leaves of *Ledum palustre*); —овое масло rosemary oil.

розниться *see* разниться.

розни/ца: в —цу at retail; продавать в —цу *v.* retail; —чный *a.* retail.

розн/ый *a.* odd, unmatched, incomplete; —ь *f.* difference, diversity.

розов процесс *see* Розе процесс.

розо/ватый *a.* rose-tinted, pinkish; —видный *a.* (bot.) rose-like, rosaceous; —во- *prefix* rose; —вокрасный *a.* rose-red; —вые, —цветные *pl.* (bot.) Rosaceae; —вый *a.* rose, rose-colored;

—вое дерево rosewood; —вое масло rose oil, attar of roses; —ловая кислота rosolic acid, corallin; —цианин *m.* rosocyanin.

**розыск** *m.* research, inquiry.

**роиться** *v.* swarm.

**рой** *m.* cluster; swarm (of bees); **р. ионов** ion cluster; —ба *f.* swarming.

**ройер** *m.*, **р.-машина** *f.* (foundry) royer (loam- and sand-preparing machine).

**рокамболь** *m.* (bot.) rocambole (*Allium scorodoprasum*).

**Роквелл: твердость по —у** (met.) Rockwell hardness.

**рок/ер, —кер** *m.* (min.) rocker, cradle (for gold-bearing sand).

**рокфор** *m.* Roquefort cheese.

**рокцелловая кислота** *see* **роцелловая кислота.**

**рол** *m.*, —евой *a.* roll; cylinder, shaft; —ик *m.* roller, castor; roll; pulley; (elec.) porcelain insulator; **ведущий р., направляющий р.** guide roller, idler.

**ролико/вый** *a.* roller, roll; **р. башмак** roller block; **р. грохот** roller screen; **р. подшипник, —подшипник** *m.* roller bearing; —вая подача roll feed; —вая цепь roller chain; sprocket chain.

**ролл** *m.* (paper) hollander, beater.

**роль** *f.* role, part; **играть р.** act (as), serve (as).

**рольганг** *m.* roller conveyer, roll-type conveyer; roll train; table (of rolling mill); **приводной р., рабочий р.** live roller, live rollers.

**роль/ный** *a.* rolled; **р. свинец** sheet lead; **листовое —ое олово** tin foil.

**ром** *m.* rum.

**роман** *m.* novel; pellitory root (of *Anacyclus pyrethrum*).

**роман/ский** *a.* Roman; **р. цемент, -цемент** *m.* Roman cement, Parker's cement (a natural cement from clay and limestone).

**ромаш/ка** *f.* (bot.) daisy, camomile (*Matricaria*); **аптечная р., дикая р., лекарственная р.** German camomile (*M. chamomilla*); **желтая р., красильная р.** yellow camomile (*Anthemis tinctoria*); **корень —ки** *see* **роман; персидская р.** pellitory of Spain

(*Anacyclus pyrethrum*); **римская р.** Roman camomile (*Anthemis nobilis*); —ник *m.* (bot.) pyrethrum.

**ромб** *m.* (geom.) rhomb, rhombus, rhombohedron; diamond; (zool.) turbot; brill (*Rhombus*).

**ромбен порфир** (petr.) rhomben porphyry.

**ромбический** *a.* (cryst.) rhombic.

**ромбо—** *prefix* rhombo—, rhomb; —видный, —образный *a.* rhomboid, rhombiform; diamond-shaped, diamond; —вый *a.* rhombus, rhombic; —вая призма rhombohedron; —гемиморфный *a.* (cryst.) rhombohemimorphous; —двупирамидальный *a.* (cryst.) rhombobipyramidal; —ид *m.* (geom.) rhomboid; —идальный *a.* rhomboid, rhomboidal; —клаз *m.* (min.) rhomboclase (a hydrous acid ferric sulfate).

**ромбоэдр** *m.* (cryst.) rhombohedron; —ический *a.* rhombohedral.

**ромеит** *m.* (min.) romeite (a calcium antimonate).

**ромен** *see* **ромашка.**

**рометалл** *m.* Rhometal (iron-nickel-chromium-silicon alloy).

**ромовый** *a.* rum; **р. завод** (rum) distillery.

**ронгалит** *m.*, —овый *a.* Rongalite (formaldehyde sodium sulfoxylate).

**ронять** *v.* drop, let fall, shed, cast off.

**рораский подъярус** (geol.) Rauracian substage.

**рос** *past sing. of* **расти.**

**рос/а** *f.* dew; mildew (plant disease); **точка —ы** dew point; —ение *n.* dew-retting (of flax); —инка *f.* dewdrop; —истый *a.* dewy.

**росичка** *f.* crabgrass (*Digitaria*).

**росколит** *m.* (min.) roscoelite (a vanadium muscovite).

**роскошный** *a.* luxurious, splendid; exuberant, luxuriant (foliage).

**роскоэлит** *see* **росколит.**

**росли** *past pl. of* **расти.**

**рослый** *a.* full-grown, tall; **р. слиток** (foundry) rising ingot.

**росн/оладанная кислота** benzoic acid; —ый ладан benzoin gum.

**росомаха** *f.* (zool.) wolverine.

**росомер** *m.* (meteor.) drosometer.

**роспуск** *m.* breaking up; dismissal; unraveling; unreeling; —**и** *pl.* log trailer.

**россбиграмма** *f.* (meteor.) Rossby diagram.

**Росси кривая** Rossi curve.

**российский** *see* **русский**.

**Россия** Russia.

**россып/ное золото** (min.) placer gold, alluvial gold, glacial gold; —**ь** *f.* scattering; (min.) placer, alluvial deposit, gravel mine; **золотоносная** —**ь** auriferous sand, gold-bearing sand.

**рост** *m.* height, size; increase, growth, development; germination; —**ом** in height; **во весь р.** full length; **давать р.** *v.* germinate; **кривая** —**a** growth curve; **остановить р.** *v.* stunt (growth).

**роствер** *m.* grating; grillage foundation.

**рост/ец** *m.* (bot.) thallus; —**овой** *a.* growth; —**овое вещество** growth stimulant; —**ок** *m.* seedling; sprout, shoot; **пускать** —**ки** *v.* germinate, sprout; —**омер** *m.* auxanometer.

**росторнит** *m.* (min.) rosthornite (a resin).

**росчин** *m.* leaven.

**росший** *past act. part. of* **расти**.

**росянк/а** *f.* (bot.) sundew (*Drosera*); —**овые** *pl.* Droseraceae.

**рот** *m.* mouth; **полость рта** oral cavity.

**рота** *f.* company; (med.) erysipelas.

**ротаметр** *m.* rotameter, float-type flow meter.

**ротанг** *m.* (bot.) rattan (*Calamus*).

**рота/ри** *n.* rotary system; —**тивный** *a.* rotative, rotary; —**тор** *m.* rotator; —**ционно-барабанный** *a.* rotary-drum.

**ротационн/ый** *a.* rotation, rotary, rotatory; **р. вентилятор** rotary blower; —**ая машина** rotary engine; —**ая радиотерапия** rotation therapy; —**ая сушилка** rotary dryer; —**ое движение** rotary motion, rotation.

**ротация** *f.* rotation; rotation (printing) machine.

**ротен/овая кислота** rotenic acid, isotubaic acid; —**он** *m.*, —**оновый** *a.* rotenone.

**ротлерин** *m.* rottlerin, kamalin.

**рото—** *prefix* mouth, stomato—.

**ротовая кислота** rothic acid.

**ротовой** *a.* mouth, stomatous, stomatic.

**ротограф** *m.*, —**ия** *f.* (phot.) rotograph.

**ротоногие** *pl.* (zool.) Stomatopoda.

**ротор** *m.*, —**ный** *a.* rotor; **р.-маховик** flywheel rotor.

**ротоскоп** *m.* rotoscope.

**рототерапия** *f.* (radiation) rotation therapy.

**роттизит** *m.* (min.) rottisite (a hydrated nickel silicate).

**Роуланда значение** (optics) Rowland's value.

**роцелл/овая кислота** roccellic acid; —**ин** *m.* roccelin, orseillin.

**рошеллева соль** Rochelle salt, potassium sodium tartrate.

**рошерит** *m.* (min.) roscherite.

**Рошона призма** Rochon prism.

**рошпан** *m.* (min.) cross brace.

**роштейн** *m.*, —**овый** *a.* (met.) raw matte, first matte; (copper) coarse metal.

**роща** *f.* grove, wood.

**РОЭ** *abbr.* (**реакция оседания эритроцитов**) erythrocyte sedimentation rate.

**ро/ют** *pr. 3 pl. of* **рыть**; —**ющий** *a.* digging.

**рояль** *m.*, —**ный** *a.* piano.

**рр** *abbr.* (**реки**) rivers; **р-р** *abbr.* (**раствор**) solution.

**РСК** *abbr.* (**реакция связывания комплемента**) complement fixation test.

**РСФСР** *abbr.* (**Российская Советская Федеративная Социалистическая Республика**) Russian Soviet Federated Socialist Republic.

**РСХ** *see* **райсемхоз**.

**рта** *gen. of* **рот**.

**РТО** *abbr.* (**Российское техническое общество**) Russian Technical Society.

**РТС** *abbr.* (**ремонтно-техническая станция**) service and supply center; (**ремонтно-тракторная станция**) tractor service station.

**рт. ст.** *abbr.* (**ртутный столб**) mercury column.

**ртутисто—** *prefix* mercuro—, mercurous.

**ртутист/ый** *a.* mercurous, mercury; —**ая соль** mercurous salt.

**ртутник** *m.* mercury-arc rectifier.

**ртутно—** *prefix* mercuri—, mercuric; **—синеродоводородная кислота** mercuricyanic acid.

**ртутн/ый** *a.* mercuric, mercury; (pharm.) mercurial; **р. выпрямитель** (elec.) mercury arc rectifier, mercury vapor rectifier; **р. столбик, —ая нить** mercury column (of thermometer); **—ая лампа** (elec.) mercury vapor lamp, mercury discharge lamp; **—ая мазь** (pharm.) mercury ointment, blue ointment; **—ая соль** mercuric salt.

**ртут/ь** *f.* mercury, Hg, quicksilver; **азотнокислая закись —и** mercurous nitrate; **азотнокислая окись —и** mercuric nitrate; **азотнокислая р.** mercury nitrate; **амидисто-хлористая р., белая осадочная р., двухлористо-амидистая р.** white precipitate, ammoniated mercury; **двуиодистая р., иодная р.** mercury biiodide, mercuric iodide; **двухлористая р.** *see* **ртуть, хлорная; закись —и** mercurous oxide; **соль закиси —и** mercurous salt; **иодистая р., желтая иодистая р., одноиодистая р.** mercurous iodide, yellow mercury iodide; **однохлористая р., полухлористая р.** *see* **ртуть, хлористая; окись —и** mercuric oxide; **красная окись —и** red mercuric oxide; **соль окиси —и** mercuric salt; **сернистая р.** mercury sulfide; **сернокислая закись —и** mercurous sulfate; **сернокислая окись —и** mercuric sulfate; **хлористая р.** mercurous chloride; **хлористо-амидистая р., хлористо-аммиачная р.** *see* **ртуть, амидисто-хлористая; хлорная р.** mercuric chloride, mercury bichloride.

**РУ** *abbr.* (рентгеновская установка) X-ray unit.

**Руан** Rouen.

**руб.** *abbr.* (рублей) rubles.

**рубазоновая кислота** rubazonic acid.

**рубанок** *m.* plane (tool).

**рубатоксин** *m.* rubatoxin.

**руба/ха** *f.* shirt; **—шка** *f.* shirt; jacket; housing; casing, lining; **водяная —шка** water jacket.

**рубеановая кислота** rubeanic acid, dithioöxamide.

**рубеж** *m.* border, boundary, limit, line,

verge; **за —ом** abroad; **—ная черта** boundary line.

**руб/еллит** *m.* (min.) rubellite (a variety of tourmaline); **—ен** *m.* rubene; **—еритриновая кислота** *see* **рубиановая кислота; —ероид** *m.* Ruberoid (roof-sheeting material); **—ефакция** *f.* (med.) rubefaction.

**рубец** *m.* scar, seam; gash, notch, slash; hem; (biol., med.) cicatrix; (anat.) rumen, first stomach.

**рубиа/нит** *m.* rubianite (old term for fuchsin); **—новая кислота** rubianic acid, ruberythric acid; **—цин** *m.* rubiacin (a madder dye).

**рубидиев/ый** *a.* rubidium; **—ая соль** rubidium salt; **—ые квасцы** rubidium alum.

**рубид/ий** *m.* rubidium, Rb; **иодистый р.** rubidium iodide; **окись —ия** rubidium oxide; **сернокислый р., сульфат —ия** rubidium sulfate.

**руби/дин** *m.* rubidine; **—ервин** *m.* rubijervine; **—ксантин** *m.* rubixanthin; **—линовая кислота** rubilic acid.

**рубильн/ик** *m.* cleaver, chopper; (elec.) knife switch, switch, cut-out; **—ый** *a.* chopping; **—ая машина** chopper, chopping machine.

**рубин** *m.* rubin, fuchsin; (min.) ruby (a gem variety of red corundum); **р.-балэ** balas ruby, balas (a variety of spinel); **—ный, —овый** *a.* ruby; **—ное стекло** ruby glass; artificial ruby; **—овая кислота** rubinic acid; **—овая обманка** (min.) ruby blende (a red variety of sphalerite); **—овая шпинель** ruby spinel, spinel.

**рубить** *v.* chop, hew, cut, fell (tree).

**рубицен** *m.* rubicene.

**руб/ка** *f.* hewing, chopping, cutting, severing, felling (of trees); cut, gash; construction, erection, building; **—леный** *a.* chopped, cut, felled.

**рубль** *m.* ruble.

**рубракс** *m.* Rubrax (an asphalt).

**рубрезерин** *m.* rubreserine.

**рубрен** *m.* rubrene.

**рубрика** *f.* heading, head; column.

**рубро/глауцин** *m.* rubroglaucin (pigment); **—глиокладин** *m.* rubrogliocladin; **—н** *m.* rubrone (a rubber compound).

**руб/цевание** *n.* scarring, cicatrization; **—цеватый** *a.* scarred, seamed, rough, grained; **—цовый** *a.* scar, seam; gash, notch; **—цовая жила** (min.) gash vein; **—чатый** *a.* seamed, ribbed, fluted; **—чик** *m.* scar; (anat.) commissure; (bot.) hylum; (text.) rib.

**рубэритриновая кислота** *see* **рубиановая кислота.**

**рубящий выключатель** (elec.) knife switch.

**руда** *f.* (min.) ore.

**рудбекия** *f.* (bot.) rudbeckia.

**рудеральный** *a.* (bot.) ruderal.

**рудимент** *m.* rudiment; **—арный** *a.* rudimentary, vestigial.

**рудисты** *pl.* (geol.) Rudistes.

**рудит** *m.* (petr.) rudite, coarse sediments.

**рудить** *v.* (met.) ore down (open hearth).

**рудник** *m.* mine, pit.

**руднични/ый** *a.* mine, mining, miner's; **р. воздух, р. газ** firedamp, mine methane; **р. лес** timber, pit props; **—ые машины** mining equipment.

**рудн/ый** *a.* mining; ore; **р. двор** stockyard; **р. ларь** ore pocket; **р. столб** shoot (of ore); **р. шлам** ore slime; **—ая мелочь** smalls, slack, fines; **—ая проба** assay; **—ая промышленность,** **—ое дело** ore mining, mining industry.

**рудо—** *prefix* ore; **—дробилка** *f.* ore crusher, crusher.

**рудоискатель** *m.* (min.) prospector; **—ный** *a.* prospecting; dowsing (rod).

**рудо/катка** *f.* rolls; **—кон** *m.* miner; **—носный** *see* **рудосодержащий.**

**рудообжиг/альщик** *m.* (met.) roaster, calciner; **—ательная печь** roasting furnace, roasting kiln, roaster, calciner.

**рудоотделитель** *m.* ore separator.

**рудопромыв/ательный** *a.* ore-washing; **—ная фабрика** ore-washing plant; **—очная машина** ore washer, specif. log washer.

**рудоразбор/ка** *f.* (min.) sorting, picking (of ore); **—ный** *a.* sorting, picking; **—ный стол** picking table; **—ная лента** picking belt; **—ное устройство** sorting device, screening device.

**рудораспределитель** *m.* ore distributor; **—ный** *a.* ore-distributing.

**рудо/содержащий** *a.* ore-bearing, metalliferous; **—спуск** *m.* ore chute.

**рудяк** *see* **ортштейн.**

**ружейн/ый** *a.* gun, rifle; **р. замок** musket lock; **р. мастер** gunsmith; **—ая граната** rifle grenade; **—я** *f.* gunsmith's shop.

**ружье** *n.* gun, rifle.

**рук/а** *f.* hand; arm; **держать в —ах** *v.* have in hand; **из вторых рук** second-hand; **из первых рук** first-hand; **махнуть —ой** *v.* overlook; **на скорую —у** in haste, offhand; **от —и** manually, by hand; **установка от —и** manual adjustment, hand adjustment; **чертеж от —и** freehand drawing; **под —ами, под —ой** at hand, handy; **сбыть с рук** *v.* rid oneself (of).

**рукав** *m.* sleeve; hose, flexible pipe; bag; branch (of river), arm (of water); second stomach (of ruminants).

**рукавиц/а** *f.* mitten; **—ы** *pl.* gauntlets.

**рукавн/ый** *a.* sleeve; hose; bag (filter, etc.); **—ое соединение** sleeve coupling, sleeve; hose coupling.

**рукавообразн/ый** *a.* sleeve-like, sleeve-shaped; **—ая залежь** (geol.) channel deposit.

**рукавчик** *m.* cuff.

**руководитель** *m.* leader, instructor, guide, supervisor, manager; **—ство** *n.* direction, guiding, management; **—ствовать** *v.* lead, guide, manage.

**руководить** *v.* lead, guide, conduct; instruct, direct, rule; supervise, manage, run, boss; **р. неправильно** mislead; **—ся** *v.* be guided, be directed, be influenced (by); follow (directions).

**руководство** *n.* guidance, lead, leadership, direction, supervision, management; handbook, manual, textbook; **—вать** *see* **руководить.**

**руководящ/ий** *a.* leading, guiding, guide; **—ая линия** guide line.

**рукодельный** *a.* handmade.

**руко/крылые** *pl.* (zool.) Chiroptera; **—ногие** *pl.* Brachiopoda.

**рукопис/ь** *f.*, **—ный** *a.* manuscript.

**рукоплескать** *v.* applaud, clap.

**рукоят/ка** *f.* **—ь** *f.* handle, hilt, shaft, grip; lever, arm; crank, crank handle; **—чик** *m.* (min.) cager.

**рулев/ой** *a.* steering, rudder, helm; **—ое**

**управление** steering gear; (aero.) control stick.

**руление** *n.* (aero.) taxying, sailing.

**рулет/ка** *f.*, **—очный** *a.* tape, tape measure; reel; **—та** *f.* (geom.) roulette.

**руло** *n.*, **—н** *m.* roll (of sheet material); **—нные кровли** roofing materials.

**руль** *m.* wheel, rudder, helm, control.

**рум.** *abbr.* (румынский) Rumanian.

**румб** *m.*, **—овый** *a.* bearing, point (of compass); rhumb (line).

**румицин** *m.* rumicin.

**Румкорфа спираль, румкорфовая катушка** (elec.) Ruhmkorff coil.

**румпфит** *m.* (min.) rumpfite (probably a variety of prochlorite).

**румынский** *a.* Rumanian

**Румыния** Rumania.

**румян/а** *f.* rouge, paint; **—еть** *v.* redden, blush; **—ец** *m.* blush; good complexion; erubescence, bloom (on fruit).

**румянка** *f.* (bot.) German camomile (*Matricaria chamomilla*); viper's bugloss (*Echium*); alkanet (*Anchusa*).

**румяный** *a.* rosy, ruddy.

**Рунге серия** Runge series.

**рундук** *m.* locker, bin.

**рун/ец** *m.* sheep tick; **—истый** *a.* fleecy; **—ный** *a.* fleece; **—о** *n.* fleece, wool; shoal (of fish).

**рупельский ярус** (geol.) Rupelian stage.

**рупия** *f.* rupee.

**рупор** *m.* mouthpiece, mouth; (rad.) horn, loudspeaker, speaker; **—ный** *a.* mouthpiece, speaker; horn-type.

**руппия** *f.* a marine herb (Ruppia).

**рус** *m.* (bot.) sumac (*Rhus*).

**рус.** *abbr.* (русский) Russian.

**руса/к** *m.*, **—чий** *a.* (zool.) hare.

**русло** *n.* bed (of river), channel, waterway, race.

**русский** *a.* Russian.

**руст,** **—ик** *m.*, **—ика** *f.* (masonry) rustic, bossage.

**русый** *a.* blond, light-colored.

**рута** *f.* (bot.) rue (Ruta); **душистая р., обыкновенная р.** common rue (*R. graveolens*).

**Рута аккумулятор** Ruth's (steam) accumulator.

**рутаекарпин** *m.* rutaecarpine.

**рутен/ат** *m.* ruthenate; **—иевый** *a.* ru-

thenium, ruthenic; **—иевая кислота** ruthenic acid; **соль —иевой кислоты, —иевокислая соль** ruthenate.

**рутен/ий** *m.* ruthenium, Ru; **двухлористый р., хлористый р.** ruthenium dichloride, ruthenious chloride; **закись —ия, одноокись —ия** ruthenium monoxide; **окись —ия** (any) ruthenium oxide; **сернистый р., сульфид —ия** ruthenium sulfide, laurite.

**рутер** *m.* rooter, road plow.

**рутерфорд/ин,** **—ит** *m.* (min.) rutherfordite (an uranyl carbonate).

**рутил** *m.* (min.) rutile (a form of titanium oxide); **игольчатый р.** acicular rutile, maidenhair.

**рутил/иден** *m.* rutylidene, 1-hendecyne; **—ин** *m.* rutylin.

**рутиловый** *a.* (min.) rutile.

**рутин** *m.* rutin.

**рутин/а** *f.*, **—ный** *a.* routine.

**рут/иновая кислота** rutinic acid; **—ный, —овый** *a.* rue; **—овка** *see* **рута;** **—овые** *pl.* (bot.) Rutaceae; **—овая кислота** rutic acid; **—овое масло** rue oil; **—онал** *m.* Rutonal, methylphenylbarbituric acid; **—оплодные** *pl.* (bot.) Rutoideae.

**Рутса вентилятор** Roots blower.

**рутьер** *see* **рутер.**

**руфи/ановая кислота** rufianic acid, quinizarinsulfonic acid; **—галловая кислота,** **—галлол** *m.* rufigallic acid, rufigallol; **—н** *m.* rufin; **—опин** *m.* rufiopin, tetrahydroxyanthraquinone.

**руфол** *m.* rufol, 1,5-anthracenediol.

**рух** *m.* (glass) devitrification; friable place.

**рухл/ость** *f.* friability; unsteadiness; **—ый** *a.* friable; unsteady.

**рухляк** *m.* (geol.) marl (a calcareous clay); **отверделый р.** hardened marl, marlstone; **—овый** *a.* marly, marlaceous.

**рухнуть** *v.* crash down; crumble away.

**ручат/ельный** *a.* guaranteeing, guarantee; **—ельство** *n.* guaranty, warrant, voucher; **—ься** *v.* guarantee, warrant, vouch (for), answer (for), certify; be sure.

**руч/еек** *m.* brook, streamlet, rill; **—ей** *m.*

brook, stream, creek, rivulet, water-course; groove, caliber, pass (of roller); зев —ья pass; конструкция —ья pass design.

**ручейники** *pl.* caddis flies (*Trichoptera*).

**ручка** *f.* small hand; handle, knob, grip, shaft; crank, crank handle; arm (of lever); (aero.) stick; penholder; **р. натяжного стержня** cotter.

**ручник** *m.* hammer.

**ручн/ой** *a.* manual, hand, handmade, hand-operated, manually operated; portable; domestic, tame; **р. привод,** —ое управление hand operation, manual operation; **с —ым приводом** hand-operated, hand-driven; **кран с —ым приводом** hand crane; —ая выгрузка, —ая погрузка freight handling; —ая загрузка hand stoking (of furnace); —ая пила hand saw; —ая работа handiwork; manual labor; —ой работы handmade; —ая тележка hand cart, push cart.

**руш/ение** *n.* falling in, collapse; pearling; —ить *v.* hull; —иться *v.* fall in, collapse, go to ruin, crumble away.

**РФК** *abbr.* (рибозофосфорная кислота) ribose-phosphoric acid.

**РФТ** *abbr.* (реактор для физических и технических исследований) physical and technical research reactor.

**РФХО** *abbr.* (Русское физико-химическое общество) Russian Physico-Chemical Society.

**РХБС** *see* эфирсульфонат.

**р-ция** *abbr.* (реакция) reaction.

**рыб/а** *f.* fish; **р.-молот** hammerfish, hammerhead; —ак *m.* fisherman; —ацкий, —ачий *a.* fishing; fisherman's; —ачество *n.* fishing; —ачить *v.* fish; —ешка *f.* young fish.

**рыб/ий** *a.* fish; **р. жир** fish oil, spec. cod-liver oil; **р. клей** fish glue, isinglass; **растительный р.** clей agar, vegetable isinglass; —ьи ягоды *see* кукольван; —ья чешуя (med.) ichthyosis, xerodermia.

**рыбин/а** *f.*, —с *m.* ribband, rising line.

**рыбка** *f.* little fish.

**рыбление** *n.* combing, hackling (of flax).

**рыбн/ый** *a.* fish, piscine; —ые отбросы fish scrap, pomace.

**рыбовод** *m.* pisciculturist; —ный, —че-

ский *a.* piscicultural; —ный завод fish hatchery; —ство *n.* pisciculture, fish breeding.

**рыболов** *m.* fisherman; —ный *a.* fishing; —ные снасти fishing tackle; —ные ягоды *see* кукольван; —ство *n.* fishing, fishery, fishing industry.

**рыбо/образный** *a.* fish-shaped; fish-bellied (girders, etc.); —промысловый *a.* fishing industry, fish; —промышленность *f.* fishing industry, fish industry; —разведение *n.* fish culture, pisciculture; —ядный *a.* (zool.) fish-eating, ichthyophagous; —ящер *m.* (pal.) ichthyosaur.

**рыбьи** *see* рыбий.

**рыв/ок** *m.* jerk; —ки *pl.* jerking.

**рыж/еватый** *a.* reddish, rusty, rust-colored; —еть *v.* become reddish, get rust-colored; —ий *a.* reddish, rust-colored; red-haired.

**рыжик** *m.* (bot.) an edible brown mushroom (*Lactarius deliciosus*); gold-of-pleasure (*Camelina*); —овое масло cameline oil, cameline seed oil.

**рыл** *past sing. of* рыть.

**рыл/о,** —ьце *n.* muzzle (of animal); nozzle, jet, spout, mouth; (bot.) stigma.

**рым** *m.* eye; **р.-болт** eye bolt.

**рыно/к** *m.* market, market place; —ч-ный *a.* market, commercial.

**рыс/ь** *f.*, —ий *a.* (zool.) lynx.

**рыт/вина** *f.* rut, groove, gully, ravine; excavation, hollow; —ый *a.* dug.

**рыть** *v.* dig, hollow out, excavate; mine; —е *n.* digging, excavation.

**рыхл/ение** *n.* cultivation, loosening (of soil); —еть *v.* become friable, get porous; —итель *m.* cultivator; ripper; —ить *v.* stir up, loosen, cultivate, mellow (soil); —окомковатый *a.* loose-aggregate, loosely lumpy (soil); —ость *f.* friability, porousness, openness; —ый *a.* friable, porous, loose, flocculent; incoherent; light, mellow (soil); —ящий *a.* stirring up, cultivating.

**рычаг** *m.* lever, arm, crank; (aero.) stick; hand spike, jack; —и *pl.* controls; действие —а leverage; плечо —а lever arm; система —ов leverage, system of levers.

**рычажн/ый** *a.* lever; **р. молот** sledge hammer; **р. реверс** reversing lever; **р. циркуль** beam compass; **—ые весы** beam balance.

**рычажок** *m.* small lever; rod.

**р.э.** *abbr.* (**радиоактивный элемент**) radioactive element.

**рэл** *m.* rel (unit of magnetic resistance).

**Рэлей** *see* **релеевский.**

**Рэнкин** *see* **Ранкин.**

**РЭС** *abbr.* (**ретикуло-эндотелиальная система**) reticulo-endothelial system.

**рэт** *m.*, **—ический ярус** (geol.) Rhaetian stage.

**рют/лер** *m.*, **—тель-машина** (molding) jar-ramming machine.

**ряб/ина** *f.* (bot.) mountain ash (*Sorbus*); pockmark; waviness, ripple; **обыкновенная р.** rowan (*S. aucuparia*); **—инник** *m.* (bot.) sorbaria; **—ить** *v.* ripple, curl; **—ишник** *m.* (bot.) tansy (*Tanacetum vulgare*); **—ой** *a.* pitted, pocked, pock-marked; spotted, speckled; **—уха** *f.* wildfire (plant disease); **—чик** *m.* (bot.) fritillaria.

**рябь** *f.* ripple, ripples, ripple marks, rippled surface; ground-swells.

**ряд** *m.* row, series, line; range, order, sequence, succession; level, layer; (pulse, etc.) train; set, bank (of machines); **—ами** in rows, in banks, in batteries; **на —у с** on a line with; **ставить на —у с** *v.* class with; **помещать в р., ставить в р.** *v.* range, put in a row, align.

**рядов/ой** *a.* ordinary, commonplace, rank-and-file, unsorted, run-of-the-mine, commercial (grade); consecutive, serial; in rows, drill (sowing); **р. уголь** run-of-mine coal; **—ая сеялка** (agr.) seed drill; **—ое замещение** adjacent substitution, neighboring substitution (in organic ring compounds).

**ряд/ок** *m.* small row; drill row; **—ом** *adv.* beside, side by side.

**ряж** *m.*, **—евый** *a.* crib, cribwork; **—евый бык** crib pier.

**ряск/а** *f.* (bot.) duckweed (*Lemna*); **—овые** *pl.* Lemnaceae.

# С

**с** *prep. instr.* with; *prep. gen.* by, for, from, on, over, since, down; *prep. acc.* for.

**с** *abbr.* (**скорость света**) velocity of light; **с.** *abbr.* (**сажень**) sajene; (**северный**) north, northern; (**секунда**) second; (**сильный**) strong; **С.** *abbr.* (**север**) north.

**с—** *prefix, particularly with verbs* de—, down from; con—, with.

**САА** *abbr.* (**сульфамат аммония**) ammonium sulfamate.

**саарский уголь** Saar coal.

**сабадилл/a** *f.* (bot.) sabadilla (*Sabadilla officinalis*); **семена —ы** sabadilla, cevadilla (seeds of *Schoenocaulon officinale*); **—ин** *m.* sabadilline, cevadilline; **—овая кислота** sabadillic acid, cevadic acid.

**сабадин** *m.* sabadine; **—ин** *m.* sabadinine, cevine.

**сабалол** *m.* sabalol.

**сабатрин** *m.* sabatrine.

**Сабатье процесс** Sabatier process.

**саббатин** *m.* sabbatin, gentiopicrin.

**сабельник** *m.* (bot.) cinquefoil (*Potentilla*).

**сабин/ан** *m.* sabinane; **—ен** *m.* sabinene; **—иновая кислота** sabinic acid, 12-hydroxydodecanoic acid; **—ол** *m.* sabinol, 6-hydroxysabinene.

**сабля** *f.* sword, saber.

**сабо** *n.* sabot.

**сабот/аж** *m.* sabotage; **—ажник** *m.* saboteur; **—ировать** *v.* sabotage.

**сабромин** *m.* Sabromin, calcium dibromobehenate.

**сабугалит** *m.* sabugalite (uranium mineral).

**сабур** *m.*, **—ный** *a.* (bot.) aloe; **американский с., древовидный с.** American aloe, century plant (*Agave americana*).

**саванна** *f.* savanna (grassland).

**савой** *m.*, **—ская капуста** Savoy cabbage (*Brassica oleracea savanda*).

**сага/пенум** *m.* sagapenum (gum resin from *Ferula persica*); **—резитаннол** *m.* sagaresitannol (acid resin).

**сагенит** *m.* (min.) sagenite (a rutile-containing quartz).

**сагитта** *f.* sagitta; —**льный** *a.* sagittal.

**саго** *n.* sago (starch).

**саговник** *m.* (bot.) fern palm (*Cycas*); —**овые** Cycadaceae; —**овый** *a.* cycadaceous; —**овое растение** cycad.

**сагов/ый** *a.* sago; —**ая пальма** (bot.) sago palm (*Sagus*).

**саграды, кора** cascara sagrada.

**САГУ** *abbr.* (Среднеазиатский государственный университет) Central Asia State University.

**сагыз** *m.* sagyz (a growth of salt crystals in the silt of salt lakes); *see also* **кок-сагыз, крым-сагыз, тау-сагыз.**

**сад** *m.* orchard; garden; —**ик** *m.* small orchard; —**ить** *see* **сажать.**

**садиться** *v.* sit, take a seat; shrink (of cloth); settle (of dust); set, sink, give way (of building); run (aground).

**садка** *f.* (agr.) planting; thickening (of liquids); shrinkage; charge, molten charge, melt; slip (of charge in blast furnace); **жидкая с.** molten charge.

**садк/ий** *a.* (paper) fast (pulp); —**ость** *f.* freeness.

**садо/вник** *m.* gardener; **лесной с.** beetle (*Myelophilus*); —**внический** *a.* gardening; pruning (tool); —**вод** *m.* horticulturist; —**водство** *n.* horticulture, gardening; cultivation of orchards; —**водческий** *a.* horticultural; orchard-growing; —**вый** *a.* orchard; garden; pruning (knife); grafting (wax).

**садок** *m.* breeding place; fish pond, livefish tank; oyster bank; rabbit warren.

**садочн/ый** *a.* charging; —**ая машина** charger, charging machine; —**ое окно** door (of furnace), charge hole.

**сажа** *f.* carbon black; soot; **белая с.** powdered silica gel; **газовая с.** gas black; **ламповая с.** lamp black; **печная с.** chimney soot.

**саж/алка** *f.* (agr.) planter; small pond; —**альник** *m.* dibble; —**альный** *a.* planting; —**альный кол** dibble; —**альщик** *m.* planter; —**ание** *n.* planting, setting; —**ать** *v.* plant; set, place, put; seat.

**сажевый** *a.* carbon black; soot.

**саженец** *m.* seedling, slip.

**сажень** *f.* sajene (obs. unit of length, 2.134 meters).

**сажепродуватель** *m.* soot blower.

**саж/истый, —ный** *a.* soot, sooty; —**ка** *f.* smut (plant disease).

**саза** *f.* (bot.) a bamboo (*Sasa*).

**сазан** *m.* (zool.) carp.

**сайбелиит** *m.* (min.) szaibelyite.

**сайда** *f.* pollack (fish).

**сайзель** *see* **сизаль.**

**сайка** *f.* kind of small loaf.

**сайлентблок** *m.* (automobile) silent block.

**сайодин** *m.* Sajodin, calcium monoiodobehenate.

**сак** *m.* bag, sack.

**Сака прокатный стан** (met.) Sack's rolling mill.

**сакалоид** *m.* a sugar plastic.

**саква** *f.* feed bag (for horses).

**саквояж** *m.* traveling bag, suitcase.

**саки** *n.* saki (a Japanese beer).

**Саккура-Тетроде формула** (thermodynamics) Sackur-Tetrode equation.

**саксат/иловая кислота** saxatilic acid; —**овая кислота** saxatic acid.

**саксаул** *m.* (bot.) haloxylon.

**саксифра/гин, —жин** *m.* (expl.) saxifragin (chiefly barium nitrate).

**саксонский синий** Saxon blue (a cobalt blue).

**сакуранин** *m.* sakuranin.

**сакхульминовая кислота** sacchulmic acid.

**сал** *see* **сиал.**

**салазк/и** *pl.* sled, toboggan; skids, slide, slide rails; sliding carriage, carriage, carrier; **контактные с.** (elec.) contact bridge; **подача —ами** sliding advancement.

**салазолон** *m.* salazolon, antipyrine salicylate.

**салака** *f.* (zool.) a kind of sprat.

**саламандр/а** *f.* salamander; —**ин** *m.* salamanderine (a salamander alkaloid).

**саламид** *m.* salamide, salicylamide.

**салантол** *m.* salantol, salacetol.

**салат** *m.*, —**ный** *a.* salad; (bot.) lettuce (*Lactuca sativa*); **с.-ромен** *m.* cos lettuce (*L. s. romana*).

**сал/ацетол** *m.* salacetol, acetosalicylic ester; —**гипнон** *m.* salhypnone, benzoylmethyl salicylate.

**салда** *f.* (agr.) hack hook.

салеит *m.* saleite (uranium mineral).

салеп *m.* salep (dried tubers of species of the *Orchis genus*).

салив/ация *f.* (physiol.) salivation; —ин *m.* salivin, ptyalin.

салиген/ин, —ол *m.* Saligenin, salicyl alcohol.

саликоил *see* салицил.

саликор *m.* salicor, blanquette (ash from soda plants).

салиметр *m.* salimeter, salt solution hydrometer.

салин *m.* ash from molasses.

салинафтол *m.* salinaphthol, betol.

салинигрин *m.* salinigrin.

салинометр *m.* salinometer.

салипирин *m.* Salipyrine, antipyrine salicylate.

салит *m.* (min.) salite, sahlite (a variety of hedenbergite pyroxene).

салить *v.* tallow, grease.

сали/фебрин *m.* Salifebrin, salicylanilide; —формин *m.* Saliformin, urotropine salicylate.

салицил *m.* salicyl; —аза *f.* salicylase; —амид *m.* salicylamide, *o*-hydroxybenzamide; —анилид *m.* salicylanilide; —ат *m.* salicylate; —ид *m.* salicylide, tetrasalicylide; —ил *m.* salicylyl; —ированный *a.* salicylated; —ировать, —овать *v.* salicylate.

салицилово/аммониевая соль ammonium salicylate; —бензиловый эфир benzyl salicylate; —бутиловый эфир butyl salicylate; —висмутовая соль bismuth salicylate; основная —висмутовая соль bismuth subsalicylate; —кальциевая соль calcium salicylate.

салициловокисл/ый *a.* salicylic acid; salicylate (of); с. хинин quinine salicylate; —ая соль salicylate.

салицилово/метиловый эфир methyl salicylate; —натриевая соль sodium salicylate; —фениловый эфир phenyl salicylate; —этиловый эфир ethyl salicylate.

салицилов/ый *a.* salicyl, salicylic; с. альдегид salicylaldehyde, salicylal; с. натр sodium salicylate; с. спирт salicyl alcohol, *o*-hydroxybenzyl alcohol; —ая кислота salicylic acid, *o*-hydroxybenzoic acid; соль —ой кис-

лоты salicylate; —ое сало (pharm.) salicylated mutton fat.

салицило/л *m.* salicylol; —нитрил *m.* salicylonitrile, *o*-hydroxybenzyl nitrile; —салициловая кислота salicylosalicylic acid, diplosal.

салицил/резорцинол *m.* salicylresorcinol; —уровая кислота salicyluric acid; —хинин *m.* salicylquinine, saloquinine.

салицин *m.*, —овый *a.* salicin, saligenin.

салический *a.* (petr.) salic, containing alumina.

Салливена реакция Sullivan's test (for cystine).

салмонсит *see* сальмонсит.

сало *n.* fat, grease; lard; tallow; suet; (ice) grease, slush; нутряное с., почечное с. suet.

салоколл *m.* salocoll, phenocoll salicylate.

салол *m.*, —овый *a.* salol, phenyl salicylate.

сало/мас *m.* hydrogenated fat; —образный *a.* tallowy; (anat.) sebaceous.

салопийский ярус (geol.) Salopian stage, middle and upper Silurian.

салотоп/енный, —ный *a.* fat-melting; tallow-melting; rendering; —ка *f.* fat melting; fat-melting plant; —ня *f.* fat-melting plant.

сало/фен *m.* Salophen, acetamidosalol; —хинин *m.* Saloquinine, quinine salicylate.

салумин *m.* Salumin, aluminum salicylate.

салуфер *m.* Salufer, sodium silicofluoride.

салфетк/а *f.*, —очный *a.* napkin; filter cloth.

сальвадорский *a.* Salvador.

сальварсан *m.* salvarsan (arsphenamine).

сальви/анин *m.* salvianin, monardein; —ния *f.* (bot.) salvinia; —ол *m.* salviol, thujone; —я *f.* (bot.) sage (Salvia).

сальд/ирование *n.* (com.) striking a balance; —ировать *v.* strike a balance; —о *n.* balance.

сальза *f.* (geol.) salse, mud cone, mud volcano.

сальмин *m.* salmine (a protamine).

сальмит *m.* (min.) salmite.

**сальмонсит** *m.* (min.) salmonsite.

**сальник** *m.*, **—овый** *a.* stuffing box; gland, packing gland; gasket, collar; drip pan; (zool.) epiploon; (anat.) omentum; **—овая коробка** stuffing box; **—овая крышка** gland.

**сальность** *f.* greasiness.

**сальн/ый** *a.* greasy, fatty, sebaceous; lardaceous; tallowy; tallow (candle); **с. корень** (bot.) comfrey (*Symphytum*); **—ая железа** (anat.) sebaceous gland.

**сальпингит** *m.* (med.) salpingitis.

**сальсапарелль** *see* **сарсапарелль.**

**сальсол/идин** *m.* salsolidine; **—ин** *m.* salsoline.

**салюмин** *see* **салумин.**

**сам** *pron.* self, himself, itself; in person; **с. по себе** alone, by itself; **—а** *f.* herself; **—и** *pl.* themselves, yourselves; **—о** *n.* itself; **—о собой разумеется** it is self-evident.

**самадер/а** *f.* (bot.) samadera (*Samadera indica*); **—ин** *m.* samaderin.

**саман** *m.* adobe, sun-baked brick; chopped straw.

**саманда/ридин** *m.* samandaridine (a salamander alkaloid); **—рин** *m.* samandarine; **—трин** *m.* samandatrine.

**саманный** *a.* adobe; **с. кирпич** adobe, sun-dried brick.

**самариев/ый** *a.* samarium, samaric; **—ая соль** samaric salt.

**самар/ий** *m.* samarium, Sm; **окись —ия** samarium oxide; **сернокислая закись —ия** samarous sulfate; **сернокислая окись —ия** samaric sulfate; **хлористый с.** samarous chloride; **хлорный с.** samaric chloride.

**самаристый** *a.* samarium, samarous.

**самарскит** *m.* (min.) samarskite.

**сама-состояние** *n.* sama condition, no thermal flow.

**самбук** *m.* (bot.) elder (*Sambucus*).

**самбу/нигрин** *m.* sambunigrin; **—цинин** *m.* sambucinin.

**самец** *m.* male.

**самин** *m.* samin.

**самиресит** *m.* (min.) samiresite (a niobate-tantalate).

**самка** *f.* female.

**само** *see* **сам.**

**само—** *prefix* self—, auto—, automatic, spontaneous.

**самобытн/ость** *f.* originality; independence; **—ый** *a.* original; independent.

**самовар** *m.* samovar, tea urn.

**самовентилирующийся** *a.* self-ventilating, automatically ventilated.

**самовнушение** *n.* autosuggestion.

**самовозбужд/ающийся** *a.* (elec.) self-exciting; **—ение** *n.* self-excitation; **—енный** *a.* self-excited.

**самовозгорание** *see* **самовоспламенение.**

**самовозникающий** *a.* spontaneous.

**самовольн/о** *adv.* arbitrarily; **—ый** *a.* self-willed; unwarranted.

**самовоспламен/ение** *n.* spontaneous combustion; spontaneous ignition, self-ignition; **—яемость** *f.* spontaneous combustibility; **—яемый, —яющийся** *a.* spontaneously inflammable.

**самовоспроизвод/ство** *n.* self-reproduction; **—ящийся** *a.* self-reproducing.

**само/всасывающий** *a.* automatic intake; **—вулканизующийся** *a.* self-vulcanizing, autovulcanizing; **—выпрямляющийся** *a.* self-straightening, self-righting; **—выравнивающийся** *a.* self-aligning; **—гасящий** *a.*, **—гашение** *n.* self-quenching.

**самогон** *m.* home brew.

**самогорание** *n.* spontaneous combustion.

**самодви/гатель** *m.* automatic engine; **—жущийся** *a.* automatic, self-powered, self-propelled, self-moving.

**само/действующий** *a.* automatic, self-acting; **—дельный** *a.* homemade, hand-made; **—деятельность** *f.* self-activity, self-help, self-service; **—диффузия** *f.* autodiffusion, self-diffusion; **—довлеющий** *a.* self-sufficient, independent; **—дувная печь** wind furnace, air furnace, draft furnace; **—жигание, —загорание** *n.* spontaneous ignition; **—заводящийся** *a.* self-starting; self-winding; **—зажимающий** *a.* self-gripping.

**самозакал/ивающийся** *a.* (met.) self-hardening, air-hardening; **—ка** *f.* air-hardened steel.

**само/закрывающийся, —замыкающийся, —запирающийся, —запорный** *a.* self-closing, automatic closing, self-locking; **—запирание** *n.* automatic closing, automatic locking; —**записывающий** *a.* self-recording, recording, graphic; —**запускающийся** *a.* self-starting; —**заражение** *n.* (med.) auto-infection; —**зарядный** *a.* (mil.) automatic (rifle); —**затухание** *n.* self-stopping, natural dying away.

**самозахватывающ/ий** *a.* self-gripping; **с. грейфер** automatic grab; —**ие клещи** self-gripping jaws.

**само/защита** *f.* self-defense; —**излучение** *n.* self-emission (of rays), spontaneous radiation.

**самоиндукц/ионный** *a.* (elec.) self-inductive; —**ия** *f.* self-induction; **коэффициент** —**ии** inductance; **реакция** —**ии** inductive reactance.

**самоионизация** *f.* self-ionization.

**самокал** *m.*, —**ка** *f.* air-hardened steel.

**самокат** *m.* bicycle; —**чик** *m.* cyclist.

**само/колебание** *n.* natural vibration; —**контролирующийся** *а.* self-supervisory; —**корректирующийся** *a.* self-correcting; —**крепление** *n.* self-attaching.

**самолет** *m.* airplane, plane, aircraft; **с.-амфибия** amphibian; **с.-истребитель** combat plane, fighter; —**ный** *a.* airplane, aircraft; airborne; —**ный челнок** (text.) fly shuttle; —**вождение** *n.* aerial navigation; —**остроение** *n.* airplane construction, aircraft industry.

**самоличн/о** *adv.* in person, personally; —**ый** *a.* personal.

**самонаведен/ие** *n.* (elec.) self-induction; (aero.) homing; —**ный** *a.* self-induced.

**само/наводящийся** *a.* self-guided, self-homing (missile); —**нагревание** *n.* spontaneous heating; —**надеянность** *f.* self-confidence; —**обвинение** *n.* self-condemnation; —**обладание** *n.* self-possession, self-control, restraint; —**обличение** *n.* self-accusation; —**обман** *m.* self-deception; —**обольщение** *n.* self-delusion; —**оборона** *f.* self-defense; —**образование** *n.* self-education, self-instruction.

**самообслужив/ание** —**ающийся** *a.* self-service; —**ающаяся установка** self-contained plant.

**само/окисление** *n.* autooxidation, self-oxidation; —**окрашенный** *a.* self-

colored; —**окупаемость** *f.* self-support; —**окупаемый** *a.* self-supporting; —**опирающийся** *a.* unsupported, independent; —**определение** *n.* self-determination; —**опрокидывающийся** *a.* self-dumping, automatic dumping; —**опыление** *n.* (bot.) self-pollination.

**самоостан/авливающийся** *a.* self-stopping, self-catching; —**ов** *m.*, —**овка** *f.* automatic stop.

**само/отвердевать** *v.* harden by itself; —**отжиг** *m.* self-annealing; —**отравление** *n.* self-poisoning; —**отталкивание** *n.* self-repulsion; —**охлаждающийся** *a.*, —**охлаждение** *n.* self-cooling; —**охрана** *f.* self-defense; self-preservation; —**очевидный** *a.* self-evident.

**самоочищ/ающийся** *a.* self-cleaning, self-purifying; —**ение** *n.* self-purification.

**само/ошлаковывающийся** *a.* self-fluxing; —**пад** *m.* free fall, free-falling drill; —**переваривание** *n.* self-digestion, autolysis; —**перегревание** *n.* self-superheating; —**передвигающийся** *a.* self-moving, automatic; —**писец** *m.* self-recorder, automatic recorder, recorder, recording instrument.

**самопишущ/ий** *a.* self-recording, recording, self-registering, registering; **с. прибор** *see* **самописец**; —**ее перо** fountain pen.

**самоплавкий** *a.* self-fluxing.

**самопоглощение** *n.* self-absorption.

**самопод/аватель** *m.*, —**ающий механизм** self-feeder, automatic feeder; —**ающий** *a.* self-feeding.

**само/поддерживающийся** *a.* self-maintaining, self-supporting, self-sustaining; self-propagating; —**пожертвование** *n.* self-sacrifice; —**поилка** *f.* drinking fountain; —**пресс** *m.* (text.) cylinder press.

**самопроизвольн/о** *adv.* spontaneously; —**ость** *f.* spontaneity; —**ый** *a.* spontaneous, involuntary; arbitrary.

**само/пуск** *m.* self-starter, automatic starter; self-starting; —**пускающийся** *a.* self-starting; —**разгружающийся** *a.* self-discharging, gravity-discharge;

—разложение, —разрушение *n*. spontaneous decomposition; —размагничивающийся *a*. self-demagnetizing; —разогревание *n*. self-heating; evolution of heat (from reaction).

саморазря/д *m*., —жение *n*. (elec.) self-discharge; —жающийся *a*. self-discharging, running down; leaking.

самораспростран/ение *n*. self-propagation; —яющийся *a*. self-propagating.

саморассеяние *n*. (nucl.) self-scattering.

саморасцепл/ение *n*. self-detachment, automatic uncoupling; —яющийся *a*. self-detaching, disconnecting automatically.

саморегистрирующий *see* самопишущий.

саморегулир/ование *n*., —овка *f*. automatic regulation, self-regulation, self-adjustment, self-alignment; —овать *v*. regulate itself, adjust itself; —ующийся *a*. self-regulating, self-adjusting.

само/резка *f*. cutter; —реклама *f*. self-advertisement; —род *m*. native phosphoric ore.

самород/ный *a*. natural; (min.) native; —ок *m*. native metal, native ore; prill, nugget (of gold).

самосад/ка *f*., —очная соль (geol.) salt deposited in lakes, seas, etc.

само/свал *m*. dump truck; —сварение *n*. autodigestion; —светящийся *a*. self-luminous; —сгорание *see* самовоспламенение; —сев *m*. self-seeding; self-sown plant; volunteer crop; —севка *f*. self-sown plant; —сжатие *n*. self-constriction; —сжатый, —сжимающийся *a*. self-constricted; —син *m*. autosyn (instrument); —синхронизирующий *a*. self-synchronizing; —склеивающийся *a*. self-sealing.

самосмаз/ка *f*., —ывание *n*. self-lubrication, automatic lubrication; —очный, —ывающий, —ывающийся *a*. self-lubricating; —чик *m*., —ывающий прибор automatic lubricator.

само/согласованный *a*. self-congruent, self-consistent; —сопротивляющийся *a*. self-resistant; —сопряженный *a*. self-conjugate; self-adjoint (equation); —сохранение *n*. self-preserva-

tion; —спекающийся *a*. clotting, coagulating; hardened; —спуск *m*. self-triggering.

самостоятельн/о *adv*. independently; —ость *f*. independence; —ый *a*. independent, self-contained, separate.

само/суйка *f*. shaping machine, shaper; —схват *m*. grab; —таска *f*. drag, dragging device; bucket conveyer, drag conveyer; pull-over, drawing device.

самотек *m*. gravity flow, flow; gravity feed; drift; honey (flowing from combs); —ом by gravity; of its own accord; нагрузка —ом gravity loading; подача —ом gravity feed.

самотечный *a*. self-flowing; automatic, spontaneous; gravity (lubrication, circulation, etc.).

самотормо/жение *n*. self-braking, automatic braking, self-locking, self-catching; —зиться *v*. stop automatically; jam; —зящий, —зящийся *a*. self-braking, self-stopping.

самоточка *f*. automatic lathe; (obs.) screw-cutting lathe.

само/убивающий пояс insecticide-impregnated strip (of paper or burlap); —убийство *n*. suicide, self-destruction; —уверенный *a*. self-confident, confident, assured; —укладывание *n*. self-packing.

самоуплотн/ение *n*., —яющийся *a*. self-packing, self-sealing.

самоуправл/ение *n*. self-government; —яющийся *a*. self-governing.

само/управный *a*. arbitrary; —уравновешивающийся *a*. self-balancing.

самоустанавлив/ание *n*. self-adjustment, automatic adjustment; —ающийся *a*. self-adjusting, automatically adjusting, self-aligning; floating.

самоустойчивость *f*. autostability.

самоуч/итель *m*. manual of self-instruction, handbook; —ка *f*. self-education; *m. and f.* self-taught person.

само/фазировка *f*. autophasing; —флюсующийся *a*. self-fluxing; —фокусировка *f*., —фокусирующийся *a*. self-focusing; —хват *m*. grip.

самоход *m*. self-feed, power feed; self-acting; creeping (of meter); —ный *a*.

automotive, self-propelled, self-moving, self-acting, power-driven, power-operated; —ная подача power feed.
**самоцвет** *m.*, —ный камень gem; —ный *a.* fine (gem).
**самоцентр/ирующийся** *a.* self-centering, self-aligning; —овка *f.* self-centering, self-alignment.
**само/черт** *m.* pantograph; —чувствие *n.* state of health, state of being; —шлакующийся *a.* self-fluxing; —экранирование *n.* (nucl.) self-shielding.
**самсонит** *m.* (min.) samsonite.
**самум** *m.* (meteor.) simoon, sandstorm.
**самшит** *m.*, —овый *a.* (bot.) box, box-tree (*Buxus sempervirens*).
**сам/ый** *a.* the very; same, selfsame; **с. верхний** the highest, the topmost; **с. предмет** the subject itself, the thing itself; **с. факт, что** the very fact that; —ое большое at the most; the biggest; **с** —ого начала from the very first.
**сан., сан—** *abbr., prefix* (санитарный) sanitary.
**санатоген** *m.* Sanatogen.
**санаторий** *m.* sanatorium.
**санация** *f.* sanitation.
**сангвина** *f.* red chalk.
**сангвин/арин** *m.* sanguinarine; —ин *m.* sanguinin.
**сандал** *m.*, —овое дерево, —ьное дерево (bot.) sandalwood (*Santalum album*); **синий с.** logwood (*Haematoxylon campechianum*); —ин *see* **санталин**; —ия *f.*, —ьный *a.* sandal; **красное —ьное дерево** red sandalwood, sanders.
**сандарак** *m.*, —овый *a.* sandarac, gum juniper; (min.) realgar; —овая смола sandarac (resin); —овое дерево sandarac tree (*Callitris quadrivalvis*); —олевая кислота sandaracolic acid; —опимаровая кислота sandaracopimaric acid.
**сандарацин** *m.* sandaracin; —овая кислота sandaracinic acid; —олевая кислота sandaracinolic acid.
**сандбергерит** *m.* (min.) sandbergerite (a zinciferous variety of tennantite).
**сандвич** *m.* sandwich.
**сани** *pl.* sledge, sleigh; sled.

**санидин** *m.*, —овый *a.* (min.) sanidine, glassy feldspar.
**саниров/ание** *n.* sanitation; —ать *v.* improve sanitary conditions.
**санитар** *m.* orderly; hospital attendant; stretcher bearer; —ия *f.* sanitation; —но-строительные изделия (cer.) sanitary-construction ware.
**санитарн/ый** *a.* sanitary; hospital (train); **с. автомобиль, с. транспорт** ambulance; —ая служба medical service; —ая техника sanitary engineering; —ое управление department of sanitation.
**санкиновое дерево** (bot.) aniseed tree (*Illicium anisatum*).
**санкциониров/анный** *a.* sanctioned; —ать *v.* sanction, assent (to).
**саннуазский ярус** (geol.) Sannoisian stage.
**саноформ** *m.* sanoform, methyl diiodosalicylate.
**саночн/ик** *m.* (min.) drawer; —ый *a.* sledge.
**сантал** *m.* santal, santalenic acid; *see also* **сандальное дерево**; —ал *m.* santalal; —ен *m.* santalene; —еновая кислота, —ин *m.* santalenic acid, santalic acid, santalin; —ил *m.* santalyl.
**санталов/ый** *a.* santal, santalic; sandalwood; —ая кислота *see* **санталеновая кислота**; —ое дерево *see* **сандальное дерево**; —ое масло sandalwood oil.
**санталол** *m.* santalol.
**сантен** *m.* santene; —овая кислота santenic acid; —ол *m.* santenol; —он *m.* santenone.
**сантехника** *f.* sanitary engineering.
**санти—** *prefix* centi— (one-hundredth); —бар *m.* centibar (unit of pressure); —грамм *m.* centigram.
**сантил** *m.* Santyl, santalyl salicylate.
**санти/литр** *m.* centiliter; —метр *m.* centimeter; —метровая волна microwave, centimeter wave; —пуаза *f.* centipoise (unit of viscosity); —стокс *m.* centistokes (unit of kinematic viscosity).
**сантол** *m.* santol.
**сантонин** *m.* santonin, santonic lactone; —овая кислота santoninic acid; **соль —овой кислоты, —овокислая соль** santoninate; —овокислый натрий

sodium santoninate; —оксим *m.* santoninoxime.

сантон/истый *a.* santonous; —овая кислота santonic acid; соль —овой кислоты, —овокислая соль santonate; —овокислый натрий sodium santonate; —он *m.* santonone.

сантонский подъярус (geol.) Santonian substage.

санторин/овая земля, —ская земля (min.) Santorin earth (a volcanic ash).

сантохлор *m.* santochlor, *p*-dichlorobenzene.

санупр *abbr.* (санитарное управление) department of sanitation.

сап *m.* (vet.) glanders.

сапа *see* сапка.

сапамин *m.* Sapamine (detergent).

сапан *m.* (bot.) sapanwood (*Caesalpinia sappan*).

саперный *a.* (mil.) sapper, undermining.

сапетка *f.* (corn) crib.

сапин *m.* sapine (isomer of cadaverine); —овая кислота sapinic acid.

сапировать *v.* (mil.) sap, undermine.

сапка *f.* (agr.) hoe.

сапогенин *m.* sapogenin, sapogenol.

сапоги *pl.* boots.

сапожн/ик *m.* shoemaker; —ичество *n.* shoe-making; —ый *a.* shoemaker's; —ый вар cobbler's wax; —ый крем, —ая вакса, —ая мазь shoe polish.

сапон/арин *m.* saponarin; —ария *f.* (bot.) saponaria; —етин *m.* saponetin; —ин *m.* saponin; —ины *pl.* saponins (amorphous glycosides).

сапонит *m.* (min.) saponite.

сапонификация *see* омыление.

сапо/тален *m.* sapotalene, trimethylnaphthalene; —тин *m.* sapotin; —тинетин *m.* sapotinetin; —токсин *m.* sapotoxin.

саппан *see* сапан.

саприн *m.* saprine (a ptomaine).

сапро— *prefix* sapro— (rotten, putrid; decaying organic matter); —генный *a.* (biol.) saprogenous; —л *m.* a cresol disinfectant.

сапропел/евый *a.* (zool.) sapropelic; —ит *m.* sapropelite (coal derived from algal materials); —ь *m.* sapropel.

сапрофит *m.* (biol.) saprophyte.

сапун *m.* breather pipe, breather;

breather valve (of pump); snore piece (of pump).

сапфир *m.*, —овый *a.* (min.) sapphire (a gem variety of blue corundum); —ин *m.* (min.) sapphirine.

сарай *m.*, —ный *a.* barn, shed; garage, carhouse; hangar.

саранч/а *f.* locust, grasshopper; —евые, —овые *pl.* Acrididae, Locustidae.

саратогские свиты (geol.) Saratogan series.

сарган *m.* (zool.) garfish.

сард *m.* (min.) sard, carnelian (a variety of cryptocrystalline quartz).

сардел/евое масло anchovy oil; —ь *f.* anchovy; sardine.

Сарджента диаграмма Sargent diagram.

сардин/а, —ка *f.* sardine, pilchard; —иан *m.* (min.) sardinian (an anglesite); —овое масло sardine oil.

сардоникс *m.* (min.) sardonyx (a variety of chalcedony).

сарептская горчица (bot.) Indian mustard (*Brassica juncea*).

саржа *f.* (text.) serge.

саркастический *a.* sarcastic.

саркин *m.* sarkin, sarcine, hypoxanthine.

саркинит *m.* (min.) sarkinite.

сарко— *prefix* sarco— (flesh); —зин *m.*, —зиновый *a.* sarcosine, methylglycine; —колла *f.* sarcocolla (gum); —коллин *m.* sarcocollin; —лемма *f.* (anat.) sarcolemma; —лит *m.* (min.) sarcolite; —ма *f.* (med.) sarcoma; —плазма *f.* (anat.) sarcoplasma; —псид *m.* (min.) sarcopside; —споридии *pl.* (zool.) Sarcosporidia; —фаги *pl.* flesh flies (*Sarcophagidae*).

сармат *m.*, —ский ярус (geol.) Sarmatian stage.

саротамнин *m.* sarothamnine.

сарпинка *f.* printed calico.

саррацен/ин *m.* sarracenine; —ия *f.* (bot.) sarracenia; —овая кислота sarracenic acid; —овый корень sarracenia root.

сарсапар/елль, —илла, —илль, —иль *f.* sarsaparilla (dried root of *Smilax officinalis*); ост-индская с. *see* мадар.

сарса/повая кислота sarsapic acid; —понин *m.* sarsasaponin.

сарторит *m.* (min.) sartorite, skleroclase.

**сарци/дин** *m.* sarcidin (antibiotic); **—н** *see* **саркин.**

**сарыч** *m.* (zool.) buzzard.

**САС** *abbr.* (**селитряно-аммиачный суперфосфат**) ammonium nitrate superphosphate.

**сассапар/елль, —ель, —илль, —иль** *see* **сарсапарелль.**

**сассафрас** *m.*, **—овый** *a.* (bot.) sassafras.

**сасси** *n.* sassy bark, casca bark (of *Erythrofloeum guinense*).

**сассолин** *m.* (min.) sassoline, sassolite (a boric acid).

**САСШ** *see* **США.**

**сателлит** *m.* (astron.) satellite; (mech.) planet pinion (of gear), planet wheel; **—овый** *a.* satellite; subordinate; **—овая шестерня** planetary gear.

**сативин** *m.* sativin; **—овая кислота** sativic acid.

**сатин** *m.* (text.) satin; **—ер** *m.* glazer; **—ет** *m.* satinet, thin satin.

**сатениров/альный, —очный** *a.* satining, glazing; **—ание** *n.* satining, glazing; finish; **—анный** *a.* satin, glazed; **—ать** *v.* satin, glaze; calender, supercalender (paper).

**сатинит** *m.* satin white (pigment).

**сатиновое дерево** satinwood.

**сатко** *n.* Satco Metal (a lead-base alloy).

**сатура/тор** *m.* saturater; (sugar; beverages) carbonator; **—ционный** *a.*, **—ция** *f.* saturation; carbonation.

**сатурея** *f.* (bot.) savory (*Satureia hortensis*).

**Сатурн** *m.* (astron.) Saturn; **система —а** Saturnian system.

**сатурн/изм** *m.* (med.) saturnism, lead poisoning; **—ово дерево** arbor Saturni, lead tree; **—овы цветы** (min.) Saturn flowers, flowers of lead, mimetite.

**сафир** *see* **сапфир.**

**сафлор** *m.* (bot.) safflower (*Carthamus tinctorius*); zaffer (impure oxide of cobalt obtained by roasting ore); **красильный с.** safflower; **—ит** *m.* (min.) safflorite (an iron-containing cobalt diarsenide); **—овый** *a.* safflower; **—овый кармин** safflower red, carthamin.

**сафой** *see* **савойская капуста.**

**сафр/анин** *m.* safranine (a phenazine dye); **—анинол** *m.* safraninol; **—анол** *m.* safranol; **—ен** *m.* safrene; **—озин** *m.* safrosin; **—ол** *m.* safrole; **—он** *m.* saffron.

**сафьян** *m.*, **—овый** *a.* morocco (leather).

**сахар** *m.* sugar; **с.-рафинад** refined sugar; **с.-сатурн** sugar of lead, lead acetate; **с.-сырец** unrefined sugar; **жженый с.** caramel; **кристаллический с.** granulated sugar; **мелкий с.** powdered sugar.

**сахар/аза** *f.* saccharase, invertase; **—ан** *m.* saccharane; **—ат** *m.* saccharate, sucrate.

**сахардан** *m.* (bot.) East Indian rosewood (*Dalbergia latifolia*); jacaranda.

**сахари/д** *m.* saccharide; **—метр** *m.* saccharimeter; **—метрия** *f.* saccharimetry.

**сахарин** *m.* saccharin, benzoyl sulfonic imide; **—овая кислота** saccharinic acid; **—оза** *f.* saccharinose, saccharin.

**сахарист/ость** *f.* saccharinity; sugar content; **—ый** *a.* sugary, saccharine, sacchariferous; (geol.) saccharoidal, saccharoid; **—ое соединение** compound of sugar, spec. sucrate.

**сахарить** *v.* sugar, sweeten with sugar.

**сахарник** *m.* (bot.) skirret (*Sium sisarum*).

**сахарно/кальциевая соль, —кислый кальций** calcium saccharate; **—кислый** *a.* saccharic acid; saccharate (of); **—кислая соль** saccharate.

**сахарн/ый** *a.* sugar, saccharine; **с. завод** sugar refinery; **с. песок** granulated sugar; **с. тростник** (bot.) sugar cane (*Saccharum officinarum*); **с. уголь** charcoal from sugar; **—ая болезнь** (med.) diabetes; **—ая голова** sugar loaf; **—ая кислота** saccharic acid, tetrahydroxyadipic acid; **соль —ой кислоты** saccharate; **—ая пудра** confectioner's sugar.

**сахаро/биоза** *f.* saccharobiose, sucrose; **—вар** *m.* sugar refiner; **—варение** *n.* sugar refining; **—видный** *a.* (geol.) saccharoidal (texture); **—за** *f.* saccharose, sucrose; **—метр** *m.* saccharometer (a fermentation tube); **—мицеты** *pl.* (bot.) saccharomycetes; **—молочная кислота** saccharolactic acid, mucic acid; —**новая кислота** saccharonic acid; —**нос** *m.* sugar-yielding plant; —**образование** *n.* formation of sugar, saccharification; (physiol.) glycogenesis; —**подобный** *a.* sugar-like, saccharine, saccharoid, sugary; —**рафинадный завод** sugar refinery; —**содержащий** *a.* sugar-containing, sacchariferous, saccharine, saccharated.

**сахельский ярус** (geol.) Sahelian stage.

**сачок** *m.* hand net, insect net.

**саше** *n.* sachet; small bag.

**сб** *abbr.* (**сборник**) collection, symposium; (**стильб**) stilb.

**сбав/ить, —лять** *v.* reduce, lower, cut, deduct, subtract; —**ка** *f.* reduction, lowering, cut (in price), deduction.

**сбалансиров/анный** *a.* balanced; —**ать** *v.* balance, neutralize.

**сбалтывать** *v.* stir, mix up, shake up.

**сбе/гание** *n.* running off; —**гать, —жать** *v.* run off, flow off; run down, rush down; run over, overflow, bubble over, rise; —**гаться** *v.* collect, gather.

**сбере/гательная касса** savings bank; —**гать, —чь** *v.* save, economize; stock, lay up; keep, reserve; —**жение** *n.* economy, saving; preservation; —**жения** *pl.* savings.

**сбивать** *v.* knock down, beat down; knock off, strike off; throw down, down; knock together, nail together, put together; churn (butter), whip (cream), beat (eggs); **с. с дороги** lead astray; —**ся** *v.* be disconcerted, be confused; churn, whip; —**ся с пути** go astray.

**сбивка** *f.* beating off, striking off; churning (of butter), whipping (of cream), beating (of eggs).

**сбивчив/ость** *f.* confusedness; —**ый** *a.* confused, indistinct; conflicting.

**сбирать** *see* **собирать.**

**сбит/ый** *a.* knocked off, out of position, out of alignment; biased; nailed together, put together; churned (butter), whipped (cream), beaten (eggs); shot down (plane); —**ь** *see* **сбивать.**

**сбли/жать, —зить** *v.* draw together, bring together; bind, connect; compare; —**жаться** *v.* approach, draw together, converge; —**жение** *n.* drawing together, approach; connecting, binding; **прививка —жением** inarching (method of plant grafting); —**женный** *a.* drawn together; contiguous, adjacent; (biol.) connivent, converging.

**сблокированный** *a.* interlinked, interlocked.

**сбоина** *f.* residue, cake; husks.

**сбой** *m.* reduction, lowering; fragments.

**сбойка** *f.* joining, joint, mortising; (min.) connector, crosscut.

**сбойня** *see* **сбоина.**

**сбоку** *adv.* at the side (of), on the side, from the side; **вид с.** side view.

**сбол/тить, —чивать** *v.* bolt, fasten, secure; —**ченный** *a.* bolted together, fastened, secured; —**чивание** *n.* bolting together, fastening.

**сбор** *m.* assemblage, assembly, gathering, collection; picking, harvesting, reaping; yield; fee; **быть в —е** *v.* be assembled.

**сборка** *f.* assemblage, assembly, assembling, putting together, building up, setting up, erecting, erection, installation, rigging, mounting, fitting, joining; crease (in cloth); (glaze) shivering; **с. подборкой** selective assembly; **предварительная с., узловая с.** preliminary assembly, subassembly.

**сборник** *m.* collection; symposium; collector, accumulator, receiver, receptacle, storage tank, sump; header, manifold.

**сборн/ый** *a.* miscellaneous, heterogeneous; accumulative, aggregate, built up, assembled; collecting; prefabricated (building, cement, etc.); mixed (fertilizer); composite (map); **с. горшок** receiver; **с. пункт** gathering place; **с. щит** cable distributor; —**ая группа** assembly; —**ая шина** (elec.) collecting main; busbar.

**сборочн/ая** *f.*, —**ый цех** assembly shop, assembly plant, fitting shop; —**ый** *a.* assembly, assembling, erecting; —**ый винт** fastening screw; —**ый конвейер** assembly belt.

**сборщик** *m.* assembler, fitter, erector, mounter; collector, picker.

**сбраживать** *v.* ferment, brew.

сбрасыв/ание *n.* discarding, disposal, dumping, dropping, throwing down; (geol.) faulting; —атель *m.* knock-off; tripper; (geol.) fault fissure; —ать *v.* discard, dispose (of), dump, drop, throw down; throw off, cast off, shed; —ающий *a.* throwing down, dumping; —ающий прибор (aero.) jettison gear; —ающая трещина (geol.) fault fissure.

сбри/вать, —ть *v.* shave, shear off.

сброженный *a.* fermented, brewed.

сброс *m.* drop; (geol.) fault, break; (land) slide; амплитуда —a fault throw; линия —a fault trace, rift; откос —a, терраса —a, фас —a fault scarp.

сбросить *see* сбрасывать.

сбросов/ый *a.* (geol.) fault; с. выступ horst; —ая глыба, —ая масса fault block; —ая гора block mountain; —ая деятельность faulting; —ая линия fault trace, furrow; —ое строение faulted structure, block faulting.

сброшенн/ый *a.* thrown down, thrown off, discarded, dumped; (geol.) faulted; с. вниз (geol.) downfaulted; —ая котловина fault basin.

сбруя *f.* harness.

сбы/вание *n.,* —т *m.* sale, marketing; market; —вать, —ть *v.* sell off, market; dispose (of), get rid (of); —ваться *v.* happen, occur, turn out, be realized; —тие *n.* diminution; —тный *a.* marketable; —точный *a.* possible, probable, feasible.

св *abbr.* (международная свеча) international candle; св. *abbr.* (свыше) over; (святой) saint; СВ *abbr.* (средние волны) medium waves; С.-В. *abbr.* (северо-восток) northeast.

сваб/ирование *n.* swabbing (for starting oil wells); —ит *m.* (min.) swabite (a calcium arsenate).

сваебойная машина ram, pile driver.

свайка *f.* pole.

свайники *pl.* (zool.) Strongyloidea.

свайн/обойный *a.* pile-driving, ram; —ый *a.* pile; —ый мост pile bridge.

свал/енный *a.* thrown down, dumped, unloaded; —ивание *n.* dumping; felting, matting; —ивать, —ить *v.* dump, unload, throw down; heap up,

accumulate; —иваться *v.* fall, collapse, tumble down; —ка *f.,* —очное место dump, dumping ground; —очный *a.* dumping, unloading.

свал/яный *a.* felted, matted; —ять *v.* felt, mat.

Свана патрон (elec.) bayonet socket; С. цоколь bayonet cap.

сванбергит *m.* (min.) svanbergite.

сваренный *a.* cooked, boiled; welded, fused.

сварив/аемость *f.* weldability; —аемый, —ающийся *a.* weldable; —ание *n.* welding; —ать *v.* weld (together), weld up, fuse; —ать в притык buttweld.

сварить *v.* boil, cook; weld.

сварка *f.* welding; с. в цепь chain welding; с. мостиком bridge welding, tie welding; с. по шву, с. швом seam welding; с. рычагом bar welding; с. точками, точечная с. spot welding.

сварн/ой, —ый *a.* welded.

сварочн/ый *a.* weld, welding; с. автомат, с. агрегат, —ая машина welder, welding machine; с. жар welding heat; с. мастер welder; с. металл weld metal; с. прут welding rod; с. цех welding shop; с. шлак hearth cinder; —ая горелка welding torch, burner, blowpipe; —ая печь welding furnace; —ая сталь weld steel, puddled steel, mild steel; —ое дело welding practice; —ое железо weld iron, wrought iron; —ое оборудование welding outfit.

свартцит *m.* swartzite (uranium mineral).

сварщик *m.* welder, welding operator.

свая *f.* pile, pier, post, pole.

сведа *f.* (bot.) seablite (*Suaeda*).

сведен/ие *n.* knowledge, information; leading down; reduction; (med.) contraction, cramp; settling (of accounts); —ия *pl.* information, data; с. в таблицу tabulation; доводить до —ия *v.* notify; принять к —ию *v.* take into consideration; сообщать —ия *v.* instruct, inform; —ный *a.* reduced; settled, closed; contracted, cramped.

сведущ/ий *a.* adept, versed (in), expert, skilled; —ее лицо expert.

свеже— *prefix* freshly, recently.

**свежевать** *v.* flay, dress (cattle).

**свеже/замороженный** *a.* quick-frozen; **—приготовленный** *a.* freshly prepared, fresh; **—просольный** *a.* freshly pickled; fresh-salted; **—разведенный** *a.* freshly diluted; fresh; **—распиленный, —срубленный** *a.* green, unseasoned (timber); **—скошенный** *a.* freshly mowed.

**свеж/есть** *f.* freshness; brilliance (of color); **—ий** *a.* fresh, recent; brilliant, bright; live (steam); green (sand, coal, etc.); virgin (neutron).

**свезт/и, —ь** *see* **свозить.**

**свекл/а, —овица** *f.*, **—овичный** *a.* (bot.) beet (*Beta*); **кормовая с.** mangel-wurzel (*B. vulgaris macrorhiza*); **листовая с., —овичник** *m.* Swiss chard (*B. v. cicla*); **сахарная с.** sugar beet (*B. v. saccharifera*); **столовая с.** garden beet (*B. v.*); **—оводство, —осеяние** *n.* sugarbeet culture; **—окопатель** *m.* beetroot harvester.

**свеклосахарн/ый** *a.* beet-sugar; **с. завод** beet-sugar refinery; **—ая патока** beetroot molasses.

**свербежни/к** *m.* (bot.) thistle; **—ца** *f.* scabious (*Scabiosa*).

**свер/гать, —гнуть** *v.* throw down, overthrow; **—жение** *n.* overthrow.

**свер/ить** *see* **сверять; —ка** *f.* collation, comparison; revision; regulation (of clock).

**сверк/ание** *n.* sparkle, sparkling, glitter, flash; **—ать, —нуть** *v.* sparkle, glitter, flash, gleam, scintillate; **—ающий** *a.* sparkling, glittering, flashing, bright.

**сверл/ение** *n.* boring, drilling, piercing; **—ила** *pl.* ship-timber beetles (*Lymexylonidae*); **—ильник** *m.* borer, driller; (bot.) samphire (*Crithmum maritimum*); **—ильноревольверный станок** turret drill.

**сверлильн/ый** *a.* boring, drilling; **с. перфоратор** auger, rotary drill; **с. станок, —ая машина** drill, drill press; **—ая стружка** borings.

**сверл/ильщик** *m.* borer, driller; **—ить** *v.* bore, drill, perforate, pierce.

**сверло** *n.* drill, borer, boring bit, bit, auger; **с.-коронка, желобчатое с., полое с.** core drill, diamond drill; **с.-развертка** finishing drill; **американ-**

**ское с., витое с., спиральное с.** twist drill.

**сверл/овщик** *m.* borer, driller, drill operator; **—озаточный** *a.* drill-sharpening; **—янка** *f.* borer, spec. ship worm.

**сверн/увшийся** *a.* clotted, curdled, coagulated; coiled (rope); **—утость** *f.* convolution; **—утый** *a.* convolute, folded, rolled; stripped (thread); coagulated; **—уть** *v.* turn; wrench; *see* **свертывать; —уться в петлю** kink (of cord, wire).

**сверст/ать, —ывать** *v.* (typ.) make up into pages.

**сверт/еть** *see* **свертывать; —ка (функций)** *f.* (math.) convolution.

**свертн/ый** *a.* screwed on; **с. вал** built-up shaft; **—ая гайка, —ая муфта** screw cap; cap screw.

**сверток** *m.* packet, package, pack, parcel.

**свертыв/аемость** *f.* coagulability; **—аемый** *a.* coagulable; **—ание** *n.* coagulation; curdling; convolution, folding; rolling, coiling; **—ать** *v.* coagulate; roll up, wrap up; turn (aside); curtail (production); **—аться** *v.* coagulate, curdle, congeal, clot; roll up, curl up, crumple; **—ающийся** *a.* coagulating, congealing.

**сверх** *prep. gen.* above, over, beyond; besides, in addition to; **с. того** moreover, over and above, besides, on top of.

**сверх—** *prefix* super—, hyper—, ultra—, extra—, excessively; **—адиабатический** *a.* superadiabatic; **—баллон** *m.* balloon tire; – **быстродействующий, —быстроходный, —быстрый** *a.* super fast, extra fast, ultra-high-speed; **—высокий** *a.* ultra-high; super—; **—густитель** *m.* (ore concentration) superthickener; **—давление** *n.* excess pressure, pressure above atmospheric; (aero.) superpressure; **—действие** *n.* peak output; **—закалка** *f.* (met.) superhardening; **—звуковой** *a.* (acous.) supersonic, ultrasonic; **—комплектный** *a.* supernumerary; **—критический** *a.* supercritical, above critical; **—критичность** *f.* supercriticality; **—легкий** *a.* super-light; **—летальный** *a.* superlethal; **—микроскоп** *m.* electron microscope.

**сверх/мощный** *a.* superpower; super—; —**никель** *m.* supernickel (copper-nickel alloy); —**отжиг** *m.* (met.) over-annealing; —**плоскость** *f.* (math.) hyperplane; —**прибыль** *f.* excess profit; —**проводимость** *f.* super-conductivity; —**сжатие** *n.* overcompression; —**скоростной** *a.* super-high-speed, extra fast; —**соприкосновение** *n.* (geom.) superosculation; —**сопряжение** *n.* hyperconjugation; —**структура** *f.* superstructure, superlattice; —**счетный** *a.* odd; —**твердый** *a.* superhard, extra hard; —**текучесть** *f.* superfluidity; —**текучий** *a.* super-fluid; —**ток** *m.* (elec.) overcurrent, excess current; —**тонкий** *a.* hyperfine; —**точный** *a.* very precise, super— (regulator); —**тяжелый** *a.* superheavy.

**сверху** *adv.* from above; at the top (of); on, upon, above, over; **с. до низу** from top to bottom; **давление с.** top pressure; **загрузка с.** top charging.

**сверх/урочный** *a.* overtime; —**фильтр** *m.* ultrafilter; —**фоторегистрация** *f.* moving-image camera photography; —**человеческий** *a.* superhuman; —**чистый** *a.* ultra-pure; —**чувствительный** *a.* supersensitive, super— (regulator); —**штатный** *a.* supernumerary; —**ъестественный** *a.* supernatural, miraculous; —**ядро** *n.* supernucleus.

**сверч/ок** *m.* cricket; —**ки** *pl.* Gryllidae.

**сверш/ать, —ить** *v.* complete, accomplish, achieve, perfect; —**аться, —иться** *v.* be completed, be achieved, come about; —**ение** *n.* completion, accomplishment, achievement.

**сверять** *v.* collate, compare; regulate (clock).

**свес** *m.* overhang, jut, projection, extension; —**ить** *see* **свешивать.**

**свест/и, —ь** *see* **сводить.**

**свет** *m.* light, daylight; world; **в —у** clear, in the clear, inside; **высота в —у** inside height, clearance; **диаметр в —у** inside diameter; **ширина в —у** clearance, clear width, clear opening; **преломление —а** refraction of light, optical refraction; **проливающий с.** luminous; **пропускающий с.** translucent; **сила —а** *see* **светосила.**

**светать** *v.* dawn, grow light.

**светил/о** *n.* star, luminary, light; —**а** *pl.* heavenly bodies.

**светильн/ик** *m.* lamp, illuminant; —**ый** *a.* illuminating; —**я** *f.* wick, taper.

**светимость** *f.* luminance; radiance; transmission (of spectrometer).

**светить** *v.* light, give light; —**ся** *v.* shine, gleam, glisten, sparkle.

**светлана** *f.* (bot.) amaryllis.

**светлеть** *v.* lighten, grow light, brighten; clear up, clarify.

**светло** *adv.* light, bright, clear; it is light; —**вина** *f.* bright spot; —**коричневый** *a.* light brown; —**красный** *a.* light red, bright red; —**окрашенный** *a.* light-colored, light; —**сть** *f.* lightness, brightness; clearness, lucidity; —**та** *f.* luminosity; —**тянутая сталь** (met.) bright-drawn steel.

**светлушка** *see* **сафлор.**

**светлый** *a.* light, bright, luminous; clear, lucid; **с. отжиг** (met.) bright annealing.

**светля/к, —чок** *m.* glow-worm, firefly.

**светность** *f.* high light.

**свето—** *prefix* light, photo—; *see also* **фото—;** —**блик** *m.* light pattern; —**боязнь** *f.* (med.) photophobia; —**вод** *m.* (nucl.) light guide.

**светов/ой** *a.* light, luminous; **с. выход,** —**ая отдача** light output; luminous efficiency; luminescence yield; **с. поток** luminous flux; **с. пучок** pencil of light; **с. сигнал** flare; **с. эфир** luminiferous ether; —**ая волна** light wave; —**ая дуга** luminous arc, (electric) arc; —**ая копия** *see* **светокопия;** —**ая мощность** luminosity, luminescence; —**ое явление** luminous phenomenon; optical phenomenon.

**свето/выход** *m.* light output; —**излучение** *n.* radiation of light; —**испускающий** *a.* light-emitting, luminous.

**светокоп/ирная бумага, —ировальная бумага** blueprint paper; —**ировальная машина** blueprinting machine; —**ировальня** *f.* blue printing room; —**ирование** *n.* blue printing; photostating; —**ия** *f.* blueprint; photostat.

**свето/лечение** *n.* (med.) phototherapy, light treatment; —**ловушка** *f.* insect trap (using light); —**любивый** *a.*

light-requiring; —маскировка *f.* blackout; —масса *see* светосостав; —мер *m.* photometer; —мерный *a.* photometric; —непроницаемый *a.* lightproof, light-tight; opaque; —носный *a.* luminiferous; —ориентация *f.* (biol.) phototropism; —печатание *n.* photographic tracing; —писное копирование blueprinting; photostating; —пись *f.* photography; —поглощение *n.* light absorption; —провод *see* световод; —прозрачный *a.* translucent.

светопроницаем/ость *f.* transparency; translucence; —ый *a.* transparent; translucent.

светопрочный *a.* fast to light, photostable.

светорассе/ивающий *a.* light-diffusing, light-scattering; —яние *n.* diffusion or scattering of light.

свето/сигнализация *f.* light signaling; —сила *f.* illuminating power; aperture ratio, speed (of lens); transmission (of spectrometer); —состав *m.* phosphor, luminous compound; —стойкий *a.* lightproof, light-resistant, fast to light (of dye), photostable; —стойкость, —устойчивость *f.* light resistance, photostability, fastness to light; —тень *f.* light and shadow; —техника *f.* lighting engineering, illumination engineering; —фильтр *m.* light filter, color filter; —фор *m.* traffic light, signal light, light signal.

светочувствительн/ость *f.* sensitivity to light, photosensitivity; speed (of film); —ый *a.* sensitive to light, photosensitive; —ая бумага light-sensitive paper, printing paper, photographic paper (for blueprints, etc.); —ая проводимость (elec.) photoconductivity; —ое сопротивление photoresistance.

светоэлектрический *a.* photoelectric; с. элемент photoelectric cell.

светящ/ийся *a.* luminous, luminescent, phosphorescent, shining; noctilucent (cloud); с. разряд (elec.) glow discharge; —аяся краска luminous paint; —аяся лампа (thermionics)

glow tube; —аяся точка luminous point, bright spot; focus.

свеч/а *f.* candle; запальная с. sparkplug; нормальная с., стандартная с. standard candle; сила света в —ах, число —ей candlepower.

свечение *n.* luminescence, luminosity, brightness, glow, phosphorescence, radiance, glimmer, glint, shimmer; lighting; белое с. incandescence, white heat; красное с. red heat.

свечеобразный *a.* candle-shaped.

свечка *see* свеча.

свечн/ой *a.* candle; —ость *f.* candle-power.

свешив/ать *v.* weigh, weigh down; hang down; —аться *v.* be weighed; hang down, overhang; —ающийся *a.* overhanging.

свив/ание *n.*, —ка *f.* coiling, twisting, twist; —ать *v.* coil, twist, wind, spin.

св. Игнатия бобы *see* Игнатия.

свидание *n.* meeting, appointment, interview.

свидетел/ь *m.* witness, onlooker; (analysis) blank sample; (chromatography) reference spot, marker; быть —ем *v.* witness, be a witness (to); —ьское показание (court) evidence.

свидетельств/о *n.* evidence, attestation, affirmation; testimony; document, certificate, record; bill (of sale); —ование *n.* witnessing, examination, verification; —овать *v.* witness, attest, bear witness (to), testify; indicate; —оваться у доктора get a health certificate; —ующий о significative, indicating.

свилеват/ость *f.* (bot.) curly grain, cross grain; —ый *a.* cross-grained; knotty, gnarled.

свиль *f.* curve, knot (in wood); cord (flaw in glass).

свинарн/ик *m.*, —я *f.* pig sty.

Свинбурна испытание (elec.) Swinburne test.

свиневодство *n.* swine breeding.

свин/ец *m.* lead, Pb; гремучий с. fulminating lead; двуокись —ца, перекись —ца lead dioxide, lead peroxide; закись —ца, недокись —ца lead suboxide; мышьяковокислый с. lead arsenate; окись —ца lead oxide, specif. lead monoxide; **соль окиси —ца** lead salt, specif. a salt of bivalent lead; **сернистый с.** lead sulfide; **сернокислый с., сульфат —ца** lead sulfate; **уксуснокислый с.** lead acetate, sugar of lead; **хлористый с.** lead chloride, plumbous chloride; **хлорный с.** lead tetrachloride, plumbic chloride; **хромовокислый с.** lead chromate.

**свинина** *f.* pork, pig.

**свинка** *f.* young pig, small pig; (met.) pig, ingot, bar; (mercury) switch; (med.) mumps; (zool.) beet pest (*Bothynoderes punctiventris*); **железо в —х, чугун в —х** pig iron.

**свиноводство** *n.* swine breeding.

**свин/ой** *a.* swine, pig; pork (meat); **с. жир, —ое сало** lard; **с. камень** (min.) swine stone (a variety of marble); **—орой** *m.* Bermuda grass (*Cynodon dactylon*).

**свинтить** *see* **свинчивать.**

**свин/ух** *m.,* **—уха** *f.* mushroom (*Agaricus violaceus*); **—ушка** *f.* mushroom (*A. placomyces* or *Paxillus involutus*).

**свинцевание** *n.* lead plating, lead lining.

**свинцовисто/кислая соль** plumbite; **— кислый натрий, —натриевая соль** sodium plumbite; **—мышьяковый блеск** (min.) dufrenoysite.

**свинцовист/ый** *a.* lead, plumbous; **—ая кислота** lead hydroxide, plumbous hydroxide; **соль —ой кислоты** plumbite; **—ая соль** plumbous salt, lead salt.

**свинцовка** *f.* (bot.) leadwort (*Plumbago*).

**свинцово/висмутовый сплав** lead-bismuth alloy; **—водород** *m.* lead hydride; **—кальциевая соль** calcium plumbate.

**свинцовокисл/ый** *a.* plumbic acid; plumbate (of); **с. натрий** sodium plumbate; **—ая соль** plumbate.

**свинцово/медный штейн** lead-copper matte; **—натриевая соль** sodium plumbate; **—оловянный сплав** (met.) lead-tin alloy; **—плавильная печь** (met.) lead furnace; **—плавильный завод** lead works; **—серый** *a.* lead-gray, lead-colored; **—суриковая покраска** red-lead coating.

**свинцов/ый** *a.* lead, plumbic; **с. аккуму-**

**лятор** (elec.) lead accumulator, battery; **с. блеск** (min.) lead glance, galena, lead sulfide; **с. глет** litharge, lead oxide; **с. груз** plumb bob; **с. корень** *see* **свинцовка; с. крон** chrome yellow; **с. купорос** lead sulfate; **с. отвес** plumb line; **с. пепел, —ая изгарина, —ая окалина** lead ash; lead dross; the gray film of oxide on lead exposed to air; **с. сахар** sugar of lead, lead acetate; **с. сурик** red lead, red lead oxide, minium; **с. уксус** vinegar of lead (basic lead acetate solution); **с. шлак** lead scoria, lead dross; **—ая бумага, —ая фольга** leadfoil; **—ая дробь** lead shot; **—ая желтая** lead yellow, lead chromate; **—ая земля** (min.) earthy cerussite; **—ая камедь** (min.) plumboresinite; **—ая камера** lead chamber (for sulfuric acid manufacture); **соль —ой кислоты** plumbic acid; **соль —ой кислоты** plumbate; **—ая почка** (min.) bindheimite (a hydrous lead antimonate); **—ая примочка** Goulard's extract (solution of basic lead acetate); **—ая решетка** (elec.) lead grid; **—ая роговая руда** (min.) horn lead, phosgenite; **—ая слюда** (min.) cerussite in micaceous form; **—ая соль** lead salt; **—ое дерево** lead tree, arbor Saturni; **—ые белила** white lead, lead carbonate.

**свинчак** *m.* (min.) galena, lead sulfide, spec. compact galena, specular galena.

**свинчатковые** *pl.* (bot.) Plumbaginaceae.

**свинч/енный** *a.* screwed, screwed together; **—ивание** *n.* screwing; **—ивать** *v.* screw, screw together.

**свин/ья** *f.,* **—ячий** *a.* pig, swine, hog; sow.

**свирепый** *a.* fierce; violent (epidemic, etc.).

**свис/ать, —нуть** *v.* hang loose, sag, trail; overhang; **—ающий** *a.* hanging, pendent; **—лый** *a.* hanging, sagging, drooping.

**свист** *m.* whistle, hiss, hissing; (rad.) howling (static); **—ать, —еть, —нуть** *v.* whistle, hiss; **—ок** *m.* whistle.

**свистящий** *a.* whistling, hissing; sibilant.

**свит/а** *f.* suite, series, set; strata; **—ы** *pl.* (geol.) formation.

**свитер** *m.* sweater.

**свит/ок** *m.* roll, scroll; (zool.) volute; **—ый** *a.* coiled, convoluted; **—ь** *see* **свивать.**

**свищ** *m.* flaw, unsound spot, air hole, honeycomb (on metals); worm hole; (med.) fistula; (anat.) sinus; **—евой** *a.* fistular, fistulous.

**свобода** *f.* freedom, liberty.

**свободно** *adv.* freely, loosely, easily; **с. надетый** loose, loose-fitting; **с. сидящий** loose-running (on shaft); **— висящий** *a.* cantilever; **—лепестный** *a.* (bot.) apopetalous; choripetalous; **—стоящий** *a.* upright, self-supported.

**свободный** *a.* free, loose, clear, open; independent, separate; available; **с. от** free from, devoid of.

**свод** *m.* arch, arc, vault, dome, cupola; canopy, roof, crown (of furnace); saddle, crest; (geol.) anticline; summary, digest; **выводить —ом** *v.* arch.

**сводик** *m.* little vault; bung.

**сводить** *v.* lead, take, conduct; bring together, converge; settle up, pay off; **с. до** reduce to; **с. на-нет** bring to nothing; **—ся** *v.* be let down; lead (to), come (to); **все это сводится к** the net result is.

**свод/ка** *f.* résumé, summary, abstract; report, bulletin; felling (of tree); **—ный** *a.* compound, composite, combined.

**свод/овой, —овый** *a.* crest, crown; arch; **—чатый** *a.* arched, vaulted, cambered.

**свое** *see* **свой.**

**своевременн/о** *adv.* in good time, opportunely; **—ость** *f.* opportuneness; **—ый** *a.* opportune, timely, well-timed.

**своеобраз/ие** *n.*, **—ность** *f.* originality, peculiarity; **—ный** *a.* original, unusual, peculiar, unique, out of the ordinary.

**своз/ить** *v.* carry, convey, transport; **—ка** *f.* conveyance, transport, removal, carting.

**свой** *a. and possessive pron.* my, his, her, its, our, your, their; one's own; domestic, home; **своего производства**

of domestic manufacture; **в свое время** at one time, formerly; **на своем** on his own; **настоять на своем** *v.* insist; **по своему** in one's own way.

**свойственн/о** *adv.* naturally; it is natural; **—ость** *f.* peculiarity, singularity; **—ый** *a.* peculiar, distinctive, characteristic, specific; natural, native, indigenous, inherent, intrinsic.

**свойств/о** *n.* property, characteristic, quality, attribute, feature, aspect, capacity, behavior; nature, character; relationship, alliance; **в —е** related; **физические —а** physical properties; **химические —а** chemical properties.

**свор/ачивание** *n.* turning, shunting; bending aside, deflection; **—ачивать, —отить** *v.* turn aside, shunt; bend aside, deflect; displace, dislodge, remove.

**СВЧ** *abbr.* (**сверхвысокая частота, сверхвысокочастотный**) ultra-high frequency.

**свык/аться, —нуться** *v.* accustom oneself (to), become accustomed.

**свыше** *prep. gen.* above, beyond, upwards (of), over.

**связанность** *f.* combined state; coherence.

**связан/ный** *a.* combined, bound, fixed, linked, tied, coupled, connected, connected up, associated, affiliated, allied; coherent; latent; **не с.** free; **химически с.** chemically combined, combined, fixed; **—о с** (it) involves.

**связать** *see* **связывать.**

**связи** *see under* **связь.**

**связист** *m.* signaler, signal man.

**связк/а** *f.* bundle, roll, sheaf, pack, bunch, batch, fagot, bale; binding, band; bond; binder; (anat.) ligament; **с. входа** (cybernetics) input bundle; **—и** *pl.* ligaments; **голосовые —и** (anat.) vocal chords.

**связной песок** (min.) auriferous sand with high clay content.

**связн/ость** *f.* connectedness, coherence; tenacity (of soil); (math.) compendency, connectedness, connection; **— ый** *a.* connected, coherent, cohesive; compendent.

**связочн/ый** *a.* bundle, bunch; (anat.)

ligamentous, ligamental; —ое железо bundle iron, fagot iron.

**связующ/ий** *a.* binding, cementing, connecting, connective, conjunctive; —ая рама bracing frame; —ая способность binding power, cementing power; —ая ткань (anat.) conjunctive tissue; —ее вещество, —ее средство binder, adhesive, glue, cement, agglutinant.

**связыв/ание** *n.* binding, bonding, combining, linking, coupling, tying together; —ать *v.* bind, combine, fix, take up; tie, link, couple, connect; cement, bond; consolidate; stay, brace; —аться *v.* be bound, be combined, combine; bind oneself (to); get involved (with); —ающий *see* **связующий**.

**связ/ь** *f.* bond, tie, connection, coupling, link, linkage, junction, jointing, joining, conjunction, bonding, binding; (elec.) coupling; contact, association, relation, closeness, cohesion, coherence, continuity; communications, communication; binder; connector, tie piece, tie rod, stay, brace, bracing, strut, truss; belt, belting; с. через излучение radiation coupling; в —и in connection (with); двойная с. (chem.) double bond; корпус —и signal corps; коэффициент —и coupling factor; поддерживать с. *v.* keep in touch; порвать с. *v.* sever a connection; система —и communicating system; (rad.) coupling system; служба —и communication service; сопротивление —и (elec.) coupling resistance; средство —и means of communication; установить с. *v.* establish communication; (elec.) connect up; химическая с. chemical bond; энергия —и (nucl.) binding energy; эффект химической —и (nucl.) chemical binding effect.

**свясло** *n.* bandage.

**свят/ой** *a.* saint; —ое дерево (bot.) guaiacum, lignum vitae (*Guaiacum officinale*); —оянское зелье (bot.) St. John's wort (*Hypericum perforatum*).

**сг** *abbr.* (сантиграмм) centigram.

**сгиб** *m.* bend, flexure, fold, crimp;

(anat.) flexion; —аемость *f.* pliability, flexibility; —аемый, —ающийся *a.* pliable, flexible, bendable; collapsible; —ание *n.* flexure, flection, bending, deflection; —атель *m.*, —ающая мышца (anat.) flexor; —ательный, —ающий *a.* bending, flexing; flexor; —ать *v.* bend, flex, fold; curve, crook; deflect; —аться *v.* bend, bend down, bow down, stoop; swerve.

**сгла/дить, —живать** *v.* smooth, smooth over; obliterate; scrape, plane; level, level down; —живаться *v.* wear smooth; —живание *n.* smoothing, smoothing out, flattening; scraping, planing; leveling; —живатель *m.* smoother, flattener.

**сгни/вать, —ть** *v.* rot, putrefy, decay.

**сговариваться** *v.* arrange (for), make arrangements (with), agree (upon); make an appointment (with).

**сгон** *m.* driving together, joining, fitting; rafting (of lumber); (pipe) sleeve; —ный *a.* driven together, joined; —ная гайка, —ная муфта screw cap; cap screw; (pipe) sleeve, union; —щик *m.* fitter; —ять *v.* drive together, join, fit; drive away, drive off; raft, float.

**сгораем/ость** *f.* combustibility, inflammability; —ый *a.* combustible, inflammable; —ые вещества combustibles.

**сгоран/ие** *n.* combustion, burning; (nucl.) burn-up; камера —ия, пространство —ия combustion chamber; мотор внутреннего —ия internal-combustion engine; продукты —ия combustion products.

**сгор/ать, —еть** *v.* burn, burn up, burn out; —ающий *a.* burning; combustible; —евший *a.* burnt.

**сгре/балка** *f.* rake; (met.) strike, puddler's rabble; —бание *n.* raking; skimming; —бать, —сти, —сть *v.* rake, rake up, rake together; skim.

**сгру/жать, —зить** *v.* unload.

**сгруппиров/ание, —ывание** *n.* grouping; —анный *a.* grouped, banked; bunched; —ать, —ывать *v.* group, bank, assemble.

**СГС** *abbr.* (сантиметр-грамм-секунда)

centimeter-gram-second (cgs system of units).

**сгустившийся** *a.* thickened, coagulated, clotted.

**сгуститель** *m.* thickener, coagulant, condenser; (paper) decker; —**ный** *a.* thickening, coagulating; —**ное средство** coagulant.

**сгуст/ить** *see* **сгущать;** —**ок** *m.* coagulum, curd, clot (of blood, etc.); bunch, cluster; blob (in photoemulsion); sheaf (of rays); **образование** —**ков** bunching, clustering.

**сгущаем/ость** *f.* condensability; compressibility (of gas); —**ый** *a.* condensable; compressible.

**сгущ/ать** *v.* thicken, condense, concentrate; compress, liquefy; coagulate, clot, curdle; **с. выпариванием** boil down, concentrate; —**аться** *v.* be condensed, be concentrated; coagulate, clot; —**ающий** *a.* condensing, concentrating; coagulating; —**ающее вещество** coagulant.

**сгущен/ие** *n.* condensation, thickening, concentration; compression, liquefaction; coagulation, clotting, curdling; gelling, setting; (phase) bunching (in cyclotron); —**ный** *a.* condensed, thickened, concentrated; compressed, liquefied; coagulated; evaporated (milk).

**сдабривать** *v.* flavor, season.

**сдавать** *v.* give up, part with; yield; rent, lease; check (baggage); —**ся** *v.* give in, surrender, acknowledge defeat; be for rent; **ему сдается** it seems to him.

**сдавл/енный** *a.* pressed, squeezed, compressed; —**ивание** *n.* pressing, squeezing, compression; pinching; throttling; —**ивать** *v.* press, squeeze, compress, condense; pinch, contract; mash, crush; throttle.

**сда/точный** *a.*, —**ча** *f.* lease; change (in small coin); surrender; checking (of baggage); —**ть** *see* **сдавать.**

**сдваив/ание** *n.* doubling, duplication; (bot.) gemination; **период** —**ания** doubling time (of nuclear reactor); —**ать** *v.* double, duplicate; combine in pairs; —**ающий** *a.* doubling; joining; coupling (rod).

**сдвиг** *m.* displacement, shift, slip; shear, shearing, shearing action; (geol.) fault, dislocation, upheaval, heave; lag; improvement, progress (in work, etc.); **с. фаз** (elec.) phase displacement, phase shift; **угол** —**а фаз** phase angle; **коэффициент** —**а** coefficient of shear; **напряжение** —**а** shear stress; **плоскость** —**а** shear plane; **площадь** —**а** shearing area; **предельное напряжение** —**а** yield stress; **работающий на с.** under shear stress; **сопротивление** —**у** shear strength, resistance to shear; **угол** —**а** angle of displacement.

**сдвиг/ание** *n.* displacing, displacement, shifting; —**ать,** —**ивать** *v.* displace, shift, slide, remove; shear; draw together; —**аться,** —**иваться** *v.* shift, shear; —**ающий** *a.* shifting, shearing; —**ающее усилие** shear, shearing, shear force; shear stress; —**овая волна** transverse wave.

**сдвижение** *n.* displacement, shifting, shearing; bringing together.

**сдвижной** *a.* movable; slip (cover); telescopic (mast).

**сдвинут/ый** *a.* displaced, shifted, removed; out of line, out of alignment, skew; **с. по фазе** out of phase; —**ь** *see* **сдвигать.**

**сдво/ение** *n.* doubling, duplication; —**енный** *a.* double, doubled, duplex; twin, twinned; binary, paired, combined in pairs, matched, coupled; (bot.) geminate; —**ить** *see* **сдваивать.**

**сдел/анный** *a.* made, manufactured; —**ано** it is done, it is made; —**ать** *v.* make, do, manufacture; accomplish, carry out; —**аться** *v.* become.

**сделка** *f.* agreement, transaction, deal, bargain; arrangement.

**сдельн/о** *adv.* by the piece, by the job; **с.-премиальная система** contract-bonus system; —**ый** *a.* piece, by the piece, job; —**ая плата,** —**ая оплата** piece-rate pay, payment by the piece; —**ая работа** piecework, contract work.

**сдельщи/к** *m.* pieceworker, workman paid by the piece; —**на** *f.* piecework.

**сдергивать** *v.* pull off, tear off, pull down, draw down.

**сдерж/анный** *a.* reserved, discreet, composed; **—ать, —ивать** *v.* check, keep in check, restrain, repress, moderate; contain, support, sustain; **—ивание** *n.* check, restraint, suppression, coercion; **—ивающий** *a.* restrictive.

**сдернуть** *see* **сдергивать.**

**сдир/ание** *n.* stripping, peeling; **—ать** *v.* strip, strip off, peel, flay, skin; bark; **—аться** *v.* peel, flake, come off.

**сдоб/а** *f.* shortening; seasoning, condiment; **—ный** *a.* rich (pastry).

**сдобрить** *see* **сдабривать.**

**сдор** *m.* beef lard.

**сду/вать, —ть** *v.* blow away, blow off.

**себам/ид** *m.* sebamide; **—иновая кислота** sebamic acid.

**себац/ил** *m.* sebacyl; **хлористый с.** sebacyl chloride; **—иловая кислота, —иновая кислота** sebacic acid, decanedioic acid; **соль —иновой кислоты** sebacate.

**себестоимость** *f.* net cost, cost price, cost (of manufacture).

**себя** *gen. and acc. reflexive pron.* oneself, myself, himself, herself, itself, ourselves, yourselves, themselves.

**сев** *m.* (agr.) sowing, planting; seed; young crop, seedlings.

**сев.** *abbr.* (**северный**) north, northern; **сев.-вост.** *abbr.* (**северо-восточный**) northeast.

**север** *m.* north.

**северн/ый** *a.* north, northern, northerly; **С. ледовитый океан** Artic Ocean; **с. полярный** Arctic; **Северная Америка** North America; **—ое сияние** aurora borealis, northern lights.

**северо/-американский** *a.* North American; **С.-Американские Соединенные Штаты** United States of America; **-восток** *m.* northeast; **-запад** *m.* northwest; **—магнитный** *a.* north-magnetic.

**сев.-зап.** *abbr.* (**северо-западный**) northwest.

**севооборот** *m.* (agr.) crop rotation.

**севр** *m.,* **—ские изделия** (cer.) Sèvres ware.

**севрю/га** *f.* starred sturgeon; **—жина** *f.* sturgeon meat.

**Сегер** *see under* **Зегер.**

**сегмент** *m.* segment, section; **—ация** *f.* segmentation; fission; **—ный, —о-образный** *a.* segmental, segmentary.

**сегнерово колесо** Segner's wheel.

**сегнето/активный, —электрический** *a.* (phys.) ferroelectric (*also called* Seignette-electric); **—ва соль** Seignette salt, Rochelle salt, potassium sodium tartrate; **—электрик** *m.* ferroelectric; **—электричество** *n.* ferroelectricity.

**сего** *see* **сей.**

**сегодня** *adv.* today, this day; **с. утром** this morning; **—шний** *a.* today's.

**сеголетка** *f.* this year's brood.

**сегрега/т** *m.,* **—ционное включение** (met.) segregate, segregant; **—ционный** *a.* segregation, segregated; **—ция** *f.* segregation; liquation.

**седалище** *n.* seat, seating; (anat.) buttock.

**седалищн/ый** *a.* (anat.) sciatic; **—ая болезнь** (med.) sciatica; **—ая кость** (anat.) ischium.

**седан** *m.* sedan.

**седан/олид** *m.* sedanolid; **—оновый ангидрид** sedanonic anhydride; **—ский черный** Sedan black.

**седатин** *m.* sedatin, valeridin; Sedatine, antipyrine.

**седел/ка** *f.,* **—ьце** *n.,* **—ьный** *a.* saddle; clamp, cleat; collar beam; pad.

**Седерберга электрод** *see* **Содерберга электрод.**

**седеть** *v.* turn gray, get gray hair.

**седимент/ация** *f.* sedimentation; **—о-метрия** *f.* sedimentometry.

**седина** *f.* gray hair; (met.) flaw.

**седло** *n.* saddle; seat (of valve); collar beam; (meteor.) col; (geol.) anticline; **—видный, —образный** *a.* saddle-shaped, saddle; **—образное соединение** (welding) saddle joint; **—вина** *f.* saddle; saddle point (of a surface); col; valley, trough; anticline, arch.

**седо/ватый** *a.* grayish; **—власый** *a.* gray-haired.

**седогептоза** *f.* sedoheptose.

**седой** *a.* gray-haired, hoary.

**седок** *m.* rider.

**седьмой** *a.* seventh.

**сеет** *pr. 3 sing. of* **сеять.**

**сезаль** *see* **сизаль.**

**сезам** *m.* (bot.) sesame, benne plant (*Sesamum indicum*); **—ин** *m.* sesamin;

—овое масло sesame oil, benne oil; —ол *m.* sesamol; —олин *m.* sesamolin.

**Сезерланда уравнение** Sutherland's equation.

**сезон** *m.* season; по —у in season; —ность *f.* seasonal fluctuation; —ный *a.* seasonal.

**сей** *pron. m.,* **сия** *f.,* **сие** *n.* this; **сии** *pl.* these; за **сим** after this, next; до **сих пор** up to now; при **сем** herewith; прилагаемый при сем enclosed (letter).

**сейвал** *m.* sei whale.

**сейгнетова соль** *see* сегнетова соль.

**сейсм** *m.,* —ическое явление seism, earthquake; —ика *f.* seismic surveying; —ический *a.* seismic, earthquake; —ичность *f.* seismicity.

**сейсмо—** *prefix* (geol.) seismo—, earthquake; —грамма, —запись *f.* seismogram; —граф, —приемник *m.* seismograph, earthquake-shock recorder; —графия *f.* seismography; —логия *f.* seismology; —метр *m.* *m.* seismometer; —метрия *f.* seismometry; —разведка *f.* seismic prospecting; —скоп *m.* seismoscope; —стойкий *a.* earthquakeproof; —стойкость *f.* seismic stability.

**сейте** *imp. of* сеять.

**сейф** *m.* safe.

**сейчас** *adv.* now, immediately, at once, presently; just now.

**сейша** *f.* seiche (apparent tide in lake).

**сек** *past sing. of* сечь.

**сек.** *abbr.* (секунда) second.

**секал/ин** *m.* secaline, trimethylamine; —оза *f.* secalose; —оновая кислота secalonic acid.

**секапс** *m.* (math.) secant.

**секатор** *m.* cutter, pruning shears.

**секач** *m.* cutter (for peat).

**секванский подъярус** (geol.) Sequanian substage.

**секвестр** *m.* (med.) sequestrum; —ация *f.* sequestration; —ировать *v.* sequester.

**секвой/ен** *m.* sequoiene; —ное дерево sequoia wood; —ное масло oil from sequoia needles; —я *f.* (bot.) sequoia.

**секикаевая кислота** sekikaic acid.

**секли** *past pl. of* сечь.

**секрет** *m.* secret; (biol.) secretion; по —у secretly, confidentially.

**секретар/ский** *a.* secretarial; —ь *m.* secretary, clerk.

**секретин** *m.* secretin.

**секретн/ость** *f.* secrecy; —ый *a.* secret, confidential; combination (lock).

**секре/торный** *a.* secretory, secreting; —ция *f.* secretion.

**сексагональный** *a.* hexagonal.

**сексифенил** *m.* sexiphenyl, hexaphenyl.

**секстан, —т** (math., surv.) sextant.

**секстильон** *m.* sextillion.

**сексуальный** *a.* sexual.

**сектор** *m.,* —ный *a.* (math.) sector; segment, zone; department.

**секунд/а** *f.,* —ный *a.* second; —омер *m.* stopwatch, timing device, timer; —омерный *a.* timing.

**секуринин** *m.* securinine.

**секут** *pr. 3 pl. of* сечь.

**секущ/ая** *f.,* —ая линия (math.) secant; —ий *a.* cutting, intersecting, secant; —ая жила (geol.) cross vein.

**секцион/ирование** *n.* sectionalizing; —ированный *a.* sectionalized; stepped, step, graded, graduated, subdivided; —ировать *v.* sectionalize, make sectional; subdivide; —ный *a.* section, sectional, divided; aliquot; dissection, dissecting; —ный котел sectional boiler.

**секция** *f.* section, unit, cell; step, stage; dissection, dissecting; autopsy.

**сел** *past sing. of* сесть.

**сел.** *abbr.* (селекция) selection; breeding; (сельский) rural.

**селагинелл/а** *f.* (bot.) a club moss (*Selaginella*); —овые *pl.* Selaginellaceae.

**селадонит** *m.* (min.) celadonite.

**селах/иловый спирт** selachyl alcohol; —олеиновая кислота selacholeic acid, 6,15-tetracosenoic acid.

**селевые воды** flood waters which erode land on denuded hills.

**селед/ка** *f.,* —очный *a.* herring.

**селезен/ка** *f.* (anat.) spleen; —очный *a.* spleen, splenic.

**селезень** *m.* (zool.) drake.

**селек/тивность** *f.* selectivity; —тивный *a.* selective, discriminative; —тор *m.* selector; sorter; (time) gate; механический —тор chopper (interrupter);

—торная схема (computers) gating circuit, gate; —ционер *m.* breeder; —ционный *a.*, —ция *f.* selection; (biol.) breeding.

селен *m.* selenium, Se; бромистый с., однобромистый с. selenium monobromide; бромный с., четырехбромистый с. selenium tetrabromide; двуокись —а selenium dioxide; синеродистый с. selenocyanogen; хлористый с., однохлористый с. selenium monochloride; хлорный с., четыреххлористый с. selenium chloride, specif. selenium tetrachloride.

селен/азол *m.* selenazole; —азолин *m.* selenazoline; —ат *m.* selenate; —ид *m.* selenide; —ил *m.* selenyl; хлористый —ил selenyl chloride.

селениновая кислота seleninic acid.

селенисто/водородная кислота *see* селеноводородная кислота; —кислый *a.* selenious acid; selenite (of); —кислый натрий, —натриевая соль sodium selenite; —кислая соль selenite; —медистый свинец (min.) zorgite (an impure clausthalite).

селенист/ый *a.* selenious, selenous, selenium; selenide (of); с. аммоний ammonium selenide; с. ангидрид selenious anhydride, selenium dioxide; с. водород hydrogen selenide; с. свинец lead selenide; с. этил ethyl selenide; —ая кислота selenious acid; соль —ой кислоты selenite; —ая медь copper selenide; —ая сера (min.) selensulfur; —ая соль selenide.

селенит *m.* selenite; (min.) selenite (a form of gypsum); —овый *a.* selenitic.

селено— *prefix* seleno—, selenium; —висмутовый блеск (min.) selenobismutite, guanajuatite; —вобариевая соль barium selenate.

селеноводород *m.* hydrogen selenide; —ная кислота hydroselenic acid; соль —ной кислоты selenide.

селеново/кислый *a.* selenic acid; selenate (of); с. натрий, —натриевая соль sodium selenate; —кислая соль selenate.

селенов/ый *a.* selenium, selenic; seleniferous; selenide (of); с. ангидрид selenic anhydride, selenium trioxide; с.

фотоэлемент, с. элемент selenium cell; —ая кислота selenic acid; соль —ой кислоты selenate.

селено/графия *f.* (astron.) selenography; —ид *m.* (elec.) selenoid; —мочевина *f.* selenourea; —нил *m.* selenonyl; —новая кислота selenonic acid; —оловянная кислота selenostannic acid; —ртутный свинец (min.) lehrbachite (an impure clausthalite); —серная кислота selenosulfuric acid; —содержащий *a.* selenium-containing, seleniferous; —углерод *m.* carbon selenide; —фен, —фуран *m.* selenophene, selenofuran; —фенол *m.* selenophenol.

селеноциан/истый водород, —овая кислота, —оводородная кислота selenocyanic acid; соль —истого водорода, соль —овой кислоты selenocyanate; с. калий potassium selenocyanate.

селеу *see* селин.

сели *see* селевые воды; *past pl. of* сесть.

селигманнит *m.* (min.) seligmannite.

селин *m.* a grass (*Aristida*).

селинон *m.* a sodium 3,5-dinitro-*o*-cresylate insecticide.

селитра *f.* saltpeter, niter, potassium nitrate; аммиачная с. ammonium nitrate; воздушная с., известковая с., кальциевая с., норвежская с. Norwegian saltpeter, calcium nitrate; гремучая с. saltpeter blasting powder; калиевая с. potassium nitrate; кубическая с., натриевая с., чилийская с. Chile saltpeter, sodium nitrate; стенная с. wall saltpeter (calcium nitrate efflorescence).

селитр/енный *see* селитряный; —оварня *f.* niter works, saltpeter works; —ообразование *n.* saltpeter formation; —яница *f.* saltpeter works; saltpeter mine; —яница, —янка *f.* (bot.) niter bush (*Nitraria*).

селитрян/ый *a.* saltpeter, containing saltpeter, nitrous, nitric; с. завод, —ая варница saltpeter works, niter works; с. налет niter efflorescence; с. щелок saltpeter lye; —ая бурта saltpeter mine; —ая земля nitrous earth; —ая известь calcium nitrate; —ая кислота nitric acid; —ая пена wall saltpeter (calcium nitrate efflorescence); —ые цветы niter efflorescence.

селиться v. settle, take up residence.

селлаит m. (min.) sellaite (a magnesium fluoride).

Селлерса резьба Sellers screw thread, U.S.S. screw thread.

село n. village.

сель m. mud-laden torrent.

сель— abbr. (сельскохозяйственный) agricultural.

сельвинит m. (min.) selwynite, yellow ocher.

сельдерей m., —ный a. (bot.) celery (Apium graveolens).

сельдь f. herring.

Сельмаш Selmash (Agricultural Machine Trust); сельмашстроение n. agricultural machine building.

сельсин m., —ный a. (elec.) selsyn, synchro; с.-датчик m. transmitting synchro.

сельск/ий a. rural; с. хозяин farmer; —ое хозяйство agriculture, farming.

сельскохозяйственн/ый a. agricultural, farm; с. инвентарь, —ое орудие farm implements; —ая промышленность agricultural industry, agriculture.

сельтерская вода seltzer water.

сельфактор m. (text.) self-acting mule.

сельхоз— abbr. (сельскохозяйственный) agricultural; —артель m. collective farm; —вуз m. agricultural institute; —пром m. agricultural industry.

сем see сей.

сем. abbr. (семейство) family.

семафор m. semaphore, signaler; —ный a. semaphore, semaphoric; —ный столб signal post; —щик m. signal man.

семг/а f., —овый a. (zool.) salmon.

семееды pl. (zool.) seed and stem chalcids (Eurytomidae).

семей/ный a. family; domestic; —ство n. family; group; set (of curves, etc.); series (of element).

семен/а pl. of семя; —истый a. seedy; —ник m. seed plant; (anat.) testicle.

семенн/ой a. seed; seminal, spermatic; suffix (bot.) spermous; с. каналец

(anat.) seminiferous tubule; с. канатик (anat.) spermatic cord; —ая клетка, —ое тельцо seminal cell, spermatozoön; —ая коробка (bot.) seed vessel; —ое ядро seed kernel; (bot.) endosperm; (physiol.) spermatic nucleus; —ые живчики, —ые нити (anat.) spermatozoa.

семено/вместилище n., —с m., —носец m. (bot.) placenta; —вод m. seed grower; —водство n., —водческий a. seed growing; —дольный a. (bot.) cotyledonous; —доля f. cotyledon; —кровелька f. (bot.) aril; —ложе n. (bot.) pericarp; seed bed; —носный a. (bot.) seed-bearing, seminiferous; —почка f. (bot.) ovule; —сушильня f. seed dryer.

семер/ка, —о seven.

семестр m. semester, term; —овый a. semi-annual, half-yearly.

Семет-Сольвэ коксовальная печь Semet-Solvay coke oven.

семи— prefix semi—; hepta—, seven; —атомный a. heptatomic; —башенный a. having seven towers; —бензол m. semi-benzene.

семивалентн/ость f. heptavalence, septivalence; —ый a. heptavalent, septivalent.

семиводный гидрат heptahydrate.

семиглавый a. having seven domes.

семигранн/ик m. (geom.) heptahedron; —ый a. heptahedral.

семидесятый a. seventieth.

семидин m. semidine.

семикарбаз/ид m. semicarbazide, aminourea; —идо— prefix 3-aminoureido— (Soviet nomenclature); —он m. semicarbazone.

семи/кратный a. sevenfold, septuple; —летний a. seven-year, septennial; —мужие n. (bot.) heptandria; —окись f. heptoxide; —полье n. seven-field crop rotation system; —полярный a. semipolar; —сотый a. seven-hundredth.

семиугольн/ик m. (geom.) heptagon; —ый a. heptagonal.

семи/циклический a. heptacyclic; —часовой a. seven-hour; —членный a. seven-membered; —членное ядро seven-membered ring.

**семматериал** *m.* seed for sowing.

**семнадцат/ый** *a.* seventeenth; **—ь** seventeen.

**семперв/ин** *m.* sempervine; **—ирин** *m.* sempervirine.

**семсе/ийт, —ит** *m.* (min.) semseyite.

**семфонд** *m.* seed fund, seed stock.

**семь** seven; **—десят** seventy; **—сот** seven hundred.

**семья** *f.* family, household; (bee) colony.

**семя** *n.* seed, grain; (anat.) sperm, semen.

**семя—** *see also* **семено—**; **—выводящий проток** (anat.) spermiduct; **—доля** *f.* (bot.) cotyledon; **—ед** *m.* seed-eating insect, grain insect; **—зачаток** *m.* (bot.) ovule; **—ложе** *n.* seedbed; **—нка** *f.* (bot.) achene, achaenocarp; **—нные растения** (bot.) seed-bearing plants, Spermatophyta; **—нный** *a. suffix* (bot.) **—**spermous; **—норушка** *f.* oil mill; **—нос, —носец** *m.* (bot.) placenta; **—носушилка** *f.* seed dryer; **—почка** *f.* (bot.) ovule; **—провод** *m.* seed tube; (anat.) seminal duct; **—чко** *n.* seed; pea (grade) coal; **—чковые** *pl.* (bot.) Pomaceae.

**Сена** the Seine.

**сен/аит** *m.* (min.) senaite; **—армонтит** *m.* (min.) senarmontite (an antimony trioxide); **—гиерит** *m.* sengierite (uranium mineral).

**сенд/кеттер** *m.* (foundry) sand-treating machine; **—слингер** *m.* sand slinger.

**сенега** *f.* senega (root of *Polygala alba*).

**сенегальск/ая камедь, —ое гумми** Senegal gum (from *Acacia senegal*).

**сенег/енин** *m.*, **—ениновая кислота** senegenin, senegeninic acid; **—ин** *m.* senegin.

**сенекский ярус** (geol.) Senecan stage.

**сенеци/н** *m.* senecine; **—онин** *m.* senecionine; **—оновая кислота** senecionic acid, senecioic acid, isopropylidene-acetic acid; **—фолидин** *m.* senecifolidine; **—фолин** *m.* senecifoline; **—фолиновая кислота** senecifolic acid.

**сенжьерит** *see* **сенгиерит**.

**сени** *f.* entrance, passage, vestibule.

**сенна** *f.* senna (dried leaves of *Cassia*).

**сенн/ик** *m.* hay barn, hay loft; **—ой** *a.* hay; **—ой пресс** hay baler; **—ая палочка** (bact.) hay bacillus.

**сено** *n.* hay; **—вал** *m.* hay loft; **—ворошение** *n.* tedding; **—ворошилка** *f.* tedder; **—вязалка** *f.* hay baler; **—еды** *pl.* (zool.) Copeognatha; **—заготовка** *f.* hay making; **—кос** *m.* mowing; hay making; haying season; **—косилка** *f.* mower; **—косный** *a.* hay-cutting; hay (field); **—косцы** *pl.* (zool.) daddy-long legs (*Phalangida*); **—кошение** *n.* hay cutting.

**сеноман** *m.*, **—ский ярус** (geol.) Senoman stage.

**сенонский ярус** (geol.) Senonian stage.

**сено/сушилка** *f.* hay dryer; **—уборка** *f.* hay making.

**сенсация** *f.* sensation.

**сенсибилиза/тор** *m.* sensitizer; **—ция** *f.* sensitization, sensitizing.

**сенсит/ивный** *a.* sensitive; **—ометр** *m.* (optics) sensitometer; **—ометрический** *a.* sensitometric; **—ометрия** *f.* sensitometry.

**сенсорный** *a.* sensory.

**сент** *m.* (acous.) cent (unit of pitch).

**сентябрь** *m.* September.

**сепар/атный** *a.* separate, independent; separative; **—атор** *m.* separator; centrifuge; **—ационный** *a.*, **—ация** *f.*, **—ирование** *n.* separation; de-sugaring (Steffen process); **—ационная способность** separative power; **—ировать** *v.* separate, isolate.

**сепиолит** *m.* (min.) sepiolite, meerschaum.

**сепия** *f.* sepia (pigment); (zool.) cuttlefish; **коричневая с.** sepia brown.

**сепс/ин** *m.* sepsine (a yeast ptomaine); **—ис** *m.* (med.) sepsis.

**септа** *f.* septum.

**септар/иевый** *a.* (geol.) septarian; **—ии** *pl.* septaria, septarian nodules or concretions.

**септик-танк** *m.* septic tank.

**септильон** *m.* septillion.

**септи/цемия** *f.* (med.) septicemia; **—ческий** *a.* septic, putrefaction.

**септориоз** *m.* septoria leaf spot (plant disease).

**сер.** *abbr.* (**серийный**) serial; (**серия**) series.

**сер—** *see also* **цер—**.

**сер/а** *f.* sulfur, S; brimstone; **бромистая с., полубромистая с.** sulfur bromide, specif. sulfur monobromide; **возогнанная с.** sublimed sulfur, flowers of sulfur; **двубромистая с.** sulfur dibromide; **двуокись —ы** sulfur dioxide; **двухлористая с., хлорная с.** sulfur chloride, sulfur dichloride; **полухлористая с., хлористая с.** sulfur monochloride; **трехокись —ы** sulfur trioxide, sulfuric acid anhydride; **цианистая с.** thiocyanogen, sulfocyanogen; cyanogen sulfide.

**сераделла** *f.* (bot.) serradella (*Ornithopus sativus*).

**Сербия** Serbia; **сербский** *a.* Serbian.

**сервантит** *m.* (min.) cervantite.

**серваризация** *f.* servarizing (application of protective aluminum coating).

**серво** *n.*, **—механизм** *m.* (elec.) servomechanism, servo unit, servosystem; **—двигатель, —мотор** *m.* servomotor (relay apparatus); **—управление** *n.* servocontrol; **—управляемый** *a.* servocontrolled; **—усилитель** *m.* servoamplifier.

**сергосин** *m.* Sergosin, methiodal sodium.

**сердечник** *m.*, **—овый** *a.* core, center; mandrel; strand (of cable); (bot.) ladies' smock (*Cardamine*); **выдвижной с.** (foundry) drawback; **—овый ящик** (foundry) core box.

**сердечн/о-сосудистый** *a.* (anat.) cardiovascular; **—ый** *a.* heart, cardiac; cordial.

**сердолик** *m.* (min.) carnelian, sard (a variety of chalcedony).

**сердц/е** *n.* (anat.) heart; **ожирение —а** (med.) fatty degeneration of the heart; **разрыв —а** heart failure.

**сердце/биение** *n.* (med.) palpitation; **- видка** *f.* (zool.) a mollusk (*Cardium*); **—видный** *a.* heart-shaped, cordiform; (bot.) cordate.

**сердцевин/а** *f.* heart, core, center; (bot.) pith; **без —ы** (bot.) pithless; **—ный** *a.* (bot.) medullary, medullar.

**серебрение** *n.* silvering, silver plating.

**серебристо—** *prefix* silver, argento—.

**серебрист/ый** *a.* silvery; silver, argentous; **с. колчедан** (min.) argentopyrite; **с. свинец** argentiferous lead; **—ая лапчатка** (bot.) silverweed (*Po-*

*tentilla anserina*); **—ая сталь** silver steel.

**серебрить** *v.* silver, silver plate.

**серебр/о** *n.* silver, Ag; **азотнокислое с., нитрат —а** silver nitrate; **бромистое с.** silver bromide; **квадрантная окись —а, недокись —а** silver suboxide; **немецкое с., новое с.** German silver, nickel silver; **окись —а** silver oxide; **роговое с.** (min.) horn silver, cerargyrite, silver chloride; **сусальное с.** tinsel; **хлористое с.** silver chloride; **цианистое с.** silver cyanide.

**серебро/носный, —содержащий** *a.* argentiferous, silver-bearing, silver-containing; **—плавочный горн** silver-refining hearth.

**серебряк** *see* **сабельник.**

**серебрянка** *f.* silver steel.

**серебряно/медный блеск** (min.) stromeyerite; **—синеродистый калий** potassium silver cyanide; **—синеродистый натрий** sodium silver cyanide, sodium argentocyanide; **—сурьмяный блеск** (min.) miargyrite.

**серебрян/ый** *a.* silver; **с. блеск** (min.) silver glance, argentite; **землистый с. блеск, —ая чернь** (min.) earthy argentite; **—ая плакировка** silver plating; **—ая соль** silver salt; **—ая утварь** silver plate; **—ая фольга** silver foil; **—ых дел мастер** silversmith.

**середин/а** *f.* middle, midst; mean; **—ка** *f.* middle piece, central portion, the very center; **—ный** *a.* middle, mean, central.

**сереж/ка** *f.* ear ring; shackle, fastening; (bot.) catkin (*Amentum*); **—ковые** *pl.* Amentaceae; **—чатый** *a.* amentaceous.

**серендибит** *m.* (min.) serendibite.

**серение** *n.* sulfuring, treating with sulfur, sulfur fumigation.

**сереть** *v.* turn gray.

**сериальн/ый** *a.* serial; **—ая структура** (geol.) seriate structure.

**сериес/-двигатель, с.-мотор** *m.* (elec.) series motor; **с.-параллельная обмотка** (elec.) series-parallel winding.

**сериесный** *a.* series; (mach.) series-wound.

**серийн/о** *adv.* (elec.) in series; **—ый** *a.* series, serial.

**серикоза** *f.* sericose, cellulose acetate.

**сериметр** *m.* silk-testing device; **—ия** *f.* testing silk for tensile strength.

**серин** *m.* serine, hydroxyalanine.

**серить** *v.* sulfur, treat with sulfur, fumigate with sulfur.

**серицин** *m.*, **—овый** *a.* sericin, silk gelatin, silk glue; **—овая кислота** sericic acid.

**серицит** *m.* (min.) sericite (a flaky form of muscovite); **—изация** *f.* sericitization; **—овый** *a.* sericitic.

**серия** *f.* series, set, bank (of machines); (pulse, etc.) train; order, succession, range; **—ми** (elec.) in series.

**серка** *f.* suint, yolk (of wool); fatty sweat.

**сермесоак** *m.* ice-cap; continental ice sheet.

**сернисто/аммониевая соль** ammonium sulfite; **—водородный** *see* **сероводородный**; **—калиевая соль** potassium sulfite; **—кальциевая соль** calcium sulfite; **кислая —кальциевая соль** calcium bisulfite.

**сернистокисл/ый** *a.* sulfurous acid; sulfite (of); **с. натрий** sodium sulfite; **—ая соль** sulfite; **кислая —ая соль** bisulfite.

**сернистонатриевая соль** sodium sulfite; **кислая с. соль** sodium bisulfite.

**сернист/ый** *a.* sulfur, sulfurous; sulfide (of); **с. азот** nitrogen sulfide; **с. аммоний** ammonium sulfide; **с. ангидрид** sulfurous anhydride, sulfur dioxide; **с. водород** hydrogen sulfide; **с. газ** sulfur dioxide; **с. голубой** sulfur blue; **с. источник** sulfur spring; **с. натрий** sodium sulfide; **с. углерод** carbon bisulfide; **с. цвет** flowers of sulfur, sublimed sulfur; **—ая кислота** sulfurous acid; **соль —ой кислоты** sulfite; **кислая соль —ой кислоты** bisulfite; **—ая медь** cuprous sulfide; **—ая руда** (min.) sulfide ore; **—ая сурьма** antimony sulfide; **—ое железо** ferrous sulfide; **—ые красители**, **—ые краски** sulfur dyes; **кислый с.** hydrosulfide (of); **кислый с. кальций** calcium hydrosulfide.

**серно/алюминиевая соль** aluminum sulfate; **—аммониевая соль** ammonium sulfate; **—бариевая соль** barium sulfate; **—ватая кислота** hyposulfuric acid, dithionic acid; **соль —ватой кислоты** hyposulfate, dithionate.

**серноватист/ая кислота** thiosulfuric acid; hyposulfurous acid; **соль —ой кислоты** thiosulfate; hyposulfite.

**серноватисто/аммониевая соль** ammonium thiosulfate; **—калиевая соль** potassium thiosulfate; **—кислый** *a.* thiosulfuric acid; thiosulfate (of); **—кислый натрий, —натриевая соль** sodium thiosulfate; **—кислая соль** thiosulfate.

**серновато/кислый** *a.* hyposulfuric acid; hyposulfate (of); dithionic acid; dithionate (of); **с. натрий, —натриевая соль** sodium hyposulfate, sodium dithionate; **—кислая соль** hyposulfate, dithionate.

**серновинная кислота** ethylsulfuric acid (formerly sulfovinic acid).

**серножелез/истая соль** ferrous sulfate; **—ная соль** ferric sulfate; **—истоаммониевая соль** ferroammonium sulfate; **—ноаммониевая соль** ferriammonium sulfate.

**серно/желтый** *a.* sulfur yellow; **—золотая соль** auric sulfate; **—известковый** *a.* sulfur-lime (spray); **—калиевая соль** potassium sulfate; **кислая —калиевая соль** potassium bisulfate; **—калиемагниевая соль** potassium magnesium sulfate; **—кальциевая соль** calcium sulfate; **—кислотное производство** sulfuric acid manufacture; **—кислотчик** *m.* sulfuric acid specialist (or manufacturer).

**сернокисл/ый** *a.* sulfuric acid; sulfate (of); **с. аммоний** ammonium sulfate; **с. натрий** sodium sulfate; **кислый с. натрий** sodium bisulfate; **с. хинин** quinine sulfate; **—ая соль** sulfate.

**серно/кобальтистая соль** cobaltous sulfate; **—кобальтовая соль** cobaltic sulfate; **—магниевая соль** magnesium sulfate; **—марганцовистая соль** manganous sulfate; **—медистая соль** cuprous sulfate; **—медная соль** cupric sulfate; **—метиловый эфир** methyl sulfate.

**сернонатриевая соль** sodium sulfate;

**кислая с. соль** sodium bisulfate; **сырая с. соль** niter cake.

**серноникелев/ая соль** nickel sulfate; **—оаммониевая соль, двойная —о-аммониевая соль** nickel ammonium sulfate.

**серно/очистительный завод** sulfur refinery; **—ртутистая соль** mercurous sulfate; **—ртутная соль** mercuric sulfate; **—свинцовистая соль** lead sulfate, plumbous sulfate; **—синеродистый** see **серосинеродистый;** **—феноловая кислота** phenolsulfuric acid; **—цинковая соль** zinc sulfate; **—этиловый эфир** ethyl sulfate.

**серн/ый** a. sulfur, sulfuric; **с. ангидрид** sulfuric anhydride, sulfur trioxide; **с. колчедан** (min.) sulfur pyrite, pyrite; **с. цвет** flowers of sulfur, sublimed sulfur; **с. черный** sulfur black; **с. эфир** ethyl ether; **—ая кислота** sulfuric acid; **—ая кислота для аккумуляторов** battery acid; **дымящая —ая кислота** fuming sulfuric acid, oleum; **соль —ой кислоты** sulfate; **кислая соль —ой кислоты** bisulfate; **—ая медь** cupric sulfide; **—ая нитка** sulfured wick, sulfur match; **—ая печень** liver of sulfur (mixture of potassium sulfide and polysulfides); **потассium sulfite;** **—ая спичка** sulfur match; **—ое железо** ferric sulfide; **—ое льняное масло** sulfur balsam; **—ое молоко** milk of sulfur, precipitated sulfur.

**серо—** prefix sulfur; gray; sero—, serum, serous; **—азот** m. nitrogen sulfide; **—бурый** a. brownish gray, dun-colored; **—вакковый конгломерат** (petr.) graywacke; **—вакцина** f. (med.) serovaccine; **—ватый** a. grayish.

**сероводород** m. hydrogen sulfide; **—истый** a. hydrosulfide (of); **—ная вода** hydrogen sulfide solution, **—ная кислота** hydrosulfuric acid, hydrogen sulfide; **соль —ной кислоты** sulfide.

**серодиагностика** f. (med.) serodiagnosis.

**серозакись кобальта** cobaltous oxysulfide.

**сероземь** m. sierozem, gray desert soil.

**серозн/ый** a. (med.) serous; **—ая жид-**

**кость** serum; **—ая оболочка** serous membrane, serosa.

**серология** f. (med.) serology.

**серо/обжигательная печь** sulfur kiln, sulfur burner; **—окись** f. oxysulfide; **—окись углерода** carbon oxysulfide, carbonyl sulfide.

**серо/синеродистый** a. thiocyanate, sulfocyanate (of); **с. аммоний** ammonium thiocyanate; **с. барий** barium thiocyanate; **—содержащий** a. sulfur-containing, sulfur.

**серость** f. grayness.

**серотерапия** f. (med.) serum therapy.

**сероуглерод** m. carbon disulfide.

**серп** m. sickle, reaping hook.

**серпентин** m. (min.) serpentine.

**серпентина** f. hairpin bend, hairpin turn.

**серпентин/изация** f. (min.) serpentinization; **—изированный** a. serpentinous; **—ит** m. serpentinite, serpentine rock; **—овый** a. serpentine.

**серпетка** f. pruning knife.

**серпиерит** m. (min.) serpierite.

**серпник** (bot.) see **сверлильник.**

**серпо/видный, —образный** a. crescent-shaped, sickle-shaped, falcate.

**серпуха** f. (bot.) saw-wort (Serratula).

**серпянка** f. sarp cloth, open canvas.

**сертификат** m. certificate.

**Сертоли клетки** (physiol.) Sertoli's cells.

**серум** m. serum.

**серусодержащий** see **серосодержащий.**

**серы** gen. of **сера.**

**серфы** pl. parasitic wasps (Serphoidea).

**серый** a. gray.

**серьга** f. ear ring; pendant; thimble, sleeve piece; stirrup; link.

**серьезн/ость** f. seriousness, gravity; **—ый** a. serious, grave.

**серянка** f. sulfured wick, sulfur match; sulfur pot.

**сескви—** prefix sesqui—; **—терпен** m. sesquiterpene.

**сессия** f. session, sitting; term (of court).

**сестон** m. (biol.) seston, microplankton.

**сестра** f. sister; (med.) nurse.

**сесть** see **садиться.**

**сете/вой** a. of **сеть;** supply-line; line (frequency); **—образный** a. reticular, net-like.

**сетк/а** f. net, netting, network; sieve,

screen; grid, grate, grating; frame; (cryst.) lattice; (anat.) reticulum; (filter) gauze; mantle (of lamp); **контур —и** (rad.) grid circuit; **эмиссия —и** (thermionics) grid emission; **—ообразный** a. net-shaped, reticular, reticulated.

**сетлер** m. settler, separator.

**сеточн/ый** a. net; grid; **с. товар** netting; **с. ток** (thermionics) grid current; **с. электрод** wire gauze electrode; **—ая утечка** (rad.) grid leak; **—ое смещение** (thermionics) grid bias; **с —ым управлением** grid-controlled.

**сетчат/ка** f. meshwork; (anat.) retina; **—окрылые** pl. (zool.) Neuroptera; **—ость** f. reticulation, netting.

**сетчат/ый** a. netted, network, net-shaped, reticulate, reticulated, reticular, veined; cellular; latticed; wire-gauze (electrode); **с. барабан** revolving screen; **с. узор** reticulation; **с. шов** mesh weld; **—ая оболочка** (anat.) retina; **—ая структура, —ое строение** reticular structure, reticulation; (met.) network structure; **—ое дно** perforated bottom.

**сет/ь** f. net, netting, mesh; circuit, system; network (of stations, etc.); (anat.) reticulum; **напряжение —и** (elec.) line voltage, voltage of the system; **электрическая с.** power-supply system.

**сечен/ие** n. cross section, section, cut, profile; size, gage; **большого —ия** heavy-gage (wire); **живое с.** cross section (of river, etc.), profile; **малого —ия** light-gage (wire); **площадь —ия** sectional area; **поперечное с.** cross section; **эффективное с.** effective cross section.

**сеч/енный** a. chopped; **—ет** pr. 3 sing. of **сечь;—ка** f. chopper, cutter; chopped straw.

**сечонка** f. (cer.) crackle.

**сечь** v. chop, chop up; **—ся** v. cut, split.

**сею/т** pr. 3 pl. of **сеять; —щий** a. sowing; sifting.

**сеялка** f. (agr.) sowing machine, seeder, drill; sifter, screen; **рядовая с.** drill.

**сеяльн/ый** a. sowing; sifting; **с. молоток** (agr.) dibbling mallet, mallet-dibbler;

**с. рожок** seed horn, sowing drill; **—ая доска** seed board.

**сея/нец** m. seedling; **—ние** n. sowing; sifting; **—нный** a. sown; sifted; **—ть** v. sow, plant, drill; sift.

**сжат/ие** n. condensation, compression; constriction, contraction, reduction, shrinkage, shrinking; packing (of powder); pinch; grip, clutch; **камера —ия** compression chamber; **конечное с.** compression pressure; **предел прочности на с.** compression strength, crushing strength; **сопротивление —ию** compressive strength; **степень —ия** compression ratio; **ход —ия** compression stroke (of piston); **эффект —ия** (elec.) pinch effect.

**сжат/о** adv. concisely, in brief form; **—ость** f. conciseness, compactness; compression; **большая степень —ости** high compression ratio; **—ый** a. condensed, compressed (air, gas); compression; compact, concise, brief; constricted, pinched; (geom.) oblate; mowed, reaped, harvested; **—ь** v. reap; see also **сжимать**.

**сжечь** see **сжигать**.

**сжиг/ание** n. combustion, burning, burning up, consumption (of fuel); **камера —ания** combustion chamber; **—ать** v. burn, burn up, consume; burn out, burn off; set on fire.

**сжиж/ать** v. liquefy; (met.) liquate out; condense, compress; **—ение** n. liquefaction; liquation; condensation; **—енный** a. liquefied; liquated; condensed.

**сжим** m. clip, grip, clamp, tongs, forceps.

**сжим/аемость** f. compressibility, condensability; contractibility; **коэффициент —аемости** compressibility factor; **—аемый** a. compressible, condensable; contractible; **—ание** n. compression, condensation; contraction, constriction, shrinkage; (med.) strangulation; see also **сжатие; —ать** v. compress, condense; contract, constrict, squeeze, press, pinch, force together; grip, hug; **—аться** v. condense; contract, shrink.

**сжимающ/ий** a. compressing, condensing; **с. ход** compression stroke (of piston); **—ая нагрузка** compression load; —ее усилие compressive force; —ийся a. constringent, contractile.

**сжимки** pl. clamp, tongs.

**С.-З.** abbr. (северо-запад) northwest.

**сзади** adv. behind, from behind, at the rear (of); **вид с.** end view.

**сзывать** see созывать.

**сиал,** —ь m. (geol.) sial.

**сиамск/ий** a. Siam, Siamese; **с. бензой,** —ая камедь Siam benzoin (resin).

**сиарезинол** m. siaresinol; —овая кислота siaresinolic acid.

**сиба** see циба—.

**сибир/ка** f. (vet.) anthrax; (bot.) sibirea (Sibiraea); —ский a. Siberian; —ская язва anthrax.

**Сибирь** Siberia.

**сиботаксис** m. (phys.) cybotaxis.

**сиву/ха** f., —шный a., —шное масло fusel oil, potato spirit.

**сиг** m. (zool.) whitefish.

**сигар/а** f. cigar; —ета, —етка f. cigarette.

**сигма** f. sigma ($\sigma$).

**сигмоидальный** a. sigmoid, sigmoidal.

**сигнал** m. signal, alarm; sign; (mil.) flare; —изатор m. alarm; signal indicator, direction indicator; (gases) warning component; —изация f., —изирование n. signaling; signal system; —изировать v. signal, sound a signal; —изирующий a. signaling; —ист see сигнальщик; —ьно-предупредительное устройство alarm system.

**сигнальн/ый** a. signal, signaling, alarm; pilot (lamp); **с. звонок** alarm bell, alarm, signal; **с. огонь** signal light; beacon; **с. прибор** alarm; —ая веревка bell cord; —ое полотнище (aero.) marker.

**сигнальщик** m. signal man, signaler; (railroad) flagman.

**сигнатура** f. (typ.) signature; label, ticket.

**сида** f. (bot.) sida; —льцея f. sidalcea.

**сиделка** f. nurse, attendant.

**сиден/ие** n. sitting; seat; —ье n. seat.

**сидеразотит** m. (min.) siderazotite.

**сидер/альный** a. green (manure); —ат m. green manure crop; —ация f. sideration, use of green manure.

**сидерит** m. (min.) siderite, chalybite, spathic iron.

**сидерический** a. (astron.) sidereal.

**сидеро—** prefix sidero— (star; iron); —графия f. siderography; —з m. (med.) siderosis; —лит m. (min.) siderolite (a meteorite); —мелан m. (petr.) sideromelane (a basalt glass); —натрит m. (min.) sideronatrite; —плезит m. (min.) siderplesite (a form of magnesite-siderite); —скоп m. sideroscope; —стат m. (astron.) siderostat; —филлит m. (min.) siderophyllite (a variety of biotite); —фильный a. siderophyllic.

**сидеть** v. sit, be seated; sit up, stay up (with); fit.

**Сидо обманка** Sidot's blende (an artificially prepared zinc sulfide).

**сидр** m. cider; —овая водка cider brandy.

**сидя/чий** a. sitting, sedentary; (biol.) sessile, fixed; —щий a. sitting; —щий в inserted in, set in.

**сиенит** m. syenite (an acidic igneous rock); —овый a. syenitic, syenite.

**сиенн/а** f., —ая земля sienna (pigment); **женная с.** burnt sienna.

**сиенодиорит** m. (petr.) syenodiorite, monzonite.

**сиенск/ий** a. sienna; —ая желть, —ая земля sienna (pigment).

**сизал,** —ь m., —ьский a. (bot.) sisal, sisal hemp (Agave sisalana).

**сизиг/ийский** a. (astron., zool.) syzygial; —ия f. syzygy.

**сизый** a. dove-colored.

**сиккатив** m. siccative, desiccant, drier.

**сиклерит** m. (min.) sicklerite.

**сикоз** m. (med.) sycosis.

**сико/мор** m. (bot.) sycamore (Ficus sycomorus); —церил m. sycoceryl; —цериловый спирт sycoceryl alcohol.

**сикромо** n. Sicromo (silicon-chromium-molybdenum steel).

**сил/а** f. force; power, strength; intensity (of light, sound); vigor, energy; **с.-час** horsepower-hour; **быть в —ах** v. have the power (to), be in a position (to); **вектор —ы** line of force; **в —у** on the strength (of), in virtue (of); **войти в —у** v. come into effect, become effective; **единица —ы** unit of force;

**живая с.** kinetic energy; **имеющий —у** (law) valid; **лошадиная с.** horsepower; **момент —ы** moment of force; **остаться в —е** v. hold good; **работать через —у** v. overwork.

**силал** m. Silal (a high-silicon cast iron).

**силан** m. silane, silicon hydride; **—ол** m. silanol, silicol.

**силевый поток** (geol.) sill.

**силезск/ий процесс** Silesian (reverberatory) process (for lead manufacture); **—ая печь** Silesian furnace (for zinc distillation).

**силекс** m. Silex (a silica glass).

**силектрон** m. Silectron (iron-silicon alloy).

**силика/гель** m. silica gel; **—н** m. silicane, silane; monosilane, silicohydride.

**силикат** m., **—ный, —овый** a. silicate; **с.-глыба** f. impure sodium disilicate; **—изация** f., **—ирование** n. silicification, silicatization; **—ный кирпич** silica brick (a fire brick).

**силико—** prefix silico—, silicon; **—алюминий** m. aluminum-silicon (a master alloy); **—бутан** m. silicobutane, tetrasilane; **—вольфрамовая кислота** silicotungstic acid; **—з, —зис** m. (med.) silicosis; **—кальций** m. calcium-silicon (alloy); **—л** m. silicol, hydroxysilane; **—ль** m. Silicol (a high-silicon alloy); **—марганец** m. manganese-silicon (alloy); **—метан** m. silicomethane, monosilane; **—н** m. silicone; **—новая смола** silicone resin; **—пропан** m. silicopropane, trisilane; **—термия** f. (met.) silicothermic process; **—уксусная кислота** silicoacetic acid; **—фосфат** m. silicophosphate; **—шпигель** m. (met.) silicon spiegel (a spiegeleisen); **—этан** m. silicoethane, disilane.

**силиманит** see **силлиманит.**

**силинг** m. ceiling.

**силитовый стержень** (elec.) Silit resistor.

**силиц/ид** m. silicide; **—ий** see **кремний; —ил** m. silicyl; **—илен** m. silicylene.

**силкин** m. a nitrocellulose rayon.

**силлиманит** m. (min.) sillimanite, fibrolite; sillimanite (a refractory material).

**силль** f. (geol.) sill.

**силов/ой** a. power, force; **с. дом, —ая станция, —ая установка** (elec.)

power house, power station, power plant; **мощная —ая установка** superpower station; **с. провод** (elec.) power line; **с. узел** (elec.) power pack; **—ая линия** line of force; **—ая постоянная** force constant; **—ая трубка, трубка —ых линий** field tube; **—ая цепь** (elec.) power circuit; **—ое поле** field of force.

**силок** m. snare, trap.

**силокс/ан** m., **—анный** a. siloxane; **—ен** m. siloxen; **—икон** m. siloxicon (a refractory material).

**силомер** m. dynamometer.

**силоприемник** m. (mech.) receiver.

**силос** m. (agr.) silo; silage.

**силосель** m. Sil-O-Cel (heat insulator).

**силосн/ый** a. (agr.) silo, ensilage; **—ая башня, —ая яма** silo; **—ые культуры** ensilage crops.

**силосо/вание** n. ensilage, storing ensilage; **—ванный корм** ensilage (fodder); **—вать** v. ensilage, silo, store in a silo; **—наполнитель** m. silo feeder; **—резка** f. ensilage cutter, shredder; **—швырялка** f. blower.

**силумин** m. (met.) Silumin (a silicon-aluminum alloy).

**силунд** m. silundum, silicon carbide.

**силур** m., **—ийский период** (geol.) Silurian period.

**силуэт** m. silhouette.

**силы** gen. and pl. of **сила.**

**силь** see **сель.**

**сильван** m. sylvan, α-methylfuran.

**сильванит** m. (min.) sylvanite, graphic tellurium.

**сильве/глицерин** m. silveglycerin; **—оловая кислота** silveolic acid.

**сильвер—** prefix silver—.

**сильвестрен** m. sylvestrene.

**сильвиалит** m. (min.) silvialite (a hypothetical molecule identical with sulfate-meionite).

**сильвин** m. (min.) sylvite (a potassium chloride); **—ит** m. sylvinite (a sylvite with rock salt).

**сильвинов/ая кислота** sylvic acid, abietic acid; **—ой кислоты** sylvate.

**силькреты** pl. (petr.) silcretes (conglomerates with silica cement).

**сильманал** m. Silmanal (silver-manganese-aluminum alloy).

**сильно** *adv.* powerfully, strongly, vigorously, highly; **—действующий** *a.* strong; aggressive, offensive, violent, drastic; **—точный** *a.* heavy-current, high-current; **—фокусирующий** *a.* strong-focusing.

**сильный** *a.* powerful, strong, vigorous; intense, sharp, severe (cold, illness, etc.); hard, heavy (rain).

**сильфон** *m.*, **—ный** *a.* bellows.

**сил/ьхром** *m.* Silchrome (a chromium-silicon steel); **—юмин** *see* **силумин.**

**сим** *abbr.* (сименс) mho; **СИМ** *abbr.* (Сибирский научно-исследовательский институт металлов) Siberian Scientific Research Institute of Metals.

**сима** *f.* (geol.) sima.

**симаруб/а** *f.* (bot.) mountain damson (*Simaruba officinalis*); **—идин** *m.* simarubidin; **кора —ы, —овая кора** simaruba bark, bitter damson.

**симбатность** *f.* (biol.) symbasis; agreement.

**симби/оз** *m.* (biol.) symbiosis, living together; **—онт** *m.* symbiont; **—отический** *a.* symbiotic.

**символ** *m.* symbol, symbolic expression, sign, image; **—изировать** *v.* symbolize, represent, stand (for); **—ический** *a.* symbolic, figurative.

**сименс** *m.*, **Сименса единица** (elec.) mho (unit of conductance).

**Сименса процесс** (met.) Siemens direct process.

**сименсит** *m.* siemensite (refractory material).

**сименс-мартеновск/ий** *a.* (met.) Siemens-Martin; **с. процесс** Siemens-Martin process, open hearth process; **—ая печь** Siemens-Martin furnace.

**симилор** *m.* similor, Mannheim gold (a variety of brass).

**симметр/изация** *f.*, **—ирование** *n.* symmetrization, balancing; **—ический**, **—ичный** *a.* symmetrical; **—ичность**, **—ия** *f.* symmetry.

**симморфоз** *m.* (chem.) addition.

**симоген** *see* **цимоген.**

**симон/еллит** *m.* (min.) simonellite (a hydrocarbon); **—иит, —ит** *m.* simonyite.

**симпат/изировать** *v.* sympathize; **—ин**

*m.* (physiol.) sympathin; **—ический** *a.* sympathetic; **—ическая реакция** sympathetic reaction, induced reaction; **—ические чернила** sympathetic ink, invisible ink; **—ия** *f.* sympathy.

**симплезит** *m.* (min.) symplesite.

**симплекс** *m.*, **—ный** *a.* (math.) simplex; (biochem.) symplex.

**симпод/иальный** *a.* (bot.) sympodial; **—ий** *m.* sympodium.

**Симпсона правило** (surv., etc.) Simpson's rule.

**симптом** *m.* symptom, sign; **—атика** *f.* (med.) symptomatology; **—атический** *a.* symptomatic.

**симул/ировать** *v.* simulate; **—ьтанный** *a.* simultaneous; **—ьтантный** *a.* combined; **—яция** *f.* simulation.

**симфиз** *m.* (anat.) symphysis.

**син—** *prefix* syn—; **—адельфит** *m.* (min.) synadelphite.

**син/актин** *m.* sinactine, *l*-tetrahydro-*epi*-berberine; **—альбин** *m.* sinalbin.

**синальдоксим** *m.* synaldoxime.

**синамин** *m.* sinamine, allyl cyanamide.

**синантроза** *f.* synanthrose, levulin.

**синап/ин** *m.*, **—иновый** *a.* sinapine; **—иновая кислота** sinapic acid; **соль —иновой кислоты, —инокислая соль** sinapate; **—олин** *m.* sinapolin, diallyl urea; **—таза** *f.* synaptase, emulsin.

**сингамия** *f.* (biol.) syngamy, conjugation.

**синген/ез** *m.* (biol.) syngenesis, sexual reproduction; **—етический** *a.* (zool., min.) syngenetic; **—ит** *m.* (min.) syngenite (a potassium-calcium sulfate).

**синглет** *m.*, **—ный** *a.* singlet.

**сингония** *f.* syngony, (crystal) system.

**сингулярный** *a.* singular.

**синдетикон** *m.* syndetic material, liquid glue.

**син-диазосоединение** *n.* syndiazo compound.

**синди/кат** *m.* syndicate; **—отактический** *a.* syndiotactic (polymer); **—цированный** *a.* syndicated; **—цировать** *v.* syndicate.

**синдром** *m.* (med.) syndrome.

**сине/ва** *f.* dark-blue color; blue stain (plant disease); **—ватобледный** *a.* livid; **—ватый** *a.* bluish; **—глазка** *f.*

day flower (*Commelina communis*); —гнойная палочка (bact.) Bacillus pyocyaneus.

синеголовник *m.* (bot.) eryngo (*Eryngium*).

синекалильный *a.* at blue heat; с. жар blue heat.

синеклиза *f.* (geol.) syneclise (broad structural depression).

синеломк/ий *a.* (met.) blue brittle, blue short, brittle at blue heat; —ость *f.* blue brittleness.

синематограф *see* кинематограф.

синемюрский ярус (geol.) Sinemurian stage.

синерг/етический эффект, —изм *m.* (physiol.) synergism; —ия *f.* synergy, correlated action.

синерезис *m.* syneresis (contraction of gel).

синерод *m.* cyanogen, ethanedinitrile; хлористый с. cyanogen chloride; —истоводородная кислота *see* синеродоводородная кислота.

синеродист/ый *a.* (lower or —ous) cyanide (of); с. водород hydrogen cyanide; с. калий potassium cyanide; с. натрий sodium cyanide; —ая кислота cyanic acid; —ая медь cuprous cyanide; —ое железо ferrous cyanide.

синеродн/ый *a.* (higher or —ic) cyanide (of); —ая медь cupric cyanide; —ая ртуть mercuric cyanide; —ое железо ferric cyanide.

синеродо— *prefix* cyan—, cyano—.

синеродоводород *m.*, —ная кислота hydrogen cyanide, hydrocyanic acid, prussic acid; соль —ной кислоты cyanide; —ный *a.* hydrocyanic, hydrocyanide (of).

синеть *v.* get blue.

синефрин *m.* synephrin.

синигрин *m.* sinigrin, potassium myronate.

син/ий *a.* blue, dark blue; с. пигмент cyanin; —яя копия, светописная —яя копия blueprint.

синиль, —ник *m.* (bot.) woad (*Isatis tinctoria*); —но— *see* синеродо—.

синильн/ый *a.* bluing, for dyeing dark blue; prussic; —ая кислота prussic acid, hydrocyanic acid; соль —ой кислоты prussiate, cyanide; желтая

—ая соль yellow prussiate, potassium ferrocyanide; красная —ая соль red prussiate, potassium ferricyanide.

синистрин *m.* sinistrin.

синить *v.* blue, make blue.

синица *f.* (zool.) titmouse.

синкаин *m.* Syncaine, procaine.

синкалин *m.* sincaline, choline.

синкарпий *m.* syncarp (a collective fruit).

синкл/аза *f.* (geol.) synclase; —иналоид *m.* synclinaloid; —иналь *f.*, —инальная складка syncline; —инальный *a.* synclinal; —инорий *m.* synclinorium, synclinore.

синнематин *m.* synnematin.

синов/иальная жидкость, —ия *f.* (anat.) synovia.

синодический *a.* (astron.) synodical.

синоменин *m.* sinomenine.

синоним *m.* synonym; —ический *a.* synonymous.

синопсис *m.* synopsis.

синопская земля *see* синопит.

синопти/к *m.*, synoptic meteorologist, weather forecaster; —ка *f.* synoptics, synoptic meteorology; —ческий *a.* synoptic; —ческая карта synoptic chart, weather map.

синтагматит *m.* (min.) syntagmatite (a variety of hornblende).

синталин *m.* Synthalin.

синтан *m.* syntan (synthetic tanning agent).

синтез *m.* synthesis; —атор *m.* synthesizer; —ированный *a.* synthesized; —ировать *v.* synthesize.

синтер *m.* sinter, sinter cake; —ование *n.*, —овочный *a.* sintering.

синтетическ/и *adv.* synthetically; —ий *a.* synthetic; —ий каучук synthetic rubber; —ая смола synthetic resin.

синт/ин *m.* synthine (synthetic mixture of hydrocarbons); —ол *m.* synthol (synthetic mixture of alcohols, aldehydes, and acids).

синтомицин *m.* synthomycin (synthetic streptomycin).

синтониз/ация *f.* syntonization, tuning; —ированный *a.* syntonized, tuned; —ировать *v.* syntonize, tune.

синтонин *m.* syntonin, muscle fibrin.

синтонический *a.* (rad.) syntonic.

**синус** *m.*, —**ный** *a.* (math.) sine; (anat.) sinus; **с.-счётчик** (elec.) sine meter; **метод** —**ов** sine method; —**оида** *f.*, —**оидальная кривая** (math.) sinusoid, sine curve; —**оидальный** *a.* sine, sine-shaped; sinusoidal; sinuous.

**синфаз/ирование** *n.* synphasing; —**ный** *a.* cophasal.

**синхизит** *m.* (min.) synchysite (parisite).

**синхонин** *m.* cinchonine (from cinchona bark).

**синхрониз/атор** *m.* synchronizer; —**ация** *f.*, —**ирование** *n.* synchronization, synchronizing, timing; —**ированный** *a.* synchronized, simultaneous; —**ировать** *v.* synchronize, bring into step; —**ирующий** *a.* synchronizing.

**синхронизм** *m.* synchronism, simultaneous occurrence; **выпасть из** —**а** *v.* fall out of step; **выше** —**а** hypersynchronous; **ниже** —**а** hyposynchronous; **приведение к** —**у** synchronization; **приводить в с.** *v.* synchronize.

**синхрон/истический** *a.* synchronistic; synchronous; —**ический**, —**ичный**, —**ный** *a.* synchronous, coincident; —**ия** *see* **синхронизм**; —**ность** *f.* synchronism; timing; —**оскоп** *m.* synchronoscope.

**синхро/скоп** *m.* (elec.) synchroscope; —**трон** *m.*, —**тронный** *a.* (nucl.) synchrotron; —**фазотрон** *m.* proton-synchrotron; —**циклотрон** *m.* (nucl.) synchrocyclotron, f-m cyclotron.

**синцианин** *m.* syncyanin (blue pigment).

**синцитий** *m.* (biol.) syncytium.

**синь** *f.* blue; blue pigment; blue stain (plant disease); **желтое с.-кали** potassium ferrocyanide; **красное с.-кали** potassium ferricyanide; **желтый с.-натр** sodium ferrocyanide; **красный с.-натр** sodium ferricyanide.

**синька** *f.* bluing; blueprint.

**синь-кали** *see under* **синь.**

**синьоритет** *m.* seniority.

**синэнергетический** *see* **синергетический.**

**синэстрол** *m.* Synestrol, hexestrol.

**синюх/а** *f.* (bot.) Jacob's ladder (*Polemonium*); (med.) cyanosis; —**овые** *pl.* Polemoniaceae.

**синяк** *m.* bruise, black and blue, black

eye; (bot.) viper's bugloss (*Echium*).

**сиомин** *m.* siomine, hexamethylene-amine tetraiodide.

**сип** *m.* (zool.) vulture.

**сипилит** *m.* (min.) sipylite (identical with fergusonite).

**сип/лость** *f.* hoarseness; —**лый** *a.* hoarse, husky; —**нуть** *v.* get hoarse.

**сиполин** *see* **циполин.**

**сипота** *f.* hoarseness.

**сипункулиды** *pl.* (zool.) Sipunculoidea.

**сирена** *f.* siren.

**сирен/евый** *a.* lilac, lilac-colored; **с. альдегид** syringaldehyde; —**евая кислота** syringic acid; —**ь** *f.* (bot.) lilac (*Syringa vulgaris*).

**сирийский** *a.* Syrian.

**сиринг/енин** *m.* syringenin, oxymethyl-coniferin; —**етин** *m.* syringetin; —**ин** *m.* syringin, lilacin; —**овая кислота** syringic acid.

**Сири/ус** *m.* (astron.) Sirius; —**я** Syria.

**сироп** *m.* syrup; —**ный** *a.* syrup, syrupy; —**ообразный** *a.* syrupy, syrup-like, viscous.

**сирота** *m.* orphan.

**сирфы** *pl.* flower flies (*Syrphidae*).

**сисмондин** *m.* (min.) sismondine, sismondite (a form of chloritoid).

**система** *f.* system, method, scheme, arrangement, organization; **индустриальная с.** industrialism.

**системат/изация** *f.* systemization; classification, filing; —**изировать** *v.* systematize; classify, arrange, file; —**ик** *m.* (biol.) taxonomist, classifier; - -**ика** *f.* systematism; systemization; taxonomy, classification; —**ический** *a.* systematic, methodical; —**ично** *adv.* systematically.

**систокс** *see* **меркаптофос.**

**систола** *f.* (physiol.) systole.

**ситец** *m.* (text.) calico, cotton print.

**ситник** *m.* coarse white bread; (bot.) rush (*Juncus*); —**овые** *pl.* Juncaceae; —**овый** *a.* rush.

**ситн/ый** *a.* sifted; —**ая мука** coarse flour, siftings.

**сито** *n.* sieve, screen, riddle, bolter, sifter, strainer; **шкала сит** mesh gage; —**видный** *see* **ситообразный.**

**ситов/ик**, —**ник** (bot.) *see* **ситник;** —**ина**

*f.* rot, putrefaction; fungus-infected wood.

**сито/вый** *a.* screen; **с. анализ** particle-size analysis; **—образный** *a.* cribriform, sieve-like; screen.

**ситостан** *m.* sitostane (isomer of cholane); **—ол** *m.* sitostanol.

**ситостерин** *m.* sitosterol.

**ситочный** *a.* sifter, sieve, screen.

**ситуаци/онный** *a.*, **—я** *f.* situation; **с. план** site plan, layout plan.

**ситус: анализ с.** (math.) analysis situs.

**ситце/вый** *a.* (text.) calico, cotton print; **—набивная машина, —печатная машина** cotton-printing machine; **—набивное производство, — печатание** *n.* calico printing, cloth printing.

**ситцы** *pl.* (text.) cotton prints.

**ситчат/ый** *a.* screen; sieve-plate (column); **с. барабан** revolving screen; **—ая плита** sieve plate; filter plate; **—ая тарелка** sieve plate (of distillation column).

**сифили/с** *m.* (med.) syphilis; **—тик** *m.*, **—тический** *a.* syphilitic.

**сифон** *m.* siphon; siphon trap; **проводить через с., сливать —ом, —ировать** *v.* siphon, siphon off.

**сифонн/ый** *a.* siphon; **с. водослив** siphon spillway; **с. запор, с. затвор, с. приемник** siphon trap; **с. трубопровод, —ая трубка** siphon, siphon tube, siphon tubing; **—ая отливка, —ая разливка** (foundry) bottom casting; **—ые зеленые водоросли** (bot.) Siphonales.

**сифоно—** *prefix* siphono—(siphon, tube); **—гамный** *a.* (bot.) siphonogamous; **—стельный** *a.* (bot.) siphonostelic; **—форы** *pl.* (zool.) Siphonophora.

**сих** *see under* **сей.**

**сихнодимит** *m.* (min.) sychnodymite (probably a variety of linnaeite).

**сицилийский** *a.* Sicilian; **Сицилия** Sicily.

**сиштоф** *m.* Si-stoff (siliceous by-product of alumina industry).

**сия/ние** *n.* shining, radiation, radiance, luminescence, glow, luster, sheen; aureole, halo; **—ть** *v.* shine, radiate, eradiate, beam; **—ющий** *a.* shining, radiant, beaming.

**СК** *abbr.* (синтетический каучук) synthetic rubber.

**скабиоза** *f.* (bot.) scabious (*Scabiosa*).

**ска/жем** let us say, say; **—занное** *n.* what has been said; **—занный** *a.* said, spoken; **—зать** *v.* say, speak, tell; **так —зать** so to speak; **—заться, —зываться** *v.* tell, show up; profess to be; **—зываться благоприятно** have a favorable effect (on); **—зываться на** affect, influence.

**скак/ание** *n.* skipping, jumping; **—ательный сустав** (anat.) hock; **—ать** *v.* skip, jump, leap, bound.

**скаккит** *m.* (min.) scacchite (a manganous chloride).

**скак/нуть** *see* **скакать; —ун** *m.* jumper; **—уны** *pl.* tiger beetles (*Cicindelidae*).

**скала** *f.* rock, crag, cliff; scale (of thermometer, etc.).

**скаленоэдр** *m.* (cryst.) scalenohedron; **—ический** *a.* scalenohedral.

**скалистый** *a.* rocky, craggy.

**скалк/а** *f.*, **—овый** *a.* rolling pin; ram, plunger, plunger piston; **расточная с.** boring bar.

**скалообразующий** *a.* (geol.) petrogenic.

**скалыв/ание** *n.* cleaving; shear, shearing, shearing action; spalling, chipping up; (nucl.) spallation; **осколок —ания** spallation fragment; **структура —ания** (geol.) shear structure; **—ать** *v.* cleave, split off, chop off; shear, shear off; pin together; copy the outline of a drawing by means of pin pricks; **—ающий** *a.* shearing; **—ающая сила** shearing force.

**скальзывать** *see* **скользить.**

**скалькировать** *v.* trace.

**скальные работы** rock excavation.

**скальп** *m.* scalp; **—ель** *m.* scalpel; **—ировать** *v.* scalp, sift.

**скальчатый** *a.* plunger (pump); **с. поршень** plunger, ram.

**скаляр** *m.*, **—ный** *a.* (math.) scalar.

**скамейка** *f.* bench, stool; bank.

**скаммон/ий** *m.* scammony (root of *Convolvulus scammonia*); **камедь —ии** scammony resin; **—ин** *m.* scammonin.

**скамья** *f.* bench.

**скандиев/ый** *a.* scandium; **—ая земля** scandia, scandium oxide; **—ая соль** scandium salt.

**сканд/ий** *m.* scandium, Sc; **окись —ия** scandium oxide; **хлористый с.** scandium chloride.

**скандинавский** *a.* Scandinavian.

**скан/дирование, —ирование** *n.* scanning, scan, analyzing; **—дировать, —ировать** *v.* scan.

**скапавший** *a.* trickled off.

**скапливать** *v.* collect, accumulate, hoard; **—ся** *v.* collect, accumulate, agglomerate, aggregate; be piled up, be heaped.

**скаполит** *m.* (min.) scapolite, wernerite; **—изация** *f.* scapolitization.

**скапывать** *v.* dig off, dig away.

**скарабей** *m.* scarab, dung beetle.

**скарифика/тор** *m.* (agr.) scarifier; **—ция** *f.* scarification.

**скарлатина** *f.* (med.) scarlet fever.

**скармливать** *v.* feed.

**скарн** *m.*, **—овый** *a.* (petr.) skarn (silicate contact gangue).

**скат** *m.* slope, incline, descent, pitch, gradient, declivity; ramp; slide, chute; (zool.) ray, skate (fish); **электрический с.** torpedo fish; **—ать** *see* **скатывать.**

**скатерть** *f.* tablecloth.

**скатить** *see* **скачивать.**

**скато/ксил** *m.* skatoxyl; **—л** *m.* skatole, methylindole.

**скатыв/ание** *n.* rolling, rolling down; rolling up; **угол —ания** angle of pitch; (geol.) angle of dip; **—ать** *v.* roll, slide; roll up; **—аться** *v.* roll down, roll off, slide off.

**скафандр** *m.* diving suit.

**скахит** *see* **скаккит.**

**скаченный** *a.* run-off.

**скачет** *pr. 3 sing. of* **скакать.**

**скачив/ание** *n.* running off; **—ать** *v.* run off, drain off, draw off.

**скачкообразн/о** *adv.* by leaps or jumps; spasmodically; **—ый** *a.* spasmodic, uneven, intermittent; abrupt; **—ая работа** skipping.

**скач/ок** *m.* jump, skip, leap, spring, bound; rapid change, drop; break, discontinuity (in curve); (potential) difference; **—ки** *pl.* skipping; **—ками** in jumps; in stages or steps, by degrees, gradually; notch by notch; **движение —ками** galloping motion;

**слой —ка** layer of discontinuity; **—ут** *pr. 3 pl. of* **скакать; —ущий** *a.* jumping.

**скашив/ание** *n.* sloping, beveling, chamfering; (agr.) mowing; **с. под углом** beveling; **—ать** *v.* slope, bevel, chamfer, cant, cut aslant; mow down.

**СКБ** code mark for synthetic butadiene rubber.

**скваж/ина** *f.* pore, aperture, chink, slit, gap, interstice, rift; borehole, drillhole; (oil) well; **со —инами** porous; **—инный** *a.* borehole; well; **—истость** *f.* porosity; **—истый** *a.* porous; blown; **—ность** *f.* porosity; duty factor.

**сквален** *m.* squalene, spinacene.

**скверн/о** *adv.* badly, poorly; **ему с.** he is not well; **—ый** *a.* bad, poor.

**сквидж** *m.* squeegee.

**сквилла** *f.* (bot.) squill (*Scilla maritima*).

**сквозить** *v.* appear through, be seen through; **сквозит** there is a draft.

**сквозн/ой** *a.* transparent, open; through, continuous; **с. болт** through bolt; **с. ветер, —як** *m.* draft, current of air; **—ая работа** (min.) open work, open cut, surface mining; **—ое отверстие** through hole.

**сквозь** *adv.* through.

**сквор/ец** *m.*, **—цовый** *a.* (zool.) starling; **—ешник** *m.* (met.) pigeon hole (flaw in casting).

**скелет** *m.* skeleton, frame, shell; **—ирование** *n.* skeletonization (of leaves by insects); **—ный** *a.* skeleton, frame; skeletal; **—ный никель** Raney nickel (catalyst).

**скепти/к** *m.* sceptic; **—ческий** *a.* sceptic, sceptical.

**скерда** *f.* (bot.) crepis.

**скетч** *m.* sketch.

**СКИ** code mark for synthetic polyisoprene rubber.

**скиаметр** *m.* skiameter, actinometer.

**скиддер** *m.* skidder.

**скид/ка** *f.* allowance, reduction, deduction, discount; **—ывать** *v.* allow, reduce, deduct; throw off, cast off.

**скимкоультер** *m.* (agr.) skim colter.

**скин-слой** *m.* skin layer.

**скинут/ый** *a.* deducted; thrown off, cast off; **—ь** *see* **скидывать.**

**скин-эффект** *m.* (elec.) skin effect.

**скип** *m.* skip, charging skip.

**скипидар** *m.*, —**ный** *a.* turpentine; —**ное дерево** (bot.) a pistachio (*Pistacia mutica*).

**скиповый** *a.* skip; **с. загрузчик** skip loader.

**скирд** *m.*, —**а** *f.*, —**овать** *v.* stack, rick, pile.

**скис/ать,** —**нуть** *v.* turn sour, sour, curdle.

**скифский ярус** (geol.) Scythian stage.

**скицировать** *v.* sketch, draft.

**склад** *m.* warehouse, storehouse, storeroom; (lumber) yard; storage, store, stock; habit; **на** —**е** in storage, in stock; **помещать в с.** *v.* put in storage, store.

**складк/а** *f.* crease, wrinkle, fold, lap, crimp, crinkle; (geol.) fold; **с.-взброс** (geol.) upthrust fold; **с. местности** (geol.) natural feature; **с.-сброс** (geol.) fault fold; **с.-сдвиг** (geol.) overthrust; **точка** —**и** plait point (in solubility curve); —**ообразование** *n.* folding, fold formation.

**складн/ой** *a.* folding, collapsible; portable; —**ая линейка** folding rule.

**складный** *a.* coherent, harmonious.

**складочн/ый** *a.* storage, warehouse, storehouse; contributed; —**ое место** storehouse; (mil.) dump.

**складск/ой** *a.* warehouse; —**ое хозяйство** stores, supply department.

**складчат/ость** *f.* (geol.) folding; —**ый** *a.* folded, plicated; (met.) wrinkled.

**складыв/аемое** *n.* (math.) addend; —**ание** *n.* putting together; addition; folding; stowing, storing; —**ать** *v.* put together, lay together; fold, fold up; accumulate, pile, store; add (up), sum up; cancel (debts).

**склеенный** *a.* glued, cemented, agglutinate.

**склеив/ание** *n.* gluing, cementing, pasting; sizing; —**ать** *v.* glue, cement, paste together, stick together; splice; size, dress; —**ающий** *a.* adhesive, adhering, sticking; —**ающее вещество** adhesive, agglutinant.

**скле/ить** *see* **склеивать;** —**йка** *f.* gluing together, pasting; splice; patch.

**склеп/анный,** —**ный** *a.* riveted; —**ка** *f.*,

—**ывание** *n.* riveting, fastening; —**машина** *f.* riveting machine; —**ывать** *v.* rivet, rivet together, clench, fasten; —**ывающий** *a.* riveting.

**склер/а** *f.* (anat.) sclera; —**енхима** *f.* (biol.) sclerenchyma.

**склерит** *m.* (med.) scleritis; (zool.) sclerite.

**склеро**— *prefix* sclero— (hard); —**з** *m.* (med., bot.) sclerosis, hardening; —**зированный** *a.* sclerosed; —**зный** *a.* sclerous, hard; —**клаз** *m.* (min.) scleroclase, scleroclasite, sartorite; —**метр** *m.* sclerometer; —**метрический** *a.* sclerometric; —**н** *m.* Scleron (aluminum-base alloy).

**склеропелит** *m.* skleropelite (an argillite sedimentary rock).

**склеропротеин** *m.* scleroprotein.

**склероскоп** *m.* scleroscope.

**склероти/ка** *f.* (anat.) sclerotic; —**ниоз** *m.* sclerotiniose (plant disease); —**новая кислота** sclerotic acid, sclerotinic acid; —**ческий** *a.* (med., bot.) sclerotic, sclerosed.

**склероций** *m.* (bot.) sclerotium.

**склизкий** *a.* slimy.

**склодовскит** *m.* sklodowskite (uranium mineral).

**склон** *m.* slope, side, descent, decline, declivity, slide; —**ение** *n.* slope, incline, inclination, declivity, dip, pitch; depression; declination, deflection, variation; **магнитное** —**ение** magnetic declination; **стрелка** —**ения** (geol.) dip needle, dipping compass; **угол** —**ения** angle of declination; angle of pitch; angle of depression; (geol.) angle of dip; —**енный** *a.* inclined, sloped; —**ить** *see* **склонять.**

**склонн/ость** *f.* inclination, tendency, disposition, propensity, bent, leaning, taste, aptitude, affinity; **иметь с.** *v.* tend, be inclined (to); —**ый** *a.* inclined, disposed, prone, ready (to).

**склон/ять** *v.* incline, bend, bias; —**яться** *v.* incline, bend; yield, comply, give in; be disposed (to), tend (to); —**яющийся** *a.* dipping.

**склянка** *f.* phial, vial, bottle, flask.

**СКН** code mark for butadiene-acrylonitrile synthetic rubber.

**скоб/а** *f.* cramp, cramp iron, clamp,

cleat, clincher, clinch; bracket, brace, frame; hook, fastening, catch, claw, detent, detainer, checking device; buckle; clip; staple; stirrup; **железная с.** cramp iron; **прибить** —ами *v.* staple; **скрепить** —ой *v.* cramp, clamp; **соединение** —ой clasp joint.

**скобель** *m.* scraper, plane, draw knife; chip ax.

**скобк/а** *f.* bracket; *see also* **скоба; в** —и, **в** —ах in brackets; **квадратные** —и brackets; **круглые** —и parentheses; **фигурные** —и braces.

**скобл/ение** *n.* scraping; —**ильный** *a.* scraping, scrape; —**ильный инструмент** scraper; —**ить** *v.* scrape, smooth, plane, shave, pare; file; grate; (med.) scarify.

**скобочная машина** stapler.

**скобяные изделия, с. товары** hardware, ironware.

**сков/анный** *a.* forged, welded (together); —**ать** *see* **сковывать.**

**сковиллит** *m.* (min.) scovillite, rhabdophanite.

**сковка** *f.* forging, welding.

**сковорода** *f.* pan, frying pan; (elec.) heating grill.

**сковород/ень,** —**ник** *m.*, **соединение в с.** dovetail (joint); **вязка** —**нем, соединение** —**нем** dovetailing.

**сковыв/ание** *n.* welding, forging; chaining; —**ать** *v.* weld, forge; chain.

**скок** *m.* hop, jump, leap, bound.

**сколачивать** *v.* knock together, put together; knock off, strike off; beat down.

**сколецит** *m.* (min.) scolecite.

**сколии** *pl.* vespoid digger wasps (*Scoliidae*).

**сколиодоновая кислота** scoliodonic acid.

**сколиоз** *m.* (med.) scoliosis.

**сколит** *m.* a bark beetle (*Scolytus*).

**сколок** *m.* pricked pattern; copy, picture; chip.

**сколотина** *f.* buttermilk.

**сколотить** *see* **сколачивать.**

**сколоть** *see* **скалывать.**

**сколь** *adv.* how, how much; **с. угодно** as much as desired.

**скольжен/ие** *n.* slipping, sliding, slide, skidding, gliding; launching (of ship); (met.) slip; slip (of induction motor);

stroke (of piston); **зеркало** —**ия** (geol.) slickenside(s); **кривая** —**ия** slip curve; **плоскость** —**ия** sliding surface; **угол** —**ия** angle of slide.

**скольз/ить,** —**нуть** *v.* slip, slide, skid; glide, skim (over); creep; —**кий** *a.* slippery; (bot.) lubricous; —**кость** *f.* slipperiness, lubricity, lubricating property, lubricating power; —**ун** *m.* slipper, slide block, guide shoe.

**скользящий** *a.* slipping, slip, skidding, sliding, gliding; glancing (blow); **с. камень** slide block; **с. контакт** (elec.) sliding contact.

**сколько** *adv.* how much, how many? **с.-нибудь** any (amount); **с. раз** how often?

**скольтер** *m.* (agr.) colter.

**скомбинированный** *a.* combined.

**скомбр/ин** *m.* scombrine; —**он** *m.* scombrone.

**скомк/анный** *a.* wrinkled, crumpled; —**ать** *v.* wrinkle, crumple.

**скомпилированный** *a.* compiled, collected.

**сконструиров/анный** *a.* constructed, engineered, designed; —**ать** *v.* construct, design; develop.

**сконфузить** *v.* confuse, disconcert.

**сконцентрированный** *a.* concentrated.

**скоп** *m.* savings; forehearth (of furnace); *suffix* —scope; **молочные** —**ы** dairy products.

**скопарин** *m.* scoparin.

**скопившийся** *a.* accumulated; (geol.) segregated.

**скопин** *m.* scopine, 2,3-epoxytropane.

**скопить** *v.* castrate; *see also* **скапливать.** —**скоп/ический** *a. suffix* —scopic; —**ия** *f. suffix* —scopy.

**скопл/ение** *n.* accumulation, heap, mass, aggregate; aggregation, stock, conglomeration, agglomerate, congregation, congestion; stock; reflux (of steam); (geol.) segregation; (med.) afflux; —**енный** *a.* accumulated, collected; —**яемый** *a.* accumulative, cumulative; —**ять** *see* **скапливать.**

**скопол/амин** *m.* scopolamine, hyoscine; *dl*-scopolamine, atroscine; —**еин** *m.* scopoleine; —**етин** *m.* scopoletin, chrysatropic acid; —**ил** *m.* scopolyl;

—ин *m.* scopoline; —иновая кислота scopolic acid.

скопометр *m.* scopometer (optical instrument); —ия *f.* scopometry.

скорбут *m.* (med.) scurvy; —ный *a.* scorbutic.

скордия *f.* (bot.) water germander (*Teucrium scordium*).

скорее *comp. of* скоро, скорый sooner, more quickly; rather, preferably; как можно с. as soon as possible.

скорифика/тор *m.* scorifier (vessel for assaying gold and silver ores); —ция *f.* scorification.

скорлуп/а *f.* shell, hull; —ный *a.* shell, shelly; crustaceous.

скорлупняк/и *pl.* (zool.) Crustacea; —овый *a.* crustacean; crustaceous.

скорлупо/ватый *a.* shell, shelly; —ватая структура (geol.) conchoidal structure; botryoidal structure; —ватое отслоение peeling; —образный *a.* conchoidal, shell-like, shell-shaped.

скорняк *m.* furrier, fur-dresser.

скоро *adv.* soon, promptly, quickly, speedily, rapidly, at a rapid rate.

скорода *see* шнит-лук.

скородит *m.* (min.) scorodite.

скороножка *f.* (zool.) centipede.

скоропашка *f.* (agr.) cultivator.

скоропечатный станок (typ.) engine press.

скоропись *f.* shorthand, stenography.

скороплодность *f.* early maturity.

скороподъемность *f.* (aero.) climbing speed.

скоропортящийся *a.* perishable.

скоропостижн/о *adv.* unexpectedly (of death); —ый *a.* sudden, unexpected.

скоропреходящий *a.* transitory, short-lived.

скороспел/ка *f.* early fruit; —ость *f.* early ripening, earliness; —ый *a.* early-ripening, early.

скоросте/мер *m.* velocity meter; —уменьшитель *m.* reducing gear.

скорости/ой, —ый *a.* velocity; high-speed; rapid.

скорострельный *a.* (mil.) quick-firing.

скорост/ь *f.* velocity, speed, quickness, rapidity, rate; с. реакции rate of reaction; включать с. *v.* put in gear; коробка —ей gear box, gear-shift box;

набирание —и acceleration, speeding up; снижение —и, уменьшение —и deceleration, slowing down; угловая с. angular velocity; указатель —и speedometer.

скоротечн/ость *f.* transience, transiency, short duration, rapidity; —ый *a.* transient, short-lived, brief, fast; (med.) fulminant; galloping (consumption).

скорпион *m.* (zool.) scorpion; —ницы *pl.*, —овые мухи scorpion flies (*Mecoptera*).

скорца *f.* scorza (epidote sand from Transylvania gold washings).

скорцонера *f.* (bot.) viper's grass (*Scorzonera*).

скорчинг *m.* (rubber) scorching.

скор/ый *a.* fast, quick, speedy, rapid, swift; first (aid); в —ом времени soon, in a short time, before long.

скос *m.* bevel, chamfering, chamfer, splay, slope, taper, tapering; feather (wedge); с. фаски chamfered edge; угол —a angle of taper.

скосарь *m.* snout beetle (*Otiorrhynchus*).

скосить *see* скашивать.

скот *m.*, —ина *f.* cattle, livestock.

ското— *prefix* cattle; scoto— (darkness); —бойня *f.* slaughter house, abattoir; —вод *m.* cattle breeder; —водство *n.* cattle breeding; —водческий *a.* cattle (ranch).

ското/графия *f.* scotography, skiagraphy; —ма *f.* (med.) scotoma; —метр *m.* (med.) scotometer.

скотосбрасыватель *m.* cowcatcher (of locomotive).

Скотта способ Scott method (of analysis).

скошенный *a.* chamfered, beveled, tapered, canted, biased; mowed (grass).

скрадывать *v.* conceal, hide.

скрайбер *m.* (carpentry) scriber.

скрап *m.* scrap, scrap iron; с.-процесс (met.) scrap process (variation of Martens process); —ный двор scrap stockyard, scrap pile.

скрасть *see* скрадывать.

Скраупа синтез Skraup synthesis.

скреб *m.* (forestry) scrub; bush; *past sing. of* скрести; —енный *a.* scraped; —ет *pr. 3 sing. of* скрести.

**скребкововковшевой транспортер** scraper conveyer, scraping bucket conveyer.

**скребковый** *a.* scraping, scraper; **с. грохот** drag screen; **с. классификатор** rake classifier (for ore concentration); **с. конвейер, с. транспортер** scraper conveyer.

**скреб/ли** *past pl. of* **скрести;** —**ло** *n.* strickle; doctor, scraping knife; —**машина** *f.* scraper, dehairer (for hides); —**ница** *f.* scrubbing brush; currycomb; —**ной** *a.* scraper; —**нуть** *see* **скрести;** —**ок** *m.* scraper, scrubber; rabble, rabbler; trowel; —**ут** *pr. 3 pl. of* **скрести;** —**ущий** *a.* scraping.

**скрепа** *f.* tie, clamp, brace.

**скрепер** *m.,* —**ный** *a.* scraper, rabbler; **с.-волокуша** dragline scraper.

**скреп/ить** *v.* tie, fasten, make fast, fix, secure (to), tack; rivet, bolt, clamp; cement; splice; brace, strengthen; —**ка** *f.* fastener, clamp; (paper) clip; split pin; splice.

**скреплен/ие** *n.* fastening, tightening, clamping; brace, bond; scarf, splice; strengthening, reinforcement; —**ный** *a.* fastened, clamped; cemented; reinforced.

**скреплять** *see* **скрепить.**

**скрепляющ/ий** *a.* fastening, clamping; cementing; strengthening, reinforcing; **с. болт** coupling bolt; **с. обруч** clamping ring; —**ая машина** stapler.

**скрести** *v.* scrape, scrub; rake.

**скрестить** *v.* cross, cross over.

**скрещ/ение, —ивание** *n.* crossing, crossing over; junction; twisting, interlacing; interbreeding; —**енный** *a.* crossed, crossed over; twisted; (biol.) hybrid; —**иваемость** *f.* combining ability; —**ивать, —иваться** *v.* cross, intersect; interbreed, crossbreed, hybridize.

**скрив/ить, —лять** *v.* bend, twist, crook; —**ленный** *a.* twisted, warped.

**скрип** *m.* creak, squeaking; (med.) crepitus; —**ение** *n.* creaking; —**еть** *v.* creak, grate, squeak; **пестрая —ица** parasol mushroom (*Lepiota procera*).

**скрипка** *f.* violin.

**скрип/нуть** *see* **скрипеть;** —**ун** *m.* long-

horned beetle (*Saperda*); (bot.) orpine (*Sedum telephium*); —**учий** *a.* creaking, creaky, grating, grinding.

**скромный** *a.* modest, unassuming, plain.

**скруб** *m.* (forestry) scrub; bush.

**скруббер** *m.,* —**ный** *a.* scrubber; absorption tower.

**скругл/ение** *n.* rounding off, roundness, curvature; —**ять** *v.* round off, round.

**скрупул** *m.* scruple; —**езный** *a.* scrupulous, meticulous.

**скрут/ить** *see* **скручивать;** —**ка** *f.* twist, twisting; twist joint; joining; splice; **шаг —ки** lay (of cable).

**скрученн/ость** *f.* twistedness; torsion; —**ые** *pl.* (bot.) Contortae.

**скруч/енный** *a.* twisted, contorted; —**ивание** *n.* torsion, twisting, coiling action; buckling, warping; (leaf) curl, roll; **момент —ивания** torque; **угол —ивания** angle of twist; —**ивать** *v.* twist, spin; roll up; —**ивающий** *a.* torsion, torsional, twisting; —**ивающее усилие** torque, torsional force, twisting force, twisting stress.

**скрыв/ание** *n.* concealment, hiding; (mil.) camouflaging; —**ать** *v.* conceal, hide, secrete; camouflage; —**аться** *v.* hide, vanish, disappear; —**ающийся** *a.* disappearing.

**скрыт/ие** *see* **скрывание;** —**ники** *pl.* minute brown scavenger beetles (*Lathridiidae*).

**скрытно** *adv.* secretly; *prefix see also* **скрыто—;** —**еды** *pl.* silken fungus beetles (*Cryptophagidae*); —**сть** *f.* secrecy; —**хоботник** *m.* snout beetle (*Ceutorrhynchus*).

**скрытный** *a.* concealed, hidden, secretive.

**скрыто—** *prefix* crypto— (hidden); —**генетический** *a.* cryptogenetic; —**жаберные** *pl.* (zool.) Cryptobranchia; —**зернистый** *a.* (petr.) cryptomerous; (geol.) cryptoclastic, compact; —**кристаллический** *a.* cryptocrystalline, microcrystalline; —**письменнографитный** *a.* (petr.) cryptographic.

**скрыт/ый** *a.* hidden, concealed, secret, cryptic; latent; stored, potential (energy); insidious (disease); —**ая теплота** latent heat; —**ое изображение** latent image; —**ое состояние**

latency, latent state; —ь *see* **скрывать.**

**скрэб** *see* **скруб.**

**СКС** code mark for butadiene-styrene synthetic rubber.

**скрюч/ивать, —ить** *v.* crook.

**СКТ** code mark for silicone rubber.

**скудель** *f.* clay, potter's clay.

**скуд/еть** *v.* thin, decline, grow poor; —**но** *adv.* scantily, sparsely; —**ность** *f.* scantiness, sparseness, poorness, barrenness; —**ный** *a.* scanty, sparse, poor, meager, lean (ore); bare, barren (soil); small, short.

**скул/а** *f.,* —**овая кость** cheek bone; —**астый** *a.* with high cheek bones; —**атник** *m.* (bot.) polypody (*Polypodium*); —**овой** *a.* (anat.) zygomatic, malar.

**скульпт/ор** *m.* sculptor; —**ура** *f.* sculpture, statuary; (pal.) ornamentation; —**урный** *a.* sculptural, plastic; modeling (clay).

**скумбрия** *f.* (zool.) mackerel.

**скумпия** *f.* (bot.) smoke tree (*Cotinus*).

**скунс** *m.* (zool.) skunk.

**скупать** *v.* buy up, corner.

**скупит** *m.* schoepite.

**скупить** *see* **скупать.**

**скупиться** *v.* stint, be sparing, grudge.

**скупка** *f.* buying up, cornering.

**скуп/ой** *a.* stingy, miserly; —**ость** *f.* stinginess, miserliness.

**скутелларин** *m.* scutellarin.

**скуттерудит** *m.* (min.) skutterudite (a cobalt arsenide).

**скученн/ость** *f.* congestion; density; —**ый** *a.* congested, crowded, pressed together, packed close; dense, compact.

**скучив/ание** *n.* crowding, heaping, boxing up; —**ать** *v.* crowd together, heap, pile, accumulate; —**аться** *v.* flock together, assemble.

**скучный** *a.* tedious, dull, sad.

**скушать** *v.* eat up.

**сл** *abbr.* **(сантилитр)** centiliter; **сл.** *abbr.* **(слабый)** weak.

**слаб/еть** *v.* weaken, waste away; diminish, run down; —**ина** *f.* slack, sag.

**слабит/ельное** *n.,* —**ельный** *a.* laxative, purgative; —**ь** *v.* purge.

**слабнуть** *v.* become weak, get feeble.

**слабо** *adv.* weakly, slightly, mildly; loosely; —**активный** *a.* mildly active; (nucl.) warm; —**возбужденный** *a.* (elec.) feebly excited; —**кипящий** *a.* light-boiling; —**кислый** *a.* weakly acid, subacid; —**летучий** *a.* not very volatile, heavy; —**натянутый** *a.* slack, loose; —**обогащенный** *a.* slightly enriched; —**половинчатый чугун** lightly mottled pig iron; —**радиоактивный** *a.* slightly radioactive; —**сильный** *a.* feeble, weak.

**слабость** *f.* weakness, feebleness; failing, weak point, disadvantage; (med.) asthenia.

**слабо/сученый** *a.* slack (silk); —**точный** *a.* weak-current; sound (cable; insulator).

**слабоум/ие** *n.* imbecility; —**ный** *a.* imbecile, feeble-minded.

**слабофокусирующий** *a.* weak-focusing.

**слабый** *a.* weak, feeble, slight, faint, light; soft, mild; low, inefficient, poor; loose, lax, slack; thin (negative).

**слав/а** *f.* fame, repute; —**иться** *v.* have a reputation (for); —**ка** *f.* (zool.) warbler; —**ный** *a.* famous, renowned; pleasant.

**славянский** *a.* Slavic, Slavonic.

**слаг/аемое** *n.* component; (math.) term; item; sum; —**ать** *v.* put together, join, add; compose; lay down; —**ать с себя** decline; —**аться** *v.* be added, be summed up, be composed (of); —**ающая** *f.* component, constituent; —**ающий** *a.* component, constituent; cumulative; —**ающее сопротивление** component resistance.

**сладить** *see* **слаживать.**

**сладк/ий** *a.* sweet; —**огорький** *a.* bittersweet; —**огорькость** *f.* bittersweetness; —**корень** *m.* wall fern (*Polypodium vulgare*); —**ость** *f.* sweetness; —**ости** *pl.* confectionery.

**слажив/ание** *n.* arrangement, agreement; —**ать** *v.* arrange, agree; piece, join.

**слал** *past sing.* of **слать.**

**сламывать** *v.* break, demolish, pull down (building).

**сланец** *m.* (petr.) schist; slate; shale; **глинистый с.** clay shale, shale;

**горючий с.** oil shale, bituminous shale.

**сланный** *a.* sent.

**сланцевание** *n.* (min.) application of slate dust for prevention of explosions.

**сланцеват/ость** *f.* schistosity, foliated structure, foliation, foliation cleavage, cleavage, cleavage structure; jointing; **—ый** *a.* schistose, schistous; foliated; flaky, scaly; slatelike, slaty; shaly; **—ая глина** shale, slate clay; **—ая структура** cleavage structure.

**сланцевидный** *a.* slate-like, slaty; schistose, schistous.

**сланцев/ый** *a.* schist, schistose, schistous; shale; slate, slaty, slate-like; foliated, foliaceous, scaly, flaky; **с. бензин** shale gasoline; **с. деготь, —ая смола** shale tar; **с. пласт** (petr.) schist; **—ая черная краска** slate black; **—ое масло** shale oil.

**сласти** *pl.* sweets, confection, confectionery; **—ть** *v.* sweeten.

**слать** *v.* send.

**слева** *adv.* from the left, to the left, leftwards, left.

**слегка** *adv.* slightly, lightly, superficially.

**след** *m.* trace, mark, track, trail; vestige; spur (of matrix); track (of ionizing particle); **ни —a** not a trace (of), no sign (of); **—ы** *pl.* traces; trace amount; **анализ —ов** trace analysis.

**след.** *abbr.* (следовательно) therefore; (следующий) following; **след. обр.** *abbr.* (следующим образом) as follows.

**следить** *v.* watch, attend, follow, keep track (of), observe, keep an eye on.

**следован/ие** *n.* sequence, succession, following; investigation; **путь —ия** travel line.

**следовательно** *adv.* therefore, consequently, hence; it follows that.

**след/овать** *v.* follow, go after, come after, succeed, result; **—ует** it is necessary, it should, one must; **—ует заметить** it should be noted; **ему —ует** he should; **как —ует** properly; as follows; **как и —овало ожидать** as was to be expected; **—ом за** immediately after; **—оуказатель** *m.* guide; (agr.) marker.

**следственный** *a.* inquest, inquiry; **с. материал** evidence.

**следствие** *n.* consequence, issue, result, effect, conclusion; **естественное с.** corollary; **причина и с.** cause and effect.

**следует** *see under* **следовать.**

**следующ/ий** *a.* following, next, sequent; **в с. раз** next time; **—им образом** as follows, in the following manner.

**следящ/ий** *a.* follow-up; tracking; servo (mechanism); **—ая система, —ое устройство** servo system; automatic control system; **элемент —ей системы** servo element.

**слежаться** *see* **слеживаться.**

**слеж/ение** *n.* following, tracing, tracking; **—ечный** *a.* track.

**слежив/аемость** *f.* caking, consolidation; tendency to cake; **—ание** *n.* caking, agglutination; deterioration in storage; **—аться** *v.* cake; deteriorate.

**слеза** *f.* tear; drop.

**слез/ание** *n.* descent; **—ать** *v.* descend, climb down, alight, dismount.

**слез/иться** *v.* water, tear; **—ка** *f.* tear drop; drop; insulating bead; **—ки** *pl.* (bot.) Job's tears (*Coix lachryma*); **—ливый** *see* **слезный; —ник** *m.* drip ring; (anat.) lachrymal gland; **—ничок** *m.* lachrymal sac.

**слезн/ый** *a.* tear, lachrymal; **с. проход** (anat.) lachrymal duct; **—ые железы** lachrymal glands.

**слезо/гонный** *a.* tear-exciting, lachrymatory; **—течение** *n.* (physiol.) lachrymation; (med.) epiphora; **—точивый газ** tear gas.

**слезть** *see* **слезать.**

**слеп/ень** *m.* horsefly, gadfly; **—ни** *pl.* horseflies (*Tabanidae*).

**слепить** *v.* dazzle, blind; paste together; mold, form.

**слепл/ивать, —ять** *v.* glue together, paste (to); mold, form; **—иваться, —яться** *v.* stick together, adhere.

**слепни** *see under* **слепень.**

**слеп/нуть** *v.* go blind, become blind, lose one's sight; **—няки** *pl.* leaf bugs (*Miridae*); **—о** *adv.* blindly; **—ой** *a.* blind, sightless; *m.* blind person; **—ой опыт** blank test, control test.

**слепок** *m.* mold, cast, stamp; model, copy, counterpart.

**слепо/рожденный** *a.* born blind; **—та** *f.* blindness.

**слесарн/ая, —я** *f.*, **—ая мастерская** locksmith's workshop; fitting shop; **—ичать** *v.* do mechanical jobs; do metal work; **—оводопроводное дело** plumbing; **—ый** *a.* locksmith's; metalworking; **—ая обработка** bench work.

**слесарство** *n.* locksmith's trade.

**слесарь** *m.* locksmith; fitter, mechanic, machinist; **с.-водопроводчик** plumber.

**слет** *m.* flight; assembly, gathering; **—ать, —еть** *v.* fly off, fly down.

**слечь** *v.* take to one's bed (from illness).

**слешер** *m.* slasher, slashing machine.

**слив** *m.* overflow, decantation, discharge; weir; sink, drain.

**слива** *f.* (bot.) prune, plum (*Prunus*).

**слив/ание** *n.*, **—ка** *f.* pouring off, decantation; pouring together, mixing; **—ать** *v.* pour off, decant, run off; pour together, mix; melt (metal); **—аться** *v.* run together, flow together, unite, fuse, combine, blend; **—ающийся** *a.* flowing together, interfluent, confluent, blending, fusing.

**сливк/и** *pl.* cream; **—оотделитель** *m.* (cream) separator.

**сливн/ой** *a.* overflow, pouring; mixed; (min.) compact; **с. носок** pouring lip, overflow lip; **с. шибер** overflow regulator, flow control; **—ая труба** overflow pipe; sewer pipe, drain; **—ое отверстие** overflow.

**слив/ный, —овый** *a.* plum, prune; **—няк** *m.* plum tree orchard; **—овые** *pl.* Prunaceae; **—овый клей, —овая камедь** plum tree gum; **—овая водка** plum brandy; **—овое масло** plum seed oil.

**сливочн/ый** *a.* cream; **—ое масло** butter; **—ое мороженое** ice cream.

**сливянка** *f.* plum brandy.

**слизевики** *pl.* (bot.) slime mold (*Myxomycetes*).

**слизевокисл/ый** *a.* mucic acid; mucate (of); **—ая соль** mucate.

**слизев/ый** *a.* mucous; slime; viscous (fermentation); **—ая кислота** mucic acid; **соль —ой кислоты** mucate;

**—ые грибы** *see* **слизевики**.

**слиз/ень** *m.* (zool.) slug; **—ни** *pl.* Limacidae.

**слизеподобный** *a.* mucin-like, mucoid.

**слизист/ый** *a.* slimy, mucilaginous; mucous; **—ая железа** (anat.) mucous gland; **—ая оболочка, —ая ткань** (anat.) mucosa, mucous membrane; **—ое вещество** mucin; **—ые споровики** (zool.) Myxosporidia.

**слиз/кий** *a.* slippery, slimy, viscous, mucous; **—нееды** *pl.* predaceous beetles of the Carabidae family; **—няк** *m.* (zool.) mollusk, snail, slug; **—ь** *f.* mucus, phlegm; slime, mucilage.

**слип** *m.* (aero.) slip stream.

**слип/ание** *n.* conglomeration, accumulation; adhesion, adherence; **—аться** *v.* conglomerate; adhere, stick together.

**слипер** *m.* sleeper (beam foundation).

**слипшийся** *a.* conglomerate; adhering.

**слитковыжиматель** *m.* (foundry) ingot stripper.

**слитн/ость** *f.* coalescence, fusion, unification; **—ый** *a.* coalescent, fused, united, unified; massive (structure).

**слитой** *a.* compact (soil).

**слит/ок** *m.* (met.) ingot, pig, bar, rod; (gold) bullion; **—ый** *a.* poured off, decanted; **—ь** *see* **сливать**.

**слич/ать** *v.* compare, collate, check; **—ение** *n.* comparison, collation, checking; **—ительный** *a.* comparative.

**слишком** *adv.* too much, too many, too; over; **с. много** too many, too much.

**слияние** *n.* fusion, union, blending, merging, consolidation, amalgamation, coalescence; confluence, junction (of rivers).

**словар/ь** *m.*, **—ный** *a.* dictionary.

**словацкий** *a.* Slovakian.

**словенский** *a.* Slovenian.

**словник** *m.* glossary.

**словно** *adv.* as, as if, as though, like.

**слово** *n.* word, term; say, speech, address; **с. в с.** word for word, verbatim; **одним —м** in short, briefly.

**словолит/ец, —чик** *m.* type founder; **—ня** *f.* type foundry.

**слог** *m.* syllable; (written) style.

**слоеват/ость** *f.* schistosity; lamination, sheeting; **—ый** *a.* schistous; slaty; foliated, scaly, flaky.

**слоевище** *n.* (bot.) thallus.

**слоев/ой** *a.* layer, bed; **—ая выемка** (min.) slicing.

**слоевцовые** *pl.* (bot.) Thallophyta; **с. бактерии** Schizomycetes.

**слоен/ие** *n.* foliation; **—ый** *a.* foliated.

**слож/ение** *n.* (math.) addition, summation; build, constitution; texture, structure; **—енный** *a.* folded; built; **—имый** *a.* (math.) summable; **—ить** *v.* add; put together, make up, compose; *see also* **слагать, складывать.**

**сложно** *adv.* complexly, complicatedly.

**сложност/ь** *f.* complexity, intricacy, complication; multiplicity; **в общей —и** on the whole, after all.

**сложноцветные** *pl.* (bot.) Compositae.

**сложноэфирн/ый** *a.* ester; **—ая кислота** ester acid; **—ое число** ester number.

**сложн/ый** *a.* complex, complicated, intricate; composite, mixed; multiple, multiplex; compound (interest); **с. индивид, —ое тело** compound; **с. профиль** configuration; **с. эфир** ester; **—ая руда** complex ore.

**слоисто/дождевое облако** nimbostratus (cloud); **—кучевое облако** stratocumulus.

**слоистость** *f.* cleavage, lamination, foliation, schistosity; stratification.

**слоист/ый** *a.* laminated, lamellar, lamellate, foliated, flaky, scaly; stratified, layer, sheet-like; (min.) schistose, schistous; (geol.) bedded; **с. излом** cleavage; **—ое облако** layer cloud, stratus; **—ое строение** schistose structure.

**слоиться** *v.* flake, scale, peel off, exfoliate.

**сло/й** *m.* layer, stratum, bed, band, scam; lamella, flake, lamina, sheet; ply, thickness; coat, coating (of paint), film; (metal) foil; (filter) bed; (hard) pan; **—ями** in layers; **отделение —ев** exfoliation; **покрывать —ями металла** *v.* laminate; **тонкий с.** film.

**слом** *m.* breaking, wrecking, demolition, demolishing; **металл на с.** scrap metal; **—анный** *a.* broken; truncated (cone); **—ать, —ить** *see* **сламывать;**

**—аться** *v.* break, snap; get out of order.

**слон** *m.* elephant; **—ик-блошка** *f.* (zool.) leaf miner; **—ики** *pl.* weevils or snout beetles (*Curculionidae*); **—овость** *f.* (med.) elephantiasis.

**слонов/ый** *a.* elephant, elephantine; **—ая болезнь** (med.) elephantiasis; **—ая бумага** ivory paper; **—ая кость** ivory; **жженая —ая кость, —ая черная, —ая чернь** ivory black; **растительная —ая кость** vegetable ivory, corajo.

**служащий** *a.* serving; *m.* employee.

**служб/а** *f.* service, attendance; office; duty, job, work, employment; (weather) bureau; **—ы** *pl.* services; outbuildings, annexes; **время —ы, продолжительность —ы, срок —ы** service, useful life, working life, age; **на —е** at work, on duty.

**служебн/ый** *a.* employee's, service; official; auxiliary; **с. персонал** staff; **—ое время** working hours; **—ое преступление** violation of duty; **—ые обязанности** official duties.

**служ/ение** *n.* service; **—итель** *m.* servant, attendant; **—ить** *v.* serve, be employed, work.

**слух** *m.* hearing; rumor, report, news; **есть —и, что, ходят —и** it is rumored that; **—ач** *m.* sound reader.

**слухов/ой** *a.* acoustic, auditory, aural, auricular; **с. аппарат** hearing aid; **с. нерв** (anat.) auditory nerve; **—ая трубка** (tel.) receiver; ear trumpet; **—ая чувствительность** aural sensitivity; **наружный с. проход** (anat.) acoustic duct.

**случ/ай** *m.* case, occurrence, incident, instance, occasion, circumstance, chance, opportunity; **в —ае** in case (of), in the event (of); **во всяком —ае** in any case, at any rate; **в противном —ае** otherwise; **в таком —ае** in that case, then; **в худшем —ае** at the worst; **в этом —ае** in this instance; **и в том и в другом —ае** in either case, in both cases; **ни в каком —ае** on no account, by no means; **на всякий с.** in any case; just in case; **по —аю** on account (of), owing (to); **закрыто по —аю ремонта** closed for repairs; при —ае at a convenient time; упустить с. *v.* miss an opportunity.

случайн/о *adv.* by chance, accidentally, casually; —ость *f.* chance, accident, emergency; (math.) contingency; (mil.) hazard; —ый *a.* chance, accidental, incidental, casual, random, occasional, haphazard, stray; nonrecurrent (waste); —ое совпадение (nucl.) accidental coincidence, random coincidence.

случ/ать, —ить *v.* couple, pair.

случ/аться, —иться *v.* happen, occur, take place, come about.

случ/ка *f.*, —ной *a.* pairing, coupling; —ная болезнь (vet.) trypanosomosis.

слуш/ание *n.* hearing; —атели *pl.* audience; —ать *v.* listen; —аться *v.* listen, pay attention (to); obey.

слущивание *n.* (med.) desquamation, scaling off.

слыхать *v.* hear.

слыш/ать *v.* hear; —аться *v.* be heard; —имость *f.* audibility; —имый *a.* audible; —но *adv.* audibly; it is reported, it is said; —ный *a.* audible, heard.

слэг *m.* slug (unit of mass).

слюд/а *f.* (min.) mica; чешуйки —ы micaceous lamina.

слюдист/оглинистый сланец (min.) micaceous slate, phyllite; —ый *a.* micaceous.

слюдообраз/ный *a.* mica-like, micaceous; —ование *n.* micatization.

слюдян/ой *a.* mica, micaceous; —ая пластинка mica sheet; —ая порода micaceous rock; —ые листики mica scale.

слюн/а *f.* saliva; —ный *a.* salivary; —ные железы (anat.) salivary glands.

слюно/гон *m.* (bot.) pellitory of Spain (*Anacyclus pyrethrum*); —гонный *a.* salivary; —гонное средство (med.) salivator; —отделение, —течение *n.* (physiol.) salivation.

сляб *m.* (met.) slab.

слябинг *m.* (met.) slabbing; slab mill.

слякот/ный *a.* miry, slushy; —ь *f.* mire, slush.

см *abbr.* (сантиметр) centimeter; см² *abbr.* (квадратный сантиметр) square

centimeter; см³ *abbr.* (кубический сантиметр) cubic centimeter; см. *abbr.* (смотри) see.

смаз/анный *a.* greased, lubricated; smeared, blurred; —ать *see* смазывать.

смазк/а *f.* grease, lubricant, oil; greasing, lubrication, oiling; величина —и, значение —и lubricating value; жидкая с. oil lubrication.

смазочн/ый *a.* lubricating, lubrication, grease; с. жир grease, axle grease; с. канал oil drain, oil channel; с. материал, —ое вещество, —ое средство lubricant; ointment, salve; —ая канавка oil groove (in machine); —ая коробка lubricator, oil can, grease cup; —ое масло lubricating oil, lubricant.

смазчик *m.* greaser, lubricator.

смазыв/аемость *f.* lubricating property; —ание *n.* lubrication, greasing, oiling; —ать *v.* lubricate, grease, oil; smear; evade (a question).

смазывающ/ий *a.* lubricating, greasing, oiling; smearing; —ая способность, —ее свойство lubricating property; —ее приспособление lubricator.

смалец *m.* lard.

смальт/а *f.* smalt (blue pigment or glass); mosaic enamel; —ин, —ит *m.* (min.) smaltine, smaltite.

смарагд *m.*, —овый *a.* (min.) emerald (a gem variety of beryl); —ит *m.* smaragdite (a variety of amphibole).

сматыв/ание *n.* winding, reeling; unreeling; —ать *v.* wind, reel, reel on; reel off, unreel, unroll, uncoil, run off, pay out.

смах/ивать, —нуть *v.* brush off.

смачив/аемость *f.* wettability; —аемый *a.* wettable; —ание *n.* wetting, moistening; —атель *m.*, —ающее вещество wetting agent; —ать *v.* wet, moisten, damp, dampen, sprinkle; soak, steep, imbue, drench; —ающий *a.* wetting.

смежно *adv.* contiguously; in the vicinity (of); —сть *f.* contiguity, adjacency, proximity, juxtaposition.

смежн/ый *a.* adjacent, contiguous, proximate, neighboring, abutting, adjoining; (math.) affine; —ое нахождение juxtaposition; —ые двойники (cryst.) contact twins; —ые области науки allied sciences.

смел/ость *f.* daring; —ый *a.* daring, bold.

смен/а *f.* change, shift, relay, exchange, interchange, replacing, renewing, relief; succession (of crops); ночная с. night shift; —ить *see* сменять.

сменный *a.* changeable, interchangeable, exchangeable, renewable, removable; staggered; с. насос relay pump; с. перебор changewheel gear.

сменяем/ость *f.* interchangeability; —ый *a.* interchangeable, removable.

сменять *v.* change, interchange, exchange, replace, remove, renew; relieve; —ся *v.* take turns, alternate; exchange (for).

смерз/ание *n.* freezing, freezing together; —лый *a.* frozen, congealed.

смер/ивать, —ить *v.* measure.

смертельный *a.* fatal, mortal, lethal.

смерти/ость *f.* mortality, death rate; коэффициент —ости, процент —ости death rate; —ый *a.* mortal; —ая казнь death penalty, capital punishment, execution.

смертоносн/ость *f.* deadliness; —ый *a.* deadly, lethal, fatal; pestilent; —ый газ lethal gas.

смерт/ь *f.* death, decease; объявление о —и obituary; удостоверение о —и death certificate.

смерч *m.* waterspout; sandstorm.

смес/еобразование *n.* carburetion (in engine); —имость *f.* miscibility; —имый *a.* miscible; —итель *m.*, —ительный бак mixer, mixing tank, blender; —итель-отстойник *m.* mixer-settler; —ительный *a.* mixing.

смести *see* сметать.

сместить *see* смещать.

смесь *f.* mixture, mix, blend, composite, composition; (rubber) stock; miscellany.

смет/а *f.* estimate, estimated cost, appraisal; составлять —у *v.* estimate.

сметан/а *f.* sour cream; —ообразный *a.* creamy, paste-like, viscous.

смет/ать *v.* sweep off; —ки *pl.* sweepings.

сметн/ый *a.* estimated, planned; —ые цены estimated prices, estimates.

сметь *v.* dare, venture, have the courage.

смеш/анный *a.* mixed, miscellaneous, composite, compound, combination, blended; (biol.) hybrid; stirred, agitated; —ать *see* смешивать; —ение *n.* mixture, mixing (together), combination, blending, merging, coalition; confusion; complication.

смешив/аемость *f.* miscibility; —аемый *a.* miscible; —ание *n.* mixing, blending; stirring, agitation; —ать *v.* mix, blend, combine; stir, agitate; mix up, confuse; —аться *v.* intermix, intermingle, interblend; be confused.

смешивающий *a.* mixing; с. аппарат mixer; —ся *a.* coalescing, fusing; miscible.

смешно *adv.* ridiculously; it is ridiculous, it is strange, it is odd; —й *a.* funny, ludicrous, ridiculous.

смещ/ать *v.* displace, shift, dislodge, remove, skew; —аться *v.* shift; (geol.) heave; —ающее напряжение bias.

смещен/ие *n.* displacement, dislodgment, shifting, shift, removal, disturbance; movement, migration; bias, distortion; deviation; (geol.) dislocation, slip, heave, upheaval; с. фаз phase shift; напряжение —ия (thermionics) grid bias; поле —ия bias field; правило —ия (nucl.) displacement law; ток —ия (elec.) displacement current; угол —ия displacement angle; —ный *a.* displaced, dislocated, out of line, skew; staggered.

смеяться *v.* laugh (at), ridicule.

СМЖ *abbr.* (спинномозговая жидкость) cerebrospinal fluid.

смилаксовые *pl.* (bot.) Smilacaceae.

смила-сапонин *m.* smila-saponin.

смилацин *m.* smilacin, sarsasaponin.

смин/ание *n.* mashing, kneading; —ать *v.* mash, knead, work; crumple; —аться *v.* collapse; —ающийся *a.* collapsible.

смир/енный *a.* submissive, quiet; —ительная рубашка (med.) strait jacket.

смирн/а *f.*, —ский ладан myrrh (gum); —ский *a.* Smyrna.

смирн/ый *a.* quiet, gentle; —ять *v.* subdue, tame.

**Смита процесс** Smith process (for copper refining).

**смит/ит** *m.* (min.) smithite; **—сонит** *m.* smithsonite (a zinc carbonate).

**смог** *past. sing. of* **смочь.**

**смок/ва, —овница** *f.* fig tree (*Ficus*); **дикая с.** sycamore (*F. sycomorus*); **индийская с.** banyan tree (*F. indica*); **райская с.** plantain (*Musa paradisiaca*).

**смол** *see* **смолка.**

**смола** *f.* resin, rosin, gum; tar, pitch; **искусственная с.** synthetic resin; **каменноугольная с.** coal tar.

**смолевка** *f.* (bot.) catchfly (*Silene*); (zool.) pine weevil (*Pissodes*).

**смол/евой** *a.* resin; tar, tarred; **—ение** *n.* resinification; tarring; **—еный** *a.* resined; tarred, pitched; **—истость** *f.* resinousness, resinous nature; tarriness, pitchiness.

**смолист/ый** *a.* resinous, resin; bituminous, pitch, tarry; **с. известняк** bituminous limestone; **с. торф** pitch peat; **с. уголь** pitch coal (bituminous coal or lignite); **—ое масло** oleoresin; **—ые материалы** naval stores; **—ые остатки** tarry residues.

**смолить** *v.* resin; tar, pitch; **—ся** *v.* become resinous, resinify.

**смолка** *f.* (bot.) German catchfly (*Lychnis viscaria*); fumigating resin.

**смолк/ать, —нуть** *v.* grow silent; cease.

**смолница** *f.* (soils) smolnitz.

**смоло/варня** *see* **смолокурня; —вка** *f.* tar pot; **—гонный** *a.* tar distilling; **—гонщик** *m.* tar distiller.

**смолокур/ение** *n.*, **—енный** *a.* tar distilling; **—енный завод, —ный завод, —ня** *f.* tar works, tar distillery.

**смолоносн/ица** *f.* (bot.) giant fennel (*Ferula*); **—ый** *a.* resiniferous; tarbearing.

**смолообраз/ование** *n.* formation of resin; gum formation (in gasoline); **—ующий** *a.* resin-forming; gumforming.

**смоло/отделитель** *m.* tar separator; **—подобный** *a.* resinoid; tarry; **—разгонка** *f.* tar distillation; **—садный** *see* **смологонный; —семянник** *m.* (bot.) pittosporum; **—содержащий** *a.* resin-

containing; gum-containing, gummy; tar-containing.

**смоль** *f.* resin; tar; **—ный** *see* **смоляной; —ня** *f.* tar works, tar factory.

**смоляк** *m.* decomposed surface peat.

**смолянка** *f.* tar barrel, tar pot.

**смолян/ой** *a.* resin, resinous, resinoid; tar, tarry, pitch; (elec.) resinous, negative; **с. желвак** resin deposit (in wood); **с. камень** (petr.) pitchstone (a variety of volcanic glass); **с. клей** resin sizing; **—ая бумага** tar paper; **—ая замазка** bituminous cement; **—ая кислота** resin acid; **соль —ой кислоты** resinate; **—ая масса** resinous compound; **—ая обманка, —ая руда** (min.) pitchblende (a variety of uraninite); **—ая пакля** tarred oakum; **—ое масло** resin oil; tar oil; **—ое озеро** asphalt lake; **—ое число** tar value; **—ые красители** coal-tar dyes.

**смолянокисл/ый** *a.* resin acid; resinate (of); **—ая медь** copper resinate; **—ая соль** resinate.

**смонтированный** *a.* assembled, erected, built up, set up, mounted.

**смораживаться** *v.* congeal, freeze.

**смородин/а** *f.*, **—ный** *a.* (bot.) currant (*Ribes*); **—ные** *pl.* Grossulariaceae.

**сморчок** *m.* (bot.) morel (*Morchella esculenta*).

**сморщ/енный** *a.* wrinkled, shriveled, crinkled, crumpled; corrugated (iron); **—ивание** *n.* wrinkling, shriveling, shrinking; crumpling; corrugation; **—ивать, —ить** *v.* wrinkle; corrugate; **—иваться, —иться** *v.* wrinkle, shrivel, shrink, crumple up, crinkle.

**смотать** *see* **сматывать.**

**смотр** *m.* inspection; **произвести с.** *v.* inspect, review; **—еть** *v.* inspect; look, view, regard; **—еть за** superintend, look after, be in charge of; **—я на, —я по** according to, depending on; **не —я на** in spite of, notwithstanding.

**смотров/ой** *a.* inspection, sight; **с. люк, —ая дверь, —ое окно, —ое отверстие** sight hole, peep hole, glory hole, inspection hole; **—ое стекло** sight glass.

**смотря** *see under* **смотреть.**

**смоч/енный** *a.* wetted, moistened, humidified; **с. термометр** wet bulb thermometer; —ить *see* смачивать.

**смочь** *v.* be able, prove able.

**смрадн/ость** *f.* stench, offensive odor; —ый *a.* foul smelling.

**смуглый** *a.* dark-complexioned, swarthy.

**смутить** *see* смущать.

**смутн/ость** *f.* dimness; confusion; —ый *a.* dim, vague; hazy, confused.

**смушка** *f.* astrakhan lamb.

**смущ/ать** *v.* disturb, perplex, confuse, embarrass; —ение *n.* confusion, embarrassment; —енный *a.* disturbed, confused, embarrassed.

**смыв** *m.* (geol.) washout; глина —а colluvial clay; —аемый *a.* wipe-off; —ание *n.* washing, washing off; erosion; —ать *v.* wash, wash off; erode; —ка *f.* (paint) remover; —ная вода wash water.

**смык/ание** *n.* joining; closing; с. невязки (surv.) adjusting traverse; —ать *v.* joint, link, couple, fit in, clamp; close; —аться *v.* interlock.

**смысл** *m.* sense, meaning, significance, purport; в —е in the sense (of); on the score (of); здравый с. common sense; нет —а there is no point (in); по —у according to the terms (of); —ить *v.* understand, know.

**смыт/ый** *a.* washed off; eroded; —ь *see* смывать.

**смычка** *f.* jointing, joint, coupling, clamp; union.

**смыч/ок** *m.*, —ковый *a.* bow; —ковая дрель bow drill.

**смягч/ать** *v.* soften; mitigate, moderate, modify, subdue, damp; —аться *v.* soften; ease off, relent; —ающий *a.* softening; (pharm.) emollient; extenuating (circumstances); —ающее средство softening agent; emollient, demulcent.

**смягчен/ие** *n.* softening; moderation, modification, damping; —ный *a.* softened; moderated, modified; subdued (color).

**смягчитель** *m.* softener, softening agent; plasticizer; —ный *a.* softening; plasticizing.

**смягчать** *see* смягчать.

**смятение** *n.* confusion, commotion.

**смят/ие** *n.* crumpling; contortion, warping; напряжение —ия bearing stress;

прочность на с. bearing strength; —ый *a.* crumpled, rumpled; contorted; —ь *v.* crumple, rumple; disrupt; (mil.) overrun; —ься *v.* get out of shape.

**сн** *abbr.* (стен) sthene.

**снаббирование** *n.* lowering and raising pipes when drilling high-pressure oil wells.

**снабж/ать, снабдить** *v.* provide, supply, furnish, deliver, feed; —ающий *a.* supply, delivery; —ение *n.* provision, supply, supplying, delivery, delivering, feed; outfit; отдел —ения purchase department; —енный *a.* provided, supplied.

**Снайдера электропечь** Snyder furnace.

**снайпер** *m.* (mil.) sniper, sharpshooter.

**снайтов/ать, —ить** *v.* lash.

**снаружи** *adv.* on the outside, on the exterior, exteriorly, outwardly.

**снаря/д** *m.* apparatus, instruments, implements; (mil.) shell, projectile, missile; с. с удушливым газом gas shell; —дить, —жать *v.* equip, furnish, fit out, outfit; —жение *n.* equipment, outfit; implements; —женный *a.* equipped, outfitted.

**снаст/ь** *f.* tackle, equipment, gear; outfit, kit; rope, cordage, rigging; —и *pl.* cordage, rigging.

**сначала** *adv.* at first, firstly, from the start, at the beginning; all over again.

**снашив/ание** *n.* wear, abrasion; —ать *v.* wear out, abrade.

**снеббер** *m.* (min.) snubber.

**снег** *m.*, —овой *a.* snow; (dry) ice; граница вечного —а, —овая линия snow line; —овал, —оочиститель, —опах *m.* snow plow; —ование *n.* refrigeration with snow; —озащита *f.* snow fence; —омер *m.* snow gage; —опад *m.* snowfall; —оподобный *a.* snow-like, snowy; —отаялка *f.* snow melter.

**снедок** *m.* (bot.) chervil (*Anthriscus cerefolium*).

**снеж/инка** *f.* snow flake; —ить *v.* snow; —нобелый *a.* snow-white; —ягодник *m.* snowberry (*Symphoricarpus*); —ный *a.* snow; —ная буря snowstorm; —ная крупа soft hail.

**Снелля закон** (phys.) Snell's law.

снес/ение *n.* removal, pulling down, demolition; —ти *see* сносить.
снеток *m.* smelt (fish).
сни/жать, —зить *v.* sink, lower, lessen, reduce, bring down; cut (price); —жаться *v.* sink, drop; —жение *n.* reduction, decrease, loss; cutting down (of prices); depression.
снизойти *see* снисходить.
снизу *adv.* underneath, below; вид с. bottom view; подача с. underfeed.
снимание *n.* taking off, taking down.
сниматель *m.* pickup.
снимать *v.* take off, take down, take away, remove, strip, strip off; skim off; gather (crop); take (readings); plot (a curve); relieve (pressure); sign (contract); photograph; с. мерку take measurements, measure; с. с работы dismiss, discharge; —ся *v.* be removed; (phot.) take; —ся с места start.
снимающ/ийся *a.* stripping; —ееся покрытие stripcoat.
снимок *m.* print, photograph; copy, counterpart; *suffix* —graph.
СНиП *abbr.* (строительные нормы и правила) construction specifications and regulations.
снисходит/ельный *a.* condescending; lenient; —ь *v.* condescend; make allowance (for).
снит/ок *see* снеток; —ь *see* сныть.
сниться *v.* dream.
снова *adv.* again, anew, afresh; начать с. *v.* make a fresh start.
снов/аль, —альщик *m.* (text.) warper; —альный *a.* warping; warp (machine); —альня *f.* warp beam; —ание *n.*, —ка *f.* warping; —ать *v.* warp.
сноп *m.* sheaf, bundle; cone, shaft, beam (of light), shower (of sparks), jet (of flame); —овидный *a.* sheaf-like; —овязалка *f.*, —вязальная машина, —вязка *f.* (agr.) binder; —онос *m.* sheaf carrier.
снорт *m.* snort valve (of blast furnace).
снос *m.* demolition, wrecking, removal, pulling down (building); drift; (min.) stripping system; terrace, bench (of open-cut mine); угол —а (aero.) drift; drift angle; —ить *v.* demolish, tear down, take down, pull down;

take, carry, drive; wash away; suffer, endure; —иться *v.* confer, communicate.
сноска *f.* reference, footnote.
сносный *a.* tolerable; passable.
снотворн/ый *a.*, —ое средство soporific, somnifacient.
сношен/ие *n.* relation, connection, communication, dealings; поддерживать —ия *v.* keep in touch (with).
СНР *abbr.* (Секция научных работников) Section of Trade Union of Scientific Workers.
СНХ *abbr.* (Совет народного хозяйства) Council of National Economy.
сныть, обыкновенная goutweed (*Aegopodium podagraria*).
снят/ие *n.* taking down, taking off; taking away, removal, skimming; taking (readings); plotting (curves); relieving (pressure); с. урожая harvesting; —ый *a.* taken down, taken off, removed; skimmed; stripped (emulsion); —ый затылок cutting clearance; со —ым затылком cleared; —ь *see* снимать.
со *see* с; со— *see* с—.
соавторы *pl.* coauthors, collaborators.
собак/а *f.* dog; —оводство *n.* dog breeding.
собач/ий *a.* dog, canine; с. зуб *see* свинорой; с. корень, с. язык (bot.) hound's tongue (*Cynoglossum officinale*); —ья капуста dog's mercury (*Mercurialis perennis*); —ья петрушка dog's parsley (*Aethusa cynapium*); —ья чума distemper.
собачка *f.* small dog, puppy; (mech.) dog; clamp dog; dog, catch, stop, detent, checking device, arresting device; (ratchet) pawl; trigger (of gun).
собир/ание *n.* gathering, assembling, collecting, collection, agglomeration; —атель *m.* gatherer, collector; (elec.) collector; (elec.) conductor.
собирательн/ый *a.* collecting, collective; с. приемник, с. сосуд collecting vessel, receiver, reservoir; drip pan, collecting basin; stock tub; —ая линза, —ое стекло condensing lens, condenser, converging lens; —ая полоса, —ая шина (elec.) busbar; —ое кольцо (elec.) collector ring, slip ring.

**собир/áть** *v.* gather, collect, catch; accumulate, stock; assemble, set up, erect, build up, install, mount, fit up; make up, get together; congregate, agglomerate; pick (harvest); **—áться** *v.* gather, collect, agglomerate, congregate; intend, plan (to), get ready (to); **—áющий** *a.* collecting; converging (lens); **—áющийся** *a.* intending, planning.

**соблазн/ительный** *a.* tempting; **—ить, —ять** *v.* tempt.

**соблю/дáть, —сти** *v.* observe, keep, maintain; **—дáться** *v.* be observed, be kept; be fulfilled; **—дéние** *n.* observance, keeping, maintenance, adherence.

**собóй** *instr. of* себя.

**собол/ь** *m.*, **—ий** *a.* (zool.) sable.

**собралит** *m.* (min.) sobralite (identical with pyroxmangite).

**собран/ие** *n.* gathering, assembly, meeting, conference, board; collection, accumulation, congregation, complex; **—ный** *a.* gathered, assembled; collected; conglomerate; assembled, erected, built up, mounted; **в —ном виде** assembled.

**собрáт** *m.* colleague, fellow member; **с. по ремеслу** fellow worker, coworker.

**собрáть** *see* собирáть.

**собрер/ол** *m.* sobrerol, pinol hydrate; **—он** *m.* sobrerone, pinol.

**собственни/к** *m.* owner, proprietor; **—ческий** *a.* proprietary.

**собственно** *adv.* properly, strictly, correctly; **с. говоря** strictly speaking.

**собственност/ь** *f.* property, possessions, real estate; ownership; **иметь в —и** *v.* own, possess; **прáво —и** proprietary rights.

**собственн/ый** *a.* own, proper; characteristic; natural, inherent, fundamental; self—; eigen—; internal (friction, resistance, etc.); **с. вес** gravity; **—ым весом** by gravity; **—ая функция** eigenfunction, fundamental function; **—ая частота** fundamental frequency; natural frequency; **—ая энергия** self-energy; **—ое значение, —ое число** (math.) eigenvalue; **—ое колебание** natural oscillation; **—ое состояние** eigenstate.

**событ/ие** *n.* event, occurrence; **—ия** *pl.* events, developments.

**сов—, сов.** *abbr.* (советский) Soviet.

**сова** *f.* (zool.) owl.

**совáть** *v.* thrust, shove, push; **—ся** *v.* intrude, interfere.

**соввлáсть** *f.* Soviet rule.

**совентáль** *m.* sovental (detergent).

**соверш/áть** *v.* accomplish, effect, perform, achieve; commit; **—áться** *v.* be accomplished; come about; **—éние** *n.* accomplishment, completion, performance, achievement, fulfillment.

**совершéнно** *adv.* quite, completely, entirely, fully, thoroughly, wholly, totally, perfectly, precisely; to all intents and purposes; **с. вéрно** precisely, absolutely, right; **—лéтие** *n.* majority; **достигнуть —лéтия** *v.* come of age; **—ротые** *pl.* (zool.) Teleostomi.

**совершéнн/ый** *a.* perfect, ideal, complete, thorough, absolute; **—ая жидкость** perfect liquid, ideal liquid.

**совершéнств/о** *n.* perfection, ideal; efficiency; **в —е** to perfection; **верх —а** acme of perfection; **—ование** *n.* perfecting, improvement, development; **—овать** *v.* perfect, improve, develop, refine; consummate, complete; **—оваться** *v.* be perfected, improve, progress.

**совершитель** *m.* accomplisher, performer.

**совершить** *see* совершáть.

**совест/ливый, —ный** *a.* conscientious, scrupulous; **—ь** *f.* conscience.

**совéт** *m.* council, board, committee; Soviet; advice, counsel, opinion; **—ник** *m.* adviser, counselor; **—овать** *v.* advise, counsel, recommend, suggest; **—оваться** *v.* consult, take counsel, discuss.

**совéтск/ий** *a.* Soviet; **С. Союз** Soviet Union; **—ая власть** the Soviet Government; **—ое государство** the Soviet State.

**совéтчик** *see* совéтник.

**совещ/áние** *n.* conference, meeting; consultation, counsel, deliberation; communication; **—áтельный** *a.* consultative, deliberative, advisory; **—**

**аться** *v.* take counsel, deliberate, confer.

**совиден** *m.* vinyl chloride-vinylidene chloride copolymer (Soviet equivalent of Saran).

**сов/иноголовки, —ки** *pl.* owlet or cutworm moths (*Noctuidae*); **—ка** *f.* cutworm (*Agrotis*); **стеблевая —ка** stem borer.

**совкаин** *m.* Sovcaine, dibucaine hydrochloride.

**Совкино** Soviet Cinematograph Enterprises, Sovkino.

**совлад/елец** *m.* joint owner, joint proprietor; **—ение** *n.* joint ownership, joint property; **—еть** *v.* own in common.

**совместим/ость** *f.* compatibility; **—ый** *a.* compatible, combinable, consistent.

**совместитель** *m.* a person holding several positions (or jobs); **—ствовать** *v.* hold two or more positions.

**совместить** *see* совмещать.

**совместно** *adv.* in common, jointly, together; **владеть с.** *v.* share; **работающий с.** collaborating, cooperating; jointly operating; **ставить с.** *v.* class (with); **—сть** *f.* compatibility; consistency (of equations).

**совместн/ый** *a.* joint, common, cooperative; **со—**; **с. объем** covolume; **—ая полимеризация** copolymerization; **—ая работа** teamwork, collaboration, cooperation; **—ое действие** joint action, cooperation; **—ое обучение** coeducation; **—ое осаждение** coprecipitation.

**совмещ/ать** *v.* combine, join; reunite, reconcile; (geom.) superpose; **—аться** *v.* coincide; **—ающийся** *a.* superposable; coinciding; **—ение** *n.* combination; blending; coincidence; **—енный** *a.* combined, integrated.

**Совнархоз** *see* **СНХ.**

**совок** *m.* shovel, scoop; trowel; dust pan.

**совокуп/ить, —лять** *v.* join, unite; **—ление** *n.* (zool.) copulation; **—ляться** *v.* copulate; **—ность** *f.* combination, association, conjunction, totality; series, set, aggregate; **в —ности** in the aggregate, in total, together; **—ный** *a.* joint, combined, collective; cumulative, aggregate.

**совол** *m.* chlorinated biphenyl.

**совпа/дать, —сть** *v.* coincide, concur, conform, tally, agree; **с. во времени** synchronize; **с. по фазе** be in phase; **с. частично** overlap; **точно с.** (printing) register; **—дающий** *a.* coincident, coincidental, concurrent, congruent, corresponding; **—дающий осями** coaxial; **—дение** *n.* coincidence, concurrence, conformity, congruence, concordance, correspondence, matching; accord, accordance; superposition; **отсчет —ия, счет —ий** (instrumentation) coincidence counting; **схема —ий, цепь —ия** coincidence circuit.

**совпрен** *m.* sovprene (a synthetic chloroprene rubber).

**совр.** *abbr.* (**современный**) contemporary.

**современн/ик** *m.* contemporary; **—ость** *f.* contemporaneousness, the present time, modernity; **—ый** *a.* contemporary, contemporaneous, modern, up-to-date, recent.

**совсем** *adv.* altogether, absolutely, completely, entirely; **с. не** not in the least, not at all; **с. не то** nothing of the sort.

**Сов/строй** *abbr.* (**Советское строительство**) Soviet construction; **—торгфлот** Sovtorgflot, the Soviet Merchant Marine; **—фото** Sovfoto (official Soviet photographic organization).

**совхоз** *m.*, **—ный** *a.* sovkhoz, state farm.

**соглас/ие** *n.* consent, compliance, concurrence, assent, accord, agreement, congruence; (geol.) conformity; **в —ии** in accordance (with); **находиться в —ии** *v.* agree; **общее с.** concensus; **—ительный** *a.* conciliatory; **—иться** *see* **соглашаться.**

**согласн/о** *adv.* harmoniously, concordantly; in conformance (with), according (to); **с. заказу** as per order; **—ость** *f.* consistency; consonance, concord; concordance; **—ый** *a.* conforming (to), in agreement (with), consistent (with); consonant (letter); **—ое напластование** (geol.) conformable strata.

**согласов/ание** *n.* concordance, agreement, conformity, correspondence, coordination, matching; consent;

approval; adjustment; (math.) congruence; —**анность** *f.* concordance, agreement, harmony, compatibility, consistency; concensus; consent; —**анность действия** teamwork; —**анный** *a.* adjusted; coordinated, coordinate, simultaneous; matched, consistent; approved; —**ать,** —**ывать** *v.* adjust, square; coordinate, correlate, match, fit; conciliate; accommodate, comply; —**аться,** —**ываться** *v.* conform, be in keeping (with), comply; cohere.

**согласующийся** *a.* conforming; compatible.

**соглаш/ать** *v.* persuade, induce; —**аться** *v.* consent, agree, comply (with); coincide; **не** —**аться** differ, disagree; —**ение** *n.* agreement, covenant, understanding, arrangement, contract; **притти к** —**ению** *v.* come to terms, come to an agreement.

**согнать** *v.* drive away, drive off.

**согнуто**— *prefix* campylo—, curved; —**семенной** *a.* (bot.) campylospermous.

**согнут/ый** *a.* bent, curved; —**ь** *v.* bend, curve, twist.

**согрев/ание** *n.* warming, heating; —**атель** *m.* heater; —**ательный** *a.* heating; —**ать** *v.* warm, heat; —**аться** *v.* get warm.

**согренит** *m.* a uranium-containing carbon compound.

**согрет/ый** *a.* warmed, heated; —**ь** *see* согревать.

**сода** *f.* soda, sodium carbonate; **с. бикарбонат, с. для теста, двууглекислая с., питьевая с.** sodium bicarbonate, baking soda; **с. для стирки, углекислая с.** washing soda, sodium carbonate; **аммиачная с.** ammonia soda, Solvay soda; **жженая с., кальцинированная с., обезвоженная с., прокаленная с.,** soda ash (commercial anhydrous sodium carbonate); **кристаллическая с.** soda crystals.

**содалит** *m.* (min.) sodalite.

**содд/иит,** —**ит** *m.* soddyite, soddite (uranium mineral).

**Содди-Фаянса закон** Soddy-Fajans law.

**содейств/ие** *n.* assistance, cooperation, concurrence; —**овать** *v.* assist, help,

cooperate; contribute, further, forward, expedite, promote.

**Содерберга электрод** Söderberg electrode.

**содержание** *n.* contents, content, percentage, capacity, volume (of a body), area (of a surface); maintenance, upkeep; housing, housing system; allowance, salary, pay; **с. и форма** form and contents; **краткое с.** summary; **кубическое с.** volume; **процентное с.** percentage, per cent content; **руда богатая** —**м** a rich ore; **с большим** —**м, с высоким** —**м** rich (in), high (in); **уголь с высоким** —**м золы** high-ash coal; **с низким** —**м** low (in), low-grade (ore), poor (in).

**содерж/ать** *v.* contain, hold, include, comprise; keep, support, maintain; **с. в себе** include, contain; —**ащий** *a.* containing; **не** —**ащий** free (of); **не** —**ащий урана** uranium-free; —**имое** *n.* contents; —**имость** *f.* capacity, volume.

**содово**— *prefix* soda; **с.-известковое умягчение** soda-lime process (for softening water).

**содов/ый** *a.* soda; **с. щелок** soda lye; —**ая вода** soda water (beverage); —**ая масса,** —**ая целлюлоза** (paper) soda pulp.

**содоклад** *m.* coreport, joint report; —**чик** *m.* reader of a joint report or paper.

**содосодержащий** *a.* containing soda.

**содр/анный** *a.* stripped, skinned, barked; —**ать** *see* сдирать.

**содрог/аться,** —**нуться** *v.* shiver, shudder.

**содружество** *n.* concord; collaboration; friendship; **с. наций** (British) commonwealth.

**соев/ище** *n.* soybean field; —**ый** *a.* soybean.

**соединен/ие** *n.* (chem.) compound; combination, combining, blending, fusion, amalgamation, consolidation, coalition, aggregation, conglutination, association; connection, connecting, joining, junction, conjunction; (mech.) coupling; union, joint, seam, bond, link; splice, splicing; fastening, binding; assembling; bridging; (elec.) contact; meshing (of gears); с.-зигзаг (elec.) zigzag connection; в —ии с in connection with; вес —ия combining weight; вступать в с., входить в с. *v.* enter into combination, react; место —ия, точка —ия joint, junction; объем —ия combining volume; органическое с. organic compound; реакция —ия addition reaction; combination; с непосредственным —ием direct-coupled; схема —ия (elec.) circuit diagram; теплота —ия heat of combination; уравнение —ия equation of combination.

**Соединенные Штаты** United States.

**соедин/енный** *a.* combined, united, connected, coupled, joined, joint; —итель *m.* connector, bond, coupler, coupling.

**соединительн/ый** *a.* connecting, coupling, binding, joint; connective, conjunctive; с. брус draw bar; с. вес combining weight; с. зажим (elec.) connecting terminal, connector; с. канал connecting channel, connecting main; с. механизм, с. привод connecting gear; с. объем combining volume; с. провод (elec.) cross connection; jumper; с. фланец flange coupling; —ая гайка flange nut, collar nut, nipple; —ая деталь coupling piece, adapter; —ая замазка cement for joints; —ая коробка (elec.) junction box; —ая линия (tel.) trunk line; —ая муфта connector, sleeve; —ая полоса, —ая шина (elec.) connecting busbar; —ая ткань (zool.) connective tissue; —ая трубка nipple; —ая труба connecting pipe; —ая тяга coupling rod, tie rod, tie piece, tie; —ая часть joint; connecting piece, connection; —ое звено connecting link, link, coupling; —ые скобки (typ.) brace.

**соедин/ить, —ять** *v.* connect, join, unite, consolidate, draw together, link, couple, bridge, fasten, attach, splice; bind, combine, fix; bond; build up; engage, mesh, put in gear; с. в (elec.) connect up, connect to; —иться, —яться *v.* unite, combine, join, congregate, coalesce, fuse; engage,

become engaged, mesh (of gears); —яемый *a.* combinable.

**сожал/ение** *n.*, —еть *v.* regret.

**сожжен/ие** *n.* burning, combustion; анализ —ием combustion analysis, analysis by combustion; печь для —ия combustion furnace; —ный *a.* burnt, scorched.

**сожительство** *n.* (biol.) symbiosis, living together.

**созаль** *m.* Sozal, aluminum phenolsulfonate.

**созвать** *see* **созывать.**

**созвездие** *n.* (astron.) constellation.

**созвуч/ие** *n.* consonance, harmony, accord; —ный *a.* in keeping (with).

**созд/авание** *n.* creation, making; —авать, —ать *v.* create, make, form, build, set up, found, establish; generate, produce; —ание *n.* creation; establishment, founding; creature; —атель *m.* creator, maker; founder, originator.

**созид/ание** *n.* erection, construction, building; creation, foundation; —атель *m.* constructor, builder; creator, founder; —ательный *a.* constructive; creative; —ать *v.* erect, construct, make, build; create, found.

**созин** *m.* sozin (a body protein).

**созн/авать, —ать** *v.* acknowledge, recognize, admit; —аваться, —аться *v.* confess, admit; —ание *n.* consciousness, sense; acknowledgment, admission; потерять —ание *v.* lose consciousness; притти в —ание *v.* regain consciousness; —ательно *adv.* consciously, knowingly; —ательность *f.* consciousness, awareness; —ательный *a.* conscious.

**созо/иодол** *m.* sozoiodol, sozoiodolic acid; соль —иодола sozoiodolate; —ловая кислота sozolic acid, o-phenolsulfonic acid.

**созрев/ание** *n.*, —ательный, —ающий *a.* ripening, maturing; aging; —ать *v.* ripen, mature, age, season; —ший *a.* ripe, mature.

**созывать** *v.* summon, call (meeting), invite; convene, gather.

**соизвол/ить, —ять** *v.* agree, consent.

**соиздатель** *m.* copublisher.

**соизменим/ость** *f.* (math.) covariance; —**ый** *a.* covariant.

**соизмерим/ость** *f.* commensurability, commensuration; —**ый** *a.* commensurable, commensurate; comparable.

**соиск/ание** *n.* competition, rivalry; —**атель** *m.* competitor, rival.

**сойка** *f.* (zool.) jay.

**сойти** *see* **сходить.**

**сок** *m.* juice, sap; liquor.

**сокалоин** *m.* socaloin.

**сокинг-секция** *f.* (rad.) a reaction coil.

**сокирки** *pl.* (bot.) larkspur (*Delphinium consolida*).

**соко/выжиматель** *m.* juice extractor, squeezer; —**вый** *a.* juice, sap; liquor; —**вый способ дубления** liquor tanning.

**сокол** *m.* poker, slice bar; trowel, smoothing trowel; (zool.) falcon, hawk.

**соколок** *m.* plane; trowel; brisket (of beef).

**сокоподъемник** *m.* air lift, montejus.

**сокосодержание** *n.* (bot.) sap content.

**сокр.** *abbr.* (сокращение) abbreviation.

**сократительн/ый** *a.* contracting, contraction; (met.) concentration; —**ая плавка** concentration smelting.

**сократить** *see* **сокращать.**

**сокращ/аемость** *f.* contractibility, contractility; —**аемый** *a.* contractible, contractile; —**ать** *v.* abbreviate, abridge, shorten; reduce, curtail, cut, lower; contract, constrict; (met.) concentrate; fire, discharge (from job); —**аться** *v.* shorten, contract, shrink; **способный** —**аться,** —**ающийся** *a.* (biol.) contractive, contractile; —**ающий** *a.* abbreviating; contracting; reducing.

**сокращен/ие** *n.* abbreviation, abridgment; reduction, curtailment, decrease, diminution; contraction, constriction; shrinkage; short cut; (met.) concentration; **с. сердца** (physiol.) systole; —**но** *adv.* briefly, shortly, in brief form; —**ность** *f.* brevity; —**ный** *a.* abbreviated, abridged, brief, concise; reduced, diminished; contracted; short-cut; (met.) concentrated.

**сокристаллизация** *f.* cocrystallization.

**сокровищ/е** *n.* treasure; —**ница** *f.* treasure house, depository, storehouse.

**сокруш/ать,** —**ить** *v.* break, crush, pulverize, wreck, demolish; —**ение** *n.* demolition, destruction; —**ительный** *a.* destructive, shattering, damaging.

**соксмет** *m.* Soxhlet apparatus (flask and condenser).

**солан/густин** *m.* solangustin; —**дрин** *m.* solandrine; —**елловая кислота** solanellic acid; —**идин** *m.* solanidine; —**ин** *m.* solanine (glycosidal alkaloid); —**ион** *m.* solanione, javanicin; —**овая кислота** solanic acid; —**орубин** *m.* solanorubin, lycopin.

**соларовое масло** *see* **соляровое масло.**

**соларсон** *m.* Solarson, chloroarsenol.

**соласодин** *m.* solasodine.

**сола/т** *m.* solate, liquefied gel; —**ция** *f.* solation, liquefaction of a gel.

**солдат** *m.* soldier; —**ик** *m.* tool post.

**солевар** *m.* salt plant worker; —**ение** *n.* salt making; —**енный завод,** —**ница,** —**ня** *f.* salt works, saltern.

**солев/ой** *a.* salt; **с. налет,** —**ые выцветы** efflorescence of salt.

**соле/выносливость** *f.* salt tolerance; —**дробилка** *f.* salt crusher; —**мер** *m.* salinometer; salimeter (hydrometer for salt solutions); —**ние** *n.* salting; pickling, curing.

**соленоид** *m.,* —**ный** *a.* (elec.) solenoid; —**альный** *a.* solenoidal; tube-like.

**соле/носный** *a.* saliferous, salt-bearing; —**ность** *f.* saltiness, salinity.

**солен/ый** *a.* salt, salty, saline, salt-bearing; briny, brackish; pickled; corned (beef); *see also* **соляной; с. огурец** pickle; —**ая вода** salt water, brine; —**ая капуста** sauerkraut.

**соленье** *n.* salted foods, pickled foods.

**солеобраз/ование** *n.* salt formation, salification; —**ователь** *m.* salt former, halogen; —**ующий** *a.* salt-forming.

**соле/подобный** *a.* salt-like, saline; —**род** *m.* salt former, halogen.

**солерос** *m.* (bot.) glasswort (*Salicornia*).

**соле/содержащий** *a.* saliferous, salt-bearing, containing salt; —**сос** *m.* salt pump (for extracting salt from brine); —**устойчивость** *f.* salt tolerance.

**соли** *gen., pl., etc. of* **соль.**

**солидар/изироваться** *v.* hold together, join; **—но** *adv.* jointly and severally; **—ность** *f.* solidarity; **—ный** *a.* solidary, having common interests.

**солидн/ость** *f.* solidity, firmness, reliability, soundness; **—ый** *a.* solid, firm, reliable, sound, sturdy, substantial.

**солидол** *m.* grease, lubricant grease.

**солидус** *m.* (met., etc.) solidus.

**соликамские соли** natural deposits of sodium and potassium salts.

**солитер** *m.* (zool.) tapeworm; solitaire (gem).

**солить** *v.* salt, brine, pickle, cure.

**солифлюкция** *f.* solifluction, soil creep.

**солка** *f.* salting, pickling.

**солнечник** *m.* John Dory (fish); heliozoan, sun animalcule; **—и** *pl.* Heliozoa.

**солнечн/ый** *a.* solar, sun, sunny; **с. камень** (min.) sunstone (a variety of oligoclase feldspar); **с. свет** sunlight; **с. удар** sun stroke; **—аи ванна** sun bath; **—ая постоянная** solar constant; **—ая система** (astron.) solar system; **—ое затмение** solar eclipse; **—ое сияние** sunshine; **—ое сплетение** (anat.) solar plexus; **—ые часы** sun dial.

**солнце** *n.* sun; sunshine; **ложное с.** (astron.) parhelion; anthelion; **—лечение** *n.* heliotherapy; **с.-рыба** *f.* sun fish; **—стояние** *n.* solstice; **—цвет** *m.* sunrose (*Helianthemum*).

**солод** *m.*, **—ильный** *a.* malt; **затертый с.** mash; **—елый** *a.* sweetish; **—еть, —ить** *v.* malt; sweeten.

**солодк/а** *f.*, **—овый** *a.* (bot.) licorice (*Glycyrrhiza glabra*).

**солодов/ание** *n.* malting; **—енный** *a.* malt; **—ник, —щик** *m.* maltster, maltman; **—ня** *f.* malt house; malt kiln; **высушивать в —не** *v.* kiln-dry.

**солодов/ый** *a.* malt; **с. камень** malting barley; **с. сахар** malt sugar, maltose; **с. ток** malt floor; **с. экстракт, —ая вытяжка** malt extract; wort.

**солодосушильня** *f.* malt kiln.

**солодь** *f.* (soils) solod, degraded solonetz.

**соложение** *n.* malting, malt production.

**солом/а** *f.*, **—енный** *a.* straw, chaff; **дре-** весная с. match-stick wood; **—енная масса** (paper) straw pulp; **—ина** *f.* straw, stalk; (bot.) culm; **—инка** *f.* a straw; **—ит** *m.* pressed straw block (or sheet); **—ка** *f.* straw, haulm, stem; **—овяз** *m.* straw binder; **—оизмельчитель** *m.* straw shredder.

**соломонова печать** *see* купена.

**соломо/резка** *f.* straw cutter, chaff cutter; **—тряс** *m.* straw shaker (of thresher).

**солонец** *m.* solonetz (dark strongly alkaline soil).

**солонина** *f.* corned beef.

**солонка** *f.* salt cellar, salt shaker.

**солоноват/ость** *f.* brackishness; **—ый** *a.* brackish, briny.

**солонцеват/ость** *f.* solonetzicity, alkalinity (of soil); **—ый** *a.* solonetzic, alkaline; saliferous.

**солончак** *m.* solonchak, saline soil; salt marsh, salt bottoms; (bot.) saltwort (*Salsola*); **—оватость** *f.* salinity; **—овый** *a.* brackish, briny, saliniferous, salty; saline (soil); (bot.) halophytic.

**солор/иновая кислота** solorinic acid; **—инол** *m.* solorinol; **—овая кислота** soloric acid; **—ол** *m.* solorol.

**солур/иновая кислота** solurinic acid; **—ол** *m.* solurol, nucleotinphosphoric acid.

**солфатара** *see* сольфатара.

**соль** *f.* salt; spec. sodium chloride; **с. закиси металла** **—ous** salt; **сернокислая с. закиси железа** ferrous sulfate; **с. окиси металла** **—ic** salt; **сернокислая соль окиси железа** ferric sulfate; **с. серной кислоты, сернокислая с.** sulfate; **с. уксусной кислоты, уксуснокислая соль** acetate; **двойная с.** double salt; **кислая с.** acid salt, bisalt; **основная с.** basic salt, subsalt.

**сольбар** *m.* a barium polysulfide insecticide and fungicide.

**сольв/ат** *m.*, **—атный** *a.* solvate; **—атация** *f.*, **—атационный** *a.*, **—ация** *f.* solvation; **—атированный** *a.* solvated; **—атохромия** *f.* solvatochroism (color shift caused by solvent).

**сольвент** *m.* solvent.

**сольвеол** *m.* solveol, diethyl phthalate.

**Сольвея способ** *see* Сольвэ способ.

**сольволи/з** *m.* solvolysis; —**тический** *a.* solvolytic, solvation.

**Сольвэ способ** Solvay process, ammonia soda process.

**сольник** *see* **солерос.**

**сольпуги** *pl.* (zool.) Solpugida.

**сольфатара** *f.* solfatara (volcanic orifice).

**солюбилизация** *f.* solubilization.

**солю/сульфон** *m.* Sulphetrone, solapsone; —**сурьмин** *m.* Solyusurmin, sodium stibogluconate.

**солянк/а** *f.* salt shaker; (bot.) saltwort (*Salsola*); —**и** *pl.* (bot.) halophytes, halophytic vegetation.

**солян/ой** *a.* salt, saline; **с. рассол** brine; **с. раствор** salt solution, saline solution; brine; —**ая вода** salt water, saline water; —**ая зола** salt ash; —**ая кислота** hydrochloric acid; **соль —ой кислоты** chloride; —**ая масса** (geol.) salt deposit, saline residue.

**солянокисл/ый** *a.* hydrochloric acid; chloride (of metals, etc.); hydrochloride (of aniline and similar bases); —**ая соль** chloride; hydrochloride.

**соляр/изация** *f.* solarization; —**ий** *m.* solarium; —**иметр** *m.* solarimeter; —**ный** *a.* solar; —**овое масло** (petroleum) solar oil.

**сом** *m.* (zool.) sheatfish.

**соматический** *a.* (zool.) somatic.

**сомато—** *prefix* somato— (body; soma, somatic); —**логия** *f.* somatology.

**сомит** *m.* (zool.) somite, body segment.

**сомкнут/ый** *a.* locked, closed; joined; —**ь** *see* **смыкать.**

**сомнамбул** *m.* somnambulist; —**изм** *m.* somnambulism.

**сомне/ваться** *v.* doubt, have doubts, question; —**ние** *n.* doubt; **без —ния** without doubt, beyond doubt, no doubt; **подвергать —нию** *v.* doubt, question.

**сомнирол** *m.* somnirol.

**сомнительн/о** *adv.* doubtfully; it is doubtful; —**ость** *f.* doubtfulness, uncertainty; —**ый** *a.* doubtful, dubious, questionable, problematical.

**сомнитол** *m.* Somnitol.

**сомнож/ество** *n.* (math.) coset, corresponding set; —**итель** *m.* (co-) factor; —**ители** *pl.* cofactors, multiplier and multiplicand.

**сомнол** *m.* somnol, chloroethanal alcoholate.

**сомон** *m.* salmon (color).

**сон** *m.* sleep.

**сонерил** *m.* Soneryl, Neonal, butethal.

**соним** *m.* (met.) sonim (a solid nonmetallic inclusion).

**Сонина полином** (math.) Sonine polynomial.

**сонлив/ость** *f.* somnolence; **неестественная с.** (med.) coma; —**ый** *a.* sleepy, drowsy; **болезненно —ый** comatose.

**сонн/ый** *a.* sleepy; **с. напиток** soporific; —**ая артерия** (anat.) carotid; —**ая болезнь** (med.) sleeping sickness; —**ая одурь** (bot.) belladonna; —**ая трава** *see* **жидовская вишня;** —**ое зелье** (bot.) mandrake (*Mandragora officinarum*); —**ые капли** sleeping draught.

**сонометр** *m.* sonometer, phonometer.

**сон-трава** *f.* pasqueflower (*Anemone pulsatilla*, *A. patens*, or *Pulsatilla patens*).

**соня** *f.* (zool.) dormouse.

**соображ/ать** *v.* consider, take into consideration; contrive; —**ение** *n.* consideration, deliberation; reason; **по различным —ениям** for diverse reasons; **принимать в —ение** *v.* take into consideration, allow (for).

**соображит/ельность** *f.* quickness, alertness, quick thinking; —**ельный** *a.* quick-witted, alert; —**ь** *see* **соображать.**

**сообразн/о** *adv.* in conformity (with), according (to); —**ость** *f.* suitability, suitableness, compatibility, conformity, compliance, congruence, coincidence; consent; —**ый** *a.* suitable, compatible, conformable, congruent, consistent.

**сообразов/ать,** —**ывать** *v.* adapt, adjust, conform; —**аться,** —**ываться** *v.* fit, suit, conform, comply.

**сообща** *adv.* together, jointly; **действие с.** consolidated action.

**сообщ/ать** *v.* communicate, inform, send word, advise, report, notify; impart, transmit; pass on (information); —**аться** *v.* be in communication (with); —**ающийся** *a.* communicating.

**сообщен/ие** *n.* communication, information, message, report, notice; (elec.) connection, contact; (tel.) traffic; **с. о погоде** weather report; **пути —ия** means of communication; **установить с.** *v.* establish communication; (elec.) connect up; **—ный** *a.* communicated; imparted, given.

**сообщ/ество** *n.* community; assemblage, association; cooperation; **—ить** *see* **сообщать; —ник** *m.* accomplice, partner; **—ничество** *n.* complicity, participation.

**соору/дить, —жать** *v.* build, construct, erect, install; frame; **—жение** *n.* building, construction, erection, installation; edifice, structure.

**соосажд/ать** *v.* coprecipitate; **—ение** *n.* coprecipitation.

**сооси/ость** *f.* coaxial alignment; **—ый** *a.* coaxial, uniaxial.

**соответственно** *adv.* accordingly, according (to), correspondingly, consequently; respectively; **с. указаниям** in accordance with instructions, as per instructions; **—сть** *f.* conformance, conformity, correspondence; suitability, pertinence.

**соответственн/ый** *a.* expedient, proper, suitable, pertinent; corresponding, conforming, congruent, homologous; **—ая часть** mate, counterpart; **—ые углы** corresponding angles.

**соответств/ие** *n.* conformity, correspondence, congruence, homology; expediency, fitness; **в —ии** in conformity (with), in accordance (with); **взаимное с.** congruence.

**соответств/овать** *v.* match, match up, fit, correlate, tally; meet, satisfy (requirements); answer (the purpose); **—ующий** *a.* appropriate, suitable, pertinent, fit; corresponding, homologous; coincident; adequate; specific, characteristic; **—ующая часть** counterpart, mate.

**соотносительн/ость** *f.* correlation; **—ый** *a.* correlative.

**соотношен/ие** *n.* correlation, relation, relationship, connection, correspondence; proportion, ratio; **с. веса** weight ratio; **с. между массой и энергией** mass-energy relation; **быть в —ии**

*v.* correspond, correlate; **установить правильное с.** *v.* bring into proper correlation, coordinate.

**сопельный** *a.* nozzle, jet.

**соперни/к** *m.* rival, competitor; **не имеющий —ка** unrivaled; **—чать** *v.* rival, compete; emulate; **—чество** *n.* rivalry, competition.

**сопка** *f.* mud volcano; bald mountain, volcanic peak (Kamchatka); coniform peak, cone-shaped hill or mountain.

**сопло** *n.*, **—вой** *a.* nozzle, jet, nipple.

**соплодие** *n.* fruit system, collective fruit.

**сополимер** *m.* copolymer; **—изация** *f.* copolymerization.

**сопостав/ить, —лять** *v.* compare, contrast; juxtapose; **—ление** *n.* comparison, contrast; correlation (of data); juxtaposition; **в —лении с** comparison with; versus.

**сопочный** *a. of* **сопка**; mud-volcano, mud-volcanic.

**сопредельный** *a.* contiguous, adjoining, adjacent.

**соприкас/ание** *see* **соприкосновение; —аться** *v.* touch, come in contact (with); border, be adjacent (to), abut; (geom.) osculate; **—аться с** have bearing on; engage, mesh; **—ающий, —ающийся** *a.* touching, contiguous, adjoining, abutting, osculating.

**соприкосновен/ие** *n.* contact, touch; contiguity, juxtaposition; (geom.) osculation; engagement; **место —ия, точка —ия** point of contact; (elec.) contact point; **поверхность —ия** contact surface; **—ность** *f.* contiguity; **—ный** *a.* contiguous; implicated (in).

**сопричастный** *a.* participant; implicated, involved.

**сопрово/дающий, —дительный** *a.* accompanying; associated; **—дить, —ждать** *v.* accompany, go with, attend, escort, convoy; follow, track; carry along, take along, entrain; **—ждение** *n.* accompaniment; convoy, escort; **—жденный** *a.* accompanied.

**сопротивлен/ие** *n.* resistance, opposition, drag; strength (of material); resistor; **с. изгибу** transverse strength; **с. износу** resistance to wear, wear resistance; **с. разрыву, с. растяжению** tensile strength; **с. срезу** shearing strength; **с. толчку, с. удару** impact strength; **линия наименьшего —ия** line of least resistance; **магазин —ия** (elec.) resistance box; **нагревание —ием** resistance heating; **оказать с.** *v.* resist; **печь —ия** resistance furnace; **полное с.** (elec.) impedance; **провод большого —ия** high-resistance line; **сила —ия** resisting force; **сила —ия воздуха** air resistance; (aero.) drag; **точка предельного —ия** yield point; **удельное с.** (elec.) specific resistance, resistivity.

**сопротивл/яемость** *f.* resistance, capacity to resist, strength; (elec.) resistivity, specific resistance; **—яться** *v.* resist, oppose; **—яющийся** *a.* resisting, resistant.

**сопрягать** *v.* conjugate, mate, join.

**сопряжен/ие** *n.*, **—ность** *f.* union, conjugation, conjunction, junction, coupling, linking, interlinking; **—ный** *a.* combined, connected, linked, coupled, paired, conjugated; interlinked; (math., chem.) conjugate; adjoint (function); **—ная двойная связь** conjugate double bond; **—ная деталь** mate; **—ная растворимость** solubilization; **—ные слои** conjugate layers; **—о** (it) involves.

**сопрячь** *see* **сопрягать.**

**СОПС** *abbr.* (**Совет по изучению производительных сил**) Council for the Study of Productive Strength.

**сопутств/ование** *n.* accompaniment; **—овать** *v.* accompany; **—ующий** *a.* accompanying, associated, attendant, concomitant; **—ующие металлы** metal impurities.

**сор** *m.* litter, rubbish, waste, dross; sor (a salina in Kazakhstan and Central Asia; in the Ob river basin, the underwater portion of a partly submerged valley).

**соразмер/ение** *n.* matching, corresponding; **—ить, —ять** *v.* match, fit together; proportion, apportion, weigh, regulate; **—но** *adv.* in proportion (to); **—ность** *f.* proportionality, symmetry; **—ный** *a.* proportional, proportionate, commensurate; fit, adequate.

**сорбент** *m.* sorbent.

**сорбин** *m.*, **—оза** *f.* sorbin, sorbinose; **—овый** *a.* sorbin, sorbic; **—овая кислота** sorbic acid, 2,4-hexadienoic acid; **соль —овой кислоты, —овокислая соль** sorbate.

**сорбир/ование** *see* **сорбция; —ованный** *a.* sorbed (absorbed or adsorbed); **—ующий** *a.* sorbing; **—ующее вещество** sorbent.

**сорбит** *m.* sorbitol; (met.) sorbite; **—изировать** *v.* (met.) sorbitize, make sorbitic; **—овый** *a.* sorbite, sorbitic.

**сорбоза** *f.* sorbose.

**сорбц/ионный** *a.*, **—ия** *f.* sorption.

**сорв/анный** *a.* torn off; stripped (screw thread); **—ать** *v.* tear off, tear away, peel off; twist off, strip; hamper (work); disrupt, break (strike).

**сорго** *n.* (bot.) sorghum; **сахарное с.** Chinese sugar cane (*S. saccharatum*); **техническое с.** broomcorn (*S. technicum*).

**сордавалит** *m.* (petr.) sordawalite (basalt glass selvage).

**Соре правило** *see* **Сорэ правило.**

**соревн/ование** *n.* competition, rivalry; **—овать, —оваться** *v.* compete, rival; **—ующийся** *a.* competing.

**Сореля цемент** Sorel cement.

**соретит** *m.* (min.) soretite (a variety of aluminous hornblende).

**сор/инка** *f.* dirt particle, dust particle; **—ить** *v.* litter.

**сормайт** *m.* sormite (a cast iron-chromium alloy).

**сорн/ость** *f.* contamination, impurity; bittiness (of surface coatings); **—ый** *a.* littered; rubbish, waste; (agr.) weedy; **—ая трава, —ое растение, —ополевое растение, —як** *m.* weed.

**сорок** forty.

**сорокавосьмигранн/ик** *m.* (cryst.) hexoctahedron; **—ый** *a.* hexoctahedral.

**сорок/алетний** *a.* forty-year; **—ачасовая неделя** forty-hour week; **—овой** *a.* fortieth; **—ножка** *f.* (zool.) centipede.

**сорт** *m.* sort, kind, variety, brand; strain, breed; nature, quality, grade; **с.-анализатор** *m.* (strain) tester; **—амент, —имент** *m.* assortment, set; grades, grading; gage (of wire).

**сортиров/ание** *n.* sorting, classification,

grading; —**анный** *a.* sorted, classified, screened; —**ать** *v.* sort, assort, classify, grade, pick, pick out, cull, screen, separate, size; —**ать по размерам** size, assort (according to size); —**ка** *f.* sorting, classification, grading, separation, sizing; batching; grader, classifier, sorter.

**сортировочн/ый** *a.* sorting, separating, distributing; **с. аппарат** sorter, separator, grader, classifier; **с. ящик** (concentration) separation box; —**ая воронка** separatory funnel; —**ая установка** grading plant; —**ое устройство** sorting device, screening device.

**сортир/овщик** *m.* sorter, grader; —**ующий** *a.* sorting, classifying, grading.

**сорт/ность** *f.* grade, rating; —**ный** *a.* high-quality; varietal; —**оведение** *n.* research on varieties; —**оводство** *n.* plant breeding.

**сортов/ой** *a.* sort, variety; section, section-shaped; (biol.) strain; commercial (timber); **с. номер** brand number; **с. прокатный стан** section mill; **с. стан** jobbing mill, shape mill; —**ая сталь** structural steel, profile steel; —**ое железо** section iron, profile iron.

**сорто/изучение** *n.* (biol.) strain investigation; —**испытание** *n.*, —**испытательный** *a.* strain testing; —**размер** *m.* grade size; —**сеть** *f.* strain-testing system; —**улучшающий** *a.* strain-improving; —**участок** *m.* strain-testing station; strain-testing plot.

**сортутить** *see* **сортучивать.**

**сортуч/ение,** —**ивание** *n.* amalgamation; —**енный** *a.* amalgamated; —**ивать,** —**ить** *v.* amalgamate; —**ка** *f.* amalgam.

**Сорэ правило** Soret's principle, Ludwig phenomenon.

**сос/альце** *n.* (zool.) sucker; haustellum (proboscis); —**альцик** *m.* fluke (parasitic worm); —**альцики** *pl.* Trematoda; —**ание** *n.* suction, sucking; —**ать** *v.* suck.

**сосед** *m.* neighbor; —**ний** *a.* neighboring, adjoining, adjacent; (math.) affine; —**ство** *n.* neighborhood, vicinity, adjacency, proximity; **по** —**ству** in the vicinity, nearby.

**сосен/ка** *f.* (bot.) small pine; —**ные** *see* **сосновые.**

**сосиска** *f.* sausage.

**соскаблив/ание** *n.* scraping off; —**ать** *v.* scrape off; pare, shave.

**соскакив/ание** *n.* jumping off, coming off, slipping; —**ать** *v.* jump off, come off, spring off, work off, slip.

**соскальзыв/ание** *n.* slide, sliding, slip; launching (of ship); —**ать** *v.* slide down, slip, slip off, skid, run off, work off; launch.

**соскоблить** *see* **соскабливать.**

**соско/видный** *a.* mammilliform, mammiform, mammillary; —**вый** *a.* nipple.

**соскользн/увший** *a.* slipped, slipped off; —**уть** *see* **соскальзывать.**

**соскочить** *see* **соскакивать.**

**соскре/бать,** —**сти** *v.* scrape off.

**сосл/анный** *a.* exiled, banished, deported; *m.* an exile; —**ать** *see* **ссылать.**

**сослуживец** *m.* colleague, fellow worker.

**сосн/а** *f.* (bot.) pine tree (*Pinus*); —**овые** *pl.* pine family (*Pinaceae*).

**соснов/ый** *a.* pine; —**ая камедь** pine resin; —**ая кислота** *see* **пиновая кислота;** —**ая смола** pine tar, wood tar; resin; —**ая шерсть** pine (needle) wool; —**ое масло** pine oil (crude turpentine).

**сосняк** *m.* pine forest.

**сосо/к** *m.* (anat.) nipple, teat; —**чек** *m.* papilla; nipple.

**сосредоточен/ие** *n.* centering, concentration; —**но** *adv.* intently; —**ность** *f.* concentration; —**ный** *a.* centered, concentrated, focused; lumped; —**ный груз** point load, single load.

**сосредоточ/ивать,** —**ить** *v.* concentrate, center, centralize, focus; —**иваться** *v.* center, focus.

**соссюрит** *m.*, —**ный,** —**овый** *a.* (min.) saussurite (a variety of zoisite); —**изация** *f.* saussuritization (a metamorphism to saussurite); —**овое габбро** (petr.) saussurite-gabbro, allalinite.

**состав** *m.* composition, constitution, make-up, formation, structure;

compound, composite; body; staff, personnel; formula (of fertilizer); amount (of property); **войти в с.** *v.* become part (of), amalgamate (with); **подвижной с.** (railroad) rolling stock; **химический с.** chemical composition.

**состав/итель** *m.* author, writer, composer, compiler; **—ить, —лять** *v.* compose, get together, compile, draw up, work out; fit up, set up, build up, construct, design; prepare, compound, concoct; constitute, form, comprise, amount, make up; **—ить план** plan, plot; **—ление** *n.* composition, compilation, drawing up; construction; constitution, formation, combination, concoction, mixing; synthesis; **—ленный** *a.* composed, made up (of).

**составляющ/ая** *f.*, **—ая часть, —ий элемент** component, ingredient, constituent; **—ий** *a.* component, constituent; **—ая сила** composite force.

**составн/ой** *a.* compound, composite, combined, complicated; compounding; built up, sectional, separable, joined, jointed; component; constituent; link, chain; telescope, telescopic; **с. цех** batch-mixing section; **—ая деталь** unit; **—ая кривая** compound curve; **—ая труба** flexible pipe; **—ая часть** component, constituent, ingredient, part, integral part; element (of compound); **твердая —ая часть** solid constituent; **—ое ядро** compound nucleus.

**состар/ивание** *n.* aging; **—ить** *v.* age; **—иться** *v.* age, grow old.

**состоян/ие** *n.* condition, state, status, position, stage; ability; (weather) condition; (chemical) compound or group; **с. тела** state of aggregation, physical form (of matter); **быть в —ии** *v.* be in a position (to), be able (to); **в —ии поставки** as received; **диаграмма —ия** structural diagram (of alloy); phase diagram; **насыщенное с.** saturated state, saturation; **прокатка в горячем —ии** hot-rolling.

**состоятельн/ость** *f.* competence; solvency; validity, strength (of argument); **—ый** *a.* solvent; well-off; well-grounded.

**состоять** *v.* consist (of), be made up (of),

comprise; **—ся** *v.* consist; happen, take place; **не —ся** fail.

**состра́гивать** *v.* plane off.

**состр/игать, —ичь** *v.* shear off, cut off.

**сострогать** *see* **состра́гивать.**

**состяз/ание** *n.* contest, competition; **—ательный** *a.* controversial, contentious; **—аться** *v.* compete; cope (with).

**сосуд** *m.* vessel, receiver, container; **—ик** *m.* (bot.) vasculum; **—исто-волокнистый** *a.* fibro-vascular; **—истый** *a.* vascular; **—истые тайнобрачные** (bot.) vascular cryptogams (*Pteridophyta*); **—орасширитель** *m.* (physiol.) vasodilator, vasodilating agent.

**сосулька** *f.* icicle.

**сосун** *m.* suction box.

**сосуществов/ание** *n.* coexistence; **—ать** *v.* coexist

**сосущ/ий** *a.* sucking; (zool.) suctorial; **—ая сила** suction; soil-water strength.

**сосц/евидный** *a.* mammiform, mammillary, mammillated; **—ы** *pl.* nipples, teats; **снабженный —ами** papillose, papillary.

**сосчит/ать, —ывать** *v.* count, calculate, sum up, add up; number.

**сот** *m.* honeycomb.

**сотвор/ение** *n.* creation, making; **—ить, —ять** *v.* create, make, fabricate.

**сотенный** *a.* centesimal, hundredth.

**сотерн** *m.* sauterne (wine).

**сотня** *f.* one hundred.

**сотоварищ** *m.* associate, partner, fellow member, fellow worker; **—ество** *n.* company, society; partnership; membership.

**сотов/ый** *a.* honeycomb, cellular; **с. мед** honey in combs; **—ая катушка** (rad.) honeycomb coil; **—ая структура** honeycomb structure, cell structure.

**сотообразный** *a.* honeycombed, cellular.

**сотрудни/к** *m.* collaborator, contributor, fellow worker, coworker; **—чать** *v.* collaborate, contribute, cooperate; **—чество** *n.* collaboration, cooperation.

**сотрясатель** *m.* shaker.

**сотрясательн/ый** *a.* shaking; shocking; **—ое движение** shaking motion, shaking; —ое сито shaking screen, shaker.

**сотряс/ать,** —ти *v.* shake, vibrate; —ающийся *a.* shaking, jigging; —е-ние *n.* shake, shaking, jarring, vibra-tion, pulsation (of sound); percussion; shock, concussion (of brain); com-motion.

**соты** *pl.* honeycomb.

**сотый** *a.* centesimal, hundredth.

**соудар/ение** *n.* collision, impact, en-counter, impingement, shock; плот-ность —ения collision density; —яться *v.* collide, encounter.

**соус** *m.* sauce, gravy.

**соучаст/вовать** *v.* participate, take part in, cooperate, collaborate; —ие *n.* participation, cooperation, collabora-tion; —ник *m.* participant, associate; —ный *a.* participating.

**софокусный** *a.* (phys.) confocal.

**софор/а** *f.* (bot.) sophora; —ин *m.* sophorin (glucoside); sophorine (alka-loid).

**соффионы** *pl.* (geol.) soffioni (emanation of vapors).

**сохнуть** *v.* dry.

**сохран/ение** *n.* preservation, conserva-tion, retention; constancy; care, cus-tody; с. энергии conservation of energy; закон —ения вещества, закон —ения массы law of conserva-tion of matter; —итель *m.* guardian, custodian; —ительный *a.* preserva-tive; —ить *see* сохранять.

**сохранн/о** *adv.* safely, securely; it is safe; —ость *f.* safety; preservation; —ый *a.* safe, secure.

**сохранять** *v.* conserve, preserve, retain; maintain, keep, observe; с. за собой reserve (for oneself); —ся *v.* be well preserved, keep, last; survive.

**соц—** *abbr.* (социальный) social, (соци-алистический) socialistic.

**соцветие** *n.* (bot.) raceme, inflorescence.

**соц/договор** *m.* socialist agreement, con-tract; —иализация *f.* socialization; —иальный *a.* social; —истический *a.* socialistic.

**социоиодол** *see* созоиодол.

**соч.** *abbr.* (сочинение) paper.

**сочевичник** *m.* (bot.) bitter vetch (Oro-bus); peavine (Lathyrus).

**сочение** *n.* trickle, ooze, dribble; (med.) suppuration.

**сочет/ание** *n.* union, conjunction, join-ing, combination; —ать *v.* unite, con-nect, join, combine; match.

**сочин/ение** *n.* composition, paper; со-брание —ений collected works; сту-денческое с. thesis; —итель *m.* author, composer; —ять *v.* compose.

**сочиться** *v.* trickle, ooze, ooze out, dribble, drip; bleed (of trees).

**сочлен** *m.* fellow member.

**сочлен/ить,** —ять *v.* joint, join, link; —ение *n.* articulation, joint, connec-tion, coupling; member, link; —ен-ный *a.* articulated, jointed, coupled, linked, interlinked, chain.

**сочн/ость** *f.* juiciness, succulence; —ый *a.* juicy, succulent; rich (color).

**сочувств/ие** *n.* sympathy; —овать *v.* sympathize.

**сошка** *f.* prop, support; rack, rest (for gun); bipod (of machine gun), tripod; share (of plow); pitman, connecting rod; рулевая с. pitman arm.

**сошлифов/ка** *f.* grinding off, abrasion; —ывать *v.* grind off, abrade.

**сошн/ик** *m.* share (of plow), colter; —ый *a.* plow.

**союз** *m.* union, association, league, alliance, combination, conjunction.

**Союз Советских Социалистических Рес-публик** The Union of Soviet Socialist Republics (USSR).

**союзн/ик** *m.* ally, associate, confederate; —ый *a.* union; allied; —ое прави-тельство the Government of the Union.

**соя** *f.* (bot.) soy, soya, soybean (Soja hispida or Glycine hispida).

**сп.** *abbr.* (спирт) ethyl alcohol (as solvent).

**спагетти** *n.* spaghetti.

**спад** *m.* decrease, drop, fall; slope, incline.

**спадаит** *m.* (min.) spadaite.

**спад/ание** *n.* fall, diminution, drop; collapse; —ать *v.* fall, fall off, de-crease, diminish, abate, lower, drop, go down, recede; collapse; —аться *v.* fall together, come together; —аю-щий *a.* decreasing; sloping.

**спазм** *m.,* —а *f.* spasm, convulsion;

—**атический**, —**одический** *a.* spasmodic, convulsive; —**олитин** *m.* adiphenine; —**отин** *m.* spasmotin, sphacelotoxin; —**отоксин** *m.* spasmotoxin.

**спаив/ание** *n.* soldering; —**ать** *v.* solder, solder together.

**спай** *m.* soldered joint, joint, seam; junction (of thermocouple).

**спайдер** *m.* (mech.) spider.

**спайка** *f.* soldering; solder; (soldered) joint, seam; junction (of thermocouple); (bot.) commissure.

**спайнолепест/ковый** *a.* (bot.) sympetalous, gamopetalous; —**ные** *pl.* Sympetalae.

**спайн/ость** *f.* cleavage; cleavability; —**ости** *pl.* cleavage cracks; —**ый** *a.* cleavage; —**ая поверхность** cleavage plane, cleavage face.

**спайщик** *m.* jointer, splicer.

**спалзывать** *v.* creep off, creep down, slip off, slip, slide.

**спалить** *v.* singe, burn.

**спальный** *a.* sleeping; **с. вагон** (railroad) sleeping car, sleeper.

**спарагмит** *m.* (petr.) sparagmite (sandstone).

**спарассол** *m.* sparassol, methyl ester of everninic acid.

**спардек** *m.* spardeck (of boat).

**спаренный** *a.* coupled, connected; duplex, twin, paired, dual.

**спарж/а** *f.*, —**евый** *a.* (bot.) asparagus (*Asparagus officinalis*); —**евые** *pl.* Asparagoideae; —**евый камень** (min.) asparagus stone (a variety of apatite); —**евая капуста** *see* **брокколи.**

**спар/ивание** *n.*, —**ивающий** *a.* coupling, pairing; —**ивать**, —**ить** *v.* couple, pair, match, mate; —**иваться** *v.* pair.

**спарнакский ярус** (geol.) Sparnacian stage.

**спартеин** *m.* sparteine, lupinidine.

**спарто** *see* **эспарто.**

**спарывать** *v.* rip off.

**спасание** *n.* rescue; saving, salvage.

**спасательн/ый** *a.* rescue, saving, safety; **с. круг, с. пояс** lifebelt; —**ая лестница** fire escape; (min.) emergency ladder; —**ая лодка** lifeboat; —**ое дело** rescue work.

**спасать** *v.* save, rescue.

**спасение** *see* **спасание.**

**спасибо** *adv.* thanks, thank you.

**спаситель** *m.* rescuer.

**спасти** *see* **спасать.**

**спастический** *a.* (med.) spastic, spasmodic.

**спасть** *see* **спадать.**

**спатулатин** *m.* spathulatine.

**спать** *v.* sleep.

**спа/янность** *f.* unity, solidarity, cohesion; —**янный** *a.* soldered; united; —**ять** *see* **спаивать.**

**СПБ** *abbr.* (Санкт-Петербург) St. Petersburg (now Leningrad).

**спейсер** *m.* spacer.

**спек** *m.* cake, sintered mass; —**аемость** *f.* tendency to cake; —**ание** *n.* caking, clinkering, sintering, agglutination, agglomeration; burning, sticking; —**аться** *v.* cake, clinker, form clinker, sinter; burn, stick; bake; —**ающая способность** clinkering capacity (of coal); —**ающийся** *a.* caking, clinkering, sintering.

**спектр** *m.* spectrum; **с. комбинационного рассеяния** Raman spectrum.

**спектральн/ый** *a.* spectral, spectrum; **с. анализ** spectrum analysis; —**ые наблюдения** spectroscopic observations; —**ые цвета** spectral colors, spectrum colors.

**спектро—** *prefix* spectro—, spectrum; —**анализатор** *m.* spectrum analyzer; —**грамма** *f.* spectrogram; —**граф** *m.* spectrograph; —**графический** *a.* spectrographic.

**спектрометр** *m.* spectrometer; —**ический** *a.* spectrometric; —**ия** *f.* spectrometry.

**спектроскоп** *m.* spectroscope; —**ически чистый** spectroscopically pure, spectropure; —**ический** *a.* spectroscopic; —**ия** *f.* spectroscopy.

**спектро/фотометр** *m.* spectrophotometer; —**химический** *a.* spectrochemical; —**химия** *f.* spectrochemistry.

**спекуларит** *see* **спекулярит.**

**спекулировать** *v.* speculate.

**спекул/ум**, —**юм** *m.* (med.) speculum; speculum metal (a copper-tin alloy).

**спекулярит** *m.* (min.) specularite, specular hematite.

**спекуля/тивный** *a.* speculative; **—ция** *f.* speculation, venture.

**спекш/ийся** *a.* caked, sintered, baked, parched; **—иеся куски** sinter.

**спелеология** *f.* speleology, study of caves.

**спел/ость** *f.* ripeness, maturity; (met.) refined state, finished state; readiness (of soil for plowing); **—ый** *a.* ripe, mature; refined, finished; rich (slag); **—ый ход** (met.) good working order, normal working; thorough refining; **—ь** *m.* (met.) refining foam (graphite in molten iron).

**Спенса печь** (met.) Spence furnace.

**спенсерит** *m.* (min.) spencerite.

**спер/ва** *adv.* at first; at the start; in the first place, firstly; **—еди** *adv.* in front, before; **вид —еди** front view, face.

**сперилит** *see* **сперрилит.**

**сперма** *f.* (zool.) sperm, spermatozoa, semen.

**спермато—** *prefix* spermato—, spermo— (sperm, seed, germ); **—генез** *m.* (biol.) spermatogenesis; **—зоид** *m.* (zool.) spermatozoön; (bot.) spermatozoid; **—логия** *f.* (bot.) spermatology; **—рея** *f.* (med.) spermatorrhea.

**спермацет** *m.* spermaceti, cetaceum; **—овое масло** sperm oil, whale oil.

**спермин** *m.* spermine (a leucomaine).

**сперрилит** *m.* (min.) sperrylite (a platinum diarsenide).

**спертый** *a.* close, stuffy; compressed.

**спессарт/ин, —ит** *m.* (min.) spessartite, spessartine (a variety of manganese-aluminum garnet).

**спеть** *v.* ripen, mature.

**спех** *m.* haste, hurry; **к —у** urgent.

**спец** *see* **специалист; спец., спец—** *abbr.* (**специальный**) special.

**специал/изация** *f.* specialization; **—изироваться** *v.* specialize; **—ист** *m.* specialist, expert; **—ьно** *adv.* specially; **—ьность** *f.* specialty, trade, department; **—ьный** *a.* special, separate, individual, specific, particular; (math.) singular.

**специи** *pl. of* **специя.**

**специфи/ка** *f.* specific, characteristic; **—кация** *f.* specification; description; **давать —кацию** *v.* specify; **—ческий**

*a.* specific; **—чность** *f.* specificity.

**специя** *f.* spice; medicament.

**спец/материалы** *pl.* special materials; **—одежда** *f.* working clothes, overalls; (protective) clothing; **—ставка** *f.* salary drawn by a specialist; **—фонд** *m.* special funds.

**спечь** *v.* bake.

**спеш/а** *adv.* in haste, hurriedly; **не с.** leisurely, at leisure; **—ить** *v.* hasten, hurry, rush; **—ка** *f.*, **—ность** *f.* haste, hurry, urgency; **—но** *adv.* hastily, in haste, hurriedly, urgently; it is urgent; **—ный** *a.* hasty, urgent, pressing; **—ная почта** special delivery.

**спз** *abbr.* (**сантипуаз**) centipoise.

**спигел/ин** *m.* spigeline; **—ия** *f.* (bot.) worm-grass (*Spigelia*).

**спидометр** *m.* speedometer.

**спикер** *m.* speaker.

**спикула** *f.* (zool.) spicule.

**спилантол** *m.* spilanthol.

**спилив/ание** *n.* sawing off; **—ать** *v.* saw off, saw down; file off, file away, file down.

**спилит** *m.* (petr.) spilite (albitized basalt); **—овый** *a.* spilitic.

**спилить** *see* **спиливать.**

**спилозит** *m.* (petr.) spilosite (spotted contact slate).

**спилок** *m.* (leather) split (hide).

**спин** *m.* spin, angular momentum (of nucleus); **с.-орбитальная связь** spin-orbit coupling; **с.-эхо** *n.* spin echo.

**спин/а** *f.* back; **—ой к —е** back to back.

**спина/стерин** *m.* spinasterol; **—цен** *m.* spinacene, squalene; **—цин** *m.* spinacine.

**спинель** *see* **шпинель.**

**спинка** *f.* back, back edge.

**спинн/ой** *a.* back; (anat.) dorsal, spinal; **с. мозг, —ая струна** spinal cord; **с. хребет** spinal column.

**спин/овый** *a.* of **спин**; **—овое квантовое число** (nucl.) spin quantum number; **—ор** *m.* spinor.

**спинтарископ** *m.* spinthariscope, scintillascope (for detecting radioactive rays).

**спинтер** *m.* (min.) spinthère, séméline (a variety of titanite).

**спирал/еобразная бактерия** (bact.) spirillum; **—изация** f. spiralization.

**спираль** f. spiral, spire, helix, snail; **—но—** prefix spiro— (spiral, coiled); **—ный** a. spiral, helical; volute (centrifugal pump); **—ная линия** spiral line, helix; **—ная рессора** coil spring.

**спир/ан** m., **—ановый** a. spiran, spiro compound; **—ацин** m. spiracin, methylcarboxylsalicylic acid; **—ей** m., **—ея** f. (bot.) spirea (*Spiraea*); **—ейные** pl. (bot.) Spiraeoideae; **—ейный** a. spiraea; **—ейная кислота** spiraeic acid (salicylic acid); **—иллы** pl. (bact.) Spirillaceae.

**спиро—** prefix spiro— (spiral, coiled; respiration); **—гира** f. (bot.) spirogyra; **—зал** m. Spirosal, monoglycol salicylate; **—ил** m. spiroyl; **—метр** m. (med.) spirometer; **—пентан** m. spiropentane; **—соединения** pl. spiro compounds, spirans; **—форм** m. Spiroform, acetylsalol; **—хета** f. (biol.) spirochaeta; **—хетоз** m. (med.) spirochetosis; **—хин** m. spirochin; **—цид** m. Spirocide, acetarsone; **—циклан** m. spirocyclan, spiro compound.

**спирт** m. alcohol, spirit; **с.-сырец** undistilled alcohol; **безводный с.** absolute alcohol; **водный с.** alcohol containing water; **древесный с.** wood alcohol, methyl alcohol; **стандартный с.** proof spirit; **твердый с.** solid alcohol (a household fuel); **этиловый с.** ethyl alcohol; **—аза** f. alcoholase.

**спиртн/ой, —ый** see **спиртовой.**

**спирто/альдегид** m. alcohol aldehyde, hydroxyaldehyde; **—амин** m. alcohol amine, hydroxyamine; **—вать** v. alcoholize; add alcohol; fortify (wine); **—вка** f. alcohol lamp; **—водочный завод** distillery.

**спиртов/ой, —ый** a. alcohol, alcoholic, spirit; **с. голубой** spirit blue; **с. раствор** alcoholic solution; **с. уровень** spirit level; **—ая лампа** spirit lamp, alcohol lamp; **—ая морилка** spirit mordant; **—ая смесь** alcoholic mixture; **—ые краски** spirit colors (alcohol-soluble dyes).

**спирто/завод** m. distillery; **—кетон** m. alcohol ketone, hydroxyketone; **—**

**кислота** f. alcohol acid, hydroxyacid; **—мер** see **спиртометр.**

**спиртометр** m. alcoholometer; **—ический** a. alcoholometric; **—ия** f. alcoholometry.

**спирто/растворимый** a. alcohol-soluble; spirit (dye); **—сырец** m. crude spirit, raw spirit; (distilling) low wine, singlings; **—устойчивый** a. alcohol-resistant, alcohol-fast; **—эфир** m. alcohol ether, hydroxyether.

**спис/ать, —ывать** v. copy, make a copy, transcribe; **—ываться с** v. correspond with; **—ок** m. copy; list, register; **вносить в —ок** v. catalog; **—ывание** n. copying.

**спица** f. spoke; knitting needle; long needle.

**спич** m. speech.

**спичечн/ица** f. matchbox; **—ый** a. match; **—ая соломка** matchwood, matchstick.

**спичка** f. match.

**сплав** m. (met.) alloy; fusion, sintering; float; **с. на алюминиевой основе** aluminum-base alloy; **с. с цинковой основой** zinc-base alloy; **белый с.** white metal; **—ить** see **сплавливать; —ка, —ление** see **сплавливание; —ленный** a. alloyed; fused, molten; floated, drifting.

**сплавл/ивание** n. (met.) alloying; melting, fusion, fusing together; floating; **сварка —иванием** fusion welding; **—ивать, —ять** v. alloy; melt, fuse, fuse together; **—иваться, —яться** v. coalesce; **—яемый** a. alloyable; **—яемый материал, —яемая загрузка** melting charge, melt.

**сплавной** a. floatable; drift (wood).

**спланировать** v. plan, project.

**спланхно—** prefix splanchno— (viscera); **—логия** f. splanchnology.

**сплачивать, —ся** v. unite, combine, join.

**сплесень** m. splice, splice joint, splicing.

**сплесн/ение, —ивание** n. splice, splicing; **—ивать, —ить** v. splice, join.

**спле/сти, —сть, —тать** v. plait, braid; interweave, intertwine, interlace; splice; **—тение** n. entanglement, complication; meshing, interweaving, interlacing; splice; (anat.) plexus.

**сплотить** see **сплачивать.**

**сплотки** *pl.* (min.) launder, trough.

**сплочен/ие** *n.*, **—ность** *f.* solidarity, cohesion, firmness; joining, scarfing.

**сплошн/ой** *a.* continuous, unbroken, uniform; solid, massive, compact; blind (wall); sheet (lightning); **с. характер** uniformity; **—ая среда** continuum; **—ость** *f.* continuity.

**сплошь** *adv.* continuously, uninterruptedly; without exception; **с. да рядом** very often, frequently.

**сплы/вать, —ть** *v.* run off, overflow; **—ваться, —ться** *v.* run together, blend, merge, mix, fuse.

**сплю/снутый, —щенный** *a.* flattened, stretched out; oblate (sphere); **—снуть, —щивать, —щить** *v.* flatten, compress, draw down; telescope; upset, jump up; **—щиваться** *v.* telescope, collapse; **—щенность** *f.* flatness; **—щивание** *n.* flattening; telescoping, collapse.

**сподио/зит** *m.* (min.) spodiosite (a calcium fluophosphate); **—филлит** *m.* spodiophyllite.

**сподок** *m.* (met.) bottom swage.

**сподручный** *a.* handy, convenient.

**сподумен** *m.* (min.) spodumene, triphane.

**спокойн/ый** *a.* calm, quiet, tranquil, quiescent, resting, at rest, restful; mild; smooth (working); latent; stagnant; (elec.) static; **с. контакт** (telegraphy) backstop; **с. ход** smooth running, steady running; **—ая нагрузка** dead load, steady load; **—ая сталь** (met.) dead melt (bubble-free steel).

**спокойств/ие, —о** *n.* calmness, calm, quietness, placidity, composure.

**сполаживание** *n.* flattening.

**споласкив/ание** *n.* rinsing; **—ать** *v.* rinse out.

**сполз/ание** *n.* sliding off, slipping, creep; **—ать, —ти** *see* **сползывать.**

**сполна** *adv.* completely, entirely, in full.

**сполос/катель** *m.* rinser; (min.) clean-up man; **—кать, —нуть** *see* **сполоскивать.**

**сполох** *see* **северное сияние.**

**спонгин** *m.* spongin.

**спонгиоз** *m.* graphitization of cast iron.

**спонтанный** *a.* spontaneous.

**спор** *m.* dispute, controversy; **об этом нет —у** it is self-evident.

**спора** *f.* (biol.) spore.

**спорадический** *a.* sporadic.

**споранг/иевый** *a.* (bot.) sporangial; **—ий** *m.* sporangium, spore case; **—ин** *m.* sporangin.

**споридия** *f.* (bot.) sporidium.

**спор/ить** *v.* dispute, argue; **—иться** *v.* succeed; **—ный** *a.* disputable, debatable, questionable, contestable, controversial.

**споро—** *prefix* (biol.) sporo—, spore; **—вики, —вые животные** *pl.* (zool.) Sporozoa; **—вместилище** *see* **спорангий; —вый** *a.* spore; **—вое растение, —фит** *m.* (bot.) sporophyte; **—карпий** *m.* (bot.) sporocarp; **—киста** *f.* (zool.) sporocyst; **—носный** *a.* (bot.) sporiferous; sporogenous; **—образование** *n.* (biol.) spore formation, sporogenesis.

**спорт** *m.* sport, mutation.

**споруляция** *f.* (bot.) sporulation.

**спорынья** *f.* (bot.) ergot, spurred rye (*Claviceps purpurea*); smut (of corn).

**спорыш** *m.* (bot.) knot weed (*Polygonum aviculare*).

**способ** *m.* method, process, means, way, manner, mode, system; **влажным —ом** wet (process); **механическим —ом** mechanically; by machine; **таким —ом** in this way.

**способн/ость** *f.* capacity, capability, power, ability, aptitude, talent, faculty; **—ability, —ibility; с. делиться** fissionability; **с. преломления** refractive power; **с. проникать** penetrating power; **—ый** *a.* capable, able, gifted; **—ый к делению** fissionable; **—ый к обработке** machinable.

**способств/ование** *n.* contribution, aid, assistance; **—овать** *v.* contribute, aid, assist, promote, further, enable, favor; **—ующий** *a.* instrumental.

**спр.** *abbr.* (**справочник**) handbook.

**справа** *adv.* to the right, from the right side.

**справедлив/о** *adv.* fairly; true; (it) holds true, (it) is correct (for); **—ость** *f.* justice, right, fairness; correctness, accuracy; **отдать ему —ость** *v.* do him justice; **по —ости** in all fairness;

justly; —ый *a.* just, fair, right; valid, true, correct, accurate.

справ/иться, —ляться *v.* consult, make inquiries, inquire, ask (about); manage, master, cope (with), handle; —ка *f.* information, reference, statement; наводить —ки *v.* make inquiries, inquire, investigate.

справочн/ая *f.* (tel.) information; —ик *m.*, —ая книга reference book, handbook, manual; directory; карманный —ик handbook, manual; —ый *a.* information, inquiry; —ый кран try cock, gage cock; —ый стол information desk.

спрашивать *v.* ask, demand, inquire; —ся *v.* ask permission.

спрессов/анный *a.* pressed; —ать, —ывать *v.* press, force together.

спринклер *m.* sprinkler; —ное оборудование sprinkler system (for fire protection).

спринц/евать, —овать *v.* syringe, inject; —овка *f.* syringe; syringing.

спровоцировать *v.* provoke, incite.

спроектированный *a.* designed, planned.

спрос *m.* (com.) demand, market; permission; с. на demand for; с. и предложение supply and demand; —ить *see* спрашивать.

спрут *m.* (zool.) octopus.

спрыг/ивание *n.* jumping off, jumping down, springing down; —ивать, —нуть *v.* jump off, jump down, spring down.

спрыс/кать, —кивать, —нуть *v.* spray, sprinkle, wet, moisten; —кивание *n.* spraying, wetting, moistening; — нутый *a.* sprayed, sprinkled, moistened.

спрягать *v.* conjugate.

спрямление *n.* alignment; squaring; rectification (of curve).

спрясть *v.* (text.) spin.

спрятать *v.* hide, conceal.

спуаз *abbr.* (сантипуаз) centipoise.

спуррит *m.* (min.) spurrite.

спуск *m.* descent, slope, incline, downgrade; lowering, downward motion; chute, drop; discharge, drain, outlet, escape; tapping, draining, emptying, drawing off, running off; trigger, release; launching (of ship); (pharm.)

cerate; —ать *v.* lower, let down; discharge, tap, tap off, draw off, drain, drain off, empty, run off; deflate; unwind; let loose, release, trip, trigger; —аться *v.* come down, descend, alight; —ающийся *a.* sloping; descending.

спускн/ой *a.* lowering; drain, discharge, outlet, escape; release, releasing; с. вентиль drain valve; с. желоб shoot, chute, slide; с. канал sewer; с. кран drain cock, petcock; с. крючок, —ая собачка trigger, releasing cam; с. механизм, —ое приспособление trigger mechanism, release; с. рычаг starting lever; —ая втулка, —ая пробка drain plug; —ая пружина trigger spring; —ая труба drain pipe, drain, discharge pipe; —ое действие trigger action; —ое отверстие drain hole, tap hole; —ые сани launching cradle.

спусковой *see* спускной.

спуст/ившийся *a.* descended; (aero.) landed; —ить *see* спускать.

спустя *prep. acc.* after, afterwards, later; немного с. a little later.

спутанно *adv.* in a tangle; —волокнистая структура (geol.) felted texture; —столбчатый *a.* diverse columnar.

спут/анный *a.* tangled, entangled, jumbled, matted; —ать *see* спутывать.

спутник *m.* fellow traveler, companion; guide; (astron.) satellite, sputnik; —и *pl.* (min.) accessory minerals, associated minerals, secondary minerals; с. платины a member of the platinum group.

спутыв/ание *n.* entanglement; —ать *v.* entangle, tangle, mix up.

спущенн/ый *a.* let down, lowered; drained, run off; extracted, strained; deflated; быть —ым на-нет *v.* taper all the way to the end.

спя/чка *f.* sleep, sleepiness; (med.) sleeping sickness; зимняя с. hibernation; —щий *a.* sleeping, dormant.

ср *abbr.* (стерадиан) steradian; ср. *abbr.* (сравни) compare; (средний) average, mean; middle.

срабатыв/аемость *f.* wearability, wearing capacity, wearing property; —ание *n.* wear, wearing away, wear and tear, abrasion, chafing; operation, action; triggering, trip; response; count (in radiation counter); —**ать** *v.* wear away, abrade; operate; trip; —**аться** *v.* wear, wear away, deteriorate, fray.

**сработ/авшийся** *a.* worn, worn out (tool), used up; —**анный** *a.* worn out; made; —**ать** *v.* make, fabricate.

**сравнен/ие** *n.* comparison; **делать с.** *v.* compare, contrast; **по** —**ию с** in comparison with, versus.

**сравни** *imp. of* **сравнивать.**

**сравнив/ание** *n.* comparing; leveling; —**ать** *v.* compare, parallel; level, make even; —**аться** *v.* equal, be equal, come up (to); —**ающее устройство** comparator.

**сравним/ость** *f.* comparability; —**ый** *a.* comparable.

**сравнительн/о** *adv.* comparatively, relatively; **с. с** versus, against; —**ый** *a.* comparative, relative, respective; —**ый период** (nucl.) comparative lifetime.

**сравн/ить** *see* **сравнивать;** —**ять** *v.* level, make even, smooth; —**яться** *v.* be equalized, become equal.

**сра/жать,** —**зить** *v.* throw down, overwhelm; —**жаться,** —**зиться** *v.* combat, fight, struggle; —**жение** *n.* battle.

**сразу** *adv.* at once, at one stroke, then and there; **с. после** right after.

**срамной** *a.* (anat.) pudendal.

**сраст/ание** *n.* growth, accretion; coalescence, coalition; concretion; healing, growing together, inosculation (of blood vessels), knitting (of bones); **двойник** —**ания** (cryst.) interpenetration twin; —**аться,** —**ись** *v.* grow together, intergrow, coalesce, interlock, entangle; inosculate, knit; —**ить** *see* **сращивать.**

**сращ/ение** *see* **срастание; неправильное с.** (med.) vicious union; —**ивание** *n.* joining, combination, union, binding (of wires), splicing; joint, splice; —**ивать** *v.* join, combine, unite, consolidate, splice; —**иваться** *see* **сростаться.**

**сред/а** *f.* medium, atmosphere, fluid, agent; surroundings, environment;

(biol.) habitat; Wednesday; **условия внешней** —**ы, условия** —**ы** environment.

**среди** *prep. gen.* in the middle (of), among; *prefix* inter—.

**средиземн/оморский,** —**ый** *a.* Mediterranean; inland.

**средина** *see* **середина.**

**срединный** *a.* middle, mean, median.

**средне—** *prefix* middle, medium, central; meso—; average; —**азиатский** *a.* Central Asia; —**активный** *a.* medium-active; (nucl.) medium-activity, semihot; —**вековый** *a.* medieval; —**вековье** *n.* Middle Ages; —**взвешенная величина,** —**взвешенное** *n.* (statistics) weighted average, weighted mean; —**годовой** *a.* average annual; —**девонский отдел** (geol.) Mesodevonic period.

**среднее** *n.* average, mean; **геометрическое с., пропорциональное с.** geometric mean.

**среднезернистый** *a.* medium-granular, medium-grained.

**среднеквадратичн/ое** *n.,* —**ый** *a.* (math.) mean square; root-mean-square, rms; —**ое значение** (elec.) root-mean-square value, effective value.

**средне/месячный** *a.* average monthly; —**порфировый** *a.* (petr.) mediophyric; —**сортный** *a.* medium-grade; —**суточный** *a.* average daily; —**схватывающийся** *a.* medium-setting (cement); —**твердый** *a.* medium-hard; —**тяжелый** *a.* medium-weight.

**средн/ий** *a.* middle, mean, average, medium, median, central; moderate, middling, intermediate; neutral; medium-textured (soil); secondary (school); —**ее арифметическое,** —**яя арифметическая** arithmetical mean; —**ее время** local mean time; —**ее время жизни** mean life; —**ее значение,** —**яя величина** mean value, mean; —**ее пропорциональное** mean proportional; —**ее ухо** (anat.) middle ear; —**ее число,** —**яя** *f.* mean, average; **выводить** —**ее число** *v.* average; —**им числом** on an average, at an average; —**ие сутки** mean solar day; —**яя ошибка** standard deviation; —**яя проба** all-level sample; —**яя**

реакция neutral reaction; —яя соль neutral salt; —яя точка midpoint; в —ем on an average, on the average, medium; выше —его above average.

средостение *n.* (anat.) mediastinum.

средоточие *n.* center, center point, point of concentration, concentration, focus.

средств/о *n.* agent, medium; —ant, —ent; means, way, facility, expedient; (pharm.) remedy; —a *pl.* means, facilities; resources, capital; —а передвижения transport facilities; с. к цели stepping stone; абсорбирующее с. absorbent; служить —ом *v.* be instrumental.

средь *see* среди.

срез *m.* cut, slice; microscopic section; shear, shearing, shearing off, shearing action; деформация —а (geol.) shearing; плоскость —а shear plane; прочность на с. shearing strength; работающий на с. under shearing stress.

срез/ание *n.* cutting, shearing, shear; truncation; —анный *a.* cut, sheared; truncated; —ать *see* срезывать; —ающий *see* срезывающий.

срезыв/аемый *a.* in shear; —ание *n.* cutting, shearing, shearing off; beveling; truncation; коэффициент —ания coefficient of shear; —ать *v.* cut away, cut off, trim, shear, shear off; slide; fail (examination); —ающий *a.* shearing; —ающая сила, —ающее усилие shear, shearing, shearing force.

срисов/ать, —ывать *v.* draw, copy.

срод/ный *a.* innate, natural; homogeneous, allied, congenial; —ственный *a.* kindred.

сродство *n.* relationship, affinity; избирательное с. affinity; химическое с. chemical affinity.

срок *m.* date, time, fixed time, term, period; deadline; с. работы, с. службы life (of equipment); —ом до within (given time); до —а ahead of schedule.

срост *m.* coupling, attachment, adhesion.

сростно— *prefix* syn—, syno—, sym—, syl— (together; associated); gamo—

(fusion); —лепестный *a.* (bot.) sympetalous; —листный *a.* (bot.) gamophyllous.

сросток *m.* attachment, adhesion; joint, junction, splice, splicing; (min.) concretion.

сросшийся *a.* grown together, united; (biol.) adnate.

срочн/о *adv.* urgently, quickly, by express; —ость *f.* urgency; —ый *a.* urgent, pressing; special-delivery (letter); —ое наблюдение (meteor.) standard observation.

сруб *m.* frame, framework, skeleton, shell, cage, cribwork, cradling; —ать, —ить *v.* cut down, cut off, fell, hew; —ка *f.* cutting down, felling; —овая крепь (min.) crib.

срыв *m.* disruption, collapse; breakaway; (nucl.) stripping; реакция —а stripping reaction; —ать *see* сорвать, срыть; —ной *a.* leaf (lettuce).

срыт/ие *n.* demolition, razing to the ground; —ь *v.* demolish, raze, level to the ground.

сряду *adv.* one after the other, uninterruptedly, continuously.

СС *abbr.* (Советский Союз) Soviet Union.

ссад/ина *f.* (med.) excoriation, abrasion, lesion; —ить *v.* excoriate, chafe, graze.

сса/дить, —живать *v.* land, put on shore; assist in coming down, help down; —диться, —живаться *v.* descend, alight; shrink (of cloth); —дка *f.* shrinking.

ССБ *abbr.* (сульфитно-спиртовая барда) (paper) sulfite waste liquor.

ссевшийся *a.* coagulated, clotted; crystallized, granulated (honey).

ссед/ание *n.* shrinkage; coagulation; settling, sinking; —аться *v.* shrink, contract; coagulate, curdle, clot; settle, sink.

ссек *m.* loin, sirloin, round (of beef).

ссесться *see* сседаться.

ссор/а *f.* disagreement, quarrel; —иться *v.* disagree, quarrel.

ссохнуться *see* ссыхаться.

СССР *abbr.* (Союз Советских Социалистических Республик) Union of Soviet Socialist Republics (USSR).

**сст** *abbr.* (сантистокс) centistokes.

**ссу/да** *f.*, **—дный** *a.* loan; **—дить, —жать,** *v.* loan, lend, advance.

**ссучить** *see* **сучить.**

**ссыл/ать** *v.* banish, exile, send away, deport; **—аться** *v.* be exiled; refer, allude (to), cite, quote; **—аясь на** with reference to; **—ка** *f.* exile, deportation; transportation; reference, citation.

**ссып/ание** *n.* pouring; **—ать** *v.* pour; **—ка** *f.* pouring; collection; **—ной** *a.* pouring; grain-collecting (center).

**ссыхаться** *v.* shrink, shrivel, dry up, contract in drying.

**ст.** *abbr.* (стадия) stage, phase; (станция) station; (старший) senior; (статья) article; (степень) degree; (стокс) stoke; (столб) column; (ступень) grade.

**стабилиз/атор** *m.* stabilizer, equalizer, balancer; regulator; **—ация** *f.* stabilization, stabilizing, settling; **—ированный, —ованный** *a.* stabilized, settled; **—ировать, —овать** *v.* stabilize, settle; regulate.

**стабилит** *m.* stabilite (diphenylethylene-diamine rubber antioxidant).

**стабиловольт** *m.* voltage-stabilizing tube.

**стабильн/ость** *f.* stability, firmness, rigidity; **—ый** *a.* stable, steadfast, firm, secure, substantial.

**ставень** *m.* shutter.

**став/ить** *v.* put, place, set, stand, station; lay down (conditions); **—ка** *f.* setting, placing, putting; rate (of pay).

**ставня** *see* **ставень.**

**ставролит** *m.* (min.) staurolite, staurotide.

**ставший** *past. act. part. of* **стать.**

**стагнация** *f.* stagnation, dead season.

**стад/иальный, —ийный** *a.*, **—ия** *f.* stage, phase; **—иальное дробление** stage crushing (of ore); **по —иям** in stages; **—ийность** *f.* vicissitude, change.

**стад/ность** *f.* herd instinct; **—ный** *a.* gregarious; **—о** *n.* herd, drove, flock; school, shoal (of fish).

**стаж** *m.* experience, record; length of service; **—ер** *m.* apprentice; **—ирование** *n.* probation.

**стаз** *m.* (physiol.) stasis.

**СТАЗРА** *abbr.* (станция защиты растений) plant protection station.

**стаивать** *v.* melt, melt away, thaw off, defrost, deice.

**стакан** *m.* glass; beaker; bucket (of well pump); socket; vessel; shell, pot; **—чик** *m.* little glass; small beaker; can, pot; (paper) cup.

**стакер** *m.* stacker.

**стал** *past sing. of* **стать.**

**сталагмит** *m.* (geol.) stalagmite; **—овый** *a.* stalagmitic.

**сталагмометр** *m.* stalagmometer; **—ический** *a.* stalagmometric.

**сталактит** *m.* (geol.) stalactite; **—овый** *a.* stalactitic.

**стале—** *prefix* steel; **—алюминий** *m.* ferroaluminum (iron-aluminum alloy); **—бетон** *m.* steel concrete; **—бронза** *f.* steel bronze; **—вар** *m.* steel worker, steel mill hand; **—ватый** *see* **сталистый;—делательный завод** steel mill.

**сталелитей/ный** *a.* steel casting; **с. завод, —ная мастерская** steel foundry, steel mill, steel works; **—щик** *m.* steel founder.

**сталеплавильн/ый** *a.* steel smelting, steel founding; **с. завод** steel mill, steel works; **—ая печь** steel furnace.

**сталепрокатный** *a.* steel rolling; **с. завод, с. стан** steel rolling mill, steel mill.

**стали** *past pl. of* **стать;** *gen., pl., etc., of* **сталь.**

**Сталинград** Stalingrad.

**сталинит** *m.* stalinite (a very hard Soviet tool alloy); tempered safety glass.

**сталистый** *a.* steely, steel-like; **с. чугун** semisteel, toughened cast iron.

**сталкивать** *v.* push, shove off; **—ся** *v.* collide, run (against, into), encounter, impinge (upon); clash, conflict, interfere.

**стало быть** *conj.* consequently, therefore, on that account, accordingly.

**сталь** *f.* steel; **с.-самозакалка, с.-самокалка** self-hardening steel, air-hardened steel, natural steel; **с.-серебрянка** silver steel (a steel alloy); **дикая с.**

wild steel; **индийская с.** Indian steel, wootz steel, wootz; **немецкая с.** German steel, natural steel; **специальная с.** special steel, steel alloy.

**стальник** *m.* (bot.) restharrow (*Ononis*).

**стальн/ой** *a.* steel; **с. баллон, —ая бутыль** steel cylinder (for gas); **с. лист** steel plate, sheet steel; **с. слиток, —ая болванка** steel ingot; **—ая отливка** steel casting; cast steel; **—ая плита** steel plate.

**стальносерый** *a.* steel gray.

**стамеска** *f.* chisel.

**стампийский ярус** (geol.) Stampian stage.

**стамуха** *f.* stamukha (ice hummock on a shoal).

**стан** *m.* mill; stature, height; camp, station; **с.-дуо** two-high mill, two-high rolling mill, twin rolling mill; **с.-трио** three-high mill, three-high rolling mill.

**станд** *m.* stand.

**стандарт** *m.* standard, standard specifications, norm, normal; sort; gage; **с.-вешер, с.-скруббер** a mechanical scrubber.

**Стандартгиз** *abbr.* (Государственное издательство стандартов) State Standards Publishing House.

**стандартиз/ация** *f.* standardization; **—ировать, —овать** *v.* standardize, calibrate, gage; **—ованный** *a.* standardized.

**стандартный** *a.* standard, normal.

**станет** *fut. 3 sing. of* **стать.**

**станина** *f.* mount, bed, bed plate, base, pedestal; bench; stand; frame, framework, carcass, casing, case, housing; column, pillar; bracket.

**станиол/ь** *m.*, **—евый** *a.* (metal) foil.

**станки-качалки** *pl.* pumps (for oil wells).

**станковая крепь** (min.) grid-type timber.

**станкостроение** *n.* machine-tool industry.

**станн/ат** *m.* stannate; **—ил** *m.* stannyl; **—ин, —ит** *m.* (min.) stannite, tin pyrites; **—ит** *m.* stannite.

**становить** *see* **ставить; —ся** *v.* become, turn, get, grow; get upon, stand on; put oneself (in).

**стан/ок** *m.*, **—очный** *a.* machine, machine tool; lathe; bench, stand; stall;

frame, bow (of saw); loom; (gun) carriage; **обработанный на —ке** machined; **токарный с.** lathe.

**станут** *fut. 3 pl. of* **стать.**

**станци/я** *f.*, **—онный** *a.* station; plant; (tel.) exchange.

**стапель** *m.* (naut.) building slip; stocks.

**стапливать** *v.* melt, fuse.

**старание** *n.* endeavor, effort, exertion; **приложить все с.** *v.* do one's level best.

**старатель** *m.* prospector, free miner.

**старательн/ость** *f.* assiduity, application; **—ый** *a.* painstaking, efficient.

**старательский** *a.* (min.) prospecting, prospector's.

**стараться** *v.* endeavor, strive, try, exert oneself.

**старейший** *a.* oldest.

**стар/ение** *n.* aging, seasoning; (met.) age hardening; (nucl.) storage for decay; **подвергаться —ению** *v.* age, season; **прошедший с.** seasoned; **—еть, —иться** *v.* grow old, age, become obsolete; **—еющий** *a.* aging; **—ик** *m.* old man; **—ина** *f.* old times, antiquity; **—инный** *a.* old-fashioned, ancient, long-established; **—ить** *v.* age, mature.

**старо/ватый** *a.* oldish, rather old; **—давний** *a.* ancient; **—дубка** *f.* (bot.) false hellebore (*Adonis vernalis*); **—модный** *a.* old-fashioned, antiquated; **—пашка** *f.* mellow soil, old arable soil; **—садка** *f.* starosadka (accumulation of seasonal layers of salt in a lake); **—сть** *f.* age, old age, senility.

**старт** *m.* start; **момент —а** initial time.

**старт/ер** *m.* starter, self-starter; **автоматический с.** self-starter; **—овый** *a.* start, starting.

**стар/уха** *f.* old woman; **—ческий** *a.* senile.

**старш/е** *compr. of* **старый,** older, elder; **—ий** *a.* oldest, eldest, senior; superior, chief, head; *m.* chief, head; **—ий рабочий, —ина** *m.* foreman; **—инство** *n.* seniority.

**стар/ый** *a.* old, ancient, senile; back (number of journal); **—ье** *n.* old things, junk.

**Стаса пипетка** Stas pipet.

**стаск/ать, —ивать** *v.* pull off, drag down.

стассанизация *f.* stassanization (sterilization by heat).

Стассано электропечь (elec.) Stassano furnace.

стассфурт/ит *m.* (min.) stassfurtite (a variety of boracite); —ские соли Stassfurt salts (chiefly potassium chlorides and sulfates).

стат *m.* unit of radioactivity equal to $3.63 \times 10^{-7}$ curies.

статбюро *abbr.* (статистическое бюро) Bureau of Statistics.

статей/ка *f.* short article, item; —ный *a.* article; chapter; clause.

статив *m.* rack, stand; surface gage.

статика *f.* (mech.) statics.

статисти/к *m.* statistician; —ка *f.* statistics; —ческий *a.* statistical, statistic.

статич/еский, —ный *a.* (mech.) static; —ность *f.* static character.

статор *m.*, —ный *a.* (mach.) stator.

статоскоп *m.* statoscope (a barometer).

статус-кво status quo.

статут *m.* statute, ordinance; —ная милия statute mile.

статуя *f.* statue.

стать *v.* begin (to); come (to); *see also* становиться.

статья *f.* article, paper; item, clause.

стафил—, —о— *prefix* staphyl—, staphylo— (uvula; staphylococcic); —иниды *pl.* rove beetles (*Staphylinidae*); —ококк *m.* (bact.) staphylococcus; —ома *f.* (med.) staphyloma.

стафисагроин *m.* staphisagroine.

стаффелит *m.* (min.) staffelite.

стахи/дрин *m.* stachydrine; —оза *f.* stachyose; —с (bot.) stachys.

стационар *m.* station; hospital; —ность *f.* stability; —ный *a.* stationary, fixed; steady; equilibrium; steady-state; hospital (patient); —ный потенциал equilibrium potential;—ный режим steady state.

стация *f.* (biol.) station, habitat.

стачивать *v.* grind off, sharpen; —ся *v.* wear off, be worn off.

стачк/а *f.* (labor) strike; —ом *m.* strike committee.

стащить *see* стаскивать.

стая *f.* flock; shoal, school (of fish).

стаять *see* стаивать.

ствол *m.* trunk, stem; shaft, shank (of tool); core, body; (min., agr.) shaft; (nerve) cord; tube; barrel (of gun); канал —a bore (of gun); —истый *a.* tubular; —овой *a.* trunk, stem; *m.* (min.) top cager.

створ *m.* line of direction; fold of door; в —е in line.

створажив/ание *n.*, —ающийся *a.* curdling; coagulating.

створка *f.* fold, flap; valve.

створоженный *a.* coagulated, curdled.

створчат/ый *a.* folding; valved, valvate; casement (window); с. клапан flap valve, clack valve; —ая дверь valve.

стеапс/аза *f.*, —ин *m.* steapsase, steapsin.

стеарат *m.* stearate.

стеарил *m.*, —овый *a.* stearyl; хлористый с. stearyl chloride.

стеарин *m.* stearin, glycerol tristearate.

стеариново/кислый *a.* stearic acid; stearate (of); с. натрий, —натриевая соль sodium stearate; —кислая соль stearate; —кислые эфиры stearic esters; —этиловый эфир ethyl stearate.

стеаринов/ый *a.* stearin, stearic; с. альдегид stearic aldehyde, stearaldehyde; с. ангидрид stearic anhydride; с. жмых, —ая лепешка stearin cake; —ая кислота stearic acid, octodecanoic acid; соль —ой кислоты stearate; —ая свеча stearin candle; —ое масло stearin oil; —ое мыло stearin soap.

стеаро— *prefix* stearo—; —ксилевая кислота, —ксиловая кислота stearoxylic acid, 9,10-dioxooctadecanoic acid; —левая кислота, —ловая кислота stearolic acid, 9-octadecynoic acid; —н *m.* stearone, 18-pentatriacontanone; —нитрил *m.* stearonitrile, octadecanenitrile; —птен *m.* stearoptene, oleoptene.

стеатит *m.* (min.) steatite (a variety of talc); a synthetic talc insulation material; —овый *a.* steatite, steatitic.

стебел/ек *m.* (biol.) pedicle, pedicel; снабженный —ьками pedicellate.

стеб/ель *m.*, —левой *a.* stem, stalk; column; shank, shaft (of tool); —ельковый, —ельчатый *a.* stalk-like, columnar; —левание *n.* stooling, letting out shoots; —левидный *a.* stem-like; (bot.) cauliform; —ледробилка, —плющилка *f.* hay crusher; —леед *m.* (zool.) Lixus iridis; —леруб *m.* stalk cutter; —листый *a.* having several stems.

стег/ать, —ивать *v.* lash; stitch, quilt.

стедит *m.* (met.) steadite.

стеенструпин *m.* (min.) steenstrupine.

стеж/ка *f.* stitch, quilting; —ок *m.* stitch.

стек/ание *n.* runoff, running off; (charge) leakage; —ать *v.* flow, flow off, run off, run out, drain, discharge; drip off, trickle; —аться *v.* flow into each other, converge; gather, collect, accumulate; —ающий *a.* draining, discharging, running out.

стеклец *m.* stekletz (lower part of massive mirabilite salt layer in Western Siberia).

стеклить *see* стекловать.

стекло *n.* glass; chimney (of kerosene lamp); с. буры fused borax; с. жизни Vitaglass; жидкое с., растворимое с. water glass, sodium silicate solution; окрашенное с., цветное с. stained glass.

стекло/бой *m.* broken glass, cullet; —вание *n.* vitrification; (polymers) glass transition, second-order transition; температура —вания glass point, second-order transition temperature, $T_g$; —варенная печь glass furnace; —варный горшок glass pot; —ватый *a.* vitreous, glassy; —вать *v.* vitrify; glaze.

стекловидн/ость *f.* glassiness, vitreousness; —ый *a.* glassy, vitreous, hyaline.

стекло/делие *n.* glass manufacture; —дув *m.* glass blower; —дувная трубка blowtube, blowpipe; —калильная печь *see* стеклоплавильная печь.

стеклообразн/ость *f.* glassiness, vitreousness; —ый *a.* glassy, glass-like, vitreous, vitriform.

стеклоочиститель *m.* windshield wiper.

стеклопакет *m.* double glass sheet.

стеклоплавильн/ый *a.* glass-melting; с. горшок glass pot, glass crucible; —ая

печь glass furnace, spec. ash furnace.

стекло/подобный *see* стеклообразный; —рез *m.* glass cutter; —тара *f.* container glassware; —ткань *f.* glass cloth.

стеклышко *n.* piece of glass; glass bead; покровное с. (micros.) cover glass.

стеклян/истый *a.* hyaloid, pellucid, glass-like; —ницы *pl.* clear-winged moths (*Aegeriidae*).

стеклянн/ый *a.* glass, vitreous, hyaline; (elec.) positive; с. кубик glass block, glass brick; с. кубок glass beaker; —ая бумага sand paper; —ая вата glass wool, spun glass; —ая нить, —ое волокно glass fiber; —ая палочка stirring rod, glass rod; —ая плита glass plate; —ая посуда, —ые изделия glassware.

стеклярус *m.* glass beads.

стекольн/ый *a.* glass, vitreous; *see also* стеклянный; с. завод glass works; с. мастер glass maker, glass manufacturer; с. шлак glass gall; —ая замазка putty; —ая печь glass furnace.

стекольщи/к *m.* glazier; —чий *a.* glazier's.

стекший *a.* discharged, run out, drained.

стела *f.* (bot.) stele.

стелаж *see* стеллаж.

стелить *v.* spread, strew, litter; —ся *v.* spread; creep; play (of flame); float, drift.

стеллаж *m.* shelving; book case; rack, stand; —и *pl.* scaffolding; —ный *a.* *of* стеллаж; stage (kiln).

стелл/арит *m.* (min.) stellarite, stellar coal (a variety of asphaltum); —ерит *m.* stellerite (a zeolite).

стеллит *m.*, —овый *a.* (min.) stellite; Stellite (a cobalt-base alloy for high-speed tools); —ировать *v.* stellite.

стеллой *m.* (met.) Stalloy (an electrical steel).

стель *see* стела.

стелька *f.* welt; inner sole, insole.

стельность *f.* (zool.) pregnancy.

стел/ющийся, —ящийся *a.* (bot.) trailing, creeping.

стемнеть *v.* get dark.

стен *m.* sthene (unit of force).

**стен/а** *f.* wall, side; **обнести —ой** *v.* wall in.

**стенд** *m.* stand; test bed; testing unit; **—ер** *m.* stand pipe.

**стенка** *f.* wall, partition; shell (of boiler).

**стенни/к** *m.* (bot.) candytuft (*Iberis*); **—ца** *f.* (bot.) wall pellitory (*Parietaria officinalis*).

**стенн/ой** *a.* wall, wall-type, mural; (biol.) parietal; **с. кирпич** building brick; **—ая селитра** wall saltpeter (calcium nitrate).

**стено—** *prefix* wall; steno— (narrow, little, close); **—битный таран** battering ram.

**стенограф** *m.* stenographer; a bark beetle (*Ips stenographus*); **—ист** *m.*, **—истка** *f.* stenographer; **—ический** *a.* stenographic; **—ия** *f.* stenography, shorthand.

**стеноз** *m.* (med.) stenosis, narrowing, constriction **—ин** *m.* Stenosine, sodium methanearsonate.

**стенструпин** *m.* (min.) steenstrupine.

**степенный** *a.* sedate; (math.) exponential; power (function).

**степен/ь** *f.* degree, extent; rate; step, stage; grade, class; ratio; order (of an equation); (math.) power; **в меньшей —и** to a lesser degree, less; **в слабой —и** to a slight degree, slightly; **второй —и** (math.) quadratic; **ни в какой —и** in no degree, in no wise, not at all; **до некоторой —и** in some measure, to a certain degree; **первой —и** (math.) linear; **показатель —и** (math.) exponent; **третья с.** (math.) third power, cube; **возводить в третью с.** *v.* raise to the third power, cube; **корень третьей —и** cube root; **ученая с.** (university) degree.

**степ/ной** *a.*, **—ь** *f.* steppe, plain.

**стер** *m.* stere, cubic meter; **—ад, —адиан** *m.* steradian (unit of measure of solid angle).

**стерв/а** *f.* carrion, carcass; **—оядные** *pl.* (zool.) scavengers; **—оядный** *a.* carrion-eating, scavenging.

**стережен/ие** *n.* guard, watch, charge; guarding, watching; **—ный** *a.* guarded.

**стерео—** *prefix* stereo— (solid, three-dimensional; spatial); **—бинокль** *m.* stereoscope.

**стереограф/ический** *a.* (geom.) stereographic; **—ия** *f.* stereography.

**стереоизомер** *m.* stereoisomer; **—ия** *f.* stereoisomerism; **—ный** *a.* stereoisomeric.

**стереокауловая кислота** stereocaulic acid.

**стерео/метр** *m.* stereometer; **—метрический** *a.* stereometric; **—метрия** *f.* stereometry, solid geometry; **—скоп** *m.* stereoscope; **—скопический** *a.* stereoscopic; **—снимок** *m.* stereoscopic photograph.

**стереотип** *m.* (typ.) stereotype; **пластинка —а** cliché; **—ировать** *v.* stereotype; **—ия** *f.* stereotypy, stereotyping; **—ный** *a.* stereotype, stereotypic; **—щик** *m.* stereotyper, stereotypist.

**стерео/труба** *f.* stereoscopic telescope; **—фонический** *a.* stereophonic; **—фотография** *f.* stereoscopic photograph (or photography).

**стереохим/ический** *a.* stereochemical; **—ическая формула** spatial formula; **—ия** *f.* stereochemistry, spatial or configurative chemistry.

**стереть** *see* **стирать.**

**стеречь** *v.* guard, take care (of), have charge (of).

**стерженщик** *m.* (foundry) core maker.

**стерж/ень** *m.*, **—невой** *a.* rod, bar; (foundry) core; stem, stalk, shank, shaft, arm; bolt, peg, pin; spindle, pivot; plug; nipple (of gun); spine; **с. управления** (nucl.) control rod.

**стержнев/ой** *a. of* **стержень**; **с. пруток** core rod; **с. трансформатор** (elec.) core-type transformer; **с. цех** core room; **с. ящик** core box; **—ая обмотка** (elec.) bar winding.

**стержнеобразный** *a.* rod-like, bar.

**стеригматоцистин** *m.* sterigmatocystin.

**стерилампа** *f.* sterilamp.

**стерилиз/атор** *m.* sterilizer; **—ация** *f.* sterilization; **—ировать, —овать** *v.* sterilize; **—ованный** *a.* sterilized; **—ующий** *a.* sterilizing; **—ующее средство** germicide.

**стерильн/ость** *f.* sterility; **—ый** *a.* sterile.

**стерины** *pl.* sterols (solid alcohols).

стерическ/ий *a.* steric, spatial; —ое затруднение steric hindrance.

стерко/билин *m.* stercobilin, urobilin; —рит *m.* (min.) stercorite, microcosmic salt; —рол *m.* stercorol, coprosterol.

стеркулиев/ая камедь sterculia gum, Indian tragacanth; —ые *pl.* (bot.) Sterculiaceae.

стерлинг *m.*, —овый *a.* sterling; фунт —ов pound sterling.

стерлядь *f.* sterlet (a small sturgeon).

стернбергит *m.* (min.) sternbergite.

стернит *m.* (zool.) sternite.

стерня *f.* (agr.) stubble; stubble field.

стерпеть *v.* bear, tolerate, endure.

стеррометалл *m.* sterro metal (a copper-zinc base alloy).

стертый *a.* worn out, rubbed off, eroded (rock).

стесать *see* стесывать.

стесн/енный *a.* crowded, restricted; —ительный *a.* inconvenient; —ить, —ять *v.* constrain, embarrass, hamper, handicap, crowd, narrow.

стесывать *v.* cut off, chop off; plane off.

стетоскоп *m.* (med.) stethoscope; defectophone (for investigating noises in machinery); —ический *a.* stethoscopic.

Стефана закон (phys.) Stefan's law.

стефан/ит *m.* (min.) stephanite, brittle silver ore (silver-antimony sulfide); —ов камень heliotrope, bloodstone (a form of quartz); —ский ярус (geol.) Stephanian stage.

стехио— *prefix* stoichio—; —логия *f.* (physiol.) stoichiology; —метрический *a.* stoichiometric; —метрия *f.* stoichiometry.

стеч/ение *n.* confluence, convergence; concurrence, coincidence; —ь *see* стекать.

стиб/амин *m.* Stibamine; —енил *m.* stibenyl, stibacetin; —иат *m.* stibiate, antimonate; —ид *m.* stibide, antimonide; —иконит, —ит *m.* (min.) stibiconite, antimony ocher; —ил *m.* stibyl, antimonyl; —илвинная кислота antimonyl tartaric acid; —ин *m.* stibine, antimonous hydride; —иотанталит *m.* (min.) stibiotantalite (a tantalo-niobate of antimony);

—лит *m.*, —ляная охра (min.) stiblite; —нит *m.* (min.) stibnite, antimonite, antimony glance.

стигма, —та *f.* (biol.) stigma; —ты *pl.* stigmata; —стан *m.* stigmastane; —станол *m.* stigmastanol; —стерин *m.* stigmasterol.

стилизованный рисунок conventionalized design.

стиллинг/ин *m.* stillingine; —оид *m.* stillingoid.

стило— *prefix* stylo— (pillar, column); —граф *m.* stylograph (pen); —лит *m.* (geol.) stylolite; —литовый *a.* stylolitic; —метр *m.* stylometer.

стилон *m.* Steelon (a polyamide fiber).

стилотипит *m.* (min.) stylotypite.

стиль *m.* style, manner, fashion.

стильб *m.* stilb (unit of brightness).

стильбаз/ин *m.* stilbazine; —ол *m.* stilbazole; —олин *m.* stilbazoline.

стильбен *m.*, —овый *a.* stilbene, toluylene; хлористый с. stilbene chloride; —диол *m.* stilbenediol, vinylene-bisphenol.

стильбит *m.* (min.) stilbite (a zeolite).

стильпно/мелан *m.* (min.) stilpnomelane (an iron silicate); —сидерит *m.* stilpnosiderite (a variety of limonite).

Стильсона ключ Stillson wrench.

стим-пойнт *m.* (min.) steam point, point (for thawing ground).

стимул *m.* stimulus, stimulant, spur; —ирование *n.* stimulation; —ировать *v.* stimulate; —ирующий *a.* stimulating, stimulant; —ятор *m.* stimulant.

стипенд/иат *m.* scholarship student; —ия *f.* stipend, scholarship.

стипитатовая кислота stipitatic acid.

стипт/ицин *m.* Stypticin, cotarnine chloride; —ол *m.* Styptol, cotarnine phthalate.

стиракол *m.* Styracol, guaiacol cinnamate.

стиракс *m.*, —овый *a.* styrax, storax (a balsam from *Liquidambar orientalis*); —овое дерево (bot.) styrax.

стир/альный *a.* washing, laundering; с. порошок detergent; —альная машина washing machine, washer; —ание *n.* rubbing off, rubbing out, erasure, erasing, obliteration; abrasion; —ать *v.* rub off, rub out, erase, efface, obliterate; abrade, erode; wipe off, dust; wash, launder; —**аться** *v.* wear, wear out, wear away, wear off, fray, rub off; wash, be washable.

**стирацин** *m.* styracine, cinnamyl cinnamate.

**стирающийся** *a.* washable.

**стирен** *m.* styrene, styrolene, phenethylene.

**стирил** *m.*, —**овый** *a.* styryl; —**овая кислота** styrilic acid; —**овый спирт** styryl alcohol, cinnamic alcohol.

**стирка** *f.* washing, laundering, laundry.

**стирол** *m.* styrene; styrol, colloidal silver; **хлористый с.** styrene chloride; —**ен** *see* **стирен**; —**еновый спирт** styrolene alcohol, cinnamic alcohol; —**овые смолы** styrene resins.

**стирон** *m.* styrone, cinnamic alcohol.

**стис/кивать,** —**нуть** *v.* squeeze, compress, jam; clutch, grip.

**стифнинов/ая кислота** styphnic acid, trinitroresorcinol; **соль** —**ой кислоты,** —**окислая соль** styphnate.

**стихать** *v.* calm down, abate, die down.

**стих/ийный** *a.* elemental, elementary; —**ийное движение** elemental upheaval; —**ия** *f.* element.

**стихнуть** *see* **стихать.**

**стихтит** *m.* (min.) stichtite.

**стицерин** *m.* stycerin; —**овая кислота** styceric acid.

**стичер** *m.* stitcher (for rubber).

**стла/нный** *a.* laid out; —**ть** *see* **стелить.**

**сто** hundred.

**Стоби печь** (elec.) Stobie furnace.

**стов/аин** *m.* Stovaine; —**арсол** *m.* Stovarsol, acetarsone.

**стог** *m.* stack, rick (of straw, etc.); —**омет,** —**ометатель** *m.* hay stacker, stacker.

**стоградусный** *a.* centigrade.

**стоечка** *f.* stand; prop, support.

**стожить** *v.* stack.

**стоимост/ь** *f.* cost, price, worth, value; **падение** —**и** depreciation.

**стоит** *pr. 3 sing. of* **стоить, стоять; с. только** one need only.

**стоить** *v.* cost, amount (to), be worth.

**стойбище** *n.* resting place (for cattle).

**стойка** *f.* stand, pedestal, pedestal base; rack, counter; rest, support, prop, brace, bracing; (aero.) strut; chuck; column, pillar, post, stake; stem, shank; tine.

**стойк/ий** *a.* stable, sturdy, firm, steadfast, persistent, persevering; hardy; *suffix* -proof, -resisting; —**ое соединение** stable compound; **химически с.** chemically stable.

**стойкость** *f.* stability, sturdiness, firmness, steadiness; persistence, perseverance, durability.

**стойло** *n.* stall, pen, sty, box, compartment; —**вый** *a.* stall; barnyard (manure).

**стоймя** *adv.* upright.

**сток** *m.* flow, discharge, discharging, drainage, escape, effluence; (discharge) outlet, run-off; channel, sewer, drain.

**Стока конвертер** Stock converter.

**Стокгольм** Stockholm.

**стокезит** *m.* (min.) stokesite.

**стокер** *m.* stoker; feeder.

**стократный** *a.* centuple, hundredfold.

**стокс** *m.* stoke (unit of kinematic viscosity).

**Стокса закон** Stokes' law.

**стол** *m.* table, desk; board; food, diet.

**столб** *m.* column, pillar, post, pole, stake, peg; sharply projecting rock (in Urals and Siberia); **жидкий с.** liquid column.

**столбенеть** *v.* fall into a stupor.

**столбец** *m.* column (of table).

**столбик** *m.* column; core; peg; (biol.) style; (anat.) columella; **с. ртути** mercury column.

**столбняк** *m.* (med.) tetanus, lockjaw; catalepsy, stupor.

**столбо/видный** *a.* columnar, pillar-like; —**вой** *a.* column, post; —**вой выключатель** (elec.) pole switch, pillar switch.

**столбур** *m.* big bud (tomato disease).

**столбчак** *m.* basalt (a basic igneous rock).

**столбчат/ый** *a.* columnar, basaltiform; acicular (crystal); palisade (cell, tissue); —**ая отдельность** (geol.) columnar structure, basaltic structure.

**столет/ие** *n.* century; —**ний** *a.* centennial; —**няя годовщина** centennial;

—ник *m.* (bot.) century plant (*Agave americana*).

столик *m.* little table; (microscope) stage.

столист/венный, —ый *a.* (bot.) centifolious; —ник *m.* centifolio.

столи/ца *f.* capital, metropolis; —чный *a.* metropolitan.

столкн/овение *n.* collision, impact, impingement, encounter; shock, percussion; interference; частота —овений collision rate; —уть *see* сталкивать.

столов/ая *f.* dining room; —ый *a.* table, desk; —ая гора, —ое плоскогорье (geol.) mesa; —ая соль table salt, sodium chloride; —ое масло salad oil.

столон *m.* (bot.) stolon, runner, offset.

столочь *v.* grind.

столп *see* столб.

столь *adv.* so; —ко *adv.* so; so much; as much, as many; —ко же as much again.

столяр *m.* carpenter, joiner, cabinet maker; с.-краснодеревец cabinet maker; —ная, —ня *f.* carpenter's shop; —ничать *v.* do carpentry work; —ный *a.* carpenter, joiner's; —ный клей joiner's glue; —ный станок joiner's bench; —ная пила buck saw.

стомат—, —о— *prefix* stomat—, stomato— (mouth); —ит *m.* (med.) stomatitis; —ология *f.* stomatology.

Стон/а машина, —ея машина (foundry) Stone's machine (for knocking out cores).

стоно/г *m.* (bot.) hart's tongue (*Scolopendrium*); —жка *f.* (zool.) centipede.

стоп *m.* stop.

стопа *f.* foot; series; ream (of paper); pile (of timber, bricks); по его —м in his footsteps.

стопер *m.* (min.) stoper, stoping drill.

стопин *m.* quick match.

стопинг *m.* (min.) stoping.

стопить *see* стапливать.

стопка *f.* stack, pile; small glass.

стопор *m.* plug, stopper; stop, catch, detent, detainer, checking device, locking device, lock; corkscrew; —ез-ка *f.* guillotine, trimmer; —ить *v.* plug, stop, stopper; fix, lock.

стопорн/ый *a.* stop, stopper, closing; с.

болт binder bolt, binding bolt; с. винт stop screw, set screw; clamping screw; с. клапан stop valve, cut-off valve, check valve; с. кран stopcock; с. механизм stopper, stop gear, arresting device, lock mechanism, locking device; с. рычаг, с. стержень stopper, stopping lever; с. штифт stop pin, stop; —ая гайка lock nut, check nut; —ое кольцо check ring; —ое приспособление, —ое устройство lock, catch.

стопоходящий *a.* (zool.) plantigrade.

стопочная заливка filling molds by stacking one on top of the other and filling the top one.

стопроцентный *a.* hundred per cent, one hundred per cent.

стоп-стержень *m.* (nucl.) scram rod.

стоптать *see* стаптывать.

сторакс *see* стиракс.

сторож *m.* guard, watchman, caretaker; на —е on the watch, on the alert; —евой *a.* watch, guard; —евая вышка watch tower; —ить *v.* watch, keep watch (over), guard; —ок *m.* catch; tongue, cock (of scales).

сторон/а *f.* side; land, place; —ой sideways, sidewards; в —е aside, apart; остаться в —е *v.* be out of the picture; в —у to the side, laterally; в другую —у in the other direction, the other way; отложить в —у *v.* put aside, lay aside; перемещение в —у lateral movement, lateral displacement; повернуть в —у *v.* turn aside; уход в —у (drilling) side tracking; во все —ы in different directions; on all sides; вывернуть на другую —у *v.* turn inside out; задняя с. back; передняя с. front, face; с —ы from the side; laterally; с другой —ы on the other hand; с его —ы for his part, from his point of view; он со своей —ы he for one, for his part.

сторонн/ий *a.* outside, irrelevant; *suffix* —hedral, —lateral; —ик *m.* adherent, supporter, advocator; *suffix* —hedron; —ичество *n.* siding, adherence, support.

стосил *m.* (bot.) ginseng (*Panax*).

стохастический *a.* stochastic, conjectural.

**сточить** *see* **стачивать.**

**сточн/ый** *a.* sewer, drain, drainage, discharge, escape; **с. колодец** cesspool, sewer; **с. край** drip edge; **с. трубопровод, —ая труба** sewer pipe, drain; **—ая жидкость** sewage; **—ая петля, —ое кольцо** curved edge; **—ые воды** waste water, sewage.

**стояк** *m.* stand pipe; upright; uprise; (foundry) riser.

**стоялый** *a.* stale, stagnant; long unused.

**стоян/ие** *n.* standing; stand (of plants); **—ка** *f.* stand, station, quarters; layover, stopover; (train) stop; (automobile) parking.

**сто/ять** *v.* stand; continue; **с. за** stand for, defend; **—ячий** *a.* standing, stationary; vertical, erect; stagnant, still; stand (pipe); floor (lamp); **—ячая волна** standing wave.

**стоящий** *a.* costing; **дорого с.** costly, expensive; **ничего не с.** worthless.

**стр** *abbr.* (**стерадиан**) steradian; **стр.** *abbr.* (**страница**) page.

**страбизм** *m.* (med.) strabismus, squint.

**страв/ить, —лять** *v.* scour, pickle, etch, cleanse; **—ление** *n.* scouring, pickling, etching, corrosion; **—ленный** *a.* scoured, pickled, etched.

**стравлив/ание** *n.* grazing; **—ать** *v.* graze, browse.

**страда** *f.* harvest time, harvesting season.

**страд/ание** *n.* suffering, pain; **—ать** *v.* suffer, undergo; **—ающий** *a.* suffering.

**страж, —а** *see* **сторож.**

**страз** *m.*, **—а** *f.* paste (jewel).

**стралит** *m.* (min.) strahlite, actinolite.

**страна** *f.* country, land, region; **с. света** point of the compass.

**страница** *f.* page, leaf.

**странн/о** *adv.* strangely, oddly; it is strange; **—ость** *f.* strangeness, oddness, oddity, singularity, peculiarity; **—ый** *a.* strange, odd, singular, peculiar.

**странствовать** *v.* wander, travel.

**страст/оцвет** *m.* passion flower (*Passiflora*) **—ь** *f.* passion, mania.

**стратегия** *f.* strategy.

**стратиграфия** *f.* (geol.) stratigraphy.

**стратифи/кация** *f.* stratification; **—цированный** *a.* stratified.

**страто/метр** *m.* stratometer (for soils); **—пеит** *m.* (min.) stratopeite (an alteration product of rhodonite); **—план** *m.* (aero.) stratoplane, stratosphere plane; **—стат** *m.* stratosphere balloon; **—сфера** *f.* (meteor.) stratosphere; **—сферный** *a.* stratospheric.

**страус** *m.*, **—овый** *a.* (zool.) ostrich; **—ник** *m.*, **—пер** (bot.) fern (*Struthiopteris germanica*).

**страх** *m.* fear, fright, apprehension; **на свой с.** at one's own risk; **под —ом** under penalty (of), on pain (of).

**страхов/ание** *n.*, **—ка** *f.* insurance; **с. от огня** fire insurance; **—ать** *v.* insure; **—ой** *a.* insurance; **—щик** *m.* insurance agent; underwriter.

**страш/илки** *pl.* leaf and stick insects (*Phasmatidae*); **—иться** *v.* fear, be in fear (of), be apprehensive; **—но** *adv.* frightfully, extremely; it is dreadful; **—ный** *a.* frightful, dreadful.

**стрежень** *m.* deep channel in river.

**стрейнер** *m.* strainer.

**стрекающие** *pl.* (zool.) Cnidaria.

**стрекоз/а** *f.* dragon fly; **—ы** *pl.* Odonata.

**стрел/а** *f.* arrow, pointer, indicator; crane arm, gib, jib, overhang beam, boom (of derrick); cantilever; rise (of arch), camber; **зубец —ы** barb.

**стрелк/а** *f.* arrow, pointer, needle, indicator, index; hand (of clock); (railroad) switch; spit, tongue (of land); (bot.) scape; **с. наклонения** dip needle; **—ование** *n.* bolting; **—овый** *a.* arrow; shooting.

**стреловидный** *a.* arrow-like, sagittal, sagittary; **с. шов** (anat.) sagittal suture.

**стреловой** *m.* crane operator.

**стрелок** *m.* rifleman.

**стрелолист** *m.* (bot.) arrowhead (*Sagittaria*).

**стрелочн/ик** *m.* (railroad) switchman.

**стрелочн/ый** *a.* arrow, needle, sagittary; (railroad) switch; **с. измерительный прибор, с. прибор** indicating instrument, indicator.

**стрельб/а** *f.* shooting, firing, marksmanship; **—ище** *n.* shooting range.

**стрельнуть** *see* **стрелять.**

**стрельчат/ка** *f.* (zool.) acronycta; **—ый** *a.* arrow-shaped, sagittary; gabled, pointed.

**стрелять** *v.* shoot, fire.

**стремительн/ость** *f.* impetus; **—ый** *a.* impetuous, precipitate.

**стрем/иться** *v.* rush; aim (at), strive (for); attempt, try; tend, converge; **—ление** *n.* tendency, inclination, leaning, propensity.

**стремнина** *f.* chute, slope; rapids (of river).

**стремя** *n.* stirrup.

**стремянка** *f.* step ladder; bridging board, gangway, footpath.

**стремящийся** *a.* rushing; striving (for).

**стренга** *f.* strand.

**стренгит** *m.* (min.) strengite (hydrous iron phosphate).

**стренда** *see* **стренга.**

**стренер** *m.* strainer, filter.

**стреп/силин** *m.* strepsilin; **—тидин** *m.* streptidine.

**стрепто—** *prefix* strepto— (twisted chain; streptococcus); **—биоза** *f.* streptobiose; **—зим** *m.* streptozyme; **—кокк** *m.* (bact.) streptococcus; **—кокковый** *a.* streptococcic; **—лин** *m.* streptolin; **—мицин** *m.* streptomycin; **—стазин** *m.* streptostasin; **трицин** *m.* streptothricin; **—цид** *m.* Streptocid, sulfanilamide; **белый —цид** *m.* Streptocid album, sulfanilamide; **—цин** *m.* streptocin.

**стресс** *m.* stress.

**стреха** *f.* eaves.

**стриг** *past sing. of* **стричь; —аль, —альщик** *m.* shearer; **—альный** *a.* shearing.

**стриговит** *m.* (min.) strigovite.

**стриг/ун** *m.* a beetle (*Myelophilus*); **—ут** *pr. 3 pl. of* **стричь; —ущий** *a.* cutting, shearing; **—ущий лишай** (med.) ring worm.

**стриж/ей** *m.* shearer; **—еный** *a.* sheared, clipped; **—ет** *pr. 3 sing. of* **стричь; —ка** *f.* shearing, clipping, clip, cropping, haircut.

**стрик** *m.* streak (plant disease).

**стриктура** *f.* (med.) stricture, narrowing.

**стриппер** *m.* stripper; **с.-кран** stripper, stripping crane.

**стриппинг-секция** *f.* stripping section (of fractionating column).

**стрихнидин** *m.* strychnidine.

**стрихнин** *m.,* **—овый** *a.* strychnine; **сернокислый с., сульфат —а** strychnine sulfate; **—овая кислота** strychninic acid.

**стрихницин** *m.* strychnicine.

**стричь** *v.* cut, clip, shear, fleece.

**строб** *m.,* **—ировать** *v.* (elec. comm.) strobe, gate; **—импульс** *m.* (computers, etc.) gate pulse; **—ирование** *n.,* **—ирующий** *a.* gating; **ширина —ирования** gate width; **—ирующая схема** gating circuit, gate.

**стробоскоп** *m.* stroboscope (speed-measuring device); **—ический** *a.* stroboscopic.

**строг/ало** *n.* plane; **—альный** *a.* planing; **—альный станок, —альная машина** planing machine, planer; **—альщик** *m.* planer (operator); **—ание** *n.* planing, shaping; **—анный** *a.* planed; **—ать** *v.* plane, shape, shave.

**строг/ий** *a.* strict, rigid, severe; **—о** *adv.* strictly, exactly; **—ость** *f.* strictness, severity.

**строевой** *a.* building, construction; **с. лес** timber.

**строен/ие** *n.* building, construction, formation; structure; constitution, composition; texture, grain; **изомерия —ия** structural isomerism; **формула —ия** structural formula.

**строенный** *a.* triple, triplex.

**строитель** *m.* builder, constructor, designer, engineer; **—ный** *a.* building, construction, structural, architectural; **—ный материал** building material; **—ная техника** civil engineering; **—ное искусство** architecture; **—ство** *n.* building, construction, erection; organization, development.

**строить** *v.* build, construct, erect; form.

**стро/й** *m.* regime, system, order; formation, line; **вывести из —я** *v.* put out of commission, disable; **выйти из —я** *v.* get out of order; (mil.) fall out.

**стройка** *f.* construction, building.

**стройн/ый** *a.* well-shaped, well-proportioned; orderly (system); **—ое целое** harmonious whole, unified whole.

**строк/а** *f.* line; row (of a determinant);

**красная с.** (typ.) break line; new paragraph; **начать с новой —и** v. indent, begin a new paragraph.

**строма** f. (biol.) stroma, binding tissue.

**строматология** f. (geol.) stromatology.

**стромболианский** a. strombolian (eruption).

**стромейерит** m. (min.) stromeyerite (a silver-copper sulfide).

**Строменджер-Слоутера способ** (welding) Strawmenger-Slaughter process.

**стронгилиды** pl. (zool.) Strongylidae.

**стронциан** m. strontia, strontium oxide; **едкий с.** caustic strontia, strontium hydroxide; **—ит** m. (min.) strontianite (a strontium carbonate); **—овый** a. strontianiferous; **—окальцит** m. (min.) strontianocalcite (a variety of calcite).

**стронциев/ый** a. strontium; **—ая соль** strontium salt.

**стронц/ий** m. strontium, Sr; **гидрат окиси —ия** strontium hydroxide; **карбонат —ия, углекислый с.** strontium carbonate; **окись —ия** strontium oxide, strontia; **хлористый с.** strontium chloride.

**строп** m. sling, strap; **—а** f. (parachute) shroud line, suspension line.

**стропил/а** pl. frame, framework, truss; **—ина** f., **—о** n., **—ьная нога, —ьная связь** truss piece, rafter, beam, joist.

**стропить** v. sling.

**строфант** m. strophanthus (seeds of *Strophanthus kombe* or *hispidus*); **—идин** m. strophanthidin; **—ин** m. strophanthin, methylouabain; **—иновая кислота** strophanthinic acid; **—обиоза** f. strophanthobiose; **—овая кислота** strophanthic acid.

**строфоида** m. (geom.) strophoid.

**строч/ить** v. sew, stitch; write, jot down; **—ка** f. short line; **—ный** a. line; horizontal; (typ.) lower-case (letter).

**строящийся** a. under construction.

**струбц/инка** f., **—инок** m., **—ынга, —ынка** f. clamp, screw clamp, vise.

**струв/ерит** m. (min.) strüverite (tapioliterutile); **—ит** m. struvite.

**струг** m. plane; draw knife; (road) grader; **—ать** v. plane, shave.

**струе— ** *prefix* jet; **—отклоняющий регулятор** jet-deflecting governor.

**стружк/а** f. shaving, chip; (sugar beet) cossette; **—и** pl. shavings, turnings, filings, borings, cuttings, chips; **—оприемник** m. waste receiver; **—оразбиватель** m. chip breaker.

**стру/истый** *see* **струйчатый; —иться** v. stream, flow; (light) radiate, shine.

**струйк/а** f. groove, channel; small jet; (geol.) stria, costella; (hydrogeology) water thread; **—овая смазка** stream lubrication.

**струйн/ый** a. jet; current, flow; **с. аппарат** jet apparatus; **с. инжектор** jet injector; **с. конденсатор** jet condenser, spray condenser; **с. насос** jet pump; **—ая воздуходувка** jet blower; **—ая горелка** jet burner; **—ое течение** jet stream.

**струйчат/ость** f. waviness; (geol.) striations; **следы —ости** (geol.) ripple marks; **—ый** a. fluid, flowing, moving; striated; braided (pattern of a stream); **—ый прибор** radiator.

**структур/а, —ность** f. structure, constitution; texture (of rock, etc.); **—ирование** n. cross-linking; vulcanization; **—ированный** a. cross-linked, structurized; vulcanized; **—ировать** v. cross-link; polymerize further; **—ночувствительный** a. structure-sensitive; **—ный** a. structural; **—ная схема** block diagram; **—ная формула** structural formula; **—ообразование** n. structure formation, aggregation (of soil); **—ообразующее удобрение** (soil) conditioner.

**струн/а** f. string; catgut; cross brace; **—ный** a. string, stringed; **—ная проволока** string (for musical instrument), piano wire; **—обетон** m. reinforced concrete; **—цы** pl. (zool.) Nematoda.

**струп** m. (med.) scab.

**стручков/ый** a. (bot.) leguminous; **с. перец** red pepper (*Capsicum annuum*); **—ые культуры** legume crops.

**стручок** m. (bot.) legume, pod; **сладкий с., цареградский с.** carob (*Ceratonia siliqua*).

**стру/я** f. jet, spray, spurt, stream, streamline, streak, spout, flow, current (of air, etc.); ray (of light); stria, striation; **бить —ей** v. jet, spout,

flush; **действие** —и jet action; **тонкой**
—**ей** in a thin stream.
**стрях/ивание** *n.* shaking off, shaking
down; —**ивать,** —**нуть** *v.* shake off,
shake down; —**ивать пыль** dust off.
**студен/еть** *v.* jellify, gel; cool down;
—**истый** *a.* jelly-like, gelatinous;
—**истая масса** jelly; —**ость** *f.* coldness, chilliness.
**студен/т** *m.,* —**ческий** *a.* student, undergraduate; **с. второкурсник** sopho-
more; **с. первокурсник** freshman; **с.-
медик** medical student; **старый с.**
senior.
**студ/еный** *a.* gelid, frigid, cold; gelled;
—**ень** *m.* jelly, gelatin; cold, frost;
—**ить** *v.* cool, refrigerate; gel.
**студия** *f.* studio.
**студне/видный,** —**образный,** —**подобный** *a.* jelly-like, gel-like, gelatinous.
**студтит** *m.* studtite (uranium mineral).
**стук** *m.* knock, clatter, rap, clash; **с. в
моторе** motor knock; —**альце** *n.*
knocker; —**ание,** —**анье** *n.* knocking;
—**ать,** —**нуть** *v.* knock, strike; rap,
beat, thump; —**аться,** —**нуться** *v.*
knock, strike; hit oneself (against);
—**отня** *f.* knocking, rattling noise.
**стул** *m.,* —**ьный** *a.* chair; anvil block;
(med.) stool; ball, block (of soil);
—**овые тиски** bench vise; —**ьчик** *m.*
stool, bench.
**ступа** *f.* mortar, beater.
**ступать** *v.* step, tread.
**ступеевая кислота** stuppeic acid.
**ступенчато** *adv.* stepwise, in steps or
stages, gradually; —**сть** *f.* gradation.
**ступенчат/ый** *a.* step, stepped, step-by-
step, in steps or stages, gradual,
graduated, graded; step-shaped, step-
like; tapering; staggered; multistage,
multistep; cascade (battery); (biol.)
scalariform; **с. выключатель** (elec.)
step switch; **с. стык** shingle splice; **с.
шкив** step pulley, cone pulley; **с.
элеватор** escalator; —**ая выборка**
(min.) benching; —**ая жила** ladder
vein; —**ая решетка** echelon grating;
—**ое разложение** stepwise decomposition.
**ступен/ь** *f.* step, tread (of stairs), rung
(of ladder); stage, phase, grade, degree; —**ями** by degrees, gradually,

step by step; —**ька** *f.* step, footboard;
spoke, rung (of ladder); (distillation)
theoretical plate.
**ступить** *see* **ступать.**
**ступица** *f.* boss, hub, nave (of wheel).
**ступка** *see* **ступа.**
**ступня** *f.* foot.
**ступпа** *f.* stupp (in mercury distillation).
**стурин** *m.* sturine.
**стучать** *v.* knock, tap, rap; hammer.
**стушев/аться,** —**ываться** *v.* keep in the
background; efface oneself.
**стывший** *past act. part. of* **стыть.**
**стыд** *m.* shame, disgrace, scandal; —**ить**
*v.* put to shame; —**иться** *v.* feel
ashamed, lose face; —**но** *adv.* shame-
fully; it is shameful.
**стык** *m.* joint, seam, junction, splice;
butt joint; **сваривать в с.** *v.* butt-
weld.
**стыков/ой** *a.* joint, butt; **с. болт** clamp
bolt; **с. шов,** —**ое соединение** butt
weld, butt joint; —**ая накладка** fish
plate, splice piece; cover plate.
**стыл** *past sing. of* **стыть.**
**стылый ход** cold-working (of furnace).
**сты/нуть,** —**ть** *v.* cool, cool off.
**стычка** *f.* (mil.) engagement, skirmish.
**стэнд** *see* **стенд.**
**Стюарт-Кирхгофа закон** Stewart-Kirch-
hoff law.
**стюартит** *m.* (min.) stewartite.
**стютцит** *m.* (min.) stuetzite.
**стэр** *see* **стер.**
**стягив/ание** *n.* tightening, contraction,
constriction; concentration; sintering;
—**ать** *v.* tighten, draw together, contract, constrict; shackle, brace; tie,
bond; agglutinate; —**аться** *v.* tighten,
be drawn together, contract, shrink;
sinter, form clinker or slag; —**ающий**
*a.* constringent, astringent; tie, binding; —**ающее средство** astringent.
**стяж/ание** *n.* acquisition; —**атель** *m.*
accumulator; —**ать** *v.* acquire, get,
obtain.
**стяжение** *n.* concretion, nodule.
**стяжка** *f.* tightening device, tie piece, tie
rod, coupling, coupler, draw bar;
swivel; **проволочная с.** stay wire.
**стяжн/ой** *a.* coupling, tie; **с. болт** tie
bolt; clamp bolt; **с. винт** clamping
screw; **с. замок** swivel; —**ая муфта**

buckle; —ая тяга tie rod, tension rod.

**стянут/ый** *a.* tightened, drawn together, constricted; coupled; —ь *see* **стягивать.**

**су-ауру** *n.* (vet.) a form of trypanosomosis.

**суб—** *prefix* sub—, under—; —**альпийский** *a.* (bot.) subalpine; —**аренда** *f.* sublease; —**арктический** *a.* subarctic; —**атомный** *a.* subatomic; —**аэральный** *a.* subaerial; —**аэратор** *m.* subaerator; —**аэрация** *f.* (flotation) subaeration.

**суббота** *f.* Saturday.

**суб/гармоника** *f.* (acous.) subharmonic, suboctave; —**гедральный** *a.* (min.) subhedral; —**грейдер** *m.* subgrader; —**группа** *f.* subgroup.

**субер/ан** *m.* suberane, cycloheptane; —**анкарбоновая кислота** suberanecarboxylic acid; —**ат** *m.* suberate; —**ен** *m.* suberene; —**ил** *m.* suberyl; —**иловый спирт** *see* **суберол.**

**суберин** *m.* suberin (wax from cork); —**овая кислота** suberic acid, octanedioic acid; **соль** —**овой кислоты,** —**овокислая соль** suberate.

**субер/ол** *m.* suberol, cycloheptanol; —**он** *m.* suberone, cycloheptanone; —**оновая кислота** suberonic acid.

**суб-инспектор** *m.* junior inspector.

**субконтрагент** *m.* subcontractor.

**субламин** *m.* Sublamine, mercuric sulfate ethylenediamine.

**сублетальный** *a.* (med.) sublethal.

**сублим/ат** *m.* sublimate; spec. corrosive sublimate, mercuric chloride; —**ационный** *a.,* —**ация** *f.,* —**ирование** *n.* sublimation; —**ированный** *a.* sublimated; —**ировать** *v.* sublimate, sublime; —**ирующийся** *a.* sublimable.

**суб/марина** *f.* submarine; —**металлический** *a.* submetallic; —**несущий** *a.* subcarrier; —**нивальный** *a.* subniveal, under the snow; —**нормальный** *a.* subnormal; —**полярный** *a.* subpolar; —**продукты** *pl.* by-products; —**секвентный** *a.* subsequent.

**субсид/ировать** *v.* subsidize; —**ия** *f.* subsidy, subvention.

**субстантивный** *a.* substantive; **с. краситель** substantive dye, direct dye.

**субстанци/альный** *a.* substantial; —**я** *f.* substance.

**субститу/т** *m.* substitute; —**ция** *f.* substitution.

**суб/страт** *m.* substratum; substrate; basement (complex of rocks); —**стратосфера** *f.* substratosphere; —**структура** *f.* substructure; —**тангенс** *m.* (geom.) subtangent; —**тенолин** *m.* subtenolin; —**тилизин** *m.* subtilysine; —**тилин** *m.* subtilin.

**субтильн/ость** *f.* slenderness, frailty; —**ый** *a.* slight, delicate, frail.

**суб/тропики** *pl.* subtropics; —**тропический** *a.* subtropical; —**трузия** *f.* subtrusion; —**фоссильный** *a.* subfossil; —**фосфорная кислота** hypophosphoric acid.

**субъект** *m.* subject; person; —**ивность** *f.* subjectivity; —**ивный** *a.* subjective; —**ивная ошибка** personal equation.

**сувойки** *pl.* Vorticella, bell animalcules.

**суглин/истый** *a.* loamy; argillaceous, clayey; —**ок** *m.* loam.

**сугроб** *m.* snow drift, snow bank.

**сугуб/о** *adv.* especially, particularly; —**ый** *a.* especial, particular.

**суд** *m.* court, tribunal; **верховный с.** supreme court; **подавать в с.** *v.* institute proceedings (against).

**судак** *m.* (zool.) pike perch.

**судан** *m.,* —**овый** *a.* sudan (dye); —**ка** *f.,* —**ская трава** Sudan grass (*Sorghum vulgare sudanese*); —**ский** *a.* Sudan, Sudanese.

**судебномедицинский** *a.* forensic.

**судебн/ый** *a.* legal, law, judicial, forensic; **с. порядок** court procedure; —**ым порядком** in legal form; **преследовать** —**ым порядком** *v.* bring action (against); **с. следователь** examining judge; —**ая химия** forensic chemistry; —**ое постановление** regulation of the law; —**ое разбирательство** lawsuit, trial.

**судейский** *a.* judicial, judge.

**судза** *f.* (bot.) perilla.

**судилищный боб** *see* **калабарские бобы.**

**судить** *v.* judge, pass judgment on; foresee, conjecture, visualize; form an opinion; —**ся** *v.* go to court, have a lawsuit.

**судно** *n.* ship, steamer, boat, vessel, craft; **с.-кран** crane ship; **с.-матка** aircraft carrier; **грузовое с.** freighter.

**судовладелец** *m.* ship owner.

**судов/ой** *a.* ship, naval, maritime; ship's (papers); **—ые припасы** naval stores.

**судок** *m.* cruet, castor; lunch box.

**судомойн/ый** *a.* dish-washing; utensil-washing; **—ая машина** dish washer.

**судопроизводство** *n.* legal procedure.

**судоро/га** *f.* cramp, spasm, convulsion, twitch; **—жный** *a.* spasmodic, convulsive; **—жное сжатие челюстей** (med.) lockjaw, tetanus.

**судостро/ение** *n.* ship building; **—итель** *m.* ship builder.

**судоход/ный** *a.* maritime, navigable, sailable; **—ство** *n.* navigation.

**судьба** *f.* fate, destiny, fortune, luck.

**суд/ья** *m.* judge, justice; **—я по** judging by, to judge from.

**суеверие** *n.* superstition.

**суезит** *m.* (min.) souesite (a native nickel-iron alloy).

**суета** *f.* rushing around, commotion, fuss.

**сужден/ие** *n.* judgment; opinion, pronouncement; **основа —ия** criterion; **правильное с.** sound reasoning, good logic; **—о** *see* **судить.**

**суж/ение** *n.* narrowing, contraction, constriction, reduction in area; necking; (med.) stenosis; **—енный** *a.* narrowed, contracted, constricted, compressed; contact; **—ивать** *v.* narrow, narrow down, constrict, shrink; draw down, taper; throttle; **—иваться** *v.* narrow down, shrink, contract; taper; **—иваться к концу** taper off; **—ивающийся** *a.* contracting; tapering.

**сузанит** *see* **сусанит.**

**сузить** *see* **суживать.**

**сузотоксин** *m.* susotoxin.

**суйма** *f.* (geol.) solidified freshly deposited salt.

**суйфунит** *m.* (min.) suifunite, ash tuff.

**сук** *m.* branch, bough, limb; knot (in wood).

**сука** *f.* (zool.) bitch.

**сукку/дифер** *m.* succudifer (juice of *Digitalis ferruginea* leaves); **—лент-ный** *a.* (bot.) succulent.

**сукно** *n.* cloth; **положить под с.** *v.* shelve, put the matter on file.

**сукновал** *m.* fuller, wool worker; **—ьная глина** fuller's earth (a decolorizing clay); **зеленая —ьная глина** (min.) green fuller's earth, smectite; **—ьня** *f.* fullery, fulling mill.

**сукнодел** *m.* cloth worker, textile manufacturer; **—ие** *n.* cloth manufacture, textile industry.

**суковатый** *see* **сучковатый.**

**сукон/ка** *f.* piece of cloth, rag; **—ный** *a.* cloth; **—ный товар** clothing; **—щик** *m.* cloth worker, weaver; clothier.

**сукрови/ца** *f.* (med.) sanies, (inflammatory) lymph; ichor; (blood) serum; **—чный** *a.* sanious; ichorous.

**сукрол** *m.* Sucrol, dulcin; **—ит** *m.* sucrolite (synthetic resin made from sugar).

**сукцин—** *prefix* succin—, succino—; **—альдегид** *see* **янтарный альдегид; —амид** *m.* succinamide, butanediamide; **—амил** *m.* succinamyl; **—аминовая кислота** succinamic acid, amidosuccinic acid; **—ат** *m.* succinate; **—елит** *m.* succinelite (succinic acid from amber).

**сукцинил** *m.* succinyl, butanedioyl; **хлористый с.** succinyl chloride; **—оянтарная кислота, —янтарная кислота** succinylsuccinic acid.

**сукцин/имид** *m.* succinimide, butanimide; **—ит** *m.* (min.) succinite (a variety of amber or of grossularite garnet); **—ол** *m.* succinol; **—онитрил** *m.* succinonitrile, ethylene cyanide; **—орезинол** *m.* succinoresinol; **—уровая кислота** succinuric acid.

**сулванит** *m.* (min.) sulvanite (a sulfovanadate of copper).

**сулема** *f.* corrosive sublimate, mercuric chloride.

**султон** *m.* sultone.

**сульванит** *see* **сулванит.**

**сульгин** *m.* Sulfaguine, sulfaguanidine.

**сульф—** *prefix* sulf—, sulfo—, thio—; **—адиазин** *m.* sulfadiazine; **—азид** *m.* sulfazide; **—актин** *m.* sulfactin; **—альдегид** *m.* sulfaldehyde, thioaldehyde; **—амид** *m.* sulfamide; **—амин** *m.* sulfamine, sulfonamide; **—амино-бензойная кислота** sulfaminobenzoic

**сульфаминов/ая кислота** sulfamic acid, sulfamidic acid; **соль —ой кислоты,**

—окислая соль sulfamate; —оаммиачная соль ammonium sulfamate; —окислый *a.* sulfamic acid; sulfamate (of).

сульфамино/кислота *see* сульфаминовая кислота; —л *m.* sulfaminol, thiooxydiphenylamine.

сульфангидрид *m.* sulfide (of phosphorus, etc.).

сульфанил/амид *m.* sulfanilamide; —овая кислота sulfanilic acid; соль —овой кислоты, —овокислая соль sulfanilate.

сульфа/нтрол *m.* sulfanthrol; —пиридин *m.* sulfapyridine.

сульфат *m.* sulfate, spec. sodium sulfate; с. калия potassium sulfate; —ация *f.*, —ирование *n.* sulfating; —изирующий обжиг (met.) sulfating roasting; —изирующее средство sulfatizing agent; —ировать *v.* sulfate; —ный *a.* sulfate, sulfatic; —ная масса, —ная целлюлоза (paper) sulfate pulp.

сульфацил *m.* Sulfacyl, N¹-acetylsulfanilamide.

сульфгидр/ат *m.* hydrosulfide; —ил *m.* sulfhydryl, mercapto—.

сульфенамид *m.* sulfenamide.

сульфид *m.*, —ный *a.* sulfide; с. натрия sodium sulfide; —ин *m.* Sulfidine, sulfapyridine; —ность *f.* sulfidity.

сульф/икислота *f.*, —иновая кислота sulfinic acid; —имид *m.* sulfimide; —ин *m.* sulfine, sulfonium.

сульфир/ование *n.* sulfonation; sulfuration, sulfurization; —ованный *a.* sulfonated; sulfurated, sulfureted, sulfurized; —овать *v.* sulfonate; sulfurize; —ующий *a.* sulfonating; sulfurizing.

сульфит *m.* sulfite, spec. sodium sulfite; с. натрия sodium sulfite; с.-целлюлоза (paper) sulfite pulp; —ация *f.* sulfitation (of fruit, etc.); —ирование *n.* sulfitization; —новарочный процесс sulfite cooking, sulfite pulping process.

сульфит/ный, —овый *a.* sulfite; с. процесс (paper) sulfite pulp process; с. щелок sulfite liquor; —ная масса, —ная целлюлоза sulfite pulp.

сульфкарб/амид *m.* thiocarbamide, thiourea; —аминовая кислота thio-

carbamic acid; —аминовый эфир thiocarbamic ester; —анил *m.* thiocarbanil, phenyl isothiocyanate; —анилид *m.* thiocarbanilide, sulfocarbanilide; —имид *m.* thiocarbimide, isothiocyanic acid.

сульфо— *prefix* sulfo—, thio—; —аммофос *m.* ammonium sulfate-phosphate; —ароматический *a.* sulfoaromatic; —бензойная кислота sulfobenzoic acid; —бензол *m.* benzenesulfonic acid; —борит *m.* (min.) sulfoborite; —галит *m.* (min.) sulfohalite; —гидрометр *m.* sulfohydrometer; —группа *f.* sulfo group; —димезин *m.* sulfodimezine, sulfamethazine; —ихтиоловая кислота sulfoichthyolic acid.

сульфокарб/амид *see* сульфкарбамид; —онат *m.* sulfocarbonate; —оновая кислота *see* сульфоугольная кислота.

сульф/окислота *f.* sulfo acid (a sulfonic acid or a sulfacid); —оксид *m.* sulfoxide; —оксиловая кислота sulfoxylic acid.

сульфомышьяков/ая кислота sulfarsenic acid, thioarsenic acid; соль —ой кислоты, —окислая соль sulfarsenate, thioarsenate; —истая кислота sulfarsenious acid, thioarsenious acid; соль —истой кислоты, —истокислая соль sulfarsenite, thioarsenite; —истокислая соль sulfarsenite, thioarsenite; —истоаммониевая соль ammonium thioarsenite; —оаммониевая соль ammonium thioarsenate.

сульфон *m.* sulfone; —ал *m.* Sulfonal, sulfonmethane; —амид *m.* sulfonamide, sulfamine; —ат *m.* sulfonate; —ий *m.*, —иевый *a.* sulfonium, sulfine; —иевое соединение sulfonium compound, sulfine; —ил *m.* sulfonyl, sulfuryl.

сульфониров/ание *n.* sulfonation; —анный *a.* sulfonated; —ать *v.* sulfonate.

сульфонитрат *m.* nitrosulfate.

сульфонов/ая кислота sulfonic acid; амид —ой кислоты sulfonamide; соль —ой кислоты, —окислая соль sulfonate; хлорангидрид —ой кислоты sulfonyl chloride.

сульфо/нокарбоновая кислота sulfonocarboxylic acid, sulfonecarboxylic acid; —оксоль *m*. a drying oil; —основание *n*. sulfur base; —пон *m*. sulfopone (a zinc sulfide-calcium sulfate pigment); —производные *pl*. sulfo derivatives; —пурпуровая кислота indigo purple; —рафан *m*. sulforaphane, raphanin; —соединение *n*. sulfo compound; —соль *f*. sulfo salt, thio salt.

**сульфосурьмян/ая кислота** sulfantimonic acid, thioantimonic acid; **соль —ой кислоты, —окислая соль** sulfantimonate, thioantimonate; **—истая кислота** sulfantimonious acid, thioantimonious acid; **соль —истой кислоты, —истокислая соль** sulfantimonite, thioantimonite.

**сульфо/уголь** *m*. sulfonated coal; — **угольная кислота** sulfocarbonic acid, thiocarbonic acid; **—уксусная кислота** sulfoacetic acid; **—феноловая кислота** phenolsulfonic acid; **—фикация** *f*. (agr. chem.) sulfofication; **—хлорид** *m*. sulfochloride.

**сульфоциан** *m*. sulfocyanogen, thiocyanogen; **—истая кислота, —овая кислота** sulfocyanic acid, thiocyanic acid; **соль —овой кислоты, —ат** *m*. sulfocyanate, thiocyanate.

**сульф/оэтиловая кислота** ethylsulfonic acid; **—уратор** *m*. sulfonator.

**сульфурил** *m*. sulfuryl, sulfonyl; **хлористый с.** sulfuryl chloride, sulfuric chloride.

**сульфуриметр** *m*. device for determining fineness of sulfur grains.

**сульфуриров/ание** *n*. sulfonation; sulfurization; **—анный** *a*. sulfonated; sulfurized, sulfureted; **—ать** *v*. sulfonate; sulfurize, fumigate with sulfur.

**сульцимид** *m*. sulcimide, N¹-cyanosulfanilamide.

**сума** *f*. bag, pouch.

**сумак** *see* **сумах.**

**сумарезинол** *m*. sumaresinol, sumaresinolic acid.

**сумасш/едший** *a*. insane, mad; *m*. madman, lunatic; **с. дом** insane asylum; **—ествие** *n*. madness, insanity.

**суматоха** *f*. confusion, disorder, bustle.

**суматрск/ий** *a*. Sumatra; **—ая камфора** Sumatra camphor, Borneo camphor.

**сумах** *m*., **—овый** *a*. (bot.) sumac (*Rhus*); **—овые** *pl*. Anacardiaceae.

**сумбул** *m*., **корень с., —ьный корень** sumbul, musk root (dried rhizome of *Ferula sumbul*); **—ьная кислота** sumbulic acid, angelic acid.

**сумежье** *n*. (bot.) mesocarp.

**сумер/ечные** *pl*. (zool.) Crepuscularia; **—ечный** *a*. crepuscular; **—ки** *pl*. crepuscule, twilight, dusk.

**суметь** *see* **уметь**; know how.

**сумк/а** *f*. bag, sack, pack, satchel, case; (zool.) pouch; (anat.) bursa, follicle, capsule; **—ообразный** *a*. sack-like, box.

**сумм/а** *f*. sum, amount; **набрать —у** *v*. make up a sum; **общая с.** total.

**сумма/рный** *a*. summary; total, gross, overall, ultimate; **—рная сила** composite force; **—тор** *m*., **—торное устройство** summator, summation device, adder.

**суммир/ование** *n*. summation, summing up, addition; **—овать** *v*. sum up, summarize, add up; **—ующий** *a*. integrating; cumulative; summation, summing; **—ующий узел, —ующее устройство** summator, adder.

**сумоч/ка** *f*. small bag, little sac; (biol.) utricle; **—ник** *m*. (biol.) sporangium; **—ник, трава —ник** (bot.) shepherd's purse (*Capsella bursa pastoris*); **—ный** *a*. sac; capsular.

**сумра/к** *m*. dusk, twilight, darkness; **—чный** *a*. dark, dusky.

**сумчат/ый** *a*. utricular; pitcher-shaped; (zool.) marsupial; (bot.) ascomycetous; **—ая болезнь** plum pocket (disease); **—ое животное** marsupial; **—ые грибы** Ascomycetes.

**сундтит** *m*. (min.) sundtite (andorite).

**сунду/к** *m*., **—чный** *a*. trunk, chest, box; **—чок** *m*. small trunk, foot locker.

**сунуть** *see* **совать.**

**суп** *m*. soup.

**супер—** *prefix* super—; **—ам** *m*. ammoniated superphosphate fertilizer; **—генный** *a*. (geol.) supergene; **—кристальные породы** supercrust rocks; **—палит** *m*. (mil.) superpalite (poison gas); **—позиция** *f*. (elec.) superposition; **—структура** *f*. superstructure; **—фосфат** *m*. superphosphate (fertilizer); —**фузивные породы** (geol.) superfusive rocks; —**чаржер** *m.* supercharger; —**элит** *m.* superstock seeds, carefully selected seeds; —**элитный** *a.* superstock.

**супес/ок** *m.*, —**ь** *f.* sandy loam; —**чаный** *a.* sandy loam, sandy.

**суплиров/ание** *n.* soupling (of silk), boiling off; —**анный** *a.* soupled, souple; —**ать** *v.* souple.

**суповой** *a.* soup.

**супон/ь**, —**я** *f.* strap, hame.

**супоросность** *f.* (zool.) pregnancy.

**супорт** *see* **суппорт.**

**суппозитории** *pl.* (pharm.) suppositories.

**суппорт** *m.*, —**ный** *a.* support, rest, carriage.

**супра/капсулин**, —**реналин**, —**ренин** *m.* Supracapsuline, Suprarenaline, Suprarenin (epinephrine); —**стерин** *m.* suprasterol; —**фосфат** *m.* supraphosphate, basic slag.

**супротивный** *a.* (bot.) accumbent, opposite.

**сургуч** *m.*, —**ный** *a.* sealing wax.

**сурдин/а**, —**ка** *f.* sourdine, mute; silencer, muffler, damper; —**ирующий** *a.* muting.

**суреп/а**, —**ица** *f.* (bot.) rape (*Brassica napus* or *campestris*); —**ица**, —**ка** *f.* winter cress (*Barbarea vulgaris*); —**ное масло** rapeseed oil, colza oil.

**сурж/а** *f.*, —**ик** *m.* maslin, mixture (of wheat and rye grain).

**сурик** *m.*, —**овый** *a.* minium, red lead, red lead oxide; **железный с.** iron minium, iron ocher, iron oxide; **свинцовый с.** red lead, minium; —**овое покрытие** coat of red lead; **красный** —**овый** minium-colored, miniaceous.

**суринамин** *m.* surinamine, methyltyrosine.

**суров/ость** *f.* austerity, sternness; —**ый** *a.* stern, severe; coarse, hard, rough; rigorous, bleak (climate); heavy (frost); unbleached (cloth); raw (silk).

**сурпалит** *m.* surpalite, diphosgene.

**суррогат** *m.* substitute; (med.) succedaneum; —**ировать** *v.* substitute.

**сурьм/а** *f.* antimony, Sb; **окись** —**ы** antimony oxide, specif. antimony trioxide; **пятиокись** —**ы** antimony

pentoxide, antimonic oxide; **пятисернистая с.** antimony pentasulfide, antimonic sulfide; **пятихлористая с., хлорная с.** antimony pentachloride, antimonic chloride; **сернокислая с.** antimony sulfate; **трехсернистая с.** antimony trisulfide, antimonous sulfide; **треххлористая с., хлористая с.** antimony trichloride, antimonous chloride; **хлорокись** —**ы** antimony oxychloride, antimonyl chloride.

**сурьмянисто/кислый** *a.* antimonous acid; antimonite (of); **с. натрий**, —**натриевая соль** sodium antimonite; —**кислая соль** antimonite.

**сурьмянист/ый** *a.* antimonous, antimony, antimonial; antimonide, stibide (of); **с. ангидрид** antimony trioxide; **с. водород** antimonous hydride, stibine; **с. никель** (min.) nickel antimonide, breithauptite; —**ая кислота** antimonous acid; **соль** —**ой кислоты** antimonite; —**ая соль** antimony salt; —**ое серебро** (min.) antimonial silver, dyscrasite.

**сурьмяно/водород** *m.* antimonous hydride, stibine; —**й** *see* **сурьмяный;** —**калиевая соль** potassium antimonate; —**кальциевая соль** calcium antimonate; —**кислый** *a.* antimonic acid; antimonate (of); —**кислый натрий**, —**натриевая соль** sodium antimonate; —**кислая соль** antimonate; —**никелевый блеск** (min.) ullmannite; —**свинцовая соль** lead antimonate.

**сурьмян/ый** *a.* antimonic, antimony, antimonial; **с. ангидрид** antimony pentoxide; **с. блеск** (min.) antimony glance, antimonite, stibnite; **с. кермес**, —**ая киноварь** (min.) kermes mineral, kermesite, red antimony sulfide; —**ая кислота** antimonic acid; **ангидрид** —**ой кислоты** antimony pentoxide; **соль** —**ой кислоты** antimonate; —**ая обманка** (min.) antimony blende, kermesite; —**ая охра** (min.) antimony ocher, stibiconite (or cervantite); —**ая соль** antimony salt; —**ая чернь** antimony black, antimonous sulfide; —**ое масло** butter of antimony, antimony trichloride; —**ое стекло** antimony glass, antimonous oxide; —ые белила antimony white (antimony trioxide); —ые цветы (min.) antimony bloom, valentinite.

**сусак** *m.*, **зонтичный с.** (bot.) flowering rush (*Butomus umbellatus*); —овые *pl.* Butomaceae.

**сусаль** *f.* tinsel; —ная нить tinsel wire; —ное золото tinsel; *see also* мусивное золото.

**сусанит** *m.* (min.) susannite (probably a modification of leadhillite).

**Сусквеганна** Susquehanna (river).

**суслик** *m.* suslik, ground squirrel, gopher.

**сусло** *n.* (grape) must; (brewing) wort; wash; —мер *m.* must-measuring device.

**суслон** *m.* sheaves, shock.

**сусляный** *a. of* сусло.

**суспен/дированный** *a.* suspended; —зия *f.* suspension; —зии *pl.* suspended matter; —зоид *m.* suspensoid, suspension, soliquoid; —зорий *m.* (med.) suspensory; (zool.) suspensorium.

**суссексит** *m.* (min.) sussexite; (petr.) sussexite (an alkalic basalt-porphyry).

**сустав** *m.* joint, articulation; hinge; **неподвижность** —ов (med.) ankylosis; —ной *a.* joint, articulation; —ной ремень link belt; —ная мязь (pharm.) antarthritic salve; —очный, —чатый *a.* jointed, articulated, hinged; telescopic, telescope; —очная муфта link box; —чатая труба flexible pipe.

**сутки** *pl.* day, 24 hours.

**суточн/ый** *a.* daily, diurnal; **с. ход** daily variation; —ая дача ration.

**сутулина** *f.* curve, bend.

**сутун/ка** *f.*, —очный *a.* (met.) billet, sheet billet, sheet bar; —очный стан billeting roll, sheet bar mill, strip mill.

**сутур/а** *f.* suture; —ная структура (geol.) sutural texture.

**суть** *f.* substance, gist, essence, essentials, kernel, pith (of the matter); **с. дела** point; *pr. 3 pl. of* быть.

**суфляр** *m.* (min.) piper, gas feeder; (geol.) fumarole; —ный газ blower gas.

**суффикс** *m.* (grammar) suffix.

**суффле** *n.* (text.) gusset.

**суффозия** *f.* (geol.) suffosion, undermining.

**сухар/ь** *m.*, —ный *a.* biscuit, rusk, dry bread; refractory kaolin clay; **с. подпятника** thrust bearing.

**сухо** *adv.* dryly, dry; it is dry; —адиабатический *a.* (meteor.) dry adiabatic; —ватый *a.* dryish, rather dry; —вей *m.* dry wind; —дол *m.* dry valley.

**сухожил/ие** *n.* (anat.) sinew, tendon; —ьный *a.* sinewy, tendinous.

**сух/ой** *a.* dry, arid, barren; **с. элемент** (elec.) dry cell; —ая перегонка dry distillation, destructive distillation; —им путем in the dry way; by land, over land; **анализ** —им путем dry method, analysis by heat; **всасывание в** —ую dry suction.

**сухоложский** *a.* Sukhoi Log.

**сухомятка** *f.* dry food.

**сухопарн/ик** *m.* steam dome, dome (of boiler); steam dryer; boiler room; —ый колпак steam dome.

**сухо/парый** *a.* lean, thin, spare; —перегонный *a.* dry-distilled; —путный *a.* overland, by dry land; terrestrial, land; —стой *m.* deadwood; dry period (of cow); —стойный *a.* dry; —сть *f.* dryness; aridity, barrenness; —тка *f.* (med.) marasmus, progressive emaciation; tabes; —фрукты *pl.* dried fruits; —цвет *m.* (bot.) everlasting (*Xeranthemum*); —щавый *a.* lean, emaciated; —ядение *n.* xerophagia, eating dry food.

**суч/ение** *n.* spinning, twisting; —ильный *a.* spinning, twisting, twist; —ильщик *m.* spinner; —ить *v.* spin, twist; throw (silk).

**сучко/ватый** *a.* knotty, nodose, gnarled, snagged, rough, scarred, grained; —рез *m.* (agr.) extension pruner.

**суч/ок** *m.*, **мертвый с.**, **роговой с.** knot ((in wood); —ья *pl.* brushwood.

**суш/а** *f.* dry land; **по** —е by land; —е *comp. of* сухо, сухой, drier; —ение *n.* drying, desiccation; —еница *f.* (bot.) everlastings (*Gnaphalium*); —еный *a.* dried, desiccated, dehydrated (food).

**сушил/ка** *f.*, —о *n.* dryer, desiccator, drying kiln, drying chamber, drying plant; **с.-вакуум** vacuum dryer.

**сушильн/ый** *a.* drying; **с. аппарат**, **с. прибор** drying apparatus, dryer, desiccator; **с. барабан** rotary dryer; **с. под** dryer, drying floor; **с. станок, —ая полка, —ая тележка, —ые стеллюги** drying rack; **с. шкаф** desiccator, dryer, drying chamber; **—ая камера** drying room; **—ая печь** drying oven, drying kiln, dryer, desiccator; **—ая установка** drying plant; **—ое масло** drying oil; **—ое средство** drying agent, drier, desiccant, siccative.

**суш/ильня** *see* **сушилка**; **—ильщик** *m.* dryer; **—ить** *v.* dry, desiccate; **—иться** *v.* dry, get dried, desiccate; bake; **—ка** *f.* drying, desiccation; weathering, seasoning, curing; **искусственная —ка** kiln drying; **—ки** *pl.* siccatives, driers; **—няк** *m.* adobe, brick clay; sun-dried clay brick; deadwood; **—ь** *f.* dryness, dry weather; dry matter.

**существенн/о** *adv.* essentially, substantially; **—ое** *n.* an essential; **—ость** *f.* importance, significance; **—ый** *a.* important, significant; material, considerable; essential, intrinsic.

**существ/о** *n.* being, creature; nature; essence, point; **по —у** essentially, in essence; in fact; **—ование** *n.* existence, being, subsistence; occurrence; **условия —ования** (biol.) habitat; **—овать** *v.* be, exist, live, subsist; be extant; **—ующий** *a.* existing, existent, subsistent; **все —ующее** all that exists.

**сущий** *a.* existing, which is; real, true.

**сущност/ь** *f.* substance, nature; essentiality, essence, point; **в —и** virtually; **в —и говоря** practically speaking.

**СУЭ** *abbr.* (сероуглеродная эмульсия) carbon disulfide emulsion.

**Суэцкий канал** Suez Canal.

**суягность** *f.* (zool.) pregnancy.

**сфабриковать** *v.* make, devise, concoct.

**сфагн/овые мхи** (bot.) Sphagnaceae; **—ум** *m.* peat moss, bog moss (*Sphagnum*).

**сфазирован/ие** *n.* phasing in; **—ный** *a.* phased.

**сфалерит** *m.* (min.) sphalerite, zinc blende.

**сфексы** *pl.* sphecid wasps (*Sphecoidea*).

**сфен** *m.* (min.) sphene, titanite; **—оид**

*m.* (cryst.) sphenoid; **—оидальный** *a.* sphenoidal, sphenoid.

**сфера** *f.* sphere, realm, range, scope, domain, province; **с. действия** zone of action, field of operation.

**сферит** *m.* (min.) spherite (a hydrous aluminum phosphate).

**сферич/еский** *a.* spherical, spheral, globular, ball-shaped, orbicular; **—ность** *f.* sphericity.

**сфероид** *m.* spheroid; **—альный** *a.* spheroidal, sphere-shaped; (met.) nodular; **—изация** *f.,* **—изирование** *n.* (met.) spheroidizing, spheroidization.

**сферо/кобальтит** *m.* (min.) spherocobaltite (a cobalt carbonate); **—кристалл** *m.* spherocrystal, spherical crystal.

**сферолит** *m.* (cryst.) spherulite, spheroidal aggregate; **—овый** *a.* spherulitic; **—овая порода** spherulitic ore.

**сферометр** *m.* spherometer; **—ический** *a.* spherometric; **—ия** *f.* spherometry.

**сферо/сидерит** *m.* (min.) spherosiderite (a variety of siderite); **—стильбит** *m.* spherostilbite; **—тека** *f.* (bot.) a powdery mildew (*Sphaerotheca morsuvae*); **—физин** *m.* spherophysine; **—форин** *m.* spherophorin.

**сферулит** *see* **сферолит**.

**сфигмо/граф** *m.* (med.) sphygmograph, pulse-recording device; **—манометр** *m.* sphygmomanometer.

**сфинго/зин** *m.* sphingosine; **—ин** *m.* sphingoin; **—миелин** *m.* sphingomyelin (phospholipin from brain).

**сфинкс** *m.* sphinx (moth).

**сфинктер** *m.* (anat.) sphincter.

**сфокусированный** *a.* focused.

**сформиров/анный** *a.* formed, molded, shaped; **—ать** *v.* form, mold, shape.

**сфрагид** *m.* (min.) sphragide, cimolite.

**СФР-грамма** *f.* moving image camera picture, streak camera picture.

**сфрезеров/анный** *a.* milled; **—ывать** *v.* mill.

**СФТИ** *abbr.* (Сибирский физико-технический институт) Siberian Physics and Technology Institute.

**с. х.** *abbr.* (сельское хозяйство) agriculture; **с-х** *abbr.* (сельскохозяйственный) agricultural; **с.-х. арт.** *see* **колхоз**.

**схват** *m.* gripping device, grab, grab

tongs, tongs; —ы *pl.* tongs; vise; ящик —a grab, grab bucket.

схват/ившийся *a.* set (cement); —ить *see* схватывать; —ка *f.* grasping; interlock; —ки, —ы *pl.* tongs; pangs (of pain); шов —ками tack weld.

схватыв/ание *n.* grasping, clutching; catching (disease); setting, hardening (of cement); —ать *v.* grasp, clutch, seize, lay hold (of); catch; set, harden; —ающий *a.* grasping, clutching; —ающийся *a.* (cement) setting, binding.

с. х-во *see* с. х.

схем/а *f.* scheme, plan, project; flow sheet, chart, schematic drawing, diagram; system, arrangement, layout; connection, circuit, network; device; (flow) pattern; с. движения материала, с. технологического потока, с. технологического процесса flow sheet; с. обогащения (concentration) flow sheet; с. соединений (elec.) connection, hook-up; составлять —у *v.* connect, hook up.

схематизировать *v.* schematize, plan; give a rough picture (of).

схематич/ески *adv.* schematically; —еский *a.* schematic, diagrammatic, outline; —ность *f.* schematism.

с.-х. и. *abbr.* (сельскохозяйственный институт) agricultural institute.

схизо— *see* шизо—.

схистоцерка *f.* schistocerca (a locust).

схлестывать *v.* whip, lash.

схлопывание *n.* (plasma) collapse.

схлынуть *v.* abate, flow away, recede.

сход *m.* descent, descending; gathering; tails, tailings; (measurement) drift.

сходимость *f.* (math.) convergence.

сходить *v.* go down, descend, come down, get off; с. за pass for; go for, fetch; с. на-нет dwindle to nothing, taper down to nothing; —ся *v.* meet, join, come together, converge; agree, coincide.

сходка *f.* meeting, assembly.

сходни *pl.* gangplank, gangway, ramp, stairs.

сходн/ый *a.* analogous, similar, like, allied, consistent; suitable; quasi—; —я *see* сходни.

сходств/енный *a.* similar, like, compati-

ble; —о *n.* similarity, likeness, resemblance, analogy, comparison; coincidence, congruity, compatibility.

сходя: не с. с места without moving, on the spot; —щийся *a.* convergent.

схождение *n.* meeting, convergence.

схожий *a.* like, alike, similar, relative.

схоластический *a.* scholastic.

СХОС *abbr.* (сельскохозяйственная опытная станция) agricultural experiment station.

сце/дить, —живать *v.* decant, draw off, tap; filter off; —жа *f.* blowpit, drainage pit; —женный *a.* decanted, drawn off; filtered off; —живание *n.* decantation; filtering.

сцен/а *f.* stage, scene; —ический *a.* stage, theatrical, scenic.

сцеп *m.* hook, link, chain, bond; —ить *see* сцеплять; —ка *f.* coupling, connecting, hitching; coupler, clutch.

сцеплен/ие *n.* coupling, linking, linkage, interlinking; cohesion, coherence, adhesion, adherence, tenacity; chain, series; meshing, engagement; clutch, grip; (elec.) connecting, contact; выключение —ия clutch release; сила —ия cohesive force, cohesion (of molecules); тяга —ия clutch rod; —ный *a.* coupled, linked, interlinked; coherent; meshed, engaged, in gear.

сцеплянки *pl.* (bot.) Conjugatae.

сцеплять *v.* couple, link, interlink, hook . together, hook up, lock; clutch, mesh, engage, put in gear, throw into gear, throw in (clutch); —ся *v.* interlock; cohere, adhere; mesh, engage.

сцепляющий *a.* coupling; engaging; с. болт catch bolt, catch; с. штифт catch; —ся *a.* cohesive.

сцепн/ой *a.* coupling; с. крюк, с. прибор, —ая тяга draw bar; с. шатун, —ое дышло coupling rod; —ая муфта clutch.

сцепщик *m.* coupler.

Сциларда-Чалмерса метод (nucl.) Szilard-Chalmers method.

сцилл/а *f.* (bot.) scilla; —аин *m.* scillain; —арабиоза *f.* scillarabiose; —арен *m.* scillaren; —ареназа *f.* scillarenase; —аридин *m.* scillaridin; —ин *m.* scillin; —ипикрин *m.* scillipicrin; —ит, —итол *m.* scyllitol; —итин *m.*

scillitin; —итиновый уксус squill vinegar (from *Scilla maritima*); —итоксин *m.* scillitoxin.

**сцимнол** *m.* scymnol.

**сцинтилл/ирование** *n.*, —яционный *a.*, —яция *f.* (nucl.) scintillation; —ирующий *a.* scintillating; —ирующее вещество, —ятор *m.* scintillator; (scintillating) phosphor; —ограф *m.* scintillograph, automatic scintillation scanner; —яционный индикатор, —яционный счетчик scintillation counter.

**сцио—** *prefix* scio— (shade, shadow); —фильный *a.* (bot.) sciophilous.

**сцитаминовые** *pl.* (bot.) Scitamineae.

**сцифоидные** *pl.* (zool.) Scyphozoa.

**СЦМ** *abbr.* (система центра масс) center-of-mass system.

**счастливый** *a.* fortunate, lucky, happy; с. крюк (oil-well drilling) grab.

**счаст/ье** *n.* happiness, fortune, chance, luck; к —ью fortunately, luckily.

**счерп/ать, —нуть, —ывать** *v.* scoop off, ladle out, skim.

**счер/тить, —чивать** *v.* copy, trace, draw.

**счесать** *see* **счесывать.**

**счесть** *see* **считать.**

**счесывать** *v.* (text.) card off (yarn).

**счет** *m.* account; bill, statement; expense; numeration; counting; score; calculation; баланс —ов balance sheet; быть на хорошем —у *v.* stand well (with); за с. at the expense (of); by means of, through; due to, because of; круглым —ом in round figures; на этот с. on that score, on that account; скорость —а counting rate; измеритель скорости —а (counting) rate meter.

**счетно-решающ/ий** *a.* computing; с. прибор, —ее устройство computer.

**счетн/ый** *a.* account; calculating; counting; countable; с. диск counter dial; с. механизм register, cash register; —ая книга account book; —ая линейка slide rule; —ая машина calculating machine, computing machine; adding machine; —ая таблица register; scale; —ая трубка counter tube; —ое устройство counter.

**счетовод** *m.* accountant; —ство *n.* accounting, bookkeeping.

**счетчик** *m.* meter, measuring device; register, indicator, recorder; integrating device; calculator, computer; (radiation) counter, counter tube; с.-зонд *m.* counter probe; с. делений fission counter; с. импульсов pulse counter; (impulse) scaler; rate meter; электрический с. electric meter.

**счеты** *pl.* abacus, counting board.

**счисл/ение** *n.* numeration, numbering; calculation; система —ения scale of notation; —енный *a.* numerated; —итель *m.* computer; —ять *v.* numerate, enumerate.

**счистить** *see* **счищать.**

**счит/ать** *v.* count, compute, reckon, rate; regard, think, consider, assume; с. за consider as, take for; —аться *v.* take into consideration, take into account; be considered, be held to be; не —аться disregard, ignore; —алось, что it was considered that; —ая на on the basis of; не —ая apart (from), exclusive (of); не —аясь regardless (of), in spite (of).

**считыв/ание** *n.* reading; plotting; computation; —ать *v.* take readings; compute; —ающее устройство reader, reading device.

**счищать** *v.* clean, clear, take off, remove.

**с.ш.** *abbr.* (северная широта) north latitude.

**США** *abbr.* (Соединенные Штаты Америки) United States of America.

**сши/вание** *n.* sewing together, stitching; joining; (polymers) cross-linking; lacing (of belt); —вать, —ть *v.* sew together; join; cross-link; lace; (med.) suture; —вка *f.* sewing together; seam, joint; suture; —тый *a.* sewed, sewn, stitched; cross-linked; vulcanized; laced (belt).

**сшихтованный** *a.* (met.) fluxed.

**съед/ать** *v.* eat up; eat away, corrode; —обность *f.* edibility; —обный *a.* edible.

**съеживаться** *v.* shrivel, shrink.

**съезд** *m.* convention, conference, congress, meeting, assembly; —ить *v.* go.

**съезжать** *v.* slide off, come off; —ся *v.* convene, meet, assemble.

съем *m.* contract, lease; removal, skimming; extraction, withdrawal; take-off; output; (agr.) picking.

съемк/а *f.* survey, surveying; plan; planning, mapping; plotting; (phot.) exposure; делать —у *v.* photograph, film; производить —у *v.* survey.

съемн/ик *m.* stripper, stripping device; remover, puller, extractor; (agr.) picker; —ый *a.* detachable, removable, withdrawable, dismountable, loose, renewable, interchangeable, replaceable.

съемочный *a.* surveying; camera.

съемщик *m.* lessee, tenant; surveyor.

съест/ной *see* съедобный; —ь *see* съедать.

съехать *see* съезжать.

сыворотка *f.* whey; (med., zool.) serum.

сывороточн/ый *a.* whey; (med., zool.) serum, serous; —ая жидкость serum; —ая закваска (cheese) rennet; —ая оболочка serous membrane, serosa.

сыгр/ать, —ывать *v.* play, perform.

сызнова *adv.* anew, afresh.

сын *m.* son.

сып/ание *n.* strewing, scattering; —ать *v.* strew, scatter; pour (grain, etc.); —ец *m.* pulverized material.

сыпной *a.* (med.) exanthematic.

сыпун *m.* fine dry sand.

сыпучесть *f.* friability.

сыпуч/ий *a.* friable, loose, free-flowing, running; (geol.) quick; с. материал, —ее тело loose material, bulk material; free-flowing material; мера —их тел dry measure; с. песок quicksand; —ка *f.* sypuchka (loose, fine-grained sand containing barite, quartz, or pyrite).

сыпь *f.* (med.) rash, eruption.

сыр *m.* cheese.

сыреть *v.* grow damp, grow moist.

сырец *m.* raw material; raw silk; adobe, brick clay; sun-dried clay brick; с.-хлопок cotton wool; пенька-с. raw hemp.

сырный *a.* cheese, cheesy, caseous.

сыровар *m.* cheese maker; —ение *n.* cheese making; —ня *f.* cheese dairy.

сыроват/ость *f.* slight dampness; —ый *a.* dampish, moist.

сыродел/ие *n.*, —ьный *a.* cheese-making.

сыродутн/ый горн, —ая шахтная печь (met.) bloomery; с. процесс blooming.

сыроежка *f.* (bot.) agaric (*Russula*).

сыр/ой *a.* damp, moist, humid, wet; raw, crude, coarse, untreated; green (wood); (foundry) green (sand, etc.); с. материал, —ые продукты raw material; формовка по с. (foundry) green sand molding.

сырок *m.* cheese curds.

сыромолот *m.* damp threshing.

сыромятн/ик *m.* raw hide dresser, tawer, tanner; —ый *a.* tawed; —ый завод, —я *f.* tawery, (alum) tannery; —ая кожа raw hide; —ое дубление tawing.

сыромять *f.* tawed leather, raw hide.

сыроподобный *a.* cheesy, caseous.

сыросека *f.* brushwood burning.

сыростестойкий *a.* dampproof, moistureproof, moisture-resistant.

сырость *f.* dampness, damp, moisture, wetness, humidity.

сырт *m.* (geol.) divide; syrt, quicksand, bog.

сырцовый *a.* raw, crude; natural (steel).

сырье *n.*, —вой *a.* raw material, stock; —вая база source of raw materials.

сыссерскит *m.* (min.) sisserskite (a variety of iridosmine).

сыт/ность *f.* substantiality (of food); —ный *a.* satisfying, filling; —ость *f.* satiation, repletion; —ый *a.* satisfied, replete; до —а to repletion.

сыть *f.* (bot.) cyperus; съедобная с. chufa (*Cyperus esculentus*).

сычу/г *m.* (zool.) abomasum; —жина *f.*, —жок *m.*, —жная закваска rennet; —жный фермент rennin (milk-coagulating enzyme).

сэбин *m.* sabin (unit of sound absorption).

сэдбюрийск/ий *a.* (geol.) Sudburian; —ая руда (min.) Sudbury ore (nickeliferous pyrrhotite).

сэлопский ярус (geol.) Salopian stage.

СЭТИ *abbr.* (Комитет содействия экспорту, транзиту и импорту) Committee to Facilitate Exports and Imports.

сюда *adv.* here, hither.

**сюжет** *m.* subject, topic.
**сюрприз** *m.* surprise.
**сюрфасография** *f.* streamlining.

**сядут** *fut. 3 pl. of* **сесть.**
**сяжки** *pl.* (zool.) antennae.
**Сясьстрой** Siasstroy.

# Т

**т** *abbr.* (температура) temperature; (тонна) ton; **т.** *abbr.* (товарищ) comrade; (том) volume; (точка) point; **Т** code for titanium in steel mark.
**та** *see* **тот.**
**таба/к** *m.,* **—чный** *a.* (bot.) tobacco (*Nicotiana tabacum*); **—ководство** *n.* tobacco growing; **—корезен** *m.* tobaccoresene; **—цин** *m.* tabacin; **—чная камфора** nicotianin.
**табашир** *m.* tabashir (a secretion of bamboo).
**таббиит** *m.* (min.) tabbyite, wurtzilite.
**табель** *f.* table, list, catalog, schedule; **—щик** *m.* timekeeper.
**табес** *m.* (med.) tabes (dorsalis).
**табл.** *abbr.* (таблица) table.
**таблет/изация** *f.* pastillation; **—ирование** *n.* tableting; (plastics) preforming; **—ировать** *v.* tablet; **—ка** *f.* tablet; pellet; cake, slab; preform; **—очный** *a.* tablet; preforming.
**таблитчатый** *a.* tabular, flat, discoid.
**табли/ца** *f.* table, list, chart, scale, schedule; **т. логарифмов** (math.) logarithmic table; **вносить в —цу** *v.* tabulate; **подвижная счетная т.** sliding scale; **составление —ц** tabulation; **—чный** *a.* table, tabular.
**табло** *n.* signal panel, mimic panel; chart.
**т. абс.** *abbr.* (температура абсолютная) absolute temperature.
**табул/ирование** *n.* tabulation; **—ированный** *a.* tabulated; **—ировать** *v.* tabulate; **—ятор** *m.* tabulator, tabulating machine.
**табун** *m.* tabun (lethal gas).
**табурет** *m.,* **—ка** *f.* stool.
**тавистокит** *m.* (min.) tavistockite.
**таволга** *f.* (bot.) spirea (*Spiraea*); filipendula.
**тавот** *m.,* **—ный** *a.* (lubricating) grease; **—ница** *f.* grease cup; lubricating cock; grease gun; **—ный пресс,** **—ный шприц,** **—онагнетатель** *m.* grease gun.

**Тавр** Taurus Mountains.
**тавр/ение** *n.* branding; **—еный** *a.* branded; **—ить, накладывать —о** *v.* brand; stamp; **—о** *n.* mark, brand, stamp.
**тавро—** *prefix* Т-, tee-; **—бимсовое железо, —бульб** *m.,* **—бульбовое железо** T-bulb iron, bulb bar.
**тавров/ый** *a.* Т-, tee; **т. угольник** T-square; **—ая балка** T-beam.
**тавто—** *see* **тауто—.**
**таган** *m.* andiron, trivet, stand.
**тагат/оза** *f.* tagatose; **—он** *m.* tagatone (ketone from *Tagates glandulifera*).
**таги/лит** *m.* (min.) tagilite; **—ровит** *m.* tagirovite (a titanium mineral).
**Таджикская АССР** the Tadjik Autonomous Socialist Soviet Republic.
**таежный** *a. of* **тайга.**
**ТАЕМ** *abbr.* (одна тысячная атомной единицы массы) millimass unit.
**тает** *pr. 3 sing. of* **таять.**
**таз** *m.* basin, pan; (mech.) bush; (anat.) pelvis; **промывать в —у** *v.* pan out (gold); **—ик** *m.* small basin, tray; (zool.) coxa.
**тазиметр** *m.* (elec.) tasimeter.
**тазо/вый** *a.* basin, pan; (anat.) pelvic; **т. пояс** pelvic girdle; **т. прибор** (text.) coiler; **—мер** *m.* (med.) pelvimeter.
**таинолит** *m.* (min.) tainolite, taeniolite.
**таинственный** *a.* secret, mysterious.
**Таити** Tahiti.
**таить** *v.* conceal, hide, shelter, secret.
**тайга** *f.* taiga (vast Siberian coniferous forest).
**тайком** *adv.* secretly, in secret.
**Тайлор** *see under* **Тэйлор.**
**тайм/ер** *m.* timer, timing unit; **—шит** *m.* time sheet.
**тайн/а** *f.* secret, secrecy, privacy; **—о** *adv.* secretly, in secret, confidentially.
**тайно—** *prefix* crypto- (hidden); **—брачие** *n.* (bot.) cryptogamy; **—брачные, —цветные** *pl.* Cryptogamia; **—брачный** *a.* cryptogamous, cryptogamic.
**тайный** *a.* secret, mysterious.

**тайфун** *m.* typhoon.

**так** *adv.* so, thus, like this; **т. же** so, as, in the same way; **т. же . . . как** as . . . as; **т. и есть** so it is; **т. или иначе** somehow or other, by some means or other; **т. как** as, because, for, since, inasmuch as, seeing that, being that; **т. например** for instance, thus; **т. сказать** so to speak; **т. точно** exactly, just so; **т. что** so that; **т. чтобы** so as to, so that; **и т. д.** and so forth.

**такамагак** *m.* tacamahac (resin).

**такелаж** *m.*, **—ный** *a.* cordage, rigging, tackle; **—ить** *v.* rig out.

**также** *adv.* also, too, likewise; **т. не** neither; **а т.** and at the same time.

**так наз.** *abbr.* (**так называемый**) so-called; **так. обр.** *abbr.* (**таким образом**) in such a manner, thus.

**таков** *a.* such, like; **все они —ы** all of them are alike, they are all like that; **—ой** *a.* such; **как —ой** as such.

**так/ой** *a.* such; **т. же** such a one, similar; **все т. же** always the same, still the same; **не т. как** unlike; **что —ое** what is it? what is the matter?

**такони/йский** *a.* (geol.) Taconian; **—т** *m.* (petr.) taconite (a ferruginous chert).

**такса** *f.* fixed price; tariff, fee, rate; **—тор** *m.* assessor, appraiser; **—ция** *f.* fixing of prices; assessment, evaluation; taxation.

**такси/катин** *m.* taxicatin; **—н** *m.* taxine; **—новая кислота** taxic acid; **—нол** *m.* taxinol.

**таксиров/ание** *n.*, **—ка** *f.* price fixing, price freezing; **—ать** *v.* fix prices; estimate, evaluate, tax; (aero.) taxi, cruise.

**таксис** *m.* (biol.) taxis, tropism.

**таксит** *m.* (petr.) taxite (probably clastic lava); **—овый** *a.* taxitic.

**—таксия** *f.* *suffix* **—taxy.**

**таксод/иевые** *pl.* (bot.) Taxodiaceae; **—ий** *m.* taxodium.

**таксо/метр** *m.* taxi meter; **—мотор** *m.* taxi.

**таксоном/ический** *a.* taxonomic; **—ия** *f.* taxonomy, classification.

**таксофон** *m.* pay telephone.

**такт** *m.* cycle (of engine); stroke; rate, tempo (of work); (music) time, measure; tact.

**тактика** *f.* tactics.

**тактильный** *a.* tactile, tangible.

**тактиты** *pl.* (petr.) tactites (silicate contact rocks from limestone).

**тактич/еский** *a.* tactic; **—ный** *a.* tactful.

**тактометр** *m.* (physiol.) tactometer.

**такыр** *m.*, **—ный** *a.* takyr (clay-surfaced desert); takyr soil, desert soil; **—изация** *f.* takyrization; **—овидный** *a.* takyr-like.

**тал** *m.* (bot.) willow (*Salix*).

**талант** *m.* talent, gift, ability; **—ливый** *a.* talented.

**таласс/емия** *f.* (med.) thalassemia, Cooley's anemia; **—о—** *prefix* thalasso— (sea).

**талатизамин** *m.* talatisamine.

**талевый** *a.* tackle, compound pulley.

**таленит** *m.* (min.) thalenite (an yttrium silicate).

**тали** *pl.* of **таль.**

**талиев/ый** *a.* thallium, thallic; **—ая соль** thallic salt.

**тал/ий** *m.* thallium, Tl; **закись —ия** thallous oxide; **соединение закиси —ия** thallous compound; **соль закиси —ия** thallous salt; **окись —ия** thallic oxide; **соединение окиси —ия** thallic compound; **соль окиси —ия** thallic salt; **сернокислая закись —ия** thallous sulfate; **сернокислая окись —ия** thallic sulfate; **сернокислый т.** thallium sulfate; **хлористый т.** thallous chloride; **хлорный т.** thallic chloride.

**таликтрин** *m.* thalictrine.

**талист/ый** *a.* thallium, thallous; **—ая соль** thallous salt.

**талит** *m.* talitol (hexahydric alcohol).

**талия** *f.* waist, middle.

**таллейохин** *m.* thalleioquin; **—олин** *m.* thalleioquinoline.

**таллен** *m.* thallene.

**талл/иевый** *see* **талиевый; —ий** *see* **талий.**

**таллин** *m.* thalline, tetrahydro-*p*-quinanisol; **сернокислый т.** thalline sulfate.

**таллингит** *m.* (min.) tallingite (a hydrated copper chloride).

**таллирование** *n.* thallation.

**таллит** *m.* (min.) thallite (a variety of epidote).

**талло—** *prefix* thallo— (young shoot).

**таллол** *m.* tallol, tall oil, liquid rosin; —**еиновая кислота** talloleic acid.

**талло/м** *m.* (bot.) thallome, thallus; —**фит** *m.* (bot.) thallophyte; —**хлор** *m.* thallochlore, lichen chlorophyll.

**таловый** *a.* willow.

**талоза** *f.* talose.

**талон** *m.* check; coupon; stub (of check).

**талоновая кислота** talonic acid.

**талослизевая кислота** talomucic acid.

**талофидный элемент** thalofide (photo-electric) cell.

**талый** *a.* melted, thawed.

**тал/ь** *f.*, —**и** *pl.* tackle, block and tackle, compound pulley; jack, hoist; **т.-лопарь** tackle-fall; **цепная т.** chain pulley block.

**Тальбота способ** Talbot (anticorrosion) process.

**тальвег** *m.* (geol.) thalweg.

**тальк** *m.* (min.) talc, talcum (a hydrous magnesium silicate); steatite, soap-stone; **волокнистый т.** fibrous talc, agalite.

**талька** *f.* (text.) skein; reel.

**тальк/апатит** *m.* (min.) talcapatite; —**ит** *m.* (min.) talcite (a variety of talc or of muscovite).

**тальков/ый** *a.* talc, talcose, talcous; talcum (powder); **т. сланец** (petr.) talc schist; —**ая земля** (min.) magnesite; magnesia.

**талькоподобный** *a.* talc-like, talcoid.

**тальми** *n.* talmi, talmi gold (gold-plated brass for jewelry).

**тальник** *m.* (bot.) willow (*Salix*).

**тальреп** *m.* turnbuckle, screw shackle, adjusting screw.

**там** *adv.* there.

**таманит** *m.* (min.) tamanite, anapaïte.

**тамар/икс, —иск** *m.* (bot.) tamarisk (*Tamarix*); —**инд** *m.* tamarind (*Tamarindus indica*); —**исковые** *pl.* Tamaricaceae.

**тамбур** *m.*, —**ный** *a.* tambour; vestibule; reel.

**тамноловая кислота** thamnolic acid.

**тамож/енный, —ный** *a.* customhouse, customs, revenue; **т. сбор, —енная пошлина** customs, custom duties; —**енное управление** customs; —**ня** *f.* customhouse.

**тампи/ко** *n.* tampico (a dyewood); —**ко-ловая кислота** tampicolic acid; —**цин** *m.* tampicin (resin).

**тампон** *m.* plug, pad, wad, lump; (med.) tampon; —**аж** *m.* tamponage; (min.) plugging, stopping up; —**ация** *f.*, —**ирование** *n.* inserting a tampon; packing; —**ировать** *v.* tampon, plug up; pack.

**танатол** *m.* thanatol, guaethol.

**танацет/ен** *m.* tanacetene; —**ил** *m.* tanacetyl; —**иловый спирт** tanacetyl alcohol; —**ин** *m.* tanacetin; —**он** *m.* tanacetone.

**танген/с** *m.* (geom.) tangent; **т.-буссоль** *f.* tangent compass; **относящийся к** —**су** tangential; —**соида** *f.* tangent curve; —**циальный** *a.* tangent, tangential; centrifugal (force).

**тангинин** *m.* tanghinine.

**тандем** *m.*, —**ный** *a.* tandem.

**танетские слои** (geol.) Thanet sands.

**танец** *m.* dance.

**Танжер** Tangiers.

**танжерин** *m.* tangerine (fruit).

**танин** *see* **таннин.**

**танк** *m.* (mil.) tank; **т.-амфибия** amphibian tank; —**аж** *m.* tank capacity; tankage (slaughterhouse waste); —**ер** *m.* tanker; oil tanker; —**ист** *m.* (mil.) member of tank crew.

**танко/вождение** *n.* (mil.) tank driving; —**вый** *a.* tank; —**недоступная местность** tankproof terrain.

**танн/аза** *f.* tannase; —**альбин** *m.* Tannalbin, albumin tannate; —**ат** *m.* tannate; —**иген** *m.* tannigen, acetan-nin; —**ил** *m.* tannyl; —**ин** *m.* tannin, tannic acid, digallic acid; —**ино-подобный** *a.* tannic.

**танно/зал, —креозот** *m.* tannosal, tan-nocreosote, creosote tannate; —**пин** *m.* Tannopin, urotropine tannin; —**форм** *m.* Tannoform, tannin-form-aldehyde.

**тантайрон** *m.* Tantiron (acid-resistant iron alloy).

**тантал** *m.* tantalum, Ta; **окись —а** tantalum oxide, specif. tantalum pentoxide, tantalic oxide; **пятихлористый т., хлорный т.** tantalum pentachloride, tantalic chloride; **трех-хлористый т., хлористый т.** tantalum trichloride, tantalous chloride.

**тантал/ат** *m.* tantalate; **—истый** *a.* tantalous, tantalum; **—ит** *m.* (min.) tantalite (iron-manganese tantalate).

**танталово/кислый** *a.* tantalic acid; tantalate (of); **т. натрий, —натриевая соль** sodium tantalate; **—кислая соль** tantalate; **—кислое железо** iron tantalate.

**танталов/ый** *a.* tantalic, tantalum; **т. ангидрид** tantalic anhydride, tantalum pentoxide; **—ая кислота** tantalic acid; **соль —ой кислоты** tantalate.

**танталофтористый калий** potassium tantalum fluoride.

**тантьема** *f.* bonus.

**танцмейстер** *m.* inside calipers.

**танцовать** *v.* dance.

**тапиока** *f.* tapioca, manioca starch.

**тапиолит** *m.* (min.) tapiolite.

**тапс/иевая кислота** thapsic acid; **—ия** *f.* (bot.) deadly carrot (*Thapsia*).

**тар/а** *f.* packing, packaging; package, can; (com.) tare; **вес в —е** crated weight (of machine); **скидка на —у** tare and tret.

**таракан** *m.*, **—ий** *a.* cockroach; **—ы, —овые** *pl.* Blattoidea.

**таракса/нтин** *m.* taraxanthin; **—стерин** *m.* taraxasterol; **—церин** *m.* taraxacerin; **—цин** *m.* taraxacin.

**тарамеллит** *m.* (min.) taramellite.

**таран** *m.* (mech.) ram; (bot.) knotweed (*Polygonum*, spec. *P. alpinum*); **—ить** *v.* ram.

**таранноновский сланец** (geol.) Tarannon shale.

**таранн/ый** *a.* ram, battering ram; **—ая косточка** (anat.) astragalus.

**тарантул** *m.* (zool.) tarantula.

**тарань** *f.* roach (fish).

**тарапакаит** *m.* (min.) tarapacaite (a potassium chromate).

**тарбуттит** *m.* (min.) tarbuttite (a basic zinc phosphate).

**таргол** *m.* targol (antiknock compound).

**тардин** *m.* tardin.

**тарел/ка** *f.*, **—очный** *a.* plate, tray, disk; **коэффициент полезного действия —ки** plate efficiency; **теоретическая т.** theoretical plate; **—очка** *f.* small plate; flare, flange; **—очный процесс** plate process (for carbon black).

**тарельчат/ый** *a.* plate, plate-like, disk, tray; **т. клапан** disk valve; **—ая колонна** plate column; **—ая колпачковая колонна** bubble tower; **—ая муфта** plate coupling, flange coupling; **—ая печь** revolving hearth; **—ое олово** plate pewter.

**тарзальный** *a.* (anat., zool.) tarsal.

**таририновая кислота** tariric acid, 5-octadecinoic acid.

**тариров/ание** *n.* taring; calibration, calibration test; **—анный** *a.* tared; **—ать** *v.* tare; calibrate (for weight).

**тариф** *m.*, **—ный** *a.* tariff; rate; **—икатор** *m.* tariff clerk; **—икация** *f.* tariffing; establishment of wage scale; **—ная сетка** tariff table; scale of wages, wage scale; **—ицировать** *v.* fix a wage scale.

**таркон/ин** *m.* tarconine; **—овая кислота** tarconic acid; **—ол** *m.* tarconol.

**тарлатан** *m.* (text.) tarlatan.

**тармакадам** *m.* tar-macadam road.

**тарновицит** *m.* (min.) tarnowitzite (a variety of aragonite).

**тарный** *a. of* **тара.**

**таро** *n.* taro (root of *Colocasia esculenta*); **т.-крахмал** taro starch.

**тароксиловая кислота** taroxylic acid.

**тартальный** *a.* bailing, bailing out.

**тартан** *m.* (text.) tartan.

**тарт/ание** *n.* bailing; **—ать** *v.* bail (out).

**тартинка** *f.* sandwich, buttered bread.

**тартр/азин** *m.* tartrazine (dye); **—аловая кислота** tartralic acid; **—амид** *m.* tartramidc; **—аминовая кислота** tartramic acid; **—ат** *m.* tartrate; **—иметр** *m.* tartrimeter; **—имид** *m.* tartrimide; **—онил** *m.* tartronyl; **—оновая кислота** tartronic acid, 2-hydroxypropanedioic acid.

**тартыши** *pl.* (ice) growler.

**тархониловый спирт** tarchonyl alcohol.

**тарын** *m.* (geol.) ice sill, ice step.

**тарэлаидиновая кислота** tarelaidinic acid.

**таск/ание** *n.* dragging, drawing; **—ать** *v.* drag, draw, tug, pull.

**таскыл** *m.* taskyl (rounded summit covered with placers).

**тасманит** *m.* (min.) tasmanite (an oxygenated hydrocarbon).

**таɑтатура** *f.* (tel.) key set, key pulser.

**татар/ка** *f.* Welsh onion (*Allium fistulosum*); **—ник** *m.* thistle, spec. cotton thistle (*Onopordon*); **—ский** *a.* Tartar. **Татреспублика** the Tartar Autonomous Socialist Soviet Republic.

**татуировать** *v.* tattoo.

**тауерная цепь** pulling chain.

**таумавит** *m.* (min.) tawmawite (a chromiferous variety of epidote).

**таумазит** *m.* (min.) thaumasite.

**таунсендовская лавина** (electronics) Townsend avalanche.

**таур/ил** *m.* tauryl; **—иловая кислота** taurylic acid; **—ин** *m.* taurine, aminoethylsulfonic acid; **—окарбаминовая кислота** taurocarbamic acid.

**таурохол/ат** *m.* taurocholate; **—евая кислота** taurocholic acid, choleic acid; **соль —евой кислоты, —евокислая соль** taurocholate; **—еиновая кислота** taurocholeic acid.

**тау-сагыз** *m.* (bot.) tau-saghyz (*Scorzonera tau-saghyz*) (a rubber-bearing plant).

**тауто—** *prefix* tauto— (the same).

**таутомер** *m.* tautomer, tautomeric substance; **—ия** *f.* tautomerism, dynamic allotropy; **—ный** *a.* tautomeric.

**таутомочевина** *f.* tautourea.

**ТАФ** *abbr.* (**триаммонийфосфат**) triammonium phosphate.

**тафия** *f.* a rum.

**тафта** *f.* (text.) taffeta.

**тахгидрит** *m.* (min.) tachhydrite.

**тахеометр** *see* **тахиметр**; **—ическая съемка, —ия** *f.* (surv.) tacheometry.

**тахи—** *prefix* tachy— (swift, quick); **—генез** *m.* (zool.) tachygenesis; **—гидрит** *see* **тахгидрит**; **—графия** *f.* tachygraphy, stenography; **—кардия** *f.* (med.) tachycardia; **—лит** *m.* (petr.) tachylite (a volcanic basic glass).

**тахиметр** *m.* tachymeter, speed indicator; (surv.) techymeter, tacheometer; **—ический** *a.* tachymetric; **—ия** *f.* tachymetry.

**тахинин** *m.* tachinin.

**тахины** *pl.* tachina flies (*Larvaevoridae*).

**тахиол** *m.* tachiol, silver fluoride.

**тахистерин** *m.* tachysterol.

**тахо/генератор** *m.* tachometer generator; **—грамма** *f.* tachogram; **—граф** *m.* tachograph, registering tachometer, speed indicator; **—метр** *m.* tachometer, speed counter; **—метрия** *f.* tachometry.

**тацетт** *m.* (bot.) narcissus (*Narcissus tazetta*).

**тач/альное шило** stitching awl; **—ать** *v.* stitch, overcast.

**тачка** *f.* wheelbarrow; truck, trolley.

**тащить** *v.* carry (along), draw along slowly, haul, pull, tow; **—ся** *v.* drag along, lag (behind), crawl, creep, plod.

**та/ющий** *a.*, **—яние** *n.* thawing, melting; **температура (точка) —яния** melting point; **—ять** *v.* thaw, melt.

**тв.** *abbr.* (**твердость**) hardness.

**Тввадделя гидрометр** Twaddel hydrometer.

**твайнер** *m.* twiner.

**ТВД** *abbr.* (**турбовинтовой двигатель**) turbo-propeller engine.

**тверд/ение** *n.* hardening, congealing, solidification; concretion; **точка —ения** solidifying point, freezing point; **—еть** *v.* harden, grow hard, solidify, congeal, set; toughen, cake.

**твердить** *v.* repeat over and over again.

**твердо** *adv.* firmly, steadfastly; consistently; thoroughly, well; **т. стоять на своем** *v.* be firm in one's decision.

**твердодревник** *m.* (bot.) ironwood (usually *Ostrya* or *Carpinus*).

**твердомер** *m.* hardness gage, durometer.

**твердоплавк/ий** *a.* difficulty fusible, infusible; **—ость** *f.* infusibility.

**твердостекловатый** *a.* durovitreous.

**твердост/ь** *f.* hardness, toughness; solidity, rigidity, stiffness, steadiness, firmness, constancy, consistency; resolution, fixedness; **т. по Бринелю** Brinell hardness; **активная т.** abrasive hardness; **показатель —и, число —и** hardness number; **средней —и** medium hard; **шкала —и** (min.) hardness scale, Mohs scale.

**твердотянутый** *a.* (met.) hard-drawn.

**тверд/ый** *a.* hard, tough, firm, solid, rigid; stable, resolute, constant, steady, consistent; crusted; fixed (price); **т. раствор** solid solution; **—ая масса** concretion; **—ое состояние**

solid state, solidity; переводить в
—ое состояние *v.* solidify; —ое тело
solid; физика —ого тела solid-state
physics.

**т. возг.** *abbr.* (температура возгонки)
sublimation temperature.

**твор/ение** *n.* creation, creating, making;
creature; work; —ец *m.* creator,
maker; author, achiever.

**творил/о** *n.,* —ьный *a.* lime pit, mortar
pit; —ьный ящик lime bin.

**творить** *v.* create, make, do, shape,
produce; slake (lime); —ся *v.* be
created, be made, be done; happen.

**творо/г** *m.* curds; pot cheese; —жистый
*a.* curdled, clotted, caseous; —житься
*v.* curdle, clot, coagulate; —жный *a.*
curdy, curdled, coagulated; caseous.

**творчес/кий** *a.* creative; —тво *n.* creative power, creative genius.

**т. воспл.** *abbr.* (точка воспламенения)
ignition point.

**т. всп.** *abbr.* (температура вспышки)
flash point.

**ТВЧ** *abbr.* (ток высокой частоты) high-
frequency current.

**ТВЭ** *abbr.* (тепловыделяющий элемент)
fuel element.

**Твэдля** *see* **Твадделя.**

**ТГУ** *abbr.* (Тбилисский государственный университет) Tbilisi State University; (Томский государственный
университет им. В. В. Куйбышева)
V. V. Kuibyshev State University.

**т. е.** *abbr.* (то-есть) that is.

**теаза** *f.* thease.

**теаллит** *m.* (min.) tcallite (a lead
sulfostannate).

**теамин** *m.* Theamin, theophylline ethanolamine.

**театр** *m.* theater.

**теба/ин** *m.* thebaine, paramorphine;
—инол *m.* thebainol; —инон *m.*
thebainone; —ол *m.* thebaol.

**тебелон** *m.* tebelon, isobutyl oleate.

**тебеневка** *f.* winter grazing.

**тебен/ол** *m.* thebenol; —он *m.* thebenone.

**тебомолочная кислота** thebolactic acid.

**Тевенина теорема** (elec.) Thévenin's
theorem.

**теве/резин** *m.* theveresin; —тин *m.*
thevetin.

**тегогликол** *m.* tegoglycol.

**теел/ин** *m.* theelin, estrone; —ол *m.*
theelol, estriol.

**тезин** *m.* thesine.

**тезис** *m.* thesis; summary; position.

**теин** *m.* theine, caffeine.

**Тейзена аппарат, Т. дезинтегратор**
Theisen cleaner (for gases).

**тейкрин** *m.* teucrin.

**тейлериоз** *m.* (vet.) theileriosis.

**Тейлор** *see under* **Тэйлор.**

**тек** *past sing. of* **течь.**

**тека** *f.* (biol.) theca; *suffix* —theca,
receptacle.

**текли** *past pl. of* **течь.**

**текомин** *m.* tecomin, lapachol.

**текс** *m.* tack.

**тексол** *m.* tecsol (alcohol denaturant).

**тексроп** *m.,* —ный *a.* Texrope (a multiple V-belt drive).

**текст** *m.* text.

**текстиль/ный** *a.* textile; —ные изделия
textiles; —щик *m.* textile worker.

**тексто/винит** *m.* a leather substitute;
—лит *m.,* —литовый *a.* textolite
(resin-impregnated laminated cloth).

**текстуальный** *a.* textual.

**текстур/а** *f.* texture, grain; (geol.) texture, fabric, structure; —диаграмма
*f.* X-ray fiber pattern; —ный *a.*
textural.

**тектит** *m.* tektite (a variety of meteorite).

**тектогидрат** *m.* tectohydrate.

**тектони/ка** *f.* tectonics, construction;
structural geology; —ческий *a.* tectonic, structural; (med.) plastic;
—ческий рельеф structure contour.

**тектор** *m.* cement gun.

**тектохинон** *m.* tectoquinone.

**текут** *pr. 3 pl. of* **течь.**

**текучест/ь** *f.* flow, fluidity, liquid state;
viscosity, consistency, body (of liq-
uid); yield (of metal); turnover (of
labor); yield; —и yield point; степень —и
consistency; температура начала —и
pour point.

**текуч/ий** *a.* flowing, fluid, running; —ая
вода running water; легко т. liquid,
very liquid; трудно т. thick,
viscous.

**текущ/ий** *a.* flowing, streaming, running,
leaking, leaky; current, present; т.

**ремонт** maintenance; —**ие события** current events.

**текший** *past act. part. of* **течь.**

**теле—** *prefix* tele— (operating at a distance; remote); —**автоматика** *f.* (elec.) telautomatics, wireless control; —**вещание** *n.* television broadcasting; —**видение** *n.*, —**визия** *f.*, —**визионный** *a.* television; —**визор** *m.* television set.

**телега** *f.* cart, wagon.

**телегониометр** *m.* telegoniometer, direction finder.

**телеграмма** *f.* telegram, wire, dispatch.

**телеграф** *m.* telegraph; —**ирование** *n.* telegraphing, telegraphy; —**ировать** *v.* telegraph, wire, cable; —**ист** *m.* telegraph operator; —**ия** *f.* telegraphy; —**ный** *a.* telegraph, telegraphic; —**ная лента** tape; —**он** *m.* telegraphone.

**тележ/ка** *f.*, —**ный** *a.* hand cart, truck, trolley, car; (train) truck; **т.-грузовик** lorry; —**ник** *m.* carter; —**ный мастер** cartwright.

**теле/зритель** *m.* televiewer, television set; —**измерение** *n.* telemetry, measurement at a distance; —**индикатор** *m.* teleindicator.

**телейтоспора** *f.* (bot.) teleutospore, teliospore.

**телекия** *f.* (bot.) oxeye (*Buphthalmum*).

**теле/метр** *m.* telemeter; —**метрия** *f.* telemetry; —**механизация** *f.* introduction of remote control; —**механика** *f.* telemechanics, remote control.

**теленок** *m.* (zool.) calf.

**теле/объектив** *m.* telephoto lens; —**регулируемый** *a.* remote-controlled.

**телескоп** *m.*, —**ировать** *v.* telescope; —**ический** *a.* telescopic; —**ия** *f.* telescopy.

**телесный** *a.* corporal; flesh (color); solid, material; solid (angle); (zool.) somatic; **т. комплекс** (met.) inclusion.

**теле/тайп** *m.* (telegraphy) teletype; —**термометр** *m.* telethermometer; —**управление** *n.* remote control; —**управляемый** *a.* remote-controlled.

**телефон** *m.* telephone; —**ирование** *n.* telephoning; —**ировать** *v.* telephone, call up; —**ист** *m.* telephone operator; —**ия** *f.* telephony.

**телефонн/ый** *a.* telephone; **т. аппарат** telephone, telephone set; —**ое сообщение** telephone communication, telephone system.

**телефонограмма** *f.* telephone message.

**телефоровые** *pl.* (bot.) Telephoraceae.

**телефотограф/ический** *a.* telephotographic, telephoto; —**ия** *f.* telephotography; telephotograph.

**телец** *m.* (zool.) calf.

**телецентр** *m.* television station.

—**телий** *m.* *suffix* (anat.) —thelium.

**телин** *see* **теелин.**

**тел/иться** *v.* calve; —**ка** *f.* heifer.

**теллур** *m.* tellurium, Te; **двуокись** —**а** tellurium dioxide; **двухлористый т.**, **хлористый т.** tellurium dichloride, tellurous chloride; **листоватый т.** (min.) foliated tellurium, nagyagite; **письменный т.** (min.) graphic tellurium, sylvanite; **сернистый т.** tellurium sulfide; **хлорный т.**, **четыреххлористый т.** telluric chloride, tellurium tetrachloride.

**теллур/ат** *m.* tellurate; —**ид** *m.* telluride; —**ий** *m.* (astron.) tellurian; —**ил** *m.* telluryl; —**иновая кислота** tellurinic acid.

**теллуристо/кислый** *a.* tellurous acid; tellurite (of); **т. натрий**, —**натриевая соль** sodium tellurite; —**кислая соль** tellurite.

**теллурист/ый** *a.* tellurous, tellurium, telluriferous; telluride (of); **т. ангидрид** tellurous anhydride, tellurium dioxide; **т. висмут** bismuth telluride; (min.) telluric bismuth, tetradymite; **т. водород** hydrogen telluride; **т. свинец** lead telluride; —**ая кислота** tellurous acid; **соль** —**ой кислоты** tellurite; —**ая слюда** (min.) tellurium mica; —**ое золото** gold telluride; —**ое серебро** silver telluride; (min.) telluric silver, hessite.

**теллурит** *m.* tellurite; (min.) tellurite, telluric ocher (a tellurium dioxide).

**теллурический** *a.* telluric, earth.

**теллуро—** *prefix* telluro—.

**теллуроводород** *m.* hydrogen telluride; —**ный** *a.* hydrotelluride (of); telluride (of); —**ная кислота** hydrotelluric acid; **соль** —**ной кислоты** telluride.

теллурово/кислый *a.* telluric acid; tellurate (of); **т. натрий, —натриевая соль** sodium tellurate; **—кислая соль** tellurate.

теллуров/ый *a.* telluric, tellurium; **т. ангидрид** telluric anhydride, tellurium trioxide; **—ая кислота** telluric acid; **соль —ой кислоты** tellurate; **—ая охра** (min.) telluric ocher, tellurite.

теллуро/ний *m.* telluronium; **—новая кислота** telluronic acid; **—синеродистая кислота** tellurocyanic acid; **—углерод** *m.* carbon telluride; **—фенол** *m.* tellurophenol.

тел/о *n.* body, solid, substance, matter; (filter) bed; shaft, shank (of tool); housing; core, center (of roll, axle); **жидкое т.** liquid; **простое т.** element; **сложное т.** compound; **твердое т.** solid.

тело— *prefix* body; telo— (end, terminal; far); **—ген** *m.* telogen.

телодвижение *n.* exercise, motion.

телок *m.* bull calf.

телол *see* теелол.

теломеризация *f.* (polymerization) telomerization.

телорез *m.* (bot.) water soldier (*Stratiotes*, spec. *S. aloides*).

телосложение *n.* build, constitution.

телоспоридии *pl.* (zool.) Telosporidia.

телофаза *f.* (biol.) telophase.

телофоровая кислота thelophoric acid.

тельфаировая кислота telfairic acid.

тельфер *m.* telpher, telpher line; **—аж** *m.* telpherage (automatic transportation).

тельце *n.* corpuscle; small body; (fat) globule.

теля/тина *f.* veal; **—тник** *m.* calf pen; dealer in calves; **—чий** *a.* calf, veal.

тем *instr. of* тот; *adv.* so much the; **т. более** the more so, all the more; **т. лучше** so much the better, all the better; **т. не менее** nevertheless, none the less, in spite of that; **т. самым** thereby; **с т., чтобы** in order to, to; on condition that, provided that.

тема *f.* theme, subject, topic; **—тический** *a.* thematic.

тембр *m.* timbre, quality, tone.

теменной *a.* (anat.) parietal.

темень *see* темнота.

темечко *see* темя.

Темза the Thames.

теми *instr. pl. of* тот.

темискамит *m.* (min.) temiskamite.

темн/ее *comp. of* темный, темно, darker; **—еть** *v.* darken, grow dark; **—о** *adv.* darkly, obscurely; it is dark.

темно— *prefix* dark—; **—багровый** *a.* dark purple; **—ватый** *a.* darkish, rather dark, rather obscure; **—желтый** *a.* dark yellow; **—калильный** *a.* black-hot; **—красный** *a.* dark red; **—окрашенный, —цветный** *a.* dark-colored; **—русый** *a.* chestnut (colored); **—рыжий** *a.* dark russet, dark red, chestnut; **—та** *f.* darkness, dark, obscurity.

темн/ый *a.* dark, dingy, dim, indistinct; obscure, vague (meaning); deep (color); non-luminous (flame); **—ая вода** (med.) amaurosis; **—ая комната** (phot.) dark room; **—ая теплота** obscure heat; **—ое пространство** dark space; **—ое пятно** (astron.) nebula.

темп *m.* tempo, time; rate, frequency.

темпель *m.* tymp (of blast furnace); **—ная плита** tymp plate.

температур/а *f.* temperature; **т. кипения** boiling point; **т. плавления** melting point; **коксование при высокой —е** high-temperature coking; **кривая —ы** temperature curve; **падение —ы, перепад —ы** temperature drop; **предел —ы** temperature limit; **пределы —ы** temperature range.

температурный *a.* temperature, heat, thermal; **т. интервал** temperature range; **т. коэффициент** temperature coefficient; **т. режим** temperature schedule; **т. шов** heat crack.

температуропроводность *f.* thermal conductivity, thermal diffusivity.

темперирование *n.* tempering.

темпирование *n.* timing (of bomb).

темплет *m.* templet.

темп-ра *abbr.* (температура) temperature.

темя *n.* (anat.) sinciput.

тенар/дит *m.* (min.) thenardite (a sodium sulfate); **—ова синь** Thenard's blue (a cobalt blue).

тенденц/иозность, **—ия** *f.* tendency,

leaning, inclination, bent, trend; **выявить —ию** v. show a tendency, tend (to); **—иозный** a. intentional, purposeful.

**тендер** m. tender, tank (of locomotive).

**тенев/ой** a. shadow; shaded, shady; **т. коэффициент** shadow factor; **—ая защита** (nucl.) shadow shielding.

**теневынослив/ость** f. (bot.) shade endurance, tolerance of shade; **—ый** a. shade-enduring.

**тенелюб** m. shade-loving plant.

**тенета** pl. net, snare, trap.

**тенз/иметр** m. tensimeter (for measuring vapor pressure); **—иометр** m. tensiometer (for measuring surface tension); **—одатчик, —ометр** m. strain gage, tensometer (for measuring deformation); **—ор** m., **—орный** a. (math.) tensor.

**тениловый спирт** thenyl alcohol, thiophenecarbinol.

**тениолит** m. (min.) taeniolite.

**тенистый** a. shady, shaded, shadowy.

**теннантит** m. (min.) tennantite.

**теннесьян** m. (geol.) Tennessean system.

**теннис** m. tennis.

**тенорит** m. (min.) tenorite (a cupric oxide).

**тенс—** see **тенз—**.

**тент** m. tent, awning.

**тень** f. shade, shadow; (astron.) umbra.

**теобром/ин** m. theobromine, 3,7-dimethylxanthine; **хлористоводородный т.** theobromine hydrochloride; **—овая кислота** theobromic acid; **—оза** f. theobromose, theobrominelithium.

**теодолит** m. (surv.) theodolite, transit compass; **—ный** a. theodolite, theodolitic.

**теор.** abbr. (**теоретически**) theoretically.

**теорем/а** f. theorem, proposition; **обратная т.** converse proposition; **—ный** a. theorematic, theoremic.

**теорет/изировать** v. theorize; **—ик** m. theorist, speculator; **—ически** adv. theoretically; **—ический** a. theoretical; **на —ических основаниях** on theoretical grounds, theoretically.

**теор/ия** f. theory; **выход 85% —ии** the yield is 85% of the theoretical; **возводить —ию, составлять —ии** v.

**тео-синте** n. (bot.) teosinte (Euchlaena mexicana or E. luxurians).

**тео/филлин** m. theophylline, 1,3-dimethylxanthine; **—цин** m. Theocin, theophylline.

**тепари** n. (bot.) a bean (Phaseolus acutifolius).

**теперешн/ий** a. present, contemporary, actual; **—ие времена** the present.

**теперь** adv. now, at the present time, at present; **т., когда** now that.

**Теплера насос** Töpler pump.

**тепл/еть** v. get warm, grow warm; **—иться** v. burn, shine (of lamp); **—ица** f. hothouse, greenhouse, conservatory; (sulfuric acid) concentrating department; **—ичный** a. hothouse.

**тепл/о** n. heat, warmth; see also **теплота**; adv. warm, warmly; it is warm; **т. образования** heat of formation; **механический эквивалент —а** conversion constant; **обмен —а** heat transfer; heat exchange; **отвод —а** cooling.

**тепло—** prefix heat, thermal, thermo—; **—бетон** m. thermoconcrete.

**тепловат/о** adv. tepidly; it is rather warm; **—ость** f. tepidity; **—ый** a. tepid, lukewarm.

**тепловоз** m. diesel locomotive; **—ный** a. diesel.

**теплов/ой** a. heat, thermal, thermic, caloric; **т. двигатель, —ая машина** heat engine; **т. процесс** thermal process, thermal phenomenon; **т. цикл** (nucl.) thermal cycle; **т. эквивалент** heat equivalent, calorific value; **т. эффект** heat effect, Joule effect; **т. эффект сгорания** heat of combustion, heat value; **—ая единица** heat unit, thermal unit; **—ая катушка** (elec.) heat coil; **—ая оболочка** heating jacket, steam jacket; **—ая обработка** heat treatment; **—ая станция** thermal power plant; **—ая трещина** heat crack; **—ая энергия** heat energy, thermal energy; **—ое значение** heat value; **—ое напряжение** thermal stress; **—ое напряжение топочной поверхности** heat liberation per unit heating surface; **—ое расширение**

**тепло/выделение** *n.* heat release, heat liberation; **—выделяющий** *a.* heat-liberating; **—выделяющий элемент** (nucl.) fuel element; **—гашение** *n.* thermoquenching.

**теплоемкость** *f.* heat capacity, thermal capacity; specific heat; **атомная т.** atomic heat capacity; **удельная т.** specific heat; **молекулярная т.** molecular heat capacity.

**теплоизлуч/ающий** *a.* heat-radiating; **—ение** *n.* heat radiation.

**теплоизол/ирующий, —яционный** *a.* heat-insulating, heat-insulation; **—ятор** *m.* heat insulator; **—яция** *f.* heat insulation, insulation against loss of heat.

**теплокровный** *a.* (zool.) warm-blooded.

**тепломер** *m.* thermometer; calorimeter; **—ный** *a.* thermometric; calorimetric.

**тепло/напряжение** *n.* heat-release rate; thermal stress; **—напряженность** *f.* thermal stress; **—непроницаемый** *a.* heatproof, impervious to heat, athermanous; **—носитель** *m.* heat carrier, heat-transfer agent; cooling agent, coolant; **—носитель-замедлитель** *m.* coolant-moderator.

**теплообмен** *m.* heat exchange; heat transfer; **—ник** *m.*, **—ный аппарат** heat exchanger; **—ник-подогреватель** *m.* exchanger-preheater.

**теплооборот** *m.* thermal economy.

**теплообраз/ование** *n.* heat production; **—ователь** *m.* heat producer, heat generator; **—ующий** *a.* heat-producing, heat-generating, heat-forming.

**тепло/отбор** *m.* heat take-off; **—отвод** *m.* heat removal, cooling; **—отводящий** *a.* heat-removing, heat-transmitting; cooling; **—отдача** *f.* heat emission; heat transfer; **—отдающий** *a.* heat-liberating, exothermic;—**передатчик** *m.* heat transmitter; heat-transfer agent; **—передача** *f.* heat transfer, transmission of heat; **—передающий** *a.* heat-transfer, heat-transmitting; **—поглощательная способность** heat absorption capacity; **—поглощающий** *a.* heat-absorbing; **—потеря** *f.* heat loss, temperature loss.

**теплопровод** *m.* steam or hot water pipe; heat conductor; **—имость, —ность** *f.* heat conductivity, thermal conductivity, heat conduction, heat transfer, heat passage; **—ник** *m.* heat conductor; **—ный, —ящий** *a.* heat-conducting, heat-conveying, heat-carrying; diathermic, diathermal, diathermanous; **—ная способность** heat conductivity.

**теплопрозрачн/ость** *f.* diathermancy; **—ый** *a.* diathermanous, diathermic.

**теплопроизвод/ительность** *f.* heat value, calorific value, heating efficiency, heating power; **—ящий** *a.* heat-producing, heat-generating.

**теплород** *m.* caloric; thermogen; **—ный** *a.* caloric, calorific, thermal.

**тепло/смена** *f.* thermal cycling; **—снабжение** *n.* heat supply; **—содержание** *n.* heat content, enthalpy.

**теплостойк/ий** *a.* heatproof, heat-resistant, thermostable; **—ость** *f.* heatproof quality, resistance to heat, thermostability.

**теплосъем** *m.* heat removal, heat extraction.

**теплот/а** *f.* heat, warmth; *see also* **тепло**; **единица —ы** heat unit, thermal unit, therm; **скрытая т.** latent heat; **удельная т.** specific heat.

**теплотворн/ость** *f.*, **—ая способность** calorific value, heat value, heating capacity, efficiency (of fuel); **—ый** *a.* calorific, heat-producing.

**теплотехник** *m.* thermotechnician, combustion engineer; **—а** *f.* thermotechnics, heat technology; heat engineering.

**теплотехнический** *a.* thermotechnical; heat-engineering; **Т. институт** Power Engineering Institute.

**тепло/устойчивый** *see* **теплостойкий**; **—фикационный** *a.* heating (plant); **—фикация** *f.* introduction of a district heating system; **—ход** *m.* ship propelled by diesel engine; **—централь** *m.* heating plant; **—чувствительный** *a.* heat-sensitive; **—электроцентраль** *m.* heating and power plant; **—энергетика** *f.* heat and power engineering; thermal power.

**теплый** *a.* warm, tepid; thermal.

**тепляк** *m.* temporary enclosure for construction work; winter shelter.

**тер** *past sing. of* **тереть.**

**тера—** *prefix* tera— (denoting a magnitude of $10^{12}$).

**тер/аконовая кислота** teraconic acid, 2-isopropylidenebutanedioic acid; — **акриловая кислота** teracrylic acid.

**тералит** *m.* (petr.) theralite (a dark nepheline gabbro).

**терапевт** *m.* therapeutist; —**ический** *a.* therapeutic.

**терапиновая кислота** terapic acid.

**терапия** *f.* therapy, therapeutics.

**терас—** *see* **террас—.**

**тератология** *f.* (med.) teratology.

**терб/ий** *m.*, —**иевый** *a.* terbium, Tb; **окись** —**ия**, —**иевая земля** terbium oxide, terbia; **хлористый т.** terbium chloride.

**тердесьен** *m.* sienna (pigment).

**тереаниловая кислота** tereanilic acid.

**теребен** *m.* terebene; —**тен** *m.* terebenthene, turpentine; —**тиловая кислота** terebentylic acid.

**теребил/ка** *f.* (flax) puller; —**ьный** *a.* pulling; gripping.

**теребинов/ая кислота** terebic acid, terebinic acid; **соль** —**ой кислоты**, —**окислая соль** terebate.

**тереб/ить** *v.* pull, pluck, pick; —**ление** *n.* pulling, picking.

**тереза** *f.* counter scales, platform scales.

**тере/камфен** *m.* terecamphene; —**санталовая кислота** teresantalic acid; —**сантол** *m.* teresantol.

**терескен** *m.* (bot.) winterfat (*Eurotia*).

**тереть** *v.* rub, chafe; grate, grind, shred.

**терефтал/евая кислота** terephthalic acid, benzene-*p*-dicarboxylic acid; —**иловый спирт** terephthalyl alcohol; —**оновая кислота** terephthalonic acid, carboxyformylbenzoic acid.

**териа/к** *m.*, —**чная кашка** (pharm.) theriac.

**территория** *see* **территория.**

**терка** *f.* grater, grinder; rasp; huller.

**терли** *past pl. of* **тереть.**

**терлингуаит** *m.* (min.) terlinguaite (an oxychloride of mercury).

**терм** *m.* term; therm (unit of heat); electron energy level; —**a** *f.* therm; hot spring, thermal spring.

**термакс** *m.* (rubber) termax.

**термал/изация** *f.* thermalization; —**лой** *m.* Thermalloy (nickel-copper-iron alloy).

**термальный** *a.* thermal; hot (spring); *see also* **тепловой, термо—.**

**термиерит** *m.* (min.) termierite (a clay resembling halloysite).

**термин** *m.* term, technical term; technicality; (pharm.) thermin; **определение** —a definition, defining.

**терминальный** *a.* terminal.

**термин/овать** *v.* term, name, designate; —**ологический** *a.* terminological, nomenclature; —**ология** *f.* terminology, nomenclature.

**терм/ион** *see* **термоион;** —**истор** *m.* thermistor, heat-variable resistor.

**термит** *m.*, —**ный** *a.* (zool.) termite; thermite (aluminum-iron oxide mixture); —**ы** *pl.* termites (*Isoptera*); —**ник** *m.* termites' nest; —**ный способ** thermite process, thermoreduction; —**ная сварка** thermite welding.

**термическ/ий** *a.* thermic, thermal; temperature-indicating; thermatomic (black); *see also* **тепловой, термо—; т. двигатель** heat engine; —**ая единица** heat unit, thermal unit, therm; —**ая катушка** (elec.) heat coil; —**ая обработка** heat treatment; —**ая стойкость** thermal stability; —**ая фосфорная кислота** phosphoric acid made by the furnace process; —**ая цепь** thermoelement; —**ое расширение** heat expansion.

**термия** *f.* therm (unit of heat).

**термо—** *prefix* thermo—, therm—, heat; *see also* **тепло—;** —**анализ** *m.* thermal analysis; —**барокамера** *f.* tank for testing temperature- and pressure-measuring equipment; —**барометр** *m.* thermobarometer; —**батарея** *f.* (elec.) thermopile; —**вольт** *m.* "iron rubber" (molded hard rubber with embedded metal components); —**гальванометр** *m.* (elec.) thermogalvanometer; —**граф** *m.* thermograph, self-registering thermometer; —**датчик** *m.* temperature-sensitive element; —**двигатель** *m.* thermomotor, heat engine; thermomagnetic motor; —**деление** *n.*

thermofission; —дин *m.* thermodin, phenacetin urethane.

термодинами/ка *f.* thermodynamics; —ческий *a.* thermodynamic; —ческая вероятность thermodynamic potential, Gibb's function.

термо/диффузионный *a.*, —диффузия *f.* thermal diffusion; (moisture) migration; —единица *f.* thermal unit, therm; —зит *m.* a slag material; —изоляционный *a.*, —изоляция *f.* thermal insulation, heat insulation; —ион *m.* (phys.) thermion; —ионизация *f.* thermal ionization; —ионный *a.* thermionic; —каутер *m.* (med.) cautery (instrument); —лиз *m.* thermolysis, decomposition by heat; —литический *a.* thermolytic; —магнитизм *m.* thermomagnetism; —магнитный *a.* thermomagnetic; —металлургия *f.* thermometallurgy.

термометр *m.* thermometer; т.-праща *f.* sling thermometer; —ический *a.* thermometer, thermometric; —ия *f.* thermometry; —ограф *m.* thermometrograph, recording thermometer.

термо/мицин *m.* thermomycin; —мотор *see* термодвигатель; —напряжение *n.* thermoelectromotive force; —натрит *m.* (min.) thermonatrite (a monohydrated sodium carbonate); —нейтральность *f.* thermoneutrality; —обработка *f.* heat treatment, thermal treatment; —отрицательный *a.* thermonegative; —пара *f.* thermocouple, thermoelectric couple; —перм *m.* Thermoperm (iron-nickel alloy); —пластичный *a.* thermoplastic; —полимеризация *f.* thermal polymerization; —положительный *a.* thermopositive; —прен *m.* thermoprene (isomerization product of rubber); —преобразователь *m.* (elec.) thermopile; —реактивный *a.* thermosetting (resin); —регулятор *m.* thermoregulator, temperature control device; —регуляция *f.* thermoregulation.

термос *m.* Thermos (bottle).

термо/синтез *m.*, —слияние *n.* thermofusion; —сифон *m.* thermosiphon; —скоп *m.* thermoscope; —сопротивление *n.* thermal resistance; —спай, —сросток *m.* thermojunction, ther-

mocouple; —стат *m.* thermostat; incubator (for microorganisms); —статический *a.* thermostatic; —столбик *m.* (elec.) thermopile; —терапия *f.* thermotherapy, heat treatment; —ток *m.* thermoelectric current; —упругий, —эластичный *a.* thermoelastic; —физика *f.* thermophysics; —физический *a.* thermophysical; —филлин *m.* thermophillin; —филлит *m.* (min.) thermophyllite (a variety of serpentine); —химический *a.* thermochemical; —химия *f.* thermochemistry; —хромирование *n.* diffusion chromizing.

термоэлектрическ/ий *a.* thermoelectric; т. ряд thermoelectric series; т. столб, —ая батарея thermopile, thermoelectric pile; т. элемент, —ая пара, —ая цепь thermoelectric couple, thermocouple, thermoelement.

термоэлектр/ичество *n.* thermoelectricity; —од *m.* thermoelectrode; —одвижущая сила thermoelectromotive force, thermoelectric power; —он *m.* thermion, thermoelectron; —онный *a.* thermoelectronic, thermionic.

термо/элемент *m.* thermoelement, thermocouple; —ядерный *a.* thermonuclear; —ядерная техника thermonucleonics.

терн, —овник *m.* (bot.) blackthorn, sloe (*Prunus spinosa*); —ие *n.*, —ии *pl.* thorns, prickles; —истый *a.* thorny; —овик *m.* briar; —овый *a.* thorn, thorny; —ослива *f.* bullace (*Prunus insititia*); *see also* терн.

терочный *a.* grinding.

терп/адиен *m.* terpadiene; —ан *m.* terpane, menthane; —анон *m.* terpanone.

терпелив/ость *f.* patience; —ый *a.* patient, persevering.

терпен *m.* terpene.

терпение *n.* patience, endurance, perseverance.

терпен/иловая кислота terpenylic acid; —овый *a.* terpene; —ол *m.* terpenol; —он *m.* terpenone.

терпентин *m.*, —ный, —овый *a.* turpentine; венецианский т. Venetian turpentine, larch resin; —ное масло turpentine.

**терп/еть** *v.* endure, bear, suffer, tolerate, stand, put up (with); undergo; **время —ит** there is plenty of time.

**терпилен** *m.* terpilene, terpinylene; **—ол** *m.* terpilenol, terpineol.

**терпим/ость** *f.* tolerance, toleration, sufferance; **—ый** *a.* tolerant, permissive; tolerable, bearable, endurable.

**терпин** *m.* terpine, dihydroxymenthane; **—гидрат** *m.* terpin hydrate; **—ен** *m.* terpinene; **—еол** *m.* terpineol, lilacin; **—ил** *m.*, **—иловый** *a.* terpinyl; **—ила-цетат**, **—иловый эфир уксусной кислоты** terpinyl acetate; **—илен** *m.* terpinylene, terpilene; **—иловая кислота** terpinylic acid; **—ол** *m.* terpinol; **—олен** *m.* terpinolene.

**терпк/ий** *a.* tart, sharp, sour, astringent; **—ость** *f.* tartness, acerbity, astringency.

**терпу/г** *m.* rasp, rasping file, grate; (zool.) rock trout; atka fish, mackerel; **—жок** *m.* needle file.

**терпурил** *m.* terpuril (detergent).

**террако́т/а** *f.*, **—овый** *a.* terra cotta.

**террамицин** *m.* Terramycin, oxytetracycline.

**террарий** *m.* terrarium.

**терра-росса** *f.* terra rossa (a red earth).

**терраса** *f.* terrace; balcony, platform; (geol.) bench.

**терра-сиенна** *f.* terra sienna, ocher.

**террас/ирование** *n.* terracing, benching; **—овидный** *a.* terrace-like, step, bench.

**терраццо** *n.* terrazzo, Venetian mosaic.

**терреевая кислота** terreic acid.

**терри/генный** *a.* (geol.) terrigenous, terrestrial; **—кон, —коник** *m.* (min.) waste pile.

**территор/иальный** *a.* territorial; **—ия** *f.* territory.

**тертый** *a.* grated; ground (pigment).

**терфенил** *m.* terphenyl, diphenylbenzene.

**терция** *f.* third.

**терчуг** *see* **терпуг.**

**терший** *past act. part. of* **тереть.**

**терять** *v.* lose, give up, give off; shed; waste; **—ся** *v.* be lost, escape; disappear; get lost; be at a loss.

**тес** *m.* thin planks, battens, deals.

**тес/ание** *n.* cutting, hewing, dressing; **—анный, —аный** *a.* cut, hewn, dressed, squared; **—ать** *v.* cut, hew, square, chip.

**тесем/ка** *f.* tape, ribbon, band, strap; **—чатый** *a.* tape-like, ribbon-like.

**тес/ка** *see* **тесание**; **—ло** *n.* adz.

**теснина** *f.* gorge, canyon, pass; narrows.

**тесн/ить** *v.* press, squeeze, cram, push, thrust, force back; **—о** *adv.* narrowly, tightly, closely, intimately; it is tight; **—овато** *adv.* rather tightly, rather narrowly, rather closely; **—оватый** *a.* rather narrow, rather crowded; **—ота** *f.* crowded state, closeness; **—ый** *a.* narrow, tight, close; intimate (mixture).

**тесовый** *a.* deal, plank; **т. гвоздь** brad.

**тессеральный** *a.* (cryst.) tesseral.

**тест** *m.* test; **—ер** *m.* tester, analyzer.

**тестикула** *f.* (anat.) testicle.

**тесто** *n.* dough, paste, pulp, viscous mass; **—ватый** *a.* pasty, pulp-like; **—месилка** *f.* kneader; **—образный** *a.* pasty, paste-like, doughy, semi-liquid; **—раскатка** *f.* dough roller.

**тестостерон** *m.* testosterone.

**тесьма** *see* **тесемка.**

**тетамон** *m.* tetamon, tetraethylammonium iodide.

**тетан/ин** *m.* tetanine (a tetanus ptomaine); **—ия** *f.* (med.) tetany; **—о-токсин** *m.* tetanotoxin; **—трен** *m.* tetanthrene; **—тетрагидрофенан-трен**; **—ус** *m.* (med.) tetanus.

**тетартоэдр/ический** *a.* (cryst.) tetartohedral; **—ия** *f.* tetartohedry.

**тетелин** *m.* tethelin.

**тетерев** *m.* (zool.) black grouse.

**тетива** *f.* string, bowstring; (construction) string board, stringer.

**тетра—** *prefix* tetra—, quadri—; **—ами-лоза** *f.* tetraamylose; **—бензилкремний** *m.* tetrabenzylsilicane, tetrabenzylsilicon; **—борная кислота** tetraboric acid; **—боронатриевая соль** sodium tetraborate.

**тетрабром—** *prefix* tetrabrom—, tetrabromo—; **—ид** *m.* tetrabromide.

**тетрагексаэдр** *m.* (cryst.) tetrahexahedron; **—ический** *a.* tetrahexahedral.

тетрагидро— *prefix* tetrahydro—; — бензол *m.* tetrahydrobenzene; —кси- *prefix* tetrahydroxy—; —фталан *m.* tetrahydrophthalan.

тетра/гира *f.* (cryst.) fourfold axis of symmetry; —гон *m.* (geom.) tetragon; —гональный *a.* tetragonal; —да *f.* tetrad; —декан *m.* tetradecane; —децил *m.*, —дециловый *a.* tetradecyl; —димит *m.* (min.) tetradymite, tellurbismuth.

тетрад/ка, —ь *f.* notebook, pad.

тетраз/ан *m.* tetrazane; —ен *m.* tetrazene; —ил *m.* tetrazyl; —ин *m.* tetrazine.

тетразо— *prefix* tetrazo—, bisazo—, bisdiazo—; —л *m.* tetrazole; —н *m.* tetrazone; —товая кислота tetrazotic acid.

тетра/иод— *prefix* tetraiod—, tetraiodo—; —каин *m.* tetracaine; —карнит *m.* tetracarnite (detergent); —козан *m.* tetracosane; —козановая кислота tetracosanic acid.

тетрал/ин *m.* Tetralin, tetrahydronaphthalene; —ит *m.* tetralite, Tetryl; —ол *m.* tetralol; —он *m.* tetralone.

тетрамер ацетилена tetrameric acetylene.

тетрамерный *a.* tetramerous.

тетраметил *m.*, —овый *a.* tetramethyl; —ен *m.* tetramethylene; —мочевина *f.* tetramethylurea.

тетрамин *m.* tetramine.

тетра/нитро— *prefix* tetranitro—; —силан *m.* tetrasilane; —спора *f.* (bot.) tetraspore; —сульфид *m.* tetrasulfide; —тионовая кислота tetrathionic acid.

тетрафенил *m.*, —овый *a.* tetraphenyl; —ен *m.* tetraphenylene; —кремний *m.* tetraphenylsilicane, tetraphenylsilicon.

тетрафторид *m.* tetrafluoride.

тетрахлор— *prefix* tetrachlor—, tetrachloro—; —ид *m.* tetrachloride; —метан *m.* tetrachloromethane, carbon tetrachloride; —этан *m.* tetrachloroethane, acetylene tetrachloride.

тетрациклин *m.* tetracycline.

тетраэдр *m.* (cryst.) tetrahedron; —ит *m.* (min.) tetrahedrite, gray copper ore; —ический *a.* tetrahedral.

тетраэтил *m.*, —овый *a.* tetraethyl; —свинец *m.* tetraethyl lead (T.E.L.).

тетридин *m.* pyrithyldione.

тетрил *m.* (expl.) Tetryl, tetranitromethylaniline.

тетриновая кислота tetrinic acid.

тетрод *m.* (rad.) tetrode.

тетро/донин *m.* tetrodonine (fugin); —доновая кислота tetrodonic acid; —за *f.* tetrose; —ксан *m.* tetroxane; —ксид *m.* tetroxide; —л *m.* tetrole, furan; —левая кислота, —ловая кислота tetrolic acid, butynoic acid.

тетрон/ал *m.* tetronal, diethylsulfone diethylmethane; —овая кислота tetronic acid; —эритрин *m.* tetronerythrin.

тетрофин *m.* tetrophine.

тетурам *m.* tetraethylthiuram disulfide.

тефиграмма *f.* (meteor.) tephigram.

тефр/ит *m.* (petr.) tephrite (alkali basalt); —озин *m.* tephrosin, hydroxydeguelin; —оит *m.* (min.) tephroite (a manganese silicate).

тефф *m.* (bot.) teff (*Eragrostis*).

тех— *abbr.* (технический) technical.

Техас, техасский *a.* Texas.

технеций *m.* technetium, Tc.

техник *m.* technician, technologist; engineer, mechanic; —a *f.* technology, technological process; technique, procedure, practice; engineering; technics, arts; —ум *m.* technical school.

техническ/ий *a.* technical; engineering; commercial, industrial; large (calorie); т. расчет engineering; —ая вода industrial water; —ая общественность technical world; —ая химия applied chemistry, industrial chemistry; —ое изготовление industrial preparation, manufacture; —ие условия technical specifications, standard specifications, specifications; указывать —ие условия *v.* specify.

технолог *m.* technologist; —ический *a.* technological; process (liquid); technical, crude (product); —ическая карта, карта —ического процесса flow sheet; —ия *f.* technology; engineering; (foods) processing, canning.

технорук *m.* supervisor of technical works, works manager.

**теций** *m.* (bot.) thecium; *suffix* (biol.) —thecium (small receptacle).

**тече/безопасный** *a.* leakproof; —искание, —испытание *n.* leak detection, leak testing; —искатель *m.* leak detector, leak tester.

**течен/ие** *n.* current, stream, course, flux, flow, run; streaming, flowing; в т. during, in the course (of); over a period (of); вверх по —ию, против —ия upstream, against the current; вниз по —ию, по —ию downstream, with the current; медленное т. ooze, oozing; обратное т. reflux; потенциал —ия streaming potential; распределение —ий, система —ий flow pattern.

**течка** *f.* (gravity) spout; (zool.) heat.

**течь** *v.* flow, stream, run; leak, escape, trickle, drip; fly, pass (of time); *f.* leaking; т. обратно *v.* reflux; с —ю leaky.

**теше/махерит** *m.* (min.) teschemacherite (acid ammonium phosphate); —нит *m.* (petr.) teschenite (alkalic dolerite).

**т. зам.** *abbr.* (точка замерзания) freezing point; **т. заст.** *abbr.* (точка застывания) solidification point.

**тиаз/ил** *m.* thiazyl; —ин *m.* thiazine; —иновые краски thiazine dyes; —ол *m.*, —оловый *a.* thiazole; —олидин *m.* thiazolidine, tetrahydrothiazole; —олил *m.* thiazolyl; —олин *m.* thiazoline, dihydrothiazole.

**ти/альдин** *m.* thialdine; —амид *m.* thiamide; —амин *m.* thiamine; —антрен *m.* thianthrene, diphenylene disulfide.

**тибетский** *a.* Tibetan; т. бык (zool.) yak.

**тибон** *m.* thibone, thiacetazone.

**тигель** *m.*, —ный *a.* crucible; —ный ухват crucible shank; —ная печь crucible furnace; —ная проба crucible test; —ные клещи crucible tongs.

**тиглинов/ая кислота** tiglinic acid, tiglic acid, 2-methyl-2-butenoic acid; соль —ой кислоты tiglate; —ый альдегид tiglic aldehyde, tiglaldehyde.

**тигмотаксис** *m.* (biol.) thigmotaxis, stereotaxis.

**тигровый** *a.* tiger; т. глаз (min.) tiger eye (a variety of phenocrystalline quartz).

**тиен/ил** *m.* thienyl; —он *m.* thienone, thienyl ketone.

**тиза** *f.* (min.) tiza, ulexite.

**Тиза способ** Thies process (for extraction of gold).

**тизана** *f.* tisane, medicinal tea.

**тизонит** *m.* (min.) tysonite, fluocerite.

**тик** *m.* (text.) ticking; (med.) tic; (bot.) *see* тиковое дерево.

**тик/анье** *n.* ticking, tick (of watch); —ать *v.* tick; —кер *m.* (rad.) ticker, chopper.

**тиков/ый** *a.* teak; —ое дерево (bot.) teak, teakwood (*Tectona grandis*).

**тикональ** *m.* Ticonal (iron-cobalt-nickel-titanium alloy).

**тиксотроп/ия** *f.* thixotropy (of gels); —ный *a.* thixotropic.

**тилазит** *m.* (min.) tilasite, fluor-adelite.

**Тиле трубка** Thiele tube.

**тили/адин** *m.* tiliadin, taraxerol; —акорин *m.* tiliacorine; —цин *m.* tilicin.

**тилькальзин** *m.* Tylcalsin, calcium acetylsalicylate.

**тиллит** *m.* (petr.) tillite (cemented till).

**тиллитин** *m.* Tyllithin, lithium acetylsalicylate.

**тилль** *f.* (geol.) till, glacial drift.

**тил/марин** *m.* tylmarin; —оз *m.* (med., bot.) tylosis; —офорин *m.* tylophorine.

**тиманнит** *m.* (min.) tiemannite (mercuric selenide).

**тимацетин** *m.* thymacetin, thymol phenacetin.

**тимберов/анный** *a.* repaired, refitted (ship); timbered; —ать *v.* repair, refit; —ка *f.* repairing.

**тим/ен** *m.* thymene; —иан *see* тимьян; —идол *m.* thymidol, methylpropylphenyl menthol; —ил *m.* thymyl; —иловый спирт thymyl alcohol; —ин *m.* thymine, 5-methyluracil; —иновая кислота thyminic acid, solurol; —иодол *m.* Thymiodol, thymol iodide; —ипин *m.* thymipin.

**тимо/видин** *m.* thymovidin; —гидрохинон *m.* thymohydroquinone; —дин *m.* thymodin, thymol iodide; —зиновая кислота thymosinic acid.

**тимол** *m.*, —**овый** *a.* thymol, 3-hydroxy-*p*-cymene; **иодистый т.** thymol iodide, diiodothymol.

**тимон** *m.* (bot.) cumin (*Cuminum cyminum*).

**тимот/ал** *m.* Thymotal, thymol carbamate; —**иновая кислота** thymotic acid; —**ол** *m.* thymotol, thymol iodide.

**тимофеевка** *f.* (bot.) timothy (*Phleum*).

**тимо/форм** *m.* thymoform; —**хингидрон** *m.* thymoquinhydrone; —**хинон** *m.* thymoquinone.

**тимпан** *m.* (anat.) tympanum, middle ear; tympanic membrane; —**альный** *a.* tympanal, tympanic; —**ит** *m.* (med.) tympanitis, inflammation of middle ear; —**ит**, —**ия** *f.* tympanites (distention from gas); —**ный** *a.* tympanic; —**ное колесо** tympanium, drum wheel.

**тимуснуклеиновая кислота** thymus nucleic acid, desoxyribonucleic acid, DNA.

**тимьян** *m.*, —**овый** *a.* (bot.) thyme (*Thymus*); —**овая камфора** thyme camphor, thymol; —**овое масло** thyme oil.

**тина** *f.* slime, mud, mire, ooze, silt, slurry, sludge; (pond) scum; (cer.) slip; (bot.) fresh-water algae (*Conferva*).

**тингуаит** *m.* (petr.) tinguaite (phonolite).

**Тиндаля явление** (light) Tyndall effect.

**тинист/ость** *f.* sliminess; —**ый** *a.* slimy, oozy, muddy.

**тинкал** *m.* (min.) tincal, crude borax; —**ьконит** *m.* tincalconite.

**тинктура** *f.* tincture, infusion.

**тиннин** *m.* thynnin.

**тинный** *a.* mud, mire, ooze; muddy, slimy; (bot.) conferval, confervaceous.

**тинолит** *m.* (min.) thinolite (a variety of tufa calcium carbonate); —**овый** *a.* thinolithic.

**тиноль** *m.* soldering paste with flux.

**тинто, вино** *n.* tent (a deep-red wine).

**тинтометр** *m.* tintometer (colorimeter).

**тио—** *prefix* thio—; —**альдегид** *m.* thioaldehyde; —**амид** *m.* thioamide; —**ангидрид** *m.* thioanhydride; —**анилин** *m.* thioaniline; —**арсенит** *m.*

thioarsenite; —**ацетамид** *m.* thioacetamide; —**бензойная кислота** thiobenzoic acid; —**геновые красители** thiogenic dyes, sulfur dyes; —**диазол** *m.* thiodiazole; —**индиго** *n.* thioindigo.

**тиокарб/амат** *m.* thiocarbamate; —**амид** *m.* thiocarbamide, thiourea; —**аминовая кислота** thiocarbamic acid; —**онил** *m.* thiocarbonyl.

**тио/каучук** *m.* thio rubber; —**кетон** *m.* thioketone; —**кислота** *f.* thioacid; —**кол** *m.* Thiocol, potassium guaiacol sulfonate; Thiokol (polysulfide rubber).

**тиоксан** *m.* thioxane; —**тен** *m.* thioxanthene, methylenediphenylene sulfide; —**тон** *m.* thioxanthone, benzophenone sulfide.

**тиокс/ен** *m.* thioxene, dimethylthiophene; —**илол** *m.* thioxylene.

**тио/л** *m.* thiol; —**лан** *m.* thiolane; —**ловая кислота** thiolic acid; —**лютин** *m.* thiolutin; —**молочная кислота** thiolactic acid; —**мочевина** *f.* thiourea, thiocarbamide; —**муравьиная кислота** thioformic acid.

**тиомышьяков/ая кислота** thioarsenic acid, sulfarsenic acid; **соль —ой кислоты, —окислая соль** thioarsenate, sulfarsenate; —**истая кислота** thioarsenious acid, sulfarsenious acid; **соль —истой кислоты, —истокислая соль** thioarsenite, sulfarsenite; —**истоаммониевая соль** ammonium thioarsenite; —**оаммониевая соль** ammonium thioarsenate.

**тиопафтен** *m.* thionaphthene, benzothiophene.

**тион/еин** *m.* thioneine, thiazine; —**ил** *m.* thionyl, sulfinyl; —**ин** *m.*, —**иновый** *a.* thionine, Lauth's violet; —**овая кислота** thionic acid; —**уровая кислота** thionuric acid, sulfamidobarbituric acid.

**тиооловянн/ая кислота** thiostannic acid; **соль —ой кислоты, —окислая соль** thiostannate; —**оаммониевая соль** ammonium thiostannate; —**окислый** *a.* thiostannic acid; thiostannate (of).

**тиопентал-натрий** *m.* thiopental-sodium, Pentothal sodium.

**тиосерн/ая кислота** thiosulfuric acid;

**соль —ой кислоты, —окислая соль** thiosulfate; **—истая кислота** thiosulfurous acid; **соль —истой кислоты, —истокислая соль** thiosulfite; **—о-натриевая соль** sodium thiosulfate.

**тио/синамин** *m.* thiosinamine, allyl thiourea; **—соединение** *n.* thio compound; **—соль** *f.* thio salt; **—спирт** *m.* thio alcohol; **—сульфат** *m.* thiosulfate, specif. sodium thiosulfate; **—сульфокислота** *f.* thiosulfonic acid.

**тиосурьмян/ая кислота** thioantimonic acid, sulfantimonic acid; **соль —ой кислоты, —окислая соль** thioantimonate; **—истая кислота** thioantimonious acid, sulfantimonious acid; **соль —истой кислоты, —истокислая соль** thioantimonite.

**тио/толен** *m.* thiotolene, methylthiophene; **—угольная кислота** thiocarbonic acid; **—уксусная кислота** thioacetic acid; **—уретан** *m.* thiourethane; **—фан** *m.* thiophane.

**тиофен** *m.* thiophene, thiofuran; **—ил** *m.* thiophenyl; **—ин** *m.* thiophenine, aminothiophene; **—карбоновая кислота** thiophenecarboxylic acid; **—овая кислота** thiophenic acid; **—ол** *m.* thiophenol, phenylthiol.

**тио/флавон** *m.* thioflavone; **—форм** *m.* thioform, basic bismuth dithiosalicylate; **—фос** *m.* Thiophos, parathion (insecticide); **—фосген** *m.* thiophosgene, thiocarbonyl chloride; **—фосфат** *m.* thiophosphate; **—фосфорил** *m.* thiophosphoryl; **—фосфорная кислота** thiophosphoric acid; **—фтен** *m.* thiophthene, bithiophene.

**тиохин—** *prefix* thioquin—.

**тиохром** *m.* thiochrome.

**тиоциан** *m.* thiocyanogen; **—ат** *m.*, **соль —овой кислоты** thiocyanate; **—овая кислота** thiocyanic acid, sulfocyanic acid; **—уровая кислота** thiocyanuric acid.

**тиоэфир** *m.* thio ether.

**тип** *m.* type, kind, model, design, pattern, make, variety; (biol.) phylum; **—изация** *f.* typification; standardization; **—ический** *a.* typical, characteristic.

**типичн/ость** *f.* typicalness; **—ый** *a.*

typical; **—ая модель** representative type.

**типовый** *a.* type; standard.

**типограф** *m.* typographer, printer; a bark beetle (*Ips typographus*); **—ический, —ский** *a.* typographic; type (metal); printing (press); printer's (ink, varnish, etc.); **—ия** *f.* printing house, printer's, press; **в —ии** at the printer's, in press; **—щик** *m.* printer.

**типолитография** *f.* printing and lithographic establishment.

**типология** *f.* typology.

**типун** *m.* (vet.) pip.

**типчак** *m.* (bot.) fescue (*Festuca sulcata*).

**тир** *m.* shooting range; tar compound.

**тираж** *m.* circulation (of a journal); impression, number of copies (of a book).

**тирамин** *m.* tyramine, *p*-hydroxyphenylethylamine.

**тиратрон** *m.* (thermionics) thyratron.

**тир-бушон** *m.* stopper, plug.

**тире** *n.* dash; hyphen.

**тирезол** *m.* thyresol, santalol methylester.

**тирео—** *prefix* thyreo—, thyro—, thyroid; **—генный** *a.* thyrogenic; **—идин** *m.* thyroidin.

**тирит** *m.* (min.) tyrite, fergusonite; thyrite (silicon resistor).

**тиро—** *see* **тирео—**.

**тировать** *v.* tar, pitch.

**тироглобулин** *m.* thyroglobulin.

**тироз/ил** *m.* tyrosyl; **—ин** *m.*, **—иновый** *a.* tyrosine, aminohydroxycinnamic acid; **—иназа** *f.* tyrosinase; **—инуровая кислота** tyrosinuric acid; **—ол** *m.* tyrosol, *p*-hydroxyphenethyl alcohol.

**тиро/идин** *m.* thyroidin; **—ксин** *m.* thyroxine.

**тиролейцин** *m.* tyroleucin.

**тиролит** *m.* (min.) tyrolite, copper froth.

**тирольский** *a.* Tyrolene.

**тиро/токсикон, —токсин** *m.* tyrotoxicon, tyrotoxin, diazobenzene hydroxide; **—трицин** *m.* tyrothricin; **—цидин** *m.* tyrocidine.

**тис** *see* **тисс**.

**тиск/ание** *n.* squeezing, pressing; **—ать** *v.* squeeze, press, cram; **—и** *pl.* vise, jaw vise, clamp; jaws; **—овый** *a.* vise; tightening.

**тисн/ение** *n.* impressing, impression, printing, stamping; **—еный** *a.* impressed, stamped, embossed; **—уть** *v.* impress, stamp, print.

**тисовое дерево** *see* **тисс.**

**тисочн/ый** *a.* vise, clamp, jaw; **т. клупик** clamps; **—ая губа** jaw.

**т. исп.** *abbr.* (**температура испарения**) vaporization temperature.

**тисс** *m.* (bot.) yew, yew tree (*Taxus*).

**Тиссо конденсатор** Tissot condenser.

**тиссов/ые** *pl.* (bot.) Taxaceae; **—ый** *a.* yew; **—ое дерево** *see* **тисс.**

**титан** *m.* titanium, Ti; **азотистый т.** titanium nitride; **двуокись** **—а** titanium dioxide; **двухлористый т.** titanium dichloride; **окись** **—а** titanium oxide; **перекись** **—а** titanium peroxide, titanium trioxide; **сернокислый т., сульфат** **—а** titanium sulfate; **четыреххлористый т.** titanium tetrachloride, titanic chloride.

**титан/авгит** *m.* (min.) titanaugite (a titaniferous variety of augite); **—ат** *m.* titanate; **—гранат** *m.* (min.) titangarnet; **—ил** *m.* titanyl; **сернокислый —ил** titanyl sulfate.

**титанист/ый** *a.* titanous, titanium, titaniferous; **т. железняк** (min.) titaniferous iron ore, ilmenite; **—ое железо** (met.) ferrotitanium; (min.) ilmenite.

**титанит** *m.* (min.) titanite, sphene.

**титанический** *see* **титановый.**

**титано—** *prefix* titano—, titanium.

**титановокисл/ый** *a.* titanic acid; titanate (of); **—ая соль** titanate.

**титанов/ый** *a.* titanic, titanium, titaniferous; **т. ангидрид** titanic anhydride, titanium dioxide; **—ая кислота** titanic acid; **соль —ой кислоты** titanate; **—ая сталь** titanium steel; **—ые белила** titanium white (titanium dioxide pigment).

**титаноливин** *m.* (min.) titanolivine, titanclinohumite (a variety of clinohumite).

**титано/магнетит** *m.* (min.) titanomagnetite; **—фтористоводородная кислота, —фтороводородная кислота** fluotitanic acid.

**титон** *m.*, **—ский ярус** (geol.) Tithonian stage.

**титр** *m.* titer, titration standard; (text.) titer, metric number; caption; **определять т., устанавливать т.** *v.* titrate; **—иметр** *m.* titrimeter; **—иметрический, —ометрический** *a.* titrimetric; **—ометрия** *f.* titrimetry.

**титров/альный** *a.* titrating, titration; **т. анализ** analysis by titration, volumetric analysis; **т. аппарат, —анный аппарат** titrating apparatus; **—ание** *n.* titration, titrimetry; **прием —ания** titration method; **—анный** *a.* titrated; **—анный раствор** titration standard, standard solution, titrant; **—анная кислота** titrating acid, standard acid; **—ать** *v.* titrate, analyze by volumetric method.

**титрующийся** *a.* titratable.

**титул** *m.* title, name; **—ованный** *a.* titled, entitled; **—ьный лист** title page.

**тиурам** *m.* thiuram.

**тиурет** *m.* thiuret (iodoform substitute).

**тиф** *m.* (med.) typhus; **брюшной т.** typhoid fever; **сыпной т.** typhus.

**тифастерин** *m.* typhasterol.

**тифдрук** *m.* intaglio printing; mezzotint.

**тифен** *m.* thiphen (hydrochloride).

**тифии** *pl.* black wasps (*Tiphidae*).

**тиф/лит** *m.* (med.) typhlitis; **—озный** *a.*, **—оид** *m.* typhoid; **—отоксин** *m.* typhotoxin.

**тихий** *a.* quiet, still, noiseless, silent; calm; mild, gentle; slow, sluggish; soft, low (sound); **Т. океан** Pacific Ocean; **т. разряд** (dielectrics) silent discharge, corona.

**тихит** *m.* (min.) tychite (a sulfate-carbonate of magnesium and sodium).

**тихо** *adv.* quietly, silently; **—океанский** *a.* Pacific; **—ход** *m.* (zool.) sloth; **—ходный** *a.* low-speed, slow-running, slow-moving, slow; **—ходы** *pl.* (zool.) Tardigrada.

**тиш/е** *comp. of* **тихий, тихо** quieter; more quietly; **—ина, —ь** *f.* stillness, quiet, silence, calm, mildness.

**т.к.** *abbr.* (**так как**) since, inasmuch as; **ТК** *abbr.* (**турбокомпрессор**) turbocompressor.

**тка/льный** *a.* weaving; **—невый** *a.* (biol.) tissue; **—нетерапия** *f.* tissue therapy; **—неэквивалентный** *a.*

(radiobiol.) tissue equivalent; —ние *see* тканье; —ный *a.* woven, cloth.

ткан/ь *f.* fabric, cloth; web; texture; (biol.) tissue; **бумажная т.** cotton cloth; **доза в —и** tissue dose (of radiation); **металлическая т., проволочная т., сетчатая т.** wire gauze; **нервная т.** (anat.) nerve tissue.

тканье *n.* weaving; (text.) pique; —вое *n.* pique; —вый *a.* cloth; (biol.) tissue; webbing (belt); —вая доза tissue dose (of radiation).

т. капл. *abbr.* (температура каплепадения) drop point.

тка/ть *v.* weave; —цкая *f.* weaver's workshop, loom department.

ткацк/ий *a.* weaver's, weaving, loom, textile; **т. станок** loom; **т. челнок** shuttle; —ая фабрика weaving mill; —ое производство weaving.

ткач *m.* weaver; **т.-усач** *m.* longicorn beetle (*Lamia textor*); —ество *n.* weaving.

ТКВРД *abbr.* (турбокомпрессорный воздушно-реактивный двигатель) turbojet engine.

т. кип. *abbr.* (точка кипения) boiling point.

т-км *abbr.* (тонна-километр) ton-kilometer.

ткнуть *see* тыкать.

т. конд. *abbr.* (температура конденсации) dew point; **т. крит.** *abbr.* (температура критическая) critical temperature.

тку/т *pr. 3 pl. of* ткать; —щий *a.* weaving.

ТКФ *abbr.* (трикальцийфосфат) tricalcium phosphate.

тлевый *a.* (zool.) aphid.

тле/ние *n.* smoldering, incomplete combustion; decay, decomposition; —ность *f.* perishability; —нный *a.* perishable; —ть *v.* smolder, burn incompletely, glow; rot, decay, molder; —ться *v.* smolder, glow; —ющий *a.* smoldering; glow, glow-discharge; —ющий разряд (elec.) glow discharge.

тл/я *f.* (zool.) aphid; rot, rottenness; —и *pl.* aphids, plant lice (*Aphididae*).

тмин *m.* (bot.) caraway (*Carum carvi*); **воложский т., римский т.** cumin

(*Cuminum cyminum*); **черный т.** nutmeg flower (*Nigella sativa*).

тминн/ый *a.* caraway; cumin; —ая водка kümmel (liqueur); —ое масло caraway oil; cumin oil.

ТМТД *abbr.* (тетраметилтиурамдисульфид) tetramethylthiuram disulfide (seed disinfectant).

т.н., т.наз. *abbr.* (так называемый) so-called.

ТНК *abbr.* (тимонуклеиновая кислота) thymus nucleic acid, desoxyribonucleic acid.

ТНТ *abbr.* (тринитротолуол) trinitrotoluene.

т. о. *abbr.* (таким образом) thus.

то *see also under* тот; **то же** ditto, same; **то ли ... то ли** either ... or; **то ... то** sometimes, at times ... at others ..., now ... now; first ... then; **а не то** if not, otherwise, or else; **да и то** even then; **если так, то** if so, then, if it is so, then; **не то, что** not that; **об этом-то** precisely about that.

тоарсийский ярус (geol.) Toarcian stage.

Тобина бронза (met.) Tobin bronze.

т-образный *a.* T-, T-shaped, tee-.

тов. *abbr.* (товарищ) comrade.

товар *m.* merchandise, goods, wares; commodity, article; —ы *pl.* goods, ware.

товарищ *m.* companion, partner, fellow, colleague, associate; **т. по торговле** partner in trade; **т. по учению** fellow student; —ество *n.* company, partnership, society, association.

товарность *f.* marketability.

товарн/ый *a.* goods, commodity; commercial; trade (mark); freight (train); truck (farming); **крытый т. вагон** box car; —ое движение freight traffic; —ое хозяйство goods economy.

товаро/ведение *n.* science of staple commodities; —обмен *m.* barter, exchange of goods; —оборот *m.* turnover of merchandise.

тогда *adv.* then, at that time; **т. же** at the same time; **т. как** while, whereas, when; **т.-то** at that (particular) time; —шний *a.* of that time, existing at that time.

того *gen. of* тот.

**тоддалия** *f.* (bot.) toddalia.

**тоддит** *m.* toddite (uranium mineral).

**то-есть** that is, that is to say.

**тождеств/енность** *f.*, **—о** *n.* identity; **—енный** *a.* identical, same, homologous.

**тоже** *adv.* also, too, likewise.

**ток** *m.* current, stream, flow; (elec.) current; (agr.) threshing floor; **без —а** without current, dead (wire); **выключаемый т., предельный т. выключения** current-breaking capacity; **допустимая нагрузка —ом** current-carrying capacity; **двигатель переменного —а** alternating current motor, a-c motor; **плотность —а** current density; **под —ом** current-carrying, live; **подать т.** *v.* make contact; **двигатель постоянного —а** direct current motor, d-c motor; **растительный т.** malt floor; **трехфазного —а** three-phase (generator, voltage, etc.); **указатель —а** (elec.) current indicator, spec. ammeter; **функция —а** (hydrodynamics) stream function.

**токайск/ий** *a.* Tokay; **—ое** *n.* Tokay wine.

**токарн/ая** *f.* turner's workshop, turnery, lathe shop; **—ичать** *v.* turn, work on a lathe, do lathework.

**токарно/винторезный станок** screw-cutting lathe; **—давильный станок** spinning lathe; **—долбежный станок, —затыловочный станок** backing-off lathe (for making screw taps), relieving lathe; **—механическая** *see* **токарная; —полировальный станок** polishing lathe; **—расточной станок** boring lathe; **—револьверный автомат** automatic turret lathe; **—револьверный станок** turret lathe; **—шлифовальный станок** grinding lathe.

**токарн/ый** *a.* lathe, worked on a lathe; turned; **т. автомат** automatic lathe; **т. полуавтомат** semiautomatic lathe; **т. резец** turning tool, cutting tool; **т. станок** lathe, turning lathe; **т. цех, —ая мастерская, —я** *see* **токарная; —ая работа** turning, lathework; **—ое ремесло** turnery, turning, lathework; **—ые стружки** turnings.

**токарь** *m.* turner, lathe hand.

**токи** *pl. of* **ток.**

**токо—** *prefix* (elec.) current; **toco—** (childbirth, offspring); **—ведущий, —несущий** *a.* current-carrying, live; **—вращатель** *m.* contact device; **—вый** *a.* current; **—генераторный** *a.* current-generating; **—дробитель** *m.* current divider.

**токология** *f.* tocology, obstetrics.

**токоограничитель** *m.* (elec.) current limiter; **—ный** *a.* current-limiting.

**токопрерыватель** *m.* (elec.) circuit breaker, interrupter.

**токоприемн/ик** *m.* (elec.) current collector, trolley; **—ый** *a.* current-collecting; **—ый ролик** trolley; **—ая дуга** bow collector.

**токопровод** *m.* (elec.) conduction; conductor; **—ящий** *a.* current-conducting, conducting, current-carrying.

**токосниматель** *m.* (elec.) collector.

**токособиратель** *m.* (elec.) current collector; **—ный** *a.* current-collecting, collector.

**токоферол** *m.* tocopherol (vitamin E).

**токс/альбумин** *m.* toxalbumin; **—афен** Toxaphene, chlorinated camphene (insecticide); **—емия** *f.* (med.) toxemia; **—икарол** *m.* toxicarol, tephrosin; **—икоз** *m.* (med.) toxicosis; (soil) sickness, **—икологический** *a.* toxicological; **—икология** *f.* toxicology; **—ин** *m.* toxin, poison; **—истерин** *m.* toxisterol; **—ический** *a.* toxic, poisonous; **—ичность** *f.* toxicity; **—офор** *m.* toxophore.

**тол** *see* **толит; —амин** *m.* Tolamine, chloramine-T; **— ан** *m.*, **—ановый** *a.* tolan, diphenylacetylene.

**толацил** *m.* tolacyl; **—амин** *m.* tolacylamine.

**толевая кровля** roofing paper.

**толерантн/ость** *f.* tolerance; **—ый** *a.* tolerance (dose, etc.).

**толиантипирин** *m.* tolyantipyrine, tolypyrine.

**толидин** *m.* tolidine, dimethylbenzidine.

**толиз/аль** *m.* tolysal, tolypyrine salicylate; **—ин** *m.* Tolysin, neocinchophen.

**толил** *m.* tolyl; tolil, dimethylbenzil; **хлористый т.** tolyl chloride, chlorotoluene; **—ен** *m.* tolylene; **—овый спирт** tolyl alcohol, tolylcarbinol.

**толимидазол** *m.* tolimidazole.

**толипирин** *m.* tolypyrine, *p*-tolyldimethylpyrazole.

**толит** *m.* (expl.) tolit, trinitrotoluene.

**толк** *m.* meaning, sense; doctrine; —и *pl.* talk, rumors; **в т. не взять** *v.* be unable to understand; **говорить** —**ом** *v.* speak reasonably, speak plainly; **добиться** —**у** *v.* get an explicit answer; **знать т.** *v.* understand; **сбить с** —**у** *v.* disconcert, baffle.

**толк/ание** *n.* push, pushing; —**атель** *m.* pusher, push rod; stamp; expediter; (mach.) tappet; plunger (of pump); —**ать** *v.* push, give a push, thrust, shove; shake, joggle; —**ач** *m.* pusher, tappet; pestle, pounder; —**ачик** *m.* March fly (*Bibio sanguinarius*).

**толкающ/ий** *a.* pushing, propelling; **т. механизм** thrust gear; **т. пропеллер** pusher propeller; **т. стержень** push rod; —**ая сила** propelling force, impelling power.

**толкли** *past pl. of* **толочь.**

**толкнуть** *see* **толкать.**

**толков/ание** *n.* interpretation, explanation, comment; —**атель** *m.* interpreter; —**ать** *v.* interpret, explain, comment; —**аться** *v.* be interpreted, be explained; —**ый** *a.* explanatory; sensible.

**толкотня** *f.* crush, crowd; jostling.

**толк/ут** *pr. 3 pl. of* **толочь;** —**ушка** *f.* rammer; pestle; —**ущий** *a.* crushing, grinding.

**Толленса проба** Tollens test.

**толока** *f.* (agr.) manuring a field by letting cattle graze there.

**толокно** *n.* oat flour, oatmeal.

**толокнянка** *f.* (bot.) bearberry (*Arctostaphylos*, spec. *A. uva ursi*).

**толокси**— *prefix* toloxy—, cresoxy—.

**толочь** *v.* pound, beat, crush, powder, comminute, triturate.

**толп/а** *f.* crowd; —**иться** *v.* crowd, cluster, group.

**толст/еть** *v.* get fat; —**ить** *v.* fatten; —**о** *adv.* thickly; fat.

**толсто**— *prefix* thick; —**ватый** *a.* rather thick; rather fat; —**головки** *pl.* (zool.) common skippers (*Hesperiidae*); —**кожий** *a.* (zool.) thick-skinned, pachydermatous; —**кожее животное** pachyderm.

**толстолист/ный,** —**овой** *a.* thick-leaved; (met.) plate; **т. стан** plate mill; —**овая сталь** plate steel, steel plate.

**толсто/ножки** *pl.* chalcid flies (*Eurytomidae*); —**пластинчатый** *a.* thickplate, in thick plates; —**слойный** *a.* thick, thick-layered; deep-bed (filter); —**стенный** *a.* thick-walled, heavy-walled; —**та** *f.* thickness.

**толстый** *a.* thick, heavy (paper), heavygage (wire); fat, stout, obese.

**толстянковые** *pl.* (bot.) Crassulaceae.

**толтры** *pl.* toltry (parallel rows of Middle Miocene reefs consisting of calcareous algae, mollusks, bryozoans, etc.).

**толу/амид** *m.* toluamide, methylbenzamide; —**анилид** *m.* toluanilide, α-phenylacetanilide.

**толуанск/ий** *a.* Tolu; **т. бальзам** tolu, balsam of Tolu; —**ая бальзамовая семянница** (bot.) Tolu balsam tree (*Toluifera balsamum*); —**ое масло** tolu oil, alpahaca oil.

**толуидин** *m.,* —**овый** *a.* toluidine, aminotoluene; —**овый голубой** Toluidine Blue.

**толуил** *m.,* —**овый** *a.* toluyl; —**ен** *m.,* —**еновый** *a.* toluylene, tolylene; stilbene; —**еновый голубой** Toluylene Blue; —**овая кислота** toluic acid, methylbenzoic acid.

**толунитрил** *m.* tolunitrile, cyanotoluene.

**толуол** *m.,* —**ьный** *a.* toluene, methylbenzene; —**сульфокислота** *f.* toluenesulfonic acid.

**толу/тиазол** *m.* toluthiazole; —**феназин** *m.* toluphenazine.

**толухин**— *prefix* toluquin—; —**олин** *m.* toluquinoline; —**он** *m.* toluquinone.

**толчейная** *f.* (met.) stamp mill.

**толчейн/ый** *a.* stamp; **т. пест** stamp; **т. постав, т. стан,** —**ая мельница,** —**ая фабрика** *see* **толчейная; т. шлам, т. шлих,** —**ая муть** ore slime; —**ая мука** pulverized ore.

**толч/ение** *n.* stamping, pounding, crushing, powdering, comminution; —**енный,** —**еный** *a.* stamped, crushed, powdered; —**ея** *f.* (met.) stamp mill;

stamp (for crushing ore); pounder, crusher.

**толчко/мер** *m.* bumpometer, impact-measuring device; **—образный** *a.* jerky, jerking; (elec.) shock.

**толч/ок** *m.* push, thrust, impulse, impetus; jerk, jolt, jar, shake, kick, percussion, concussion; collision, impact; (elec.) shock; (ionization) burst; **—ки** *pl.* jerks, jerking; **—ками** by jerks, jerkily, by starts or jolts, percussively, intermittently; **движение —ками** jerky motion; **действующий —ками** pulsating, intermittent; **истечение —ками** intermittent delivery; **влияние —ков** pulsating effect; **дать т.** *v.* start; **приемник —ков** shock absorber.

**толщ/а** *f.* thickness, mass; layer; (geol.) stratum, series (of rock); **—ина** *f.* thickness, width, depth, size, caliber, gage (of wire); obesity, fatness; **—иномер** *m.* thickness gage, calipers.

**толь** *m.* asphaltic roofing paper, tar paper.

**только** *adv.* only, merely, but, just; **т.-т.** barely, just; **т.-что** just now, just; **не т.** not only.

**том** *m.* volume.

**Томаса-Гилькрайста способ, Т.-Джильхриста способ** *see* **томасирование.**

**томасиров/ание** *n.* Thomas-Gilchrist process, production of iron or steel by Thomas process; **—ать** *v.* produce iron or steel by the Thomas process.

**томасов** *see under* **томасовский.**

**томасовск/ий** *a.* (met.) Thomas, Thomas-Gilchrist; **т. конвертер** Thomas converter, basic Bessemer converter; **т. чугун** Thomas pig (iron), basic pig (iron); **т. шлак, —ая мука** *see* **томас-фосфат; —ая сталь** Thomas steel, basic steel, basic Bessemer steel; **—ое железо** Thomas iron, basic iron.

**томас/овый** *see* **томасовский; —фосфат, —шлак** *m.* Thomas phosphate, basic slag (fertilizer).

**томат** *m.* (bot.) tomato (*Lycopersicum esculentum*); **—ин** *m.* tomatine.

**томбуй** *m.* buoy, float.

**томильн/ый** *a.* (met.) malleablizing; **т. колодец, —ая печь** (met.) soaking pit, soaking furnace.

**томит** *m.* (min.) tomite, sapromyxite.

**томительный** *a.* tiresome, wearisome.

**томить** *v.* tire, exhaust, weary, fatigue; braise (meat); (met.) malleablize; **т. голодом** starve; **—ся** *v.* get tired, tire.

**—томия** *f.* *suffix* **—tomy** (cutting; incision operation).

**томл/ение** *n.* fatigue; (met.) malleablizing, cementation, blistering; **—енка —янка** *f.*, **—еная сталь** converted steel, cement steel, blister steel; **—еный** *a.* wearied, tired; malleablized; **—еный чугун** malleable cast iron.

**томн/ость** *f.* languor, lassitude; **—ый** *a.* languid.

**томография** *f.* (med.) tomography (X-ray diagnosis).

**томорин** *m.* Tomorin (rodenticide).

**томпак** *m.* tombac (any copper and zinc alloy).

**Томсена процесс** Thomsen process (for manufacture of soda and alumina).

**томсенолит** *m.* (min.) thomsenolite.

**томсон/ит** *m.* (min.) thomsonite (a zeolite); **—овское рассеяние** (nucl.) Thomson scattering.

**тому** *dat. of* **тот.**

**тон** *m.* tone, tint; note.

**тоналит** *m.* (petr.) tonalite.

**тональный** *a.* tone; audio—.

**тонг** *m.* joint tongue.

**тонгрийский ярус** (geol.) Tongrian stage.

**тоненький** *see* **тонкий.**

**тонер** *m.* toner, lake (pigment).

**тонзил/лит** *m.* (med.) tonsillitis; **—ярный** *a.* tonsillar.

**тонизирующее средство** (med.) tonic.

**тоника** *f.* (acous.) keynote.

**тонина** *f.* fineness, dispersity.

**тонит** *m.* (expl.) tonite.

**тоническ/ий** *a.*, **—ое средство** tonic.

**тонка** *f.*, **бобы т.** (bot.) tonka bean (*Dipteryx odorata* or *Coumarouna odorata*).

**тонкан** *m.* Toncan (a ferrous alloy).

**тонк/ий** *a.* thin, fine, minute, fine-grained; intimate (mixture); delicate (adjustment); keen (hearing); light-gage (sheet); **т. слой, —ая пластинка** lamina; **—ая структура** (optical spectroscopy) fine structure; **—о** *adv.* thinly, finely, fine.

**тонко—** *prefix* thin, fine.

**тонковое дерево** *see* **тонка.**

**тонко/волокнистый** *a.* fine-fibered, fine-fibrous; fibrillous, fibrillose; **—волоченый** *a.* fine-drawn (wire); **—жилковатый** *a.* fine-grained (wood); **—зернистый** *a.* fine-grained, fine; **—измельченный** *a.* finely pulverized, finely divided, fine (powder); **—канальчатый** *a.* fine-tubular; **—кожий** *a.* thin-skinned.

**тонколист/ный,** **—овой** *a.* thin leaf, thin-leaved; (met.) sheet; **т. стан** sheet mill; **т. непрерывный стан** strip mill; **—овое железо** sheet iron.

**тонконог** *m.* (bot.) koeleria.

**тонко/оттянутый** *a.* fine-drawn, finely drawn (wire); **—песчаный** *a.* fine-sandy; **—пленчатый** *a.* thin-filmed, thin-pellicular; **—полосный** *a.* stratified; **—прядильный** *a.* fine-spinning; **—пряды** *pl.* (zool.) swifts (*Hepialidae*); **—размолотый,** **—распыленный** *a.* finely divided, finely pulverized; **—рунный** *a.* fine-wooled (sheep); **—слоистый,** **—слойный** *a.* thin-layer; thinly laminated, laminated, lamellar; close-grained (wood).

**тонкостенн/ость** *f.* thinness of walls; **—ый** *a.* thin-walled, thin-section.

**тонкост/ь** *f.* thinness, fineness, sharpness, delicacy; **—и** *pl.* details, ins and outs.

**тонмейстер** *m.* (sound) mixer, monitor man.

**тонна** *f.* ton; **большая т., длинная т.** long ton; **—ж** *m.* tonnage.

**тоннель** *see* **туннель.**

**тонно/километр** *m.* kilometer-ton (unit of work); **—фут** *m.* foot-ton.

**тонсиль** *m.* tonsil.

**тонус** *m.* (med.) tone, tonicity.

**тонуть** *v.* drown, sink.

**тончайший** *a.* very fine, capillary.

**тоншнейдер** *m.* pug mill, clay cutter.

**тоньше** *comp. of* **тонкий, тонко,** thinner, finer.

**тоня** *f.* fishery; haul; (hydraulics) crawl.

**топаз** *m.*, **—овый** *a.* (min.) topaz (an aluminum fluosilicate); **восточный т., золотистый т.** oriental topaz (a variety of sapphire corundum); **дымчатый т.** smoky topaz; **—овое масло** topaz oil (lubricant); **—олит**

*m.* (min.) topazolite (a variety of andradite garnet).

**топ/ание** *n.* stamping; **—ать** *v.* stamp.

**топенант** *m.* lift, jigger.

**топильн/ый** *a.* heating; **—ое пространство** combustion chamber, fire chamber; combustion space.

**топинамбур** *m.* (bot.) Jerusalem artichoke (*Helianthus tuberosus*).

**топить** *v.* heat; fire, stoke; melt; drown; **—ся** *v.* burn; melt, be melted; be drowned.

**топический** *a.* (med.) topical, local.

**топк/а** *f.* furnace, burner; fire box, fire chamber, combustion chamber; heating, firing, stoking; fire; melting; **автоматическая т., механическая т.** automatic stoking; stoker; **с газовой —ой** gas-heated; **устье —и** stoke hole.

**топк/ий** *a.* swampy, muddy; suitable for fuel, combustible; **—ость** *f.* swampiness, muddiness.

**топлен/ие** *n.* heating; melting; **—ный, —ый** *a.* heated; melted.

**топливн/ик** *m.*, **—ое пространство** fire box, heating chamber, combustion chamber; **—ый** *a.* fuel; **—ая нефть, —ое масло** fuel oil.

**топливо** *n.* fuel; **древесное т.** firewood; **жидкое т.** liquid fuel; fuel oil; **твердое т.** solid fuel; **—добывающий** *a.* fuel (industry); **—несущий, —содержащий** *a.* fuel-carrying, fuel-bearing; **—провод** *m.* fuel line; **—снабжение** *n.* fuel supply.

**топлый** *a.* soaked, wet.

**топнуть** *see* **топать.**

**топограф** *m.* topographer; surveyor; **—ический** *a.* topographic; **—ия** *f.* topography.

**тополев/ый** *a.* poplar; **—ые почки** poplar buds, balm of Gilead buds.

**топология** *f.* (math.) topology.

**тополь** *m.* (bot.) poplar (*Populus*).

**топор** *m.* ax; **т.-колун** chopper; **—ик** *m.* hatchet; **—ище** *n.* helve, shaft (of ax).

**топорн/ость** *f.* clumsiness, coarseness; **—ый** *a.* clumsy, coarse, rough, rough-hewn; ax, hatchet; **—ый камень** (min.) nephrite (a variety of amphibole).

**топорщить,** —**ся** *v.* distend, swell up.

**топот** *m.* stamping, trampling.

**топотип** *m.* (zool.) topotype.

**топохим/ический** *a.* topochemical, localized reaction; —**ия** *f.* topochemistry.

**топочн/ый** *a.* furnace; heating; **т. газ** flue gas; fuel gas; **т. порог** fire bridge, baffler; **т. ход,** —**ая труба** flue, furnace flue; —**ая арматура** furnace fittings; —**ая дверка** fire door, stoking door; —**ая коробка** fire box, combustion chamber; —**ая плита** hearth plate; —**ое отверстие** fire hole; —**ое пространство** fire box, combustion chamber; furnace, hearth.

**топтать** *v.* trample, tread (upon).

**топь** *f.* swamp, marsh, quagmire, bog.

**тор** *m.* (math.) tore, torus, anchor ring.

**торак/о—** *prefix* thoraco— (thorax, thoracic, chest); —**с** *m.* thorax.

**торамин** *m.* toramin (ammonium trichlorobutyl malonate).

**торба** *f.* bag.

**торб/анит** *m.* (min.) torbanite (a variety of cannel coal); —**ернит** *m.* torbernite, copper uranite.

**торг** *m.* bargaining, trade; auction.

**торгов/ать** *v.* trade, deal, negotiate, sell; —**аться** *v.* bargain; —**ец** *m.* tradesman, dealer, merchant.

**торговл/я** *f.* commerce, trade, business, traffic (in); **предмет** —**и** commodity; **основные предметы** —**и** staple commodities.

**торгово-промышленный** *a.* pertaining to commerce and industry.

**торгов/ый** *a.* trading, trade, commercial, mercantile; **т. знак,** —**ая марка** trademark; **т. флот** merchant marine, merchant shipping; —**ая палата** Chamber of Commerce, Board of Trade; —**ое дело** business; —**ое качество** commercial grade, technical grade; —**ое предприятие** business enterprise, business; —**ое судно** freighter, cargo ship.

**торгпред** *m.* official trade representative of the USSR; —**ство** *n.* Trade Delegation.

**тор/ец** *m.* end, end plane, butt, face; **вид с** —**ца** end view; **подрезать т.** *v.* face.

**торжеств/енность** *f.* solemnity; —**енный** *a.* solemn, triumphal, gala; grand (meeting); —**о** *n.* triumph, celebration; —**овать** *v.* triumph (over), celebrate.

**торзио/граф** *m.* torsiograph; —**метр** *m.* torsion meter, torque meter; —**н** *m.*, —**нный** *a.* torsion.

**тор/ианит** *m.* thorianite (a thorium oxide mineral); —**ид** *m.* thoride.

**ториев/ый** *a.* thorium; —**ая земля** thoria, thorium oxide; —**ая соль** thorium salt.

**тор/ий** *m.* thorium, Th; **окись** —**ия** thorium oxide, thoria; **сернокислый т., сульфат** —**ия** thorium sulfate; **хлористый т.** thorium chloride; **эманация** —**ия** thoron, Tn; —**ийсодержащий** *a.* thorium-bearing; —**ированный** *a.* thoriated (filament); —**ит** *m.* (min.) thorite (thorium silicate).

**торица** *f.* (bot.) spurry (*Spergula*).

**торичеллиева** *see* **торричеллиева.**

**торичник** *m.* (bot.) sandspurry (*Spergularia*).

**торкрет,** —**бетон** *m.* gunite; —**ирование** *n.* guniting, gunite work; —**ировать** *v.* gunite, cement with a cement gun.

**тормаз** *see* **тормоз.**

**торментол** *m.* tormentol.

**торможен/ие** *n.* braking, brake action, frictional action, drag; checking, retardation, inhibition; slowing down, deceleration; throttling; damping; (distillation column) loading; **способность** —**ия** (nucl.) stopping power; —**ный** *a.* braked, stopped; retarded, inhibited; throttled.

**тормоз** *m.* brake, drag; **ручной т.** hand brake; —**ить** *v.* brake, stop; retard, inhibit; slow down, decelerate; throttle.

**тормозн/ой** *a.* brake, braking; *m.* brakeman; **т. башмак,** —**ая колодка** brake shoe; **т. вал** brake shaft; **т. подвес** brake carrier, brake support; **т. путь** braking distance; **т. эффект** braking efficiency, retardation efficiency; —**ая коробка** brake housing; —**ая лента** brake band; —**ая система** brake assembly; —**ая способность** (nucl.) stopping power; —**ая тяга**

brake rod; —ое излучение brems-strahlung (electromagnetic radiation); —ое приспособление brake, stopping device.

рмозящ/ий *a.* braking; inhibiting; damping; т. агент inhibitor; т. момент, —ее сопротивление, —ее усилие braking resistance, retarding torque; —ая поверхность braking surface, brake surface; —ее действие brake action.

рнадо *n.* (meteor.) tornado.

рогуммит *m.* thorogummite (a thorium-uranium silicate mineral).

роид *m.* (geom.) toroid; —альный, —ный *a.* toroidal, toroid.

рон *m.* thoron, Tn; thorium emanation.

роп/ить *v.* hasten, hurry, precipitate, rush, urge (on), push (on, forward); —иться *v.* make haste, hurry, be in a hurry, speed; не —ясь unhurriedly, leisurely.

роплив/о *adv.* hurriedly, with speed; —ость *f.* haste, hurry, speed; —ый *a.* hasty, hurried, speedy, quick, prompt.

рос *m.*, —истый лед ice pack; —ы *pl.* (ice) hummock.

ро/тунгстит *m.* (min.) thorotungstite; —ураннинит *m.* thorouraninite.

рпед/а *f.*, —ировать *v.* (mil., oil-well drilling) torpedo.

рпидный *a.* (med.) torpid.

рр *m.* torr (1 mm. of mercury column).

эричеллиева пустота Torricellian vacuum (of a barometer).

)с *m.* torso, trunk, body.

)сио— *see* торзио—.

)т *m.* tart, pastry, pie.

)твейтит *m.* (min.) thortveitite (a silicate of the yttrium metals).

)тонский подъярус (geol.) Tortonian substage.

)ф *m.* peat, turf; болотный т. bog peat; волокнистый т., моховой т. fibrous peat, peat moss; —окрошка *f.* peat dust; —ообразование *n.* peat formation; —оподобный *a.* peat-like, peaty; —оразработка *f.* peat mining; —орезка *f.* turf cutter; —отук *m.* peat-fertilizer mixture; —офосфат *m.* peat phosphate; —яник *m.* peat moss, turf peat; peat bog.

торфянист/ый *a.* peaty, turfy; —ая земля peaty earth, black earth, mold.

торфян/ой *a.* peat, peaty; т. грунт, —ая земля peat soil, peat mold, bog earth, muck soil; т. мох (bot.) peat moss (*Sphagnum*); т. уголь peat charcoal, charred peat; —ая залежь peat deposit, peat bog; —ая мука powdered peat; —ое болото peat bog.

торцев/ать *see* торцовать; —ой *see* торцовый.

торцовать *v.* face, pave (with small blocks).

торцов/ый *a.* front, face; end; end-window (counter); (geol.) mullion, rodding (structure); blockwood (pavement); т. ключ socket wrench, box wrench; т. коллектор *see* лобовой коллектор; т. щит fender, guard; —ая плита faceplate, surface plate; —ая поверхность plane surface; —ая фрезеровка face milling; —ое соединение edge joint.

торч/ание *n.* protrusion, projection; —ать *v.* protrude, project, stick out; —ащий *a.* upright; —ком *adv.* on end, upright, vertically.

торшон *m.* (paper) linen-finish texture.

тот *m. pron.*, та *f.*, то *n.* that; те *pl.* those; тот же the same, the selfsame; один и тот же one and the same; тот и другой both, the one and the other; тот или другой either; ни тот ни другой neither; тот, кто the one who, whoever; до того to such an extent, to such a degree, so much; тому назад ago; к тому же besides, moreover.

тотальный *a.* total.

т. отв. *abbr.* (точка отвердения) solidification point, setting point.

тотчас *adv.* immediately, instantly, directly, without delay, right away, promptly.

тохлорин *m.* Tochlorine, chloramine-T.

точен/ие *n.* sharpening, whetting, grinding; turning, working on a lathe; —ый *a.* sharpened, chiseled; turned, machined.

точечка *see* точка.

точечносваренный *a.* spot-welded.

точечн/ый *a.* point, punctate; dot;

dotted (line); spot (welding); localized (impact); **т. электрод** point electrode; **—ая коррозия** pitting; **—ая масса** (phys.) mass point.

**точил/ка** *f.*, **—о** *n.* whetstone, grindstone, sharpener; **круглое —о** grinding wheel, polishing wheel.

**точильн/ый** *a.* grinding, sharpening; **т. брусок, т. камень** whetstone, grindstone; **т. материал** abrasive; **т. сланец** whet slate; **т. станок** sharpener; lathe, turning lathe, grinding lathe; **—ая машина** grinding machine; **—ое колесо** grinding wheel, polishing wheel.

**точ/ильня** *f.* grind mill; **—ильщик** *m.* knife grinder, sharpener; **—ильщики** *pl.* (zool.) deathwatches (*Anobiidae*); **—ить** *v.* sharpen, whet, grind, hone; turn (on lathe); eat, gnaw, corrode.

**точк/а** *f.* point, dot, period, spot; (typ.) point (0.254 mm.); sharpening, grinding; **т. в —у** exactly, to a T, in the same manner; **т. кипения** boiling point; **т. плавления** melting point; **т. с запятой** semicolon; **в трех —ах** three-point; **попасть в —у** *v.* hit the mark; **т.-тире** *n.* dot-and-dash (code).

**точно** *adv.* exactly, precisely, closely, accurately, punctually, duly; as, like, as if; **т. так** exactly so, just so; **т. так же** in exactly the same manner; **т. такой** exactly the same.

**точност/ь** *f.* exactness, preciseness, precision, accuracy; punctuality; closeness, degree, fineness, delicacy (of adjustment); (elec. comm.) fidelity; **в — и** exactly, punctually; **с —ью до** correct to, correct within; **с высокой —ью** high-fidelity.

**точн/ый** *a.* exact, precise, accurate, correct, punctual, sharp, distinct, explicit, definite, strict, close; fine, delicate, sensitive (adjustment); precision (instrument, tool, work); **—ое управление** sensitive control; **—ые науки** exact sciences.

**точь-в-точь** *adv.* exactly, in the same way.

**тошн/ить** *v.* feel sick, feel nauseated; **ему —о** he is nauseated; **—ота** *f.* nausea; **—отворный** *a.* nauseating, nauseous.

**тощ/ать** *v.* grow thin, waste away; **—ий** *a.* lean, poor (ore, gas); empty; skim (milk), skim-milk; gaunt, meager, emaciated, thin; **—ая кишка** (anat.) jejunum.

**т.п.** *abbr.* (тому подобное) similar, like; such as.

**т. пл.** *abbr.* (точка плавления) melting point.

**ТПН** *abbr.* (трифосфопиридиннуклеотид) triphosphopyridine nucleotide, TPN.

**тр.** *abbr.* (труды) transactions.

**т-ра** *abbr.* (температура) temperature.

**трав/а** *f.* grass, herb, weed; **ароматичные —ы, лекарственные —ы** herbs; **морская т.** seaweed.

**травелер** *m.* traveler.

**траверс** *m.* traverse; crossarm; transom; **—а** *f.* crosspiece, crossbar; crossover; crosshead (of engine); tie beam, tie piece; stay, brace; transverse member, transverse beam.

**травертин** *m.* (min.) travertine, calcsinter, calc tufa (a form of calcite).

**травильн/ый** *a.* etching; pickling, scouring; **т. порошок** etching powder; **т. чан** pickling tank; **—ая ванна, —ая жидкость** pickling bath.

**травинка** *f.* blade (of grass), herb.

**травить** *v.* corrode, attack, etch, pickle, dip, scour, cleanse; mordant; stain; poison; pay out (rope), unwind, uncoil; **т. желтым** dye yellow; **т. кислотой** pickle.

**травка** *f.* blade (of grass), herb.

**травление** *n.* etching, corrosion, attack; pickling, dipping, scouring, cleansing; **испытание —м** etching test.

**травма** *f.* trauma, wound, injury; **—тизировать** *v.* traumatize; **—тический** *a.* traumatic, wound; **—товая кислота** traumatic acid; **—тол** *m.* traumatol, iodocresol; **—тология** *f.* traumatology.

**травник** *m.* herbarium.

**траво—** *prefix* grass; weed; **—косилка** *f.* lawn mower; **—косный** *a.* grass-cutting; grass (land); **—очиститель** *m.* weeder; weed killer, herbicide; **—полье** *n.* grassland farming; **—польный** *a.* grassland, grass-arable; **—сеяние** *n.* grass cultivation; **—стой**

*m.* herbage; —**ядный** *a.* herbivorous; phytophagous.

**травян/истый** *a.* grassy, herbaceous; —**ой** *a.* grass, grassy; herb, herbal; —**ая вошь** (zool.) aphid; —**ое дерево** (bot.) grass tree (*Xanthorrhoea australis*).

**травящий** *see* **травильный.**

**траг/акант, —аниит, —ант** *m.*, —**антовая камедь** tragacanth, gum dragon (exudation from *Astragalus* species).

**траг/едия** *f.* tragedy; —**ический** *a.* tragic.

**традесканция** *f.* (bot.) spiderwort (*Tradescantia*).

**традици/онный** *a.* traditional; —**я** *f.* tradition.

**траектор/ия** *f.* trajectory, path, track; **веер** —**ий** (mil.) sheaf of fire; **вершина** —**ии** culminating point; **сноп** —**ий** (mil.) cone of fire.

**тразентин** *m.* (pharm.) Trasentine.

**т. разл.** *abbr.* (**температура разложения**) decomposition temperature; **т. размягч.** *abbr.* (**температура размягчения**) softening point.

**трайлер** *see* **трейлер.**

**трак** *m.* track, track link.

**т-ра кип.** *abbr.* (**температура кипения**) boiling point.

**тракт** *m.* highway, road; channel, route; loop, circuit; (anat.) tract.

**тракт/ат** *m.* treatise; treaty; —**овать** *v.* treat; —**овка** *f.* treatment, interpretation (of problem).

**трактовый** *a.* highway, road.

**трактор** *m.* tractor; **т.-тягач** truck-tractor; —**изация** *f.* tractorization; —**ист** *m.* tractor driver; —**ный** *a.* tractor; tractor-drawn; —**остроение** *n.* tractor manufacture.

**трактриса** *f.* (geom.) tractrix.

**трал** *m.* trawl, trawl line, trawl net; —**е-ние** *n.* trawling; —**ер, —ьщик** *m.* trawler, mine sweeper, sweeper; —**ить** *v.* trawl; creep (of submarine).

**трамблер** *m.* distributor (of motor).

**трамб/ование** *n.*, —**овочный, —ующий** *a.* ramming, tamping; —**ованный** *a.* rammed, tamped; —**овать** *v.* ram, tamp, pack; stamp; —**овка** *f.* rammer, ram, tamper; stamper; ramming, tamping; —**овочная машина** ram-

ming machine (for coke-oven charge); —**овщик** *m.* packer.

**трамвай** *m.*, —**ный** *a.* trolley, trolley car; —**ная сеть** network of trolley tracks.

**трамлер** *see* **трамблер.**

**трамплин** *m.* spring board (for planes).

**транзистор** *m.* (electron.) transistor; **на** —**ах** transistorized; —**изация** *f.* transistorization.

**транзит** *m.*, —**ный** *a.* transit; —**ивность** *f.* (math.) transitive relation; —**ивный** *a.* transitive.

**транзитрон** *m.* (thermionics) transitron.

**транс** *m.* (med.) trance.

**транс—** *prefix* trans—; *see also* **транз—**; —**атлантический** *a.* transatlantic.

**трансверт/ер, —ор** *m.* (elec.) transverter.

**транс/грессия** *f.* (geol.) transgression, unconformability of overlap; **согласная т.** parallel transgression; —**дуктор, —дюсер** *m.* (elec.) transducer; —**континентальный** *a.* transcontinental; —**крибировать** *v.* transcribe.

**транскристалл/изация** *f.* transcrystallization; —**ический** *a.* transcrystalline.

**транскюр/иевый** *a.*, —**ий** *m.* transcurium.

**транслир/овать** *v.* translate, relay, retransmit; —**ующий** *a.* translating, relaying.

**трансля/тор** *m.* (elec. comm.) translator; —**ция** *f.*, —**ционный** *a.* translation, translating, relaying, relay, retransmitting; repeater.

**трансми/ссия** *f.*, —**ссионный** *a.* transmission, transmitting; —**ттер** *m.* transmitter.

**транс/мутация** *f.* (biol.) transmutation; —**океанский** *a.* transoceanic; —**парант** *m.* (phot.) transparency; ruled paper; —**пирация** *f.* transpiration; —**пирировать** *v.* transpire; —**плантация** *f.* (med.) transplantation; (bot.) grafting; —**плутониевый** *a.*, —**плутоний** *m.* transplutonium.

**транспо/зиция** *f.*, —**нирование** *n.*, —**нировка** *f.* transposition; —**нировать** *v.* transpose.

**транспорт** *m.* transport, transportation, conveyance, conveying, hauling, transit, transfer; —**абельный** *a.* transportable, portable; —**ер** *m.*, —**ерный**

*a.* transporter, conveyor; carrier; **ленточный —ер, —ерная лента** conveyer belt, feed belt; **—ерный червяк** worm conveyer, screw conveyer.

**транспортир** *m.* protractor.

**транспортир/ование** *n.* transportation, conveying, conveyance, handling, handling operation; **система —ования** transportation system; **—ованный** *a.* transported, conveyed; **—овать** *v.* transport, convey, carry, haul, transfer; **—овочный, —ующий** *a.* transport, conveying; **—овочная лента** conveyer belt.

**транспорти/ик** *m.* transport worker; **—ый** *a.* transport, conveying; **—ый винт** screw conveyer, worm conveyer; **—ая лента** conveyer belt; **—ая труба** conveyer pipe, conduit; **—ое средство** means of transportation; conveying device.

**транссудация** *f.* transudation.

**трансуран/ид** *m.* transuranide; **—овый** *a.* transuranium, transuranic (element).

**трансфер, —т** *m.*, **—тный** *a.* transfer; **—кар** *m.* transfer car.

**трансформатор** *m.*, **—ный** *a.* (elec.) transformer; converter; **т.-повыситель, повышающий т.** step-up transformer; **т.-понизитель, т.-редуктор, понижающий т.** step-down transformer; **т. частоты** (rad.) frequency modulator; **—ный усилитель** transformer-coupled amplifier.

**трансформ/ационный** *a.*, **—ация** *f.*, **—ирование** *n.* transformation, conversion, change; **коэффициент —ации** (elec.) transformation ratio; **—изм** *m.* (biol.) transformism; **—ировать** *v.* transform, convert, change; **—ирующий** *a.* transforming.

**трансфузия** *f.* transfusion.

**трансцендент/альный, —ный** *a.* (math.) transcendental.

**транш/ея** *f.*, **—ейный** *a.* trench, ditch, pit, dug-out.

**трап** *m.* ladder, gangway; *see* **трапп.**

**трапец/евидный, —иевидный** *a.* (geom.) trapeziform; **—оидальный** *a.* trapezoid, trapezoidal; buttress (screw thread); **—ия** *f.* trapezium; trapezoid;

trapeze; **—оэдр** *m.* (cryst.) trapezohedron.

**т-ра плавл.** *abbr.* (**температура плавления** melting point.

**трапп** *m.*, **—овый** *a.* (petr.) trap, traprock.

**трапспаут** *m.* trap spout (of water jacket).

**трас, —с** *m.* (petr.) trass (natural pozzolana).

**трасса** *f.* route, course, run (of cable), layout; line, direction.

**трасс/ант** *m.* (com.) drawee; **—ат** *m.* drawer.

**трассир/овать** *v.* trace, locate; stake out; **—овка** *f.* tracing, location, location survey; laying, laying out, layout; **—ующий** *a.* tracing; **—ующая пуля** (mil.) tracer bullet.

**трассовый** *a.* (petr.) trass.

**трат/а** *f.* expense, expenditure; consumption; waste, wasting; **—ить** *v.* expend, disburse, spend; consume; waste.

**тратта** *f.* (com.) bill of exchange, draft.

**траубевский закон** Traube's rule.

**траулер** *m.* trawler.

**траурница** *f.* a butterfly (*Vanessa antiopa*).

**трафарет** *m.*, **—ный** *a.* stencil; routine; **—ить** *v.* stencil.

**трафик** *m.* traffic.

**трах/еальный** *a.* (anat., bot.) tracheal; **—еид** *m.* (bot.) tracheid; **—еит** *m.* (med.) tracheitis; **—еинодышащие, —ейные** *pl.* (zool.) Tracheata; **—ейный** *a.* (anat.) tracheal; **—еотомия** *f.* (med.) tracheotomy; **—ея** *f.* (anat.) trachea; **—илины** *pl.* (zool.) jellyfish (*Trachylina*).

**трахит** *m.* trachyte (an alkaline felsite rock); **—ный, —овый** *a.* trachyte, trachytic.

**трахома** *f.* (med.) trachoma.

**ТРД** *abbr.* (**турбореактивный двигатель**) turbojet engine; **ТРДВ** *abbr.* (**турбореактивный двигатель, винтовой**) turbopropeller jet engine.

**требов/ание** *n.* demand, requirement, requisition, request, claim; **—ательность** *f.* exactions; **—ательный** *a.* demanding, exacting, particular; **—ать** *v.* demand, claim, require, request, want, ask, call (for); —**ать настой-чиво** insist; —**аться** v. be required, be requested, be necessary.

**треб/уемый** a. required, requisite, specified; —**уемая мощность** required power, input; —**ующий** a. requiring, in want (of), requesting, demanding.

**тревог/а** f. alarm, anxiety, fear, concern; **бить** —**у** v. sound an alarm, give an alarm; **быть в** —**е** v. be anxious (about); **сигнал** —**и** alarm signal, alarm.

**тревож/ить** v. alarm, disturb, worry; —**иться** v. be alarmed, be anxious, worry; —**ный** a. alarming, troubling, uneasy; —**ный сигнал** alarm.

**трегал/аза** f. trehalase; —**оза** f. trehalose.

**трегер** m. carrier.

**трегерит** m. trögerite (uranium mineral).

**трезвость** f. soberness.

**трезвучие** n. (music) triad.

**трезвый** a. sober, sound, judicious.

**трезуб/ец** m. trident; —**чатый,** —**ый** a. trident, tridentate, three-toothed, three-pronged.

**трейбование** see **капелирование**.

**трейлер** m. trailer.

**трек** m. (nucl.) track.

**трелев/ать** v. haul, skid; —**ка** f., —**очный** a. hauling.

**трельяж** m. trellis, lattice, latticework.

**тремадокский** a. (geol.) Tremadoc.

**трематоды** pl. (zool.) Trematoda.

**тремблер** m. (elec.) trembler.

**тремолит** m. (min.) tremolite (a variety of amphibole).

**трензель** m., —**ное железо** snaffle bit; **большой т.** (mach.) quadrant; **малый т.** (mech.) tumbler.

**трен/ие** n. friction, rubbing; **т. покоя** friction of rest; **без** —**ия** frictionless; **внутреннее т.** internal friction; viscosity; **жила** —**ия** (geol.) attrition vein; **сопротивление от** —**ия** frictional resistance; **тормоз** —**ия** friction brake; **электричество** —**ия** frictional electricity.

**трениров/анный** a. trained; conditioned; activated (catalyst); —**ать** v. train; condition; age; —**ка** f., —**очный** a. training; conditioning; aging.

**трено/га** f. tripod; derrick crane; —**гий,** —**жный** a. tripod, three-legged; —**жник** m., —**жный штатив** tripod.

**трентонский** a. (geol.) Trenton.

**тренцов/альная машина** worming machine (for rope); —**ать** v. worm.

**треншальтер** m. (elec.) cut-out switch.

**трео/за** f. threose; —**зовая кислота** threosic acid; —**нин** m. threonine; —**новая кислота** threonic acid.

**трепал/ка** f., —**о** n. brake, swingle, scutcher, beater (for fibers); —**ьный** a. braking, scutching; —**ьная машина** disintegrator; —**ьщик** m. stripper, beater.

**трепан** m. (surgery) trepan, trephine; trepan, trepanning tool; —**ация** f. trepanation.

**трепание** n. braking, swingling, scutching, beating (of fibers).

**трепанировать** v. trepan, perforate with a trepan.

**треп/аный** a. braked, scutched (fiber); —**ать** v. pull about; fray; brake, scutch, swingle, beat, break; —**аться** v. fray.

**трепел** m. (min.) tripoli, tripoli earth, tripolite; **английский т.** rottenstone; —**ьный** a. tripoli, tripoline.

**трепет** m. tremble, trepidation, palpitation, shiver; —**ание** n. trembling, palpitation, shivering, shaking, tremors, throbbing; —**ать** v. tremble, palpitate, shiver, shake; —**ный** a. trembling, palpitating.

**трепешник** m. (bot.) sanicle (*Sanicula europaea*).

**трепло** n. scutching blade (for fibers).

**треск** m. crack, crackle, snap, decrepitation.

**треска** f. cod, codfish.

**треск/ание** n. cracking, crackling, splitting; —**ать** v. crack, split, cleave; —**аться** v. crack, crackle, split, cleave; chap.

**тресковый** a. cod; **т. жир** cod liver oil.

**трескотня** f. rattle, continuous crackling.

**трескучник** m. (bot.) weld, dyer's weed (*Reseda luteola*).

**тресн/увший,** —**утый** a. cracked, decrepitated; —**уть** v. crack, fracture, split, burst; chap; —**уться** v. knock, strike, hit (against).

**трест** *m.* trust, combine; **правление —а** trust board.

**треста** *f.* stock, treated plant fibers.

**трестиров/ание** *n.* foundation of a trust; **—ать** *v.* organize into a trust.

**трет** *pr. 3 sing. of* **тереть.**

**трет—** *abbr.* (**третичный**) tertiary.

**третейский** *a.* arbitral; **т. анализ** umpire analysis, umpire assay; **т. суд** court of arbitration; **т. судья** arbitrator, referee.

**третекс** *m.* a building material made of wood pulp.

**трет/ий** *a.* third; **—ья копия** triplicate; **в —ьих** in the third place, thirdly.

**третичный** *a.* tertiary, ternary; **т. период** (geol.) Tertiary period; **т. спирт** tertiary alcohol.

**третник** *m.* soft solder.

**третной** *a.* every four months; mottled.

**третняк** *see* **третник.**

**треть** *f.* a third, one third.

**третьина** *f.* (bot.) buckbean (*Menyanthes trifoliata*).

**треугольн/ик** *m.* (geom.) triangle; **—ый** *a.* triangular, three-cornered.

**треф** *m.* (rolling mill) wobbler, wabbler.

**трефоль** *see* **трилистник.**

**трех—** *prefix* tri—, three, triple; **—атомный** *a.* triatomic; trihydric (alcohol); **—бромистый** *a.* tribromide (of).

**трехвалентн/ость** *f.* trivalence; **—ый** *a.* trivalent.

**трехвалковый** *a.* three-roller; **т. стан** three-roller mill, three-high mill.

**трех/ваттный** *a.* (elec.) three-watt; **—водный гидрат** trihydrate; **—главая мышца** (anat.) triceps; **—гнездный** *a.* three-cell, three-celled; (bot.) trilobate; **—горлый** *a.* three-necked (bottle).

**трехгранн/ик** *m.* (geom.) trihedron; **—ый** *a.* trihedral; three-surfaced; bounded by three surfaces.

**трех/дименсионный** *a.* three-dimensional; **—дневный** *a.* three-day; **—дольный** *a.* (bot.) trilobate, three-lobed; **—жильный** *a.* three-strand, triple-core, triple (cable); **—замещенные** *pl.* trisubstitution products, triderivatives; **—замещенный фосфат кальция** tricalcium phosphate; **—заходная резьба** triple (screw) thread.

**трехзуб/чатый, —ый** *a.* trident, tridentate, three-pronged.

**трех/иодистый** *a.* triiodide (of); **—каскадный** *a.* three-stage; triple-cascade; **—кислотный** *a.* triacid; **—колонный** *a.* three-column, three-legged; **—контактный** *a.* (elec.) three-pronged, three-pin (plug); **—контурный** *a.* three-circuit; **—корпусный** *a.* three-unit; triple; triple-effect (evaporator); **—красочный** *a.* three-color; **—кратный** *a.* threefold, triple, three-stage; **—кремнеземик** *m.* trisilicate (group of minerals); **—кулачковый** *a.* three-jawed; **—ламповый** *a.* (rad.) three-tube; **—летие** *n.* triennial; **—летний** *a.* triennial, three-year; **—линейный** *a.* trilinear; **—листный** *a.* trifoliate; **—листовой** *a.* three-sheet; **—лопастный** *a.* three-bladed; trifoliate; (bot.) trilobate; **—лучевая щель** (pal.) trilete markings.

**трехманнит** *m.* (min.) trechmannite (a sulfarsenite of silver).

**трех/мерный** *a.* three-dimensional; **—месячный** *a.* three-month, quarterly; **—минутный** *a.* three-minute; **—моторный** *a.* three-motor (airplane); **—недельный** *a.* three-week; **—ниточная резьба, —оборотная резьба** triple (screw) thread; **—обмоточный** *a.* triple-wound; **—окись** *f.* trioxide; **—основной** *a.* tribasic; **—осный** *a.* triaxial.

**трех/палубный** *a.* three-deck; **—палый, —перстный** *a.* (zool.) tridactylous; **—плечий** *a.* three-arm, three-armed; **—полье** *n.* three-field system (of crop rotation); **—польный** *a.* three-crop; **—полюсный** *a.* tripolar, triple-pole; **—проводный** *a.* three-wire, three-line, triple; **—процентный** *a.* three per cent; **—путный** *a.* three-way, three-lane (highway); **—реберный** *a.* tricostate; **—рядный** *a.* three-row, triserial, triple; three-range, three-tier; **—сернистый** *a.* trisulfide (of); **—скальчатый** *a.* triple-plunger (pump).

**трехслой/ка** *f.* three-ply; **—ные** *pl.* (zool.) Triploblastica; **—ный** *a.* three-ply, three-layer; triple-covered (wire).

**трехсот/летие** *n.* tercentenary; **—ый** *a.* tercentennial; three-hundredth.

**трех/срезный** *a.* triple-shear; **—створчатый** *a.* three-valved; **—стержневой** *a.* three-legged; three-rod; **—сторонний** *a.* trilateral, trihedral, three-sided; **—струйный** *a.* triple-jet; **—ступенчатый** *a.* three-stage, three-step, three-stepped; triple-cascade; **—тонный** *a.* three-ton.

**трехфазн/ый** *a.* (elec.) triphase, three-phase; **т. генератор, генератор —ого тока** three-phase generator.

**трехформенн/ость** *f.* (cryst.) trimorphism; **—ый** *a.* trimorphous.

**треххлористый** *a.* trichloride (of).

**трехходов/ой** *a.* three-way, three-pass, three-throw; **т. кран** three-way cock, T-valve; **—ая деталь** T-piece; **—ая нарезка** triple (screw) thread.

**трехцвет/ка** *f.* (bot.) pansy (*Viola tricolor*); **—ность** *f.* trichromatism; (cryst.) trichroism; **—ный** *a.* tricolored, trichromatic; (bot.) trifloral.

**трех/цилиндровый** *a.* three-cylinder; **—частичный** *a.* three-piece.

**трехчетверт/ка** *f.* three quarters; **—ной** *a.* three-quarter.

**трехчлен** *m.*, **—ное количество** (math.) trinomial; **—истый** *a.* (zool.) triarticulate; **—ный** *a.* trinomial, trinominal, ternary, three-membered.

**трех/ъярусный, —этажный** *a.* three-story, three-storied; three-tier; **—ъядерный** *a.* with three nuclei; **—ъязычный** *a.* trilingual.

**трещ/ание** *n.* cracking, crackling, rattling; **—ать** *v.* crack, crackle, rattle; burst, split; **—етка** *see* **трещотка.**

**трещин/а** *f.*, **—ный** *a.* crack, cleft, fissure, fracture, crevice, slit, split, chink, break, flaw; (geol.) joint; **—ная вода** (geol.) interstitial water; **—ное строение** fracture pattern.

**трещиноват/ость** *f.* parting, jointing, fracturing; block disintegration; **—ый** *a.* cracked, full of cracks, fissured, split, cleft; broken up, crumbling (rock).

**трещотка** *f.* ratchet drill; clack; click; **сверлильная т.** ratchet drill.

**три** three; *prefix* tri—, three; **—ада** *f.* triad; **—адный** *a.* triad, ternary.

**триаз/ан** *m.* triazane; **—ен** *m.* triazene; diazoamine; **—ин** *m.* triazine; **—инил** *m.* triazinyl.

**триазо—** *prefix* triazo—, azido—; **—бензол** *m.* triazobenzene, phenyl azo-imide.

**триазол** *m.* triazole, pyrrodiazole; **—ил** *m.* triazolyl; **—он** *m.* triazolone, keto-triazole.

**триакантин** *m.* triacanthine.

**триаконтан** *m.* triacontane.

**триаконтаэдр** *m.* (geom.) triacontahedron; **—ический** *a.* triacontahedral.

**триамино—** *prefix* triamino—.

**триаммоний** *m.* triammonium.

**триаморфный** *a.* (cryst.) triamorphous.

**триангель** *m.* (railroad) brake beam.

**триангул/ировать** *v.* (surv.) triangulate; **—ятор** *m.* triangulator; **—яция** *f.* triangulation.

**триарилметан** *m.*, **—овый** *a.* triaryl-methane.

**триас** *m.* (geol.) Trias; **—овый** *a.* Triassic.

**триацет/ат** *m.* triacetate; **—ил** *m.* triacetyl; **—илцеллюлоза** *f.* cellulose triacetate; **—ин** *m.* triacetin, glyceryl triacetate.

**триба** *f.* (biol.) tribe.

**трибензил** *m.* tribenzyl.

**трибка** *f.* gear, driving gear.

**трибо—** *prefix* tribo— (friction); **—люминесценция** *f.* triboluminescence; **—метр** *m.* tribometer, friction gage.

**трибочная сталь** pinion steel.

**трибоэлектричество** *n.* triboelectricity.

**трибром—** *prefix* tribrom—, tribromo—; **—производные** *pl.* tribromo derivatives; **—уксусная кислота** tribromo-acetic acid; **—фенол** *m.* tribromo-phenol.

**трибсталь** *f.* pinion steel.

**трибунал** *m.* tribunal, court.

**трибут/ил** *m.* tributyl; **—ирин** *m.* tributyrin, butyrin.

**тривалерин** *m.* trivalerin, phocenin.

**тривариантный** *a.* trivariant.

**тривиальн/ость** *f.* triviality; **—ый** *a.* trivial.

**триггер** *m.* trigger; (elec. comm.) flip-flop.

**тригидр/ат** *m.* trihydrate; **—окси—** *prefix* trihydroxy—.

**тригир/а** *f.* (cryst.) threefold axis of symmetry; **—ный** *a.* trigonal (system).

**триглицерид** *m.* triglyceride.

**тригон** *m.* trigon; trigone; —**альный** *a.* trigonal, triangular; —**додекаэдр** *m.* (cryst.) trigondodecahedron.

**тригонеллин** *m.* trigonelline, nicotinic methylbetaine.

**тригонометр/ический** *a.* trigonometric, trigonometrical; —**ия** *f.* trigonometry; **плоская** —**ия** plane trigonometry.

**три/декан** *m.* tridecane; —**дециловая кислота** tridecylic acid, tridecoic acid; —**димит** *m.* (min.) tridymite (a hexagonal silica).

**тридцати/гранник** *m.* triacontahedron; —**двухгранник** *m.* polyhedron with thirty-two sides.

**тридцат/ый** *a.* thirtieth; —**ь** thirty.

**триер** *m.* seed separator, grain cleaner, grader; sifter; screening machine; —**овать** *v.* screen, sort, grade.

**трижды** *adv.* thrice, three times, threefold.

**тризм** *m.* (med.) trismus.

**три/калий** *m.* tripotassium; —**кальцийфосфат** *m.* tricalcium phosphate.

**трикапр/ин** *m.* tricaprin, glyceryl tricaprinate; —**оин** *m.* tricaproin, glyceryl tricapronate.

**трикарбоновый** *a.* tricarboxylic (acid).

**триклин/ический, —ный** *a.* (cryst.) triclinic, anorthic, asymmetric.

**трикозан** *m.* tricosane.

**трико** *n.*, —**таж** *m.*, —**тажное изделие** tricot, knitted fabric, jersey.

**трикрез/ил** *m.* tricresyl; —**ол** *m.* tricresol (mixture of cresol isomers).

**трилистн/ик** *m.* (bot.) trefoil, clover (*Trifolium*); **водяной т.** buckbean, bogbean (*Menyanthes trifoliata*); —**иковидный** *a.* cloverleaf; —**ый** *a.* three-leaved, trifoliate.

**трилит** *m.* (expl.) trilite, trinitrotoluene.

**триллион** *m.* trillion.

**трилобин** *m.* trilobine.

**трилобит** *m.* trilobite (fossil crustacean).

**трилон** *m.* Trilon (chelating agent).

**тримезиновая кислота** trimesic acid.

**тример** *m.* trimer (a polymer of three molecules); —**ит** *m.* (min.) trimerite; —**ный** *a.* trimeric.

**тримет/ил** *m.*, —**иловый** *a.* trimethyl; —**иламин** *m.* trimethylamine; —**илен**

*m.* trimethylene; —**ин** *m.* (pharm.) trimethadione.

**триметрический** *a.* trimetric, orthorhombic.

**тримм/ер** *m.* trimmer; (aero.) stabilizer, elevator tab; —**инг-машина** *f.* trimming machine, trimmer.

**тримолекулярный** *a.* trimolecular.

**триморф/изм** *m.* (cryst.) trimorphism; —**ный** *a.* trimorphous.

**тримужний** *a.* (bot.) triandrous.

**тринадцат/ый** *a.* thirteenth; —**ь** thirteen.

**тринатрийфосфат** *m.* trisodium phosphate.

**тринидадский** *a.*, **Тринидад** Trinidad; **т. асфальт** Trinidad asphalt.

**тринитро**— *prefix* trinitro—; —**бензол** *m.* trinitrobenzene; —**ксилол** *m.* trinitroxylene; —**толуол** *m.* trinitrotoluene, TNT; —**фенол** *m.* trinitrophenol, picric acid.

**тринкерит** *m.* (min.) trinkerite.

**тринол** *m.* (expl.) trinol, trinitrotoluene.

**трином** *m.* (math.) trinomial.

**трио** *see* **трио-стан.**

**триод** *m.* (thermionics) triode, three-electrode tube; **кристаллический т.** transistor; **на кристаллических —ах** transistorized.

**триоз/а** *f.* triose; —**офосфат** *m.* triosephosphate.

**три/окись** *f.* trioxide; —**оксазол** *m.* trioxazole; —**оксан** *m.* trioxane, paraformaldehyde; —**окси**— *prefix* trioxy—; trihydroxy—; —**оксим** *m.* trioxime; —**оксиметилен** *m.* trioxymethylene, paraformaldehyde; —**олеин** *m.* triolein, olein; —**олефин** *m.* triolefin.

**трионал** *m.* trional, sulfonethylmethane.

**трио-стан** *m.* three-high (rolling) mill.

**триостр/енник** *m.* (bot.) triglochin; —**иевый** *a.* tricuspidate, three-pointed.

**трип** *m.* imitation velvet.

**трипальмитин** *m.* tripalmitin, palmitin.

**трипан/блау** *n.* Trypan Blue, Diamine Blue; —**овый** *a.* trypan; —**озомоз** *m.* (vet.) trypanosomiasis; —**осома** *f.* trypanosome (parasitic protozoan); —**рот** *m.* Trypan Red.

**трип/арсамид** *m.* tryparsamide; —**афлавин** *m.* Trypaflavine, acriflavine.

**трипкеит** *see* **триппкеит.**

**триплан** *m.* (aero.) triplane.

**трипл/екс** *m.* triplex; laminated safety glass; —**ет** *m.*, —**етный** *a.* triplet (spectral line); —**ит** *m.* (min.) triplite; —**оид** *m.*, —**оидный** *a.* (biol.) triploid; —**оидит** *m.* (min.) triploidite.

**триппер** *m.* (med.) gonorrhea.

**триппкеит** *m.* (min.) trippkeite (a copper arsenite).

**трипропил** *m.*, —**овый** *a.* tripropyl; —**а-мин** *m.* tripropylamine.

**трипротамин** *m.* triprotamine, sturine.

**трипс** *m.* (zool.) thrips; —**ы** *pl.* Thripidae (family); Thysanoptera (order).

**трипсин** *m.* trypsin, tryptase.

**триптан** *m.* triptane, 2,2,3-trimethylbutane.

**трипто/н** *m.* tryptone; —**фан** *m.* tryptophan, indolylalanine; —**фил** *m.* tryptophyl.

**трипугиит** *m.* (min.) tripuhyite (an iron antimonate).

**тририцинолеин** *m.* triricinolein, ricinolein.

**трисазо**— *prefix* trisazo—.

**три/сахарид** *m.* trisaccharide; —**сектри-са** *f.* (math.) trisectrix; —**секция** *f.* trisection; —**силан** *m.* trisilane; —**силикат** *m.* trisilicate; —**ста** three hundred; —**стеарин** *m.* tristearin, stearin; —**сульфид** *m.* trisulfide.

**трите** *imp. of* **тереть.**

**тритетраэдр** *m.* (cryst.) tritetrahedron.

**тритиан** *m.* trithiane.

**тритий** *m.* tritium (isotope of hydrogen).

**тритил** *m.* trityl, triphenylmethyl.

**тритио**— *prefix* trithio—; —**новая кис-лота** trithionic acid; **соль** —**новой кислоты,** —**новокислая соль** trithionate; —**угольная кислота** trithiocarbonic acid.

**тритицин** *m.* triticin (carbohydrate from *Triticum*).

**трито/мит** *m.* (min.) tritomite; —**н** *m.* (zool.) triton, newt, eft; triton, t (nucleus of tritium); Triton (detergent); —**пин** *m.* tritopine.

**триумф** *m.* triumph; —**альный** *a.* triumphal; —**атор** *m.* triumpher.

**трифан** *m.* (min.) triphane, spodumene.

**трифенил** *m.* triphenyl; —**ен** *m.* triphen-

ylene; —**карбинол** *m.* triphenylcarbinol.

**три/феррин** *m.* triferrin, iron paranucleinate; —**филин** *m.* (min.) triphylite; —**фоль** *f.* (bot.) buckbean, bogbean (*Menyanthes trifoliata*).

**трифонид** *m.* ichneumon fly (*Ichneumon jucundus*).

**трифторид** *m.* trifluoride.

**трихальцит** *m.* (min.) trichalcite.

**трихин/а,** —**елла** *f.* (zool.) trichina; —**еллез,** —**оз** *m.* (med.) trichinosis; —**еллезный,** —**озный** *a.* trichinous.

**трихиноил** *m.* triquinoyl.

**трихит** *m.* (min.) trichite (a hair-like crystallite).

**трихлор**— *prefix* trichlor—, trichloro—; —**бензол** *m.* trichlorobenzene; —**и-стый** *a.* trichloride (of); —**метан** *m.* trichloromethane, chloroform; —**оук-сусная кислота, —уксусная кислота** trichloroacetic acid; —**этан** *m.* trichloroethane; —**этилен** *m.* trichloroethylene.

**трихо**— *prefix* tricho—, trich— (hair); —**грамма** *f.* (zool.) Trichogramma; —**монацид** *m.* trichomonacide; —**мониоз, —моноз** *m.* (vet.) trichomoniasis; —**тецин** *m.* trichothecin; —**фитоз** *m.* (med.) trichophytosis, ringworm; —**цидин** *m.* trichocidin.

**трихро/изм** *m.* (cryst.) trichroism; —**ич-ный** *a.* trichroic; —**матичный** *see* **трехцветный.**

**три/цепс** *m.* (anat.) triceps; —**циан** *m.* tricyanogen; —**циклен** *m.* tricyclene; —**циклический** *a.* tricyclic; —**щетин-ник** *m.* (bot.) trisetum; —**эдр** *m.* (geom.) trihedron; —**эдрический** *a.* trihedral.

**триэн** *m.* tryen, Yatren.

**триэтил** *m.*, —**овый** *a.* triethyl; —**амин** *m.* triethylamine.

**триэтокси**— *prefix* triethoxy—.

**троакар** *m.* (surgery) trocar.

**трог** *m.* (geol.) glacial trough.

**трог/ание** *n.* touching, stirring; **т. с места** starting; —**ать** *v.* touch, affect; start; —**аться** *v.* touch, be in contact (with); stir, move; taint, spoil; —**ать-ся с места** start; **не** —**ая с места** without disturbing.

**троговая долина** *see* **трог.**

**трое** three; **на т.** in three parts.

**троекратн/о** *adv.* three times, thrice, triply; **—ый** *a.* threefold, three.

**троетес** *m.*, **—ный гвоздь** three-inch nail, plank nail.

**троечница** *f.* (bot.) barrenwort (*Epimedium*).

**тро/ить** *v.* divide into three; (agr.) trifallow; **—ичный** *a.* ternary; trinity.

**тройка** *f.* triplet, triad, set of three; trefoil; team of three.

**тройлит** *m.* (min.) troilite (a ferrous sulfide).

**тройник** *m.*, **—овый** *a.* tee, T-piece, T-joint, T-pipe, T-bend; three stands; three inches thick; trilling, six-rayed twinned crystal; (elec.) branch box, T-junction box; **—овая муфта** T-junction box; **—овое образование** trilling.

**тройничн/ость** *f.* triplicity; **—ый** *a.* triple; (anat.) trifacial.

**тройн/ой** *a.* triple, triplicate, three, tri-, ternary; triangular; **т. процесс** (met.) triplex process; **—ая ось** (cryst.) triad axis; **—ая связь** triple bond; **—ая соль** trisalt; **—ая точка** triple point; **—ое деление** (nucl.) ternary fission; **—ое правило** (math.) rule of three; **—я** triplets.

**тройский вес** Troy weight.

**тройственн/ость** *f.* triplicity; **—ый** *a.* triple.

**тройчат/ка** *f.* triad, group of three; **—ный** *a.* ternate, arranged in threes.

**троктолит** *m.* (petr.) troctolite (a variety of gabbro).

**троллеит** *m.* (min.) trolleite.

**троллей** *m.*, **—ный** *a.* (elec.) trolley; **—ный провод** trolley wire; **—ная вагонетка** trolley car.

**тромб** *m.* (med.) thrombus, blood clot.

**тромба** *see* **смерч**.

**тромб/аза** *f.*, **—ин** *m.* thrombase, thrombin, zymoplasm; **—оген** *m.* thrombogen, serozyme; **—оз** *m.* (med.) thrombosis; coagulation, clotting; **—опения** *f.* (med.) thrombopenia; **—опластин** *m.* thromboplastin; **—оцит** *m.* thrombocyte, blood platelet.

**тром/ель, —мель** *m.* (min.) trommel, revolving sieve, washing drum.

**Троммера проба** Trommer's test (for glucose in urine).

**тромолит** *m.* Tromolit (iron-nickel-cobalt-aluminum-copper alloy).

**трона** *f.* (min.) trona (sodium sesquicarbonate).

**тронк** *m.*, **—овый** *a.*, **—овый поршень** trunk, trunk piston; **—овый двигатель** trunk engine.

**трон/утый** *a.* touched, affected; spoiled, tainted; **—уть** *see* **трогать**; **—уться** *v.* be affected; spoil, go bad; start.

**троостит** *m.* (min.) troostite (a variety of willemite); (met.) *see* **тростит**.

**—троп** *m. suffix* **—**trope.

**тропа** *f.* path, pathway, walk, track.

**тропа/кокаин** *m.* tropacocaine, benzoyl-pseudotropine; **—н** *m.* tropane, N-methylnortropane; **—нол** *m.* tropanol; **—нолкарбоновая кислота** tropanolcarboxylic acid; **—нон** *m.* tropanone.

**троп/ат** *m.* tropate; **—ацин** *m.* tropacine; **—еин** *m.* tropeine; **—ентан** *m.* tropentane; **—еолин** *m.* tropeolin; **—идин** *m.* tropidine, N-methylnortropidine; **—изм** *m.* tropism.

**тропик** *m.* tropic; **—и** *pl.* tropics; **т. козерога** Capricorn; **т. рака** Cancer; **между —ами** intertropical.

**троп/ил** *m.* tropyl; **—илиден** *m.* tropilidene, 1,3,5-cycloheptatriene; **—илий** *m.* tropylium; **—ин** *m.* tropine, N-methyltropoline; (biol.) tropin.

**тропинка** *f.* little path, footpath.

**тропин/карбоновая кислота** tropinecarboxylic acid, ecgonine; **—овая кислота** *see* **тропиновая кислота**.

**тропическ/ий** *a.* tropic; torrid (zone); jungle (fever); **—ая растительность** tropical vegetation.

**—троп/ия** *f. suffix* **—**tropy; **—ный** *a. suffix* **—**tropic (turning, changing).

**тропо—** *prefix* tropo— (turn, turning, change).

**троповая кислота** tropic acid, phenylhydracrylic acid.

**тропо/пауза** *f.* (meteor.) tropopause, top of troposphere; **—сфера** *f.* troposphere; **—сферный** *a.* troposphere, tropospheric.

**трос** *m.* cable, rope, (steel) line.

**тростильн/ый** *a.* twisting; **—ая машина** (text.) slubbing frame.

**тростин/а, —ка** *f.* reed, cane.

**тростит** *m.* (met.) troostite (a transition substance in steel); **—овый** *a.* troostitic.

**тростить** *v.* twist, splice.

**трост/ник** *m.*, **—никовый** *a.*, **—ь** *f.*, **—яной** *a.* (bot.) cane, spec. reed (*Phragmites*); **индийский т.** rattan (*Calamus*); **сахарный т.** sugar cane; **—никовый мат** rush matting; **—никовый сахар** cane sugar; **—янка** *f.* hard grass (*Sclerochloa*).

**тротил** *m.* (expl.) trotyl, trinitrotoluene.

**тротуар** *m.*, **—ный** *a.* sidewalk, footpath; pavement, platform; **движущийся т.** conveyer; **край —а** curb.

**троф/ический** *a.* trophic, nutrition; **—ный** *a. suffix* trophic; **—о—** *prefix* tropho— (food, nourishment); **—о-невроз** *m.* (med.) trophoneurosis.

**трохо/вая кислота** trochoic acid; **—ида** *f.* (geom.) trochoid; **—идальный, —идный** *a.* trochoid, trochoidal; **—идальный анализатор** trochoidal (mass) analyzer (a mass spectrometer); **—сфера** *f.* (zool.) trochosphere, trochophore; **—трон** *m.* trochotron (trochoidal mass spectrometer or electronic beam-switching tube).

**трощен/ие** *n.* twisting, torsion; (text.) slubbing; throwing (of silk); **—ый** *a.* twisted; thrown.

**трояк/ий** *a.* triple, threefold; **—о** *adv.* in three different ways.

**труб/а** *f.* pipe, tube; flue, funnel, shaft; duct, conduit; trumpet; **—ы** *pl.* piping, tubing; **—ач** *m.* stentor (trumpet-shaped protozoan); **туранский —ачик** tree cricket (*Oecanthus turanicus*).

**трубк/а** *f.* tube, small pipe; (tel.) receiver; **согнутая т. в виде U** U-tube; **—оверты** *pl.* (zool.) Attelabidae; **—овидный, —ообразный** *a.* tubiform, tubular; **—оцветный** *a.* (bot.) tubuliflorous.

**трубн/ый** *a.* pipe, tube; **—ые принадлежности** pipe fittings.

**трубо—** *prefix* pipe, tube; **—волочильный станок** tube-drawing bench; **—дер** *m.* tube extractor; **—держатель** *m.* pipe support, tube holder; **—испытательный аппарат** pipe-testing apparatus, pipe prover; **—литейное производство** pipe casting; **—ловка** *f.* pipe grab; **—нарезной станок** pipe-threading machine; **—отвод** *m.* branch pipe; **—очиститель** *m.* pipe cleaner, tube cleaner, reamer.

**трубопровод** *m.* pipe-line, supply line; conduit, duct; piping system, piping, tubing; manifold (of engine); **впускной т.** intake manifold; **—ная сеть** pipe system, piping system, piping; **—чик** *m.* pipe fitter, plumber.

**трубопрокат/ка** *f.*, **—ный** *a.* pipe rolling, tube rolling; **—ный завод, —ный стан** tube mill, tube-rolling mill.

**трубо/расширитель** *m.* tube beader, tube expander; **—рез** *m.* pipe cutter, tube cutter; **—резный станок** pipe-cutting machine; **—рог** *m.* whelk (marine snail); **—формовочная машина** pipe-molding machine; **—цвет** *m.* trumpet flower (*Tecoma radicans*); **—чист** *m.* chimney sweep, sweeper; **—чка** *f.* little tube.

**трубочн/ый** *a.* pipe, tube; **т. камень** (petr.) pipestone, catlinite (a red shale); **—ая глина** pipe clay.

**трубчатый** *a.* tubular, tubulated, hollow; piping; **т. котел** tubular boiler.

**трубы** *gen. and pl. of* **труба**; **т.-зонды** *pl.* (agr.) fumigating tubes.

**труд** *m.* labor, work, toil; (scientific) treatise; **—ы** *pl.* transactions, proceedings (of society), works (of author); **без —а** without difficulty, without effort, easily; **с большим —ом** with great difficulty; **биржа —а** labor bureau; **взять на себя т.** *v.* take the trouble; **положить много —а** *v.* take great pains; **физический т.** manual labor.

**трудиться** *v.* work, labor, toil.

**трудно** *adv.* with difficulty, difficultly; it is difficult; **—вато** *adv.* with some difficulty; it is rather difficult; **—ватый** *a.* rather difficult; **—дробимый** *a.* strong, tough; **—обрабатываемый** *a.* churlish, difficult to work; **—определимый** *a.* nondescript, difficult to define; **—плавкий** *a.* difficultly fusible; infusible, refractory; —раствори́мый *a.* difficultly soluble; —сть *f.* difficulty, hardship; —теку́щий *a.* viscous, thick.

тру́дный *a.* difficult, hard, laborious, heavy (work).

трудо/во́й *a.* labor, earned by labor; —день *m.* work day; —ёмкий *a.* labor-consuming, laborious; —люби́вый *a.* hard-working, industrious; —лю́бие *n.* industriousness, industry; —спосо́бность *f.* capacity for work; —спосо́бный *a.* efficient, able-bodied.

труд/ы́ *pl. of* труд; —я́щийся *a.* working; *m.* worker; здравоохране́ние —я́щихся occupational health.

тру́кс/еллин *m.* truxelline; —иллин *m.* truxilline; —и́лловая кислота́ truxillic acid; —и́новая кислота́ truxinic acid.

труп *m.* corpse; —ножировоско́вой *a.* adipocerous.

тру́пн/ый *a.* corpse; т. воск, т. жировоск adipocere (mixture of calcium and potassium palmitates); т. яд ptomaine; —ое окочене́ние rigor mortis.

тру́с/ить *v.* be afraid; shake, scatter; —ли́вый *a.* cowardly, timid, apprehensive.

трут *m.* tinder, punk (niter-treated agaric); agaric (dried fruit body of *Polyporus officinalis*); *pr. 3 pl. of* тере́ть.

тру́тень *m.* drone, drone bee.

тру́тн/ик *m.* (bot.) tinder fungus; —и́ца *f.* tinder box, lighter.

трутови́к *m.* (bot.) agaric (*Polyporus*); —о́вые *pl.* pore fungi (*Polyporaceae*).

Трутона правило Trouton's rule.

трух/а́ *f.* rot, rotten wood; —лый, —ля́вый *a.* rotten.

тру́щий, —ся *a.* rubbing, friction.

трюм *m.* bilge, hold (of freighter).

Трюмана мастика́тор Truman's masticator.

трю́мный *a.* bilge, hold.

трю́фел/евые грибы́, —и *pl.* (bot.) Tuberaceae; —ь *m.*, —ьный *a.* truffle (*Tuber*); олений —ь stinkhorn (*Phalus*).

тряп/и́чный *a.* rag; —ка *f.* rag, piece of waste; —ьё *n.* rags.

тряс/е́ние *n.* shaking, shivering, trem-

bling; —и́лка *f.* (mech.) shake.

тряси́н/а *f.*, —ный *a.* marsh, swamp, bog, mire, morass; quaking bog.

тря́ск/а *f.* jolting, jolt, joggling; —ий *a.* jolting; shaky; rough (road); —о-формо́вочная маши́на (molding) jar-ramming machine, jolt-ramming machine.

тряс/ти́ *v.* shake, jolt, joggle; —ти́сь *v.* shake, joggle; shiver, tremble; —унка *f.* (bot.) quaking grass (*Briza*); —учка *f.* shaker; (med.) intermittent fever; (bot.) quaking grass; —у́щийся *a.* shaking, shaky, quaking.

тряхну́ть *see* трясти́.

тсе-тсе *see* цеце.

т. стекл. *abbr.* (температу́ра стеклова́ния) glass point.

тсу́г/а *f.* (bot.) hemlock (*Tsuga*); —и́новая кислота́ tsugic acid.

ТСЭ *abbr.* (Техни́ческая Сове́тская Энциклопе́дия) Technical Soviet Encyclopedia.

ТТ *abbr.* (теорети́ческая таре́лка) (distillation) theoretical plate.

ТТХ *abbr.* (хло́ристый трифенилтетразо́л) triphenyltetrazolium chloride.

ту *f. acc. of* тот; ТУ *abbr.* (трихлорфенокси́уксусная кислота́) trichlorophenoxyacetic acid.

туале́тные изде́лия toilet preparations.

ту́ба/вая кислота́ tubaic acid; —зид *m.* Tubazid, isonicotinic acid hydrazide; —ин *m.* tubain (resin from derris root); —нол *m.* tubanol.

туберку́л *m.* (med.) tubercle; —ёз *m.* tuberculosis; -ёзный *a.* tuberculous, tubercular, consumptive; —ин *m.* tuberculin; —остеари́новая кислота́ tuberculostearic acid, 10-methyl-stearic acid.

туберо́з/а *f.* (bot.) tuberose (*Polianthes tuberosa*); —ный *a.* tuberose; tuberous, nodular; —ное ма́сло tuberose oil.

ту́бо/кура́рин *m.* tubocurarine (paracurarine); —токси́н *m.* tubotoxin (rotenone).

тубу/ла́тный *a.* tubulate, tubulated; —лус, —с *m.* tubulure, tubule, tube.

туга́йный *a.* tugaic (soil).

туг/о *adv.* tightly, fast; slowly, with difficulty; ему́ прихо́дится т. he finds it difficult; —о́й *a.* tight, close; stiff, unyielding; dull; —онатянутый *a.* tightly drawn, taut, tense.

**тугоплавк/ий** *a.* difficultly fusible, high-melting; infusible, refractory; hard (glass); —**ость** *f.* infusibility, refractoriness.

**тугость** *f.* tightness, stiffness, slowness.

**туда** *adv.* there, thither; **т. и обратно** back and forth, to and fro.

**туе/вик** *m.* (bot.) thujopsis; —**вый** *a.* thuja; —**вая кислота** thujic acid; —**вое масло** thuja oil, oil of white cedar; —**н** *m.* thujene, tanacetene; —**тин** *m.* thujetin; —**тиновая кислота** thujetic acid.

**туже** *comp. of* **туго, тугой,** tighter.

**тужиться** *v.* exert oneself.

**тужурка** *f.* short coat.

**туз** *m.* dinghy.

**тузем/ец** *m.* native; —**ный** *a.* native, indigenous.

**тузл/ук** *m.,* —**уковать** *v.,* —**учный** *a.* (leather) brine.

**туй/евое масло** *see* **туевое масло;** —**ен** *see* **туен;** —**игенин** *m.* thujigenin.

**туйил** *m.,* —**овый** *a.* thujyl; **хлористый т.** thujyl chloride; —**амин** *m.* thujyl amine; —**овый спирт** *see* **туйол.**

**туй/ин** *m.* thujin; —**оид** *m.* thujoid; —**ол** *m.* thujol, hydroxythujene, absinthol; —**он** *m.* thujone, tanacetone; —**ородин** *m.* thujorhodin, rhodoxanthin; —**я** *see* **туя.**

**тук** *m.,* —**овый** *a.* manure, fertilizer.

**туко/мешалка** *f.* fertilizer mixer; —**нагрузчик** *m.* fertilizer loader; —**разбрасыватель,** —**распределитель** *m.* fertilizer spreader, manure spreader; —**смесь** *f.* fertilizer mixture; —**смешение** *n.* fertilizer mixing.

**тула сплав** tula metal (a silver-copper-lead alloy).

**тулейка** *f.* shank.

**Тулета раствор** (min.) Thoulet solution, Sonstadt solution.

**тул/ий** *m.* thulium, Tm; **окись —ия** thulium oxide; **хлористый т.** thulium chloride; —**ит** *m.* (min.) thulite (a variety of zoisite).

**туловище** *n.* trunk, body, torso, bulk.

**туляремия** *f.* (med.) tularemia, rabbit fever.

**туман** *m.* fog, mist, haze, vapor, spray,

film; —**ить** *v.* fog, darken, make obscure; —**иться** *v.* get foggy, grow dark, become obscure, get dim; —**ность** *f.* fogginess, mistiness, mist, haziness; (astron.) nebula; —**ный** *a.* foggy, misty, hazy, cloudy; nebulous, vague, obscure; —**омер** *m.* fog meter; —**ообразователь** *m.* fog generator; mist sprayer; —**ообразовательный** *a.* mist (spraying); —**ообразующая установка** mist sprayer.

**тумба** *f.* curbstone; pedestal, cabinet leg; stub pole, fender.

**тумблер** *m.* tumbler; (elec.) toggle switch.

**туменол** *m.* Tumenol, ichthammol.

**тумский камень** (min.) axinite.

**тунг** *m.* (bot.) tung tree (*Aleurites*); **т. Форда,** —**овое дерево** tung oil tree (*A. fordii*); **японский т.** mu tree (*A. cordata*); —**овое масло** tung oil.

**тунгстен** *see* **вольфрам.**

**тунгстит** *m.* (min.) tungstite, tungstic ocher (tungsten trioxide).

**тундр/а** *f.,* —**овый** *a.,* —**овая полоса** tundra (treeless plain).

**тунец** *m.* tunny (fish).

**тунеяд/ец** *m.* parasite; —**ный** *a.* parasitic, parasitical; —**ство** *n.* parasitism.

**туникаты** *pl.* (zool.) Tunicata, Urochorda.

**туницин** *m.* (zool.) tunicin.

**туннель** *m.,* —**ный** *a.* tunnel, subway; duct, conduit; —**ная сушилка** tunnel dryer.

**тупеть** *v.* become blunt, grow dull.

**тупик** *m.,* —**овый** *a.* blind alley, blind pass, impasse, cul-de-sac, dead end; (railroad) siding; **попасть в т.** *v.* be at a loss, be at a deadlock; **стать в т.** *v.* be perplexed, be at a standstill; —**овый упор** buffer stop.

**тупить** *v.* blunt, dull, take off the edge.

**туповат/ость** *f.* bluntness; —**ый** *a.* rather blunt, rather dull, dullish.

**тупой** *a.* blunt, dull, stub; obtuse (angle).

**тупо/конечный** *a.* blunt-pointed, blunt; —**носый** *a.* blunt-nosed, blunt-pointed, blunt; —**сть** *f.* bluntness, dullness; —**угольный** *a.* obtuse-angled; obtuse (triangle).

**тур** *m.* round; gabion; mountain goat.

**тур.** *abbr.* (турецкий) Turkish; (**туркестанский**) Turkestan.

**туранит** *m.* (min.) turanite (a hydrous copper vanadate).

**тураноза** *f.* turanose.

**турацин** *m.* turacin.

**турбеллярии** *pl.* (zool.) Turbellaria.

**турбидиметр** *m.* turbidimeter; **—ический** *a.* turbidimetric, nephelometric (analysis); **—ия** *f.* turbidimetry.

**турбин/а** *f.*, **—ный** *a.* turbine; **т.-компаунд** compound turbine; **—ный эксгаустер** turbine-driven exhauster; **—ная установка** turbine plant.

**турбино—** *prefix* turbino—, turbine.

**турбо—** *prefix* turbo—, turbine; **—агрегат** *m.* turbo-unit; **—альтернатор** *m.* turbo-alternator; **—бур** *m.* turbine drill; **—вентилятор** *m.*, **—воздуходувка** *f.* turboblower, turbofan; **—винтовой** *a.* turbopropeller; **—воз** *m.* turbine locomotive; **—возбудитель** *m.* (elec.) turbo-exciter; **—генератор** *m.* (elec.) turbogenerator.

**турбодинамо** *n.*, **—машина** *f.* (elec.) turbodynamo.

**турбо/компрессор** *m.* turbocompressor, turboblower; **—логоушер** *m.* (min.) turbowasher; **—насос** *m.* turbine pump; **—преобразователь** *m.* (elec.) turboconverter; **—реактивный** *a.* turbojet; **—строение** *n.* turbine construction; **—трансформатор** *m.* turbine transformer; **—эксгаустер** *m.* turbine-driven exhauster.

**турбулентн/ость** *f.* turbulence; **—ый** *a.* turbulent; **—ое движение** eddy.

**турбулизация** *f.* agitation.

**тургит** *m.* (min.) turgite, hydrohematite.

**тургор** *m.* (bot.) turgor.

**турель** *f.* turret; ring mount.

**турецк/ий** *a.* Turkish; **т. боб** (bot.) kidney bean (*Phaseolus*); **т. перец** red pepper, paprika; **—ое седло** (anat.) sella turcica.

**турингит** *see* тюрингит.

**туркестан** Turkestan.

**туркм.** *abbr.* (туркменский) Turkmen.

**Туркменская СССР** Turkmen Soviet Socialist Republic.

**турма** *f.* coal bin (made of cement).

**турмалин** *m.*, **—овый** *a.* (min.) tourmaline; **благородный т.** gem tourmaline,

rubellite; **—изация** *f.* tourmalinization; **—овый роговик** tourmaline hornstone, cornubianite (hornfels).

**турменная кислота** tower (sulfuric) acid.

**турмер/ин** *m.* turmerin; **—овая кислота** turmeric acid.

**турнбул/лева синь, —ьская синь** Turnbull's blue, insoluble Prussian blue.

**турне** *n.* tour, round, circuit.

**турнейский** *a.* (geol.) Tournaisian.

**турнепс** *m.* (bot.) turnip (*Brassica campestris rapifera*).

**турнер/ит** *m.* (min.) turnerite (a variety of monazite); **—ова желть** Turner's yellow, Cassel yellow.

**турникет** *m.* tourniquet; turnstile; turnpike.

**турок** *m.* Turk.

**туронский** *a.* (geol.) Turonian.

**турпет** *m.* turpeth root (of *Ipomoea turpethum*); **—ин** *m.* turpethin (resin); **—ный минерал** turpeth mineral, turbith mineral (mercuric subsulfate).

**Турция** Turkey.

**турьит** *see* тургит.

**тускарора** wild rice (*Zizania aquatica*).

**тускл/о** *adv.* dimly, without luster; **—оватость, —ость** *f.* dimness, lack of luster, dullness, tarnish, cloudiness; **—оватый** *a.* rather dim; **—осерый** *a.* dull gray; **—ый** *a.* dim, lusterless, dull, tarnished, dingy, faint, crepuscular.

**тускн/ение** *n.* fogging, tarnishing; **—еть, —уть** *v.* grow foggy, tarnish, get dim, get dull; **—еющий** *a.* tarnishing.

**Туссена формула** (meteor.) Toussaint's formula.

**туссол** *m.* tussol, antipyrine mandelate.

**тут** *adv.* here; then; (bot.) *see* тута; **т.-же** then and there, immediately.

**тута** *f.* (bot.) mulberry (*Morus*).

**тутин** *m.* tutin.

**тутов/ник, —ое дерево** *see* тута; **—одство** *n.* mulberry culture; **—ые** *pl.* Moraceae; **—ый** *a.* mulberry.

**тутокаин** *m.* tutocaine, butamin.

**туф** *m.* (petr.) tuff; tufa; **вулканический т.** volcanic tuff, tuff; tuff cone; **известковый т.** lime tuff, travertine; **землистый т.** earthy tuff; tufaceous earth.

**туф/елька** *f.* slipper animalcule, paramecium; **—ля** *f.* slipper, shoe.

**туфо/вый** *a.* (petr.) tuff, tuffaceous; tufa, tufaceous; **т. камень** tuff; tufa; **—вая земля** tufaceous earth; **—образный, —подобный** *a.* tufa-like, tufaceous.

**тухл/ость** *f.* putrefaction, decomposition; **—ый** *a.* putrefied, rotten, spoiled, tainted; **—ятина** *f.* tainted meat.

**тухнуть** *v.* putrefy, get spoiled; go out (of fire).

**тухолит** *m.* (min.) tucholite.

**туция** *f.* (zinc) tutty.

**туча** *f.* cloud, rain cloud; swarm.

**тучн/ость** *f.* fertility, richness (of soil); obesity, fatness; **—ый** *a.* fertile, rich; obese, fat, corpulent; succulent.

**туша** *f.* carcass.

**тушев/ание** *n.* shading (of a drawing), wash, washing (with ink); **—анный** *a.* shaded; **—ать** *v.* shade, wash, tint.

**туш/ение** *n.* extinguishing, putting out (fire); stewing; slaking (coke); quenching (luminescence); **—итель** *m.* extinguisher, sprinkler; **—ительный** *a.* extinguishing; **—ить** *v.* extinguish, put out, blow out; stew; braize (meat); slake, quench; damp; (elec.) switch off, turn off.

**тушканчик** *m.* jerboa (a rodent).

**тушь** *f.*, **китайская т.** India ink.

**ту/я** *f.* (bot.) thuja; **западная т.** arborvitae (*Thuja occidentalis*); **эфирное масло —и** *see* туевое масло.

**туя—** *prefix* thuja—, thuya—; **—кетон** *m.* thuyaketone; **—ментол** *m.* thuyamenthol; **—плицин** *m.* thujaplicin.

**ТХК, ТХУК** *abbr.* (трихлоруксусная кислота) trichloroacetic acid; **ТХФМ** *abbr.* (трихлорфенолят меди) copper trichlorophenolate (seed disinfectant).

**тч.** *abbr.* (точка) point; **т.ч.** *abbr.* (так что) so that; **т/ч** *abbr.* (тонн в час) tons per hour.

**тщательн/о** *adv.* carefully, with great care, thoroughly, in detail; **—ость** *f.* care, carefulness, attention; accuracy; **—ый** *a.* careful, thorough; accurate.

**тщедуш/ие** *n.* debility, feebleness, weakness; **—ный** *a.* infirm, feeble, weak.

**тщетн/о** *adv.* vainly, in vain, to no purpose; **—ость** *f.* vainness, uselessness, futility; **—ый** *a.* vain, useless, futile.

**тыкать** *v.* poke, prod, thrust.

**тыкв/а** *f.*, **—енный** *a.* (bot.) squash, gourd (*Cucurbita*); **горькая т., дикая т., лесная т.** colocynth (*Citrullus colocynthis*); **крупная т.** winter squash (*Cucurbita maxima*); **летняя т., обыкновенная т., столовая т.** summer squash (*Cucurbita pepo*); pumpkin; **мозговая т.** vegetable marrow; **мускатная т.** squash (*Cucurbita moschata*); **посудная т.** bottle gourd (*Lagenaria vulgaris*); **—енные** *pl.* Cucurbitaceae; **—ообразный** *a.* gourd-shaped.

**тыл** *m.* rear, back, back areas; **с —а** at the rear, from the rear; **—овой, —ьный** *a.* back, rear, from the rear; **—ок** *m.* back, back edge (of tool).

**тын** *m.*, **—овый** *a.* paling; stockade.

**тыс.** *abbr.* (тысяча) thousand.

**тысяча** thousand.

**тысяче—** *prefix* thousand, milli—; **—голов** *m.* (bot.) cowherb (*Vaccaria segetalis*); **—гранник** *m.* (geom.) chiliahedron; **—летие** *n.* millennium.

**тысяче/листник** *m.* (bot.) yarrow (*Achillea* spec. *A. millefolium*); **чихотный т.** sneezewort (*A. ptarmica*); **—ног** *m.*, **—ножка** *f.* (zool.) millepede.

**тысячн/ый** *a.* thousandth; **—ая доля** one thousandth.

**тычин/ка** *f.* (bot.) stamen; **—ковый, —очный** *a.* staminal, staminate; **—коносный** *a.* staminate, staminiferous, stamen-bearing; **—очная нить** (bot.) connective; stamen.

**тычка** *f.* center punch, prick punch.

**тыч/ок** *m.*, **—ковый** *a.* (masonry) header, bondstone, bonder; blow, hit, shove, prod, knock; peg, pin; **—ковая гайка** castle nut.

**тьма** *f.* dark, darkness, obscurity.

**тьорзанит** *m.* (min.) thiorsanite (a variety of anorthite).

**тэгит** *m.* (elec.) tegit (insulator).

**Тэйлора печь** Taylor producer; **Т. ряд** (math.) Taylor's series; **Тэйлор-Уайта способ** Taylor-White process (for toughening steel).

**тэкс** *m.* tack.

**ТЭН** *abbr.* (тетранитропентаэритрит)

pentaerythrityl tetranitrate, PETN; **ТЭПФ** *abbr.* (тетраэтилпирофосфат) tetraethyl pyrophosphate; **ТЭС** *abbr.* (тетраэтилсвинец) tetraethyl lead; (тепловая электростанция) thermal electric power plant.

**тэта** *f.* theta (θ).

**тэфф, абиссинский** (bot.) a grain (*Eragrostis teff*).

**ТЭЦ** *abbr.* (теплоэлектроцентраль) heat and electric power plant.

**тюб/ик** *m.* tube; —**инг** *m.* tubing, piping.

**Тюдора аккумулятор** (elec.) Tudor accumulator.

**тюк** *m.* bale, pack, package; **т.-рулон** *m.* round bale; **прессовать в —и, укладывать в —и, —овать** *v.* bale, pack; —**овый** *a.* baled.

**тюлевый** *a.* tulle.

**тюлен/евый** *a.* seal-skin; —**ий** *a.*, —**ь** *m.* (zool.) seal; —**ий жир** seal oil; —**ина** *f.* flesh of the seal.

**тюль** *m.* (text.) tulle.

**тюльпан** *m.*, —**ный, —овый** *a.* (bot.) tulip (*Tulipa*); —**ное дерево** tulip tree (*Liriodendron tulipifera*); —**ообразный** *a.* tulip-shaped, funnelshaped, funneled.

**тюрбина** *see* **турбина**.

**тюрбо** *n.* turbot (flatfish).

**Тюри регулятор** (elec.) Thury regulator.

**тюринг/ит** *m.* (min.) thuringite; —**ский** *a.* (geol.) Thuringian.

**тюрьма** *f.* prison, jail.

**тютень** *see* **тигель**.

**тюфяк** *m.* mattress.

**тюямунит** *m.* tyuyamunite (uranium mineral).

**тяг/а** *f.* pull, draw, draft, current; traction, pulling, hauling; thrust; pull rod, connecting rod, side rod, rod, shaft; stay, brace; (laboratory) hood; **искусственная т., форсированная т.** forced draft; blast draft; **регулятор —и** damper; **с нижней —ой** downdraft (carburetor, etc.); **сила —и** tractive force, traction force, traction; pull (of propeller); **служба —и** transport service, railway service; **соединительная т.** coupling bar, draw bar.

**тягание** *n.* litigation.

**тягач** *m.* tow car; tractor, truck tractor.

**тяговооруженность** *f.* (aero.) thrust-weight ratio.

**тягов/ый** *a.* traction, tractional, tractive; **т. двигатель, т. мотор** (elec.) traction motor; **т. канат** traction rope, pull rope, hauling rope; **т. крюк** draw hook, draw bar hook; **т. паровоз** traction engine, road locomotive; **т. прибор** draw gear; **т. стержень** draw bar, drag bar; —**ая рессора** draw spring, draw bar spring; —**ая цепь** pull chain; —**ое колесо** winch wheel; —**ое оборудование** haulage equipment; —**ое усилие** tractive force, pulling force, pull.

**тягомер** *m.* draft gage, draft indicator, suction gage; blast meter, blast indicator; traction dynamometer.

**тягост/ный** *a.* burdensome, wearisome; distressing; —**ь** *f.* burden, weight, load.

**тягот/а** *f.* weight, load, burden, heaviness, hardship; —**ение** *n.* gravitation, gravity, attraction, pull; **коэффициент —ения** gravity constant; **поле —ения** gravitational field; —**еть** *v.* gravitate, be attracted; weigh; —**ить** *v.* overload, overwhelm, weigh, hang (upon), hang heavy; —**иться** *v.* feel the weight (of), feel the burden (of).

**тягун** *m.* (glass) lehr, annealing furnace.

**тягуч/есть** *f.* ductility; malleability; tenacity, toughness; viscosity (of liquid); —**ий** *a.* ductile; malleable; tenacious, tough; tensile, tractile; viscous (liquid), viscid, ropy.

**тяж** *m.* drawing rod, (brake) rod; strand, cord; trace, shaft brace.

**тяж/ба** *f.*, —**ебный** *a.* lawsuit; competition.

**тяжел/еть** *v.* get heavy; —**о** *adv.* heavily; with difficulty; it is heavy; it is difficult; —**оватый** *a.* rather heavy.

**тяжеловес** *m.* (min.) Siberian topaz (either blue or colorless).

**тяжеловесн/ость** *f.* ponderosity, heaviness; —**ый** *a.* ponderous, heavy.

**тяжело/водный** *a.* heavy-water; —**грузный** *a.* heavily loaded; —**суглинистый** *a.* clayey loam.

**тяжел/ый** *a.* heavy, weighty, ponderous; hard, difficult, burdensome; serious; close (air); rich (food); serious (illness);

substantial; —ая вода heavy water, deuterium oxide; —ая жидкость gravity solution; —ая индустрия heavy industry; —ого типа, для —ой работы heavy-duty (machine).

**тяжение** *n.* stress.

**тяжест/ь** *f.* weight, weightiness, gravity, heaviness, load, burden; severity; **сила** —**и** gravity, force of gravity; **силой** —**и** by gravity; **центр** —**и** center of gravity.

**тяжкий** *a.* grave, weighty, serious, severe.

**тяжник** *m.* draw band.

**тянут/ый** *a.* drawn out; pulled, hauled; —**ь** *v.* draw, draw out, stretch; pull, haul, drag; —**ь дело** delay, put off, prolong, protract; —**ься** *v.* stretch, extend, lengthen; range, run, go along, sweep; last, seem long, drag on, hold out, linger; strive, strive to equal.

**тянущ/ий** *a.* drawing, pulling; **т. пропеллер** tractor propeller; —**ая сила** pull.

**Тянь-цзин** Tientsin.

**тяп/ание** *n.* hacking; —**ать,** —**нуть** *v.* hack, chop, cut; —**ка** *f.* chopper, cleaver; hoe.

# У

**у** *prep. gen.* by, near, at, on, to; of; **у него есть** he has, he possesses, he owns; **у них на заводе** at their plant; **попросить у него** *v.* ask him.

**У** code for carbon in steel mark.

**у—** *prefix* de—, ab—, away from.

**уабаин** *m.* ouabain, G-Strophanthin.

**уади** *n.* (geol.) wadi (a valley).

**уайтрот** *m.* white rot (of trees).

**уайт-спирит** *m.* white spirit (turpentine substitute).

**УАСХН** *abbr.* (Украинская академия сельскохозяйственных наук) Ukrainian Academy of Agricultural Sciences.

**уатт** *m.* (elec.) watt; *see also* **ватт.**

**Уатта регулятор** (elec.) Watt governor.

**уаттметр** *see* **ваттметр.**

**убав/ить,** —**лять** *v.* diminish, lessen, abate, subdue; curtail, reduce, abridge; —**иться,** —**ляться** *v.* diminish, decrease, lessen, abate; —**ка** *f.* shortening, curtailment, reduction, decrease; discount; —**ление** *n.* diminishing, decreasing, reducing; —**ленный** *a.* diminished, decreased, reduced.

**убег/ать** *v.* run away, make off; —**ающий** *a.* run-away.

**убедительн/ость** *f.* persuasiveness, conclusiveness; —**ый** *a.* persuasive, convincing, conclusive, demonstrative, earnest (request); **быть** —**ым** *v.* carry conviction, be convincing.

**убедить** *see* **убеждать.**

**убежать** *see* **убегать.**

**убежд/ать** *v.* convince, persuade, satisfy;

prevail (upon), induce, urge; —**аться** *v.* be convinced, be satisfied, be persuaded; ascertain; —**ение** *n.* conviction, persuasion; **не поддающийся** —**ению** inconvincible; —**енность** *f.* conviction, assurance; —**енный** *a.* convinced, positive (of), certain.

**убежище** *n.* refuge, shelter, cover, dugout.

**убел/енный** *a.* whitened, bleached; —**ивание** *n.* whitening, bleaching; —**ивать,** —**ить,** —**ять** *v.* whiten, bleach.

**убер/егать,** —**ечь** *v.* preserve, protect, guard, keep safe.

**убив/ание** *n.* killing, butchering; —**ать** *v.* kill, butcher, slaughter; —**ающий** *a. suffix* —cidal, —destroying; —**ающее средство** *suffix* —cide.

**убийств/енный** *a.* deadly, killing, murderous; —**о** *n.* murder, assassination; slaughter, butchery.

**убир/аемый** *a.* (aero.) retractable; —**ать** *v.* remove, take off, take away, carry away, withdraw, dispose (of); harvest, reap, gather in, store; furnish, trim, decorate; —**аться** *v.* clear off, get out of the way; be gathered in; put in order; —**ающийся** *a.* disappearing.

**убит/ый** *a.* killed; —**ь** *see* **убивать.**

**ублюд/ковый,** —**очный** *a.* hybrid; mongrel, cross-bred; —**ковые породы** (geol.) hybrid rocks; —**ок** *m.* hybrid, halfbreed.

**убог/ий** *a.* lean, poor; —**ая руда** poor ore, halvans, halvings.

**убоина** *f.* meat; fattened cattle.

**убой** *m.* slaughter, slaughtering; **—ный** *a.* slaughter; dressed (weight of meat).

**убо́рист/ость** *f.* closeness, compactness; **—ый** *a.* close, compact.

**уборка** *f.* removal; harvest, reaping, gathering in, picking, plucking; (flax) pulling; harvesting season; putting in order, arranging.

**убо́рная** *f.* lavatory.

**убо́рочн/ый** *a.* harvesting; **—ая машина** harvester, picker; windrower.

**убо́рщик** *m.* attendant, office cleaner; harvester, picker; windrower.

**убр/анный** *a.* removed; harvested, reaped; **—ать** *see* **убирать**.

**убыв/ание** *n.* decrease; subsidence; **—ать** *v.* decrease, diminish, lessen, decline; subside, sink, ebb, fall (of tide); **—ающий** *a.* decreasing, diminishing; **закон —ающего плодородия** law of diminishing returns.

**убыль** *f.* decrease, diminution; subsidence, ebb; loss, waste, leak; wear and tear, depreciation; **итти на у.** *see* **убывать**.

**убыт/ок** *m.* damage, loss; disadvantage; **—очность** *f.* unprofitableness; **—очный** *a.* unprofitable, losing; wasteful; detrimental; **—ь** *see* **убывать**.

**уваж/ать** *v.* respect, esteem, consider; **—ение** *n.* respect, regard, deference, appreciation; **с —ением** respectfully yours; **—ительный** *a.* valid, satisfactory, allowable; worthy of consideration; **—ить** *v.* comply (with a request).

**увал** *m.* rounded, low ridge; heights.

**уванит** *m.* (min.) uvanite (a hydrous uranium vanadate).

**увар** *m.* boiling away; loss on boiling; **—енный** *a.* boiled down, evaporated down, concentrated; **—ивание** *n.*, **—ка** *f.* boiling down; evaporating down, concentration; loss on boiling; **—ивать, —ить** *v.* boil down, boil away, evaporate down, concentrate.

**уваровит** *m.* (min.) uvarovite (a calcium-chromium garnet).

**уведом/ительный** *a.* informative; **—ить, —лять** *v.* inform, advise, notify, give notice; **—ление** *n.* information, notification, notice.

**увезти** *see* **увозить**.

**увекове́ч/ение, —ивание** *n.* recording; immortalization; **—ивать, —ить** *v.* record; immortalize, perpetuate.

**увеличен/ие** *n.* increase, growth, augmentation; enhancement; enlargement, magnification, increment; extension (of operations); **у. жесткости** hardening; **—ный** *a.* increased, enlarged, magnified.

**увеличив/ание** *see* **увеличение**; **—ать** *v.* increase, augment, raise; enlarge, magnify; boost, amplify, intensify, enhance; extend; **—аться** *v.* increase, be on the increase, grow, augment, swell, become larger; **—ающий** *a.* increasing; magnifying.

**увеличитель** *m.* enlarger; **—ный** *a.* enlarging, magnifying, augmentative; **—ное стекло** magnifying glass, magnifier.

**увеличить** *see* **увеличивать**.

**увенч/ание** *n.* crowning; **—анный** *a.* crowned, capped; **—ать, —ивать** *v.* crown, cap, crest; complete, finish; **—аться успехом** be successful.

**уверен/ие** *n.* assertion, assurance; **—но** *adv.* confidently, positively; **—ность** *f.* assurance, sureness, confidence, certainty; **можно с —ностью сказать** it is safe to say; **—ный** *a.* assured, sure, confident, positive, certain.

**уверить** *see* **уверять**.

**увернуть** *see* **увертывать**.

**уверовать** *v.* come to believe.

**уверт/ка** *f.* subterfuge, evasion, dodge; **—ливость** *f.* evasiveness; **—ливый** *a.* evasive, elusive; **—ывать** *v.* wrap up; **—ываться** *v.* evade, elude, escape, avoid, dodge, shirk.

**уверять** *v.* assure, persuade, convince; **—ся** *v.* become convinced, make sure.

**увесист/ость** *f.* heaviness, weightiness; **—ый** *a.* heavy, weighty.

**увести** *see* **уводить**.

**увеч/ить** *v.* maim, cripple, mutilate, disable; **—ность** *f.* disability; **—ный** *a.* crippled, disabled, lame; *m.* cripple; **—ье** *n.* mutilation, personal injury.

**увещ/ание** *n.* exhortation, admonition, admonishment; **—ательный** *a.* exhortative, admonitory; **—ать, —евать** *v.* exhort, admonish, talk (to).

**увивать** *v.* entwine, wrap around, twist.

**увид/áть, —еть** *v.* see, catch sight (of), set eyes (on); perceive, understand; **—еться** *v.* see each other, meet.

**увил/ивание** *n.* elusion, evasion, dodging; **—ивать, —ьнуть** *v.* elude, evade, dodge.

**уви/новая кислота** uvic acid; **—олевый** *a.* uviol, ultraviolet-transmitting (glass); **—тиновая кислота** uvitic acid, 5-methylisophthalic acid; **—тоновая кислота** uvitonic acid.

**увить** *see* увивать.

**увлажнен/ие** *n.* moistening, damping, humidifying, wetting; (text.) conditioning; **—ность** *f.* moisture, dampness, humidity; **степень —ности** moisture content; **—ный** *a.* moistened, wetted, humid.

**увлажнитель** *m.* moistener, humidifier; **—ный** *a.* moistening, humidifying; (text.) conditioning.

**увлажни/ть, —ять** *v.* moisten, damp, humidify, wet, sprinkle; **—яющий** *a.* moistening, humidifying; damp (air).

**увлек/атель** *m.* (azeotropic distillation) withdrawing agent; **—ательный** *a.* absorbing, interesting, exciting; **—ать** *v.* entrain, carry along, carry away; absorb, interest, fascinate; **—ать при осаждении** carry down by precipitation, coprecipitate; **—ать пыль водой** settle dust with water, sprinkle down; **—аться** *v.* be absorbed (in), take a fancy (to); be carried away.

**увлеч/ение** *n.* entrainment, carrying away; interest, enthusiasm; **—енный** *a.* entrained, carried along, entrapped; interested; **—ь** *see* увлекать.

**увод** *m.* leading away; **—ить** *v.* lead away, carry off; discharge, drain off.

**увоз** *m.* removal, carrying off; **—ить** *v.* remove, carry off, carry away, drive away, take away.

**уволить** *see* увольнять.

**увольн/ение** *n.* dismissal, discharge; **—ительный** *a.* discharge; **—ять** *v.* dismiss, discharge, expel; discard; free, exempt (from).

**УВЧ** *abbr.* (ультравысокочастотный) ultrahigh-frequency.

**увяд/ание** *n.* wilting, withering; wilt (plant disease); **—ать** *v.* wilt, wither, fade; waste away; **—ший** *a.* wilted, withered.

**увяз/ать, —нуть, —ывать** *v.* tie up, pack up; link up, connect, bring into harmony (with); sink, stick (in); **—ываться** *v.* be tied up; **—ка** *f.* tying up, linking; agreement; (stratigraphic) correlation; **—очный** *a.* tying, packing; **—ывание** *n.* tying up, linking, connecting.

**увянуть** *see* увядать.

**угад/ать, —ывать** *v.* guess; **—ывание** *n.* guessing.

**угар** *m.*, **—ный** *a.* waste, loss; (text.) waste, refuse; loss in burning; consumption (of fuel); carbon monoxide fumes; charcoal fumes; **едкий у.** corrosive fumes; **—ный газ** carbon monoxide.

**уга/сание** *n.* dying away, fading, extinction; damping-off (of seedlings); **—сать, —снуть** *v.* die away, fade, go out, become extinct; **—сить, —шать** *v.* extinguish; **—сший** *a.* extinct; **—шенный** *a.* extinguished.

**угле—** *prefix* carbon; coal; **—аммиачная соль, —аммониевая соль** ammonium carbonate; **—бариевая соль** barium carbonate; **—висмутовая соль** bismuth carbonate; **основная —висмутовая соль** bismuth subcarbonate; **—вод** *m.*, **—водный** *a.* carbohydrate.

**углеводород** *m.* hydrocarbon; **кольчатый у.** cyclic hydrocarbon; **непредельный у.** unsaturated hydrocarbon; **предельный у.** saturated hydrocarbon; **—истый** *a.* hydrocarbon, hydrocarbonaceous, containing hydrocarbons; **—истое соединение** hydrocarbon.

**углевыжигательн/ый** *a.* charring; **—ая печь** charcoal kiln.

**угле/держатель** *m.* carbon holder (of electric arc lamp); **—дробилка** *f.* coal crusher; **—железистая соль** ferrous carbonate; **—железная соль** ferric carbonate; **—жжение** *n.* charcoal burning, charring, carbonization; **—жог** *m.* charcoal burner; **—зернистый** *a.* granulated carbon; **—калиевая соль** potassium carbonate; **кислая**

—калиевая соль potassium bicarbonate; —кальциевая соль calcium carbonate.

углекислот/а f. carbonic acid, carbon dioxide; соль —ы carbonate; твердая у. dry ice.

углекисл/ый a. carbonic acid; carbonate (of); у. аммоний ammonium carbonate; у. газ carbon dioxide; у. натрий sodium carbonate; у. охладитель carbon dioxide refrigerant, liquid carbon dioxide; —ая соль carbonate; кислая —ая соль acid carbonate, bicarbonate; основная —ая соль basic carbonate, subcarbonate.

угле/коп m. coal miner, collier; —крезиловый эфир cresyl carbonate; —литиевая соль lithium carbonate; — магниевая соль magnesium carbonate.

углемарганцов/ая соль manganic carbonate; —истая соль manganous carbonate.

углемед/истая соль cuprous carbonate; —ная соль cupric carbonate; основная —ная соль cupric subcarbonate.

угле/мойка f. coal washer; coal concentration plant; —натриевая соль sodium carbonate; кислая —натриевая соль sodium bicarbonate; —никелевая соль nickel carbonate; —носный a. coal-bearing, carboniferous.

углеобжигательный a. carbonizing, charring; у. завод charcoal works.

угле/образователь m. carbon-forming material; coal-yielding material; —отбойная машина coal cutter; —промывочный a. coal-washing; —промышленность f. coal mining, coal industry; —разборка f. sorting of coal.

углерод m. carbon, C; двуокись —a carbon dioxide; недокись —a carbon suboxide; окись —a carbon monoxide; сернистый у. carbon bisulfide; хлорокись —a carbonyl chloride, phosgene; четыреххлористый у. carbon tetrachloride.

углеродист/ый a. carbon, carbonic, carbonaceous, carboniferous; carbide (of); у. алюминий aluminum carbide; у. водород hydrocarbon; —ая связь carbon bond; —ая сталь carbon

steel; —ая сурьма antimony carbide; —ое железо iron carbide.

углеродный a. carbon, carbonic, carbonaceous.

угле/свинцовистая соль lead carbonate; основная у. соль lead subcarbonate; —фикация f. (geol.) coalification, carbonification (metamorphism); — цинковая соль zinc carbonate; —цинковый элемент carbon-zinc cell.

угли pl. of уголь.

углистый a. carbonaceous, carbon-like; coal, coal-like; у. железняк (min.) black band iron ore (carbonaceous iron carbonate); у. сланец (petr.) carbonaceous shale, ampelite.

угло-бимсовое железо, угло-бульбовое железо bulb angle iron, bulb angle.

углов gen pl. of угол.

угловато adv. angularly, at an angle; prefix гонио—, anguli—; —зернистый a. angular-grained; —круглый a. subangular; round-cornered; —листный a. (bot.) goniophyllous; —нервный a. (bot.) angulinerved.

угловат/ость f. angularity; —ый a. angular.

углов/ой a. angle, angular; corner; directional (correlation); у. коэффициент slope (of a graph); у. лист corner plate; у. рычаг crank; у. эффект corner effect (of wind); —ая передача angular drive; —ая связь; —ое скрепление angle brace; —ая скорость angular velocity; —ая частота (elec.) angular frequency; —ое железо corner iron; —ое лекало angle gage; —ое соединение corner joint.

углом see under угол.

угломер m., —ный инструмент goniometer, angle gage, protractor.

углуб/ить see углублять; —ка see углубление.

углубл/ение n. hollow, depression, recess, pocket, concave, cavity, hole; sump, pit; socket; notch, indentation, spot; slot, rabbet; deepening, sinking, immersion; (geol.) dip; (anat.) alveolus; —енный a. deepened, depressed; —еньице f. (biol.) alveola; —ять v. deepen, make deeper, excavate; depress, sink, recess, concave; —яться *v.* deepen, become deeper; dip; go far into; examine closely, investigate.

**углы** *pl. of* **угол.**

**угля** *gen. of* **уголь.**

**угляк** *m.* (min.) black diamond, carbonado.

**угнать** *see* **угонять.**

**угнет/ать** *v.* oppress, depress, weigh heavy (on); **—ение** *n.* oppression; **—енный** *a.* oppressed, depressed.

**уговарив/ание** *v.* persuasion, urging; **—ать** *v.* persuade, urge, exhort; **—аться** *v.* agree, be persuaded.

**уговор** *m.* agreement, understanding; **с —ом** on condition; **—ить** *v.* persuade, prevail (upon), induce; **—иться** *v.* come to an agreement.

**угод/а** *f.* pleasure, gratification; **в —у** to please, to oblige; **—ить** *see* **угождать; как ему —но** as he pleases, as he chooses; **сколько —но** as much as is desired; **что —но** anything at all.

**угод/ье** *n.* land, area; **—ья** *pl.* grounds; **лесные —ья** forests; **полевые —ья** arable lands.

**угожд/ать** *v.* gratify, please, humor; **—ение** *n.* gratification, humoring, compliance.

**уг/ол** *m.* angle; corner; **за —лом** around the corner; **под —лом** at an angle, obliquely; **под прямым —лом** at right angles (to), perpendicular (to); **передача под —лом** angular drive; **сечение под —лом** oblique section; **установка под —лом** angular adjustment; **сдвиг —лов** angular displacement.

**уголек** *m.* (illum.) carbon filament.

**уголов/ный** *a.* criminal, penal; **—щина** *f.* criminal act.

**уголок** *m.* corner; angle bracket.

**уголь** *m.* coal; carbon; **активированный у.** activated carbon; **болотный у., илистый у.** mud coal, coal slime; **бумажный у.** paper coal (a variety of lignite); **бурый у.** lignite, brown coal; **графитовый у.** graphitic carbon; **древесный у., растительный у.** charcoal; **жирный у.** soft coal, bituminous coal; **землистый у.** sooty coal; **ископаемый у.** coal; **каменный у.** coal (above rank of lignite; usually bitu-

minous coal); **превращать в у.** *v.* carbonize.

**угольник** *m.* try-square, square; corner iron; elbow, pipe bend; crank; **листовой у., полосовой у.** corner plate; **стыковой у.** angle bracket.

**угольный** *a.* angle, angular; corner; *see also* **угловой.**

**угольн/ый** *a.* coal; carbon, carbonic; **у. ангидрид** carbon dioxide; **у. бассейн, у. район** coal field; **у. газ** coal gas; **у. муссор, у. сор, —ая мелочь** small coal, slack, coal dirt; **у. рудник, —ая копь** coal mine, colliery; **у. сланец** bituminous shale; **у. стержень** carbon (of electric arc lamp); **у. тигель** carbon crucible, graphite crucible; **у. электрод** carbon electrode; **—ая бумага** carbon paper; **—ая дуговая лампа** carbon arc lamp; **сварка —ой дугой** carbon arc welding; **—ая кислота** carbonic acid, carbon dioxide; **соль —ой кислоты** carbonate; **—ая набойка** brasque, steep; **—ая щетка** (elec.) carbon brush, brush.

**угольщик** *m.* collier; coal freighter; charcoal burner.

**угон** *m.* driving away; creep (deformation); **—ять** *v.* drive away; **—яться** *v.* overtake, catch up (with), equal.

**угор/ать, —еть** *v.* be poisoned by carbon monoxide.

**угорок** *m.* mound, hillock.

**угорь** *m.* (med.) blackhead, comedo; (zool.) eel.

**уго/стить, —щать** *v.* treat, entertain.

**угреватый** *a.* pimpled, pimply.

**угри** *pl.* (vet.) measles; (med.) acne.

**угриц/евидные, —ы** *pl.* (zool.) Anguillulidae.

**угро/жать** *v.* threaten, menace, impend; **—жающий** *a.* threatening, menacing, impending, imminent; precarious (situation); **—за** *f.* threat, hazard.

**уд.** *abbr.* (удельный) specific.

**уда** *f.* hook; fishhook.

**удабривать** *see* **удобрять.**

**удав** *m.* (zool.) boa constrictor.

**удаваться** *v.* succeed, be a success, turn out well; **не у.** fail.

**удав/ить, —ливать** *v.* strangle, choke; **—ление** *n.* strangulation.

**удален/ие** *n.* removal, withdrawal, disposal (of), elimination; driving off, expulsion, expelling, discharging, drawing off; departure, escape; evacuation; extraction; depriving, impoverishment; recession; —ectomy (surgical removal); **у. кишки** (med.) enterectomy; **у. серы** desulfurization; **поле —ия ионов** (instrumentation) clearing field; —**ный** *a.* removed, eliminated; expelled, discharged, drawn off; remote, outlying, distant.

**удал/ившийся** *a.* withdrawn; escaped; —**итель** *m.* eliminator; (paint) remover, stripper; —**ить** *v.* remove, eliminate, withdraw, draw off, draw out, take away, empty; clear away, dispose (of); free (from); drive off, expel; avert; deprive (of); extract; —**иться** *v.* be removed; withdraw, retire, recede, move away, go away.

**удал/ой,** —**ый** *a.* enterprising, daring.

**удалять** *see* **удалить.**

**удар** *m.* blow, stroke, strike, hit, knock, tap, thump; impact, impingement, collision, smash, clash; shock, percussion, kick; impulse; detonation; (elec.) shock; (sun) stroke; clap (of thunder); beat (of pulse); (hydraulic) hammer; —**ами** percussively; by starts or jolts, jerkily; **испытание на у.** (met.) impact test; **одним—ом** with one blow, at one stroke; **поглотитель** —**а** shock absorber; **прочность на у., сопротивление** —**у** impact strength; **сила** —**а** force of impact; **теория** —**а** (radiobiol.) hit theory; **точка** —**а** point of impact; **центр** —**а** point of impact; center of percussion, center of oscillation.

**ударение** *n.* stress, emphasis; **делать у. на** *v.* emphasize; **ставить у.** *v.* stress, accent.

**удар/ить** *see* **ударять;** —**ник** *m.* shock worker; firing pin, striking pin, striker (in torpedo); tapper, telegraph key; pellet; —**но-вращательный** *a.* percussive-rotary (drilling).

**ударн/ый** *a.* shock; impact; pulsating; percussion, percussive; most important; **у. винт** stop screw, adjusting screw; **у. грохот** impact screen; **у. инструмент** churn drill; **у. колпачок** percussion cap; **у. нож** breaking knife; **у. перфоратор,** —**ое сверло** percussion drill, hammer drill; **у. раствор** (electrodeposition) striking solution; —**ая бригада** shock brigade; —**ая волна** shock wave; —**ая вязкость** impact toughness; impact strength; —**ая гранатная трубка,** —**ая трубка** percussion fuse; —**ая проба,** —**ое испытание** (met.) impact test; drop test; hammer test; —**ая сварка** percussive welding; —**ая сила** striking power; force of impact; —**ая стена** deflecting wall, baffle; —**ое бурение** percussive boring; —**ое действие** (mil.) perforating effect (of shell); —**ые темпы** high pressure (of work); **в** —**ом порядке** with dispatch, with concentration of all forces.

**удар/оглушитель** *m.* shock absorber; —**очувствительность** *f.* sensitivity to shock; —**яемый** *a.* knocked-on (atom).

**ударять** *v.* strike, hit, knock, kick; chop; —**ся** *v.* strike, hit, knock (against), collide (with), impinge; interfere.

**удаться** *see* **удаваться.**

**удач/а** *f.* luck, success, good fortune; —**но** *adv.* successfully, well; —**ный** *a.* lucky, successful, fortunate.

**уд. в.** *see* **уд. вес.**

**удваив/ание** *n.* doubling, redoubling; duplication; splitting; —**ать** *v.* double, redouble; duplicate; split; —**аться** *v.* double, be doubled, redouble.

**уд. вес** *abbr.* (**удельный вес**) specific gravity; **уд. вл.** *abbr.* (**удельная влажность**) specific humidity.

**удво/ение** *see* **удваивание;** —**енный** *a.* doubled, double, twofold; duplicate; —**итель** *m.* doubler; duplicator; —**ить** *see* **удваивать.**

**удевятерять** *v.* multiply by nine.

**удел** *m.* lot, portion; —**ение** *n.* allotment; sparing (attention, etc.); —**ить** *see* **уделять.**

**удельно** *adv.* specifically, very.

**удельн/ый** *a.* specific, unit; **у. вес** specific gravity; density; relative significance; proportion; **у. объем** specific volume; **у. съем стекломассы** specific melting efficiency of glass furnace; **—ая емкость, —ая проводимость** (elec.) permittivity; **—ая когезионная энергия** cohesive energy density.

**уделять** *v.* allot, portion; spare, give, pay (attention).

**удерж/ание, —ивание** *n.* retention, keeping, holding, reservation; containment, confinement; occlusion; trapping; **агент —ивания** hold-back agent; **—ать, —ивать** *v.* retain, hold, confine; keep back, hold back, withhold; restrain; detain, delay; maintain; **—ивать за собой** retain, reserve for oneself; **—иваться** *v.* hold on; refrain, restrain oneself; **—иваемость** *f.*, **—ивающая сила** retentivity; adherence (of insecticides); **—ивающий** *a.* retaining, retentive; holding; **—ивающая способность** (distillation) holdup.

**удесятер/енный** *a.* tenfold, decuple; **—ить, —ять** *v.* multiply by ten, decuple.

**удивительн/о** *adv.* wonderfully; it is wonderful, it is remarkable; **не у., что** it is no wonder that; **—ость** *f.* wonderfulness; **—ый** *a.* wonderful, astonishing, surprising, amazing; **ничего —ого** no wonder.

**удив/ить, —лять, приводить в —ление** *v.* astonish, surprise, amaze; **—иться, —ляться** *v.* be surprised, wonder; **—ление** *n.* surprise, wonder, astonishment; **—ленный** *a.* surprised.

**удилище** *n.* (fishing) rod.

**удило** *n.* bit (for horse).

**удить** *v.* angle (for fish).

**удлинен/ие** *n.* lengthening, elongation, prolongation, extension, expansion, stretch; **коэффициент —ия** coefficient of expansion; **относительное у., удельное у.** specific elongation; **—ный** *a.* elongated, lengthened, extended, stretched out; oblong.

**удлин/итель** *m.* extension, extension piece, extension arm; lengthener; attenuator; **—ительный** *a.* extension, lengthening; **—ить, —ять** *v.* lengthen, elongate, prolong, extend, expand, enlarge; **—иться, —яться** *v.* lengthen, stretch; **—яемость** *f.* extensibility;

**—яющийся** *a.* extensible; lengthening, stretching.

**удобн/о** *adv.* conveniently, easily; comfortably; it is convenient; **—ость** *f.* convenience, ease, facility; comfort; **—ый** *a.* convenient, handy, easy, expedient; comfortable; **—ый случай** favorable occasion, opportunity.

**удобоварим/ость** *f.* digestibility; **—ый** *a.* digestible.

**удобоисполним/ость** *f.* feasibility, practicability; **—ый** *a.* feasible, practicable, easy to carry out.

**удобоносим/ость** *f.* portability; **—ый** *a.* portable, easily carried.

**удобообтекаем/ый** *a.* streamlined; **—ое тело** streamline.

**удобоперевозим/ость** *f.* transportability; **—ый** *a.* transportable.

**удобопереносимый** *a.* portable.

**удобопонятн/ость** *f.* comprehensibility; **—ый** *a.* comprehensible, intelligible.

**удоборазрезаем/ость** *f.* sectility; **—ый** *a.* sectile.

**удоборегулируемый** *a.* adjustable, easily regulated.

**удобосмешиваем/ость** *f.* miscibility; **—ый** *a.* miscible, mixable.

**удобоуправляем/ость** *f.* maneuverability; **—ый** *a.* maneuverable.

**удобр/ение** *n.* (agr.) fertilizer, manure, dressing; fertilization, manuring, application (of fertilizer); **—енный** *a.* fertilized, manured; **—итель** *m.*, **—ительное вещество** fertilizer; **—ить, —ять** *v.* fertilize, manure, topdress.

**удобство** *n.* convenience, accommodation, facility; comfort, ease.

**удовлетвор/ение** *n.*, **—енность** *f.* satisfaction; **—енно** *adv.* with satisfaction; **—енный** *a.* satisfied, content; **—ительно** *adv.* satisfactorily; **—ительность** *f.* satisfactoriness; **—ительный** *a.* satisfactory, adequate; **—ить, —ять** *v.* satisfy, meet (demand).

**удовольств/ие** *n.* gratification, pleasure, enjoyment; **—оваться** *v.* be satisfied, content oneself (with).

**удой** *m.* milking, yield of milk; **—ливая корова, —ная корова** good milker; **—ник** *m.* milk pail; **—ность** *f.* milk yield.

**удометр** *m.* udometer, rain gage.

**удорож/ание** *n.* rise in price; **—ать, —ить** *v.* raise the price.

**удостаивать** *v.* honor (with), award, confer (a degree), pay (attention); deign, vouchsafe.

**удостовер/ение** *n.* certificate, testimonial; attestation; **в у.** in witness (of); **сортовое у.** certificate; **—итель** *m.* witness, attestor; **—ить, —ять** *v.* certify, attest, bear witness, testify; **—иться, —яться** *v.* ascertain, prove, convince oneself, make sure (of).

**удостоить** *see* **удостаивать.**

**удочка** *f.* fishing rod, rod.

**удружить** *v.* do a friendly service.

**удрученный** *a.* dejected, depressed.

**удуш/ать, —ить** *v.* stifle, suffocate, asphyxiate, strangle, smother; **—ающий** *a.* suffocating, choking; **—ение** *n.* suffocation, asphyxiation, smothering; **—енный** *a.* suffocated, stifled, asphyxiated; **—ливый** *a.* suffocating, stifling; **—ливый газ** suffocating gas, poison gas; **снаряд с —ливым газом** (mil.) gas shell, chemical shell; **—ье** *n.* (med.) asthma.

**уедин/ение** *n.* solitude, seclusion; **—енность** *f.* solitariness; **—енный** *a.* isolated, solitary, secluded, remote; **—ить, —ять** *v.* isolate, separate, detach, insulate.

**уезд** *m.*, **—ный** *a.* county, district.

**уезжать** *v.* go away, depart, leave.

**уемистый** *a.* capacious, roomy, spacious.

**уехать** *see* **уезжать.**

**уж** *m.* (zool.) grass snake; *adv.* already.

**ужал/ение** *n.* sting, stinging; **—енный** *a.* stung; **—ить** *v.* sting.

**ужар/ивать, —ить** *v.* roast to a point; reduce by roasting.

**ужас** *m.* horror, dismay, fright; **к своему —у** to one's dismay; **притти в у.** *v.* be horrified; **—но** *adv.* terribly, horribly, awfully, very; **—ный** *a.* terrible, horrible, awful, dreadful.

**уже** *comp. of* **узкий, узко,** narrower; *adv.* already; even only; as long ago as; **у. в 1942 г.** as long ago as 1942; **у. малое количество** even a small amount; **у. не** no longer; **его у. нет** he is no longer here.

**ужение** *n.* angling (for fish).

**ужестчение** *n.* (electron.) ruggedization.

**уживаться** *v.* be accustomed (to), get along (with).

**ужин** *m.* supper; (agr.) harvest, reaping; **—ать** *v.* eat supper.

**ужовка** *f.* porcelain shell.

**ужов/ник** *m.* (bot.) adder's tongue (*Ophioglossum vulgatum*); (pharm.) symphytum; **—ый** *a.* snake.

**УЗ** *abbr.* (ультразвук) ultrasonics; (ультразвуковой) ultrasonic.

**уза** *f.* propolis, bee glue.

**узакон/ение** *n.* legalization; statute, ordinance, decree; **—ивать, —ить, —ять** *v.* legalize, make legal.

**узарин** *m.* uzarin.

**узб.** *abbr.* (узбекский) Uzbek.

**узд/а** *f.* bridle; check, restraint; **—ечка** *f.* (anat., zool.) frenulum, frenum.

**узел** *m.* node; knot, loop; bundle, pack; (mach.) block, unit, assembly, subassembly; joint, joint connection; (railroad) junction, terminal; knot (in wood); (anat.) ganglion; branch point (in cross-linked polymer); **у. решетки** (cryst.) lattice point; **у. тока** (elec.) current node; **—ок** *m.* small knot; small bundle; (bot.) nodule.

**узик** *m.* (bot.) tormentil (*Potentilla tormentilla*).

**узкий** *a.* narrow, tight.

**узко** *adv.* narrowly, tightly; **—горлый** *a.* narrow-necked (bottle); **—колейный** *a.* narrow-gage; **—листный** *a.* (bot.) narrow-leaved, angustifoliate; **—лучевой** *a.* narrow-beam; **—надкрылые** *pl.* false blister beetles (*Oedemeridae*); **—полосный** *a.* narrow-band; **—телки** *pl.* cylindrical bark beetles (*Colydiidae*).

**узловат/ость** *f.* knottiness, nodosity; **—ый** *a.* knotty, nodose, nodular, knobby, torose; (anat.) ganglionic.

**узлов/ой** *a.* knot, node, nodal; junction; unit; **у. лист, —ая накладка** junction plate, gusset plate, gusset; **у. пункт, —ая станция** junction point, junction; **у. шарнир** multiple joint; **—ая система** (zool.) sympathetic nervous system; **—ая точка** junction point, point of junction; (acous.) node.

**узло/вязатель** *m.* knotter; **—вязательная машина** knotting machine; **—ловитель** *m.* (paper) knotter, knot screen.

**узна/вание** *n.* recognition; learning, knowledge; **—вать, —ть** *v.* recognize, identify, know; learn, find out.

**узор** *m.* pattern, design, arrangement, markings, figure; **—ный, —чатый** *a.* figured, ornamented.

**узость** *f.* narrowness, tightness.

**УзССР** *abbr.* (Узбекская Советская Социалистическая Республика) Uzbek Soviet Socialist Republic.

**узура** *f.* (med.) wasting away of bone and tissue.

**узурпировать** *v.* usurp.

**узус** *m.* usage, customary practice.

**узы** *pl.* bonds, ties.

**Уильямсона реакция** Williamson reaction.

**УИМ** *abbr.* (Уральский научно-исследовательский институт черных металлов) Ural Scientific Research Institute of Ferrous Metals.

**Уимшерста машина** (elec.) Wimshurst machine.

**уинлокский** *a.* (geol.) Wenlock.

**уинтаит** *m.* (min.) uintaite, gilsonite (a bitumin).

**уипсток** *m.* (drilling) whip stock.

**УИПФХ** *abbr.* (Украинский научно-исследовательский институт прикладной физико-химии) Ukrainian Scientific Research Institute of Applied Physical Chemistry.

**Уитмор** Whitmore (name).

**Уитстона мостик, уитстонов мост** (elec.) Wheatstone bridge.

**Уитфильда газогенератор** Whitfield producer.

**уйти** *see* **уходить.**

**указ** *m.* decree, edict, enactment.

**указ/ание** *n.* indication, hint; direction, instruction, designation; **имеются —ания** it has been reported; **—анный** *a.* indicated, specified; **—атель** *m.* indication, sign; (chem.) indicator; indicator, indicator dial, dial; pointer, needle, arrow; detector; guide; index, directory, catalog; (railroad) time-table; (street) sign; (math.) characteristic.

**указательн/ый** *a.* indicating, indicatory; **у. механизм** indicator; **у. палец** forefinger, index finger; **—ая пластинка** dial; **—ая стрелка** pointer.

**указ/ать, —ывать** *v.* indicate, denote; point out, show, direct, explain, demonstrate; **—ывать на** point to; indicate, imply; **следует у.** it should be noted; **—ка** *f.* pointer, fescue, marker; **—ный** *a.* standard; **—ывающий** *a.* indicating; directing.

**укалывать** *v.* prick.

**укат/ать, —ывать** *v.* roll, smooth; **—ить** *v.* roll away; drive off; **—ывание** *n.* rolling, smoothing.

**УКВ** *abbr.* (ультракороткие волны) ultrashort waves; (ультракоротко-волновый) ultrashort wave.

**укидывать** *v.* bestrew, scatter.

**укип/ание** *n.* boiling away, evaporation; **—ать** *v.* boil away, boil enough.

**уклад** *m.* usage, way of life; (met.) natural steel.

**уклад/ка** *f.* packing; stacking up; setting; laying, installation (of pipes, etc.); placement (of concrete); **—очный** *a.* packing; **—чик** *m.* packer, stacker; (parachute) rigger.

**укладыв/ание** *n.* packing, stowing; piling, stacking; **—ать** *v.* pack, pack up; stow; pile, stack; set, lay; pave, embed; **—аться** be packed, be stowed, be put away; pack up; go, fit (into), be contained (in); be laid out; lie down; **—ающийся** *a.* folding.

**уклон** *m.* slope, dip, slant, incline, declivity, pitch, gradient, grade (of road), downgrade; ramp; taper, bias, canting, bevel; bias, trend, inclination; deviation; **под у.** at a slant, downgrade, downhill; **итти под у.** *v.* slope.

**уклон/ение** *n.* deviation, deflection, digression, error, aberration, declination; canting, swerving; evasion, avoiding; **—ист** *m.* deviator; **—иться, —яться** *v.* deviate, vary; swerve, sheer; evade, avoid, shun; **—яться от** diverge from; **—омер, —ометр** *m.* inclinometer; declinometer; **—чивость** *f.* evasiveness; **—чивый** *a.* evasive.

**уключина** *f.* ragbolt; oarlock.

**уков/ать, —ывать** *v.* (met.) condense, tighten by forging; reinforce with metal sheets; **—ка** *f.* forging reduction ratio.

**укол** *m.* prick, pricking; (med.) injection, puncture; **—оть** *see* **укалывать.**

**укомплектован/ие** *n.* completion; manning; replacement; **—ный** *a.* completed; manned; staffed, with a complete staff.

**укор** *m.* reproach, blame.

**укорачив/ание** *n.* shortening, contraction, reduction; **—ать** *v.* shorten, contract, reduce, abridge, lessen; take up (belt).

**укорен/ение** *n.* implanting, inculcating; rooting, taking root; **—ившийся** *a.* rooted, inveterate, of long standing; **—ить, —ять** *v.* implant, inculcate; **—иться, —яться** *v.* take root.

**укоризн/а** *f.* reproach; **—енный** *a.* reproachful; reproachable, censurable.

**укорить** *see* **укорять.**

**укор/отитель** *m.* (pulse) chopper; **—отить** *see* **укорачивать; —очение** *see* **укорачивание; —оченный** *a.* shortened, contracted, abbreviated, abridged; stub.

**укорять** *v.* reproach.

**укос** *m.* (agr.) mowing; (hay) crop, yield.

**укосина** *f.* strut, angle brace; cantilever; (crane) jib, boom, overhang beam.

**укосн/ение** *n.* delay, slowness; **—ительный** *a.* slow; **—ительное движение** decelerating motion, deceleration.

**укр.** *abbr.* (украинский) Ukrainian.

**Украйна** Ukraine.

**украсить** *see* **украшать.**

**украсть** *v.* steal, make off (with); tap.

**украш/ать** *v.* adorn, decorate, ornament, embellish, set off; **—ение** *n.* decoration, ornament; **—енный** *a.* decorated.

**укреп/ить, —лять** *v.* strengthen, fortify, consolidate, solidify; brace, reinforce, stiffen; fix, set, make fast, fasten; **—ление** *n.* strengthening, fortifying, fortification, consolidation; reinforcement, stiffening; fixing, fastening; corroboration; (bridge) head; (mil.) defense; **—ленный** *a.* strengthened, fortified; reinforced, stiffened; fixed, fastened; embedded; **—ляющее** *n.*,

**—ляющее средство** tonic, restorative; **—ляющий** *a.* strengthening; reinforcing; bracing, invigorating, restorative; **—ляющая часть** (fractionation) rectifying section.

**укромный** *a.* secluded; comfortable.

**укроп** *m.*, **—ный** *a.* (bot.) dill (*Anethum graveolens*); fennel (*Foeniculum vulgare*); **аптечный у., сладкий у.** sweet fennel (*F. dulce*); **водяной у., конский у.** water fennel, horsebane (*Oenanthe phellandrium*); **морской у.** samphire (*Crithmum maritimum*); **собачий у.** dog fennel, mayweed (*Anthemis cotula*); **—ное дерево** sassafras wood.

**укро/тить, —щать** *v.* subdue, curb; pacify, appease; **—щение** *n.* subdual; pacification.

**укрупн/ение** *n.* enlargement, coarsening; consolidation; coagulation, flocculation; **—итель** *m.* coagulant; **—ить, —ять** *v.* enlarge, coarsen; consolidate, combine; coagulate, flocculate.

**укрыв/ание** *n.* concealing, concealment; **—ательство** *n.* concealment; **—ать** *v.* conceal, cover, sheathe; screen, shelter; **—аться** *v.* cover oneself, seek shelter, hide; **—истость** *f.* covering power (of paint).

**укрыт/ие** *n.* cover, covering, sheathing; shelter, housing; concealment; **—ый** *a.* covered, sheltered, housed; concealed; **—ь** *see* **укрывать.**

**уксус** *m.* vinegar; **превращать в у.** *v.* acetify.

**уксусно/алюминиевая соль, —глиноземная соль** aluminum acetate; **—амиловый эфир** amyl acetate; **—аммиачная соль, —аммониевая соль** ammonium acetate; **—бариевая соль** barium acetate; **—бутиловый эфир** butyl acetate; **—железистая соль** ferrous acetate; **—железная соль** ferric acetate; **—известковая соль, —кальциевая соль** calcium acetate; **—изоамиловый эфир** isoamyl acetate; **—калиевая соль** potassium acetate.

**уксуснокисл/ый** *a.* acetic acid; acetate (of); **у. калий** potassium acetate; **у. хинин** quinine acetate; **у. этил** ethyl acetate; **—ая соль** acetate.

**уксусно/крезиловый эфир** cresyl acetate;

—магниевая соль magnesium acetate; —медистая соль cuprous acetate; —медная соль cupric acetate; —метиловый эфир methyl acetate; —натриевая соль sodium acetate; —пропиловый эфир propyl acetate; —ртутистая соль mercurous acetate; —ртутная соль mercuric acetate; —свинцовая соль lead acetate; —этиловый эфир ethyl acetate.

**уксусн/ый** *a.* vinegar; acetic; **у. альдегид** acetaldehyde, ethanal; **у. ангидрид** acetic anhydride; **у. сахар** sugar of lead, lead acetate; **у. шелк** acetate silk; **у. эфир** acetic ester, ethyl acetate; **у. эфир целлюлозы** cellulose acetate; —**ая кислота** acetic acid, ethanoic acid; **ледяная —ая кислота** glacial acetic acid; **амид —ой кислоты** acetamide; **ангидрид —ой кислоты** acetic anhydride; **соль —ой кислоты** acetate; **основная соль —ой кислоты** subacetate; —**ая пленка** flower of vinegar; —**ая эссенция** vinegar essence; —**ое брожение** acetic fermentation, acetification; —**ое дерево** (bot.) staghorn sumac (*Rhus typhina*).

**укупор/ивание** *n.*, —**ка** *f.* corking, capping, sealing; packing; —**ивать, —ить** *v.* cork, cap, seal; pack; —**очный** *a.* corking, capping, sealing; packing, pack; —**очная машина** sealing machine, capping machine; —**щик** *m.* corker; packer.

**укус** *m.*, —**ить** *v.* bite, sting.

**укут/анный** *a.* wrapped up, covered; —**ать, —ывать** *v.* wrap up, muffle up, cover; —**ывание** *n.* wrapping up.

**улавлив/ание** *n.* collecting, catching, capture, trapping, interception; recovery (from waste); blanketing (of gold-bearing sands or slimes); —**атель** *see* **уловитель;** —**ать** *v.* collect, catch, pick up, capture, entrap; recover; discover, detect, discern; locate; seize (an opportunity); —**ающая башня** entrainment tower.

**уладить** *see* **улаживать.**

**улажив/ание** *n.* settling, composing, reconciliation; —**ать** *v.* settle, compose, reconcile, make up, arrange, adjust.

**улегаться** *see* **укладываться.**

**улей** *m.*, —**ный** *a.* beehive, hive.

**улекс/ин** *m.* ulexine, cytisine; —**ит** *m.* (min.) ulexite, boronatrocalcite.

**улет** *m.* flying away, flight, migration (of birds); —**ание** *n.* flying away, escape; —**ать, —еть** *v.* fly away, escape.

**улетуч/иваемость** *f.* volatility; —**иваемый** *a.* volatile; —**ивание** *n.* volatilization; —**иваться, —иться** *v.* volatilize, evaporate; escape, disappear; —**ивающийся** *a.* volatilizing; volatile; disappearing.

**улечься** *see* **укладываться.**

**улигит** *m.* (min.) uhligite.

**улика** *f.* evidence, proof.

**улит/ка** *f.* (zool.) snail; (anat.) cochlea; helix; spiral conveyer; —**ки** *pl.* (zool.) Gastropoda; —**кообразный** *a.* spiral, helical; conchoidal; —**очный** *a.* snail; helical; scroll; byssus (silk).

**улица** *f.* street.

**улич/ать, —ить** *v.* convict; expose; detect; —**ение** *n.* conviction; detection; —**итель** *m.* detector.

**уличный** *a.* street; outdoor.

**улов** *m.* catch, take, yield; —**имый** *a.* perceptible; —**итель** *m.* catcher, separator, interceptor; trap; detector, locator (of sound); —**ить** *see* **улавливать.**

**уловка** *f.* trick, ruse, stratagem.

**уловлен/ие** *see* **улавливание;** —**ный** *a.* caught, collected; recovered; detected, located.

**улож/ение** *n.* packing up; (law) code; —**енный** *a.* packed, put away; laid; —**ить** *see* **укладывать.**

**улуч/ать, —ить** *v.* seize, catch; find.

**улучш/ать, —ить** *v.* improve, better, make better, amend, ameliorate, refine; —**аться, —иться** *v.* improve, become better; —**ающее вещество** ameliorant, conditioner, stabilizer; surfactant (surface active agent); —**ающийся** *a.* improving, progressing; —**ение** *n.* improvement, amelioration; amendment, refinement, development, adaptation; (met.) heat treatment; —**енный** *a.* improved.

**улыб/аться, —нуться** *v.* smile.

**ульевой** *a.* beehive, hive; **у. процесс** beehive process (of coking).

**Ульмана реакция** Ullmann reaction.

**ульман/ит, —нит** *m.* (min.) ullmannite (a sulfantimonide of nickel).

**ульмат** *m.* ulmate.

**ульмин** *m.* ulmin (an elm gum; an organic substance in soil, etc.); **—овый** *a.* ulmin, ulmic; **—овый бурый** ulmin brown, Van Dyke brown; **—овая кислота** ulmic acid, geic acid; **соль —овой кислоты, —овокислая соль** ulmate.

**ульрихит** *m.* (petr.) ulrichite; (min.) ulrichite (a form of uraninite).

**ульстерский** *a.* (geol.) Ulsterian.

**ультимат/ивный** *a.* ultimate; ultimatum; **—ум** *m.* ultimatum.

**ультра—** *prefix* ultra—, excessively; **—акустика** *f.* (acous.) ultrasonics; **—высокий** *a.* ultrahigh; **—динный** *a.* (rad.) ultradyne; **—звук** *m.* ultrasound (ultrasonic vibrations); ultrasonics; **—звуковой** *a.* ultrasonic, supersonic; **—короткий** *a.* ultrashort; **—красный** *see* **инфракрасный; —малый** *a.* minute, trace.

**ультрамарин** *m.,* **—овый** *a.* ultramarine, artificial lapis-lazuli; **—овый желтый** ultramarine yellow, barium chromate.

**ультрамикро/метр** *m.* ultramicrometer; **—н** *m.* ultramicron; **—скоп** *m.* ultramicroscope; **—скопический** *a.* ultramicroscopic; **—химический** *a.* ultramicrochemical.

**ультра/милонит** *m.* ultra-mylonite (flinty crush rock); **—основный** *a.* ultrabasic; **—основные породы, —щелочные породы** (petr.) ultrabasic rocks; **—полярный** *a.* ultrapolar; **—фильтр** *m.* ultrafilter; **—фильтрация** *f.* ultrafiltration; **—фиолетовый** *a.* ultraviolet (rays); **—центрифуга** *f.* ultracentrifuge.

**ум** *m.* mind, intellect, intelligence, understanding; **ему пришло на ум** it occurred to him.

**у.м.** *abbr.* (уровень моря) sea level.

**умаление** *n.* belittling, disparagement; depreciation, decrease, lessening.

**умаливание** *n.* supplication, entreating.

**умалить** *see* **умалять.**

**умалишенный** *m.* lunatic, insane person.

**умалчив/ание** *n.* suppression, keeping secret; **—ать** *v.* say nothing (of), pass over in silence.

**умалять** *v.* belittle, disparage; depreciate; **—ся** *v.* diminish, lessen.

**уматывать** *v.* wind around, wrap.

**умащивать** *v.* pave, floor.

**умбелл/аровая кислота** umbellaric acid; **—атин** *m.* umbellatine; **—иферон** *m.* umbelliferone, 4-hydroxycoumarin; **—овая кислота** umbellic acid, *p*-hydroxycoumaric acid; **—оновая кислота** umbellonic acid; **—уловая кислота** umbellulic acid; **—улон** *m.* umbellulone.

**умбиликаровая кислота** umbilicaric acid.

**умбра** *f.,* **земля у.** umber (pigment).

**уме/лый** *a.* skilful, expert; **—ние, —нье** *n.* skill, ability, dexterity; know-how.

**уменьш/аемое, —ающееся** *n.* (math.) minuend; **—аемый** *a.* reducible; **—ать, —ить** *v.* diminish, lessen, lower, reduce, decrease, minimize, abate, ease, ease up; alleviate (pain); narrow; **—аться, —иться** *v.* diminish, lessen, decrease, drop, fall, decline, abate, dwindle; **—ение** *n.* diminution, lessening, decrease, reduction, contraction, shrinkage, abatement, attenuation; short-cut; **—енный** *a.* diminished, lessened, decreased, reduced; **—ительный** *a.* diminutive.

**умерение** *n.* moderation, tempering, mitigation, restraining.

**умеренн/о** *adv.* moderately; **—ость** *f.* moderation; **—ый** *a.* moderate, medium, mild, temperate; **—ый пояс** (meteor.) temperate zone.

**умереть** *see* **умирать.**

**умерить** *see* **умерять.**

**умертвить** *see* **умерщвлять.**

**умерший** *a.* dead, deceased; *m.* the dead, the deceased.

**умерщвл/ение** *n.* killing, destruction; **—ять** *v.* kill, destroy, put to death.

**умерять** *v.* moderate, mitigate, modify, damp; **—ся** *v.* be moderated; abate.

**умесить** *see* **умешивать.**

**умест/ительный** *a.* spacious, roomy; **—ить** *see* **умещать.**

**умести/ость** *f.* pertinence, appropriateness, aptness, relevancy; **—ый** *a.*

pertinent, appropriate, relevant, well-timed, timely.

**умет** *m.* (mil.) trench; dust, refuse.

**уметь** *v.* be able, know how.

**умешивать** *v.* knead, mix in, work up.

**умещать** *v.* put, pack, find room (for); **—ся** *v.* go in, fit in.

**уминать** *v.* compress, consolidate; squeeze, press, tread down; knead, work.

**умир/ание** *n.* dying, expiration; **—ать, —еть** *v.* die, die off, expire; **—ающий** *a.* dying.

**умир/ить, —отворить, —отворять, —ять** *v.* pacify, appease, conciliate.

**умно** *adv.* cleverly, wisely, sensibly.

**умнож/ать, —ить** *v.* increase, augment; (math.) multiply; **у. на** multiply by; **—аться** *v.* increase, multiply, be multiplied; **—ение** *n.* rise, increase; multiplication; breeding (of nuclear fuel); **трубка —ения** (electron) multiplier tube; **—итель** *m.* multiplier.

**умный** *a.* intelligent, clever, sensible, wise.

**умозаключ/ать** *v.* conclude, infer; **—ение** *n.* conclusion, inference.

**умозр/ение** *n.* speculation, theory; **—ительно** *adv.* theoretically; **—ительность** *f.* theoretical nature; **—ительный** *a.* speculative, theoretical.

**умол** *m.* grinding; loss in grinding.

**умолачивать** *v.* thresh, beat.

**умолить** *see* умолять.

**умолот** *m.* threshing; yield (of grain); **—ить** *see* умолачивать.

**умолч/ание** *n.* suppression, omission; reticence, silence; **—ать** *see* умалчивать.

**умолять** *v.* supplicate, entreat, implore.

**умопомешательство** *n.* insanity, lunacy.

**уморить** *v.* kill, cause one's death.

**умостить** *see* умащивать.

**умственный** *a.* mental, intellectual.

**умудр/енный** *a.* taught, made wiser; **—ить, —ять** *v.* teach, make wiser; **—иться, —яться** *v.* contrive, manage, find a way.

**умформер** *m.* (elec.) converter, motor generator; transformer; dynamotor.

**умывальн/ик** *m.*, **—ая раковина** wash basin, wash stand; **—ый** *a.* wash, washing; **—я** *f.* wash room, lavatory.

**умыв/ание** *n.* washing, wash; (pharm.) lotion; **—ать, —аться** *v.* wash.

**умыс/ел** *m.* design, intention, purpose, premeditation; **без —ла** unintentionally; **с —лом** on purpose, purposefully; **—лить** *see* умышлять.

**умыт/ый** *a.* washed; **—ь** *see* умывать.

**умышленн/о** *adv.* intentionally, on purpose, purposely, deliberately; **—ость** *f.* deliberateness; **—ый** *a.* intentional, deliberate, designed, premeditated.

**умышлять** *v.* plot, scheme, design.

**умягч/ать, —ить** *v.* soften.

**умять** *see* уминать.

**унав/аживание, —ожение** *n.* (agr.) manuring; **—аживать, —оживать, —озить** *v.* manure, top-dress.

**унаследовать** *v.* inherit.

**УНГ** *abbr.* (уранилнитратгексагидрат) uranyl nitrate hexahydrate.

**унгварит** *m.* (min.) ungvarite, unghwarite (a variety of chloropal).

**унгулиновая кислота** ungulinic acid.

**ундека/диен** *m.* undecadiene; **—лактон** *m.* undecalactone, peach aldehyde; **—н** *m.* undecane, hendecane; **—нафтен** *m.* undecanaphthene; **—нафтеновая кислота** undecanaphthenic acid.

**ундеколевая кислота** undecolic acid.

**ундецен** *m.* undecene, hendecene; **—ил** *m.* undecenyl; **—овая кислота** undecenoic acid, undecylic acid.

**ундецил** *m.*, **—овый** *a.* undecyl, hendecyl; **—ен** *m.* undecylene, hendecene; **—еновая кислота** undecylenic acid, 9-hendecenoic acid; **—овая кислота** undecylic acid, hendecanoic acid; **—овый альдегид** undecylic aldehyde, hendecanal; **—овый спирт** undecylic alcohol, hendecyl alcohol.

**унести** *see* уносить.

**уни—** *prefix* uni— (one, single); **—вариантный** *a.* univariant.

**универсал** *m.* (astron., surv.) theodolite.

**универсально** *adv.* universally; **у.-шлифовальный станок** universal grinding machine; **—сть** *f.* universality.

**универсальн/ый** *a.* universal, all-purpose; multipurpose, general-purpose; versatile; **у. инструмент** (astron., surv.) theodolite; **у. ключ** universal wrench; **у. станок** universal lathe;

—ая газовая постоянная universal gas constant *R*.

университет *m.*, —ский *a.* university.

уни/жать, —зить *v.* lower, reduce; degrade, humiliate; —жение *n.* lowering; degradation, humiliation, abasement.

уник/альный *a.*, —ум *m.* unique.

унимать *v.* appease, pacify; stop (blood), alleviate (pain).

униполярн/ость *f.* unipolarity; —ый *a.* unipolar.

унисон *m.*, —ный *a.* unison.

унитаз *m.* toilet bowl.

уни/тарный *a.* unitary; —фикация *f.* unification, unitization; —филяр *m.* declinometer; —филярный *m.* unifilar; —фицировать *v.* unify, unitize.

уничиж/ать, —ить *v.* disparage; —ение *n.* disparagement, contempt; —ительный *a.* disparaging, contemptuous.

уничтож/ать, —ить *v.* destroy, annihilate, exterminate, eliminate, do away (with); abolish, nullify, cancel, cancel out, neutralize; demolish, obliterate; extinguish; dissipate, deplete; взаимно —ающиеся погрешности compensating errors; —ение *n.* destruction, annihilation, extermination, elimination, disposal (of); abolishment, cancellation, cancelling; demolition; —енный *a.* destroyed, exterminated; cancelled; —итель *m.* annihilator; —ительный *a.* destructive.

уния *f.* union.

ункомпагрит *m.* (min.) uncompahgrite (melilite-rich pyroxenite).

унос *m.* taking, bearing, carrying away, entrainment; carryover; (boiler) priming; team; —ить *v.* take away, carry away, carry off.

ун-т *abbr.* (университет) university.

унтерцуг *m.* (min.) timber support.

унцевый *a.* ounce, one-ounce.

унцинатовая кислота uncinatic acid.

унция *f.* ounce (28.3 grams).

унывать *v.* be disheartened, lose heart.

унять *see* унимать.

Уокера компенсатор фаз (elec.) Walker phase-advancer.

уошер *m.* washer.

упадать *see* упасть.

упад/ок *m.* decline, decay, decadence;

fall, decrease, ebb; descent, dip; у. сил breakdown, collapse; период —ка period of decline; приходить в у. *v.* fall into decay, decline; состояние —ка decadent stage; —очный *a.* decadent.

упаков/ать, —ывать *v.* pack, pack up, put up, wrap up; —ка *f.*, —ывание *n.* packing, wrapping, boxing, baling; wrapper, package; вес в —ке shipping weight; плотной —ки close-packed; —очный *a.* packing, wrapping; baling (press); —очный коэффициент, —очный множитель (nucl.) packing fraction; —щик *m.* packer.

упар/ивание *n.* concentration, concentration by evaporation; steaming; —ивать, —ить *v.* concentrate, evaporate, boil down; steam, stew; —очный *a.* steaming.

упас *m.* (bot.) upas (*Antiaris toxicaria*).

упасть *v.* fall, fall down; descend, decline.

упах/ать, —ивать *v.* till, plow thoroughly.

Упварда элемент Upward (chlorine) cell.

упек *m.* loss in baking; —ать *v.* bake well, bake thoroughly; —аться *v.* lose in baking, bake out.

упереть *see* упирать.

упечь *see* упекать.

упирать *v.* set, place, fix; rest, prop, lean (against); —ся *v.* be fixed; rest, push, thrust, strike (against), lean (against); run into (of a road); persist (in); resist; —ся в push against, abut against, butt against.

упит/анность *f.* fatness; —анный *a.* well-fed; —ать, —ывать *v.* feed up, fatten.

упих/ать, —ивать, —нуть *v.* push in, shove in.

упла/та *f.* payment, paying, reimbursement, disbursement; подлежащий —те payable; —тить, —чивать *v.* pay, disburse.

уплотнен/ие *n.* condensation, thickening; consolidation, compression, squeezing, contraction, shrinkage; packing, settling, flattening; compaction, tightening, sealing, luting; seal, gasket, gland, packing; sintering; —ный *a.* condensed, thickened, compressed; packed, sealed; consolidated.

**уплотнитель** *m.* thickener; packer; **—ный** *a.* thickening; packing, sealing; **—ная втулка** sealing bush.

**уплотни/ить, —ять** *v.* condense, thicken, concentrate; compress, squeeze, contract; pack, tighten, make tight, make impervious, seal (off, in, out); consolidate; **—яться** *v.* condense, thicken; contract, shrink; sinter, form clinker or slag.

**уплотняющ/ий** *a.* thickening; packing, sealing; impermeable; blanketing (gas); **—ая жидкость** sealing liquid; **—ая масса** packing material, packing; **—ее кольцо** packing ring, gasket ring.

**уплощенный** *a.* depressed; compressed.

**уплы/вать, —ть** *v.* swim away, go away, float away; pass away, elapse.

**уподоб/ить, —лять** *v.* liken, compare; **—ление** *n.* likening, comparison.

**упоко/ение** *n.* repose, rest; **—ительный** *a.* restful.

**упол—** *abbr.* (**уполномоченный**) representative.

**уполаживание** *n.* flattening.

**уполз/ать, —ти** *v.* creep away, crawl away.

**уполномоч/ение** *n.* authorization; power of attorney; **—енный** *a.* authorized; *m.* authorized agent, representative, delegate; **—ивать, —ить** *v.* authorize, empower, commission.

**уполовник** *m.* skimmer; (casting) ladle.

**упомин/ание** *n.* mention, mentioning, reference; **ничего стоящего —ания** nothing to speak of; **—ать** *v.* mention, make mention (of), refer, make reference (to).

**упомянут/ый** *a.* mentioned, referred (to); **—ь** *see* **упоминать.**

**упор** *m.*, **—ка** *f.* rest, prop, support, stay, brace; dog, stop, arresting device, checking device, catch, detent, detainer; **делать у.** *v.* emphasize.

**упорно** *adv.* obstinately, persistently; **—сть** *f.* obstinacy, persistence, tenacity.

**упорн/ый** *a.* stubborn, obstinate, unyielding, persistent, tenacious; stop, thrust; fixed (center); *suffix* **—**proof, **—**resistant; **у. болт** stop; **у. диск** bearing disk, bearing socket; **у. кулачок** stop, detent; **у. подшипник** thrust bearing; **у. шариковый подшипник, у. шарикоподшипник** ball and thrust bearing; **у. рычаг** stop, stop lever; **у. торец** anvil; **у. угольник** back square; **у. штифт** stop, stop pin; **—ая скоба** stop piece, check clamp; **—ое кольцо** thrust collar.

**упорство** *see* **упорность; —вать** *v.* persist (in); be stubborn.

**упорядоч/ение** *n.* regulation, ordering; **—енность** *f.* orderliness; **—енный** *a.* well regulated, ordered; **—ивать, —ить** *v.* regulate, put in good order.

**употр.** *abbr.* (**употребительный**) customary; (**употребляется**) is used.

**употребит/ельность** *f.* usualness; frequency (of usage); use; **—ельный** *a.* usual, customary, generally used, practiced; **—ь** *see* **употреблять.**

**употреблен/ие** *n.* use, employment, application, usage; **вводить в у.** *v.* bring into use, introduce; **вышедший из —ия** obsolete, disused, antiquated; **для внутреннего —ия** (med.) for internal use; **—ный** *a.* used.

**употреблять** *v.* use, make use (of), employ, apply; **—ся** *v.* be used, be in use, be employed.

**управ/а** *f.* board; office; satisfaction, justice; **—дел** *m.* business manager; **—итель** *m.* manager; **—ить** *see* **управлять.**

**управлен/ие** *n.* management, government, administration; handling, operation, controlling, control, regulation; steering, guiding, direction; (aero.) controls; board; **у. на расстоянии** remote control; **выключатель —ия** master switch; **дурное у.** mismanagement, maladministration; **механизм —ия** operating gear; steering gear; **пост —ия** pulpit, control position; **рычаг —ия** control lever; **с электронным —ием** electronically controlled; **щит —ия** instrument control board, control panel.

**управляем/ость** *f.* controllability, control, maneuverability; **—ый** *a.* controllable, maneuverable; guided, controlled; **—ый по радио** radio-controlled; trolled.

**управлять** *v.* manage, control, regulate, handle, run, operate (machine), drive; govern, rule; boss; guide, direct; **—ся** *v.* be managed, be controlled; manage, get along, handle, overcome.

**управляющ/ий** *a.* managing, controlling, control, operating; *m.* manager, superintendent, director; **у. вал** camshaft; **у. делами** business manager; **—ая кнопка** control button; **—ее звено** controller; **—ее сочленение** master joint (of manipulator).

**упражн/ение** *n.* exercise, practice, drill; **—ять** *v.* exercise; **—яться** *v.* exercise, practice.

**упраздн/ение** *n.* abolition, elimination; **—ить, —ять** *v.* abolish, eliminate, annul.

**упрашивать** *v.* beg, entreat, urge.

**упревать** *v.* stew, be stewed; perspire.

**упре/дить, —ждать** *v.* forestall, anticipate, prevent; precede; **—ждение** *n.* anticipation, prevention; preceding, lead; advance; **угол —ждения** (elec.) angle of lead.

**упрек** *m.* reproach, reproof; **—ать, —нуть** *v.* reproach, reprove.

**упр/елый** *a.* stewed, cooked; perspired; **—еть** *see* **упревать.**

**упросить** *see* **упрашивать.**

**упростить** *see* **упрощать.**

**упроч/ение** *n.* strengthening, consolidation; fixing, securing; **—ивать, —ить** *v.* strengthen, consolidate; fix, secure, make firmer; **—нение** *n.* hardening, toughening; **механическое —нение** (met.) strain hardening; **—нять** *v.* substantiate; strengthen.

**упрощ/ать** *v.* simplify; **у. до** reduce to; **—ение** *n.* simplification; **—енный** *a.* simplified; reduced; short.

**упруг/ий** *a.* elastic, springy, resilient, flexible; expansible (gas); taut; **у. гистерезис** elastic hysteresis; **—ая деформация** elastic deformation or strain; **—ая линия** line of deflection; **—ая отдача** recoil; **—ая постоянная** elastic constant; stiffness constant; modulus of elasticity; **—ое восстановление** elastic recovery; (met.) spring-back; **—ое основание** cushion; **—ое последействие** elastic lag, elastic after-effect; **—ое столкновение** elastic collision; **—о** *adv.* elastically, resiliently; **—ожидкий** *a.* elastic-fluid.

**упругост/ь** *f.* elasticity, resilience, spring, rebound, flexibility; tension; extensibility, expansibility, buoyancy (of gas); **у. пара** vapor tension; **у. при изгибе** elasticity of flexure; **у. при сжатии** elasticity of compression; **модуль —и** modulus of elasticity, rigidity modulus; **сила —и** elastic force, elasticity; tension; **предел —и** elastic limit.

**упру/дить, —живать** *v.* dam, dam up.

**упружить** *v.* make elastic or springy; **—ся** *v.* be elastic, be springy.

**упрягать** *v.* harness.

**упряж/ка** *f.* team; (min.) shift; **—ной, —ный** *a.* harness; draw; draft (horse); **—ной крюк** draw hook; **—ной прибор** draw gear, coupling gear; **—ная тяга** draw bar; **—ь** *f.* harness, gear.

**упрям/иться** *v.* persist, be obstinate; **—ство** *n.* persistence, obstinacy; **—ый** *a.* persistent, obstinate, stubborn.

**упрячь** *see* **упрягать.**

**упу/скать, —стить** *v.* let escape, let slip, omit, overlook, miss (an opportunity); **—щение** *n.* omission, neglect; **—щенный** *a.* omitted, neglected, overlooked.

**упятер/енный** *a.* quintuple, fivefold; **—ить, —ять** *v.* quintuple, increase fivefold.

**ур.** *abbr.* (уральский) Ural.

**уравнен/ие** *n.* equation, relation; leveling; **у. первой степени** simple equation; **химическое у.** chemical equation; **—ный** *a.* leveled; equated.

**уравн/ивание** *n.* leveling, grading; equalization, compensation; **—ивать** *v.* level, grade, even, smooth; equalize, compensate; equate, make equal; steady; **—ивающий** *a.* leveling; compensating; **—иловка** *f.* wage leveling; **—итель** *m.* leveler, grader; equalizer, balancer, balance gear; regulator; **—итель хода** governor.

**уравнительн/ый** *a.* leveling, grading; equalizing, compensating, balancing, balancer; regulating; **у. агрегат** balancer, equalizer; **у. винт** set screw, adjusting screw; **у. маятник** compensator, compensation pendulum; **у. метод** compensation method; **у. чан, —ая башня** (concentration) surge tank; **—ая обмотка** (elec.) compensating winding.

**уравновесить** *see* **уравновешивать.**

**уравновешенн/ость** *f.* equilibrium, balance, steadiness; **—ый** *a.* equilibrated, compensated, balanced, counterpoised, equable, level, steady.

**уравновешив/ание** *n.* equilibration, balancing; **—ать** *v.* put in equilibrium, equilibrate, balance, counterbalance, counteract, equalize, neutralize; **—ающий** *a.* equalizing, balancing.

**уравнять** *see* **уравнивать.**

**ураган** *m.,* **—ный** *a.* hurricane.

**ураз/ин** *m.* urazine, diurea; **—ол** *m.* urazole, hydrazodicarbonimide; urasol, acetylmethylene-disalicylic acid.

**уразум/евать, —еть** *v.* understand, comprehend.

**ураконит** *m.* (min.) uraconite, uranic ocher.

**Урал** Ural (mountains, river, or region).

**УРАЛГИНЦВЕТМЕТ** *abbr.* (**Уральский государственный научно-исследовательский институт цветных металлов**) Ural State Scientific Research Institute of Non-ferrous Metals.

**уралий** *m.* uralium (probably identical with rhenium).

**урал/ий, —ин** *m.* Uralin, chloral urethane.

**уралит** *m.* (min.) uralite (pyroxene altered to amphibole); Uralite (a fireproof asbestos material); Uralit (wood preservative); **—изация** *f.* uralitization.

**урал/ортит** *m.* (min.) uralorthite (a variety of allanite); **—ьский** *a.* Ural.

**урамил** *m.* uramil, 5-aminobarbituric acid.

**урамин** *m.* uramine, guanidine.

**уран** *m.* uranium, U; **двуокись —а, закись —а** uranium dioxide, uranous oxide; **закись-окись —а** uranoso-uranic oxide, uranous uranate; **соль закиси —а** uranous salt; **окись —а** uranic oxide, uranium trioxide; **соль окиси —а** uranic salt; **сернокислая закись —а** uranous sulfate; **сернокислый у.** uranium sulfate.

**Уран** *m.* (astron.) Uranus.

**уран/ат** *m.* uranate; **—ид** *m.* uranide.

**уранил** *m.,* **—овый, —ьный** *a.* uranyl; **—сульфат** *m.,* **сернокислый у.,** uranyl sulfate, uranium sulfate; **хлористый у.** uranyl chloride, uranium dioxydichloride; **—овая соль** uranyl salt.

**уранин** *m.* uranin, sodium fluorescein; (min.) pitchblende; **—ит** *m.* (min.) uraninite, pitchblende.

**уранисто—** *prefix* uranoso—, uranous.

**уранист/ый** *a.* uranium, uranous; **—ая соль** uranous salt.

**уранит** *m.* (min.) uranite; **известковый у.** lime uranite, autunite; **—овый** *a.* uranitic.

**урано—** *prefix* urano—, uranium, uranic.

**ураново/кислый** *a.* uranic acid; uranate (of); **у. натрий, —натриевая соль** sodium uranate; **—кислая соль** uranate.

**уранов/ый** *a.* uranium, uranic; **у. ангидрид** uranic anhydride, uranium trioxide; **у. блок** (nucl.) slug; **у. желтый** uranium yellow, sodium uranate; **у. котел, у. реактор** nuclear reactor; **у. свинец** uranium lead (a form of radium); **—ая кислота** uranic acid; **соль —ой кислоты** uranate; **—ая слюда** (min.) uran mica, uranite; **—ая смолка, —ая смоляная обманка, —ая смоляная руда** (min.) pitchblende; **—ая соль** uranium salt; **—ая чернь** a group of uranium oxide minerals.

**урано/графия** *f.* uranography, descriptive astronomy; **—добывающий** *a.* uranium-mining; **—лепидит** *m.* (min.) uranolepidite; **—лит** *m.* uranolite (a meteorite); **—метрическая съемка** method of prospecting for uranium ores; **—метрия** *f.* (astron.) uranometry; **—ниобит** *m.* (min.) uranoniobite (a variety of uraninite); **—носный, —содержащий** *a.* uraniumcontaining, uraniferous; **—пилит** *m.* (min.) uranopilite; **—пластика** *f.* (med.) uranoplasty; **—спинит** *m.* (min.) uranospinite; **—сферит** *m.*

(min.) uranospherite; —**таллит** *m.*
(min.) uranothallite; —**темнит** *m.*
(min.) uranotemnite; —**тил, —фан**
*m.* (min.) uranotil, uranophane; —**тит**
*m.* (min.) uranotite; —**торианит** *m.*
(min.) uranothorianite; —**торит** *m.*
(min.) uranothorite (a variety of
thorite); —**хальцит** *m.* (min.) urano-
chalcite; —**цирцит** *m.* (min.) uranocircite; —**шпатит** *m.* uranospathite.

**урао** *n.* (min.) urao, trona (hydrous sodium carbonate).

**урари** *n.* urari, curare; —**н** *m.* curarine.

**урасол** *see* **уразол.**

**урат** *m.* urate (salt of uric acid); —**емия**
*f.* (med.) uratemia; —**ол** *m.* uratol,
Ural toluene (dehydrogenated tree-
stump turpentine).

**урацил** *m.* uracil, 2,6-dioxopyrimidine.

**урбанит** *m.* (min.) urbanite (an iron-
schefferite).

**урвать** *see* **урывать.**

**ургон** *m.*, —**ский ярус** (geol.) Urgonian
stage.

**урдит** *m.* (min.) urdite (a variety of
monazite).

**уреаза** *f.* urease, urase.

**урегулиров/ание** *n.* regulation; —**ать** *v.*
regulate, regularize; settle (a question); compensate, adjust.

**уредоспора** *f.* (bot.) uredospore.

**урез/ать** *see* **урезывать;** —**ка** *f.* abridgment, curtailment.

**урезыв/ание** *n.* curtailment; —**ать** *v.*
cut down, curtail, abridge, reduce.

**уреид** *m.* ureide.

**урема** *f.* bottom land.

**урем/ический** *a.* (med.) uremic; —**ия** *f.*
uremia.

**уреометр** *m.* ureometer, ureameter.

**урет** *m.* urete; —**ан** *m.* urethan, ethyl
carbamate; —**идин** *m.* uretidine,
tetrahydrourete; —**илан** *m.* urethyl-
ane, methyl carbamate; —**ин** *m.*
uretine, 1,2-dihydrourete.

**уретр/а** *f.* (anat.) urethra; —**альный** *a.*
urethral; —**ит** *m.* (med.) urethritis;
—**оскоп** *m.* (med.) urethroscope.

**уридин** *m.* uridine, uracil-*d*-riboside.

**уриказа** *f.* uricase.

**уриконский** *a.* (geol.) Uriconian.

**урильник** *m.* urinal.

**урин/а** *f.* urine; —**оид** *m.* urinoid, cyclo-

hexene-3-one; —**ометр** *m.* urinometer.

**ур. м.** *abbr.* (уровень моря) sea level.

**урмона** *f.* swampy coniferous forest.

**урна** *f.* urn.

**ур-ние** *abbr.* (уравнение) equation.

**уро**— *prefix* uro— (urea; urine; urinary
tract; urination); —**билин** *m.* urobilin, hydrobilirubin; —**бромогематин**
*m.* urobromohematin.

**уров/ень** *m.* level, plane, surface; standard; **у. моря** sea level; **у. стояния**
(water) table; **банка —ня** leveling
bottle; **в у.** flush (with); **жизненный
у.** standard of living; **на одном —не**
on a level (with), level (with), on one
level; **на —не земли, на —не пола**
at ground level; **поверхность —ня**
level surface; **спиртовой у.** spirit
level; **ширина —ня** (nucl.) level
width.

**уровнемер** *m.* level gage.

**урогематин** *m.* urohematin.

**урод,** —**ец** *m.*, —**ина** *f.* monster, freak;
—**иться** *v.* bear a good crop; —**ливость** *f.* deformity, abnormality,
defect; —**ливый** *a.* deformed, mis-
shapen, abnormal; —**ование** *n.* dis-
figuration, mutilation; —**овать** *v.*
disfigure, mutilate, deform, cripple;
—**ство** *n.* disfigurement, deformity,
malformation.

**урожай** *m.* harvest, crop, yield; **снимать
у., собирать у.** *v.* harvest, reap;
—**ность** *f.* fruitfulness, productivity,
yielding capacity, yield; —**ный** *a.*
fruitful, productive; harvest.

**урожать** *v.* produce, bear, yield.

**урожд/аться** *v.* be born; —**енный** *a.*
born.

**уроженец** *m.* native, indigene.

**урозин** *m.* urosine, lithium quinate.

**урок** *m.* lesson; task, assignment.

**урокан/ин** *m.* urocanin; —**иновая кислота** urocaninic acid; —**овая кислота**
urocanic acid, imidazoleacrylic acid.

**уроксантин** *m.* uroxanthin.

**уролог** *m.* (med.) urologist; —**ия** *f.*
urology.

**урометр** *m.* urometer, urinometer.

**урон** *m.* loss, damage, harm; **наносить
у.** *v.* damage.

**уронид** *m.* uronide.

**уронить** *v.* drop.

**уро/новая кислота** uronic acid; **—порфирин** *m.* uroporphyrin; **—протовая кислота** uroprotic acid; **—птерин** *m.* uropterin; **—рубин** *m.* urorubin; **—сульфан** *m.* sulfanilylurea; **—токсин** *m.* urotoxin; **—тропин** *m.* urotropin, hexamethylenetetramine; **—фан** *m.* urophan; **—ферин** *m.* uropherine, theobromine lithium; **—фос** *m.* urophosphate (fertilizer); **—хлораловая кислота** urochloralic acid; **—хром** *m.* urochrome; **—цитрал** *m.* urocitral, theobromine sodium citrate.

**уроч/ище** *n.* well-delineated area; natural boundary, natural landmark, survey mark; **—ный** *a.* fixed, determined.

**уроэритрин** *m.* uroerythrin.

**урс/ановая кислота** ursanic acid; **—ин** *m.* ursin, arbutin; **—ол** *m.* Ursol, *p*-phenylenediamine; **—оловая кислота, —он** *m.* ursolic acid, urson, prunol; **—оновая кислота** ursonic acid.

**уругвайский** *a.* Uruguay, Uruguayan.

**урузен** *m.* urusene.

**уруть** *f.* (bot.) water milfoil (*Myriophyllum*).

**урушиновая кислота** urushic acid, laccol.

**урыв/ать** *v.* snatch; **—ками** in snatches, at odd moments, by fits and starts.

**урюк** *m.* dried apricot.

**ус** *m.* whisker; barb; (zool.) antenna, feeler; (bot.) tendril, runner; awn (of grass); (whale) bone; guard bar; rail wing; miter; **соединение в у.** miter joint, miter.

**усадебный** *a. of* **усадьба.**

**усад/ить** *see* **усаживать; —ка** *f.* shrinking, shrinkage, contraction, shriveling; loss, disappearance; setting, planting; **давать —ку** *v.* shrink; **коэффициент —ки** shrinkage factor.

**усадочн/ый** *a.* shrinkage, contraction; **у. масштаб** shrink rule, shrinkage rule, contraction gage; **—ая мера** shrinkage allowance; **—ая раковина** shrink hole; (met.) pipe, piping, shrinkage cavity.

**усадьба** *f.* farm, farmstead.

**усаживать** *v.* seat, settle (down); plant, set; **—ся** *v.* take a seat, get settled.

**усат/ка** *f.* bearded wheat (*Triticum vulgare* var. *aristata*); **—ый** *a.* bearded; (bot.) awned, aristate.

**усач** *m.* barbel (fish); capricorn beetle; **—и** *pl.* long-horned beetles (*Cerambycidae*).

**усв/аивание, —оение** *n.* assimilation, appropriation, adoption; mastering; (biol.) uptake; anabolism; **—аивать, —оить, —оять** *v.* assimilate, appropriate, adopt; master, understand, familiarize oneself (with); **—ояемость** *f.* assimilability, availability; comprehensibility; **—ояемый** *a.* assimilable, available, accessible.

**усе/вать, —ивать** *v.* strew, sow; stud.

**усек/ать** *v.* cut off, truncate; **—новение** *n.* decapitation, beheading.

**усерд/ие** *n.* diligence, assiduity, zeal; **—но** *adv.* diligently; **—ный** *a.* diligent, industrious, painstaking, zealous.

**усесться** *see* **усаживаться.**

**усечен/ие** *n.* cutting off, truncation; (med.) excision; **—ный** *a.* cut off, truncated, topped; **—ный конус** (geom.) truncated cone, frustum of a cone; **—ная пирамида** truncated pyramid, frustum of pyramid.

**усечь** *see* **усекать.**

**усе/янный** *a.* sown, strewn; studded, dotted; (petr.) sempatic; **—ять** *see* **усевать.**

**усидчивый** *a.* persevering, assiduous.

**усик** *m.* (bot.) tendril; (zool.) antenna, feeler, horn; barbel; **—оватый** *a.* antennal.

**усилен/ие** *n.* strengthening, reinforcement; growth, rise, gain, increase, boost; intensification (of light, sound, etc.); (phot.) intensification; amplification, magnification; aggravation, heightening; **коэффициент —ия** (rad.) amplification factor; (elec. comm.) gain; **способ —ия** cumulative method; **—но** *adv.* intensely, strenuously, hard, to the best of one's ability; **—ный** *a.* strengthened, reinforced, fortified; increased; intensified; amplified, magnified; urgent (request); high-caloric (diet).

**усилив/ать** *v.* strengthen, reinforce, fortify, stiffen; intensify, heighten, increase, boost; amplify, magnify; aggravate, strain; —**аться** *v.* strengthen, become stronger, become more pronounced; become vigorous; intensify, increase; exert oneself; —**а-ющий** *a.* strengthening; intensifying; amplifying; magnifying; —**ающий ингредиент** (rubber) active filler; —**ающий экран** (radiobiol.) intensifying screen.

**усил/ие** *n.* stress, strain, pull, force; effort, exertion, endeavor, struggle; **прилагать** —**ия** *v.* exert oneself, make efforts, take pains; **срезывающее у.** shearing force; **употреблять все** —**ия** *v.* do one's best.

**усилитель** *m.* amplifier; intensifier, booster; (rubber) active filler; **у. импульсов** (nucl.) pulse amplifier; **у. индуктора** (elec.) magneto booster; **у. напряжения** (elec.) booster; **у. с бегущей волной** traveling-wave accelerator; **у.-дискриминатор** *m.* amplifier-discriminator; —**ный** *a.* intensifying, boosting.

**усилить** *see* **усиливать.**

**ускольз/ать,** —**нуть,** —**ывать** *v.* slip away, slip off; escape.

**ускорен/ие** *n.* acceleration, speeding up, hastening; **у. хода** acceleration, speeding up; **измеритель** —**ия,** —**иемер** *m.* accelerometer; **сила** —**ия** accelerating force; —**ный** *a.* accelerated, fast, express.

**ускор/итель** *m.* accelerator, accelerant; —**ительный** *a.* accelerating, accelerative; —**ить,** —**ять** *v.* accelerate, quicken, hasten, speed, speed up, intensify; expedite, favor; —**яющий** *a.* accelerating; —**яющее усилие** accelerating force.

**уславливаться** *see* **условиться.**

**усластить** *v.* sweeten.

**услать** *see* **усылать.**

**услащ/ать,** —**ивать** *see* **усластить.**

**усл. ед.** *abbr.* (**условная единица**) arbitrary unit.

**уследить** *v.* follow.

**услов/ие** *n.* condition, stipulation, specification, understanding, proviso, clause; circumstance; —**ия** *pl.* condi-

tions; terms (of contract); mode; **по** —**ию** according to agreement; **под** —**ием, при** —**ии, с** —**ием** on condition (that), provided, providing; **при прочих равных** —**иях** other conditions being equal, other things being equal; **при сходных** —**иях** under similar conditions; **ни при каких** —**иях** under no circumstances; **ставить** —**ием** *v.* stipulate, condition; (geom.) postulate.

**услов/иться,** —**ливаться** *v.* agree, arrange, make arrangements, settle, contract; —**ленный** *a.* agreed (upon), fixed, stipulated.

**условно** *adv.* conditionally; provisionally; —**сть** *f.* conditionality; convention.

**услови/ый** *a.* conditional, provisory; arbitrary (unit); quasi—, apparent; conventional; nominal; **у. знак,** —**ое обозначение** conventional sign, conventional symbol; legend; **у. масштаб** representative scale; —**ое топливо** ideal fuel, comparison fuel.

**усложн/ение** *n.* complication; —**енный** *a.* complicated; modified (resin); —**ить,** —**ять** *v.* complicate.

**услуг/а** *f.* service, good turn, favor; **к его** —**ам** at his service, at his disposal; **оказать** —**у** *v.* render a service.

**услышать** *v.* hear.

**усматривать** *v.* find, discover, discern, see, perceive; look (after), attend (to).

**усмир/ить,** —**ять** *v.* suppress, put down; appease, pacify.

**усмотр/ение** *n.* discerning, observing; judgment, discretion; option; —**еть** *see* **усматривать.**

**уснаровая кислота** usnaric acid.

**усн/етиновая кислота** usnetinic acid; —**етовая кислота** usnetic acid; —**идиновая кислота** usnidic acid; —**идол** *m.* usnidol; —**иновая кислота** usninic acid, usnic acid.

**уснуть** *v.* fall asleep.

**усовершенствов/ание** *n.* improvement, development, advance, advent, refinement, adaptation; —**анный** *a.* improved, perfected, elaborated, advanced; —**атель** *m.* improver, developer; —**ать** *v.* improve, develop, perfect; —**аться** *v.* improve, be improved.

**усовик** *m.* rail wing.

**усомниться** *v.* doubt, have misgivings.

**усоногие** *pl.* (zool.) Cirripedia.

**усох/нуть** *see* **усыхать**; **—ший** *a.* dried.

**усп.** *abbr.* (**успехи**) progress.

**успе/вать, —ть** *v.* have time, be able; succeed, be successful, obtain good results; make progress, improve.

**успех** *m.* success; improvement, progress, advance, advancement; **—и** *pl.* progress; **делать —и** *v.* succeed; improve, advance, make progress; **добиться —а** *v.* achieve success, succeed.

**успешн/о** *adv.* successfully; **—ость** *f.* successfulness, success, effectiveness; **—ый** *a.* successful, effective.

**успокаив/ание** *n.* quieting, soothing; moderation, decrement, waning; (elec.) damping; de-excitation; (met.) dead melting, killing, quieting (of steel); **гидравлическое у.** (elec.) liquid damping; **—ать** *v.* soothe, quiet, steady, calm, reassure, set at ease; damp; **—аться** *v.* quiet down, compose oneself; settle down, slacken, abate; **—ающий** *a.* quieting, soothing; damping; **—ающий порошок** sedative; **—ающее средство** lenitive, palliative, tranquilizer.

**успоко/ение** *see* **успокаивание**; **—енный** *a.* quieted, quiet; (elec.) damped; (met.) killed (steel); **—ившийся** *a.* moderated, abated.

**успокоитель** *m.* arrester; (elec.) damper; **жидкий у.** liquid damper; **—ное** *n.* sedative; **—ный** *a.* soothing, restful; sedative; reassuring; (elec.) damping; **—ная обмотка** (elec.) damper winding, damper; **—ная цепь** (elec.) damping circuit.

**успокоить** *see* **успокаивать**.

**Усп. хим.** *abbr.* (**Успехи химии**) Progress of Chemistry (journal).

**усредн/ение** *n.* neutralization; averaging; **—енный** *a.* neutralized; averaged-out, average, mean; **—итель** *m.* neutralizer, neutralizing agent; **—ять** *v.* neutralize; average (out); **—яющий** *a.* neutralizing.

**уссингит** *m.* (min.) ussingite.

**УССР** *abbr.* (**Украинская Советская Социалистическая Республика**) Ukrainian Soviet Socialist Republic.

**уст.** *abbr.* (**устарелый**) obsolete.

**устав** *m.* statute, rules, regulations, code (of regulation).

**уставать** *v.* get tired, tire.

**устав/ить, —ливать, —лять** *v.* set, arrange, place, put; fill, cover; **—ка** *f.* setting, placing, putting.

**устаивать** *see* **устоять**.

**устал/остный** *a.* fatigue; **—остная прочность** (rubber) fatigue stress; **—ость** *f.* fatigue, weariness, lassitude; **испытание на —ость** fatigue test; **предел —ости** fatigue limit, fatigue point, endurance limit; **—ый** *a.* tired, fatigued, weary, worn out; **—ь** *f.* fatigue; **без —и** untiringly, unceasingly.

**устанавлив/аемый** *a.* adjustable; **—ание** *see* **установка, установление**.

**устанавливать** *v.* set, put, place, arrange; establish, determine, fix, settle, ascertain, find out, locate, distinguish, define; align, adjust, regulate; (mach.) mount, set up, install, erect, fit, rig up; (elec.) make (contact); **у. на** adjust for; **у. по** set by, set to; **—ся** *v.* be set, be settled, be fixed, be established, be determined; determine, decide.

**установ/ившийся** *a.* set, settled, steady, smooth; **—ить** *see* **устанавливать**.

**установк/а** *f.* setting, placing, arrangement, seating; setting up, assembling, assembly, mounting, erecting, erection, fitting, putting together, installation, installing, laying; establishment; adjustment, regulation; plant, unit, set-up; outfit, equipment, apparatus; device, contrivance; aim, purpose, tendency; **у. для опрыскивания** sprayer, spraying unit; **у. для переработки** processing plant; **у. на** adjustment for; **у. на нуль** zero adjustment; **у. на фокус** focusing; **иметь —у на** *v.* aim at; **дать —у** *v.* give indications; **допускающий —у по** adjustable for; **силовая у.** power plant; **точная у.** fine adjustment.

**установл/ение** *n.* establishment, institution; determination, determining, fixing, ascertainment; (elec.) rating; statute, law; **—енный** *a.* established, fixed, specified, standard, regulation, set (form); mounted, rigged up, installed; **—ять** see **устанавливать**.

**установочн/ый** a. adjusting, adjustable, regulating; installation; **у. болт** adjuster bolt; **у. винт** set screw, adjusting screw; **—ая мера** reference gage; **—ое приспособление** adjusting device, adjuster; control gear.

**установщик** m. adjuster, fitter, erector, installer, mounter.

**устар.** abbr. (**устарелый**) obsolete.

**устар/еваемость, —елость** f. obsolescence, obsoleteness; **—евший, —елый** a. obsolete, antiquated, out of date; **—еть** v. become obsolete.

**устать** see **уставать**.

**устели-поле** n. (bot.) ceratocarpus.

**устилаговая кислота** ustilagic acid.

**уст/илание** n. covering, paving, flooring; strewing, spreading; **—илать, —лать** v. cover, floor, pave; strew, spread.

**уст/ин** m. Ustin, nornidulin; **—ицеаин** m. ustizeain.

**уст/ичный** see **устьичный; —ный** a. oral, verbal.

**устой** m. abutment, buttress, pier, column; basis, foundation; cream (on milk).

**устойчив/о** adv. stably, steadily, firmly; **—ость** f. stability, steadiness, firmness, rigidity; immunity, resistance; **—ый** a. stable, steady, firm, rigid; durable, resistant; persistent (gas); suffix **—proof, —resistant; —ое соединение** stable compound; **делать —ым** v. stabilize, steady.

**устоять** v. resist, hold out (against), withstand; **—ся** v. settle, precipitate; gather, form cream (of milk).

**устраив/ать** v. arrange, make arrangements (for), accommodate; organize; make, construct; place, settle, establish, install; suit, be convenient (for); **—аться** v. get established, get settled; be arranged, be set up.

**устран/ение** n. removal, elimination, separation, setting aside, clearing; correction (of faults); **у. напряжения** stress relief; **—ить, —ять** v. remove, eliminate, set aside, clear out, dispose (of), do away (with); smooth away; **—иться, —яться** v. be removed; withdraw, stand aside, keep (from).

**устраш/ать, —ить** v. frighten, appall; **—ающий** a. formidable, redoubtable.

**устрем/ить, —лять** v. direct, turn, fix; **—ление** n. directing, turning; tendency, striving; rush.

**устри/ца** f., **—чный** a. oyster; **—цевод-ство** n. oyster culture; **—цевые** pl. Ostracea; **—цеобразный червец** oyster-shell scale; **—чный завод** oyster farm.

**устро/енный** a. arranged; organized; **—итель** m. organizer; **—ить** see **устраивать**.

**устройство** n. arrangement, layout; organization, establishment, installation; device, attachment, appliance, apparatus, facility; working principle (of machine); **—ing** device, **—er**; **пусковое у.** starting device, starter.

**уступ** m. shelf, ledge, bank, terrace, step; (geol.) bench, scarp; recess; bend; shoulder; spur (of hill); **—ы** pl. (min.) benching; **—ами** benched, terraced; step-like, graduated, graded, gradual; **работа —ами** (min.) benching; **расположенный —ами** arranged in steps, stepped, staggered.

**уступ/ать, —ить** v. yield, give in, submit; consent; give up, resign; abate; **—ительный** a. concessive; **—ка** f. concession; deduction, discount, reduction, abatement; **делать —ки** v. compromise (with), meet halfway.

**уступ/ный** a. (min.) bench, benched; **—ная выемка** benching; **—ообразный** a. benched; stepped, in steps; **—чатый** a. stepped, step-shaped, staggered.

**уступчив/ость** f. compliance; **—ый** a. compliant, pliable, yielding, submissive.

**усть/е** n. mouth, issue; opening, aperture, orifice; mouthpiece; outflow, discharge; estuary (of river); **—евый** a. mouth; estuarine; **—ице** n. (biol.) stoma; **—ичный** a. stomatal.

**усугуб/ить, —лять** v. redouble, aggravate, make worse; **—ление** n. aggravation.

**усуш/ивать, —ить** v. dry, parch; **—ка** f. drying, shrinkage (on drying), wastage.

**УСХ** *abbr.* (управление сельского хозяйства) agricultural department.

**усы** *pl. of* ус.

**усылать** *v.* send away.

**усып/ание** *n.* strewing, scattering; —ать *v.* strew, scatter, cover, litter.

**усып/ительный, —ляющий** *a.* soporific, hypnotic, narcotic; —ительное средство soporific, somnifacient; —ить, —лять *v.* lull, make drowsy; narcotize; anesthetize.

**усы/хание** *n.* drying, desiccation, shrinking, shrinkage; —хать *v.* dry, shrink; —шка *f.* shrinkage, loss on drying.

**ута/ивание** *n.*, —йка *f.* concealment, suppression; —ивать, —ить *v.* conceal, hide, keep secret; suppress.

**утапливать** *v.* melt down.

**утаптывать** *v.* tread, trample down.

**утварь** *f.* utensils, implements.

**утвердит/ельно** *adv.* affirmatively, in the affirmative; —ельный *a.* affirmative, positive; —ь *see* утверждать.

**утвержд/ать** *v.* affirm, assert, maintain; confirm, corroborate, ratify; approve, accept; prove; strengthen, consolidate; —ают, —ается it is claimed; —аться *v.* be affirmed, be confirmed; strengthen oneself; —ение *n.* affirmation, assertion, statement; confirmation, corroboration; approval; strengthening, consolidation, fixing; —енный *a.* affirmed; confirmed, corroborated; approved.

**утекать** *v.* flow away, flow off, run off, leak; disperse.

**утенок** *m.* duckling.

**утепл/ение** *n.* heating, warming; —енный *a.* heated; hot; —итель *m.* heater; —ить, —ять *v.* heat, warm.

**утерамин** *m.* Uteramine, tyramine.

**утереть** *see* утирать.

**утер/ивать, —ять** *v.* lose, forfeit; —янный *a.* lost, forfeited.

**утес** *m.* rock, crag, cliff, bluff, ridge; —истый *a.* rocky, craggy; —ник *m.* (bot.) furze, gorse (*Ulex*, spec. *U. europaeus*).

**утеч/ка** *f.* leakage, leaking, leak, escape, loss, wastage, stray; dissipation, dispersion; issue, effluent, runoff; коэффициент —ки (elec.) dispersion coefficient, leakage factor; —ь *see* утекать.

**утеш/ать, —ить** *v.* console, comfort, relieve; —ение *n.* consolation, comfort, relief; —ительный *a.* consoling, comforting, relieving.

**утилиз/ация** *f.* utilization, salvaging; цех —ации salvage department; —ировать *v.* utilize, salvage, recover; —ируемый *a.* utilizable, available.

**утил/итарный** *a.* utilitarian; —ь *m.*, —ь-сырье *n.* utilizable refuse, utility waste, utilizable scrap, (metal) junk; (cer.) bisque; —ьный *a.* utilized; scrap; —ьный обжиг (cer.) body firing, bisque firing.

**утиный** *a.* duck; у. нос guide blade (of conveyer).

**утир/ание** *n.*, —ка *f.* wiping; —ать, —еть *v.* wipe.

**утих/ание** *n.* abatement, subsidence, dying down; —ать, —нуть *v.* abate, subside, quiet down; —ший *a.* abated, moderated.

**утка** *f.* (zool.) duck; long-necked hydrogenation flask.

**уткать** *v.* weave a pattern into.

**утко/водство** *n.* duck breeding; —нос *m.* (zool.) platypus.

**уток** *m.* (text.) weft.

**утол/ение** *n.* slaking, quenching (of thirst); satisfaction (of hunger); alleviation (of pain); —ить *see* утолять.

**утол/стить, —щать** *v.* thicken, make thicker; —щение *n.* thickening, thicker part, swelling, expansion, bulging, bulge, bulb, node; (welding) reinforcement; rib, boss, camber; —щенный *a.* reinforced; thickened.

**утолять** *v.* slake, quench (thirst); satisfy (hunger); alleviate (pain).

**утомительн/ость** *f.* tiresomeness; —ый *a.* tiresome, fatiguing.

**утом/ить, —лять** *v.* fatigue, tire; —ление *n.* fatigue, weariness; (met.) fatigue; exhaustion, depletion (of soil); —ленный *a.* fatigued, tired, weary.

**утон/ение** *n.* thinning, tapering; —енный *a.* thinned, tapered, taper; —ить *see* утонять.

**утонуть** *see* утопать.

**утонч/ать, —ить** *v.* make thinner, thin, thin out, narrow down; refine; —аться, —иться *v.* become thinner, narrow down, taper; —ающийся *a.* tapering.

утончен/ие *n.* thinning (down), tapering; refining; —ность *f.* refinement, subtlety; —ный *a.* refined, subtle, fine.

утон/ьшать, —ять *v.* thin, make thinner; —ьшение *n.* thinning, tapering.

утоп *m.* deadhead.

утоп/ать *v.* be drowned, sink; —ить, —лять *v.* drown; bury, embed; —ление *n.* drowning; burying, embedding; —ленный *a.* drowned; buried, embedded, recessed, sunk, countersunk (head), flush; built-in; —ленная головка countersink; —ленного типа flush, flush-type.

утоптать *see* утаптывать.

утор *m.* notch; chine, fissure; croze (of barrel); —ить *v.* open; make a croze; —ник *m.* crozer; notcher.

уточн/ение *n.* making more precise; more exact definition; specification; —енный *a.* refined, improved; —ить *v.* make more precise, define more accurately, specify.

уточный *a.* (text.) weft.

уточнять *see* уточнить.

утраивать *v.* treble, triple.

утрамбов/анный *a.* rammed, tamped, packed; —ать, —ывать *v.* ram, tamp, pack; —ка *f.*, —ывание *n.*, —ывающий *a.* ramming, tamping, packing.

утра/та *f.* loss; exhaustion, depletion (of soil); —тить, —чивать *v.* lose; —ченный *a.* lost; —чивание *n.* loss, losing.

утренний *a.* morning, early.

утриров/ание *n.*, —ка *f.* overdoing, exaggeration; —ать *v.* overdo, exaggerate, carry too far.

утр/о *n.* morning; в 5 часов —а at 5 а.м.

утроб/а *f.* womb; —ный *a.* uterine; —ный плод fetus.

утро/ение *n.* trebling, tripling, triplication; —енный *a.* triple, threefold, three times as great; —итель *m.* trebler, tripler; —ить *see* утраивать.

утром *adv.* in the morning, а.м.

утру/дить, —ждать *v.* trouble, inconvenience; —диться, —ждаться *v.* take trouble, trouble oneself.

утруска *f.* spillage, leakage.

утряс/ать, —ти, —ывать *v.* shake down.

утучн/ение *n.* enrichment, fertilization, manuring (of soil); fattening; —ить, —ять *v.* enrich, fertilize, manure; fatten.

утфель *m.* (sugar) massecuite.

утюг *m.* iron (for pressing); road drag; —ообразный *a.* shaped like an iron; bow-shaped, bow.

утюж/ение *n.*, —ка *f.* ironing, pressing; dragging (of road); —ить *v.* iron, press; drag, scrape; —ный *a.* iron.

утягивать *v.* bind, tie; draw tight, pull.

утяжел/ение *n.* charging, loading; (text.) weighting; —енный *a.* heavy; weighted; —итель *m.* weighting compound; —ить, —ять *v.* charge, load; make heavy; weight.

утяжина *f.* (met) shrinkage cavity, shrink hole, pipe.

утянуть *see* утягивать.

утятина *f.* duck (meat).

УФ *abbr.* (ультрафиолетовый) ultraviolet; (усилитель фототоков) photocurrent amplifier.

УФАН *abbr.* (Уральский филиал Академии Наук) Ural Branch of the Academy of Sciences.

уфимский *a.* Ufa.

ухаб *m.*, —ина *f.* hole, hollow, pit, bump, rut (in road); —ы *pl.* ups and downs; —истый *a.* rough, uneven, rutty.

ухажив/ание *n.* tending, nursing, care; (mach.) handling, treatment; —ать *v.* attend (to), tend, nurse, take care (of); handle, treat; service (machines); cultivate (plants).

ухание *n.* slip (of charge in blast furnace).

ухват *m.* shank, grip; oven fork; grab; —ить, —ывать *v.* grip, grasp, catch hold (of); —иться за *v.* seize (an opportunity); —ка *f.* way, manner, trick; grip.

ухи/триться, —тряться, —щряться *v.* contrive, manage, find a way; —щрение *n.* device, contrivance, shift, dodge; —щренный *a.* clever, cunning.

ух/о *n.* (anat.) ear; (mech.) ear, lug, hanger, eye; морское у. (zool.) abalone; наружное у. (anat.) auricle; среднее у. middle ear; воспаление среднего —а (med.) otitis; тугой на у. hard of hearing.

**уховертк/а** *f.* (zool.) earwig; —**и** *pl.* Dermaptera.

**уход** *m.* departure, going away, leaving, withdrawal; (frequency) drift; resignation (from work); care, nursing, attention, attendance; handling, maintenance, upkeep; **у. за** caring for, servicing; treatment, management; **монтер по** —**у** maintenance man, service man; **не требующий** —**а** maintenance-free; —**ить** *v.* go away, depart, leave, withdraw, retreat; issue, go out; be evolved; —**ящий** *a.* departing, leaving, outgoing; —**ящая вода** discharge water, waste water.

**ухудш/ать,** —**ить** *v.* make worse, aggravate, impair, deteriorate; —**аться,** —**иться** get worse, deteriorate; —**ение** *n.* change for the worse, deterioration, decline.

**уцелеть** *v.* survive, remain uninjured, escape destruction, be left intact.

**уцеп/иться,** —**ляться** *v.* catch hold (of), seize, grip, grasp, clutch.

**уч.** *abbr.* (**участок**) plot; (**учебный**) educational; (**ученый**) scientist.

**участв/овать** *v.* take part (in), participate, have a hand (in), partake, be involved (in); —**ующий** *a.* participating; *m.* participant.

**участ/ие** *n.* share, sharing, part, participation, partnership; interest, concern; **при** —**ии** with the assistance (of), with the cooperation (of); **принимать у.** *v.* take part (in), participate, take interest (in).

**участит/ель** *m.* amplifier; —**ь** *see* **учащать.**

**участковый** *a.* section, sectional, district.

**участник** *m.* participant, participator, partner; member; competitor.

**участ/ок** *m.* section, part, portion; region, district, locality, zone; piece, parcel (of land), lot, plot, strip; division, allotment; **дробить на** —**ки** *v.* parcel out; break into lots.

**участь** *f.* lot, portion, destiny, fate.

**учащ/ать** *v.* make more frequent, increase the frequency (of); thicken; repeat; —**ение** *n.* increase of frequency; repetition.

**учащий** *m.* teacher; —**ся** *m.* student.

**учеб/а** *f.* studying; training; —**ник** *m.* textbook, manual.

**учебн/ый** *a.* educational, training; school; practice (bomb); **у. курс** course of studies, curriculum; —**ая стрельба** (mil.) artillery practice; —**ое время** (school) term; —**ое заведение** educational institution, school.

**учен/ие** *n.* teaching, instruction; tuition; learning, studying; apprenticeship, training; science; doctrine; **отдать в у. мастеру** *v.* apprentice; —**ик** *m.,* —**ица** *f.* student; apprentice; —**ик-летчик** *m.* flying cadet; —**ический** *a.* pupil's, student; —**ичество** *n.* apprenticeship.

**учено** *adv.* scientifically; —**сть** *f.* learning, erudition.

**учен/ый** *a.* scientific, learned, academic, scholarly; *m.* scientist, man of learning, scholar; **у.-атомник, у.-ядерник** *m.* nuclear scientist; **Государственный у. совет** State Scientific Council; —**ое общество** scientific society; —**ые степени** university degrees.

**ученье** *see* **учение.**

**учесть** *see* **учитывать.**

**учет** *m.* calculation, estimate; accounting; discount; registration; record keeping, metering; follow-up; **плановый у.** follow-up; **производить у. товара** *v.* take stock; **стать на у.** *v.* register oneself.

**учетвер/ение** *n.* quadrupling; —**енный** *a.* quadruplicate, quadruple; —**ить,** —**ять** *v.* quadruple, multiply by four.

**учет/ный** *a.* discount; registration (form); accounting; **у. процент** rate of discount; —**чик** *m.* accountant; calculator.

**училище** *n.* school, college.

**учинение** *n.* making, committing.

**учин/ивать,** —**ить** *v.* mend, repair.

**учин/ить,** —**ять** *v.* make, commit.

**учитель** *m.,* —**ница** *f.* teacher, instructor; —**ский** *a.* teacher's; magistral; —**ство** *n.* teaching, duties of a teacher; —**ствовать** *v.* teach, be a teacher.

**учитыв/ание** *n.* taking into account; discounting; —**ать** *v.* take into account, take into consideration, consider, allow (for); discount; не —ая disregarding.

**учить** *v*. teach, instruct, train; learn, study; —ся *v*. learn, study.

**учре/дитель** *m*. founder, institutor, establisher; —дить, —ждать *v*. found, establish, set up, start; —ждение *n*. establishment, institution; institute.

**ушат** *m*. bucket, small tub, small vat.

**ушестер/енный** *a*. sextuple; —ить, —ять *v*. sextuple, increase sixfold.

**уши** *pl. of* **ухо**.

**ушиб** *m*. bruise; (med.) contusion; —ание *n*. bruising; —ать, —ить *v*. bruise, hurt, contuse.

**ушив/альник**, —атель *m*. lace, lacing, belt fastener; —ание *n*. sewing up; lacing up; —ать *v*. sew up; lace up.

**ушир/ение** *n*. widening, enlargement, spread, amplification; —итель *m*. extension; —ительный *a*. widening, enlarging; —ить, —ять *v*. widen, enlarge, broaden.

**ушить** *see* **ушивать**.

**ушко** *n*. small ear, ear, lug, loop, handle; (anat., zool.) auricle; eye (of needle,

etc.); tab, tag; thimble, sleeve piece; —головый винт eye bolt.

**ушн/ой** *a*. ear, aural, otic; —ая боль earache; —ая раковина (anat.) cochlea; —ая сера ear wax; —ое зеркало (med.) otoscope.

**ущелье** *n*. forge, ravine, canyon, pass, gulch, rift; notch, gap.

**ущем/ить**, —лять *v*. pinch, nip, jam; (med.) strangulate; —ление *n*. strangulation, constriction; —ленный *a*. strangulated.

**ущерб** *m*. damage, injury, harm, loss, detriment, disadvantage; в у. to the detriment (of), to the prejudice (of); на —е on the decline, in the waning stage; наносить у. *v*. damage, injure, impair.

**Уэбба** Webb's.

**Уэкфильд** Wakefield.

**Уэльс** Wales; уэльский *a*. Welsh.

**уютный** *a*. comfortable, cozy.

**уязвимый** *a*. vulnerable.

**уясн/ить**, —ять *v*. elucidate, explain, clear up; size up (situation); understand.

# Ф

**ф** *abbr*. (фарада) farad; (фот) phot; **Ф** code for vanadium in steel mark.

**Фабер-дю-Фора печь** Faber du Faur furnace (for desilverization of zinc crusts).

**фабзав/ком** *abbr*. (фабрично-заводский комитет) factory committee; —уч *abbr*. (фабрично-заводское учебное заведение) factory workshop school.

**фабианол** *m*. fabianol.

**фабра** *f*. black dye.

**фабрик/а** *f*. factory, shop, mill, works, plant; —ант *m*. manufacturer, maker, producer; —ат *m*. manufactured product, product; —аты *pl*. manufactured goods, industrial goods; —ация *f*. manufacture, manufacturing, production, making, fabrication; —овать *v*. manufacture, produce, make, fabricate.

**фабрить** *v*. dye black.

**фабрично-заводск/ий** *a*. industrial, manufacturing, factory; —ие изделия industrial goods.

**фабричн/ый** *a*. factory, manufacturing; **ф.** рабочий factory hand, mill hand; —ая марка, —ое клеймо trademark, brand, name plate, label; —ая цена cost price, net cost; —ое законодательство labor legislation; Factory Acts; —ое производство manufacturing, manufacture.

**фавероль** *f*. (bot.) horse bean.

**фавор** *m*. favor; —ит *m*. favorite.

**—фаг** *m*. *suffix* (biol.) —phag, —phage.

**фагарамид** *m*. fagaramide.

**фагацид** *m*. fagacid (acid resin).

**фагеденический** *a*. (med.) phagedenic.

**фагин** *m*. fagine.

**—фагия** *f*. *suffix* (biol.) —phagy, —phagia.

**фагоцит** *m*. (biol.) phagocyte; —арный *a*. phagocytic; —оз *m*. phagocytosis.

**фаз/а** *f*. phase, stage; в —е, находящийся в —е, совпадающий по —е in phase; не в —е, сдвинутый по —е out of phase; жидкой —ы liquid phase; правило фаз phase rule;

равенство фаз, совпадение фаз (elec.) phase coincidence; phase-rule equilibrium; разность фаз, сдвиг фаз, смещение фаз (elec.) phase difference, phase displacement; смещение —ы phase shift (for scattering); угол сдвига фаз phase angle.

фазан *m.* (zool.) pheasant.

фазелин *m.* phaselin.

фазео/лин *m.* phaseolin (protein of *Phaseolus vulgaris*); phaseoline (alkaloid); —лунатин *m.* phaseolunatin; —лунатиновая кислота phaseolunatinic acid; —маннит *m.* phaseomannite, inosite.

фаз/ии *pl.* (zool.) Phasiidae; —ин *m.* phasin.

фазиров/ание *n.*, —ка *f.* phasing; —анный *a.* phased; —ать *v.* phase.

фаз/ис *see* фаза; —ный *a.* phase; (mach.) phase-wound.

фазо— *prefix*, —вый *a.* phase; —вый множитель (elec.) phase factor; —вый переход phase transition; —вая обмотка (elec.) phase winding; —вая характеристика (elec.) phase response; —вращатель, —регулятор *m.*, —сдвигающее устройство phase shifter, phase-shifting transformer; —выравниватель, —компенсатор *m.* phase compensator; phase advancer; phase modifier; —импульсный *a.* pulse-position; —индикатор, —метр, —указатель *m.* (elec.) phase indicator, phase meter, power-factor meter; —разделитель *m.* phase separator; —расщепитель *m.* phase splitter; —расщепляющий *a.* phase-splitting; —сдвигающий, —смещающий *a.* phase-shifting; —трон *m.* (nucl.) synchrocyclotron, frequency-modulated cyclotron; —тропия *f.* phasotropy, dynamic isomerism.

фай *m.* (text.) faille, poult-de-soie.

файнс *m.* fines.

файнштейн *m.* (met.) converter matte.

файрфрекс *m.* Firefrax (fireproof cement).

файялит *see* фаялит.

факел *m.*, —ьный *a.* torch, flare; jet, tongue (of flame); ф.-лоцман pilot flame; —ьный свет torch light.

фако/идальный *a.* (petr.) phacoidal (structure); —лит *m.* (min.) phacolite (a variety of chabazite); —метр *m.* (optics) phacometer.

факсимил/е *n.*, —ьный *a.* facsimile, replica.

факт *m.* fact.

фактис *m.* factice (a rubber substitute from linseed oil).

фактическ/и *adv.* by facts; in fact, practically, virtually; —ий *a.* based on facts, actual; practical, virtual, active; present; —ое значение virtual value.

фактор *m.* factor, coefficient, agent; —ы *pl.* factors, elements; —иал *m.* (math.) factorial; —иальный *a.* factor, factorial.

фактория *f.* trading station, trading post.

фактура *f.* (com.) invoice, bill; surface finish, texture; composition.

факультативный *a.* facultative, optional.

факультет *m.* faculty; (math.) factorial.

факция *f.* faction.

фаланга *f.* (anat.) phalanx; (zool.) solpugid.

фалда *f.* tail, skirt, flap.

фалевка *f.* crusher, grinder.

фалерц *see* фальерц.

фаллопиевы трубы (anat.) Fallopian tubes.

фалунит *m.* (min.) fahlunite, falunite (a variety of altered cordierite).

фаль/банд *m.* (petr.) fahlband (metamorphic ore band); —ерц *m.* (min.) fahlerz, fahlore, tetrahedrite, gray copper ore.

фальсифи/кация *f.*, —цирование *n.* falsification, adulteration; —цированный *a.* adulterated; —цировать *v.* falsify, adulterate; —цирующий *a.* adulterating; —цирующее вещество adulterant.

фальц *m.* rabbet, groove, furrow, channel; fold; —аппарат *m.* folder; —губель *m.* fillister, rabbet plane; —евать, —овать *v.* rabbet, groove; fold, crease; —овка *f.* rabbeting, grooving; folding; horning; fillister, rabbet plane.

фальцовочный *a.* rabbeting, grooving; folding; horning; ф. молоток horning hammer, bumping hammer; ф. пресс horning press (punch press); ф. станок rabbeting machine; squeezer.

**фальшборт** *m.* bulwark.

**фальшив/ка** *f.* forged document; —o *adv.* falsely; —ость *f.* falseness; —ый *a.* spurious, false, counterfeit (money); pseudo—.

**фальшфейер** *m.* false fire, blue light.

**фаля** *f.* spring lock.

**фаматинит** *m.* (min.) famatinite.

**фаменский ярус** (geol.) Famennian stage.

**фамилия** *f.* family name, surname.

**фамильярн/ость** *f.* familiarity; —ый *a.* familiar, unceremonious.

**ФАН** *abbr.* (Филиал Академии Наук СССР) Branch of the Academy of Sciences USSR.

**фанатик** *m.* fanatic.

**фангломерат** *m.* (petr.) fanglomerate (a pebbly deposit in an alluvial fan).

**фанер/а** *f.*, —ит *m.* veneer; plywood; клееная ф., многослойная ф. plywood.

**фанерн/ый** *a.* veneer; plywood; ф. лист plywood, plywood sheet; —ая работа veneering, veneer work; —ое дерево plywood.

**фанеро—** *prefix* phanero—, visible; veneer, plywood; —гам *m.* (bot.) phanerogam, spermatophyte; —пильная машина veneer sawing machine.

**фанза** *f.* (text.) foulard.

**фановая труба** suction pipe, draft pipe.

**фанодорн** *m.* Phanodorn, cyclobarbital.

**фанта/зия** *f.* fantasy, fancy, imagination; —стический, —стичный *a.* fantastic, imaginary.

**фантом** *m.* (radiology) phantom; model (of body); —ный *a.* phantom.

**ФАО** *abbr.* (Организация по вопросам продовольствия и сельского хозяйства ООН) United Nations Food and Agricultural Organization.

**фаолит** *m.* faolite (a resin-asbestos material).

**фара** *f.* (automobile) headlight; landing light.

**фарад** *m.*, —а *f.* (elec.) farad (unit of capacity); —еево явление (light) Faraday effect; —ей *m.* (elec.) faraday, Faraday unit.

**Фарадея закон** Faraday's law; **Ф.** клетка (elec.) Faraday cage; **Ф.** число *see* фарадей.

**фарадизация** *f.* (med.) faradization.

**фарадиол** *m.* faradiol.

**фарад/ический** *a.* faradic; —метр *m.* (elec.) faradmeter.

**фараонова змея** Pharaoh's serpent (stick of mercuric thiocyanate); ф. мышь (zool.) ichneumon (a carnivore).

**фаратсигит** *m.* (min.) faratsihite (intermediate between kaolinite and nontronite).

**фарватер** *m.* fairway, waterway, channel.

**Фаренгейта шкала** Fahrenheit (thermometer) scale.

**фаринг/еальный** *a.* (anat.) pharyngeal; —ит *m.* (med.) pharyngitis; —оскоп *m.* pharyngoscope.

**фарино/за** *f.* farinose; —том *m.* farinotome (for determining starch and protein in grain).

**фармако—** *prefix* pharmaco— (drug, medicine; poison); —гнозия *f.* pharmacognosy; —лит *m.* (min.) pharmacolite (a calcium arsenate); —лог *m.* pharmacologist; —логический *a.* pharmacological; —логия *f.* pharmacology; —пея *f.* pharmacopoeia; —сидерит *m.* (min.) pharmacosiderite (a basic iron arsenate); —химия *f.* pharmaceutical chemistry.

**фармацевт** *m.* pharmacist, druggist; —ика *f.* pharmaceutics; —ический *a.* pharmaceutical; —ические препараты, – ические товары pharmaceuticals, drugs.

**фармация** *f.* pharmacy.

**фарнез/ал** *m.* farnesal; —ен *m.* farnesene; —еновая кислота farnesenic acid; —ол *m.* farnesol.

**фароелит** *m.* (min.) faroelite (probably identical with thomsonite).

**фаррара способ** (met.) Farrar's process.

**фарту/к** *m.*, —чный *a.* apron.

**фарфор** *m.* porcelain, china; молочный ф. milk glass, glass porcelain; —овидный *a.* porcelain-like, porcelaneous.

**фарфоров/ый** *a.* porcelain; ф. завод china factory; —ая глина china clay (a type of kaolin); —ая посуда, —ые изделия china, porcelain ware; —ая

**яшма** (min.) porcelain jasper, porcellanite.

**фарфорообжигательная печь** porcelain kiln.

**фарш** *m.* stuffing, sausage meat; —**ировать** *v.* stuff.

**фары** *pl. of* **фара.**

**фас** *m.* face, front, facade; **ф. ступени** (geol.) scarp.

**фасад** *m.* facade, face, front; elevation, view; **боковой ф.** side view, profile; **передний ф.** front view, frontal view; —**ная керамика** facade earthenware.

**фас/ет** *m.,* —**етка** *f.* facet; face; bevel edge; —**етный** *a.* facet; beveled (mirror); —**еточный** *a.* facet; compound (eye); —**ка** *f.* face, facet; (bevel) edge, bevel, chamfer, chamfering.

**фасов/ать** *v.* pack (up); —**ка** *f.,* —**очный** *a.* packing.

**фасоль** *f.* (bot.) bean (*Phaseolus*); **обыкновенная ф.** kidney bean (*P. vulgaris*).

**фасон** *m.* style, make, fashion; —**ирование** *n.* fashioning, shaping; —**ировать** *v.* fashion, shape; —**но-токарный станок** shaping lathe, forming lathe.

**фасонн/ый** *a.* fashioned, shaped, molded; shape, form, profile; irregular, irregularly shaped; section, sectionshaped; **ф. валок** grooved roll; **ф. калибр** (rolling) section groove; **ф. резец** forming tool, form cutter; shaping tool; **ф. фрезер,** —**ая фреза** profile cutter; **ф. шаблон** curve gage; **ф. штамп** shaping die; —**ая гладилка** trowel; —**ая наковальня** die block; —**ая обработка** profiling; —**ая плита** die plate; —**ая сварка** shape welding; —**ая фрезеровка** form milling; —**ая штамповка** molding; —**ое железо** profile iron, structural iron; —**ое отверстие** irregularly shaped hole; —**ые части** fittings (for pipes, etc.).

**фассаит** *m.* (min.) fassaite (a variety of augite pyroxene).

**фасци/ация** *f.* (bot.) fasciation; —**ола** *f.* (zool.) fasciole; —**олез** *m.* (vet.) fascioliasis; —**я** *f.* (anat.) fascia.

**Фаулера раствор** Fowler solution (of potassium arsenite); **Ф. ряд** Fowler's

series (of helium spectrum lines).

**фаулерит** *m.* (min.) fowlerite (a variety of rhodonite).

**фаун/а** *f.* (zool.) fauna; —**овый** *a.* faunal.

**фаут/ная древесина** defective wood; —**ы** *pl.* defects (in wood).

**фауясит** *m.* (min.) faujasite.

**фахверк** *m.,* —**овое сооружение** framework; —**овый** *a.* framework; frame (building).

**фацелия** *f.* (bot.) phacelia.

**фацет** *see* **фасет.**

**фаци/альный** *a.* phase; (biol., geol.) facies, environmental; —**я** *f.* facies, phase, environment.

**фашин/а** *f.,* —**ный** *a.* fascine, fagot; —**изация** *f.,* —**ная работа** reinforcement with fascines; —**ник** *m.* brushwood, fagot wood.

**фаялит** *m.* (min.) fayalite (member of olivine group).

**фаянс** *m.,* —**овый** *a.,* —**овая посуда** (cer.) earthenware; faience, glazed pottery.

**Фаянс-Содди правило** Fajans-Soddy law.

**ф. гр.** *abbr.* (**федоровская группа симметрии**) (cryst.) Fedorov symmetry group.

**ФДМ** *abbr.* (**фенилдиметилмочевина**) phenyldimethylurea.

**фебрифугин** *m.* febrifugine (alkaloid).

**февраль** *m.* February.

**фед** *m.* Fed (Soviet miniature camera).

**федер** *m.* (cinematography) fader.

**федер/альный** *a.* federal; —**ация** *f.* federation, league.

**фединг** *m.* fading, fade-out.

**федометр** *m.* Fadeometer (for testing dye fastness).

**федоров/ит** *m.* (min.) federovite (a variety of pyroxene); —**ский** *a.* Fedorov.

**Фезера анализ** Feather analysis.

**фейерверк** *m.* fireworks.

**фейнцуг** *m.* drawing of fine wire.

**фейринг** *m.* (aero.) fairing.

**фейфка** *f.* tube, pipe.

**фейхоа** *f.* (bot.) feijoa (*Feijoa sellowiana*).

**фекал/ии** *pl.,* —**ьная масса** feces, excrements; —**ьный** *a.* fecal.

**фекулометр** *m.* feculometer (for determining moisture content of starch).

**фелингов раствор, —а жидкость** (sugar) Fehling solution.

**фелландрен** *m.* phellandrene, 1(7),2-*p*-menthadiene.

**феллановая кислота** fellanic acid.

**феллема** *f.* (bot.) phellem, cork.

**фелло—** *prefix* phello— (cork); **—ген** *m.* (bot.) phellogen, cork cambium; **—геновая кислота** phellogenic acid; **—дерма** *f.* (bot.) phelloderm, secondary cortex; **—новая кислота** phellonic acid; **—пластика** *f.* phelloplastics.

**фельдшер** *m.* surgeon's assistant, orderly.

**фельдшпат** *m.* (min.) feldspar; **—изация** *f.* feldspathization; **—изироваться** *v.* feldspathize, change to feldspar; **—иты** *pl.* feldspathoids; **—овый** *a.* feldspar, feldspathic.

**фельетон** *m.* newspaper article.

**фельзит** *m.* felsite (a group of acidic igneous rocks); **—овый** *a.* felsite, felsitic.

**фельзобаниит** *m.* (min.) felsöbanyite.

**фельзофир** *m.* (petr.) felsophyre, felsite-porphyry; **—овый** *a.* felsophyric.

**фелькерит** *m.* (min.) voelckerite, oxyapatite.

**фемический** *a.* (petr.) femic.

**фен** *m.* phene, benzene ring; foehn (wind).

**фен—** *prefix* phen—.

**фенадон** *m.* Fenadone, methadone hydrochloride.

**феназ/арсиновая кислота** phenazarsinic acid; **—ин** *m.* phenazine, dibenzoparadiazine; **—инфуран** *m.* phenazinfuran; **—он** *m.* phenazone; **—оний** *m.* phenazonium.

**фенакаин** *m.* phenacaine, Holocaine.

**фенакит** *m.* (min.) phenacite, phenakite.

**фенамин** *m.* phenamine (Soviet term for amphetamine); phenocoll hydrochloride.

**фенантр/ахинон, —енхинон** *m.* phenanthraquinone, phenanthrenequinone; **—ен** *m.* phenanthrene; **—енон** *m.* phenanthrenone, phenanthrone; **—иазин** *m.* phenanthriazine; **—идин** *m.* phenanthridine; **—идон** *m.* phenanthridone; **—ил** *m.* phenanthryl; **—оказин** *m.* phenanthroxazine; **—ол** *m.* phenanthrol, hydroxyphenan-

threne; **—олин** *m.* phenanthroline; **—он** *m.* phenanthrone.

**фенарсазин** *m.* phenarsazine.

**фенат** *m.* phenate.

**фенацет/еин** *m.* phenacetein, phenacetolin; **—ин** *m.* phenacetin, acetophenetide; **—ол** *m.* phenacetol, phenoxyacetone; **—уровая кислота** phenaceturic acid.

**фенацил** *m.*, **—овый** *a.* phenacyl; **—иден** *m.* phenacylidene; **—идин** *m.* phenacylidin; **—овый спирт** phenacyl alcohol, hydroxyacetophenone.

**фенацит** *see* **фенакит**.

**фенгит** *m.* (min.) phengite (a variety of high-silica muscovite).

**фенгомазин** *m.* phenhomazine.

**фендиоксин** *m.* phendioxin, dibenzodioxin.

**фенет/идин** *m.* phenetidine, ethoxyaniline; **—ил** *m.* phenetyl, ethoxyphenyl; **—ол** *m.* phenetole, ethoxybenzene.

**фенигрековое семя** fenugreek seed.

**фенидон** *m.* (phot.) Phenidone.

**фенли** *m.* phenyl; **хлористый ф.** phenyl chloride, chlorobenzene.

**фенил/амин** *m.* phenylamine, aniline; **—ат** *m.* phenylate, phenate, phenolate; **—ацетилен** *m.* phenylacetylene, ethynylbenzene; **—гидразин** *m.* phenylhydrazine, hydrazinobenzene; **—ен** *m.*, **—еновый** *a.* phenylene; **—ендиамин** *m.* phenylenediamine, benzenediamine; **—иден** *m.* phenylidene; **—ин** *m.* phenindione; **—карбинол** *m.* phenylcarbinol, benzyl alcohol; **—масляная кислота** phenylbutyric acid; **—мочевина** *f.* phenylurea.

**фениловый** *a.* phenyl, phenylic; **ф. спирт** phenylic alcohol, phenol, carbolic acid; **ф. эфир** phenyl ether, phenoxybenzene; **ф. эфир салициловой кислоты** phenyl salicylate; **ф. эфир уксусной кислоты** phenyl acetate.

**фенил/он** *m.* Phenylone, antipyrine; **—уксусная кислота** phenylacetic acid, alpha-toluic acid; **—фосфиновая кислота** phenylphosphinic acid; **—фосфористая кислота** phenylphosphorous acid, phosphenylic acid; **—хинолин** *m.* phenylquinoline, phenylchinoline; **—ьный** *see* **фениловый**;

—**этан** *m.* phenylethane, phenylic acid; —**этанол** *m.* phenylethanol, phenylethyl alcohol.

**фенин** *m.* phenin, phenacetin.

**фенит** *m.* (petr.) fenite; —**изация** *f.* fenitization.

**феницин** *m.* phoenicin.

**феницит** *m.* (min.) phoenicite, phoenicochroite.

**фен/метил** *m.* phenmethyl; —**o**— *prefix* (chem.) pheno—, phen— (phenyl, benzene); pheno— (showing).

**феновый** *a.* (meteor.) foehn.

**фено/за** *f.* phenose; —**кол, —колл** *m.* phenocoll (hydrochloride), phenamine; —**крист, —кристалл** *m.* (petr.) phenocryst, porphyritic crystal; — **кристаллический** *a.* phenocrystic; phenocrystalline, phanerocrystalline.

**феноксазин** *m.* phenoxazine.

**фенокси**— *prefix* phenoxy—; —**бензол** *m.* phenoxybenzene, phenyl ether.

**фенол** *m.* phenol, carbolic acid; —**аза** *f.* phenolase; —**о-альдегидные смолы** phenol-aldehyde resins; —**овый** *see* **фенольный**.

**фенолог/ический** *a.* (biol.) phenological; —**ия** *f.* phenology.

**фенол/осульфокислота** *f.*, —**сульфоновая кислота** phenolsulfonic acid; **соль —сульфоновой кислоты** phenolsulfonate; —**рот** *m.* phenol red (indicator); —**серная кислота** phenolsulfuric acid, phenylsulfuric acid.

**фенолсульфоново/алюминиевая соль** aluminum phenolsulfonate; —**бариевая соль** barium phenolsulfonate; —**кальциевая соль** calcium phenolsulfonate; —**кислый** *a.* phenolsulfonic acid; phenolsulfonate (of); —**кислый цинк, —цинковая соль** zinc phenolsulfonate; —**кислая соль** phenolsulfonate, sulfophenylate.

**фенол/фталеин** *m.* phenolphthalein; — **фталид** *m.* phenolphthalide; —**фталин** *m.* phenolphthalin; —**хинин** *m.* phenolquinine, quinine carbolate; — **ьный** *a.* phenol, phenolic; —**ьная смола** phenol resin, phenolic; —**ят** *m.* phenolate, phenate.

**феномен** *m.* phenomenon; —**альный** *a.* phenomenal; —**ология** *f.* phenomenology.

**фено/морфолин** *m.* phenomorpholine, dihydro-1,4-benzoxazine; —**и** *m.* phenone; —**нафтазин** *m.* phenonapthazine, benzophenazine; —**пирин** *m.* phenopyrine, antipyrine phenate; —**пласт** *m.* phenoplast, phenolic (resin); phenolayer; —**прен** *m.* phenoprene, 2-phenylbutadiene-1,4; —**салил** *m.* phenosalyl; —**сафранин** *m.* phenosafranine; —**стал** *m.* phenostal, diphenyl oxalate; —**тиазин** *m.* phenothiazine, thiodiphenylamine; —**тип** *m.* (biol.) phenotype; —**хинон** *m.* phenoquinone.

**фентиазин** *see* **фенотиазин**.

**фенх/ан** *m.* fenchane; —**анол** *m.*, —**иловый спирт, —ол** *m.* fenchol, fenchyl alcohol; —**анон, —он** *m.* fenchone; —**елевый** *a.*, —**ель** *m.* (bot.) fennel (*Foeniculum vulgare*); —**ен** *m.* fenchene; —**еновая кислота** fenchenic acid; —**ил** *m.* fenchyl; —**окамфорон** *m.* phenchocamphorone; —**оксим** *m.* fenchoxime; —**оловая кислота** fencholic acid.

**фенэтил** *m.*, —**овый** *a.* phenethyl; — **амин** *m.* phenethylamine; —**ен** *m.* phenethylene, styrene; —**овый спирт** phenethyl alcohol, benzylcarbinol.

**фео**— *prefix* pheo— (dun-colored); —**фитин** *m.* pheophytin; —**форбид** *m.* pheophorbid; —**хром** *m.* pheocrome.

**фер/берит** *m.* (min.) ferberite (iron tungstate); —**ганит** *m.* ferganite (a hydrous uranium vanadate); —**гюсонит** *m.* fergusonite, tyrite.

**Фери калориметр** Féry calorimeter.

**ферма** *f.* (agr.) farm; girder, rib, truss.

**Ферма принцип** Fermat's principle.

**фермат** *m.* fermate (fungicide).

**фермент** *m.* enzyme, ferment; —**ативный, —ивный** *a.* fermentative, fermentation, zymotic; enzymic, enzymatic; —**ация** *f.* fermentation; —**ировать** *v.* ferment.

**фермер** *m.* farmer; —**ское хозяйство** farm; —**ство** *n.* farming.

**Ферми график** (nucl.) Fermi plot; **возраст по Ф.** Fermi age.

**ферми/-газ** *m.* Fermi gas; —**евский** *a.* Fermi; —**й** *m.* fermium, Fm; —**он** *m.* (nucl.) fermion.

**ферморит** *m.* (min.) fermorite.

**фермуар** *m.* clasp, catch, snap; chisel.

**фернамбук** *m.*, —овое дерево (bot.) Brazil wood (*Caesalpinia brasiliensis*).

**фернандинит** *m.* (min.) fernandinite.

**фернико** *n.* Fernico (iron-cobalt-nickel alloy).

**ферон** *m.* pheron, esterase carrier.

**Ферранти явление** (elec.) Ferranti effect.

**Феррариса насос** Ferraris pump.

**феррат** *m.* ferrate; —оген *m.* ferratogen, ferric nucleinate.

**ферри** *n.* Ferry (nickel-copper alloy).

**феррит** *m.*, —овый *a.* ferrite.

**ферритунгстит** *m.* (min.) ferritungstite.

**феррихром** *m.* Ferrichrome (iron-nickel-cobalt-chromium alloy).

**ферро**— *prefix* ferro—, iron; —аксинит *m.* (min.) ferroaxinite; —алюминий *m.* (met.) ferroaluminum; —бор *m.* (met.) ferroboron; —ванадий *m.* (met.) ferrovanadium; —вольфрам *m.* (met.) ferrotungsten, tungsten steel; —кальцит *m.* (min.) ferrocalcite; —кобальт *m.* (met.) ferrocobalt; —лит *m.* ferrolite (iron ore rock); —магнетизм *m.* ferromagnetism; —магнитный *a.* ferromagnetic; —магнитная область magnetic domain; —манган, —марганец *m.* (met.) ferromanganese; —молибден *m.* (met.) ferromolybdenum; —натрит *m.* (min.) ferronatrite.

**феррроникел/ит** *m.* (min.) ferronickelite; —ь *m.* (met.) ferronickel.

**ферросилиц/ий** *m.*, —иевый *a.* (met.) ferrosilicon; —иевый процесс ferrosilicon process, Pidgeon process (for magnesium).

**ферро/сплав** *m.* (met.) ferroalloy; —типия *f.* (phot.) ferrotype; —титан *m.* (met.) ferrotitanium; —титанит *m.* (min.) ferrotitanite; —торит *m.* (min.) ferrothorite; —фосфор *m.* (met.) ferrophosphorus; —хром *m.* (met.) ferrochrome, ferrochromium; —церий *m.* (met.) ferrocerium; —циркон *m.* (met.) ferrozirconium; —электрический *a.* ferroelectric.

**фертильный** *a.* fertile.

**ферул/а** *f.* (bot.) ferula; **ф.-альдегид** *m.* ferulaldehyde; *p*-coniferaldehyde; —ен *m.* ferulene; —овая кислота ferulic acid, *m*-methoxy-*p*-hydroxy-cinnamic acid.

**фестон** *m.* festoon; (bot.) scallop; —чатый *a.* scalloped.

**Фетера формула** Feather's formula.

**фетр** *m.*, —овый *a.* felt.

**фефка** *f.* (soldering) finger pipe.

**Фехнера закон** (illum.) Fechner's law.

**фехраль** *m.* (elec.) a high-resistance alloy similar to Fecraloy.

**фзу** *see* **фабзавуч.**

**фиалк/а** *f.*, —овый *a.* violet (*Viola odorata*); трехцветная **ф.** pansy (*V. tricolor*); —овые *pl.* Violaceae; —овое масло violet oil; масло —ового корня orris root oil.

**Фиата печь** Fiat furnace.

**фибра** *f.* fiber; spec. a leatheroid material; a fiberboard.

**фибрилл/а** *f.* fibril, small fiber; —овый *a.* fibrillar, fibrillate; —ярный *a.* fibrillar; fibrous (protein).

**фибрин** *m.* fibrin; —оген *m.* fibrinogen; —озный *a.* fibrinogenous, fibrinous; —олиз *m.* fibrinolysis; —олизин *m.* fibrinolysin.

**фибробласт** *m.* (zool.) fibroblast, lamellar cell; —ический *a.* fibroblastic.

**фибро/вый** *a.* fiber, fibrous; —зный *a.* fibrous; —ин *m.* fibroin; —лизин *m.* fibrolysin; —лит *m.* (min.) fibrolite, sillimanite; (construction) Fibrolit, fiberboard; —ма *f.* (med.) fibroma, fibrous tumor; —пластин *m.* fibroplastin, paraglobulin; —феррит *m.* (min.) fibroferrite (a hydrated ferric sulfate).

**фиг.** *abbr.* (**фигура**) figure, illustration.

**фиг/а** *f.*, —овый *a.* fig; —овое дерево (bot.) fig tree (*Ficus carica*).

**фигур/а** *f.* figure, illustration, diagram; shape, form; —ально *adv.* figuratively; —альный *a.* figurative, metaphorical, symbolic; —ация *f.* figuration; —ировать *v.* figure, act (as).

**фигурн/ый** *a.* figure, figured; fancy (pattern); shaped, irregularly shaped; **ф. контур** irregular outline; **ф. резец** form tool, forming cutter; —ые скобки braces.

**фидер** *m.*, —ный *a.* feeder, feeder cable.

**фидлерит** *m.* (min.) fiedlerite.

**физ.** *abbr.* (**физический**) physical.

**физал/ин** *m.* physalin; **—ис** *m.* (bot.) physalis.

**физет** *see* **физетовое дерево.**

**физетеровая кислота** physeteric acid, 5,6-tetradecenoic acid.

**физетин** *m.* fisetin, tetrahydroxyflavone.

**физетовое дерево** young fustic (wood of *Rhus cotinus*).

**физетолеиновая кислота** physetoleic acid, hypogaeic acid.

**физиатрия** *f.* (med.) physiatrics.

**физик** *m.* physicist; **ф.-атомник** *m.* nuclear physicist; **—a** *f.* physics; **—a твердого тела** solid-state physics.

**физико—** *prefix* physico—, physical; **ф.-металлургический** *a.* physicometallurgical; **ф.-химический** *a.* physicochemical, physical chemistry.

**физиограф/ический** *a.* physiographic; **—ия** *f.* physiography, physical geography.

**физиолог** *m.* physiologist; **—ический** *a.* physiological; **—ия** *f.* physiology.

**физио/пластика** *f.* plastic surgery; **—терапевт** *m.* physical therapist; **—терапия** *f.* physiotherapy, physical therapy.

**физит** *m.* physite, erythrol.

**физическ/ий** *a.* physical; manual (labor). **—ие свойства** physical properties.

**физ/культура** *f.* physical culture, gymnastics; **—мат** *abbr.* (**физико-математический факультет**) physical-mathematical faculty.

**физод/аловая кислота** physodalic acid; **—овая кислота** physodic acid.

**физостигмин** *m.* physostigmine, eserine; **салициловокислый ф.** physostigmine salicylate.

**Фика диффузия** Fickian diffusion; **Ф. закон** (nucl.) Fick's law.

**фико—** *prefix* (bot.) phyco— (seaweed, algae); **—ксантин** *m.* phycoxanthin; **—логия** *f.* (bot.) phycology, study of algae; **—мицеты** *pl.* (bot.) Phycomycetes; **—феин** *m.* phycophaein; **—хром** *m.* phycochrome.

**фикоцериловый спирт** ficocerylic alcohol.

**фико/церитрин** *m.* phycoerythrin; **—циан** *m.* phycocyanin; **—эритрин** *m.* phycoerythrin.

**фикс** *m.* fixed price; **ф.-пункт** *m.* fixed

point; **—аж** *m.* fixing, fixation; fixer, fixative, fixing bath; **—ажная ванна** (phot.) fixing bath; **—атив** *m.*, **—ирующий реагент** fixative, fixing agent; **—атор** *m.* catch, lock; locator, index, index pin; fixative; (nitrogen) fixer; **—атуар** *m.* fixature, pomade; **—ация** *f.*, **—ирование** *n.* fixation, fixing; immobilization (of nuclear waste); **—ированный** *a.* fixed; immobilized, frozen in; **—ировать** *v.* fix; stop, lock, secure, make fast; immobilize; record, register, rate; **—ирующий** *a.* fixing.

**фиктивн/ость** *f.* fictitiousness; **—ый** *a.* fictitious, false, imitation, dummy; theoretical, hypothetical.

**фикус** *m.* (bot.) fig (*Ficus*).

**фикция** *f.* fiction.

**филадельфия** Philadelphia.

**филант** *m.* a sphecid wasp (*Philanthus triangulum*).

**филария** *f.* (zool.) filaria (parasitic nematode).

**филата** *f.* (min.) cross board (of support).

**филатура** *f.* (text.) spinning.

**филе** *n.* (food) filet.

**филен/ка** *f.* panel, paneling, slat; **обшивать —кой** *v.* panel; **—чатый** *a.* panel, paneled; **—чатая дверь** panel door.

**филер** *m.* filler.

**фили** *pl. of* **филум,** (biol.) phyla.

**филиал** *m.* branch, branch office, affiliated branch, affiliated society; **ф. завода** branch works; **—ьный** *a.* branch, affiliated); **—ьное отделение** branch.

**филигран** *m.* filigree, filigree work.

**филиксовая кислота** filixic acid.

**филиппи железа** (zool.) Filippi's glands.

**филицин** *m.* filicin, filicic acid anhydride; **—овая кислота** filicinic acid.

**филлад** *see* **филлит.**

**филлантин** *m.* phyllanthin.

**филлер** *m.* filler, filling material.

**филлигенин** *m.* phillygenin.

**филлин** *m.* phyllin, chlorophyll derivative.

**филлипсит** *m.* (min.) phillipsite.

**филлирин** *m.* phyllyrin.

**филлит** *m.* (petr.) phyllite (related to slate).

**филло—** *prefix* phyllo— (leaf).

**филловит** *m.* (min.) fillowite (similar to dickinsonite).

**филло/генетический** *a.* phyllogenetic, leaf-producing; —**гемин** *m.* phyllohemin; —**дий** *m.* (bot.) phyllode; —**кладий** *m.* (bot.) phylloclade, leaf-like branch; —**ксера** *f.* (zool.) phylloxera; —**пиррол** *m.* phyllopyrrole; —**порфирин** *m.* phylloporphyrin; —**стахис** *m.* (bot.) bamboo (*Phyllostachys*); —**стиктоз** *m.* phyllosticta infection (of plants); —**таксия** *f.* (bot.) phyllotaxy, phyllotaxis; —**эритрин** *m.* phylloerythrin.

**фило**— *prefix* phylo— (phylum; tribe, race); —**генез** *m.*, —**гения** *f.* (biol.) phylogenesis, phylogeny, race history; —**генетический** *a.* phylogenetic.

**филодендрон** *m.* (bot.) philodendron.

**философ** *m.* philosopher; —**ический** *a.* philosophic; —**ия** *f.* philosophy.

**филум** *m.* (biol.) phylum.

**фильде/кос** *m.* (text.) lisle thread; —**косовый** *a.* lisle; —**перс** *m.* high-grade lisle.

**фильдинга газогенератор** Fielding producer.

**фильера** *f.* draw plate; die; (text.) spinneret.

**фильм** *m.*, —**a** *f.* film.

**фильмарон** *m.* Filmaron, aspidinofilicin.

**фильм/отека** *f.* film library; —**офон** *m.* sound recorder; —**пак** *m.* (phot.) film pack.

—**фильн/ость** *f. suffix* (biol.) —phily; —**ый** *a. suffix* —philous, -seeking.

**фильтр** *m.* filter; **тело** —a filter bed; —**ат** *m.* filtrate; —**ация** *f.* filtration; seepage, percolation; transmissibility; permeability; **коэффициент** —**ации** coefficient of transmissibility, transmissibility; permeability.

**фильтровальн/ый** *a.* filter, filtering; **ф. насос** filter pump; **ф. слой** filter bed; —**ая бумага** filter paper; —**ая набивка** filter pad; —**ая сетка** filter gauze.

**фильтров/ание** *see* **фильтрация**; —**анный** *a.* filtered; —**ать** *v.* filter; —**очный** *see* **фильтровальный**.

**фильтр/одержатель** *m.* filter ring, filter support; —**поглотитель** *m.* absorption filter; —**пресс** *m.* filter press; —**уемый, —ующийся** *a.* filterable;

**легко** —**уемый** easy to filter; —**ующий** *see* **фильтровальный**.

**филярный** *a.* filar, thread-like.

**фимоз** *m.* (med.) phimosis.

**фин.** *abbr.* (финский) Finnish; **фин**— *abbr.* (финансовый) financial.

**финал** *m.* end, conclusion; —**ьный** *a.* final.

**финанс/ирование** *n.* financing; —**ировать** *v.* finance; —**овый** *a.* financial; —**ы** *pl.* finances.

**финвал** *m.* finback whale.

**фингеровщик** *m.* (min.) skip loader.

**финик** *m.*, —**овый** *a.* date (fruit); **морской ф.** (zool.) sea date (*Lithodomus*); —**овая пальма** date palm (*Phoenix dactylifera*).

**финиметр** *m.* gage for gas cylinders.

**фининспектор** *m.* assessor.

**финифт/ь** *f.* enamel; —**яный** *a.* enamel, enameled.

**финиш** *m.* finish; **момент** —a terminal time; —**ер** *m.* finisher, finishing machine.

**финка** *see* **финна.**

**Финляндия** Finland.

**финн/а** *f.* cysticercus (larval tapeworm); —**ы** *pl.* (med.) measles; cysticerci; —**оз** *m.* (med.) cysticercosis; —**озный** *a.* infested with cysticerci; measly (meat).

**финский** *a.* Finnish.

**фиолетовый** *a.* violet; **ф. пигмент** anthocyanin.

**фион** *m.* phyone, adenohypophyseal growth hormone.

**фиорд** *m.* fiord.

**фиорит** *m.* (min.) fiorite, siliceous sinter.

**фирм/а** *f.*, —**енный** *a.* firm, company.

**фирн** *m.*, —**овый** *a.* firn (snow).

**фискальный** *a.* fiscal.

**фистацит** *see* **эпидот.**

**фисташк/а** *f.* pistachio nut; (bot.) *see* **фисташник**; —**ово-зеленый** *a.* pistachio-green.

**фисташков/ый** *a.* pistachio; **ф. лак** mastic varnish; —**ая водка** mastic (liquor); —**ая смола** mastic (resin); —**ое дерево** (bot.) mastic tree (*Pistacia lentiscus*); —**ое масло** pistachio oil.

**фисташник** *m.* (bot.) pistachio, green almond (*Pistacia vera*).

**фистул/а** *f.* (med.) fistula; **—озный, —ярный** *a.* fistulose, fistulous, fistular.

**фисци/евая кислота, —он** *m.* physcic acid, physcion; **—ол** *m.* physciol.

**фит—** *prefix* phyt—, phyto— (plant, vegetable); *suffix* —phyte (plant); **—аза** *f.* phytase; **—альбумин** *m.* phytalbumin, vegetable albumin; **—ан** *m.* phytane; **—ен** *m.* phytene; **—еновая кислота** phytenic acid; **—ил** *m.* phytyl.

**фитил/едержатель** *m.* wick holder; **—ь** *m.,* **—ьный** *a.* wick, fuse; rosin-core (solder); cored-carbon (arc lamps).

**фитин** *m.* phytin.

**фитинг** *m.* fitting; **—и** *pl.* fittings.

**фитингофит** *m.* (min.) vietinghofite.

**фитиновая кислота** phytic acid, inositol-hexaphosphoric acid.

**фито—** *see* **фит—**; **—генический** *a.* phytogenic; **—гормон** *m.* phytohormone; **—графия** *f.* phytography, descriptive botany; **—климат** *m.* plant climate; **—л** *m.* phytol; **—лакцин** *m.* phytolaccin; phytolaccine (alkaloid); **—лякка** *f.* (bot.) phytolacca; **—метрия** *f.* phytometry; **—монады** *pl.* (zool.) phytomonadina; **—н** *m.* (bot.) phyton; **—нцид** *m.* phytoncide; **—патология** *f.* phytopathology, plant pathology; **—стерин** *m.* phytosterol; **—стеролин** *m.* phytosterolin; **—фаг** *m.* phytophagan, phytophagous beetle, plant-eating insect; **—фагия** *f.* phytophagy; **—фармакология** *f.* phytopharmacology; **—фтороз** *m.* phytophthora infection (of plants); **—химический** *a.* phytochemical; **—химия** *f.* phytochemistry; **—хром** *m.* (bot.) phytochrome; **—ценоз** *m.* phytocenosis, plant community; **—цидное действие** plant damage (by sprays).

**Фиттига реакция** Fittig reaction.

**фитэритрин** *m.* phyterythrin (red coloring matter of plants).

**фифленый** *a.* serrated, serrate.

**фихтелит** *m.* (min.) fichtelite (a paraffinic hydrocarbon).

**Фицджеральда-Лоренца сокращение** Fitzgerald-Lorentz contraction.

**фише** *n.* Fichet generator.

**фишерит** *m.* (min.) fischerite.

**Фишер-Тропша процесс** Fischer-Tropsch (indirect hydrogenation) process.

**фишка** *f.* plug.

**ф-ка** *abbr.* (фабрика) factory.

**ф-ла** *abbr.* (формула) formula.

**флавазин** *m.* flavazine.

**флаван** *m.* flavan; **—илин** *m.* flavaniline; **—ин** *m.* flavin; **—ол** *m.* flavanol, 3-hydroxyflavone; **—он** *m.* flavanone, 2,3-dihydroflavone.

**флав/аспидовая кислота** flavaspidic acid; **—иановая кислота** flavianic acid; **—ин** *m.* flavin, quercetin; **—индулин** *m.* flavinduline; **—ицид** *m.* flavicid.

**флаво/ксантин** *m.* flavoxanthin; **—л** *m.* flavol, 2,6-anthracenediol; **—мицин** *m.* flavomycin; **—н** *m.,* **—новый** *a.* flavone, 2-phenylchromone; **—пурин** *m.* flavopurin, alizarin X; **—пурпурин** *m.* flavopurpurin, 1,2,6-trihydroxyanthraquinone.

**флаг** *m.* flag, banner.

**флагеллаты** *pl.* (zool.) Flagellata.

**флажный** *a. of* флаг.

**флайолотит** *m.* (min.) flajolotite.

**флакон** *m.* small bottle, flask.

**фламандский** *a.* Flemish.

**фламбиров/ание** *n.* flambing; (med.) flambage, singeing; **—ать** *v.* flame, pass through or over a flame; sterilize (with flame); singe (cloth).

**фланг** *m.,* **—овый** *a.* flank, side.

**Фландрия** Flanders.

**фланел/ь** *f.,* **—евый** *a.* flannel; **—ет** *m.* flannelette.

**фланец** *m.* flange, collar, ring, bush; **соединительный ф.** flange sleeve, flange coupling.

**фланжиров/альный** *see* **фланжировочный**; **—ать** *v.* flange; **—ка** *f.* flanging.

**фланжировочн/ый** *a.* flange, flanging; **ф. пресс, ф. станок, —ая машина** flanger, flanging machine.

**фланце/вать** *see* **фланжировать**; **—вый** *a.* flange, flanged; **—загибочный станок, —загибочная машина, —отгибочная машина** flanging machine.

**фланцованный** *a.* flanged.

**флат** *m.,* **—овая бумага** flat (sheet) paper.

**флаттер** *m.* (aero.) flutter.

**флеб—, —о—** *prefix* phleb—, phlebo— (vein); **—ит** *m.* (med.) phlebitis.

**флегма** *f.* phlegm; (fractional distillation) reflux, bottoms, residue.

**флегматизация** *f.* (expl.) flegmatization.

**флегматичный** *a.* phlegmatic, sluggish.

**флегмов/ый** *a. of* **флегма; —ое число** reflux ratio.

**флегмона** *f.* (med.) phlegmon.

**флекс/инг-машина** *f.* (rubber) flexing machine; **—ия** *f.* flection; **—ометр** *m.* flexometer; **—ор** *m.* (anat.) flexor; **—ура** *f.* flexure; (geol.) fold.

**флеп** *m.* flap.

**флер** *m.* gauze; crepe; **—ница** *f.* golden-eyed fly (*Chrysopa*).

**флец** *m.,* **—овый** *a.* (geol.) fletz, bed, layer.

**флигель** *m.* wing, annex.

**флиндерсин** *m.* flindersin.

**флинкит** *m.* (min.) flinkite.

**флинт, —глас** *m.* flint glass.

**флиппер** *m.* (rubber) flipper; **—овальный станок** bead flipper machine.

**Флиссинген** Flushing.

**флиш** *m.* (geol.) flysch.

**фло/бабен** *m.* phlobabene; **—бафен** *m.* phlobaphene; **—гистон** *m.* phlogiston; **—гоз** *m.* (med.) phlogosis, inflammation; **—гозин** *m.* phlogosin; **—гопит** *m.* (min.) phlogopite (a magnesium mica).

**флокен** *m.* floc, floccule, flake.

**флокит** *m.* (min.) flokite (probably identical with mordenite).

**флокс** *m.* (bot.) phlox; **—ин** *m.* phloxin (aniline dye).

**флокул/ированный** *a.* flocculated, flocculent; **—ировать** *v.* flocculate; **—яция** *f.* flocculation.

**флора** *f.* (bot.) flora.

**флорамид** *m.* floramid (urea fertilizer).

**флорент/ийский, —инский** *a.* Florentine; **ф. лак** Florentine lake, cochineal carmine; **—ин** *m.* (text.) florentine.

**флоренцит** *m.* (min.) florencite.

**Флоренция** Florence.

**флоретин** *m.* phloretin; **—овая кислота** phloretic acid, *p*-hydroxyhydrocinnamic acid.

**флоридин** *m.,* **—овые глины** Floridin, fuller's earth.

**флориз/еин, —ин** *m.* phlorizein, phlorizin.

**флористический** *a.* (bot.) flora, floral; floristic.

**флорицин** *m.* polymerized castor oil.

**флоро/глуцид** *m.* phloroglucide; **—глуцин, —глюцин** *m.* phloroglucinol, 1,3,5-benzenetriol; **—глуцит** *m.* phloroglucitol, methylenetriol; **—за** *f.* phlorose, alpha-glucose; **—л** *m.* phlorol, *o*-ethylphenol; **—н** *m.* phlorone, *p*-xyloquinone.

**флорризин** *see* **флоризеин.**

**флорхинил** *m.* phloroquinyl.

**флот** *m.* fleet, navy; **воздушный ф.** air force; **торговый ф.** merchant marine.

**флотац/ия** *f.,* **—ионный** *a.* (met.) flotation; **ф. маслом** oil flotation.

**флотилия** *f.* flotilla, small fleet.

**флотир/ование** *see* **флотация; —ованный** *a.* floated, floated off; **—овать, —оваться** *v.* float, float off; **—уемость** *f.* floatability; **—уемый** *a.* floatable; **—ующийся** *a.* floating; floatable.

**флото/машина** *f.* flotation machine, flotation cell; **—реагент** *m.* flotation agent.

**флотский** *a.* fleet, naval.

**флотура** *f.* floater (in glass furnace).

**флоэма** *f.* (bot.) phloem.

**флуавил** *m.* fluavil.

**флуат** *m.* Fluate (preservative); **—ирование** *n.* fluating, fluosilicate coating.

**флудинг** *m.* flooding.

**флукту/ационный** *a.,* **—ация** *f.* fluctuation; **—ировать** *v.* fluctuate; **—ирующий** *a.* fluctuating.

**флуо—** *see also* **флюо—** .

**флуор—** *see also* **фтор—.**

**флуор/ан** *m.* fluoran; **—антен** *m.* fluoranthen, idryl; **—ен** *m.* fluorene, diphenylenemethane; **—еновая кислота** fluorenic acid; **—енол** *m.* fluorenol, fluorene alcohol; **—енон** *m.* fluorenone, diphenylene ketone.

**флуоресцеин** *m.* fluorescein, resorcinolphthalein; **—калий** *m.* potassium fluorescein; **—овая бумага** fluorescein paper, Zellner's paper (indicator).

**флуоресц/енция** *f.,* **—ирование** *n.* fluorescence; **—ин** *m.* fluorescin; **—ировать** *v.* fluoresce; **—ирующий** *a.* fluorescent.

**флуор/ид** *m.* fluoride; **—ил** *m.* fluoryl

—иламин *m.* fluorylamine, amino-fluorene; —илиден *m.* fluorylidene; —иметр, —ометр *m.* fluorometer (for measuring fluorescence); —инден *m.* fluorindene; —ит *see* флюорит; —ометрия *f.* fluorometry; —он *m.* fluorone, 3-isoxanthone; —оскоп *m.* fluoroscope; —офор *m.* fluorophore.

флуоцерит *m.* (min.) fluocerite, tysonite.

флуэллит *m.* (min.) fluellite.

флюат *see* флуат.

флювио— *prefix* fluvio—, river; —гляциальный *a.* (geol.) fluvioglacial; —граф *m.* fluviograph.

флюг/арка *f.*, —ер *m.* weather vane, wind vane, vane; (chimney) cowl, deflector; wind sock (of airdrome); столбовой —ер wind cone.

флюид *m.* fluid; —альный *a.* fluid, fluidal, fluid-like; —альная структура (geol.) fluidal structure, flow structure; —изация *f.* fluidization; —изированный *a.* fluidized; —изировать *v.* fluidize.

флюкс *m.* flux; —ия *f.* fluxion; —метр *m.* (elec.) fluxmeter; —ующий *a.* fluxing, flux.

флюктуация *see* флуктуация.

флюкция *see* флюксия.

флюор— *see also* флуор—.

флюорит *m.* (min.) fluorite, fluorspar.

флюоцерит *see* флуоцерит.

флюс *m.* flux, fusing agent; (med.) gumboil; —ование *n.* fluxing, fluxation, fluxion; —ованный *a.* fluxed; —овый *a.* flux.

флюсофен *m.* (met.) flowing furnace.

флюсующий *a.* fluxing; ф. материал fluxing agent, flux.

флютбет *m.* apron (of dam), spillway dam; spillway, by-channel.

флютерит *m.* (min.) uranothallite.

фля/га *f.* flask, canteen, phial; (milk) can; —жка *f.* little flask.

флянцевый *see* фланцевый.

фляшерия *f.* septicemia (in caterpillars).

ФМ *abbr.* (фазовая модуляция) phase modulation.

фн. *abbr.* (фунт) pound.

фоб/ия *f.* (med.) phobia; —ность *f.* *suffix* —phoby, —phobic nature; —ный *a. suffix* —phobic, —phobous, -shunning.

фоглит *m.* voglite (uranium mineral).

фоердит *m.* (expl.) foerdite.

Фоже газогенератор Faugé producer.

фойе *n.* foyer, lobby.

фойяит *m.* (petr.) foyaite (nepheline-syenite); —овый *a.* foyaitic.

фок/альный *a.* focal; —ометр *m.* (optics) focimeter; —ус *m.* focus, focal point; (X-rays) focal spot; trick; приводить в —ус, собирать в —усе, —усировать *v.* focus, bring into focus; установка на —ус, —усирование *n.*, —усировка *f.* focusing; —усирующий *a.* focusing; —усный *a.* focus, focal; —усное пятно focus, focal point; —усное расстояние focal length.

фолада *f.* (zool.) pholas (a mollusk).

фол/ацин *m.*, —евая кислота folacin, folic acid, pteroylglutamic acid, vita-min B$_c$.

фолерит *m.* (min.) pholerite (near kaolinite).

фолиант *m.* folio; volume.

фоли/евая кислота *see* фолевая кислота; —нерин *m.* folinerin, oleandrin.

фоллетаж *m.* apoplexy (grape disease).

фолликул *m.*, —а *f.* (anat., bot.) follicle; —ин *m.* folliculin, estrone; —ярный *a.* follicular.

фольбортит *m.* (min.) volborthite.

фольварк *m.* farm, estate.

фольг/а *f.*, —овый *a.* foil; нанесение —и foliation, application of foil (to mirror); —одержатель *m.* foil holder.

фольгерит *m.* (min.) folgerite (pent-landite).

фомка *f.* forcer.

фомоз *m.* phomosis, phoma infection (of plants).

фон *m.* background; (tel.) background noise, crackling; (acous.) phon (unit of volume); (polarography) base electrolyte; (agr.) preceding crop or fertilization; *suffix* —phone.

фонар/ик *m.* small lantern, lamp; карманный ф., электрический ф. flash-light; —ный *a.* lantern, lamp.

фонарь *m.* lantern, lamp, search light; skylight; connector, connecting piece; карманный ф., электрический ф. flashlight; передовой ф. headlight (of automobile); **полный ф.** (molding) core barrel.

**фонд** *m.*, **—овый** *a.* fund, stock.

**фонический** *a.* phonic, acoustic.

**фоно—** *prefix* phono— (sound); **—вый** *a. of* **фон**; **—грамма** *f.* phonogram; sound track; **—граф** *m.* phonograph; **—графический** *a.* phonographic; — **лит** *m.* phonolite, clinkstone (an igneous rock); **—литический** *a.* phonolite, phonolitic; **—метр** *m.* phonometer; **—н** *m.* phonon (lattice-vibration quantum); **—скоп** *m.* phonoscope.

**фонтан** *m.* fountain; flowing (oil) well.

**фонтанель** *f.* (anat., med.) fontanel.

**фонтанир/овать** *v.* gush, spout; **—ующий** *a.* gushing, spouting, flowing.

**фор—** *prefix* fore—, pre—, preliminary; *suffix* (chem.) **—phore**; (zool.) **—phorus.**

**Фора аккумулятор** (elec.) Faure accumulator.

**фораминиферы** *pl.* (zool.) Foraminifera.

**форвакуум** *m.* preliminary vacuum, rough exhaust.

**форгенин** *m.* forgenin, tetramethylammonium formate.

**Форда воронка** (viscosity determination) Ford cup.

**форез** *m.* phoresis, cataphoresis.

**форелленштейн** *m.* (petr.) forellenstein, troctolite (a gabbro).

**форель** *f.* (zool.) trout.

**Фореста система** Forest system.

**форзац** *m.* (typ.) fly leaf.

**фориды** *pl.* humpbacked flies (*Phoridae*).

**фор/камера** *f.* prechamber, antechamber, precombustion chamber, mixing chamber; **—контакт** *m.* preliminary catalytic purifier.

**Форлендера правило** Vorländer's rule (of substitution in benzene nucleus).

**форм/а** *f.* form, shape, contour, configuration; mold, cast; structure, build, make, model; mode (of operation or interaction); (typ.) form; uniform; **отливать в —у** *v.* mold, cast; **придавать —у** *v.* shape, form.

**формазил** *m.* formazyl, formazyl hydride; **—карбоновая кислота** formazylcarboxylic acid.

**формал** *see* **формаль.**

**формализм** *m.* formalism.

**форм/алин** *m.* Formalin (formaldehyde solution); **—аль** *m.* formal, dimethoxymethane; **—альдегид** *m.* formaldehyde, methanal; **—альдоксим** *m.* formaldoxime.

**формальн/ость** *f.* formality; **—ый** *a.* formal.

**форм/амид** *m.* formamide, methanamide; **—амидин** *m.* formamidine; **—амин** *m.* formamine, hexamethylenetetramine; **—аминт** *m.* formamint; **—анилид** *m.* formanilide, N-phenylformamide; **—анит** *m.* (min.) formanite.

**формат** *m.* (typ.) size, form.

**формация** *f.* formation, structure.

**формвар** *m.* Formvar, polyvinyl formal resin.

**форменный** *a.* formal, regular, prescribed; positive.

**формиат** *m.* formate.

**формий** *see* **формиум.**

**формил** *m.*, **—овый** *a.* formyl; **—ен** *m.* formylene, methenyl; **—ирование** *n.* formylation; **—ировать** *v.* formylate, introduce formyl radical (into).

**формин** *m.* Formin, hexamethylenetetramine.

**формир/ование** *see* **формование**; **—овать** *see* **формовать**; **—овочный**, **—ующий** *see* **формовочный**; **—ующее устройство** (pulse) shaper.

**формиум** *m.* (bot.) New Zealand flax (*Phormium tenax*).

**форм-мочевина** *f.* urea-formaldehyde (a nitrogenous fertilizer).

**формов/альный** *see* **формовочный**; **—ание** *n.* molding, casting; formation, forming, shaping; training (of plant); **—анный** *a.* molded, cast; formed; **—ать** *v.* mold, cast; form, shape, model, fashion; **—ка** *f.* molding, casting; mold frame; formation, shaping, modeling; **—ка в песке** sand casting; **—ой** *a.* mold; **—ая глина** *see* **формовочная глина**; **—очная** *f.* molding room.

**формовочн/ый** *a.* molding, mold, molder's, casting; molded; plastic; forming, form; **ф. песок** molding sand; **ф. пресс** molding press, stamping press; **ф. станок**, **—ая машина** molding machine; extruding machine; **—ая глина**, **—ая земля** (foundry) loam;

—ые чернила (foundry) blacking, blackwash.

**формовщик** *m.* molder.

**формо/гидразид** *m.* formohydrazide, formyl hydrazide; —за *f.* formose, *i*-fructose; —ксим *m.* formoxime, formaldoxime; —литное число formolite number (of oil); —ль *m.* formol; —нитрил *m.* formonitrile, hydrocyanic acid.

**формула** *f.* formula.

**формулиров/анный** *a.* formulated; conceived; —ать *v.* formulate, word, lay down; —ка *f.* formulation.

**формуляр** *m.* log, logbook; data card, form; (library) card; —ный *a.* official.

**формфактор** *m.* (elec.) form factor.

**форон** *m.* phorone.

**форониды** *pl.* (zool.) Phoronidea.

**форсажная камера** (rockets) afterburner.

**форсиров/ание** *n.*, —ка *f.* forcing; spiking (of nuclear reactor); —анный *a.* forced; —ать *v.* force, push, boost, speed up; spike.

**форстерит** *m.* (min.) forsterite (a magnesium silicate).

**форсун/ка** *f.* sprayer, atomizer, jet; force pump; (oil) burner, spray burner; —очная сажа lamp black.

**форт** *m.* fort; —ификация *f.* fortification.

**фортка** *f.* airport, air vent.

**фортоин** *m.* Fortoin, methylenedicotoin.

**форточка** *see* фортка.

**форхерит** *m.* (min.) forcherite (an opal).

**форцепсы** *pl.* forceps.

**форцит** *m.* (expl.) forcite.

**форшальт-турбина** *f.* front turbine.

**форшахта** *f.* (min.) front shaft.

**форштосс** *m.* adaptor.

**фосген** *m.*, —овый *a.* phosgene, carbonyl chloride; —ит *m.* (min.) phosgenite, horn lead, hornblei.

**фосмука** *f.* phosphate rock meal.

**фоссилиз/ация** *f.* (geol.) fossilization; —ированный *a.* fossilized; —ировать *v.* fossilize.

**фостоновая кислота** phostonic acid.

**фосф/аген** *m.* phosphagen; —азид *m.* phosphazide; —азин *m.* phosphazine; —азобензол *m.* phosphazobenzene; —азол *m.* phosphazol; —анилин *m.* phosphaniline, phenylphosphine.

**фосфат** *m.* phosphate; ф. кальция

calcium phosphate; —аза *f.* phosphatase; —ация *f.* phosphatization; —ид *m.* phosphatide, phospholipin; —ин *m.* phosphatin; —ирование *n.* parkerizing (rustproofing process); —ная порода phosphate rock; —шлаки *pl.* phosphate slag (fertilizer).

**фосфенил** *m.* phosphenyl; хлористый ф. phosphenyl chloride; —истая кислота phosphenylous acid; —овая кислота phosphenylic acid, phenylphosphorous acid.

**фосф/ид** *m.* phosphide; —ил *m.* phosphyl.

**фосфин** *m.* phosphine, phosphorous hydride; —истая кислота phosphonous acid [$RP(OH)_2$ *or* $R_2POH$]; —овая кислота phosphonic acid [$RPO(OH)_2$ *or* $R_2PO(OH)$]; —огруппа *f.* phosphono group.

**фосфит** *m.* phosphite; ф. натрия sodium phosphite.

**фосфо—** *prefix* phospho—, phosphorus; —бензол *m.* phosphobenzene; —гипс *m.* phosphogypsum (a phosphorus pentoxide-gypsum fertilizer); —кислота *f.* phospho acid, phosphonic acid.

**фосфон/ий** *m.*, —иевый *a.* phosphonium; хлористый ф. phosphonium chloride, chlorophosphonium; —овый *a.* phosphonic.

**фосфор** *m.* phosphorus, P; phosphor, luminescent material; белый ф., желтый ф. white phosphorus, yellow phosphorus, ordinary phosphorus; закись —а phosphorus trioxide, phosphorous anhydride; красный ф. red phosphorus; пятиокись —а phosphorus pentoxide; пятихлористый ф., хлорный ф. phosphorus pentachloride; трехводородистый ф. hydrogen phosphide, phosphine; трехлористый ф., хлористый ф. phosphorus trichloride.

**фосфо/рат** *m.* phosphorate; —ресслерит *m.* (min.) phosphor-roesslerite (magnesium phosphate pentadecahydrate).

**фосфоресц/енция** *f.*, —ирование *n.* phosphorescence; —ировать *v.* phosphoresce; —ирующий *a.* phosphorescent, luminescent; luminous (paint).

**фосфориз/ация** *f.* phosphorization; — **ировать** *v.* phosphorize, combine with phosphorus, treat with phosphorus.

**фосфорил** *m.* phosphoryl; **хлористый ф.** phosphoryl chloride, phosphorus oxychloride; — **ирование** *n.* phosphorylation.

**фосфористо/калиевая соль, — кислый калий** potassium phosphite; — **кислый** *a.* phosphorous acid; phosphite (of); — **кислая соль** phosphite; — **этиловый эфир** ethyl phosphite.

**фосфорист/ый** *a.* phosphorus, phosphorous; phosphide (of); **ф. ангидрид** phosphorous anhydride, phosphorus trioxide; **ф. водород** hydrogen phosphide, phosphine; **ф. кальций** calcium phosphide; **ф. марганец** manganese phosphide; (met.) phosphormanganese; **ф. свинец** lead phosphide; — **ая бронза** (met.) phosphor bronze; — **ая кислота** phosphorous acid; **соль — ой кислоты** phosphite; — **ая медь** copper phosphide; — **ое железо** iron phosphide; (met.) ferrophosphorus.

**фосфорит** *m.* (min.) phosphorite; phosphate rock; **костяной ф.** (min.) osteolite, earthy apatite; — **ная мука** phosphate fertilizer; — **ование** *n.* (agr.) phosphate fertilizing; — **овый** *a.* phosphorite, phosphoritic; — **оподобный** *a.* phosphoritic.

**фосфорич/еский** *a.* phosphorescent; **ф. свет,** — **ность** *see* фосфоресценция.

**фосфорно/алюминиевая соль** aluminum phosphate; — **аммониевая соль** ammonium phosphate; — **аммониево-натриевая соль** sodium ammonium phosphate.

**фосфорноват/ая кислота** hypophosphoric acid; **соль — ой кислоты** hypophosphate; — **истая кислота** hypophosphorous acid; **соль — истой кислоты** hypophosphite.

**фосфорноватисто/аммониевая соль** ammonium hypophosphite; — **бариевая соль** barium hypophosphite; — **кальциевая соль, — кислый кальций** calcium hypophosphite; — **кислый** *a.* hypophosphorous acid; hypophosphite (of); — **кислая соль** hypophosphite; — **натриевая соль** sodium hypophosphite.

**фосфорновато/кальциевая соль, — кислый кальций** calcium hypophosphate; — **кислый** *a.* hypophosphoric acid; hypophosphate (of); — **кислая соль** hypophosphate.

**фосфорно/вольфрамовая кислота** phosphotungstic acid; — **железистая соль** ferrous phosphate; — **железная соль** ferric phosphate; — **калиевая соль** potassium phosphate; **кислая — калиевая соль** potassium dihydrogen phosphate, monopotassium phosphate; — **кальциевая соль** calcium phosphate; **кислая — кальциевая соль** acid calcium phosphate, monocalcium phosphate.

**фосфорнокисл/ый** *a.* phosphoric acid; phosphate (of); **ф. кальций** calcium phosphate; **ф. хинин** quinine phosphate; — **ая соль** phosphate.

**фосфорно/крезиловый эфир** cresyl phosphate; — **магниевая соль** magnesium phosphate; — **марганцовая соль** manganic phosphate; — **марганцовистая соль** manganous phosphate.

**фосфорномолибденов/ая кислота** phosphomolybdic acid; — **оаммониевая соль** ammonium phosphomolybdate.

**фосфорно/натриеаммониевая соль** sodium ammonium phosphate; — **натриевая соль** sodium phosphate; — **однокальциевая соль** monocalcium phosphate, calcium acid phosphate.

**фосфорн/ый** *a.* phosphorus, phosphoric; **ф. ангидрид** phosphoric anhydride, phosphorus pentoxide; — **ая кислота** phosphoric acid; **соль — ой кислоты,** — **ая соль** phosphate.

**фосфоро—** *prefix* phosphoro—, phosphorus; — **бактерин** *m.* phosphorobacterin (fertilizer); — **бензол** *m.* phosphorobenzene; — **водород** *m.* hydrogen phosphide, phosphine; — **метр** *m.* phosphorometer (optical instrument); — **подобный** *a.* phosphorous, like phosphorus; — **рганический** *a.* organophosphorus; — **светящийся** *a.* phosphorescent.

**фосфосидерит** *m.* (min.) phosphosiderite.

**фосфуранилит** *m.* (min.) phosphuranylite.

**фот** *m.* phot (unit of illumination); **ф.-час** phot-hour.

**фот/ен** *m.* photene; —**иния** *f.* (bot.) photinia.

**фото** *n.* photograph; *prefix* photo—, light; photographic; photoelectric; —**анализатор** *m.* photoanalyzer (a pulse-height analyzer); —**аппарат** *m.* camera; —**варистор** *m.* photovaristor (cadmium sulfide or lead telluride); —**возбужденный** *a.* photoexcited.

**фотоген** *m.,* —**овый** *a.* photogen, bog-head naphtha; photogen, phosphorescent plant or animal; —**ический** *a.* photogenic.

**фото/гравюра** *f.* photogravure; photoengraving; —**грамметрия** *f.* photogrammetry (photographic surveying).

**фотограф** *m.* photographer; —**ирование** *n.* photographing; —**ировать** *v.* photograph; —**ически** *adv.* photographically.

**фотографическ/ий** *a.* photographic; **ф. аппарат** camera; **ф. снимок** photograph, snapshot; —**ая пленка** film.

**фотография** *f.* photography; photograph; **моментальная ф.** snapshot.

**фото/деление** *n.* (nucl.) photofission; —**динамика** *f.* (biol.) photodynamics; —**запись** *f.* photographic recording; —**затвор** *m.* camera shutter; —**звезда** *f.* photostar (in nuclear emulsion); —**дозиметр** *m.* photodosimeter, film badge; —**импульс** *m.* photoimpact; —**ионизация** *f.* photoionization; —**источник** *m.* photosource; —**камера** *f.* camera; —**катализ** *m.* photocatalysis; —**катализатор** *m.* photocatalyst; —**катод** *m.* photoelectric cathode; —**лампа** *f.* photoelectric cell; phototube; —**лиз** *m.* photolysis; —**лит** *m.* photolyte; —**литический** *a.* photolytic.

**фотолитограф/ический** *a.* photolithographic; —**ия** *f.* photolithography.

**фото/логический** *a.* photologic; —**логия** *f.* photology, optics; —**люминесценция** *f.* photoluminescence; —**мезон** *m.* (nucl.) photomeson.

**фотометр** *m.* photometer; —**ирование** *n.* photometry, photometric evaluation or recording of light intensity; —**ировать** *v.* measure with a photometer, take a reading with a photometer;

—**ический** *a.* photometric; —**ия** *f.* photometry.

**фото/механический** *a.* photomechanical; —**множитель** *see* **фотоумножитель**; —**н** *m.,* —**ный** *a.* photon (quantum of electromagnetic radiation); —**нейтрон** *m.* (nucl.) photoneutron; —**образование,** —**рождение** *n.* photoproduction; —**н** *m.* photon; —**окисление** *n.* photooxidation; —**передатчик** *m.* picture transmitter; —**периодизм** *m.* (bot.) photoperiodism; —**план** *m.* photomap; —**пластинка** *f.* (phot.) plate; —**пленка** *f.* (phot.) film; —**полимеризация** *f.* photopolymerization; —**проводимость** *f.* photoconductivity; —**протон** *m.* (nucl.) photoproton; —**разведка** *f.* photographic reconnaissance; —**расщепление** *n.* (nucl.) photodisintegration.

**фотосинт/ез** *m.* (bot.) photosynthesis; —**етический** *a.* photosynthetic.

**фото/снимок** *m.* photograph; —**сопротивление** *n.* photoresistor; photoresistance; —**старение** *n.* photodegradation; light aging; —**стат** *m.* photostat; —**сфера** *f.* (astron.) photosphere; —**съемка** *f.* photographing; photograph; —**терапия** *f.* (med.) phototherapy; —**техника** *f.* photographic technology; —**типический** *a.* phototypic; —**типия** *f.* phototype; —**ток** *m.* photocurrent, photoelectric current.

**фототроп/ический** *a.* phototropic; —**ия** *f.* phototropy, phototropism.

**фото/удар** *m.* photoimpact; —**умножитель** *m.,* —**умножительный** *a.* (electron.) photomultiplier; —**упругий** *a.* photoelastic; —**фильный** *a.* (biol.) photophilous, light-loving; —**фобный** *a.* (biol.) photophobic; —**фор** *m.* (med., zool.) photophore; —**форез** *m.* photophoresis; —**химический** *a.* photochemical; —**химический элемент** photochemical cell; —**химия** *f.* photochemistry.

**фотохром** *m.* photochrome; —**атический** *a.* photochromatic; —**ия** *f.* photochromy.

**фото/чувствительность** *f.* photosensitivity, photoelectric sensitivity;

—чувствительный *a.* photosensitive; —эдс photo-emf; —эклектор *m.* light trap (for insects).

фотоэлектричес/кий *a.* photoelectric; ф. элемент, —кая ячейка photoelectric cell; —тво *n.* photoelectricity.

фотоэлектро/движущая сила photoelectromotive force; —н *m.* photoelectron; —нный *a.* photoelectronic; —нный умножитель photomultiplier.

фотоэлемент *m.* photocell, photoelectric cell; phototube; photoemissive element; эмиссионный ф. photoemissive cell.

фото/эмиссия *f.* photoemission; —эмульсия *f.* photographic emulsion.

фотоэффект *m.* photoeffect, photoelectric effect; внешний ф. photoemission; внутренний ф. photoconductive effect; порог —a photoelectric threshold.

фотоядерный *a.* photonuclear.

фоцен/ин *m.* phocenin, trivalerin; —овая кислота phocenic acid, valeric acid.

фоциметр *m.* (phot.) focimeter.

ФП *abbr.* (фильтр-поглотитель) absorption filter.

фр. *abbr.* (фракция) fraction.

фрагарол *m.* fragarol.

фрагмент *m.* fragment; —арный *a.* fragmentary; —ация *f.* fragmentation.

фрадицин *m.* fradicin (antibiotic).

фраза *f.* phrase, sentence.

фразерин *m.* fraserin.

фракс/етин *m.* fraxetin; —идубильная кислота fraxitannic acid; —ин *m.* fraxin.

фракциониров/ание *n.*, —ка *f.* fractionation; —анный *a.* fractionated, fractional; —анная конденсация fractional condensation; —анная перегонка fractional distillation; —ать *v.* fractionate; —очная колонна fractionating column.

фракционн/о *adv.* fractionally; by degrees, in steps; —ый *a.* fractional; factional; fractionating (column).

фракция *f.* fraction, cut; faction, group.

фрамуга *f.* fixed frame; transom.

франгул/а-эмодин *m.* frangula emodin, emodin; —ин *m.* frangulin; —иновая

кислота frangulinic acid, frangulic acid.

франк *m.* franc (money).

Франка-Кондона принцип Franck-Condon principle; Ф.-Рида механизм Frank-Read mechanism.

франкеит *m.* (min.) franckeite.

франкиров/апис *n.*, —ка *f.* prepayment (of postage); —анный *a.* prepaid, postpaid; —ать *v.* prepay, pay the postage.

Франклина доска Franklin's plate.

франклин/изация *f.* (med.) franklinization; —ит *m.* (min.) franklinite (a zinc-manganese spinel); —овский ток (elec.) Franklin's current.

франко *adv.* (com.) prepaid, free; ф.-борт, ф.-судно free on board; ф. место работ delivered at the job.

франколит *m.* (min.) francolite (a variety of apatite).

франконит *m.* frankonite (decolorant).

франкфуртский *a.* Frankfort; ф. черный Frankfort black (a vegetable black).

франский *a.* (geol.) Frasnian.

Франсуа-Рексрота печь (coking) Francois-Rexroth furnace.

франц. *abbr.* (французский) French.

франций *m.* francium, Fr.

Франция France.

французск/ий *a.* French; ф. ключ monkey wrench; —ая синь French blue; —ое дерево *see* бакаут.

фраунгоферовы линии (light) Fraunhofer lines.

фрахт *m.*, —овый *a.* freight; —овать *v.* freight, charter; —овка *f.* freightage; —овщик *m.* freighter.

фрачник *m.* (zool.) borer (*Lixus*).

Фраша способ Frasch process (for sulfur mining).

фреатический *a.* (geol.) phreatic.

фрегат *m.* frigate (ship); (zool.) frigate.

Фреде реактив Fröhde's reagent (for alkaloids).

фрез *m.*, —а *f.* cutter, milling cutter, mill; rototiller, rotary plow; —а-развертка *f.* hole-boring cutter; —барабан *m.* drum shredder (for peat).

фрезер *m.* cutter, milling cutter; —ный *a.* milling, cutting; shredded (peat); —ный резец milling cutter, cutter, cutting tool; —ный станок milling machine, miller, cutting machine.

фрез/ерование *n.*, —еровка *f.*, —ование *n.* milling, cutting, notching; tilling, rototilling, breaking up (of soil); —ерованный *a.* milled; tilled; —еровать, —овать *v.* mill, cut; till, break up; —еровочный *a.* milling, cutting; —еровщик *m.* milling machine operator.

фрейбергит *m.* (min.) freibergite, argentiferous tetrahedrite.

фрейеслебенит *m.* (min.) freieslebenite.

Фрейнд/а метод Freund's method (for cycloparaffins; —лиха уравнение Freundlich equation.

фрейфал *m.* free fall, free-falling drill.

фрейялит *see* фрейалит.

фреквентин *m.* frequentin; —овая кислота frequentic acid, citromycetin.

Фремонта испытание (met.) Fremont (impact) test.

фремонтит *m.* (min.) fremontite, natramblygonite, natromontebrasite.

френезия *f.* (med.) phrenesia, phrenitis.

Френеля формула Fresnel's (reflection) formula.

френозин *m.* phrenosin; —овая кислота phrenosinic acid, cerebronic acid.

Френсиса реактивнуая трбина Francis water turbine.

френцелит *m.* (min.) frenzelite, guanajuatite, selenobismutite.

Френье насос Frenier pump.

фреон *m.* Freon (refrigerant).

фретинг-коррозия *f.* (met.) fretting corrosion.

фриг/атор *m.* an ice-salt refrigeration system; —ориметр *m.* frigorimeter; coolometer; —ория *f.* frigoric unit (minus calorie).

фриделит *m.* (min.) friedelite.

Фрид/ель-Крафтса реакция Friedel-Crafts reaction; —лендера синтез Friedlander synthesis (of quinolines).

фриз *m.* frieze, border, rib.

фризеит *m.* (min.) frieseite (a variety of sternbergite).

фризовый *a.* frieze, border, bordered.

Фрика печь (elec.) Frick furnace.

фрикативный *a.* fricative (sound).

фрикцион *m.* (friction) clutch.

фрикционн/ый *a.* friction, frictional; ф.

конус friction cone, cone clutch; ф. привод friction drive; —ая муфта friction clutch; —ая передача friction gear, friction gearing.

фринин *m.* phrynin.

Фриса перегруппировка Fries rearrangement (of phenol ethers).

фрит/а, —та *f.*, —товый *a.* (glass) frit.

фриттер *m.* (tel.) acoustic shock absorber.

фритчеит *m.* (min.) fritzscheite.

фришев/альный *a.* refining; —ание *n.* refining, refinement, fining, fining process; —ать *v.* refine, fine; revive (litharge).

фронт *m.*, —овой *a.* front; edge; ф. ремонта машин number of machines under repair simultaneously; —альный *a.* frontal, front; —ит *m.* (med.) inflammation of frontal sinus.

фронто/генез *m.*, —образование *n.* (meteor.) frontogenesis; —лиз *m.* frontolysis, breakdown of atmospheric front; —н *m.* pediment.

фр. пат. *see* франц. *and* пат.

Фруда критерий Froude number.

фрукт *m.* fruit.

фруктигенин *m.* fructigenin.

фрукто— *prefix* fructo—, fruit.

фруктов/ый *a.* fruit; ф. сахар fruit sugar, fructose; ф. экстракт fruit flavor; ф. эфир, —ая эссенция fruit essence.

фруктоз/а *f.* fructose, fruit sugar; —амин *m.* fructosamine, isoglucosamine; —ан *m.* fructosan, sugar anhydride; —ид *m.* fructoside.

фрукто/сниматель *m.* fruit picker; —сушилка *f.* fruit dryer, fruit-dehydrating oven.

фрю-ван/ер, —нер *m.* (min.) frue vanner, slime washer.

ф-с *abbr.* (фот-секунда) phot-second.

фт. *abbr.* (фут) foot.

фтал— *prefix* phthal—; —азин *m.* phthalazine, 2,3-benzodiazine; —азол *m.* phthalylsulfothiazole; —азон *m.* phthalazone, 1-oxyphthalazine; —амид *m.* phthalamide; —аминовая кислота phthalamic acid, *o*-carbamylbenzoic acid; —анил *m.* phthalanil; N-phenylphthalimide; —ат *m.* phthalate.

**фталево/бутиловый эфир** butyl phthalate; **—кислый** *a.* phthalic acid; phthalate (of); **—кислая соль** phthalate; **—этиловый эфир** ethyl phthalate.

**фталев/ый** *a.* phthalic; **ф. альдегид** phthalic aldehyde, phthalaldehyde; **ф. ангидрид** phthalic anhydride, phthalandione; **—ая кислота** phthalic acid, 1,2-benzenedicarboxylic acid; **соль —ой кислоты** phthalate.

**фтал/еин** *m.* phthalein; **—ид** *m.* phthalide, isobenzofuranone; **—иден** *m.* phthalidene; **—идил** *m.* phthalidyl.

**фталил** *m.* phthalyl; **хлористый ф.** phthalyl chloride; **—овый спирт** phthalyl alcohol, 1,2-xylenediol.

**фтал/имид** *m.* phthalimide, 1,3-isoindoledione; **—ин** *m.* phthalin; **—иновая кислота** *see* **фталевая кислота**; **—ирование** *n.* phthalation.

**фтало—** *prefix* phthalo—; **—ил** *m.* phthaloyl; **—н** *m.* phthalone; **—нитрил** *m.* phthalonitrile, dicyanobenzene; **—новая кислота** phthalonic acid, carbobenzoylformic acid; **—фенон** *m.* phthalophenone, diphenylphthalein; **—цианин** *m.* phthalocyanine.

**фталуровая кислота** phthaluric acid.

**фталь—** *see* **фтал—**.

**фтанит** *m.* (min.) phthanite (silicified shale).

**фтивазид** *m.* phthivazide (antituberculotic).

**фтириаз** *m.* (med.) phthiriasis.

**фтор** *m.* fluorine, F; **окись —a** fluorine oxide; *prefix* fluor—, fluoro—, fluorine.

**фторангидрид** *m.* acid fluoride; **ф. хромовой кислоты** chromyl fluoride.

**фтор/апатит** *m.* (min.) fluorapatite; **—ацетат** *m.* fluoroacetate.

**фторбор/ная кислота** fluoboric acid; **соль —ной кислоты, —нокислая соль** fluoborate; **—этилен** *m.* fluoroboroethylene.

**фторирoв/ание** *n.* fluorination, introduction of fluorine (into); **—анный** *a.* fluorinated; **—ать** *v.* fluorinate.

**фтористоводородная кислота** *see* **фтороводородная кислота.**

**фтористый** *a.* fluorine; (lower or **—ous**)

fluoride (of); **ф. аммоний** ammonium fluoride; **ф. водород** hydrogen fluoride, anhydrous hydrofluoric acid; **ф. калий** potassium fluoride; **ф. кремний** silicon fluoride; **ф. метил** methyl fluoride; **ф. натрий** sodium fluoride; **основной ф.** oxyfluoride (of).

**фторн/ый** *a.* fluorine; (higher or **—ic**) fluoride (of); **—ое олово** stannic fluoride.

**фторо—** *prefix* fluoro—; **—апатит** *m.* (min.) fluorapatite, common apatite; **—бензол** *m.* fluorobenzene, fluobenzene.

**фтороводород** *m.* hydrogen fluoride, anhydrous hydrofluoric acid; **—ный** *a.* hydrofluoric, hydrofluoride (of); **—ная кислота** hydrofluoric acid; **соль —ной кислоты** fluoride.

**фторокись** *f.* oxyfluoride.

**фторопласт** *m.* polyfluoroethylene resin; **ф.-3** polychlorotrifluoroethylene (same as Kel-F); **ф.-4** polytetrafluoroethylene (same as Teflon).

**фторо/силикат** *m.* fluosilicate; **—титановая кислота** fluotitanic acid; **—углерод** *m.* carbon tetrafluoride, tetrafluoromethane; **—форм** *m.* fluoroform, trifluoromethane.

**фтор/производные** *pl.* fluorine derivatives, fluorine compounds; **—силикат** *m.* fluosilicate; **—хлорметан** *m.* fluorochloromethane; **—циан** *m.* cyanogen fluoride.

**ФТТ** *abbr.* (Физика твердого тела) Solid State Physics (Journal).

**фуга** *f.* seam, crack.

**фуганок** *m.* plane, smoothing plane.

**фугас** *m.* (mil.) land mine; **самовзрывный ф.** contact mine, mine; **—ность** *f.* fugacity; **—ный** *a.* explosive; high-explosive (shell, bomb); **—ное действие** explosive effect (of shell); brisance.

**фугативность** *f.* fugacity.

**фуггерит** *m.* (min.) fuggerite (a member of the gehlenite-akermanite series).

**фугетивность** *f.* fugacity.

**фугин** *m.* fugin, fugutoxin.

**фугов/ально-склеечный станок** combined jointing and gluing machine; **—альный** *a.* jointing, mortising; **—альный станок** jointing machine;

—**ание** *n.* jointing; —**ать** *v.* joint, mortise, join; plane.

**фуговой фонарь** arc lamp.

**фузаин** *m.* fusain, mineral charcoal.

**фуза/нин** *m.* fusanin; —**нол** *m.* fusanol; —**рин** *m.* fusarine, fusafungine; —**риновая кислота** fusaric acid; —**риоз** *m.* fusariose (any Fusarium infection of plants); fusarium wilt; —**риозный** *a.* fusarial; —**рубин** *m.* fusarubin.

**фукеит** *m.* (min.) fouqueite (probably same as clinozoisite).

**Фуко ток** (elec.) Foucault current, eddy current.

**фуко/за** *f.* fucose, 2,3,4,5-tetrahydroxy-hexanal; —**зит** *m.* (min.) fucosite; —**ксантин** *m.* fucoxanthine; —**новая кислота** fuconic acid.

**фуксин** *m.* fuchsin, magenta red; —**осернистая кислота** fuchsin sulfurous acid (Schiff's reagent).

**фукс/ит** *m.* (min.) fuchsite (a variety of muscovite); —**ия** *f.* (bot.) fuchsia.

**Фуксово стекло** water glass, sodium silicate.

**фуксон** *m.* fuchsone, quinonediphenyl-methane.

**фуксшванц** *m.* dovetail saw.

**фуку/зин** *m.* fucusine, fucusamine; —**зол** *m.* fucusol; —**с** *m.* rockweed (*Fucus*).

**фулаксит** *m.* phulaxite.

**фулерфон** *m.* (telegraphy) fullerphone.

**фулл/ерова земля, —еровская земля, —онова земля** fuller's earth.

**фульв/анол** *m.* fulvanol; —**ен** *m.* fulvene, 5-methylenecyclopentadiene; —**овая кислота, —окислота** fulvic acid; —**оплюмиерин** *m.* fulvoplumierin.

**фульг/еновая кислота** fulgenic acid; —**ид** *m.* fulgide; —**урит** *m.* fulgurite (tube of glassy rock formed by lightning).

**фульмин/ат** *m.*, **соль —овой кислоты, —овокислая соль** fulminate; —**овая кислота** fulminic acid; —**овосеребряная соль** silver fulminate; —**уровая кислота** fulminuric acid, isocyanuric acid; **соль —уровой кислоты, —уровокислая соль** fulminurate.

**фуляр** *m.* (text.) foulard.

**фумагиллин** *m.* fumagillin.

**фумар/амид** *m.* fumaramide; —**ил** *m.* fumaryl; **хлористый —ил** fumaryl chloride; —**ин** *m.* fumarine, protopine; Fumarin (a rodenticide); —**овая кислота** fumaric acid, *trans*-butenedioic acid; **соль —овой кислоты, —овокислая соль** fumarate; —**оидная конфигурация** fumaroid; —**ола** *f.* (geol.) fumarole, smoke hole; fumarole deposit; —**протоцетраровая кислота** fumaroprotocetraric acid.

**фумиг/ант** *m.* fumigant; —**атин** *m.* fumigatin; —**атор** *m.* fumigator; —**ацин** *m.* fumigacin, helvolic acid; —**ационный** *a.*, —**ация** *f.* fumigation.

**фунги—** *prefix* fungi—; —**сид, —цид** *m.* fungicide; —**стерин** *m.* fungisterol; —**цидин** *m.* fungicidin, nystatin.

**фунгоцин** *m.* fungocin.

**фундамент** *m.* foundation, substructure, groundwork, bed, base.

**фундаментальн/о** *adv.* fundamentally; —**ость** *f.* fundamentality, solidity; —**ый** *a.* fundamental, solid, substantial; foundation.

**фундаментн/ый** *a.* foundation, base; —**ая плита** foundation plate, bed plate, base.

**фундированный** *a.* funded; solid (income).

**фундук** *m.* hazelnut (*Corylus maxima*).

**фуникулер** *m.* funicular, funicular railway, cable railway.

**функия** *f.* (bot.) plantain lily (*Funkia*).

**функцион/ал** *m.* (math.) functional; —**альный** *a.* functional; nutrient-deficiency (disease); —**ирование** *n.* functioning, operation; —**ировать** *v.* function, operate, run; behave; —**ирующий** *a.* functioning, functional.

**функция** *f.* function; purpose, service; **x как ф. у** $x$ as a function of $y$, $x$ versus $y$ (on diagram).

**фунт** *m.* pound; **ф.-вес** pound-force; **ф.-калория** *f.* centigrade heat unit, Chu; **ф.-масса** *f.* pound-mass; —**овый** *a.* pound, one-pound; —**офут** *m.* foot-pound.

**фура** *f.* wagon, van.

**фураж** *m.*, —**ный** *a.* (agr.) forage, fodder; **сухой ф.** hay; —**ировать** *v.* forage; —**ировка** *f.* forage, foraging.

**фуразан** *m.* furazan, oxdiazole.

**фуран** *m.*, —**овый** *a.* furan, furfuran; —**дион** *m.* furandione, maleic anhydride; —**карбоновая кислота** furancarboxylic acid, pyromucic acid; —**оза** *f.* furanose; —**озид** *m.* furanoside.

**фурацилин** *m.* Furacin, Furacilin, nitrofurazone.

**фургон** *see* **фура**.

**Фурдриниера машина** (paper making) Fourdrinier machine.

**фурил** *m.* furyl; furil, difurylglyoxal; —**иден** *m.* furylidene; —**овый спирт** furfuryl alcohol, furfuralcohol.

**фурма** *f.* (met.) tuyere.

**фурмарьерит** *m.* fourmarierite (uranium mineral).

**фурменн/ый** *a.* (met.) tuyere; **ф. патрубок** blast connection; —**ая амбразура** tuyere arch; —**ая коробка** tuyere box, blast box.

**фурмов/ание** *n.* punching; —**щик** *m.* puncher.

**фурнель** *m.* (min.) a chute.

**фурнирный** *a.* veneer, veneering.

**фурнитура** *f.* supplies, accessories.

**фуро/диазол** *m.* furodiazole, oxdiazole; —**ил** *m.* furoyl; **хлористый** —**ил** furoyl chloride, pyromucyl chloride; —**илирование** *n.* furoylation; —**ин** *m.* furoin; —**л** *m.*, —**ловый** *a.* furol, furfural, 2-furancarbonal; —**моназол** *m.* furomonazole; —**новая кислота** furonic acid, furfurylacetic acid.

**фурункул** *m.* (med.) furuncle, boil; —**ез** *m.* furunculosis.

**фурфур/акролеин** *m.* furfuracrolein; —**ал** *m.* furfural, 2-furancarbonal; —**алкоголь** *m.* furfuralcohol, furfuryl alcohol; —**амид** *m.* furfuramide, furfuryl amide; —**ан** *m.* furfuran, furan; —**бутилен** *m.* furfurbutylene, butylfurfuran.

**фурфурил** *m.*, —**овый** *a.* furfuryl; **уксуснокислый ф.** furfuryl acetate; —**иден** *m.* furfurylidene, fural; —**овый спирт** furfuryl alcohol, furylcarbinol.

**фурфурин** *m.* furfurine.

**фурфуровый** *a.* furfuric; **ф. альдегид** furfuraldehyde, furfural; **ф. спирт** furfuralcohol, furfuryl alcohol.

**фурфур/оин** *m.* furfuroin, furfuryl-fural;

—**ол** *m.* furfural; —**ол-флороглюцид** furfuralphloroglucide; —**ольная смола** furfural resin; —**остильбен** *m.* furfurostilbene.

**Фурье ряд** (math.) Fourier series.

**фусоотделитель** *m.* tar separator in by-product coking process.

**фус/тик** *m.*, —**тиковое дерево** fustic (wood of *Chlorophora tinctoria*); —**тин** *m.* fustin; —**цин** *m.* fuscin.

**фусы** *pl.* heavy coal-tar products formed in by-product coking process.

**фут** *m.* foot (0.305 meter); **указный ф.** foot rule; **ф.-ламберт** *m.* equivalent foot-candle.

**футеров/анный** *a.* lined (furnace); —**ать** *v.* line, fettle; —**ка** *f.*, —**очный** *a.* (refractory) lining, fettling.

**футляр** *m.* case, casing, cover, sheath, jacket; box, container, housing.

**фут/овый** *a.* foot, one-foot; —**о-свеча, —свеча** *f.* (illum.) foot-candle; —**о-тонна, —тонна** *f.* foot-ton (unit of work); —**о-фунт, —фунт** *m.* foot-pound; —**шток** *m.* foot rule; depth gage, sounding rod.

**фуфайка** *f.* sweater, vest.

**фухерит** *m.* (min.) foucherite (probably identical with borickite).

**фуцит** *m.* fucitol.

**фушунский** *a.* Fushun.

**ф-ч** *abbr.* (фот-час) phot-hour.

**фырк/ать**, —**нуть** *v.* sniff, snort; —**ающий клапан** snort valve (a butterfly valve); blow valve.

**фьорд** *see* **фиорд**.

**фьюминг-процесс** *m.* fuming process (zinc and lead extraction from slag).

**ФЭ** *abbr.* (фотоэлемент) photocell.

**фэр** *abbr.* (физический эквивалент рентгена) physical roentgen equivalent, rep.

**фэрфильдит** *m.* (min.) fairfieldite (a hydrous calcium-manganese phosphate).

**ФЭУ** *abbr.* (фотоэлектронный умножитель) photomultiplier.

**фюзеляж** *m.*, —**ный** *a.* (aero.) fuselage, body, framework.

**фюзен** *m.* fusain, mineral charcoal.

**фюльгебель** *m.* micrometer.

## X

**X** code for chromium in steel mark; **X.** *abbr.* (химия) chemistry.

**хабазит** *see* **шабазит.**

**хавег** *m.* Haveg (phenol-formaldehyde resin).

**хави—** *see* **шави—.**

**хадакристалл** *m.* chadacryst, enclosed crystal.

**хаживать** *see* **ходить.**

**хаз** *m.* rear end of hide; **—овый конец** fag end, frayed end.

**хайпер—** *see also* **гайпер—, гипер—.**

**хакафос** *m.* a mixed fertilizer.

**хаки** *m.* khaki.

**халат** *m.* robe, coverall.

**халатн/ость** *f.* negligence; **—ый** *a.* negligent, indifferent, careless, remiss.

**халва** *f.* halva (confectionery).

**халибит** *m.* (min.) chalybite, siderite, spathic iron ore.

**халикоз** *m.* chalicosis (a lung disease).

**халикты** *pl.* mining bees (*Halictidae*).

**халиловский** *a.* Khalilovo; **х. чугун** a naturally alloyed iron.

**халко—** *see* **халько—.**

**халцедон** *m.*, **—овый** *a.* (min.) chalcedony (a form of cryptocrystalline quartz); **зеленый х.** chrysoprase.

**халькантит** *m.* (min.) chalcanthite, blue vitriol.

**халько—** *prefix* chalco— (copper); **— алюмит** *m.* (min.) chalcoalumite; **—граф** *m.* chalcograph beetle (*Tomicus chalcographus*); **—графия** *f.* chalcography, line engraving; **—зин** *m.* (min.) chalcosine, chalcocite, copper glance; **—ламприт** *m.* (min.) chalcolamprite (a member of the pyrochlore group); **—лит** *m.* (min.) chalcolite, copper uranite; **—менит** *m.* (min.) chalcomenite; **—н** *m.* chalcone, benzalacetophenone; **—пирит** *m.* (min.) chalcopyrite, copper pyrites; **—сидерит** *m.* (min.) chalcosiderite; **—стибит** *m.* (min.) chalcostibite, wolfsbergite; **—трихит** *m.* (min.) chalcotrichite, plush copper ore; **—фанит** *m.* (min.) chalcophanite, hydrofranklinite; **—филлит** *m.* (min.) chalco-

phyllite, copper mica; **—цит** *m.* (min.) chalcocite, copper glance.

**хальфовый** *a.* esparto.

**хальциды** *pl.* (zool.) chalcids (*Chalcididae*).

**халява** *see* **холява.**

**хамелеон** *m.* (zool.) chameleon; chameleon mineral (potassium manganate); (chem.) potassium permanganate.

**хам/емии** *pl.* aphid flies (*Chamaemyidae*); **—еропс** *m.* (bot.) fan palm (*Chamaerops*); **—овая кислота** chamic acid.

**хамса** *f.* khamsa, anchovy (fish).

**хао/с** *m.* chaos, disorder, confusion; **—тически** *adv.* chaotically, in disorder, at random; **—тический, —тичный** *a.* chaotic, disorganized, without order, random; turbulent.

**хар/а** *f.* (bot.) chara; **—ы** *pl.* Characeae.

**характер** *m.* character, nature, type; (lather) behavior; **х. работы** type of work; method of operation; **—изовать** *v.* characterize; **—изующий** *a.* characteristic, specific, essential.

**характеристика** *f.* characteristic, character, property; (math.) characteristic (of logarithm); characteristic curve; curve; characterization; response, performance (of machine); (elec.) rating; **графическая х., кривая х.** characteristic curve; **рабочая х.** performance curve.

**характеристич/еский, —ный** *a.* characteristic; performance; **—еская вязкость** intrinsic viscosity; **—еская диаграмма** performance diagram; **— ные данные** performance figures.

**характерн/о** *adv.* characteristically; significantly; it is characteristic; it is significant; **—ый** *a.* characteristic, representative, specific, special; **—ая особенность, —ая черта** characteristic, feature.

**характерограф** *m.* (elec.) automatic recorder for volt-ampere characteristics.

**харг** *m.* (bot.) wild cotton (*Gomphocarpus fruticosus*).

**харк/ание** *n.* expectoration, spitting; **—ать, —нуть** *v.* expectorate, spit.

**харлэкский отдел** (geol.) Harlech series.

**харовые** *pl.* (bot.) Characeae.

**хартия** *f.* charter.

**хартшифер** *m.* (petr.) hard slate.

**Харьков** Kharkov.

**хата** *f.* hut; **х.-лаборатория** *f.* (agr.) Kolkhoz laboratory.

**хатский ярус** (geol.) Chattian stage.

**хатьма** *f.* (bot.) lavatera.

**хауз-турбина** *f.* house turbine (supplying electricity for use in the power house).

**Хаукинса элемент** Hawkins' cell.

**хаульмугр/ен** *m.* chaulmoogrene; **—иловый спирт** chaulmoogryl alcohol; **—овая кислота** chaulmoogric acid, cyclopentenyltridecanoic acid; **—овое масло** chaulmoogra oil.

**Хауэлла печь** Howell furnace.

**хвал/а** *f.* praise; **—ебный** *a.* eulogistic, laudatory; **—ение** *n.* praising; **—еный** *a.* praised; **—ить** *v.* praise, commend, eulogize.

**хвастать, —ся** *v.* boast, brag.

**хват/ательный** *a.* (biol.) prehensile; **—ать** *v.* snatch, seize, catch hold (of), catch, grasp, clutch, bite; carry; suffice, be sufficient, last; **у него не —ает** he is short (of); **—аться** *v.* snatch (at), grasp, get hold (of); **—ающий** *a.* (zool.) prehensile; **—ить** *v.* suffice, be sufficient; hit, strike; **—иться** *v.* remember suddenly; **—ка** *f.* seizing, clutching; grasp, clutch, grip.

**х-во** *abbr.* (хозяйство) economy; farm.

**хвоевертка** *f.* (zool.) evetria.

**хвойн/ик** *m.* (bot.) ephedra; **—иковые** *pl.* Ephedraceae; **—ые** *pl.* conifers (*Coniferae*); **—ый** *a.* coniferous, cone-bearing; acerose; **—ый спирт** coniferyl alcohol; **—ый экстракт** pine extract; **—ое дерево** conifer.

**хворост** *m.* brushwood, dry branches.

**хвор/ый** *a.* sickly, puny; **—ь** *f.* sickliness, illness, ailment.

**хвост** *m.* tail, tail piece; (aero.) tail group; line, queue; shank, shaft (of tool); spike; last runnings (in distillation); **—ы** *pl.* (min.) tails, tailings, residue; **заносить х.** *v.* (aero.) skid; **плестись в —е** *v.* lag behind; **спуск на х.** (aero.) tail spin, tail dive.

**хвостат/ые** *pl.* (zool.) Caudata, Urodela; **—ый** *a.* tailed, caudate.

**хвост/ик** *m.* little tail; **—ист** *m.* lagger, trailer; **—ище** *n.* huge tail; **—овик** *m.* stem, shaft (of tool).

**хвостов/ой** *a.* tail, caudal; rear, posterior, hindmost; residual, waste (gases); **х. молот** tilt hammer; **—ая вена** caudal vein.

**хвосты** *pl. of* хвост.

**хвощ** *m.* (bot.) horsetail (*Equisetum*); **—евые, —и** *pl.* Equisetaceae.

**хвоя** *f.* (bot.) coniferous needle.

**хевея** *f.* (bot.) hevea; **бразильская х.** para rubber tree (*Hevea brasiliensis*).

**Хевисайда слой** Heaviside layer, ionosphere.

**Хегелера печь** Hegeler furnace.

**хедер** *m.* header (grain-harvester).

**хейлит** *m.* (med.) cheilitis.

**хейр/амин** *m.* cheiramine; **—антин** *m.* cheiranthin; **—антовая кислота** cheiranthic acid; **—ин** *m.* cheirin; **—инин** *m.* cheirinine; **—олин** *m.* cheirolin.

**хел/ант** *m.* chelating agent; **—ат** *m.* chelate, chelate compound; **—ация** *f.* chelation.

**хелеритрин** *m.* chelerythrine.

**хелидон/аминовая кислота** chelidonamic acid; **—ин** *m.* chelidonine; **хлористоводородный —ин** chelidonine hydrochloride; **—овая кислота** chelidonic acid, pyronedicarboxylic acid; **соль —овой кислоты, —овокислая соль** chelidonate; **—оид** *m.* chelidonoid.

**хелицероносные** *pl.* (zool.) Chelicerata.

**хелонин** *m.* chelonin.

**Хельбергера печь** Helberger furnace.

**хемилюминесценция** *f.* chemiluminescence.

**хемо—** *prefix* chemo—; *see also* химио—; **—з** *m.* (med.) chemosis; **—лиз** *m.* chemolysis; **—синтез** *m.* (physiol.) chemosynthesis; **—смоз** *m.* chemosmosis; **—сорбция** *f.* chemisorption; **—таксис** *m.* (biol.) chemotaxis; **—тропизм** *m.* (biol.) chemotropism.

**Хендерсона способ** Henderson process (of treating copper sulfide ores).

**хеневиксит** *m.* (min.) chenevixite.

**хенна** *see* хна.

хено/подин *m*. chenopodin; —таурохолевая кислота chenotaurocholic acid; —холевая кислота chenocholic acid.

херес *m*. sherry.

хермес *m*. coniferous tree aphid (*Chermes*).

Хертера-Дриффильда характеристика Hurter and Driffield characteristic curve.

хескер *m*. (agr.) husker; —ный *a*. husking.

хессилит *see* шессилит.

хет/а *f*. chaeta, seta, spine, bristle; —огнаты *pl*. (zool.) Chaetognatha.

хетомин *m*. chetomin.

хетчер *m*. hatcher, incubator.

Хеффа сепаратор Huff separator (electrostatic concentrator for ores).

хиазм *m*., —а *f*. (biol.) chiasm, chiasma.

хиастолит *m*. (min.) chiastolite, macle (a variety of andalusite).

хибикон *m*. Hibicon, benzchlorpropamide.

хивиатит *m*. (min.) chiviatite.

Хивисайда *see* Хевисайда.

ХИК *abbr*. (Химический институт имени Л.Я. Карпова) L.Ia. Karpov Chemical Institute.

хил *see* хилус.

хил/еть *v*. grow feeble, grow sickly; —ость *f*. feebleness, sickliness.

хилус *m*. (physiol.) chyle.

хилый *a*. feeble, weak, sickly.

хим— *abbr*. (химический) chemical; ХИМ *abbr*. (Харьковский научно-исследовательский институт металлов) Kharkov Scientific Research Institute of Metals.

химаза *f*. chymase.

химаппарат *m*. chemical apparatus, chemical equipment.

химафил/ин *m*. chimaphilin; —оид *m*. chimaphiloid.

химбомба *f*. chemical bomb, gas bomb.

ХИМГАЗ *abbr*. (Всесоюзный научно-исследовательский институт химической переработки газов) All-Union Scientific Research Institute of the Chemical Treatment of Gases.

химера *f*. (biol.) chimera.

химеричн/ость *f*. impracticability; —ый *a*. impracticable, chimerical, absurd.

хим/завод *m*. chemical plant, chemical works; —изация *f*. chemization, introduction of chemical processes into the national economy; —изм *m*. chemism; chemical mechanism; chemical affinity.

химик *m*. chemist; х.-консультант, х.-эксперт consulting chemist; х.-органик *m*. organic chemist; х.-пищевик food chemist.

химик/алии, —аты *pl*. chemicals.

химико— *prefix* chemico—, chemical; —аналитические весы analytical balance; —термическая обработка chemical heat treatment; —технологический *a*. chemical engineering.

химиловый спирт chimyl alcohol.

химио— *prefix* chemo—; *see also* хемо—; —терапия *f*. chemotherapy; —синтез *m*. chemosynthesis; —цептор *m*. chemoceptor.

химически *adv*. chemically; х. связанный chemically combined; х. чистый chemically pure.

химическ/ий *a*. chemical; —ая бомба (mil.) chemical bomb, gas bomb; —ая война chemical warfare; —ая реакция, —ое действие chemical reaction; —ая служба chemical warfare service; —ая технология chemical technology; chemical engineering; —ая чистка dry cleaning (of clothes); —ое соединение chemical compound; —ое стекло chemical laboratory glassware; —ие материалы, —ие препараты, —ие продукты chemicals.

химия *f*. chemistry; неорганическая х. inorganic chemistry; органическая х. organic chemistry; прикладная х. applied chemistry.

химозин *m*. chymosin, rennase.

химотрипсин *m*. chymotrypsin (enzyme).

химпоглотитель *m*. chemical absorber.

Химпромторг *abbr*. (Химическая торгово-промышленная контора) Chemical Commerce Bureau.

химсостав *m*. chemical composition.

химус *m*. (physiol.) chyme.

хин— *prefix* quin—, quinine; —а *f*. quina, cinchona bark; —азин *m*.

quinazine, quinoxaline; —**азитиновая кислота** quinasitinic acid, о-amidobenzoylglyoxalic acid; —**азолин** *m.* quinazoline, phenmiazine; —**азолон** *m.* quinazolone, oxyquinazoline; —**акридин** *m.* quinacridine; —**ализарин** *m.* quinalizarin, 1,2,5,8-tetrahydroanthraquinone.

**хинальдин** *m.*, —**овый** *a.* quinaldine, 2-methylquinoline; —**овая кислота** quinaldic acid, 2-quinolinecarboxylic acid.

**хин/амидин** *m.* quinamidine; —**амин** *m.* quinamine; —**амицин** *m.* quinamicine; —**ан** *m.* quinane, desoxyquinine; —**анафтол** *m.* quinanaphthol, quinaphthol; —**ат** *m.* quinate; —**гидрон** *m.*, —**гидроновый** *a.* quinhydrone; —**долин** *m.* quindoline; —**ен** *m.* quinene.

**хинид/амин** *m.* quinidamine; —**ин** *m.* quinidine.

**хинизарин** *m.*, —**овый** *a.* quinizarin, 1,4-dihydroxyanthraquinone.

**хинизатин** *m.* quinisatin; —**овая кислота** quinisatinic acid.

**хинин** *m.* quinine; **сернокислый х., сульфат** —**a** quinine sulfate.

**хинин/дол** *m.* quinindole; —**овый** *see* **хинный**; —**овая кислота** quininic acid; —**он** *m.* quininone.

**хинировать** *v.* (text.) cloud, weave or print chiné.

**хин/ит** *m.* quinite, quinitol, cyclohexanediol; —**ицин** *m.* quinicine.

**хинно/дубильная кислота** *see* **хинодубильная кислота;** —**кислый** *a.* quinic acid; quinate (of); —**кислый хинин** quinine quinate; —**кислая соль** quinate.

**хинн/ый** *a.* quinine; **х. корень** (bot.) China root (*Smilax china*); —**ая кислота** quinic acid, hexahydrotetrahydroxybenzoic acid; **соль** —**ой кислоты** quinate; —**ая кора** cinchona bark; **королевская** —**ая кора** yellow cinchona, calisaya bark; —**ое дерево** (bot.) cinchona; —**ое основание** quinine base; —**ые цветы** quinine flowers.

**хино—** *prefix* quino—; —**a** *f.* quinoa (seeds of *Chenopodium quinoa*); —**вин** *m.* quinovin, chinovin; —**воза** *f.*

quinovose (glucoside); chinovose (carbohydrate); —**дубильная кислота** quinotannic acid, cinchonatannin; —**зол** *m.* Quinosol, 8-hydroxyquinoline sulfate; —**ид** *m.*, —**идный** *a.* quinoid, paraquinoid; —**идин** *m.* quinoidine; —**ил** *m.* quinoyl.

**хинок/итиол** *m.* hinokitiol, thujaplicin; —**овая кислота** hinokic acid.

**хиноксал/ил** *m.* quinoxalyl; —**ин** *m.* quinoxaline, quinazine; —**он** *m.* quinoxalone.

**хинол** *m.* quinol, hydroquinone; —**изин** *m.* quinolizine; —**ил** *m.* quinolyl, quinoyl.

**хинолин** *m.*, —**овый** *a.* quinoline, 1-benzazine; —**карбоновая кислота** quinolinecarboxylic acid; —**овая кислота** quinoline acid; quinolinic acid, 2,3-pyridinedicarboxylic acid; —**ол** *m.* quinolinol, hydroxyquinoline.

**хино/лон** *m.* quinolone; —**н** *m.* quinone; —**нил** *m.* quinonyl; —**танниновая кислота** *see* **хинодубильная кислота;** —**токсин** *m.* quinotoxine; —**тропин** *m.* quinotropine, urotropine quinate; —**фталон** *m.* quinophthalone; —**хинолин** *m.* quinoquinoline, 1,10-naphthodiazine.

**хинуклидин** *m.* quinuclidine.

**хио/кокцин** *m.* chiococcine; —**лит** *m.* (min.) chiolite; —**нантин** *m.* chionanthin; —**нантоид** *m.* chionanthoid.

**хирад** *m.* Hyrad, irradiated polyethylene.

**хират/ин** *m.* chiratin; —**огенин** *m.* chiratogenin.

**хиретта** *f.* (bot.) chiretta (*Swertia chirata*).

**хиреть** *see* **хилеть.**

**хиро—** *prefix* chiro—; —**нол** *m.* chironol.

**хирург** *m.* surgeon; —**ический** *a.* surgical; —**ия** *f.* surgery.

**хит/енидин** *m.* chitenidine; —**енин** *m.* chitenine; —**ин** *m.* chitin; —**инизация** *f.* chitinization; —**иновый** *a.* chitin, chitinous.

**хитоза** *f.* chitose; —**мин** *m.* chitosamine (glucosamine); —**н** *m.* chitosan.

**хитоновая кислота** chitonic acid.

**хитоны** *pl.* (zool.) Loricata.

**хитр/о** *adv.* cleverly, skillfully, cunningly; —**осплетение** *n.* stratagem;

cobweb, tangle;—**ость** *f.* cunning, slyness; trick, dodge, stratagem; —**ый** *a.* clever, sly, crafty, cunning.

**хищение** *n.* tampering.

**хищн/ецы** *pl.* assassin bugs (*Reduviidae*); —**ые** *pl.* (zool.) Carnivora; —**ый** *a.* predatory; predaceous (insect).

**хладагент** *m.* refrigerant; coolant.

**хладнит** *m.* (min.) chladnite (a variety of enstatite).

**хладнокровный** *a.* cold-blooded; cool, collected, indifferent.

**хладноломк/ий** *a.* (met.) cold short, brittle at atmospheric temperature; —**ость** *f.* cold shortness, cold brittleness.

**хладностойкий** *a.* cold-resistant, antifreezing; **х. состав** antifreeze.

**хладо/агент** *see* **хладагент**; —**бойня** *f.* slaughterhouse; —**ломкость** *see* **хладноломкость**; —**стойкий** *see* **хладностойкий**; —**текучесть** *f.* cold flow; —**транспорт** *m.* refrigerated transportation (of perishables).

**хламидоспор/а** *f.* (bot.) chlamydospore; —**ин** *m.* chlamydosporin.

**хл.-бум.** *abbr.* (**хлопчатобумажный**) cotton.

**хлеб** *m.* bread, loaf; cereals, grain; **убирать х.** *v.* harvest (grain); —**а** *pl.* grain crop; —**ец** *m.* small loaf of bread.

**хлебн/ый** *a.* bread; grain, cereal; **х. амбар** granary; **х. комарик** Hessian fly; **х. спирт** grain alcohol, ethyl alcohol; —**ая биржа** corn exchange; —**ая плесень** bread mold (*Mucor mucedo*); —**ое дерево** (bot.) bread-fruit (*Artocarpus incisa*); —**ые растения** cereal plants, cereals.

**хлебо—** *prefix* grain; bread; —**завод** *m.* bakery; —**заготовка** *f.* grain harvesting, grain storage.

**хлебок** *m.* sip, mouthful, spoonful.

**хлебопаш/енный** *a.* agricultural; —**ество** *n.* agriculture; grain farming; —**ествовать** *v.* farm; —**ец** *m.* farmer.

**хлебо/пек** *m.* baker; —**пекарная ценность** baking value; —**пекарня** *f.* bakery; —**печение** *n.* bread baking; —**роб** *m.* grain grower; —**род** *m.* abundant grain crop; —**торговля** *f.*

grain trade; —**уборочный** *a.* harvest, harvesting.

**хлев** *m.* cattle shed, barn, pen.

**хлест/ание,** —**анье** *n.* whipping, lashing, flapping; gushing, spouting; —**ать,** —**нуть** *v.* whip, lash, flap; gush out, spout, flow, pour (of rain).

**хлоантит** *m.* (min.) chloanthite (a nickel diarsenide).

**хлоп/ание,** —**анье** *n.* banging, knocking; whipping, flapping; popping; —**ать** *v.* bang, slam, knock, clap; whip, flap.

**хлопинит** *m.* khlopinite, chlopinite (a niobium tantalate).

**хлопко—** *prefix* cotton; —**вод** *m.* cotton grower; —**водство** *n.* cotton growing.

**хлопков/ый** *a.* cotton; **х. пух** linters; —**ое масло** cottonseed oil; —**ое семя** cottonseed; —**ые очески** cotton waste.

**хлопко/очески** *pl.* cotton waste; —**очиститель** *m.,* —**очистительная установка** (cotton) gin; —**очистка** *f.* ginning; —**прядение** *n.* cotton spinning; —**роб** *m.* cotton grower; —**трепалка** *f.* batting machine; —**уборочная машина** cotton picker.

**хлопнуть** *see* **хлопать**.

**хлопок** *m.* cotton; floc, flake; **х.-сырец** cotton wool.

**хлопот/ать** *v.* take trouble; solicit, petition; bustle about; —**ливый** *a.* busy (person); troublesome (business); —**ня** *f.* concern, care; fuss, bustle; —**ы** *pl.* trouble, cares.

**хлопушка** *f.* firecracker; gate valve; (bot.) catch fly (*Silene venosa*).

**хлопчатник** *m.,* —**овый** *a.* (bot.) cotton plant (*Gossypium*); —**овое масло** cottonseed oil.

**хлопчато—** *prefix* cotton.

**хлопчатобумажн/ый** *a.* cotton; **х. порох** guncotton, pyroxylin; —**ая материя,** —**ая ткань** cotton, cotton fabric.

**хлопчат/ый** *a.* cotton; —**ая бумага** cotton, cotton fabric.

**хлопь/е** *n.,* —**я** *pl.* flocs, flakes; —**ями** in flakes, in flocculent form; **в виде —ев** in the form of flakes, flocculent; **образование —ев, —еобразование** *n.* flocculation; —**евидный, —еобразный** *a.* flaky, flocculent, flocky.

**хлор** *m.* chlorine, Cl, chlorine gas; **гидрат** —а chlorine hydrate; **двуокись** —a chlorine dioxide, chlorine peroxide; **окись** —a chlorine oxide.

**хлор**— *prefix* chlor—, chloro—; chloride; —**азин** *m.* Chlorazine, chloramine-T; —**азол** *m.* chlorazol; —**акон** *m.* Chloracon, benzchlorpropamide.

**хлорал** *m.* chloral, trichloroethanal; **сернистоводородный х.** chloral hydrosulfide; —**гидрат** *m.* chloral hydrate; —**ид** *m.* chloralide; —**оза** *f.* chloralose, anhydroglucochloral.

**хлор/алун** *m.* chloralum; —**алуровая кислота** chloraluric acid; —**аль** *see* **хлорал;** —**алюминит** *m.* (min.) chloraluminite; —**амид** *m.* chloramide, chloral amide; —**амил** *m.* amyl chloride; —**амилен** *m.* chloroamylene; —**амин** *m.* chloramine; —**амфеникол** *m.* chloramphenicol, Chloromycetin (antibiotic).

**хлорангидрид** *m.* acid chloride; **х. азотной кислоты** nitroxyl chloride; **х. серной кислоты** sulfuryl chloride; **х. стеариновой кислоты** stearyl chloride; **х. уксусной кислоты** acetyl chloride.

**хлоранил** *m.* chloranil, tetrachloroquinone; —**амид** *m.* chloranilamide; —**ин** *m.* chloraniline; —**овая кислота** chloranilic acid; **соль** —**овой кислоты,** —**овокислая соль** chloranilate.

**хлор/апатит** *m.* (min.) chlorapatite (a variety of apatite); —**астролит** *m.* (min.) chlorastrolite (probably a mixture of zeolites); —**ат** *m.* chlorate; —**атит** *m.* (expl.) chloratite; —**атор** *m.* chlorinator (for water purification).

**хлорацет/ат** *m.* chloroacetate; —**ил** *m.* chloroacetyl; —**он** *m.* chloroacetone; —**оновая кислота** chloroacetonic acid; —**офенон** *m.* chloroacetophenone, phenacyl chloride.

**хлорбенз/ил** *m.* chlorobenzyl; benzyl chloride; —**ойная кислота** chlorobenzoic acid; —**ол** *m.* chlorobenzene.

**хлор/бромбензол** *m.* chlorobromobenzene; —**бутадиен** *m.* chlorobutadiene; —**винил** *m.* vinyl chloride.

**хлоргидр/ат** *m.* hydrochloride; chlorine hydrate; —**ин** *m.,* —**иновый** *a.* chlorohydrin; —**ирование** *n.* hydro-

chlorination, addition of hydrogen chloride.

**хлор/дан,** —**индан** *m.* chlordan (insecticide); —**екс** *m.* Chlorex, *sym*-dichloroethyl ether; —**закись кобальта** cobaltous oxychloride; —**замещенный** *a.* chlorine-substitution, chloro—; —**ид** *m.*, —**идный** *a.* chloride; —**идин** *m.* Chloridin, pyrimethamine; —**изация,** —**инация** *see* **хлорирование;** —**ил** *m.* chloryl; —**илен** *m.* chlorylene, trichloroethylene; —**ин** *m.* chlorinated polyvinyl chloride fiber; chlorine (the porphyrin); —**ион** *m.* chlorion, chloride ion.

**хлорир/ование** *n.* chlorination; —**ованный** *a.* chlorinated; —**овать** *v.* chlorinate; —**ующий** *a.* chlorinating; —**ующий агент** chlorinating agent; —**ующий обжиг** chlorination roasting.

**хлорис** *m.* (bot.) finger grass (*Chloris*).

**хлористоводородн/ый** *a.* hydrochloride (of); **х. газ** hydrogen chloride, anhydrous hydrochloric acid; **х. хинин** quinine hydrochloride; —**ая кислота** hydrochloric acid, aqueous hydrogen chloride; **соль** —**ой кислоты** chloride.

**хлористо/калиевая соль,** —**кислый калий** potassium chlorite; —**кислый** *a.* chlorous acid; chlorite (of); —**кислая соль** chlorite.

**хлорист/ый** *a.* chlorine, chlorous; (lower or —**ous**) chloride (of); **х. алюминий** aluminum chloride; **х. бензил** benzyl chloride; **х. водород** hydrogen chloride; **х. карбонил** carbonyl chloride, phosgene; **х. этил** ethyl chloride; —**ая кислота** chlorous acid; **соль** —**ой кислоты** chlorite; —**ая медь** cuprous chloride; —**ое железо** ferrous chloride; **основной х.** oxychloride (of).

**хлорит** *m.* chlorite; (min.) chlorite; —**изация** *f.* (min.) chloritization; —**овый** *a.* chlorite; (min.) chloritic; —**оид** *m.* (min.) chloritoid, ottrelite.

**Хлор-ИФК** *abbr.* (изопропил-N-3-хлорфенилкарбамат) isopropyl N-(3-chlorophenyl)carbamate.

**хлор/кали** *n.* potassium chloride; —**кальций** *m.,* —**кальциевый** *a.* calcium chloride; —**каучук** *m.* chlorinated rubber; —ксилол *m.* chloroxylene; —манганокалит *m.* (min.) chlormanganokalite; —масляная кислота chlorobutyric acid; —метан *m.* chloromethane; —метил *m.* chloromethyl; methyl chloride; —метилбутан *m.* chloromethylbutane; —нитробензол *m.* chloronitrobenzene.

хлорно/аммониевая соль ammonium perchlorate; —бариевая соль barium perchlorate; —ватая кислота chloric acid; соль —ватой кислоты chlorate.

хлорноватисто/калиевая соль potassium hypochlorite; —кальциевая соль calcium hypochlorite; —кислый *a.* hypochlorous acid; hypochlorite (of); —кислый натрий, —натриевая соль sodium hypochlorite; —кислая соль hypochlorite.

хлорноватист/ый *a.* hypochlorous; х. ангидрид hypochlorous acid anhydride, chlorine monoxide; —ая кислота hypochlorous acid; соль —ой кислоты hypochlorite; —ые эфиры hypochlorite esters.

хлорновато/алюминиевая соль aluminum chlorate; —аммониевая соль ammonium chlorate; —бариевая соль barium chlorate; —калиевая соль potassium chlorate; —кислый *a.* chloric acid; chlorate (of); —кислый натрий, —натриевая соль sodium chlorate; —кислая соль chlorate; —медная соль copper chlorate.

хлорно/калиевая соль, —кислый калий potassium perchlorate; —кислый *a.* perchloric acid; perchlorate (of); —кислая соль perchlorate; —серебряная соль silver perchlorate.

хлорн/ый *a.* chlorine; (higher or —ic) chloride (of); х. ангидрид perchloric anhydride, chlorine heptoxide; х. гремучий газ chlorine detonating gas (mixture of chlorine and hydrogen); —ая вода chlorine water; —ая известь bleaching powder, calcium hypochlorite mixture; —ая кислота perchloric acid; соль —ой кислоты perchlorate; —ая медь cupric chloride; —ая ртуть mercuric chloride; —ое железо ferric chloride; —ое олово stannic chloride; основной х.

oxychloride (of); основная —ая медь copper oxychloride.

хлоро—*prefix* chloro—, chlor—, chlorine.

хлороводород *m.* hydrogen chloride; —ный *see* хлористоводородный.

хлоро/генин *m.* chlorogenine, alstonine; —геновая кислота chlorogenic acid; —гидрин *m.* chlorohydrin; —з *m.* (med.) chlorosis; —иодистый *a.* chloroiodide, iodochloride (of); —какодил *m.* cacodyl chloride; —кальцит *m.* (min.) chlorocalcite, hydrophilite.

хлорокись *f.* oxychloride; х. углерода carbonyl chloride, phosgene; х. фосфора phosphorus oxychloride, phosphoryl chloride.

хлоро/ксил *m.* Chloroxyl (cinchophen hydrochloride); —ксилен *m.* chloroxylene, xylyl chloride; —меланит *m.* (min.) chloromelanite (a variety of jadeite); —метр *m.* chlorometer, chloridometer; —метрия *f.* chlorometry; —мицетин *m.* Chloromycetin, chloramphenicol.

хлоропал *m.* (min.) chloropal, nontronite.

хлоро/палладиевая кислота chloropalladic acid; —пласт *m.* (biol.) chloroplast.

хлороплатин/ат *m.*, соль —овой кислоты, —овокислая соль chloroplatinate, platinichloride; —истая кислота chloroplatinous acid; соль —истой кислоты, —истокислая соль, —ит *m.* chloroplatinite, platinochloride; —овая кислота chloroplatinic acid.

хлоро/прен *m.*, —преновый *a.* chloroprene, 2-chloro-1,3-butadiene; —рафин *m.* chlororaphin; —торит *m.* (min.) chlorothorite; —углерод *m.* carbon chloride, carbon tetrachloride; —фаит *m.* (min.) chlorophaite (a chlorite); —фан *m.* (min.) chlorophane (a variety of fluorite).

хлорофилл *m.*, —овый *a.* (bot.) chlorophyll; —ид *m.* chlorophyllide; —ин *m.* chlorophyllin; —ит *m.* (min.) chlorophyllite (an alteration product of cordierite).

хлороформ *m.*, —енный, —овый *a.* chloroform, trichloromethane; —ировать *v.* chloroform.

**хлор/ошпинель** *f.* (min.) chlorospinel, ceylonite; —**парафин** *m.* chloroparaffin; —**пентан** *m.* chloropentane; —**пикрин** *m.* chloropicrin; —**платинат** *see* хлороплатинат; —**производные** *pl.* chlorine derivatives, chlorine compounds; —**промазин** *m.* chlorpromazine; —**пропан** *m.* chloropropane; —**смесь** *f.* a carbon disulfide-carbon tetrachloride insecticide; —**содержащий** *a.* chlorine-containing; —**сульфоновая кислота** chlorosulfonic acid; —**тен** *m.* a chlorinated α-pinene insecticide; —**толуол** *m.* chlorotoluene, benzyl chloride.

**хлоруксусн/ая кислота** chloroacetic acid; **соль** —**ой кислоты**, —**окислая соль** chloroacetate; —**оэтиловый эфир** ethyl chloroacetate; —**ые эфиры** chloroacetic esters.

**хлор/фен** *m.* a chlorinated camphene insecticide (equivalent to Toxaphene); —**фензон** *see* эфирсульфонат; —**фенол** *m.* chlorophenol; —**циан** *m.* cyanogen chloride; —**цинк** *m.* zinc chloride; —**щавелевая кислота** chlorooxalic acid; —**этан**, —**этил** *m.* chloroethane, ethyl chloride; —**этанол** *m.* chloroethanol, chlorocarbinol; —**этен**, —**этилен** *m.* chloroethylene, vinyl chloride; —**этиловый эфир** chloroethyl ether; —**этон** *m.* chloretone, chlorobutanol; —**юр** *see* хлорид; —**янтарная кислота** chlorosuccinic acid.

**хлф.** *abbr.* (хлороформ) chloroform (as solvent).

**хлын/увший** *a.* gushing; irruptive; —**уть** *v.* gush (out), spout, well; rush, pour.

**хлюпание** *n.* sucking noise, suction noise.

**ХМ** *abbr.* (хлорат магния) magnesium chlorate.

**хмеле/водство** *n.* (agr.) hop growing; —**вой** *a.* hop; brewer's (yeast); —**вая мука** hop dust, lupulin; —**граб** *m.* (bot.) hop hornbeam (*Ostrya*); —**к** *m.* hop clover; —**подобный** *a.* hop-like, like hops.

**хмел/ить** *v.* intoxicate; —**ица** *f.* (bot.) staminate hop; —**ь** *m.* hops; intoxication; (bot.) hop (*Humulus lupulus*); —**ьник** *m.* hop field; —**ьное** *n.* intoxicating liquor; —**ьной** *a.* brewing; intoxicating; intoxicated.

**хмыз** *m.* spray, sprig, twig.

**хна** *f.* henna (dye); (bot.) henna plant (*Lawsonia inermis*).

**хобот** *m.* trunk, proboscis; (lathe) tool holder; —**ок** *m.* proboscis (of insect).

**ход** *m.* motion, movement, travel, progress, headway; course, path, way, passage, passing, going; rate, speed, gait, pace; functioning, operation, running, working (of furnace), process (of smelting, etc.); action, blow (of press), stroke (of piston); gear, thread, pitch (of screw); shape, trend, dependence (of curve); range (of magnet); entrance (to building, etc.); train (of thought); **х. вверх** upstroke (of piston), rise, ascent; **х. вниз** downstroke, fall, descent; **х. дел** course of events; **х. назад** back stroke; reverse motion; **быть в —у** *v.* run, work, be in operation; **величина —а**, **высота —а** delivery head; **временной х.** time dependence (of curve); **длина —а** stroke; **на —у** on the go, in operation, running, in progress; in running order; **на полном —у** at full speed; (furnace) full blast; **на резиновом —у** rubber-tired (vehicle); **быть на —у** *v.* be in operation, run; **пускать в х.**, **пустить в х.** *v.* put into operation, put into service; start up, set going, set in motion, put into action; **разность —а** (optical) path difference; **свободный х.** free running, free play.

**ходатай** *m.* intercessor, mediator; —**ствовать** *v.* intercede, petition; apply (for).

**ходильный** *a.* ambulatory.

**ходить** *v.* go, run, work; pass (of current, etc.); tend, take care (of).

**ходк/ий** *a.* salable, marketable; —**ость** *f.* marketability.

**ходов/ой** *a.* going, running; leading; track, path; salable, marketable; **х. валик** feed shaft; **х. винт** lead screw, leader, guide screw; **х. золотник** throttle valve; **х. механизм** running gear; **х. ролик** traveler, traveling roller, runner; —**ая гайка** sliding nut;

—ая пружина mainspring (of clock-work); —ая часть undercarriage, un-derframe (of machine).

ходок *m.* conduit, passage (in mine).

ходоуменьшитель *m.* reducing gear; —ный *a.* speed-reducing.

ходул/я *f.*, —ьный *a.* stilt.

ходуном: ходить х. *v.* shake, rock.

ход/ьба *f.* walking; —ячий *a.* walking; current.

хождение *n.* walking; nursing, caring (for); иметь х. *v.* be current, pass.

хоз—, хоз. *abbr.* (хозяйственный) econ-omy, economic; (хозяйство) econ-omy; husbandry; —расчет *m.* cost accounting; self-support; —часть *f.* economic department.

хоз/яин *m.* master; boss; landlord, owner, proprietor; (biol., min.) host; сельский х. farmer; —яйка *f.* mis-tress, landlady; housewife; —яйни-чать *v.* manage a household; farm; boss.

хозяйственн/ик *m.* economist; —о *adv.* economically; —ость *f.* economy; —ый *a.* economic, economical; farm; household; —ый год fiscal year; на —ом расчете self-supporting.

хозяйство *n.* economy; farm; farming, husbandry; industry; establishment, household; (power) plant; домашнее х. household; коллективное х. co-operative farm; народное х. national economy; сельское х. farming, agri-culture; —вать *see* хозяйничать.

Хойля сплав Hoyle's metal (lead-tin-antimony alloy).

хол/алин *m.*, —евая кислота cholalin, cholic acid; —ан *m.* cholane; —ано-вая кислота cholanic acid; cholaic acid; —антрен *m.* cholanthrene; —евокислый *a.* cholic acid; cholate (of); —евокислая соль, соль —евой кислоты cholate; —еиновая кислота choleic acid, deoxycholic acid; cho-leinic acid.

холеный *a.* well cared for (animal).

холер/а *f.* (med.) cholera; —ик *m.* choleric person; —ический *a.* chol-eric; —ный *a.* cholera, choleraic; —ный вибрион cholera bacillus, comma bacillus; —ный яд cholera

virus; —овидный *a.* choleroid, chol-eraic.

холест/ан *m.* cholestane; —анон *m.* cho-lestanone; —ен *m.* cholestene; —енон *m.* cholestenone; —ерил *m.* choles-teryl.

холестерин *m.*, —овый *a.* cholesterol; —овая кислота cholesteric acid; соль —овой кислоты, —овокислая соль cholesterate; —овокислый *a.* choles-teric acid; cholesterate (of).

холе/стерол *see* холестерин; —строфан *m.* cholestrophan, dimethylparabanic acid; —телин *m.* choletelin; —цистит *m.* (med.) cholecystitis.

холин *m.*, —овый *a.* choline, bilineurine; —овая кислота cholinic acid.

холка *f.* (zool.) withers, ridge, crest.

холл *m.* hall, entrance hall.

Холле съемное днище Holley detachable bottom.

Холля способ Hall process (for alu-minum); Х. явление (elec.) Hall effect.

холм *m.* hill, hillock, mound, hummock, hog-back; (sand) dune.

холмий *see* гольмий.

холм/ик *m.* hillock, mound, hummock; —истый *a.* hilly, rolling, undulating.

хологон *m.* Chologon, dehydrocholic acid.

холод *m.* cold, chill; —а *pl.* cold weather; градусы —а degrees of frost, degrees below freezing; на —у in the cold; выдавливание на —у cold pressing; насыщать на —у *v.* saturate in the cold, saturate in the cold state; проба на —у cold test.

холодеть *v.* grow cold, cool, chill.

холодильник *m.* refrigerator, cooler; con-denser; х. смешения condensing jet, mixing condenser; башенный х. cooling tower; вторичный х. after-cooler; обратный х., обратно постав-ленный х. reflux condenser.

холодильн/ый *a.* cooling, refrigerating, refrigerative, refrigerant; condensing; х. агент cooling agent, coolant; х. вагон (railroad) refrigerator car; х. чан cooler; —ая машина refrigerating machine, refrigerator; cooler; —ая промышленность refrigeration in-dustry; —ая смесь freezing mixture;

—ая соль freezing salt; —ая техника refrigeration engineering; —ая установка refrigerating plant, cooling plant; freezing plant; cold storage plant; condensing plant; —ое вещество, —ое средство refrigerant, refrigerating agent; —ое дело refrigeration; —ое пространство cooling jacket.

холодиновая кислота cholodinic acid.

холодить v. cool, chill, refrigerate.

холодно adv. cold, coldly; it is cold; —ватый a. rather cold, chilly; —катаный a. (met.) cold-rolled; —кровный a. cold-blooded; —ломкий a. (met.) cold short; —ломкость f. cold shortness; —обработанный a. (met.) coldworked, cold-wrought, hard-wrought; —сть f. coldness; —тянутый a. (met.) cold-drawn, hard-drawn.

холодн/ый a. cold, frigid, chilly; х. пояс frigid zone; —ая клепка cold riveting; —ые красители ice colors (azo dyes); прокатанный в —ом состоянии (met.) cold-rolled.

холодо/производительность f. refrigerating capacity; —стойкий a. resistant to cold; winter-hardy (plant); —стойкость f. resistance to cold; hardiness.

холоидановая кислота choloidanic acid.

холостить v. castrate.

холост/ой a. idle, loose-running, loose, free; empty, blank, dummy; inert (fuel element); (elec.) dead; single, unmarried; х. впуск, х. выпуск, —ая нагрузка no load; х. заряд, х. патрон blank cartridge; х. ролик idler; х. ход idling, idle motion, idle running, free running, running without load, running light; no load; idle stroke; работать на —ом ходу, работать в —ую v. idle, run idle, run without load; —ая колоша bed charge; —ая проба blank test, control test; —ая работа idling, no load, no-load working, running light; —ое пятно (chromatography) reference spot.

холостяк m. bachelor.

холоталлин m. cholothallin.

холощение n. castration.

холст m., —инный, —яной a. canvas; fabric, cloth, linen; (text.) lap;

грубый х. sacking; —ина f. a piece of canvas; linen; —инка f. (text.) gingham; —овая машина sliver lap machine.

холщевый see холстинный.

холява f. (glass) hand-blown cylinder.

хомут m. collar, yoke, ring, hoop, stirrup; clamp, clip; стяжной х. band; —ик m. collar; clip; lug.

хомяк m. (zool.) hamster.

хон m. hone, honing head.

хондра f. (geol.) chondrule.

хондрилл/а f., —овый a. (bot.) chondrilla.

хондрин m. chondrin (cartilage protein).

хондрио— prefix (biol.) chondrio— (grit, grain, cartilage); —м m., —ма f. chondriome; —сома f. chondriosome.

хондрит m. (geol.) chondrite; (med.) chondritis.

хондро— prefix chondro— (grain; cartilage); —арсенит m. (min.) chondrarsenite (a variety of sarkinite); —дин m. chondrodine; —дит m. (min.) chondrodite (a member of the humite group).

хондроз/амин m. chondrosamine; —аминовая кислота chondrosamic acid; —ин m. chondrosin; —иновая кислота chondrosinic acid.

хондро/ин m. chondroine; —итин m. chondroitin; —итовая кислота chondroitic acid; —логия f. chondrology, study of cartilages; —ма f. (med.) chondroma; —ниновая кислота chondroninic acid; —новая кислота chondronic acid; —протеин m. chondroprotein.

хонинг m., —ование n. honing (of cylinder bores, etc.); х.-головка honing head, hone; х.-станок honing machine; —ировать, —овать v. hone.

хонолиты pl. (geol.) chonoliths (irregular intrusive masses).

хопер see хоппер.

хопкалит see гопкалит.

хоппер m. hopper; hopper car.

хорватский a. Croatian.

Хорвуда процесс Horwood (flotation) process.

хорд/а f. (math.) chord; (anat.) chord, notochord; span (of arc); —альный a.

chordal; —овые *pl.* (zool.) Chordata; —овый *a.* chord; chorded.

хорек *see* хорь.

хорея *f.* (med.) chorea, St. Vitus' dance.

хорлестрофан *m.* chorlestrophan.

хорография *f.* chorography (of a region).

хоронить *v.* bury, inter; hide, conceal.

хорош/енько *adv.* well, thoroughly, properly, soundly; —ий *a.* good; high (yield, etc.); —о *adv.* well; highly; —о растворимый *a.* readily soluble.

Хорснея процесс (met.) Horsney process.

хорь *m.*, —ковый *a.* (zool.) pole cat, skunk.

хот/ение *n.* desire, volition; —еть *v.* wish, want, desire; —еться *v.* be desirable; ему хочется he wants, he desires, he would like (to).

хот/ь, —я *conj.* though, although; х. бы if only, even if; —я *pr. act. part. of* хотеть.

хох/латка *f.* (bot.) corydalis; —латки *pl.* (zool.) the prominents (*Notodontidae*); —латый *a.* tufted, crested, cristate; —литься *v.* bristle up; —ол *m.* tuft, crest; —олок *m.* (bot.) pappus.

хочет *pr. 3 sing. of* хотеть.

храбрый *a.* brave, courageous.

хранение *n.* keeping, custody; storing, storage; conservation, preservation; отдавать на х. *v.* deposit, store; холодное х. cold storage.

хран/илище *n.* storehouse, storage; depository, safe; reservoir; —итель *m.* keeper, custodian, guardian; —ить *v.* keep, hold, store, preserve.

храп *m.* grab, crampon; snore piece (of pump); snore; —еть *v.* snore; snort.

храповик *m.* ratchet, ratchet wheel; х. и собачка ratchet and pawl.

храпов/ой, —ый *a.* ratchet; х. механизм ratchet, ratchet gearing; х. экскаватор clamshell excavator; —ая собачка pawl; —ое колесо ratchet wheel.

храпок *m.* strainer; snore piece (of pump).

хреб/ет *m.* (anat.) spine, spinal column, backbone; crest, ridge (of mountain); range, chain (of mountains); —тообразный *a.* ridged.

хрен *m.*, —овый *a.* (bot.) horse radish (*Cochlearia armoracea*).

хрестоматия *f.* reader.

хриз/азин *m.* chrysazin, 1,8-dihydroxyanthraquinone; —азол *m.* chrysazol, 1,8-anthracenediol; —алида *f.* (zool.) chrysalis, pupa; —амин *m.* chrysamine, flavophenine; —амминовая кислота chrysamminic acid, chrysammic acid; —анилин *m.* chrysaniline; —аниловая кислота chrysanilic acid; —анисовая кислота chrysanisic acid, 3,5-dinitro-4-aminobenzoic acid; —антема *f.* (bot.) chrysanthemum; —антемин *m.* chrysanthemin; —аробин *m.* chrysarobin; —атроповая кислота chrysatropic acid, scopoletin; —ен *m.* chrysene, benzophenanthrene; —еновая кислота chrysenic acid, betaphenyl-naphtholcarboxylic acid; —идин *m.* chrysidine; —ин *m.* chrysin, 5,7-dihydroxyflavone.

хризо— *prefix* chryso— (gold, gold-colored); —берил *m.* (min.) chrysoberyl, cymophane; —идин *m.* chrysoidin; chrysoidine, 2,4-diaminoazobenzene; —кал *m.* chrysocale (a copper-zinc-lead alloy); —кетон *m.* chrysoketone; —колла *f.* (min.) chrysocolla (a hydrous copper silicate); —лeповая кислота chrysolepic acid, picric acid; —лин *m.* chrysolin (dye); —лит *m.* (min.) chrysolite, olivine, peridot; —монады *pl.* (zool.) chrysomonadina; —пикрин *m.* chrysopicrin, vulpic acid; —праз *m.* (min.) chrysoprase (a variety of chalcedony); —тил *m.* (min.) chrysotile, serpentine asbestos; —токсин *m.* chrysotoxin.

хризофан/ин *m.* chrysophanin; —овая кислота, —ол *m.* chrysophanic acid, chrysophanol.

хризо/фенин *m.* chrysophenine; —фениновая кислота chrysophenic acid; —фисцин *m.* chrysophyscin, physcion; —флуорен *m.* chrysofluorene, 1,2-benzofluorene; —хинон *m.* chrysoquinone, chrysenequinone.

хрип *m.*, —ение *n.* hoarseness; rattle, crepitation; —еть *v.* speak hoarsely; rattle, crepitate, crackle; —лый *a.* hoarse, husky; —нуть *v.* become hoarse; —ота *f.* hoarseness.

хроатол *m.* chroatol, terpene hydro-iodide.

**хроиколит** *m.* choicolyte.

**хром** *m.* chromium, Cr; chrome; **гидрат закиси** —a chromous hydroxide; **гидрат окиси** —a chromic hydroxide; **закись** —a chromous oxide, chromium monoxide; **соль закиси** —a chromous salt; **окись** —a chromic oxide; **соль окиси** —a chromic salt; **сернокислая закись** —a chromous sulfate; **сернокислая окись** —a chromic sulfate; **сернокислый x.** chromium sulfate; **хлористый x.** chromous chloride; **хлорный x.** chromic chloride.

**хром/акс** *m.* Chromax (ferrous alloy); **—алой** *m.* chromaloy (chromium alloy).

**хроман** *m.* chroman, dihydrobenzopyran.

**хромансил, —ь** *m.* Cromansil (a chromium-manganese-silicon steel).

**хромат** *m.* chromate; **—ермография** *f.* chromathermography; **—ид** *m.* (biol.) chromatid; **раскалывание —идов, распад —идов** chromatid break; **—изм** *m.* chromatism, chromatic aberration; **—ика** *f.* chromatics, science of colors; **—ин** *m.* (biol.) chromatin; **—иновый** *a.* (biol.) chromatic; **—ический, —ичный** *a.* chromatic, color; **—ное наполнение** chromating (anticorrosion treatment).

**хромато/грамм** *m.,* **—грамма** *f.* chromatogram; **—графический** *a.* chromatographic (analysis); **—графия** *f.* chromatography; **—скоп** *m.* chromatoscope; **—фор** *m.* (biol.) chromatophore, pigment cell.

**хроматроп** *m.* (phys.) chromatrope.

**хромать** *v.* limp, be lame; lag behind.

**хромгельб** *m.* chrome yellow (a lead chromate pigment).

**хромель** *m.* Chromel (chromium-nickel alloy).

**хромил** *m.* chromyl; **хлористый x.** chromyl chloride, chromic oxychloride.

**хромиров/ание** *n.* (met.) chrome plating; chromizing, chromium-coating; chrome tanning (of leather); **—анный** *a.* chrome-plated; chrome-tanned; **—ать** *v.* chrome-plate; chrome, chrome-tan.

**хромисто/железистая соль** ferrous chromite; **—кальциевая соль** calcium chromite; **—кислый** *a.* chromous acid; chromite (of); **—кислая соль** chromite; **—магниевая соль** magnesium chromite; **—синеродистый калий** potassium chromicyanide.

**хромист/ый** *a.* chromium, chromous, chrome; **x. железняк** (min.) chrome iron ore, chromite; **x. пикотит** (min.) chrompicotite; **—ая кислота** chromous acid; **соль —ой кислоты** chromite; **—ая слюда** (min.) chrome mica; **—ая соль** chromous salt; **—ая сталь** (met.) chrome steel, chromium steel; **—ое железо** (met.) ferrochrome; (min.) chrome iron ore, chromite.

**хромит** *m.* chromite; (min.) chromite, chrome iron ore; **—ит** *m.* (min.) chromitite; **—овый кирпич** chromite (refractory) brick.

**хромо—** *prefix* chromo— (color; pigment, pigmentation; chrome, chromium); **—бариевая соль** barium chromate; **—ванадиевая сталь** chrome-vanadium steel.

**хромово/аммониевая соль** ammonium chromate; **—бариевая соль** barium chromate; **—калиевая соль** potassium chromate; **—кислый** *a.* chromic acid; chromate (of); **—кислый свинец** lead chromate; **—кислая соль** chromate.

**хромовольфрамовая сталь** chrome-tungsten steel.

**хромово/медная соль** cupric chromate; **—натриевая соль** sodium chromate; **—ртутистая соль** mercurous chromate; **—ртутная соль** mercuric chromate; **—свинцовистая соль** lead chromate.

**хромовщик** *m.* chrome tanner.

**хромов/ый** *a.* chromium, chromic, chrome; **x. ангидрид** chromic anhydride, chromium trioxide; **x. желтый** chrome yellow (lead chromate pigment); **x. сок, x. экстракт** chrome tan liquor; **—ая зеленая** chrome green; **—ая кислота** chromic acid; **соль —ой кислоты** chromate; **кислая соль —ой кислоты** bichromate; **хлорангидрид —ой кислоты** chromyl chloride; **—ая кожа** chrome leather; **—ая краска** chrome color; **—ая соль** chromic salt; **—ая сталь** chrome steel, chromium steel; **—ая шпинель**

(min.) chrome spinel, picotite; —ое дубление chrome tanning; —ое железо (met.) ferrochrome; —ые квасцы chrome alum, ammonium chromic sulfate.

хромоген *m.*, —ная группа chromogen; —ный *a.* chromogenic.

хромо/дубильный раствор chrome tan liquor; —зин *m.* chromosin; —зома *see* хромосома.

хромой *a.* lame, limping.

хромо/кадмиевая желть chrome cadmium yellow (pigment); —кислый *see* хромовокислый.

хромолитограф/ия *f.* chromolithography; —ский *a.* chromolithographic; —ский оттиск chromolithograph, color print.

хромо/марганцевый *a.* chrome-manganese (steel); —метр *m.* chromometer, colorimeter; —молибденовый *a.* chrome-molybdenum; —н *m.* chromone, 1,4-benzopyrone; —натриевая соль sodium chromate; —никелевый *a.* chrome-nickel.

хромоногий *a.* lame.

хромоскоп *m.* chromoscope.

хромосом/а *f.*, —ный *a.* (biol.) chromosome; разрыв —ы, —ный разрыв chromosome break.

хромосфера *f.* (astron.) chromosphere.

хромота *f.* lameness.

хромо/тип *m.* chromotype, color print; —типия *f.* chromotypy, color printing; —троп *m.* chromotrope; —тропия *f.* chromotropy, chromoisomerism; —троповая кислота chromotropic acid; —фор *m.*, —форная группа chromophore; —форм *m.* chromoform; —фотография *f.* chromophotography, color photography; —фотометр *m.* chromophotometer (colorimeter); —циклит *m.* (min.) chromocyclite (a variety of apophyllite).

хромпик *m.* bichromate, spec. potassium bichromate; аммониевый х. ammonium bichromate; калиевый х. potassium bichromate; натриевый х. sodium bichromate.

хромпикотит *m.* (min.) chrompicotite.

хронизатор *m.* timer.

хроник *m.* chronic invalid.

хроник/а *f.* chronicle; —ер *m.* chronicler, reporter.

хронир/ование *n.* timing; —овать *v.* time; —ующее устройство timer.

хроническ/и *adv.* chronically; —ий *a.* chronic, lingering.

хроно— *prefix* chrono— (time); —грамма *f.* chronogram; —граф *m.* chronograph; —логический *a.* chronological; —логия *f.* chronology.

хронометр *m.*, —овый *a.* chronometer, timekeeper; —аж *m.* timing; exact timing of operations; time metering; time study; time card system; —ажная карта time card; —ический *a.* chronometric; —ия *f.* chronometry; —овый спуск chronometer escapement.

хроно/скоп *m.* chronoscope; stopwatch; —счетчик *m.* time meter; —трон *m.* chronotron (a mass spectrometer).

хрупк/ий *a.* friable, brittle, fragile, frangible; —оломкий *a.* short-brittle; —ость *f.* friability, brittleness, frangibility; embrittlement; испытание на —ость friability test, brittleness test.

хруст *m.* crunch, crackle; cartilage.

хрусталик *m.* (anat.) crystalline lens.

хрусталь *m.* crystal; crystal glass, cut glass; английский х. flint glass; —ный *a.* crystal, crystalline.

хруст/ение *n.* crunching, crackling, crepitation; —еть, —нуть *v.* crunch, crackle, crepitate.

хрущ *m.* cockchafer, may beetle; —ак *m.* beetle of the Tenebrionidae family; мучной —ак meal worm (*Tenebrio molitor*); —ик *m.* beetle of the Scarabaeidae family.

хр/юкать *v.* grunt; —як *m.* boar.

хрящ *m.* cartilage, gristle; gravel, grit; —и *pl.* (met.) shot; —еватость *f.* gristliness; —еватый *a.* gristly, cartilaginous; gravelly; курчавый —евик *see* ирландский мох; —евина *f.* gristle.

хрящев/ой *a.* cartilaginous, chondral; gravelly (soil); х. клей chondrin; х. сахар chondroglucose; —ая опухоль (med.) chondroma.

хрящеперый *a.* (zool.) selachian.

**ХСЗ** *abbr.* (Химизация социалистического земледелия) Chemization of socialistic agriculture.

**ХТИ** *abbr.* (Харьковский технологический институт) Kharkov Technological Institute.

**хтонизотермический** *a.* (geol.) chthonisothermic.

**худ/ение** *n.* growing thin, getting thin; —**еть** *v.* grow thin, lose weight.

**худжира** *f.* khudzhira (dry lake in the steppes).

**худо** *adv.* badly, ill; *n.* harm, evil.

**худоба** *f.* thinness, leanness, emaciation.

**худож/ественный** *a.* artistic; —**ник** *m.* artist, painter.

**худо/й** *a.* bad, ill, inferior; thin, lean, meager; —**сочие** *n.* (med.) cachexia; —**сочный** *a.* cachectic; —**щавость** *f.* thinness; —**щавый** *a.* thin, lean.

**худш/ий** *a.* worse, the worst; **в** —**ем случае** at the worst; **еще х.** still worse.

**хуже** *comp. of* **худо**, worse; **х. всего то,**

что the worst of it is that; **тем х.** so much the worse.

**Хуп/ера масса** Hooper (insulating) material; —**са способ** Hoopes process (for aluminum refining).

**хурма** *f.* (bot,) persimmon (*Diospyros*).

**хурхит** *see* **черчит.**

**хутор** *m.*, —**ской** *a.* farm, farmstead; —**янин** *m.* farmer.

**хуттонит** *m.* (min.) huttonite.

**ХФДМ** *abbr.* (N-хлорфенил-N-N-диметил мочевина) N-chlorophenyl-N-N-dimethylurea; **4-ХФУК** *abbr.* (4-хлорфеноксиуксусная кислота) 4-chlorophenoxyacetic acid.

**ХХТИ** *abbr.* (Харьковский химико-технологический институт имени С. М. Кирова) S.M. Kirov Kharkov Institute of Chemical Technology.

**х.ч.** *abbr.* (химически чистый) chemically pure.

**хэдер** *see* **хедер.**

**Хэуорса синтез** Haworth synthesis.

# Ц

**ц** *abbr.* (центнер) centner, hundredweight; **°Ц** *abbr.* (градус Цельсия) degree centigrade.

**Цаги, ЦАГИ** *abbr.* (Центральный аэрогидродинамический институт) Central Aero-Hydrodynamic Institute; **Цаги трубка** a water meter.

**цанг/а** *f.*, —**и** *pl.*, —**овый** *a.* tongs, tweezers, forceps; holder, clamp; (lathe) chuck; —**овый патрон** drawin chuck.

**цап/ать** *v.* hoe, hack; —**ка** *f.* hoe, chopper; cornerplate.

**цапля** *f.* (zool.) heron.

**цапон/-лак** *m.*, —**овый лак** a cellulose nitrate varnish.

**цапф/а** *f.*, —**овый** *a.* pin, pivot, journal (of shaft); trunnion; shank; **шаровая ц.** ball journal; —**овый мост** trunnion bascule bridge.

**царап/ание** *n.* scratching, abrasion; scratches; —**анный** *a.* scratched, abraded; —**ать,** —**нуть** *v.* scratch, abrade; —**ина** *f.* scratch, abrasion, mark, notch.

**царатит** *m.* (min.) zaratite, emerald nickel.

**царга** *f.* sheet-steel cylinder or drum.

**царск/ий** *a.* czar; king; **ц. корень, ц. костыль** (bot.) masterwort (*Imperatoria ostruthium*); —**ая вена** (anat.) basilic vein; —**ая водка** aqua regia (a mixture of hydrochloric and nitric acids); —**ая мазь** basilicon ointment, resin ointment; —**ая синь** smalt (pigment); —**ие кудри** (bot.) Turk's-cap lily (*Lilium martagon*).

**царств/о** *n.* kingdom, empire; —**ование** *n.*, —**овать** *v.* reign, rule (over); —**ующий** *a.* reigning, ruling.

**цве/ль** *f.* mold, mustiness; efflorescence; —**сти** *v.* become moldy; effloresce; (bot.) bloom, blossom; flourish, thrive.

**цвет** *m.* color, tint; (bot.) flower, blossom, bloom; **игра** —**ов** iridescence; **основные** —**а, первичные** —**а** primary colors; **углубление** —**а** bathochromic change.

**цвет/ение** *n.* (bot.) blooming, blossoming, flowering, florescence; flower, blossom; efflorescence; —**ень** *m.* pollen, beebread; —**истый** *a.* flowery; —**ковый** *a.* flowering, phanerogamous.

**ЦВЕТМЕТИН** *abbr.* (Центральный институт металлургии цветных металлов и прикладной минералогии) Central Institute of the Metallurgy of Non-Ferrous Metals and Applied Mineralogy.

**цветн/ой** *a.* chromatic, colored; floral; stained (glass); (met.) non-ferrous; **ц. спектр** color spectrum, chromatic spectrum; **—ая капуста** *see under* капуста; **—ая литография** chromolithography; **—ая реакция** color reaction; **—ость** *f.* chromaticity; color index.

**цвето/видный** *a.* flower-shaped; **—водство** *n.* floriculture, flower-growing.

**цветов/ой** *a.* color, chromatic; chromaticity; **—ая реакция на** color reaction for; **—ая температура** (phot.) color temperature.

**цвето/воспроизводящий** *a.* chromatogenic; **—деление** *n.* (phot.) color separation.

**цветоед** *m.* beetle of the Nitidulidae or Curculionidae families.

**цветозамещаемый** *a.* allochromatic.

**цветоизмен/яемость** *f.* allochroism, change of color; **—яющий** *a.* versicolor; **—яющийся** *a.* (med.) allochroic.

**цветок** *m.* flower, blossom, bloom.

**цвето/ложе** *n.* (bot.) receptacle; **—мер** *m.* colorimeter; (sugar) decolorimeter; **—метр** *m.* colorimeter; **—метрический** *a.* colorimetric; **—метрия** *f.* colorimetry; **—насыщенность** *f.* color saturation; **—ножка** *f.* (bot.) peduncle; **—нос** *m.* floriferous shoot; **—носный** *a.* flower-bearing, floriferous; **—ощущение** *n.* color sensation; **—рассеяние** *n.* (optics) chromatic aberration, chromatic dispersion; **—устойчивость** *f.* color fastness.

**цветоч/ек** *m.* little flower; **—ник** *m.* flower pot; (zool.) boll weevil; **—ный** *a.* flower, floral; **—ный покров** (bot.) perianth; **—ный щиток** (bot.) corymb.

**цвет/уха** *f.* seed stalk; premature blooming; **—ушность** *f.* bolting, producing seed prematurely; **—ущий** *a.* flowering, blossoming; flourishing; efflorescent.

**цви/зелит** *m.* (min.) zwieselite (a variety of triplite); **—ттер** *m.* (min.) zwitter (a variety of greisen).

**ц/га** *abbr.* (центнеров на гектар) centners per hectare.

**ЦГЛ** *abbr.* (Центральная генетическая лаборатория) Central Genetic Laboratory.

**ЦГС** *see* **СГС.**

**цеаксантин** *m.* zeaxanthine.

**цев/адиллин** *m.* cevadilline, sabadilline; **—адин** *m.* cevadine, veratrine; **—адиновая кислота** cevadic acid, tiglic acid; **соль —адиновой кислоты** cevadate; **—иллин** *m.* cevilline; **—ин** *m.* cevine.

**цевитаминовая кислота** cevitamic acid, ascorbic acid, vitamin C.

**цевка** *f.* bobbin, spool, reel; spindle, pin; pirn tube; (mach.) teat.

**цевочник** *m.* (bot.) stonecrop (*Sedum acre*).

**цевочн/ый** *a.* bobbin, spool; **—ая обмотка** (elec.) bobbin winding; **—ое зацепление** cogging; mangle gear; **—ое зубчатое колесо** mangle gear; **—ое колесо** cog wheel.

**цедил/ка** *f.*, **—о** *n.* filter, strainer.

**цедильн/ый** *a.* filter, filtering, straining; **ц. колпак, ц. мешок** filter bag; **ц. холст** filter cloth; **—ая бумага** filter paper; **—ая подушка** filter pad.

**цедить** *v.* filter, strain; percolate; decant.

**цедр/а** *f.* shred of lemon or orange peel; **—арин** *m.* cedrarine, orexin; **—ат** *see* **цитрон; —ен** *m.* cedrene; **—ин** *m.* cedrin; **—ол** *m.* cedrol, cedrene camphor; **—он** *m.* cedron (seeds of *Simaba cedron*); **—онин** *m.* cedronine.

**цежен/ие** *n.* filtering, straining; percolation; decantation; **—ный** *a.* filtered, strained; percolated; decanted.

**цезальпин/иевые** *pl.* (bot.) Caesalpiniaceae; **—ия** *f.* caesalpinia.

**цезиев/ый** *a.* cesium; **—ая соль** cesium salt; **—ые квасцы** cesium alum, cesium aluminum sulfate.

**цез/ий** *m.* cesium, Cs; **окись —ия** cesium oxide; **сернокислый ц., сульфат —ия** cesium sulfate; **хлористый ц.** cesium chloride; **—ированный** *a.* cesium-coated.

**цезол** *m.* cesol (methyl chloride ester of

nicotinic acid).

**Цейзеля реакция** Zeisel reaction.

**цейкент** *m.* (min.) zeuxite (probably tourmaline).

**цейланит** *m.* (min.) ceylanite, ceylonite, black spinel.

**цейлонский** *a.* Ceylon; ц. мох (bot.) Ceylon moss (*Gracilaria lichenoides*).

**Цейнера диаграмма** Zeuner valve diagram.

**цейнерит** *m.* (min.) zeunerite.

**Цейсса линза** Zeiss lens.

**цейхгауз** *m.* arsenal, armory.

**цек** *m.* crackle; crazing.

**цековка** *see* зенковка.

**целеби/ость** *f.* salubrity; curative property; —ый *a.* salutary, curative, medicinal, healing; salubrious, wholesome, healthful; —ое средство remedy.

**целев/ой** *a.* object, purpose; ц. взнос specific appropriation; —ая установка object.

**целесообразн/ость** *f.* expediency; —ый *a.* expedient; expeditious.

**целестин** *m.,* —овый *a.* (min.) celestine, celestite (strontium sulfate).

**целе/указание** *n.* target designation, target indication; —установка *f.* aim, object.

**целеустремленн/ость** *f.* purpose, endeavor; —ый *a.* purposeful; goal-seeking.

**целибуха** *see* рвотный орех.

**целидония** *f.* (bot.) greater celandine (*Chelidonium majus*).

**целик** *m.* pillar, block (of untouched ore); natural soil; (gun) sight.

**целиком** *adv.* wholly, totally, entirely, completely; ц. и полностью fully.

**целин/а** *f.* virgin soil; —ный *a.* virgin.

**целит** *m.* Celite (a diatomaceous earth).

**целительн/ость** *f.* salubrity; —ый *a.* healing, curative, medicinal; salubrious, wholesome; —ое средство remedy, medicament.

**цел/ить,** —иться *v.* aim (at), point (at), direct (at), allude (to); —кий *a.* aiming well, true.

**целлит** *m.* cellite (cellulose acetate plastic).

**целло/биоза,** —за *f.* cellobiose, cellose; —зольв *m.* Cellosolve, 2-ethoxyethanol; —зольвацетат *m.* Cellosolve

acetate; —идин *m.* celloidin, collodion wool; —н *m.,* —новый *a.* Cellon, tetrachloroethane; Cellon (a cellulose acetate plastic); —новая кислота cellonic acid; —тропин *m.* cellotropin, monobenzoyl-arbutin; —фан *m.* cellophane.

**целлул/оза** *see* целлюлоза; —оид *m.,* —оидный *a.* celluloid.

**целлюларный** *see* целлюлярный.

**целлюлоз/а** *f.,* —ный *a.* cellulose; (paper) pulp; ацетат —ы, уксусно-кислая ц. cellulose acetate; —ная смола cellulose pitch (from evaporation of sulfite liquor); —но-бумажный *a.* paper and pulp; —ность *f.* cellulosity.

**целлюлоид** *see* целлулоид.

**целлюлярн/ость** *f.* cellularity; —ый *a.* cellular.

**цел/ое** *n.* the whole, the entire; (math.) integer; в —ом upon the whole, in all, altogether; молекула в —ом the whole molecule, the entire molecule; за одно ц. in block, in one piece, unit; отлитый за одно ц. *see* цельнолитой.

**целозия** *f.* (bot.) celosia.

**целом** *m.* (zool.) coelom; *see also under* целое.

**целометр** *m.* (astron.) caelometer.

**целомные** *pl.* (zool.) Coelomata.

**целост/ность** *f.* completeness, entireness, entirety; —ный *a.* complete, entire; —ь *f.* wholeness, entireness, integrity; в —и completely, entirely; intact.

**цел/ый** *a.* whole, entire, integral, unbroken, complete, intact, sound; ц. и невредимый safe and sound; —ая величина integral; —ое число whole number, integer; по —ым неделям for weeks at a time.

**цел/ь** *f.* goal, aim, mark, target; intention, object, objective, end, purpose; задаваться —ью, поставить себе —ью *v.* aim (at); не достигающий —и ineffectual; отвечать —и *v.* answer the purpose; попадать в ц. *v.* hit the mark; с —ью with a view (to), in order (to); purposely, on purpose; указатель движущихся —ей moving target indicator.

**цельз/иан** *m.* (min.) celsian (a barium feldspar); **—ия** *f.* (bot.) celsia.

**цельно** *adv. and prefix* wholly, entirely, all, in a single piece; **—головые рыбы** (zool.) Holocephali; **—катаный** *a.* (met.) seamless rolled; **—кованый** *a.* seamless forged; **—крайний** *a.* entire; **—литой** *a.* (foundry) cast in block, unit cast, one-piece; **—металлический** *a.* all-metal; **—резиновый** *a.* all-rubber; **—сварной** *a.* all-welded; **—стальной** *a.* all-steel; **—сть** *f.* wholeness, entirety, totality, integrity; **—тянутый** *a.* seamless (pipe).

**цельный** *a.* whole, entire, integral, total; one-piece, solid; whole, unskimmed (milk).

**Цельсия термометр** centigrade thermometer; **Ц. шкала** Celsius (thermometer) scale, centigrade scale.

**цемент** *m.* cement; **ц.-пушка** cement gun.

**цементационн/ый** *a.* cementing; (met.) cementation, carbonization; **—ая печь** *see* цементовочная печь; **—ая смесь** carbonizer.

**цемент/ация** *f.* cementing; (met.) cementation, carburization, carbonization, case-hardening; contact deposition of copper from solution by zinc; **поверхностная ц.** casehardening; **—ирная печь** *see* цементовочная печь.

**цементиров/ание** *see* цементация; **—анный** *a.* cemented; (met.) carbonized, carburized, casehardened, cement (steel); **—ать** *v.* cement; carbonize, carburize, caseharden, subject to cementation; **—ать с поверхности** caseharden.

**цементирующ/ий** *a.* cementing; **ц. порошок** cement; **—ая связка** cement, bond; **—ое вещество** cement, bond; (met.) carbonizer.

**цементит** *m.* cementite (iron carbide).

**цементн/ый** *a.* cement; **ц. брус** cement block; **ц. мергель** cement rock; **ц. раствор** cement mortar; **—ая затирка** cement floor; **—ая медь** cement copper; **—ая печь** *see* цементовочная печь; **—ая сталь** (met.) cement steel, cementation steel, blister steel; **—ое молоко** cement grout.

**цементов/альный** *a.* cementing, cement; **—ание** *see* цементация; **—ать** *see* цементировать; **—очный** *a.* cementation; **—очная печь** (met.) cementation furnace.

**цемент/омет** *m.*, **—пушка** *f.* cement gun.

**цемянки** *pl.* broken brick, rubble, grog (added to mortars).

**цен/а** *f.* price, value, worth, cost, charge; **ц. без скидки** net price; **ц. деления** scale division; **—ою** at the cost (of); **крайние —ы** rock-bottom prices; **скидка —ы** discount.

**ценз** *m.*, **—овый** *a.* qualification, right.

**цензор** *m.* censor; **—ство** *n.* censorship.

**цензур/а** *f.* censorship; **дозволено —ой** licensed; **—ный** *a.* censorial; **—овать** *v.* censor, license.

**ценит/ель** *m.* appraiser, valuer, judge; **—ь** *v.* value, estimate, rate, appreciate; **высоко —ь** prize, rate high; **слишком высоко —ь** overrate; **—ься** *v.* be valued, be appreciated.

**ценн/ость** *f.* value, rate, price; importance; **—ый** *a.* valuable, negotiable; registered (mail).

**ценогенезис** *m.* (biol.) cenogenesis.

**ценоз** *m.* (med.) cenosis, morbid discharge.

**ценокрепис** *m.* (zool.) chalcid (*Caenocrepis bothynoderi*).

**цент** *m.* (acous., coin) cent.

**центаур/еидин** *m.* centaureidin; **—ин** *m.* centaurin (glucoside); centaurine (alkaloid).

**центи—** *see* санти—; **—бел** *m.* (acous.) centibel.

**центнер** *m.* centner, hundredweight (50 kg.; USSR—100 kg.).

**центр** *m.* center; nucleus (of crystal); **вращающийся ц., передний ц., подвижной ц.** live center; **задний ц., упорный ц.** fixed center; **между —ами** center to center; **неподвижный ц.** dead center; **установка по —у** center adjustment.

**централиз/ация** *f.* centralization; **—ировать, —овать** *v.* centralize; **—ованный** *a.* centralized.

**центральный** *a.* central, center.

**Центриздат** *abbr.* (Центральное издательство народов СССР) The Central

Publishing Office of the Peoples of the USSR.

**центрир/ование** *see* **центровка; —ованный** *a.* centered; **—овать** *v.* center; **—ующий** *a.* centering; **—ующее острие** center point.

**центрифуг/а** *f.* centrifuge, centrifugal machine, wringer; **—ирование** *n.* centrifugation, centrifugal separation; **—ированный** *a.* centrifuged; **—ировать, —овать** *v.* centrifuge.

**центробеж/ка** *f.* (centrifugal) extractor; **—но** *adv.* centrifugally, by centrifugal means.

**центробежн/ый** *a.* centrifugal; **ц. вентилятор** centrifugal fan; **ц. дезинтегратор** centrifugal mill; **ц. насос** centrifugal pump, rotary pump; **—ая сила** centrifugal force; **—ая форсунка** centrifugal atomizer.

**центров/альный** *a.* centering; **ц. станок** lathe for boring center holes in cylinders; **—ать** *see* **центрировать; —ка** *f.* centering, alignment, boring conical center holes; **линия —ки** center line; **производить —ку** *v.* center, align; **—очный** *a.* centering, center; **—очный циркуль** divider calipers; **—ый** *a.* center, central, centric.

**Центрогонти** *abbr.* (**Центральный государственный научно-технический институт**) State Central Institute of Technology.

**центро/ида** *f.* (astron.) centroid; **— клиналь** *f.* (geol.) centrocline; **— клинальный** *a.* centroclinal; **—план** *m.* center of airplane wing; **—сома** *f.* (biol.) centrosome.

**центростремительн/ость** *f.* centripetenсу; **—ый** *a.* centripetal; **—ая сила** centripetal force; **—ое ускорение** centripetal acceleration.

**центрофуга** *see* **центрифуга.**

**центура** *f.* center bit.

**ценуроз** *m.* (vet.) coenurosis, gid.

**цеолит** *m.* (min.) zeolite (division); **—изация** *f.* zeolitization; **—овый** *a.* zeolite, zeolitic; **—овая земля** mealy zeolite; **—ообразный** *a.* zeolitic.

**цеорин** *m.* zeorin.

**цеофиллит** *m.* (min.) zeophyllite (a hydrofluosilicate of calcium and iron).

**цеп** *m.* (agr.) flail.

**цепенатяжное устройство** chain tightener.

**цепенеть** *v.* grow torpid, be benumbed.

**цепень** *m.* tapeworm (*Taenia*).

**цеп/еобразный** *a.* chain-like; (biol.) catenate, catenulate; **—и** *gen., pl., etc. of* **цепь.**

**цеп/кий** *a.* cohesive, adhesive, tenacious; clutching, gripping; (zool.) prehensile, scansorial; trailing (plant); **—кость** *f.* cohesiveness, adhesiveness, tenacity; grasping, prehensility; **—лять** *v.* hook, catch hold (of); **—ляться** *v.* adhere, cling; clutch, grasp.

**цепни** *pl. of* **цепень.**

**цепн/ой** *a.* chain; (math.) catenary, catenarian; continued; ladder (network); suspension (bridge); **ц. блок, —ое колесо** sprocket, sprocket wheel; **ц. ключ** chain tongs (pipe wrench); **ц. тормоз** drag chain; **ц. транспортер** chain conveyer; **—ая линия** (math.) catenary; **—ая подача** chain feed; **—ая реакция** chain reaction; **—ое правило** (math.) chain rule; **— реагирующий** *a.* chain-reacting.

**цепоч/ка** *f.* chain, series, network; little chain; **—ный** *see* **цепной.**

**цеппелин** *m.* zeppelin, air ship.

**цеп/ь** *f.* chain; network; bond; (elec.) circuit; range (of mountains); **ц. атомов углерода** carbon chain; **вводить в ц.** *v.* (elec.) connect, connect up; **коэффициент —и** circuit factor.

**цераз/ин** *m.* cerasin; **—ит** *m.* (min.) cerasite (a variety of iolite).

**церан** *m.* cerane, isohexacosane.

**церанограф** *m.* (meteor.) ceraunograph.

**церат** *m.* cerate; **—ин** *m.* ceratin, keratin; **—иназа** *f.* ceratinase; **—ония** *f.* (bot.) carob (*Ceratonia*).

**цербер/етин** *m.* cerberetin; **—идин** *m.* cerberidin; **—ин** *m.* cerberin.

**церва** *f.* (bot.) dyer's rocket (*Reseda luteola*).

**цервантит** *m.* (min.) cervantite (an antimony tetroxide).

**церви/кальный** *a.* (anat.) cervical, neck; **—цит** *m.* (med.) cervicitis.

**церебр/альный** *a.* (anat.) cerebral, brain; **—ин** *m.* cerebrin; cerebrine, cerebrum siccum; **—иновая кислота** cerebric acid; —оза *f.* cerebrose, galactose; —озид *m.* cerebroside, galactoside; —он *m.* cerebron; —оновая кислота cerebronic acid; —оспинальный *a.* (med.) cerebrospinal.

**цере/вистерин** *m.* cerevisterol (a yeast sterol); —зин *m.* (min.) ceresin, ozocerite; —зит *m.* Ceresit (waterproofing compound).

**церемон/иальный** *a.* ceremonial, ceremonious; —иться *v.* stand upon ceremony; —ия *f.* ceremony.

**церера** *f.* (astron.) Ceres.

**церид** *m.* ceride; —ин *m.* ceridin, cerolin.

**цериев/ый** *a.* cerium, ceric; —ая земля ceria, cerium dioxide; —ая соль ceric salt.

**цериз** *m.* cerise, cherry red.

**цер/ий** *m.* cerium, Ce; азотнокислая закись —ия cerous nitrate; азотнокислая окись —ия ceric nitrate; закись —ия cerous oxide; соль закиси —ия cerous salt; окись —ия ceric oxide, cerium dioxide; соль окиси —ия ceric salt; углекислый ц. cerium carbonate, specif. cerous carbonate; фтористый ц. cerous fluoride; фторный ц. ceric fluoride; хлористый ц. cerous chloride; щавелевокислый ц. cerium oxalate, specif. cerous oxalate.

**церил** *m.* ceryl; —ен *m.* cerylene; —овый *a.* ceryl, cerylic; —овый спирт ceryl alcohol, 1-hexacosanol.

**церин** *m.* cerin (a sterol); cerotic acid; —овая кислота cerinic acid, cerotic acid.

**церист/ый** *a.* cerium, cerous; —ая соль cerous salt.

**церит** *m.* (min.) cerite.

**церк/а** *f.* (zool.) cercus; —оспореллез *m.* cercosporella infection (of plants); —оспороз *m.* cercospora infection.

**ЦЕРН** *abbr.* (Европейская организация ядерных исследований) European Organization for Nuclear Research, CERN.

**цернезьен** *m.* (geol.) Cernaysian.

**церо—** *prefix* cero—, wax; cerium, ceric; —вый *see* цериевый; —графия *f.* cerography, wax printing; —зин *m.* cerosin, cerosinyl cerosate; —зинил *m.* cerosinyl; —зиновая кислота cerosic acid, tetracosanic acid; соль

—зиновой кислоты, —зиновокислая соль cerosate; —ксилин *m.* ceroxylin; —леин *m.* cerolein; —лин *m.* cerolin; ceridin; —мелиссовая кислота ceromelissic acid.

**церот/ен** *m.* cerotene; —ин *m.* cerotin, ceryl cerotate; —иновая кислота cerotinic acid, cerotic acid, heptacosanoic acid; соль —иновой кислоты, —иновокислая соль cerotate; —ол *m.* cerotol, ceryl alcohol.

**церул/евая кислота** cerulic acid; —еин *m.* cerulein; —еит *m.* (min.) ceruleite; —игнол *m.* cerulignol; —игнон *m.* cerulignone, cedriret; —ин *m.* coeruline, soluble indigo.

**церуссит** *m.* (min.) cerussite, lead spar, white lead ore.

**цесарка** *f.* (zool.) guinea hen.

**цестоды** *pl.* (zool.) Cestoda.

**цет/ан** *m.* cetane, hexadecane; —ановое число cetane rating (of diesel oil); —ат *m.* cetate; —ен *m.* cetene, hexadecylene; —енилен *m.* cetenylene.

**цетил** *m.,* —овый *a.* cetyl, hexadecyl; хлористый ц., —хлорид cetyl chloride; —ен *m.* cetylene, cetene; —ид *m.* cetylide; —овая кислота cetylic acid, palmitic acid; соль —овой кислоты, —овокислая соль cetylate; —овый спирт cetyl alcohol, 1-hexadecanol; —овый эфир cetyl ether.

**цетин** *m.* cetin, cetyl cetylate; —овая кислота cetic acid.

**цетрар/ин** *m.,* —иновая кислота cetrarin, cetrarinic acid; —ия *f.* (bot.) cetraria; —овая кислота cetraric acid.

**цефал—, —о—** *prefix* cephal—, cephalo— (head); —ин *m.* cephalin, kephalin; —оподы *pl.* (zool.) Cephalopoda; —оспорин *m.* cephalosporin; —отаксус *m.* (bot.) cephalotaxus.

**цефарантин** *m.* cepharanthine.

**цефаровихит** *m.* (min.) zepharovichite (probably an impure wavellite).

**цефаэлин** *m.* cephaeline.

**цех** *m.* works, plant, mill; shop, workshop; department, section; trade corporation, trade union, guild; —и *pl.* works; —ком *m.* shop committee.

**цехов/ой** *a.* works; shop; department; —ое выражение shop term; —ые условия working conditions.

**цехштейн** *m.* (geol.) Zechstein, upper division of the Permian.

**цеце** *f.* tsetse (fly).

**цецидий** *m.* (bot., zool.) cecidium, gall.

**циамелид** *m.* cyamelide, *s*-trioxanetriimine.

**циан** *m.* cyanogen, ethane dinitrile; **хлористый ц.** cyanogen chloride.

**циан**— *prefix* cyan—, cyano—, cyanic; **—амид** *m.*, **—амидный** *a.* cyanamide, cyanogen amide; **—амид кальция** calcium cyanamide; **—анилид** *m.* cyananilide, phenyl cyanamide; **—ат** *m.* cyanate; **—бензил** *m.* cyanbenzyl; **—газ** *m.* hydrogen cyanide; **—гидрин** *m.*, **—гидринный** *a.* cyanohydrin.

**цианид** *m.*, **—ный** *a.* cyanide; **черный ц.** *see* **цианплав**; **—ин** *m.* cyanidin (an anthocyanidin); cyanidine; **—ный процесс** cyanide process (of gold extraction).

**циан/изация** *f.*, **—ирование** *n.* (met.) cyanidation, cyaniding; cyanation; **—изировать** *v.* cyanide; **—ин** *m.* cyanin; cyanine, quinoline blue.

**цианистоводородн/ый** *a.* hydrocyanic; hydrocyanide (of); **—ая кислота** hydrocyanic acid; **соль —ой кислоты** cyanide.

**цианист/ый** *a.* cyanogen, cyano—; (lower or —ous) cyanide (of); *see also* **синеродистый**; **ц. водород** hydrogen cyanide; **ц. калий** potassium cyanide; **—ая кислота** hydrocyanic acid.

**цианит** *see* **кианит.**

**цианкали** *n.* potassium cyanide; **желтое ц.** potassium ferrocyanide; **красное ц.** potassium ferricyanide.

**цианкобаламин** *m.* cyanocobalamin, vitamin $B_{12}$.

**циано**— *prefix* cyano—; *see also* **циан**—; **—воаммониевая соль** ammonium cyanate.

**циановодород** *m.* hydrogen cyanide; **—ный** *see* **цианистоводородный.**

**цианово/калиевая соль** potassium cyanate; **—кислый** *a.* cyanic acid; cyanate (of); **—кислый цинк, —цинковая соль** zinc cyanate; **—кислая соль** cyanate; **—натриевая соль** sodium cyanate.

**цианов/ый** *a.* cyanic, cyanogen; (higher or —ic) cyanide (of); *see also* **синеродный**; **—ая кислота** cyanic acid; **соль —ой кислоты** cyanate; **—ая ртуть** mercuric cyanide; **—ые водоросли** (bot.) Cyanophyceae.

**циано/генератор** *m.* hydrogen cyanide generator; **—з** *m.* (med.) cyanosis; **—какодил** *m.* cacodyl cyanide; **—кись** *f.* oxycyanide; **—л** *m.*, **—ловый** *a.* cyanol, aniline; **—метр** *m.* cyanometer; **—типия** *f.* (phot.) cyanotype (process), blueprinting; **—уксусная кислота** cyanoacetic acid; **—форм** *m.* cyanoform, tricyanomethane.

**циан/плав** *m.* calcium and sodium cyanide mixture; **—угольная кислота** cyanocarbonic acid, cyanformic acid; **—уксусная кислота** cyanoacetic acid; **—уксусноэтиловый эфир** ethyl cyanoacetate; **—этилирование** *n.* cyanoethylation; **—урамид** *m.* cyanuramide; **—урин** *m.* cyanurin; **—уровая кислота** cyanuric acid; **соль —уровой кислоты** cyanurate.

**ЦИАТИМ** *abbr.* (Центральный научно-исследовательский институт авиационных топлив и масел) Central Scientific Research Institute of Aviation Fuels and Lubricants.

**циба** *f.* ciba (dye).

**цибет** *m.* (zool.) civet, civet cat; **—он** *m.* civetone, 9-cycloheptadecen-1-one.

**циботактический** *a.* cybotactic (arrangement of molecules).

**цивет** *see* **цибет.**

**цивилиз/ация** *f.* civilization; **—ованный** *a.* civilized; **—овать** *v.* civilize.

**цивильный** *a.* civil.

**цигад/енин** *m.* zygadenine; **—ит** *m.* (min.) zygadite (a variety of albite feldspar).

**цигер** *m.* cheese albumin.

**цигнолин** *m.* Cignolin, 1,8,9-anthratriol.

**цигота** *f.* (biol.) zygote.

**—цид** *suffix* **—**cide; **—ный** *a.* *suffix* —cidal.

**цидонин** *m.* cydonin (gum).

**циейзен** *see* **циэйзен.**

**цикад/а** *f.* (zool.) cicada; (bot.) cycad; **певчие —ы** (zool.) Cicadidae; **—ка** *f.* leaf hopper (*Cicadellida*); **—овые** *pl.* (zool.) Cicadidae; (bot.) Cycadaceae.

**цикл** *m.* cycle, cycle process; round,

circuit; ring; period; **испытавший ц.** cycled; **разрыв —а** (chem.) ring cleavage.

**цикламен** *m.* (bot.) cyclamen.

**цикл/амин** *m.* cyclamin, arthranitin; **—аминол** *m.* cyclaminol; **—амиретин** *m.* cyclamiretin; **—ан** *m.* cyclane, naphthene; **—еин** *m.* cycleine; **—ен** *m.* cyclene; **—ид** *m.* (geom.) cyclide; **—изация** *f.* cyclization, ring formation.

**циклина** *f.* scraper.

**циклит** *m.* cyclite, benzyl bromide.

**циклич/еский** *a.* cycle, cyclic; continuous; circular-orbit; **—еская кривая** cycle curve; **—еского типа** batch (dissolver); **—еское соединение** cyclic compound; **—ность** *f.* cycle of operations.

**цикло—** *prefix* cyclo— (circle; cycle; cyclic compound); **—бутан** *m.* cyclobutane, tetramethylene; **—бутен** *m.* cyclobutene; **—бутил** *m.* cyclobutyl.

**циклогекс/адиен** *m.* cyclohexadiene, dihydrobenzene; **—ан** *m.* cyclohexane, hexamethylene; **—анол** *m.* cyclohexanol, Hexalin; **—ен** *m.* cyclohexene, 1,2,3,4-tetrahydrobenzene; **—ил** *m.* cyclohexyl.

**циклоген/ез** *m.* (meteor.) cyclogenesis, development of a cyclone; **—етический** *a.* cyclogenetic.

**циклогепт/ан** *m.* cycloheptane, suberane; **—анол** *m.* cycloheptanol, suberol; **—ен** *m.* cycloheptene, suberene.

**циклоид/а** *f.* (geom.) cycloid; **—альный, —ный** *a.* cycloid, cycloidal.

**циклометр** *m.* cyclometer, revolution counter; **—ический** *a.* cyclometric; **—ия** *f.* cyclometry.

**циклон** *m.*, **—ный** *a.* (meteor.) cyclone; (min.) cyclone, dust extractor; (fumigation) a cyanide-impregnated absorbent; **—ический** *a.* cyclone, cyclonic; **—ообразование** *see* **циклогенез.**

**цикло/октадиен** *m.* cyclooctadiene; **—олефин** *m.* cycloölefin; **—пальдовая кислота** cyclopaldic acid; **—парафин** *m.* cycloparaffin, naphthene.

**циклопент/адиен** *m.* cyclopentadiene; **—ан** cyclopentane, pentamethylene;

**—ен** *m.* cyclopentene; **—ил** *m.* cyclopentyl.

**циклоп/ин** *m.* cyclopin; **—ит** *m.* (min.) cyclopite (a variety of anorthite); **—ический** *a.* cyclopean, gigantic; **—оловая кислота** cyclopolic acid.

**циклопроп/ан** *m.* cyclopropane, trimethylene; **—ен** *m.* cyclopropene; **—ил** *m.* cyclopropyl.

**цикло/птерин** *m.* cyclopterin; **—ран** *m.* cycloran (detergent); **—строфический** *a.* (meteor.) cyclostrophic; **—трон** *m.*, **—тронный** *a.* (nucl.) cyclotron (an accelerator).

**цикля** *f.* scraper.

**циковка** *see* **зенковка.**

**цикор/ий** *m.*, **—иевый** *a.* (bot.) chicory (*Cichorium* spec. *C. intybus*); **салатный ц.** endive (*C. endivia*).

**цикут/а** *f.* (bot.) water hemlock (*Cicuta virosa*); **—ен** *m.* cicutene; **—ин** *m.* cicutine; **—оксин** *m.* cicutoxin.

**цилиндр** *m.* cylinder, roller, roll, drum; (urine) cast; (Faraday) cup; **тело —а** cylinder barrel; **—ический** *a.* cylindrical; **—овый** *a.* cylinder; **—оида** *f.* (geom.) cylindroid; **—осверлильный** *a.* cylinder-boring; **—ошлифовальный** *a.* cylinder-grinding; **—сток** *m.* heavy cylinder oil.

**циллой** *m.* Zilloy, prime western zinc.

**ЦИМ** *abbr.* (Центральный институт материалов) Central Institute of Materials; (Центральный институт металлов) Central Institute of Metals.

**цимал** *m.* Zimal (zinc-base alloy).

**цимар/игенин** *m.* cymarigenin; **—ин** *m.* cymarin; **—иновая кислота** cymaric acid; **—оза** *f.* cymarose, 3-methyldigitoxose.

**циматолит** *m.* (min.) cymatolite (a variety of altered spodumene).

**цименил** *m.* cymenyl, cymyl.

**цимет** *m.* Cimet (a chrome iron).

**цимидин** *m.* cymidine, carvacrylamine.

**цимил** *m.* cymyl.

**цими/нит** *m.* (petr.) ciminite (latiteporphyrite); **—цин** *m.* cimicin; **—циновая кислота** cimicic acid; **—фугин** *m.* cimicifugin, macrotin.

**цимоген** *m.* cymogene (butane product).

**цимол** *m.* cymene, isopropyltoluene.

**цимолиз** *see* **зимолиз.**

**цимолит** *m.* (min.) cimolite (a clay).

**цимофан** *m.* (min.) cymophane, chrysoberyl.

**цинанхотоксин** *m.* cynanchotoxin.

**цинапин** *m.* cynapine.

**цинаш** *m.* tin ashes, stannic oxide.

**цинвальдит** *m.* (min.) zinnwaldite (an iron-lithia mica).

**цинга** *f.* (med.) scurvy.

**цингерон** *m.* zingerone.

**цингибер/ен** *m.* zingiberene, 1-methyl-4-propenyl cyclohexane; **—ол** *m.* zingiberol.

**цинготн/ый** *a.* (med.) scorbutic; **—ая трава** scurvy grass (*Cochlearia*).

**цинен** *m.* cinene, limonene; **—овая кислота** cinenic acid.

**цинеол, —ь** *m.* cineole, eucalyptole; **—овая кислота** cineolic acid.

**цинерария** *f.* (bot.) cineraria.

**цинк** *m.* zinc, Zn; **азотнокислый ц.** zinc nitrate; **иодистый ц.** zinc iodide; **окись —а** zinc oxide; **сернокислый ц., сульфат —а** zinc sulfate; **хлористый ц.** zinc chloride; **хромовокислый ц.** zinc chromate.

**цинк/алкил** *m.* zinc alkyl; **—амид** *m.* zinc-amide; **—ат** *m.* zincate; **—вейс** *m.* zinc white, zinc oxide; **—грау** *n.* zinc gray; **—дибраунит** *m.* (min.) zinc-dibraunite (a variety of braunite); **—диэтил** *see* **цинкэтил; —енит** *m.* (min.) zinkenite; **—иодэтил** *m.* zinc ethyliodide; **—ит** *m.* (min.) zincite, red oxide of zinc; **—метил** *m.* zinc methyl, dimethylzinc.

**цинков/альный** *a.* galvanizing; **—ание** *n.* zincing, zinc plating, galvanizing; **—анный** *a.* zinc-plated, galvanized; **—ать** *v.* zinc, zinc-plate, galvanize.

**цинково/кислый** *a.* zincic acid; zincate (of); **ц. натрий, —натриевая соль** sodium zincate; **—кислая соль** zincate; **—кобальтовая соль** cobalt zincate.

**цинковщик** *m.* zinc metallurgist.

**цинков/ый** *a.* zinc; **ц. железный шпат** (min.) ferriferous smithsonite; **ц. желтый, ц. крон** zinc yellow, zinc chromate; **ц. купорос** zinc vitriol, zinc sulfate; (min.) goslarite; **ц. цвет** zinc flowers, zinc oxide; **ц. шпат** (min.) zinc spar, smithsonite; **—ая зеленая** zinc green, cobalt green; **—ая кислота** zincic acid; **соль —ой кислоты** zincate; **—ая обманка** (min.) zinc blende, sphalerite; **—ая окись** zinc oxide; **—ая окшара** blue powder (zinc dust); **—ая пыль** zinc dust; **—ая соль** zinc salt; **—ая шпинель** (min.) zinc spinel, gahnite; **—ое масло** zinc butter, zinc chloride; **—ые белила** zinc white, zinc oxide; **—ые огарки** zinc ash, zinc calx; **—ые цветы** (min.) zinc bloom, hydrozincite.

**цинкограф** *m.* zincograph; **—ический** *a.* zincographic; **—ия** *f.* zincography, etching on zinc.

**цинк/одестилляционная печь** zinc distillation furnace, zinc furnace; **—озит** *m.* (min.) zinkosite (zinc sulfate); **—оплавильный завод** zinc smelter, zinc works; **—органическое соединение** organic zinc compound; **—этил** *m.* zinc ethyl, diethyl zinc.

**циннам/ал, —аль, —альдегид** *m.* cinnamaldehyde; **—ат** *m.* cinnamate; **—еин** *m.* cinnamein, benzyl cinnamate; **—ен** *m.* cinnamene, styrene; **—енил** *m.* cinnamenyl, styryl.

**циннамил** *m.*, **—овый** *a.* cinnamyl; **хлористый ц.** cinnamyl chloride; **—овая кислота** cinnamylic acid, cinnamic acid; **—овый спирт** cinnamyl alcohol, cinnamic alcohol.

**циннамо/ил** *m.* cinnamoyl; **—мум** *m.* (bot.) cinnamon (*Cinnamomum*); **—н** *m.* cinnamone, styryl ketone; **—нитрил** *m.* cinnamonitrile.

**цинния** *f.* (bot.) zinnia.

**циннолин** *m.* cinnoline, 1,2-benzodiazine; **—овая кислота** cinnolic acid.

**циновка** *see* **цыновка.**

**цино/глосин** *m.* cynoglossine; **—дин** *m.* cynodine; **—ктонин** *m.* cynoctonine; **—токсин** *m.* cynotoxin.

**циноп** *see* **цинаш.**

**цинубель** *m.* roughing plane.

**цинур/еновая кислота** cynurenic acid; **—ин** *m.* cynurine.

**цинх/аин** *m.* cinchaine, *i*-propylhydrocupreine; **—амидин** *m.* cinchamidine, hydrocinchonidine; **—ен** *m.* cinchene.

**цинхо/дубильная кислота** cinchotannic acid, quinotannic acid; **—л** *m.* cinchol;

—**лепидин** *m.* cincholepidine; —**лин** *m.* cincholine; —**лойпон** *m.* cincholoipone; —**мероновая кислота** cinchomeronic acid.

**цинхон/а** *f.* cinchona (bark); —**амин** *m.* cinchonamine; —**ан** *m.* cinchonane, desoxycinchonine; —**идин** *m.* cinchonidine, chinidine; —**илин** *m.* cinchoniline; —**ин** *m.* cinchonine; —**иновая кислота** cinchoninic acid, 4-quinolinecarboxylic acid; —**ицин** *m.* cinchonicine, cinchotoxine; —**овая кислота** cinchonic acid.

**цинхотени/дин** *m.* cinchotenidine; —**н** *m.* cinchotenine; —**цин** *m.* cinchotenicine.

**цинхо/тин** *m.* cinchotine, hydrocinchonine; —**токсин** *m.* cinchotoxine; —**тропин** *m.* cinchotropin; —**фен** *m.* cinchophen, atophan; —**церотин** *m.* cinchocerotin.

**цинциннатьян** *m.* (geol.) Cincinnatian.

**ципол/ин, —лин** *m.* (min.) cipolino marble, muscovite marble.

**циппеит** *m.* zippeite (uranium mineral).

**циприн** *m.* (min.) cyprine (a variety of vesuvianite).

**циралит** *m.* Ziralit (a zirconia-alumina refractory).

**цирен** *m.* salt pan.

**цирин** *see* **алланит.**

**цирк** *m.* circus; (geol.) cirque.

**циркаллой** *m.* Zircalloy (a zirconium alloy).

**циркелит** *m.* (min.) zirkelite.

**цирковой** *a.* circus; (geol.) cirque.

**циркон** *m.* (min.) zircon (zirconium silicate); **ц.-фавас** *m.* (min.) zircon favas; —**иат** *m.* zirconate.

**циркониев/ый** *a.* zirconium; *see also* **цирконовый;** —**ая земля** zirconia, zirconium oxide; —**ая соль** zirconium salt.

**циркон/ий** *m.* zirconium, Zr; **двуокись** —**ия, окись** —**ия** zirconium dioxide, zirconium oxide, zirconia; **сернокислый ц., сульфат** —**ия** zirconium sulfate; **хлористый ц.** zirconium chloride.

**циркон/ил** *m.* zirconyl; **хлористый ц.** zirconyl chloride, zirconium oxychloride; —**истый** *a.* zirconium.

**цирконов/ый** *a.* zirconium, zirconic; **ц.**

**ангидрид** zirconic anhydride, zirconium oxide; —**ая кислота** zirconic acid, zirconium hydroxide; **соль** —**ой кислоты** zirconate.

**циркообразный** *a.* (geol.) cirque.

**циркулин** *m.* Circulin (antibiotic).

**циркулир/овать** *v.* circulate; —**ующий** *a.* circulating, circulation; distributing.

**циркуль** *m.* dividers; calipers; compass (for drawing); **делительный ц., измерительный ц., разметочный ц.** dividers; **калиберный ц.** calipers.

**циркуляр** *m.* circular; —**ка** *f.* circular saw; —**ный** *a.* circular; circulatory, circulating.

**циркулятор** *m.* circulator.

**циркуляц/ионный** *a.* circulation, circulating; **ц. насос** circulating pump; **ц. подогреватель** circulation feed water heater; —**ия** *f.* circulation; circuit; **котел с** —**ей** circulation boiler.

**циров/ание** *n.,* —**ка** *f.* engine turning, guilloche; —**ать** *v.* engine-turn.

**цирроз** *m.* (med.) cirrhosis.

**цирролит** *m.* (min.) cirrolite, kirrolite.

**циртолит** *m.* (min.) cyrtolite (a form of altered zircon).

**цирцея** *f.* (bot.) circaea.

**цис—** *prefix* cis—.

**цискон** *m.* Ziscon (aluminum-zinc alloy).

**цис-соединение** *n. cis*-compound.

**циссоида** *f.* (math.) cissoid.

**цист/а** *f.* (biol.) cyst; —**амин** *m.* cystamine, hexamethylenetetramine; —**еин** *m.* cysteine, β-mercaptoalanine; —**еиновая кислота** cysteic acid.

**цистерна** *f.* cistern, reservoir, tank; **вагон-ц.** (railroad) tank car.

**цис-терпин** *m. cis*-terpine.

**цист/ин** *m.* cystine; —**ит** *m.* (med.) cystitis; —**ицеркоз** *m.* cysticercosis, cysticercus infestation; —**опурин** *m.* cystopurin; —**оскоп** *m.* (surgery) cystoscope.

**цис-транс-изомерия** *f. cis-trans*-isomerism.

**ЦИТ** *abbr.* (**Центральный институт труда**) Central Institute of Labor.

—**цит** *m. suffix* (biol.) —cyte (cell).

**цитаза** *f.* cytase.

**цитарин** *m.* Citarin.

**цитата** *f.* citation, quotation.

**цитвар/ь** *f.*, —**ный** *a.* (bot.) santonica, worm seed (*Artemisia maritima*); —**ный корень** zedoary (rhizome of *Curcuma zedoaria*); —**ное масло** wormseed oil; zedoary oil; —**ное семя** wormseed, santonica; zedoary seed.

**цити/диловая кислота** cytidylic acid; —**дин** *m.* cytidine, cytosine riboside; —**зин** *m.* cytisine, ulexine.

**цитиров/ание** *n.* citation, quotation; —**ать** *v.* cite, quote, extract.

**цититон** *m.* (pharm.) cytisine solution.

**цито**— *prefix* (biol.) cyto— (cell; cytoplasm); —**ген** *m.* cytogene; —**генетика** *f.* cytogenetics; —**диагностика** *f.* (med.) cytodiagnosis; —**зин** *m.*, —**зиновый** *a.* cytosine; —**лиз** *m.* cytolysis, dissolution of cells; —**лизин** *m.* cytolysin; —**логия** *f.* cytology; —**плазма** *f.* cytoplasm; —**плазматический** *a.* cytoplasmic; —**токсин** *m.* cytotoxin; —**хром** *m.* cytochrome.

**цитравинная кислота** citratartaric acid.

**цитракон/ил** *m.* citraconyl; —**овая кислота** citraconic acid, methylmaleic acid; —**овый ангидрид** citraconic anhydride.

**цитр/ал** —**аль** *m.* citral, geranial; —**амид** *m.* citramide; —**анилид** *m.* citranilide; —**аниловая кислота** citranilic acid; —**ат** *m.*, —**атно**— *prefix*, —**атный** *a.* citrate; —**ен** *m.* citrene; —**идиновая кислота** citridic acid, aconitic acid; —**ил** *m.* cityryl, lemon oil.

**цитрин** *m.* citrin, vitamin P; citrine ointment, mercuric nitrate ointment; (min.) citrine (a yellow variety of quartz); —**ин** *m.* citrinin.

**цитро/ванилин, —ваниль** *m.* citrovanillin; —**мицетин** *m.* citromycetin, frequentic acid; —**н** *m.* (bot.) citron (*Citrus medica*); —**нат** *m.* candied citron or lemon peel.

**цитронелл/а** *f.* citronella grass (*Cymbopogon nardus*); —**ал, —аль** *m.* citronellal, citronellaldehyde; —**ил** *m.* citronellyl; —**илацетат** *m.*, —**иловый эфир уксусной кислоты** citronellyl acetate; —**овая кислота** citronellic acid; —**овое масло** citronella oil; —**ол** *m.* citronellol.

**цитро/нил** *m.* citronyl, citronella oil;

—**нин** *m.* citronin, dinitrodiphenylamine; —**фен** *m.* citrophen.

**цитрулл/ин** *m.* citrulline; citrullin, colocynthin; —**ол** *m.* citrullol.

**цитрус** *m.*, —**овый** *a.* (bot.) citrus; —**овые** *pl.* Aurantiaceae.

**циттавит** *m.* (min.) zittavite (a variety of lignite).

**циферблат** *m.*, —**ный** *a.* dial, dial plate, face; —**ный индикатор** dial gage.

**цифр/а** *f.* cipher, figure, number, numeral, character; digit; **обозначать** —**ами** *v.* figure; —**ователь** *m.*, —**овая машина, —овой вычислитель** digital computer; —**овой** *a.* cipher; numbered, figured; digital; —**овые данные** figures, numerical data.

**цицания** *f.* (bot.) wild rice (*Zizania*).

**цицеро** *n.* (тур.) pica.

**цицеров/ая кислота** ciceric acid; **соль** —**ой кислоты, —окислая соль** cicerate.

**циэйзен** *m.* die, draw plate.

**ЦК** *abbr.* (Центральный комитет) Central Committee.

**цмин** *m.* (bot.) everlasting (*Helichrysum*).

**ЦНИГРИ** *abbr.* (Центральный научно-исследовательский горноразведочный институт) Central Scientific Research Mining-Prospecting Institute; **ЦНИИКОП** *abbr.* (Центральный научно-исследовательский институт консервной и овощесушильной промышленности) Central Research Institute of the Canning and Vegetable Drying Industry; **ЦНИИЧМ** *abbr.* (Центральный научно-исследовательский институт черной металлургии) Central Scientific Research Institute of Ferrous Metallurgy; **ЦНИКП** *abbr.* (Центральный научно-исследовательский институт кожевенной промышленности) Central Research Institute of the Leather Industry; **ЦНИЛхимстрой** *abbr.* (Центральный научно-исследовательская лаборатория стройматериалов химической промышленности) Central Scientific Research Laboratory of Construction Materials of the Chemical Industry.

**ЦНС** *abbr.* (центральная нервная система) central nervous system.

**цоизит** *m.* (min.) zoisite.

**цойсия** *f.* lawn grass (*Zoysia*); **ц.-матрелла** *f.* Manila grass (*Z. matrella*).

**цокол/евка** *f.*, **—евочный** *a.* basing, base; **—ь** *m.*, **—ьный** *a.* foundation, base, pedestal; socle, block; socket, base (of electric bulb).

**ЦОС** *abbr.* (**Центральная опытная станция**) Central Experiment Station.

**Ц-система** *f.* center-of-mass system.

**ЦСУ** *abbr.* (**Центральное статистическое управление**) Central Statistical Bureau; **ЦСУА** *abbr.* (**Центральная станция удобрений и агропочвоведения**) Central Station of Fertilizers and Agronomical Soil Science.

**цуг** *m.* train (of waves).

**цуга** *see* **тсуга**.

**цукат** *m.* candied peel.

**цунами** *f.* tsunami, seismic sea wave.

**цуниит** *m.* (min.) zunyite.

**цынг—** *see* **цинг—**.

**цыновка** *f.* mat.

**цыпл/енок** *m.* chick, baby chicken; **—ята** *pl.* chicks; **—ячий** *a.* chicken.

**ЦЭС** *abbr.* (**Центральный электротехнический совет**) Central Electro-Technical Council; (**центральная электростанция**) central electric power plant·

**Цюрих** Zurich.

# Ч

**ч.** *abbr.* (**час**) hour; (**часть**) part.

**чаб/ер** *m.* (bot.) savory (*Satureia*, spec. *S. hortensis*); **—рец** *m.* thyme (*Thymus*).

**чави—** *see* **шави—**.

**чавыча** *f.* quinnat, king salmon.

**чад** *m.* smoke, fumes; steam; **—ить** *v.* smoke, fume; steam.

**чаеподобный** *a.* tea-like.

**чай** *m.* tea; tea plant (*Thea*); infusion; **китайский ч.** *see* **чайное дерево**.

**чайка** *f.* (zool.) sea gull, tern.

**чайн/ик** *m.* teapot; **—ые** *pl.* (bot.) Theaceae; **—ый** *a.* tea; infusion; **—ый настой, —ый отвар** tea infusion; **—ое дерево** (bot.) tea plant (*Thea sinensis*).

**чайот** *m.* (bot.) chayote (*Sechium edule*).

**чалка** *f.* fastening cord, mooring.

**чалт/ык** *m.*, **—ычная почва** chaltyk (soil).

**чальмерзит** *m.* (min.) chalmersite (identical with cubanite).

**чан** *m.*, **—овый** *a.* vat, tub, tank; trough, pit; **ч.-фильтр** filter tank, filtering basin.

**чарка** *f.* glass, jigger (of liquor), a unit of liquid measure equal to 0.123 liter.

**чарнокит** *m.* (petr.) charnockite (hypersthene granite).

**чаровница** *see* **черноцвет**.

**час** *m.* hour; **—ы** *pl.* hours; clock, watch; 12 **—ов дня** twelve o'clock, noon; **через ч.** in an hour.

**часов/ой** *a.* one hour's, an hour's; clock, watch; *m.* sentinel, sentry, watch, guard; **ч. механизм** clockwork; **ч. пояс** time zone; **—ая стрелка** hour hand (of clock); **по ч. стрелке** clockwise, from left to right; **против ч. стрелки** counterclockwise, from right to left; **—ое дело** horology; **—ое масло** watch oil, neat's-foot oil; **—ое стекло** watch glass, (large size) clock glass; **—щик** *m.* watch maker, clock maker, horologist.

**часовъярский** *a.* Chasov Yar.

**части** *gen.*, *pl.*, etc. *of* **часть**.

**части/ца** *f.* particle, bit, grain, fraction, speck, corpuscle; molecule; **ч.-мишень** *f.* target particle; **ч.-предшественник** *m.* precursor; **—чка** *f.* particle, very fine particle, spicule.

**частичн/о** *adv.* partially, partly, incompletely; **—ый** *a.* partial, fractional; particle, particulate; corpuscular, molecular; **—ый платеж** instalment; **—ая формула** molecular formula.

**частное** *n.* (math.) quotient.

**частност/ь** *f.* particularity; **в —и** in particular; **останавливаться на —ях** *v.* dwell on details, particularize.

**части/ый** *a.* private; partial; peculiar, exceptional, individual, particular; **—ая производная** (math.) partial derivative; **—ая собственность** private property; **—ым образом** privately, confidentially, unofficially.

**часто** *adv.* often, constantly, frequently;

close, thickly; —**кол** *m.* paling, palisade.

**частомер** *m.* (elec.) frequency meter.

**частот/а** *f.*, frequency; thickness, closeness; periodicity; **ч. среза, пограничная ч., предельная ч.** (elec.) cut-off frequency; **диапазон частот, полоса частот** frequency band; **печь большой —ы** high-frequency furnace; **печь малой —ы** low-frequency furnace; **ток высокой —ы** high-frequency current; **ток низкой —ы** low-frequency current.

**частотн/о-временной** *a.* time-and-frequency; —**о-зависимый** *a.* frequency-dependent, frequency-sensitive; —**о-импульсный** *a.* pulse-frequency; —**о-модулированный** *a.* frequency-modulated; —**ый** *a.* frequency; —**ая характеристика** frequency response; **с —ой модуляцией** frequency-modulated, f-m.

**частотомер** *m.* (elec.) frequency meter.

**частух/а** *f.* (bot.) water plantain (*Alisma*); —**овые** *pl.* Alismaceae.

**частый** *a.* frequent, dense, thick; (text.) close-woven; quick (pulse).

**част/ь** *f.* part, portion, share, fraction, proportion; fragment, piece, segment; member; department, section; step, stage; **ч. целого** integrant, component; —**ей на** parts per; —**ью** partly; **большей —ью** for the most part; **большая ч.** the greater part, the majority; **на —и** apart, to pieces; **разобрать на —и** *v.* take apart, dismantle; **одна пятая ч.** one fifth; **по —и** in connection (with); **по —ам** in parts, in instalments; piecemeal; partially; **интегрирование по —ям** (math.) partial integration.

**часы** *pl.* of **час**; **ч.-хронометр** timekeeper, timepiece.

**чаталы** *pl.* props (for fruit trees).

**чатертоновский** *see under* **Четтертона**.

**чаулмугр**— *see* **хаульмугр**—.

**чах/лость** *f.* weakness, unhealthiness; —**лый** *a.* weak, consumptive; stunted, dwarfed (vegetation); —**нуть** *v.* fade away, wither away.

**чахот/ка** *f.* (med.) consumption, pulmonary tuberculosis; —**очный** *a.* consumptive, tubercular.

**чаша** *f.* bowl, cup; dish, basin, pan; beaker.

**чаше/видный,** —**образный** *a.* cup-shaped, cup; bowl-shaped; —**листник** *m.* (bot.) sepal; —**цветник** *m.* (bot.) calycanthus.

**чашеч/ка** *f.* small cup; (bot.) calyx, bell; —**ный** *a.* cup-shaped, cup.

**чашк/а** *f.* cup, bowl; (Petri) dish; pan (of balance); (knee) cap; bob (of pendulum); housing; cistern (of barometer); —**ообразный** *a.* cup-shaped, cup.

**чаща** *f.* thicket, brushwood, brake, jungle.

**чаще** *comp. of* **часто, частый,** more often, more frequently; **ч. всего** mostly; **как можно ч.** as often as possible.

**чв-ч** *abbr.* (**человекочас**) man-hour.

**ч.д.а.** *abbr.* (**чистый для анализа**) analytical grade (reagent).

**чебак** *m.* bream (fish).

**чебер** *see* **чабер.**

**чебрец** *see* **чабрец.**

**чевкинит** *m.* (min.) tscheffkinite, chevkinite.

**чего** *gen. of* **что**, what.

**чеддит** *m.* (expl.) cheddite.

**чей** *pron. m.*, **чье** *n.*, **чья** *f.*, **чьи** *pl.* whose.

**чек** *m.* check; (agr.) check plot; rice field.

**чек/а** *f.* pin, pin bolt, cotter, cotter pin, key, wedge, chock; splint; **закрепить —ой** *v.* key.

**чекан** *m.* stamp, die; coinage, coin; calker; chisel; —**ить** *v.* stamp, hammer; mint, coin; engrave, chisel, chase, emboss; calk; (agr.) pinch out, pick out; —**ка** *f.* stamping, die stamping; engraving, chasing, relief work; fullering, calking; beading (of pipes); calking chisel, calking iron; fullering tool; pinching (of plants); chopping (of cotton); —**ный** *a.* stamped; coined; engraved, chased; calked; —**ная работа** stamping; relief work, embossing.

**чеканочный** *a.* stamping; coining; calking; **ч. молоток** set hammer; **ч. пресс** stamping press, coining press; embossing press; **ч. штамп** embossing die.

**чеканщик** *m.* stamper; coiner; chaser; calker.

**чекмарная соль** (geol.) partly solidified, recently deposited salt.

**чекмарь** *m.* rammer, beater; smoother.

**чековая книжка** check book.

**челибуха** *see* **чилибуха.**

**Челлин/а печь** *see* **Кьеллина печь; —и гало** (meteor.) Cellini's halo.

**челн, —ок** *m.,* **—очный** *a.* shuttle, rabbit; canoe, dug-out; **—окодержатель** *m.* shuttle carrier; **—очная жила** (min.) wavy vein; **—очница** *f.* (weaving) breast beam end; **—оч-ницы** *pl.* (zool.) Cymbidae.

**человек** *m.* man, person, human being; **сила —а** manpower; **—одень** *m.* man-day; **—очас** *m.* man-hour.

**человеч/ек** *m.* manikin, dummy; **—е-ский** *a.* human; **—еский род** mankind; **—ество** *n.* mankind, humanity; **—ный** *a.* human, man's.

**челюст/ной** *a.* jaw; (anat.) maxillary; **—ь** *f.* jaw, jaw bone; **верхняя —ь** maxilla; **нижняя —ь** mandible.

**чем** *instr. of* **что,** with what, what; *conj.* than, more; **ч. дальше, тем хуже** from bad to worse; **ч. позже, тем лучше** the later the better; **о ч.?** what about, of what? **он не при ч.** he has nothing to do with it; **остаться не при ч.** *v.* lose.

**чемерица** *f.* (bot.) false hellebore (*Veratrum*).

**чемодан** *m.* suitcase.

**чемплэн** *m.* (geol.) Champlainian period, middle Ordivician.

**чему** *dat. of* **что,** to what; **к ч.** to what; what for, why.

**ченевиксит** *m.* (min.) chenevixite.

**чепец** *m.* cap.

**Чепмана насос** Chapman pump.

**чепманайзинг-процесс** *m.* Chapmanizing process (nitriding of iron or steel).

**чепрак** *m.* back of hide; saddle cloth.

**чепуха** *f.* nonsense.

**черва** *f.* grub (of bee).

**червеобразн/ые** *pl.* (zool.) Apoda; **—ый** *a.* vermiform, vermicular, worm-like; **—ый отросток** (anat.) appendix.

**червецы** *pl.* scale insects (*Coccidae*); nematode worms (*Mermithidae*); **мучнистые ч.** mealy bugs (*Pseudococcidae*).

**черви** *pl. of* **червь; —веть** *v.* become wormy; **—вый** *a.* wormy, worm-eaten.

**червлен/ый** *a.* scarlet, bright red; purple; **—ь** *f.* scarlet (pigment).

**черво—** *prefix* vermi—, worm; **—водня** *f.* silkworm breeding house.

**червонный** *a.* red; pure (gold).

**черво/точина** *f.* worm hole; dry rot; **—точный** *a.* worm-eaten; **—ядный** *a.* vermivorous, worm-eating.

**черв/ь** *m.* worm; **круглые —и** Nemathelminthes; **плоские —и** Platyhelminthes.

**червяги** *pl.* (zool.) Coeciliadae.

**червяк** *m.,* **—овый** *a.* (zool., mech.) worm.

**червячно-фрезерный станок** worm milling machine.

**червячн/ый** *a.* worm, screw; **ч. бур** worm auger; **ч. конвейер, ч. транспортер** worm conveyer, screw conveyer; **ч. привод** worm gear drive; **—ая передача, —ая шестерня, —ое колесо** worm gear, worm wheel, worm; **—ая фреза** hobbing cutter, hob, gear cutter; **регулировка —ого механизма** worm adjustment.

**чердак** *m.* garret, attic, loft.

**черед** *see* **очередь.**

**череда** *f.* (bot.) bur marigold (*Bidens*).

**черед/ование** *n.* alternation, alternating, rotation; **—овать, —оваться** *v.* alternate, take turns, rotate, interchange; (elec.) reverse; **—ующийси** *a.* alternating, alternate, staggered; cycling.

**через** *prep. acc.* across, over; per, via, by, through, from; in, after; within (a given time); **ч. борт** overboard; **ч. день** in a day; every other day, on alternate days.

**череззерница** *f.* seedless spike (of cereal).

**черем/ица, —ша** *f.* (bot ) ramson (*Allium ursinum*); **—уха** *f ,* **—уховый** *a.* bird cherry (*Padus; Prunus padus*).

**Черенкова излучение** Cerenkov radiation.

**черенкование** *n.* (bud) grafting; propagation by cuttings.

**черенковский** *a.* Cerenkov (radiation; counter).

**черен/ковый** *a.* grafting, scion; cutting, slip; sucker; (bot.) pedunculate; stick (sulfur); —ок *m.* graft, scion; cutting, slip; (bot.) peduncle, stalk; (tool) shank, handle, stock, grip.

**череп** *m.* (anat.) skull, cranium; (cer.) body; grog.

**черепах/а** *f.,* —**овый** *a.* (zool.) tortoise, turtle; tortoise shell.

**черепаш/ий** *a.* slow; tortoise, turtle; **ч. панцырь,** —**ья чешуя** tortoise shell; —**ка** *f.* shield bug (*Eurygaster*).

**черепи/на** *f.* broken tile; —**тчатый** *a.* tiled; roof-tile, tegular; —**ца** *f.* tile, roof tile; drain tile; **крытый** —**цей** tiled.

**черепичн/ый** *a.* tile; (zool.) tegular; **ч. завод** tile factory, tilery; —**ая кровля** tile roofing, tiling; —**ая печь** tile kiln.

**черепной** *a.* cranial, skull.

**череп/ок** *m.* crock; (cer.) body; **набор** —**ка** formation of cast from slip.

**черепокожный** *a.* (zool.) testaceous, testacean; **ч. моллюск** testacean.

**чересло** *n.* (agr.) colter, cutter.

**черес/полосица** *f.* overlapping (of lands); —**строчный** *a.* interlaced.

**чересчур** *adv.* too, excessively.

**черешковый** *a.* peduncular, stalk.

**черешня** *f.* (bot.) mazzard (*Cerasus avium*).

**череш/ок** *m.* (bot.) petiole, peduncle, stalk; —**чатый** *a.* petiolate.

**черимойя** *f.* (bot.) cherimoyer (*Anona cherimolia*).

**черкез** *m.* (bot.) saltwort (*Salsola Richteri*).

**чермигит** *m.* (min.) tschermigite, ammonia alum.

**черн/ение** *n.* blacking, blackening; (foundry) blackening, facing; —**еный** *a.* blackened; —**еть** *v.* become black, get black, blacken, darken.

**черника** *f.* (bot.) whortleberry, bilberry (*Vaccinium myrtillus*).

**чернил/а** *pl.* ink; —**овыводитель** *m.* ink eradicator; —**ьница** *f.* inkstand, inkwell.

**чернильноорешковая кислота** gallic acid; **ч. дубильная кислота** tannic acid.

**чернильн/ый** *a.* ink; **ч. камень** inkstone, copperas; **ч. орешек** gallnut, (nut) gall; **ванна** —**ых орешков** gall steep.

**чернить** *v.* blacken, smoke; black out.

**черни/ца** *see* **черника;** —**чник** *m.* whortleberry bush; —**чный** *a.* whortleberry.

**чернобур/ый** *a.* dark brown; silver (fox); —**ая сажа** bister, wood-pulp black.

**чернобыл,** —**ьник** *m.* (bot.) mugwort, wormwood (*Artemisia vulgaris*).

**черноватый** *a.* blackish, dark.

**черновик** *m.* rough copy, draft.

**черновина** *f.* black dot, black spot.

**чернов/ой** *a.* rough, coarse; preliminary (operation); intermediate; shaping; **ч. металл** crude metal; **ч. набросок** rough sketch; **ч. прокатный стан, ч. стан** (met.) roughing mill, breaking down mill; **ч. проход,** —**ая проходка** roughing cut; breaking down; **ч. резец** roughing tool; —**ая обработка** roughing out, rough finishing; —**ая прокатка** roughing, roughing down; —**ая форма** (glass) parison mold; —**ые валки** roughing rolls, roughing-down rolls, breaking-down rolls.

**черноголов/ка** *f.* (bot.) self-heal (*Prunella*); —**ник** *m.* burnet (*Poterium*).

**Черногория** Montenegro.

**черногорка** *f.* (bot.) adonis.

**чернозем** *m.,* —**ный** *a.* chernozem, black earth; —**овидный** *a.* chernozem-like; —**ообразование** *n.* chernozem formation.

**черно/клен** *m.* (bot.) maple (*Acer tataricum*); —**книжие** *n.* black magic; —**кожий** *a.* black, negro; —**корень** *m.* (bot.) hound's tongue (*Cynoglossum*); —**кудренник** *m.* (bot.) black horehound (*Ballota nigra*); —**лесье** *n.* deciduous forest; —**ломкий** *a.* (met.) black-hot short, brittle at black heat; —**пишущий аппарат** ink writer, inker; —**рабочий** *m.* manual laborer, unskilled workman.

**чернослив** *m.* (bot.) plum; prune; **сухой ч.** prune.

**черно/та** *f.* blackness; —**тал** *m.* (bot.) laurel-leaf willow (*Salix pentandra*); —**телки** *pl.* darkling beetles (*Tenebrionidae*); —**цвет** *m.* (bot.) enchanter's nightshade (*Circaea*).

**черну/ха,** —**шка** *f.* (bot.) nutmeg flower (*Nigella sativa*).

**черн/ый** *a.* black; unskilled, manual (labor); rough, coarse; (met.) ferrous;

back (entrance); **ч. корень** *see* **чернокорень;** —**ая варка** (paper) black cook; —**ая доска** blackboard; —**ая металлургия** iron and steel industry; —**ая ножка** stem wilt (plant disease); —**ое дерево** (bot.) ebony (*Diospyros ebenum*); **травить под** —**ое дерево** *v.* ebonize.

**чернышевит** *m.* (min.) tschernichewite (a variety of soda-iron amphibole).

**чернь** *f.* black (pigment); black enamel; niello (on silver).

**черп/ак** *m.,* —**аковый** *a.,* —**алка** *f.* scoop, ladle; bucket, pail; grab bucket, grab; —**аковая разгрузка** scoop discharge; —**альный** *a.* scooping, ladling; —**альная ложка** ladle; —**ать,** —**нуть** *v.* scoop, ladle, dip out, draw out; dredge, excavate; —**ачный** *a.* scoop, ladle; bucket; —**ачный элеватор** bucket elevator, bucket dredge.

**черств/еть** *v.* get stale; —**ость** *f.* staleness; —**ый** *a.* stale, hard, dry (bread).

**черт.** *abbr.* (**чертеж**) diagram, drawing.

**черт/а** *f.* trait, characteristic, feature; line, mark; (min.) streak; —**ы** *pl.* pattern; **в** —**е** in the boundaries (of); **в общих** —**ах** in general outline, in a few words.

**чертеж** *m.* plan, design, scheme; sketch, draft, diagram, representation, drawing, illustration, chart; —**ная** *f.* drafting room; —**ник** *m.* draftsman; designer.

**чертежн/ый** *a.* drafting, drawing, graphic; —**ая игла** drawing point; —**ая кнопка** thumb tack; —**ая линейка** rule, ruler, straightedge; —**ое перо** lettering pen.

**черт/илка** *f.* scriber, marking tool, scratch awl; drop point; —**ильный** *see* **чертежный;** —**ить** *v.* draw, sketch, trace, design, plot; —**ок** *m.* thumbtack.

**чертополох** *m.* (bot.) thistle (*Carduus*).

**черточка** *f.* line.

**черчен/ие** *n.* drawing, sketching, tracing, designing; —**ный** *a.* drawn, sketched, designed.

**черч/иллит** *m.* (min.) churchillite, mendipite; —**ит** *m.* (min.) churchite.

**чесалка** *f.* (hemp, flax) comb, ripple,

hackle; (text.) carding machine; (bot.) fuller's teasel (*Dipsacus fullonum*).

**чесаль/ник,** —**щик** *m.* (text.) carder, comber; —**ный** *a.* carding, combing, hackling; —**ный гребень** comb; —**ный станок** hackling bench.

**чес/ание** *n.* combing, hackling (of flax), carding; scratching; —**аный** *a.* combed, hackled, carded; —**ать** *v.* comb, hackle, card; scratch; curry (horse); —**аться** *v.* itch; —**ка** *f.* combing; scratching.

**чесно/к** *m.,* —**чный** *a.* (bot.) garlic (*Allium sativum*); **дикий ч., заячий ч., медвежий ч.** water germander (*Teucrium scordium*).

**чесот/ка** *f.* itch, rash; (med.) scabies; mange; —**ный,** —**очный** *a.* scabby, scabious, mangy.

**чессилит** *m.* (min.) chessylite, azurite.

**чествовать** *v.* honor, celebrate.

**честерлит** *m.* (min.) chesterlite (a variety of microcline).

**честерьян** *m.* (geol.) Chesterian series.

**честн/ость** *f.* honesty, integrity; —**ый** *a.* honest, upright, straightforward.

**честолюб/ивый** *a.* ambitious; —**ие** *n.* ambition.

**честь** *f.* honor; *v.* deem; **он делает ч. своей профессии** he is a credit to his profession; **отдавать ч.** *v.* give credit (to); **считать за ч.** *v.* consider it an honor, deem it a favor; **это делает ему ч.** this does him credit.

**чесу/нча,** —**ча, че-су-ча** *f.* pongee, tussah (silk).

**чет** *m.* pair, even number; —**а** *f.* pair, couple; **он ему не** —**а** he is no match for him.

**четверг** *m.* Thursday.

**четвер/ичный** *a.* (statistics) quartile; —**ка,** —**ня** *f.* four, group of four; —**ной** *a.* fourfold, quadruple, tetra—; quaternary; tetrad (axis).

**четверо** four; **их ч.** there are four of them; —**ногий** *a.* (zool.) quadruped, four-footed; —**ногое животное** quadruped; —**який** *a.* fourfold.

**четверт/ичный** *a.* quaternary; (geol.) Quaternary; —**ка** *see* **четверть;** —**ная** *f.* unit of measure (one fourth of a vedro); —**ной** *a.* one-fourth, quarter; (met.) quaternary, four-component (alloy); —ый *a.* fourth; —ая часть one fourth, a quarter.

четверт/ь *f.* one fourth, a quarter; (geom.) quadrant; unit of measure (20.991 dkl.); ч. второго a quarter past one o'clock; без —и пять a quarter to five o'clock.

четверть/волновой *a.* quarter-wave; — оборотный *a.* quarter-turn.

четкий *a.* legible, clear, sharp.

четко/видный, —образный *a.* beaded.

четкость *f.* legibility, clearness, sharpness, definition; accuracy.

четн/о-нечетный *a.* even-odd; —ость *f.* (phys.) parity; —о-четный *a.* even-even; —ый *a.* even (number).

четочн/ый *a.* beaded; ч. водоподъемник chain pump; —ая жила (min.) wavy vein; —ая молния beaded lightning.

Четтертона композиция, четтертон-компаунд, четтертоновская мастика Chatterton compound.

четыре four; *prefix see* четырех—; —жды *adv.* four times, multiplied by four, fourfold; —ста four hundred; —угольник *see* четырехугольник.

четырех— *prefix* quadri—, tetra—, four; —атомный *a.* tetratomic; —бромистый *a.* tetrabromide (of).

четырехвалентн/ость *f.* tetravalence; —ый *a.* tetravalent.

четырехвалковый прокатный стан, ч. стан four-roll mill, four-roller mill, four-high rolling mill.

четырехводный гидрат tetrahydrate.

четырехгранн/ик *m.* (geom.) tetrahedron; —ый *a.* tetrahedral.

четырех/жаберные *pl.* (zool.) Tetrabranchia; —замещенные *pl.* tetrasubstitution products, tetraderivatives; — иодистый *a.* tetraiodide (of); —коленчатый *a.* four-throw (shaft); —конечный *a.* four-point; —кратный *a.* fourfold, quadruple; —кулачковый *a.* four-jawed; —летний *a.* four-year; —лопастный *a.* four-blade; (bot.) tetralobate; —мерный *a.* four-dimensional; —местный *a.* four-seater (car).

четырехног/ий *a.* (zool.) quadruped, four-footed; —ое животное quadruped.

четырех/окись *f.* tetroxide; —основный *a.* tetrabasic; —осный *a.* (cryst.)

tetraaxial, four-axis; —палый *a.* (zool.) tetradactyl, four-digited; — перое долото four-blade bit; —полье *n.* four-field crop rotation.

четырехполюсн/ик *m.* quadripole; —ый *a.* quadripole, quadripolar, tetrapolar, four-pole, four-polar.

четырех/процентный *a.* four per cent; —прядный *a.* four-strand; —рожковый *a.* four-pronged; —рукавный *a.* four-armed; —ручный *a.* (zool.) quadrumanous, four-handed; —рядный *a.* tetraserial, four-row; —сернистый *a.* tetrasulfide (of); —смысленность *f.* four-ambiguity; —сотый *a.* four-hundredth; —сплавный *a.* quaternary, four-component (alloy); — створчатый *a.* (bot.) quadrivalve.

четырехсторонн/ий *a.* quadrilateral, four-sided; —ик *m.* quadrilateral figure.

четырех/ступенчатый *a.* four-stage, four-stepped; —тактный *a.* (mach.) four-cycle, four-stroke; —тионовая кислота tetrathionic acid; —точечный *a.* four-point; —углеродное кольцо four-carbon ring.

четырехугольн/ик *m.* tetragon, quadrangle; —ый *a.* tetragonal, quadrangular, four-angled.

четырех/фазный *a.* four-phase; —фтористый *a.* tetrafluoride (of).

четыреххлористый *a.* tetrachloride (of); ч. кремний silicon tetrachloride.

четырех/хоботные *pl.* (zool.) Tetrarhynchoidea; —ходовой *a.* four-way; — цикловый *a.* four-cycle; —частичный *a.* four-piece; —член *m.* (math.) quaternion; —члениковые *pl.* (biol.) Tetramera; —членный *a.* four-membered, four-period; (biol.) tetramerous; —шкальный *a.* four-scale; —шкальная система (cryst.) four-axis system; —этажный *a.* four-story.

четырнадцат/ый *a.* fourteenth; —ь fourteen.

чефер *m.* chafer.

чефрас *m.* (bot.) sandalwood (*Santalum*).

чех/лик *m.* (bot.) calyptra, cap, covering; известковый ч. an industrial limestone; —ликовидный *a.* hood-shaped;

—**ловидность** *f.* cattail fungus infection (of plants); —**лоноски** *pl.* (zool.) casebearers (*Coleophoridae*); —**ол** *m.* cover, covering, case, hood; jacket, can, sheathe.

**Чехословакия** Czechoslovakia.

**чечеви/ца** *f.* lens; (bot.) lentil (*Lens esculenta*); —**цеобразный** *a.* lens-shaped, lenticular; —**чка** *f.* (bot.) lenticel; —**чный** *a.* lentil; lenticular; —**чная руда** (min.) pea ore, bean ore (usually a variety of limonite).

**чешет** *pr. 3 sing. of* **чесать.**

**чешский** *a.* Czechoslovakian.

**чешуе/крылые** *pl.* (zool.) Lepidoptera; —**носный** *a.* scale-bearing, scaly; —**перые** *pl.* Squamipennes (fish).

**чешуистый** *a.* scaly, squamous.

**чешуй/ка** *f.* scale, lamella, plate; —**ница** *f.* (zool.) silverfish (*Lepisma saccharina*).

**чешуйчат/ые** *pl.* (zool.) Squamata; —**ый** *a.* scaly, scaled, squamose, squamosal, lamellar, laminated, foliated, flaky, flaked, platy; (geol.) imbricate (structure); —**ая структура** flaky texture, lamellar structure.

**чеш/ут** *pr. 3 pl. of* **чесать;** —**ущий** *a.* combing; scratching.

**чешуя** *f.* scale, squama; plate, lamella; husk; (tectonic) sliver.

**чизел/евать** *v.* break subsurface soil; —**ь** *m.* chisel (subsoil cultivator).

**чий** *m.* a grass (*Lasiagrostis*).

**чикаг/оголубой** *m.*, —**ский голубой** Chicago blue (pigment).

**чикл** *m.* chicle (gum).

**чил/дренит** *m.* (min.) childrenite; —**еит** *m.* chileite (an alteration product of pyrite); —**енит** *m.* chilenite.

**Чили** Chile.

**чили/буха** *f.* (bot.) nux vomica (*Strychnos nux-vomica*); —**га** *f.* pea tree (*Caragana*).

**чилийск/ий** *a.* Chile, Chilean; —**ая мельница** Chile mill, edge mill, chaser.

**чилим** *m.* (bot.) water caltrop (*Trapa*); spec. water chestnut (*T. natans*).

**чилин** *see under* **чилийский.**

**чиллагит** *m.* (min.) chillagite (a lead tungstate-molybdate).

**ЧИМ** *abbr.* **(частотно-импульсная** модуляция) pulse-frequency modulation.

**чиминит** *see* **циминит.**

**чин** *m.* rank, grade.

**чина** *f.* (bot.) vetchling (*Lathyrus*); **посевная ч.** chickling vetch (*L. sativus*).

**чинар** *m.*, —**а** *f.* (bot.) plane (*Platanus*), spec. European plane tree (*P. orientalis*).

**чингил** *m.* chingil (rock glacier in the Armenian Upland).

**чинить** *v.* mend, patch, repair; sharpen (pencil); make, do, commit; **ч. препятствия** put obstacles in the way, impede.

**чинк** *m.* chink (scarp on the edge of the Usturt Plateau).

**чинка** *f.* mending, repair, overhauling.

**чинколобвит** *see* **склодовскит.**

**чиновн/ик** *m.* official, civil servant, public servant; —**ический** *a.* bureaucratic; —**ый** *a.* of high rank.

**чинтермалическая линия** (meteor.) isotherm, an isotherm based on simultaneous observations.

**чинук** *m.* (meteor.) chinook.

**чиполин** *see* **циполин.**

**чир** *m.* whitefish.

**чирей** *m.* (med.) boil, furuncle.

**чирк/ать,** —**нуть** *v.* strike (a match).

**численн/о** *adv.* numerically, in number; —**ость** *f.* number, quantity; (mil.) strength; —**остью** in number; —**ый** *a.* numeral, numerical; —**ое значение** numerical value.

**числитель** *m.* (math.) numerator; —**ный** *a.* numeral; **имя** —**ное количественное** cardinal number; **имя** —**ное порядковое** ordinal number.

**числить** *v.* count; —**ся** *v.* be counted, be reckoned; be (on the list).

**числ/о** *n.* number, quantity; population; date; **ч. М** Mach number; **ч. месяца** date; **без** —**а** countless, innumerable; undated; **в том** —**е** among them; **первое ч.** the first of the month; **помечать** —**ом** *v.* date.

**числов/ой** *a.* numeral, numerical; —**ое значение** numerical value.

**чистец** *m.* (bot.) hedge nettle (*Stachys*).

**чистилка** *f.* cleanser; (plow) staff.

**чистиль/ник,** —**щик** *m.* (bot.) wild cucumber (*Ecballium elaterium*).

**чист/ильщик** *m.* cleaner, cleanser; —**ить** *v.* clean, cleanse, wash, scrub, scour, scrape; dredge (a canal); clear (woods); weed out (a field); purge (gas pipe); —**ка** *f.* cleaning, cleansing, washing, scrubbing, scouring, scraping; dredging; clearing; weeding out; purging; —**о** *adv.* cleanly, purely, neatly; —**овик** *m.* clean copy.

**чистов/ой** *a.* clean, finish, finishing; **ч. инструмент, ч. резец** finishing tool, smoothing tool; **ч. прокатный стан** planishing roll; **ч. пропуск, ч. проход** (rolling) planishing pass; **ч. стан** finishing mill; —**ая обработка,** —**ая отделка** finishing (off), finishing work.

**чисто/кровный** *a.* thoroughbred, purebred, full-blooded, pedigreed; —**линейный** *a.* (biol.) pure-strain; —**плотность** *f.* cleanliness; —**плотный** *a.* clean, neat; —**породный** *a.* purebred; —**сердечный** *a.* frank, sincere; —**сортность** *f.* purity (of strain or breed).

**чистот/а** *f.* cleanliness, cleanness, purity, fineness; clarity, clearness; (acous.) fidelity; **ч. поверхности** smoothness, degree of surface finish; **размер в —е** finished size.

**чистотел** *m.* (bot.) celandine (*Chelidonium*).

**чистотянутая сталь** bright-drawn steel.

**чистоуст** *m.* (bot.) osmund (*Osmunda*).

**чист/ый** *a.* clean, pure, uncontaminated, immaculate; neat; clear, blank (page); proper (fraction); net (weight, energy, profit); mere (chance); finished, smooth; absolute (alcohol); **ч. для анализа** analytically pure, analytical grade; —**ая отделка** finishing, finish; **химически ч.** chemically pure.

**чистяк** *m.* (bot.) pilewort (*Ficaria*).

**чит/аемость** *f.* readability; —**альный** *a.* reading; —**альня** *f.* reading room; —**атель** *m.* reader; —**ать** *v.* read; deliver (a lecture).

**чих/ание** *n.* sneezing; (med.) sternutation; —**ательный** *a.* sternutatory, sternutative; —**ательный газ** sneezing gas, poison gas sternutative; —**ать**

*v.* sneeze; —**отная гулявица,** —**отная трава** sneezewort (*Achillea ptarmica*).

**чищалка** *f.* (boring) spoon.

**чище** *comp. of* **чисто, чистый,** cleaner, more cleanly, purer.

**член** *m.* member, fellow; article; (math.) term; (anat.) limb; **ч.-корреспондент** associate member; —**ик** *m.* segment, joint.

**членисто/ногие** *pl.* (zool.) Arthropoda; —**сть** *f.* articulation, segmentation.

**член/истый** *a.* articulate, hinged, jointed, segmented; —**овредительство** *n.* mutilation, maiming, crippling; —**ораздельный** *a.* articulate, distinct.

**членс/кий** *a.* member, membership; **ч. билет** membership card; —**тво** *n.* membership, fellowship.

**ЧМ** *abbr.* (частотно-модулированный) frequency-modulated, f-m.

**чоб/ор,** —**рик** *see* **богородская трава.**

**чоп** *m.* tap or plug for tank.

**чоппер** *m.* (rubber) chopper, chopping machine, shredder.

**чортов палец** (geol.) belemnite (an extinct cephalopod); —**а вода** (ammonium sulfate manufacture) condensate from the gas after the saturator; —**а кожа** moleskin.

**чрев/атый** *a.* pregnant; fraught (with); —**о** *n.* womb.

**чреда** *see* **очередь.**

**чрез** *see* **через.**

**чрезвычайн/о** *adv.* extremely, exceedingly, highly, immensely, extra; —**ость** *f.* extreme, excessiveness; —**ый** *a.* extreme, excessive, extraordinary.

**чрезмерный** *a.* excessive, extreme, immoderate, inordinate, redundant; over—; **ч. разряд** overdischarge.

**чрен** *m.* trough, tub, tank, vat.

**чтение** *n.* reading, perusal.

**чтенный** *a.* deemed.

**чтец** *m.* reader, lecturer.

**что** *pron.* what, which, whatever; why, how; *conj.* that; **ч.-либо, ч.-нибудь** something, anything; **ч.-то** something; rather; **ни во ч. не ставить** *v.* not to value; **ни за ч.** not for anything, not under any circumstances.

**чтоб,** —**ы** *conj.* in order that, in order to, so that; **ч. не** lest; **вместо того, ч.** instead of.

**чтущий** *a.* deeming.

**чубарый** *a.* mottled, speckled.

**чубук** *m.* grape stalk; stem (of pipe).

**чубушник** *m.* (bot.) mock orange (*Philadelphus*).

**Чувашская АССР** the Chuvash Autonomous Soviet Socialist Republic.

**чувствительн/ость** *f.* sensitivity, sensitiveness, sensibility, susceptibility, excitability; (acous.) response; **ч. по току** current sensitivity; **время — ости** (nucl.) sensitive time; **относительнаи ч.** (elec.) sensitivity; **—ый** *a.* sensitive, sensible, susceptible, responsive, delicate; (zool.) sensory; transition (color); painful, severe; **сделать —ым** *v.* sensitize.

**чувство** *n.* feeling, sensation, sense; **лишиться чувств** *v.* lose consciousness, faint; **обман чувств** illusion; delusion; **органы чувств** (anat.) organs of sense; **притти в ч.** *v.* regain consciousness, recover one's senses; **—вание** *n.* sensation, feeling; **—вать** *v.* feel, experience; **—вать себя больным** feel ill.

**Чугаева реакция** Tschugajew's reaction (for nickel).

**чугаль** *m.* a heat-resistant cast iron-aluminum alloy.

**чугун** *m.* cast iron; pig; **ч. в болванках, ч. в свинках, доменный ч., сырцовый ч., штыковой ч.** pig iron; **белый ч.** white iron; **болванка —а** (iron) pig; **литейный ч.** cast iron; **серый ч.** gray iron.

**чугунка** *f.* portable iron stove; a dark-colored, crude salt.

**чугунн/ый** *a.* cast iron; **—ая отливка, —ое литье** cast iron; iron casting, pig iron casting; **—ая соль** a dark-colored, crude salt; **—ая трава** (bot.) vervain (*Verbena*).

**чугуно/возный ковш** (met.) ladle car; **—литейная** *f.*, **—литейный завод** cast iron foundry, iron foundry; **—литейщик** *m.* iron founder; **—плавильный завод** smelter; iron works.

**чуд/еса** *pl.* of **чудо**; **—есный** *a.* wonderful, miraculous, extraordinary; **—есная палочка** (bact.) *Bacillus prodigiosus;* **—иться** *v.* wonder (at), be surprised; seem; **—ище** *see* **чудовище.**

**чудн/о** *adv.* wonderfully, marvelously; oddly, strangely; it is strange; **—ой** *a.* strange, odd, queer; **—ый** *a.* wonderful, marvelous, outstanding; **—ая сеть** (anat.) network of fine blood vessels.

**чудо** *n.* miracle, wonder.

**чудовищ/е** *n.* monster, freak; **—ность** *f.* monstrosity, enormity; **—ный** *a.* monstrous.

**чужд/аться** *v.* avoid, shun; **—ый** *a.* foreign, strange, hostile, alien, extraneous.

**чуже/земец, —странец** *m.* stranger, alien, foreigner; **—земный** *a.* strange, alien, foreign, outside; **—родный** *a.* alien, foreign; (geol.) allogenic.

**чужеядн/ый** *a.* parasitic; **—ое растение** (bot.) parasite.

**чуж/ой** *a.* foreign, strange; extraneous; *m.* foreigner, stranger; **жить на ч. счет** *v.* be a parasite; **присвоить —ую мысль** *v.* plagiarize, borrow an idea.

**чулан** *m.*, **—ный** *a.* pantry; storeroom.

**чул/ок** *m.* stocking; (mach.) housing; (incandescent) mantle; **—ки** *pl.* stockings, hosiery; **—очник** *m.* stocking maker; **—очновязальная машина** hosiery-knitting machine; **—очный** *a.* stocking, hosiery; **—очные изделия** hosiery.

**чума** *f.* (med.) plague, pestilence (spec. bubonic plague); **водяная ч.** *see* **элодея; собачья ч.** distemper.

**чумбур** *m.* halter.

**чуметь** *v.* have distemper.

**чумиза** *f.* (bot.) foxtail millet (*Setaria italica*).

**чумичка** *f.* skimmer, ladle.

**чум/ка** *f.* (vet.) distemper; **—ной** *a.* pestilential, plague-stricken.

**чур/бак, —бан** *m.* block, blockwood, log; chunk, lump; **—ка** *f.* chock, block.

**чутк/ий** *a.* sensitive, delicate, responsive; considerate; **—ость** *f.* sensitivity, delicacy; tact.

**чуточку** *adv.* very slightly.

**чуть** *adv.* hardly, barely, scarcely; **ч. не** almost, nearly; **ч. что, он беспокоится** he worries over every trifle; **ч. что не** all but.

**чутье** *n.* scent; hearing.

**чуфа** *f.* (bot.) chufa (*Cyperus esculentus*).

**чучело** *n.* dummy, stuffed animal; scarecrow.

**чушк/а** *f.*, **—овый** *a.* (met.) pig, ingot, bar; (zool.) young sow; **чугун в —ах** pig iron; **—олом, —оломатель** *m.* pig breaker.

**чушь** *see* чепуха.

**чуять** *v.* smell, scent, feel, sense.

**чье** *see* чей.

**Чьеллина печь** *see* Кьеллина печь.

**чьи, чья** *see* чей.

**Чэдвика способ** Chadwick process.

**Чэддока штатив** Chaddock support.

**чэзи** *n.* (geol.) Chazy subdivision.

**Чэпман** *see under* Чепман.

# Ш

**ш.** *abbr.* (широкий) broad, wide.

**шабазит** *m.* (min.) chabazite.

**шабдар** *m.* clover (*Trifolium resupinatum*).

**шабер** *m.* scraper, scrape; (paper) doctor; **ш.-крючок** hook scraper.

**шаблон** *m.*, **—ный** *a.* template, gage, pattern; model, copy; (master) form, mold; stencil; (foundry) sweep; bobbin, spool; (elec.) former; **ш.-высотомер** center height gage; **затачивать по —у** *v.* grind to gage; **изготовлять по —у** *v.* copy; **формовать —ом** *v.* (foundry) sweep.

**шаблонн/ый** *see under* шаблон; trite, unoriginal; **—ая обмотка** (elec.) former winding; **—ая формовка** (foundry) sweep molding.

**шабоит** *m.* (min.) szaboite (a variety of hypersthene).

**шабот** *m.* anvil block.

**шабр/ение** *n.*, **—овка** *f.* scraping, scouring; **—ить** *v.* scrape, scour; **—ованный** *a.* scraped, scoured; **—овщик** *m.* scraper.

**шави/бетол** *m.* chavibetol, 5-allylguaiacol; **—кол** *m.* chavicol, *p*-allylphenol; **—цин** *m.* chavicine; **—циновая кислота** chavicic acid.

**шавозот** *m.* chavosot (*p*-allylphenol).

**шаг** *m.* step, pace; (mech.) pitch, spacing; **ш. за —ом** step by step, stepwise; **с малым —ом** closely spaced; **с переменным —ом** variable-pitch; **—ать** *v.* pace, step; **—ающий** *a.* (mach.) walking; **—нуть** *v.* take a step; **—овый** *a.* step, step-type, step-by-step; pitch; **—омер** *m.* (surv.) pedometer, pace counter; pitch counter, pitch gage (for gears).

**шагрен/евая кожа, —ь** *m.* shagreen

(leather); **—ировать** *v.* produce a shagreen finish.

**шадрик** *m.* leached ashes, crude potash.

**шайба** *f.* washer, disk, collar; plate.

**шайбелиит** *m.* (min.) szaibelyite.

**шайка** *f.* small tub.

**шакша** *f.* (tanning) bark liquor, ooze, purée; bate, drench (for leather).

**шаланда** *f.* scow, mud scow, barge.

**шалаш** *m.* hut.

**шалнер** *see* шарнир.

**шалфей** *m.*, **—ный** *a.* (bot.) sage (*Salvia*); **аптечный ш., лекарственный ш.** garden sage (*S. officinalis*).

**шальтер** *m.* switch.

**шальштейн** *m.*, **—овый** *a.* (petr.) schalstein (sheared basalt).

**шамберленовый** *a.* Chamberlain.

**шамбо** *n.* sewer, septic tank.

**шамозит** *m.* (min.) chamosite.

**шамот** *m.*, **—а** *f.* chamotte (a fire clay), refractory clay; grog.

**шамот/ный, —овый** *a.* chamotte, fireclay; grog; **ш. камень, ш. кирпич** firebrick, refractory brick; **ш. порошок** (cer.) grog; **—ная глина** fireclay; **—ная футеровка** fireclay lining, refractory lining.

**шампакол** *m.* champacol, guaiol.

**шампанское** *n.* champagne (wine).

**шампиньон** *m.* (bot.) meadow mushroom (*Agaricus campestris* or *Psalliota campestris*); **—ница** *f.* mushroom cellar.

**шампунь** *m.* shampoo.

**шамуа** *see* замша; **—зит** *m.* (min.) chamoisite, chamosite.

**шандор/а** *f.*, **—ный** *a.*, **—ная балка** dam beam, dam timber; shutter (of dam); **—ный щит** dam walling.

**шандра** *f.* (bot.) horehound (*Marrubium*).

**шанк/ер, —р** *m.* (med.) chancre; **мягкий**

ш. chancroid (venereal disease); —**ерный** *a.* chancrous.

**шанс** *m.* chance; —**ы** *pl.* odds; **иметь
—ы** *v.* stand a good chance.

**Шанхай** Shanghai.

**шанц/евый** *a.* digging (tool); —**овать** *v.*
intrench; —**ы** *pl.* fieldwork.

**шапагат** *m.* twine.

**шапбахит** *m.* (min.) schapbachite.

**Шапеле электропечь** (elec.) Chapelet
furnace.

**шапирограф** *m.* (manifolding) a hectograph.

**шапка** *f.* cap; (geol.) caprock.

**шаповал** *m.* fuller, felt maker.

**шапоч/ка** *f.* little cap; —**ник** *m.* hatter;
—**ный** *a.* hat.

**шапп** *m.* (text.) schappe (thread).

**шар** *m.* ball, globe, sphere, orb; **ш.-зонд**
(meteor.) sounding balloon; **ш.-пилот**
(meteor.) pilot balloon; **воздушный
ш.** balloon; **земной ш.** globe, the
earth; **поплавковый ш.** ball float.

**шарас** *m.* charas (drug from hemp resin).

**шарголин** *m.* a leather substitute.

**Шардонне искусственный шелк** Char-
donnet silk, nitrocellulose rayon.

**шаржир-машина** *f.* (met.) charging
machine, charger.

**шар-зонд** *see under* **шар.**

**шариаж** *m.* (geol.) an overthrust folding.

**шарик** *m.* little ball, ball; globule, bead,
pellet; bubble; bulb (of thermom-
eter); (blood) corpuscle.

**шариков/ый** *a.* ball; **ш. клапан** ball
valve; **ш. подпятник, ш. упорный
подшипник** ball thrust bearing; **ш.
подшипник,** —**ая опора** ball bearing;
—**ая трубка** bulb tube.

**шарикоподшипник** *m.,* —**овый** *a.* ball
bearing; **упорный ш.** ball thrust
bearing.

**шарлах** *m.* —**овый** *a.* scarlet (pigment).

**шарлот** *m.* (bot.) shallot (*Allium as-
calonicum*).

**Шарля закон** Charles (gas) law.

**шармутьен** *m.* (geol.) Charmouthian
stage.

**шарнасьен** *m.* (geol.) Sharnacian substage.

**шарнир** *m.* hinge, joint, articulation,
link; **на —е, на —ах** hinged; **универ-
сальный ш.** universal joint, ball-and-

socket joint; —**ноукрепленный** *a.*
hinged, tilting.

**шарнирн/ый** *a.* hinge, joint, link,
swivel; hinged, jointed, articulated,
articulate; knuckle-joint, hinge-joint;
toggle-action (shears); **ш. болт** link
bolt; swing bolt; **ш. клапан** flap
valve; **ш. ремень** link belt; **ш. узел,**
—**ая связь,** —**ое соединение,** —**ое
сочленение** hinge joint; ball-and-
socket joint; —**ая муфта** link box;
—**ая опора** tip bearing, tilting bearing; —**ая цепь** link chain.

**шаровидн/ость** *f.* sphericity, globularity;
—**ый** *a.* spherical, spheroidal, globular; bubble (cap); —**ая порода** (min.)
sphere ore, cocarde ore; spherulite.

**шаров/ка** *f.* (agr.) cultivation; (bot.)
globe flower (*Trollius*); —**ки** *pl.*
(zool.) Cyrtidae; —**ница** *f.* globe
daisy (*Globularia*).

**шаров/ой** *a.* ball, sphere, spherical;
(geol.) spherulitic; **ш. затвор** ball
lock, ball catch; **ш. клапан,** —**ая
клапанная заслонка** ball valve, ball
check; **ш. шарнир,** —**ое соединение,**
—**ое соединение муфтой,** —**ое шар-
нирное соединение,** —**ое сочленение**
ball-and-socket joint; **ш. шип** ball
journal; —**ая мельница** ball mill;
—**ая пята,** —**ая цапфа** ball pivot.

**шарообразный** *see* **шаровидный.**

**шарош/ечный** *a.* cutting, milling; **ш.
станок,** —**ка** *f.* (milling) cutter, milling machine; burr; mill; —**ечная
головка** cutter block.

**Шарпи копер** (met.) Charpy impact
machine; **Ш. метод** Charpy method.

**шар-пилот** *see under* **шар.**

**шарпит** *m.* (min.) sharpite.

**шартрез** *m.* chartreuse (liqueur).

**шарф** *m.* scarf.

**шарьяж** *m.* (geol.) overthrust, overthrust folding, overthrust mass.

**шасси** *n.* chassis, underframe, carriage;
(aero.) landing gear.

**шаста слои** (geol.) Shasta series.

**шаст/алка** *f.* grain awner, hummeling
maching; —**ание** *n.* awning.

**шат/ание** *n.* swaying; hesitation, vacillation; loafing; —**ать** *v.* shake, rock,
sway; —**аться** *v.* get loose, be loose,

shake, be shaky; loaf; —ающийся *a.* loose.

шатер *m.*, —ный *a.* tent; marquee.

шатировка *f.* shading.

шатк/ий *a.* unsteady, wavering, rickety, precarious; —ость *f.* unsteadiness, vacillation, weakness, precariousness.

шатнуть *see* шатать.

шатровый *a.* tent; hipped (roof).

шаттукит *m.* (min.) shattuckite (a hydrous copper silicate).

шатун *m.* connecting rod, pitman, link, rocker; pump; tiller, guide lever.

шафлор *see* сафлор.

шафран *m.*, —ный, —овый *a.* (bot.) saffron (*Crocus*, spec. *C. sativus*); —ножелтый *a.* saffron-yellow.

шахмат/ный *a.* chess; checkerboard, checkered, staggered, alternate; checkrow (planting); ш. узор checkerwork; —ная структура (min.) chessboard structure; в —ном порядке, —ообразный *a.* checkered, staggered, alternate; —ы *pl.* chess.

шахт/а *f.* mine, pit, shaft, well; column; compartment; —ер *m.* miner; —ный *a.* mine, mining, pit, shaft; —ная вагонетка mine car; —ная печь shaft furnace.

шаш/ель, —ень *m.* shipworm, borer.

шашка *f.* saber, sword; (smoke) pot; (blasting) cartridge; (expl.) charge; (rockets) burner, grain.

шв. *abbr.* (шведский) Swedish.

шва *gen. of* шов.

швабр/а *f.* mop, swab; чистить —ой *v.* mop, mop up, swab.

швартов *m.*, —ый *a.* mooring, hawser (of ship); —ать *v.* moor.

швартцембергит *m.* (min.) schwartzembergite.

Шварцвальд the Black Forest.

швацит *m.* (min.) schwazite (a mercurial variety of tetrahedrite).

шведск/ий *a.* Swedish; ш. ключ monkey wrench; —ая зелень *see* Шееле зелень; —ая спичка safety match.

швейник *m.* sewer.

швейнфуртск/ий *a.* Schweinfurt; —ая зелень Schweinfurt green, Paris green.

швейный *a.* sewing.

швейц. *abbr.* (швейцарский) Swiss.

Швейцария Switzerland.

швейцарский *a.* Swiss; ш. песчаник (min.) Swiss sandstone (a conglomerate).

швейцеров реактив Schweitzer's reagent (for cellulose).

швелевание *n.* low-temperature carbonization, low-temperature distillation.

швеллер *m.*, —ный *a.* channel, channel bar, channel iron; —ное железо channel iron.

швель/газ *m.* gas from low-temperature carbonization, partially burned gas; —кокс *m.* low-temperature coke; —шахта *f.* distillation shaft of gas producer.

швермер *m.* (blasting) squib.

Швеция Sweden.

швингтурбина *f.* (text.) scutcher.

швиц/камера *f.* steaming room (for leather); —ование *n.* steaming, sweating; —овать *v.* steam, sweat.

швырковые дрова firewood.

швыр/нуть, —ять *v.* throw, fling; —ялка *f.* spinner; blower; —яние *n.* throwing, flinging.

шевелилка *f.* agitator, stirrer.

шевелин *m.* a heat-insulation material from flax wastes.

шевел/ить, —ьнуть *v.* move, stir, budge.

шев/ер *m.* shaver; —ингование *n.*, —инг-процесс *m.* shaving.

шевиот *m.* (text.) cheviot; serge.

Шеврёля соль Chevreul's salt, cuprous-cupric sulfite.

шевро *n.* kid (leather).

шеврон *m.* (mil.) chevron, stripe; —ный *a.* chevron, herringbone (pattern); —ная передача helical gearing.

шевская смола cobbler's wax.

шеддок *m.* (bot.) shaddock (*Citrus maxima*).

шедит *see* чеддит.

шедший *past act. part. of* идти.

Шееле зелень, шеелева зелень Scheele's green (acid copper arsenite).

шеелиз/ировать, —овать *v.* scheelize (treat wine with glycerin).

шее/лит *m.* (min.) scheelite (calcium tungstate); —рерит *m.* (min.) scheererite (a hydrocarbon).

Шези формула Chezy's formula (for pipe friction).

**шейв/ер** *see* **шевер; —ингование, —инг-процесс** *see* **шевинг-процесс.**

**шей/ка** *f.* neck, collar; pin, pivot journal, journal (of shaft); (anat.) cervix; web (of rail); recess; **образование —ки** (met.) necking down; **—ный** *a.* neck; (anat.) cervical, jugular.

**шейхцерия** *f.* (bot.) scheuchzeria.

**шексо** *n.* (min.) an impure Hungarian soda.

**шел** *past sing. of* **идти.**

**шелест** *m.* rustle, rustling, murmer; **—еть, —ить** *v.* rustle.

**шелк** *m.* silk; **ш.-супль, полувареный ш.** souple silk; **ш.-сырец, невареный ш.** raw silk; **дикий ш.** tussore, tussah silk; **искусственный ш.** artificial silk, rayon.

**шелко/видный, —вистый** *a.* silky, silk-like, with a silky luster, sericeous; **—вина** *f.* silk thread; **—вица** *f.* (bot.) mulberry tree (*Morus*).

**шелковичн/ый** *a.* silk; **ш. червь** silkworm; **—ая кислота** bombic acid; **соль —ой кислоты, —окислая соль** bombate; **—ое дерево** *see* **шелковица.**

**шелковод** *m.* silkworm breeder, sericulturist; **—ный** *a.*, **—ство** *n.* silkworm breeding, sericulture.

**шелков/ый** *a.* silk; **ш. клей** silk glue, cericin; **—ая бумага** tissue paper.

**шелкокрутильная фабрика** silk mill.

**шелкопряд** *m.* silkworm; **кольчатый ш.** tent caterpillar; **непарный ш.** gypsy moth; **—ы** *pl.* caterpillars of the Bombycidae, Attacidae, or Lasiocampidae families; **—ение** *n.* silk spinning; **—ильня** *f.* silk mill.

**шеллак** *m.*, **—овый** *a.* shellac.

**шеллан** *m.* shellane (compressed natural gas).

**шеллачный** *see* **шеллаковый.**

**шеллен** *m.* shellene.

**шелл/ер** *m.* (corn) sheller; **—машина** *f.* hulling mill, decorticator.

**шеллоловая кислота** shellolic acid.

**шелохнуть, —ся** *v.* move, stir, agitate.

**шелудив/еть** *v.* become mangy; **—ость** *f.* rhizoctonia (plant disease); **—ый** *a.* mangy, scabby.

**шелух/а** *f.* peel, rind, skin, jacket, husk, hull, pod; scale (of fish); shell meal (fertilizer); **—овый** *a.* scaly.

**шелуш/ение** *n.* peeling, shelling, hulling, husking; scaling, exfoliation; (med.) desquamation; **—ильная машина** sheller, hulling machine, husker; **—ить** *v.* shell, hull, husk; **—иться** *v.* peel, scale, scale off, exfoliate; desquamate.

**шелыга** *f.* apex (of arch), crown.

**шельский век** (geol.) Chellian stage.

**шельф** *m.*, **—овый** *a.* shelf, ledge; **—овый ледник** (geol.) ice shelf.

**шелюг/а** *f.* willow (*Salix acutifolia* or *S. daphnoides*); **—ование** *n.* willow planting.

**Шена прокатный стан** (met.) Schoen mill.

**Шенгерра способ** Schoenherr process (of nitrogen fixation).

**шенит** *m.* (min.) schoenite (a variety of picromerite).

**Шено процесс** (met.) Chenot process.

**Шен-Пунга двигатель** Schön-Punga motor.

**Шенрока таблица** (sugar) Schoenrock table.

**шепард** *m.* (met.) crane for charging cupola furnace.

**шепел/явить, —ять** *v.* lisp.

**шепинг** *m.*, **ш.-машина** *f.* shaper, shaping machine, horizontal planing machine.

**шепит** *m.* schoepite (uranium mineral).

**шеп/нуть** *see* **шептать; —от** *m.* whisper.

**шептала** *f.* dried peach.

**шептало** *n.* sear (of machine gun).

**шептать** *v.* whisper.

**Шепф** Schöpf (name).

**Шерарда способ** (met.) Sherard process.

**шерардиз/ация** *f.*, **—ирование** *n.* (met.) sherardization, sherardizing (galvanization of iron); **—ованный** *a.* sherardized; **—овать** *v.* sherardize.

**шерба** *f.* (min.) unit of weight (200 kg.).

**шербер** *m.* (met.) cupel, roasting dish, scorifier; **—ная проба** scorification.

**шербет** *m.* sherbet.

**шеренга** *f.* rank, file.

**Шерер** Scherer (name).

**шерерит** *see* **шеерерит.**

**шеретовка** *f.* hulling mill.

**шериданит** *m.* (min.) sheridanite (a talc-like chlorite).

шерл *m.* (min.) schorl, black tourmaline; —овый *a.* schorl, schorlaceous; —о-вая порода schorl rock.

шерникит *m.* (min.) schernikite (a variety of lepidolite-muscovite).

шерохов/альный *a.*, —ание *n.*, —ка *f.* roughing; buffing, polishing; —а-тость *f.* roughness; —атый *a.* rough, coarse, broken; —ики *pl.* (zool.) Echinodermata.

шерст/еподобный, —истый *a.* wooly, wool-like, fleecy; —инка *f.* wool thread; —ный *see* шерстяной.

шерсто/бит, —бой *m.* wool beater; wool carder; —битный, —бойный *a.* wool-beating; wool-carding; —бойня *f.* wool-beating mill; —мойка, —мойня *f.* wool washing; wool-washing plant; wool washer; —носный *a.* wool-bearing; —прядильный *a.* wool-spinning.

шерсточесальн/ый *a.* wool-carding; —ая машина wool carder.

шерст/ь *f.* wool; —як *m.* (bot.) eriochloa.

шерстян/ой *a.* wool, woolen; ш. жир wool fat, wool grease; suint, yolk; ш. пот suint, yolk; —ая пряжа wool yarn; —ое масло wool oil.

шерт *see* роговик.

шертинг *m.* (text.) shirting.

шерфование *n.* (leather) trimming.

шерхебель *m.* rough plane, jack plane.

шершав/еть *v.* grow rough, get rough, roughen; —ость *f.* roughness; —ый *a.* rough; —ый валец roughing mill.

шершень *m.* (zool.) hornet.

шессилит *m.* (min.) chessylite, azurite.

шест *m.* pole, rod, stick.

шествие *n.* procession, train, march.

шестерен/ка *see* шестерня; —ный, —чатый *a.* pinion, gear; —чатый привод pinion drive, gear drive; —чатая передача gear and pinion.

шестер/ик *m.*, —ка *f.* six, group of six; six-inch thickness; six-strand rope; six-inch nail; —ной *a.* six, sixfold; —ная ось (cryst.) hexad axis.

шестерня *f.* pinion, cog wheel, toothed wheel, gear, drive gear; ведущая ш. pinion gear, drive gear; коническая ш. bevel gear.

шестеро six; их ш. there are six of them.

шести— *prefix* hex—, hexa—, six;

—атомный *a.* hexatomic; hexahydric (alcohol); —валентный *a.* hexavalent; —валковый *a.* six-roller, six-high (rolling mill); —водный гидрат hexahydrate.

шестигранн/ик *m.* (geom.) hexahedron, cube; —ый *a.* hexahedral, cubic.

шести/десятый *a.* sixtieth; —дневка *f.* six-day week; —дневный *a.* six-day; —замещенные *pl.* hexasubstitution products, hexa-derivatives; —заряд-ный револьвер six-chambered revolver, six-shooter; —кратный *a.* sixfold, sextuple.

шестилет/ие *n.* six years, six-year period; —ний *a.* six-year, six-year-old.

шестилучев/ой *a.* hexactinal, six-rayed; hexagonal; —ые *pl.* (zool.) Hexacorallia.

шести/минутный *a.* six-minute; —муж-ний *a.* (bot.) hexandrous; —ногий *a.* (zool.) hexapod, six-legged; —основ-ный *a.* hexabasic; —польный *a.* (agr.) six-field (crop rotation); —про-водный *a.* six-wire; —сотый *a.* six-hundredth.

шестисторонн/ий *a.* (geom.) hexahedral, six-sided; hexagonal; —ик *m.* hexahedron; (cryst.) cube.

шестиугольн/ик *m.* (geom.) hexagon; —ый *a.* hexagonal.

шести/фазный *a.* six-phase; —фтори-стый *a.* hexafluoride (of); —членный *a.* six-membered; —электродная лампа (rad.) hexode.

шестнадцатигранн/ик *m.* (cryst.) diocta-hedron; —ый *a.* dioctahedral.

шестнадцат/ый *a.* sixteenth; —ь six-teen.

шестоват/ый *a.* columnar, stalked; (met.) spiky; —ая структура (min.) columnar structure.

шест/ой *a.* sixth; в —ых sixthly, in the sixth place; одна —ая one sixth.

шесток *m.* hearth.

шесть six; —ю ш. six times six; —десят sixty; —сот six hundred.

шеф *m.* chief, master; chef; patron; ш.-электрик chief electrician; —ство-вать *v.* patronize.

Шеффера кислота Schäffer's acid, Armstrong's acid.

**шефферит** *m.* (min.) schefferite.

**Шеффильд** Sheffield.

**шея** *f.* neck; vent.

**шибер** *m.*, **—ный** *a.* gate valve, gate, slide valve, slide plate; slide, slider, slide bar; damper (of chimney); **—ный вентиль** gate valve, slide valve.

**шибуол** *m.* shibuol.

**шизо—** *prefix* schizo—, split; **—генез** *m.*, **—гония** *f.* (biol.) schizogony, schizogenesis; **—мицеты** *pl.* (bot.) Schizomycetes; **—френия** *f.* (med.) schizophrenia.

**шикимол** *m.* shikimol, safrole.

**шиконин** *m.* shikonin.

**шикша** *f.* crowberry (*Empetrum*).

**шил** *past sing. of* **шить.**

**шиллер-шпат** *m.* (min.) schiller spar, bastite (an altered enstatite).

**шиллинг** *m.* shilling (coin).

**шило** *n.* awl, pricker; **—видный** *a.* awl-shaped, subulate.

**шильн/ик** *m.* (bot.) awlwort (*Subularia*); **—ый** *a.* awl; **—ая трава, —як** *m.* (bot.) broom, spec. dyer's broom (*Genista tinctoria*).

**шильце** *n.* small awl; (bot.) plumule, pip.

**ШИМ** *abbr.* (широтно-импульсная модуляция) pulse-width modulation.

**шимм** *m.* shim; **—ирование** *n.* (instrumentation) shimming.

**шимоза** *f.* melinite (picric acid).

**шимпанзе** *n.* (zool.) chimpanzee.

**шина** *f.* tire; (elec.) busbar, bus; (med.) cast, splint; (foundry) ear (of mold); **внутренняя ш.** inner tube; **массивная ш.** solid tire, truck tire; **распределительная ш., сборная ш., собирательная ш.** (elec.) busbar.

**шинировать** *see* **хинировать.**

**шинков/альный** *a.*, **—ание** *n.* (food) chopping, shredding; **—ать** *v.* chop, shred.

**шинколобвит** *m.* (min.) chinkolobwite, sklodowskite.

**шинн/ый** *a. of* **шина;** **—ое железо** band iron, hoop iron.

**шиншилла** *f.* (zool.) chinchilla.

**шип** *m.* pin, dowel pin; tongue, joint tongue, tenon; journal, pivot; horn, lug, projection; spine, thorn, prickle;

thorn needle; crampon; calking, calk; (zool.) sturgeon; **ш. и гнездо** tenon and mortise; **соединение —ом** tenon joint; **соединение —ом в гнездо** joining by mortise and tenon.

**шип/ение** *n.* hissing, hiss, fizzing, sizzle, effervescing; scratching (of phonograph needle); **—еть** *v.* hiss, fizz, sizzle, effervesce.

**шиповник** *m.* (bot.) dog rose (*Rosa canina*).

**шипонос** *m.* a parasitic worm (*Echinorhyncus*); **—ки** *pl.* tumbling flower beetles (*Mordellidae*).

**шипорезный** *a.* tenon-cutting; tenon (saw); **ш. станок** tenoner, tenoning machine.

**шипуч/есть** *f.* frothiness, foaminess, effervescence; **—ий** *a.* frothy, sparkling, effervescent, carbonated, soft (drinks); **—ее вино** sparkling wine, champagne.

**шипящий** *a.* hissing, fizzing, sibilant.

**шир.** *abbr.* (ширина) width.

**шире** *comp. of* **широкий, широко,** broader, wider; more broadly, more widely.

**шир/ение** *n.* broadening, widening, stretching; (text.) tentering; **—илка** *f.* expanding roller; **—ильная машина** (text.) stenter, tenter.

**ширин/а** *f.* width, breadth, gage (of rail); latitude; **по —е** edgewise, on edge; **пять футов —ы** five feet wide.

**ширит/ельный** *a.* stretching; **—ельная машина** stretcher; **—ь** *v.* stretch, widen, make wider, enlarge; **—ься** *v.* widen, spread, expand, enlarge.

**ширма** *f.* screen, shield.

**ширмерит** *m.* (min.) schirmerite.

**широк/ий** *a.* broad, wide, extensive; **—ая публика** the public at large; **—о** *adv.* broadly, widely, extensively.

**широковещ/ание** *n.*, **—ательный** *a.* (rad.) broadcast, broadcasting.

**широко/горлый** *a.* wide-necked (bottle); **—диапазонный** *a.* wide-range; **—захватный** *a.* wide-cut.

**ширококолейный** *a.* wide-gage, full-gage; **ш. путь** wide-gage track, wide gage.

**ширококостный** *a.* big-boned.

**ширококрыл/ые** *pl.* (pal.) Eurypterida; **—ый** *a.* broad-winged, large-winged.

широколист/венный, —ый *a.* broad-leaved; —ница *f.* (bot.) polypody (*Polypodium*).

широко/полосный *a.* wide-strip, broad-band; wide-range; strip (mill); — раскрытный *a.* wide-angle; —слойный *a.* broad-zoned; coarse-grained (wood); —ходовой *a.* loose.

широт/а *f.* latitude; —но-импульсный *a.* pulse-width; —но-модулированный *a.* width-modulated; —ный *a.* latitudinal.

ширпотреб *abbr.* (товары широкого потребления) commodities; цех —а salvaging department.

ширь *see* ширина.

шисто— *prefix* schisto— (cleft; fissure); —церка *f.* locust (*Schistocerca*); —цит *m.* (med.) schistocyte.

шит-асфальт *m.* sheet asphalt.

шитиха *f.* (blasting) squib.

шит/ый *a.* sewn; —ь *v.* sew, stitch; —ье *n.* sewing.

Шифа реактив Schiff's reagent, thioacetic acid.

шифер *m.* (petr.) slate; schist; shale; —вейс *m.* flake white (white lead); —ный *a.* slate, slaty, slate-like; schist, schistose; shale; scaly, flaky, foliated, foliaceous; —ная чернь mineral black (graphitic slate); —ное масло shale oil.

шифон *m.* (text.) chiffon.

шифр *m.* code, cipher; (libraries) classification number; —атор *m.* coder, encoder; —ованный *a.* written in code, ciphered, cipher, cryptographic; coded (message); —овать *v.* write in code, code.

Шиффа реактив *see* Шифа реактив.

шихан *m.* shikhan (monadnock consisting of a limestone reef in Bashkiria).

шихта *f.* (met.) charge, furnace charge, burden, batch, mixture; (petr.) schist; gas absorber (in mask); —рник *m.* (met.) mixing shed, mixing place; —рный *see* шихтовый.

шихтов/ание *n.*, —ка *f.* (met.) burdening, blending, mixing, preparing a mixture, calculating a charge; burden, charge; —ать *v.* burden, blend, mix, prepare a mixture, prepare a burden,

calculate a charge; —очный *a.* burdening, mixing, charging.

шихт/овый *a.* (met.) burden, charge, charging; ш. бункер stock bin; ш. двор, —плац *m.* mixing place; stock-yard.

шишак *see* шлемник.

шишель *m.*, —ный *a.* (foundry) core; —ник *m.* core maker; —ный ящик, —ная втулка core box.

шишечка *f.* bump, lump, knob, button.

шишечный *a.* (foundry) core; ш. каркас, ш. шпиндель core mandrel, core rod.

шишк/а *f.* bump, lump; tuber, knob; (bot.) cone; (foundry) core, mold core; отливать с —ой *v.* cast hollow; фальшивая ш. (foundry) drawback.

шишко/ватый *a.* bumpy, gnarled, knobby, torose, torous; tuberculate, nodular; —видный *a.* bumpy, knobby; cone-like; —видная железа (anat.) pineal gland; —носный *a.* (bot.) cone-bearing, coniferous.

шкал/а *f.* scale, range, dial; (time) base; ш. твёрдости scale of hardness; круговая ш. dial; со —ой graduated.

шканечный журнал logbook, log.

шкант *m.* dowel.

шкап *see* шкаф.

шкатулка *f.* box, case.

шкаф *m.*, —ной *a.* closet, locker; cupboard, cabinet, case; safe; (exhaust) hood; ш.-колонка column case; сушильный ш. desiccator.

шкафут *m.* gangway.

шкафчик *m.* small closet, locker.

шквал *m.* squall, gust of wind; flaw; —истый *a.* squally; —овой *a.* squall.

шквар *see* шкварки.

шквар/а, —ина *f.* scoria, dross, scum; (fat extraction) residue; —ки *pl.* crackling (crisp fat); —ный, —очный *a.* low-grade (fat).

шкворень *m.* pin, bolt, draw bolt, king bolt, king rod; (automobile) kingpin.

шкив *m.* pulley, sheave; ш.-маховик flywheel pulley, flywheel; —ообразный *a.* pulley-like, pulley; disk-like, discoid, discoidal.

школа *f.* school.

школьн/ик *m.* student, pupil; —ый *a.* school; —ый совет school board.

**шкраб** *abbr.* (школьный работник) student worker.

**шкуна** *f.* schooner.

**шкур/а** *f.*, **—ный** *a.* hide, skin, pelt; **—ка** *f.* abrasive cloth or paper; **стеклянная —ка** sandpaper.

**шлаг** *m.* explosive shell in a rocket.

**шлагбаум** *m.* barrier, bar, toll gate, lifting gate, swing gate; turnpike, toll road.

**шлак** *m.* slag, dross, scoria; cinder, sinter; (coal) clinker; tails; poison (in nuclear reactor); **волокнистый ш.** slag wool, slag, mineral wool; **топочный ш.** cinder; **—обетон** *m.* slag concrete (made of cement, slag and sand).

**шлаков/ание** *n.* slag formation, scorification; **—атый** *see* **шлаковидный**; **—ать** *v.* slag, form slag, scorify, clinker.

**шлако/видный** *a.* slaggy, scoriaceous, drossy; **—вик** *m.* slag chamber, slag pocket; cleaner, dust catcher (in furnace); **—вня** *f.* slag pot; skimmer; **—воз** *m.* slag car, slag buggy; **—вщик** *m.* cinder pit man.

**шлаков/ый** *a.* slag, slaggy, cinder, scoriaceous, drossy; clinker; **ш. камень, ш. кирпич** slag brick, slag block; **ш. конгломерат, ш. нарост, ш. слиток** cake (of slag or clinker); **ш. под печи** slag hearth; **ш. свинец** slag lead, slaggy lead; **—ая вата, —ая шерсть** slag wool, slag, mineral wool; **—ая камера** slag chamber, slag pocket; **—ая корка, —ая настыль** slag crust; clinker; **—ое железо** cinder iron.

**шлако/выпор** *m.* (foundry) out gate; **—выпускное окно** slag hole, cinder tap, cinder notch.

**шлакообраз/ный** *a.* slaggy, scoriaceous; **—ование** *n.* slag formation, scorification; **—ователь** *m.* slag former, slag-forming constituent; **—овательный** *a.* slag-forming.

**шлако/отделитель, —сниматель, —уловитель** *m.* slag separator, slag remover, skimmer, skim gate; **—подобный** *a.* slaggy, scoriaceous, drossy; **—приемник** *m.* slag catcher, cinder pocket; **—содержащий** *a.* slag-containing, slaggy, containing clinker;

**—удаление** *n.* slag removal, cinder removal.

**шлакующийся** *a.* slagging, clinkering.

**шлам** *m.*, **—овый** *a.* slime, mud, ooze, sludge; slurry; sediment, silt, residue, bottoms; tarry residue (in engine); drilling mud; (cer.) slip; **ш.-ваннер** *m.* (concentration) slime vanner; **—герд** *m.* slime pit; slime table; **—овый реактор** slurry (nuclear) reactor; **—овый стол** slime table; buddle; slime washer.

**шламо/образный** *a.* slime-like, slimy; slurry (nuclear fuel); **—образование** *n.* sludging; **—отделитель, —разделитель** *m.* slime separator; **—уловитель** *m.* slime extractor, sludge extractor.

**шланг** *m.*, **—овый** *a.* hose.

**шлеечная машина** (text.) thread extractor, thread picker.

**шлейка** *f.* strap.

**шлейф** *m.* (elec.) loop, circuit; tail (of curve); (agr.) leveler, drag, float; **ш.-борона** *f.* smoothing harrow; **—овать** *v.* smooth, plane; **—овый осциллограф** loop oscillograph.

**шлем** *m.* helmet; top section (of converter); (mech.) neck; (still) head; **предохранительный ш.** helmet, head guard.

**шлемгерд** *see* **шламгерд.**

**шлем/ник, —овник** *m.* (bot.) skullcap (*Scutellaria*); **—овой, —овый** *a.* helmet.

**шлеп/ать, —нуть** *v.* slap, splash.

**шлеппер** *m.* dragging device, tug, tappet, pull-over; transfer table; **вводящий ш.** (rolling) pull-over transfer; **выводящий ш.** pull-off transfer.

**шлет** *pr. 3 sing. of* **слать.**

**шли** *past pl. of* **идти.**

**шликер** *m.* (met.) dross; (cer.) slip; **съем —ов** dressing, skimming.

**Шлиппе соль** Schlippe's salt, sodium sulfantimonate.

**шлипс** *m.* tool extractor, tool grab.

**шлир/а** *f.*, **—ы** *pl.* schlieren (regions of varying refraction as in liquids); (petr.) schlieren, streaks, striae, indistinct inclusions; (glass) thread or tear-shaped flaw; **—овое строение** streaky structure.

**шлите** *imp. of* **слать.**

**шлиф** *m.*, **—ной** *a.* section, microsection, polished section, slide; cross-sectional view; ground-glass joint; **—ной напильник** smooth file, smooth-cut file.

**шлифовальн/ый** *a.* polishing, buffing, burnishing, grinding, abrasive; **ш. круг** polishing wheel, polishing disk; **ш. материал** abrasive; **ш. порошок** polishing powder, grinding powder; **ш. состав** grinding compound; **ш. станок** polishing machine, grinder; **—я** *f.* polishing room, grindery.

**шлифов/альщик, —щик** *m.* polisher, grinder; **—ание** *n.*, **—ка** *f.* polishing, burnishing, grinding, abrasion, abrading; **—анный** *a.* polished, burnished, ground; **—ать** *v.* polish, burnish, grind, abrade.

**шлифтик** *m.* smoothing plane.

**шлифующий** *see* **шлифовальный.**

**шлих** *m.*, **—овый** *a.* (ore) slime, schlich, slick; concentrate; alluvial sand.

**шлихта** *f.* (text.) size; dressing.

**шлихтов/альный** *a.*, **—ание** *n.*, **—ка** *f.* smoothing, planing, finishing; dressing; (text.) sizing; (met.) planishing; **—альная шкурка** fine emery cloth; **—анный** *a.* finished; dressed, sized; **—ать** *v.* smooth, plane, finish; dress, size; planish; (foundry) blackwash, apply a wash (to molds).

**шлихштейн** *m.* (met.) lead matte.

**шлиц** *m.* slit, slot, groove; **—евать** *v.* slit, make slits, slot, groove; **—евой** *a.* slit, slot; castle-type; **—евая ножовка** slitting saw; **—евая фреза** slot cutter; **—ованный** *a.* slit, grooved, splined.

**шлюз** *m.*, **—ный** *a.* sluice, lock, gate valve, sluice valve; **—ник** *m.* sluice keeper; **—ный сбор** lockage (toll); **—ование** *n.* locking, damming; **—ованный** *a.* locked, dammed; lock (canal); **—овать** *v.* sluice.

**шлюп** *m.* sloop; **—ка** *f.* launch, small boat.

**шлю/т** *pr. 3 pl. of* **слать; —щий** *a.* sending.

**шлямбур** *m.* jumper (borer).

**шлямовочная машина** stripping machine.

**шляп/а** *f.*, **—ный** *a.* hat; **—ка** *f.* cap, head (of nail, etc.).

**шляпо/видный, —образный** *a.* hat-shaped; (bot.) pileate.

**шлях** *m.* road.

**шляхтхебель** *m.* plane.

**шмак** *m.* sumac (dye); **—овка** *f.* dyeing with sumac.

**шмальт/а** *f.* smalt, cobalt blue; **—ин** *m.* (min.) smaltite, cobalt arsenide.

**шмель** *m.* bumble bee; **ш. кукушка** lodger bee (*Psithyrus*).

**шмикит** *m.* (min.) szmikite.

**шнебергит** *m.* (min.) schneebergite.

**Шнейдера печь** Schneider's (zinc) furnace.

**шнейдерит** *m.* (expl.) schneiderite.

**шнек** *m.*, **—овый** *a.* auger; worm, endless screw; worm conveyer, screw conveyer; **ш.-смеситель** pug mill; **—овый транспортер** worm conveyer, screw conveyer.

**шнит/-лук, —тлук** *m.* (bot.) chives (*Allium schoenoprasum*); **—т-салат** *m.* cut-leaved lettuce (*Lactuca sativa* var. *secalina*).

**Шнорра земля** (min.) Schnorr's earth.

**шнур** *m.* cord, string, twine; lace, lacing, braid; (elec.) flex, flexible cord, flexible cable; (blasting) fuse; (nucl.) pinch.

**шнуров/ание** *n.*, **—ка** *f.* lacing, tying; **—ать** *v.* lace, tie; **—ой** *a.* string, cord, lace; corded (book).

**шнур/ок** *m.* little cord, lace, twine; (blasting) fuse; **—ки** *pl.* laces.

**Шоба копер** Schob impact strength tester.

**шов** *m.*, **—ный** *a.* seam, joint, junction; depression, groove; (anat.) commissure; (med., bot.) suture; **без шва** seamless; **неплотность шва** joint leakage; **—ная сварка** seam welding.

**шодди** *n.* shoddy (wool).

**Шодрона элемент** (elec.) Chaudron's thermopile.

**шок** *m.*, **—ировать** *v.* shock; **—кер** *m.* shocker.

**шоколад** *m.*, **—ный** *a.* chocolate; **—ное дерево** *see* **какао.**

**Шомодьи** Somogyi (name).

**шомолнокит** *m.* (min.) szomolnokite (a hydrous ferrous sulfate).

**шомпол** *m.* ramrod, ram, rammer, tamping stick, tamper; **—ьное ружье** muzzle loader.

**шоопирование** *n.* Schoope process, metallization process, metal pulverization.

**шопот** *see* **шепот.**

**Шор: твердость по —у** Shore hardness.

**шора** *f.* (min.) a supporting framework.

**шорломит** *m.* (min.) schlorlomite (a titanium garnet).

**шорн/ая** *f.* saddler's shop; **—ик** *m.* harness maker; **—ый** *a.* harness (leather).

**шорох** *m.* noise, rustling.

**шортволл-машина** *f.* (min.) shortwall machine (coal cutter).

**шоссе** *n.*, **—йный** *a.*, **—йная дорога** highway, paved road.

**шоссиров/ание** *n.* highway construction; macadamization; **—ать** *v.* build a highway, improve a road; macadamize.

**шотвельд** *m.* shot welding.

**Шотки эффект** (thermionics) Schottky effect, shot effect.

**шотл.** *abbr.* (**шотландский**) Scotch.

**Шотландия** Scotland.

**шотланд/ка** *f.*, **—ская материя** (text.) plaid; **—ский** *a.* Scotch.

**шотовское стекло** *see under* **шоттовское.**

**Шоттена реакция** Schotten's reaction.

**Шоттки** *see* **Шотки.**

**шоттовское стекло** Schott (Jena) glass.

**шофер** *m.* (automobile) driver.

**шпага** *f.* sword.

**шпагат** *m.* binder twine.

**шпадель** *see* **шпатель.**

**шпажка** *f.* finishing tool.

**шпажник** *m.* (bot.) gladiolus.

**шпаклев/ание** *n.*, **—ка** *f.* spachtling, filling, filling up, puttying; filler, putty; first coat (of paint); **—ать** *v.* spachtle, fill, putty, stop (holes); apply a ground coat (of paint).

**шпала** *f.* crosstie, sleeper.

**шпалер/а** *f.*, **—ник** *m.* espalier; trellis, latticework.

**шпан** *m.* span piece, bar.

**шпанголит** *m.* (min.) spangolite.

**шпангоут** *m.* rib (of ship), frame.

**шпанка** *f.* (bot.) black cherry; (zool.) merino sheep; Spanish fly.

**шпанрама** *f.* (text.) stenter, tenter, stretching frame.

**шпанск/ий** *a.* Spanish; **—ая пила** pit saw, cleaving saw; **—ие мушки** Spanish flies, cantharides.

**шпарить** *v.* scald.

**шпарутка** *f.* (text.) temple.

**шпат** *m.* (min.) spar; (vet.) obs. name for arthritis; spavin; **бурый ш.** brown spar, ferruginous dolomite; **горький ш.** bitter spar, crystalline dolomite; **досчатый ш., дощатый ш.** tabular spar, wollastonite; **малиновый ш.** rhodochrosite; **пенистый ш.** foam spar, earth foam, aphrite; **полевой ш.** feldspar; **синий ш.** blue spar, azure spar, lazulite; **тяжелый ш.** heavy spar, barite, baryte, barytes.

**шпатель** *m.* spatula.

**шпатлев/ание, —ка** *see* **шпаклевание.**

**шпато/видный** *a.* (min.) spathiform, sparry, spar; **—вый** *a.* spar, sparry, spathic; **—вый гипс** sparry gypsum, selenite; **—вый железняк** spathic iron, siderite, chalybite.

**шпахтель** *m.* spatula.

**шпация** *f.* (typ.) space.

**шпей/за** *f.*, **—совый** *a.* (met.) speiss; **—зофен** *m.* copper furnace; **—скобальт** *m.*, **—совый кобальт** (min.) smaltite.

**шпек** *see* **шпик.**

**шпелейзофен** *see* **шпейзофен.**

**шпенек** *m.* pin, peg, prong.

**шперак** *m.* beak iron, bickern, horn (of anvil).

**шпергель** *m.* (bot.) spergula.

**шпиатр** *m.* type metal.

**шпиг** *m.*, **—а** *f.* lard.

**шпигель** *m.* (met.) spiegel, spiegeleisen; specular (cast) iron; Cordovan leather; **—ная вагранка** spiegel cupola.

**шпигов/альный** *a.*, **—ание** *n.* larding; **—анный** *a.* larded; **—ать** *v.* lard.

**шпик** *m.*, **—овать** *v.* lard.

**шпилить** *v.* pin, fasten with a pin.

**шпиль** *m.* spire, steeple; needle, pin, pivot; reel, capstan, windlass.

**шпилька** *f.* small nail, tack; hairpin; peg, dowel; prong; cotter pin; (text.) spindle; **соединение на —x** dowel joint; **установочная ш.** dowel pin.

**шпинат** *m.* spinach (*Spinacia oleracea*).

**шпингалет** *m.* latch, catch, bolt.

**шпиндель** *m.*, **—ный** *a.* spindle, pivot,

axle, arbor, shaft, mandrel; stem (of valve); **рассверливающий ш.** boring bar; **—ная бабка** headstock.

**шпинел/евый** *a.*, **—ь** *f.* (min.) spinel; **—лид** *m.* spinellide (a member of the spinel group).

**шпинтон** *m.* tail spindle.

**шпион** *m.* spy; (min.) twist drill.

**шпитц/лутен** *m.*, **—лютте** *n.* (ore concentration) spitzlutte.

**шпиц** *m.* spire, steeple; **—евание** *n.* pointing; **—кастен** *m.* (ore concentration) spitzkasten, funnel box, V-vat; **—лютте** *see* **шпитцлутен**; **—метр** *m.* water gage.

**шплейзофен** *m.*, **—ное гнездо** (met.) refining hearth.

**шплинт** *m.* splint; split pin, cotter pin; pin, key.

**шпод** *m.* (min.) grapnel.

**шпон** *m.* (typ.) lead; veneer sheet (of wood), plywood.

**шпонка** *f.* dowel; joint tongue; (mach.) key; **направляющая ш.**, **скользящая ш.** sliding key.

**шпоночно-долбежный станок** key-slotting machine, key seater; **ш.-фрезерный станок** keyway milling machine, slot milling machine.

**шпоночн/ый** *a.* joint tongue; cotter, key; **ш. болт** key bolt; **ш. паз**, **—ая канавка** key bed, key seating, keyway.

**шпора** *f.* spur; (mech.) lug.

**шпорник** *m.* (bot.) delphinium.

**шпред/ер** *m.*, **—инг-машина** *f.* spreader (for rubberizing cloth); **—ингование** *n.*, **—ировка** *f.* spreading, rubberizing.

**шприц** *m.* syringe, injector, squirt, sprayer; (med.) hypodermic syringe; (grease) gun; wash bottle; **—гусс** *m.* die casting; **ш.-машина** *f.* extruder; **ш.-процесс** *m.* extrusion process; pipe manufacture; **—евание** *n.* extrusion; **—евать** *v.* extrude; **—ованный** *a.* extruded.

**шпрот** *m.*, **—овый** *a.* (zool.) sprat.

**шпул/едержатель** *m.* bobbin holder; **—ька** **—я** *f.* (text., elec.) spool, bobbin; **—ьная машина** winding machine, winder.

**шпунт** *m.* groove, slot, channel; pile; **ш. и гребень** groove and tongue; **—**

**губель** *see* **шпунтубель**; **—ина** *f.* pile plank.

**шпунтов/альный** *a.* grooving, rabbeting; **—ание** *n.* grooving, rabbeting; groove and tongue; **—анный** *a.* grooved; **—ать** *v.* groove, rabbet; tongue, groove and tongue; **—ник** *m.* grooving plane; **—ый** *a.* groove, grooved, grooved and tongued; **—ый ряд** sheet piling; **—ая свая** pile plank; **—ое соединение** groove-and-tongue joint, grooving and tonguing.

**шпунтубель** *m.* grooving plane, rabbet plane, tongue plane.

**шпур** *m.* (math.) spur (of matrix); (geom.) trace; (min.) blast hole, bore hole; (met.) furnace outlet, gutter.

**шпур/овая печь**, **—офен** *m.* (met.) concentration furnace; **—штейн** *m.* concentrated matte, concentration metal; **синий —штейн** blue concentrated metal, blue metal (a copper matte).

**ШР** *abbr.* (**Шоппер-Риглер**) (paper) Schopper-Riegler (pulp freeness, degrees).

**шрадан** *see* **октаметил**.

**шрам** *m.* scar.

**шрапнель** *f.*, **—ный** *a.* (mil.) shrapnel.

**шрауфит** *m.* (min.) schraufite (resin).

**шраффировать** *v.* shade, hatch, line.

**шредер** *m.* shredder, shredding machine; **—овать** *v.* shred.

**Шредингера волновая функция** Shroedinger wave function.

**шрейбер/зит** **—сит** *m.* (min.) shreibersite (an iron-nickel phosphide).

**шре/кингерит** *m.* (min.) schroekingerite (a uranium sulfate-carbonate); **—ттерит** *m.* (min.) schroetterite.

**шрифт** *m.* type, character.

**шрот** *m.* small shot; grist, groats; oil cake; **ш.-эффект** *m.* (thermionics) Schrott effect, shot effect.

**шт.** *abbr.* (**штука**) thing; piece; (**штат**) state.

**штаб** *m.* (mil.) staff, headquarters; **ш.-офицер** field officer; **главный ш.** general staff.

**штабел/евать** *v.* pile, stack; **—ер** *m.* stacker; **—ь** *m.* pile, stack, stockpile.

**штабик** *m.* molding.

**штабн/ой** *a.* staff; **—ая служба** staff duty.

штамб *m.*, —овый *a.* stem, trunk, body (of tree); bole.

штамм *m.* (bact.) strain, line.

штамп *m.* stamp, punch, puncher, die; вырезывающий ш. blanking die.

штампов/альный *see* штамповочный; —ание *n.*, —ка *f.* stamping, die stamping, punching; pressing; extrusion; drop forging; горячая —ка drop forging; —анный *a.* stamped, punched; pressed; wafer; drop-forged; stock (phrase); —ать *v.* stamp, punch; press; impress, emboss; coin; drop-forge.

штамповочн/ый *a.* stamping, punching; pressing; ш. молот drop hammer; die; ш. пресс stamping press, punch press; ш. станок stamp; —ые работы punch-press work.

штампов/щик *m.* stamp operator, puncher; —ый *a.* stamp, punch; *see also* штамповочный; —ые краски printing inks.

штанг/а *f.*, —овый *a.* bar, rod; pole, beam, arm; spear; stem (of valve); буровая ш. boring bar; —ен высоты —енрейсмасс, —енрейсмус *m.* height gage; —ензубомер *m.* gear-tooth gage; —енциркуль *m.* slide gage, sliding calipers; —овая крепь (min.) roof bolting; —овое бурение bar drilling; —удлинитель *m.* push rod; —щик *m.* (surv.) rodman, staffman.

штандоль *m.* stand oil, lithographic oil (polymerized linseed oil).

штанцевание *n.* stamping, punching.

штаны *pl.* trousers, breeches.

штапель *m.*, —ный *a.* staple.

штарковский эффект (phys.) Stark effect.

штат *m.* state; staff, establishment; быть в —е *v.* be on the staff.

штатив *m.* support, stand, holder; (test tube) rack; base, foot; tripod.

штатный *a.* state, official; regular; staff.

штатский *a.* civil, civilian; *m.* civilian.

штауфер *m.*, —ка *f.*, Штауффера масленка Stauffer lubricator; —ная букса grease box, grease cup.

штейгер *m.* mine boss, head miner.

штейн *m.* (met.) matte; белый ш., сокращенный ш. white metal (smelted copper); голубой ш. blue metal (a copper matte); корки —а matte scrap.

штейнаш *m.* stone ash (a mixture of potash and potassium hydroxide).

штейнгут *m.* (cer.) thin white ware.

штеккер *m.*, —ный *a.* (elec.) plug.

Штейнмеца закон (elec.) Steinmetz law.

штейновый *a.* (met.) matte.

штеккер *m.*, —ный *a.* (elec.) plug.

штеклинг *m.* (agr.) steckling, slip.

штемпел/евание *n.* stamping, die stamping; —евать *v.* stamp, impress; postmark; —ь *m.*, —ьный *a.* stamp, punch, die; seal; plunger (of press); почтовый —ь postmark.

штенгель *m.* stem, stalk; exhaust tube.

штендер *m.* (min.) pillar, support.

штепсел/евать *v.* (elec.) plug in; —ь *m.*, —ьный *a.*, —ьная вилка plug; —ьная коробка junction box; —ьная розетка plug socket, receptacle.

Штерна-Герлаха эффект Stern-Gerlach effect.

штернбергит *m.* (min.) sternbergite.

штиблеты *pl.* boots.

штил/евой *a.* still, calm; —евая полоса, —ь *m.* calm.

штирийский *a.* Styrian; Штирия Styria.

Штифеля способ Stiefel (disk-piercing) process.

штифт *m.* joint pin, pin, spike; dowel; stem, pivot; (elec.) plug; —ик *m.* brad.

штихель *m.* engraving tool, graver, burin.

штихмас, —с *m.* inside caliper gage, pin gage, end-measuring rod; раздвижной ш. adjustable caliper gage.

шток *m.* coupling rod, rod (of piston, etc.); (geol.) boss, stock, shoot, block (of ore); —верк *m.* (min.) stockwork; —лак *m.* stick lac.

штокроза *f.* hollyhock (*Althaea rosea*).

штольн/я *f.*, —евый *a.* (min.) gallery, drift, tunnel; adit, entrance; passage; выемочная ш. drift tunnel.

штольцит *m.* (min.) stolzite (a lead tungstate).

штоп/альный *a.*, —ка *f.* darning, mending; —ать *v.* darn, mend.

штопор *m.*, —ный *a.* corkscrew; (aero.)

spin; **спуск —ом** (aero.) spinning; **—ить** *v.* spin.

**штора** *f.* blind, curtain.

**шторм** *m.*, **—овой** *a.* storm, gale.

**штосгерд** *m.* (min.) impact buddle, jolting buddle.

**штоссель** *m.* rammer, stamper; tappet.

**штоф** *m.* (text.) damask; old unit of liquid measure (1.23 l.).

**штранц** *m.* strand, beach.

**штраф** *m.* fine, penalty; **—овать** *v.* fine.

**штревель** *m.* (min.) tamping bar, tamper.

**штрейкбрехер** *m.* strike breaker, scab.

**штрек** *m.* (min.) drift, drive; **выемка —ами** drift mining, drifting.

**Штреккера реакция** Strecker reaction.

**штренгит** *m.* (min.) strengite.

**штрипка** *f.* strap.

**штрипс** *m.*, **—овый** *a.* (met.) strip; **—о- вый стан** strip mill, skelp mill; **—овая сталь** strip steel; steel strip, skelp.

**штрих** *m.* stroke, touch; trait, feature; mark, line, dash; hatchure; (math.) prime; **—оватость** *f.* streak (plant disease); **—оватый** *a.* hatched, striated; **—овать** *v.* hatch, crosshatch, shade; **—овка** *f.* hatch, hatching, hatchure, shading, striation; **—овой** *a.* dash; hatch; facsimile (transmission); **—овой пунктир, —овая линия** dash line; **—овой пунктир, —овая линия** dash line; **—передача** *f.* facsimile transmission; **ш.-точечный пунктир** dot-and-dash line.

**штудировать** *v.* study.

**штука** *f.* thing; piece, sample, specimen.

**штукатур** *m.* plasterer; **—ить** *v.* plaster, stucco; **—ка** *f.* plaster, plastering, stucco.

**штуковать** *v.* piece, patch; fine-draw.

**штукофен** *m.* (met.) high bloomery furnace.

**штуп** *m.* stupp, mercurial soot.

**штурвал** *m.* steering wheel, pilot wheel; (aero.) control stick; star wheel; turnstile; **—ьчик** *m.* star knob.

**штурм** *m.* attack.

**штурман** *m.* (aero.) pilot; (navy) mate.

**штурмов/ать** *v.* attack; **—ик** *m.* stormovik (attack plane); **—ой** *a.* attack (bomber); scaling (ladder).

**штуф** *m.* (min.) a large specimen of ore,

a lump of (high-grade) ore; **—ный** *a.* lump; **—ный сульфид** (met.) massive sulfide; **—ная руда** lump ore.

**штуцер** *m.*, **—ный** *a.* connecting pipe, connecting branch, sleeve; carbine, rifle.

**штучн/ый** *a.* thing; piece; inlaid; **ш. ка- мень** block rubble; **—ая цена** unit price.

**штыб** *m.* fines; tails; culm (an anthracite dust); **—оотбрасыватель, —оотвал** *m.* culm remover.

**штык** *m.* bayonet; (met.) bar, ingot, pig; (agr.) depth of spade; **ш.-нож, ш.- тесак** (mil.) sword bayonet; **чугун в —ах** pig iron; **—овка** *f.* turning over (soil).

**штыков/ой, —ый** *a.* bayonet; (met.) bar, ingot, pig; **ш. затвор** bayonet lock, bayonet catch; **ш. контакт** (elec.) plug; **—ая медь** ingot copper, pig copper, copper bar.

**штыр/ь** *m.*, **—евой** *a.* pin, dowel; shaft, spindle; pintle, pivot pin; probe.

**штэк-фильтр** *m.* (min.) filter drain (perforated pipe in wall).

**Штюве диаграмма** Stüve (adiabatic) diagram.

**шуба** *f.* fur coat.

**шубригель** *see* **штангенциркуль.**

**шуга** *f.* slush ice, floating anchor ice.

**Шульце-Гарди правило** Schulze-Hardy rule (of colloid coagulation).

**шум** *m.* noise, sound.

**шумановская область** (phys.) Schumann region.

**шум/еть** *v.* make noise; **—иха** *f.* uproar; spangle, tinsel, shining platelet; **—ный** *a.* noisy, loud; **—овка** *f.* crackle; skimmer, ladle.

**шумо/глушитель, —заглушитель** *m.* muffler, silencer; **—мер** *m.* noise gage; **—пеленгатор** *m.* (naut.) hydrophone.

**шумящий** *a.* noisy; roaring (flame); (vet.) emphysematous (carbuncle).

**шунгит** *m.* (min.) schungite, shungite (an amorphous form of carbon).

**шунт** *m.* (elec.) shunt; by-pass.

**шунтиров/ание** *n.*, **—ка** *f.* (elec.) shunting; **—анный** *a.* shunted; **—ать** *v.* shunt.

**шунт/ирующий** *a.* (elec.) shunting; bypass; **—ование** *see* **шунтирование;**

—овать *see* шунтировать; —овой *a.*
shunt; (mach.) shunt-wound; by-
pass; —омер *m.* shunt meter.
шуров/ание *n.*, —ка *f.* rabbling, stirring,
poking; —ать *v.* rabble, stir, poke;
stoke, kindle; —ой *see* шуровочный.
шуровочн/ый *a.* rabble, rabbling; ш.
лом, ш. сокол, —ая лопата rabbler,
rabble, poker; —ая плита dead plate
(of furnace); —ое отверстие stirring
hole, poke hole; fire hole; —ое приспособление stirring device, stirrer,
rabble.
шуруп *m.* wood screw.
шурф *m.* perforation, hole; (min.) prospecting pit, bore pit, pit; —обур *m.*

portable drill; —ование *n.*, —овка *f.*
prospecting, pitting; —овать *v.* perforate; prospect, make pits; —овочная машина pitting machine; —овщик *m.* digger, excavator.
шурш/ание *n.*, —ащий *a.* crackling,
rustling; —ать *v.* crackle, rustle.
шуст *m.* auger.
шут/ить *v.*, —ка *f.* jest, joke.
шуцлак *m.* protective lacquer.
шхеры *pl.* sea cliffs, rocks.
шхуна *f.* schooner.
шь/ет *pr. 3 sing. of* шить; —ют *pr. 3 pl.*;
—ющий *a.* sewing.
шэпинг *see* шепинг.

# Щ

щавелево/амиловый эфир amyl oxalate;
—аммониевая соль ammonium oxalate; —бутиловый эфир butyl oxalate; —железистая соль ferrous oxalate; —железная соль ferric oxalate;
—калиевая соль potassium oxalate;
—кальциевая соль calcium oxalate.
щавелевокисл/ый *a.* oxalic acid; oxalate
(of); щ. анилин aniline oxalate; щ.
ряд oxalic acid series; —ая соль
oxalate; кислая —ая соль bioxalate.
щавелево/медная соль cupric oxalate;
—метиловый эфир methyl oxalate;
—натриевая соль sodium oxalate;
—никелевая соль nickel oxalate;
—уксусная кислота oxalacetic acid;
—этиловый эфир ethyl oxalate.
щавелев/ый *a.* oxalic; (bot.) sorrel; —ая
кислота oxalic acid, ethanedioic acid;
соль —ой кислоты oxalate; кислая
соль —ой кислоты bioxalate.
щавел/ек *m.* (bot.) sheep sorrel (*Rumex
acetosella*); —ь *m.*, —ьный *a.* dock
(*Rumex*); кислый —ь, обыкновенный —ь sorrel (*Rumex acetosa*).
щадит/ель *m.* shock absorber; —ельный
*a.* sparing; merciful; —ь *v.* spare; be
merciful.
щебен/ить *v.* fill with rubble; —ка *see*
щебень; —очный *a.* rubble; —очный
слой ballast (of road bed).
щебень *m.* rubble, crushed stone, broken
stone, gravel, ballast; chips, chippings,
rubbish; (geol.) detritus; мелкий щ.

rubble, chippings; шлаковый щ.
broken slag.
щедрин/а, —ка *f.* pockmark.
щедр/ость, —ота *f.* liberality, generosity;
—ый *a.* liberal, generous.
щек/а *f.* cheek; jowl; jaw (of vise, crusher); side, sidepiece, flange; —овая
дробилка, —одробилка *f.* (mach.)
jawbreaker; —овая стена overhanging wall; —овые плиты jaw plates
(of crusher).
щеколда *f.* latch, catch, pawl, finger,
trigger, trip gear.
щекообразный *a.* jaw-shaped.
щекот/ать *v.* tickle; —ливый *a.* ticklish;
delicate.
щел. *abbr.* (щелочный) alkaline.
щеле/видный *a.* slit-like; —вой *a.* slot,
slotted, slit, chink.
щел.-зем. *abbr.* (щелочноземельный) alkaline earth.
щел/ина, —ка *see* щель; —истый *a.*
rimose, full of fissures.
щелк/ание *n.* clicking, snapping; —ать,
—нуть *v.* click, snap.
щелковская зелень Soviet variant of
Paris green (insecticide).
щелкуны *pl.* click beetles (*Elateridae*).
щелок *m.* lye, alkali, caustic; liquor;
натровый щ. caustic soda solution.
щелоч/ение *n.* alkalization; lixiviation;
—ерастворимый *a.* alkali-soluble;
—еустойчивый *see* щелочноупор-
ный; —ить *v.* alkalize; lixiviate.

**щелочно**— *prefix* alkali—; —**земельный металл** alkali earth metal.

**щелочн/ой** *a.* alkaline, alkali, caustic; **щ. металл** alkali metal; **щ. раствор** alkaline solution, alkali solution; —**ая земля** alkali earth; —**ое свойство** alkalinity; **сделать** —**ым** *v.* render alkaline, alkalize.

**щелочно/сть** *f.* alkalinity, concentration of alkali; —**упорный**, —**устойчивый** *a.* alkaliproof, alkali-resisting.

**щелочь** *f.* alkali; **водная едкая щ.** alkali hydroxide.

**щелчок** *m.* click.

**щель** *f.* chink, slit, crack, fissure, cleft; aperture, gap; peephole; flaw; **голосовая щ.** (anat.) glottis.

**щем/ить** *v.* pinch, smart; —**ление** *n.* pinching, smarting; —**ло** *n.* vise, press; brace (of drill).

**щенок** *m.* puppy; cub; whelp.

**щеп/а** *f.* chips, shavings, splinters, slivers; kindling; —**ально-драночный станок** peeling machine; —**ание** *n.* chipping; splitting, cleaving; —**ать** *v.* chip, splinter, split, cleave; bite, sting, smart.

**щепетильный** *a.* scrupulous, punctilious.

**щеп/ить** *see* **щепать**; —**ка** *f.* chip, sliver, splinter, shaving; *pl.* kindling; —**коловитель** *m.* (paper) sliver screen; —**ные изделия** light wood materials.

**щепот/ка**, —**очка**, —**ь** *f.* pinch.

**щерба** *f.* chip; fish broth.

**щерб/атый** *a.* chipped; pockmarked; full of chinks; gap-toothed; —**ина** *see* **щель**, **щерба**.

**щет** *m.* (bot.) horsetail (*Equisetum*).

**щетин/а** *f.*, —**ный** *a.* bristle, stubble; —**истый** *a.* bristly, setaceous, setose; —**иться** *v.* bristle; —**ка** *f.* chaeta, seta, bristle; —**ко**, —**о**— *prefix* bristle, seti—; —**коносный** *a.* aristate; —**(к)охвосты** *pl.* (zool.) bristletails (*Thysanura*); —**кочелюстные** *pl.* arrowworms (*Chaetognatha*); —**ник** *m.* bristle grass (*Setaria*); —**ница** *f.* (bot.) spikenard (*Aralia racemosa*); —**оватый** *a.* bristly; —**овидный** *a.* setiferous; —**ообразный** *a.* bristle-shaped, setiform.

**щет/ка** *f.* brush; **искрение** —**ок** (elec.) brush sparking; —**кодержатель** *m.*

brush holder; —**очка** *f.* little brush; —**очник** *m.* brush maker; —**очный** *a.* brush; —**очный палец** (elec.) brush spindle, brush holder arm, brush stud; —**очная траверза** brush yoke.

**щечка** *see* **щека**.

**щечный** *a.* (anat.) cheek, buccal, malar.

**щи** *pl.* cabbage soup.

**щикол/ка**, —**отка** *f.* ankle.

**щип/альный** *a.* plucking; —**ание** *n.* plucking; pinching, nipping; —**ать**, —**нуть** *v.* pluck; pinch, nip; nibble, crop, browse (on); —**аться** *v.* pinch; —**ец** *m.* gable; —**ок** *m.* nip, pinch, tweak.

**щипц/еобразный** *a.* forcipate, forceps-like; —**овый** *a.* forceps, tongs; gable (roof); —**ы** *pl.* forceps, tongs, pincers, pliers; (electrode) holder.

**щипчики** *pl.* forceps, pincers, tweezers.

**щирица** *f.* (bot.) amaranth (*Amaranthus*).

**щит** *m.* shield, screen, blind; switchboard; board, panel; (turtle) shell; **щ. от грязи** mudguard; **щ. управления** control panel; **распределительный щ.** switchboard.

**щит/ковидный** *a.* (bot.) corymbose; —**ники** *pl.* stink bugs (*Pentatomidae*).

**щитовидный** *a.* shield-shaped, scutellate; thyroid (gland); (bot.) peltate.

**щитовк/а** *f.* scale insect; **калифорнийская щ.** San Jose scale; —**и** *pl.* armored scales (*Diaspidinae*).

**щитовник** *m.* wood fern (*Dryopteris*).

**щиток** *m.* shield, screen, cover; dashboard, panelboard, (instrument) board; (bot.) cyme, corymb; (zool.) thorax.

**щитоноска** *f.* a leaf beetle (*Cassida*).

**щитообразный** *a.* shield-shaped, scutellate.

**щука** *f.* (zool.) pike, pickerel (fish).

**щуп** *m.* feeler, probe, sounding borer; dip rod; (met.) test rod, trial rod; thickness gage, clearance gage; —**алец** *m.* (text.) feeler; —**альный** *a.* feeler, feeling, probing; —**альце** *n.* (zool.) tentacle, feeler; antenna; —**альцежвалы** *pl.* (zool.) Chelicerae; —**альценогие** *pl.* (zool.) Palpigradi; —**ание** *n.* feeling, touching probing; —**ать** *v.* feel, touch, probe.

**щупл/ость** *f.* undeveloped state (of seeds); —**ый** *a.* sickly, weak, undersized.

**щурить** *v.* screw up (eyes), squint.

**щучий** *a.* pike (fish).

**щучка** *f.* hair grass (*Aira*); tussock grass (*Deschampsia caespitosa*).

# Э

**э** *abbr.* (эрг) erg; (эрстед) oersted; (электрон) electron.

**эбен, американский** granadilla (fruit of *Passiflora*).

**эбенов/ые** *pl.* (bot.) Ebenaceae; —**ый** *a.* ebony; —**ое дерево** *see* черное дерево.

**Эбергарда явление** (phot.) Eberhard effect.

**эбланин** *m.* eblanin, pyroxanthine.

**эбонит** *m.,* —**овый** *a.* ebonite, hard rubber.

**эбуллиоскоп** *m.* ebullioscope; —**ический** *a.* ebullioscopic; —**ия** *f.* ebullioscopy.

**эбурин** *m.* eburine (a synthetic ivory).

**эв** *abbr.* (электрон-вольт) electron volt.

**эв—** *see also* **эй—**.

**эваку/ация** *f.,* —**ационный** *a.* evacuation; —**ированный** *a.* evacuated; —**ировать** *v.* evacuate, empty, exhaust.

**эвальвация** *f.* evaluation, estimation.

**эван/зит,** —**сит** *m.* (min.) evansite.

**эвапор/атор** *m.* evaporator; —**ация** *f.* evaporation, vaporization; —**иты** *pl.* (geol.) evaporites; —**ометр** *m.* (meteor.) evaporimeter.

**эвгедральн/ость** *f.* (petr.) euhedral character; —**ый** *a.* euhedral, automorphic.

**эвген—** *see* евген—, эйген—.

**эвгленовые** *pl.* (zool.) Euglenoidina.

**эвгранитовый** *a.* (geol.) eugranitic, granitoid.

**эвдиалит** *m.* (min.) eudialyte.

**эвдиометр** *m.* eudiometer; —**ический** *a.* eudiometric; —**ия** *f.* eudiometry, gasometry, gasometric analysis.

**эвдоксин** *see* эйдоксин.

**эвердур** *m.* Everdur (a copper alloy).

**эверитова соль** Everitt's salt, potassium ferrous ferrocyanide.

**эверн/иин** *m.* everniine; —**иновая кислота** everninic acid, evernesic acid; —**овая кислота** evernic acid; —**уровая кислота** evernuric acid.

**эвипал** *m.* Evipal, hexobarbital.

**эвкалипт** *m.,* —**овый** *a.* (bot.) eucalyptus; —**ен** *m.* eucalyptene; —**овое масло** eucalyptus oil; —**ол** *m.* eucalyptole, cineole; —**олен** *m.* eucalyptolene.

**эвклаз** *m.* (min.) euclase (a member of the datolite group).

**эвкод/ал** *m.* Eucodal, dihydrohydroxycodeinone; —**еин** *m.* eucodeine, methyl codeine bromide.

**эвкоммия** *see* эйкоммия.

**эвкрит** *see* эйкрит.

**эвксенит** *m.* (min.) euxenite.

**эвктолит** *m.* (petr.) euctolite.

**эвнатрол** *m.* eunatrol, sodium oleate.

**эвод/ен** *m.* evodene; —**иамин** *m.* evodiamine.

**эвольвент/а** *f.,* —**ный** *a.* (geom.) evolvent; (geom.) evolute.

**эволюта** *f.* (geom.) evolute.

**эволюц/ионировать** *v.* evolve, develop, unfold; evolutionize; —**ионистический** *a.* evolutionistic; —**ионный** *a.* evolution, evolutionary; —**ия** *f.* evolution.

**эвпа/рин** *m.* euparin; —**торин** *m.* eupatorine (alkaloid); eupatorin (glucoside).

**эври—** *prefix* eury— (wide, broad); —**птериды** *pl.* (pal.) Eurypterida.

**эврит** *m.* (petr.) eurite, petrosilex.

**эвритермный** *a.* (zool.) eurythermal.

**эвритомуха** *f.* eurytomid, chalcid fly, spec. clover seed chalcid (*Bruchophagus gibbus*).

**эвстатический** *a.* (geol.) eustatic.

**эвтаксит** *m.* eutaxite (banded volcanic rock); —**овое строение** eutaxitic structure, banded structure, platy parting (flow layers).

**эвтект/ика** *f.,* —**ический** *a.* eutectic; —**оид** *m.,* —**оидный** *a.* (met.) eutectoid.

**эвфорб/ий** *m.* euphorbium (resin); —**ин** *m.* euphorbin; —**иновая кислота** euphorbic acid.

**эвшель** *m.* (met.) zaffer (a cobalt oxide).

**Эгейское море** the Aegean Sea.

**эгида** *f.* aegis; protection.
**эгилопс** *m.* (bot.) aegilops.
**эгирин** *m.* (min.) aegirite, acmite.
**эгле** *n.*, **—вое дерево** (bot.) Bengal quince (*Aegle marmelos*).
**эгоистич/еский**, **—ный** *a.* egoistic, self-centered, narrow.
**эгутер** *m.* (paper) dandy roll.
**ЭД** *abbr.* (электродиализ) electrodialysis.
**эдаф/ология** *f.* edaphology, science of soils; **—он** *m.* edaphon, soil life; **—онический** *a.* edaphic.
**Эдвина процесс** (met.) Edwin process.
**эдельвейс** *m.* (bot.) edelweiss (*Leontopodium*).
**Эдера жидкость** Eder's solution.
**эдестин** *m.* edestin (a seed globulin).
**эджер** *m.* edger.
**эджрайт** *m.* Age-Rite (antioxidant for rubber).
**Эдисона явление** (elec.) Edison effect.
**—эдр** *m. suffix* —hedron; **—ический** *a. suffix* —hedral.
**эдс** *abbr.* (электродвижущая сила) electromotive force.
**ЭДТА** *abbr.* (этилендиаминтетрацетат) ethylenediaminetetraacetic acid sodium salt; **ЭДТУ** *abbr.* (этилендиаминтетрауксусная кислота) ethylenediaminetetraacetic acid.
**Эдуарда черепицы** Edward's tiles.
**э.ед.** *abbr.* (электронная единица) electronic unit.
**эжектор** *m.*, **—ный** *a.* ejector, ejector pump; lift-out attachment, lifting out device, grapnel.
**эзенбек/ин** *m.* esenbeckine; **—овая кислота** esenbeckic acid.
**эзер/амин** *m.* eseramine; **—идин** *m.* eseridine; **—ин** *m.*, **—иновый** *a.* eserine, physostigmine; **сернокислый —ин** eserine sulfate.
**эзоксин** *m.* esoxin.
**эзофагоскоп** *m.* (med.) esophagoscope.
**ЭИН** *abbr.* (Энергетический институт Академии наук СССР) Institute of Power Engineering of the Academy of Sciences, USSR.
**эй—** *see also* **эв—**; **—галлол** *m.* eugallol, pyrogallol monoacetate.
**эйген/величина** *f.*, **—верт** *m.* (math.) eigenvalue, proper value.
**эйген/ин** *m.* eugenin; **—овая кислота**

eugenic acid, eugetinic acid; eugenol; **—ол** *m.* eugenol, 4-allylguaiacol; **коричнокислый —ол** eugenol cinnamate.
**эйдален** *m.* eudalene, 7-isopropyl-1-methyl naphthalene.
**Эйде** *see under* **Биркеланд.**
**эйдесмол** *m.* eudesmol.
**эйджрайт** *see* **эджрайт.**
**эйдидимит** *m.* (min.) eudidymite.
**эйдоксин** *m.* eudoxine, bismuth Nosophen.
**эйкаин** *m.* eucaine.
**эйкайрит** *m.* (min.) eucairite.
**эйкалипт** *see* **эвкалипт.**
**эйкарвон** *m.* eucarvone.
**эйкоз/ан** *m.* eicosane; **—ановая кислота** eicosanic acid; **—анол** *m.*, **—иловый спирт** eicosanol, eicosyl alcohol, arachidic alcohol; **—ил** *m.* eicosyl; **—илен** *m.* eicosylene.
**эйкозоль** *m.* a casein paint for leather.
**эйколит** *m.* (min.) eucolite (similar to eudialyte).
**эйком/ия**, **—мия** *f.* (bot.) Chinese gutta-percha tree (*Eucommia ulmoides*); **—миевые** *pl.* Eucommiaceae.
**эйконоген** *m.* (phot.) Eikonogen.
**эйкриптит** *m.* (min.) eucryptite.
**эйкрит** *m.* (petr.) eucrite.
**эйксант/ин** *m.* euxanthin; **—иновая кислота** euxanthinic acid, euxanthic acid, purreic acid; **—оген** *m.* euxantogen, mangiferin; **—он** *m.* euxanthone, purrone, 1,7-dihydroxyxanthone; **—оновая кислота** euxanthonic acid.
**эйксенит** *m.* (min.) euxenite, polycrase.
**эйкупин** *m.* Eucupin, *i*-amylhydrocupreine.
**эйлер/ианский** *a.*, **—ов** (math.) Eulerian, Euler's.
**эйлиз/ин** *m.* eulysin; **—ит** *m.* (petr.) eulysite (a peridotite).
**эйлиптол** *m.* eulyptol.
**эйлит/ин**, **—ит** *m.* (min.) eulytin, eulytite.
**эйм/енол** *m.* Eumenol; **—идрин** *m.* Eumydrin, atropine methyl nitrate.
**эйнатрол** *see* **эвнатрол.**
**эйнштейний** *m.* einsteinium, Es.
**эйоним/ин** *m.* euonymin; **—ит** *m.* euonymit, dulcitol; **—оид** *m.* euonymoid.
**эйосмит** *m.* (min.) euosmite (fossil resin).

**эйпар/ал** *m.* euparal (synthetic resin); **—ин** *m.* euparin.

**эйпат/ирин** *m.* eupatirin, stevioside; **—орин** *m.* eupatorin.

**эйпир/ин** *m.* eupyrine; **—хроит** *m.* (min.) eupyrchroite (a variety of apatite).

**эйпиттон** *m.*, **—овая кислота** eupittone, eupittonic acid, hexamethoxyaurine.

**эйралит** *m.* (min.) euralite (a chlorite).

**эйрезол** *m.* Euresol, resorcinol monoacetate.

**Эйри спираль** (optics) Airy's spiral.

**эйрибин** *m.* eurybin.

**эйрит** *m.* (petr.) eurite (a felsite).

**эйробин** *m.* eurobin, chrysarobin triacetate.

**эйродин** *m.* eurhodine.

**эйрофен** *m.* europhen, isobutyl-*o*-cresol iodide.

**эйстенин** *m.* eustenin, theobromine sodium iodide.

**эйтаксит** *see* **эвтаксит.**

**эйтаннин** *m.* eutannin.

**эйтиохроновая кислота** euthiochronic acid.

**эйфельский ярус** (geol.) Eifelian stage.

**эйфилл/ин** *m.* Euphylline, theophylline ethylenediamine; **—ит** *m.* (min.) euphyllite (a mica).

**эйфорбий** *see* **эвфорбий.**

**эйфорин** *m.* euphorine, phenylurethan.

**эйфоти/д** *m.* (petr.) euphotide, gabbro; **—ческий** *a.* euphotic, gabbro.

**эйфтальмин** *m.* euphthalmine, eucatropine.

**эйфурбин** *m.* euphurbin.

**Эйхгорна гидрометр** Eichhorn's hydrometer.

**эйхинин** *m.* Euquinine, quinine ethylcarbonate.

**эйхроит** *m.* (min.) euchroite.

**эйхроновая кислота** euchroic acid, mellitic acidimide.

**эйч-металл** *m.* Aich's metal (a copper-zinc-iron alloy).

**эка—** *prefix* eka—; **—алюминий** *m.* eka-aluminum, gallium; **—бор** *m.* eka-boron, scandium; **—силиций** *m.* ekasilicon, germanium; **—толит** *m.* ekatolite (calcite filling the fir-like cavities in nepheline syenite); **—элемент** *m.* ekaelement.

**экбалин** *m.* ecbalin, elateric acid.

**экболин** *m.* ecboline.

**экв.** *abbr.* (эквивалент, эквивалентный) equivalent.

**Эквадор** Ecuador.

**экватор** *m.* equator; **—иал** *m.* equatorial (telescope); **—иальный** *a.* equatorial.

**экв. ед.** *abbr.* (эквивалентная единица) equivalent unit.

**экви—** *prefix* equi—.

**эквивалент** *m.* equivalent, weight equivalent; **—ность** *f.* equivalence; **—ный** *a.* equivalent; **—ная стоимость** equivalent value; **закон —ных отношений** law of definite proportions.

**эквидистантный** *a.* equidistant.

**экви/зетовая кислота** equisetic acid, aconitic acid; **—ленин** *m.* equilenin.

**эквилибр** *m.* equilibrium, balance; **—ировать** *v.* equilibrate, balance; **—истика** *f.* equilibration, equipoise.

**эквилин** *m.* equilin.

**эквимолекулярный** *a.* equimolecular.

**эквимолярный** *a.* equimolar.

**эквипотенциальный** *a.* equipotential.

**ЭКГ** *abbr.* (электрокардиограмма) electrocardiogram.

**экгон/идин** *m.* ecgonidine, *dl*-anhydroecgonine; **—ин** *m.* ecgonine, tropinecarboxylic acid.

**экдемит** *m.* (min.) ecdemite, heliophyllite.

**экз.** *abbr.* (экземпляр) copy; specimen.

**экз—** *see also* **экс—**; **—альгин** *m.* Exalgin, methylacetanilide; **—альтация** *f.* (chem.) exaltation.

**экзам/ен** *m.*, **—енационный** *a.*, **—енация** *f.* examination; **—енатор**, **—инатор** *m.* examiner; **—еновать** *v.* examine.

**экзантема** *f.* (med.) exanthema.

**экзарация** *f.* (geol.) exaration, furrowing.

**экзегетический** *a.* (math.) exegetic.

**экзема** *f.* (med.) eczema; **—тозный** *a.* eczematous.

**экземпляр** *m.* copy; specimen, sample; model; **в трех —ах** in triplicate.

**экзо—** *prefix* exo— (outside, outer); ecto—; **—асковый** *a.* (bot.) exoascaceous; **—гамия** *f.* (biol.) exogamy; **—генный** *a.* exogenous, produced outside; **—дерма** *f.* (biol.) exoderm.

**экзоморф/изм** *m.* (geol.) exomorphism; **—ный** *a.* exomorphic (contact rocks).

**экзосмо/с** *m.* exosmosis; **—тический** *a.* exosmotic.

**экзотерический** *a.* exoteric; external.

**экзотерм/ический, —ный** *a.* exothermic, heat-liberating; **—ическое соединение** exothermic compound; **—ичность** *f.* exothermic nature.

**экзо/тический** *a.* exotic; **—токсин** *m.* (bact.) exotoxin; **—трофный** *see* **эктотрофный; —ты** *pl.* exotic plants or animals; **—фтальм** *m.* (med.) exophthalmia; **—энергетический** *a.* (phys.) exoenergic.

**эквивок** *m.* equivocality, ambiguity; ambiguous term.

**экипаж** *m.* vehicle, carriage; crew.

**экипиров/анный** *a.* equipped, furnished; **—ать** *v.* equip, furnish, fit out; **—ка** *f.* equipment, fitting out, outfit; housing; **—очный** *a.* equipment.

**эккер** *m.* (surv.) cross-staff.

**эклиметр** *m.* inclinometer; clinometer.

**эклип/с** *see* **затмение; —тика** *f.*, **—тический** *a.* (astron.) ecliptic.

**эклогит** *m.* eclogite (a garnet-pyroxene rock); **—овый** *a.* eclogite, eclogitic.

**экмолин** *m.* ekmolin (Soviet antibiotic).

**эко—** *prefix* eco— (habitat, environment).

**эколид** *m.* Ecolid, chlorisondamine chloride.

**эколог/ический** *a.* (biol.) ecological; **—ия** *f.* ecology, bionomics.

**эконом/айзер, —изатор** *m.* economizer, waste gas heater; **—етр** *m.* econometer; **—ика** *f.* economics; economy, economic structure; **—ист** *m.* economist; **—ить** *v.* economize, save, cut down expenses.

**экономическ/ий** *a.* economical; commercial; **—ая горелка** pilot burner; **—ая игла** economizer (in carburetor), waste heat utilizer.

**экономичн/ость** *f.* economy; efficiency; **—ый** *a.* economical; efficient.

**эконом/ия** *f.* economy, saving; **—ничать** *v.* economize, save; **—ность** *f.* economy; **—ный** *a.* economical; **—совет** *m.* Council of Economics.

**экран** *m.* screen, shield; baffle, deflector; **э. для защиты от** (nucl.) shield.

**экранир/ование** *n.* screening, shielding, insulation; (elec.) screening effect; (electrochem.) shadowing; **коэффициент —ования, постоянная —ования** screening number, screening constant (of element); **эффект —ования, —ующее действие** screening effect; **—ованный** *a.* screened, shielded; **—ованная камера** (nucl.) hot cell (of hot laboratory); **—овать** *v.* screen, screen off, shield; **—ующий** *a.* screening, shielding; **—ующая сетка** (thermionics) screen grid.

**экс—** *prefix* ex—; *see also* **экз—; —анол** *m.* polyisobutylene used as a lubricating oil additive.

**эксанталовая кислота** ecsantalic acid.

**эксгаустер** *m.* exhauster, exhaust fan, suction fan, aspirator.

**эксикатор** *m.* exsiccator, desiccator, dryer.

**эксит/он** *m.*, **—онный** *a.* (electron.) exciton; **—рон** *m.* excitron.

**экскаватор** *m.* excavator, power shovel, digger, dredge; **кабельный э., канатный э.** drag-line excavator; **—ный** *a.* excavator, excavation; **—ные работы** excavation, excavation work.

**экскавация** *f.* excavation, digging; cutting (of road).

**экскре/ментный** *a.* excremental; **—менты** *pl.* excrement, feces; **—ты** *pl.* (physiol.) excreta, excretions; **—ция** *f.* excretion, elimination.

**экскурс** *m.* digression; **—ионный** *a.*, **—ия** *f.* excursion, trip.

**эксосмос** *see* **экзосмос.**

**экспан/дор, —зер** *m.* expander; **зионный, —сионный** *a.* expansion; **—сивный** *a.* expansive; **—син** *m.* Expansine, patulin (antibiotic); **—сиометр** *m.* expansion gage; **—сия** *f.* expansion, expanse.

**экспед/ировать** *v.* expedite, facilitate; dispatch, send; **—итор** *m.* file clerk; forwarding agent; **—иционный** *a.* expeditionary; dispatch; **—иционные исследования** field work; **—иция** *f.* expedition; dispatch office.

**экспеллер** *m.* expeller.

**экспенд/ер** *m.* (tire manufacture) expander; **—ирование** *n.* expanding.

**эксперимент** *m.* experiment, test, trial;

**—ально** *adv.* experimentally; **—альный** *a.* experimental, experiment; tentative; pilot (plant); research (nuclear reactor); **—атор** *m.* experimenter; **—ирование** *n.* experimentation; **—ировать** *v.* experiment.

**эксперт** *m.* expert; examiner, inspector; **—иза** *f.* expert's opinion, consultation, arbitration; examination, appraisal, valuation, estimation; certificate.

**экспираторный** *a.* expiratory.

**экспликация** *f.* explication, explanation; legend, key (of diagram).

**эксплоат—** *see* **эксплуат—**.

**эксплуататор** *m.* exploiter; **—ский** *a.* exploiting.

**эксплуатационн/ый** *a.* exploitation, operation, operating, working; service, performance, field (test); cruising (power of engine); **э. режим** operating conditions, working conditions; **—ая надежность** serviceability; **—ые качества** performance; **—ые расходы** operating costs, cost of operation, maintenance cost.

**эксплуат/ация** *f.* exploitation, operation; maintenance; improvement; working (of land, mines); **ввести в —ацию** *v.* put into service, put into operation; **отдел —ации** maintenance division; **условия —ации** operating conditions, working conditions; **—ировать** *v.* exploit, use, operate, run, work.

**экспоз/е** *n.* exposé, exposure; **—иция** *f.* exposition, exhibition, display; exposure (to light, etc.); exposure time; **коэффициент —иции** exposure factor.

**экспон/ат** *m.* exhibit; **—ент** *m.* exhibitor; (math.) exponent, index; **—ента** *f.* exponential (curve); **—ентный, —енциальный** *a.* exponential; **—ировать** *v.* exhibit, show; expose (to light, etc.); irradiate; **—ометр** *m.* exposure meter; spec. intensitometer, X-ray exposure meter.

**экспорт** *m.* export, exportation; **—ер** *m.* exporter; **—ирование** *n.* exportation; **—ировать** *v.* export; **—ный** *a.* export, exportable; **—ная торговля** export; **—ное дело** export business.

**экспресс** *m.* express; **э.-анализ** quick analysis, approximate analysis; **э.-лаборатория** field laboratory; **э.-старение** accelerated aging.

**экспромтом** *adv.* impromptu, extempore, without preparation.

**экспропри/ация** *f.* expropriation; **—ировать** *v.* expropriate, dispossess.

**экссуд—** *see* **эксуд—**.

**экстенз/ометр** *see* **экстенсометр**; **—ор** *m.* (anat.) extensor.

**экстенсивн/ость** *f.* extensiveness; **—ый** *a.* extensive.

**экстенсометр** *m.* extensometer.

**экстерн** *m.* extramural student.

**экстерьер** *m.* exterior.

**экстинкция** *f.* extinction.

**экстирп/атор** *m.* extirpator, cultivator; **—ация** *f.* extirpation, weed extermination.

**экстра—** *prefix* extra—.

**экстраваганти/ость** *f.* extravagance; **—ый** *a.* extravagant, liberal.

**экстрагент** *m.* extractant, extracting agent.

**экстрагир/ование** *n.* extraction, separation; **—ованный** *a.* extracted; **—о-вать** *v.* extract; **—уемый** *a.* extractable; **—ующий** *a.* extracting.

**экстрак/т** *m.* extract; **—тивный** *a.* extractive, extractable; **—тивное вещество** extractive; **—тор** *m.* extractor; **—ционный** *a.*, **—ция** *f.* extraction; **—ционная перегонка** extractive distillation; **—ционная фосфорная кислота** wet-process phosphoric acid.

**экстралин** *m.* an antiknock additive for gasoline.

**экстраординарный** *a.* extraordinary, unusual, uncommon; **э. профессор** professor adjunct; reader.

**экстрапол/ирование** *n.*, **—яция** *f.* extrapolation; **—ированный** *a.* extrapolate, extrapolated; **—ировать** *v.* extrapolate.

**экстраток** *m.* (elec.) extra current.

**экстрациклическое соединение** extracyclic compound.

**экстрем/альный** *a.*, **—ум** *m.* (math.) extreme.

**экстренн/о** *adv.* specially; **—ый** *a.* special, urgent; emergency; unforeseen (expenses).

**экструзия** *f.* extrusion.

**эксуд/ат** *m.* (med.) exudate; —**ация** *f.* exudation.

**эксфолиация** *f.* exfoliation.

**эксцельсиор** *m.* excelsior (wood shavings).

**эксцентрик** *m.*, —**овый** *a.* (mach.) eccentric; cam, cam gear; —**овый вал** camshaft; —**овый привод** cam drive.

**эксцентри/ситет** *m.*, —**чность** *f.* (mach., math.) eccentricity; —**ческий**, —**чный** *a.* eccentric, off-center.

**эксцесс** *m.* excess.

**эксцизия** *f.* excision, cutting out.

**экто—** *prefix* ecto— (outside, external); —**генез** *m.* ectogenesis; —**генный** *a.* ectogenic; (bact.) ectogenous; —**дерма** *f.* (zool.) ectoderm; —**мия** *f.* *suffix* —ectomy (surgical removal); —**пия** *f.* (med.) ectopy; —**плазма** *f.* (biol.) ectoplasm; —**трофный** *a.* (bot.) ectotrophic, nourished from without.

**экугин** *m.* echugin, echujin.

**Экштейна-Эйбнера основание** Eckstein-Eibner base, ethylideneaniline.

**элаидин** *m.*, —**овый** *a.* elaidin; —**овая кислота** elaidic acid, *trans*-9-octadecenoic acid; **соль —овой кислоты,** —**овокислая соль** elaidate.

**эла/ил** *m.* elayl, ethylene; —**ин** *m.* elain (obs. name for ethylene).

**элаио/метр** *m.* elaiometer (oil-expressing device); —**пласт** *m.* (bot.) elaioplast.

**эларсон** *m.* Elarson, strontium chloroarsenobehenolate; —**овая кислота** elarsonic acid.

**эласмы** *pl.* chalcid flies (*Elasmidae*).

**эластанс** *m.* (elec.) elastance.

**эластик** *m.* rubber; rubber tire.

**эластин** *m.* elastin (a protein).

**эластич/еский**, —**ный** *a.* elastic, resilient, springy, flexible, supple; —**ность** *f.* elasticity, resilience, spring, flexibility.

**эластомер** *m.* elastometer.

**элат/ерин** *m.* elaterin; —**ерит** *m.* elaterite, mineral caoutchouc; —**еровая кислота** elateric acid, ecbalin; —**ерон** *m.* elaterone; —**ин** *m.* elatine; —**иновая кислота** elatinic acid; —**овая кислота** elatic acid.

**элбон** *m.* Elbon, cinnamoyl-*p*-hydroxyphenylurea.

**эл.-графич.** *abbr.* (электронно-графический) electron-diffraction.

**элеватор** *m.*, —**ный** *a.* elevator, hoist, lift; (grain) elevator.

**электрет** *m.* electret (a dielectric material).

**электриз/атор** *m.* electrizer; —**ация** *f.*, —**ование** *n.* electrification, electrifying; —**ованный** *a.* electrified; —**овать** *v.* electrify, electrize; charge; —**уемость** *f.* electrifiableness; —**уемый**, —**ующийся** *a.* electrifiable.

**электрик** *m.* electrician; electric blue.

**электрит** *see* электрет.

**электрифи/кация** *f.* electrification; —**цированный** *a.* electrified; —**цировать** *v.* electrify.

**электрически** *adv.* electrically, by means of electricity.

**электрическ/ий** *a.* electric, electrical; *see also* электро—; **э. заряд** electric charge; **э. привод** electric drive; **с —им приводом** electrically driven; **э. фонарь** flashlight; —**ая восприимчивость** dielectric susceptibility; —**ая отдача** electrical efficiency; —**ая проводка** electric wiring; —**ая проницаемость** dielectric constant, permittivity; —**ая прочность** dielectric strength; —**ая станция** (electric) power plant; —**ая цепь** electric circuit; **отрицательно э.** electronegative; **положительно э.** electropositive.

**электричеств/о** *n.* electricity; **э. трения** frictional electricity; **возбуждение —а, производство —а** generation of electricity.

**электро** *n.* electro, electrotype.

**электро—** *prefix* electro—, electric; —**акустика** *f.* electroacoustics; —**анализ** *m.* electroanalysis; —**биология** *f.* electrobiology; —**бус** *m.* electrobus; —**вагонетка** *f.* electric truck, power truck.

**электроваленти/ость** *f.* electrovalence; —**ый** *a.* electrovalent; —**ые соединения** electrovalent compounds.

**электро/воз** *m.* electric locomotive; —**возбудительный** *see* электродвижущий; —**воспламенитель** *m.* electric fuse; —**взрыватель** *m.* (min.) electric exploder; —водокачка *f.* electric pump; —вязкостный *a.* electroviscous.

электрогенератор *m.* electric generator, generator; —ный *a.* generator; electricity-generating.

электрогониометр *m.* electrogoniometer, phase indicator.

электрограф/ический *a.* electrographic; —ия *f.* electrography.

электрод *m.* electrode; напряжение —ов electrode potential.

электродвигатель *m.* electric motor; —ный *a.* electric motor; electromotive.

электродвижущ/ий *a.* electromotive; э. ряд electromotive series, displacement series; —ая сила electromotive force.

электродетонатор *m.* (min.) electric exploder.

электродиализ *m.* electrodialysis.

электродинам/ика *f.* electrodynamics; —ический *a.* electrodynamic; —о-метр *m.* electrodynamometer.

электрод/ный *a.* electrode; —одержатель *m.* electrode holder.

электро/дойка *f.* electric milking; —доменная печь electric blast furnace.

электродуг/а *f.* electric arc; —овая сварка electric arc welding, arc welding.

электро/емкость *f.* capacity; —закалка *f.* (met.) electrotempering; —запал *m.* electric fuse; —защита *f.* cathodic protection (against corrosion); —звуковой *a.* electroacoustic; —золь *m.* electrosol; —изгородь *f.* electric fence; —измерительный прибор electric meter; —изолирующий *a.* electric insulating.

электроиндук/тивный *a.* electroinductive, inductive; —ция *f.* electroinduction, induction.

электро/калориметр *m.* electrocalorimeter, electric resistance calorimeter; —капилярный *a.* electrocapillary; —кара *f.* power truck; —кароттаж *m.* (min.) electric logging; —кинетика *f.* electrokinetics; —кинетический *a.* electrokinetic; —коррозия *f.* electrocorrosion; —корунд *m.* synthetic corundum; —кратовый *a.* electro-

cratic (colloid); —крекинг *m.* (petroleum) electrocracking; —культура *f.* (bot.) electroculture; plant raising in electrically heated hotbeds and hothouses.

электролиз *m.* electrolysis; подвергать —у *v.* electrolyze; —атор, —ер *m.* electrolyzer; —ация *f.* electrolyzing; —ный *a.* electrolysis, electrolytic; —ованный *a.* electrolyzed; —овать *v.* electrolyze, decompose by electrolysis.

электролит *m.* electrolyte; —ический, —ный *a.* electrolytic; —ический элемент electrolytic cell; —ическое покрытие (met.) electrodeposition.

электролюминесцен/тный *a.* electroluminescent; —ция *f.* electroluminescence.

электромагн/етизм *m.* electromagnetism; —ит *m.* electromagnet; —итиза-ция *f.* electromagnetization; —итный *a.* electromagnetic.

электромашинный *a.* dynamoelectric (amplifier).

электромер *m.* electromer; —ия *f.* electromerism.

электрометалл *m.* (welding) filler metal; —ургия *f.* electrometallurgy.

электрометр *m.* electrometer; —ический *a.* electrometric; —ия *f.* electrometry.

электромехани/ка *f.* electromechanics; electrical engineering; —ческий *a.* electromechanical.

электро/миграция *f.* electromigration; —монтер *m.* electrician; —мотор *m.* electromotor, electric motor; —мотриса *f.* a small electric truck; —мощность *f.* electric power.

электрон *m.* electron; Elektron (magnesium-base alloy); э. отдачи recoil electron; э. связи bonding electron; э.-вольт *m.* electron volt, ev (unit of energy).

электро/наседка *f.* (electric) incubator; —натирание *n.* (met.) an electrodeposition process.

электрон/ика *f.* electronics; —но-лучевой *a.* electron-beam; cathode-ray (tube); —но-позитронный *a.* electron-positron; —но-разрядный *a.* electron-discharge.

электронн/ый *a.* electron, electronic; э.

луч electron beam; **э. прожектор,** **—ая пушка** electron gun; **—ая лампа** electron tube; (rad.) vacuum tube; **—ая формула** electronic formula; **—ое облако** electron cloud; **—ое сродство** electron affinity.

**электроно/грамма** *f.* electron-diffraction pattern; **—граф** *m.* electron-diffraction camera; **—графический** *a.* electron-diffraction; **—графия** *f.* electron diffraction (study).

**электро/оборудование** *n.* electrical equipment; **—оптика** *f.* electrooptics; **—осадитель** *m.* electric precipitator; **—осаждение** *n.* electrodeposition, electrolytic precipitation; **—осмос** *m.* electroösmosis; **—отрицательность** *f.* electronegativity; **—отрицательный** *a.* electronegative; **—очистка** *f.* electrical precipitation (of gases); **—пайка** *f.* electric welding; **—пастух** *m.* electric fence.

**электропечь** *f.* electric furnace; **э. прямого действия** direct arc furnace; **дуговая э.** electric arc furnace.

**электропиролиз** *m.* electropyrolysis.

**электропитание** *n.* electric power supply.

**электроплав/ильный** *a.*, **—ка** *f.* (met.) electrosmelting; **—ильная печь** electrosmelting furnace.

**электро/подъемник** *m.* electric elevator; **—покрытие** *n.* (met.) electrodeposition, electroplating; **—полировка** *f.* (met.) electrolytic polishing; **—положительный** *a.* electropositive; **—предприятие** *n.* electrical works; **—привод** *m.* electric drive.

**электропровод/имость** *f.* electrical conductance; **—ка** *f.* (electric) wiring; **—ность** *f.* electric conductivity, specific conductance; **—ящий** *a.* conducting.

**электро/производительность** *f.* electrical efficiency; **—пушка** *f.* (met.) iron-notch gun (in blast furnace); **—пылеуловление** *n.* electrical dust precipitation; **—разведка** *f.* (min.) electric geophysical exploration; **—резка** *f.* (electric) arc cutting; **—сварка** *f.*, **—сварочный** *a.* electric welding; arc welding; **—сверло** *n.* electric drill; **—свечение** *n.* electroluminescence; **—связь** *f.* electric communica-tion; **—сеть** *f.* power supply net-work; **—сила** *f.* electric power; **—синтез** *m.* electrosynthesis.

**электроскоп** *m.* electroscope; **э.-дозиметр** radioscope; **—ический** *a.* electroscopic; **—ия** *f.* electroscopy.

**электросмоз** *see* **электроосмоз.**

**электросталь** *f.* electric steel.

**электростанция** *f.* power plant.

**электростати/ка** *f.* electrostatics; **—ческий** *a.* electrostatic.

**электро/стенолиз** *m.* electrostenolysis; **—сторож** *m.* electric fence; **—стрикция** *f.* electrostriction; **—таль** *f.* electrically operated compound pulley; **—терапия** *f.* electrotherapy.

**электротерм/ический** *a.* electrothermal; **—ия** *f.* electrothermics.

**электротехни/к** *m.* electrician, electrical engineer; **—ка** *f.* electrical technology, electrical engineering; **—ческий** *a.* electrotechnical, electrical, electrical engineering.

**электро/тигель** *m.* electric crucible; **—типия** *f.* electrotypy; **—тяга** *f.* electric traction; **—управляемый** *a.* electrically controlled; **—фильность** *f.* electrophilicity; **—фильный** *a.* electrophilic; **—фильтр** *m.* electrostatic precipitator, Cottrell precipitator; **—фон** *m.* electrophone; **—фор** *m.* electrophorus; **—форез** *m.* electrophoresis; **—формовка** *f.* electroforming.

**электрохим/ический** *a.* electrochemical; **э. ряд** electrochemical series, electromotive series, displacement series; **—ия** *f.* electrochemistry.

**электро/хозяйство** *n.* electric plant; **—централь** *m.* power house, power plant; **—часы** *pl.* electric clock; **—шерардизация** *f.* (met.) electrosherardizing; **—эндосмос** *m.* electroendosmosis; **—энергия** *f.* electric energy, electric power; **—ядерный** *a.* electronuclear.

**электрум** *m.* (min.) electrum (native gold-silver alloy).

**электуар/ий, —иум** *m.* (pharm.) electuary, confection.

**элемент** *m.* element; unit, component; (elec., electrolytic) cell; (elec.) couple;

(meteor.) factor; member (of construction); **э.-индикатор** *m.* indicator element; **э. с одной жидкостью** single-fluid cell; **гальванический э.** galvanic cell, voltaic cell; **жидкостный э., наливной э.** wet cell; **периодическая система —ов** periodic system (of the elements); **сухой э.** dry cell.

**элементарн/ость** *f.* elementariness; **—ый** *a.* elementary, elemental, simple; fundamental; ultimate (analysis); **—ая ячейка** (cryst.) unit cell; **—ое звено** monomer unit, mer.

**элементный** *a.* element; (elec.) cell.

**элементоорганический** *a.* hetero-organic.

**элемецин** *m.* elemecin.

**элем/и** *n.*, **смола э.**, **—иевый** *a.* elemi, elemi gum; **—ин** *m.* elemin; **—ицин** *m.* elemicin, 1-allyl-3,4,5-trimethoxybenzene; **—овая кислота** elemic acid; **—ол** *m.* elemol; **—оновая кислота** elemonic acid.

**элео—** *prefix* eleo—, elaeo— (oil).

**элеолит** *m.* (min.) eleolite, elaeolite (a variety of nephelite); **—овый** *a.* elaeolithic.

**элеомаргариновая кислота** eleomargaric acid, octadecadienoic acid.

**элеометр** *m.* elaeometer (oil hydrometer).

**элеонорит** *m.* (min.) eleonorite.

**элеостеариновая кислота** eleostearic acid, octadecatrienoic acid.

**элерон** *m.* (aero.) aileron, flap.

**элефантиазис** *m.* (med.) elephantiasis.

**элиазит** *m.* (min.) eliasite (a variety of gummite).

**эликсир** *m.* elixir.

**элимин/ант** *m.* (math.) eliminant; **—атор** *m.* eliminator; **—ация** *f.* elimination; **—ировать** *v.* eliminate.

**элинвар** *m.* Elinvar (an iron-nickel-chromium alloy).

**элипс** *see* **эллипс.**

**элит** *m.* (min.) ehlite (probably same as pseudomalachite).

**элит/а** *f.*, **—ный** *a.* (genetics) elite, superior stock, selected varieties.

**эллаг/ендубильная кислота, —овая кислота** ellagic acid, gallogen.

**эллахерит** *m.* (min.) oellacherite (a variety of muscovite).

**эллинг** *m.* launch, slipway; shipyard, dock; airship hangar.

**эллипс, —ис** *m.* (geom.) ellipse; **—оид** *m.* ellipsoid; **—оидальный** *a.* ellipsoid, ellipsoidal.

**эллиптич/еский** *a.* elliptic, elliptical; **—ность** *f.* ellipticity.

**эл. магн. ед.** *abbr.* (электромагнитная единица) electromagnetic unit.

**элодея** *f.* (bot.) water thyme (*Elodea*).

**элонгация** *f.* elongation, stretch.

**элотрон** *m.* a gamma spectrometer using recoil electrons.

**эл.-ст. ед.** *abbr.* (электростатическая единица) electrostatic unit.

**эль** *m.* ale.

**Эльба** the Elbe (river).

**Эльбса реакция** Elbs reaction.

**эльван** *m.* (petr.) elvan (quartz-porphyry or granite).

**эльделин** *m.* eldeline.

**Эльзас** Alsace; **эльзасский** *a.* Alsatian.

**Эльм/а огонь, святого —са огонь** (meteor.) St. Elmo's fire; **—ора процесс** Elmore (flotation) process.

**эльпидит** *m.* (min.) elpidite.

**эльсвортит** *m.* (min.) ellsworthite (a uranium-bearing pyrochlore).

**элю/ант** *m.* eluant; **—ат** *m.* eluate; **—ация** *see* **элюирование.**

**элюв/иальный** *a.* (geol.) eluvial; **—ий** *m.* eluvium, residual rock.

**элю/ент** *m.* elutriator, elutriating agent; **—ирование** *n.*, **—триация, —ция** *f.* elution, washing, extraction; elutriation (separation of radioactive elements by ion exchanger); **—ировать** *v.* elute, extract; **—ирующий** *a.* eluting; elutriating; **—ционно-разделительный** *a.* elution-partition.

**эмаграмма** *f.* (meteor.) emagram.

**эмал/евый** *a.*, **—ь** *m.* enamel; **—евпроволока** *f.* enameled wire; **—ирование** *n.*, **—ировка** *f.*, **—ировочный** *a.* enameling, glazing; **—ированный** *a.* enameled, glazed; enamel (ware); **—ировать, покрыть —ью, —ьировать** *v.* enamel, glaze.

**эман** *m.* eman (unit of radioactivity equal to $10^{-10}$ curies per liter); **—атор** *m.* emanator; **—ационный** *a.*, **—ация** *f.* emanation, Em; emission; **коэффициент —ации** emanating power;

—ий *m.* emanation, emanon, Em; —ирование *n.*, —ирующий *a.* emanating; —ометр *m.* emanometer (for measuring radioactivity).

эмбел/иевая кислота, —ин *m.* embelic acid, embelin; соль —иевой кислоты, —иевокислая соль embeliate.

эмбенская нефть Emba crude oil.

эмблема *f.* emblem.

эмбол/ит *m.* (min.) embolite (silver chlorobromide); —ия *f.* (med.) embolism.

эмбрио— *prefix* embryo—, embryonic; —генез *m.*, —гения *f.* embryogeny.

эмбриолог *m.* embryologist; —ический *a.* embryological; —ия *f.* embryology.

эмбрион *m.* embryo; —альный *a.* embryonic.

ЭМГ *abbr.* (электромиограмма) electromyogram.

эме *see* эл. магн. ед.

эмеральдин *m.* emeraldin (dye).

эмет/амин *m.* emetamine; —ик *see* рвотный камень; —ин *m.* emetine; —ический *a.* emetic; —этилин *m.* emetethyline.

эмигр/ант *m.* emigrant; refugee; —ационный *a.* emigration, emigrant; —ация *f.* emigration; —ировать *v.* emigrate.

эми/ссионный *a.* emission, emissive, emitting; —ссионая способность emissive power, emissivity; —ссия *f.* emission; удельная —ссия emissivity; —тер *m.*, —терный *a.* (electron.) emitter; —тировать *v.* emit, give off; —тируемый *a.* emitted; —тирующий *a.* emitting, emissive.

эмкар *m.* (vet.) gangrene.

эммер *m.* (bot.) emmer (*Triticum dicoccum*).

эммонсит *m.* (min.) emmonsite (a hydrated ferric tellurite).

эмодин *m.* emodin; —овая кислота emodinic acid; —ол *m.* emodinol.

эмоц/иональный *a.* emotional; —ия *f.* emotion.

эмпиема *f.* (med.) empyema.

эмпиревматический *a.* empyreumatic, tarry.

эмпир/изм *m.* empiricism; —ически *adv.* empirically, experimentally; —ический *a.* empirical, experimental; —ическая формула empirical formula.

эмплектит *m.* (min.) emplectite (a member of the zinkenite group).

эмпрессит *m.* (min.) empressite (probably identical with muthmannite).

эмульг/атор *m.* emulsifier; —ация *f.*, —ирование *n.* emulsification; —ирующий агент emulsifying agent, emulsifier.

эмульсер *m.* emulsifier; air lift.

эмульсин *m.* emulsin, synaptase.

эмульс/ионный *a.*, —ия *f.* emulsion; э. реагент, —ификатор, —ор *m.* emulsifying agent, emulsifier; —ирование *n.*, —ификация *f.* emulsification; —ированный *a.* emulsified; —ировать, делать —ию, переводить в —ию *v.* emulsify; —оид *m.* emulsoid, emulsion; —ол *m.* self-emulsifying oil.

эмфизема *f.* (med.) emphysema.

эмшер *m.* (geol.) Emscherian stage.

эмшерский бассейн Imhoff (septic) tank.

ЭМЭ *abbr.* (эмпирический матричный элемент) empirical matrix element.

энант/ема *f.* (med.) enanthema; —ил *m.* enanthyl; —иловая кислота enanthylic acid, enanthic acid; —ин *m.* enanthin, heptine.

энантио— *prefix* enantio— (opposite); —морф *m.* (cryst.) enantiomorph; —морфизм *m.* enantiomorphism; —морфный *a.* enantiomorphous, similar but not superposable; —тропия *f.* (cryst.) enantiotropy; —тропный *a.* enantiotropic.

энантов/ый *a.* enanthic; э. альдегид enanthic aldehyde, enanthal; э. эфир enanthic ether, cognac oil, ethyl pelargonate; —ая кислота enanthic acid; соль —ой кислоты, —окислая соль enanthate.

энанто/л *m.* enanthol, heptyl alcohol; —токсин *m.* enanthotoxin.

энаргит *m.* (min.) enargite.

энгельманова сосна Engelmann spruce (*Picea engelmanii*).

энгидрос *m.* (min.) enhydros (a form of chalcedony).

Энглера вискозиметр Engler's viscosimeter.

эндекан *see* ундекан.

**эндекаэдр** *m.* (cryst.) hendecahedron; —**ический** *a.* hendecahedral.

**эндем/ический** *a.* endemic, local; —**ия** *f.* (med.) endemic, endemic disease; —**ы** *pl.* endemic animals or plants.

**эндивий, э. цикорий** *m.* (bot.) endive (*Cichorium endivia*).

**эндлихит** *m.* (min.) endlichite (a variety of vanadinite).

**эндо**— *prefix* endo— (within); —**гамический** *a.* endogamous; —**гамия** *f.* (biol.) endogamy; —**генный** *a.* endogene, endogenic; —**дерма** *f.* (zool.) endoderm; —**кард** *m.* (anat.) endocardium; —**кардит** *m.* (med.) endocarditis.

**эндокрин** *m.* (physiol.) endocrine; —**ные железы** (anat.) endocrine glands; —**ология** *f.* endocrinology; —**опатия** *f.* (med.) endocrinopathy.

**эндокроцин** *m.* endocrocin.

**эндокси**— *prefix* endoxy—.

**эндометилен** *m.* endomethylene.

**эндомицин** *m.* endomycin.

**эндоморф** *m.* (cryst.) endomorph; —**ный** *a.* endomorphic; —**оз** *m.* endomorphism.

**эндо/паразит** *m.* endoparasite, internal parasite; —**плазма** *f.* (biol.) endoplasm.

**эндосмо/метр** *m.* (phys.) endosmometer; —**с** *m.* endosmosis; —**тический** *a.* endosmotic.

**эндо/сперма** *f.* (bot.) endosperm; —**субтилизин** *m.* endosubtilysin; —**телий** *m.* (zool.) endothelium.

**эндотерм/ический, —ный** *a.* endothermic, heat-absorbing; —**ическое соединение** endothermic compound; —**ичность** *f.* endothermic nature.

**эндо/тия** *f.* endothia blight (of plants); —**токсин** *m.* endotoxin; —**трофный** *a.* (bot.) endotrophic, nourished from within; —**фермент** *m.* endoenzyme, intracellular enzyme.

**эндрюзит** *m.* (min.) andrewsite (near chalcosiderite).

**энезол** *m.* Enesol, mercuric salicylarsenate.

**энервация** *f.* (med.) enervation.

**энерратор** *m.* hydrotransmitter.

**энергети/к** *m.* power engineer, power worker; —**ка** *f.* energetics; power

engineering, power; —**ческий** *a.* energy, power; energetic, energic, energy-producing.

**энергичн/о** *adv.* energetically, vigorously; —**ый** *a.* energetic, vigorous, lively, active; —**ая реакция** vigorous reaction.

**энерг/ия** *f.* energy, power; **возбуждать** —**ию** *v.* energize; **затрата** —**ии** energy consumption; **кинетическая э.** kinetic energy; **растрата** —**ии** dissipation of energy, energy loss; **скрытая э.** stored energy, potential energy; **тепловая э., термическая э.** heat energy.

**энерго**— *prefix* power; energy; —**база** *f.* source of power supply; —**выделение** *n.*, —**отдача** *f.* release of energy, energy liberation; —**емкость** *f.* energy capacity, power capacity, energy content (of fuel); —**машиностроение** *n.* power machinery construction; —**силовая установка, —установка** *f.* power plant; —**снабжение** *n.* power supply; —**содержание** *n.* energy content; —**центр** *m.* power center; —**эквивалентный** *a.* power-equivalent.

**энзим** *m.*, —**ный** *a.* enzyme.

**энзоот/ический** *a.* enzootic, afflicting animals; —**ия** *f.* enzootic disease.

**энигматит** *m.* (min.) enigmatite.

**энидин** *m.* enidin.

**энимики** *pl.* (geol.) Animikian series.

**энин** *m.* enin.

**энкаусти/ка** *f.* encaustic, encaustic painting; —**ческий** *a.* encaustic (tile, etc.).

**энкринит** *m.* (min.) encrinite; —**овый** *a.* encrinitic.

**эннеадекан** *m.* enneadecane, nonadecane.

**эннеаэдр** *m.* (geom.) enneahedron; —**ический** *a.* enneahedral.

**энниатин** *m.* enniatin.

**энное количество** unspecified number, *n.*

**энол** *m.* enol; —**ат** *m.* enolate; —**ьная форма** enol form.

**энстатит** *m.* (min.) enstatite.

**энтальпия** *f.* (phys.) enthalpy, heat content.

**энтер/ит** *m.* (med.) enteritis; —**о**—*prefix* entero— (intestine); —**околит**

*m.* (med.) enterocolitis; —**отомия** *f.* enterotomy.

**энто—** *prefix* ento— (within, inner); *see also* **эндо—**; —**зоон** *m.* entozoon, animal parasite.

**энтомолог** *m.* entomologist; —**ический** *a.* entomological; —**ия** *f.* entomology.

**энтоолитовый** *a.* (petr.) entoölitic.

**энтр. ед.** *abbr.* (**энтропийная единица**) entropy unit, eu.

**энтрилодер** *m.* (min.) entry loader, scraper loader.

**энтроп/ийный** *a.*, —**ия** *f.* (phys.) entropy.

**энтузиазм** *m.* enthusiasm.

**энуклеация** *f.* enucleation.

**энцефалит** *m.* encephalitis, brain fever.

**энциклопед/ический** *a.* encyclopedic; —**ия** *f.* encyclopedia.

**эоген** *m.* (geol.) Eogene period.

**эозин** *m.* eosin, tetrabromofluorescein; —**офил** *m.* (biol.) eosinophile; —**о-фильный** *a.* eosinophilic.

**эозо/йский** *a.* (geol.) Eozoic, pre-Cambrian; —**новая структура**, —**он** *m.* (geol.) eozoon (a banded structure).

**эолов/а арфа** aeolian tones; —**о-обломочный** *a.* (geol.) anemoclastic; —**ый** *a.* (geol.) aeolian, windborne; —**ый многогранник** ventifact; —**ые отложения** aeolian rocks, wind deposits.

**эосфорит** *m.* (min.) eosphorite (near childrenite).

**эоцен** *m.* (geol.) Eocene epoch; —**овая формация** Eocene formation.

**эпархейский** *a.* (geol.) Eparchean.

**эпейроген/ез, —езис** *m.* (geol.) epeirogenesis; —**етический, —ический** *a.* epeirogenic; —**ия** *f.* epeirogeny.

**эпи—** *prefix* epi—; —**бласт** *m.* (biol.) epiblast, ectoderm; —**борнеол** *m.* epiborneol, 3-camphanol; —**бромгидрин** *m.* epibromohydrin, bromopropylene oxide.

**эпиген/ез** *m.* (geol.) epigenesis; —**етический** *a.* epigenetic; —**ит** *m.* (min.) epigenite; —**ный** *a.* epigene.

**эпигидрин** *m.* epihydrin, propylene epoxide; —**овая кислота** epihydrinic acid, glycidic acid; —**овый спирт** epihydric alcohol, glycidol.

**эпигуанин** *m.* epiguanine, methylguanine.

**эпидем/иология** *f.* (med.) epidemiology; —**ический** *a.*, —**ия** *f.* epidemic.

**эпидерм/а** *f.*, —**ис** *m.* (biol.) epidermis; —**ический** *a.* epidermic.

**эпи/десмин** *m.* (min.) epidesmine; —**дидимит** *m.* (min.) epididymite; —**диорит** *m.* (petr.) epidiorite (altered diabase); —**дозит** *m.* (petr.) epidosite, pistacite rock.

**эпидот** *m.*, —**овый** *a.* (min.) epidote, pistacite; **зеленый э.** arendalite; —**изация** *f.* epidotization.

**эпизод** *m.* episode; —**ический** *a.* incidental, occasional.

**эпизона** *f.* (geol.) epizone, shallow zone (of metamorphism).

**эпизоот/ический** *a.* (vet.) epizootic; —**ия** *f.* epizooty, epizootic disease.

**эпи/кадмиевый** *a.* (nucl.) epicadmium; —**каин** *m.* epicaine; —**камфора** *f.* epicamphor, 3-camphanone; —**катехол** *m.* epicatechol.

**эпикластический** *a.* (petr.) epiclastic.

**эпилеп/сия** *f.* (med.) epilepsy; —**тик** *m.*, —**тический** *a.* epileptic.

**эпиляция** *f.* epilation, depilation, hair removal.

**эпимер, —ид** *m.* epimer, epimeride (isomer); —**ный** *a.* epimeric.

**эпи/морф** *m.* (cryst.) epimorph; —**нефрин** *m.* epinephrine (adrenaline); —**нин** *m.* Epinine; —**озин** *m.* epiosin, methyldiphenyleneamidozol; —**параклаз** *m.* (geol.) epiparaclase, overthrust; —**планктонный** *a.* (biol.) epiplanktonic; —**положение** *n.* epiposition; —**породы** *pl.* (geol.) epirocks (metamorphic); —**рамноза** *f.* epirhamnose.

**эпирогенезис** *see* **эпейрогенез.**

**эпи/скоп** *m.* episcope (projector); —**стильбит** *m.* (min.) epistilbite; —**столит** *m.* (min.) epistolite; —**тека** *f.* (bot.) epitheca; —**телиальный** *a.* (biol.) epithelial; —**телий** *m.* epithelium; —**телиома** *f.* epithelioma, epithelial cancer; —**тепловой, —термальный** *a.* epithermal; —**трохоида** *f.* (geom.) epitrochoid; —**физ** *m.* (anat.) epiphysis; —**фит** *m.* (bot.) epiphyte; —**фитный** *a.* epiphytic.

**эпихлор/гидрин** *m.* epichlorohydrin,

chloropropylene oxide; —ит *m.* (min.) epichlorite (a variety of chlorite).

**эпицентр** *m.* epicenter, zero point.

**эпицикл** *m.* (astron.) epicycle; —**ический** *a.* epicyclic; —**оида** *f.* (geom.) epicycloid.

**эпи/эритроза** *f.* epierythrose; —**этилин** *m.* epiethylin, glycidyl ethyl ether; —**янтинит** *m.* epijanthinite (uranium mineral).

**Эплтона слой** Appleton layer (of ionosphere).

**эпокси—** *prefix* epoxy—; —**дирование** *n.* epoxidation; —**дный** *a.* epoxy (resin).

**эпоха** *f.* epoch, period, time, age.

**э.п.р.** *abbr.* (электронный парамагнетический резонанс) (spectroscopy) electron paramagnetic resonance.

**эпсом/ит** *m.* (min.) epsomite, natural Epsom salt; —**ская соль** Epsom salts, magnesium sulfate heptahydrate.

**Эпштейна прибор** (elec.) Epstein hysteresis tester.

**эпюр** *m.*, —**а** *f.* projection diagram; stress-strain diagram; line, curve.

**эпюр/ат** *m.* (fractionation) intermediate product; —**ационная колонна** a fractionating column.

**эр/а** *f.* era; **наша э.** Christian Era; **в 60 г. нашей —ы** 60 A.D. **до нашей —ы** B.C.

**эратический** *see* **эрратический.**

**эрб/иевый** *a.*, —**ий** *m.* erbium, Er; —**иевая земля, окись —ия** erbia, erbium oxide; **сернокислый —ий** erbium sulfate.

**эрг** *m.* erg (unit of work); **э.-секунда** erg-second.

**ЭРГ** *abbr.* (электроретинограмма) electroretinogram.

**эргамин** *m.* ergamine, histamine.

**эргин** *m.* ergine; —**овый двигатель** ergine motor.

**эргметр** *m.* (elec.) ergmeter.

**эрго—** *prefix* ergo— (ergot; work); —**базин, —метрин** *m.* Ergobasine, Ergometrine; —**граф** *m.* (med.) ergograph; —**зин** *m.* ergosine; —**стан** *m.* ergostane; —**стерин** *m.* ergosterol; —**тамин** *m.* ergotamine; —**тизм** *m.* (med.) ergotism; —**тин** *m.* ergotine;

—**тинин** *m.* ergotinine; —**тиновая кислота** ergotic acid; —**тионеин** *m.* ergothioneine; —**токсин** *m.* ergotoxine; —**флавин** *m.* ergoflavin; —**хризин** *m.* ergochrysin.

**эрекция** *f.* (physiol.) erection.

**эремурус** *m.* (bot.) eremurus.

**эреп/син** *m.*, —**таза** *f.* erepsin, ereptase.

**эретизм** *m.* (med.) erethism.

**эрзац** *m.* substitute.

**Эри** Lake Erie.

**эриантус** *m.* plume grass (*Erianthus*).

**эригероновое масло** erigeron oil.

**эризимин** *m.* erysimin.

**эрийский ярус** (geol.) Erian stage.

**эрикит** *m.* (min.) erikite.

**эриколин** *m.* ericolin.

**Эриксена испытание** (met.) Erichsen test.

**эрин/ит** *m.* (min.) erinite (a variety of montmorillonite); —**оид** *m.* Erinoid, artificial horn (a casein thermoplastic).

**эрио/диктиол** *m.* eriodictyol; —**дин** *m.* eriodin; —**метр** *m.* (text.) eriometer; —**нит** *m.* (min.) erionite (a zeolite near stilbite).

**эритем/а** *f.* (med.) erythema; —**альность** *f.* erythemal factor; —**ный** *a.* erythematous; erythema (dose).

**эритр/ен** *m.*, —**еновый** *a.* erythrene, 1,3-butadiene; —**ин** *m.*, —**иновый** *a.* erythrin; erythrine (alkaloid); (min.) erythrite, cobalt bloom; —**инин** *m.* erythrinine; —**иновая кислота** erythric acid; —**ит** *m.* erythrite, erythritol, tetrahydroxybutane.

**эритро—** *prefix* erythro— (red; erythrocyto—); —**глюций** *m.* erythroglucin, erythrol; —**декстрин** *m.* erythrodextrin; —**за** *f.* erythrose; —**зин** *m.* erythrosine; —**ксилин** *m.* erythroxyline, cocaine; —**л** *m.* erythrol, erythritol; 3-butene-1,2-diol; —**лакцин** *m.* erythrolaccin; —**литмин** *m.* erythrolitmin; —**мицин** *m.* erythromycin; —**новая кислота** erythronic acid; —**сидерит** *m.* (min.) erythrosiderite; —**филл** *m.* (bot.) erythrophyll; —**флеин** *m.* erythrophleine; —**цефаелин** *m.* erythrocephaelin; —**цинкит** *m.* (min.) erythrozincite; —**цит** *m.* erythrocyte, red blood corpuscle.

**эритрулоза** *f.* erythrulose.

**эрицин** *m.* ericin, Mesotan; —ол *m.* ericinol.

**эрквеин** *m.* herquein (antibiotic).

**Эрленмейера колба** Erlenmeyer flask, erlenmeyer.

**эрлифт** *m.* air lift.

**Эрлиха теория** Ehrlich (side-chain) theory.

**эрлих/ин** *m.* ehrlichin; —овский *a.* Ehrlich.

**эрмитов/о сопряжение** (math.) Hermitian conjugate; —ский *a.* Hermitian, Hermite.

**эродиров/анный** *a.* eroded, weathered; —ать *v.* erode, wear away.

**эроз/ивный** *a.* erosive, wearing; corrosive; —неустойчивый, —ионноустойчивый *a.* erosion-resistant; —ионный *a.* erosion, erosional; —ия *f.* erosion, weathering (of rocks, etc.).

**эрратический** *a.* (geol.) erratic, transported.

**эрс** *abbr.* (эрстед).

**эрстед** *m.* (elec.) oersted (magnetic unit); —метр *m.* oerstedmeter.

**эрстит** *m.* Oerstit (magnetic alloy).

**Эру печь** (met.) Heroult furnace.

**эрудиция** *f.* erudition, learning, knowledge.

**эруковая кислота** erucic acid, *cis*-13-docosenoic acid.

**эруптивн/ый** *a.* eruptive, effusive, volcanic; igneous; —ые породы (geol.) eruptive rocks.

**эруц/идовая кислота** erucidic acid, brassic acid; —иловый спирт erucylic alcohol.

**эрштедт** *see* эрстед.

**Э.С.** *abbr.* (энергия связи) binding energy.

**эсе** *see* эл.-ст. ед.

**эскадр/а** *f.*, —он *m.*, —енный *a.* squadron; troop; —енный броненосец battleship.

**эскалатор** *m.* escalator.

**эскариоль** *m.* (bot.) escarole (*Cichorium endivia* var. *scariola*).

**эскарп** *m.* (geol.) scarp, escarpment, cliff.

**эскер** *m.* (geol.) esker.

**эскиз** *m.* sketch, draft, rough draft, outline; э. от руки freehand sketch; —ный *a.* sketch; sketchy; —ный чертеж outline sketch, draft.

**эскимосский** *a.* Eskimo.

**эскул/етин** *m.* esculetin, 6,7-dihydroxycoumarin; —етиновая кислота esculetinic acid; —ин *m.*, —иновая кислота esculin, esculinic acid, bicolorin.

**эспар/то** *n.* esparto grass (*Stipa tenacissima*); —товый *a.* esparto, esparto grass; —цет *m.* sainfoin (*Onobrychis*).

**эспатит** *m.* Espatite (Soviet ion-exchange resin).

**эсперин** *m.* esperin.

**эссексит** *m.* essexite (nepheline monzonite and related rocks).

**эссенция** *f.* essence; летучая э. essential oil, volatile oil.

**эссонит** *m.* (min.) essonite, cinnamon stone (a variety of grossularite garnet).

**эст.** *abbr.* (эстонский) Estonian.

**эстакад/а** *f.*, —ный *a.* scaffold bridge, gantry, trestle; pier; stockade (breakwater); —ный кран gantry crane; —ный мост scaffold bridge, gantry; —ный рельсовый путь elevated railroad.

**эстамп** *m.* print, plate, engraving.

**эстезиометр** *m.* esthesiometer (for measuring tactile sensibility).

**Эстеля способ** Estelle method (for electrolytic iron).

**эстер** *see* эфир, сложный; —ификация *f.* esterification.

**эстивация** *f.* (biol.) estivation.

**эстолид** *m.* estolide.

**Эстония** Estonia; **эстонский** *a.* Estonian.

**эстрагол** *m.* estragole, *p*-allylanisole.

**эстрагон** *m.*, —овый *a.* (bot.) tarragon (*Artemisia dracunculus*).

**эстрада** *f.* platform, stage.

**эстр/адиол** *m.* estradiol; —атриен *m.* estratriene; —ин, —он *m.* estrone, theelin; —иол *m.* estriol, theelol.

**эстуар/иевый** *a.* (geol.) estuarine; —ий *m.* estuary, frith, firth.

**Эстьена аппарат** Estienne apparatus.

**эсхинит** *see* эшинит.

**эта** *pron. f.* this, that.

**этаж** *m.* story, floor, level; здание в пять —ей five-story building; нижний э., первый э. ground floor.

**этажерка** *f.* set of shelves; bookcase.

**этажный** *a.* story, floor; storied; stepped, step-like, graduated, graded, gradual;

multiple-stage, multistage; **э. выключатель** (elec.) floor switch; **э. клапан** multiple-seated valve; **э. котел** multiple-stage boiler.

**эталон** *m.* standard (of weights or measures); calibrating device, calibration instrument.

**эталониров/ание** *n.* standardization, standardizing; calibration; gaging; **—анный** *a.* standardized; calibrated; gaged; **—ать** *v.* standardize, adjust; calibrate; gage, test (instrument).

**эталонн/ый** *a.* standard; calibrating, calibration; reference (source, etc.); **э. аппарат** calibrating device; **—ое сопротивление** standard resistance.

**эталь** *m.* ethal, cetyl alcohol.

**этаминал** *m.* pentobarbital.

**этан** *m.*, **—овый** *a.* ethane; **—ал, —аль** *m.* ethanal, acetaldehyde; **—алевая кислота** ethanal acid, glyoxalic acid; **—амид** *m.* ethanamide, acetamide; **—диаль** *m.* ethanedial, glyoxal; **—дикарбоновая кислота** ethanedicarboxylic acid; **—дикислота** *f.*, **—диовая кислота** ethanedioic acid, oxalic acid; **—диол** *m.* ethanediol, glycol; **—овая кислота** ethanoic acid, acetic acid; **—оил** *m.* ethanoyl, acetyl; **—ол** *m.* ethanol, ethyl alcohol.

**этансульфо/кислота** *f.*, **—новая кислота** ethanesulfonic acid.

**этантиол** *m.* ethanethiol, ethyl mercaptan; **—овая кислота** ethanethiolic acid, thiolacetic acid.

**этап** *m.*, **—ный** *a.* stage; halting place; **—ный пункт** depot.

**Этвеша правило** (phys.) Eötvös rule.

**этез/ии** *pl.* etesian winds; **—ийный** *a.* etesian, periodical.

**этен** *m.* ethene, ethylene; **—ил** *m.* ethenyl; **—иламид** *m.* ethenylamide, acetamidine; **—илиден** *m.* ethenylidene; **—ол** *m.* ethenol, vinyl alcohol.

**этериз/ация** *f.* (med.) anesthetization (with ether); **—ировать** *v.* anesthetize.

**этерин** *m.* etherin (obs. name for ethylin).

**этерифи/кация** *f.* esterification; etherification; **—ковать, —цировать** *v.* esterify; etherify, convert into ether.

**этернит** *m.* Eternit (an asbestos-cement roofing material).

**эти** *pron. pl.* these, those.

**этиден** *m.* ethidene, ethylidene.

**этика** *f.* ethics.

**этикет/ирование** *n.* labeling; **—ка** *f.* label, tag, nameplate.

**этил** *m.* ethyl; **бромистый э.** ethyl bromide, bromoethane; **перекись —а** ethyl peroxide; **сернокислый э.** ethyl sulfate; **хлористый э.** ethyl chloride, chloroethane.

**этил/ал** *m.* ethylal; **—амин** *m.* ethylamine; **—анилин** *m.* ethylaniline; **—ат** *m.* ethylate (ethoxide or alcoholate); **—ацетат** *m.* ethyl acetate; **—бензол** *m.* ethylbenzene.

**этилен** *m.* ethylene, ethene; **бромистый э.** ethylene bromide; **окись —а** ethylene oxide; **хлористый э.** ethylene chloride.

**этилен/гликоль** *m.* ethylene glycol; **—диамин** *m.* ethylenediamine; **—имин** *m.* ethylenimine; **—молочная кислота** ethylene lactic acid, hydracrylic acid; **—овый** *a.* ethylene; **—овый ряд** ethylene series; **—овая связь** ethylene linkage, double bond; **—хлоргидрин** *m.* ethylene chlorohydrin.

**этилиден** *m.* ethylidene; **хлористый э.** ethylidene chloride; **—гликол** *m.* ethylidene glycol; **—мочевина** *f.* ethylidene urea.

**этилиров/ание** *n.* ethylation; **—анный** *a.* ethylated; **—ать** *v.* ethylate, introduce the ethyl radical.

**этил/карбонат** *m.* ethyl carbonate; **—меркаптан** *m.* ethyl mercaptan; **—молочная кислота** ethyllactic acid; **—ово-спиртовый** *a.* ethyl-alcoholic.

**этилов/ый** *a.* ethyl; **э. спирт** ethyl alcohol, ethanol; **э. эфир** ethyl ether, ether; ethyl ester; **э. эфир масляной кислоты** ethyl butyrate; **э. эфир уксусной кислоты** ethyl acetate; **—ая жидкость** mixture of lead tetraethyl and organic chlorides and bromides.

**этилол** *m.* ethylol, hydroxyethyl.

**этилосерн/ая кислота** ethylsulfuric acid; **соль —ой кислоты, —окислая соль** ethylsulfate; **—истая кислота** ethylsulfurous acid; **—окислый** *a.* ethylsulfuric acid; ethylsulfate (of); **—онатриевая соль** sodium ethylsulfate.

**этил/сульфокислота** *f.*, —**сульфоновая кислота** ethylsulfonic acid, ethanesulfonic acid; —**толуол** *m.* ethyltoluene; —**целлюлоза** *f.* ethylcellulose.

**этимология** *f.* etymology.

**этин** *m.* ethyne, acetylene; —**ил** *m.* ethynyl.

**этиолирование** *n.* etiolation, blanching.

**этиолог/ический** *a.* etiological; —**ия** *f.* etiology (investigation of causes).

**этионовая кислота** ethionic acid, ethylenesulfonic acid.

**этиопорфирин** *m.* etioporphyrin.

**этит** *m.* (min.) aetite, eaglestone (nodule).

**этич/еский,** —**ный** *a.* ethic, ethical.

**этмолит** *m.* ethmolith (plutonic mass of rock).

**Этна** Mt. Etna.

**этна** *f.* aetna (insulating material).

**это** *pron. n.* this, that, it.

**этокс/алил** *m.* ethoxalyl; —**ибензойная кислота** ethoxybenzoic acid; —**илирование** *n.* ethoxylation.

**этот** *pron. m.* this, that.

**этрол** *m.* etrol (a plastic).

**Эттеля раствор** Öttel's solution.

**Эттингсгаузена эффект** (elec.) Ettingshausen effect.

**эттрингит** *m.* (min.) ettringite.

**этуаль** *m.* star.

**эу**— *see also* **эв**—, **эй**—; —**лофиды** *pl.* chalcid flies (*Eulophidae*); —**мицин** *m.* eumycin.

**эф.** *abbr.* (эфир) ethyl ether (as solvent).

**эфедр/а** *f.* (bot.) ephedra; —**ин** *m.* ephedrine; —**овые** *pl.* Ephedraceae.

**эфеля** *pl.* (min.) crushed gold ore; sand-clay refuse.

**эфемер** *m.* (bot.) ephemeral; —**иды** *pl.* (zool.) Ephemeridae; (astron.) ephemerides; —**ный** *a.* ephemeral, short-lived, transitory.

**Эфиопия** Ethiopia; **эфиопский** *a.* Ethiopian.

**эфир** *m.* ester; ether, spec. ethyl ether; **э. бензойной кислоты** benzoic acid ester; **э. уксусной кислоты** acetic acid ester; **азотистоэтиловый эфир** ethyl nitrite; **кислотный э.** acid ester, ester; **простой э.** ether; **сложный э.** ester; **этиловый э. бензойной**

**кислоты** ethyl benzoate; **этиловый э. уксусной кислоты** ethyl acetate; —**ат** *m.* etherate; —**номасличный** *a.* essential-oil.

**эфир.** *abbr.* (эфирный) ethereal (solution in ethyl ether).

**эфирн/ый** *a.* ester; ether; ethereal; —**ая кислота** ether acid; lampic acid (obs.); —**ая смола** ester gum; —**ое масло,** —**ое летучее масло** essential oil, volatile oil; —**ые пары** ether fumes.

**эфир/окислота** *f.* ether acid, acid ester; —**омасличный** *a.* aromatic, essential-oil; —**онос** *m.* essential-oil (bearing) plant; —**оносный** *a.* aromatic; —**ообразование** *n.* ester formation, esterification; ether formation, etherification; —**оподобный** *a.* ester-like; ether-like; —**сульфонат** *m.* a chlorophenylchlorobenzenesulfonate miticide (equivalent of Ovotran).

**эфлоресценция** *f.* efflorescence.

**эффект** *m.* effect, result; capacity.

**эффективн/ость** *f.* effectiveness, efficiency; **предел** —**ости** effective range; —**ый** *a.* effective, efficient; active; considerable; —**ая мощность** effective power; —**ое сечение** (nucl.) cross section.

**эффектный** *a.* effective.

**эфферентный** *a.* (physiol.) efferent.

**эффуз/ивный** *a.* (petr.) effusive, extrusive; —**иометр** *m.* effusiometer (for determining gas density); —**ия** *f.* effusion; —**ор** *m.* effuser.

**эхи/ин** *m.* echiine; —**каучин** *m.* echicaoutchin; —**накозид** *m.* echinacoside.

**эхино**— *prefix* echino— (spiny; sea urchin); —**кокк** *m.* echinococcus (tapeworm); —**коккоз** *m.* (vet.) echinococcosis, echinococcus infection; —**псин** *m.* echinopsine; —**ринх** *m.* echinorhynchus (parasitic worm).

**эхит/амин** *m.* echitamine, ditaine; —**енин** *m.* echitenine; —**ин** *m.* echitin.

**эхиуриды** *pl.* (zool.) Echiuroidea.

**эхицерин** *m.* echicerin; —**овая кислота** echiceric acid.

**эхо** *n.* echo; —**лот** sounding device; **измерение** —**лотом** echo sounding; —**мессер** *m.* (tel.) singing point tester.

эци/альный *a.* (bot.) aecium, aecial; —дий *m.* aecidium; —й *m.* aecium.

Эчисона электропечь, Эчсона электропечь Acheson electric furnace.

эшафот *m.* scaffold.

эшелон *m.* echelon; —ная линза, —ное стекло echelon lens.

эшинит *m.* (min.) eschynite, aeschynite.

ЭЭГ *abbr.* (электроэнцефалограмма) electroencephalogram.

# Ю

Ю. *abbr.* (юг) south; code for aluminum in steel mark.

юб/ка *f.*, —очный *a.* skirt; (elec.) petticoat (of insulator).

Ю.-В. *abbr.* (юго-восток) southeast.

ювелир *m.* jeweler; —ный *a.* jewelry.

ювенильный *a.* juvenile, young.

юг *m.* south; на юг southward.

югл/андин *m.* juglandin; —он *m.* juglone, 5-hydroxy-14-naphthoquinone; —оновая кислота juglonic acid.

юго-запад *m.* southwest.

Югославия Yugoslavia.

югулярный *a.* (anat.) jugular.

юж., южн. *abbr.* (южный) south, southern.

Южная Америка South America.

южнобережный *a.* south coast.

южн/ый *a.* south, southern, southerly; Ю. Ледовитый океан Antarctic Ocean; ю. полюс antarctic pole; ю. полярный круг antarctic circle; —ое сияние aurora australis.

Ю.-З. *abbr.* (юго-запад) southwest.

Юза аппарат Hughes' apparatus.

Юитт Hewitt (name).

Юкавы потенциал (nucl.) Yukawa potential.

Юкатан Yucatan.

юкка *f.* (bot.) yucca; —сапонин *m.* yuccasaponin.

Юкон Yukon (river).

юлеп *m.* julep.

юлиенит *m.* (min.) julienite.

юлокротин *m.* yulocrotine.

юлол *m.* julol; —идин *m.* julolidine, 1,2,5-6-tetrahydrojulol.

юмит *m.* humite (coal from humic material).

Юм-Розери правило (met.) Hume-Rothery rule.

Юнга модуль Young's modulus, longitudinal elasticity.

юнгерманниевые *pl.* (bot.) Jungermaniaceae.

юнгит *m.* (min.) youngite.

Юнгнера аккумулятор (elec.) Jungner accumulator.

юнипер/ин *m.* juniperin; —овая кислота juniperic acid, 16-hydroxyhexadecanoic acid; —ол *m.* juniperol.

Юнкерса калориметр Junker's calorimeter.

юн/ость *f.* youth; (geol.) immaturity; —ошеский *a.* youthful, young, juvenile; —ошество *n.* youth, young people; —ый *a.* young, youthful; immature.

Юпитер (astron.) Jupiter.

юр *m.* height, bluff; на —у in an exposed place.

Юра the Jura mountains.

юра *see* юрский период.

Юра способ Ure's process (for mercury loss).

юр/идический *a.* juridical; —исдикция *f.* jurisdiction; —испруденция *f.* jurisprudence, science of law; —ист *m.* jurist, lawyer; student of law.

юрский период (geol.) Jurassic period.

юстир/ные весы balance for weighing gold; —овать *v.* adjust, correct; —овка *f.* adjustment, correction, alignment.

юстиция *f.* justice.

юта *see* джут.

Юта Utah.

юфть, юхта *f.* Russia leather.

ююба *f.* (bot.) jujube (*Zizyphus jujuba*).

# Я

я *pron.* I.

ябин *m.* yabine.

яблоко *n.* apple; (eye) ball; (mech.) ball.

яблон/евые *pl.* (bot.) Pomaceae; —ный *a.* apple tree, apple; —овка *f.* apple brandy; —я *f.* (bot.) apple tree (*Pyrus malus* or *Malus*); малорослая —я apple tree (*Malus pumila*).

Яблочкова свеча (illum.) Jablochkoff candle.

яблочно/кальциевая соль calcium malate; —кислый *a.* malic acid; malate (of); —кислая соль malate; —этиловый эфир ethyl malate.

яблочн/ый *a.* apple, pomaceous; malic; (mech.) ball; я. пресс cider press; я. шарнир ball coupling, cup-and-ball, ball and socket joint; —ая кислота malic acid, *l*-hydroxybutanedioic acid; соль —ой кислоты malate.

ябор/анди-листья *pl.* jaborandi (leaves of *Pilocarpus pennatifolius*); —идин *m.* jaboridine; —ин *m.* jaborine.

Ява Java.

яван/ицин *m.* javanicin; —ский *a.* Javanese.

яв/ить, —лять *v.* show, display, exhibit, manifest; —ляться *v.* appear, make one's appearance; be; seem; у него —илась мысль it occurred to him; —ка *f.* appearance; presence; —ление *n.* phenomenon, effect; appearance, occurrence; (ionizing) event; (med.) symptom; химическое —ление chemical phenomenon.

явно *adv.* evidently, visibly, clearly.

явно— *prefix* phanero— (visible, apparent); —брачный *a.* (bot.) phanerogamous.

явнокристаллическ/ий *a.* phanerocrystalline, obviously crystalline; —ая порода (petr.) phanerite, granitoid.

явн/ость *f.* evidence, obviousness, clearness; —ый *a.* evident, obvious, clear, plain, apparent; (math.) explicit.

явор *m.*, —овый *a.* (bot.) plane (*Platanus*); Eurasian maple (*Acer pseudoplatanus*).

явский *a.* Java, Javanese.

явств/енность *f.* clearness, distinctness; —енный *a.* clear, distinct; —овать *v.* be clear, be obvious, be apparent; appear.

ягель *m.* (bot.) lichen, spec. reindeer moss (*Cladonia rangiferina*).

ягн/енок *m.*, —иться *v.* lamb; —ятник *m.* lammergeyer (vulture).

ягод/а *f.*, —ный *a.* berry; —ица *f.* breech, buttocks; —ичный *a.* breech; gluteal; —ковые *pl.* (bot.) Thymelaeaceae; —ник *m.* berry bush; berry patch; —ообразный *a.* berry-like, baccate.

яд *m.* poison, venom; toxin; virus.

яд. ед. *abbr.* (ядерная единица) nuclear unit.

ядерночистый *a.* nuclear-pure.

ядерн/ый *a.* nuclear; kernel; я. котел, я. реактор nuclear reactor; —ая техника nucleonics; —ая физика nuclear physics; —ое горючее, —ое топливо (nucl.) fuel, fissionable material; —ое деление nuclear fission.

ядерщик *m.* nuclear physicist.

—ядный *a. suffix* —vorous, —phagous, eating.

ядовит/ость *f.* toxicity; virulence, malignity; —ый *a.* poisonous, toxic; virulent, venomous; noxious (gas); —ый зуб fang (of snake); —ое начало (med.) virus.

ядо/носный *a.* poison-bearing, toxiferous; poisonous, venomous; —химикаты *pl.* toxic chemicals (insecticides, fungicides, herbicides).

ядр/еный *a.* vigorous, healthy; juicy, succulent, fresh; full (of grains); —истый *a.* having big kernels; —ица *f.* peeled, whole buckwheat.

ядр/о *n.* nucleus, kernel; center, core (of reactor, etc.); heartwood; substance, gist; (benzene) ring; (cannon) ball, bullet; (anat.) testicle; я.-мишень *f.* target nucleus; атомное я. atomic nucleus; разрыв —а, расщепление —а ring cleavage; удаление —а (biol.) enucleation; физика атомного —а nuclear physics; —отехника *f.* nucleonics; —ышко *n.* (biol.) nucleolus.

яе/ин *m.* yajeine; —нин *m.* yajenine.

яз. *abbr.* (язык) language.

язв/а *f.* (med.) ulcer, sore; красная я. coral spot (plant disease); моровая я. plague, pestilence; сибирская я. malignant anthrax; —енник *m.* (bot.)

anthyllis; —**енный** *a.* ulcerous; —**ина** *f.* pit; —**ины** *pl.* pitting; с —**инами** pitted.

**язык** *m.*, —**овый** *a.* tongue; language; clapper (of bell); bolt (of lock); **воспаление** —**а** (med.) glossitis; —**отруб** *m.* (bot.) salpiglossis; —**оцветные** *pl.* (bot.) Liguliflorae.

**языч/ковый** *a.* tongue; (bot.) ligulate, ray; **я. контакт** (elec.) snap contact, rubbing contact; —**ник** *m.* (bot.) adder's tongue (*Ophioglossum vulgatum*); —**ный** *a.* tongue; lingual; —**ок** *m.* little tongue; catch, lug; tag; (acous.) reed; (anat.) uvula; (bot.) ligule.

**яич/ко** *n.* ovule, egg; (anat.) testicle; **придаток** —**ка** (anat.) epididymis; —**ник** *m.* (anat.) ovary; —**ница** *f.* scrambled eggs, omelette; —**ный** *a.* egg.

**яйла** *f.* yaila (monoclinal limestone plateau dissected by karst valleys in the Crimea).

**яйце**— *prefix* egg, ovi—; —**видный**, —**образный** *a.* egg-shaped, oviform, ovoid, oölitic, oval; —**вод**, —**провод** *m.* (anat.) oviduct; —**еды** *pl.* egg parasites (*Scelionidae*); —**клад** *m.* (zool.) ovipositor; —**кладка** *f.* oviposition, egg laying; —**кладущий**, —**родный**, —**родящий** *a.* (zool.) oviparous, egg-laying; —**клетка** *f.* (zool.) ovicell, egg cell; —**носкость** *f.* egg yield.

**яйцо** *n.* egg; (biol.) ovum.

**як** *m.* (zool.) yak.

**якоби/ан** *m.* (math.) Jacobian (functional determinant); —**евский** *a.* Jacobian, Jacobi's.

**якобсит** *m.* (min.) jacobsite.

**якобсонов орган** (zool.) Jacobson's organ.

**якобы** *particle* as if, as though, supposedly.

**якор/ный** *a.*, —**ь** *m.* anchor; (elec.) armature; (acous.) reed; **я.** *a.* anchor-type.

**Якутская АССР** Yakut Autonomous Soviet Socialist Republic.

**ялап/а** *f.* jalap (root of *Ipomoea purga* or *Exogonium*); —**ин** *m.* jalapin, orizabin; —**иновая кислота** jalapic acid;

—**иноловая кислота** jalapinolic acid, *d*-11-hydroxyhexadecanoic acid; —**ная смола** jalap resin.

**ялик** *m.* skiff, dinghy, wherry.

**ялов/еть** *v.* be barren; be dry (of cow); —**ица** *f.* dry cow; —**ка** *f.* cowhide; —**ость** *f.* barrenness, sterility; —**ый** *a.* barren, sterile; dry.

**яльпаит** *m.* (min.) jalpaite (cupriferous argentite).

**яма** *f.* pit, well, depression, hole; ditch, trench; (air or gas) pocket.

**ямайск/ий** *a.* Jamaica; **я. перец** (bot.) pimento, allspice (*Myrtus pimenta*); —**ое горькое дерево** (bot.) Jamaica quassia (*Picrasma excelsa*).

**ямайцин** *m.* jamaicin.

**ямб/овая кора** jambul (bark of *Eugenia jambolana*); —**оза** *f.* (bot.) rose apple (*Myrtus jambos* or *Jambosa vulgaris*); —**озин** *m.* jambosine; —**улол** *m.* jambulol.

**ям/ка**, —**очка** *f.* little pit, pit, hole, depression; с —**ками** pitted.

**ямс** *m.* (bot.) Chinese yam (*Dioscorea*).

**ямчат/ость** *f.* pitted condition; pit (plant disease); —**ый** *a.* pitted.

**январь** *m.* January.

**янгонин** *m.* yangonin.

**янтарно/аммониевая соль** ammonium succinate; —**кислый** *a.* succinic acid; succinate (of); —**кислый алюминий** aluminum succinate; —**кислая соль** succinate; —**этиловый эфир** ethyl succinate.

**янтарн/ый** *a.* amber; succinic; **я. альдегид** succinic aldehyde, succinaldehyde; **я. ангидрид** succinic anhydride, succinyl oxide; —**ая земля** (min.) amber, succinite; —**ая кислота** succinic acid, butanedioic acid; **соль** —**ой кислоты** succinate; **хлорангидрид** —**ой кислоты** succinyl chloride; —**ая смола** amber resin; —**ое масло** amber oil.

**янтарь** *m.* amber; **черный я.** (min.) black amber, jet.

**янтинит** *m.* (min.) ianthinite (a hydrous uranium dioxide).

**янусовый зеленый** Janus green (intra-vitam stain).

**Ян-Цзы-Цзян** the Yang-Tse-Kiang.

япакон/ин *m.* japaconine; —итин *m.* japaconitine, acetylbenzoyl japaconine.

Япония Japan.

японск/ий *a.* Japanese; я. воск Japan wax; я. лак Japan lacquer, Japan varnish; —ая кислота japonic acid (a tannic acid); —ое лаковое дерево (bot.) Japanese wax tree (*Rhus succedanea*).

яр *m.* steep bank, cliff, crag; (zool.) heat.

ярд *m.* yard (measure).

яремный *a.* (anat.) jugular.

ярк/ий *a.* bright, clear, luminous; strong, intense (light); rich (color); —о *adv.* brightly; —окрасный *a.* bright red, ruby; —остно-модулированный *a.* intensity-modulated; —ость *f.* brightness, brilliance, luminosity, intensity.

ярлы/к, —чок *m.* label, tag.

ярмарка *f.* (agr.) fair.

ярмо *n.* (elec.) yoke; framework, carcass.

яров/изация *f.* vernalization, yarovization (method of treating seeds and bulbs); early stage of growth; —изированный *a.* vernalized; —ое *n.*, —ой хлеб summer grain crop; —ой *a.* spring (rye, wheat), summer-crop.

ярозит *m.* (min.) jarosite.

ярочка *f.* yearling ewe, ewe lamb.

ярровит *m.* (min.) jarrowite (thinolite).

Ярроу котел Yarrow boiler.

ярунок *m.* miter box, miter block.

ярус *m.* story, floor; deck, tray (of dryer); (geol.) stage, formation, layer, stratum; —ный *a.* story, floor; tray (dryer); stage; multistage; stepped, steplike, graded, graduated, gradual.

ярутка *f.* (bot.) pennycress (*Thlaspi*).

ярый *a.* violent; eager; unbleached (wax).

ярь *f.* spring (grain) crop; green color; я.-медянка, медная я. verdigris, basic cupric acetate; green copper rust.

яр-яр *m.* yara-yara, β-naphthyl methyl ether.

ясен/евый, —ный *a.* (bot.) ash, ashen; —евое дерево, —ь *m.* ash (*Fraxinus*); —ец *m.* dittany (*Dictamnus* or *Cunila*); китайский —ь ailanthus.

ясколка *f.* (bot.) chickweed (*Cerastium*).

ясли *pl.* manger, crib (for cattle feed).

ясменник *m.* (bot.) woodruff (*Asperula*).

ясмон *m.* jasmone.

ясн/еть *v.* clear up; —о *adv.* clearly, brightly; in plain terms; evidently; it is clear; it is obvious; —ость *f.* clearness, brightness; plainness; внести —ость в *v.* clear (the situation).

яснотка *f.* (bot.) dead nettle (*Lamium*).

ясный *a.* clear, bright; distinct, definite, precise; lucid, explicit; transparent; distinctly audible; obvious, apparent, evident, pronounced.

ассиды *pl.* (zool.) Jassidae.

ястреб *m.* (zool.) hawk; Hawk (a brand of white metal); —инка *f.* (bot.) hawkweed (*Hieracium*); —иный *a.* hawk; accipitral, hawk-like.

ятрен *m.* Yatren, chiniofon.

ятрофин *m.* jatrophine.

ятрохим/ический *a.* (med.) iatrochemical; —ия *f.* iatrochemistry.

ятрышник *m.* (bot.) orchis.

ятулийский *a.* (geol.) Jatulian.

яулингит *m.* (min.) jaulingite (a resin resembling succinite).

яхобаб *m.* astrakhan hide.

яхонт *m.* gem, jewel, precious stone; красный я. ruby; синий я. sapphire.

яхта *f.* yacht.

ячеист/ый *a.* cellular, porous, honeycombed, alveolar, vesicular, cavernous; —ое состояние porosity.

ячейк/а *f.* nucleus; (biol.) cell; cell, unit, compartment, cubicle; honeycomb; mesh (of screen); stage (in scaling circuit); —овый *a.* nuclear; cellular; —ообразный *a.* cellular, cellulated, honeycomb.

ячея *f.* cell.

ячменевые *pl.* (bot.) Hordeae.

ячменн/ый *a.* barley; я. отвар barley water; я. сахар malt sugar, maltose; —ое зерно barley corn.

ячмень *m.* (bot.) barley (*Hordeum*); (med.) sty; многорядный я. common barley (*H. vulgare*).

ячневый *a.* ground-barley, crushed-barley.

яшма *f.* (min.) jasper, jasperite (a form of cryptocrystalline quartz); агатовая я. jasper-agate; молочная я. galactite.

яшмов/ый *a.* (min.) jasper, jaspidean;

**и. агат** jasper-agate; **я. фарфор** (cer.) jasperated china; **—ая каменная посуда** (cer.) jasper ware, Wedgwood ware.

**яшмоподобный** *a.* (min.) jasper-like, jasperoid, jaspoid.

**ящери/ца** *f.* (zool.) lizard; **—чный** *a.* lizard; saurian.

**ящик** *m.* box, chest, case, container; bin; cage; drawer (of desk); (rad.) cabinet; **я.-решето** *n.* drain box.

**ящичный** *a.* box; **я. отжиг** pot annealing, close annealing; **я. питатель** hopper feeder, hopper.

**ящур** *m.* (vet.) foot and mouth disease.